M

• Internal & External Stables • Steel Framed Buildings & Barns
• Horse Exercisers • Windows & Doors • Lunge & Paddock Pens
• Stocks & Solaria • Accessories

www.monarch-equestrian.co.uk   01902 605566   sales@monarch-equestrian.co.uk

Injured Jockeys Fund

The Injured Jockeys Fund provides appropriate support in a prompt and sympathetic manner to those jockeys past or present who are injured, unable to ride, or generally in need.

As a not-for-profit, self funding organisation we are reliant on the support and generosity of our supporters.

To find out how you can become involved and support the Injured Jockeys Fund or make a donation, please visit us at:

www.ijf.org.uk or call: **01638 662246**

Sir Anthony McCoy OBE
President - Injured Jockeys Fund

Compassion • Care • Support

Injured Jockeys Fund (Registered Charity No. 1107395)

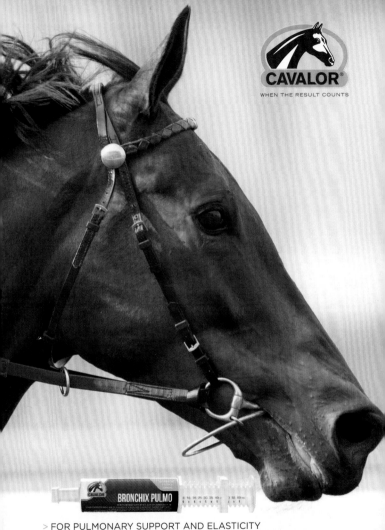

CAVALOR®
WHEN THE RESULT COUNTS

BRONCHIX PULMO

> FOR PULMONARY SUPPORT AND ELASTICITY

www.cavalor.com | Consumer line 7/7 +44 (0)1352 746100

Plug & Play - All you need is a regular 16 amp outlet to operate

MK

WWW.MOLENKONING.COM

UNITED KINGDOM

MOLENKONING IS THE WORLDS LEADING MANUFACTURER OF HORSE WALKERS & REHABILITATION EQUIPMENT

Walkers · Fences · Roofs · Horsepower Plates · Solariums

CHEVAL
LIBERTÉ

Cheval Liberté UK are the official UK & Ireland Distributor of Molenkoning Products

T: 01490 413 152   E: sales_uk@molenkoning.com

W: www.molenkoning.com

TOP QUALITY
HAY

ENGLISH, AMERICAN, CANADIAN, HAYLAGE

FIBRE SELECT
THE RANGE OF DUST EXTRACTED HIGH QUALITY HAY IN FULLY PACKAGED BALES TO SUIT YOUR REQUIREMENTS

RANSLEY HAY

Contact Philip Ransley
Tel 01233 731001 / 733189   Mob 07860 915000
Email philip.ransley@ransleyhay.co.uk

For all enquiries in Ireland please contact
Tom Daly on 00353 868 220 557

– STROMSHOLM –

HOOFCARE & SOUNDNESS

www.stromsholm.co.uk

Equine
Biosecurity
Aware

The NEW Non-Slip Nail
Carrera Secure

tungsten pin

The high quality **tungsten pin** provides **excellent grip** & **much better wear**. Fits all Kerckhaert's aluminium Kings race plates.

Ask your farrier for details.

SUPER SOUND

The fastest selling race plate on the market!

The Super Sound® is the **premium aluminium** race plate in the Kerckhaert program.

Kerckhaert has the **biggest** selection of steel and aluminium **thoroughbred horseshoes** for both training and racing.

Contact us:

Milton Keynes Head Office
Tel: 01908 233909

Also available at our:

Newmarket Race Division
& Lambourn Race Division

Britain

STRÖMSHOLM
– KERCKHAERT GROUP –

Worldwide

KERCKHAERT
– ROYAL HORSESHOE FACTORY –

Cutting the cost of
horse healthcare

✓ Request a product & we will price match

✓ BHA anti-doping guidance

✓ Free delivery over £29*

Your horse's health is our priority, a fair price is our promise.

*Some exclusions apply. See our website T&Cs for more information.

evetdrug.co.uk

EQUINE MEDICATION | SUPPLEMENTS | WORMERS | THERAPY | FIRST AID

Feed the best to be the best

Highclere Castle Horse Feeds

Natural whole feed

Your horse's digestion is the engine room for all success and oats are the fuel.

Support your horses stamina and speed

Prepare your mares for foaling

Feed your yearlings for growth and condition

Our oats have powered winners of over £9m in the last five years.

Horses thrive on our Ryegrass Haylage (200kg bales)

HIGHCLERE CASTLE HORSE FEEDS

Call 01635 250600 or 07950 010692
www.highclerecastlehorsefeeds.co.uk

CALDERS & GRANDIDGE

G

1820

Experts in pressure treated timber
products for all your equine needs.

Top quality treated timber
fencing and handmade gates
manufactured on-site.

View the range at
www.caldersandgrandidge.com
Email enquiries@caldersandgrandidge.com
or call our experts on 01205 358866

BY APPOINTMENT TO
HER MAJESTY THE QUEEN

NEW

POWERING YOUR WINNERS

Ultra low starch

With lecithin & pectin

Suitable for equines prone to gastric ulcers as part of a balanced diet

Part of the new and improved SPILLERS Racing Range.
For more information visit www.spillers-feeds.com

For more information call our Care-Line: 01908 226623 or visit www.spillers-feeds.com

©Mars, 2020.

Respiratory problems in racehorses are the second highest reason for lost training days

Exposure to respirable dust is a major cause of respiratory problems in horses.

Use Haygain's unique steaming technology to reduce the risk of respirable dust and pathogens found in all hay and haylage.

Don't risk losing out: For a healthier horse, make Haygain part of your feeding routine.

Source: Rossdale PD et al. K (1985) Epidemiological Study of Wastage Among Racehorses, Vet Rec, 116:66-69.

www.haygain.com | T: 01488 854005

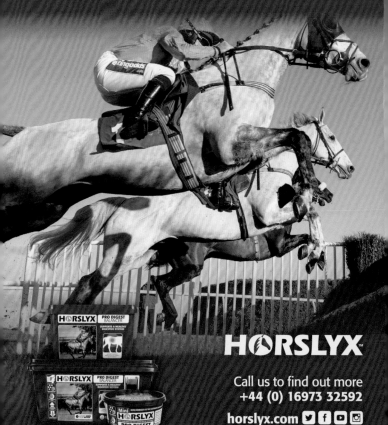

Healthy Gut, Healthy Horse

HORSLYX™

HORSLYX PRO DIGEST BALANCER SUPPORTS A HEALTHY DIGESTIVE SYSTEM

HORSLYX PRO DIGEST BALANCER SUPPORTS A HEALTHY DIGESTIVE SYSTEM

Mini HORSLYX PRO DIGEST

Call us to find out more
+44 (0) 16973 32592

horslyx.com

WOODHOUSE ™

DELIVERING SUCCESSFUL EVENTS

1890
130
YEARS
2020

Stables, Horse Walks & Trade Stands

Tel: 0115 9899 899
www.lhwoodhouse.co.uk

RACING POST SHOP

Classic *reads*

HENRIETTA KNIGHT

£20

STARTING FROM SCRATCH INSPIRED TO BE A JUMP JOCKEY

Foreword by Sir Anthony McCoy

RACING POST LEGENDS

TIGER ROLL THE LITTLE LEGEND

EDITED BY ANDREW PENNINGTON

£20

Order now

 racingpost.com/shop 01933 304858

HORSES
IN TRAINING 2020

130th YEAR OF PUBLICATION

Raceform

INDEX TO GENERAL CONTENTS

Editor
Richard Lowther; Raceform Ltd., 27 Kingfisher Court, Hambridge Road, Newbury, G14 5SJE-mail: richard.lowther@racingpost.com

Production Editor
Adrian Gowling; Bloodstock Services, Weatherbys

Typesetting
Andy Ball; Printing Services, Weatherbys, Sanders Road, Wellingborough, NN8 4BX.

Orders
Raceform Ltd., Sanders Road, Wellingborough, Northants NN8 4BX.
Tel: 01933 304858www.racingpost.com/shopE-mail: Shop@racingpost.com

Advertisements
kay.brown@archantdialogue.co.uk and gary.millone@ archantdialogue.co.uk

ISBN
978-1-83950-040-4

Printed and bound by CPI William Clowes, Copland Way, Beccles NR34 7TL
© Raceform Ltd 2020

INDEX TO ADVERTISERS

2020

RACING FIXTURES

AND SALE DATES

(SUBJECT TO ALTERATION)

Flat fixtures are in **Black Type**; Jump in Light Type; Irish in *Italic*;
asterisk (★) indicates an evening or Twilight meeting;
† indicates an All Weather meeting. Sale dates are at foot of fixtures

MARCH

Sun	Mon	Tues	Wed	Thur	Fri	Sat
1 Huntingdon *Leopardstown* Sedgefield	**2** Chepstow *Leopardstown* Wetherby **Wolverhampton†★**	**3** Exeter Newcastle **Southwell†★**	**4** Catterick Bridge Fontwell Park **Kempton Park†★** **Lingfield Park†**	**5** Carlisle **Newcastle†★** **Southwell†** *Thurles* Wincanton	**6** *Dundalk†★* Ffos Las Leicester Sandown Park **Wolverhampton†★**	**7** Ayr **Chelmsford City†★** *Gowran Park* Hereford Sandown Park **Wolverhampton†**
8 *Naas* Southwell (Mixed) Warwick	**9** Plumpton Stratford-On-Avon Taunton **Wolverhampton†★**	**10** Cheltenham **Newcastle†★** Sedgefield **Southwell†**	**11** Cheltenham Huntingdon **Kempton Park†★** **Lingfield Park†**	**12** **Chelmsford City†★** Cheltenham Doncaster Hexham Cheltenham Sale	**13** Cheltenham *Dundalk†★* Fakenham **Lingfield Park†** **Southwell†★**	**14** Fontwell Park Kempton Park *Navan* Newcastle Uttoxeter **Wolverhampton†★**
15 Carlisle *Limerick* Market Rasen	**16** Hereford Kelso Southwell	**17** *Down Royal* Taunton Wetherby *Wexford*	**18** Haydock Park Ludlow Plumpton Ascot Sale	**19** Chepstow Huntingdon Sedgefield	**20** *Dundalk†★* **Lingfield Park†** Musselburgh Newbury **Newcastle†★**	**21** Bangor-On-Dee Kelso **Lingfield Park†** Newbury **Southwell†★** *Thurles*
22 Carlisle *Downpatrick* Exeter *Naas*	**23** **Lingfield Park†** Wincanton **Wolverhampton†★**	**24** *Clonmel* Hereford Hexham **Southwell†★**	**25** **Kempton Park†★** Market Rasen Newcastle **Southwell†**	**26** Cork Ffos Las **Lingfield Park†** Warwick **Wolverhampton†★**	**27** *Dundalk†★* Fontwell Park **Lingfield Park†** **Newcastle†★** Wetherby	**28** **Doncaster** **Kempton Park†** *Navan* Stratford-On-Avon Uttoxeter **Wolverhampton†★**
29 Ascot *Curragh* **Doncaster** *Limerick*	**30** **Bath** Ludlow **Newcastle†★**	**31** **Lingfield Park†** **Musselburgh** Southwell				

APRIL

Sun	Mon	Tues	Wed	Thur	Fri	Sat
■	■	■	**1** *Leopardstown* **Lingfield Park**† Market Rasen Wincanton **Wolverhampton**†★ Ascot Sale	**2** Aintree **Chelmsford City**†★ *Limerick* **Southwell**† Taunton Goffs UK Aintree Sale	**3** Aintree **Kempton Park**†★ **Leicester** Sedgefield *Wexford*★	**4** Aintree Chepstow *Dundalk*† **Lingfield Park**† Newcastle **Wolverhampton**†★
5 Ffos Las *Leopardstown* Plumpton	**6** Kelso **Redcar** **Windsor**	**7** Exeter **Pontefract** Southwell Keeneland Sale	**8** **Catterick Bridge** *Gowran Park*★ **Kempton Park**†★ **Nottingham** **Wolverhampton**†	**9** Bath **Chelmsford City**†★ *Clonmel*★ Hereford Wetherby Osarus Sale	**10** **Chelmsford City**† **Lingfield Park**† **Newcastle**†	**11** Carlisle *Cork* *Fairyhouse* Haydock Park **Kempton Park**† Musselburgh Newton Abbot **Wolverhampton**†★
12 *Cork* *Fairyhouse* Ffos Las Market Rasen Plumpton **Southwell**†	**13** Chepstow *Cork* *Fairyhouse* Fakenham Huntingdon Plumpton **Redcar** **Wolverhampton**† Tattersalls Sale	**14** **Lingfield Park**† **Newmarket** Warwick Tattersalls Sale	**15** **Beverley** Cheltenham *Dundalk*★ **Kempton Park**†★ **Newmarket** Tattersalls Sale	**16** Cheltenham **Newcastle**†★ **Newmarket** **Ripon**	**17** Ayr *Ballinrobe*★ **Bath**★ Exeter★ Fontwell Park **Newbury**	**18** Ayr Bangor-On-Dee **Brighton**★ *Curragh* **Newbury** **Nottingham**★ **Thirsk**
19 *Dundalk*† Stratford-On-Avon *Tramore* Wincanton	**20** Hexham Kempton Park★ Newton Abbot **Pontefract** *Tramore*★ **Windsor**★	**21** *Fairyhouse*★ Ludlow Sedgefield **Southwell**★ **Wolverhampton**†★ Yarmouth	**22** **Catterick Bridge** *Dundalk*†★ **Epsom Downs** **Lingfield Park**†★ Perth Taunton★ Goffs UK Sale	**23** **Beverley** **Chelmsford City**†★ Exeter★ Perth *Tipperary*★ Warwick Cheltenham Sale	**24** Chepstow★ Cork **Doncaster** *Kilbeggan*★ Perth **Sandown Park** Worcester★	**25** **Doncaster**★ **Haydock Park** **Leicester** *Limerick* *Navan* **Ripon** Sandown Park **Wolverhampton**†★
26 Salisbury Wetherby	**27** Ayr **Lingfield Park**† *Naas*★ **Southwell**† **Thirsk**★ **Windsor**★	**28** Ayr★ Brighton **Lingfield Park**† **Nottingham** *Punchestown*★ Yarmouth	**29** Ascot Brighton★ **Chelmsford City**† Pontefract *Punchestown*★ **Wolverhampton**†	**30** **Chelmsford City**†★ Musselburgh *Punchestown*★ **Redcar** **Southwell**† **Wolverhampton**†★ Tattersalls Sale Goffs Punchestown Sale	■	■

MAY

Sun	Mon	Tues	Wed	Thur	Fri	Sat
31 Fakenham Kilbeggan *Listowel* **Nottingham**					**1** *Cheltenham★* **Chepstow** **Lingfield Park** **Musselburgh** **Newcastle†★** *Punchestown★* Tattersalls Sale	**2** **Doncaster** **Goodwood** *Hexham★* **Newmarket** *Punchestown* **Thirsk** *Uttoxeter*
3 **Hamilton Park** **Newmarket** **Salisbury** *Sligo*	**4** **Brighton** *Curragh* *Down Royal* Kempton Park *Gowran Park* **Nottingham** **Windsor**	**5** *Ayr* *Ballinrobe★* **Chester** Fakenham *Gowran Park* *Southwell★* **Wolverhampton†★**	**6** **Chester** *Fontwell Park★* *Gowran Park★* *Kelso* **Kempton Park†★** *Newton Abbot*	**7** **Chelmsford City†★** **Chester** *Huntingdon* *Tipperary★* *Wincanton★* *Worcester*	**8** **Ascot** **Bath** **Beverley** *Cork★* *Downpatrick* *Market Rasen★* **Ripon★** *Warwick* **Wolverhampton†**	**9** **Ascot** *Cork* **Haydock Park (Mixed)** *Hexham* **Lingfield Park** *Naas* **Nottingham** **Thirsk★** *Warwick★* Arqana Sale
10 *Killarney* *Leopardstown* *Ludlow* *Plumpton*	**11** **Catterick Bridge** *Killarney★* **Musselburgh** *Roscommon★* *Southwell★* **Windsor★** **Wolverhampton†**	**12** *Ayr★* **Beverley** **Chepstow** *Killarney★* *Sedgefield* **Wetherby★** *Tattersalls (IRE) Sale*	**13** **Bath★** *Newton Abbot* *Perth★* *Worcester* **York**	**14** *Clonmel★* *Fontwell Park★* **Newmarket★** *Perth* **Salisbury** **York**	**15** *Aintree★* **Hamilton Park★** *Kilbeggan★* *Leopardstown★* **Newbury** **Newmarket** **York**	**16** *Bangor-On-Dee* **Doncaster★** *Navan* **Newbury** **Newmarket** **Thirsk** *Uttoxeter★* *Wexford* Arqana Sale
17 *Naas* **Ripon** *Stratford-On-Avon*	**18** **Carlisle** *Ffos Las* **Leicester★** **Redcar** **Windsor★** Goffs UK Sale	**19** *Hexham★* *Huntingdon★* **Lingfield Park†** **Nottingham** *Sligo★* **Wolverhampton†** Goffs UK Sale	**20** **Ayr** *Cork★* **Kempton Park†★** *Southwell★* *Warwick* **Yarmouth** Goffs UK Sale	**21** **Chelmsford City†★** **Lingfield Park** *Market Rasen* **Sandown Park★** *Tipperary★* **Wolverhampton†**	**22** **Bath** **Brighton** *Downpatrick★* **Haydock Park** **Pontefract★** *Wexford★* *Worcester★* BBAG Sale Tattersalls (IRE) Sale	**23** **Beverley** *Cartmel* **Catterick Bridge** **Chester** *Curragh* *Ffos Las★* **Haydock Park** **Salisbury★**
24 *Curragh* *Fontwell Park* *Kelso* *Uttoxeter*	**25** *Ballinrobe★* *Cartmel* **Chelmsford City†** *Huntingdon* **Leicester** **Redcar** **Windsor**	**26** *Ballinrobe★* **Brighton** **Leicester** **Lingfield Park★** *Ludlow★* **Redcar**	**27** **Beverley** *Cartmel★* *Gowran Park★* **Hamilton Park** *Newton Abbot* *Warwick★*	**28** *Carlisle★* *Fairyhouse★* **Goodwood** **Haydock Park** *Limerick★* **Ripon** **Sandown Park★** Cheltenham Sale	**29** *Carlisle* **Catterick Bridge★** *Down Royal★* **Goodwood** **Haydock Park★** *Stratford-On-Avon★* *Tramore★* **Yarmouth**	**30** **Goodwood** **Haydock Park** **Lingfield Park★** *Listowel* **Newmarket** *Stratford-On-Avon★* *Tramore* **York**

JUNE

Sun	Mon	Tues	Wed	Thur	Fri	Sat
	1 Gowran Park Listowel Southwell **Windsor**★ **Wolverhampton**† **Yarmouth**★	**2** Bangor-On-Dee **Brighton** **Lingfield Park**†★ **Newcastle**†★ Tipperary★ Ascot Sale	**3** Curragh★ Fontwell Park **Kempton Park**†★ Newton Abbot **Nottingham** **Ripon**★ Wexford	**4** **Chelmsford City**†★ Ffos Las **Hamilton Park** Leopardstown★ Uttoxeter **Wolverhampton**†★	**5** **Bath**★ **Catterick Bridge** Clonmel★ **Doncaster**★ **Epsom Downs** **Goodwood**★ Market Rasen	**6** **Chepstow**★ **Doncaster** **Epsom Downs** Hexham **Lingfield Park**★ **Musselburgh** Navan Punchestown Worcester
7 **Goodwood** Perth Punchestown	**8** **Ayr** **Leicester** **Pontefract**★ Roscommon★ **Windsor**★	**9** **Chelmsford City**†★ **Lingfield Park** Roscommon★ **Salisbury** **Wetherby**★ Goffs Sale	**10** Cork★ Fontwell Park **Hamilton Park**★ **Haydock Park** **Kempton Park**†★ **Yarmouth** Goffs Sale	**11** **Haydock Park**★ Leopardstown★ **Newbury** **Nottingham** Uttoxeter★ **Yarmouth**	**12** Aintree★ **Chepstow** Fairyhouse★ **Goodwood**★ Gowran Park★ Newton Abbot★ **Sandown Park** **York** Osarus Sale	**13** **Bath** **Chester** Downpatrick Hexham **Leicester**★ Limerick **Sandown Park** Worcester★ **York**
14 **Doncaster** Downpatrick **Salisbury**	**15** **Ayr** Kilbeggan★ **Nottingham**★ **Thirsk** **Windsor**★ Goffs London Sale	**16** **Ascot** **Beverley** **Brighton**★ Sligo★ Stratford-On-Avon **Thirsk**	**17** **Ascot** **Chelmsford City**†★ **Hamilton Park** **Ripon**★ Uttoxeter Wexford★	**18** **Ascot** **Chelmsford City**† Ffos Las★ Leopardstown★ **Lingfield Park**†★ **Ripon**	**19** **Ascot** **Carlisle**★ Down Royal★ **Goodwood**★ Limerick★ Market Rasen **Newmarket**★ **Redcar**	**20** **Ascot** **Ayr** Down Royal **Haydock Park**★ **Lingfield Park**★ **Newmarket** Perth **Redcar**
21 Hexham **Pontefract** Worcester	**22** Ballinrobe★ **Chepstow** Southwell **Windsor**★ **Wolverhampton**†★	**23** **Beverley** **Brighton** **Newbury**★ Newton Abbot★	**24** **Bath**★ **Carlisle** **Kempton Park**†★ Naas★ **Salisbury** Worcester Tattersalls (IRE) Sale	**25** **Hamilton Park**★ **Leicester**★ **Newcastle**† **Newmarket** **Nottingham** Tipperary★ Tattersalls (IRE) Sale	**26** Cartmel **Chester**★ Curragh★ **Doncaster** **Newcastle**†★ **Newmarket**★ **Yarmouth**	**27** **Chester** Curragh **Doncaster**★ **Lingfield Park**★ **Newcastle**† **Newmarket** **Windsor** **York** SGA Sale
28 Cartmel Curragh Uttoxeter **Windsor**	**29** Ffos Las **Pontefract** **Windsor**★ **Wolverhampton**†★	**30** **Brighton** **Chepstow**★ **Hamilton Park** Stratford-On-Avon★ Arqana Sale				

JULY

Sun	Mon	Tues	Wed	Thur	Fri	Sat
			1 **Bath**★ *Bellewstown*★ **Kempton Park†**★ **Musselburgh** **Thirsk** Worcester Arqana Sale	**2** *Bellewstown*★ **Epsom Downs**★ **Haydock Park** **Newbury**★ Perth *Tipperary*★ **Yarmouth** Arqana Sale	**3** *Bellewstown*★ **Beverley** **Chelmsford City†**★ **Doncaster** **Haydock Park**★ Newton Abbot **Sandown Park** *Wexford*★	**4** *Bellewstown*★ **Beverley** **Carlisle** **Chelmsford City†** **Haydock Park** **Leicester** *Naas* **Nottingham**★ **Sandown Park**
5 *Ayr* *Fairyhouse* *Limerick* Market Rasen	**6** *Ayr* **Ripon**★ *Roscommon*★ **Windsor**★ Worcester	**7** **Brighton**★ **Pontefract** Uttoxeter★ **Wolverhampton†**★	**8** **Bath**★ **Catterick Bridge** *Fairyhouse*★ **Kempton Park†**★ **Lingfield Park** *Tramore*★ **Yarmouth** Tattersalls Sale	**9** **Carlisle** **Doncaster** **Epsom Downs**★ *Leopardstown*★ **Newbury**★ **Newmarket** Tattersalls Sale	**10** **Ascot** **Chepstow**★ **Chester**★ *Cork*★ Ffos Las★ *Kilbeggan*★ **Newmarket** **York** Tattersalls Sale	**11** **Ascot** **Chester** **Hamilton Park**★ *Limerick* *Navan* **Newmarket** **Salisbury**★ **York**
12 *Dundalk†* Perth Sligo Stratford-On-Avon	**13** **Ayr** **Brighton** *Killarney*★ *Roscommon*★ **Windsor**★ **Wolverhampton†**★ *Fasig-Tipton Sale*	**14** **Bath** **Beverley** **Chelmsford City†**★ Downpatrick *Killarney*★ Southwell★ Ascot Sale Fasig-Tipton Sale	**15** **Catterick Bridge** *Killarney*★ **Lingfield Park** Uttoxeter **Wolverhampton†**★ **Yarmouth**★	**16** **Chepstow** **Epsom Downs**★ **Hamilton Park** *Killarney* **Leicester** *Leopardstown*★ Worcester★	**17** **Hamilton Park**★ **Haydock Park** *Kilbeggan*★ *Killarney* **Newbury** **Newmarket**★ **Nottingham** **Pontefract**★ Goresbridge Sale	**18** Cartmel *Curragh* **Doncaster**★ **Haydock Park**★ Market Rasen **Newbury** **Newmarket** **Ripon**
19 *Curragh* Newton Abbot **Redcar** Stratford-On-Avon *Tipperary*	**20** **Ayr** *Ballinrobe*★ **Beverley**★ Cartmel **Windsor**★	**21** *Ballinrobe*★ **Chelmsford City†**★ **Musselburgh** **Nottingham**★ Southwell	**22** **Bath** **Catterick Bridge** **Leicester**★ **Lingfield Park** *Naas*★ **Sandown Park**★	**23** **Doncaster**★ *Leopardstown*★ *Limerick*★ **Newbury**★ **Sandown Park** Worcester **Yarmouth**	**24** **Ascot** **Chepstow**★ *Cork*★ *Down Royal*★ **Newmarket**★ **Thirsk** Uttoxeter **York**★	**25** **Ascot** **Chester** Gowran Park **Lingfield Park**★ **Newcastle†** **Newmarket** **Salisbury**★ **York**
26 **Pontefract** Uttoxeter	**27** **Ayr** *Galway*★ Newton Abbot **Windsor**★ **Wolverhampton†**★	**28** **Beverley** *Galway*★ **Goodwood** Perth★ Worcester★	**29** *Galway*★ **Goodwood** **Leicester**★ Perth **Redcar** **Sandown Park**★ Goffs UK Goodwood Sale	**30** **Epsom Downs**★ Ffos Las★ *Galway* **Goodwood** **Nottingham** Stratford-On-Avon	**31** Bangor-On-Dee **Bath**★ *Galway*★ **Goodwood** **Musselburgh**★ **Newmarket**★ **Wolverhampton†**	

AUGUST

Sun	Mon	Tues	Wed	Thur	Fri	Sat
30 Beverley Goodwood Yarmouth	**31** Cartmel **Chepstow** Downpatrick **Epsom Downs** **Ripon** Roscommon★ **Southwell†**					**1** Chelmsford City† Doncaster Galway Goodwood Hamilton Park★ Lingfield Park★ Newmarket Thirsk
2 Chester Galway Market Rasen	**3** Carlisle★ Cork **Kempton Park†** Naas **Ripon** **Windsor★**	**4** Catterick Bridge Ffos Las **Nottingham★** Roscommon★	**5** Bath Brighton **Kempton Park†** **Pontefract** Sligo **Yarmouth★** — Goffs UK Sale	**6** Brighton **Haydock Park** Leopardstown★ **Newcastle†** **Sandown Park★** Sligo★ **Yarmouth**	**7** Brighton **Chelmsford City†** **Haydock Park** **Musselburgh** **Newmarket★** **Thirsk** Tipperary★ Wexford★	**8** Ascot Ayr★ **Chelmsford City†** Cork **Haydock Park** Kilbeggan **Lingfield Park★** **Newmarket** **Redcar**
9 Curragh Downpatrick **Leicester** **Windsor** — Fasig-Tipton Sale	**10** Ayr Ballinrobe★ **Ripon** **Windsor★** **Wolverhampton†★** — Fasig-Tipton Sale Tattersalls (IRE) Sale	**11** **Chepstow** **Lingfield Park†** **Nottingham** — Tattersalls (IRE) Sale	**12** **Beverley** Gowran Park★ **Kempton Park†** **Newcastle†★** **Salisbury** — Tattersalls (IRE) Sale	**13** **Beverley** **Ffos Las★** Leopardstown★ **Lingfield Park** **Salisbury** Tramore★ **Yarmouth**	**14** **Chelmsford City†★** Curragh★ **Newbury** **Newmarket★** **Nottingham** **Thirsk★** Tramore★ **Wolverhampton†**	**15** Bath★ **Doncaster** Dundalk† Market Rasen★ **Newbury** **Newmarket** Perth **Ripon** Tramore★ — Arqana Sale
16 Pontefract Southwell Tramore — Arqana Sale	**17** Bangor-On-Dee★ **Catterick Bridge** **Lingfield Park†** Roscommon★ **Windsor★** — Arqana Sale	**18** **Carlisle★** **Hamilton Park** **Kempton Park†** Sligo★ — Arqana Sale Ascot Sale	**19** Bath **Carlisle** **Kempton Park†★** Killarney Worcester★ **York**	**20** Chepstow Fontwell Park★ Killarney★ **Leicester★** Stratford-On-Avon **York**	**21** Kilbeggan★ Killarney★ **Musselburgh** **Newcastle†★** **Salisbury★** **Sandown Park** **Wolverhampton†★** **York**	**22** **Chelmsford City†★** **Chester** Curragh★ Killarney **Lingfield Park†★** Newton Abbot **Sandown Park** **Wolverhampton†**
23 Brighton Naas Worcester	**24** Ballinrobe★ **Brighton** **Chepstow** **Ripon★**	**25** Bangor-On-Dee **Salisbury★** **Yarmouth** — Goffs UK Sale	**26** Bellewstown★ **Catterick Bridge** **Kempton Park†★** **Lingfield Park** **Musselburgh** Stratford-on-Avon★ — Goffs UK Sale	**27** Bellewstown★ **Carlisle** **Ffos Las** Fontwell Park★ **Newbury** Sedgefield★ Tipperary★ — Goffs UK Sale	**28** **Chelmsford City†** Curragh★ Down Royal★ **Ffos Las** **Goodwood★** **Hamilton Park★** **Newmarket** **Thirsk**	**29** **Beverley** Cartmel **Chelmsford City†** **Goodwood** Navan **Newmarket** **Redcar★** **Windsor★**

SEPTEMBER

Sun	Mon	Tues	Wed	Thur	Fri	Sat
		1 **Epsom Downs** *Laytown★* Newton Abbot★ **Ripon** Osarus Sale	**2** **Bath** *Gowran Park* **Hamilton Park★** Hexham★ **Lingfield Park** Uttoxeter Osarus Sale	**3** **Chelmsford City★** *Clonmel★* **Haydock Park** **Salisbury** Sedgefield Worcester★	**4** **Ascot** *Down Royal★* **Haydock Park** **Kempton Park†★** *Kilbeggan★* **Musselburgh★** **Newcastle†** BBAG Sales	**5** **Ascot** **Haydock Park** **Kempton Park†** *Navan* Stratford-On-Avon **Thirsk** *Wexford* **Wolverhampton†★**
6 *Fontwell Park* **York**	**7** **Brighton** *Galway★* Newton Abbot Perth **Windsor★**	**8** **Catterick Bridge** *Galway★* **Goodwood** **Leicester** **Newcastle†★** Ascot Sale	**9** **Carlisle** *Cork★* **Doncaster** Uttoxeter **Wolverhampton†★**	**10** **Chelmsford City†** **Chepstow** **Doncaster** **Epsom Downs** Goffs UK Yorton Sale	**11** *Ballinrobe★* **Chester** **Doncaster** **Salisbury★** **Sandown Park**	**12** **Bath** **Chelmsford City†** **Chester** **Doncaster** *Leopardstown* **Lingfield Park** **Musselburgh★** Goffs Sale
13 **Bath** *Curragh* **Flos Las**	**14** **Brighton** **Thirsk** **Wolverhampton†★** Worcester Keeneland Sale	**15** **Kempton Park†★** **Redcar** Southwell **Yarmouth** Goffs UK Sale Keeneland Sale	**16** **Beverley** *Kelso★* **Sandown Park** *Sligo* **Yarmouth** Goffs UK Sale Keeneland Sale	**17** **Ayr** **Chelmsford City†** *Naas* **Pontefract** **Yarmouth** Keeneland Sale	**18** **Ayr** *Downpatrick* *Dundalk†★* **Kempton Park†★** **Newbury** Newton Abbot SGA Sale Keeneland Sale	**19** **Ayr** **Catterick Bridge** **Chelmsford City†** *Gowran Park* *Navan* **Newbury** **Newmarket** **Wolverhampton†★** SGA Sale Keeneland Sale
20 **Hamilton Park** *Listowel* Plumpton Keeneland Sale	**21** *Fairyhouse★* **Hamilton Park** **Leicester** *Listowel* Warwick **Wolverhampton†★** Keeneland Sale	**22** **Beverley** **Lingfield Park†** *Listowel* **Newcastle†★** Warwick Tattersalls (IRE) Sale Keeneland Sale	**23** **Goodwood** **Kempton Park†★** *Listowel* Perth **Redcar** Tattersalls (IRE) Sale Keeneland Sale	**24** **Kempton Park†★** *Listowel* **Newmarket** Perth **Pontefract** Keeneland Sale	**25** *Dundalk†★* **Haydock Park** *Listowel* **Newcastle†★** **Newmarket** Worcester Keeneland Sale	**26** **Chelmsford City†★** **Chester** *Curragh* **Haydock Park** *Listowel* Market Rasen **Newmarket** **Ripon** Keeneland Sale
27 *Curragh* **Epsom Downs** **Musselburgh**	**28** **Bath** **Hamilton Park** **Newcastle†★** Newton Abbot *Roscommon*	**29** **Ayr** *Cork* Sedgefield **Wolverhampton†★** Worcester Goffs Sale	**30** Bangor-On-Dee Huntingdon **Kempton Park†★** **Nottingham** Goffs Sale			

OCTOBER

Sun	Mon	Tues	Wed	Thur	Fri	Sat
				1	**2**	**3**
				Chelmsford City†★	**Ascot**	**Ascot**
				Clonmel	*Dundalk†★*	Fontwell Park
				Salisbury	Fontwell Park	Gowran Park
				Southwell	*Gowran Park*	**Newmarket**
				Warwick	Hexham	**Redcar**
					Newcastle†★	**Wolverhampton†★**
				Goffs Sale	Goffs Sale	Arqana Sale
4	**5**	**6**	**7**	**8**	**9**	**10**
Kelso	Pontefract	**Brighton**	Kempton Park†★	**Ayr**	Chepstow	Chelmsford City†★
Tipperary	Stratford-On-Avon	**Catterick Bridge**	Ludlow	Chelmsford City†★	*Downpatrick*	Chepstow
Uttoxeter	*Tipperary*	*Galway*	Navan	Exeter	*Dundalk†★*	*Fairyhouse*
	Windsor	**Leicester**	Nottingham	**Southwell†★**	**Kempton Park†★**	Hexham
	Wolverhampton†★	**Southwell†★**	Sedgefield	*Thurles*	**Newmarket**	*Limerick*
				Worcester	**York**	**Newmarket**
						York
		Tattersalls Sale	Tattersalls Sale	Tattersalls Sale		
11	**12**	**13**	**14**	**15**	**16**	**17**
Curragh	**Musselburgh**	Hereford	**Bath**	**Brighton**	*Dundalk†★*	**Ascot**
Goodwood	**Windsor**	Huntingdon	Kempton Park†★	Carlisle	Fakenham	**Catterick Bridge**
Limerick	**Wolverhampton†★**	**Leicester**	Nottingham	Chelmsford City†★	**Newcastle†★**	*Flos Las*
Newton Abbot	**Yarmouth**	**Newcastle†★**	Wetherby	*Curragh*	**Redcar**	*Leopardstown*
		Punchestown	Punchestown	**Southwell†★**	Uttoxeter	Market Rasen
				Tramore		Stratford-On-Avon
				Wincanton		**Wolverhampton†★**
					BBAG Sale	BBAG Sale
	Tattersalls Sale	Tattersalls Sale	Tattersalls Sale	Tattersalls Sale	Tattersalls Sales	Tattersalls Sale
18	**19**	**20**	**21**	**22**	**23**	**24**
Cork	Plumpton	Exeter	Fontwell Park	Carlisle	Cheltenham	Chelmsford City†★
Kempton Park	**Pontefract**	*Gowran Park*	Kempton Park†★	Chelmsford City†★	**Doncaster**	Cheltenham
Naas	**Windsor**	**Kempton Park†★**	Navan	Ludlow	*Dundalk†★*	**Doncaster**
Sedgefield	**Wolverhampton†★**	**Newcastle†**	**Newmarket**	Southwell	**Newbury**	*Galway*
		Yarmouth	Worcester	*Thurles*	**Newcastle†★**	Kelso
				Wolverhampton†★	*Sligo*	*Leopardstown*
						Newbury
		Arqana Sale	Arqana Sale		Arqana Sale	
		Goffs UK Sale	Goffs UK Sale	Arqana Sale	Goresbridge Sale	
25	**26**	**27**	**28**	**29**	**30**	**31**
Aintree	Ayr	Bangor-On-Dee	*Dundalk†★*	Chelmsford City†★	*Down Royal*	Ascot
Galway	*Galway*	**Catterick Bridge**	Fakenham	*Clonmel*	*Dundalk†★*	Ayr
Wexford	**Leicester**	Chepstow	Kempton Park†★	**Lingfield Park†**	**Newcastle†★**	*Down Royal*
Wincanton	**Newcastle†★**	**Southwell†★**	**Nottingham**	Newton Abbot	**Newmarket**	**Newmarket**
	Redcar		Taunton	**Southwell†★**	Uttoxeter	Wetherby
	Wexford			Stratford-On-Avon	Wetherby	**Wolverhampton†★**
	Tattersalls Sale	Tattersalls Sale	Tattersalls Sale	Tattersalls Sale	Tattersalls Sale	

NOVEMBER

Sun	Mon	Tues	Wed	Thur	Fri	Sat
1 Carlisle Cork Huntingdon *Naas*	**2** Hereford **Kempton Park†** Plumpton **Wolverhampton†★** Goffs Sale	**3** Exeter *Fairyhouse* **Newcastle†★** **Redcar** **Southwell†** Goffs Sale	**4** *Dundalk†* **Kempton Park†★** **Lingfield Park†** Musselburgh **Nottingham** Goffs Sale	**5** **Chelmsford City†★** **Kempton Park†★** Market Rasen Newbury Sedgefield *Thurles* Ascot Sale	**6** *Dundalk†★* Fontwell Park Hexham **Newcastle†★** Warwick Osarus Sale Tattersalls (IRE) Sale	**7** Aintree **Chelmsford City†★** **Doncaster** Kelso *Naas* Wincanton Tattersalls (IRE) Sale
8 Ffos Las *Navan* Sandown Park Tattersalls (IRE) Sale	**9** Carlisle Chepstow *Fairyhouse* Kempton Park Keeneland Sale Tattersalls (IRE) Sale	**10** Hereford Huntingdon Lingfield Park Tattersalls (IRE) Sale Keeneland Sale	**11** Ayr Bangor-On-Dee Exeter Tattersalls (IRE) Sale Keeneland Sale	**12** *Clonmel* Ludlow Sedgefield Taunton Tattersalls (IRE) Sale Keeneland Sale	**13** Cheltenham *Dundalk†★* Newcastle Southwell Cheltenham Sale Tattersalls (IRE) Sale Keeneland Sale	**14** Cheltenham **Lingfield Park†** Punchestown Uttoxeter Wetherby **Wolverhampton†★** Tattersalls (IRE) Sale Keeneland Sale
15 Cheltenham Cork Fontwell Park Punchestown Goffs Sale Keeneland Sale	**16** **Kempton Park†★** Leicester Plumpton **Wolverhampton†** Arqana Sale Goffs Sale Keeneland Sale	**17** Fakenham Limerick Lingfield Park **Newcastle†★** **Southwell†** Arqana Sale Goffs Sale Keeneland Sale	**18** *Dundalk†* Ffos Las Hexham **Kempton Park†★** Warwick Arqana Sale Goffs Sale Keeneland Sale	**19** **Chelmsford City†★** Market Rasen **Newcastle†** *Thurles* Wincanton Goffs Sale Keeneland Sale	**20** Ascot Catterick Bridge Chepstow *Dundalk†★* **Newcastle†★** Goffs Sale Keeneland Sale	**21** Ascot *Gowran Park* Haydock Park Huntingdon **Lingfield Park†** **Wolverhampton†★** Goffs Sale Keeneland Sale
22 Exeter *Navan* Uttoxeter Goffs Sale	**23** Kempton Park Ludlow Musselburgh Tattersalls Sale	**24** Punchestown Sedgefield Southwell **Wolverhampton†★** Tattersalls Sale	**25** Hereford **Kempton Park†★** **Lingfield Park†** Wetherby Tattersalls Sale	**26** **Chelmsford City†★** Lingfield Park **Southwell†** Taunton *Thurles* Tattersalls Sale	**27** **Chelmsford City†★** Doncaster *Dundalk†★* Newbury **Southwell†** Tattersalls Sale	**28** Bangor-On-Dee Doncaster *Fairyhouse* Newbury Newcastle **Wolverhampton†★** Tattersalls Sale
29 Carlisle *Fairyhouse* Leicester Tattersalls Sale	**30** Ayr Fakenham **Wolverhampton†★** Tattersalls Sale					

DECEMBER

Sun	Mon	Tues	Wed	Thur	Fri	Sat
		1 *Dundalk†★* Lingfield Park Southwell **Wolverhampton★**	**2** Haydock Park **Kempton Park★** **Lingfield Park★** Ludlow	**3** **Chelmsford City†★** *Clonmel* Leicester Market Rasen Wincanton	**4** *Dundalk†★* Exeter **Newcastle†★** Sandown Park Sedgefield	**5** Aintree Chepstow *Navan* Sandown Park Wetherby **Wolverhampton†★**
		Tattersalls Sale	*Tattersalls Sale*	*Tattersalls Sale*	*Goffs UK Sale*	*Arqana Sale*
6 *Cork* Huntingdon Kelso *Punchestown*	**7** Musselburgh Plumpton **Wolverhampton†★**	**8** Fontwell Park **Southwell†★** *Tramore* Uttoxeter	**9** Hexham **Kempton Park†★** Leicester **Lingfield Park†**	**10** **Chelmsford City†★** Newcastle Taunton Warwick	**11** Bangor-On-Dee Cheltenham Doncaster *Dundalk†★* **Southwell†★**	**12** Cheltenham Doncaster Fairyhouse Hereford **Newcastle†** **Wolverhampton†★**
Arqana Sale	*Arqana Sale*	*Arqana Sale*				
13 Carlisle Southwell	**14** Ayr *Flos Las* *Naas* Plumpton	**15** Catterick Bridge Wincanton **Wolverhampton†★**	**16** *Dundalk†★* **Kempton Park†★** **Lingfield Park†** Ludlow Newbury	**17** **Chelmsford City†★** Exeter Hereford **Southwell†**	**18** Ascot *Dundalk†★* **Southwell†** Uttoxeter **Wolverhampton†★**	**19** Ascot Haydock Park **Lingfield Park†** *Navan* Newcastle **Wolverhampton†★**
20 Fakenham **Southwell†** *Thurles*	**21** Lingfield Park Musselburgh	**22**	**23**	**24**	**25**	**26** *Down Royal* Fontwell Park Huntingdon Kempton Park *Leopardstown* *Limerick* Market Rasen Sedgefield Wetherby Wincanton **Wolverhampton†**
27 Chepstow Kempton Park *Leopardstown* *Limerick* Wetherby **Wolverhampton†**	**28** Catterick Bridge Leicester *Leopardstown* *Limerick* **Lingfield Park†**	**29** Doncaster Kelso *Leopardstown* *Limerick* Newbury **Southwell†**	**30** Haydock Park **Lingfield Park†** Taunton	**31** **Lingfield Park†** *Punchestown* Uttoxeter Warwick		

DATES OF PRINCIPAL RACES
(SUBJECT TO ALTERATION)

JANUARY

Ballymore Novices' Hurdle (Cheltenham)	1st
Paddy Power Broken Resolutions Already Dipper Novices' Steeplechase (Cheltenham)	1st
Markel Insurance Handicap Steeplechase (Cheltenham)	1st
Paddy Power Handicap Steeplechase (Cheltenham)	1st
Paddy Power 68 sleeps to Cheltenham Handicap Hurdle (Cheltenham)	1st
Dornan Engineering Relkeel Hurdle (Cheltenham)	1st
EBF Stallions & Cheltenham Pony Club Standard Open National Hunt Flat Race (Cheltenham)	1st
Betway Hogmaneigh Handicap Hurdle (Musselburgh)	1st
Betway 'Auld Reekie' Handicap Steeple Chase (Musselburgh)	1st
Metal Man Chase (Tramore)	1st
32Red Handicap Stakes (Kempton Park)	4th
Impeccable Pig Inn Handicap Steeplechase (Sedgefield)	4th
Unibet Handicap Steeplechase (Sandown Park)	4th
Unibet Mares' Hurdle Race (Sandown Park)	4th
Unibet Tolworth Novices' Hurdle (Sandown Park)	4th
Unibet Veterans Handicap Steeplechase Final (Sandown Park)	4th
32red.com Handicap Hurdle (Sandown Park)	4th
Sky Sports Racing Sussex National Handicap Steeple Chase (Plumpton)	5th
Slaney Novices' Hurdle (Naas)	5th
32Red Conditions Stakes (Kempton Park)	8th
Betway Conditions Stakes (Newcastle)	8th
Bombardier Golden Beer Qualifier (Newcastle)	8th
Watt Fences North Yorkshire Grand National H'cap Steeple Chase (Catterick Bridge)	9th
Charnwood Forest Mares' Steeple Chase (Leicester)	9th
Weatherbys Chatteris Fen Juvenile Hurdle (Huntingdon)	10th
Unibet Lanzarote Handicap Hurdle (Kempton Park)	11th
32Red Silviniaco Conti Steeple Chase (Kempton Park)	11th
McCoy Contractors Civil Engineering Classic Handicap Steeple Chase (Warwick)	11th
Ballymore Leamington Novices' Hurdle (Warwick)	11th
McCoy Contractors 2020 Construction News Award Finalist Hampton Novices' Chase (Warwick)	11th
Pertemps Network Handicap Hurdle (Warwick)	11th
Dan Moore Memorial Handicap Steeple Chase (Fairyhouse)	11th
Moscow Flyer Novices' Hurdle (Punchestown)	12th
Killiney Novices' Steeple Chase (Punchestown)	12th
Wincanton Somerset National Handicap Steeple Chase (Wincanton)	16th
Matchbook Clarence House Steeple Chase (Ascot)	18th
bet365 Handicap Steeple Chase (Ascot)	18th
Matchbook Holloway's Hurdle Race (Limited Handicap) (Ascot)	18th
Warfield Mares' Hurdle (Ascot)	18th
OLBG.com Mares' Hurdle Race (Ascot)	18th
Patrick Coyne Memorial Altcar Novices' Steeple Chase (Haydock Park)	18th
Peter Marsh Limited Handicap Steeple Chase (Haydock Park)	18th
New One Unibet Champion Hurdle Trial (Haydock Park)	18th
Sky Bet Supreme Trial Rossington Novices' Hurdle (Haydock Park)	18th
Weatherbys Portman Cup Steeple Chase (Taunton)	18th
Navan Handicap Hurdle (Navan)	18th
Coolmore EBF Mares Novices' Steeple Chase (Thurles)	19th
Kinloch Brae Steeple Chase (Thurles)	19th
32Red Conditions Stakes (Kempton Park)	20th
Goffs Thyestes Handicap Steeple Chase (Gowran Park)	23rd
Galmoy Hurdle (Gowran Park)	23rd
Pertemps Lady Protectress Mares' Steeple Chase (Huntingdon)	24th
Sky Bet Best Odds Guaranteed Handicap Steeple Chase (Doncaster)	24th
Festival Trials Day Trophy Steeple Chase (Handicap) (Cheltenham)	25th
galliardhomes.com Cleeve Hurdle Race (Cheltenham)	25th
JCB Triumph Hurdle Trial (Juvenile Hurdle Race) (Cheltenham)	25th
Betbright Cotswold Steeple Chase (Cheltenham)	25th
Ballymore Novices' Hurdle Race (Cheltenham)	25th
Steel Plate and Sections Handicap Hurdle (Cheltenham)	25th
Timeform Novices' Handicap Steeple Chase (Cheltenham)	25th
Napoleons Casino & Restaurant Owlerton Sheffield Lightning Novices' Steeple Chase (Doncaster)	25th
Sky Bet Handicap Steeple Chase (Doncaster)	25th
Albert Bartlett River Don Novices' Hurdle Race (Doncaster)	25th
Yorkshire Rose Mares' Hurdle Race (Doncaster)	25th
Solerina Mares Novice Hurdle (Fairyhouse)	25th
Limestone Lad Hurdle (Naas)	26th
Woodlands Novice Chase (Naas)	26th
Ladbrokes Home Of The Odds Boost EBF Fillies' Handicap Stakes (Wolverhampton)	27th
Molson Coors Dick Hunt Handicap Steeple Chase (Wincanton)	30th

FEBRUARY

Betway Cleves Stakes (Lingfield Park)..1st
Betway Winter Derby Trial Stakes (Lingfield Park)...1st
Heroes Handicap Hurdle Race (Sandown Park)..1st
888Sport Contenders Hurdle (Sandown Park)...1st
888Sport Scilly Isles Novices' Steeple Chase (Sandown Park)...1st
888Sport Handicap Steeple Chase (Sandown Park)...1st
888Sport Masters Handicap Steeple Chase (Sandown Park)...1st
William Hill Towton Novices' Steeple Chase (Wetherby)...1st
bet365 Edinburgh National Handicap Steeple Chase (Musselburgh)...1st
bet365 Scottish County Hurdle (Musselburgh)..1st
BHP Insurances Irish Champion Hurdle (Leopardstown)...1st
Ladbrokes Dublin Chase (Leopardstown)...1st
Ladbrokes Liffey Handicap Hurdle (Leopardstown)...1st
Frank Ward Solicitors Arkle Novice Chase (Leopardstown)..1st
Goffs (Colts & Geldings) Irish National Hunt Flat Race (Leopardstown)..1st
Sandyford Handicap Steeple Chase (Leopardstown)...1st
Nathaniel Lacy Golden Cygnet Novice Hurdle (Leopardstown)..1st
bet365 Scottish Triumph Hurdle Juvenile Hurdle (Musselburgh)...2nd
Leopardstown Chase (Leopardstown)...2nd
Chanelle Group Brave Inca Novice Hurdle (Leopardstown)..2nd
Paddy Mullins EBF Mares Handicap Hurdle (Leopardstown)..2nd
Flogas Novice Chase (Leopardstown)...2nd
William Fly Glencullen Handicap Hurdle (Leopardstown)...2nd
Coolmore Stud Deep Run Mares INH Flat Race (Leopardstown)..2nd
Tattersalls Ireland Spring 4YO Hurdle (Leopardstown)..2nd
Unibet Irish Gold Cup (Leopardstown)..2nd
Mansionbet Sidney Banks Memorial Novices' Hurdle (Huntingdon)..6th
Mansionbet Handicap Hurdle (Huntingdon)..6th
Betfair Handicap Hurdle Race (Newbury)...8th
Betfair Denman Steeple Chase (Newbury)..8th
Betfair Exchange Steeple Chase (registered as the Game Spirit) (Newbury)..8th
St Mary's Lands Warwick Mares' Hurdle (Warwick)...8th
Betway Kingmaker Novices' Steeple Chase (Warwick)..8th
Warwick Castle Handicap Steeple Chase (Warwick)..8th
Bet At racingtv.com Novices' Hurdle (Exeter)..9th
Racing TV on Sky 426 Veterans' Handicap Steeple Chase (Qaualifier) (Exeter)..9th
Join Racing TV Now Mares' Steeple Chase (Exeter)..9th
EBF Novice Hurdle (Punchestown)...9th
Grand National Trial Handicap Steeple Chase (Punchestown)...9th
Opera Hat Mares Steeple Chase (Naas)..9th
Malcolm Jefferson Memorial Steeple Chase (Kelso)...13th
Timeform Morebattle Hurdle (A Limited Handicap) (Kelso)...13th
Powerstown Novice Hurdle (Clonmel)..13th
Weatherbys Jane Seymour Mares' Novices' Hurdle Race (Sandown Park)...14th
Sodexo Reynoldstown Novices' Steeple Chase (Ascot)...15th
Betfair Ascot Steeple Chase (Ascot)...15th
Keltbray Swinley Chase (Limited Handicap) (Ascot)..15th
Thames Materials Novices' Hurdle (Ascot)..15th
Ascot Supports Berkshire Community Foundation Handicap (Ascot)...15th
Albert Bartlett Prestige Novices' Hurdle Race (Haydock Park)...15th
William Hill Rendlesham Hurdle Race (Haydock Park)..15th
Grand National Trial (Handicap Steeple Chase) (Haydock Park)...15th
Betway Kingwell Hurdle Race (Wincanton)...15th
Red Mills Steeple Chase (Gowran Park)...15th
Red Mills Trial Hurdle (Gowran Park)..15th
32Red Conditions Stakes (Kempton Park)...16th
Boyne Hurdle (Navan)..16th
Ten Up Novice Steeple Chase (Navan)...16th
sunracing.co.uk Handicap Stakes (Newcastle)..19th
Ladbrokes Home Of The Odds Boost Conditions Stakes (Newcastle)...19th
Napoleons Casino & Restaurant Sheffield Veterans' Handicap Steeple Chase (Doncaster)............................19th
Quevega Mares' Hurdle (Punchestown)...19th
Michael Purcell Novice Hurdle (Thurles)...20th
Healthy Pets Devon National Handicap Steeple Chase (Exeter)..21st
Budbrooke Handicap Steeple Chase (Warwick)...21st
888Sport Steeple Chase (Handicap) (Kempton Park)..22nd
888Sport Take 'Em On Adonis Juvenile Hurdle Race (Kempton Park)..22nd
888 Sport Pendil Novices's Steeple Chase (Kempton Park)..22nd
Skybet Dovecote Novices' Hurdle Race (Kempton Park)...22nd
Vertem Eider Handicap Steeple Chase (Newcastle)..22nd
Betway Hever Sprint Stakes (Lingfield Park)...22nd
Betway Winter Derby (Lingfield Park)..22nd
At The Races Bobbyjo Steeple Chase (Fairyhouse)...22nd

Winning Fair Juvenile Hurdle (Fairyhouse)..22nd
Netbet Casino National Spirit Hurdle Race (Fontwell Park)..23rd
Nas na Riogh Novice Handicap Chase (Naas)..23rd
Paddy Power Johnstown Novice Hurdle (Naas)...23rd
Paddy Power Newlands Steeple Chase (Naas)..23rd
Ladbrokes Fillies Handicap Stakes (Newcastle)...27th
Patton Stakes (Dundalk)..28th
Ladbrokes Spring Cup Stakes (Lingfield Park)..29th
totescoop6 Premier Kelso Hurdle Race (Kelso)..29th
Belhaven Brewery Premier Steeple Chase (Kelso)...29th
Edinburgh Gin Premier Kelso Novices' Hurdle (Kelso)..29th
William Hill Supporting Greatwood Gold Cup (Newbury)..29th
William Hill Supporting Greatwood Veterans' Handicap Steeple Chase (Newbury)...29th
888Sport Take 'Em On Mares' Novices' Hurdle (Doncaster)...29th
888Sport Bet £10 Get £30 Handicap Steeple Chase (Doncaster)..29th
888Sport Grimthorpe Handicap Steeple Chase (Doncaster)..29th
Flyingbolt Novice Steeple Chase (Navan)...29th

MARCH

Sedgefield Racecourse Handicap Steeple Chase (Sedgefield)...1st
TRI Equestrian Carrickmines Handicap Steeple Chase (Leopardstown)...1st
Move Over To Matchbook Handicap Stakes (Kempton Park)...4th
100% Profit Boost At 32redsport.com Handicap Stakes (Kempton Park)...4th
Road To The Kentucky Derby' Conditions Stakes (Kempton Park)...4th
Matchbook Imperial Cup Handicap Hurdle Race (Sandown Park)...7th
European Breeders' Fund 'National Hunt' Novices' Hurdle Race (Sandown Park)..7th
sunracing.co.uk Lincoln Trial Handicap Stakes (Wolverhampton)...7th
sunracing.co.uk Lady Wulfruna Stakes (Wolverhampton)...7th
Betway Heed Your Hunch Handicap Stakes (Wolverhampton)...7th
Shamrock Handicap Steeple Chase (Gowran Park)..7th
Directors Plate Novice Steeple Chase (Naas)...8th
Irish Racing Writers Kingsfurze Novices' Hurdle (Naas)..8th
Leinster National (Naas)...8th
Unibet Champion Hurdle Champion Trophy (Cheltenham)...10th
Racing Post Arkle Challenge Trophy Steeple Chase (Cheltenham)..10th
Sky Bet Supreme Novices' Hurdle Race (Cheltenham)..10th
Ultima Handicap Steeple Chase (Cheltenham)..10th
Festival Mares' Hurdle Race (Cheltenham)...10th
Close Brothers Novices' Handicap Steeple Chase (Cheltenham)..10th
National Hunt Novices' Steeple Chase (Cheltenham)..10th
Betway Queen Mother Champion Steeplechase (Cheltenham)...11th
RSA Insurance Novices' Steeple Chase (Cheltenham)...11th
Glenfarclas Steeple Chase (A Cross Country Steeple Chase) (Cheltenham)..11th
Ballymore Novices' Hurdle Race (Cheltenham)...11th
Coral Cup (Handicap Hurdle Race) (Cheltenham)...11th
Weatherbys Champion Bumper NH Flat Race (Cheltenham)..11th
Boodles Juvenile Handicap Hurdle Race (registered as Fred Winter) (Cheltenham)..11th
Marsh Novices' Steeple Chase (registered as Golden Miller) (Cheltenham)..12th
Brown Advisory & Marriebelle Stable Plate Handicap Steeple Chase (Cheltenham)..12th
Paddy Power Stayers' Hurdle Race (Cheltenham)..12th
Ryanair Steeple Chase (registered as Festival Trophy) (Cheltenham)...12th
Fulke Walwyn Kim Muir Challenge Cup Amateur Riders Handicap Steeple Chase (Cheltenham)................................12th
Dawn Run Mares' Novices' Hurdle (Cheltenham)..12th
Marsh Novices' Steeple Chase (Cheltenham)..12th
Pertemps Network Final Handicap Hurdle (Cheltenham)...12th
Magners Cheltenham Gold Cup Steeple Chase (Cheltenham)...13th
JCB Triumph Hurdle Race (Cheltenham)..13th
Johnny Henderson Grand Annual Steeple Chase Challenge Cup (Cheltenham)..13th
Randox Health County Handicap Hurdle Race (Cheltenham)...13th
Albert Bartlett Novices' Hurdle Race (Cheltenham)...13th
St James's Place Foxhunter Challenge Cup Hunters' Steeple Chase (Cheltenham)...13th
Martin Pipe Conditional Jockeys Handicap Hurdle (Cheltenham)..13th
Matchbook Silver Bowl Handicap Steeple Chase (Kempton Park)..14th
Matchbook VIP Silver Plate Handicap Hurdle (Kempton Park)..14th
Brit Plant Direct Novices' Handicap Steeple Chase (Uttoxeter)...14th
Marston's Pedigree Handicap Hurdle (Uttoxeter)..14th
Marston's 61 Deep Midlands Grand National Steeple Chase (Uttoxeter)..14th
An Uaimh Chase (Navan)..14th
EBF Novice Final Handicap Chase (Navan)..14th
Aglionby Veterans' Handicap Steeple Chase (Carlisle)...15th
Dawn Run EBF Mares Novice Chase (Limerick)...15th
Shannon Spray EBF Mares Novice Hurdle (Limerick)...15th
Northern Lights Juvenile Hurdle Series Final (Handicap Hurdle) (Musselburgh)...20th
Northern Lights Two Miles Hurdle Series Final (Handicap Hurdle) (Musselburgh)..20th
Northern Lights Mares' Hurdle Series Final (Handicap Hurdle) (Musselburgh)...20th

Northern Lights Stayers' Hurdle Series Final (Handicap Hurdle) (Musselburgh)..20th
EBF & TBA Mares' 'National Hunt Novices' Hurdle Finale (Limited Handicap) (Newbury)............................21st
Be Wiser Insurance Juvenile Handicap Hurdle (Newbury)..21st
Conditional Jockeys' Veterans' Chase Series Final Handicap Steeple Chase (Newbury)............................21st
Liz Adam Memorial Handicap Steeple Chase (Kelso)..21st
Bernhard Lighting Rig Handicap Hurdle (Kelso)...21st
Paxtons Exclusively Kverneland Handicap Hurdle (Kelso)..21st
Native Upmanship Novice Chase (Thurles)..21st
Northern Lights Two Mile Chase Series Final Handicap Steeple Chase (Carlisle).......................................22nd
Northern Lights Staying Chase Series Final Handicap Steeple Chase (Carlisle)...22nd
Northern Lights Middle Distance Chase Series Final Handicap Steeple Chase (Carlisle)............................22nd
EBF Park Express Stakes (Naas)..22nd
Devoy Stakes (Naas)...22nd
Unibet Lincoln (Heritage Handicap) (Doncaster)...28th
Unibet Cammidge Trophy Stakes (Doncaster)..28th
Unibet Doncaster Mile Stakes (Doncaster)...28th
Matchbook Magnolia Stakes (Kempton Park)...28th
Better Odds With Matchbook Handicap Stakes (Kempton Park)..28th
Matchbook Betting Podcast Rosebery Handicap Stakes (Kempton Park)...28th
Colts & Fillies Club Juvenile Handicap Hurdle (Ascot)...29th
First Days Charity Novices' Handicap Steeple Chase (Ascot)..29th
Sky Sports Racing Veterans' Handicap Steeple Chase (Ascot)...29th
Irish Lincolnshire (Curragh)...29th
Hugh McMahon Memorial Novice Chase (Limerick)..29th
Kevin McManus Bumper INH Flat Race (Limerick)...29th
Betway Casino Handicap Stakes (Newcastle)...30th
Betway Live Casino Handicap Stakes (Newcastle)...30th

APRIL

Heritage Stakes (Leopardstown)...1st
Woodford Reserve Cardinal Conditions Stakes (Chelmsford City)..2nd
Doom Bar Anniversary 4yo Juvenile Hurdle Race (Aintree)...2nd
Betway Bowl Steeple Chase (Aintree)..2nd
Betway Aintree Hurdle (Aintree)..2nd
Close Brothers Red Rum Handicap Steeple Chase (Aintree)...2nd
Devenish 'Manifesto Novices' Steeple Chase (Aintree)..2nd
Goffs Nickel Coin Mares' Standard Open National Hunt Flat Race (Aintree)..2nd
Randox Health Foxhunters' Open Hunters' Steeple Chase (Aintree)..2nd
Randox Health Topham Steeple Chase (Handicap) (Aintree)..3rd
Betway Top Novices' Hurdle Race (Aintree)...3rd
JLT Melling Steeple Chase (Aintree)..3rd
Betway Mildmay Novices' Steeple Chase (Aintree)..3rd
Merseyrail Handicap Hurdle Race (Aintree)...3rd
Pinsent Masons Handicap Hurdle (Aintree)...3rd
Doom Bar Sefton Novices' Hurdle Race (Aintree)..3rd
Weatherbys Private Banking Champion Standard Open NHF (Aintree)...3rd
Gaskells Waste Management Handicap Hurdle Race (Aintree)...4th
Ryanair Liverpool Stayers' Hurdle Race (Aintree)...4th
Doom Bar Maghull Novices' Steeple Chase (Aintree)...4th
Randox Health Grand National Steeple Chase (Handicap) (Aintree)..4th
Betway Handicap Steeple Chase (Aintree)...4th
Betway Mersey Novices' Hurdle Race (Aintree)...4th
Ballysax Stakes (Leopardstown)...5th
Leopardstown 1000 Guineas Trial Stakes (Leopardstown)..5th
Leopardstown 2000 Guineas Trial Stakes (Leopardstown)..5th
Barry Hills Further Flight Stakes (Nottingham)...8th
£20 Free Bets At totesport.com Handicap Stakes (Chelmsford City)...10th
Sun Racing All-Weather Championships Apprentice Handicap Stakes (Lingfield Park).................................10th
Betway All-Weather Marathon Championships Conditions Stakes (Lingfield Park).......................................10th
Ladbrokes All-Weather Fillies' And Mares' Championships Conditions Stakes (Lingfield Park).....................10th
Betway All-Weather Sprint Championships Conditions Stakes (Lingfield Park)...10th
Ladbrokes 3 Year Old All-Weather Championships Conditions Stakes (Lingfield Park)................................10th
Betway Easter Classic All-Weather Middle Distance Championships Conditions Stakes (Lingfield Park)........10th
Sun Racing All-Weather Mile Championships Conditions Stakes (Lingfield Park)...10th
Ladbrokes Burradon Stakes (Newcastle)...10th
Queen's Cup Stakes (Heritage Handicap) (Musselburgh)...11th
William Hill Scottish Sprint Cup (Heritage Handicap) (Musselburgh)...11th
Royal Mile Handicap Stakes (Musselburgh)...11th
Bet At racingtv.com Handicap Stakes (Kempton Park)..11th
Racing TV Fillies' Conditions Stakes (Kempton Park)...11th
Racing TV Conditions Stakes (Kempton Park)..11th
Racing TV Snowdrop Fillies' Stakes (Kempton Park)..11th
Wise Betting At racingtv.com Handicap Stakes (Kempton Park)..11th
Racing TV Queen's Prize Handicap Stakes (Kempton Park)..11th
Betway Challenger Staying Chase Series Final Handicap Steeple Chase (Haydock Park)............................11th

bet365 Novices' Championship Final Handicap Hurdle (Sandown Park) 25th
bet365 Handicap Hurdle (Sandown Park) 25th
Betway Old Boston Handicap Stakes (Haydock Park) 25th
Betway Edge Green Handicap Stakes (Haydock Park) 25th
EBF Stallions King Richard III Stakes (Leicester) 25th
Visit attheraces.com Handicap Stakes (Ripon) 25th
MCH Hutchinson Memorial Handicap Stakes (Ripon) 25th
Committed Stakes (Navan) 25th
Salsabil Stakes (Navan) 25th
Vintage Crop Stakes (Navan) 25th
Prix Ganay (Parislongchamp) 26th
Woodlands Sprint Stakes (Naas) 27th
Boylesports Champion Chase (Punchestown) 28th
Evening Herald Champion Novice Hurdle (Punchestown) 28th
Growise Novice Chase (Punchestown) 28th
Kilashee Handicap Hurdle (Punchestown) 28th
Meriebelle Stable Commonwealth Cup Trial Stakes (registered as the Pavilion Stakes) (Ascot) 29th
Longines Sagaro Stakes (Ascot) 29th
Ascot Shop Paradise Stakes (Ascot) 29th
Attheraces Champion Bumper INH Flat Race (Punchestown) 29th
Bibby Financial Punchestown Gold Cup (Punchestown) 29th
Guinness Handicap Chase (Punchestown) 29th
Irish Daily Mirror War of Attrition Novice Hurdle (Punchestown) 29th
Liss A Paoraigh Mares Bumper INH Flat Race (Punchestown) 29th
totepool Chelmer Fillies' Stakes (Chelmsford City) 30th
Ballymore Eustace Handicap Hurdle (Punchestown) 30th
Ladbrokes World Series Hurdle (Punchestown) 30th
Shawiya Mares Novice Hurdle (Punchestown) 30th
Ryanair Novice Chase (Punchestown) 30th
Three.ie Handicap Steeple Chase (Punchestown) 30th

MAY

Glencarraig Lady Mares Handicap Steeple Chase (Punchestown) 1st
Punchestown Champion Hurdle (Punchestown) 1st
Punchestown Novice Handicap Chase (Punchestown) 1st
Tattersalls Ireland Champion Novice Hurdle (Punchestown) 1st
QIPCO Jockey Club Stakes (Newmarket) 2nd
QIPCO 2000 Guineas Stakes (Newmarket) 2nd
Zoustar Palace House Stakes (Newmarket) 2nd
Lightning Spear Newmarket Stakes (Newmarket) 2nd
Unibet EBF Daisy Warwick Fillies' Stakes (Goodwood) 2nd
Conqueror Fillies' Stakes (Goodwood) 2nd
Aes Champion 4yo Hurdle (Punchestown) 2nd
Ballymore Handicap Hurdle (Punchestown) 2nd
EBF Mares Champion Hurdle (Punchestown) 2nd
Charm Spirit Dahlia Stakes (Newmarket) 3rd
QIPCO 1000 Guineas Stakes (Newmarket) 3rd
Tweenhills Pretty Polly Stakes (Newmarket) 3rd
Athasi Stakes (Curragh) 4th
Mooresbridge Stakes (Curragh) 4th
Tetrach Stakes (Curragh) 4th
First Flier Stakes (Curragh) 4th
Arkle Finance Cheshire Oaks (Chester) 5th
MBNA Chester Vase (Chester) 5th
Vintage Tipple Stakes (Gowran Park) 5th
Boodles Diamond Ormonde Stakes (Chester) 6th
Homeserve Dee Stakes (Chester) 6th
Victor McCalmont Stakes (Gowran Park) 6th
Sportpesa Chester Cup (Heritage Handicap) (Chester) 7th
Homeserve Huxley Stakes (Chester) 7th
Polonia Stakes (Cork) 8th
Tote Victoria Cup (Ascot) 9th
Carey Group Buckhounds Stakes (Ascot) 9th
Pertemps Network Spring Trophy Stakes (Haydock Park) 9th
Swinton Handicap Hurdle Race (Haydock Park) 9th
RaceBets Million Chartwell Fillies' Stakes (Lingfield Park) 9th
RaceBets Derby Trial Stakes (Lingfield Park) 9th
RaceBets Money Back All Losers Oaks Trial Fillies' Stakes (Lingfield Park) 9th
EBF Weatherbys General Stud Book Kilvington Stakes (Nottingham) 9th
Blue Wind Stakes (Naas) 9th
Sole Power Stakes (Naas) 9th
Emirates Poule d'Essai Des Pouliches (Parislongchamp) 10th
Emirates Poule d'Essai Des Poulains (Parislongchamp) 10th
Killarney Handicap Hurdle (Killarney) 10th
Tourist Attraction Mares Hurdle (Killarney) 10th

Amethyst Stakes (Leopardstown) 10th
Derrinstown 1000 Guineas Trial Stakes (Leopardstown) 10th
Derrinstown Derby Trial Stakes (Leopardstown) 10th
Tori Global Supports The Samaritans Stakes (registered as Royal Windsor) (Windsor) 11th
An Riocht Chase (Killarney) 11th
Tattersalls Musidora Stakes (York) 13th
Duke of York Clipper Logistics Stakes (York) 13th
British Stallion Studs EBF Westow Stakes (York) 14th
Al Basti Equiworld Dubai Dante Stakes (York) 14th
Al Basti Equiworld Dubai Middleton Stakes (York) 14th
Matchbook Yorkshire Cup (York) 15th
Langley Solicitors British EBF Marygate Fillies' Stakes (York) 15th
Oaks Farm Stables Fillies' Stakes (registered as Michael Seely Memorial Stakes) (York) 15th
Seamus and Rosemary McGrath Memorial Savel Beg Stakes (Leopardstown) 15th
Al Shaqab Lockinge Stakes (Newbury) 16th
Al Rayyan Stakes (registered as the Aston Park) (Newbury) 16th
Shalaa Carnarvon Stakes (Newbury) 16th
Haras de Bouquetot Fillies' Trial Stakes (Newbury) 16th
Betway Fairway Stakes (Newmarket) 16th
Betway King Charles II Stakes (Newmarket) 16th
Yeats Stakes (Navan) 16th
Coolmore Stud Juvenile Fillies' Stakes (Naas) 17th
Lacken Stakes (Naas) 17th
Whitehead Memorial Stakes (Naas) 17th
Weatherbys Hamilton Stakes (registered as Leisure Stakes) (Windsor) 18th
Tennent's Lager British Stallion Studs EBF Rothesay Stakes (Ayr) 20th
Matchbook Henry II Stakes (Sandown Park) 21st
Matchbook Heron Stakes (Sandown Park) 21st
Armstrong Aggregates Temple Stakes (Haydock Park) 23rd
Armstrong Aggregates Sandy Lane Stakes (Haydock Park) 23rd
EBF British Stallion Studs Cecil Frail (sponsored by Armstrong Aggregates) Stakes (Haydock Park) ... 23rd
Lanwades Stud Stakes (Curragh) 23rd
Marble Hill Stakes (Curragh) 23rd
Tattersalls Irish 2000 Guineas Stakes (Curragh) 23rd
Weatherbys Greenlands Stakes (Curragh) 23rd
Tattersalls Irish 1000 Guineas Stakes (Curragh) 24th
Tattersalls Gold Cup (Curragh) 24th
Gallinule Stakes (Curragh) 24th
Prix d'Ispahan (Parislongchamp) 24th
Saxon Warrior Coolmore Prix Saint Alary (Parislongchamp) 24th
Mayo Grand National (Ballinrobe) 26th
Height of Fashion Stakes (Goodwood) 28th
Matchbook VIP Henry II Stakes (Sandown Park) 28th
Matchbook Betting Podcast National Stakes (Sandown Park) 28th
Matchbook Brigadier Gerard Stakes (Sandown Park) 28th
British Stallion Studs EBF Cocked Hat Stakes (Goodwood) 29th
Pertemps Network Stratford Foxhunters Champion Steeple Chase (Stratford) 29th
Betfair Tapster Stakes (Goodwood) 30th
Betfair Festival Stakes (Goodwood) 30th
Betway John of Gaunt Stakes (Haydock Park) 30th
Betway Pinnacle Stakes (Haydock Park) 30th
Betway Achilles Stakes (Haydock Park) 30th
William Hill Bronte Cup Fillies' Stakes (York) 30th
British Stallion Studs EBF Nottinghamshire Oaks Stakes (Nottingham) 31st
QIPCO Prix du Jockey Club (Chantilly) 31st

JUNE

Ballyogan Stakes (Curragh) 3rd
Silver Stakes (Curragh) 3rd
Glencairn Stakes (Leopardstown) 4th
Nijinsky (for King George V Cup) Stakes (Leopardstown) 4th
Investec Oaks Stakes (Epsom) 5th
Investec Coronation Cup (Epsom) 5th
Investec Surrey Stakes (Epsom) 5th
Investec Diomed Stakes (Epsom) 6th
Princess Elizabeth Stakes (sponsored by Investec) (Epsom) 6th
Investec Derby Stakes (Epsom) 6th
Investec Corporate Banking 'Dash' (Heritage Handicap) (Epsom) 6th
Stobo Castle Ladies' Day Gold Cup Fillies Stakes (registered as Maggie Dickson Stakes) (Musselburgh) .. 6th
Midsummer Sprint Stakes (Cork) 10th
Munster Oaks Stakes (Cork) 10th
Johnnie Lewis Memorial British EBF Stakes (registered as Abingdon Stakes) (Newbury) 11th
Ballycorus Stakes (Leopardstown) 11th
equinITy Technology Ganton Stakes (York) 12th
Randox Health Scurry Stakes (Sandown Park) 13th

JULY

Darley July Cup (Newmarket) 11th
bet365 Superlative Stakes (Newmarket) 11th
bet365 Bunbury Cup (Heritage Handicap) (Newmarket) 11th
Sportpesa City Plate Stakes (Chester) 11th
John Smith's Silver Cup Stakes (York) 11th
John Smith's City Walls Stakes (York) 11th
John Smith's Cup (Heritage Handicap) (York) 11th
Qatar Prix Jean Prat (Deauville) 12th
Cairn Rouge Stakes (Killarney) 13th
Juddmonte Grand Prix de Paris (Parislongchamp) 14th
Bourn Vincent Memorial Handicap Steeple Chase (Killarney) 14th
Icon Meld Stakes (Leopardstown) 16th
British Stallion Studs EBF Glasgow Stakes (Hamilton Park) 17th
Irish Thoroughbred Marketing Rose Bowl Stakes (Newbury) 17th
Weatherbys Super Sprint (Newbury) 18th
bet365 Hackwood Stakes (Newbury) 18th
bet365 Stakes (registered as Steventon Stakes) (Newbury) 18th
Ric & Mary Hambro Aphrodite Fillies' Stakes (Newmarket) 18th
Betway Summer Handicap Hurdle (Market Rasen) 18th
Betway Summer Plate Handicap Steeple Chase (Market Rasen) 18th
Kerrygold Irish Oaks Stakes (Curragh) 18th
Jebel Ali Anglesey Stakes (Curragh) 18th
Minstrel Stakes (Curragh) 18th
Kilboy Estate Stakes (Curragh) 19th
Sapphire Stakes (Curragh) 19th
Sweet Mimosa Stakes (Naas) 22nd
British Stallion Studs EBF Star Stakes (Sandown Park) 23rd
Silver Flash Stakes (Leopardstown) 23rd
Tyros Stakes (Leopardstown) 23rd
Vinnie Roe Stakes (Leopardstown) 23rd
Acorn Insurance British EBF Valiant Stakes (Ascot) 24th
British Stallion Studs EBF Lyric Fillies' Stakes (York) 24th
Her Majesty's Plate Stakes (Down Royal) 24th
King George VI and Queen Elizabeth QIPCO Stakes (Ascot) 25th
Princess Margaret Keeneland Stakes (Ascot) 25th
Wooldridge Group Pat Eddery Stakes (Ascot) 25th
Moet & Chandon International Stakes (Heritage Handicap) (Ascot) 25th
Sky Bet York Stakes (York) 25th
Sky Bet Go Racing In Yorkshire Summer Festival Pomfret Stakes (Pontefract) 26th
Qatar Lennox Stakes (Goodwood) 28th
Qatar Vintage Stakes (Goodwood) 28th
Qatar Goodwood Cup (Goodwood) 28th
Castlegar Novice Hurdle (Galway) 28th
Markel Insurance Molecomb Stakes (Goodwood) 29th
Qatar Sussex Stakes (Goodwood) 29th
thetote.com Galway Plate (Handicap Chase) (Galway) 29th
Qatar Richmond Stakes (Goodwood) 30th
Qatar Gordon Stakes (Goodwood) 30th
Qatar Nassau Stakes (Goodwood) 30th
Corrib EBF Fillies' Stakes (Galway) 30th
Ballybrit Novice Steeple Chase (Galway) 30th
Guinness Galway Hurdle (Handicap) (Galway) 30th
L'Ormarins Queens Plate Glorious Stakes (Goodwood) 31st
Qatar King George Stakes (Goodwood) 31st
Bombay Sapphire Glorious Stakes (Goodwood) 31st
Bonhams Thoroughbred Stakes (Goodwood) 31st
Theo Fennell Oak Tree Stakes (Goodwood) 31st
Golden Mile (Heritage Handicap) (Goodwood) 31st

AUGUST

Qatar Lillie Langtry Stakes (Goodwood) 1st
Stewards Cup (Heritage Handicap) (Goodwood) 1st
British Stallion Studs EBF Chalice Stakes (Newmarket) 1st
Mervue Handicap Hurdle (Galway) 1st
MBNA Queensferry Stakes (Chester) 2nd
Prix Rothschild (Deauville) 2nd
Ballyroan Stakes (Leopardstown) 6th
El Gran Senor Stakes (Tipperary) 7th
Rose of Lancaster Stakes (Haydock Park) 8th
British Stallion Studs EBF Dick Hern Stakes (Haydock Park) 8th
German-Thoroughbred.com Sweet Solera Stakes (Newmarket) 8th
Give Thanks Stakes (Cork) 8th
Platinum Stakes (Cork) 8th
Keeneland Phoenix Stakes (Curragh) 9th
QREC Phoenix Sprint Stakes (Curragh) 9th

LARC Prix Maurice de Gheest (Deauville) 9th
British Stallion Studs EBF Upavon Fillies' Stakes (Salisbury) 12th
Hurry Harriet Stakes (Gowran Park) 12th
Tattersalls Sovereign Stakes (Salisbury) 13th
Invesco Desmond Stakes (Leopardstown) 13th
Byerley Stud Stakes (registered as St Hugh's Stakes) (Newbury) 14th
Ballycullen Stakes (Curragh) 14th
Curragh Stakes (Curragh) 14th
Royal Whip Stakes (Curragh) 14th
Unibet Hungerford Stakes (Newbury) 15th
Unibet Geoffrey Freer Stakes (Newbury) 15th
Denford Stakes (formerly Washington Singer Stakes) (Newbury) 15th
EBF Stallions Highfield Farm Flying Fillies' Stakes (Pontefract) 16th
Prix du Haras de Fresnay-Le-Buffard Jacques Le Marois (Deauville) 16th
Juddmonte International Stakes (York) 19th
Sky Bet Great Voltigeur Stakes (York) 19th
Tattersalls Acomb Stakes (York) 19th
Mount Brandon Handicap Hurdle (Killarney) 19th
Darley Yorkshire Oaks (York) 20th
British EBF & Sir Henry Cecil Galtres Stakes (York) 20th
Sky Bet Lowther Stakes (York) 20th
Goffs UK Premier Yearling Stakes (York) 20th
Weatherbys Hamilton Lonsdale Cup (York) 21st
Coolmore Nunthorpe Stakes (York) 21st
Al Basti Equiworld Gimcrack Stakes (York) 21st
Longines Irish Champions Weekend EBF Stonehenge Stakes (Salisbury) 21st
Ruby Stakes (Killarney) 21st
Sportpesa Chester Stakes (Chester) 22nd
Betway Solario Stakes (Sandown Park) 22nd
Betway Atalanta Stakes (Sandown Park) 22nd
Sky Bet Strensall Stakes (York) 22nd
Sky Bet City of York Stakes (York) 22nd
Julia Graves Roses Stakes (York) 22nd
Sky Bet Ebor (Heritage Handicap) (York) 22nd
Debutante Stakes (Curragh) 22nd
Futurity Stakes (Curragh) 22nd
Lough Leane Handicap Chase (Killarney) 22nd
Darley Prix Morny - Finale des Darley Series (Deauville) 23rd
Darley Prix Jean Romanet (Deauville) 23rd
Abergwaun Stakes (Tipperary) 27th
Fairy Bridge Stakes (Tipperary) 27th
Flame of Tara Stakes (Curragh) 28th
Round Tower Stakes (Curragh) 28th
Snow Fairy Stakes (Curragh) 28th
William Hill Beverley Bullet Sprint Stakes (Beverley) 29th
Ladbrokes Prestige Stakes (Goodwood) 29th
Ladbrokes Celebration Mile (Goodwood) 29th
Ladbrokes March Stakes (Goodwood) 29th
Price Bailey Chartered Accountants Hopeful Stakes (Newmarket) 29th
Sky Sports Racing Winter Hill Stakes (Windsor) 29th
Sri Lanka August Stakes (Windsor) 29th
Weatherbys Bank Supreme Stakes (Goodwood) 30th
BSS EBF Ripon Champion Two Year Old Trophy Stakes (Ripon) 31st

SEPTEMBER

Shadwell Dick Poole Fillies' Stakes (Salisbury) 3rd
Betfair Sprint Cup (Haydock Park) 5th
Betfair Superior Mile (Haydock Park) 5th
Betfair Ascendant Stakes (Haydock Park) 5th
Sun Racing September Stakes (Kempton Park) 5th
Sun Racing Sirenia Stakes (Kempton Park) 5th
LNER Supporting CALM Garrowby Stakes (York) 6th
Prix du Moulin de Longchamp (Parislongchamp) 6th
Oyster Stakes (Galway) 8th
DC Training And Development Services Scarbrough Stakes (Doncaster) 9th
DFS Park Hill Stakes (Doncaster) 10th
May Hill Stakes (Doncaster) 10th
Weatherbys Racing Bank £300,000 2 Year Old Median Auction Stakes (Doncaster) 10th
Japan Racing Association Sceptre Stakes (Doncaster) 11th
Magners Rose Doncaster Cup (Doncaster) 11th
Weatherbys Global Stallions App Flying Scotsman Stakes (Doncaster) 11th
Wainwright Flying Childers Stakes (Doncaster) 11th
Hird Rail Group Park Stakes (Doncaster) 12th
Pommery Champagne Stakes (Doncaster) 12th
St Leger Stakes (Doncaster) 12th

Sportpesa Stand Cup Stakes (Chester) 12th
QIPCO Irish Champion Stakes (Leopardstown) 12th
Clipper Logistics Solonoway Stakes (Leopardstown) 12th
Coolmore Matron Stakes (Leopardstown) 12th
Kilternan Stakes (Leopardstown) 12th
KPMG Golden Fleece Stakes (Leopardstown) 12th
Ingabelle Stakes (Leopardstown) 12th
Comer Group International St Leger Stakes (Curragh) 13th
Derrinstown Stud Flying Five Stakes (Curragh) 13th
Goffs Vincent O'Brien National Stakes (Curragh) 13th
Moyglare Stud Blandford Stakes (Curragh) 13th
Moyglare Stud Stakes (Curragh) 13th
Qatar Prix Vermeille (Parislongchamp) 13th
Chasemore Farm Fortune Stakes (Sandown Park) 16th
EBF Stallions John Musker Fillies' Stakes (Yarmouth) 16th
Doonside Cup Stakes (Ayr) 17th
Shadwell Stud / EBF Stallions Harry Rosebery Stakes (Ayr) 18th
Al Maktoum Cup Arran Scottish Fillies' Sprint Stakes (Ayr) 18th
Dubai Duty Free Cup Stakes (Newbury) 18th
Firth of Clyde Stakes (Ayr) 19th
Ayr Gold Cup (Heritage Handicap) (Ayr) 19th
Dubai Duty Free Legacy Cup (Newbury) 19th
Dubai International Airport World Trophy (Newbury) 19th
Dubai Duty Free Mill Reef Stakes (Newbury) 19th
Cordell Lavarack Stakes (Gowran Park) 19th
Blenheim Stakes (Fairyhouse) 21st
Listowel Stakes (Listowel) 21st
Latrigue 4yo Handicap Hurdle (Listowel) 22nd
British Stallion Studs EBF Foundation Stakes (Goodwood) 23rd
Guinness Kerry National (Handicap Steeple Chase) (Listowel) 23rd
Tattersalls Stakes (Newmarket) 24th
Jockey Club Rose Bowl Stakes (Newmarket) 24th
Ladbrokes Handicap Hurdle (Listowel) 24th
Shadwell Joel Stakes (Newmarket) 25th
Shadwell Rockfel Stakes (Newmarket) 25th
Princess Royal Muhaarar Stakes (Newmarket) 25th
Tasleet British EBF Rosemary Stakes (Newmarket) 25th
Mukhadram Godolphin Stakes (Newmarket) 25th
Diamond Stakes (Dundalk) 25th
Juddmonte Royal Lodge Stakes (Newmarket) 26th
Juddmonte Cheveley Park Stakes (Newmarket) 26th
Juddmonte Middle Park Stakes (Newmarket) 26th
bet365 Cambridgeshire (Heritage Handicap) (Newmarket) 26th
Ferry Ales Brewery Prelude Handicap Hurdle (Market Rasen) 26th
Beresford Stakes (Curragh) 27th
CL and MF Weld Park Stakes (Curragh) 27th
Loughbrown Stakes (Curragh) 27th
Renaissance Stakes (Curragh) 27th
Kilbegnet Novice Chase (Roscommon) 28th
Navigation Stakes (Cork) 29th

OCTOBER

Londonmetric Noel Murless Stakes (Ascot) 2nd
Star Appeal Stakes (Dundalk) 2nd
Mucklemeg Mares Bumper INH Flat Race (Gowran Park) 2nd
Pat Walsh Memorial Mares Hurdle (Gowran Park) 2nd
Property Raceday Targets £3m Cumberland Lodge Stakes (Ascot) 3rd
John Guest Bengough Stakes (Ascot) 3rd
Challenge Cup (Heritage Handicap) (Ascot) 3rd
UK Hi-Fi Show Live Rous Stakes (Ascot) 3rd
Child Bereavement UK British EBF Stakes (registered as October Stakes) (Ascot) 3rd
Kingdom of Bahrain Sun Chariot Stakes (Ascot) 3rd
Tattersalls £150,000 October Yearling Auction Stakes (Newmarket) 3rd
Racing TV EBF Stallions Guisborough Stakes (Redcar) 3rd
Redcar Two Year Old Trophy Stakes (Redcar) 3rd
Gowran Champion Steeple Chase (Gowran Park) 3rd
Qatar Prix du Cadran (Parislongchamp) 3rd
Qatar Prix de Royallieu (Parislongchamp) 3rd
Qatar Prix de la Foret (Parislongchamp) 4th
Qatar Prix de l'Arc de Triomphe (Parislongchamp) 4th
Prix de l'Opera Longines (Parislongchamp) 4th
Prix de l'Abbaye de Longchamp Longines (Parislongchamp) 4th
Qatar Prix Marcel Boussac - Criterium des Pouliches (Parislongchamp) 4th
Qatar Prix Jean-Luc Lagardere (Grand Criterium) sponsored by Manateq (Parislongchamp) 4th
Concorde Stakes (Tipperary) 4th

Joe Mac Novice Hurdle (Tipperary) 4th
Like A Butterfly Novice Chase (Tipperary) 4th
Tipperary Hurdle (Tipperary) 4th
Unibet Persian War Novices' Hurdle Race (Chepstow) 9th
bet365 Fillies' Mile (Newmarket) 9th
Darley Pride Stakes (Newmarket) 9th
Godolphin Lifetime Care Oh So Sharp Stakes (Newmarket) 9th
Newmarket Academy Godolphin Beacon Project Cornwallis Stakes (Newmarket) 9th
Godolphin Stud & Stable Staff Awards Challenge Stakes (Newmarket) 9th
bet365 Old Rowley Cup (Heritage Handicap) (Newmarket) 9th
Cotswold Stone Supplies Ltd Silver Trophy Handicap Hurdle Race (Chepstow) 10th
Darley Dewhurst Stakes (Newmarket) 10th
Darley Stakes (Newmarket) 10th
Godolphin Flying Start Zetland Stakes (Newmarket) 10th
Dubai Autumn Stakes (Newmarket) 10th
Dubai British EBF Boadicea Stakes (Newmarket) 10th
Dubai Cesarewitch (Heritage Handicap) (Newmarket) 10th
coral.co.uk Rockingham Stakes (York) 10th
Low Cost Vans Novices' Steeple Chase (Chepstow) 10th
Martin Molony Stakes (Limerick) 10th
Lanwades and Staffordstown Studs Silken Glider Stakes (Curragh) 11th
Legacy Stakes (Curragh) 11th
Waterford Testimonial Stakes (Curragh) 11th
Greenmount Park Novice Hurdle (Limerick) 11th
Ladbrokes Munster National Handicap Chase (Limerick) 11th
Cailain Alainn Mares Hurdle (Limerick) 11th
British Stallion Studs EBF Beckford Stakes (Bath) 14th
Buck House Novice Steeple Chase (Punchestown) 14th
Carvills Hill Steeple Chase (Punchestown) 14th
Mercury Stakes (Dundalk) 16th
Queen Elizabeth II Stakes sponsored by QIPCO (Ascot) 17th
QIPCO British Champions Sprint Stakes (Ascot) 17th
QIPCO British Champions Long Distance Cup (Ascot) 17th
QIPCO Champion Stakes (Ascot) 17th
QIPCO British Champions Fillies & Mares Stakes (Ascot) 17th
Killavullan Stakes (Leopardstown) 17th
Trigo Stakes (Leopardstown) 17th
Matchbook VIP Hurdle (Kempton Park) 18th
Matchbook Betting Exchange Novices' Hurdle (Kempton Park) 18th
Kinsale Handicap Steeple Chase (Cork) 18th
Bluebell Stakes (Naas) 18th
Garnet Stakes (Naas) 18th
ebfstallions.com Silver Tankard Stakes (Pontefract) 19th
Vertem Futurity Trophy (Doncaster) 24th
MFB Group Franking Services Stakes (registered as Doncaster Stakes) (Doncaster) 24th
Cancom Stakes (registered as the Horris Hill Stakes) (Newbury) 24th
Teddington RBL Poppy Appeal Stakes (registered as the St Simon Stakes) (Newbury) 24th
Racing TV Stakes (registered as Radley Stakes) (Newbury) 24th
Eyrefield Stakes (Leopardstown) 24th
Knockaire Stakes (Leopardstown) 24th
Criterium de Saint-Cloud (Saint-Cloud) 24th
Virgin Bet Monet's Garden Old Roan Steeple Chase (Aintree) 25th
Bettyville Steeple Chase (Wexford) 25th
Prix Royal-Oak (Parislongchamp) 25th
Criterium International (Parislongchamp) 25th
Ladbrokes River Eden Stakes (Lingfield Park) 29th
Ladbrokes Fleur De Lys Fillies' Stakes (Lingfield Park) 29th
Irish Stallion Farms EBF Bosra Sham Fillies' Stakes (Newmarket) 30th
Weatherbys Hamilton Wensleydale Juvenile Hurdle (Wetherby) 30th
bet365 Handicap Steeple Chase (Wetherby) 30th
Hamptons EBF Mares Novice Hurdle (Down Royal) 30th
WKD Hurdle (Down Royal) 30th
Cooley Stakes (Dundalk) 30th
Price Bailey Ben Marshall Stakes (Newmarket) 31st
Weatherbys TBA James Seymour Stakes (Newmarket) 31st
British Stallion Studs EBF Montrose Fillies' Stakes (Newmarket) 31st
Sodexo Gold Cup Handicap Steeple Chase (Ascot) 31st
Byrne Group Handicap Steeple Chase (Ascot) 31st
Sodexo Handicap Hurdle (Ascot) 31st
bet365 Charlie Hall Steeple Chase (Wetherby) 31st
bet365 West Yorkshire Hurdle Race (Wetherby) 31st
bet365 Mares' Hurdle (Wetherby) 31st
Kauto Star Steeple Chase (Down Royal) 31st
Mac's Joy Handicap Hurdle (Down Royal) 31st
Skymas Steeple Chase (Down Royal) 31st

NOVEMBER

Colin Parker Memorial Intermediate Steeple Chase (Carlisle) 1st
Paddy Power Cork Grand National Handicap Steeple Chase (Cork) 1st
Paddy Power EBF Novice Chase (Cork) 1st
Paddy Power EBF Novice Hurdle (Cork) 1st
Finale Stakes (Naas) 1st
Matchbook Floodlit Stakes (Kempton Park) 2nd
Coral Haldon Gold Cup Steeple Chase (Limited Handicap) (Exeter) 3rd
BDN Construction Ltd Bud Booth Mares' Steeple Chase (Market Rasen) 5th
British EBF Gillies Fillies' Stakes (Doncaster) 7th
Wentworth Stakes (Doncaster) 7th
Unibet Elite Hurdle Race (Wincanton) 7th
John Romans Park Homes Rising Stars Novices' Steeple Chase (Wincanton) 7th
Badger Beers Silver Trophy Handicap Steeple Chase (Wincanton) 7th
Brown Lad Handicap Hurdle (Naas) 7th
Fishery Lane 4yo Hurdle (Naas) 7th
Poplar Square Steeple Chase (Naas) 7th
Virgin Bet Future Stars Intermediate Steeple Chase (Sandown Park) 8th
For Auction Novice Hurdle (Navan) 8th
Fortria Chase (Navan) 8th
Lismullen Hurdle (Navan) 8th
Canter Carpet Mares' Novices' Steeple Chase (Bangor-On-Dee) 11th
Clonmel Oil Chase (Clonmel) 12th
EBF TA Morris Memorial Mares Chase (Clonmel) 12th
Ballymore Novices' Hurdle Race (Cheltenham) 13th
Betway Churchill Stakes (Lingfield Park) 14th
Betway Golden Rose Stakes (Lingfield Park) 14th
Betvictor Gold Cup Steeple Chase (Handicap) (Cheltenham) 14th
Betvictor Smartcards Handicap Steeple Chase (Cheltenham) 14th
JCB Triumph Hurdle Trial (registered as Prestbury Juvenile Hurdle) (Cheltenham) 14th
SIA Big Bucks Handicap Hurdle (Cheltenham) 14th
Karndean Mares' Standard Open National Hunt Flat Race (Cheltenham) 14th
Morgiana Hurdle (Punchestown) 14th
Craddockstown Novice Chase (Punchestown) 14th
Unibet Greatwood Hurdle Race (Handicap) (Cheltenham) 15th
Racing Post Arkle Trophy Trial Novices' Steeple Chase (Cheltenham) 15th
Sky Bet Supreme Trial Novices' Hurdle Race (Cheltenham) 15th
Shloer Cheltenham Steeple Chase (Cheltenham) 15th
High Sheriff Of Gloucestershire And Racing Remember Standard Open NH Flat Race (Cheltenham) 15th
Florida Pearl Novice Steeple Chase (Punchestown) 15th
Grabel Mares Hurdle (Punchestown) 15th
BSS EBF Hyde Stakes (Kempton Park) 18th
Thurles Chase (Thurles) 19th
Coral Hurdle Race (Ascot) 21st
Christy 1965 Steeple Chase (Acot) 21st
Betfair Exchange Handicap Hurdle Race (Haydock Park) 21st
Betfair Steeple Chase (Haydock Park) 21st
Betfair Newton Novices' Hurdle (Haydock Park) 21st
Aries Girl Mares Bumper INH Flat Race (Navan) 22nd
Ladbrokes Troytown Handicap Steeple Chase (Navan) 22nd
Monksfield Novice Hurdle (Navan) 22nd
Racing TV Mares' Hurdle (Kempton Park) 23rd
Ladbrokes Long Distance Hurdle Race (Newbury) 27th
Ladbrokes Novices' Steeple Chase (Newbury) 27th
Ladbrokes Trophy Steeple Chase (Newbury) 28th
Ladbrokes John Francome Novices' Chase (Newbury) 28th
Ladbrokes Intermediate Hurdle (Limited Handicap) (registered as Gerry Feilden Hurdle) (Newbury) 28th
Ladbrokes Mares' Novices' Hurdle (Newbury) 28th
Betfair Fighting Fifth Hurdle Race (Newcastle) 28th
Betfair Rehearsal Handicap Steeple Chase (Newcastle) 28th
Ballyhack Handicap Steeple Chase (Fairyhouse) 28th
Houghton Mares' Steeple Chase (Carlisle) 29th
Bar One Drinmore Novice Chase (Fairyhouse) 29th
Bar One Hattons Grace Hurdle (Fairyhouse) 29th
Bar One Royal Bond Novice Hurdle (Fairyhouse) 29th
New Stand Handicap Hurdle (Fairyhouse) 29th
Porterstown Handicap Steeple Chase (Fairyhouse) 29th
Winter Festival Juvenile Hurdle (Fairyhouse) 29th

DECEMBER

32Red Wild Flower Stakes (Kempton Park) 2nd
Ballymore Winter Novices' Hurdle Race (Sandown Park) 4th
Randox Health Becher Handicap Steeple Chase (Aintree) 5th
Vigin Bet Many Clouds Steeple Chase (Aintree) 5th

Download The App At Virgin Bet Fillies' Juvenile Hurdle (Aintree) 5th
Betfair Tingle Creek Steeple Chase (Sandown Park) 5th
randoxhealth.com Henry VIII Novices' Steeple Chase (Sandown Park) 5th
Jumeirah Hotels And Resorts December Handicap Hurdle (Sandown Park) 5th
Klairon Davis EBF Novice Chase (Navan) 5th
Navan Novice Hurdle (Navan) 5th
Foxrock Handicap Steeple Chase (Navan) 5th
Proudstown Handicap Hurdle (Navan) 5th
Fitzdares Peterborough Steeple Chase (Huntingdon) 6th
Henrietta Should Be Knighted Mares Standard Open NH Flat Race (Huntingdon) 6th
Kerry Group Cork Stayers Novice Hurdle (Cork) 6th
Kerry Group Hilly Way Steeple Chase (Cork) 6th
Lombardstown EBF Mares Novice Chase (Cork) 6th
John Durkan Memorial Steeple Chase (Punchestown) 6th
Voler La Verdette Mares Novice Hurdle (Punchestown) 6th
Actioncoach Lady Godiva Mares' Novices' Steeple Chase (Warwick) 10th
December Handicap Steeple Chase (Cheltenham) 11th
Albert Bartlett Bristol Novices' Hurdle Race (Cheltenham) 12th
Caspian Caviar Gold Cup (Handicap Steeple Chase) (Cheltenham) 12th
Unibet International Hurdle Race (Cheltenham) 12th
bet365 December Novices' Steeple Chase (Doncaster) 12th
bet365 Summit Juvenile Hurdle Race (Doncaster) 12th
Thoroughbred Breeders' Association Mares' Steeple Chase (Cheltenham) 16th
Sky Bet Supreme Trial Novices' Hurdle Race (registered as the Kennel Gate) (Ascot) 18th
Jaquart Noel Novices' Steeple Chase (Ascot) 18th
St Andrews Holdings Championship Standard Open NH Flat Race (Ascot) 18th
Betway Quebec Stakes (Lingfield Park) 19th
JLT Long Walk Hurdle Race (Ascot) 19th
Betfair Exchange Trophy (Handicap Hurdle Race) (Ascot) 19th
Smarkets Betting Exchange Mares' Novices' Hurdle (registered as Abram Mares' Hurdle) (Haydock Park) 19th
Future Champions Bumper INH Flat Race (Navan) 19th
Tara Handicap Hurdle (Navan) 19th
Boreen Belle EBF Mares Novice Hurdle (Thurles) 20th
Ladbrokes Kauto Star Novices' Steeple Chase (Kempton Park) 26th
Ladbrokes Christmas Hurdle Race (Kempton Park) 26th
Ladbrokes King George VI Steeple Chase (Kempton Park) 26th
racingtv.com Rowland Meyrick Handicap Steeple Chase (Wetherby) 26th
Knight Frank Juvenile Hurdle (Leopardstown) 26th
Racing Post Novice Steeple Chase (Leopardstown) 26th
Greenmount Park Novice Chase (Limerick) 26th
coral.co.uk Future Champions Finale Juvenile Hurdle Race (Chepstow) 27th
Coral Welsh Grand National (Handicap Steeple Chase) (Chepstow) 27th
Ladbrokes Wayward Lad Novices' Steeple Chase (Kempton Park) 27th
Ladbrokes Desert Orchid Steeple Chase (Kempton Park) 27th
Paddy Power Dial A Bet Chase (Leopardstown) 27th
Paddy Power Future Champions Novice Hurdle (Leopardstown) 27th
Paddy Power Handicap Chase (Leopardstown) 27th
Dorans Pride Novice Hurdle (Limerick) 27th
Savills Christmas Chase (Leopardstown) 28th
Squared Financials Christmas Hurdle (Leopardstown) 28th
Tim Duggan Memorial Handicap Chase (Limerick) 28th
Betway Challow Novices' Hurdle Race (Newbury) 29th
Yorkshire Silver Vase Mares' Steeple Chase (Doncaster) 29th
Fort Leney Novice Chase (Leopardstown) 29th
Ryanair December Hurdle (Leopardstown) 29th
Willis Tower Watson EBF Mares Hurdle (Leopardstown) 29th
Sporting Limerick 4yo Hurdle (Limerick) 29th
Byerley Stud Mares' Novices' Hurdle (Taunton) 30th

The list of Principal Races has been supplied by the BHA and Horse Racing Ireland and is provisional. In all cases, the dates, venues, and names of sponsors are correct at time of going to press, but also subject to possible alteration.

Front cover - Archimento and N Over J among the bluebells in Angmering Park, home to William Knight's Lower Coombe Stables in West Sussex (photo by Edward Whitaker)

INDEX TO TRAINERS
†denotes Permit to train under N.H. Rules only

Name	Team No.
BROWN, MR ALAN	067
BROWN, MR ANDI	068
BROWN, MR DAVID	069
†BRYANT, MISS MICHELLE	070
BUCKLER, MR BOB	071
BURCHELL, MR DAI	072
BURKE, MR K. R.	073
BURKE, MR KEIRAN	074
†BURNS, MR HUGH	075
BURROWS, MR OWEN	076
BUTLER, MR JOHN	077
BUTLER, MR PADDY	078
†BUTTERWORTH, MRS BARBARA	079

C

Name	Team No.
†CABBLE, MISS LOUISE	080
CAMACHO, MISS JULIE	081
CAMPION, MR MARK	082
CANDLISH, MS JENNIE	083
CANDY, MR HENRY	084
CANN, MR GRANT	085
CANTILLON, MR DON	086
CARR, MRS RUTH	087
CARROLL, MR DECLAN	088
CARROLL, MR TONY	089
CARSON, MR TONY	090
CARTER, MR LEE	091
CASE, MR BEN	092
CHAMINGS, MR PATRICK	093
CHANNON, MR MICK	094
CHAPMAN, MR MICHAEL	095
†CHAPMAN, MR RYAN	096
CHAPPET, MR FABRICE	097
CHAPPLE-HYAM, MRS JANE	098
CHAPPLE-HYAM, MR PETER	099
CHARALAMBOUS, MR PETER	100
CHARLTON, MR ROGER	101
CHISMAN, MR HARRY	102
CLEMENT, MR NICOLAS	103
CLOVER, MR TOM	104
CLUTTERBUCK, MR KEN	105
COAKLEY, MR DENIS	106
COLE, MR PAUL	107

Name	Team No.
COLLIER, MR TJADE	108
COLLINS, MR PAUL	109
COLTHERD, MR STUART	110
†CONWAY, MR SEAN	111
CORBETT, MRS SUSAN	112
†CORNWALL, MR JOHN	113
COULSON, MR JAKE	114
COWARD, MISS JACQUELINE	115
COWELL, MR ROBERT	116
COX, MR CLIVE	117
COYLE, MR TONY	118
CRAGGS, MR RAY	119
CRATE, MR PETER	120
CRISFORD, MR SIMON	121
CROOK, MR ANDREW	122
CURRAN, MR SEAN	123
CURTIS, MISS REBECCA	124
CUTHBERT, MISS HELEN	125

D

Name	Team No.
D'ARCY, MR PAUL	126
DACE, MR LUKE	127
DALGLEISH, MR KEITH	128
DALY, MR HENRY	129
DANDO, MR PHILLIP	130
DARTNALL, MR VICTOR	131
DASCOMBE, MR TOM	132
DAVIDSON, MR TRISTAN	133
DAVIES, MR JOHN	134
DAVIES, MISS SARAH-JAYNE	135
DAVIS, MISS JO	136
DAVISON, MISS ZOE	137
†DAY, MR ANTHONY	138
DE BEST-TURNER, MR WILLIAM	139
DE GILES, MR ED	140
DEACON, MR GEOFFREY	141
DENNIS, MR DAVID	142
†DENNIS, MR TIM	143
DICKIN, MR ROBIN	144
†DIXON, MR JOHN	145
DIXON, MR SCOTT	146
†DIXON, MR STEVEN	147
DOBBIN, MRS ROSE	148

Name	Team No.
†DODGSON, MR ASHLEY	149
DODS, MR MICHAEL	150
DORE, MR CONOR	151
DOW, MR SIMON	152
DOWN, MR CHRIS	153
DREW, MR CLIVE	154
DRINKWATER, MR DAVID W.	155
DRINKWATER, MR SAMUEL	156
DU PLESSIS, MISS JACKIE	157
DUFFIELD, MRS ANN	158
DUKE, MR BRENDAN W.	159
DUNCAN, MR IAN	160
†DUNGER, MR NIGEL	161
DUNLOP, MR ED	162
DUNLOP, MR HARRY	163
DUNN, MRS ALEXANDRA	164
DUNNETT, MRS CHRISTINE	165
DURACK, MR SEAMUS	166
DYSON, MISS CLAIRE	167

E

Name	Team No.
EARLE, MR SIMON	168
EASTERBY, MR MICHAEL	169
EASTERBY, MR TIM	170
†ECKLEY, MR BRIAN	171
EDDERY, MR ROBERT	172
EDMUNDS, MR STUART	173
†EDWARDS, MR GORDON	174
ELLISON, MR BRIAN	175
ELSWORTH, MR DAVID	176
†ENDER, MISS SARA	177
ENGLAND, MRS SAM	178
EUSTACE, MR JAMES	179
EVANS, MR DAVID	180
EVANS, MR JAMES	181
†EVANS, MRS MARY	182
EVANS, MRS NIKKI	183
EWART, MR JAMES	184
EYRE, MR LES	185

F

Name	Team No.
FAHEY, MR RICHARD	186
FAIRHURST, MR CHRIS	187
FANSHAWE, MR JAMES R.	188

Name	Team No.
FARRELLY, MR JOHNNY	189
FEILDEN, MISS JULIA	190
FELL, MR ROGER	191
FELLOWES, MR CHARLIE	192
FERGUSON, MR JAMES	193
FFRENCH DAVIS, MR DOMINIC	194
FIERRO, MR GUISEPPE	195
FIFE, MRS MARJORIE	196
FITZGERALD, MR TIM	197
FLINT, MR JOHN	198
FLOOD, MR DAVID	199
FLOOK, MR STEVE	200
FORBES, MR TONY	201
†FORD, MRS PAM	202
FORD, MRS RICHENDA	203
FORSEY, MR BRIAN	204
FORSTER, MISS SANDY	205
FOSTER, MISS JOANNE	206
FOX, MR JIMMY	207
FRANCE, MISS SUZZANNE	208
†FRANKLAND, MR DEREK	209
FROST, MR JAMES	210
FROST, MR KEVIN	211
FRY, MR HARRY	212
FRYER, MISS CAROLINE	213
FURTADO, MR IVAN	214

G

Name	Team No.
GALLAGHER, MR JOHN	215
GALLAGHER, MR THOMAS	216
GANSERA-LEVEQUE, MRS ILKA	217
GARDNER, MRS SUSAN	218
†GASSON, MRS ROSEMARY	219
GEORGE, MR PAUL	220
GEORGE, MR TOM	221
GIFFORD, MR NICK	222
GILLARD, MR MARK	223
GIVEN, MR JAMES	224
GOLDIE, MR JIM	225
GOLLINGS, MR STEVE	226
GORDON, MR CHRIS	227
GOSDEN, MR JOHN	228
GRAHAM, MRS HARRIET	229

Name	Team No.	Name	Team No.
GRANT, MR CHRIS	230	HILL, MRS LAWNEY	271
GRASSICK, MR JAMES	231	HILLS, MR CHARLES	272
GRAY, MR CARROLL	232	HOAD, MR MARK	273
GREATREX, MR WARREN	233	HOBBS, MR PHILIP	274
GREENALL, MR OLIVER	234	HOBSON, MISS CLARE	275
GRETTON, MR TOM	235	HOBSON, MR RICHARD	276
GRIFFITHS, MR DAVID C.	236	HODGE, MR JOHN	277
GRISSELL, MRS DIANA	237	HODGES, MR RON	278
GROUCOTT, MR JOHN	238	†HOGARTH, MR HENRY	279
GUEST, MR RAE	239	HOLLINSHEAD, MISS SARAH	280
GUEST, MR RICHARD	240	HOLLINSHEAD, MRS STEPH	281
GUNDRY, MS POLLY	241	HOLT, MR JOHN	282
H		HONEYBALL, MR ANTHONY	283
HAGGAS, MR WILLIAM	242	†HOWELL, MS GEORGIE	284
HALES, MR ALEX	243	HUGHES, MRS DEBBIE	285
HALFORD, MR MICHAEL	244	HUGHES, MR RICHARD	286
HAMER, MRS DEBRA	245	HUMPHREY, MRS SARAH	287
HAMILTON, MRS ALISON	246	†HUNTER, MR KEVIN	288
†HAMILTON, MR ANDREW	247	HURLEY, MISS LAURA	289
†HAMILTON, MRS ANN	248	**I**	
HAMMOND, MR MICKY	249	INGRAM, MR ROGER	290
HANMER, MR GARY	250	IVORY, MR DEAN	291
HANNON, MR RICHARD	251	**J**	
HARKER, MR GEOFFREY	252	JACKSON, MISS TINA	292
†HARPER, MR RICHARD	253	†JAMES, MISS HANNAH	293
HARRINGTON, MRS JESSICA	254	JAMES, MR LEE	294
HARRIS, MISS GRACE	255	JARDINE, MR IAIN	295
HARRIS, MR MILTON	256	JARVIS, MR WILLIAM	296
HARRIS, MR RONALD	257	JEFFERSON, MISS RUTH	297
HARRIS, MR SHAUN	258	JEFFREYS, MR D J	298
HARRISON, MISS LISA	259	JENKINS, MR J. R.	299
HASLAM, MR BEN	260	JEWELL, MRS LINDA	300
HAWKE, MR NIGEL	261	JOHNSON, MR BRETT	301
†HAWKER, MR MICHAEL	262	JOHNSON, MR KENNY	302
HAWKER, MR RICHARD	263	†JOHNSON, MRS SUSAN	303
†HAYNES, MR JONATHAN	264	JOHNSON HOUGHTON, MISS EVE	304
HAYWOOD, MISS GAIL	265	JOHNSTON, MR MARK	305
†HEARD, MR COLIN	266	JONES, MR ALAN	306
HEDGER, MR PETER	267	**K**	
HENDERSON, MR NICKY	268	†KEHOE, MRS FIONA	307
HENDERSON, MR PAUL	269	KEIGHLEY, MR MARTIN	308
HERRINGTON, MR MICHAEL	270	KEIGHTLEY, MR SHAUN	309

Name	Team No.	Name	Team No.
KELLETT, MR CHRISTOPHER	310	**MARTIN, MR ANDREW J.**	350
KELLEWAY, MISS GAY	311	**†MARTIN, MISS NICKY**	351
KENIRY, MRS STEF	312	**MASON, MR CHRISTOPHER**	352
KENT, MR NICK	313	**MASON, MRS JENNIFER**	353
†KERR, MR LEONARD	314	**†MATHIAS, MISS JANE**	354
KING, MR ALAN	315	**MCBRIDE, MR PHILIP**	355
KING, MR NEIL	316	**MCCAIN, MR DONALD**	356
KIRBY, MR PHILIP	317	**MCCARTHY, MR TIM**	357
KIRK, MR SYLVESTER	318	**MCENTEE, MR PHIL**	358
KITTOW, MR STUART	319	**MCGRATH, MR MURTY**	359
KNIGHT, MR WILLIAM	320	**MCGREGOR, MRS JEAN**	360
KUBLER, MR DANIEL	321	**MCJANNET, MR LUKE**	361
L		**MCLINTOCK, MS KAREN**	362
LACEY, MR TOM	322	**MCPHERSON, MR GRAEME**	363
LAFFON-PARIAS, MR CARLOS	323	**MEADE, MR MARTYN**	364
†LAMPARD, MR NICK	324	**MEADE, MR NOEL**	365
†LANDY, MR JUSTIN	325	**MEEHAN, MR BRIAN**	366
LANIGAN, MR DAVID	326	**MENUISIER, MR DAVID**	367
LAVELLE, MISS EMMA	327	**MENZIES, MISS REBECCA**	368
LAWES, MR TOBY	328	**MIDDLETON, MR PHIL**	369
LEAVY, MR BARRY	329	**MIDGLEY, MR PAUL**	370
LEE, MISS KERRY	330	**MILLMAN, MR ROD**	371
LEECH, MRS SOPHIE	331	**MITCHELL, MR RICHARD**	372
LEESON, MISS TRACEY	332	**†MITFORD-SLADE, MR RICHARD**	373
LEWIS, MRS SHEILA	333	**MOFFATT, MR JAMES**	374
LITTMODEN, MR NICK	334	**MOHAMMED, MR ISMAIL**	375
LLEWELLYN, MR BERNARD	335	**MONGAN, MRS LAURA**	376
LLOYD-BEAVIS, MISS NATALIE	336	**MOORE, MR ARTHUR**	377
LONG, MR JOHN E.	337	**MOORE, MR GARY**	378
LONGSDON, MR CHARLIE	338	**MOORE, MR J. S.**	379
LOUGHNANE, MR DAVID	339	**MORGAN, MISS KELLY**	380
LOUGHNANE, MR MARK	340	**MORGAN, MISS LAURA**	381
LYCETT, MR SHAUN	341	**MORRIS, MR MOUSE**	382
M		**MORRIS, MR PATRICK**	383
MACKIE, MR JOHN	342	**MORRISON, MR HUGHIE**	384
†MADDISON, MR PETER	343	**MOUBARAK, MR MOHAMED**	385
MADGWICK, MR MICHAEL	344	**MUIR, MR WILLIAM**	386
MAIN, MRS HEATHER	345	**MULHALL, MR CLIVE**	387
MAKIN, MR PHILLIP	346	**MULHOLLAND, MR NEIL**	388
MALZARD, MRS ALYSON	347	**MULLANEY, MR LAWRENCE**	389
MANN, MR CHARLIE	348	**MULLINEAUX, MR MICHAEL**	390
MARGARSON, MR GEORGE	349	**MULLINS, MR SEAMUS**	391

Name	Team No.	Name	Team No.
MULLINS, MR WILLIAM P	392	PHILLIPS, MR RICHARD	431
MURPHY, MISS AMY	393	PICKARD, MISS ELLA	432
MURPHY, MR MIKE	394	†PICKARD, MISS IMOGEN	433
MURPHY, MR OLLY	395	PINFIELD, MR TIM	434
MURPHY, MR PAT	396	PIPE, MR DAVID	435
MURTAGH, MR BARRY	397	POGSON, MR CHARLES	436
N		PORTMAN, MR JONATHAN	437
NAYLOR, DR JEREMY	398	POULTON, MRS CAMILLA	438
†NEEDHAM, MR JOHN	399	PRESCOTT BT, SIR MARK	439
NELMES, MRS HELEN	400	PRICE, MISS KATY	440
NEWCOMBE, MR TONY	401	PRICE, MR RICHARD	441
NEWLAND, DR RICHARD	402	PRITCHARD, MR PETER	442
NEWTON-SMITH, MISS ANNA	403	**Q**	
NICHOLLS, MR ADRIAN	404	QUINN, MR DENIS	443
NICHOLLS, MR PAUL	405	QUINN, MR JOHN	444
NIVEN, MR PETER	406	QUINN, MR MICK	445
NORMILE, MRS LUCY	407	**R**	
NORTON, MR JOHN	408	RALPH, MR ALASTAIR	446
O		REED, MR TIM	447
O'BRIEN, MR A. P.	409	REES, MR DAVID	448
O'BRIEN, MR DANIEL	410	†REES, MRS HELEN	449
O'BRIEN, MR FERGAL	411	REGAN, MR SEAN	450
O'KEEFFE, MR JEDD	412	RICHARDS, MRS LYDIA	451
O'MEARA, MR DAVID	413	RICHARDS, MR NICKY	452
†O'NEILL, MRS DANNI	414	RICHES, MR JOHN DAVID	453
O'NEILL, MR JOHN	415	RIMELL, MR MARK	454
O'NEILL, MR JONJO	416	ROBERTS, MR DAVE	455
O'SHEA, MR JOHN	417	ROBERTS, MR MIKE	456
OLIVER, MR HENRY	418	ROBINSON, MISS SARAH	457
OSBORNE, MR JAMIE	419	ROBSON, MISS PAULINE	458
OWEN, MISS EMMA	420	†ROSS, MR RUSSELL	459
OWENS, MR PATRICK	421	ROTHWELL, MR BRIAN	460
P		ROWE, MR RICHARD	461
PALMER, MR HUGO	422	ROWLAND, MISS MANDY	462
PATTINSON, MR MARK	423	RUSSELL, MS LUCINDA	463
PAULING, MR BEN	424	RYAN, MR JOHN	464
PEARCE, MR SIMON	425	RYAN, MR KEVIN	465
PEARS, MR OLLIE	426	**S**	
PERRATT, MISS LINDA	427	SADIK, MR AYTACH	466
PERRETT, MRS AMANDA	428	SANDERSON, MR GARY	467
PHELAN, MR PAT	429	SAUNDERS, MR MALCOLM	468
PHILLIPS, MR ALAN	430	SAYER, MRS DIANNE	469

Name	Team No.
SCARGILL, DR JON	470
†SCOTT, MR DERRICK	471
SCOTT, MR GEORGE	472
SCOTT, MR JEREMY	473
SCOTT, MISS KATIE	474
SCUDAMORE, MR MICHAEL	475
SHAW, MR DEREK	476
SHAW, MRS FIONA	477
†SHEARS, MR MARK	478
SHEPPARD, MR MATT	479
SHERWOOD, MR OLIVER	480
SIDDALL, MISS LYNN	481
SIGNY, MR OLIVER	482
SIMCOCK, MR DAVID	483
SKELTON, MR DAN	484
SLY, MRS PAM	485
SMART, MR BRYAN	486
SMITH, MR CHARLES	487
SMITH, MR JULIAN	488
SMITH, MR MARTIN	489
†SMITH, MISS PAULA	490
SMITH, MR R. MIKE	491
SMITH, MR RALPH J.	492
SMITH, MRS SUE	493
SMITH, MISS SUZY	494
SMYLY, MR GILES	495
SNOWDEN, MR JAMIE	496
SOWERSBY, MR MIKE	497
SPEARING, MR JOHN	498
SPENCER, MR RICHARD	499
SPENCER, MR SEB	500
SPILLER, MR HENRY	501
SQUANCE, MR MICHAEL	502
STACK, MR FOZZY	503
STANFORD, MR EUGENE	504
STEELE, MR DANIEL	505
STEPHEN, MRS JACKIE	506
STEPHENS, MRS KATIE	507
STEPHENS, MR ROBERT	508
STONE, MR WILLIAM	509
STOREY, MR WILF	510
STOUTE, SIR MICHAEL	511
STRONGE, MRS ALI	512
STUBBS, MRS LINDA	513
SUMMERS, MR ROB	514
SYMONDS, MR TOM	515

T

Name	Team No.
TATE, MR JAMES	516
TATE, MR TOM	517
TEAL, MR ROGER	518
THOMAS, MR SAM	519
†THOMASON-MURPHY, MRS JOANNE	520
THOMPSON, MR DAVID	521
THOMPSON, MR RONALD	522
†THOMPSON, MR VICTOR	523
THOMSON, MR SANDY	524
TINKLER, MR NIGEL	525
TIZZARD, MR COLIN	526
TODD, SIR MARK	527
TODHUNTER, MR MARTIN	528
TREGONING, MR MARCUS	529
TUER, MR GRANT	530
TUITE, MR JOSEPH	531
TURNER, MR BILL	532
TUTTY, MRS KAREN	533
TWISTON-DAVIES, MR NIGEL	534

U

Name	Team No.
UNETT, MR JAMES	535
USHER, MR MARK	536

V

Name	Team No.
VARIAN, MR ROGER	537
VAUGHAN, MR ED	538
VAUGHAN, MR TIM	539
VON DER RECKE, MR CHRISTIAN	540

W

Name	Team No.
WADHAM, MRS LUCY	541
WAGGOTT, MISS TRACY	542
WAINWRIGHT, MR JOHN	543
†WALEY-COHEN, MR ROBERT	544
WALFORD, MR MARK	545
WALFORD, MR ROBERT	546
WALKER, MR ED	547
WALL, MR CHRIS	548
WALL, MR TREVOR	549

Name	Team No.	Name	Team No.
WALLIS, MR CHARLIE	550	WILLIAMS, MR CHRISTIAN	574
WALTON, MRS JANE	551	WILLIAMS, MR DAI	575
†WALTON, MR JASON	552	WILLIAMS, MR EVAN	576
WALTON, MRS SHEENA	553	WILLIAMS, MR IAN	577
WARD, MR JASON	554	WILLIAMS, MRS JANE	578
WARD, MR TOM	555	WILLIAMS, MR NICK	579
†WATKINS, MISS TRACEY	556	WILLIAMS, MR NOEL	580
WATSON, MR ARCHIE	557	WILLIAMS, MR OLLY	581
WATSON, MR FRED	558	WILLIAMS, MR STUART	582
WATT, MRS SHARON	559	WILLIAMS, MISS VENETIA	583
WAUGH, MR SIMON	560	WILLIAMSON, MRS LISA	584
WEATHERER, MR MARK	561	WILSON, MR ANDREW	585
WEBBER, MR PAUL	562	WINGROVE, MR KEN	587
WEST, MR ADAM	563	WINKS, MR PETER	588
WEST, MISS SHEENA	564	WINTLE, MR ADRIAN	589
WEST, MR SIMON	565	†WOODMAN, MISS REBECCA	590
WESTON, MR DAVID	566	WOODMAN, MR STEVE	591
WESTON, MR TOM	567	WOOLLACOTT, MRS KAYLEY	592
WHILLANS, MR ALISTAIR	568	**Y**	
WHILLANS, MR DONALD	569	†YORK, MR PHILLIP	593
WHITAKER, MR RICHARD	570	YOUNG, MRS LAURA	594
†WHITEHEAD, MR ARTHUR	571	†YOUNG, MR WILLIAM	595
WHITTINGTON, MR HARRY	572		
WIGHAM, MR MICHAEL	573		

Want the BIGGEST offers?

Daily PROMOS?

Biggest BOOKIES?

racingpost.com/freebets

For The Must-Have Racing Offers
RACING POST

Racing Post backs responsible gambling.
18+ begambleaware.org 0808 8020 133

London Thoroughbred Services Ltd

Management and Selection of Broodmares
International Bloodstock Transactions
Stallion Management and Syndication
Valuations
Insurance
Transport

Member of Federation of Bloodstock Agents (GB)

London Thoroughbred Services Ltd
West Blagdon, Cranborne
Dorset
BH21 5RY

Tel: 01725 517711
Email: lts@lts-uk.com
Website: www.lts-uk.com

PROPERTY OF HER MAJESTY
The Queen

Colours: Purple, gold braid, scarlet sleeves, black velvet cap with gold fringe

Trained by **Sir Michael Stoute**, Newmarket

1 **CALCULATION,** 4 br g Dubawi (IRE)—Estimate (IRE)
2 **SEXTANT,** 5 b g Sea The Stars (IRE)—Hypoteneuse (IRE)
3 **SOVEREIGN GRANT,** 4 b c Kingman—Momentary

THREE-YEAR-OLDS

4 **FIRST RECEIVER,** b c New Approach (IRE)—Touchline
5 **GLITTERING GIFT,** ch g Dubawi (IRE)—Golden Stream (IRE)
6 **QUICK WALTZ,** b f Australia—Momentary
7 **VINDICATE,** ch c Lope de Vega (IRE)—Aurore (IRE)

TWO-YEAR-OLDS

8 **EVALUATION,** b c 10/2 Dubawi (IRE)—Estimate (IRE) (Monsun (GER))
9 **GEOMETRIST,** b f 11/3 Kingman—Hypoteneuse (IRE) (Sadler's Wells (USA))
10 **JUST FINE (IRE),** b c 10/2 Sea The Stars (IRE)—Bint Almatar (USA) (Kingmambo (USA))
11 **PORTFOLIO (JPN),** b f 9/1 Deep Impact (JPN)—Diploma (Dubawi (IRE))

Trained by **William Haggas**, Newmarket

12 **DESERT CARAVAN,** 4 b g Oasis—Dream Sequence (IRE)
13 **SPACE WALK,** 4 b g Galileo (IRE)—Memory (IRE)

THREE-YEAR-OLDS

14 **AWARD SCHEME,** b f Siyouni (FR)—Queen's Prize
15 **DUSTY DREAM,** b f Dubawi (IRE)—Memory (IRE)
16 **FRUITION,** b g Oasis Dream—Ananas
17 **KEW PALACE,** b f Kingman—Shama (IRE)
18 **PORTRAY,** b g Dubawi (IRE)—Placidia (IRE)
19 **SOUND MIXER,** b f Cable Bay (IRE)—Medley

TWO-YEAR-OLDS

20 **CHALK STREAM,** b c 8/2 Sea The Stars (IRE)—Golden Stream (IRE) (Sadler's Wells (USA))
21 **COMPANIONSHIP,** b f 4/3 Galileo (IRE)—Sweet Idea (AUS) (Snitzel (AUS))
22 **LIGHT REFRAIN,** b f 13/1 Frankel—Light Music (Elusive Quality (USA))
23 **PINEAPPLE RING,** b f 4/2 Kingman—Ananas (Nayef (USA))
24 **SECRET HAUNT,** b f 31/3 Dubawi (IRE)—Enticement (Montjeu (IRE))
25 **WINK OF AN EYE,** b c 9/2 Dubawi (IRE)—Momentary (Nayef (USA))

PROPERTY OF HER MAJESTY
The Queen

Trained by **Richard Hannon**, Marlborough

TWO-YEAR-OLDS
26 COLLINSBAY, b c 16/2 Cable Bay (IRE)—Kinematic (Kyllachy)
27 SAFE PASSAGE, b f 23/2 Paco Boy (IRE)—Daring Aim (Daylami (IRE))

Trained by **Roger Charlton**, Beckhampton

THREE-YEAR-OLDS
28 CODE OF CONDUCT, b c Siyouni (FR)—Sequence (IRE)
29 EVENING SUN, b c Muhaarar—Fiery Sunset

TWO-YEAR-OLDS
30 ENCOURAGE, b c 7/3 Iffraaj—Good Hope (Cape Cross (IRE))

Trained by **Michael Bell**, Newmarket

31 YOUTHFUL, 4 b g Shamardal (USA)—Good Hope

THREE-YEAR-OLDS
32 APPROXIMATE, b f Dubawi (IRE)—Estimate (IRE)
33 CHOSEN STAR, ch f Dubawi (IRE)—Yodelling (USA)
34 CLOUD DRIFT, b g Toronado (IRE)—Humdrum
35 FORMALITY, b c Frankel—Silver Mirage
36 HIGH SHINE, b f Paco Boy (IRE)—Hypoteneuse (IRE)
37 OTAGO, b g Cable Bay (IRE)—Spinning Top

TWO-YEAR-OLDS
38 BOOKMARK, b f 12/3 New Approach (IRE)—Free Verse (Danehill Dancer (IRE))
39 CLOSENESS, b f 22/3 Iffraaj—Pack Together (Paco Boy (IRE))
40 HUMMING BEE, b c 13/4 Oasis Dream—Humdrum (Dr Fong (USA))
41 INVEIGLE, b c 6/2 Dark Angel (IRE)—Sand Vixen (Dubawi (IRE))
42 REALIST, b c 27/2 Camelot—Silver Mirage (Oasis Dream)
43 STIMULATE, b f 4/2 Motivator—Shama (IRE) (Danehill Dancer (IRE))
44 SUN FESTIVAL, b c 23/3 Toronado (IRE)—Raymi Coya (CAN) (Van Nistelrooy (USA))

Trained by **Andrew Balding**, Kingsclere

45 NATURAL HISTORY, 5 b g Nathaniel (IRE)—Film Script

THREE-YEAR-OLDS
46 KING'S LYNN, b c Cable Bay (IRE)—Kinematic
47 PUNCTUATION, br c Dansili—Key Point (IRE)

TWO-YEAR-OLDS
48 TACTICAL, b c 14/2 Toronado (IRE)—Make Fast (Makfi)

PROPERTY OF HER MAJESTY

The Queen

Trained by **John Gosden**, Newmarket

THREE-YEAR-OLDS
49 DAUNTLESS, b g Dubawi (IRE)—Enticement
50 DESERT FLYER, b f Shamardal (USA)—White Moonstone (USA)
51 INNOVATION, b f Dubawi (IRE)—Free Verse
52 LIGHTNESS (IRE), b f Shamardal (USA)—Serene Beauty (USA)

TWO-YEAR-OLDS
53 ENTHRAL, (IRE) b f 26/1 Exceed And Excel (AUS)—Aurora Leigh (Dubawi (IRE))
54 PIED PIPER, ch c 1/2 New Approach (IRE)—Pure Fantasy (Fastnet Rock (AUS))
55 SHEPHERD'S DELIGHT, b c 10/4 Golden Horn—Fiery Sunset (Galileo (IRE))
56 WAKENING (IRE), br f 3/3 Dark Angel (IRE)—Dancing Sands (IRE) (Dubawi (IRE))

Trained by **Richard Hughes**, Upper Lambourn
Horses not allocated at time of publication

To be allocated

TWO-YEAR-OLDS
57 EASTERN DAWN, b f 28/1 Iffraaj—Dawn Glory (Oasis Dream)
58 ORCHESTRAL, b c 5/4 Lope de Vega (IRE)—Set To Music (IRE) (Danehill Dancer (IRE))
59 ORDEROFSUCCESSION, b f 3/4 Siyouni (FR)—Sequence (IRE) (Selkirk (USA))
60 SENTENCE, b f 26/4 Dubawi (IRE)—Caraboss (Cape Cross (IRE))
61 SERGEANT MAJOR, b c 10/4 Siyouni (FR)—Aurore (IRE) (Fasliyev (USA))
62 THOUGHT PROCESS, b f 3/4 Galileo (IRE)—Memory (IRE) (Danehill Dancer (IRE))
63 TYNWALD, b c 21/2 Toronado (IRE)—Queen's Prize (Dansili)
64 VITAL FORCE (IRE), b f 3/2 Invincible Spirit (IRE)—Bergamask (USA) (Kingmambo (USA))
65 WELL SPENT, b f 30/4 Siyouni (FR)—Pleasemetoo (IRE) (Vale of York (IRE))

Trained by **Nicky Henderson**, Lambourn

66 HAMILTON'S FANTASY, 5 b m Mount Nelson—Romantic Dream
67 ITALIAN SUMMER, 5 br m Milan—Midsummer Magic
68 KEEN ON, 6 b g Kayf Tara—Romantic Dream
69 RAPID FLIGHT, 4 b g Midnight Legend—Spring Flight
70 STEAL A MARCH, 5 b g Mount Nelson—Side Step
71 SUNSHADE, 7 b m Sulamani (IRE)—Spring Flight

Trained by **Charlie Longsdon**, Chipping Norton

72 CONJURING TRICK, 5 b m Great Pretender (IRE)—Magic Score
73 FORTH BRIDGE, 7 b g Bernardini (USA)—Sally Forth
74 HEATHER SONG, 6 b m Kayf Tara—Bella Macrae
75 JETTISON, 4 b f Malinas (GER)—Side Step
76 NO TRUMPS, 6 b m Black Sam Bellamy (IRE)—Magic Score

SOME TRAINERS' STRINGS ARE TAKEN FROM THE BHA RACING ADMINISTRATION WEBSITE AND INCLUDE HORSES LISTED ON THERE AS IN 'PRE-TRAINING', 'AT GRASS' OR 'RESTING'

---

1 MR N. W. ALEXANDER, Kinneston

Postal: **Kinneston, Leslie, Glenrothes, Fife, KY6 3JJ**
Contacts: **PHONE 01592 840774 MOBILE 07831 488210**
EMAIL nicholasalexander@kinneston.com WEBSITE www.kinneston.com

1 **ARNICA**, 7, b g Champs Elysees—Cordoba **Mr J. K. McGarrity**
2 **ARTIC MANN**, 6, b g Sulamani (IRE)—Line Artic (FR) **Mr T. J. Hemmings**
3 **BALLYNANTY (IRE)**, 8, gr g Yeats (IRE)—Reina Blanca **J Douglas Miller & Ken McGarrity**
4 **BENNY'S SECRET (IRE)**, 10, br g Beneficial—Greenhall Rambler (IRE) **Katie & Brian Castle**
5 **BIBLICAL (FR)**, 5, ch g Harbour Watch (IRE)—Prophecie (FR) **Mr John J Murray & Mrs Lynne MacLennan**
6 **BROADWAY JOE (IRE)**, 6, b g Milan—Greenhall Rambler (IRE) **Clan Gathering**
7 **BUFFALO BALLET**, 14, b g Kayf Tara—Minora (IRE) **Alexander Family**
8 **CALIVIGNY (IRE)**, 11, b g Gold Well—Summer Holiday (IRE) **Alexander Family**
9 **CENTENIER (FR)**, 4, b g Rail Link—Calling Grace (FR) **Mrs J. A. Morris**
10 **CHANTING HILL (IRE)**, 6, b m Milan—Kitty Dillon (IRE) **Quandt & Cochrane**
11 **CHARM OFFENSIVE (FR)**, 6, b m Le Triton (USA)—Go Lison (FR) **The Nags to Riches Partnership**
12 **CHRISTMAS IN USA (FR)**, 8, b g Shaanmer (IRE)—Diamond of Diana (FR) **Bowen & Nicol**
13 **CLAN LEGEND**, 10, ch g Midnight Legend—Harrietfield **Clan Gathering**
14 **COUNTERMAND**, 8, b g Authorized (IRE)—Answered Prayer **Mr R. J. C. Wilmot-Smith**
15 **CRAIGANBOY (IRE)**, 11, b g Zagreb (USA)—Barnish River (IRE) **Quandt, Cochrane, Lysaght**
16 **DANCE OF FIRE**, 8, b g Norse Dancer (IRE)—Strictly Dancing (IRE) **Team Kinneston Club**
17 **DIAMOND BRIG**, 8, b g Black Sam Bellamy (IRE)—Lady Brig **Mr T. J. Hemmings**
18 **DUBAI DAYS (IRE)**, 6, b g Dubai Destination (USA)—Comeragh Girl (IRE) **Mr T. J. Hemmings**
19 **EAGLE RIDGE (IRE)**, 9, b g Oscar (IRE)—Azaban (IRE) **Ken McGarrity and Murray Cameron**
20 **EBONY JEWEL (IRE)**, 6, b g Westerner—Lady Roania (IRE) **Mrs L. Maclennan**
21 **ELVIS MAIL (FR)**, 6, gr g Great Pretender (IRE)—Queenly Mail (FR) **The Ladies Who**
22 **ETOILE D'ECOSSE (FR)**, 6, gr m Martaline—Etoile de Mogador (FR) **Douglas Miller, Coltman, Dunning, Turcan**
23 **FERNHILL LAD (IRE)**, 5, b g Dylan Thomas (IRE)—Sarahall (IRE) **Coltman Cundall Matterson & Stephenson**
24 **FINAL REMINDER (IRE)**, 8, b m Gold Well—Olde Kilcormac (IRE) **Katie & Brian Castle**
25 **FLY RORY FLY (IRE)**, 8, b g Milan—Thousand Wings (GER) **Turcan D-Miller Stewart Burnham Dunning**
26 4, B f Midnight Legend—Gaspaisielle **Mr N. W. Alexander**
27 **GINGER MAIL (FR)**, 4, gr g Sinndar (IRE)—Queenly Mail (FR) **Mr N. W. Alexander**
28 **GIPSY LEE ROSE (FR)**, 6, gr m Walk In The Park (IRE)—Vanoo d'Orthe (FR) **Mrs S. M. Irwin**
29 **JOLIE CRICKETTE (FR)**, 8, b m Laverock (IRE)—Crickette River (FR) **Mrs J. A. Morris**
30 **KOALA KEEL (IRE)**, 4, b g Kirkwall—Kayf Keel **Mr N. W. Alexander**
31 **LAKE VIEW LAD (IRE)**, 10, gr g Oscar (IRE)—Missy O'Brien (IRE) **Mr T. J. Hemmings**
32 **LANDECKER (IRE)**, 12, br g Craigsteel—Winsome Breeze (IRE) **Mr N. W. Alexander**
33 **LET THERE BE LOVE (IRE)**, 5, b g Shantou (USA)—Zolotaya **Katie & Brian Castle**
34 4, Ch f Mahler—Lindy Lou **Hugh Hodge Ltd**
35 **MANETTI (IRE)**, 8, b g Westerner—Mrs Wallensky (IRE) **Sandy's Angels**
36 **MARLEE MASSIE (IRE)**, 11, b g Dr Massini (IRE)—Meadstown Miss (IRE) **Mr N. W. Alexander**
37 **MARYLINE TRITT (FR)**, 4, b f Kap Rock (FR)—Tritone Crick (FR) **Mr N. W. Alexander**
38 **MCGINTY'S DREAM (IRE)**, 9, b g Flemensfirth (USA)—Laboc **Kinneston Racing**
39 **MORE MADNESS (IRE)**, 13, b g Dr Massini (IRE)—Angelic Angel (IRE) **J. F. Alexander**
40 5, B m Shirocco (GER)—Mtpockets (IRE) **A. Ownership Change Pending**
41 **MY SON JOHN**, 6, b g Bahri (USA)—Cogolie (FR) **Mr J. Threadgall**
42 **NAUTICAL MISS (IRE)**, 5, b br m Imperial Monarch (IRE)—
                                                Yourfinalanswer (IRE) **Mr HW Turcan & Sir Simon Dunning**
43 **NICEANDEASY (IRE)**, 7, b g Kalanisi (IRE)—High Priestess (IRE) **Katie & Brian Castle**
44 **NOT THE CHABLIS (IRE)**, 6, b g Scorpion (IRE)—De Street (IRE) **Turcan, Dunning, Price, Stewart, Burnham**
45 **OFF THE HOOK (IRE)**, 8, b m Getaway (GER)—Call Her Again (IRE) **Mrs I. Hodge**
46 **PENNY RIVER**, 5, b m Kayf Tara—River Alder **Katie & Brian Castle**
47 **RACING PULSE (IRE)**, 11, b g Garuda (IRE)—Jacks Sister (IRE) **J. F. Alexander**
48 4, B g Milan—Rose Tanner (IRE) **Mr N. W. Alexander**
49 **RYEDALE RACER**, 9, b g Indian Danehill (IRE)—Jontys'lass **Bissett Racing**
50 **SILK OR SCARLET (IRE)**, 8, ch g Mahler—Spirit of Clanagh (IRE) **Ken McGarrity & Dudgeon, Cundall, Liddle**
51 **SPIRIT OF KAYF**, 9, b g Kayf Tara—Over Sixty **Mrs J. A. Morris**

MR N. W. ALEXANDER - continued

52 **TED VEALE (IRE)**, 13, b g Revoque (IRE)—Rose Tanner (IRE) **Alexander Family**
53 **TRAVAIL D'ORFEVRE (FR)**, 4, gr g Martaline—Lady Needles (IRE) **Bowen & Nicol**
54 **UP HELLY AA KING**, 9, ch g And Beyond (IRE)—Gretton **Jean Matterson & J Douglas Miller**
55 **UPANDATIT (IRE)**, 5, b g Winged Love (IRE)—Betty Beck (IRE) **Miss J. G. K. Matterson**
56 **WAKOOL (FR)**, 4, gr g Motivator—Symba's Dream (USA) **Turcan, Borwick, Dunning & Fleming**

THREE-YEAR-OLDS
57 **GUSTAV'S DREAM (IRE)**, ch f Mahler—Lindy Lou **Hugh Hodge Ltd**
58 B f Gentlewave (IRE)—Spinning Away **Mr N. W. Alexander**

TWO-YEAR-OLDS
59 B f 27/02 Blue Bresil (FR)—Little Glenshee (IRE) (Terimon) **Mr N. W. Alexander**
60 B f 28/04 Clovis du Berlais (FR)—Swift Getaway (IRE) (Getaway (GER)) **Mr N. W. Alexander**

Other Owners: Mr N. W. Alexander, Alexander Family, Mr L. Borwick, Mr A. J. Bowen, Lady Burnham, Mr M. Cameron, Mr B. C. Castle, Mrs C. Castle, The Hon T. H. V. Cochrane, Mrs M. C. Coltman, Mr R. H. Cundall, Mrs J. Douglas Miller, Dudgeon, Cundall, Liddle, Sir Simon Dunning, Miss D. F. Fleming, C. Lysaght, Mrs L. Maclennan, Miss J. G. K. Matterson, Mr J. K. McGarrity, Mr J. J. Murray, Mr A. G. Nicol, Mrs D. C. S. Price, Miss S. Quandt, Mr O. G. Stephenson, A. D. Stewart, H. W. Turcan.

Assistant Trainer: Catriona Bissett.

NH Jockey: Lucy Alexander. **Conditional Jockey:** Grant Cockburn. **Apprentice Jockey:** Lucy Alexander. **Amateur Jockey:** Mr Kit Alexander.

---

2 | **MISS LOUISE ALLAN, Newmarket**
Postal: **2 London Road, Newmarket, Suffolk, CB8 0TW**
Contacts: **MOBILE 07703 355878**
EMAIL louiseallan1@hotmail.co.uk

1 **FAGO (FR)**, 12, b br g Balko (FR)—Merciki (FR) **Ms A. E. Embiricos**
2 **HARD TOFFEE (IRE)**, 9, b g Teofilo (IRE)—Speciale (USA) **Miss V. L. Allan**
3 **PHOENIX DAWN**, 6, b g Phoenix Reach (IRE)—Comtesse Noire (CAN) **The Early Birds**
4 **THEREDBALLOON**, 14, ch g Sulamani (IRE)—Sovana (FR) **Miss V. L. Allan**

THREE-YEAR-OLDS
5 B f Beat All (USA)—High Meadow Rose

TWO-YEAR-OLDS
6 **FULL MOON RISING**, b c 25/04 Sea The Moon (GER)—Lady Hen (Efisio) **A. Coombs & J. W. Rowley**
7 **GOLDEN WATTLE (IRE)**, ch f 09/02 Australia—Chrysanthemum (IRE) (Danehill Dancer (IRE)) (100000) **Brook Stud**
8 **KHUFU**, b c 24/01 Exceed And Excel (AUS)—Miss Chicane (Refuse To Bend (IRE)) (38095) **Brook Stud**
9 B f 09/02 Golden Horn—Viola da Braccio (IRE) (Vettori (IRE)) (14000) **Brook Stud**

Other Owners: Miss V. L. Allan, A. C. Coombs, Ms A. E. Embiricos, Mr J. W. F. Rowley.

---

3 | **MR CONRAD ALLEN, Newmarket**
Postal: **Trainer did not wish details of their string to appear**

4   MR SAM ALLWOOD, Whitchurch
Postal: **Church Farm, Church Lane, Ash Magna, Whitchurch, Shropshire, SY13 4EA**
Contacts: **PHONE 07738 413579**
EMAIL sj-allwood@hotmail.co.uk

1 **BEMPTON CLIFFS (IRE)**, 5, gr g Canford Cliffs (IRE)—Grand Lili **Mr M Dunlevy & Mrs H McGuinness**
2 **BITASWEETSYMPHONY (IRE)**, 5, b g Mahler—Libertango (IRE) **Bostock Dunlevy McGuinness Bradshaw**
3 **FREE SKI (IRE)**, 6, ch g Sans Frontieres (IRE)—Celtic Peace (IRE) **R. B. Francis**
4 **JOBSONFIRE**, 8, b g Sulamani (IRE)—Seviot **Allwood Clifton Thomas**
5 **KITEINAHURRICANE (IRE)**, 5, b br g Court Cave (IRE)—Katsura **S. J. Allwood**
6 **OUR DELBOY**, 8, gr g Multiplex—Dawn's Della **Mrs E. Benson**
7 **OUT ON THE TEAR (IRE)**, 6, b g Arcadio (GER)—Madame Coco (IRE) **Sam Allwood Racing Club**
8 **SHENEEDEDTHERUN (IRE)**, 10, b m Kayf Tara—Lady Moon (FR) **Sam Allwood Racing Club**

Other Owners: S. J. Allwood, Mrs B. A. Bostock, Mr P. E. Bradshaw, Mr P. Clifton, Mr M. Dunlevy, Mrs H. A. McGuinness, Miss
S. M. Thomas.

5   MR ERIC ALSTON, Preston
Postal: **Edges Farm Stables, Chapel Lane, Longton, Preston, Lancashire, PR4 5NA**
Contacts: **PHONE 01772 612120 MOBILE 07879 641660 FAX 01772 619600**
EMAIL eric1943@supanet.com

1 **ACCLAIM THE NATION (IRE)**, 7, b g Acclamation—Dani Ridge (IRE) **Mr C. F. Harrington**
2 **BOUDICA BAY (IRE)**, 5, b m Rip Van Winkle (IRE)—White Shift (IRE) **The Grumpy Old Geezers**
3 **FOX HILL**, 4, b f Foxwedge (AUS)—Siryena **Whitehills Racing Syndicate**
4 **HARRY'S RIDGE (IRE)**, 5, b g Acclamation—Dani Ridge (IRE) **Mr C. F. Harrington**
5 **JABBAROCKIE**, 7, b g Showcasing—Canina **M Balmer, K Sheedy, P Copple, C Dingwall**
6 **KEY CHOICE**, 4, ch g Iffraaj—Strictly Silca **Mr L. Carlisle**
7 **MAGHFOOR**, 6, b g Cape Cross (IRE)—Thaahira (USA) **Jo-co Partnership**
8 **MAID IN INDIA (IRE)**, 6, br m Bated Breath—Indian Maiden (IRE) **Mr C. F. Harrington**
9 **REDROSEZORRO**, 6, b g Foxwedge (AUS)—Garter Star **Red Rose Partnership**
10 **SPIRIT POWER**, 5, b g Swiss Spirit—Verasina (USA) **The Selebians**

THREE-YEAR-OLDS
11 B f Fountain of Youth (IRE)—Albertine Rose **Mr & Mrs G. Middlebrook**
12 B g Intrinsic—Brer Rabbit
13 **CAPTAIN CORCORAN (IRE)**, b g Anjaal—Hms Pinafore (IRE) **Whitehills Racing Syndicate 2**

TWO-YEAR-OLDS
14 **DELGADA (IRE)**, ch f 02/05 Belardo (IRE)—
Twiggy's Girl (IRE) (Manduro (GER)) (4289) **Whitehills Racing Syndicate 3**

Other Owners: Mrs D. L. Cooney, Mr E. Cooney.

Assistant Trainer: Mrs Sue Alston.

6   MR CHARLIE APPLEBY, Newmarket
Postal: **Godolphin Management Co Ltd, Moulton Paddocks, Newmarket, Suffolk, CB8 7PJ**
WEBSITE www.godolphin.com

1 **AMERICAN GRAFFITI (FR)**, 4, ch g Pivotal—Adventure Seeker (FR)
2 **BARNEY ROY**, 6, b g Excelebration (IRE)—Alina (IRE)
3 **BEYOND REASON (IRE)**, 4, b f Australia—No Explaining (IRE)
4 **CIRQUE ROYAL**, 4, b g Cape Cross (IRE)—Botanique (IRE)
5 **CROSS COUNTER**, 5, b g Teofilo (IRE)—Waitress (USA)
6 **D'BAI (IRE)**, 6, b g Dubawi (IRE)—Savannah Belle

MR CHARLIE APPLEBY - continued

7 **EXPRESSIONISM (IRE)**, 4, b f Galileo (IRE)—Lady Springbank (IRE)
8 **FIRST NATION**, 6, b g Dubawi (IRE)—Moyesii (USA)
9 **GHAIYYATH (IRE)**, 5, b h Dubawi (IRE)—Nightime (IRE)
10 **GHOSTWATCH (IRE)**, 5, b g Dubawi (IRE)—Nature Spirits (FR)
11 **GLORIOUS JOURNEY**, 5, b g Dubawi (IRE)—Fallen For You
12 **GOOD FORTUNE**, 4, b g New Approach (IRE)—Mazuna (IRE)
13 **ISPOLINI**, 5, b g Dubawi (IRE)—Giants Play (USA)
14 **JALMOUD**, 4, ch g New Approach (IRE)—Dancing Rain (IRE)
15 **KEY VICTORY (IRE)**, 5, b g Teofilo (IRE)—Patroness
16 **LOXLEY (IRE)**, 5, b g New Approach (IRE)—Lady Marian (GER)
17 **MAGIC LILY**, 5, ch m New Approach (IRE)—Dancing Rain (IRE)
18 **MOONLIGHT SPIRIT (IRE)**, 4, b c Dubawi (IRE)—Moonsail
19 **MUBTASIM (IRE)**, 6, b g Arcano (IRE)—Start The Music (IRE)
20 **MYTHICAL MAGIC (IRE)**, 5, b g Iffraaj—Mythie (FR)
21 **OLD PERSIAN (IRE)**, 5, b h Dubawi (IRE)—Indian Petal
22 **ON THE WARPATH**, 5, ch g Declaration of War (USA)—Elusive Pearl (USA)
23 **PERSUADING (IRE)**, 4, b g Oasis Dream—Short Skirt
24 **QUORTO (IRE)**, 4, b c Dubawi (IRE)—Volume
25 **SECRET ADVISOR (FR)**, 6, b g Dubawi (IRE)—Sub Rose (IRE)
26 **SPACE BLUES (IRE)**, 4, ch c Dubawi (IRE)—Miss Lucifer (FR)
27 **SPOTIFY (FR)**, 6, b g Redoute's Choice (AUS)—Gwenseb (FR)
28 **WALTON STREET**, 6, b g Cape Cross (IRE)—Brom Felinity (AUS)
29 **ZAKOUSKI**, 4, b g Shamardal (USA)—O'Giselle (AUS)

THREE-YEAR-OLDS

30 **AL DABARAN**, b c Dubawi (IRE)—Bright Beacon
31 **AL MAYSAN**, b c Dubawi (IRE)—Perfect Light (IRE)
32 **AL SUHAIL**, b c Dubawi (IRE)—Shirocco Star
33 **ALPEN ROSE (IRE)**, b f Sea The Stars (IRE)—Valais Girl
34 **ALTHIQA**, gr f Dark Angel (IRE)—Mistrusting (IRE)
35 **AMBER ISLAND (IRE)**, b f Exceed And Excel (AUS)—Raphinae
36 **ANTIANARA (USA)**, b br f Medaglia d'Oro (USA)—Miss Empire (USA)
37 **ARABIAN GIRL (IRE)**, b f Shamardal (USA)—Majestic Queen (IRE)
38 **BALLET QUEEN**, ch f Dubawi (IRE)—Giants Play (USA)
39 **BEAUTIFUL ILLUSION (IRE)**, b f Shamardal (USA)—Long Lashes (USA)
40 **BOCCACCIO (IRE)**, b c Dubawi (IRE)—J Wonder (USA)
41 **BRIGHT MELODY (IRE)**, b g Dubawi (IRE)—Lyric of Light
42 **CHEROKEE MIST (CAN)**, ch g City Zip (USA)—Forest Gamble (USA)
43 **CIGOLI (IRE)**, b c Galileo (IRE)—Posset
44 **COMMUNICATE**, b f Dubawi (IRE)—Discourse (USA)
45 **CONFIDENTIAL ACT (USA)**, ch c American Pharoah (USA)—Kindle (USA)
46 **DECLARING LOVE**, b gr f Dubawi (IRE)—Wedding March (IRE)
47 **DESERT PEACE (USA)**, b c Curlin (USA)—Stoweshoe (USA)
48 **DISCOVERY ISLAND**, b g Dubawi (IRE)—Sperry (IRE)
49 **DISTANT GODDESS**, b f Dubawi (IRE)—Bastet (IRE)
50 **DIVINE BLESSING**, b f Teofilo (IRE)—Najoum (USA)
51 **EASTERN WORLD (IRE)**, ch c Dubawi (IRE)—Eastern Joy
52 **ENDLESS ECHOES (IRE)**, b f Shamardal (USA)—Sahraah (USA)
53 **ETERNAL PRINCE**, b c New Approach (IRE)—La Arenosa (IRE)
54 **ETERNAL SUNSET**, b f Dubawi (IRE)—Karenine
55 **EXPRESS ROUTE (USA)**, b g Quality Road (USA)—Strawberry Sense (USA)
56 **EXPRESSIONIST (IRE)**, ch g Night of Thunder (IRE)—Permission Slip (IRE)
57 **FALLING MIST (IRE)**, b f Invincible Spirit (USA)—Spinning Cloud (USA)
58 **FIRST WINTER (IRE)**, b g Dubawi (IRE)—Abhisheka (IRE)
59 **FLAMEWOOD (USA)**, b g Medaglia d'Oro (USA)—Fire And Flame (USA)
60 **FULL VERSE (IRE)**, b g Kodiac—Anthem Alexander (IRE)
61 **GLOBAL STORM (IRE)**, ch g Night of Thunder (IRE)—Travel (USA)
62 **HIGHLAND DANCER (IRE)**, b f Galileo (IRE)—Keenes Royale
63 **HYSTERICAL (IRE)**, gr f Galileo (IRE)—Laugh Out Loud

MR CHARLIE APPLEBY - continued

64 **IMPERIAL EMPIRE,** ch g Dubawi (IRE)—Falls of Lora (IRE)
65 **JOYFUL SONG (IRE),** b f Teofilo (IRE)—Good Friend (IRE)
66 **KING'S COMMAND,** b g Dubawi (IRE)—O'Giselle (AUS)
67 **KINGSWEAR,** b c Dubawi (IRE)—Galatee (FR)
68 **LATE ROMANCE,** b f Dubawi (IRE)—Voleuse de Coeurs (IRE)
69 **LAW OF PEACE,** b c Shamardal (USA)—Certify (USA)
70 **LAZULI (IRE),** b c Dubawi (IRE)—Floristry
71 **LIGHT BLUSH (IRE),** b f Kodiac—Marsh Daisy
72 **LYRICAL APPROACH,** b f New Approach (IRE)—Dancing Sands (IRE)
73 **MAN OF PROMISE (USA),** b c Into Mischief (USA)—Involved (USA)
74 **NATIONAL TREASURE (IRE),** b f Camelot—Flawless Beauty
75 **NATIVE TRIBE,** b c Farhh—Anything Goes (IRE)
76 **NEVER ALONE,** b g Dubawi (IRE)—Yummy Mummy
77 **OCEAN HEIGHTS,** ch g Dubawi (IRE)—Ethereal Sky (IRE)
78 **ODE TO DUTY (USA),** b br c Dubawi (IRE)—Odeliz (IRE)
79 **OTTOMAN COURT,** b g Shamardal (USA)—Tulips (IRE)
80 **PATH OF THUNDER (IRE),** ch g Night of Thunder (IRE)—Sunset Avenue (USA)
81 **PINATUBO (IRE),** b c Shamardal (USA)—Lava Flow (IRE)
82 **PLEDGE OF PEACE (IRE),** b g New Approach (IRE)—Hoodna (IRE)
83 **POET'S MIND (USA),** b g Dubawi (IRE)—Arethusa (USA)
84 **POWER OF TIME (IRE),** b c Galileo (IRE)—Terror (IRE)
85 **QUEEN OF JAZZ (IRE),** b f Camelot—Musical Sands
86 **RAINBOW FALLS (IRE),** ch f Dubawi (IRE)—Colour (AUS)
87 **REFLECTIONIST (FR),** br g Sea The Stars (IRE)—Elle Same
88 **REGAL LEGACY,** b g Dubawi (IRE)—Marie de Medici (USA)
89 **RENAISSANCE QUEEN,** ch f Pivotal—Indian Petal
90 **RHYTHM OF LIFE (IRE),** ch f New Approach (IRE)—Khothry (IRE)
91 **ROYAL CASTLE (IRE),** ch c Dubawi (IRE)—Braided (USA)
92 **ROYAL CRUSADE,** b c Shamardal (USA)—Zibelina (IRE)
93 **SACRED DANCE,** b f Sea The Stars (IRE)—Janey Muddles (IRE)
94 **SAKURA PETAL,** ch f Dubawi (IRE)—Dancing Rain (IRE)
95 **SAQQARA KING (USA),** gr ro c American Pharoah (USA)—Joyful Victory (CAN)
96 **SECRET VICTORY,** ch c Dubawi (IRE)—Hidden Gold (IRE)
97 **SPECTRUM OF LIGHT (IRE),** br g Golden Horn—Elegant Shadow (GER)
98 **SPRING OF LOVE,** b f Invincible Spirit (IRE)—Desert Blossom (IRE)
99 **STATE CROWN (IRE),** ch c New Approach (IRE)—Patroness
100 **STORMY MOUNTAIN (IRE),** gr f Dark Angel (IRE)—Aspen (AUS)
101 **STORY OF LIGHT (IRE),** b g Dark Angel (IRE)—Beautiful Ending
102 **STRONG RHYTHM (IRE),** b g Dubawi (IRE)—Anjaz (USA)
103 **SUMMER ROMANCE (IRE),** gr f Kingman—Serena's Storm (IRE)
104 **SYMBOL OF LOVE,** b f Shamardal (USA)—Policoro (IRE)
105 **TOLMOUNT,** b g Dubawi (IRE)—Fintry (IRE)
106 **VIRTUOUS LADY,** b f Dubawi (IRE)—Great Virtues (IRE)
107 **VISIBLE CHARM (IRE),** b g Invincible Spirit (IRE)—Mare Nostrum
108 **VOLKAN STAR (IRE),** b g Sea The Stars (IRE)—Chicago Dancer (IRE)
109 **VOTTORIA LIGHT,** b c Shamardal (USA)—Trieste
110 **WELL OF WISDOM,** b c Oasis Dream—Alessandria
111 **WILD HUNT,** b c Dubawi (IRE)—Rumh (GER)
112 **YA HAYATI (USA),** b c Dubawi (IRE)—Wedding Toast (USA)

TWO-YEAR-OLDS

113 B c 20/02 Invincible Spirit (IRE)—Aimhirgin Lass (IRE) (Pivotal) (394680)
114 B c 03/05 Dubawi (IRE)—Albasharah (USA) (Arch (USA))
115 B c 15/04 Dubawi (IRE)—Alessandria (Sunday Silence (USA))
116 B c 11/04 Dubawi (IRE)—Alina (IRE) (Galileo (IRE)) (3600000)
117 Ch f 14/01 Sea The Stars (IRE)—Anna Mia (GER) (Monsun (GER)) (703560)
118 B c 31/03 Frankel—Anna Salai (USA) (Dubawi (IRE))
119 B br c 15/02 Pioneerof the Nile (USA)—Arethusa (USA) (A P Indy (USA))
120 B f 20/01 Dubawi (IRE)—Baisse (High Chaparral (IRE))

MR CHARLIE APPLEBY - continued

121 B c 20/03 Shamardal (USA)—Balsamine (USA) (Street Cry (IRE))
122 B f 10/02 Dubawi (IRE)—Be Fabulous (GER) (Samum (GER))
123 B f 14/04 Dark Angel (IRE)—Beatrix Potter (IRE) (Cadeaux Genereux) (858000)
124 B c 28/02 Lope de Vega (IRE)—Bikini Babe (IRE) (Montjeu (IRE)) (750000)
125 B f 24/02 Kingman—Blue Angel (IRE) (Oratorio (IRE))
126 B c 14/02 Sea The Stars (IRE)—Bourree (GER) (Siyouni (FR)) (197340)
127 B c 26/03 Dubawi (IRE)—Bright Beacon (Manduro (GER))
128 B c 20/02 Dubawi (IRE)—Chachamaidee (IRE) (Footstepsinthesand) (200000)
129 Ch c 30/03 Dubawi (IRE)—Choose Me (IRE) (Choisir (AUS)) (343200)
130 B c 05/02 Dubawi (IRE)—Come Alive (Dansili)
131 B c 03/02 Dubawi (IRE)—Dalkova (Galileo (IRE))
132 B c 28/04 Siyouni (FR)—Davantage (FR) (Galileo (IRE)) (205920)
133 B f 18/01 Dubawi (IRE)—Desert Blossom (IRE) (Shamardal (USA))
134 B c 05/02 Shamardal (USA)—Devonshire (IRE) (Fast Company (IRE))
135 Ch c 11/02 New Approach (IRE)—Dibajj (FR) (Iffraaj) (190000)
136 B f 23/04 Dubawi (IRE)—Discourse (USA) (Street Cry (IRE))
137 B c 25/04 Sea The Stars (IRE)—Dolce Strega (IRE) (Zoffany (IRE)) (85000)
138 B f 30/04 Dubawi (IRE)—Eastern Joy (Dubai Destination (USA))
139 B c 03/03 Dubawi (IRE)—Elle Shade (Shamardal (USA))
140 B c 31/03 Dubawi (IRE)—Emily Bronte (Machiavellian (USA))
141 B c 10/04 Sea The Stars (IRE)—Emreliya (IRE) (Danehill Dancer (IRE)) (725000)
142 B f 27/02 Dubawi (IRE)—Entertainment (Halling (USA))
143 Ch c 24/02 Dubawi (IRE)—Epitome (IRE) (Nashwan (USA))
144 B c 12/04 War Front (USA)—Eternal Bounty (IRE) (Galileo (IRE))
145 Ch f 06/02 Shamardal (USA)—Final Stage (Street Cry (IRE))
146 B c 16/04 Dubawi (IRE)—Fintry (IRE) (Shamardal (USA))
147 B c 11/02 Dubawi (IRE)—First Victory (IRE) (Teofilo (IRE))
148 B c 04/03 Dubawi (IRE)—Firth of Lorne (IRE) (Danehill (USA))
149 B f 09/04 Medaglia d'Oro (USA)—Fitful Skies (IRE) (Dubawi (IRE))
150 B c 23/03 Frankel—Fleche d'Or (Dubai Destination (USA)) (3100000)
151 Ch c 11/03 Frankel—Gale Force (Shirocco (GER)) (200000)
152 B c 29/03 Dubawi (IRE)—Gallipot (Galileo (IRE))
153 B f 09/04 Dubawi (IRE)—Ghurra (USA) (War Chant (USA)) (700000)
154 B c 09/02 Dubawi (IRE)—Gonbarda (GER) (Lando (GER))
155 B c 18/02 Kingman—Grace And Favour (Montjeu (IRE)) (2300000)
156 B c 20/03 Dubawi (IRE)—Halay (Dansili)
157 B c 03/04 Dubawi (IRE)—Hanky Panky (IRE) (Galileo (IRE))
158 Ch f 12/04 Dubawi (IRE)—Hibaayeb (Singspiel (IRE))
159 B f 23/03 Dubawi (IRE)—Hidden Gold (IRE) (Shamardal (USA))
160 B c 03/04 Shamardal (USA)—Important Time (IRE) (Oasis Dream)
161 Ch c 09/04 Dubawi (IRE)—Indian Petal (Singspiel (IRE))
162 Ch c 30/03 Galileo (IRE)—Jacqueline Quest (IRE) (Rock of Gibraltar (IRE)) (1100000)
163 **JAVANA,** ch f 23/03 New Approach (IRE)—Criticism (Machiavellian (USA))
164 B f 14/02 Dubawi (IRE)—Just The Judge (IRE) (Lawman (FR))
165 B c 19/02 Kingman—Kamakura (USA) (Medaglia d'Oro (USA)) (625000)
166 B c 02/04 Dubawi (IRE)—Karenine (High Chaparral (IRE))
167 B c 28/02 Dubawi (IRE)—Kazziana (Shamardal (USA))
168 Ch f 04/02 Dubawi (IRE)—Khawlah (IRE) (Cape Cross (IRE))
169 B c 13/02 Dansili—Knocknagree (IRE) (Galileo (IRE)) (320000)
170 B c 01/03 Dubawi (IRE)—Koora (Pivotal) (400000)
171 Ch f 11/03 New Approach (IRE)—La Arenosa (IRE) (Exceed And Excel (AUS))
172 B c 23/01 Frankel—La Mortola (Dubawi (IRE)) (300000)
173 B f 21/05 Dubawi (IRE)—Lacey's Lane (Street Cry (IRE))
174 B f 15/03 Sea The Stars (IRE)—Lava Flow (IRE) (Dalakhani (IRE))
175 B c 23/02 Shamardal (USA)—Local Time (Invincible Spirit (IRE))
176 B br c 07/02 Sea The Stars (IRE)—Lopera (GER) (Monsun (GER)) (875000)
177 Gr c 31/01 Dubawi (IRE)—Lumiere (Shamardal (USA))
178 B br f 17/03 Medaglia d'Oro (USA)—Macaroon (USA) (Tapit (USA))
179 B f 06/03 Dubawi (IRE)—Majestic Queen (IRE) (Kheleyf (USA))

MR CHARLIE APPLEBY - continued

180 B c 19/04 New Approach (IRE)—Marie Baa (FR) (Anabaa (USA)) (90000)
181 B c 28/03 Dubawi (IRE)—Marie de Medici (USA) (Medicean)
182 B c 04/02 Into Mischief (USA)—Mary Rita (USA) (Distorted Humor (USA))
183 B f 05/04 Dark Angel (IRE)—Mayhem (IRE) (Whipper (USA)) (686400)
184 Br c 19/03 Dubawi (IRE)—Minidress (Street Cry (IRE))
185 B f 25/05 Night of Thunder (IRE)—Miss Lucifer (FR) (Noverre (USA))
186 B c 21/01 Dubawi (IRE)—Miss Marjurie (IRE) (Marju (IRE)) (1100000)
187 B c 09/02 Frankel—Mistrusting (IRE) (Shamardal (USA))
188 Ch c 11/04 Shamardal (USA)—Modern Ideals (New Approach (IRE))
189 B f 22/03 Dubawi (IRE)—Mujarah (IRE) (Marju (IRE))
190 B c 10/03 Sea The Stars (IRE)—My Spirit (IRE) (Invincible Spirit (IRE)) (429000)
191 Ch c 10/03 Dubawi (IRE)—Nightime (IRE) (Galileo (IRE))
192 B f 24/02 Sea The Stars (IRE)—Pabouche (IRE) (Dubawi (IRE))
193 B f 15/03 Dubawi (IRE)—Panegyric (Monsun (GER))
194 B c 22/03 Hard Spun (USA)—Peace Camp (USA) (Storm Cat (USA))
195 B f 27/01 Dubawi (IRE)—Perfect Light (IRE) (Galileo (IRE))
196 B c 23/03 Dubawi (IRE)—Pleascach (IRE) (Teofilo (IRE))
197 B c 15/04 Dubawi (IRE)—Pomology (USA) (Arch (USA))
198 B f 31/01 Dubawi (IRE)—Princesse Dansante (IRE) (King's Best (USA))
199 B c 22/02 Dubawi (IRE)—Punctilious (Danehill (USA))
200 B f 04/02 Dubawi (IRE)—Pure Diamond (Street Cry (IRE))
201 Ch f 09/02 Speightstown (USA)—Raffle Ticket (USA) (A P Indy (USA))
202 Ch c 14/04 Dubawi (IRE)—Rumh (GER) (Monsun (GER))
203 B f 11/05 Shamardal (USA)—Sahraah (USA) (Kingmambo (USA))
204 B f 13/03 Dubawi (IRE)—Secret Gesture (Galileo (IRE))
205 B f 15/02 Shamardal (USA)—Sense of Fun (USA) (Distorted Humor (USA))
206 B c 17/04 Shamardal (USA)—Serene Beauty (USA) (Street Cry (IRE))
207 Ch f 30/01 Siyouni (FR)—Siamsaiocht (IRE) (Teofilo (IRE)) (386100)
208 B f 10/03 Shamardal (USA)—Sound Reflection (USA) (Street Cry (IRE))
209 B f 12/04 More Than Ready (USA)—Speckled (USA) (Street Cry (IRE))
210 Ch c 17/02 Sea The Stars (IRE)—Summer Flower (IRE) (Oasis Dream)
211 B f 02/05 Shamardal (USA)—Surprise Moment (IRE) (Authorized (IRE))
212 B f 01/04 Dubawi (IRE)—Tanzania (USA) (Darshaan)
213 B c 05/05 Sea The Stars (IRE)—Tasaday (USA) (Nayef (USA))
214 B c 11/05 Shamardal (USA)—Tashelka (FR) (Mujahid (USA))
215 Br f 11/03 Shamardal (USA)—Tearless (Street Cry (IRE))
216 B f 20/02 Medaglia d'Oro (USA)—Thunder Bay (USA) (Distorted Humor (USA))
217 B c 17/03 New Approach (IRE)—Token of Love (Cape Cross (IRE)) (320000)
218 Ch c 07/03 Dubawi (IRE)—Tulips (IRE) (Pivotal)
219 B f 22/04 Exceed And Excel (AUS)—Veil of Silence (IRE) (Elusive Quality (USA))
220 B c 11/02 Medaglia d'Oro (USA)—Velvety (USA) (Bernardini (USA))
221 B f 09/02 Sea The Stars (IRE)—Villarrica (USA) (Selkirk (USA))
222 B f 15/02 Shamardal (USA)—Violante (USA) (Kingmambo (USA))
223 B br f 24/02 Invincible Spirit (IRE)—Wadaa (USA) (Dynaformer (USA)) (600000)
224 Ch f 28/02 Dubawi (IRE)—Winters Moon (IRE) (New Approach (IRE))
225 WIRKO (GER), b c 01/03 Kingman—Weltmacht (Mount Nelson) (600600)
226 Ch c 29/03 Dubawi (IRE)—Yodelling (USA) (Medaglia d'Oro (USA))
227 B c 19/03 Dubawi (IRE)—Zibelina (IRE) (Dansili)

Assistant Trainer: Alex Merriam, Marie Murphy.

Flat Jockey: William Buick, James Doyle.

7 MR MICHAEL APPLEBY, Oakham
Postal: **The Homestead, Langham, Oakham, Leicestershire, LE15 7EJ**
Contacts: **PHONE 01572 722772 MOBILE 07884 366421**
EMAIL mickappleby@icloud.com WEBSITE www.mickappleby.com

1 **ADAMS PARK**, 5, b g Mastercraftsman (IRE)—Ile Deserte **ValueRacingClub.co.uk**
2 **AIRSHOW**, 5, ch g Showcasing—Belle des Airs (IRE) **Middleham Park Racing XXXIV**
3 **AQUARIUS (IRE)**, 4, b f Charm Spirit (IRE)—Puzzled (IRE) **Mr C. Bacon**
4 **BAILE GHILIBERT (IRE)**, 8, b g Majestic Missile (IRE)—Reddening **Mr & Mrs T. W. Readett-Bayley**
5 **BANCNUANAHEIREANN (IRE)**, 13, b g Chevalier (IRE)—Alamanta (IRE) **Mr W. Sewell & Mr Michael Appleby**
6 **BARRINGTON (IRE)**, 6, b g Casamento (IRE)—Mia Divina **Mr Frank McAleavy & Mr Ian McAleavy**
7 **BEDTIME BELLA (IRE)**, 4, b f Slade Power (IRE)—Slope **Rod In Pickle Partnership**
8 **BEECHWOOD JAMES (FR)**, 4, b c Sunday Break (JPN)—Mururoa (FR) **Middleham Park Racing CXII**
9 **BESCABY**, 5, b m Helmet (AUS)—Tidal **Houghton Bloodstock**
10 **BEST HAAF**, 4, b g Haafhd—Beyeh (IRE) **T. R. Pryke**
11 **BLUELION**, 4, ch g Sleeping Indian—Shirley's Pride **Mick Appleby Racing**
12 **BUSY STREET**, 8, b g Champs Elysees—Allegro Viva (USA) **Kings Head Duffield Racing Partnership**
13 **CALIMA CALLING (IRE)**, 4, ch f Gale Force Ten—Incoming Call (USA) **Mrs A. Garavaglia Drion**
14 **CALIN'S LAD**, 5, ch g Equiano (FR)—Lalina (GER) **Lycett Racing 100 Club**
15 **CALL OUT LOUD**, 8, b g Aqlaam—Winner's Call **Kings Head Duffield Racing Partnership**
16 **CAPE HIDEAWAY**, 8, b g Mount Nelson—Amiata **Kings Head Duffield Racing Partnership**
17 **CASE KEY**, 7, gr g Showcasing—Fluttering Rose **T. R. Pryke**
18 **CASEMENT (IRE)**, 6, b g Casamento (IRE)—Kirk Wynd **On the Case Partnership**
19 **CASH N CARRIE**, 6, b m Casamento (IRE)—Tales of Erin (IRE) **Mick Appleby Racing**
20 **CASHEL (IRE)**, 5, b g Sepoy (AUS)—Snow Dust **Mr L. A. Bellman**
21 **CASPIAN PRINCE (IRE)**, 11, ch g Dylan Thomas (IRE)—Crystal Gaze (IRE) **Mr S Louch & Mr M Appleby**
22 **CHANNEL PACKET**, 6, b h Champs Elysees—Etarre (IRE) **I. R. Hatton**
23 **CHESS MOVE (IRE)**, 5, b g Kodiac—Azia (IRE) **Mr C. Bacon**
24 **CHINESE ALPHABET**, 4, b g Leroidesanimaux (BRZ)—Kesara **Mr C. K. R. Cheung**
25 **CLIPSHAM TIGER (IRE)**, 4, b g Bungle Inthejungle—Texas Queen **Mr F. Morley**
26 **COMPETITION**, 8, b g Multiplex—Compolina **ValueRacingClub.co.uk**
27 **CRIMSON KING (IRE)**, 4, b g Kingman—Toi Et Moi (IRE) **Mr N. Hassan**
28 **DANZENA**, 5, b m Denounce—Danzanora **Mr A. M. Wragg**
29 **DANZENO**, 9, b g Denounce—Danzanora **Mr A. M. Wragg**
30 **DECORATION OF WAR (IRE)**, 5, b g Declaration of War (USA)—
Sea Paint (IRE) **Castle Racing & the Horse Watchers**
31 **DEINONYCHUS**, 9, b g Authorized (IRE)—Sharp Dresser (USA) **I. R. Hatton**
32 5, B h Schiaparelli (GER)—Di's Dilemma **Mr & Mrs T. W. Readett-Bayley**
33 **DOCTOR JAZZ (IRE)**, 5, b g Most Improved (IRE)—Daliyana (IRE) **The Horse Watchers & Matthew Taylor**
34 **DOUBLE REFLECTION**, 5, b m Showcasing—Green And Bleue **Mr C. Bacon**
35 **DREADNOUGHTUS**, 4, ch c Americain (USA)—Sharp Dresser (USA) **I. R. Hatton**
36 **DREAM WORLD**, 5, b m Dream Ahead (USA)—Tetard (IRE) **Rod In Pickle Partnership**
37 **ELHAFEI (USA)**, 5, br g Speightstown (USA)—Albamara **Geegeez.Co.Uk Ma**
38 **EPONINA (IRE)**, 6, b m Zoffany (IRE)—Dame Rochelle (IRE) **Mrs E. Cash**
39 4, Br f Foxwedge (AUS)—Etarre (IRE) **I. R. Hatton**
40 **ETON PRIDE (FR)**, 6, ch m Coastal Path—Lady Jannina **E. R. Hanbury**
41 **FANTASY KEEPER**, 6, b g Mayson—Expressive **The Fantasy Fellowship B**
42 **FIRST VOYAGE (IRE)**, 7, ch g Dubawi (IRE)—Concordia **Mr D. G. Skelton**
43 **FORSETI**, 4, b g Charm Spirit (IRE)—Ravensburg **Geegeez.Co.Uk Ma**
44 **FREE LOVE**, 4, b f Equiano (FR)—Peace And Love (IRE) **The North South Syndicate**
45 **GLORY OF PARIS (IRE)**, 6, b g Sir Prancealot (IRE)—Paris Glory (USA) **Mr C. Bacon**
46 **GOOD OLE WINNIE**, 4, b f Gale Force Ten—Dalliefour (IRE) **Rockingham Reins Limited**
47 **GRANDEE DAISY**, 4, ch f Sepoy (AUS)—Chili Dip **Mr M. J. Goggin**
48 **GREATEST JOURNEY**, 8, ch g Raven's Pass—Sensationally **The Hobbits**
49 **I LOVE YOU BABY**, 4, b f Cityscape—Ashtaroth **Craig & Laura Buckingham**
50 **INDIGO PRINCESS**, 7, b m Native Ruler—Red To Violet **Mr P. A. Jarvis**
51 **IT MUST BE FAITH**, 10, b g Mount Nelson—Purple Rain (IRE) **Mick Appleby Racing**
52 **JACKPOT ROYALE**, 5, b g Sixties Icon—Sofia Royale **Mr Wayne Brackstone, Mr Steve Whitear**
53 **JORVIK PRINCE**, 6, br g Kheleyf (USA)—Wotatomboy **The Working Men**
54 **KARABUNGA DUDE**, 6, b g Black Sam Bellamy (IRE)—Danarama **J & A Young (Leicester) Ltd**

MR MICHAEL APPLEBY - continued

55 **KASBAAN**, 5, br g Dansili—Aghareed (USA) **The Horse Watchers**
56 **KATTANI (IRE)**, 4, b g Tamayuz—Katiola (IRE) **Kaizen Racing**
57 **KHAAN**, 5, ch h Kheleyf (USA)—Sharp Dresser (USA) **I. R. Hatton**
58 **KYBOSH (IRE)**, 4, b g Dansili—Super Sleuth (IRE) **Mr L. A. Bellman**
59 **LADY CARDUROS (IRE)**, 6, b m Byron—Saranjo (IRE) **Mr J. Ross**
60 **LADY DIVA**, 6, ch m Black Sam Bellamy (IRE)—Divisa (GER) **E. R. Hanbury**
61 **LINCOLN PARK**, 4, b c Kyllachy—Twilight Pearl **Mr G. Dewhurst**
62 **LION HEARTED (IRE)**, 6, b g Lope de Vega (IRE)—Ros The Boss (IRE) **Slipstream Racing**
63 **LOCH NESS MONSTER (IRE)**, 4, b g War Command (USA)—Celestial Dream (IRE) **Mr M. J. Taylor**
64 **MALIKA I JAHAN (FR)**, 4, b f Australia—Have Faith (IRE) **The Horse Watchers**
65 **MICHELE STROGOFF**, 7, b g Aqlaam—Maschera d'Oro **Mr L. Coleman-Carr**
66 6, B g Black Sam Bellamy (IRE)—Midnight Fun **M. Appleby**
67 **MOHAREB**, 4, b g Delegator—Irrational **Mr I. Lawrence**
68 **MOON TROUBLE (IRE)**, 7, ch g Lope de Vega (IRE)—Shake The Moon (GER) **Mr Rob Oliver & the Horse Watchers**
69 **MOONRAKER**, 8, ch g Starspangledbanner (AUS)—Licence To Thrill **The Kettlelites**
70 **MOTAWAAFEQ (FR)**, 4, b c Wootton Bassett—Crossed Fingers (IRE) **Middleham Park Racing II**
71 **N OVER J**, 5, b g Kodiac—Risk A Look **Mr N. Hassan**
72 **NO SHOES NATION**, 4, ch f Monsieur Bond (IRE)—Stunning Icon **Mr S. Tolley**
73 **PAGEANT MASTER (IRE)**, 4, ch g Casamento (IRE)—Skiphall **Slipstream Racing**
74 **PERUVIAN LILY (FR)**, 4, ch f Mayson—Rosa Mundi **The Horse Watchers**
75 **PROXY**, 4, b f Frankel—Vote Often
76 **QUDURAAT**, 4, ch f Teofilo (IRE)—Ejadah (IRE) **Mrs B. A. Matthews**
77 **RESTIVE (IRE)**, 7, b g Rip Van Winkle (IRE)—I Hearyou Knocking (IRE) **M. Appleby**
78 **SAINT MAC**, 5, b g Nathaniel (IRE)—Noahs Ark (IRE) **T. R. Pryke**
79 **SEA OF MYSTERY (IRE)**, 7, b g Sea The Stars (IRE)—Sassenach (IRE) **Mr Frank McAleavy & Mr Ian McAleavy**
80 6, B m Royal Applause—Sharp Dresser (USA) **I. R. Hatton**
81 **SIX STRINGS**, 6, b g Requinto (IRE)—Island Music (IRE) **S & R Racing Partnership**
82 **STAR OF SOUTHWOLD (FR)**, 5, bl g Le Havre (IRE)—Into The Wild (FR) **Middleham Park Racing XXXIII**
83 **STONE MASON (IRE)**, 4, b c Pivotal—Victoria Star (IRE) **The Horse Watchers**
84 **STRICT (IRE)**, 4, b g Slade Power (IRE)—Thawrah (IRE) **Honestly Racing**
85 **SUMMER ANGEL (IRE)**, 5, gr m Mastercraftsman (IRE)—City Image (IRE) **Mr C. Bacon**
86 **TAN ARABIQ**, 7, b g Arabian Gleam—Tanning **Sarnian Racing**
87 **TEMUJIN (IRE)**, 4, b g Moohaajim (IRE)—Alhena (IRE) **Rockingham Reins Limited**
88 **THAT IS THE SPIRIT**, 9, b g Invincible Spirit (IRE)—Fraulein **Mr William Esdaile**
89 **TIGRAY (USA)**, 4, gr g Tapit (USA)—Daisy Devine (USA) **Honestly Racing**
90 **VALE OF ROCK (IRE)**, 7, b m Vale of York (IRE)—Pirans Rock (IRE) **Kenneth George Kitchen**
91 **WILLIAM ASHFORD (IRE)**, 8, ch g Art Connoisseur (IRE)—Song of Sixpence (IRE) **Mr D. A. Lynch**
92 **WILLY SEWELL**, 7, b g Multiplex—Cherished Love (IRE) **Mr W. J. Sewell**
93 **YER TEKKIN MICK**, 5, b g Native Ruler—Lord Conyers (IRE) **Mrs E. Cash**
94 **ZAPPER CASS (FR)**, 7, b g Elusive City (USA)—Moonlight Cass (IRE) **M. Appleby**

THREE-YEAR-OLDS

95 **ABBALEKA**, b c Equiano (FR)—Megaleka **North Cheshire Trading & Storage Ltd**
96 **AMI LI BERT (IRE)**, ch c Dragon Pulse (IRE)—Taalluf (USA) **S & R Racing Partnership**
97 **AYR HARBOUR**, b c Harbour Watch (IRE)—Sorella Bella (IRE) **Jabra Racing**
98 **BRINGING GLORY (IRE)**, b c Bated Breath—Roseraie (IRE) **Mr S. G. Morris**
99 **BULLDOZER (IRE)**, b c Hallowed Crown (AUS)—Phi Phi (IRE) **The Horse Watchers**
100 **CASARUAN**, b c Casamento (IRE)—Aruan **B. D. Cantle**
101 B f Equiano (FR)—Enford Princess **Mr C. A. Blyth**
102 **FANTASY LOVER (IRE)**, b f Due Diligence (USA)—Jollification (IRE) **The Fantasy Fellowship**
103 **FASHION FREE**, b f Muhaarar—Ighraa (IRE) **Mr L. J. M. J. Vaessen**
104 **FEEL GOOD FACTOR**, ch f Dutch Art—Meeting Waters **Craig & Laura Buckingham**
105 **GARSMAN (IRE)**, b g Garswood—Regina **The Horse Watchers**
106 **GOLD BROCADE (IRE)**, ch f Dragon Pulse (IRE)—Primal Snow (USA) **Dr C. K. C. Tan**
107 **GRACIE'S GIRL**, b f Heeraat (IRE)—Queens Revenge **Mr R. Oliver**
108 **HARBOUR POINT**, b c Harbour Watch (IRE)—Stunning Icon **Mr S. Tolley**
109 **HELMET HOUSE**, ch f Helmet (AUS)—Wentworth House **B. D. Cantle**
110 **LITTLE MISS MADAM**, b f Bollin Eric—Caribbean Pearl (USA) **Mr N. C. Hoare**
111 **MERRYWEATHER**, b f Dunaden (FR)—Pearl Princess (FR) **The Horse Watchers**

MR MICHAEL APPLEBY - continued

112 **NIKOLAYEVA**, b f Archipenko (USA)—Nezhenka **ValueRacingClub.co.uk**
113 **OUT FOR A DUCK**, b f Due Diligence (USA)—Three Ducks **Midest 1**
114 **RAADEA**, ch g Showcasing—Dream Melody **Mr C. Bacon**
115 **RED HOTTIE**, ch f Hot Streak (IRE)—Descriptive (IRE) **Head Over Hils**
116 **RED JASPER**, ch g Showcasing—Spate (IRE) **Mr C. Bacon**
117 **ROYAL COUNCIL (IRE)**, b gr g Clodovil (IRE)—Queen Zain (IRE) **Mr C. Bacon**
118 **SHOW 'EM JOY**, b f Showcasing—Black Belt Shopper (IRE) **Minster Developments**
119 **SPEED MERCHANT (IRE)**, ro g Zebedee—Tanyeli (IRE) **Slipstream Racing**
120 **TRIPLE SPEAR**, br g Showcasing—Secret Romance **Minster Developments**
121 **XIAN EXPRESS (IRE)**, ch g Dragon Pulse (IRE)—Wind Inher Sleeves (USA) **Dr C. K. C. Tan**

Trainer did not supply details of their two-year-olds.

Other Owners: M. Appleby, Mr M. Bisogno, Mr W. M. Brackstone, Mrs J. A. Brooke, Mr C. Buckingham, Mrs L. K. Buckingham, Miss H. Butler, Mr J. Cannon, Mr B. Carter, Castle Racing, Mr A. J. T. D'Arcy, Mr C. Dixon, Mr M. Dixon, Mr S. Furniss, GG Thoroughbreds I, Mr G. Gill, Mr M. Harris, Mr R. Hunnisett, Mr A. A. F. Iredale, Mr R. N. J. Lane, Mr S. Louch, Mr R. Maddocks, Mr F. McAleavy, Mr I. McAleavy, Mr S. Nightingale, Mr R. Oliver, Mr C. Pigram, Mr J. Ross, Mr W. J. Sewell, Mr P. J. Shaw, Mr S. A. Sowray, Mr M. J. Taylor, The Horse Watchers, Mr S. J. Whitear.

Assistant Trainer: Jonathan Clayton.

Flat Jockey: Silvestre De Sousa, Luke Morris, Andrew Mullen, Alistair Rawlinson. **NH Jockey:** Richard Johnson, Jack Quinlan.
Apprentice Jockey: Kevin Lundie. **Amateur Jockey:** Miss Serena Brotherton.

MR RICHARD ARMSON, Melbourne
Postal: **Scotlands Farm, Burney Lane, Staunton-Harold, Melbourne, Derbyshire, DE73 8BH**

1 **ALBURN**, 10, b g Alflora (IRE)—Burn Brook **R. J. Armson**
2 **BOB'S CALL (IRE)**, 11, b g Scorpion (IRE)—Whizz **R. J. Armson**
3 **HURRICANE VIC**, 10, b g Mount Nelson—Fountains Abbey (USA) **R. J. Armson**
4 **KEYNOTE (IRE)**, 5, b g Dragon Pulse (IRE)—Taalluf (USA) **R. J. Armson**
5 **KILCARAGH BOY (IRE)**, 11, b g King's Theatre (IRE)—Histologie (FR) **R. J. Armson**
6 **MAX O (IRE)**, 10, b g Brian Boru—Myglass (IRE) **R. J. Armson**
7 5, B g Imperial Monarch (IRE)—Presenting Lazarus (IRE) **R. J. Armson**

MR PETER ATKINSON, Northallerton
Postal: **Yafforth Hill Farm, Yafforth, Northallerton, North Yorkshire, DL7 0LT**
Contacts: **PHONE 01609 772598 MOBILE 07751 131215**

1 **IRISH ROE (IRE)**, 9, b m Vinnie Roe (IRE)—Betty's The Best (IRE) **Mrs L. Atkinson**
2 **REVERANT CUST (IRE)**, 9, gr g Daylami (IRE)—Flame Supreme (IRE) **Mr P. G. Atkinson**
3 **RIBEYE**, 5, b g Lucarno (USA)—Elusive Swallow **Mrs L. Atkinson**

MR MICHAEL ATTWATER, Epsom
Postal: **Tattenham Corner Stables, Tattenham Corner Road, Epsom Downs, Surrey, KT18 5PP**
Contacts: **PHONE 01737 360066 MOBILE 07725 423633**
EMAIL Attwaterracing@hotmail.co.uk WEBSITE www.attwaterracing.com

1 **ANGEL'S ACCLAIM (IRE)**, 6, gr m Dark Angel (IRE)—Miss Otis **Dare To Dream Racing**
2 **APRON STRINGS**, 4, b f Mayson—Royal Ivy **Canisbay Bloodstock**
3 **ASK THE GURU**, 10, b g Ishiguru (USA)—Tharwa (IRE) **Canisbay Bloodstock**
4 **BIG TIME MAYBE (IRE)**, 5, b g Dandy Man (IRE)—Divine Design (IRE) **Dare To Dream Racing**
5 **BONGO BEAT**, 9, ch g Beat Hollow—Steppin Out **Canisbay Bloodstock**
6 **DANIEL DRAVOT**, 4, b g Nathaniel (IRE)—Zubova **Mr J. M. Duggan & Mr S. Brown**
7 **DELAGATE THIS LORD**, 6, b g Delegator—Lady Filly **Mrs M. S. Teversham**
8 **EMBANKMENT**, 11, b g Zamindar (USA)—Esplanade **Canisbay Bloodstock**
9 **FREE TALKIN**, 5, b m Equiano (FR)—Where's Broughton **Canisbay Bloodstock**

MR MICHAEL ATTWATER - continued

10 **HORNBY**, 5, b g Equiano (FR)—Kindia (IRE) **Canisbay Bloodstock**
11 **JUANITO CHICO (IRE)**, 6, br g Pour Moi (IRE)—Miss Kittyhawk (IRE) **The Attwater Partnership**
12 **JUST THAT LORD**, 7, ch g Avonbridge—Lady Filly **Mrs M. S. Teversham**
13 **LAWN RANGER**, 5, b g Cityscape—Baylini **Canisbay Bloodstock**
14 **LEE ROY**, 4, ch c Leroidesanimaux (BRZ)—Steppin Out **Canisbay Bloodstock**
15 **LEP**, 4, b g Nathaniel (IRE)—Liel **Dare To Dream Racing**
16 **MISS DITSY (IRE)**, 4, b f Most Improved (IRE)—Maramkova (IRE) **Five Horses Ltd**
17 **MR FOX**, 4, b g Foxwedge (AUS)—Shared Moment (IRE) **The Attwater Partnership**
18 **MUSIC MAJOR**, 7, br g Bertolini (USA)—Music Maid (IRE) **The Attwater Partnership**
19 **NATCH**, 5, b g Nathaniel (IRE)—Angara **Mr A. C. D. Main**
20 **NOBLE DEED**, 10, ch g Kyllachy—Noble One **Canisbay Bloodstock**
21 **OUR LORD**, 8, gr g Proclamation (IRE)—Lady Filly **Mrs M. S. Teversham**
22 **PASSING CLOUDS**, 5, b g Kheleyf (USA)—Steppin Out **Canisbay Bloodstock**
23 **PINK FLAMINGO**, 4, b f Dream Ahead (USA)—Naivasha **Dare To Dream Racing**
24 **PURFORD GREEN**, 11, ch m Kyllachy—Mo Stopher **Canisbay Bloodstock**
25 **REAL ESTATE (IRE)**, 5, b g Dansili—Maskunah (IRE) **Mr A. C. D. Main**
26 **SAVOY BROWN**, 4, b g Epaulette (AUS)—Kindia (IRE) **Canisbay Bloodstock**
27 **SCENIC LADY**, 4, b f Frozen Power (IRE)—Dazzling View (USA) **The Attwater Partnership**
28 **SHEILA'S FANCY (IRE)**, 6, ch g Casamento (IRE)—Fancy Vivid (IRE) **Dare To Dream Racing**
29 **SOLAR PARK (IRE)**, 4, ch c Kendargent (FR)—Solandia (IRE) **Haxted Racing**
30 **SOMETHING LUCKY (IRE)**, 8, gr g Clodovil (IRE)—Lucky Leigh **Dare To Dream Racing**
31 **STORM BOY**, 5, b h Paco Boy (IRE)—Evenstorm (USA) **B. Gubby**
32 **THE CRUISING LORD**, 4, b g Coach House (IRE)—Lady Filly **Mrs M. S. Teversham**
33 **TRACTIVE EFFORT**, 7, b g Rail Link—Anastasia Venture **Canisbay Bloodstock**
34 **WARRANTED**, 7, b g Authorized (IRE)—Steppin Out **Canisbay Bloodstock**

THREE-YEAR-OLDS

35 **CHROMIUM**, gr f Cable Bay (IRE)—Ghedi (IRE) **Dare To Dream Racing**
36 **DILIGENT LADY**, b f Due Diligence (USA)—Lady Filly **Mrs M. S. Teversham**
37 **FARHHMORECREDIT**, b c Farhh—Espresso Romano **Mr J. S. Muscat**
38 **JOEY'S GIFT**, b g War Command (USA)—Cadeau Speciale **The Attwater Partnership**
39 **LADY CODEE**, b f Coach House (IRE)—Lady Prodee **Mrs M. S. Teversham**
40 **LADY PHYLLIS**, b f Coach House (IRE)—Lady Phill **Mrs M. S. Teversham**
41 **SEA BRIGHT**, b g Fulbright—Mary Sea (FR) **Diamonds Are Forever**
42 **STRANGE BREW**, b f Helmet (AUS)—Baylini **Canisbay Bloodstock**
43 **URTZI (IRE)**, b f Due Diligence (USA)—Yankee Belle (USA) **The Attwater Partnership**

Other Owners: Mr S. Brown, Mr J. M. Duggan, Mrs J. A. Gawthorpe, Miss J. Hunt, R. F. Kilby, Mr A. C. D. Main, Mrs L. Main, Miss M. E. Stopher.

Assistant Trainer: S. Sawyer.

MR JEAN-RENE AUVRAY, Calne
Postal: **West Nolands Farm, Nolands Road, Yatesbury, Calne, Wiltshire, SN11 8YD**
Contacts: **MOBILE 07798 645796**
EMAIL jr.auvray@outlook.com WEBSITE www.jrauvrayracing.co.uk

1 **ARGYLE (IRE)**, 7, gr g Lawman (FR)—All Hallows (IRE) **Auvray, Kelly, Law & Spratt**
2 **FIRST LINK (USA)**, 5, b m First Defence (USA)—Magic Motif (USA) **Mr S. K. McPhee**
3 **KNOCKMAOLE BOY (IRE)**, 8, b g Echo of Light—Kashmir Lady (FR) **N. R. Kelly**
4 **NAFAAYES (IRE)**, 6, ch m Sea The Stars (IRE)—Shamtari (IRE) **Nigel Kelly & Stuart McPhee**
5 **STREETS OF FIRE (IRE)**, 6, br m Milan—Flaming Brandy (IRE) **Lady E. Mays-Smith**

THREE-YEAR-OLDS

6 **TRIGGER HAPPY (IRE)**, b g Gutaifan (IRE)—Boom And Bloom (IRE) **Auvray, Kelly, Law & Spratt**

TWO-YEAR-OLDS

7 B f 01/04 Vadamos (FR)—Star Waves (IRE) (Sea The Stars (IRE)) **Mr S. K. McPhee**

12 MR ALAN BAILEY, Newmarket
Postal: **Cavendish Stables, Hamilton Road, Newmarket, Suffolk, CB8 7JQ**
Contacts: **PHONE 01638 664546 MOBILE 07808 734223 FAX 01638 664546**
EMAIL baileya12@sky.com
Licence will switch to JOSEPH PARR in Spring 2020 pending BHA approval

1 **BALTIC EAGLE (GER)**, 6, ch g Adlerflug (GER)—Baltic Gift **Mr B. Syversen**
2 **CLEM A**, 4, b g Helmet (AUS)—Mondovi **The Skills People Group Ltd**
3 **COME ON BEAR (IRE)**, 5, b m Dandy Man (IRE)—Blusienka (IRE) **M7 Come On Bear LLP**
4 **ENIGMATIC (IRE)**, 6, b g Elnadim (USA)—Meanwhile (IRE) **Trevor & Ruth Milner**
5 **ESSPEEGEE**, 7, b g Paco Boy (IRE)—Goldrenched (IRE) **The Skills People Group Ltd**
6 **GNAAD (IRE)**, 6, b g Invincible Spirit (IRE)—Areyaam (USA) **Capla Developments & A Bailey**
7 **GRASMERE (IRE)**, 5, b m Society Rock (IRE)—Silk Point (IRE) **MPR XLIV, Mr C Martin, Mrs A Shone**
8 **MARYELLEN**, 4, b f Mayson—Granny McPhee **A J McNamee & L C McNamee**
9 **SIR HAMILTON (IRE)**, 5, b g Canford Cliffs (IRE)—Cawett (IRE) **Mr B. Syversen**
10 **SIRIUS SLEW**, 4, b g Epaulette (AUS)—Slewtoo **Trevor & Ruth Milner**
11 **YOUR MOTHERS' EYES**, 4, b c Aussie Rules (USA)—Sanctum **Capla Developments & A Bailey**

THREE-YEAR-OLDS

12 B f Epaulette (AUS)—Carrauntoohil (IRE) **Mr E. Rayner**
13 **LADY ISABEL (IRE)**, b f Hallowed Crown (AUS)—Meanwhile (IRE) **Trevor & Ruth Milner**
14 B f Gale Force Ten—Margie (IRE) **Mr E. Rayner**
15 **NATIVE STAR (IRE)**, b g Nathaniel (IRE)—Purple Pearl (IRE) **Js Racing**

Other Owners: A. Bailey, Mr O. J. Jorgensen, Mr C. M. Martin, A. J. McNamee, Mr L. McNamee, Middleham Park Racing Xliv & A&j Ryan, Mrs R. L. Milner, Mr T. Milner, T. S. Palin, M. Prince, Mrs M. Shone, Mr P. Stubbins, Mr B. Syversen.

Assistant Trainer: Joseph Edwin Parr.

Amateur Jockey: Miss Jessica Cooley.

13 MRS CAROLINE BAILEY, Holdenby
Postal: **Holdenby Lodge, Spratton, Northants, NN6 8LG**
Contacts: **HOME 01604 883729 PHONE 01604 770234 MOBILE 07831 373340 FAX 01604 770423**
EMAIL caroline.bailey66@yahoo.com WEBSITE www.carolinebaileyracing.co.uk

1 **BOLDMERE**, 7, b g Multiplex—Pugnacious Lady **W. J. Odell**
2 **BRIERY BUNNY**, 8, b m Lucarno (USA)—Blackbriery Thyne (IRE) **Mrs H. Plumbly**
3 **CARLO ROCKS (IRE)**, 10, b g Carlo Bank (IRE)—Rock Garden (IRE) **Mrs S. Tucker**
4 **COOLE LION (IRE)**, 6, b g Presenting—Kayanti (IRE) **C. W. Booth**
5 **CROSSPARK**, 10, b g Midnight Legend—Blue Shannon (IRE) **C. W. Booth**
6 **DONT TELL THE WIFE**, 6, b g Midnight Legend—Dizzy Frizzy **Bailey, Jessup, & Lloyd**
7 **DYLIEV (FR)**, 7, ch m Dylan Thomas (IRE)—Coreliev (IRE) **Herron, Nicholson, & Proctor**
8 **ELKSTONE**, 9, b g Midnight Legend—Samandara (FR) **Tredwell, Robinson, Proctor & Nicholson**
9 **HOWYA HUN (IRE)**, 6, b m Stowaway—Glencree Rose (IRE) **Mrs J. M. Dixon Smith**
10 **JUST A DEAL**, 5, b g Arvico (FR)—Monte Mayor Golf (IRE) **G. T. H. Bailey**
11 **LADY MASTER**, 7, b m Native Ruler—Elmside Katie **Mr P. Dixon Smith**
12 **LORD SPARKY**, 6, ch g Sulamani (IRE)—Braybrooke Lady (IRE) **The On The Bridle Partnership**
13 **MALAPIE (IRE)**, 12, b g Westerner—Victorian Lady
14 **MATCHMAKING (GER)**, 5, ch g Mastercraftsman (IRE)—Monami (GER) **J. B. Wallwin**
15 **PELLADY**, 6, b m Le Fou (IRE)—Suetsu (IRE) **Mrs S. Tucker**
16 **THE CAPTAIN (IRE)**, 7, b g Millenary—Quilt **Mr C Flinton & Mr G Bailey**
17 **THOMAS SHELBY (IRE)**, 9, b g Witness Box (USA)—Deemiss (IRE) **Mrs A. Vaughan-Jones**

Other Owners: G. T. H. Bailey, C. Flinton, Mr M. S. Herron, Mr B. P. Jessup, Mr R. B. Lloyd, Mr K. M. Nicholson, Mr P. S. C. Proctor, Mrs B. D. Robinson, J. Tredwell.

NH Jockey: Sean Bowen, Harry Skelton. **Amateur Jockey:** Mr Thomas McClorey.

14 MR KIM BAILEY, Cheltenham

Postal: **Thorndale Farm, Withington Road, Andoversford, Cheltenham, Gloucestershire, GL54 4LL**
Contacts: **PHONE 01242 890241 MOBILE 07831 416859 FAX 01242 890193**
EMAIL info@kimbaileyracing.com **WEBSITE** www.kimbaileyracing.com

1 **ADJOURNED**, 5, gr g Rip Van Winkle (IRE)—Bite of The Cherry **The Jury**
2 **ALIANDY (IRE)**, 9, b g Presenting—Water Rock **A & S Enterprises Ltd**
3 **ANOTHER VENTURE (IRE)**, 9, ch g Stowaway—Hard Luck (IRE) **Racing For Maggie's Partnership**
4 **ARTHUR'S SIXPENCE**, 6, b g Vinnie Roe (IRE)—Loose Change (IRE) **Stillmoremoneythan**
5 **BLAZON**, 7, b g Dansili—Zante **The Blazing Optimists**
6 **BOBHOPEORNOHOPE (IRE)**, 5, b g Westerner—Bandelaro (IRE) **Mr J. F. Perriss**
7 **CATCH ME NOT**, 5, b m Flemensfirth (USA)—Dorabelle (IRE) **Mr & Mrs Paul & Clare Rooney**
8 **CHARBEL (IRE)**, 9, b g Iffraaj—Eoz (IRE) **Mrs Julie Martin & David R. Martin**
9 **CHAZZA (IRE)**, 6, b g Mahler—Presenting Proform (IRE) **This Horse Is For Sale Partnership**
10 **COMMODORE BARRY (IRE)**, 7, br g Presenting—Specifiedrisk (IRE) **The Commodores**
11 **COTTEEMCAVENNIGOAL (IRE)**, 5, b g Kalanisi (IRE)—Brega Queen (IRE) **Mr S. L. Keane**
12 **CRESSWELL LEGEND**, 9, b g Midnight Legend—Cresswell Willow (IRE) **Mrs V. W. H. Johnson**
13 **DANDY DAN (IRE)**, 7, b g Midnight Legend—Playing Around **Mr P. J. Andrews**
14 **DIAMOND GAIT**, 7, b m Passing Glance—Milliegait **Mr N. Carter**
15 **DOES HE KNOW**, 5, b g Alkaased (USA)—Diavoleria **Yes He Does Syndicate**
16 **DONNIE BRASCO (FR)**, 7, b g Buck's Boum (FR)—Parislatino (FR) **Thefiftyshadesofneigh Syndicate**
17 **DRUMREAGH (IRE)**, 8, bm m Court Cave (IRE)—Mollyash (IRE) **Bucks Fizz**
18 **DUKE OF EARL (FR)**, 4, br g Noroit (GER)—Visiorienne (FR) **Mr P. J. Andrews**
19 **EL PRESENTE**, 7, b g Presenting—Raitera (FR) **Davies Pilkington Yarborough Brooke**
20 **ESPOIR DE ROMAY (FR)**, 6, b g Kap Rock (FR)—Miss du Seuil (FR) **The Midgelets**
21 **FIRST FLOW (IRE)**, 8, b g Primary (USA)—Clonroche Wells (IRE) **A. N. Solomons**
22 **FLIRTATIOUS GIRL (IRE)**, 4, b f Flemensfirth (USA)—
                                        Another Gaye (IRE) **Mrs I. C. Sellars & Major & Mrs P. Arkwright**
23 **FUBAR (IRE)**, 6, ch g Le Fou (IRE)—Petite Mielle (IRE) **Mr & Mrs Bevan**
24 **GREY FELIX**, 4, gr g Fair Mix (IRE)—Ruby Crown **Exors of the Late Mr I. F. W. Buchan**
25 **GREY FLINT**, 5, gr g Fair Mix (IRE)—Ruby Crown **Exors of the Late Mr I. F. W. Buchan**
26 **HAPPYGOLUCKY (IRE)**, 6, br g Jeremy (IRE)—Mydadsabishop (IRE) **Lady Dulverton**
27 **HES NO TROUBLE (IRE)**, 7, b g Scorpion (IRE)—She's No Trouble (IRE) **Jockey Club Ownership (SW 2018)**
28 **HOLLYMOUNT HOLLY (IRE)**, 6, ch m Doyen (IRE)—Parsee (IRE) **Mr J. F. Perriss**
29 **ILLUMINATED BEAUTY (IRE)**, 7, b m Flemensfirth (USA)—Native Beauty (IRE) **Mr J. F. Perriss**
30 **IMPERIAL AURA (IRE)**, 7, b g Kalanisi (IRE)—Missindependence (IRE) **Imperial Racing Partnership 2016**
31 **IMPERIAL ICON (IRE)**, 5, ch g Shantou (USA)—Bobomy (IRE) **Imperial Racing Partnership**
32 **INCA ROSE**, 5, ch g Malinas (GER)—Cinderella Rose **The Coln Valley Partnership**
33 **JAVA POINT (IRE)**, 5, b g Stowaway—Classic Sun (GER) **Fanning, Griffith, Haddock**
34 **LADY OF THE NIGHT**, 7, b m Midnight Legend—Even Flo **Mr J. F. Perriss**
35 **LORD APPARELLI**, 5, ch g Schiaparelli (GER)—La Marette **The Schiaparellis**
36 **LOTS OF LUCK (IRE)**, 6, b g Millenary—Lovely Hand (IRE) **Mr J. F. Perriss**
37 **MINELLA WARRIOR (IRE)**, 8, b g King's Theatre (IRE)—Bobbi's Venture (IRE) **Mrs Julie Martin & David R. Martin**
38 **MISS GEMSTONE**, 6, ch m Midnight Legend—Real Treasure **The Real Partnership**
39 **MON PALOIS (FR)**, 8, b g Muhaymin (USA)—Gastinaise (FR) **Mrs E. A. Kellar**
40 **NEWTIDE (IRE)**, 7, br g Getaway (GER)—C'Est Fantastique (IRE) **Lady Dulverton**
41 **OWBEG (IRE)**, 5, b g Notnowcato—Rumson Way (IRE) **Mr M. Kiely**
42 **PARTY FUZZ**, 5, b g Great Pretender (IRE)—Very Special One (IRE) **Mr P. J. Andrews**
43 **POND ROAD (FR)**, 6, ch g No Risk At All (FR)—Califea (FR) **No Risk Syndicate**
44 **PRINCE LLYWELYN**, 6, ch g Schiaparelli (GER)—La Marette **Mr P. Bennett-Jones**
45 **RHOSNEIGR (IRE)**, 5, ch g Iffraaj—Sadinga (IRE) **Mrs Julie Martin & David R. Martin**
46 **ROBIN THE RAVEN (IRE)**, 8, b g Robin des Pres (FR)—Omyn Supreme (IRE) **S W Racing**
47 **ROCKY'S TREASURE (IRE)**, 9, b g Westerner—Fiddlers Bar (IRE) **Mr J. F. Perriss**
48 **ROSE TO FAME**, 6, b m Fame And Glory—Cinderella Rose **Jones Broughtons Wilson Weaver**
49 **ROSMUC RELAY (IRE)**, 8, br g Presenting—Aughrim Vic (IRE) **Mr J. F. Perriss**
50 **SADLERMOR (IRE)**, 6, b g Morozov (USA)—Lucyjane (IRE) **Elphick, Sperling & KBR**
51 **SEA STORY**, 7, b m Black Sam Bellamy (IRE)—Charlottes Webb (IRE) **John & Susie Kottler, Emma Buchanan**
52 **SHANACOOLE PRINCE (IRE)**, 7, ch g Primary (USA)—Shanacoole Rose (IRE) **Mr & Mrs Mark Laws**
53 **SHANTOU EXPRESS (IRE)**, 5, ch g Shantou (USA)—Spanker **The Second Chancers**
54 **SHINOBI (IRE)**, 4, ch g Iffraaj—Ninja Lady **Shinobithemoney**

MR KIM BAILEY - continued

55 **SILVER KAYF**, 8, gr g Kayf Tara—Silver Spinner **The Lucky Spinners**
56 **STATION MASTER (IRE)**, 9, b g Scorpion (IRE)—Gastounette (IRE) **Mrs P. A. Perriss**
57 **SUBWAY SURF (IRE)**, 6, b m Milan—Dante Rouge (IRE) **Surf On The Turf**
58 **TALK OF FAME**, 5, b g Fame And Glory—Princess Oriane (IRE) **Lady Dulverton**
59 **THE BULL MCCABE (IRE)**, 6, b g Yeats (IRE)—Twilight View (IRE) **Park View**
60 **THE EDGAR WALLACE (IRE)**, 5, b g Flemensfirth (USA)—Annalecky (IRE) **Mr P. J. Andrews**
61 **THIBAULT**, 7, b g Kayf Tara—Seemarye **Mr T. D. J. Syder**
62 **THOSE TIGER FEET (IRE)**, 6, b g Shantou (USA)—Luca Lite (IRE) **Mr P. J. Andrews**
63 **TRWYN DU (IRE)**, 4, b g Valirann (FR)—Broken Thought (IRE) **Julie & David R Martin & Dan Hall**
64 **TWO FOR GOLD (IRE)**, 7, b g Gold Well—Two of Each (IRE) **May We Never Be Found Out Partnership 2**
65 **VINNDICATION (IRE)**, 7, b g Vinnie Roe (IRE)—Pawnee Trail (IRE) **Moremoneythan**
66 **VOYBURG (IRE)**, 4, br g Sageburg (IRE)—Slevoy Ahoy (IRE) **The Ten Sages**
67 **WANDRIN STAR (IRE)**, 9, b g Flemensfirth (USA)—Keralba (USA) **Mrs P. A. Perriss**
68 **WHAT A BALOO (IRE)**, 5, b g Jeremy (USA)—Luca Lite (IRE) **Share My Dream**
69 **YEAVERING BELLE**, 6, ch m Midnight Legend—Fruit Yoghurt **The Belle Stars**
70 **YOUNEVERCALL (IRE)**, 9, b g Yeats (IRE)—Afarka (IRE) **Youneverknow Partnership**

Other Owners: Major P. W. F. Arkwright, Mrs Sandra G. E. Arkwright, Mrs C. Bailey, Mr K. C. Bailey, Mr R. H. Beevor, Mr O. S. W. Bell, Mrs C. Bevan, Mr Q. Bevan, Sir F. Brooke, Sir M. F. Broughton, Mr S. W. Broughton, Mrs E. S. Buchanan, Mr D. J. Burke, Mr S. R. Cannon, Mr N. Carter, Exors of the Late Mr D. M. Clancy, Mr K. T. Clancy, M. E. T. Davies, Mr O. Fanning, Mr N. Griffith, Mrs H. M. Haddock, D. A. Hall, Lady M. P Hatch, Mrs N. Jones, Mr J. Kottler, Mrs S. E. Kottler, Mrs J. M. Laws, Mr M. J. Laws, D. R. Martin, Mrs J. M. T. Martin, Mr R. A. Pilkington, Mrs N. P. Sellars, Mr R. Sheppard, Mrs R. B. Weaver, Mr J. Webber, T. C. Wilson, The Earl Of Yarborough.

Assistant Trainer: Matthew Nicholls.

NH Jockey: David Bass. **Conditional Jockey:** Ned Curtis, Chester Williams.

---

15 | **MR LIAM BAILEY, Middleham**
Postal: **2 Little Spigot, Coverham, Middleham, Leyburn, North Yorkshire, DL8 4TL**
Contacts: **PHONE 07807 519220**
EMAIL liambailey_foulricefarm@hotmail.com

1 **AUXILIARY**, 7, b g Fast Company (IRE)—Lady Xara (IRE) **Mrs C M Clarke, Foulrice Park Racing Ltd**
2 **BOGARDUS (IRE)**, 9, b g Dalakhani (IRE)—Sugar Mint (IRE) **Foulrice Park Racing Limited**
3 **BUYER BEWARE (IRE)**, 8, br g Big Bad Bob (IRE)—Adoring (IRE) **Mr C. R. Stirling**
4 **CANFORD'S JOY (IRE)**, 5, b g Canford Cliffs (IRE)—Joyful (IRE) **Mrs C M Clarke, Foulrice Park Racing Ltd**
5 **CAPTAIN PEAKY**, 7, b g Captain Gerrard (IRE)—Multi-Sofft **Foulrice Park Racing Limited**
6 **COOKIE RING (IRE)**, 9, b g Moss Vale (IRE)—Talah **Mrs A. M. Stirling**
7 **DANCING SPEED (IRE)**, 4, b g Dandy Man (IRE)—Air Maze **Wyndrinkers Racing**
8 **DIXIELAND (IRE)**, 4, b g Red Jazz (USA)—Signora Lina (IRE) **Wyndrinkers Racing**
9 **DUCK EGG BLUE (IRE)**, 6, b m Haatef (USA)—Sapphire Spray (IRE) **Mrs S. Porteous**
10 **FILLYDELPHIA (IRE)**, 9, b m Strategic Prince—Lady Fonic **FPR Syndicate 7**
11 **FRAMLEY GARTH**, 8, b g Clodovil (IRE)—Two Marks (USA) **FPR Yorkshire Syndicate**
12 **HAJJAM**, 6, b g Paco Boy (IRE)—Amanda Carter **Mrs C M Clarke, Foulrice Park Racing Ltd**
13 **HOW BIZARRE**, 5, ch g Society Rock (IRE)—Amanda Carter **Harswell Thoroughbred Racing, Fpr Ltd**
14 **LAGENDA**, 7, b g Dick Turpin (IRE)—Whirly Dancer **Oakfield Racing**
15 **LIFE KNOWLEDGE (IRE)**, 8, ch g Thewayyouare (USA)—
Rosa Bellini (IRE) **Mrs C M Clarke, Foulrice Park Racing Ltd**
16 **MAGREVIO (IRE)**, 4, b g Helmet (AUS)—Queen Althea (IRE) **Mrs C. M. Clarke**
17 **OPTIMA PETAMUS**, 8, gr g Mastercraftsman (IRE)—
In A Silent Way (IRE) **Mrs C M Clarke, Foulrice Park Racing Ltd**
18 **PRINCESS NEARCO (IRE)**, 5, b m Elzaam (AUS)—Royal Jubilee (IRE) **Mrs C M Clarke, Foulrice Park Racing Ltd**
19 **QUANAH (IRE)**, 4, ch g Dandy Man (IRE)—Boucheron **Mrs A. M. Stirling**
20 **STRONSAY (IRE)**, 4, b g Gale Force Ten—Perfect Blossom **Mrs C M Clarke, Foulrice Park Racing Ltd**
21 **TEMPLE OF WONDER (IRE)**, 4, b g Clodovil (IRE)—Noble Fantasy (GER) **Mr C. R. Stirling**
22 **TYRELL (IRE)**, 7, b g Teofilo (IRE)—Sleeveless (USA) **Mr R Boswell & Colin Stirling**

MR LIAM BAILEY - continued

THREE-YEAR-OLDS
23 **JUNGLE BOOK (GER)**, ch c Sea The Moon (GER)—Josefine (GER) **Mrs C M Clarke, Foulrice Park Racing Ltd**

TWO-YEAR-OLDS
24 B c 26/03 Garswood—Grafitti (Dansili) (4761) **Harswell Thoroughbred Racing**

Other Owners: Mr R. Boswell, Mrs C. M. Clarke, Foulrice Park Racing Limited, Harswell Thoroughbred Racing, Mr M. Kirby, Mr C. R. Stirling, Miss M. A. Stirling, Mr R. J. Stirling.

---

16   MR GEORGE BAKER, Chiddingfold
Postal: **Robins Farm, Fisher Lane, Chiddingfold, Godalming, Surrey, GU8 4TB**
Contacts: **PHONE 01428 682059 MOBILE 07889 514881**
EMAIL gbakerracing@gmail.com WEBSITE www.georgebakerracing.com

1 **ADELANTE (FR)**, 4, ch f Zoffany (IRE)—Make Up **Adams & Baker**
2 **AMISI**, 4, ch f Nayef (USA)—Amicella **Mrs P. A. Scott-Dunn**
3 **ATOMIC JACK**, 5, b g Nathaniel (IRE)—Indigo River (IRE) **George Baker and Partners - Super Six**
4 **BARNEY FREDERICK (FR)**, 4, b g Sunday Break (JPN)—Miss Alabama (FR) **Chelgate Limited**
5 **BARRITUS**, 5, b g Exceed And Excel (AUS)—Flambeau **Barton Partnership**
6 **BORDERFORCE (FR)**, 7, b g American Post—Miss Vic (USA) **Watt & Pittam Partnership**
7 **CONFAB (USA)**, 4, gr g Exchange Rate (USA)—Callmenancy (USA) **Confidence Partnership**
8 **CONFILS (FR)**, 4, b f Olympic Glory (IRE)—Mambo Mistress (USA) **Confidence Partnership**
9 **CONFRERIE (IRE)**, 5, b g Society Rock (IRE)—Intellibet One **New Confidence Partnership**
10 **CULTURE (FR)**, 4, b g Dream Ahead (USA)—Talon Bleu (FR) **Highclere Thoroughbred Racing - Dream On**
11 **DANTE'S VIEW (IRE)**, 4, ch g Galileo (IRE)—Daivika (USA) **Mr J. G. N. Head**
12 **DAZIBAO (FR)**, 7, ch g Muhaymin (USA)—Adjinne (FR) **Turf Club 2018**
13 **DIVA SPIRIT (IRE)**, 5, b m Invincible Spirit (IRE)—Lady Glinka (IRE) **FTP Equine Holdings Ltd**
14 **GEORGE BAKER (IRE)**, 13, b g Camacho—Petite Maxine **George Baker & Partners**
15 **GEORGE OF HEARTS (FR)**, 5, gr g Kendargent (FR)—Bugie d'Amore **Mr D. Howden**
16 **GRAIGNES (FR)**, 4, b c Zoffany (IRE)—Grey Anatomy **FTP Equine Holdings Ltd**
17 **HARRY HURRICANE**, 8, b g Kodiac—Eolith **Dare To Dream Racing**
18 **HIERONYMUS**, 4, b g Dutch Art—Sleek **Mrs Pao, Mr Stafford & Mr Tucker**
19 **HIGHWAY ONE (USA)**, 6, b m Quality Road (USA)—Kinda Wonderful (USA) **On The Game Partnership**
20 **INFANTA ISABELLA**, 6, b m Lope de Vega (IRE)—Shemissa (IRE) **The Chriselliam Partnership**
21 **LA MAQUINA**, 5, b g Dutch Art—Miss Meltemi (IRE) **George Baker and Partners - Super Six**
22 **MAMILLIUS**, 7, b g Exceed And Excel (AUS)—Laika Lane (USA) **The Mamillius Partnership**
23 **MANTON GRANGE**, 7, b g Siyouni (FR)—Emulate **Goltz And Baker Partnership**
24 **SAUVIGNON**, 9, b m Yeats (IRE)—Dalriath **W12 Syndicate**
25 **SHARP REPLY (IRE)**, 6, b g Holy Roman Emperor (IRE)—Sabindra **Miss N. Thompson**
26 4, B f Mount Nelson—Sparkling Montjeu (IRE) **Mrs C. E. Cone**
27 **THE LAMPLIGHTER (FR)**, 5, b g Elusive City (USA)—Plume Rouge **The Lamplighter Syndicate**
28 **WARGRAVE (IRE)**, 4, b c Galileo (IRE)—Scream Blue Murder (IRE) **Mr P. Bowden**
29 **WATER'S EDGE (IRE)**, 4, b g Footstepsinthesand—Sommer Queen (IRE) **Carbine Of London Racing**

THREE-YEAR-OLDS
30 **BOWLING RUSSIAN (IRE)**, b g Lope de Vega (IRE)—Minute Limit (IRE) **Equi ex Incertis Partners**
31 **DEVORGILLA**, b c Sir Percy—Sweetheart Abbey **Miss S. Bannatyne**
32 **DIVA KAREEM (IRE)**, b f Al Kazeem—Pennard (IRE) **FTP Equine Holdings Ltd**
33 **DIVA ROCK**, b f Zoffany (IRE)—Dashing (IRE) **FTP Equine Holdings Ltd**
34 **DYAMI (FR)**, b br c Bated Breath—Zaltana (USA) **Mark & Lavinia Sherwood**
35 **FEAR NAUGHT**, gr g Brazen Beau (AUS)—Tanda Tula (IRE) **Seaton Partnership**
36 **JOHN THE DIVA (FR)**, b g Rajsaman (FR)—Souvigny (FR) **FTP Equine Holdings Ltd**
37 **KYLLISHI**, b c Kyllachy—Ishiamber **Mrs P. A. Scott-Dunn**
38 **LES HOGUES (IRE)**, b f Bated Breath—Hatsepsut Queen (FR) **FTP Equine Holdings Ltd**

MR GEORGE BAKER - continued

TWO-YEAR-OLDS

39 **BONNET**, ch f 31/03 Helmet (AUS)—Tanda Tula (IRE) (Alhaarth (IRE)) **Seaton Partnership**
40 B c 07/02 Hunter's Light (IRE)—Charlie's Queen (IRE) (Myboycharlie (IRE)) (29172) **FTP Equine Holdings Ltd**
41 **CHLOHOLTEEN**, b c 07/02 Clodovil (IRE)—
　　　　　　　　　　　　Shemissa (IRE) (Fairy King (USA)) **Chris Wright, C Forsyth, H Wright, T Stinnes**
42 Ch f 29/03 Prince Gibraltar (FR)—Diamond Star (IRE) (Daylami (IRE)) (10296) **FTP Equine Holdings Ltd**
43 **FOR LOVE OF LOUISE**, b f 03/04 Nathaniel (IRE)—
　　　　　　　　　　　　A Legacy of Love (IRE) (Sea The Stars (IRE)) **Mrs B. A. Karn-Smith**
44 B f 18/04 Oasis Dream—Hidden Cove (IRE) (Nayef (USA)) (38610) **FTP Equine Holdings Ltd**
45 B f 17/02 Gio Ponti (USA)—High Heeled Hope (USA) (Salt Lake (USA)) (55000) **Mr D. Howden**
46 B br f 10/02 Goken (FR)—Magical Flower (Oasis Dream) (30030) **FTP Equine Holdings Ltd**
47 B c 25/03 Bobby's Kitten (USA)—Minute Limit (IRE) (Pivotal) **JR Wallis and Partners**
48 B c 28/03 Starspangledbanner (AUS)—Naturotopia (FR) (Northern Park (USA)) (42900)
49 **SIMPLY LOVELY (FR)**, ch c 05/03 Kheleyf (USA)—Reech Band (Choisir (AUS)) (64350) **Mrs M. Stadelmann**
50 **SIR JOSEPH SWAN**, b g 02/04 Paco Boy (IRE)—Candle (Dansili) **Mrs B. A. Karn-Smith**
51 B br f 03/03 Shalaa (IRE)—Social (Dansili) (13728) **FTP Equine Holdings Ltd**
52 Ch f 05/03 Mukhadram—Sweetheart Abbey (Dancing Spree (USA)) **Miss S. Bannatyne**
53 Gr f 20/02 Lethal Force (IRE)—Syrna (FR) (Kendor (FR)) (20592) **FTP Equine Holdings Ltd**

Other Owners: Mr Simon Ackroyd, Mr J. F. Adams, Miss Emily Asprey, Mr G. Baker, Mrs Nona Baker, The Earl Of Brecknock, Sir Francis Brooke, Mr WH Carson, Miss Rebecca Curtis, Sir Alex Ferguson, Mr A Flintoff, Mr Richard Foden, Mr David Howden, Miss L Hurley, Mr Piers Inkin, Mrs EL James, Mrs Camilla Johnson, Mr Nicholas Jones, Colonel Sandy Malcolm, Mr Nick Milne, Mrs A. Pao, Mr Bryant Park, Mr Richard Pilkington, Sir Thomas Pilkington, Mr J. Pittam, Mr William Russell, Mr Don Shanks, Mrs L. M. Sherwood, Mr M. A. Sherwood, Earl Spencer, Mr N. J. Stafford, S. P. Tucker, Mr Stephen Wallis, M. H. Watt, Mr Nick Wheeler.

Assistant Trainer: Patrick Murphy, Valerie Murphy.

Flat Jockey: Pat Cosgrave, Nicola Currie, Cieren Fallon. **NH Jockey:** Marc Goldstein.

17	**MR ANDREW BALDING, Kingsclere**

Postal: **Park House Stables, Kingsclere, Newbury, Berkshire, RG20 5PZ**
Contacts: **PHONE 01635 298210 FAX 01635 298305**
EMAIL admin@kingsclere.com WEBSITE www.kingsclere.com

1 **AGENT BASTERFIELD (IRE)**, 4, b g Raven's Pass (USA)—Maridiya (IRE) **Mr Philip Fox & Partner**
2 **ALOUNAK (FR)**, 5, b h Camelot—Awe Struck **King Power Racing Co Ltd**
3 **BADESSA**, 4, b f Dunaden (FR)—Le Badie (IRE) **Farleigh Racing**
4 **BANGKOK (IRE)**, 4, b c Australia—Tanaghum **King Power Racing Co Ltd**
5 **BAROSSA RED (IRE)**, 4, ch g Tamayuz—I Hearyou Knocking (IRE) **Another Bottle Racing 2**
6 **BE MORE**, 4, b f Shamardal (USA)—Pearl Dance (USA) **Cayton Park Stud Limited**
7 **BELL ROCK**, 4, b g Kingman—Liberally (IRE) **Mrs F. H. Hay**
8 **BERKSHIRE BLUE (IRE)**, 5, b g Champs Elysees—Lemon Rock **Berkshire Parts & Panels Ltd**
9 **BYE BYE LADY (FR)**, 4, b f Sea The Stars (IRE)—Peinture Rose (USA) **King Power Racing Co Ltd**
10 **CHIL CHIL**, 4, b f Exceed And Excel (AUS)—Tiana **King Power Racing Co Ltd**
11 **CLEONTE (IRE)**, 7, ch g Sir Percy—Key Figure **King Power Racing Co Ltd**
12 **CWYNAR**, 5, b m Kodiac—Modern Art **Mr N. D. Morris**
13 **DASHING WILLOUGHBY**, 4, b g Nathaniel (IRE)—Miss Dashwood **Mick and Janice Mariscotti**
14 **DIOCLETIAN (IRE)**, 5, b g Camelot—Saturday Girl **Mr R. J. C. Wilmot-Smith**
15 **EDINBURGH CASTLE (IRE)**, 4, b g Sea The Stars (IRE)—Evensong (GER) **Mrs F. H. Hay**
16 **ENCAPSULATION (IRE)**, 4, b f Zoffany (IRE)—Supercharged (IRE) **Mrs B. M. Keller**
17 **FOX CHAIRMAN (IRE)**, 4, b c Kingman—Starfish (IRE) **King Power Racing Co Ltd**
18 **FOX LEICESTER (IRE)**, 4, gr g Dark Angel (IRE)—Pop Art (IRE) **King Power Racing Co Ltd**
19 **FOX PREMIER (IRE)**, 4, b g Frankel—Fann (USA) **King Power Racing Co Ltd**
20 **FOX SHINJI**, 4, b c Iffraaj—Keene Dancer **King Power Racing Co Ltd**
21 **FOX TAL (IRE)**, 4, b c Sea The Stars (IRE)—Maskunah (IRE) **King Power Racing Co Ltd**
22 **FOXTROT LADY**, 5, ch m Foxwedge (AUS)—Strictly Dancing (IRE) **Mr J. C. Smith**

23 **GENETICS (FR)**, 6, b g Manduro (GER)—Garmerita (FR) **DJT Racing Partnership**
24 **GOOD BIRTHDAY (IRE)**, 4, b g Dabirsim (FR)—Chica Loca (FR) **King Power Racing Co Ltd**
25 **GRACE AND DANGER (IRE)**, 4, b f Teofilo (IRE)—Opinionated (IRE) **N M Watts/D Powell/Mrs I A Balding**
26 **HAPPY POWER (IRE)**, 4, gr c Dark Angel (IRE)—Tamarisk (GER) **King Power Racing Co Ltd**
27 **HAVANA ROCKET (IRE)**, 4, b g Havana Gold (IRE)—Mawaakeb (USA) **Mr A. M. Balding**
28 **INCLYNE**, 4, ch f Intello (GER)—Lady Brora **Kingsclere Racing Club**
29 **JOHNNY DRAMA (IRE)**, 5, b g Lilbourne Lad (IRE)—Quelle Histoire (IRE) **King Power Racing Co Ltd**
30 **JOHNNY KIDD**, 4, ch g Australia—Sabreon **Chelsea Thoroughbreds-shakin' All Over 1**
31 **LOOK AROUND**, 4, b f Kingman—Magic America (USA) **Mr G. Strawbridge**
32 **LUCK OF CLOVER**, 4, b f Phoenix Reach (IRE)—Diktalina **Lisahully Investments Ltd**
33 **MAYNE (IRE)**, 4, b g Dansili—Pink Damsel (IRE) **Mrs F. H. Hay**
34 **MORANDO (FR)**, 7, gr g Kendargent (FR)—Moranda (FR) **King Power Racing Co Ltd**
35 **NATURAL HISTORY**, 5, b g Nathaniel (IRE)—Film Script **Her Majesty The Queen**
36 **OLOROSO (IRE)**, 4, ch g Fast Company (IRE)—Convidada (IRE) **Roger Hetherington & Jeremy Carey**
37 **PIPER ARROW**, 4, b g War Command (USA)—Zeyran (IRE) **Mr D. E. Brownlow**
38 **PIVOINE (IRE)**, 6, b g Redoute's Choice (AUS)—Fleur de Cactus (IRE) **King Power Racing Co Ltd**
39 **PURDEY'S GIFT**, 4, b c Camelot—Saphira's Fire (IRE) **Sheikh J. D. Al Maktoum**
40 **RANCH HAND**, 4, b g Dunaden (FR)—Victoria Montoya **Kingsclere Racing Club**
41 **RIVERFRONT (FR)**, 4, gr g Reliable Man—Why Worry (FR) **Mr L Register & Partner**
42 **SEA SCULPTURE (IRE)**, 4, b g Archipenko (USA)—Seaflower Reef (IRE) **Kingsclere Racing Club**
43 **SHAILENE (IRE)**, 5, ch m Rip Van Winkle (IRE)—Snow Key (USA) **Mr G. Strawbridge**
44 **SHINE SO BRIGHT**, 4, gr c Oasis Dream—Alla Speranza **King Power Racing Co Ltd**
45 **SNEAKY PEEK**, 4, b f Nayef (USA)—Casual Glance **Kingsclere Racing Club**
46 **SPIRIT WARNING**, 4, b g Charm Spirit (IRE)—Averami **Kingsclere Racing Club**
47 **STONE OF DESTINY**, 5, b g Acclamation—Irishstone (IRE) **King Power Racing Co Ltd**
48 **STRAIGHT RIGHT (FR)**, 6, b g Siyouni (FR)—Sailor Moon (IRE) **King Power Racing Co Ltd**
49 **STRICT TEMPO**, 4, ch f Norse Dancer (IRE)—Strictly Dancing (IRE) **Mr J. C. Smith**
50 **TOP POWER (FR)**, 4, ch g Le Havre (IRE)—Altamira **King Power Racing Co Ltd**
51 **TRIBAL CRAFT**, 4, ch f Mastercraftsman (IRE)—Snoqualmie Star **Mr J. C. Smith**
52 **TUK POWER**, 4, b f Dubawi (IRE)—Soon (IRE) **King Power Racing Co Ltd**
53 **ZWAYYAN**, 7, ch g Pivotal—Mail The Desert (IRE) **King Power Racing Co Ltd**

THREE-YEAR-OLDS

54 **ALL YOU WISH**, b c Showcasing—Moment of Time **M M Stables**
55 **ANGEL GREY (IRE)**, gr f Gutaifan (IRE)—Violet's Gift (IRE) **Mr J. Maldonado**
56 **APPLAUDABLE (IRE)**, b c Acclamation—Bahati (IRE) **Biddestone Racing XV**
57 **ARCTIC VEGA**, ch c Lope de Vega (IRE)—Childa (IRE) **PDR Properties**
58 **ASCRAEUS**, b f Poet's Voice—Sciacca (IRE) **Promenade Bloodstock Limited**
59 **BERKSHIRE MIELE**, b f Swiss Spirit—Berkshire Honey **Berkshire Parts & Panels Ltd**
60 **BERKSHIRE PHILLY**, ch f Roderic O'Connor (IRE)—Berkshire Beauty **Berkshire Parts & Panels Ltd**
61 **BERKSHIRE ROCCO (FR)**, ch c Sir Percy—Sunny Again **Berkshire Parts & Panels Ltd**
62 **BERKSHIRE SAVVY**, b g Mukhadram—Zubova **Berkshire Parts & Panels Ltd**
63 **BERLIN TANGO**, b c Dansili—Fantasia **Mr G. Strawbridge**
64 **BRONZE RIVER**, b g Archipenko (USA)—Avon Lady **Mick and Janice Mariscotti**
65 **CADEAU D'OR (FR)**, ch g Le Havre (IRE)—Hill of Grace **John & Anne Soul**
66 **CASTLEINTHESAND (IRE)**, ch f Footstepsinthesand—Portico **Kennet Valley Thoroughbreds VII**
67 **CHILD STAR**, b f Charm Spirit (IRE)—Stybba **Qatar Racing Limited**
68 **COLTRANE (IRE)**, b c Mastercraftsman (IRE)—Promise Me (IRE) **Mick and Janice Mariscotti**
69 **DAMAGE CONTROL**, ch g Zoffany (IRE)—One So Marvellous **Mick and Janice Mariscotti**
70 **DREAM ROUND (IRE)**, b f Gleneagles (IRE)—Mythie (FR) **Thurloe Thoroughbreds XLVIII**
71 **ELHAM VALLEY (IRE)**, gr c Tin Horse (IRE)—Dame du Floc (IRE) **Martin & Valerie Slade & Partner**
72 **FOX DUTY FREE (IRE)**, b c Kingman—Bugie d'Amore **King Power Racing Co Ltd**
73 Ch c New Approach (IRE)—Gainful (USA) **Mr A. A. A. J. Al-Thani**
74 **GAME AND SET**, b f Zoffany (IRE)—Grace And Favour **Mr N. M. H. Jones**
75 **GROUP ONE POWER**, b c Lope de Vega (IRE)—Lady Aquitaine (USA) **King Power Racing Co Ltd**
76 **GROVE FERRY (IRE)**, b g Excelebration (IRE)—Rebelline (IRE) **Martin & Valerie Slade & Partner**
77 **HERODOTUS (IRE)**, b g Iffraaj—Merry Me (IRE) **Mrs F. H. Hay**
78 **HORN OF PLENTY**, b f Golden Horn—Gaze **Mildmay Racing**
79 **IRISH TWEED**, b f Roderic O'Connor (IRE)—Lady Brora **Kingsclere Racing Club**
80 **IRON HEART**, b c Muhaarar—Kiyoshi **Qatar Racing Limited**
81 **ISAAC MURPHY (FR)**, b c Makfi—Compose **Mr R. J. C. Wilmot-Smith**
82 **KAFEE (IRE)**, b c Make Believe—Dream Date (IRE) **Mr A. Al-Abdulrazzaq**

83 **KALSARA,** b f Muhaarar—Kalsa (IRE) **Mr J. A. Oldham**
84 **KAMEKO (USA),** b br c Kitten's Joy (USA)—Sweeter Still (IRE) **Qatar Racing Limited**
85 **KASHI (FR),** b br g Manduro (GER)—La Ville Lumiere (USA) **B Greenwood, I Dodds-Smith & R Homburg**
86 **KHALIFA SAT (IRE),** b c Free Eagle (IRE)—Thermopylae **A. Al Shaikh**
87 **KING'S LYNN,** b c Cable Bay (IRE)—Kinematic **Her Majesty The Queen**
88 **LA HULOTTE (IRE),** ch f Lope de Vega (IRE)—Vakiyla (FR) **Mrs C. J. Wates**
89 **LARKSPEED,** b f Al Kazeem—Perfect Delight **Dr Bridget Drew & Partners**
90 **LILY LIKE,** gr f Kodiac—Lixirova (FR) **Mr G. Strawbridge**
91 **MACHIOS,** br g Maxios—Astragal **Lord J. Blyth**
92 **MAHANAKHON POWER,** b c Gleneagles (IRE)—Lady Eclair (IRE) **King Power Racing Co Ltd**
93 **MEDIKA (IRE),** b f Australia—Weeping Wind **Rifa Mustang Europe Ltd**
94 **MIA DOLAN (USA),** b br f Hat Trick (JPN)—Kazam (USA) **Mr L. L. Register**
95 **MON CHOIX,** b g Pivotal—Privacy Order **Mr A. A. A. J. Al-Thani**
96 **MONTANARI,** ch c Sea The Moon (GER)—Pax Aeterna (USA) **Mick and Janice Mariscotti**
97 **MORNING FURY,** b f Bated Breath—Midnight Sky **Wardley Bloodstock**
98 **NEVER DARK,** b c No Nay Never (USA)—Dark Missile **Mr J. C. Smith**
99 **NYAH,** b f Assertive—Dyanita **Mrs L. M. Alexander**
100 **OPERA GIFT,** b c Nathaniel (IRE)—Opera Glass **Mr J. C. Smith**
101 **PAPA POWER,** b c Nathaniel (IRE)—Mosqueras Romance **King Power Racing Co Ltd**
102 Ch c Lope de Vega (IRE)—Party (IRE) **PDR Properties**
103 **PERFECT SUNSET,** b f Iffraaj—Perfect Star **Dr Bridget Drew & Partners**
104 **PUNCTUATION,** b c Dansili—Key Point (IRE) **Her Majesty The Queen**
105 **QUICKSTEP LADY,** b f Australia—Strictly Dancing (IRE) **Mr J. C. Smith**
106 **REALITY OF DREAMS (USA),** ch f Gio Ponti (USA)—Escape To Victory **Mrs B. M. Keller**
107 **RICK BLAINE (IRE),** b g Ruler of The World (IRE)—Saturday Girl **Chelsea Thoroughbreds - Casablanca**
108 **RODIN,** b c Mayson—Moon Goddess **The Pink Hat Racing Partnership**
109 **SHADN (IRE),** b br f No Nay Never (USA)—Amethyst (IRE) **Mr K. Yoshida**
110 **SORTEO (IRE),** b f Invincible Spirit (IRE)—Sweepstake (IRE) **Sheikh J. D. Al Maktoum**
111 **SPANISH ANGEL (IRE),** b g Gutaifan (IRE)—City Dazzler (IRE) **Mr J. Maldonado**
112 **SPRING GLOW,** gr f Mukhadram—Spring Dream (IRE) **Rainbow Racing**
113 **STANFORD (IRE),** ch c Zoffany (IRE)—Almost Always (IRE) **Mr M. A. R. Blencowe**
114 **SYMBOLIZE (IRE),** ch c Starspangledbanner (AUS)—French Flirt **Sheikh J. D. Al Maktoum**
115 **THAI POWER (IRE),** b c Kingman—Roscoff (IRE) **King Power Racing Co Ltd**
116 B f Showcasing—Tiana **Sheikh J. D. Al Maktoum**
117 **TOP DROP (IRE),** ch g Tamayuz—Solandia (IRE) **Another Bottle Racing 2**
118 **UGANDA HEIGHTS,** ch g Free Eagle (IRE)—Uvinza **Mrs A. R. Ruggles**
119 **VIA DE VEGA (FR),** ch c Lope de Vega (IRE)—Via Milano (FR) **PDR Properties**
120 **WILD HERO (IRE),** b g Zoffany (IRE)—Thought Is Free **Mrs F. H. Hay**
121 **X EIGHT,** b g Exceed And Excel (AUS)—Chortle **King Power Racing Co Ltd**

TWO-YEAR-OLDS

122 B c 07/03 Sea The Moon (GER)—A L'Anglaise (Invincible Spirit (IRE)) (45000) **Al Rabban Racing & Partner**
123 **ALCOHOL FREE (IRE),** b f 23/03 No Nay Never (USA)—Plying (USA) (Hard Spun (USA)) **Mr J. C. Smith**
124 B c 14/05 Estidhkaar (IRE)—Alltherightmoves (IRE) (Namid) (22308) **Park House Partnership**
125 **AURIFEROUS (IRE),** b c 30/01 Golden Horn—Sequester (Selkirk (USA)) (65000) **Mick and Janice Mariscotti**
126 Gr c 07/03 Dark Angel (IRE)—Avenante (Champs Elysees) (50000) **Hillwood Racing**
127 **AYO GORKHALI,** b c 09/01 The Gurkha (IRE)—
                                              Trip To Glory (FR) (Where Or When (IRE)) (25740) **P Fox/P Elson & Partner**
128 B c 20/03 The Gurkha (IRE)—Bergamot Orange (USA) (War Front (USA)) (55000) **Mr N. M. Watts**
129 B f 26/03 Hot Streak (IRE)—Berkshire Beauty (Aqlaam) **Berkshire Parts & Panels Ltd**
130 B c 06/03 Camacho—Cafetiere (Iffraaj) (72000) **Mr M. A. R. Blencowe**
131 B c 20/02 Cable Bay (IRE)—Cape Spirit (IRE) (Cape Cross (IRE)) **Kingsclere Racing Club**
132 B f 22/04 Sir Percy—Cape Victoria (Mount Nelson) **Kingsclere Racing Club**
133 **CHOSEN TARGET,** b c 21/01 Golden Horn—Handana (IRE) (Desert Style (IRE)) (30000) **A. Al Shaikh**
134 **CLASSIC LORD (GER),** ch c 21/02 Lord of England (GER)—
                                              Classic Diva (GER) (Sholokhov (IRE)) (17160) **Park House Partnership**
135 **CLIP,** b f 04/02 Iffraaj—Concise (Lemon Drop Kid) **St Albans Bloodstock & Partner**
136 **DAISY WARWICK,** b f 26/03 Kingman—Our Poppet (IRE) (Warning) **Hot To Trot Racing**
137 B c 26/02 Awtaad (IRE)—Dame Hester (IRE) (Diktat) (350000) **King Power Racing Co Ltd**
138 **DANCE AT NIGHT,** b c 13/03 Dark Angel (IRE)—Strictly Dancing (IRE) (Danehill Dancer (IRE)) **Mr J. C. Smith**
139 B c 28/02 Kodi Bear (IRE)—Dat Il Do (Bahamian Bounty) (14586) **Park House Partnership**
140 Gr ro c 22/03 Kendargent (FR)—Divine Touch (Kheleyf (USA)) (25740) **Park House Partnership**

MR ANDREW BALDING - continued

141 **DUNADINA,** ch f 05/04 Dunaden (FR)—Dauphine (IRE) (Doyen (IRE)) **Lord J. Blyth**
142 **ENFIN (IRE),** b f 14/04 Teofilo (IRE)—Zeiting (IRE) (Zieten (USA)) **Mr Brendan Hayes**
143 **EXPERT OPINION,** b c 23/02 Worthadd (IRE)—Calypso Choir (Bahamian Bounty) **Mr J. C. Smith**
144 **FLYIN' HIGH,** b c 20/03 Siyouni (FR)—Zee Zee Top (Zafonic (USA)) (150000) **Castle Down Racing**
145 B f 24/04 Zoffany (IRE)—Fontley (Sadler's Wells (USA)) (55000) **Thurloe for Royal Marsden Cancer Charity**
146 B f 09/02 Muhaarar—Fort Del Oro (IRE) (Lope de Vega (IRE)) (125000) **Al Rabban Racing & Ballylinch Stud**
147 **GOLDEN CRUSADER,** b c 30/03 Golden Horn—Ihsas (IRE) (Rahy (USA)) (49764) **Relentless Dreamers Racing**
148 Ch c 03/03 Pivotal—Gosbeck (Dubawi (IRE)) (38609) **Park House Partnership**
149 B c 14/03 Tamayuz—Hidden Valley (Haafhd) **Kingsclere Racing Club**
150 B c 18/02 Twilight Son—Hill Welcome (Most Welcome) (20000) **Park House Partnership**
151 Br c 06/04 Gutaifan (IRE)—Ibecke (Exceed And Excel (AUS)) (15444) **Park House Partnership**
152 B c 27/02 Sea The Stars (IRE)—Ignis Away (FR) (Gold Away (IRE)) (343200) **Qatar Racing Limited**
153 B c 31/03 Zoffany (IRE)—Impressionist Art (USA) (Giant's Causeway (USA)) **Mrs F. H. Hay**
154 B c 02/03 Vadamos (FR)—In Dubai (USA) (Giant's Causeway (USA)) (53195) **Mr. J Palmer-Brown & Partner**
155 B c 04/05 Manduro (GER)—Inhibition (Nayef (USA)) **Kingsclere Racing Club**
156 B c 24/04 Holy Roman Emperor (IRE)—Izola (Beat Hollow) (32604) **Kennet Valley T/breds III**
157 **JUAN DE MONTALBAN (IRE),** ch c 11/02 Lope de Vega (IRE)—
                                        Abilene (Samum (GER)) (85000) **Mick and Janice Mariscotti**
158 B f 15/04 Nathaniel (IRE)—Lady Brora (Dashing Blade) **Kingsclere Racing Club**
159 **LION HUNTER (AUT),** ch c 05/02 Hunter's Light (IRE)—
                                        Lightning Debut (Pivotal) (3861) **B. McGuire & I. A. Balding**
160 B c 26/02 Nathaniel (IRE)—Lizzie Tudor (Tamayuz) **Ms K. Gough**
161 B br c 09/04 Golden Horn—Lombatina (FR) (King's Best (USA)) (200000) **King Power Racing Co Ltd**
162 Ch c 22/04 Territories (IRE)—Lorient (Champs Elysees) (85800) **Mrs F. H. Hay**
163 **MAY NIGHT,** ch c 04/02 Mayson—Dream Melody (Selkirk (USA)) (20952) **Mr M. Payton**
164 Ch c 09/02 Lope de Vega (IRE)—Moi Meme (Teofilo (IRE)) (350000) **Apollo Racing & DTA Racing**
165 Ch c 17/04 New Approach (IRE)—Mu'ajiza (Pivotal) (60000) **Qatar Racing Ltd & Dragon Racing Ltd**
166 **NAPPER TANDY,** b c 23/02 Mukhadram—Diktalina (Diktat) **Lisahully Investments Ltd**
167 **NEBULOSA,** b f 08/05 Archipenko (USA)—Nimiety (Stormy Atlantic (USA)) **Miss K. Rausing**
168 **NEENEE'S CHOICE,** b c 24/04 Paco Boy (IRE)—
                                        Galaxy Highflyer (Galileo (IRE)) (50000) **Mick and Janice Mariscotti**
169 B c 16/05 Shalaa (IRE)—Noelani (Indian Ridge) (111540) **Mrs F. H. Hay**
170 B c 17/04 Mukhadram—Perfect Cover (IRE) (Royal Applause) (8000) **Park House Partnership**
171 B f 16/04 Australia—Pivotalia (IRE) (Pivotal) (42900) **Sheikh J. D. Al Maktoum**
172 B g 05/05 Nayef (USA)—Preveza (FR) (Dalakhani (IRE)) **Mr & Mrs M Pendarves**
173 B c 16/02 Frankel—Promised Money (IRE) (Dark Angel (IRE)) (475000) **King Power Racing Co Ltd**
174 Ch c 27/03 Lope de Vega (IRE)—Queen of Power (IRE) (Medicean) (48047) **PDR Properties & Apollo Racing**
175 Br f 22/02 Iffraaj—Queen's Dream (GER) (Oasis Dream) **Sir Alex Ferguson**
176 B c 13/03 Lope de Vega (IRE)—Qushchi (Encosta de Lago (AUS)) (500000) **Qatar Racing Limited**
177 **RECOVERY RUN,** b c 28/01 Nathaniel (IRE)—Regal Splendour (Pivotal) (32603) **Another Bottle Racing 2**
178 **RIVAL,** b c 22/01 Iffraaj—Pamona (IRE) (Duke of Marmalade (IRE)) (100000) **Highclere Thoroughbreds**
179 B c 24/04 Lope de Vega (IRE)—Rosie Cotton (IRE) (King's Best (USA)) (102960) **PDR Properties & Apollo Racing**
180 **SCOOP (IRE),** b f 27/04 Belardo (IRE)—Kapria (FR) (Simon du Desert (FR)) **Mr Brendan Hayes**
181 B f 29/01 Acclamation—Scots Fern (Selkirk (USA)) (30000) **Mrs P Veenbaas & Partner**
182 B f 17/04 Camelot—Secret Pursuit (IRE) (Lawman (FR)) **Mr Guy Brook**
183 B c 08/02 Fascinating Rock (IRE)—See Emily Play (IRE) (Galileo (IRE)) (12000) **Park House Partnership**
184 Ch c 20/02 Free Eagle (IRE)—Set Fire (IRE) (Bertolini (USA)) (77220) **Mrs. Susan Roy & Mr. D. Burke**
185 B c 31/03 Sir Percy—Shadow Dancing (Unfuwain (USA)) (98000) **Sheikh J. D. Al Maktoum**
186 **SHE IS FIERCE,** ch f 18/01 New Approach (IRE)—She Is Great (IRE) (Dalakhani (IRE)) (50000) **Al Adiyat Racing**
187 **SPANISH COLT (IRE),** b c 09/04 Kodiac—Fairywren (IRE) (Approve (IRE)) **Mr J. Maldonado**
188 B c 01/02 Kingman—Spin (IRE) (Galileo (IRE)) (514800) **King Power Racing Co Ltd**
189 **SPIRIT MIXER,** ch f 21/02 Frankel—Arabian Queen (Dubawi (IRE)) **Mr J. C. Smith**
190 **STAG PARTY (FR),** b g 25/04 Rajsaman (FR)—Invitee (Medicean) **Mr L. L. Register**
191 B c 11/04 Zoffany (IRE)—Starfish (IRE) (Galileo (IRE)) (400000) **King Power Racing Co Ltd**
192 **SUNFLOWER SEED,** ch f 25/03 Showcasing—Sunflower (Dutch Art) **Mr N. M. H. Jones**
193 B f 04/05 Cityscape—Sweet Mandolin (Soviet Star (USA)) **Messrs. J C & S R Hitchins**
194 **TACTICAL,** b c 14/02 Toronado (IRE)—Make Fast (Makfi) **Her Majesty The Queen**
195 B c 01/03 Dark Angel (IRE)—Tamarisk (GER) (Selkirk (USA)) (425000) **King Power Racing Co Ltd**
196 **TANGLEWOOD TALES,** ch c 28/01 Nathaniel (IRE)—Camdora (IRE) (Arcano (IRE)) **Lord J. Blyth**

MR ANDREW BALDING - continued

197 B c 21/03 American Pharoah (USA)—Topic (USA) (Discreet Cat (USA)) (186011) **Qatar Racing Limited**
198 TWILIGHT TROUBLE, b c 01/03 Twilight Son—
Poly Pomona (Green Desert (USA)) (24761) **Relentless Dreamers Racing**
199 B c 03/03 Cityscape—Victoria Pollard (Sir Percy) **Kingsclere Racing Club**
200 Ch c 20/03 Australia—What A Treasure (IRE) (Cadeaux Genereux) (280000) **King Power Racing Co Ltd**
201 B c 10/03 Lord of England (GER)—Wildlife Lodge (GER) (Konigstiger (GER)) (25740) **Park House Partnership**
202 YOUTH SPIRIT (IRE), b c 04/04 Camelot—Rocana (Fastnet Rock (AUS)) (85800) **A. Al Shaikh**

Other Owners: Mr H. A. Al Jehani, Al Rabban Racing, Mr A. K. M. K. Al-Rabban, Another Bottle Racing, Mr A. M. Balding, Mrs E. A. M. Balding, I. A. Balding, Mr J. Bridgman, N. R. R. Drew, Miss P. B. Drew, Dr S. B. Drew, P. E. Felton, Mrs E. J. Gregson-Williams, Mr R. W. Gregson-Williams, Mr N. G. R. Harris, Mr S. Hill, Lady A. Hobhouse, Sir C. J. S. Hobhouse, Mrs E. A. Ireland, Mr G. R. Ireland, Mr D. M. James, Mrs Fiona Marner, Lady E. Mays-Smith, Exors of the Late Mr R. P. B. Michaelson, Mildmay Racing, P Fox/P Elson & Partner, PDR Properties, Mr T. J. Ramsden, Mr L. L. Register, Mr N. M. Watts.

Assistant Trainer: Nigel Walker.

Flat Jockey: Rob Hornby, Oisin Murphy, David Probert. **Apprentice Jockey:** Josh Bryan, William Carver, William Cox, Bradley Harris, Callum Hutchinson, Marie Perrault.

---

18   MR RICHARD J. BANDEY, Tadley
Postal: **Plantation House, Wolverton, Tadley, Hampshire, RG26 5RP**
Contacts: **PHONE 01635 298963**

1 BUCK'S BEAUTIFUL (FR), 6, ch m Maresca Sorrento (FR)—Buck's Beauty (FR) **The Plantation Picnic Club**
2 COACHELLA GREEN (IRE), 8, b m Westerner—Turquoise Green (IRE) **Mr D. A. Hunt**
3 CUP OF COFFEE (FR), 6, b m Dragon Dancer—Danser Sur La Lune (FR) **Mr D. A. Hunt**
4 ELYAQIM (FR), 6, b g Spider Flight (FR)—Sinceres (FR) **Mr C. J. Boreham**
5 EYESOPENWIDEAWAKE (IRE), 9, b g Stowaway—Namesake **The King's Men**
6 FIRST ASSEMBLY (IRE), 6, b g Arcadio (GER)—Presenting Katie (IRE) **Mr S. R. Cross**
7 FLINTARA, 5, b m Kayf Tara—Flinders **Leith Hill Chasers**
8 GIRVANNA (FR), 4, gr g Soave (GER)—Irresistible Anna (FR) **Mr C. J. Boreham**
9 GOLEADOR NAO (FR), 4, b g Coastal Path—Quetzalya (FR) **Mr T. D. J. Syder**
10 SAWPIT SIENNA, 5, b m Dylan Thomas (IRE)—Sawpit Supreme **Mr D. A. Hunt**
11 THE BOLSHOI BANDIT (IRE), 4, b g Sholokhov (IRE)—Milleners Gem (IRE) **Wendy & Malcolm Hezel**
12 THE BOOGIEMAN, 6, b g Delegator—Great Quest (IRE) **Headdock & Bandey**

THREE-YEAR-OLDS
13 MOVE OVER DARLIN, b f Helmet (AUS)—Mystery Code **J. C. Sillett**

Other Owners: Mr R. J. Bandey, Mr A. Headdock, Mr M. W. Hezel, Mrs W. M. Hezel.

---

19   MISS CHELSEA BANHAM, Newmarket
Postal: **Mulligans Cottage, Cowlinge, Newmarket, Suffolk, CB8 9HP**
Contacts: **PHONE 07387 169781**

1 AT YOUR SERVICE, 6, b g Frankel—Crystal Gaze (IRE) **Chelsea Banham Pre Training ltd**
2 AXEL JACKLIN, 4, b g Iffraaj—Reroute (IRE) **Mr A. Searle**
3 CAFE ESPRESSO, 4, b f Sir Percy—Forest Express (AUS) **Chelsea Banham Pre Training ltd**
4 CHOCCO STAR (IRE), 4, b f Lawman (FR)—Sharplaw Star **Mr J. Edwards**
5 CRAKADAWN, 4, ch f Excelebration (IRE)—Atacama Sunrise **Chelsea Banham Pre Training ltd**
6 HOLY TIBER (IRE), 5, b m Holy Roman Emperor (IRE)—Quiet Waters (USA) **Mr M. Bartram**
7 INDEPENDENCE DAY (IRE), 7, b h Dansili—Damson (IRE) **Chelsea Banham Pre Training ltd**
8 LADY OF YORK, 6, b m Sir Percy—Parsonagehotelyork (IRE) **Chelsea Banham Pre Training ltd**
9 MAKAMBE (IRE), 5, gr g Dark Angel (IRE)—Pink Diva (IRE) **Mr T. F. Parrett**
10 MIAELLA, 5, b m Captain Gerrard (IRE)—Sweet Applause (IRE) **Mr M. Bartram**

MISS CHELSEA BANHAM - continued

11 **ROSARNO (IRE)**, 6, b g Fastnet Rock (AUS)—Jouet **Chelsea Banham Pre Training ltd**
12 **VOICE OF A LEADER (IRE)**, 9, b g Danehill Dancer (IRE)—Thewaytosanjose (IRE) **Chelsea Banham Pre Training ltd**

TWO-YEAR-OLDS

13 **ADMIRABLE LAD**, ch c 01/04 Bated Breath—
                                        Admirable Spirit (Invincible Spirit (IRE)) **Longview Stud & Bloodstock Ltd**
14 **CAPRICIOUS**, b f 10/01 Harzand (IRE)—Adaptability (Mastercraftsman (IRE)) **Longview Stud & Bloodstock Ltd**
15 B f 07/03 Sir Percy—Lady Bling (Showcasing) (8500) **Chelsea Banham Pre Training ltd**
16 **RESOLUTE LASS**, ch f 06/03 Charming Thought—Sinaadi (IRE) (Kyllachy) **Longview Stud & Bloodstock Ltd**
17 B c 29/04 Bated Breath—Sweet Applause (IRE) (Acclamation) **Mr M. Bartram**
18 **TOPLIGHT**, b c 14/02 Bated Breath—Operettist (Singspiel (IRE)) (10000) **Longview Stud & Bloodstock Ltd**
19 Ch c 03/05 Poet's Voice—Who Splashed Me (Medicean) **Mr M. Bartram**

---

20 | **MR JACK BARBER, Crewkerne**
Postal: **Higher Peckmoor, Henley, Crewkerne, Somerset, TA18 8FF**
Contacts: **PHONE 01460 76555 MOBILE 07904 185720**
EMAIL **info@jackbarberracing.co.uk WEBSITE www.jackbarberracing.co.uk**

1 **AMZAC MAGIC**, 8, b g Milan—Queen's Banquet **A. A. Hayward**
2 **ASK THE WEATHERMAN**, 11, b g Tamure (IRE)—Whatagale **Mr David Martin & Mr Paul Barber**
3 **BALLYJIM (IRE)**, 9, br g Jimble (FR)—Ballinacraig (IRE) **Mr J. Barber**
4 **DARCY WARD (FR)**, 7, b g Doctor Dino (FR)—Alzasca (FR) **Mr J. Barber**
5 **DOYANNIE (IRE)**, 6, ch m Doyen (IRE)—Annie May (IRE) **Barber, Donlan-Abrahams & Sim**
6 **EARTH KING (IRE)**, 4, b g Shirocco (GER)—Beach Beauty (IRE) **Mrs C. E. Penny**
7 **EARTH STAR (IRE)**, 4, br g Presenting—Madam Bovary (IRE) **R. M. Penny**
8 4, B g Ocovango—Fire And Ice (IRE) **Mr J. Barber**
9 **FLYING SARA**, 5, b m Malinas (GER)—Samandara (FR) **Peckmoor Flyers**
10 **GULSHANIGANS**, 8, b g Sakhee (USA)—Gulshan
11 5, Gr m Geordieland (FR)—Just Here (IRE) **Barber, Dolan-Abrahams & Dare**
12 **LAMANVER BEL AMI**, 6, b g Black Sam Bellamy (IRE)—Lamanver Homerun **Wessex Racing Club**
13 **MIDNIGHT MALIN**, 4, b f Malinas (GER)—Dancingtilmidnight **Mrs S. J. Maltby**
14 **NORTON HILL (IRE)**, 4, b g Fame And Glory—Charming Leader (IRE) **Mr & Mrs J. J. Barber & Mr A. Norman**
15 5, B g Black Sam Bellamy (IRE)—One Wild Night **Tony Hayward & Jack Barber**
16 **ONEUPMANSHIP (IRE)**, 5, ch g Mahler—Letthisbetheone (IRE) **Charlie Walker & Phil Fry**
17 **SHINTORI (FR)**, 8, b g Enrique—La Masai (FR) **Mrs R. E. Vicary**
18 **THE VOCALIST**, 8, b m Recharge (IRE)—Ivy Edith **Mr & Mrs D. Bennett, S Higgs & G Martin**
19 **THREE IN ONE (IRE)**, 8, b g Court Cave (IRE)—Star Bui (IRE) **Wessex Racing Club**
20 **WHAT'LLBEWILLBE (IRE)**, 6, b g Mahler—Letterwoman (IRE) **C. C. Walker**
21 4, Gr f Geordieland (FR)—Wibble Wobble **Mr J. Barber**

Other Owners: Mr J. Barber, Mr J. J. Barber, P. K. Barber, Barber, French, Newton & Wright, Mr D. Bennett, Lady Nadine Cobham, Mr J. M. Dare, Mr E. J. Dolan-Abrahams, R. P. Fry, A. A. Hayward, Mr D. J. Martin, Mr & Mrs Bennett, Mr & Mrs D Martin and S Higgs, A. J. Norman, A. G. Sim, C. C. Walker.

---

21 | **MRS STELLA BARCLAY, Garstang**
Postal: **Lancashire Racing Stables, The Paddocks, Strickens Lane, Barnacre, Garstang, Lancashire, PR3 1UD**
Contacts: **PHONE 01995 605790 MOBILE 07802 764094**
EMAIL **paul@lancashireracingstables.co.uk**

1 **BENNY IN MILAN (IRE)**, 9, b g Milan—Chaparral Lady (IRE) **Keith Dodd & Network Racing**
2 **CASTLE NORTH (IRE)**, 8, b g Stowaway—Fitanga (FR) **Mr A. T. Clarke**
3 **DAZACAM**, 6, b m Camacho—Dazakhee **Mr & Mrs D. Yates**
4 **DEOLALI**, 6, b g Sleeping Indian—Dulally **Matt Watkinson Racing Club**
5 **GLENRUA (IRE)**, 7, b g Stowaway—Ceol Rua (IRE) **Keith Dodd & Network Racing**

MRS STELLA BARCLAY - continued

6 **LEODIS (IRE)**, 8, ch g Shirocco (GER)—Leonica **Keith Dodd & Network Racing**
7 **LITTLE STEVIE**, 8, b g Overbury (IRE)—Candy's Room (IRE) **Keith Dodd & Network Racing**
8 **MANSFIELD**, 7, b g Exceed And Excel (AUS)—Jane Austen (IRE) **The Style Council**
9 **MARIETTA ROBUSTI (IRE)**, 5, b m Equiano (FR)—La Tintoretta (IRE) **Matt Watkinson Racing Club**
10 **MAURICIO (IRE)**, 6, ch g Helmet (AUS)—Essexford (IRE) **The Haydock Badgeholders**
11 **MELABI (IRE)**, 7, b g Oasis Dream—Briolette (IRE) **Matt Watkinson Racing Club**
12 **MISSESGEEJAY**, 10, br m Beat All (USA)—Riverbank Rainbow **The Coz Syndicate**
13 **ONDA DISTRICT (IRE)**, 8, b g Oasis Dream—Leocorno (IRE) **Matt Watkinson Racing Club**
14 **SHARRABANG**, 4, b g Coach House (IRE)—Dulally **Matt Watkinson Racing Club**
15 **STREPITANT**, 7, b g Dubawi (IRE)—Shawanda (IRE) **Andy Clarke & the Four Aces**
16 **WEDDING BREAKFAST (IRE)**, 6, ch m Casamento (IRE)—Fair Countenance (IRE) **Matt Watkinson Racing Club**
17 **WILDMOUNTAINTHYME**, 4, b f Doncaster Rover (USA)—Awaywithefairies **Mr P. J. Metcalfe**

THREE-YEAR-OLDS

18 **ANNIEMATION (IRE)**, b g Acclamation—Cafetiere **Mr W. Buckley**
19 **BELLE VOCI**, gr f Hellvelyn—Oricano **CCCNLP**
20 **DREW BREEZE (IRE)**, ch g Camacho—Three Cheers (IRE) **Mr R. Tedstone**
21 B f Coach House (IRE)—Ella Rosie **Mrs S. E. Barclay**
22 **FRANBELLA**, b gr f Hellvelyn—Aiaam Al Wafa (IRE) **Francesco Auriemma & Stella Barclay**
23 Gr f Hellvelyn—Sambarina (IRE) **Mr P. M. Clarkson**
24 **STARTER FOR TEN**, b g Bated Breath—Scariff Hornet (IRE) **Mr R. Tedstone**
25 **ZUCKERBERG (IRE)**, ch g Camacho—Queenie Keen (IRE) **Mr R. Tedstone**

TWO-YEAR-OLDS

26 B f 21/03 Coach House (IRE)—Betty's Pride (Lion Cavern (USA)) **Betty's Brigade**
27 B br f 06/05 Coach House (IRE)—China Lily (USA) (Street Cry (IRE)) **Mr P. J. Metcalfe**
28 B c 20/04 Coach House (IRE)—Ella Rosie (Dubai Destination (USA)) **Mrs S. E. Barclay**
29 B f 02/02 Heeraat (IRE)—Princess of Rock (Rock of Gibraltar (IRE)) **Peter Sedgwick**

Other Owners: Alan Appleton, John Ball, Tony Ball, Jim Barnes, Paul Bushell, John Calderbank, John Greaves, Gary Marshall, Frank Martindale, Richard Mattinson, Geoff & Jan Metcalfe, David Price, Jeremy Simm, Trevor Willis.

---

22 **MRS TRACEY BARFOOT-SAUNT, Wotton-under-Edge**
Postal: **Cosy Farm, Huntingford, Charfield, Wotton-under-Edge, Gloucestershire, GL12 8EY**
Contacts: **PHONE 01453 520312 MOBILE 07976 360626 FAX 01453 520312**

1 **BOMBAY BASIL (IRE)**, 6, b g Artan (IRE)—Taipan Sue (IRE) **A Good Days Racing**
2 **HERE COMES MOLLY (IRE)**, 9, ch m Stowaway—Grange Melody (IRE) **Mrs T. M. Barfoot-Saunt**
3 **HOLEINTHEWALL BAR (IRE)**, 12, b g Westerner—Cockpit Lady (IRE) **Mrs T. M. Barfoot-Saunt**
4 **TIMBER HOUSE (IRE)**, 8, ch g Golden Lariat (USA)—Panglao Island (IRE) **P. J. Ponting**
5 **TROTTER**, 6, b g Piccolo—Vintage Steps (IRE) **Mrs T. M. Barfoot-Saunt**
6 **TWICE THE MUSTARD**, 7, ch g Haafhd—Molly Pitcher (IRE) **Mr G. C. Barfoot-Saunt**

MRS TRACEY BARFOOT-SAUNT - continued

---

23 **MR MAURICE BARNES, Brampton**
Postal: **Tarnside, Farlam, Brampton, Cumbria, CA8 1LA**
Contacts: PHONE **016977 46675** MOBILE **07760 433191**
EMAIL **anne.barnes1@btinternet.com**

1 **APACHE PILOT**, 12, br g Indian Danehill (IRE)—Anniejo **Mr M. A. Barnes**
2 **ARGENT ET OR (FR)**, 7, br g Saint des Saints (FR)—Gold Or Silver (FR) **The Edinburgh Woollen Mill Ltd**
3 **BAFANA BLUE**, 9, b g Blueprint (IRE)—Anniejo **Hogarth, Morris, Percival & Irving**
4 **BOBBY BOUCHER (IRE)**, 7, b g Big Bad Bob (IRE)—Undercover Glamour (USA) **Miss H. M. Crichton**

MR MAURICE BARNES - continued

5 **BY ORDER OF (IRE)**, 5, b g Shantou (USA)—Guydus (IRE) **Mr M. A. Barnes**
6 **DEERFOOT**, 4, ch g Archipenko (USA)—Danceatdusk **Mr M. A. Barnes**
7 **DOLLY DANCER (IRE)**, 6, b m Yeats (IRE)—Scrapper Jack (IRE) **Mr E. Cassie**
8 **FAIR LADY**, 6, b m Fair Mix (IRE)—Lady Sambury **J. R. Wills**
9 **FARLAM KING**, 7, br g Crosspeace (IRE)—Second Bite **Castle Racing & Partner**
10 **FAROCCO (GER)**, 7, b g Shirocco (GER)—Fantasmatic (GER) **Miss A. P. Lee**
11 **FISHER GREEN (IRE)**, 7, b g Rip Van Winkle (IRE)—Prealpina (IRE) **D. Carr**
12 **FLYING JACK**, 10, b g Rob Roy (USA)—Milladella (FR) **The 3 Whisperers**
13 **INDIAN VOYAGE (IRE)**, 12, b g Indian Haven—Voyage of Dreams (USA) **D. Carr**
14 **ITSNOTYOUITSME**, 7, b g Milan—Brochrua (IRE) **J. Wade**
15 **KNOCKOURA (IRE)**, 8, b g Westerner—Lisselton Thatch (IRE) **The Edinburgh Woollen Mill Ltd**
16 **LADY SAMBACK**, 8, ch m Black Sam Bellamy (IRE)—Bob Back's Lady (IRE) **J. R. Wills**
17 **LOULOUMILLS**, 10, b m Rob Roy (USA)—Etching (USA) **Mr G. R. S. Nixon & Mr M. Barnes**
18 **LUCARMNOLADY**, 5, ch m Lucarno (USA)—Bonne Anniversaire **Mr M. A. Barnes**
19 **NO SUCH NUMBER**, 12, b g King's Best (USA)—Return (USA) **Miss H. M. Crichton**
20 **OH NO**, 8, b g Indian Danehill (IRE)—See My Girl **Mr J. Duckworth**
21 **OISHIN**, 8, b g Paco Boy (IRE)—Roshina (IRE) **Mr M. A. Barnes**
22 **PLACEDELA CONCORDE**, 7, b g Champs Elysees—Kasakiya (IRE) **Hogarth, Morris & Percival Racing**
23 **QUICK BREW**, 12, b g Denounce—Darjeeling (IRE) **The Wizards**
24 **REGARDE MOI**, 12, b g King's Best (USA)—Life At Night (IRE) **Mr M. A. Barnes**
25 **ROLLERRULER**, 6, b g Native Ruler—Roll Over Rose (IRE) **Mr R. W. Powell**
26 **ROMA BANGKOK**, 4, b g Mount Nelson—Magika **Mr M. A. Barnes**
27 **SAINT ARVANS (FR)**, 6, b g Motivator—Castellina (USA) **D. Carr**
28 **SMART PACO**, 6, ch g Paco Boy (IRE)—La Gifted **Mr M. A. Barnes**
29 **SPINNING SCOOTER**, 10, b g Sleeping Indian—Spinning Coin **Miss Hazel Crichton & Partner**
30 **TOO WISE MAN (IRE)**, 8, b g Dansant—Screen Idol (IRE) **D. M. Proos**
31 **TOP CAT DJ (IRE)**, 12, ch g St Jovite (USA)—Lady Coldunell **Miss A. P. Lee**
32 **VICTORY ECHO (IRE)**, 7, b g Cloudings (IRE)—Serendipity (IRE) **The Edinburgh Woollen Mill Ltd**
33 **WILD SAM (IRE)**, 10, b g Bachelor Duke (USA)—Pure Spin (USA) **K Jardine R Griffiths**

Other Owners: Mr M. A. Barnes, Castle Racing, Miss H. M. Crichton, Mr J. G. Graham, K. Greenwell, Mr R. M. Griffiths, Mr G. R. Hogarth, Mr K. Irving, Mr K. Jardine, Mr S. G. Johnston, Mr R. N. J. Lane, Mr A. J. Morris, Mr S. Nightingale, G. R. S. Nixon, Mr V. A. Percival, The Whisperers, Mr R. N. Towler.

Conditional Jockey: Dale Irving.

---

24   **MR BRIAN BARR, Sherborne**
Postal: **Tall Trees Stud, Longburton, Sherborne, Dorset, DT9 5PH**
Contacts: **PHONE 01963 210173 MOBILE 07826 867881**
EMAIL brianbarrracing@hotmail.com WEBSITE www.brianbarrracing.co.uk
TWITTER @brianbarrracing

1 **BELLA AMOURA**, 4, b f Nathaniel (IRE)—Dream Wild **Hitchins & Partners**
2 **BONNE NUIT**, 5, b g Arvico (FR)—Frosted Grape (IRE) **Miss T. R. Johnson**
3 **CHOP CHOP (IRE)**, 4, b f Rip Van Winkle (IRE)—Mince **Brian Barr Racing Club**
4 **GATES PASS**, 5, b br g Showcasing—Molly Mello (GER) **Brian Barr Racing Club**
5 **IDEAL GRACE**, 4, ch f Poet's Voice—Sunday Bess (JPN) **Mr P. Bona**
6 **INDEPENDENCE (USA)**, 4, br g More Than Ready—Frivolous Alex (USA) **Hitchins & Partner**
7 **IOWEU**, 7, br m Cockney Rebel (IRE)—Doliouchka **Brian Barr Racing Club**
8 **JOHNI BOXIT**, 5, ch g Sakhee's Secret—Pink Supreme **Brian Barr Racing Club**
9 **KAHDIAN (IRE)**, 10, br g Rock of Gibraltar (IRE)—Katiykha (IRE) **Daisy Hitchins & Neil Budden**
10 **LARGE ACTION**, 4, b g Iffraaj—Titian's Pride (USA) **Nick Bradley Racing 46 & Partners**
11 **MADALLI (IRE)**, 6, ch m Sans Frontieres (IRE)—Parkality (IRE) **Allison Family & Partner**
12 **MAJORETTE**, 6, ch m Major Cadeaux—So Discreet **Chris Clark & Daisy Hitchins**
13 **MANS NOT TROT (IRE)**, 5, b g Kodiac—Turuqaat **Brian Barr Racing Club**
14 **PERLE ROSE (IRE)**, 8, b m Milan—Powhatan Squaw (IRE) **Miss D. Hitchins**
15 **TOOLATETODELEGATE**, 6, b m Delegator—Little Caroline (IRE) **Brian Barr Racing Club**

MR BRIAN BARR - continued

THREE-YEAR-OLDS
16 Bl f Mukhadram—Dusting (IRE)
17 **PARKER'S BOY,** b g Hot Streak (IRE)—Shannon Spree **Mr T. Parker**
18 B c Hallowed Crown (AUS)—Peaceful Soul (USA)
19 **SIRBOWTIEMAN (GER),** b g Gale Force Ten—Sabaidee (IRE) **The Bow Tie Racegoers**

TWO-YEAR-OLDS
20 B c 20/04 Hellvelyn—Annie Kenney (Showcasing)
21 Ch f 25/02 Cityscape—Norfolk Sky (Haafhd)

Other Owners: Mr I. Allison, Mr N. Bradley, Mr N. Budden, Mr C. J. Clark, Miss D. Hitchins, Miss S. Holden, Mrs G. Morgan, Nick Bradley Racing 46, Mr J. A. Osborne.

Assistant Trainer: Daisy Hitchins.

NH Jockey: Paul O'Brien. **Amateur Jockey:** Mr A Butterfield.

---

25 | **MR RON BARR, Middlesbrough**
Postal: Carr House Farm, Seamer, Stokesley, Middlesbrough, Cleveland, TS9 5LL
Contacts: **PHONE 01642 710687 MOBILE 07711 895309**
EMAIL christinebarr1@aol.com

1 **DOMINANNIE (IRE),** 7, b b m Paco Boy (IRE)—English Rose (USA) **Mrs V. G. Davies**
2 **ELENORA DELIGHT,** 5, b m Dansili—Missy O' Gwaun (IRE) **Mr G. I. Davies**
3 **GO BANANAS,** 5, b m Bahamian Bounty—Ribbon Royale **R. E. Barr**
4 **GRACEFUL ACT,** 12, b m Royal Applause—Minnina (IRE) **Mr D. Thomson & Mrs R. E. Barr**
5 **MIDNIGHT WARRIOR,** 10, b g Teofilo (IRE)—Mauri Moon **Mr K. Trimble**
6 **MIGHTASWELLSMILE,** 6, b m Elnadim (USA)—Intishaar (IRE) **Mr K. Trimble**
7 **MITCHUM,** 11, b g Elnadim (USA)—Maid To Matter **S Haykin & R Barr**
8 **PEARL'S CALLING (IRE),** 5, ch m Dandy Man (IRE)—Celtic Heroine (IRE) **Mrs V. G. Davies**

Other Owners: Mrs C. Barr, R. E. Barr, Miss S. Haykin, D. Thomson.

Assistant Trainer: Mrs C. Barr.

Amateur Jockey: Miss V. Barr.

---

26 | **MR DAVID BARRON, Thirsk**
Postal: Maunby House, Maunby, Thirsk, North Yorkshire, YO7 4HD
Contacts: PHONE 01845 587435 FAX 01845 587331
EMAIL david.barron@maunbyhouse.com

1 **ABOVE THE REST (IRE),** 9, b g Excellent Art—Aspasias Tizzy (USA) **L. G. O'Kane**
2 **ANOTHER BATT (IRE),** 5, ch g Windsor Knot (IRE)—Mrs Batt (IRE) **L. G. O'Kane**
3 **ATEESCOMPONENT (IRE),** 4, b g Shirocco (GER)—Hula Ballew **Tees Components Ltd**
4 **BARYSHNIKOV,** 4, ch g Mastercraftsman (IRE)—Tara Moon **Harrowgate Bloodstock Ltd**
5 **BOB BEACH,** 4, ch g Harbour Watch (IRE)—Annie Beach (IRE) **Mrs S. C. Barron**
6 **CLON COULIS (IRE),** 6, b m Vale of York (IRE)—Cloneden (IRE) **Ms Colette Twomey**
7 **FAKE NEWS,** 5, b g Paco Boy (IRE)—Day Creek **Dr N. J. Barron**
8 **GUNMETAL (IRE),** 7, gr g Clodovil (IRE)—March Star (IRE) **Ne-chance & Mr L O' Kane**
9 **KYNREN (IRE),** 6, b g Clodovil (IRE)—Art of Gold **Elliott Brothers & Peacock & Partner**
10 **LOFTY,** 4, b g Harbour Watch (IRE)—Curly Come Home **Mr H. D. Atkinson**
11 **MR COCO BEAN (USA),** 6, b g Gio Ponti (USA)—Ing Ing (FR) **Mr S. G. Raines**
12 **NORTH WIND (IRE),** 4, b g No Nay Never (USA)—Kawn **Penton Hill Racing Limited**
13 **RAILPORT DOLLY,** 5, b m Rail Link—Polly Adler **Mr A. C. Cook**
14 **RECKLESS ENDEAVOUR (IRE),** 7, b g Kodiac—Red Fanfare **Ne-chance & Mr L O' Kane**

MR DAVID BARRON - continued

15 **SALTIE GIRL,** 4, b f Intikhab (USA)—Marine Girl **T D Barron & Partner**
16 **SORBONNE,** 4, ch g Cityscape—Sorcellerie **Mr D Ellis & Partner**
17 **VENTUROUS (IRE),** 7, ch g Raven's Pass (USA)—Bold Desire **Mr Laurence O'Kane/ Harrowgatebloodstock Ltd**
18 **VIGORITO,** 4, b f Arcano (IRE)—Lucy Parsons (IRE) **Harrowgate Bloodstock Ltd & Associate**

THREE-YEAR-OLDS

19 **BINYON,** b g Poet's Voice—Pretty Majestic (IRE) **Harrowgate Bloodstock Ltd**
20 **CARRIESMATIC,** b f Passing Glance—Concentrate **Keep The Faith Partnership**
21 **CLASS CLOWN (IRE),** ch g Intense Focus (USA)—Joli Elegant (IRE) **Dr N. J. Barron**
22 **DEEVIOUS BEAU,** b g Brazen Beau (AUS)—Vespasia **Mr R Miquel & Partner**
23 **DOT THE EYES,** b f Due Diligence (USA)—Amitola (IRE) **Dr N. J. Barron**
24 **GENERAL JOE (IRE),** ch g Siyouni (FR)—Shapoura (FR) **Peter Jones**
25 **GRANNY GREY (IRE),** ch f Tagula (IRE)—Ever Evolving (FR) **Mr P. Toes**
26 **GREYFIRE,** gr g Shooting To Win (AUS)—Ancestral Way **Mr D Ellis & Syps Ltd**
27 Ch g Shirocco (GER)—Hula Ballew **Tees Components Ltd**
28 **JOSHUA R (IRE),** b g Canford Cliffs (IRE)—Khobaraa **Mr M. Rozenbroek/ Harrowgatebloodstock Ltd**
29 **MERESIDE BLUE,** b f Sepoy (AUS)—Blue Oyster **Mereside Racing Limited**
30 **MIGHTY MARIACHI,** b g Lethal Force (IRE)—Lead A Merry Dance **Mrs D. Dalby**
31 **MODULAR MAGIC,** b g Swiss Spirit—Lucy Parsons (IRE) **Mr P McKenna, Mr L O Kane & Partner**
32 **MOSSBAWN,** b g Brazen Beau (AUS)—Maziona **Mr Laurence O'Kane/ Harrowgatebloodstock Ltd**
33 **POET'S LADY,** gr f Farhh—La Gessa **L. G. O'Kane**
34 B f Casamento (IRE)—Sheezastorm (IRE) **Harrowgate Bloodstock Ltd**
35 **VIVA VOCE (IRE),** b g Intense Focus (USA)—Moonbi Haven (IRE) **Dr N. J. Barron**
36 **WILLING TO PLEASE,** b f Iffraaj—Tebee's Oasis **Minster Stud**

TWO-YEAR-OLDS

37 **ARTHUR NORSE (IRE),** ch c 29/03 Anjaal—
                                She's Neat (IRE) (Frozen Power (IRE)) (6435) **Mrs Anne Atkinson & Partner**
38 B f 14/04 Tagula (IRE)—Ashtaroute (USA) (Holy Bull (USA)) (857) **Mr M. J. Rozenbroek**
39 **ATIYAH,** br f 31/03 Swiss Spirit—Jofranka (Paris House) (761) **Mrs Anne Atkinson & Partner**
40 **CONTACT (IRE),** gr c 04/03 Gutaifan (IRE)—La Tulipe (FR) (Authorized (IRE)) (42900) **Mr H. D. Atkinson**
41 **ESTICKY END (IRE),** b g 25/04 Estidhkaar (IRE)—Hay Now (IRE) (Key of Luck (USA)) (1500) **Dr N. J. Barron**
42 B c 19/02 Prince of Lir (IRE)—Harmony Bay (IRE) (Fast Company (IRE)) (21450) **P. D. Savill**
43 B f 09/02 Bobby's Kitten (USA)—Kashoof (Green Desert (USA)) (4000) **Peter Jones**
44 B f 01/04 Fast Company (IRE)—Khobaraa (Invincible Spirit (IRE)) **Mr A. C. Cook**
45 B g 18/04 Swiss Spirit—La Zamora (Lujain (USA)) **Mr M. J. Rozenbroek**
46 B g 12/04 Fountain of Youth (IRE)—
                                Lucy Parsons (IRE) (Thousand Words) (2000) **Harrowgate Bloodstock Ltd & Associate**
47 B c 16/02 Gutaifan (IRE)—Mary Thomas (IRE) (Zoffany (IRE)) (3861) **Mereside Racing Limited & Partner**
48 Br c 19/02 Mayson—Olive Mary (Authorized (IRE)) (6000) **Dr N. J. Barron**
49 B f 04/03 Alhebayeb—Passion Fruit
50 Gr f 14/03 Mukhadram—Perfect Haven (Singspiel (IRE)) (7500) **Mr M. J. Rozenbroek**
51 B br g 02/04 Pride of Dubai (AUS)—Princess Patsky (USA) (Mr Greeley (USA)) (3809) **Mr M. J. Rozenbroek**
52 B f 21/03 Moohaajim (IRE)—Rozene (IRE) (Sleeping Indian) **Mr M. J. Rozenbroek**
53 Ch f 08/04 Pearl Secret—Setting Forth (IRE) (Daggers Drawn (USA))
54 B br f 12/03 Hot Streak (IRE)—Star Trek (Dalakhani (IRE)) (761) **Mr A. C. Cook**
55 B f 15/02 Equiano (FR)—Tebee's Oasis (Oasis Dream) (4761) **Minster Stud**
56 B f 18/04 Epaulette (AUS)—Western Tune (IRE) (Piccolo)
57 Br g 27/04 Havana Gold (IRE)—Zaaneh (IRE) (Aqlaam) (4285)

Other Owners: C. R. Elliott, J. M. Elliott, Mr M. Hilton, Mr N. N. Kane, Mrs G. M. Swinglehurst, J. M. Swinglehurst, D. R. Tucker, Mr J. Wells.

Assistant Trainer: Nicola-Jo Barron.

27 MISS REBECCA BASTIMAN, Wetherby

Postal: **Goosemoor Farm, Warfield Lane, Wetherby, West Yorkshire, LS22 5EU**
Contacts: **PHONE 01423 359397, 01423 359783 MOBILE 07818 181313**
EMAIL **rebeccabastiman@hotmail.co.uk**

1 **AFTER JOHN**, 4, b g Dutch Art—Rosacara
2 **AMAZING GRAZING (IRE)**, 6, b g Intense Focus (USA)—North Light Rose (USA) **The Redhotgardogs 2**
3 **BE BOLD**, 8, ch g Assertive—Marysienka **Mr N Barber & Partner**
4 **DARK DEFENDER**, 7, b g Pastoral Pursuits—Oh So Saucy **Rebecca Bastiman Racing**
5 **DONNELLY'S RAINBOW (IRE)**, 7, b g Lilbourne Lad (IRE)—Donnelly's Hollow (IRE) **Miss R. Bastiman**
6 **EDGAR ALLAN POE (IRE)**, 6, b g Zoffany (IRE)—Swingsky (IRE) **I B Barker / P Bastiman**
7 **ELERFAAN (IRE)**, 6, b g Shamardal (USA)—Gorband (USA) **Ms M. Austerfield**
8 **FRENCH FLYER (IRE)**, 5, b g Pour Moi (IRE)—Leavingonajetplane (IRE) **Miss R. Bastiman**
9 **FUMBO JUMBO (IRE)**, 7, b m Zebedee—Baraloti (USA) **Miss R. Bastiman**
10 **GHALIB (IRE)**, 8, ch g Lope de Vega (IRE)—Gorband (USA) **Ms M. Austerfield**
11 **HAYADH**, 7, gr g Oasis Dream—Warling (IRE) **Miss R. Bastiman**
12 **HIGHLIGHT REEL (IRE)**, 5, b g Big Bad Bob (IRE)—Dance Hall Girl (IRE) **Grange Park Racing Club & Partner**
13 **JACOB'S PILLOW**, 9, b g Oasis Dream—Enticing (IRE) **Miss R. Bastiman**
14 **JOSIEBOND**, 4, ch f Monsieur Bond (IRE)—Smiddy Hill **I. B. Barker**
15 **LEESHAAN (IRE)**, 5, b g Bated Breath—La Grande Elisa (IRE) **Mrs P. Bastiman**
16 **LOGI (IRE)**, 6, b g Kodiac—Feet of Flame (USA) **Let's Be Lucky Racing 12**
17 **LOW PROFILE**, 5, ch g Galileo (IRE)—Dynaforce (USA) **Ms M Austerfield & the 8 Amigos**
18 **MAJESTE**, 6, b g Acclamation—Winged Valkyrie (IRE) **Let's Be Lucky Racing 17 & Partner**
19 **MILTON ROAD**, 5, b g Mazameer (IRE)—Blakeshall Girl **Mr W. L. Donaldson**
20 **ROARING FORTIES (IRE)**, 7, b g Invincible Spirit (IRE)—Growling (IRE) **Miss R. Bastiman**
21 **ROYAL BRAVE**, 9, b g Acclamation—Daqtora **James Edgar & William Donaldson**
22 **SINGMAN (IRE)**, 4, b g Dandy Man (IRE)—Singitta **Ms M. Austerfield**
23 **SPOTTON (IRE)**, 4, b g Tamayuz—Farbenspiel (IRE) **Ms M. Austerfield**
24 **STAYCATION (IRE)**, 4, b g Acclamation—Staceymac (IRE) **Miss R. Bastiman**
25 **TIERCEL**, 7, b g Olden Times—Sharp Mode (USA) **Miss R. Bastiman**
26 **VICTORY ANGEL (IRE)**, 6, b g Acclamation—Golden Shadow (IRE) **Miss R. Bastiman**
27 **WENSLEY**, 5, b g Poet's Voice—Keladora (USA) **Mr John Smith & Mrs P. Bastiman**
28 **ZESHOV (IRE)**, 9, b g Acclamation—Fathoming (USA) **Miss R. Bastiman**
29 **ZUMURUD (IRE)**, 5, gr g Zebedee—Thaisy (USA) **Ms M. Austerfield**

THREE-YEAR-OLDS
30 **ALMUERZO LOCO (IRE)**, gr g Zebedee—Chica Loca (FR) **Ms M Austerfield & the 8 Amigos**
31 **NOBBY NUTS (IRE)**, ch g Zoffany (IRE)—Scarlet Belle

Other Owners: Ms M. Austerfield, Mr E. N. Barber, I. B. Barker, Mrs P. Bastiman, Miss R. Bastiman, R. G. Capstick, Mr A. D. Crombie, D. J. Dickson, Mr W. L. Donaldson, Mr J. D. Edgar, Mr R. A. Gorrie, Mr S. T. Gorrie, Grange Park Racing Club, Let's Be Lucky Racing 17, Mr J. McAvoy, RedHotGardogs, Hugh T. Redhead, Mr J. Smith, The 8 Amigos.

Assistant Trainer: Harvey Bastiman.

Flat Jockey: Phil Dennis.

28 MR BRIAN BAUGH, Audley

Postal: **Brooklands, Park Lane, Audley, Stoke-on-Trent, Staffordshire, ST7 8HR**
Contacts: **PHONE 01782 706222 MOBILE 07547 495236**
EMAIL **bpjbaugh@aol.com**

1 **DAVID'S BEAUTY (IRE)**, 7, b m Kodiac—Thaisy (USA) **Mr G. B. Hignett**
2 **NORTH KOREA (IRE)**, 4, b f Bungle Inthejungle—Betty Fontaine (IRE) **Mr G. B. Hignett**
3 **SHESADABBER**, 4, b f Heeraat (IRE)—Saorocain (IRE) **Mr G. B. Hignett**

THREE-YEAR-OLDS
4 **DABBERSGIRL**, b f Heeraat (IRE)—Shustraya **Mr G. B. Hignett**

Assistant Trainer: S Potts.

29 **MR RALPH BECKETT, Andover**
Postal: Kimpton Down Stables, Kimpton, Andover, Hampshire, SP11 8QQ
Contacts: **PHONE** 01264 772278 **MOBILE** 07802 219022
EMAIL trainer@rbeckett.com

1 **AIR PILOT**, 11, b g Zamindar (USA)—Countess Sybil (IRE) **Lady Cobham**
2 **ALEEF (IRE)**, 7, b g Kodiac—Okba (USA) **Westerberg**
3 **ALOE VERA**, 4, b f Invincible Spirit (IRE)—Almiranta **Miss K. Rausing**
4 **ANTONIA DE VEGA (IRE)**, 4, b f Lope de Vega (IRE)—Witches Brew (IRE) **Waverley Racing**
5 **BABBO'S BOY (IRE)**, 4, gr g Mastercraftsman (IRE)—Bunood (IRE) **Amo Racing Limited**
6 **BATTERED**, 6, b g Foxwedge (AUS)—Swan Wings **King Power Racing Co Ltd**
7 **BREATH CAUGHT**, 5, b g Bated Breath—Double Crossed **Amo Racing Limited**
8 **BRIYOUNI (FR)**, 7, b g Siyouni (FR)—Brianza (USA) **Mrs I. M. Beckett**
9 **BURIRAM (IRE)**, 4, b g Reliable Man—Wild Step (GER) **King Power Racing Co Ltd**
10 **CHARTERED**, 4, b f Frankel—Time Saved **R. Barnett**
11 **CLIFFS OF DOONEEN (IRE)**, 5, b g Galileo (IRE)—Devoted To You (IRE) **The Anagram Partnership**
12 **DAVE DEXTER**, 4, b g Stimulation (IRE)—Blue Crest (FR) **Mrs Philip Snow & Partners I**
13 **DIOCLES OF ROME (IRE)**, 5, b g Holy Roman Emperor (IRE)—Serisia (IRE) **Mrs Philip Snow & Partners**
14 **DOLPHIN VISTA (IRE)**, 7, b g Zoffany (IRE)—Fiordiligi **Westerberg**
15 **FELICIANA DE VEGA**, 4, b f Lope de Vega (IRE)—Along Came Casey (IRE) **Waverley Racing**
16 **FUTURE INVESTMENT**, 4, b g Mount Nelson—Shenir **R.N.J. Partnership**
17 **HERE AND NOW**, 6, b g Dansili—Look Here **Mr R. J. Arculli**
18 **HEREBY (IRE)**, 4, b f Pivotal—Look Here **J. H. Richmond-Watson**
19 **HEY GRACIE**, 4, b f Delegator—Capestar (IRE) **D & J Newell**
20 **JUNIUS BRUTUS (FR)**, 4, ch g Cockney Rebel (IRE)—Tricked **King Power Racing Co Ltd**
21 **MANUELA DE VEGA (IRE)**, 4, b f Lope de Vega (IRE)—Roscoff (IRE) **Waverley Racing**
22 **MISTY**, 4, b f Oasis Dream—Ceilidh House **Mrs I. M. Beckett**
23 **MITCHUM SWAGGER**, 8, b g Paco Boy (IRE)—Dont Dili Dali **The Anagram Partnership**
24 **MODERN MILLIE**, 4, b f Sixties Icon—Hairspray **Mr R.A.Pegum & Partner**
25 **MOON KING (FR)**, 4, br g Sea The Moon (GER)—Maraba (IRE) **Merriebelle Irish Farm Limited**
26 **MRS IVY**, 4, ch f Champs Elysees—Just Wood (FR) **Make A Circle I**
27 **NETTE ROUSSE (GER)**, 4, ch f Mastercraftsman (IRE)—
                                        Nina Celebre (IRE) **H.H. Sheikh Mohammed bin Khalifa Al-Thani**
28 **ROCK EAGLE**, 5, ch g Teofilo (IRE)—Highland Shot **J. C. Smith**
29 **SAM COOKE (IRE)**, 4, b g Pour Moi (IRE)—Saturday Girl **Chelsea Thoroughbreds - Wonderful World**
30 **SKYMAX (GER)**, 4, br g Maxios—Set Dreams (FR) **Bermuda Racing Limited**
31 **SPEED KING**, 4, b g Kingman—Speed Cop **J. C. Smith**
32 **TIGERSKIN**, 4, ch g Nathaniel (IRE)—Jamboretta (IRE) **Mr A. D. G. Oldrey & Mr G. C. Hartigan**
33 **VICTORY CHIME (IRE)**, 5, b g Campanologist (USA)—Patuca **Mr A. Nevin**

THREE-YEAR-OLDS

34 **AFFABLE**, br f New Approach (IRE)—Al Baidaa **Highclere T'Bred Racing-Rosie Swale Pope**
35 **AFRAID OF NOTHING**, b f Charm Spirit (IRE)—Lady Dragon (IRE) **Qatar Racing Limited**
36 **ALBAFLORA**, gr f Muhaarar—Almiranta **Miss K. Rausing**
37 **ANNIE DE VEGA**, ch f Lope de Vega (IRE)—Annie's Fortune (IRE) **Waverley Racing**
38 **APOLLINAIRE**, b g Poet's Voice—Affaire de Coeur **ADC Bloodstock**
39 **ARABIAN MOON**, b g Al Kazeem—Midnight Dance (IRE) **J. C. Smith**
40 **BIGGLES**, b c Zoffany (IRE)—At A Clip **Lady Cobham**
41 **BOUND EDITION**, b c Dansili—Honor Bound **H.H. Sheikh Mohammed bin Khalifa Al-Thani**
42 **CALATRAVA**, b f Havana Gold (IRE)—Intizara **Mr C. M. Humber**
43 **CALM DOWN (FR)**, b f Intello (GER)—Sydarra (FR) **Tweenhills Fillies**
44 **CHAMADE**, b f Sepoy (AUS)—Colima (IRE) **Mr & Mrs David Aykroyd**
45 **DECLARED INTEREST**, b f Declaration of War (USA)—Wiener Valkyrie **The Eclipse Partnership**
46 **DEFT**, ch f Dubawi (IRE)—Prowess (IRE) **Mr J L Rowsell & Mr M H Dixon**
47 **DIRTY DANCER (FR)**, b f No Nay Never (USA)—Super Marmelade (IRE) **Westerberg**
48 **DUTCH SCHULTZ**, b g Golden Horn—Karpina **Chelsea Thoroughbreds - The Bronx**
49 **EVENING SPIRIT**, b f Invincible Spirit (IRE)—Evita Peron **Newsells Park Stud Limited**
50 **GOLDEN CYGNET**, b f Cable Bay (IRE)—Dark Swan (IRE) **The Prince of Wales & The Duchess of Cornwall**
51 **GRACE NOTE**, b f Swiss Spirit—Darling Grace **Mrs D. J. James**
52 **GRAIN OF SENSE (IRE)**, ch g Teofilo (IRE)—Grain of Truth **Clarendon Partnership**

MR RALPH BECKETT - continued

53 **GREAT AMBASSADOR,** ch g Exceed And Excel (AUS)—Snoqualmie Girl (IRE) **J. C. Smith**
54 **HEART REEF (FR),** b f Australia—Ignis Away (FR) **Qatar Racing Limited**
55 **HELVEZIA (IRE),** b f Holy Roman Emperor (IRE)—Dame d'Honneur (IRE) **Westerberg**
56 **ICE STATION ZEBRA,** b f Showcasing—Moretta Blanche **P. K. Gardner T/A Springcombe Park Stud**
57 **IMPATIENT,** b g More Than Ready (USA)—Regardez **J. H. Richmond-Watson**
58 **INKY BLINDER,** b g Hunter's Light (IRE)—Shallika (IRE) **D & J Newell**
59 **JACKSONIAN,** ch c Frankel—Kalima **K. Abdullah**
60 **JEANNE GREY (IRE),** b f Camelot—Empress of France (USA) **H.H. Sheikh Mohammed bin Khalifa Al-Thani**
61 **JELLYSTONE (IRE),** b g Kodiac—Scholarly **Quantum Leap Racing VIII**
62 **JOHN LOCKE,** ch g Mastercraftsman (IRE)—Sacred Shield **K. Abdullah**
63 **KINROSS,** b c Kingman—Ceilidh House **J. H. Richmond-Watson**
64 **LA FOGLIETTA,** ch f Lope de Vega (IRE)—Mamma Morton (IRE) **R. J. Cornelius**
65 **LADY SANSA (IRE),** ch f Lope de Vega (IRE)—Luce (IRE) **Ballylinch Stud**
66 **LUCANDER (IRE),** b g Footstepsinthesand—Lady Sefton **Mrs M. E. Slade & Mr B. Ohlsson**
67 **MARCELA DE VEGA,** b f Lope de Vega (IRE)—Lunar Phase (IRE) **Waverley Racing**
68 **MASCAT,** ch c Zoffany (IRE)—Critical Acclaim **Mr Y. Nasib**
69 **MAX VEGA (IRE),** ch c Lope de Vega (IRE)—Paraphernalia (IRE) **The Pickford Hill Partnership**
70 **MAXIMILIUS (GER),** br gr g Soldier Hollow—Macuna **Mrs L. Mann & Mr N. Attenborough**
71 **MEPHISTO (IRE),** gr g Kendargent (FR)—Save Me The Waltz (FR) **Highclere T'Bred Racing - Helen Skelton**
72 f Anjaal—Mrs Beeton (IRE) **Mr K. McAuliffe**
73 **NEWBOLT (IRE),** gr c Bated Breath—Nirva (IRE) **Manor Farm Partnership**
74 **NIGHT OF FASHION (IRE),** b f Camelot—Shirley A Star (USA) **Mr A. Rosen**
75 **PAGAILLE (GER),** b f Teofilo (IRE)—Pearls Or Passion (FR) **H.H. Sheikh Mohammed bin Khalifa Al-Thani**
76 **PRINCE ALEX,** b g Excelebration (IRE)—Interchange (IRE) **Amo Racing Limited**
77 **ROME IMPERIAL (IRE),** b f Siyouni (FR)—Ascot Lady (IRE) **Mr N. Martin**
78 **ROSADORA (IRE),** ch f Camacho—Adoring (IRE) **Mr G. C. B. Brook**
79 Gr f Lope de Vega (IRE)—Safiyna (FR) **Waverley Racing**
80 **SEA THE SIX,** b f Sea The Stars (IRE)—Lunesque (IRE) **Montcastle Racing**
81 **STAGIAIRE,** b f Sea The Moon (GER)—So In Love **Miss K. Rausing**
82 **SUMMIT REACH,** b c Dansili—Casual **K. Abdullah**
83 **SUN TIDE,** ch f Siyouni (FR)—Midsummer **K. Abdullah**
84 **TOMFRE,** b c Cable Bay (IRE)—Kurtanella **Mrs Philip Snow & Partners**
85 **TREFOIL,** b f Teofilo (IRE)—Prairie Flower (IRE) **J. H. Richmond-Watson**
86 **UNCLE SWAYZE,** b g Dandy Man (IRE)—Hold On Tight (IRE) **Millennium Madness & Partner**
87 **VAPE,** gr g Dark Angel (IRE)—Puff (IRE) **Mr & Mrs David Aykroyd**
88 **WITHIN REACH,** b f Oasis Dream—Grasped **K. Abdullah**
89 **WYCLIF,** b c Archipenko (USA)—Altruiste **Quantum Leap Racing IX**

TWO-YEAR-OLDS

90 **A LEGACY,** b f 08/02 Archipenko (USA)—All At Sea (Sea The Stars (IRE)) **Miss K. Rausing**
91 B f 06/02 Charm Spirit (IRE)—An Ghalanta **Qatar Racing Limited**
92 **AVETA (FR),** b f 26/03 Gleneagles (IRE)—Embiyra (IRE) (Tamayuz) (45000) **Mrs Lynn Turner & Mr Guy Brook**
93 B f 04/03 Kodiac—Beculile **Qatar Racing Limited**
94 **BULLACE,** b c 23/02 Toronado (IRE)—Redstart (Cockney Rebel (IRE)) **Mr A. D. G. Oldrey & Mr G. C. Hartigan**
95 **CASUARINA,** b f 11/02 Sea The Moon (GER)—Caribana (Hernando (FR)) **Miss K. Rausing**
96 **CHERCHEZ,** b f 12/02 Nathaniel (IRE)—Regardez (Champs Elysees) **J. H. Richmond-Watson**
97 B gr c 23/04 Vadamos (FR)—Chinese White (IRE) (Dalakhani (IRE)) (42900) **The Lucra Partnership**
98 **CITY CODE,** b c 05/03 Kodiac—City Girl (IRE) (Elusive City (USA)) **J. C. Smith**
99 B c 14/05 Oasis Dream—Daana Qatar (Galileo (IRE)) **H.H. Sheikh Mohammed bin Khalifa Al-Thani**
100 **DARK MOTIVE,** b f 05/03 Motivator—
Dark Swan (IRE) (Zamindar (USA)) **The Prince of Wales & The Duchess of Cornwall**
101 **DESERT EMPIRE (IRE),** b c 20/02 Vadamos (FR)—Got To Dance (Selkirk (USA)) (18000) **A. Al Shaikh**
102 **EMINENT VICTORY (IRE),** b c 10/03 Fulbright—Fearless Flyer (IRE) (Brave Act) (30000) **Mr Khalifa Dasmal**
103 B f 01/03 Dubawi—Emulous **K. Abdullah**
104 B f 23/04 Lope de Vega (IRE)—Ennaya (FR) (Nayef (USA)) **Montcastle Racing**
105 **FIESTY,** ch f 22/02 Siyouni—Forte (New Approach) **Mr J L Rowsell & Mr M H Dixon**
106 Gr c 20/05 Mastercraftsman (IRE)—Fleur de Nuit (Montjeu (IRE)) (42900) **The Lucra Partnership**
107 B f 30/03 Iffraaj—Forest Crown (Royal Applause) **The Eclipse Partnership**
108 **FREE WILL,** b f 10/03 Lope de Vega (IRE)—Free Rein (Dansili) **The Eclipse Partnership**

MR RALPH BECKETT - continued

109 GALAH, b f 01/03 Australia—Lunar Spirit (Invincible Spirit (IRE)) **Mr & Mrs David Aykroyd**
110 B c 22/02 Zoffany (IRE)—Genuine Quality (USA) (Elusive Quality (USA)) (60000) **Mrs M. E. Slade & Mr B. Ohlsson**
111 B c 15/01 Footstepsinthesand—Harpist (IRE) (Danehill Dancer (IRE)) (32604) **Miss T. A. Ashbee**
112 HERE AGAIN, ch f 05/05 Pivotal—Look Here (Hernando (FR)) **J. H. Richmond-Watson**
113 HOLLYWOOD LADY, b f 08/02 Sea The Stars (IRE)—Opera Gal (IRE) (Galileo (IRE)) **J. C. Smith**
114 ICONIC QUEEN, b f 17/05 Invincible Spirit (IRE)—Barshiba (IRE) (Barathea (IRE)) **J. C. Smith**
115 Ch f 11/02 Twilight Son—Inflammable (Montjeu (IRE)) (11428) **Purple'n Blues**
116 JAARPITA (IRE), b f 25/02 Australia—Anklet (IRE) (Acclamation) (28000) **Mr P Stokes & Mr S Krase**
117 JUST TELLEM (IRE), b c 20/04 Bungle Inthejungle—Art of Gold (Excellent Art) (80000) **Mr P. Mellett**
118 B c 01/03 Invincible Spirit—Lilyfire **K. Abdullah**
119 B c 25/03 Sea The Moon (GER)—Mambo Gold (USA) (Medaglia d'Oro (USA)) (25000) **The Lucra Partnership**
120 B f 01/03 Invincible Spirit (IRE)—Mechanism **K. Abdullah**
121 Gr f 01/03 Giant's Causeway (USA)—
        Meseika (USA) (Medaglia d'Oro (USA)) **H.H. Sheikh Mohammed bin Khalifa Al-Thani**
122 B g 04/05 New Bay—Mishrar (IRE) (Authorized (IRE)) (30030) **The Lucra Partnership**
123 B f 25/02 Dandy Man (IRE)—Mitzi Winks (USA) (Lookin At Lucky (USA)) (80000) **Al Rabban Racing**
124 B f 21/02 Lope de Vega—Moderah (Makfi) **Qatar Racing Limited**
125 B c 01/03 Fastnet Rock—Modesta **K. Abdullah**
126 B f 09/02 Hot Streak (IRE)—Moretta Blanche (Dansili) **P. K. Gardner T/A Springcombe Park Stud**
127 Gr f 21/03 Hellvelyn—Nassuvian Pearl (Bahamian Bounty) **Melody Racing**
128 OMAN (IRE), ch c 24/04 Australia—Awohaam (IRE) (Iffraaj) (140000) **Mr Y. Nasib**
129 B c 01/03 Oasis Dream—Ombre **K. Abdullah**
130 PARAMARIBO (IRE), b c 09/03 Sea The Moon (GER)—Homepage (Dansili) (130000) **C. H. McGhie**
131 B c 13/02 Al Kazeem—Parnell's Dream (Oasis Dream) **Mr & Mrs David Aykroyd**
132 B f 02/02 Kodiac—Rainbow's Arch (Dubawi (IRE)) (27000) **Mrs H. I. Slade**
133 Ch c 02/04 Champs Elysees—Red Riddle (Verglas) (55000) **The Lucra Partnership**
134 RHODA'S CHOICE, b f 07/04 Shalaa—Al Mas **Mr P Stokes & Mr S Krase**
135 SAMMY SUNSHINE (GER), ch f 10/04 Sea The Moon—Summertime (Sholokhov) **Sunshine Partnership**
136 SARAMENHA, ch f 26/03 Mastercraftsman (IRE)—
        Topaze Blanche (Zamindar (USA)) **H.H. Sheikh Mohammed bin Khalifa Al-Thani**
137 SCOPE (IRE), ch c 24/03 Teofilo (IRE)—Look So (Efisio) **J. H. Richmond-Watson**
138 SERENA'S QUEEN (IRE), gr f 16/03 Iffraaj—
        Serena's Storm (IRE) (Statue of Liberty (USA)) **Kaniz Bloodstock Investments Ltd**
139 SERENA'S SYMPHONY (IRE), gr f 19/03 Gleneagles (IRE)—
        Princess Serena (USA) (Unbridled's Song (USA)) **Kaniz Bloodstock Investments Ltd**
140 SHABABIYA, b f 12/04 Charm Spirit (IRE)—Ana Shababiya (Teofilo (IRE)) **A. Al Shaikh**
141 SPEEDFUL, b c 13/01 Charm Spirit (IRE)—Shiba (FR) (Rail Link) (30000) **Mr Khalifa Dasmal**
142 Ch f 17/01 Lope de Vega (IRE)—Stone Roses (FR) (Rip Van Winkle (IRE)) **SRB Equine**
143 WILLIAM BLIGH, b c 25/03 Territories (IRE)—Arbella (Primo Dominie) (50000) **Chelsea Thoroughbreds**

Other Owners: Mr N. B. Attenborough, D. P. Aykroyd, Mrs L. M. Aykroyd, Mrs I. M. Beckett, Mr F. Brady, Mr G. C. B. Brook, Clarendon Syndicate, Mrs C. Dallas, Lady G. De Walden, M. H. Dixon, G. C. Hartigan, Mr R. Hull, Mr S. D. Krase, Mrs L. Mann, Mr N. Martin, Mr K. McAuliffe, Mrs Philip Snow & Partners, D. J. M. Newell, Mrs J. Newell, Mr B. Ohlsson, A. D. G. Oldrey, Mr N. D. Peppiatt, J. L. Rowsell, Mr B. A. Scanlon, N. Skinner, Mr H. I. Slade, Mrs H. L. Smyly, Mrs B. A. Snow, Mrs J. I. Snow, Mr P. G. C. A. Stokes, Miss A. M. Sundstrom, The Millennium Madness Partnership, Mrs L. Turner.

Assistant Trainer: Adam Kite, Emma Wilkinson.

Flat Jockey: Harry Bentley, Rob Hornby, Richard Kingscote, Oisin Murphy.

---

30 **MR MICHAEL BELL, Newmarket**
Postal: Fitzroy House, Newmarket, Suffolk, CB8 0JT
Contacts: **PHONE** 01638 666567 **MOBILE** 07802 264514 **FAX** 01638 668000
EMAIL office@fitzroyhouse.co.uk **WEBSITE** www.michaelbellracing.co.uk

1 BIGHEARTED, 4, ch f Farhh—Bianca Nera **Mr M. E. Perlman**
2 EAGLES BY DAY (IRE), 4, b br c Sea The Stars (IRE)—Missunited (IRE) **Clipper Group Holdings Ltd**
3 GEETANJALI (IRE), 5, b m Roderic O'Connor (IRE)—Scylla Cadeaux (IRE) **Mr H. J. Merry**

MR MICHAEL BELL - continued

4 HOUSE EDGE, 5, gr g Nathaniel (IRE)—Bezique **Mr Edward J. Ware**
5 INHALE, 4, b f Bated Breath—Innocent Air **Mrs P Shanahan, T E Hyde, Mrs T P Hyde**
6 LACAN (IRE), 9, b g New Approach (IRE)—Invincible Isle (IRE) **M. L. W. Bell Racing Ltd**
7 LOVEHEART, 4, b f Dubawi (IRE)—Love Divine **Lordship Stud**
8 PLATFORM NINETEEN (IRE), 4, ch g Australia—Susan Stroman **The Royal Ascot Racing Club**
9 YOUTHFUL, 4, b g Shamardal (USA)—Good Hope **Her Majesty The Queen**

THREE-YEAR-OLDS

10 ANNO MAXIMO (GER), b g Maxios—Queen's Hall **O.T.I. Racing**
11 APPROXIMATE, b f Dubawi (IRE)—Estimate (IRE) **Her Majesty The Queen**
12 BOTTOM BAY, b c Oasis Dream—Coconut Kreek **Lady Bamford**
13 BRAZEN SAFA, b f Brazen Beau (AUS)—Insaaf **Ontoawinner 9 & Partner**
14 BUSHTUCKER TRIAL (IRE), b g Bungle Inthejungle—Universal Circus **Mr Christopher Wright & Mr David Kilburn**
15 BY JOVE, b g Nathaniel (IRE)—Calima Breeze **Sarah & Wayne Dale 2**
16 BY MY SIDE (IRE), ch f Siyouni (FR)—Fill My Heart (IRE) **Mr S. Hanson**
17 CHOSEN STAR, ch f Dubawi (IRE)—Yodelling (USA) **Her Majesty The Queen**
18 CLEVER CANDY, b f Intello (GER)—True Course **Mr C Philipps Mr T Redman & Mr T Trotter**
19 CLOUD DRIFT, b g Toronado (IRE)—Humdrum **Her Majesty The Queen**
20 CRAYLANDS, b f Golden Horn—Madame Defarge (IRE) **W. J. and T. C. O. Gredley**
21 DORADICA, b f Oasis Dream—Require **The Duke of Devonshire**
22 DUTCH PAINTING, b f Dutch Art—Lisiere (IRE) **Mr R. A. Green**
23 FAREWELL KISS (IRE), ch f Exceed And Excel (AUS)—Kiss Me Goodbye **M. L. W. Bell Racing Ltd**
24 FATHER OF JAZZ, b c Kingman—Bark (IRE) **W. J. and T. C. O. Gredley**
25 FESTIVE LOVE, ch f Frankel—Eva's Request (IRE) **Lady Bamford**
26 FORMALITY, b c Frankel—Silver Mirage **Her Majesty The Queen**
27 FRANKLY MR SHANKLY (GER), b g Maxios—Four Roses (IRE) **Patrick & Scott Bryceland**
28 GIBRALTAR (IRE), b g Tamayuz—Red Halo (IRE) **Mr Edward J. Ware**
29 HIGH SHINE, b f Paco Boy (IRE)—Hypoteneuse (IRE) **Her Majesty The Queen**
30 ITMUSTHAVEBEENLOVE (IRE), b f Galileo (IRE)—Nijoom Dubai **MagniersTaborShanahanWachman**
31 JUDGMENT OF PARIS, b g Champs Elysees—Iridescence **Mr Edward J. Ware**
32 LA DRAGONTEA, b f Lope de Vega (IRE)—La Concorde (FR) **Bartisan Racing Ltd**
33 LADY LIGHT, ch f Showcasing—Bird Key **China Horse Club International Limited**
34 LED ASTRAY, b f Oasis Dream—Oshiponga **Clipper Group Holdings Ltd**
35 LORD WARBURTON (IRE), ch g Zoffany (IRE)—Portrait of A Lady (IRE) **The Fitzrovians 3**
36 LYDFORD, b c Fastnet Rock (AUS)—Miss Brown To You (IRE) **W. J. and T. C. O. Gredley**
37 MAXI BOY, b c Oasis Dream—Lavender And Lace **Amo Racing Limited**
38 MISTER BLUE, b gr c Dark Angel (IRE)—Sarita **Lady Bamford**
39 MR KIKI (IRE), b g No Nay Never (USA)—Jacquelin Jag (IRE) **Amo Racing Limited**
40 NEVENDON, b c Nathaniel (IRE)—Unex Mona Lisa **W. J. and T. C. O. Gredley**
41 OPINE (IRE), b g Authorized (IRE)—Tocqueville (FR) **Secular Stagnation**
42 OTAGO, b g Cable Bay (IRE)—Spinning Top **Her Majesty The Queen**
43 PEPPER BAY, b f Cable Bay (IRE)—Selinka **5 Hertford Street Racing Club**
44 RAY'S THE ONE, br g Mount Nelson—Tenpence **Mr & Mrs Ray Jenner & Partner**
45 SEVENTEEN O FOUR (IRE), ro g Gutaifan (IRE)—Bali Breeze (IRE) **Mr Edward J. Ware**
46 SHE'S AMAZING, ch f Showcasing—Nandiga (USA) **Eight Investment Holdings Ltd**
47 SPARKLING OLLY (IRE), b f Gleneagles (IRE)—Sogno Verde (IRE) **Amo Racing Limited**
48 SPRING CAMPAIGN (IRE), ch f Dandy Man (IRE)—Doctrine **Clipper Group Holdings Ltd**
49 STEPNEY CAUSEWAY, b c New Approach (IRE)—Wake Up Call **W. J. and T. C. O. Gredley**
50 STONE CIRCLE (IRE), ch c No Nay Never (USA)—Candlehill Girl (IRE) **The Fitzrovians 3**
51 SUNSET KISS, b f Kingman—Because (IRE) **Lady Bamford**
52 TEXAS TEA PARTY, b f Mastercraftsman (IRE)—Diamond Bangle (IRE) **W. J. and T. C. O. Gredley**
53 THELMA TODD (IRE), ch f Australia—Sugar House (USA) **Chelsea Thoroughbreds - Los Angeles**
54 VIA VERITAS (USA), b br f Street Sense (USA)—Win McCool (USA) **Mrs J & Mrs Mv Magnier & Mrs P Shanahan**
55 ZMILE, b f Medaglia d'Oro (USA)—Cay Dancer **W. J. and T. C. O. Gredley**

TWO-YEAR-OLDS

56 AESTHETE, b c 05/04 Muhaarar—Miss Brown to You (Fasliyev) **W. J. and T. C. O. Gredley**
57 ALEXI BOY, b c 23/03 Kingman—Putyball (USA) (Silver Deputy (CAN)) (188760) **Amo Racing Limited**
58 B c 06/02 Kodiac—Allegation (FR) (Lawman (FR)) (38000) **Patrick & Scott Bryceland**

MR MICHAEL BELL - continued

59 B f 23/02 Bobby's Kitten—Bipartisan (Bahamian Bounty) **Mr M. E. Perlman**
60 B f 13/04 Cable Bay (IRE)—Blondikova (Pivotal) (30476) **Chelsea T'breds Corbani Cumani Jackson**
61 **BLUE HERO (CAN),** b c 03/03 Air Force Blue (USA)—Pomarine (USA) (Aptitude (USA)) (60060) **Mr K Sohi Mrs I Corbani and Partners**
62 **BOOKMARK,** b f 12/03 New Approach (IRE)—Free Verse (Danehill Dancer (IRE)) **Her Majesty The Queen**
63 **CLOSENESS,** b f 22/03 Iffraaj—Pack Together (Paco Boy (IRE)) **Her Majesty The Queen**
64 Gr f 21/02 Anjaal—Conciliatory (Medicean) (11428) **Mr C. N. Wright**
65 Ch f 09/05 Gleneagles—Crossover (Cape Cross) **Mrs P Shanahan**
66 **CRYSTAL GUARD (IRE),** b c 19/02 Lope de Vega (IRE)—
                                      Crystal Melody (Nureyev (USA)) (70000) **Mr Barnes Mrs Breitmeyer & Mrs Corbani**
67 B f 08/02 Twilight Son—Diamond Run (Hurricane Run (IRE)) **Mascalls Stud**
68 **DUJAC,** b f 11/04 Muhaarar—All For Laura (Cadeaux Genereux) (42000) **Wood Hall Stud & Mrs I. Corbani**
69 Ch f 07/04 Fast Company (IRE)—Emma Dora (IRE) (Medaglia d'Oro (USA)) (5714) **The Fitzrovians 4**
70 **ENVIRONMENTALIST,** b c 15/02 Oasis Dream—Diamond Bangle (IRE) (Galileo (IRE)) **W. J. and T. C. O. Gredley**
71 B c 09/02 Due Diligence (USA)—Flighty Clarets (IRE) (Bahamian Bounty) (61904) **Amo Racing Limited**
72 **GENEVA DIVA,** b f 19/01 Frankel—Swiss Diva (Pivotal) **Lordship Stud**
73 **GEORGE BANCROFT,** ch c 23/02 Australia—Extensive (Cacique) **W. J. and T. C. O. Gredley**
74 **HAPPINESS NEEDSART,** b f 29/01 Sea the Moon—Ebb (Acclamation) **W. J. and T. C. O. Gredley**
75 **HEATHERDON MATRON,** b f 07/03 Equiano (FR)—Ile Deserte (Green Desert (USA)) (15000) **The Heatherdonians**
76 **HOLY BEE (IRE),** ch f 21/03 Declaration of War (USA)—
                                      Scarlet Honey (FR) (Holy Roman Emperor (IRE)) **Mrs I. Corbani**
77 **HORSEFLY (IRE),** b f 03/04 Camelot—Forthefirstime (Dr Fong (USA)) (20000) **Mrs G Rowland-Clark & Partner**
78 **INVEIGLE,** b c 06/02 Dark Angel (IRE)—Sand Vixen (Dubawi (IRE)) **Her Majesty The Queen**
79 **LADY SKYE,** b f 26/04 Acclamation—Chutney (IRE) (Exceed And Excel (AUS)) (95000) **Amo Racing Limited**
80 B c 07/02 Bobby's Kitten—Late Night Movie (IRE) (Holy Roman Emperor (IRE)) (24000) **The Fitzrovians 4**
81 **LOCHANTHEM,** b f 18/01 Fast Company (IRE)—
                                      Locharia (Wolfhound (USA)) (45000) **Mrs B Green Mr H Bethell & Mrs I Corbani**
82 **MASTERMAN (FR),** ch c 28/03 Reliable Man—
                                      Quenching (IRE) (Street Cry (IRE)) (47619) **Amo Racing Limited & Mr S Hanson**
83 **MR LUIGI,** b c 11/05 Bobby's Kitten—
                                      Tottie (Fantastic Light (USA)) (20000) **Amo Racing Limited & Mr A. C. Elliott**
84 **MR RYDER,** b c 20/04 Pearl Secret—Jackline (Diktat) (35000) **Amo Racing Limited & Mr A. C. Elliott**
85 **OLYMPIC THEATRE,** b c 23/03 Mayson—Madame Vestris (IRE) (Galileo (IRE)) (25740) **The Fitzrovians 3**
86 Br c 30/04 Le Havre (IRE)—Pearly Steph (FR) (Oasis Dream) (45000) **Mr S. Mizon**
87 **REALIST,** b c 27/02 Camelot—Silver Mirage (Oasis Dream) **Her Majesty The Queen**
88 B c 27/04 Dabirsim (FR)—Rindiseyda (IRE) (Arakan (USA)) (18876) **The Fitzrovians 4**
89 **SAVEASEA,** b c 04/03 Sea the Moon—Crystal Mountain (Monashee Mountain) **W. J. and T. C. O. Gredley**
90 **STANLEY BALDWIN,** br c 07/03 Showcasing—Madame Defarge (Motivator) **W. J. and T. C. O. Gredley**
91 **STIMULATE,** b f 04/02 Motivator—Shama (IRE) (Danehill Dancer (IRE)) **Her Majesty The Queen**
92 **SUN FESTIVAL,** b c 23/03 Toronado (IRE)—Raymi Coya (CAN) (Van Nistelrooy (USA)) **Her Majesty The Queen**
93 **TALL ORDER (IRE),** b c 16/02 Muhaarar—Fate (FR) (Teofilo (IRE)) **Mr S. Hanson**
94 **THE VEGAS RAIDER,** gr c 31/03 Kendargent (FR)—
                                      Matorio (FR) (Oratorio (IRE)) (60060) **Middleham Park Racing CXIII & Partner**
95 **TONY MONTANA,** gr c 19/04 Frankel—Tropical Paradise (IRE) (Verglas (IRE)) (500000) **Amo Racing Limited**
96 Ch f 07/02 Territories—Tutti Frutti (Teofilo) **Abdullatif M Al-Abdulrazzaq**
97 **VEDUTE,** b c 22/02 Holy Roman Emperor—Quads (Shamardal) **Mr R. A. Green**
98 B f 11/04 Showcasing—Whim (Nayef (USA)) (60000) **Bartisan Racing Ltd**

Other Owners: Amo Racing Limited, R. F. Barnes, Mr H. A. Bethell, Mrs H. B. J. Breitmeyer, Mr S. Bridge, Mr P. Bryceland, Mr S. Bryceland, Chelsea Thoroughbreds Ltd, Chelsea Thoroughbreds- Thelma Todd, Mrs I. Corbani, Mrs S. J. Dale, Sarah & Wayne Dale, Mr W. R. Dale, Mr A. C. Elliott, Mrs P. J. Green, Mr S. Hanson, Mrs E. A. Harris, T. F. Harris, B. M. W. Hearn, Mrs S. J. Hearn, Mrs C. Hyde, T. Hyde, Mrs J. A. Jenner, Mr R. M. Jenner, D. Kilburn, M. L. W. Bell Racing Ltd, Mrs E. Magnier, Mrs S. Magnier, Middleham Park Racing CXIII, Mr N. J. O'Brien, Ontoawinner 9, T. S. Palin, Mr C. E. L. Philipps, M. Prince, Mr T. J. Ramsden, Mr T. S. Redman, Mrs G. E. Rowland-Clark, Mrs L. M. Shanahan, Mr K. Sohi, M. Tabor, Mr T. Trotter, Mrs K. J. Wachman, Wood Hall Stud Limited, Mr C. N. Wright.

Assistant Trainer: Nick Bell.

Flat Jockey: Jamie Spencer, Hayley Turner. **Apprentice Jockey:** Joe Bradnam, Russell Harris.

31 | MR JAMES BENNETT, Wantage
Postal: **2 Filley Alley, Letcombe Bassett, Wantage, Oxfordshire, OX12 9LT**
Contacts: **PHONE 01235 762163 MOBILE 07771 523076**
EMAIL jbennett345@btinternet.com

1 **GONZAGA**, 5, b g Oasis Dream—Symposia
2 **MOOD FOR MISCHIEF**, 5, b g Nathaniel (IRE)—Tina's Spirit (IRE)
3 **THE LAST MELON**, 8, ch g Sir Percy—Step Fast (USA)

Assistant Trainer: Jackie Blackwell.

Flat Jockey: Racheal Kneller. **NH Jockey:** David Bass, Jonathan Burke.

---

32 | MR ALAN BERRY, Cockerham
Postal: **Moss Side Racing Stables, Crimbles Lane, Cockerham, Lancashire, LA2 0ES**
Contacts: **PHONE 01524 791179 MOBILE 07880 553515**
EMAIL berryracing@hotmail.com

1 **BOLD STATEMENT (IRE)**, 5, b g Arcano (IRE)—Kylemore (IRE) **Mr A. Berry**
2 **DON'T DO IT (IRE)**, 5, b g Casamento (IRE)—Innclassic (IRE) **Mr A. Berry**
3 **ECONOMIC CRISIS (IRE)**, 11, ch m Excellent Art—Try The Air (IRE) **William Burns & Alan Berry**
4 4, B f Slade Power (IRE)—Ekhraaj (USA)
5 **I'LL BE GOOD**, 11, b g Red Clubs (IRE)—Willisa **Mr A. Berry**
6 **JUSTICE SHALLOW (FR)**, 4, ch g Shakespearean (IRE)—Try The Air (IRE) **T. W. Blane**
7 5, B m Lilbourne Lad (IRE)—Kasalla (IRE) **Exors of the Late Mr P. J. Rands**
8 **LEANNES LADY (IRE)**, 8, b m Ask—Wizzy (IRE) **Mr A. Berry**
9 **LOOK WHO IT ISNAE (IRE)**, 4, b f Thewayyouare (USA)—Forest Delight (IRE) **Mr A. Berry**
10 **MAX GUEVARA (IRE)**, 4, b g Alhebayeb (IRE)—Assumption (IRE) **A Parr & A Berry**
11 **NOTWHATIAM (IRE)**, 10, b g Morozov (USA)—Riverfort (IRE) **Sureness Limited**
12 **ONE FOR BRAD (IRE)**, 5, b m Watar (IRE)—Our Jaffa (IRE) **Kirkby Lonsdale Racing**
13 **RED HOT FUSION**, 6, b g Kodiac—Unfortunate **Mr A. Berry**
14 4, B f Alhebayeb (IRE)—Ribald

THREE-YEAR-OLDS
15 **ARTHUR WALSH (IRE)**, b g Zebedee—Peach Bloom **Ms H. Murray**
16 **BOB'S OSS (IRE)**, b g Anjaal—Prisca **A Parr & A Berry**
17 **MAYBELLENE (IRE)**, b f Camacho—Chute Hall Lady (IRE) **W Burns, A Parr & A Berry**
18 **UNAUTHORISED ACT (IRE)**, b f Elzaam (AUS)—Forest Delight (IRE) **Mr A. Berry**

Other Owners: Mr A. Berry, W. Burns, A. B. Parr.

Assistant Trainer: John A. Quinn.

---

33 | MR JOHN BERRY, Newmarket
Postal: **Beverley House Stables, Exeter Road, Newmarket, Suffolk, CB8 8LR**
Contacts: **PHONE 01638 660663**
EMAIL johnwathenberry@yahoo.co.uk WEBSITE www.johnberryracing.com

1 **ALSAMARA**, 5, b m New Approach (IRE)—Altitude **J. C. De P. Berry**
2 **DAS KAPITAL**, 5, b g Cityscape—Narla **J. C. De P. Berry**
3 **DEAR ALIX**, 5, b g Schiaparelli (GER)—Desiree (IRE) **Mrs E. L. Berry**
4 **DELATITE**, 8, b g Schiaparelli (GER)—Desiree (IRE) **The Beverley House Stables Partnership**
5 **DEREHAM**, 4, b g Sir Percy—Desiree (IRE) **Mrs E. L. Berry**
6 **FREE BIRD**, 5, b m Phoenix Reach (IRE)—Love Supreme (IRE) **The Free Birds**
7 **HEAVEN UP HERE (IRE)**, 5, b m Holy Roman Emperor (IRE)—High Fun (FR) **J. C. De P. Berry**
8 **HIDDEN PEARL**, 4, ch f Dunaden (FR)—Volkovkha **The Sisters of Mercy & John Berry**
9 **HOPE IS HIGH**, 7, b m Sir Percy—Altitude **Emma Berry & John Berry**

MR JOHN BERRY - continued

10 **KRYPTOS**, 6, b g Cacique (IRE)—Posteritas (USA) **Mr A. W. Fordham**
11 **LOVING PEARL**, 4, b f Dunaden (FR)—Forever Loved **Mr A. W. Fordham**
12 **ROY ROCKET (FR)**, 10, gr g Layman (USA)—Minnie's Mystery (FR) **McCarthy & Berry**
13 **SACRED SPRITE**, 5, b m Nathaniel (IRE)—Lively Sprite **Mr K. T. Yap**
14 **THE ROCKET PARK (IRE)**, 7, b g Rock of Gibraltar (IRE)—Snowpalm **L. C. Wadey**

THREE-YEAR-OLDS

15 **SO LOVED**, b f Gregorian (IRE)—Forever Loved
16 B g Nayef (USA)—Sweet Child O'Mine
17 **THE SIMPLE TRUTH (FR)**, gr g Rajsaman (FR)—Minnie's Mystery (FR) **Mr A. W. Fordham**

Other Owners: Mrs E. L. Berry, J. C. De P. Berry, Mr Justin Byrne, Mrs Rebecca Byrne, Mr David Collings, Mrs Anne Flaherty, Mr Brendan Granahan, Mr & Mrs Patrick Haycock, Mr Mark Hillyard, Mr Neil Hilsden, Mr Alan Mayne, Mrs Iris McCarthy, Miss L. I. McCarthy, Mr Stephen McCormick, Mr Barry Moule, Mrs Jane Moule, Mr Eamonn Mullarkey, Mr Trevor O'Rourke, Mrs M.L. Parry, Mr Robert Shergold, Mr Richard Sims, Mr P. Steele-Mortimer, The 1997 Partnership, The Sisters Of Mercy, Mr Michael Tidmarsh, L. C. Wadey, Mr Ian Walton.

Flat Jockey: Nicola Currie, John Egan, Josephine Gordon. **NH Jockey:** Will Kennedy, Jack Quinlan. **Amateur Jockey:** Mr R. Birkett.

---

34 MR JOHN BEST, Sittingbourne
Postal: **Eyehorn Farm, Munsgore Lane, Borden, Sittingbourne, Kent, ME9 8JU**
Contacts: MOBILE **07889 362154**
EMAIL john.best@johnbestracing.com WEBSITE www.johnbestracing.com

1 **AFRICAN BLESSING**, 7, ch g Mount Nelson—Bella Beguine **Mr J. O. C. Tomkins**
2 **BANTA BAY**, 6, b g Kheleyf (USA)—Atnab (USA) **Jones, Fuller & Paine**
3 **BERRAHRI (IRE)**, 9, b g Bahri (USA)—Band of Colour (IRE) **White Turf Racing UK**
4 **BETTY'S HEART (IRE)**, 4, b f Camacho—Sheer Delight (IRE) **Gentlemen That Lunch**
5 **CASA COMIGO (IRE)**, 5, b g Cape Cross (IRE)—Belanoiva (IRE) **Mr S. D. Malcolm**
6 **CRYSTAL CAROLE**, 4, b f Canford Cliffs (IRE)—Crystal Gale (IRE) **Mrs V. J. Williams**
7 **EDDYSTONE ROCK (IRE)**, 8, ch g Rock of Gibraltar (IRE)—Bayberry (UAE) **Curtis, Malt & Williams**
8 **ELMEJOR (IRE)**, 4, b g Xtension (IRE)—Lyca Ballerina **Curtis Bloodstock**
9 **FEARLESS LAD (IRE)**, 10, b g Excellent Art—Souffle **Mrs J. O. Jones**
10 **FOR RICHARD**, 4, b g Muhtathir—Retainage (USA) **Mr J. Coleman**
11 **HIORNE TOWER (FR)**, 9, b g Poliglote—Hierarchie (FR) **Mrs J. O. Jones**
12 **IGNATIUS (IRE)**, 4, b g Casamento (IRE)—Free Lance (IRE) **Keaveney & Butcher**
13 **MULLARKEY**, 6, b g Mullionmileanhour (IRE)—Hannah's Dream (IRE) **Thomson & Partners**
14 **PENTIMENTO**, 4, b g Garswood—M'Selle (IRE) **Walter & Geraldine Paine**
15 **PLANTADREAM**, 5, b g Planteur (IRE)—Phantom Ridge (IRE) **H. J. Jarvis**
16 **PRIONSA (IRE)**, 4, b g Roderic O'Connor (IRE)—Lovingit (IRE) **Hucking Horses V**
17 **SALVE DEL RIO (IRE)**, 5, b g Rio de La Plata (USA)—Salve Aurora (GER) **Mark Curtis & Mike Stanley**
18 **SEAQUINN**, 5, b m Equiano (FR)—Marine Girl **Harris & Beckett**
19 **TEBAY (IRE)**, 5, b g Elzaam (AUS)—Maid of Ale (IRE) **Mr J. R. Best**
20 **TIPPERARY JACK (USA)**, 4, b c Violence (USA)—Indian Miss (USA) **Curtis & Tomkins**
21 **TORBELLINO**, 4, b f Maxios—Tiny Smile (IRE) **Ballantine Curtis Jenkins & Malt**
22 **TOROCHICA**, 4, ch f Toronado (IRE)—Biased **Curtis Bloodstock**

THREE-YEAR-OLDS

23 B f Helmet (AUS)—Balletlou (IRE) **Mr S. D. Malcolm**
24 **BOBS LAD**, b g Casamento (IRE)—Foxie Girl **Mrs J. O. Jones**
25 **HAVANA KNIGHT**, b g Havana Gold (IRE)—Goolagong Girl (IRE) **H. J. Jarvis**
26 **MEET THE PARENTS**, b g Casamento (IRE)—Elounta **Laura Malcolm & Partners**
27 B f Casamento (IRE)—Queen Ranavola (USA)
28 **RODNEY LE ROC**, b g Garswood—French Accent **TMS & Beckett**
29 **TREGURRIAN**, ch g Equiano (FR)—Hvasavi (IRE) **H. J. Jarvis**
30 **TRIPTOTHECITY**, ch f Casamento (IRE)—Triplicity **Lingfield Park Owners Group 2019**

MR JOHN BEST - continued

TWO-YEAR-OLDS

31 B c 28/02 Mayson—Elounta (Dubawi (IRE)) **Laura Malcolm & Partners**
32 B gr c 20/03 Outstrip—French Accent (Elnadim (USA))
33 B f 03/03 Garswood—Princess Spirit (Invincible Spirit (IRE)) (5000)
34 SANTIBURI SPIRIT, gr ro f 08/05 Outstrip—Santiburi Spring (Mullionmileanhour (IRE)) (952) **Hill Paine & Partners**

Other Owners: Mr J. R. Best, Mr P. Butcher, Mr M. B. Curtis, Curtis Bloodstock, Fuller & Paine, Mr G. R. Jones, Mr A. Keaveney, Mr M. Keaveney, Mrs L. C. G. Malcolm, Mr S. D. Malcolm, Mike Stanley Racing, Mr M. Stanley, Miss H. J. Williams.

Assistant Trainer: Michelle Brister.

35
MRS SUZI BEST, Lewes
Postal: **The Bungalow, Grandstand Stables, The Old Racecourse, Lewes, East Sussex, BN7 1UR**
Contacts: **MOBILE 07804 487296**
EMAIL sbestracing@yahoo.com

1 ADRAKHAN (FR), 9, b g Martaline—Annee de La Femme (IRE) **Ms F.A. O'Sullivan & Mr D G Edmonston**
2 ANNAJEMIMA, 6, b m Firebreak—Leaping Flame (USA) **Mr J. J. Callaghan**
3 4, B c Fame And Glory—Annas Theatre
4 BASHFUL BOY (IRE), 4, b g Magician (IRE)—Bacheliere (USA) **Milldean Racing Syndicate**
5 CORRIE LAKE (IRE), 7, ch m Stowaway—Corrie Hall (IRE) **Miss F. O'Sullivan**
6 5, B m Flemensfirth (USA)—D'Gigi
7 DE PLOTTING SHED (IRE), 10, b g Beneficial—Lady Willmurt (IRE) **Kelly, Beal and Vasey**
8 DEREK DUVAL (USA), 6, b g Lope de Vega (IRE)—Lady Raj (USA) **Milldean Racing Syndicate**
9 GLOBAL WONDER (IRE), 5, b g Kodiac—Traveller's Tales **Global Wonder Partnership**
10 GOOD TIME AHEAD (IRE), 6, b g Iffraaj—Good Time Sue (IRE) **Mr M. J. Benton**
11 HIGHWAY TO SUCCESS (IRE), 4, b g Fast Company (IRE)—
Dubai's Success **Jack Callaghan & Christopher Dillon**
12 LONDON GLORY, 7, b g Archipenko (USA)—Reflected Image (IRE)
13 MILLDEAN SILVA (IRE), 7, ch m Presenting—Impudent (IRE) **Milldean Racing Syndicate**
14 NAUTICAL HAVEN, 6, b g Harbour Watch (IRE)—Mania (IRE) **Milldean Racing Syndicate**
15 NEW STREET (IRE), 9, gr g Acclamation—New Deal **Mr J. J. Callaghan**
16 OFFICER DRIVEL (IRE), 9, b g Captain Rio—Spiritville (IRE) **Miss R. Woodman**
17 OUTRATH (IRE), 10, b g Captain Rio—Silver Grouse (IRE) **Mr L. Best**
18 RED CHARMER (IRE), 10, b g Red Clubs (IRE)—Golden Charm (IRE) **Mr J. J. Callaghan**
19 RETURNING GLORY, 5, b g Exceed And Excel (AUS)—Tanzania (USA) **F. A. O'Sullivan & John Collins**
20 SIX GUN SERENADE (IRE), 9, b g Kalanisi (IRE)—Zenaide (IRE) **Mr J. J. Callaghan**
21 THATS MY RABBIT (IRE), 11, b g Heron Island (IRE)—Minnie Turbo (IRE) **Mr A Coupland & Mr John Collins**

Other Owners: Mr P. J. Arrow, Mr J. J. Callaghan, Mr J. Collins, Mr A. R. Coupland, Mr C. J. Dillon, Mr D. Edmonston, Miss F. O'Sullivan.

Assistant Trainer: Mr Tom Best.

36
MR JAMES BETHELL, Coverham
Postal: **Thorngill Stables, Coverham, Middleham, North Yorkshire, DL8 4TJ**
Contacts: **PHONE 01969 640360 MOBILE 07831 683528 FAX 01969 640360**
EMAIL james@bethellracing.co.uk WEBSITE www.bethellracing.com

1 BOB'S GIRLFRIEND, 4, ch f Sakhee (USA)—Maid of Perth **R. F. Gibbons**
2 BRIARDALE (IRE), 8, b g Arcano (IRE)—Marine City (JPN) **J. Carrick & Clarendon Thoroughbred Racing**
3 CALL ME MADAM, 5, b m Passing Glance—Shazana **R. F. Gibbons**
4 DAWAAWEEN (IRE), 4, ch f Poet's Voice—Ghandoorah (USA) **Mr Michael Dawson OBE**
5 HESSLEWOOD (IRE), 4, b g Slade Power (IRE)—Rochitta (USA) **Clarendon Thoroughbred Racing**
6 MOSS GILL (IRE), 4, b g No Nay Never (USA)—Sharaarah (IRE) **G Van Cutsem & Partner**
7 MUDAWWAN (IRE), 6, b g Invincible Spirit (IRE)—Louve Sacree (USA) **Clarendon Thoroughbred Racing**

MR JAMES BETHELL - continued

8 **PORTLEDGE (IRE)**, 6, b g Acclamation—Off Chance **Mr A. Buckingham**
9 **RICH APPROACH (IRE)**, 4, b g Dawn Approach (IRE)—Kiss Me Goodbye **The Vickers & Clark Racing Partnership**
10 **STRAWBERRYANDCREAM**, 5, ch m Cityscape—Miss Apricot **Mrs S. Bethell**
11 **ULSHAW BRIDGE (IRE)**, 5, b g High Chaparral (IRE)—Sharaarah (IRE) **Geoffrey van Cutsem & Partners**
12 **WELL FUNDED (IRE)**, 4, b f Camelot—Malikayah (IRE) **Clarendon Thoroughbred Racing**
13 **WINTON**, 4, b g Harbour Watch (IRE)—Arctic Song **Clarendon Thoroughbred Racing**

THREE-YEAR-OLDS

14 **ABBOTSIDE**, b g Mukhadram—Gregoria (IRE) **J. Carrick & Clarendon Thoroughbred Racing**
15 **BENEDICTINE**, ch f Toronado (IRE)—Melrose Abbey (IRE) **Mr J. E. Dance**
16 **CHESHIRE**, ch f Nathaniel (IRE)—Hazy Dancer **Clarendon Thoroughbred Racing**
17 **EAGLE'S FOOT**, b c Free Eagle (IRE)—Carmens Fate **The Eagle's Foot Syndicate**
18 **IDOAPOLOGISE**, b g Havana Gold (IRE)—Shiba (FR) **Clarendon Thoroughbred Racing**
19 **JERVAULX**, gr g Champs Elysees—Perfect Haven **Clarendon Thoroughbred Racing**
20 **RICH BELIEF**, b g Make Believe—Realt Eile (IRE) **The Vickers & Clark Racing Partnership**
21 **STOCKBRIDGE TAP**, ch c Nayef (USA)—Last Supper **R. F. Gibbons**
22 **SUMMERBRIDGE (IRE)**, ch f Ruler of The World (IRE)—
                                          Huffoof (IRE) **J. Carrick & Clarendon Thoroughbred Racing**

TWO-YEAR-OLDS

23 B c 02/05 Sixties Icon—Aromatherapy (Oasis Dream)
24 **EXALTED LEADER**, b c 01/03 Acclamation—
                        Authoritarian (Authorized (IRE)) (32000) **Geoffrey van Cutsem & Partners**
25 **GRANTLEY (IRE)**, b c 03/03 Charm Spirit (IRE)—
                        Peig (IRE) (Refuse To Bend (IRE)) (18000) **Clarendon Thoroughbred Racing**
26 Ch g 25/03 Cityscape—Miss Apricot (Indian Ridge) (952) **Clarendon Thoroughbred Racing**
27 **RICH DREAM (IRE)**, b c 21/02 Make Believe—
                        Poppet's Lovein (Lomitas) (40000) **The Vickers & Clark Racing Partnership**
28 B c 15/04 Muhaarar—Royal Eloquence (IRE) (Duke of Marmalade (IRE)) **Mr J. A. Tabet**
29 **THE QUEENS LADIES**, b f 27/03 Heeraat (IRE)—
                        Blades Princess (Needwood Blade) (7619) **HP Racing The Queens Ladies**
30 B f 30/04 Outstrip—True Pleasure (IRE) (Choisir (AUS)) (761) **Clarendon Thoroughbred Racing**

Other Owners: Mr J. D. Bethell, Mrs S. Bethell, Mr J. Carrick, Clarendon Thoroughbred Racing, Mr M. Clark, T. Hyde, J. Carrick & Clarendon Thoroughbred Racing, Mr D. Y. Vickers, R. T. Vickers, Mr G. N. van Cutsem.

Assistant Trainer: Edward Bethell.

---

37 | **MR WILLIAM BETHELL, Arnold**
Postal: **Arnold Manor, Arnold, Hull, North Humberside, HU11 5JA**
Contacts: **PHONE 01964 562996**
EMAIL wabethell@btinternet.com

1 **FITSAOHA (FR)**, 5, b m Barastraight—Kelle Home (FR) **W. A. Bethell**
2 **MIAMI PRESENT (IRE)**, 10, b br g Presenting—Miami Nights (GER) **W. A. Bethell**
3 **MY PAINTER (IRE)**, 9, b m Jeremy (USA)—Last Cry (FR) **W. A. Bethell**
4 **NEWBERRY NEW (IRE)**, 8, b g Kodiac—Sunblush (UAE) **W. A. Bethell**
5 **STEEL HELMET (IRE)**, 6, ch g Helmet (AUS)—Marine City (JPN) **W. A. Bethell**
6 **VERSIFIER**, 8, b m Yeats (IRE)—Daprika (FR) **W. A. Bethell**

38 | MR GEORGE BEWLEY, Appleby-In-Westmorland
Postal: **Jerusalem Farm, Colby, Appleby-In-Westmorland, Cumbria, CA16 6BB**
Contacts: PHONE **017683 53003** MOBILE **07704 924783**
EMAIL **bewleyracing@outlook.com** WEBSITE **www.georgebewleyracing.co.uk**

1 **ARCANJA (IRE)**, 6, gr g Arcadio (GER)—Nanja Monja (IRE) **J. Wade**
2 **ARTICLE FIFTY (IRE)**, 7, b g Doyen (IRE)—Annie Go (IRE) **Jgs, Richardson, Davidson & Bewley**
3 **BREAKING THE ICE (IRE)**, 5, b g Frozen Power (IRE)—Specific (IRE) **G. T. Bewley**
4 **CLASSICAL MILANO (IRE)**, 9, b g Milan—Miss Baden (IRE) **Victoria Bewley,John Gibson&e G Tunstall**
5 **CLONDAW FIXER (IRE)**, 8, b g Court Cave (IRE)—The Millers Tale (IRE) **G. T. Bewley**
6 **INNIS SHANNON (IRE)**, 10, br m Stowaway—Put On Hold (IRE) **Mrs Lesley Bewley & Mr John Gibson**
7 **KENNEDYS FIELD (IRE)**, 7, b g Multiplex—Supreme Lady (IRE) **Victoria Bewley & Lizzy Annett**
8 **LAWTOP LEGEND (IRE)**, 8, b g Milan—Nolagh Supreme (IRE) **JGS Partnership**
9 **LITTLE MILLIE (IRE)**, 8, b m Milan—Sweetbitter (FR) **Southdean Racing Club**
10 **MAH MATE BOB (IRE)**, 8, b g Mahler—Bobset Leader (IRE) **J. Wade**
11 **MAHLER SUPREME (IRE)**, 6, b g Mahler—Site Alite (IRE) **Miss M. D. Myco**
12 **MINNIMO**, 5, ch g Motivator—Alessandra **Mr E. G. Tunstall**
13 **OUR MORRIS (IRE)**, 9, b g Milan—Broken Gale (IRE) **Mr R Fisher & Bewley**
14 **PASS RUSHER (IRE)**, 5, b g Doyen (IRE)—Coolrush (IRE) **Mr A. Udale**
15 **RAISE YOUR HAND (IRE)**, 5, br g Imperial Monarch (IRE)—Midnight Dasie (IRE) **Mrs E. Annett**
16 **REIGN BACK DANCER (IRE)**, 6, b g Jeremy (USA)—Back The Queen (IRE) **Miss M. D. Myco**
17 **SAVOY COURT (IRE)**, 9, b g Robin des Champs (FR)—North Star Poly (IRE) **Eales, Brown & Lloyd**
18 **WAR AT SEA (IRE)**, 6, gr g Mastercraftsman (IRE)—Swirling (IRE) **Mrs Lesley Bewley & Mr John Gibson**
19 **WHATEVA NEXT (IRE)**, 5, b g Dubai Destination (USA)—Belon Breeze (IRE) **Mr A. Udale**

Other Owners: Mrs E. Annett, Mr G. Baird, Mr S. J. Baird, G. T. Bewley, Mrs L. Bewley, Miss V. F. Bewley, Mr E. R. Brown, Mr L. J. Davidson, Mr K. F. Eales, Mr R. A. Fisher, Mr J. H. Gibson, Mr J. H. Graham, Mrs J. Lloyd, Mr W. Richardson, Mr E. G. Tunstall.

NH Jockey: Jonathon Bewley, Colm McCormack, Craig Nichol.

39 | MR SAEED BIN SUROOR, Newmarket
Postal: **Godolphin Office, Snailwell Road, Newmarket, Suffolk, CB8 7YE**
Contacts: PHONE **01638 569956**
WEBSITE **www.godolphin.com**

1 **AL MUREIB (IRE)**, 4, ch g Dubawi (IRE)—Lava Flow (IRE)
2 **AUTUMN LEAF (IRE)**, 4, b f Shamardal (USA)—Beautiful Forest
3 **BEDOUIN'S STORY**, 5, b g Farhh—Time Crystal (IRE)
4 **BENBATL**, 6, b h Dubawi (IRE)—Nahrain
5 **BIN BATTUTA**, 6, ch g Dubawi (IRE)—Land of Dreams
6 **CANTINIERE (USA)**, 5, b m War Front (USA)—Up (IRE)
7 **COMMANDER COLE**, 6, b g Kyllachy—Welsh Angel
8 **DESERT FIRE (IRE)**, 5, b h Cape Cross (IRE)—Crystal House (CHI)
9 **DREAM CASTLE**, 6, b g Frankel—Sand Vixen
10 **DREAM LOCATION**, 4, b f Invincible Spirit (IRE)—Siyaadah
11 **DUBAI BLUE (USA)**, 4, b f More Than Ready (USA)—Speckled (USA)
12 **DUBAI HORIZON (IRE)**, 6, b g Poet's Voice—Chibola (ARG)
13 **DUBAI LEGACY (USA)**, 4, b g Discreet Cat (USA)—Afsana (USA)
14 **DUBAI LUXURY**, 4, b f Teofilo (IRE)—Isobel Archer
15 **GENTLE LOOK**, 4, ch g Dubawi (IRE)—Rosewater (IRE)
16 **GHALY**, 4, ch c Dubawi (IRE)—Hanky Panky (IRE)
17 **GIFTS OF GOLD (IRE)**, 5, b g Invincible Spirit (IRE)—Sanna Bay (IRE)
18 **GLOBAL HERO**, 4, ch c Dubawi (IRE)—Rehn's Nest (IRE)
19 **GLOBAL HUNTER (IRE)**, 4, b c Kodiac—Romie's Kastett (GER)
20 **GOLD STAR**, 6, b g Nathaniel (IRE)—Tanzania (USA)
21 **GREAT EXAMPLE**, 4, b c Cape Cross (IRE)—Gower Song
22 **HIGH END**, 6, b br g Dubawi (IRE)—Crystal Music (USA)

MR SAEED BIN SUROOR - continued

23 **JALAAD (IRE)**, 5, b g Kodiac—Surrey Storm
24 **LAND OF LEGENDS (IRE)**, 4, b c Iffraaj—Homily
25 **LAST LOOK (IRE)**, 4, b f Pivotal—Gonbarda (GER)
26 **MAJOR PARTNERSHIP (IRE)**, 5, gr h Iffraaj—Roystonea
27 **MIDNIGHT MEETING (IRE)**, 5, b h Dubawi (IRE)—Inner Secret (USA)
28 **MOUNTAIN HUNTER (USA)**, 6, b g Lonhro (AUS)—Tamarillo
29 **MUTAFAWWIG**, 4, b c Oasis Dream—Reunite (IRE)
30 **NSNAS (IRE)**, 4, b c Bated Breath—Burn The Breeze (IRE)
31 **PERFECT NUMBER**, 4, b f Cape Cross (IRE)—Wizara (IRE)
32 **PERFECT WINTER (IRE)**, 4, b f Invincible Spirit (IRE)—Heartily (IRE)
33 **PURE BEAUTY**, 4, b f Shamardal (USA)—Dark Orchid (USA)
34 **QUIET NOTE**, 4, b f Invincible Spirit (IRE)—Lady Marian (GER)
35 **REACTION TIME**, 5, b g Dubawi (IRE)—Cloudspin (USA)
36 **ROYAL MARINE (IRE)**, 4, b g Raven's Pass (USA)—Inner Secret (USA)
37 **SEARCH FOR LIGHT (IRE)**, 4, gr f New Approach (IRE)—Fire Blaze (IRE)
38 **SILENT HUNTER**, 4, b c Dutch Art—Yellow Rosebud (IRE)
39 **SILVER LINE (IRE)**, 6, gr g Dark Angel (IRE)—Admire The View (IRE)
40 **SILVER RIVER**, 6, gr g Tamayuz—Tashelka (FR)
41 **VOLCANIC SKY**, 5, b g Street Cry (IRE)—Short Skirt
42 **WESAM (IRE)**, 4, b c Slade Power (IRE)—Many Colours
43 **WHITE MOUNTAIN**, 4, b f Raven's Pass (USA)—Mujarah (IRE)
44 **YATTWEE (USA)**, 7, b br g Hard Spun (USA)—Alzerra (UAE)

THREE-YEAR-OLDS

45 **ARABIAN ROMANCE (IRE)**, b f No Nay Never (USA)—Cabelo (IRE)
46 **ARABIAN WARRIOR**, b c Dubawi (IRE)—Siyaadah
47 **ARABIC CHARM (IRE)**, b f Exceed And Excel (AUS)—Fond Words (IRE)
48 **ARABIC WELCOME (IRE)**, b br c Shamardal (USA)—Bint Almatar (USA)
49 **BACK FROM DUBAI (IRE)**, b g Exceed And Excel (AUS)—Emirates Rewards
50 **BEAUTIFUL COLOUR**, b f Shamardal (USA)—Pomology (USA)
51 **BEAUTIFUL SCENERY (IRE)**, b f Shamardal (USA)—Mont Etoile (IRE)
52 **BIG MEETING (IRE)**, b br c Shamardal (USA)—Beta
53 **BIG TEAM (USA)**, b br c Speightstown—Kotuku
54 **BLUE FLAME (IRE)**, gr c Dark Angel (IRE)—Bluefire
55 **BRIGHT START (USA)**, b br c Medaglia d'Oro (USA)—Blue Petrel (USA)
56 **BRIGHT SUNSET (IRE)**, b f Night of Thunder (IRE)—Calando (USA)
57 **BRILLIANT LIGHT**, b g Sea The Stars (IRE)—Flame of Gibraltar (IRE)
58 **CITY WALK (IRE)**, b c Brazen Beau (AUS)—My Lucky Liz (IRE)
59 **CREEK HORIZON**, b g Invincible Spirit (IRE)—Satin Kiss (USA)
60 **DEEP SNOW**, b f Bated Breath—Polar Circle (USA)
61 **DESERT CAMP (IRE)**, b c Wootton Bassett—Louarn (IRE)
62 **DESERT DESTINATION (IRE)**, b c Night of Thunder (IRE)—Scarlett Rose
63 **DUBAI LIFE (USA)**, b br f Dubawi (IRE)—Carnival Court (USA)
64 **DUBAI MIRAGE (IRE)**, ch c Dubawi (IRE)—Calipatria
65 **DUBAI QUALITY (IRE)**, ch f Dubawi (IRE)—Local Time
66 **DUBAI SOUQ (IRE)**, b c Dubawi (IRE)—Balsamine (USA)
67 **DUBAI WELCOME**, gr ro c Dubawi (IRE)—Emily Bronte
68 **EGYPTIAN KING**, b c Iffraaj—Viola d'Amour (IRE)
69 **ELECTRICAL STORM**, b g Dubawi (IRE)—Mujarah (IRE)
70 **FAADIYAH (IRE)**, ch f New Approach (IRE)—Ghasabah
71 **FAAKHIRAH (IRE)**, b f Dawn Approach (IRE)—Rawaaq
72 **FESTIVAL OF COLOUR (IRE)**, b c Kodiac—Redmaven (IRE)
73 **FINAL SONG (IRE)**, b f Dark Angel (IRE)—Rahiyah (USA)
74 **FINAL STORY (USA)**, b c Into Mischief (USA)—Katherine'skadence (USA)
75 **FIRST MAGIC (USA)**, b f More Than Ready (USA)—Danelagh (AUS)
76 **FIRST SNOWFALL**, b f Dubawi (IRE)—Flying Cloud (IRE)
77 **FIRST TARGET**, b c Showcasing—Excelette (IRE)
78 **FLOODWATER (IRE)**, b c Teofilo (IRE)—Emboss (IRE)
79 **FRESH SNOW (IRE)**, b gr f Dark Angel (IRE)—Snow Rose (USA)

MR SAEED BIN SUROOR - continued

80 **FUTURE KING (IRE),** b c Dark Angel (IRE)—Relation Alexander (IRE)
81 **GREAT HONOUR (IRE),** b c Gleneagles (IRE)—No Explaining (IRE)
82 **GREAT IMAGE (IRE),** b g Exceed And Excel (AUS)—Beautiful Forest
83 **HATTA MOUNTAINS (IRE),** b c Society Rock (IRE)—Shehila (IRE)
84 **HIDDEN EMOTION (USA),** b f City Zip (USA)—Looking Glass (USA)
85 **HISTORIC (IRE),** b br c Shamardal (USA)—Galician
86 **KHABAAB (IRE),** b c Teofilo (IRE)—Thaahira (USA)
87 **KHATM,** b c Dubawi (IRE)—Hawaafez
88 **LIVE YOUR DREAM (IRE),** b c Iffraaj—Dream Book
89 **LONG TRADITION (IRE),** b c Shamardal (USA)—Irish History (IRE)
90 **MAKING HISTORY (IRE),** b g Dubawi (IRE)—Important Time (IRE)
91 **MILITARY MARCH,** b c New Approach (IRE)—Punctilious
92 **MOUNTAIN LAKE,** b f New Approach (IRE)—Bitter Lake (USA)
93 **MOVING LIGHT (IRE),** ch c Night of Thunder (IRE)—North East Bay (USA)
94 **MY VISION,** b g Showcasing—Shembara (FR)
95 **NATION'S BEAUTY (IRE),** gr f Dark Angel (IRE)—Nahoodh (IRE)
96 **NATURE LOVER,** b f Raven's Pass (USA)—Everglades
97 **NIGHT HUNTER (USA),** gr c Tapit (USA)—Wickedly Wise (USA)
98 **OPEN STORY,** b c Night of Thunder (IRE)—Linda Radlett (IRE)
99 **ORIENTAL NIGHT (IRE),** b br f Shamardal (USA)—Oriental Step (IRE)
100 **PERFECT ARCH (IRE),** b g Dawn Approach (IRE)—Willow Beck
101 **PICTURE FRAME,** b f Showcasing—Hello Glory
102 **PLATINUM STAR (IRE),** b c Lope de Vega (IRE)—Toquette (IRE)
103 **QUEEN OF THE SEA (IRE),** b f Sea The Stars (IRE)—Knyazhna (IRE)
104 **QUIET EVENING (IRE),** b f Teofilo (IRE)—Prussian
105 **QUIET PLACE (IRE),** b f Kodiac—Need You Now (IRE)
106 **RAAEB (IRE),** ch c Raven's Pass (USA)—Kalaatah (USA)
107 **RAASED (IRE),** b g Teofilo (IRE)—Yanabeeaa (USA)
108 **REAL WORLD (IRE),** b c Dark Angel (IRE)—Nafura
109 **ROYAL ARRIVAL (IRE),** b br c Shamardal (USA)—Rock Opera (SAF)
110 **ROYAL PARTNERSHIP,** b c Shamardal (USA)—Adoringly (IRE)
111 **ROYAL VOTE (USA),** ch c Elusive Quality (USA)—Silent Bond (USA)
112 **SAAFY,** b c Shamardal (USA)—Jilnaar (IRE)
113 **SEA BAY,** b f Iffraaj—Welsh Anthem
114 **SEA CAVE,** b c Sepoy (AUS)—Vitoria (IRE)
115 **SECRET MOMENT (IRE),** b c Exceed And Excel (AUS)—Devotee (USA)
116 **SHAPE THE FUTURE (GER),** ch c Rock of Gibraltar (IRE)—Suzanita (IRE)
117 **SHINING EXAMPLE (IRE),** b c Shamardal (USA)—Kailani
118 **SILENT ESCAPE (IRE),** ch f New Approach (IRE)—Rosewater (IRE)
119 **SOLAR FLAME (IRE),** b f Invincible Spirit (IRE)—Michita (USA)
120 **SOUTH COAST (USA),** b f War Front (USA)—Moyne Abbey (USA)
121 **STAND STRONG (IRE),** b c No Nay Never (USA)—Hurricane Emma (USA)
122 **STUNNING BEAUTY (IRE),** ch f Shamardal (USA)—Short Skirt
123 **SUMMER HOUSE,** ch f Lope de Vega (IRE)—Soon (IRE)
124 **TOMOUH DUBAI,** ch f Dubawi (IRE)—West Wind
125 **UNTOLD STORY,** ch c Teofilo (IRE)—Tanzania (IRE)
126 **WARM SUNSET (IRE),** b f Oasis Dream—Predicted
127 **WARNING SHOT,** ch c Exceed And Excel (AUS)—Margravine (USA)

TWO-YEAR-OLDS

128 Ch f 05/03 New Approach (IRE)—Adoringly (IRE) (Dubawi (IRE))
129 Br f 13/05 Muhaarar—Al Ishq (FR) (Nureyev (USA))
130 B f 12/04 Sea The Stars (IRE)—Anjaz (USA) (Street Cry (IRE))
131 B f 02/05 Golden Horn—Aviacion (BRZ) (Know Heights (IRE))
132 B f 09/03 Territories (IRE)—Beautiful Ending (Exceed And Excel (AUS))
133 Ch c 07/02 Fast Company (IRE)—Beautiful Forest (Nayef (USA))
134 Ch f 22/03 Teofilo (IRE)—Belonging (Raven's Pass (USA))
135 Gr c 06/03 Dark Angel (IRE)—Betimes (New Approach (IRE))
136 B c 22/02 Exceed And Excel (AUS)—Braided (USA) (Elusive Quality (USA))

MR SAEED BIN SUROOR - continued

137 B c 16/05 Dubawi (IRE)—Certify (USA) (Elusive Quality (USA))
138 B f 24/03 Invincible Spirit (IRE)—City Glam (ARG) (Grand Reward (USA))
139 B f 11/04 Shamardal (USA)—Country Music (Street Cry (IRE))
140 B f 15/02 Teofilo (IRE)—Dufay (IRE) (Dubawi (IRE))
141 Br c 06/02 Dubawi (IRE)—Dutota Desejada (BRZ) (First American (USA))
142 Ch f 29/01 Dawn Approach (IRE)—Emirates Rewards (Dubawi (IRE))
143 Br c 12/05 Invincible Spirit (IRE)—Eshaadeh (USA) (Storm Cat (USA))
144 B f 30/04 Territories (IRE)—Etive (USA) (Elusive Quality (USA))
145 Gr c 18/05 Dark Angel (IRE)—Floristry (Fasliyev (USA))
146 Ch c 05/04 Dubawi (IRE)—Flying Cloud (IRE) (Storming Home)
147 B c 14/05 Teofilo (IRE)—Haughtily (IRE) (Invincible Spirit (IRE))
148 B c 22/01 Dawn Approach (IRE)—Huma Bird (Invincible Spirit (IRE))
149 Ch c 01/03 Pivotal—Hush Money (CHI) (Hussonet (USA))
150 B c 26/04 Dawn Approach (IRE)—Inner Secret (USA) (Singspiel (IRE))
151 B f 25/03 Shamardal (USA)—Inspiriter (Invincible Spirit (IRE))
152 Gr f 30/04 Dark Angel (IRE)—Jealous Again (USA) (Trippi (USA))
153 B f 20/04 Awtaad (IRE)—Khulood (USA) (Storm Cat (USA))
154 B c 21/03 Teofilo (IRE)—Lea Valley (Araafa (IRE))
155 B f 10/04 Invincible Spirit (IRE)—Long Lashes (USA) (Rock Hard Ten (USA))
156 Ch c 21/02 Dubawi (IRE)—Mandinga (BRZ) (Top Hat (BRZ))
157 B f 30/04 Sea The Stars (IRE)—Measured Tempo (Sadler's Wells (USA))
158 B c 23/02 Belardo (IRE)—Music Chart (USA) (Exchange Rate (USA))
159 Ch c 27/01 New Approach (IRE)—Nadia (Nashwan (USA))
160 Gr c 02/04 Shamardal (USA)—Nahoodh (IRE) (Clodovil (IRE))
161 B c 17/03 Invincible Spirit (IRE)—New Style (USA) (Street Cry (IRE))
162 B c 22/03 Dark Angel (IRE)—Patroness (Dubawi (IRE))
163 B f 23/04 Dubawi (IRE)—Placidia (IRE) (Sea The Stars (IRE))
164 B f 02/02 Teofilo (IRE)—Praia (Dubawi (IRE))
165 B c 23/02 Dawn Approach (IRE)—Pulcinella (IRE) (Dubawi (IRE))
166 Gr c 21/03 Dark Angel (IRE)—Raphinae (Dubawi (IRE))
167 Br grf 18/04 Exceed And Excel (AUS)—Safiyna (FR) (Sinndar (IRE)) (72000)
168 B f 13/02 Iffraaj—Secret Hint (Oasis Dream) (70000)
169 Ch c 27/02 Iffraaj—Show Day (IRE) (Shamardal (USA))
170 B c 03/02 Golden Horn—Silk Words (Dubawi (IRE))
171 Ch c 02/03 The Last Lion (IRE)—Snow Powder (IRE) (Raven's Pass (USA))
172 B gr c 21/03 Dark Angel (IRE)—Speirbhean (IRE) (Danehill (USA))
173 B c 21/03 Showcasing—Springlike (IRE) (Acclamation) (135000)
174 B c 27/04 Night of Thunder (IRE)—Sundrop (JPN) (Sunday Silence (USA))
175 Ch f 06/04 Night of Thunder (IRE)—Utrecht (Rock of Gibraltar (IRE))
176 Ch c 18/02 Helmet (AUS)—Vituisa (Bering)
177 B c 03/04 Dubawi (IRE)—Wavering (IRE) (Refuse To Bend (IRE))
178 B c 20/05 Dark Angel (IRE)—Windsor County (USA) (Elusive Quality (USA))
179 B c 08/02 Invincible Spirit (IRE)—Winter Queen (Dubawi (IRE))

---

40 | **MRS EMMA-JANE BISHOP, Cheltenham**
Postal: Brockhill, Naunton, Cheltenham, Gloucestershire, GL54 3BA
Contacts: **MOBILE** 07887 845970 **FAX** 01451 850199
EMAIL emmabishopracing@hotmail.com **WEBSITE** www.emmabishopracing.com

1 ANOTHER GLANCE, 4, br f Passing Glance—Roberta Back (IRE)
2 ARQUEBUSIER (FR), 10, br g Discover d'Auteuil (FR)—Djurjura (FR) **Mr R. Foulquies**
3 BAJARDO (IRE), 12, b g Jammaal—Bit of Peace (IRE) **Mrs J. Arnold**
4 GLANCE BACK, 9, b g Passing Glance—Roberta Back (IRE) **Select Racing Club & Mrs M J Arnold**
5 MACKSVILLE (IRE), 7, gr g Mastercraftsman (IRE)—Fairest of All (IRE) **Mrs J. Arnold**
6 MAX DYNAMO, 10, b g Midnight Legend—Vivante (IRE) **Mrs M. J. Wilson**
7 SHEEZA LEGEND, 6, b m Midnight Legend—Roberta Back (IRE) **Emma Bishop Racing Club**
8 STAAR (IRE), 6, b g Sea The Stars (IRE)—Bitooh **Mrs J. Arnold**

Other Owners: Mrs J. Arnold, Mr Michael J. Arnold, Mrs E. J. Bishop, The Select Racing Club Limited.

41 MR FRANK BISHOP, Kidderminster
Postal: **Parkside, Blakeshall, Wolverley, Kidderminster, Worcestershire, DY11 5XW**
Contacts: **MOBILE 07900 407647**

1 **APRILS ROSE**, 4, b f Mazameer (IRE)—Shejiyeh (IRE)
2 **EMPTY PROMISES**, 4, b g Mazameer (IRE)—Rathlin Sound **Mr F. A. Bishop**
3 **FENNANN**, 9, b g Dutch Art—Embraced **Mr M. R. Baldry**
4 **NO MORE PROMISES**, 4, b g Mazameer (IRE)—Pnyka (IRE) **Mr F. A. Bishop**

THREE-YEAR-OLDS
5 **DIAMONDS DREAM**, b f Captain Gerrard (IRE)—Blakeshall Diamond **Mr F. A. Bishop**

TWO-YEAR-OLDS
6 B f 27/04 Mazameer (IRE)—Deftera Fantutte (IRE) (Amadeus Wolf) **Mr M. R. Baldry**
7 B f 17/04 Mazameer (IRE)—Pursuit of Purpose (Dansili) **Mr M. R. Baldry**

Assistant Trainer: Mr Martin Bishop.

42 MR KEVIN BISHOP, Bridgwater
Postal: **Barford Park Stables, Spaxton, Bridgwater, Somerset, TA5 1AF**
Contacts: **PHONE 01278 671437 MOBILE 07816 837610**
EMAIL hevbishop@hotmail.com

1 **FLOW WITH EVE**, 11, b m With The Flow (USA)—Vercheny **Michael & Will Potter**
2 **JUST GO FOR IT**, 7, b m Passing Glance—Just Jasmine **Mrs S. G. Atkinson**
3 **JUST SPOT**, 13, ch m Baryshnikov (AUS)—Just Jasmine **K. Bishop**
4 5, B m Tikkanen (USA)—La Cyborg (FR) **Mr B. V. Lund**
5 **LETS GO DUTCHESS**, 10, b m Helissio (FR)—Lets Go Dutch **K. Bishop**
6 4, B c Dandy Man (IRE)—Montego Breeze **Mr B. V. Lund**
7 **MRS TROUT**, 10, b m Midnight Legend—Art Affair (GER) **M. Potter**
8 **PRECIOUS GROUND**, 10, b g Helissio (FR)—Wild Ground (IRE) **Mr K. Jones**
9 **ROSSERK ABBEY (IRE)**, 7, ch g Fruits of Love (USA)—Here Comes Alli (IRE) **Mr B. V. Lund**
10 **SHOWMETHEWAYAVRILO**, 7, ch g Showcasing—Avrilo **Mr B. V. Lund**
11 **SOMERSET JEM**, 11, b g Sir Harry Lewis (USA)—Monger Lane **Slabs & Lucan**
12 **THE GREAT RAYMONDO**, 8, b g Passing Glance—Fantasy Parkes **Slabs & Lucan**
13 **THESTOPPERDUNNE (IRE)**, 7, b g Craigsteel—Island Heron (IRE) **Mr B. V. Lund**
14 5, B br m Stowaway—Tizzy Frizzy **Mr B. V. Lund**

THREE-YEAR-OLDS
15 **HANDFUL OF GOLD (IRE)**, ch f No Nay Never (USA)—Golden Passion (IRE) **Mr B. V. Lund**
16 Ch c Tamayuz—Shaddeya (IRE) **Mr B. V. Lund**

Assistant Trainer: Heather Bishop.

Amateur Jockey: Mr Conor Smith.

43 MISS LINDA BLACKFORD, Tiverton
Postal: **Shortlane Stables, Rackenford, Tiverton, Devon, EX16 8EH**
Contacts: **PHONE 01884 881589 MOBILE 07887 947832**
EMAIL overthelast@outlook.com WEBSITE www.overthelast.com

1 **ACROSS THE PARK (IRE)**, 6, b g Presenting—Miss Baresi (IRE) **Easylife Partnership**
2 **ALKADEMON (IRE)**, 6, br g Alkaadhem—Cats Concert (IRE) **Over The Last Racing**
3 **ATOMIC ARTICLE (IRE)**, 6, b m Vinnie Roe (IRE)—Atomic Winner (IRE) **Mrs V. W. Jones & Mr B. P. Jones**
4 **LADY WETHERED (IRE)**, 8, br m Westerner—Vics Miller (IRE) **Mr M. P. Beer**
5 **MOUNTAIN OF MOURNE (IRE)**, 11, ch g Mountain High (IRE)—Katies Native (IRE) **Over The Last Racing**

MISS LINDA BLACKFORD - continued

6 **POET'S REFLECTION (IRE)**, 5, b m Dylan Thomas (IRE)—
Lola's Reflection **Mr D. Cocks & Mrs S. Livesey-van Dorst**
7 **ROWLEY PARK (IRE)**, 7, b g Golan (IRE)—Atomic Winner (IRE) **The Rowley Partnership**
8 **ROYAL CHIEFTAIN (IRE)**, 10, b g Beneficial—Jensharandsue (IRE) **Over The Last Racing**
9 **STEEL EXPRESS (IRE)**, 8, b g Craigsteel—Assidua (IRE) **Nerves of Steel Partnership**

Other Owners: Miss L. A. Blackford, Mr D. J. Cocks, B. P. Jones, Mrs V. W. Jones, Mrs S. H. Livesey-Van Dorst, Mrs Susan Quick.

Assistant Trainer: M. J. Vanstone.

NH Jockey: James Best, Micheal Nolan, Nick Scholfield. **Conditional Jockey:** Sean Houlihan.

44

MR MICHAEL BLAKE, Trowbridge
Postal: Staverton Farm, Trowbridge, Wiltshire, BA14 6PE
Contacts: **PHONE 01225 782327 MOBILE 07971 675180**
EMAIL mblakestavertonfarm@btinternet.com **WEBSITE** www.michaelblakeracing.co.uk

1 **BOLISTER (FR)**, 9, b g Le Balafre (FR)—Girlish (FR) **G. L. Moore**
2 **BOUNTY PURSUIT**, 8, b g Pastoral Pursuits—Poyle Dee Dee **Racing For A Cause**
3 **CHAMPS DE REVES**, 5, b g Champs Elysees—Joyeaux **Staverton Owners Group**
4 **COOLE CODY (IRE)**, 9, b g Dubai Destination (USA)—Run For Cover (IRE) **H. M. W. Clifford**
5 **EXCELLENT TEAM**, 8, b g Teofilo (IRE)—Seradim **Mrs J. M. Gould**
6 **FREE GIFT**, 4, b g Makfi—Aldeburgh Music (IRE) **Mrs J. M. Gould**
7 **FREEDOM AND WHEAT (IRE)**, 4, b g Fast Company (IRE)—Rustam **Racing For A Cause**
8 **HIMEMIYA**, 7, b m Shirocco (GER)—Himitas (FR) **M. J. Blake**
9 **HURRICANE ARCADIO (IRE)**, 6, b g Arcadio (GER)—Back To Favour (IRE) **Mr A. D. Potts**
10 **INIESTA (IRE)**, 9, b g Galileo (IRE)—Red Evie (IRE) **Mrs J. M. Gould**
11 **JUST MAYBE**, 6, b g Mayson—Phantasmagoria **The Maysonettes**
12 **LOVE DREAMS (IRE)**, 6, b g Dream Ahead (USA)—Kimola (IRE) **Mr A. D. Potts**
13 **MERDON CASTLE (IRE)**, 8, b g Acclamation—Siren's Gift **West Wilts Hockey Lads**
14 **ONE BIG DREAM**, 7, b m Indian Haven—Jade Chequer **Mr C. W. G. Shields**
15 **TIS FANTASTIC (FR)**, 5, gr g Montmartre (FR)—Anadara (FR) **The Moonlighters**
16 **TRIO D'ECAJEUL (FR)**, 6, b g Diamond Boy (FR)—Daresta (FR) **West Wilts Hockey Lads**
17 **WAITINONASUNNYDAY (IRE)**, 7, gr g Tikkanen (USA)—Coppenagh Lady (IRE) **West Wilts Hockey Lads**

THREE-YEAR-OLDS

18 **MR ZEE (IRE)**, b c Zebedee—Monsusu (IRE) **H. M. W. Clifford**

Other Owners: Mr M. Borgatti, Mr R. C. Butcher, Mrs V. A. Butcher, Mr S. Moir, Mr M. Murphy.

Assistant Trainer: Sharon Blake.

45

MR MICHAEL BLANSHARD, Upper Lambourn
Postal: Lethornes Stables, Upper Lambourn, Hungerford, Berkshire, RG17 8QP
Contacts: **PHONE 01488 71091 MOBILE 07785 370093 FAX 01488 73497**
EMAIL blanshard.racing@btconnect.com **WEBSITE** www.michaelblanshard.com

1 **ACCOMPLICE**, 6, b m Sakhee's Secret—Witness **The Reignmakers**
2 **FAMOUS DYNASTY (IRE)**, 6, b g Famous Name—Daffodil Walk (IRE) **Lady E Mays Smith & Partners**
3 **MOON ARTIST (FR)**, 4, b f Archipenko (USA)—Moonavvara (IRE) **Moon Artist Partnership**
4 **MRS BENSON (IRE)**, 5, ch m Rip Van Winkle (IRE)—Ebble **The Reignmakers**
5 **PENNEYS HUN (IRE)**, 7, b g Arakan (USA)—De Street (IRE) **Lady E. Mays-Smith**
6 **VINO ROSSO (IRE)**, 4, b f Zebedee—Fonseca (IRE) **The Reignmakers**

MR MICHAEL BLANSHARD - continued

THREE-YEAR-OLDS

7 **AMERICAN PIE (IRE)**, ch f Raven's Pass (USA)—Arizona Sun (IRE) **Mr B Oakley**
8 **DILIGENT LASS**, b f Due Diligence (USA)—Sunny York (IRE) **Lady E. Mays-Smith**
9 **LA POSEUR (IRE)**, b f Camacho—Jessie K **M Blanshard & Partners**
10 **SHOWING**, ch f Showcasing—Blaugrana (IRE) **The Reignmakers**

TWO-YEAR-OLDS

11 **LADYROC**, b f 29/03 Charm Spirit (IRE)—Craighall (Dubawi (IRE)) (7500) **Mr V. G. Ward**
12 B f 26/02 Outstrip—Thiel (Teofilo (IRE)) (1000)
13 Ch f 16/04 Belardo (IRE)—Whisp (GER) (Rainbow Quest (USA)) (5000) **Kildaragh Stud**

Other Owners: Mr M. T. W. Blanshard, Mr D. Cannings, Lady E. Mays-Smith, B. Mitchell, J & S Mitchell.

---

46 **MISS GILLIAN BOANAS, Saltburn**
Postal: **Groundhill Farm, Lingdale, Saltburn-By-The-Sea, Cleveland, TS12 3HD**
Contacts: **MOBILE 07976 280154**
EMAIL gillianboanas@aol.com

1 4, B g Arcadio (GER)—Arequipa (IRE) **Miss G. L. Boanas**
2 **BABY JANE (IRE)**, 5, b m Oscar (IRE)—Young Lady (IRE) **Miss G Boanas & Mr M Foxton**
3 **BESTIARIUS (IRE)**, 8, b g Vinnie Roe (IRE)—Chione (IRE) **Rug, Grub & Pub Partnership**
4 **BROCTUNE RED**, 5, ch g Haafhd—Fairlie **Mrs M. B. Thwaites**
5 **CRIXUS'S ESCAPE (IRE)**, 7, ch g Beneficial—Tierneys Choice (IRE) **Mr R. Collins**
6 **FAME AND HOPE (IRE)**, 5, b m Fame And Glory—Kaituna (IRE) **Mr John Coates Mr Richard Smith**
7 **FLEETWOOD BLACK**, 4, b f Black Sam Bellamy (IRE)—Fleet Footed **Mrs S. Williamson**
8 **GENERALISATION (IRE)**, 7, b g Arcadio (GER)—Will She Smile (IRE) **Miss G. L. Boanas**
9 **GREAT COLACI**, 7, b g Sulamani (IRE)—Fairlie **Rug, Grub & Pub Partnership**
10 **JUST CALL ME AL (IRE)**, 7, br g Presenting—Tonaphuca Girl (IRE) **M.B.Thwaites G Boanas G Halder**
11 4, Ch g Schiaparelli (GER)—La Calinda **Tees Components Ltd**
12 **LADY VINETTA**, 5, b m Sulamani (IRE)—Vinetta **The Thoughtful Partnership**
13 **LOCH LINNHE**, 8, b g Tobougg (IRE)—Quistaquay **Miss G Boanas & Mr M Foxton**
14 **NOBEL ROSE**, 6, ch m Sholokhov (IRE)—Florarossa **Miss G. L. Boanas**
15 5, Ch m Presenting—Northern Native (IRE) **Tees Components Ltd**
16 **OLIVER'S BETTY**, 5, br m Dick Turpin (IRE)—Luck Will Come (IRE) **Miss G. L. Boanas**
17 **POUND OFF YOU**, 4, ch f Haafhd—Let It Be **Miss G. L. Boanas**
18 **SULTANS PRIDE**, 8, b g Sulamani (IRE)—Pennys Pride (IRE) **Reveley Racing 1 & Partner**
19 **SWEET VINETTA**, 6, gr m Fair Mix (IRE)—Vinetta **The Supreme Partnership**
20 **TEESCOMPONENTS LAD**, 7, b g Midnight Legend—Northern Native (IRE) **Tees Components Ltd**
21 **TEESCOMPONENTSTRIG**, 5, ch g Black Sam Bellamy (IRE)—La Calinda **Tees Components Ltd**
22 **TEESCOMPONENTSYESS (IRE)**, 4, b g Shirocco (GER)—Northern Native (IRE) **Tees Components Ltd**
23 4, B f Milan—Young Lady (IRE) **Miss G. L. Boanas**

Other Owners: Miss G. L. Boanas, J. W. Coates, M. E. Foxton, D. A. Green, Mr G. S. Halder, Mr K. S. Matthews, Reveley Farms, Reveley Racing 1, R. V. Smith, Mrs M. B. Thwaites.

---

47 **MRS MYRIAM BOLLACK-BADEL, Chantilly-Lamorlaye**
Postal: **20 Rue Blanche, 60260 Lamorlaye, France**
Contacts: **HOME +33 3 44 21 33 67 MOBILE +33 6 10 80 93 47 FAX +33 3 44 21 33 67**
EMAIL myriam.bollack@gmail.com

1 **ARDEATINA**, 5, ch m Harbour Watch (IRE)—May West **F. de Chatelperron**
2 **AVEC LAURA**, 7, ch h Manduro (GER)—Sign of Life **Mme M. Bollack-Badel**
3 **GLORIA**, 5, gr m Showcasing—Go East (GER) **Philippe Ezri**
4 **GOUREL (FR)**, 6, b g Le Havre (IRE)—Racemate **Philippe Ezri**
5 **GREEN SIREN (FR)**, 4, ch f Siyouni (FR)—Green Speed (FR) **J. C. Smith**

MRS MYRIAM BOLLACK-BADEL - continued

6 **NI CHAUD NI FROID (FR)**, 4, ch f Norse Dancer (IRE)—Numerologie (FR) **Alain Badel**
7 **PRINCE KERALI (FR)**, 4, b g Sinndar (IRE)—Perpetual Glory **Ecurie Noel Forgeard**
8 **SINGSTREET (FR)**, 4, b g Evasive—Sinnderelle (FR) **Ecurie Noel Forgeard**

THREE-YEAR-OLDS

9 **ARGENTINE (FR)**, ch f Rio de La Plata (USA)—Albicocca (FR) **Mr Patrick Fellous**
10 **BOUMA (FR)**, b f Motivator—Wild Guest **Oscar Ortmans**
11 **BOUMMA DREAM**, b f Charm Spirit (IRE)—Holy Moly (USA) **Oscar Ortmans**
12 **DADAISTE (FR)**, b f Dabirsim (FR)—Summer Wave (IRE) **Meta Cantillon**
13 **DARE**, b f Bated Breath—Heronetta **Oscar Ortmans**
14 **GREEN SPIRIT (FR)**, b g Charm Spirit (IRE)—Green Speed (FR) **J. C. Smith**
15 **HANZI BELINE (FR)**, gr f Zanzibari (USA)—Hold The Thought **Benoit Chalmel**
16 **PASSEFONTAINE (FR)**, b f Wootton Bassett—Perpetual Glory **Ecurie Noel Forgeard**
17 Gr f Outstrip—Rancho Montoya (USA) **Oscar Ortmans**
18 **REPENTIR**, b f Roderic O'Connor (IRE)—Miaplacidus (IRE) **Mme M. Bollack-Badel**
19 **ROYALE OFFENSE (IRE)**, ch f Al Kazeem—Tete Orange **Benoit Chalmel**
20 **SALINAS GRANDE (FR)**, b f Muhtathir—Sinnderelle (FR) **Ecurie Noel Forgeard**
21 **SOUNDPROOF (FR)**, b f Norse Dancer (IRE)—Speed of Sound **J. C. Smith**
22 **SUPERIOR BADOLAT (IRE)**, gr c Dark Angel (IRE)—Royal Fortune (IRE) **Geoffroy Herber-Suffrin**
23 **UM ALJADEELA (IRE)**, b f Iffraaj—Ajaadat **Philippe Stein**
24 **WING DANCER (FR)**, b f Norse Dancer (IRE)—Angel Wing **J. C. Smith**
25 **ZELOTE (FR)**, b g Literato (FR)—Zython **Ecurie Noel Forgeard**

TWO-YEAR-OLDS

26 B f 07/03 Marcel (IRE)—Ayun (USA) (Swain (IRE)) (3000) **Oscar Ortmans**
27 **COGOLIN (FR)**, ch c 18/04 Goken (FR)—Albicocca (FR) (Naaqoos) **Mr Patrick Fellous**
28 **GREEN GLORY (FR)**, b c 06/04 Olympic Glory (IRE)—Green Speed (FR) (Green Tune (USA)) **J. C. Smith**
29 **MOVING FLAME**, b c 25/02 Motivator—Elusive Flame (Elusive City (USA)) **J. C. Smith**
30 **PHEDRE (FR)**, b f 22/03 Myboycharlie—Perpetual Glory (Dansili) **Ecurie Noel Forgeard**
31 **ZYGFRYD (FR)**, ch c 17/04 Literato (FR)—Zython (FR) (Kabool) **Zygfryd Partnership**

Assistant Trainer: Alain Badel, **Head Girl:** Mrs Laura Martaud, **Travelling Head:** Mr Philippe Celier.

Flat Jockey: Alexis Badel.

48

MR MARTIN BOSLEY, Chalfont St Giles
Postal: **Bowstridge Farm, Bowstridge Lane, Chalfont St. Giles, Buckinghamshire, HP8 4RF**
Contacts: **PHONE 01494 875533 MOBILE 07778 938040**
EMAIL **martin@martinbosley.com WEBSITE www.martinbosleyracing.com**

1 **ASSEMBLED**, 4, gr g Iffraaj—Bezique **Ms J. Williams**
2 **CATHEADANS FIYAH**, 4, b f Firebreak—Dualagi **Bayard Racing**
3 **CATHEADANS FURY**, 6, ch m Firebreak—Dualagi **M.A.S.A.**
4 **CHAMPION CHASE (FR)**, 8, b g Voix du Nord (FR)—Darling Frisco (FR) **Mr M. R. Bosley**
5 **EXCEEDING POWER**, 9, b g Exceed And Excel (AUS)—Extreme Beauty (USA) **The Chalfonts**
6 **FRONT FIVE (IRE)**, 8, b g Teofilo (IRE)—Samdaniya **M.A.S.A.**
7 **KARALIUS (NZ)**, 5, b g Cape Blanco (IRE)—Imbudo (AUS) **Mr D. Stenning**
8 **MIDNIGHT JITTERBUG**, 8, b g Midnight Legend—Heebie Jeebie **Mrs E. A. Prowting**
9 **NAWAR**, 5, b g Henrythenavigator (USA)—Nouriya **Quartet Racing**
10 **NORSE CASTLE**, 7, b g Norse Dancer (IRE)—Hursley Hope (IRE) **M.A.S.A.**
11 **OLYMPIC LEGEND (IRE)**, 6, ch g Choisir (AUS)—Margaret's Dream (IRE) **M.A.S.A.**
12 **VEGAS BOY (IRE)**, 5, ch g Society Rock (IRE)—Consensus (IRE) **N Bashir, N Dearman & R Ridout**
13 **ZEFFERINO**, 6, ch g Frankel—Turama **J. Carey**

THREE-YEAR-OLDS

14 B g Delegator—Dualagi **Bayard Racing**
15 **LOVE MY LIFE (IRE)**, ch f Ivawood (IRE)—Cradle Brief (IRE) **Mr N. W. Dearman, Mr N. Bashir, Mr R. J. Ridout**

MR MARTIN BOSLEY - continued

TWO-YEAR-OLDS

16 SENNEN, b c 24/04 Outstrip—Makara (Lion Cavern (USA)) (4000) **Mr M. J. Watson**

Other Owners: Mr N. Bashir, G Carson, Mr N. W. Dearman, F Hazeldine, Mr R. J. Ridout, V Weatherley, M West, K Whitaker.

49	**MR MARCO BOTTI, Newmarket**

Postal: **Prestige Place, Snailwell Road, Newmarket, Suffolk, CB8 7DP**
Contacts: **PHONE 01638 662416 MOBILE 07775 803007 FAX 01638 662417**
EMAIL office@marcobotti.co.uk WEBSITE www.marcobotti.co.uk

1 **ALJARI**, 4, b c Quality Road (USA)—Rhagori **Mr R. El Youssef**
2 **BIG DADDY KANE**, 4, b g Sea The Moon (GER)—Soft Morning **K. Sohi & Partners**
3 **CASINA DI NOTTE (IRE)**, 6, ch g Casamento (IRE)—Nightswimmer (IRE) **Mrs L. Botti**
4 **CROWNED EAGLE**, 6, b g Oasis Dream—Gull Wing (IRE) **Excel Racing & Les Boyer**
5 **EXCEED LOOSE**, 4, b f Exceed And Excel (AUS)—Killachy Loose **K Sohi & Partner**
6 **FARES POET (IRE)**, 4, b c Poet's Voice—Moon Over Water (IRE) **Mr W. Moraes**
7 **FELIX**, 4, ch g Lope de Vega (IRE)—Luminance (IRE) **K Sohi & Partner**
8 **FUTURISTIC (IRE)**, 4, b g Shamardal (USA)—Aqlaam Vision **Mr Manfredini & Partner**
9 **GEIZY TEIZY (IRE)**, 4, b f Lawman (FR)—For Joy **Nick Bradley Racing 30 & Sohi & Partner**
10 **GUROOR**, 4, ch f Lope de Vega (IRE)—Shalwa **Fabfive**
11 **INTELDREAM**, 4, b g Intello (GER)—Libys Dream (IRE) **Fabfive**
12 **KYLLACHY GALA**, 7, b g Kyllachy—Tenuta di Gala (IRE) **Excel Racing**
13 **LATIN KNIGHT**, 4, b g Sea The Stars (IRE)—Latin Love (IRE) **Heart of the South Racing 112**
14 **PERFECIMPERFECTION (IRE)**, 4, b f Camelot—Sunbird **Mr R Bruni & Partner**
15 **SERAPHIM**, 4, gr f Dark Angel (IRE)—Moma Lee **Excel Racing & Partner**
16 **SWEET CELEBRATION (IRE)**, 4, b f Exceleration (IRE)—Snow Dust **MPR, Ventura Racing 5 & Partner**
17 **UNDERCOLOURS (IRE)**, 4, b g Exceleration (IRE)—Puddles (FR) **Fabfive**
18 **WAIT FOREVER (IRE)**, 5, b h Camelot—Mount McLeod (IRE) **Mr R Bruni & Partner**
19 **WILLKOMMEN**, 4, b c Epaulette (AUS)—Weeza (IRE) **Mrs L. Botti**
20 **YIMKIN (IRE)**, 4, b f Kingman—Orpha **Promenade Bloodstock Limited**

THREE-YEAR-OLDS

21 **AL HURR**, b c Muhaarar—Mensoora (SAF) **Sheikh M. B. K. Al Maktoum**
22 **AMICIA**, ch f Camacho—Fiancee (IRE) **O'Connell, Saveall-Green, Regan, James 1**
23 **BADREPUTATION**, b g Iffraaj—Cats Eyes **Mr Manfredini & Partner**
24 **BATCHELOR BOY (IRE)**, ch c Footstepsinthesand—Kathoe (IRE) **Middleham Park Racing CXX & Partner 1**
25 **BUZZTOTHEMOON**, ch c Dandy Man (IRE)—Luna Mission (IRE) **Mr J. Allison**
26 **CIPANGO**, b c Dutch Art—Poppets Sweetlove **Mr A. Hakam**
27 **DARK SCIMITAR (USA)**, b br c Verrazano (USA)—Don't Stop to Shop (USA) **Marrone de Bianco Partnership 1**
28 **DIMA**, b f Declaration of War (USA)—Lady Nouf **Mr I. H. Al Sagar**
29 **DONO**, b g Mayson—Dan Loose Daughter **Scuderia Blueberry S.R.L. & Partner 2**
30 **ELAS GIRL**, b f Golden Horn—Elas Diamond **Newsells Park Stud Limited**
31 **ENDURED (IRE)**, b c Shamardal (USA)—Wadaat **Mr B. C. M. Wong**
32 **FAIR MAN**, b c Kingman—Fair Dubawi (IRE) **Scuderia Blueberry SRL**
33 **FAIRMET**, b f Helmet (AUS)—Fairdal **Scuderia Blueberry SRL**
34 **FAIRY LACHY**, b f Kyllachy—Fairy Oasis **Scuderia Blueberry SRL**
35 **FOLLIA**, b f Toronado (IRE)—Filona (IRE) **Scuderia Blueberry SRL**
36 **GLADICE**, b f Intello (GER)—Amurra **Mr I. H. Al Sagar**
37 **GLITTER QUEEN**, b f Night of Thunder (IRE)—Ile Flottante **Scuderia Effevi SRL**
38 **HABIT ROUGE**, b c Helmet (AUS)—Hurricane Harriet **Ambrosiana Racing & Partner**
39 **HARBOUR OF GRACE (FR)**, b f Le Havre (IRE)—Dalamar **Eclipse Thoroughbred Partners**
40 **INNER TREASURES**, b c Gleneagles (IRE)—Native Picture (IRE) **Aldo E Carlo Borsani Snc 1**
41 **KING CHARLES (USA)**, b c Lemon Drop Kid (USA)—
La Reine Lionne (USA) **The Honorable Earle I. Mack & Partner**
42 **LADY DE VEGA**, b f Lope de Vega (IRE)—Red Boots (IRE) **Heart of the South Racing 115 & Partner**
43 **LADY RED MOON**, b f Havana Gold (IRE)—Sparkling Montjeu (IRE) **Mr Giulio Spozio & Partner**
44 **LETHAL SHADOW**, b g Lethal Force (IRE)—Danehill Shadow (IRE) **Scuderia Blueberry S.R.L. & Partner 2**

MR MARCO BOTTI - continued

45 **LYRICIST VOICE,** b c Poet's Voice—Lyricist **Les Boyer Partnership**
46 **MADE IN ITALY (IRE),** b f Mukhadram—Delicatezza **Ambrosiana Racing & Les Boyer**
47 **MALOTRU,** b c Casamento (IRE)—Magika **The Honorable Earle I. Mack & Les Boyer**
48 **NO NAY BELLA (IRE),** b f No Nay Never (USA)—

                       Illuminating Dream (IRE) **Middleham Park Racing CXXI & Partners**
49 **PRESIDENTIAL SWEET (ITY),** b f Golden Horn—Biz Bar **Mr Giovanni Parri & Patner**
50 **PRETTY IN GREY,** gr f Brazen Beau (AUS)—Maglietta Fina (IRE) **Scuderia Archi Romani**
51 **PROMISES (IRE),** b f Bated Breath—Symposia
52 **PROSILI (IRE),** b f Dansili—Propaganda (IRE) **Mr W. Moraes**
53 **SETTIMA LUNA,** ch f Roderic O'Connor (IRE)—Donatia **Mr Giulio Spozio & Partner**
54 **SILVER SAMURAI,** gr c Cable Bay (IRE)—High Tan **What A Time To Be Alive 1**
55 **SKY LAKE (GER),** b f Dabirsim (FR)—Salona (GER) **Scuderia Archi Romani & Partner**
56 **VERTICE (IRE),** ch f Toronado (IRE)—Asima (IRE) **Sheikh K. A. I. S. Al Khalifa**
57 **WAILEA NIGHTS (IRE),** br f Lawman (FR)—Jersey Brown (IRE) **Sheikh K. A. I. S. Al Khalifa**
58 **ZERO LIMITS,** gr g Outstrip—Mpumalanga **Milan Racing Club 1**

TWO-YEAR-OLDS

59 Ch c 15/02 Speightster (USA)—Allerton (USA) (Cape Blanco (IRE)) **Prestige Five**
60 B c 30/04 Mshawish (USA)—Alpaca Fina (CAN) (Big Brown (USA)) **Prestige Five**
61 B c 08/03 Flintshire—Amurmar (IRE) (Galileo (IRE)) **A J Suited Partnership**
62 **ATALIS BAY,** b c 30/03 Cable Bay (IRE)—Atalis (Holy Roman Emperor (IRE)) (800) **Scuderia Blueberry SRL**
63 B c 23/04 Dawn Approach (IRE)—Badalona (Cape Cross (IRE)) (20000)
64 **CAPTAIN HELMET,** ch c 01/04 Helmet (AUS)—Captain Secret (Captain Gerrard (IRE)) **Scuderia Blueberry SRL**
65 **CASSOWARY (IRE),** ch f 10/02 Australia—Arose (Fastnet Rock (AUS)) (12870) **Saveall Green & James 1**
66 Gr c 07/02 Lope de Vega (IRE)—Claba di San Jore (IRE) (Barathea (IRE)) (100000) **Mr P. Hunt**
67 B c 05/04 Swiss Spirit—Dubawi's Spirit (FR) (Dubawi (IRE)) (12380)
68 B c 14/04 Fastnet Rock (AUS)—Gerika (FR) (Galileo (IRE)) (55770) **La Tesa SPA**
69 B f 15/02 Showcasing—Heavenly Scent (Galileo (IRE)) (25000)
70 **LADY ARGENTO (IRE),** b f 18/02 Australia—Cronsa (GER) (Martino Alonso (IRE)) (68640) **La Tesa SPA**
71 B f 03/04 Adaay (IRE)—Letterfromamerica (USA) (Ghostzapper (USA)) (16190)
72 B c 23/04 Estidhkaar (IRE)—Luvmedo (IRE) (One Cool Cat (USA)) (25714)
73 Ch f 03/05 Territories (IRE)—Mail Express (IRE) (Cape Cross (IRE)) (14000) **Scuderia Archi Romani**
74 B c 08/03 Exceed And Excel (AUS)—Moon Over Water (IRE) (Galileo (IRE)) (62000) **Mr R. Al Kamda**
75 **NIGHT FORCE (IRE),** gr c 08/03 Dark Angel (IRE)—

                       Sleeping Beauty (IRE) (Oasis Dream) (11000) **Mr Abbas Alalawi & Partner**
76 B br f 20/03 Invincible Spirit (IRE)—Polygon (USA) (Dynaformer (USA)) (40000) **Mrs E. Adamski**
77 B br c 14/04 Helmet (AUS)—Ruffled (Harlan's Holiday (USA)) **Mr C. J. Murfitt & Partner**
78 B c 23/03 Fastnet Rock (AUS)—Shalwa (Galileo (IRE)) (6000)
79 Ch f 26/03 Exceed And Excel (AUS)—Sky Crystal (GER) (Galileo (IRE)) (150000) **London Calling Syndicate**
80 **TRICOLORE (ITY),** b c 15/02 Twilight Son—Tribulina (Dansili) (12870) **La Tesa Spa & Partner**
81 Ch c 13/03 Twilight Son—Wakeup Little Suzy (IRE) (Peintre Celebre (USA)) (42000) **Mr E. Elhrari**
82 Ch c 28/03 Mehmas (IRE)—Yasmeena (USA) (Mr Greeley (USA)) (24024)
83 B c 03/03 Pride of Dubai (AUS)—Yeah Baby (IRE) (Danehill Dancer (IRE)) (28571)
84 **ZAURAK,** b f 22/03 Zoffany (IRE)—Pursuitofthestars (IRE) (Sea The Stars (IRE)) (25000)

Other Owners: Mrs E. Adamski, Mrs E. Agostini, Mr P. Agostini, Mr A. Alalawi, Ambrosiana Racing, Mr C. Austin, Mr A. Baragiola, Miss E. M. Baragiola, Miss E. M. Baragiola, Mr L. Biffi, Mrs L. Botti, Mr N. Bradley, Mr R. Bruni, Mr T. Denham, Mr A. J. Driver, Excel Racing, Mr P. Fisher, Mrs E. F. Harte, Heart of the South Racing 115, Miss S. Holden, Mr J. G. James, La Tesa SPA, Les Boyer Partnership, E. I. Mack, Mr G. Manfredini, Marrone de Bianco Partnership, Middleham Park Racing CXX, Middleham Park Racing CXXI, Middleham Park and Ventura Racing 5, Milan Racing Club, Mr C. J. Murfitt, Nick Bradley Racing 30, Mr M. A. O'Connell, O'Connell, Saveall-Green, Regan, James, T. S. Palin, Dr G. Parri, Mr R. B. Patel, M. Prince, Mr G. Saveall-Green, Saveall-Green & James, Scuderia Archi Romani, Scuderia Blueberry SRL, Mr K. Sohi, Mr G. G. S. Spozio, What A Time To Be Alive.

Assistant Trainer: Alberto Baragiola, Lucie Botti.

Apprentice Jockey: Stefano Cherchi.

50 | MR GEORGE BOUGHEY, Newmarket
Postal: Flat 3 The Gallops, Old Station Road, Newmarket , Suffolk, CB8 8LA
Contacts: **PHONE 07765 132508**
EMAIL george@georgeboughey.com

1 **ABSOLUTIO (FR)**, 4, b g Kendargent (FR)—La Joie (FR)
2 **COTTON CLUB (IRE)**, 9, b g Amadeus Wolf—Slow Jazz (USA)
3 **INVOLVED**, 5, b g Havana Gold (IRE)—Trick Or Treat
4 **JACK BERRY HOUSE**, 4, b g Harbour Watch (IRE)—Dularame (IRE)
5 **SONGKRAN (IRE)**, 4, b g Slade Power (IRE)—Choose Me (IRE)
6 **THREE C'S (IRE)**, 6, b g Kodiac—Ms Mary C (IRE)

THREE-YEAR-OLDS
7 **ARCTIC VICTORY (IRE)**, b f Ivawood (IRE)—Impressive Victory (USA)
8 **BALTIC WOLVE**, b g Australia—Baltic Comtesse (FR)
9 Ch g Mukhadram—Blossom Mills
10 **LUA DE MEL (IRE)**, b f Casamento (IRE)—Selfara

TWO-YEAR-OLDS
11 **ASTIMEGOESBY**, ch c 14/02 Mehmas (IRE)—Chantaleen (FR) (Falco (USA)) (38095)
12 Ch c 15/04 Toronado (IRE)—Blossom Mills (Bahamian Bounty) (36000)
13 B f 20/01 Oasis Dream—Julia Dream (Montjeu (IRE))
14 B f 02/03 Adaay (IRE)—Khaki (IRE) (Key of Luck (USA)) (21449)
15 B c 07/02 Ivawood (IRE)—Lady Lizabeth (IRE) (Lord Shanakill (USA)) (11153)
16 Ch f 01/04 Equiano (FR)—Mi Rubina (IRE) (Rock of Gibraltar (IRE))
17 **MIRAGE MAC**, ch f 17/04 Bobby's Kitten (USA)—Megachurch (USA) (Pulpit (USA)) (22000)
18 Ch f 19/04 Australia—Queens Park (FR) (King's Best (USA)) (33000)
19 B c 12/03 Pride of Dubai (AUS)—Stunned Silence (USA) (Officer (USA)) (9437)
20 B f 11/04 Starspangledbanner (AUS)—Sugar Hiccup (IRE) (Refuse To Bend (IRE)) (14000)
21 Ch c 25/03 The Last Lion (IRE)—Three Times (Bahamian Bounty) (15872)

51 | MR DARAGH BOURKE, Lockerbie
Postal: Cherrybank, Waterbeck, Lockerbie, Dumfries and Galloway, DG11 3EY
Contacts: **MOBILE 07495 948493**

1 **ALLTHATGLISTENS (IRE)**, 7, b m Gold Well—Avenging Angel (IRE) **Mrs L. J. McLeod**
2 **COLORADO GOLD**, 7, ch m Beat Hollow—Crevamoy (IRE) **Distillery Racing Club**
3 **GALLAHERS CROSS (IRE)**, 8, b g Getaway (GER)—Raheen Lady (IRE) **Mr L. Schwartz**
4 **GOLDEN CHANCER**, 6, b g Gold Well—Princess Oriane (IRE) **Mr S. Lowther**
5 **LOSTOCK HALL (IRE)**, 8, b g Lord Shanakill (USA)—Cannikin (IRE) **Mrs L. J. McLeod**
6 **METRO BOULOT DODO (IRE)**, 7, br g Robin des Champs (FR)—Lizzy Langtry (IRE) **Mrs K. Cole**
7 **MISTER FLEMINGTON (IRE)**, 9, ch g Flemensfirth (USA)—Deep Supreme (IRE) **Mr A. Kanji**
8 **OLD JEWRY (IRE)**, 6, b g Le Fou (IRE)—Clerken Bridge (IRE) **Mr A. Kanji**
9 **OUR LUCAS (IRE)**, 8, b br g Jeremy (USA)—Alassio (USA) **M. Sawers**
10 **PADDY MELIA (IRE)**, 8, b g Generous (USA)—Corcullentra Lass (IRE) **Cherrybank Crusaders**
11 **PADDY THE PANDA (IRE)**, 5, b g Flemensfirth (USA)—Pandorama Lady (IRE) **Mr S. Lowther**
12 **PADS (IRE)**, 10, b br g Luso—Augusta Victoria **Mr S. Lowther**
13 **SALTMARKET (IRE)**, 5, b g Multiplex—Kiera Marie (IRE) **M. Sawers**
14 **TRONGATE (IRE)**, 8, b g Dansant—Val Eile (IRE) **M. Sawers**

Other Owners: A. B. Graham.

52 MR PETER BOWEN, Haverfordwest
Postal: Yet-Y-Rhug, Letterston, Haverfordwest, Pembrokeshire, SA62 5TB
Contacts: PHONE 01348 840486 MOBILE 07811 111234 FAX 01348 840486
EMAIL info@peterbowenracing.co.uk WEBSITE www.peterbowenracing.co.uk

1 ALF 'N' DOR (IRE), 9, ch g Flemensfirth (USA)—Greenflag Princess (IRE) **The Hedonists & Karen Bowen**
2 APPLE BANK, 6, b m Apple Tree (FR)—Elfailwen **J. C. De Lisle Wells**
3 ATOMIC RUMBLE (IRE), 7, b g Oscar (IRE)—Atomic Betty (IRE) **Mr C. B. Compton & Mrs Karen Bowen**
4 BEGGAR'S WISHES (IRE), 9, b g Oscar (IRE)—Strong Wishes (IRE) **Roddy Owen & Paul Fullagar**
5 COLBY (IRE), 7, b g Witness Box (USA)—Wet And Dry (IRE) **Patrick/unsworth**
6 COUGAR'S GOLD (IRE), 9, b g Oscar (IRE)—Top Her Up (IRE) **Mr W. E. V. Harries**
7 CRUISING BYE, 14, b g Alflora (IRE)—Althrey Flame (IRE) **F. Lloyd**
8 DALKINGSTOWN, 6, ch g Malinas (GER)—True Rose (IRE) **Roddy Owen & Paul Fullagar**
9 DR ROBIN (IRE), 10, b g Robin des Pres (FR)—Inter Alia (IRE) **Peter Bowen Racing Club**
10 DRIFT ROCK, 6, ch g Malinas (GER)—Araucaria (IRE) **Amanda & Patrick Bancroft**
11 EQUUS DANCER (IRE), 6, b g Jeremy (USA)—Celtic Cailin (IRE) **Roddy Owen & Paul Fullagar**
12 FAIR EXCHANGE (IRE), 10, ch g Beneficial—Kazan Lady (IRE) **Mr G. W. Briscoe**
13 FRANCKY DU BERLAIS (FR), 7, b g Saint des Saints (FR)—Legende du Luy (FR) **Roddy Owen & Paul Fullagar**
14 GENERAL MALARKEY (IRE), 8, b g Scorpion (IRE)—Andreas Benefit (IRE) **Baker, Dodd, Cooke & Heler**
15 GET AN OSCAR (IRE), 6, ch m Getaway (GER)—Lady Perspex (IRE) **Peter Bowen Racing Club**
16 HIGHWAY STAR (FR), 8, b g Vision d'Etat (FR)—Lyli Rose (FR) **Mr A. R. E. Morgan**
17 LANDOFSMILES (IRE), 7, b g Beneficial—Sadie Supreme (IRE) **Miss Jayne Brace & Mr Gwyn Brace**
18 LEAVING HOME (IRE), 7, b g Getaway (GER)—Snuff (FR) **Mrs N. Unsworth**
19 LERMOOS LEGEND, 5, b g Midnight Legend—Absalom's Girl **Mr J. A. Martin**
20 LORD BRYAN (IRE), 9, b g Brian Boru—Run Cat (IRE) **Miss Jayne Brace & Mr Gwyn Brace**
21 LORD NAPIER (IRE), 7, b g Galileo (IRE)—Jacqueline (IND) **F. Lloyd**
22 MAC TOTTIE, 7, b g Midnight Legend—Tot of The Knar **Steve & Jackie Fleetham**
23 4, B g Ballingarry (IRE)—Milutonga Has (FR) **Mrs K. Bowen**
24 MINELLA DADDY (IRE), 10, b g Flemensfirth (USA)—Old Moon (IRE) **Roddy Owen & Paul Fullagar**
25 MO TOTTIE, 6, b m Midnight Legend—Tot of The Knar **Steve & Jackie Fleetham**
26 MON ELDORADO (FR), 8, b g Gentlewave (IRE)—Miryea (FR) **Mr M. B. Bowen**
27 MONTANNA, 6, ch g Notnowcato—Asi (USA) **F. Lloyd**
28 MORE BUCK'S (IRE), 10, ch g Presenting—Buck's Blue (FR) **P Duffy, D Semmens, V Williams & M Bowen**
29 NO QUARTER ASKED (IRE), 5, b g Jeremy (USA)—Louis's Teffia (IRE) **Roddy Owen & Paul Fullagar**
30 ONTOPOFTHEWORLD (IRE), 11, ch g Desert King (IRE)—Zaffre (IRE) **Saith O Ni & Karen Bowen**
31 ORSINO (IRE), 6, b g Galileo (IRE)—Birmanie (USA) **Peter Bowen Racing Club**
32 ROOSTER COGBURN (IRE), 7, b g Westerner—Hollygrove (IRE) **G. J. Morris**
33 SOURIYAN (FR), 9, b g Alhaarth (IRE)—Serasana **G. J. Morris**
34 STATUARIO, 5, b g Helmet (AUS)—Cat Hunter **Mrs N. Unsworth**
35 5, B m Getaway (GER)—Top Nurse (IRE) **Mrs K. Bowen**
36 WELLS DE LUNE (FR), 9, b g Irish Wells (FR)—Pepite de Lune (FR) **The Smith Swinburne Partnership**

Other Owners: Mr J. B. Baker, Mrs A. Bancroft, P. A. Bancroft, Mrs M. B. G. Bowen, Mrs K. Bowen, Mr M. B. Bowen, D. G. Brace, Miss M. J. Brace, Mr C. B. Compton, Mr P. G. Cooke, Mr G. T. G. Dodd, Mr D. P. Duffy, Paul Duffy, David Semmens, Viv Williams, P. G. Fullagar, Mr M. J. Heler, R. R. Owen, Mrs V. J. Patrick, B. S. Port, S. D. Reeve, Mr D. M. Semmens, D. A. Smith, R. D. J. Swinburne, The Hedonists, Mrs N. Unsworth.

Assistant Trainer: Karen Bowen, Michael Bowen.

NH Jockey: James Bowen, Sean Bowen.

53 MR ROY BOWRING, Edwinstowe
Postal: Fir Tree Farm, Edwinstowe, Mansfield, Nottinghamshire, NG21 9JG
Contacts: PHONE 01623 822451 MOBILE 07973 712942
EMAIL srbowring@outlook.com

1 ABOUT GLORY, 6, b g Nayef (USA)—Lemon Rock **S. R. Bowring**
2 DECISION MAKER (IRE), 6, b g Iffraaj—Consensus (IRE) **K. Nicholls**
3 FIRST EXCEL, 8, ch g First Trump—Exceedingly Good (IRE) **S. R. Bowring**
4 FOOLAAD, 9, ch g Exceed And Excel (AUS)—Zayn Zen **K. Nicholls**
5 JEANS MAITE, 4, b f Burwaaz—Misu's Maite **S. R. Bowring**

54 **MR JIM BOYLE, Epsom**
Postal: South Hatch Stables, Burgh Heath Road, Epsom, Surrey, KT17 4LX
Contacts: WORK 07719 554147 MOBILE 07719 554147
WORK EMAIL info@jamesboyle.co.uk HOME EMAIL Jimboyle17@hotmail.com
EMAIL pippaboyle@hotmail.com WEBSITE www.jamesboyle.co.uk

1 **AMARETTO**, 5, b g Kyllachy—Dan Loose Daughter **A. B. Pope**
2 **BECKY SHARP**, 5, b m Foxwedge (AUS)—Perfect Practice **Harrier Racing 1**
3 **CRISTAL SPIRIT**, 5, b g Nathaniel (IRE)—Celestial Girl **Reynolds Farm Syndicate**
4 **DESERT LAND (IRE)**, 4, b g Kodiac—La Chicana (IRE)
5 **EXEC CHEF (IRE)**, 5, ch g Exceleration (IRE)—Donnelly's Hollow (IRE) **Inside Track Racing Club**
6 **FANNY CHENAL**, 4, b f Kodiac—Maakrah **Mr H. E. Wigan**
7 **GIBRALTARIAN (IRE)**, 4, b f War Command (USA)—Star of Gibraltar **Mr D. A. Poole**
8 **HARROGATE (IRE)**, 5, br g Society Rock (IRE)—Invincible Me (IRE) **Goff, Walsh & Zerdin**
9 **HATEYA (IRE)**, 5, b m Footstepsinthesand—Selfsame (USA) **Inside Track Racing Club**
10 **ISLE OF WOLVES**, 4, b g Nathaniel (IRE)—L'Ile Aux Loups (IRE) **Inside Track Racing Club**
11 **LEROY LEROY**, 4, b g Compton Place—Small Fortune **The 'In Recovery' Partnership**
12 **PEACE PREVAILS**, 5, ch m Declaration of War (USA)—Miss Mediator (USA) **Mr M. Aljoe**
13 **SHINING**, 4, b f Lethal Force (IRE)—Spring Clean (FR) **The Clean Sweep Partnership**

THREE-YEAR-OLDS

14 **ANGELS ROC**, b g Roderic O'Connor (IRE)—Divine Pamina (IRE) **Sir D. J. Prosser**
15 **BAD COMPANY**, b g Fast Company (IRE)—Clearing **The Clean Sweep Partnership**
16 **BEAT THE HEAT**, b g Hot Streak (IRE)—Touriga **Inside Track Racing Club**
17 **BONUS**, b g Roderic O'Connor (IRE)—Spring Clean (FR) **The Clean Sweep Partnership**
18 **PURE PURFECTION (IRE)**, b f Dream Ahead (USA)—Rose of Africa (IRE) **Maid In Heaven Partnership**
19 **RHYTHMIC MOTION**, ch f Toronado (IRE)—Sonnetation (IRE) **The 'In Recovery' Partnership**
20 **SLAVONIC DANCE (IRE)**, b c Muhaarar—Najam
21 **SPREADSHEET (IRE)**, b g Exceed And Excel (AUS)—Mundana (IRE) **Reynolds Farm Syndicate**

TWO-YEAR-OLDS

22 **AVENTURINA**, b f 14/02 Charming Thought—Clearing (Sleeping Indian)
23 B c 14/02 Fast Company (IRE)—Hawk Dance (IRE) (Hawk Wing (USA)) (14000)
24 B c 14/03 Le Havre (IRE)—Sea The Sun (GER) (Sea The Stars (IRE)) (80000)
25 B c 24/03 Mukhadram—Spring Clean (FR) (Danehill (USA)) **The Clean Sweep Partnership**

---

55 **MR RICHARD BRABAZON, Curragh**
Postal: Rangers Lodge, The Curragh, Co. Kildare, R56 Y443, Ireland
Contacts: MOBILE +353 87 251 5626
EMAIL richardbrabazon@eircom.net WEBSITE www.richardbrabazon.ie

1 **HAYYEL (IRE)**, 5, b m Dark Angel (IRE)—Ravissante (IRE) **Celbridge Estates**
2 **RUNNING WAVE (IRE)**, 4, b f Big Bad Bob (IRE)—Flowing Air (IRE) **Richard Brabazon**
3 **SON AND SANNIE (IRE)**, 4, b g Es Que Love (IRE)—Anamundi **Leon Carrick & John Collins**

THREE-YEAR-OLDS

4 **PIRATE LASS (IRE)**, b f Born To Sea (IRE)—Grand Treasure (IRE) **Cafe Du Journal Syndicate**

---

56 **MR DAVID BRACE, Bridgend**
Postal: Llanmihangel Farm, Pyle, Bridgend, Mid Glamorgan, CF33 6RL
Contacts: PHONE 01656 742313

1 **BRACHO**, 8, b g Dr Massini (IRE)—Branston Lily **Mr D. Brace**
2 **COLORADO DOC**, 9, b g Dr Massini (IRE)—First Royal (GER) **Mr D. Brace**
3 **DELKANTRA (IRE)**, 10, b g Putra Pekan—Delheim (IRE) **Mr D. Brace**

MR DAVID BRACE - continued

4 **DON'T LAUGH AT ME,** 5, b g Schiaparelli (GER)—Nurse Brace **Mr D. Brace**
5 **GATS AND CO,** 5, b g Dr Massini (IRE)—Vineuil (FR) **Mr D. Brace**
6 **PATSIO (IRE),** 12, b g Moscow Society (USA)—Supreme Favour (IRE) **Mr D. Brace**
7 **PINK EYED PEDRO,** 9, b g Dr Massini (IRE)—Poacher's Paddy (IRE) **Mr D. Brace**
8 **QUICK N' EASY (IRE),** 10, ch g Vertical Speed (FR)—Tarmons Duchess (IRE) **Mr D. Brace**
9 **RASASEE (IRE),** 7, gr g Rip Van Winkle (IRE)—Gleaming Silver (IRE) **Mr D. Brace**
10 **WILLIAM MONEY (IRE),** 13, b g Cloudings (IRE)—All of A Kind (IRE) **Mr D. Brace**
11 **WITCHDOCTOR,** 5, b g Dr Massini (IRE)—Commanche Token (IRE) **Mr D. Brace**

Assistant Trainer: Robbie Llewellyn.

Conditional Jockey: Connor Brace.

---

57 MR MILTON BRADLEY, Chepstow
Postal: **Meads Farm, Sedbury Park, Chepstow, Gwent, NP16 7HN**
Contacts: **PHONE 01291 622486 FAX 01291 626939**

1 **ALFIE'S ANGEL (IRE),** 6, b g Dark Angel (IRE)—Penolva (IRE) E. A. Hayward
2 **AMERICAN TOM (FR),** 9, b g American Post—Kirkla (FR) **Mr M. J. D. Matthews**
3 **AUTUMN SPLENDOUR (IRE),** 4, b g Dandy Man (IRE)—Harvest Joy (IRE) E. A. Hayward
4 **BURAUQ,** 8, b g Kyllachy—Riccoche (IRE) D. Smith
5 **CREEK HARBOUR (IRE),** 5, b g Kodiac—Allegheny Creek (IRE) **Mr C. A. Price**
6 **ENGLISHMAN,** 10, b g Royal Applause—Tesary E. A. Hayward
7 **IMHOTEP,** 4, b g Kingman—African Rose J. M. Bradley
8 **MARNI GREY,** 6, gr g Sulamani (IRE)—Ruby Lady **Mr L. J. Williams**
9 **MOONGAZER,** 4, br f Kuroshio (AUS)—Sonnellino J. M. Bradley
10 **MR POTTER,** 7, ch g Assertive—Enclave (USA) **Mr R. W. Prince**
11 **MURAAQEB,** 6, b g Nathaniel (IRE)—Tesary E. A. Hayward
12 **RISING SUNSHINE (IRE),** 7, b g Dark Angel (IRE)—Little Audio (IRE) **Mr P. Banfield & Mr J. M. Bradley**
13 **SATCHVILLE FLYER,** 9, ch g Compton Place—Palinisa (FR) **Mr A. D. Cooke**
14 **SPRING HOLLY (IRE),** 4, b f Zebedee—Blue Holly (IRE) E. A. Hayward
15 **TEMPLE ROAD (IRE),** 12, b g Street Cry (IRE)—Sugarhoneybaby (IRE) J. M. Bradley
16 **THE NIGHT WATCH,** 4, b g Dutch Art—Scarlet Runner E. A. Hayward
17 **TINTERN SPIRIT (IRE),** 4, b f Swiss Spirit—Tintern D Smith (saul) & J M Bradley
18 **UNSUSPECTED GIRL (IRE),** 7, b m Rip Van Winkle (IRE)—Sweet Sioux J. M. Bradley
19 **WAR PLAN,** 4, b g War Command (USA)—Divine Grace (IRE) J. M. Bradley
20 **WYE BOTHER (IRE),** 4, b f Born To Sea (IRE)—Enchantment E. A. Hayward
21 **YFENNI (IRE),** 4, ch f Dutch Art—Paisley E. A. Hayward

THREE-YEAR-OLDS

22 **PORT WINSTON (IRE),** b g Harbour Watch (IRE)—Volkovkha E. A. Hayward

Other Owners: P. Banfield, J. M. Bradley, D. Smith.

Flat Jockey: Tom Marquand, Luke Morris, Franny Norton. **Apprentice Jockey:** Kerrie Raybould.

---

58 MR MARK BRADSTOCK, Wantage
Postal: **Old Manor Stables, Foresters Lane, Letcombe Bassett, Wantage, Oxfordshire, OX12 9NB**
Contacts: **WORK 01235 760780 HOME 01235 760780 PHONE 01235 760754 MOBILE 07887 686697**
EMAIL mark.bradstock@btconnect.com WEBSITE www.markbradstockracing.co.uk

1 **BENDY BOW,** 5, br g Malinas (GER)—Maid of Oaksey The BB Partnership
2 **CRAWFORD,** 4, b g Kayf Tara—Maid of Oaksey The Billy Partnership
3 **DOWN TO THE SEA (FR),** 6, ch g No Risk At All (FR)—Majoritaire (FR) Cracker and Smodge Partnership
4 **EGLANTIER (FR),** 6, b g Bonbon Rose (FR)—Kyalami (FR) UK Gunite Ltd
5 **FLINTHAM,** 11, b g Kayf Tara—Plaid Maid (IRE) The Rasher Partnership

MR MARK BRADSTOCK - continued

6 **I'M HERE (IRE)**, 7, ch g Hurricane Run (IRE)—Is It Here (IRE) **The Hooch Partnership**
7 **IDOLS'S EYE (FR)**, 5, b g Diamond Boy (FR)—Rose Caline (FR) **M. F. Bradstock**
8 **JAISALMER (IRE)**, 8, b g Jeremy (USA)—Shara (IRE) **The Jeremy Partnership**
9 **JAKAMANI**, 6, b g Sulamani (USA)—Kentford Grebe **Miss C Fordham & Mr C Vernon**
10 **PEDDLER (IRE)**, 6, b g Scorpion (IRE)—Don't Waste It (IRE) **Peddler Partnership**
11 **SOUTHFIELD LILY**, 4, b f Yeats (IRE)—Chamoss Royale (FR)
12 **SOUTHFIELD MEGAN**, 4, b f Dylan Thomas (IRE)—Southfield Etoile
13 **SOUTHFIELD TORR**, 7, gr ro g Fair Mix (IRE)—Chamoss Royale (FR) **Mrs Angela Hart & Mrs Angela Yeoman**
14 **STEP BACK (IRE)**, 10, ch g Indian River (FR)—Stepitoutmary (IRE) **Cracker and Smodge Partnership**
15 **STOOP LEAD (IRE)**, 6, b g Jeremy (USA)—The Only Girl (IRE) **Outside Cards**

Other Owners: Mr P. B. T. Armitage, Mr P. I. Armitage, Mrs A. L. Bell-Simmonds, M. F. Bradstock, C. Elgram, Miss C. Fordham, Mrs A. R. Hart, Miss A. C. Loveng, Mr J. B. G. Macleod, Mr J. Reilly, Mr J. R. Rowlands, Mr R. W. Tyrrell, C. A. Vernon, Mrs A. B. Yeoman.

Assistant Trainer: Sara Bradstock, **Head Girl:** Lily Bradstock, **Racing Secretary:** Samantha Partridge.

NH Jockey: Nico De Boinville.

---

59 **MR BARRY BRENNAN, Lambourn**
Postal: 2 Rockfel Road, Lambourn, Hungerford, Berkshire, RG17 8NG
Contacts: MOBILE 07907 529780
EMAIL barrybrennan2@hotmail.co.uk WEBSITE www.barrybrennanracing.co.uk

1 **BLIMEY CHARLIE**, 5, b g Foxwedge (AUS)—Bianca Sforza **F. J. Brennan**
2 **DARAZ LEGACY**, 6, ch m Schiaparelli (GER)—Daraz Rose (IRE) **F. J. Brennan**
3 **HOPE'S WISHES**, 10, b m Kayf Tara—Otarie (FR) **M. J. Hills**
4 **KALAYA (IRE)**, 4, b f Thewayyouare (USA)—Kalabaka (IRE) **D. R. T. Gibbons**
5 **LIGHTENTERTAINMENT (IRE)**, 12, b g King's Theatre (IRE)—Dochas Supreme (IRE) **D. R. T. Gibbons**
6 **OURMULLION**, 6, b g Mullionmileanhour (IRE)—Queen Ranavola (USA) **F. J. Brennan**
7 **WAPPING (USA)**, 7, b g Smart Strike (CAN)—Exciting Times (FR) **Mr K. P. Brennan**

THREE-YEAR-OLDS

8 **DEPARDIEU**, ch g Leroidesanimaux (BRZ)—Stellaire **F. J. Brennan**
9 **WELL IN COMMAND (IRE)**, b g War Command (USA)—Yeah Baby (IRE) **F. J. Brennan**

---

60 **MR JOHN BRIDGER, Liphook**
Postal: Upper Hatch Farm, Liphook, Hampshire, GU30 7EL
Contacts: PHONE 01428 722528 MOBILE 07785 716614
EMAIL jbridger@sky.com

1 **AEGEAN MIST**, 4, ch f Mayson—Aegean Shadow **Theobalds Stud**
2 **ARCTIC FLOWER (IRE)**, 7, gr m Roderic O'Connor (IRE)—Just In Love (FR) **Mrs D. Finch, K. Finch**
3 **DELICATE KISS**, 6, b m Delegator—Desert Kiss **Mrs D. J. Ellison, Mr B. Olkowicz, Mrs D. A. Ellison**
4 **FAIRY MIST (IRE)**, 13, b g Oratorio (IRE)—Prealpina (IRE) **Mr J. J. Bridger**
5 **FIRENZE ROSA (IRE)**, 5, b m Zebedee—Our Nana Rose (IRE) **Mr & Mrs K. Finch**
6 **MONTYS ANGEL (IRE)**, 10, b m Definite Article—Montys Bank (IRE) **China Racing Club**
7 **PETTOCHSIDE**, 11, b g Refuse To Bend (IRE)—Clear Impression (IRE) **Mr P. Cook**
8 **PHAROH JAKE**, 12, ch g Piccolo—Rose Amber **J J Bridger Mrs J Stamp**
9 **PORTO FERRO (IRE)**, 6, b m Arcano (IRE)—Sassari (IRE) **Mr J. J. Bridger**
10 **STARCHANT**, 4, b f Gregorian (IRE)—Aegean Mystery **Mr J. J. Bridger**

THREE-YEAR-OLDS

11 **AMNAA**, b c Bungle Inthejungle—She Mystifies **Watts & Spooner**
12 **ASK SIRI (IRE)**, b c Clodovil (IRE)—Coy (IRE) **Stewart Bridger Bxps**

MR JOHN BRIDGER - continued

13 **BAILEYS FREEDOM,** b c Muhaarar—Baileys Jubilee **Watts & Spooner**
14 **HOPE BAY (IRE),** b f Camelot—Summer Bliss **Mr & Mrs K. Finch**
15 **INDIAN STAR,** b f Indian Haven—Piccostar **Double-R-Racing**
16 **KAHPEHLO,** b f Helmet (AUS)—Anosti **Mr & Mrs K. Finch**
17 **LOVE NOT MONEY,** b f Dawn Approach (IRE)—Maggie Lou (IRE) **W. A. Wood**
18 **SANTORINI SAL,** b c Gregorian (IRE)—Aegean Mystery **Mystery Partnership**
19 **SHANI,** b f Heeraat (IRE)—Limegrove **China Racing Club**

TWO-YEAR-OLDS

20 **KARLUK RIVER,** b f 28/04 Outstrip—Kodiac Island (Kodiac) (2380)
21 **MATIRA BAY (IRE),** b f 30/04 Vadamos (FR)—Blue Holly (IRE) (Blues Traveller (IRE)) (6000) **Mrs D. Finch, K. Finch**
22 **PIAZOLLA (IRE),** b c 15/05 Outstrip—Kilakey (Key of Luck (USA)) (1000) **Mr & Mrs K. Finch**
23 **SILVER REFLECTION,** gr f 04/03 Gutaifan (IRE)—Pivotal Bride (Dubawi (IRE)) (4800) **Mrs D. Finch, K. Finch**
24 **VERRE DORE,** b f 25/04 Heeraat (IRE)—Nairobi (FR) (Anabaa (USA)) (2857)

Other Owners: Mr J. J. Bridger, Mr J. E. Burrows, Mr P Cook, D Higgs J J Bridger, DBD Partnership, Mrs D. Finch, Mr & Mrs K. Finch, K. Finch, Exors of the Late Mr G. K. Panos, K. Panos, Mr D. J. C. Paton, Mr W. J. Spooner, Mrs J. M. Stamp, Mrs D. Stewart, Mr M. Watts.

Assistant Trainer: Rachel Cook.

---

61 MR DAVID BRIDGWATER, Stow-on-the-Wold
Postal: **Wyck Hill Farm, Wyck Hill, Stow-on-the-Wold, Cheltenham, Gloucestershire, GL54 1HT**
Contacts: PHONE **01451 830349** MOBILE **07831 635817** FAX **01451 830349**
EMAIL **sales@bridgwaterracing.co.uk** WEBSITE **www.bridgwaterracing.co.uk**

1 **AMANGIRI (IRE),** 7, b g Zamindar (USA)—Anjella (GER) **CWB Partnership**
2 4, B g Midnight Legend—Aster (IRE) **P. J. Cave**
3 **CLARENDON,** 4, b g Australia—Lady Gloria **Mr A. J. Duffield**
4 **COBY NINE (GER),** 7, b g Arcadio (GER)—Timing **The Roworth Family Syndicate**
5 **COHESION,** 7, b g Champs Elysees—Winter Bloom (USA) **Mr A. J. Duffield**
6 **COMOTION (FR),** 5, b g Kapgarde (FR)—Second Emotion (FR) **Terry & Sarah Amos**
7 **DAME DU SOIR (FR),** 7, br m Axxos (GER)—Kassing (FR) **Cwb Plus 1 Partnership**
8 **ENRICHISSANT (FR),** 6, b br g Speedmaster (GER)—Quibble (FR) **Simon & Liz Hunt**
9 **FORT GABRIEL (FR),** 9, ch g Ange Gabriel (FR)—Forge Neuve (FR) **CWB Plus 2 Partnership**
10 **FUKUTO (FR),** 5, b g Cokoriko (FR)—Hargaux de Saisy (FR) **Simon Hunt & Bob Wilson**
11 **GAIA VALLIS (FR),** 4, b f Saint des Saints (FR)—Toccata Vallis (FR) **David Bridgwater Racing**
12 4, B g Balko (FR)—Golden Firebird (IRE) **Mr S. Hunt**
13 **IN A TIZZ (FR),** 4, b f Nicaron (GER)—Line Tzigane (FR) **Terry & Sarah Amos**
14 **KEEL OVER,** 9, b g Gamut (IRE)—Kayf Keel **Taymar Racing**
15 **LITTLE RICH (IRE),** 5, b g Arakan (USA)—Brioney (IRE) **Building Bridgies**
16 **MAKTAY,** 4, b g Makfi—Cinta **Taymar Racing**
17 **MEBA FISTA (FR),** 4, b g No Risk At All (FR)—Argovie (FR) **Mr S. Hunt**
18 **NO APPROVAL (IRE),** 7, b g Approve (IRE)—Night Cam (IRE) **The Happy Horse Partnership**
19 **OAKLEY HALL (IRE),** 8, b g Milan—Rockwell College (IRE) **David Bridgwater Racing**
20 **PIRATE SAM,** 5, b g Black Sam Bellamy (IRE)—Teenero **JA & RJ Chenery & Partners**
21 **THE CONDITIONAL (IRE),** 8, b g Kalanisi (IRE)—Gorrie Vale (IRE) **P. J. Cave**
22 **URANUS DES BORDES (FR),** 4, b g Kapgarde (FR)—Queen des Bordes (FR) **Mr S. Hunt**
23 **WAHWONAISA,** 8, b g Kalanisi (IRE)—Clandestine **AM Bostock DG Bostock**
24 **WENCESLAUS (GER),** 8, b g Tiger Hill (IRE)—Warrior Czarina (USA) **Deauville Daze Partnership**
25 **ZAMANI (GER),** 4, ch g Mamool (IRE)—Zuccarella (GER) **Mr R. Wilson**

THREE-YEAR-OLDS

26 B c Authorized (IRE)—Ahdaaf (USA) **Mr S. Hunt**
27 B c Diamond Boy (FR)—Lazoukine (FR) **Mr S. Hunt**
28 **SAQUEBOUTE (FR),** b f Slickly Royal (FR)—Grande Cavale (FR) **Mr S. Hunt**

MR DAVID BRIDGWATER - continued

TWO-YEAR-OLDS
29 Bl g 23/01 Great Pretender (IRE)—Athinea (FR) (Enrique) (13728) **Mr S. Hunt**
30 IT'S FOR YOU MUM (FR), gr f 10/02 Lord du Sud (FR)—Odile (FR) (Smadoun (FR)) **Mr S. Hunt**

Other Owners: Mrs S. P. Amos, T. P. Amos, Mrs A. M. Bostock, D. G. Bostock, D. G. Bridgwater, Mrs J. A. Chenery, Mr R. J. Chenery, Mrs J. A. Chenery & Mr R. J. Chenery, David Bridgwater Racing, Mr A. Gunn, Miss L. M. Haywood, Mrs E. A. Hunt, Mr S. Hunt, Mr R. Wilson.

Assistant Trainer: Mrs Lucy K. Bridgwater.

NH Jockey: Tom Scudamore. **Conditional Jockey:** Daniel Hiskett, Callum McKinnes. **Apprentice Jockey:** Poppy Bridgwater

---

62 MR ROBYN BRISLAND, Newark
Postal: **Mill Top Equestrian Centre, Danethorpe, Newark, Nottinghamshire**
Contacts: **MOBILE 07771 656081**
EMAIL robbris@me.com

1 ALWAYS AMAZING, 6, ch g Kyllachy—Amazed **Mr N. Andersen**
2 ANDRE AMAR (IRE), 4, b g Dandy Man (IRE)—Heaven's Vault (IRE) **Mrs J. Brisland**
3 APACHE BLAZE, 5, b m Champs Elysees—Polar Circle (USA) **Ferrybank Properties Limited**
4 ATALANTA QUEEN, 5, b m Canford Cliffs (IRE)—Champagne Aerial (IRE) **Ferrybank Properties Limited**
5 BEAUTIFUL ARTIST (USA), 5, b m Lonhro (AUS)—She's A Beauty (USA) **Mrs J. Brisland**
6 BLUELLA, 5, b m Equiano (FR)—Mata Hari Blue **Mr M. J. Golding**
7 BLUETTA, 4, b f Heeraat (IRE)—Mata Hari Blue **Mr M. J. Golding**
8 CASO DO LAGO (IRE), 9, b g Balmont (USA)—Dasha **Mrs J. Brisland**
9 COLD HARBOUR, 5, b g North Light (IRE)—Pilcomayo (IRE) **Mrs J. Brisland**
10 COMPASS POINT, 5, b h Helmet (AUS)—Takarna (IRE) **Mrs J. Brisland**
11 DEEDS NOT WORDS (IRE), 9, b g Royal Applause—Wars (IRE) **Mrs J. Brisland**
12 FOXY ELOISE, 5, b m Foxwedge (AUS)—Eleanor Eloise (USA) **Mrs J. Brisland**
13 GOLDFOX GREY, 4, gr g Equiano (FR)—Beautifull Mind (IRE) **Goldfox Racing**
14 GREG, 4, gr g Gregorian (IRE)—Takarna (IRE) **Mrs J. A. Cornwell**
15 HARBOUR FRONT, 4, b g Iffraaj—Wosaita **Mrs J. A. Cornwell**
16 HARBOUR STORM, 5, br g Sayif (IRE)—Minette **Mrs J. A. Cornwell**
17 HENRIETTA'S DREAM, 6, b m Henrythenavigator (USA)—Timeless Dream **From The Front Racing**
18 MIRABELLE PLUM (IRE), 4, b f Casamento (IRE)—Spirit of Alsace (IRE) **Mrs J. Brisland**
19 MULTITALENTED, 7, b g Multiplex—Star Welcome **Miss A. Deniel**
20 NAVAJO STAR (IRE), 6, b m Mastercraftsman (IRE)—Champagne Aerial (IRE) **Ferrybank Properties Limited**
21 NICK VEDDER, 6, b g Rip Van Winkle (IRE)—Devotion (IRE) **Mrs J. Brisland**
22 NINETEENRBO'MALLEY, 8, b g Beat All (USA)—My Nora (IRE) **Mr E. G. O'Malley**
23 OBLATE, 4, b f Epaulette (AUS)—Lady Benedicte (IRE) **Houghton Bloodstock**
24 RULER OF NATIVES, 4, b g Native Ruler—Misty Pearl **Goldfox Racing**
25 4, B f Native Ruler—Satin Princess (IRE)
26 4, B g Gregorian (IRE)—Sea Whisper **Mrs J. A. Cornwell**
27 SIX TIL TWELVE (IRE), 4, b g Bungle Inthejungle—Cuiseach (IRE) **Mrs J. Brisland**

THREE-YEAR-OLDS
28 Ch c Anjaal—Abbotsfield (IRE)
29 B f Toronado (IRE)—Anna's Vision (IRE)
30 B c Sayif (IRE)—Bahie
31 BIG IMPACT, b c Lethal Force (IRE)—Valandraud (IRE) **Mr N. P. Hardy**
32 BRASS CLANKERS, b c Helmet (AUS)—Millsini **Mrs J. Brisland**
33 FLIGHT OF THUNDER (IRE), b f Night of Thunder (IRE)—Thames Pageant
34 FUMBLEINTHEFOREST, b f Bungle Inthejungle—Blacke Forest **Goldrush Racing**
35 GINGER BOX, gr ro f Mastercraftsman (IRE)—Ellbeedee (IRE) **Cross Channel Racing Club**
36 HOORAYFORTHEGREY, gr g Henrythenavigator (USA)—Jillolini **Mr & Mrs James Sumsion**
37 Ch f Power—Moynsha Lady (IRE)
38 MR DUEPEARL, b c Due Diligence (USA)—Midnight Pearl (USA) **Mr & Mrs J Sumsion**

MR ROBYN BRISLAND - continued

39 **NAVAJO DAWN (IRE)**, b f Dawn Approach (IRE)—Patience Alexander (IRE) **Ferrybank Properties Limited**
40 **NEVER IN RED (IRE)**, b c Anjaal—Bank On Black (IRE) **Mrs J. Brisland**
41 **PEARL OF INDIA**, b f Sleeping Indian—Misty Pearl **Goldfox Racing**
42 **PULL HARDER CON**, b c Mayson—Cut The Cackle (IRE) **Mr C. J. Harding**
43 **PURPLE SANDPIPER**, b c Mayson—The Lady Lapwing **Mrs F A Veasey & Mrs Jo Brisland**
44 B br c French Navy—Quail Landing **Mrs Jackie Cornwell & Partner**
45 B c Alhebayeb (IRE)—Regal Kiss
46 **WHITE LION**, b g Haafhd—Shirley's Pride
47 **YOUAREFULLOFCHAT**, gr f Lethal Force (IRE)—Chatalong (IRE) **Mrs A. L. Heayns**

Other Owners: Mrs J. Brisland, Mrs J. A. Cornwell, Mr P. D. Ebdon, Mr M. J. Golding, J H & N J Foxon Ltd, Mrs B. Sumsion, Mr J. Sumsion, Mrs F. A. Veasey.

Flat Jockey: Martin Harley, Luke Morris.

63	**MR ANTONY BRITTAIN, Warthill** Postal: **Northgate Lodge, Warthill, York, YO19 5XR** Contacts: **PHONE 01759 371472 FAX 01759 372915** **EMAIL email@antonybrittain.co.uk WEBSITE www.antonybrittain.co.uk**

1 **ANOTHER ANGEL (IRE)**, 6, b g Dark Angel (IRE)—Kermana (IRE) **Mr Antony Brittain**
2 **BEATBYBEATBYBEAT**, 7, ch m Poet's Voice—Beat As One **Mr Antony Brittain**
3 **CANFORD BAY (IRE)**, 6, b g Canford Cliffs (IRE)—Maundays Bay (IRE) **Northgate Racing**
4 **DAAFR (IRE)**, 4, b g Invincible Spirit (IRE)—Kitty Love (USA) **Mr Antony Brittain**
5 **DRAKEFELL (IRE)**, 5, b h Canford Cliffs (IRE)—Cake (IRE) **Northgate Racing**
6 **INTERNATIONAL LAW**, 6, gr g Exceed And Excel (AUS)—Cruel Sea (USA) **John & Tony Jarvis & Partner**
7 **KLIPPERTY KLOPP**, 4, ch g Monsieur Bond (IRE)—First Harmony **Mr Antony Brittain**
8 **KLOPP**, 4, b f Monsieur Bond (IRE)—Caranbola **Mr Antony Brittain**
9 **LUCKY LODGE**, 10, b g Lucky Story (USA)—Melandre **Mr Antony Brittain**
10 **MUTABAAHY (IRE)**, 5, b g Oasis Dream—Habaayib **Mr Antony Brittain**
11 **ONE ONE SEVEN (IRE)**, 4, b g Arcano (IRE)—Maany (USA) **John & Tony Jarvis & Partner**
12 **PUCHITA (IRE)**, 5, b m Acclamation—Violet Ballerina (IRE) **Mr Antony Brittain**
13 **QAARAAT**, 5, b g Acclamation—Ladyship **Mr Antony Brittain**
14 **SLOWMO (IRE)**, 4, b g Kodiac—Motion Lass
15 **TATHMEEN (IRE)**, 5, b g Exceed And Excel (AUS)—Deyaar (USA) **Mr Antony Brittain**
16 **THAWRY**, 5, b g Iffraaj—Salacia (IRE) **Mr Antony Brittain**
17 **TRAVELLER (FR)**, 6, b g Henrythenavigator (USA)—Nantes (GER) **John & Tony Jarvis & Partner**

THREE-YEAR-OLDS

18 **MOMENTUM**, b f Swiss Spirit—Valiantly **Ryedale Racing**
19 **PACIFIC COAST**, b g Monsieur Bond (IRE)—Sea Crest **Mr Antony Brittain**
20 **SOUTH LIGHT (IRE)**, b f Elzaam (AUS)—Rien Ne Vas Plus (IRE) **Mrs N. McGreavy**
21 **VAN DIJK**, b g Cable Bay (IRE)—Stresa **Mr Antony Brittain**

TWO-YEAR-OLDS

22 B c 21/03 Albaasil (IRE)—Caranbola (Lucky Story (USA))
23 B f 05/03 Albaasil (IRE)—Guadaloup (Loup Sauvage (USA))
24 B f 08/03 Albaasil (IRE)—Melandre (Lujain (USA))
25 B c 05/04 Albaasil (IRE)—Sea Crest (Xaar)

Other Owners: Mr Antony Brittain, Mr A. Jarvis, Mr J. Jarvis, Northgate Grey.

Flat Jockey: Cam Hardie.

64   MRS JULIA BROOKE, Middleham
Postal: Brough Farm, Middleham, Leyburn, North Yorkshire, DL8 4SG
Contacts: MOBILE 07776 186581
EMAIL jb@juliabrookeracing.com

1 **DRUMLEE CITY (IRE)**, 8, b g City Honours (USA)—Alentio (IRE) **Mr H. Redknapp**
2 **DUTY GIRL (IRE)**, 7, b m Vinnie Roe (IRE)—Clogher Cailin (IRE) **Mr J. Platts**
3 **EMMA BEAG (IRE)**, 9, b m Westerner—Emma Jane (IRE) **Maurice Friel, Mrs Mary Sadler & Partner**
4 **FIDDLERS BOW (IRE)**, 11, b g Whitmore's Conn (USA)—
                                              Soraleda (IRE) **MT Buckley & Brough Farm Racing Partners**
5 **FOREWARNING**, 6, b g Cacique (IRE)—Buffering **Ladsdoracing & Partner**
6 **FREQUENCY CODE (FR)**, 4, ch g Le Havre (IRE)—Stylish **Mrs J. A. Brooke**
7 **GET THE FACTS (IRE)**, 6, b g Publisher (USA)—Ollar Rose **Mrs M. Hatfield & Mrs S. Kramer**
8 **GLOBETROTTER (IRE)**, 6, ch g Helmet (AUS)—Shimna **Sowray Brothers**
9 **KILDAVEN SPIDER (IRE)**, 9, b m Daylami (IRE)—Royal Revoque (IRE) **M T Buckley & Julia Brooke Racing Club**
10 **LONGTIMESINCEJASPR (IRE)**, 6, b m Stowaway—A Tanner Rate (IRE) **J. D. Gordon**
11 **MELONY**, 5, b m Scorpion (IRE)—Bet Davis (IRE) **Miss S. J. Turner**
12 **PETE SO HIGH (GER)**, 6, b g High Chaparral (IRE)—Paulaya (GER) **Mrs J. A. Brooke**
13 **PIAZON**, 9, br g Striking Ambition—Colonel's Daughter **The Body Warmers**
14 **SAUCHIEHALL STREET (IRE)**, 5, b g Mastercraftsman (IRE)—Top Trail (USA) **The Dalby Family**
15 **SHORT FLIGHT (IRE)**, 8, b g Trans Island—Surricate (FR) **Mrs J. A. Brooke**
16 **TRUE ROMANCE (IRE)**, 6, gr g Mastercraftsman (IRE)—Full of Love (IRE) **Mr K. S. Ward**

TWO-YEAR-OLDS

17 B g 02/02 Epaulette (AUS)—Corsage (IRE) (Acclamation) (6666)

Other Owners: Mrs J. A. Brooke, Brough Farm Racing Partnership, Mr M. T. Buckley, Mrs J. A. Dalby, Mr P. N. Dalby, Mr M. Friel, Mrs M. Hatfield, Julia Brooke Racing Club, Mrs S. Kramer, Ladsdoracing, Mr J. Platts, Mr P. T. H. Porter, Mrs M. Sadler, Mr S. A. Sowray, Mr C. Waters.

65   LADY SUSAN BROOKE, Llandrindod Wells
Postal: Tyn-y-Berth Farm, Dolau, Llandrindod Wells, Powys, LD1 5TW
Contacts: PHONE 01597 851190 MOBILE 07977 114834
EMAIL suebrooke@live.co.uk

1 **ANNIEAREYOUOK**, 5, br m Passing Glance—Ellerslie Jackie **Lady Brooke**
2 **MIDNIGHT MAKEOVER**, 6, b m Midnight Legend—Makeover **Lady Brooke**
3 **ORCHESTRATED (IRE)**, 9, b g Mahler—Rose Island **Lady Brooke**
4 **RIVER PURPLE**, 13, b g Bollin Eric—Cerise Bleue (FR) **Lady Brooke**
5 **SNOWPIERCER (FR)**, 6, b g Astarabad (USA)—My Darling Rose (FR) **Lady Brooke**
6 **SPOCK (FR)**, 15, b g Lost World (IRE)—Quark Top (FR) **Lady Brooke**
7 **STARCROSSED**, 8, b g Cape Cross (IRE)—Gretna **Lady Brooke**
8 **TINCTORIA**, 10, b m Oratorio (IRE)—Blue Indigo (FR) **Lady Brooke**
9 **VINNIE RED (IRE)**, 11, ch g Vinnie Roe (IRE)—Conzara (IRE) **Lady Brooke**
10 **YOURHOLIDAYISOVER (IRE)**, 13, ch g Sulamani (IRE)—Whitehaven **Lady Brooke**

Assistant Trainer: Lorna Brooke.

Amateur Jockey: Miss Lorna Brooke.

66 **MR ROY BROTHERTON, Pershore**
Postal: **Mill End Racing Stables, Netherton Road, Elmley Castle, Pershore, Worcestershire, WR10 3JF**
Contacts: **PHONE 01386 710772 MOBILE 07973 877280**

1 **AUNTIE JUNE,** 4, ch f Piccolo—Basle **Mr M. A. Geobey**
2 **CNOC SION (IRE),** 10, b g Gold Well—Bondi Babe (IRE) **Jan Carpenter & Bill Young**
3 **DEISE VU (IRE),** 12, b g Brian Boru—Deise Dreamer (IRE) **Elmley Queen**
4 **DUN BAY CREEK,** 9, b g Dubai Destination (USA)—Over It **Elmley Queen 2**
5 **FILAMENT OF GOLD (USA),** 9, b g Street Cry (IRE)—Raw Silk (USA) **Mr M. A. Geobey**
6 **FILBERT STREET,** 5, ch g Poet's Voice—Tinnarinka **R. Brotherton**
7 **MIRACLE GARDEN,** 8, ch g Exceed And Excel (AUS)—Sharp Terms **Mr M. A. Geobey**

Other Owners: R. Brotherton, Mrs J. A. Carpenter, Mr N. A. Lavender Jones, Mr M. A. Savage, Mr B. K. C. Young.

Assistant Trainer: Justin Brotherton.

NH Jockey: Jamie Moore.

67 **MR ALAN BROWN, Malton**
Postal: **Lilac Farm, Yedingham, Malton, North Yorkshire, YO17 8SS**
Contacts: **PHONE 01944 728090 MOBILE 07970 672845**
EMAIL ad.brown@hotmail.co.uk WEBSITE www.alanbrownracing.co.uk

1 **ATRAFAN (IRE),** 6, b g Atraf—Up Front (IRE) **Mr F. E. Reay**
2 **BLACKCURRENT,** 4, b g Kuroshio (AUS)—Mamounia (IRE) **Burton Agnes Bloodstock**

THREE-YEAR-OLDS

3 **BLACKJACK,** b g Sleeping Indian—Medam **The Hon Mrs E. S. Cunliffe-Lister**
4 **CASTASHADOW,** b g Harbour Watch (IRE)—Dareesha (IRE) **A. D. Brown**
5 **JEMS BOND,** ch g Monsieur Bond (IRE)—Saphire **Mr S. Pedersen & Mr Frank Reay**
6 Gr g Ruler of The World (IRE)—Silver Halo **Max Europe Ltd**
7 **THOMAS HAWK,** b g Gregorian (IRE)—Miss Mohawk (IRE) **Mrs M. A. Doherty**

TWO-YEAR-OLDS

8 **FORZA LORENZA,** ch f 27/02 Monsieur Bond (IRE)—Redalani (IRE) (Redback) **S. E. Pedersen**
9 **LILY'S GIFT,** b f 09/04 Poet's Voice—Nefetari (Kodiac) **Mr Frank Reay & Mr A. D. Brown**
10 B f 22/03 Albaasil (IRE)—Medam (Medicean) **Burton Agnes Bloodstock**

Other Owners: A. D. Brown, S. E. Pedersen, Mr F. E. Reay.

68 **MR ANDI BROWN, Newmarket**
Postal: **Southfields Stables, Hamilton Road, Newmarket, Suffolk, CB8 7JQ**
Contacts: **PHONE 01638 669652 MOBILE 07980 393263 FAX 01638 669652**
EMAIL southfieldsstables@btinternet.com WEBSITE www.southfieldsstables.co.uk

1 **KIRTLING,** 9, gr g Araafa (IRE)—Cape Maya **Faith Hope and Charity**
2 **TIMSSAAH,** 5, b g Showcasing—Swan Wings **Miss L. J. Knocker**

THREE-YEAR-OLDS

3 **JUNGLE BOOGALOO (IRE),** b f Bungle Inthejungle—Newton Bomb (IRE) **Mrs A L Lofts & Mrs Nicky Scott Knight**

Other Owners: Mrs A. L. Lofts, Mrs N. M. Scott Knight.

Assistant Trainer: Miss Linsey Knocker.

69

MR DAVID BROWN, Whitby
Postal: 6 Linden Lane, Newholm, Whitby, North Yorkshire, YO21 3QX
Contacts: PHONE 01636 613793 MOBILE 07889 132931
EMAIL david@davidbrownracing.com

1 **GRAYBOY**, 4, gr g Aussie Rules (USA)—Grace Hull **Mr R. Hull**
2 **GUPTA**, 4, b g Equiano (FR)—Lanai (IRE) **Mr R. Hull**
3 **JONBOY**, 5, b g Delegator—Cavallo da Corsa **Mr R. Hull**
4 **NATIONAL ANTHEM**, 5, ch h Intikhab (USA)—Song of Passion (IRE) **Mr M. Mckay**

THREE-YEAR-OLDS

5 **CAPTAIN MOORHOUSE (IRE)**, b g War Command (USA)—Shirley Blade (IRE) **Mr R. Hull**
6 **CRUISING**, b g Helmet (AUS)—Lanai (IRE) **Mr R. Hull**
7 **JAZZ STYLE (IRE)**, b g Red Jazz (USA)—Gypsy Style **Mr R. Hull**
8 **MEWS HOUSE**, ch c Coach House (IRE)—Beauty Pageant (IRE) **D H Brown & Mr Clive Watson**

TWO-YEAR-OLDS

9 **CAN CAN GIRL (IRE)**, b f 02/03 Champs Elysees—Osthurry (IRE) (Hurricane Run (IRE)) (17000) **Bratwa**
10 **ROADRUNNER (IRE)**, b c 12/05 Make Believe—Flanders (IRE) (Common Grounds) (17000) **Bratwa**

Other Owners: Mr D. H. Brown, Mr C. Watson.

Assistant Trainer: Dushyant Dooyea.

Flat Jockey: Tom Eaves, Philip Makin.

70

MISS MICHELLE BRYANT, Lewes
Postal: Bevern Bridge Farm Cottage, South Chailey, Lewes, East Sussex, BN8 4QH
Contacts: PHONE 01273 400638 MOBILE 07976 217542
EMAIL bear_2009@live.co.uk

1 **CHURCHTOWN GLEN (IRE)**, 7, b g Getaway (GER)—Annagh Lady (IRE) **Miss M P Bryant, David & Eileen Bryant**
2 **KILLABRAHER CROSS (IRE)**, 13, gr g Kasmayo—Enoughrose (IRE) **Miss M. P. Bryant**

Other Owners: Mr D. Bryant, Mrs E. Bryant, Miss M. P. Bryant.

Amateur Jockey: Miss M. P. Bryant.

71

MR BOB BUCKLER, Bridgwater
Postal: Gibb Hill, Courtway, Spaxton, Bridgwater, Somerset, TA5 1DR
Contacts: PHONE 01278 671268 MOBILE 07785 773957
EMAIL rbuckler@btconnect.com WEBSITE www.robertbucklerracing.co.uk

1 **ALL KINGS (IRE)**, 11, b g Milan—Rilmount (IRE) **R. H. Buckler**
2 4, B c Dylan Thomas (IRE)—Arctic Flow **Mrs H. R. Dunn**
3 **BARBARIAN**, 4, b g Black Sam Bellamy (IRE)—Mizzurka **Golden Cap**
4 **CUSHUISH**, 7, b m Yeats (IRE)—My Petra **R. H. Buckler**
5 **FLOWING CADENZA**, 6, b m Yeats (IRE)—Over The Flow **Mrs H. R. Dunn**
6 **GIBB HILL**, 6, ch g Frozen Fire (GER)—River Reine (IRE) **Mrs D Gamble & R H Buckler**
7 **REGAL FLOW**, 13, b g Erhaab (USA)—Flow **Mrs H. R. Dunn**
8 **SAKANDI**, 5, b m Frozen Fire (GER)—River Reine (IRE) **4 Gals and a filly**
9 **UNWIN VC**, 6, b g Black Sam Bellamy (IRE)—Becky B **Golden Cap**

Other Owners: R. H. Buckler, Mrs D. R. Gamble.

Head Lad: Giles Scott.

Conditional Jockey: Sean Houlihan.

72 **MR DAI BURCHELL, Ebbw Vale**
Postal: Drysiog Farm, Briery Hill, Ebbw Vale, Gwent, NP23 6BU
Contacts: **PHONE 01495 302551 MOBILE 07980 482860**

1 **DAWN'S LITTLE LADY**, 8, b m Dr Massini (IRE)—Kopylova **Mr L. Davies**
2 **EASKEY LAD (IRE)**, 5, b g Most Improved (IRE)—Lilakiya (IRE) **Miss S. Carter**
3 **FACT FLOW (IRE)**, 11, br g Whitmore's Conn (USA)—Beaver Run (IRE) **The Bill & Ben Partnership**
4 **FURIOUSLY FAST (IRE)**, 8, b g Fast Company (IRE)—Agouti **W. D. Burchell**
5 **GOOD IMPRESSION**, 5, b g Showcasing—Daintily Done **B. M. G. Group**
6 **WINGED ISLE**, 5, b g Winged Love (IRE)—Zaffaranni (IRE) **Mrs G. A. Davies**

Assistant Trainer: Ruth Burchell.

Flat Jockey: Hollie Doyle. **NH Jockey:** Robert Dunne, Alan Johns. **Conditional Jockey:** Jordan Nailor. **Amateur Jockey:** Miss Jodie Hughes.

73 **MR K. R. BURKE, Leyburn**
Postal: Spigot Lodge, Middleham, Leyburn, North Yorkshire, DL8 4TL
Contacts: **PHONE 01969 625088 MOBILE 07778 458777 FAX 01969 625099**
EMAIL karl@karlburke.co.uk WEBSITE www.karlburke.co.uk

1 **ANGEL PALANAS**, 6, b g Mayson—Scottish Exile (IRE) **Mr Mark Bates & Mrs E Burke**
2 **ASTRO JAKK (IRE)**, 4, b g Zoffany (IRE)—By The Edge (IRE) **Mr J. E. Dance**
3 **BARON RUN**, 10, ch g Bertolini (USA)—Bhima **Mr Eric Burke & Partner**
4 **BORN TO BE ALIVE (IRE)**, 6, b g Born To Sea (IRE)—Yaria (IRE) **Mr T Dykes & Mrs E Burke**
5 **DAWN BLAZE**, 4, ch g Dawn Approach (IRE)—Danat Al Atheer **Hambleton Racing Ltd XXXV & E Burke**
6 **EXALTED ANGEL (FR)**, 4, b g Dark Angel (IRE)—Hurryupharriet (IRE) **Pau-perth Partnership & Mrs E Burke**
7 **HAREEM QUEEN (IRE)**, 4, gr f Dark Angel (IRE)—Dulcian (IRE) **Mr J. E. Dance**
8 **KELLY'S DINO (FR)**, 7, b g Doctor Dino (FR)—Sabolienne (FR) **Mr Liam Kelly & Mrs E Burke**
9 **LITTLE INDIA (FR)**, 4, ch f Manduro (GER)—Jolie Laide (FR) **Hope Eden Racing Ltd & Mrs E Burke**
10 **LORD OBERON**, 5, b g Mayson—Fairy Shoes **Mr D J MacKay & Mrs E Burke**
11 **MAKTHECAT (FR)**, 4, b g Makfi—Troiecat (FR) **Hambleton Racing Ltd XXXV & E Burke**
12 **MILAGRE DA VIDA (IRE)**, 4, b f Bated Breath—Eucharist (IRE) **Mr J. E. Dance**
13 **MODAKHAR (IRE)**, 4, b g Battle of Marengo (IRE)—Lost Highway (IRE) **Mr Carl Waters & Mrs E Burke**
14 **MOUNT ARARAT (IRE)**, 5, b g Sea The Stars (IRE)—Divine Authority (IRE) **Mrs E. M. Burke**
15 **PARALLEL WORLD (IRE)**, 4, b g Morpheus—Miss Glitters (IRE) **Ontoawinner 14 & Mrs E Burke**
16 **RAYDIANCE**, 5, b g Mayson—Iridescence **Ontoawinner 14 & Mrs E Burke**
17 **SELF ASSESSMENT (IRE)**, 4, b g Elzaam (AUS)—Little Miss Diva (IRE) **Hold Your Horses Racing & Mrs E Burke**
18 **SHALLOW HAL**, 4, b g Mayson—Bazelle **Ontoawinner 14 & Mrs E Burke**
19 **TRUE MASON**, 4, b g Mayson—Marysienka **K. A. Dasmal**
20 **VITRALITE (IRE)**, 4, br c Moohaajim (IRE)—Nellie Forbush **S. P. C. Woods**
21 **YOU'RE FIRED (IRE)**, 9, b g Firebreak—My Sweet Georgia (IRE) **Hope Eden Racing Ltd & Mrs E Burke**

THREE-YEAR-OLDS

22 **ANCYRE (FR)**, gr f Silver Frost (IRE)—Alexia Fedorovna (USA) **Bloodstock Agency Limited**
23 **ANGEL OF THE GLEN (FR)**, b f Gleneagles (IRE)—Archangel Gabriel (USA) **Hunscote Stud Limited**
24 Ch g Libertarian—Angel Voices (IRE) **Mrs E. M. Burke**
25 **ASMUND (IRE)**, b g Zebedee—Suffer Her (IRE) **Ontoawinner, Mr R McKeown & E Burke**
26 **BOUND FOR HEAVEN**, b f Gleneagles (IRE)—Sugar Mill **Mr J. E. Dance**
27 **BRODICK**, b f Teofilo (IRE)—Bedecked (IRE) **Mrs M. Bryce**
28 **BURSEA LADY**, ch f Showcasing—Million Faces **Ontoawinner 9**
29 **CLASSY MOON (USA)**, b g Malibu Moon (USA)—Contentious (USA) **Mr C. J. Waters**
30 **DANIEL DERONDA**, b c Siyouni (FR)—Madonna Dell'orto **Mr F. Gillespie**
31 **DANNY OCEAN (IRE)**, b g Dandy Man (IRE)—Loud Applause **Ontoawinner 14 & Mrs E Burke**
32 **DO YOU LOVE ME (IRE)**, b f Galileo (IRE)—Green Room (USA) **Phoenix Thoroughbred Limited**
33 **DUBAI STATION**, b c Brazen Beau (AUS)—Princess Guest (IRE) **Ahmad AlShaikh & Co**
34 **DULCIMA (IRE)**, ch f Australia—Boast **Mr M Smith & Mr D Kilpatrick**
35 **ELECTRIC MISTRESS (IRE)**, b f Dandy Man (IRE)—Aunt Nicola **Tweenhills Fillies & Mrs E Burke**

MR K. R. BURKE - continued

36 **EMARATY HERO,** b c Lope de Vega (IRE)—Valtina (IRE) **A. Al Shaikh**
37 **EMMA CAPPELEN,** b f Kingman—Centime **Anna Sundstrom & Robert Sinclair**
38 **FINERY,** b f Al Kazeem—Elysian **Cheveley Park Stud Limited**
39 **FLAMES OF YORK,** b g Rock of Gibraltar (IRE)—Special Miss **Mr Tim Dykes & Hope Eden Racing Ltd**
40 **FORESHORE,** b g Footstepsinthesand—Skinny Love **Tim Dykes, Chris Emmerson & Jon Hughes**
41 **GOOSE LIGHTNING,** gr g Lethal Force (IRE)—Florett (IRE) **Hambleton Racing Ltd XXXV & E Burke**
42 **GRAVITY FORCE,** b c Fountain of Youth (IRE)—Itsinthestars **Bearstone Stud Limited**
43 **GUIPURE,** ch f Dutch Art—Interlace **Cheveley Park Stud Limited**
44 **HESSSA,** b f Zoffany (IRE)—Ana Shababiya (IRE) **A. Al Shaikh**
45 **HOOROO (IRE),** b g Hallowed Crown (AUS)—Hflah (IRE) **Nick Bradley Racing 2 & Mrs E Burke**
46 **HOYLAKE,** b g Gutaifan (IRE)—Flames To Dust (GER) **Nick Bradley Racing 5 & E Burke**
47 **JAMAIS ASSEZ (USA),** b g Invincible Spirit (IRE)—Ana Luna **R Sinclair, A Sundstrom & Ilse Smits**
48 **JUNINHO (IRE),** b g Gutaifan (IRE)—Soxy Doxy (IRE) **Mr G. White**
49 **LADY LATTE (IRE),** b f Anjaal—Cappuccino (IRE) **Mr Mo Charge & Mrs E Burke**
50 **LADYLEYS BELUGA,** b f Showcasing—Terse **Ontoawinner 14 & Mrs E Burke**
51 **LITTLE RED SOCKS (IRE),** b f Acclamation—Wild Academy (IRE) **Phoenix Ladies Syndicate**
52 **LORD OF THE LODGE (IRE),** b c Dandy Man (IRE)—Archetypal (IRE) **Mrs E. M. Burke**
53 **MACHO TIME (IRE),** b g Camacho—Galeaza **J. C. Fretwell**
54 **MACHO TOUCH (IRE),** b f Camacho—Hint of Red (IRE) **Pau - Perth Partnership**
55 **MOMENTSAFTAMIDNITE (USA),** b g Declaration of War (USA)—
Funny Bay (USA) **Hope Eden Racing Ltd & Mrs E Burke**
56 **MOON POWER,** b f Exceed And Excel (AUS)—Shepherdia (IRE) **King Power Racing Co Ltd**
57 **MOONBOOTZ (IRE),** ch g No Nay Never (USA)—Orange Pip **Titanium Racing Club**
58 **NEVER IN PARIS (IRE),** b f No Nay Never (USA)—Meeting In Paris (IRE) **Ontoawinner, A Marsh & E Burke**
59 **PRODUCTIVE (IRE),** b c Dark Angel (IRE)—Thawrah (IRE) **Phoenix Thoroughbred Limited**
60 **PSYCHIC POWER (IRE),** b f Slade Power (IRE)—Magie Noire (IRE) **Mr J. E. Dance**
61 **PURPLE KNIGHT (FR),** b g Requinto (IRE)—Narva (USA) **Ontoawinner, Strecker & Burke**
62 **RAYONG,** b c Mayson—Lydiate (IRE) **King Power Racing Co Ltd**
63 **RAYYAN,** b g Siyouni (FR)—Hurryupharriet (IRE) **Al Shaqab Racing UK Limited**
64 **SEIZE THE TIME (IRE),** ch f Siyouni (FR)—Teeba (USA) **Phoenix Thoroughbred Limited**
65 **SOCIALLY SHADY,** ch g Zoffany (IRE)—Executrix **Mr Liam Kelly & Mrs E Burke**
66 **SOLEMN PLEDGE,** b f Showcasing—Lovers' Vows **Pau-perth Partnership & Mrs E Burke**
67 **SPLENDIDLY,** ch g Garswood—Regal Riband **Mr J Laughton & Mrs E Burke**
68 **SPRING BLOOM,** ch g Power—Almond Branches **J. C. Fretwell**
69 **SUPERIORITY (IRE),** b f Exceed And Excel (AUS)—Janina **Mr J Laughton & Mrs E Burke**
70 B g Zebedee—Sweet'n Sassy (IRE) **Mrs E. M. Burke**
71 B g Camacho—Toparali **Mr M. McHale**
72 **TOTAL DISTRACTION,** b g Fountain of Youth (IRE)—Mad Annie (USA) **Mr R. Bentley**
73 **WAR OF CLANS (IRE),** b g Ivawood (IRE)—Precautionary **Ontoawinner 14 & Mrs E Burke**
74 **WOKE (IRE),** b br f Showcasing—Analysis **Mr H. J. Strecker**
75 **WONDERWORK (IRE),** b g Night of Thunder (IRE)—First Party **Mr H Strecker & Mrs E Burke**
76 **YES ALWAYS (IRE),** b f No Nay Never (USA)—Flavia Tatiana (IRE) **The Cool Silk Partnership**

TWO-YEAR-OLDS

77 B c 20/01 Elzaam (AUS)—Adaptation (Spectrum (IRE)) (38610)
78 **AMASOVA,** ch f 16/02 Pivotal—Russian Heroine (Invincible Spirit (IRE)) **Cheveley Park Stud Limited**
79 B f 08/03 Twilight Son—Arabian Music (IRE) (Kheleyf (USA)) (10476) **Mr Carl Waters & Mrs E Burke**
80 Gr c 27/03 Footstepsinthesand—Artistica (IRE) (Spectrum (IRE)) (53195) **More Turf Racing & Mrs E Burke**
81 B f 10/02 Dabirsim (FR)—
Aster Nox (USA) (Elusive Quality (USA)) (15444) **Hold Your Horses Racing & Mrs E Burke**
82 Ch f 25/03 Bated Breath—Birthstone (Machiavellian (USA)) (23000) **J. C. Fretwell**
83 B f 12/02 Dabirsim (FR)—Bleu Nil (IRE) (Dansili) (30030) **Ecurie Normandie Pur Sang**
84 **BOOGIE TIME (IRE),** b c 03/02 Kodiac—Get Up And Dance (Makfi) (61904) **Mr Carl Waters & Mrs E Burke**
85 **BRIGHT APPARITION,** b c 26/02 Charm Spirit (IRE)—
Katie's Diamond (FR) (Turtle Bowl (IRE)) (30000) **Mr D J MacKay & Mrs E Burke**
86 B f 09/03 Dandy Man (IRE)—Chellalla (Elnadim (USA)) (18876)
87 B f 13/03 Garswood—Dangerous Moonlite (IRE) (Acclamation) (25714) **Ontoawinner 14 & Mrs E Burke**
88 Ch c 07/03 Dandy Man (IRE)—
Days of Summer (IRE) (Bachelor Duke (USA)) (45714) **Ontoawinner 14 & Mrs E Burke**

MR K. R. BURKE - continued

89 **DISTINCTION (IRE)**, b c 03/05 Kodiac—
Tajbell (IRE) (New Approach (IRE)) (72000) **Mr Carl Waters & Mrs E Burke**
90 B f 07/03 Mehmas (IRE)—Elkmait (Trade Fair) (110000) **Mr Carl Waters & Mrs E Burke**
91 **EMIRATI DREAM (IRE)**, b c 06/05 Buratino (IRE)—Radiant Energy (IRE) (Spectrum (IRE)) (12869) **A. Al Shaikh**
92 **INHALER**, b c 08/02 Elzaam (AUS)—Desire (Kyllachy) (30476) **Mr A. Mohamdi**
93 **INTRUSIVE**, b c 28/01 Fountain of Youth (IRE)—Intrusion (Indesatchel (IRE)) (2380) **Bearstone Stud Limited**
94 B c 10/02 Gutaifan (IRE)—Mayorstone (IRE) (Exceed And Excel (AUS)) (26000)
95 **MINEANDYOURS**, b g 20/03 Garswood—Celestial Dawn (Echo of Light) (3333) **Miss K Buckle & Mrs E Burke**
96 **MISS MILBY (IRE)**, b f 24/02 Camacho—Mrs Huffey (Acclamation) (4976) **Ontoawinner 14 & Mrs E Burke**
97 Ch c 16/04 Garswood—Mysterious Girl (IRE) (Teofilo (IRE)) (13000) **Hambleton Racing Ltd XXXV & E Burke**
98 **NORTH OF AMAZING**, b c 20/04 Havana Gold (IRE)—
Princess Guest (IRE) (Iffraaj) (125000) **Mrs B Keller & Mrs E Burke**
99 B f 21/03 Cable Bay (IRE)—Norway Cross (Cape Cross (IRE)) (65000) **Mr M. S. Al Shahi**
100 **OMANY AMBER**, gr f 04/03 Gregorian (IRE)—Londonnetdotcom (IRE) (Night Shift (USA)) (15000) **K. A. Dasmal**
101 Ch c 23/03 Anjaal—Onomatomania (USA) (Mr Greeley) (58000) **Mr Genesis Thoroughbreds Partnership**
102 **REBEL AT DAWN (IRE)**, b c 01/04 Dandy Man (IRE)—
Ragtime Dancer (Medicean) (64761) **Mr Carl Waters & Mrs E Burke**
103 **RED FASCINATOR**, b f 16/02 Kodiac—Red Turban (Kyllachy) **Cheveley Park Stud Limited**
104 B c 07/02 Garswood—Rosebride (Mayson) (49523)
105 Ch c 10/02 Australia—Seven Veils (Danehill Dancer (IRE)) (85800) **Phoenix Thoroughbred Limited**
106 Ch f 14/02 Night of Thunder (IRE)—Shohrah (IRE) (Giant's Causeway (USA)) (45000)
107 B c 12/02 Kodi Bear (IRE)—Siesta Time (Oasis Dream) (14586)
108 **SIMONS KING (IRE)**, b c 01/05 Kingman—Sanaya (IRE) (Barathea (IRE)) (120120) **Ecurie Normandie Pur Sang**
109 B f 10/04 Dandy Man (IRE)—Solstice (Dubawi (IRE)) (47619) **Mr Carl Waters & Mrs E Burke**
110 **SONDERBAR**, b c 07/03 Siyouni (FR)—Sandbar (Oasis Dream) (30030) **Ecurie Normandie Pur Sang**
111 **SOUND OF DUBAI (IRE)**, b c 08/03 Estidhkaar (IRE)—
Low Cut Affair (IRE) (Fast Company (IRE)) (20952) **A. Al Shaikh**
112 **STYLISH PERFORMER (IRE)**, ch c 17/03 Dandy Man (IRE)—
Va Pensiero (IRE) (High Chaparral (IRE)) (17142) **Pau - Perth Partnershp**
113 Ch c 21/03 Pivotal—Sugar Mill (Oasis Dream) (80952) **Mr Carl Waters & Mrs E Burke**
114 Ch c 12/04 Mehmas (IRE)—Takara Girl (FR) (Kodiac) (23166) **Ecurie Normandie Pur Sang**
115 B c 04/05 Mayson—Tipperary Boutique (IRE) (Danehill Dancer (IRE)) (22307)
116 B c 12/02 Soldier Hollow—Totsiyah (IRE) (Dalakhani (IRE)) (34320) **Ecurie Normandie Pur Sang**
117 B c 13/04 Poet's Voice—Vanity's Girl (IRE) (Compton Place) (34320)
118 B f 15/03 Territories (IRE)—Varnish (Choisir (AUS)) (20000) **K. A. Dasmal**
119 Gr f 14/03 Markaz (IRE)—Vera Lilley (IRE) (Verglas (IRE)) (23594) **Nick Bradley Racing 35 & E Burke**
120 **WEST WAY NEVER (IRE)**, b f 31/03 No Nay Never (USA)—
Western Mystic (GER) (Doyen (IRE)) (47190) **Ecurie Normandie Pur Sang**
121 **WIZARD D'AMOUR**, gr ro c 21/05 Dutch Art—Holistic (Pivotal) (200000) **Mr Carl Waters & Mrs E Burke**

Other Owners: A. Al Shaikh, Mr A. A. Al Shaikh, Mr M. Bates, Mr N. Bradley, Mr S. Bridge, Miss K. Buckle, Mr E. J. Burke, Mrs E. M. Burke, Mr M. Charge, Mrs F. H. B. Cork, Mr J. F. P Cork, Mr P Doughty, Mr T. J. Dykes, Mr A. N. Eaton, Dr C. I. Emmerson, Chris Emmerson & Jon Hughes, Hambleton Racing Ltd, Hambleton Racing Ltd XXXV, Mr N. Hayes, Hold Your Horses Racing, Mr G. W. Holden, Miss S. Holden, Hope Eden Racing Limited, Mr E. J. Hughes, Mrs J. Hughes, Mrs B. M. Keller, Mr L. Kelly, Mr D. F. Kilpatrick, Mr J. Laughton, Mr D. J. MacKay, Mr A. R. W. Marsh, Mr R. C. McKeown, More Turf Racing, Mount Racing Club, Nick Bradley Racing 2, Nick Bradley Racing 35, Nick Bradley Racing 5, Mr N. J. J. O'Brien, Ontoawinner, Ontoawinner 14, Owners for Owners Constitutional, Pau - Perth Partnership, Mr D. Redvers, Mr R. Sinclair, Mr M. Smith, Mrs I. Smits, Mr H. J. Strecker, Miss A. M. Sundstrom, Mr S. R. H. Turner, Tweenhills Fillies, Mr C. J. Waters.

Assistant Trainer: Mrs Elaine Burke, Kelly Burke, Lucy Burke, Joe O'Gorman, **Pupil Assistant:** Ian Hickey.

Flat Jockey: Ben Curtis, Clifford Lee. **Apprentice Jockey:** Rhona Pindar, Harrison Shaw.

74 **MR KEIRAN BURKE, Sturminster Newton**
Postal: **Rudge Hill Farm, Rivers Corner, Sturminster Newton, Dorset**
Contacts: **MOBILE 07855 860993**

1 EVERLANES, 7, br m Shirocco (GER)—Good Thinking **Barrow Hill**
2 GAMBLING GAMUT (IRE), 8, ch g Gamut (IRE)—Red Promise (IRE) **Rags to Richies**
3 GOLDEN POET (IRE), 8, b g Urban Poet (USA)—Little Linnet **K B Racing**
4 JULLY LES BUXY, 10, b m Black Sam Bellamy (IRE)—Jadidh **Mr M. S. Rose**
5 KALABEE (IRE), 5, b g Kalanisi (IRE)—American Honey (IRE) **The Clowns**
6 MINE'S A PINT, 8, b g Network (GER)—Ryme Bere (FR) **Goodfellers Racing**
7 MR MAGILL (FR), 8, b g Hamairi (IRE)—Marie Cuddy (IRE) **K B Racing**
8 PUTDECASHONTHEDASH (IRE), 7, b g Doyen (IRE)—Be My Adelina (IRE) **Goodfellers Racing**
9 SPIRIT OF ROME (IRE), 6, ch m Mastercraftsman (IRE)—Zagreb Flyer **The Clowns**
10 THE HOTELIER (IRE), 5, b g Yeats (IRE)—Miranda's Way (IRE) **SMLC Racing**
11 WHATCOLOURISHE (IRE), 7, br m Ask—Ardnataggle (IRE) **Rags to Richies**

Other Owners: Mr K. M. F. Burke, Miss E. Rogers.

75 **MR HUGH BURNS, Alnwick**
Postal: **Rose Cottage, Hedgeley Hall, Powburn, Alnwick, Northumberland, NE66 4HZ**
Contacts: **PHONE 01665 578647 MOBILE 07503 539571**
EMAIL hughburns123@hotmail.co.uk

1 CARLITOS BAY (IRE), 9, b g Definite Article—Avitta (IRE) **Mr H. Burns**
2 CLABARE, 9, b g Proclamation (IRE)—Choral Singer **Mr H. Burns**
3 COUNTRY DELIGHTS (IRE), 7, b m Mahler—Nadwell (IRE) **Mr H. Burns**
4 MYLITTLEOULBUDDY (IRE), 7, b m Darsi (FR)—She Will Return (IRE) **Mr H. Burns**
5 SPIRIT OF DREAMS (IRE), 5, b m Dream Ahead (USA)—Easy To Thrill **Mr H. Burns**

76 **MR OWEN BURROWS, Lambourn**
Postal: **Kingwood House Stables Ltd, Lambourn Woodlands, Hungerford, Berkshire, RG17 7RS**
Contacts: **PHONE 01488 73144**
WORK EMAIL enquiries@kingwoodhousestables.co.uk

1 ALFARQAD (USA), 5, b br g War Front (USA)—Love And Pride (USA) **Hamdan bin Rashid Al Maktoum**
2 BAASEM (USA), 4, ch g New Approach (IRE)—Ausus (USA) **Hamdan bin Rashid Al Maktoum**
3 BARAAJEEL, 4, b g Kodiac—Madany (IRE) **Hamdan bin Rashid Al Maktoum**
4 BUSTAAN (USA), 4, b f Distorted Humor (USA)—Aryaamm (IRE) **Sheikh Ahmed Al Maktoum**
5 DAWAAM (USA), 4, b c Kitten's Joy (USA)—Nereid (USA) **Hamdan bin Rashid Al Maktoum**
6 ELWAZIR, 5, ch g Frankel—Dash To The Front **Hamdan bin Rashid Al Maktoum**
7 FAKHOOR (IRE), 5, b g Oasis Dream—Darajaat (USA) **Hamdan bin Rashid Al Maktoum**
8 HABUB (USA), 5, b h War Front (USA)—Sweet Lulu (USA) **Hamdan bin Rashid Al Maktoum**
9 MIZAAH (IRE), 7, b g Invincible Spirit (IRE)—Miss Beabea (IRE) **Hamdan bin Rashid Al Maktoum**
10 MUHAARAR'S NEPHEW, 4, b g Mukhadram—Rufoof **Hadi Al-Tajir**
11 MURAAD (IRE), 4, gr g Dark Angel (IRE)—Hidden Girl (IRE) **Hamdan bin Rashid Al Maktoum**
12 SAWWAAH, 5, b g New Approach (IRE)—Mudaaraah **Hamdan bin Rashid Al Maktoum**
13 SHABAABY, 5, br g Kyllachy—On The Brink **Hamdan bin Rashid Al Maktoum**
14 TABDEED, 5, b g Havana Gold (IRE)—Puzzled (IRE) **Hamdan bin Rashid Al Maktoum**
15 WADILSAFA, 5, b h Frankel—Rumoush (USA) **Hamdan bin Rashid Al Maktoum**

THREE-YEAR-OLDS
16 AL FAYYAAFY, ch c Le Havre (IRE)—Adjudicate **Hamdan bin Rashid Al Maktoum**
17 ALMUFEED (IRE), b g Mukhadram—Anqooda (USA) **Hamdan bin Rashid Al Maktoum**
18 ALQIFAAR (USA), gr ro f The Factor (USA)—Atayeb (USA) **Hamdan bin Rashid Al Maktoum**
19 DAANY (IRE), b g Pivotal—Ejadah (IRE) **Hamdan bin Rashid Al Maktoum**

MR OWEN BURROWS - continued

20 **DAHEER (USA)**, ch c Speightstown (USA)—Elraazy (USA) **Hamdan bin Rashid Al Maktoum**
21 **DALEELATY**, ch f Showcasing—Bright Glow **Hamdan bin Rashid Al Maktoum**
22 **DANYAH (IRE)**, b g Invincible Spirit (IRE)—Cuis Ghaire (IRE) **Hamdan bin Rashid Al Maktoum**
23 **DARRAAJ (IRE)**, gr g Dark Angel (IRE)—Cut No Ice (IRE) **Hamdan bin Rashid Al Maktoum**
24 **DAYSAN (USA)**, b c Temple City (USA)—Malibu Pier (USA) **Hamdan bin Rashid Al Maktoum**
25 **EADLIBB**, b f Casamento (IRE)—Zahrat Dubai **Sheikh Ahmed Al Maktoum**
26 **HAFEETH (USA)**, b c Frankel—Munasara (USA) **Hamdan bin Rashid Al Maktoum**
27 **HAIDARAH**, b g Invincible Spirit (IRE)—Natagora (FR) **Hamdan bin Rashid Al Maktoum**
28 **HAIKAL**, ch c Mukhadram—Arwaah (IRE) **Hamdan bin Rashid Al Maktoum**
29 **HAMAAYIM (FR)**, b f Oasis Dream—Goleta (IRE) **Hamdan bin Rashid Al Maktoum**
30 **HAMMAD (USA)**, b g Teofilo (IRE)—Saifaana (USA) **Hamdan bin Rashid Al Maktoum**
31 **HANAFY (USA)**, ch g Animal Kingdom (USA)—Uroobah (USA) **Hamdan bin Rashid Al Maktoum**
32 **HAWAAJIS (IRE)**, b f Dansili—Rasmeyaa (IRE) **Hamdan bin Rashid Al Maktoum**
33 **HOORREYA**, b f Dansili—Rumoush (USA) **Hamdan bin Rashid Al Maktoum**
34 **HUKUM (IRE)**, b c Sea The Stars (IRE)—Aghareed (USA) **Hamdan bin Rashid Al Maktoum**
35 **HUWAITEB**, b g Oasis Dream—Zahoo (IRE) **Hamdan bin Rashid Al Maktoum**
36 **ITKAANN (IRE)**, b c Gutaifan (IRE)—Mimisel **Sheikh Ahmed Al Maktoum**
37 **JEDDEYD (IRE)**, b c Make Believe—Lady Shanghai (IRE) **Sheikh Ahmed Al Maktoum**
38 **KASHAAF**, b c Gutaifan (IRE)—Cape Factor (IRE) **Sheikh Ahmed Al Maktoum**
39 **KHAALIS (IRE)**, b c Muhaarar—Alexander Goldrun (IRE) **Hamdan bin Rashid Al Maktoum**
40 **KHAYYAAL (USA)**, ch f Speightstown (USA)—Wonderful (IRE) **Hamdan bin Rashid Al Maktoum**
41 **MADEYNA (USA)**, ch f Animal Kingdom (USA)—Nasmatt **Sheikh Ahmed Al Maktoum**
42 **TAAWFAN (IRE)**, b f Night of Thunder (IRE)—Ameerat **Sheikh Ahmed Al Maktoum**
43 **THAKI (IRE)**, b g Lope de Vega (IRE)—Mickleberry (IRE) **Hamdan bin Rashid Al Maktoum**
44 **THAKWAAN (IRE)**, b br g Golden Horn—Mudawanah **Hamdan bin Rashid Al Maktoum**
45 **THUMUR (USA)**, b br c Golden Horn—Time Being **Hamdan bin Rashid Al Maktoum**
46 **WIDAAD**, b f Muhaarar—Mudaaraah **Hamdan bin Rashid Al Maktoum**
47 **ZAGRAH**, b f Dansili—Rewaaya (IRE) **Hamdan bin Rashid Al Maktoum**
48 **ZEIMAAM (IRE)**, ch c Slade Power (IRE)—Jathaabeh **Sheikh Ahmed Al Maktoum**

TWO-YEAR-OLDS

49 Ch f 12/02 Lope de Vega (IRE)—Accipiter (Showcasing) **Hamdan bin Rashid Al Maktoum**
50 B c 19/02 Awtaad (IRE)—African Moonlight (UAE) (Halling (USA)) **Hamdan bin Rashid Al Maktoum**
51 B f 21/04 Kodiac—Airfield (Dansili) (260000) **Hamdan bin Rashid Al Maktoum**
52 B c 04/04 Sepoy (AUS)—Baheeja (Dubawi (IRE)) **Sheikh Ahmed Al Maktoum**
53 Gr c 12/03 Havana Gold (IRE)—Blanc de Chine (IRE) (Dark Angel (IRE)) **Hamdan bin Rashid Al Maktoum**
54 Gr c 04/05 Markaz (IRE)—Bunditten (IRE) (Soviet Star (USA)) **Hamdan bin Rashid Al Maktoum**
55 B c 29/01 Cable Bay (IRE)—Conservatory (Observatory (USA)) (140000) **Hamdan bin Rashid Al Maktoum**
56 B c 27/02 Lope de Vega (IRE)—Dark Crusader (IRE) (Cape Cross) (364649) **Hamdan bin Rashid Al Maktoum**
57 Ch c 11/03 Lope de Vega (IRE)—Dash To The Front (Diktat) (500000) **Hamdan bin Rashid Al Maktoum**
58 B f 07/04 Exceed And Excel (AUS)—Dispel (Oasis Dream) (95238) **Hamdan bin Rashid Al Maktoum**
59 B c 09/03 Adaay (IRE)—Dolly Colman (IRE) (Diamond Green (FR)) (120000) **Sheikh Ahmed Al Maktoum**
60 B f 11/04 Dark Angel (IRE)—Fatanah (IRE) (Green Desert (USA)) **Hamdan bin Rashid Al Maktoum**
61 B f 31/03 Lope de Vega (IRE)—Gile Na Greine (IRE) (Galileo (IRE)) **Hamdan bin Rashid Al Maktoum**
62 **HAAJOOS (USA)**, gr c 16/02 Speightstown (USA)—
Broadway Show (USA) (Unbridled's Song (USA)) **Hamdan bin Rashid Al Maktoum**
63 B gr c 03/03 Oasis Dream—Hathrah (IRE) (Linamix (FR)) **Hamdan bin Rashid Al Maktoum**
64 B f 23/03 Oasis Dream—Hedaaya (IRE) (Indian Ridge) **Hamdan bin Rashid Al Maktoum**
65 B c 12/05 Siyouni (FR)—Jane Eyre (Sadler's Wells (USA)) (350000) **Hamdan bin Rashid Al Maktoum**
66 B c 13/02 Muhaarar—Kate The Great (Xaar) **Hamdan bin Rashid Al Maktoum**
67 **MAWKEB (USA)**, b c 03/05 Kitten's Joy (USA)—
Illegal Search (USA) (Officer (USA)) **Hamdan bin Rashid Al Maktoum**
68 B c 30/01 Oasis Dream—Mia Diletta (Selkirk (USA)) **Hamdan bin Rashid Al Maktoum**
69 **MUJASSID (USA)**, br f 18/04 Dark Angel (IRE)—
Hatheer (USA) (Storm Cat (USA)) **Hamdan bin Rashid Al Maktoum**
70 Ch c 07/03 Shamardal (USA)—Mutebah (USA) (Marju (IRE)) **Hamdan bin Rashid Al Maktoum**
71 B f 23/02 Elusive Quality (USA)—Nasmatt (Danehill (USA)) **Sheikh Ahmed Al Maktoum**
72 B c 10/02 Mehmas (IRE)—Pardoven (IRE) (Clodovil (IRE)) (140000) **Hamdan bin Rashid Al Maktoum**
73 B c 12/04 Muhaarar—Path of Peace (Rock of Gibraltar (IRE)) (100000) **Sheikh Ahmed Al Maktoum**

MR OWEN BURROWS - continued

74 B c 30/04 Adaay (IRE)—Place In My Heart (Compton Place) (200000) **Hamdan bin Rashid Al Maktoum**
75 B c 20/02 Oasis Dream—Raaqy (IRE) (Dubawi (IRE)) **Hamdan bin Rashid Al Maktoum**
76 B f 06/03 More Than Ready (USA)—Safarjal (IRE) (Marju (IRE)) **Hamdan bin Rashid Al Maktoum**
77 B f 05/04 Kingman—Shimah (USA) (Storm Cat (USA)) **Hamdan bin Rashid Al Maktoum**
78 B f 15/02 Awtaad (IRE)—Sweet Secret (Singspiel (IRE)) (100000) **Sheikh Ahmed Al Maktoum**
79 B c 22/01 Invincible Spirit (IRE)—Tamadhor (Arcano (IRE)) **Hamdan bin Rashid Al Maktoum**
80 B f 01/04 Lope de Vega (IRE)—Thai Haku (IRE) (Oasis Dream) **Hamdan bin Rashid Al Maktoum**

Assistant Trainer: Robert McDowall.

MR JOHN BUTLER, Newmarket
Postal: **The Cottage, Charnwood Stables, Hamilton Road, Newmarket, Suffolk, CB8 7JQ**
Contacts: **MOBILE 07764 999743**
EMAIL johnbutler1@btinternet.com

1 ADMODUM (USA), 7, ch g Majestic Warrior (USA)—Unbridled Treasure (USA) **Mr A. Campbell**
2 BATED BEAUTY (IRE), 5, ch m Bated Breath—Benedicte (IRE) **Miss S. Barton**
3 BOMBASTIC (IRE), 5, ch g Raven's Pass (USA)—Star of The West **Mr J. Butler**
4 BRIGAND, 5, b g Dick Turpin (IRE)—Juncea **Power Geneva Ltd**
5 BURGUILLOS (IRE), 7, ch g Lope de Vega (IRE)—Hazy Dancer **Miss A. Haynes**
6 CAT ROYALE (IRE), 7, b g Lilbourne Lad (IRE)—Call This Cat (IRE) **Whiterok Ltd**
7 CONNEMERA QUEEN, 7, ch m Major Cadeaux—Cashleen (USA) **Mr J. Butler**
8 DECLAMATION (IRE), 10, ch g Shamardal (USA)—Dignify (IRE) **Twenty 19**
9 DELEYLL, 6, ch g Sepoy (AUS)—Strings **Power Geneva Ltd**
10 DOOGAN'S WARREN (IRE), 5, br g Canford Cliffs (IRE)—Ochre (IRE) **Mr J. Butler**
11 ENZO (IRE), 5, b g Exceed And Excel (AUS)—Zamhrear **Mr J. Butler**
12 FACE LIKE THUNDER, 5, b g Passing Glance—Violet's Walk **Whiterok Ltd**
13 FAIR POWER (IRE), 6, b g Power—Pitrizzia **Mr N. Holmes**
14 FALCAO (IRE), 8, b g Majestic Missile (IRE)—Cafe Lassere (USA) **Mr J. Butler**
15 GENUINE APPROVAL (IRE), 7, ch m Approve (IRE)—Genuinely (IRE) **Madeira Racing**
16 HAVEONEYERSELF (IRE), 5, b g Requinto (IRE)—Charismas Birthday (IRE) **Mr J. Butler**
17 HIDDEN DREAM (FR), 5, b m Oasis Dream—Hideaway Heroine (IRE) **Mr J. Butler**
18 INAAM (IRE), 7, b g Camacho—Duckmore Bay (IRE) **Power Geneva Ltd**
19 JOYFUL DREAM (IRE), 6, ch m Dream Ahead (USA)—Tearsforjoy (USA) **Mr G. Dolan**
20 KATALAN (GER), 7, b g Adlerflug (GER)—Kalla **Miss A. Haynes**
21 KEEP ON LAUGHING (IRE), 5, b m Henrythenavigator (USA)—Outshine **Evans Sneath Enterprises Ltd**
22 KINGSLEY KLARION (IRE), 7, b g Arcano (IRE)—May Day Queen (IRE) **Madeira Racing**
23 MARTIN KING, 4, b c Oasis Dream—I'm A Dreamer (IRE) **Mr J. Butler**
24 MARTINEO, 5, b g Declaration of War (USA)—Woodland Scene (IRE) **Power Geneva Ltd**
25 MIME DANCE, 9, b g Notnowcato—Encore My Love **Mr J. Butler**
26 NEVER TO FORGET, 5, b g Medicean—Fontaine House **Evans Sneath Enterprises Ltd**
27 PECHEURS DE PERLES (IRE), 6, b g Pour Moi (IRE)—Annacloy Pearl (IRE) **Northumbria Leisure Ltd**
28 PINCHPOINT (IRE), 5, ch g Excelebration (IRE)—Al Amlah (USA) **Mr J. Butler**
29 PLUNGER, 5, ch g Helmet (AUS)—Percolator **Mr J. Butler**
30 PUSHKIN MUSEUM (IRE), 9, gr g Soviet Star—Chaste **Power Geneva Ltd**
31 RED INVADER (IRE), 10, b g Red Clubs (IRE)—Tifariti (USA) **Twenty 19**
32 ROCK IN SOCIETY (IRE), 5, ch g Society Rock (IRE)—Arabela (IRE) **Mr D. James**
33 RUBY GATES (IRE), 7, b m Avonbridge—Wild Academy (IRE) **Mr D. James**
34 SOAR ABOVE, 5, gr ro g Lethal Force (IRE)—Soar **Mr J. Butler**
35 SUPERSEDED (IRE), 4, gr g Exceed And Excel (AUS)—Satwa Ruby (FR) **Northumbria Leisure Ltd**
36 THE ESTABLISHMENT, 5, b g Exceed And Excel (AUS)—Sweet Coincidence **Mr J. Butler**
37 TIGER LYON (USA), 5, b g Kitten's Joy (USA)—Hold It (USA) **Mr J. Butler**
38 TIME TO SEA (IRE), 6, b g Born To Sea (IRE)—Eastern Glow **C Benham/ D Whitford/ L Quinn/ K Quinn**
39 TOOFI (FR), 9, b g Henrythenavigator (USA)—Silver Bark **Northumbria Leisure Ltd**
40 UZINCSO, 4, b g Mayson—Capacious **Recycled Products Limited**
41 WANEEN (IRE), 7, b g Approve (IRE)—Million All Day (IRE) **Mr J. Butler**
42 WARRIOR GODDESS, 5, b m Henrythenavigator (USA)—Azenzar **Mr J. Butler**

MR JOHN BUTLER - continued

43 **WELOOF (FR),** 6, b g Redoute's Choice (AUS)—Peinted Song (USA) **Power Geneva Ltd**
44 **ZAIN ARION (IRE),** 7, b m Danehill Dancer (IRE)—Shaanara (IRE) **Mr A. Al Banwan**

THREE-YEAR-OLDS

45 **JALWAN (USA),** b c Wicked Strong (USA)—City Run (USA) **Mr N. Buresli**
46 **JEREJAK,** b c Nathaniel (IRE)—Penang Power **Northumbria Leisure Ltd**

Other Owners: Mr C. F. Benham, Mr J. Butler, Mrs S. Horne, K. J. Quinn, Mr L. M. Quinn, K. Quinn/ C. Benham, Mr D. L. Whitford.

Assistant Trainer: Alice Haynes.

78	**MR PADDY BUTLER, Lewes**

Postal: Homewood Gate Racing Stables, Novington Lane, East Chiltington, Lewes, East Sussex, BN7 3AU
Contacts: **PHONE 01273 890124 MOBILE 07973 873846**
EMAIL homewoodgate@aol.com

1 **ESTIBDAAD (IRE),** 10, b g Haatef (USA)—Star of Siligo (USA) **Miss M. P. Bryant**
2 **FITZY,** 4, b g Epaulette (AUS)—Zagarock **Miss M. P. Bryant**
3 **FLOWERS ON VENUS (IRE),** 8, ch g Raven's Pass (USA)—Chelsea Rose (IRE) **Miss M. P. Bryant**
4 **HARAZ (IRE),** 7, b g Acclamation—Hanakiyya (IRE) **Christopher W Wilson & Partner**
5 **JUMPING JACK (IRE),** 6, b g Sir Prancealot (IRE)—She's A Character **Miss M P Bryant, David & Eileen Bryant**
6 **MERCERS,** 6, b m Piccolo—Ivory's Joy **Homewoodgate Racing Club**
7 **UAE SOLDIER (USA),** 5, b g Dansili—Time On **Mrs E. Lucey-Butler**
8 **UNDOCUMENTED (IRE),** 8, b m Mountain High (IRE)—Dont Cod Yourself (IRE) **Homewoodgate Racing Club**

Other Owners: Mr D. Bryant, Mrs E. Bryant, Miss M. P. Bryant, Mrs E. Lucey-Butler, C. W. Wilson.

Assistant Trainer: Mrs E Lucey-Butler.

Amateur Jockey: Miss M. Bryant, Miss J. Oliver.

79	**MRS BARBARA BUTTERWORTH, Appleby**

Postal: Bolton Mill, Bolton, Appleby-in-Westmorland, Cumbria, CA16 6AL
Contacts: **PHONE 017683 61363 MOBILE 07778 104118**

1 **AGE OF GLORY,** 11, b g Zamindar (USA)—Fleeting Moon **Miss E. Butterworth**
2 **BLACK LABEL,** 9, b g Medicean—Black Belt Shopper (IRE) **Miss E. Butterworth**
3 **BROTHER SCOTT,** 13, b g Kirkwall—Crimson Shower **Miss E. Butterworth**
4 **CHERRY PRINCESS,** 10, gr m Act One—Francia **Mrs B. Butterworth**
5 **IBN AL EMARAT (IRE),** 5, b g Excelebration (IRE)—Grace of Dubai (FR) **Miss E. Butterworth**
6 **PERSEID (IRE),** 10, br g Robin des Pres (FR)—Cowanstown Miss (IRE) **Mrs B. Butterworth**
7 **SNOWED IN (IRE),** 11, gr g Dark Angel—Spinning Gold **Miss E. Butterworth**

Assistant Trainer: Miss Elizabeth Butterworth.

NH Jockey: Sean Quinlan.

80 **MISS LOUISE CABBLE, Bridgwater**
Postal: **Rowden Farm, Spaxton, Bridgwater, Somerset, TA5 1DF**
Contacts: **MOBILE 07703 045260**

1 **JUST DEEGEETEEBEE**, 4, b g Malinas (GER)—Rising Bell **A. G. Fear**
2 **JUST TARA**, 8, b m Kayf Tara—Rising Bell **A. G. Fear**
3 **MISTER TIMMYTUCKS**, 7, b g Kayf Tara—No Need For Alarm **A. G. Fear**
4 **ROSEYROO (IRE)**, 13, b m Brian Boru—Rose Island **A. G. Fear**
5 **SPICY FRUITY (IRE)**, 10, b g Fruits of Love (USA)—Rocksham (IRE) **A. G. Fear**
6 **WONDERFUL DREAMER (IRE)**, 7, b g Vocalised (USA)—Go Hiontach (USA) **A. G. Fear**

81 **MISS JULIE CAMACHO, Malton**
Postal: **Star Cottage, Welham Road, Norton, Malton, North Yorkshire, YO17 9QE**
Contacts: **PHONE 01653 696205 MOBILE 07950 356440, 07779 318135 FAX 01653 696205**
EMAIL julie@jacracing.co.uk WEBSITE www.juliecamacho.com

1 **BILL CODY (IRE)**, 5, b g Declaration of War (USA)—Call This Cat (IRE) **Judy & Richard Peck**
2 **BURGUNDY (IRE)**, 5, b m Holy Roman Emperor (IRE)—China Tea (USA) **Elite Racing Club**
3 **BURTONWOOD**, 8, b g Acclamation—Green Poppy **Judy & Richard Peck & Partner**
4 **CHOSEN WORLD**, 6, b g Intikhab (USA)—Panoptic **The Kirkham Partnership**
5 **DREAM MOUNT (IRE)**, 5, b g Dream Ahead (USA)—Mistify (IRE) **J. Allison, B Ahkong & Partner**
6 **I KNOW HOW (IRE)**, 5, b g Epaulette (AUS)—Blue Crystal (IRE) **Judy & Richard Peck & Partner**
7 **I'LL BE BRIEF**, 4, b f Epaulette (AUS)—Shesastar **Miss J. A. Camacho**
8 **JUDICIAL (IRE)**, 8, b g Iffraaj—Marlinka **Elite Racing Club**
9 **KODIAC DANCER (IRE)**, 4, b f Kodiac—Kaiulani (IRE) **Mr & Mrs G. Turnbull**
10 **KUREDU (IRE)**, 4, b g Intello (GER)—Wait It Out (USA) **Miss J. A. Camacho**
11 **LORETTA (IRE)**, 4, b f Iffraaj—Marlinka **Elite Racing Club**
12 **LORTON**, 4, b f Sepoy (AUS)—Oilinda **G. B. Turnbull Ltd**
13 **MAJESTIC STONE (IRE)**, 6, b g Casamento (IRE)—Pretty Majestic (IRE) **Majestic Stone Partnership**
14 **MAKANAH**, 5, b g Mayson—Diane's Choice **Axom LXXI**
15 **MARVEL**, 4, b g Poet's Voice—Baralinka (IRE) **Owners Group 010**
16 **MEA CULPA (IRE)**, 4, b g Dandy Man (IRE)—La Dama Boba (IRE) **Miss J. A. Camacho**
17 **MYTHICAL SPIRIT (IRE)**, 6, b m Dragon Pulse (IRE)—Call This Cat (IRE) **Judy & Richard Peck & Partner**
18 **SPIRIT OF WEDZA (IRE)**, 8, b g Footstepsinthesand—Sampers (IRE) **Owners Group 005**
19 **TRUE NORTH (IRE)**, 5, b g Henrythenavigator (USA)—Cosmic Fire (FR) **Owners Group 018**

THREE-YEAR-OLDS
20 **ADMIRAL PERCY**, ch c Sir Percy—Oceans Apart **Owners Group 003**
21 **CAPTAIN CORELLI (IRE)**, ch g Anjaal—Disprove (IRE) **Judy & Richard Peck**
22 **DEBS SAYS NO**, ch f Teofilo (IRE)—India Spirit **Miss J. A. Camacho**
23 **LATTERHEAD (IRE)**, b f Raven's Pass (USA)—Sequined (USA) **G B Turnbull & Julie Camacho**
24 **LOW FELL**, b f Make Believe—Never Change (IRE) **G B Turnbull & Julie Camacho**
25 **MAURICE DANCER**, b g Kodiac—Kind of Hush (IRE) **Elite Racing Club**
26 **PROCLAIMER**, b c Free Eagle (IRE)—Pious **Owners Group 033**
27 **THE GREY BAY (IRE)**, b g Gutaifan (IRE)—Coursing **Judy & Richard Peck**
28 **WAITANGI**, b g Dawn Approach (IRE)—Thinking Spirit **Miss J. A. Camacho**

Other Owners: Mr B. Ahkong, Mr J. Allison, Miss J. A. Camacho, Mr R. E. Dean, G. B. Turnbull Ltd, Mrs J. M. Peck, Judy & Richard Peck, Mr R. S. Peck, Mrs R. E. Pritchard, Mrs D. J. Rush, Mr C. Verity.

Assistant Trainer: Steve Brown.

Flat Jockey: Paul Mulrennan, Callum Rodriguez.

82 MR MARK CAMPION, Malton

Postal: Whitewell House Stables, Whitewall, Malton, North Yorkshire, YO17 9EH
Contacts: PHONE 01653 692729 MOBILE 07973 178311 FAX 01653 600066
EMAIL info@markcampion-racing.com WEBSITE www.markcampion-racing.com

1 **CIVIL ENSIGN (FR)**, 6, b g Rob Roy (USA)—Petillante Royale (FR) **Whitewall Racing**
2 **KNIGHT IN ARMOUR (IRE)**, 5, b g Camelot—Madeira Mist (IRE) **Whitewall Racing**
3 **MELDRUM WAY (IRE)**, 7, b g Getaway (GER)—Meldrum Hall (IRE) **Mark Campion Racing Club**
4 **MOUNTAIN RAPID (IRE)**, 8, ch m Getaway (GER)—Founding Daughter (IRE) **Whitewall Racing**
5 **SE YOU**, 5, b g Sepoy (AUS)—Lady Hestia (USA) **Mark Campion Racing Club**
6 **TROIS BON AMIS (IRE)**, 6, gr g Lilbourne Lad (IRE)—Vanozza (FR) **Whitewall Racing**

Assistant Trainer: Mrs F. Campion.

83 MS JENNIE CANDLISH, Leek

Postal: Basford Grange Farm, Basford, Leek, Staffordshire, ST13 7ET
Contacts: PHONE 07976 825134, 07889 413639 FAX 01538 360324
EMAIL jenniecandlish@yahoo.co.uk WEBSITE www.jenniecandlishracing.co.uk

1 **AENGUS (IRE)**, 10, b g Robin des Champs (FR)—Which Thistle (IRE) **Anthony,Barrett,Baxter,Budd,Deane,Lloyd**
2 **ANNEBELLE (IRE)**, 5, b m Jeremy (USA)—Garryduff Eile (IRE) **Mr B. J. Hall**
3 **ARTHUR'S REUBEN**, 7, b g Malinas (GER)—Ambitious Annie **Mr A. J. White**
4 **BARNAY**, 5, b g Nayef (USA)—Barnezet (GR) **D. Ashbrook**
5 **BRANDY PAD (IRE)**, 6, b g Watar (IRE)—Acountry Lane (IRE) **Mr P. & Mrs G. A. Clarke**
6 **BRYDEN BOY (IRE)**, 10, b g Craigsteel—Cailin Vic Mo Cri (IRE) **Alan Baxter & Brian Hall**
7 **CANADIAN GEORGE (FR)**, 5, b g George Vancouver (USA)—Connaissance (IRE) **Mr A. J. Baxter**
8 **CATCHMEIFYOUCAN (IRE)**, 6, b m Touch of Land (FR)—Irish Honey (IRE) **A Baxter, C Burke & N Sobreperez**
9 **CHEDDLETON (IRE)**, 5, br g Shirocco (GER)—Over Sixty **Mr P. & Mrs G. A. Clarke**
10 **CLICK AND COLLECT**, 8, b g Humbel (USA)—Galena (GER) **D. Ashbrook**
11 **CONFRONTATIONAL (IRE)**, 6, b g Footstepsinthesand—Chevanah (IRE) **Mr B. W. Verinder**
12 **COSHESTON**, 7, ch g Black Sam Bellamy (IRE)—Rare Ruby (IRE) **Mrs J. M. Ratcliff**
13 **CRACK DU NINIAN (FR)**, 5, b g Le Houssais (FR)—Syphaline (FR) **Mr P. & Mrs G. A. Clarke**
14 **CRONINS HILL (IRE)**, 6, b g Scorpion (IRE)—Nicholl's Justice (IRE) **J. L. Marriott**
15 **DAPA LAD (IRE)**, 5, b g Yeats (IRE)—Flame of Dixie (IRE) **Mr A. J. White**
16 **FOLLOW YOUR FIRE (IRE)**, 5, b g Le Fou (IRE)—Jollie Bollie (IRE) **Pam Beardmore & Jennie Candlish**
17 **FOR JIM (IRE)**, 8, gr g Milan—Dromhale Lady (IRE) **Ms J. Candlish**
18 **FORTIFIED BAY (IRE)**, 8, b g Makfi—Divergence (USA) **Mr A. J. Baxter**
19 **GOLAN CLOUD (IRE)**, 7, b g Golan—Mite Be Cloudy (IRE) **Ms J. Candlish**
20 **HAPPY HOLLOW**, 8, b g Beat Hollow—Dombeya (IRE) **Mr A. J. Baxter**
21 **ISLAND FLAME (IRE)**, 7, b m Kodiac—Noble Flame (IRE) **Mr P. Bona**
22 **LEESWOOD LILY**, 7, b m Afflora (IRE)—Showtime Annie **Mr M. M. Allen**
23 **MARTHA YEATS (IRE)**, 5, b m Yeats (IRE)—Stratosphere **Mrs F. M. Draper**
24 **MINT CONDITION**, 6, b g Black Sam Bellamy (IRE)—Winning Counsel (IRE) **Whites Property Limited**
25 **MULLINAVAT (IRE)**, 11, b g Beneficial—Kilfane (IRE) **Mr M. M. Allen**
26 **OSCARS LEADER (IRE)**, 7, b g Oscar (IRE)—Lead'er Inn (IRE) **J. L. Marriott**
27 **OUTCROP (IRE)**, 6, b g Rock of Gibraltar (IRE)—Desert Sage **Alan Baxter & Brian Hall**
28 **OZARK**, 4, b f Archipenko (USA)—Shimoni **Mr J. Williams**
29 **PAKIE'S DREAM (IRE)**, 6, b g Arcadio (GER)—Emily's Princess (IRE) **Mr A. J. Baxter**
30 **QUICK PICK (IRE)**, 9, b g Vinnie Roe (IRE)—Oscars Arrow (IRE) **4 Left Footers & A Blewnose**
31 **RED GIANT (IRE)**, 9, ch g Beneficial—Barrack Star (IRE) **Mr V. A. Healy**
32 **SHOW PALACE**, 7, ch g Showcasing—Palais Polaire **Paul Wright Bevans & Jennie Candlish**
33 **SLEEPY HAVEN (IRE)**, 10, b g Indian Haven—High Society Girl (IRE) **Mr A. J. Baxter**
34 **SPECIAL BRUTE (GER)**, 5, b g Maxios—Secrets **Ms J. Candlish**
35 **SPIRIT OF HALE (IRE)**, 9, ch g Stowaway—Roseboreen (IRE) **Mrs A. V. Hall**
36 **SPLASH THE CASH (IRE)**, 7, b m Scorpion (IRE)—Goldfeather (IRE) **Alan Baxter & Terry Hastie**
37 **STAR ASCENDING (IRE)**, 8, ch g Thousand Words—Sakaka **Mr P. Wright-Bevans**
38 **STOP TALKING (IRE)**, 8, b m Gamut (IRE)—Miss Snapdragon (IRE) **Anthony,Barrett,Baxter,Budd,Deane,Lloyd**
39 **TANARPINO**, 9, ch g Tobougg (IRE)—Got Tune (FR) **Mr P. & Mrs G. A. Clarke**

MS JENNIE CANDLISH - continued

40 **THE HORSECHESNUT (IRE)**, 12, ch g Definite Article—Ballinahowliss (IRE) **Mr M. M. Allen**
41 **THEFLYINGPORTRAIT (IRE)**, 11, gr g Portrait Gallery (IRE)—Skule Hill Lass (IRE) **The Mere Partnership**
42 **TIME FOR ANOTHER (IRE)**, 7, ch g Shantou (USA)—Borleagh Blonde (IRE) **Ms J. Candlish**
43 **TOMMY THE RASCAL**, 10, b g Multiplex—Tina Gee **Mr A. J. White**
44 **TOO MUCH TO ASK (IRE)**, 7, b g Ask—Chinara (IRE) **Whites Property Limited**
45 **ULVERSTON (IRE)**, 5, b g Yeats (IRE)—So Supreme (IRE) **Mr P. & Mrs G. A. Clarke**
46 **ZOLFO (IRE)**, 8, gr g Cloudings (IRE)—Hardy Lamb (IRE) **Matt Barrett & Alan Baxter**

THREE-YEAR-OLDS

47 **CAMACHO MAN (IRE)**, ch c Camacho—Ezilii (IRE) **Whites Property Limited**

Other Owners: Mr M. Barrett, Mr A. J. Baxter, Mrs P. M. Beardmore, Mr C. Burke, Ms J. Candlish, Mrs G. A. Clarke, Mr P. Clarke, Mr B. J. Hall, Mr T. Hastie, Mr N. Sobreperez, Mr P. Wright-Bevans.

Assistant Trainer: Alan O'Keeffe.

Flat Jockey: Joe Fanning. **NH Jockey:** Sean Quinlan. **Conditional Jockey:** Darragh O'Keeffe.

---

84 MR HENRY CANDY, Wantage
Postal: **Kingstone Warren, Wantage, Oxfordshire, OX12 9QF**
Contacts: PHONE **01367 820276, 01367 820514 MOBILE 07836 211264 FAX 01367 820500**
EMAIL **henrycandy@btconnect.com**

1 **ALFRED BOUCHER**, 4, gr g Aussie Rules (USA)—Policy Term (IRE) **Mr R. Allcock**
2 **CANAL ROCKS**, 4, br g Aussie Rules (USA)—In Secret **The Earl Cadogan**
3 **FOUR FEET (IRE)**, 4, b g Harbour Watch (IRE)—Royal Connection **Henry D. N. B. Candy**
4 **GREENSIDE**, 9, b g Dubawi (IRE)—Katrina (IRE) **Clayton, Frost, Kebell & Turner**
5 **KURIOUS**, 4, b f Kuroshio (AUS)—Easy To Imagine (USA) **Hot To Trot Racing 2**
6 **LA LUNE**, 4, ch f Champs Elysees—Moonlight Mystery **Alizeti Partners, Clive & Pamela Brandon**
7 **LIMATO (IRE)**, 8, b g Tagula (IRE)—Come April **P. G. Jacobs**
8 **MADELEINE BOND**, 6, ch m Monsieur Bond (IRE)—Spin A Wish **Candy, Pritchard & Thomas**
9 **MAIDEN CASTLE**, 4, b g Nayef (USA)—Danae **Girsonfield Ltd**
10 **NEFARIOUS (IRE)**, 4, ro c Zebedee—Tellelle (IRE) **Mr A. Davis**
11 **PAST MASTER**, 7, gr g Mastercraftsman (IRE)—Millestan (IRE) **Mr D B Clark & Mr H Candy**
12 **QUARRY BEACH**, 4, b f Dutch Art—Free Offer **The Earl Cadogan**
13 **SOLDIER'S SON**, 4, b g Epaulette (AUS)—Elsie's Orphan **Henry D. N. B. Candy**
14 **TWILIGHTING**, 4, b f Kyllachy—Night Affair **Six Too Many**

THREE-YEAR-OLDS

15 **AVANZATA**, b f Al Kazeem—Avessia **P. G. Jacobs**
16 **BESIDES**, ch f Zoffany (IRE)—Beshayer (FR) **Major M. G. Wyatt**
17 **BIMBLE (IRE)**, b f Acclamation—Cape Violet (IRE) **Mr A. Davis**
18 **BLESSED (IRE)**, b c Canford Cliffs (IRE)—Bless You **T & A Frost**
19 **BY STARLIGHT (IRE)**, b f Sea The Stars (IRE)—Step Lightly (IRE) **Mr A. Davis**
20 **CANDLEMAS**, b f Mukhadram—Candoluminescence **Henry D. N. B. Candy**
21 **CATHERINE BAY**, b f Hot Streak (IRE)—Respondez **The Earl Cadogan**
22 **EXPEDIENT (IRE)**, b c Kyllachy—Mabinia (IRE) **Cheveley Park Stud Limited**
23 **GIOVANNI TIEPOLO**, b c Lawman (FR)—Leopard Creek **Mr R. Allcock**
24 **HONORE DAUMIER (IRE)**, b c Lawman (FR)—Feis Ceoil (IRE) **Mr R. Allcock**
25 **HOORAY HENRY**, gr c Brazen Beau (AUS)—All That Jas (IRE) **First Of Many**
26 **JOUSKA**, b f Cable Bay (IRE)—Quiet Protest (USA) **Mr A. Davis**
27 **LIGHT BAY**, b f Cable Bay (IRE)—Key Light (IRE) **Mr H Candy & Mrs D Blackburn**
28 **LITTLE FORTUNE**, b f Swiss Spirit—Chevise (IRE) **Fortune Racing**
29 **MARIETTY**, b f Music Master—Bikini **Mrs S. Lidsey**
30 **MISS MORRIS**, ch f Cityscape—In Your Time **Hunscote Stud Limited**
31 **NUMINOUS (IRE)**, ch g Anjaal—Emma Dora (IRE) **Mr A. Davis**
32 **PUBLICISE**, b f Dream Ahead (USA)—Furbelow **Cheveley Park Stud Limited**
33 **RACHEL WALL (IRE)**, b f Kodiac—Anne Bonney **Cheveley Park Stud Limited**

34 **RAT N MOUSE (IRE),** gr f Gutaifan (IRE)—Rhythm And Rhyme (IRE) **Henry D. N. B. Candy**
35 **SCEPTRED ISLE,** b f Cityscape—Danae **Girsonfield Ltd**
36 **WOODCOCK (IRE),** gr g Gutaifan (IRE)—Tooley Woods (IRE) **Henry D. N. B. Candy**

TWO-YEAR-OLDS

37 **ALLERBY,** b f 08/05 Iffraaj—Alice Alleyne (IRE) (Oasis Dream) **Major M. G. Wyatt**
38 **GEORGE MORLAND,** b c 19/04 Camacho—Baharah (USA) (Elusive Quality (USA)) (20952) **Mr R. Allcock**
39 **KINGSTON STAR (IRE),** b f 06/02 Gutaifan (IRE)—Star of Malta (Kyllachy) (5714) **Mr C. M. Humber**
40 B c 06/05 Charm Spirit (IRE)—Last Slipper (Tobougg (IRE)) (15000) **Mr D B Clark & Mr H Candy**
41 **LUCKY BAY,** b f 15/01 Beat Hollow—Free Offer (Generous (IRE)) **The Earl Cadogan**
42 Gr f 03/04 Hellvelyn—Nihal (IRE) (Singspiel (IRE)) **Mr Michael Aram**
43 B f 31/03 Cable Bay (IRE)—Pavonine (High Chaparral (IRE)) (9000) **Henry Candy & Partners**
44 **ROSA BONHEUR,** ch f 29/03 Camacho—Fire Line (Firebreak) **Mr R. Allcock**
45 **RUN TO FREEDOM,** b c 09/05 Muhaarar—Twilight Mistress (Bin Ajwaad (IRE)) **G. A. Wilson**
46 **SANCTIFIED,** b f 14/02 Equiano (FR)—Bookiesindexdotnet (Piccolo) **Mr A. Davis**
47 Gr c 14/05 Mayson—Silver Halo (Paris House) (16000) **Simon Broke & Partners**
48 **SONOROUS,** ch f 27/02 Pearl Secret—Speed Princess (IRE) (Fast Company (IRE)) (52380) **Mr A. Davis**
49 B f 13/03 Oasis Dream—Spring Fling (Assertive) **Six Too Many**
50 B f 21/03 Mehmas (IRE)—Symbol of Peace (IRE) (Desert Sun) (42857) **First Of Many**
51 **TWILIGHT CALLS,** b c 30/01 Twilight Son—Zawiyah (Invincible Spirit (IRE)) (24761) **Cheveley Park Stud Limited**
52 Ch f 15/02 Pearl Secret—Urban Art (FR) (Siyouni (FR)) (30476) **Mr A. Davis**
53 **VIGNONI,** b c 14/03 Helmet (AUS)—Mondovi (Kyllachy) (10000) **P. G. Jacobs**

Other Owners: Henry D. N. B. Candy.

Assistant Trainer: Amy Scott.

---

85 | **MR GRANT CANN, Lower Hamswell**
Postal: **Park Field, Hall Lane, Lower Hamswell, Bath, Gloucestershire, BA1 9DE**
Contacts: **PHONE 01225 891674 MOBILE 07968 271118**

1 **BERTIE MY BOY (IRE),** 11, b g Millenary—Slievemhuire (IRE) **J. G. Cann**
2 **CADEAU DU BRESIL (FR),** 8, b g Blue Bresil (FR)—Melanie du Chenet (FR) **J. G. Cann**
3 **GOOSEN MAVERICK (IRE),** 9, b g Morozov (USA)—Bonny River (IRE) **J. G. Cann**
4 **HOW'S MY FRIEND,** 15, b g Karinga Bay—Friendly Lady **The Hussey's Hustlers**
5 **I'M IN CHARGE,** 14, b g Rakaposhi King—Cloudy Pearl **J. G. Cann**
6 **JOHN DANIELL,** 15, b g Overbury (IRE)—Hottentot **The Hussey's Hustlers**
7 **MR SATCO (IRE),** 12, b g Mr Combustible (IRE)—Satlin (IRE) **Little Loxbrook Babes and Bays**
8 **QUEEN OF THE COURT (IRE),** 7, b m Court Cave (IRE)—Waydale Hill **J. G. Cann**

Other Owners: Miss A. M. Bush, J. G. Cann.

---

86 | **MR DON CANTILLON, Newmarket**
Postal: **63 Exeter Road, Newmarket, Suffolk, CB8 8LP**
Contacts: **PHONE 01638 668507 MOBILE 07709 377601**

1 **HUNTSMANS JOG (IRE),** 6, b g Milan—Faucon **D. E. Cantillon**
2 **NAVARRA PRINCESS (IRE),** 5, b m Intense Focus (USA)—Navarra Queen **D. E. Cantillon**
3 **PUSHMI PULLYU (IRE),** 4, b f Roderic O'Connor (IRE)—Russian Rave **Ms J. F. Chapple-Hyam**
4 **WHATS NOT TO LIKE (GER),** 9, b g Saddex—Wild Girl (GER) **D. E. Cantillon**

87 MRS RUTH CARR, Stillington

Postal: Mowbray House Farm, Easingwold Lane, Stillington, York, North Yorkshire, YO61 1LT
Contacts: WORK 01347 823776 MOBILE 07721 926772
EMAIL ruth@ruthcarrracing.co.uk, chrissie@ruthcarrracing.co.uk WEBSITE www.ruthcarrracing.co.uk

1 ABUSHAMAH (IRE), 9, b g Nayef (USA)—Adaala (USA) **Grange Park Racing VIII & Mrs R Carr**
2 ALQAAB, 5, gr g Swiss Spirit—Skiing **J Greaves, R Willcock & Ruth Carr**
3 ATHMAD (IRE), 4, b g Olympic Glory (IRE)—Black Mascara (IRE) **Mrs R. A. Carr, R J H Limited**
4 BE PERFECT (USA), 11, b g Street Cry (IRE)—Binya (GER) **The Beer Stalkers & Ruth Carr**
5 BOBBY JOE LEG, 6, ch g Pastoral Pursuits—China Cherub **Mrs A. Clark**
6 CHAPLIN BAY (IRE), 8, b g Fastnet Rock (AUS)—
Green Castle (IRE) **Miss B Houlston, Mrs M Chapman & Mrs R Carr**
7 DARK POET, 4, b g Lethal Force (IRE)—Poetic Dancer **Mrs R. A. Carr, Michael Hill**
8 EXPLAIN, 8, ch g Kyllachy—Descriptive (IRE) **The Beer Stalkers & Ruth Carr**
9 FINAL FRONTIER (IRE), 7, b g Dream Ahead (USA)—Polly Perkins (IRE) **V. Khosla**
10 FORESEEABLE FUTURE (FR), 5, b g Harbour Watch (IRE)—Russian Spirit **RHD & Ruth Carr**
11 FOXY REBEL, 6, ch g Cockney Rebel (IRE)—Foxholes Lodge **Mr Graham Scruton, Mr Dennis Williamson**
12 FRANK ROGERS, 5, b g Compton Place—Bubblina **Mrs S. J. Doyle**
13 GUNMAKER (IRE), 6, b g Canford Cliffs (IRE)—Can Dance **Align In The Sand**
14 IFTON, 4, b g Iffraaj—Flambeau **RHD**
15 INDIAN WARRIOR, 5, b g Sepoy (AUS)—Night Gypsy **Grange Park Racing Club and Ruth Carr**
16 KATHEEFA (USA), 6, gr g Street Cry (IRE)—Wid (USA) **Mrs R. A. Carr, Michael Hill**
17 KHAZAF, 5, b g Dawn Approach (IRE)—Winds of Time (IRE) **Mrs R. A. Carr**
18 KIBAAR, 8, b g Pastoral Pursuits—Ashes (IRE) **Mrs R. A. Carr, Mrs S. Hibbert**
19 KYLIE RULES, 5, b r m Aussie Rules (USA)—Africa's Star (IRE) **J A and Mrs M A Knox**
20 LOULIN, 5, ch g Exceed And Excel (AUS)—Wimple (USA) **G. Murray**
21 MAGICAL EFFECT (IRE), 8, ch g New Approach (IRE)—Purple Glow (IRE) **Miss Vanessa Church**
22 MARCELLA, 5, b m Showcasing—Cool In The Shade **Mrs M. E. Verity**
23 MARK'S CHOICE (IRE), 4, b g Bungle Inthejungle—Ramamara (IRE) **Cragg Wood Racing**
24 MESHARDAL (GER), 10, b g Shamardal (USA)—Melody Fair (IRE) **The Hollinbridge Partnership & Ruth Carr**
25 MONAADHIL (IRE), 6, b g Dark Angel (IRE)—Urban Daydream (IRE) **Mrs R. A. Carr**
26 MUTAMADED (IRE), 7, b g Arcano (IRE)—Sahaayeb (IRE) **The Bottom Liners & Mrs R. Carr**
27 MUTANAASEQ (IRE), 5, ch g Red Jazz (USA)—Indaba (IRE) **The Bottom Liners & Mrs R. Carr**
28 ORIENTAL SPLENDOUR (IRE), 8, br g Strategic Prince—Asian Lady **Mr J. A. Swinburne & Mrs Ruth A. Carr**
29 PIPERS NOTE, 10, ch g Piccolo—Madam Valentine **Cragg Wood Racing**
30 POWER PLAYER, 4, b g Slade Power (IRE)—Varnish **Grange Park Racing XIII & Ruth Carr**
31 POYLE VINNIE, 10, b g Piccolo—Poyle Dee Dee **Formulated Polymer Products Ltd**
32 REPUTATION (IRE), 7, b g Royal Applause—Semaphore **Fulbeck Horse Syndicate Ltd**
33 SHEPHERD'S PURSE, 8, b g Pastoral Pursuits—Neyraan **The Chancers & Mrs R Carr**
34 SUWAAN (IRE), 6, ch g Exceed And Excel (AUS)—Janina **Mr J. A. Swinburne & Mrs Ruth A. Carr**
35 TAMKEEN, 5, ch g Kyllachy—Regatta (USA) **Mrs Marion Chapman & Mrs Ruth A. Carr**
36 TORQUE OF THE TOWN (IRE), 4, gr g Zebedee—Elaysa **Slaters Arms Racing & Ruth Carr**
37 TRICORN (IRE), 6, b g Helmet (AUS)—Special Dancer **Lady O'Reilly, J P Hames & T Dorman**
38 VERDIGRIS (IRE), 5, b m Intense Focus (USA)—Nimboo (USA) **Ms G. F. Khosla**
39 VIVAX (IRE), 4, b g Dandy Man (IRE)—Princess Mood (GER) **Ged Martin Nick & Mrs R Carr**
40 ZEBULON (IRE), 6, gr g Zebedee—Novelina (IRE) **Bruce Jamieson, Barbara Dean, Ruth Carr**

THREE-YEAR-OLDS

41 Ch f Monsieur Bond (IRE)—China Cherub **Mrs A. Clark**
42 DON'T JOKE, ch g Slade Power (IRE)—Lady Frances **Grange Park Racing XIV & Ruth Carr**
43 MAC MCCARTHY (IRE), ch g Anjaal—Kitty Softpaws (IRE) **The Venturers & Mrs R Carr**
44 NOSTALGIC AIR, b f Hot Streak (IRE)—Steal The Curtain **Mr J Berry, Mrs M Chapman, Mrs R Carr**
45 OUTTAKE, br g Outstrip—Cambridge Duchess **Mrs R. A. Carr**
46 SHARP EXHIBIT (IRE), ch f Showcasing—Sharp Relief (IRE) **The Beer Stalkers & Ruth Carr**
47 TREVIE FOUNTAIN, b g Fountain of Youth (IRE)—Fantacise **Grange Park Racing Vii & Ruth Carr**

TWO-YEAR-OLDS

48 Ch f 10/05 Monsieur Bond (IRE)—China Cherub (Inchinor) **Mrs A. Clark**
49 B 04/04 Due Diligence (USA)—Royal Blossom (IRE) (Royal Applause) **Mrs R. A. Carr**
50 Gr g 25/02 Hellvelyn—Sas (IRE) (Zebedee) **Mrs R. A. Carr**
51 Gr f 16/03 Lethal Force (IRE)—Sugar Mountain (IRE) (Lomitas) **Dennis Clayton & Ruth Carr**

MRS RUTH CARR - continued

Other Owners: Mr J. M. Barker, J. Berry, T. J. E. Brereton, Mrs R. A. Carr, Mrs M. Chapman, Miss V. A. Church, Mr D. G. Clayton, Mr A. D. Crombie, Mr T. W. Deadman, Mrs B. I. Dean, Mr T. M. Dorman, Mr C. Dufferwiel, Mr F. H. Eales, Ged Martin Nick, Grange Park Racing VII, Grange Park Racing VIII, Grange Park Racing X1V, Grange Park Racing XIII, Mr J. A. Greaves, J. P. Hames, Mrs S Hibbert & Mrs R Carr, Mr Michael Hill, Hollinbridge Partnership, Miss B. J. Houlston, Dr K. Howard, Mrs P. Howard, Mr M. Howarth, Mr A. B. Jamieson, Mr D. R. Kelly, Mr P Newell, Lady C. J. O'Reilly, R J H Limited, RHD Research Limited, Mr G. A. Shields, Mr E. T. Surr, Mr J. A. Swinburne, The Beer Stalkers, The Bottom Liners, Mr R. Willcock, Mr R. W. Wilson.

Assistant Trainer: Mrs M. Chapman, **Racing Secretary:** Mrs Chrissie Skyes.

Flat Jockey: Jack Garritty, James Sullivan. **Amateur Jockey:** Miss Emily Bullock.

---

88   MR DECLAN CARROLL, Malton
Postal: **Santry Stables, Langton Road, Norton, Malton, North Yorkshire, YO17 9PZ**
Contacts: **MOBILE 07801 553779**
EMAIL declancarrollracing@gmail.com

1 HONEY GG, 5, b m Mayson—Local Fancy **The Commissioning Team**
2 HOUSE DEPOSIT, 4, ch g Sepoy (AUS)—Rosaceous **Ray Flegg & John Bousfield**
3 JACKAMUNDO (FR), 4, b g Fast Company (IRE)—Luxie (IRE) **Mr D. Fantom**
4 JEM SCUTTLE (USA), 4, ch g City Zip (USA)—Elegantly Wild (IRE) **Mr F. Gillespie**
5 JUS PIRES (USA), 6, b g Scat Daddy (USA)—Liza Lu (USA) **The Bramblers, Flegg & Bousfield**
6 MACHREE (IRE), 5, b m Lord Shanakill (USA)—Faleena (IRE) **Mr B Cooney**
7 MARTINA FRANCA, 6, b m Paco Boy (IRE)—Teggiano (IRE) **Mr B Cooney**
8 MOTAHASSEN (IRE), 6, br g Lonhro (AUS)—Journalist (IRE) **Mrs S. A. Bryan**
9 MUSHARRIF, 8, b g Arcano (IRE)—Cefira (USA) **Ray Flegg & John Bousfield**
10 MUSIC SEEKER (IRE), 6, b g Henrythenavigator (USA)—Danehill Music (IRE) **Mrs S. A. Bryan**
11 QUEEN MIA (IRE), 4, ch f Famous Name—Agnetha (GER) **Mr J Blackburn & Partner**
12 RADJASH, 6, b g Shamardal (USA)—White Moonstone (USA) **Mrs S. A. Bryan**
13 RHOSGOBEL (IRE), 4, b f Dandy Man (IRE)—Hunting Goddess **Dreams**
14 ROCK SOUND (IRE), 5, ch g Lope de Vega (IRE)—Thoughtless Moment (IRE) **The Bramblers**
15 SHAWAAMEKH, 6, b g Born To Sea (IRE)—Frances Stuart (IRE) **Highgreen Partnership**
16 SOMMER KATZE (FR), 4, b g Sommerabend—Forward Feline (IRE) **Mr F. Gillespie**
17 TRINITY LAKE, 4, b g Dansili—Mirror Lake **Dreams**

THREE-YEAR-OLDS

18 HI HARRY (IRE), b g Epaulette (AUS)—Emerald Fire **T. M. Jennings**
19 POTENCIA (IRE), b f Free Eagle (IRE)—Appetina **Yenilecas Syndicate**
20 RUBY DREAM, b g Oasis Dream—Russelliana **Mick Larkin & George Jackson**
21 SECRET DIARY, b f Mukhadram—Yearbook **Clipper Group Holdings Ltd**
22 SPARTAN FIGHTER, b c Dutch Art—Survived **Clipper Group Holdings Ltd**
23 B f Due Diligence (USA)—Teggiano (IRE) **Mr B Cooney**
24 TOFFEE HAMMER, b g Hot Streak (IRE)—Heliograph **Blackburn, Turton, & Johnston**
25 TOM TULLIVER, b g Hot Streak (IRE)—Belle Isle **Mr F. Gillespie**

TWO-YEAR-OLDS

26 B c 28/04 Estidhkaar (IRE)—Greek Spirit (IRE) (Invincible Spirit (IRE)) (8000) **Dreams**
27 B c 02/03 Kodiac—Herridge (IRE) (Bahamian Bounty) (105000) **Mr John Dance**
28 B c 30/01 Acclamation—Masonbrook Lady (IRE) (Canford Cliffs (IRE)) (13000) **Dreams**
29 B c 05/04 Equiano (FR)—Mirdhak (Dansili) (28314) **Mr D. Fantom**
30 B c 14/04 Pearl Secret—Miss Macchiato (IRE) (Holy Roman Emperor (IRE)) **Mr John Dance**
31 B f 27/03 Exceed And Excel (AUS)—Super Saturday (IRE) (Pivotal) (52000) **Mr John Dance**
32 TWEET TWEET, ch f 14/04 Twilight Son—
                         Tweety Pie (IRE) (Rock of Gibraltar (IRE)) **C H Stephenson & Mrs P A Johnson**
33 ZAHRISA, b f 27/03 Harzand (IRE)—Isa (Approve (IRE)) **Mrs P A Johnson**

MR DECLAN CARROLL - continued

Other Owners: Mr J. N. Blackburn, Mr H. J. Bousfield, Mrs D. Carroll, D. Carroll, R. J. Flegg, Mr E. H. M. Frost, Mr G. Jackson, Mr T. Johnston, Mr M. Larkin, Mrs Y. Lavin, Mrs L. Maher, Mrs N. McDonnell, Ms C. Mulrennan, Ms S. O'Dowd, C. H. Stephenson, The Bramblers, Mr A. Turton.

Assistant Trainer: Kym Dee.

Apprentice Jockey: Jessica Anderson, Cian Macredmond, Zak Wheatley.

89	**MR TONY CARROLL, Cropthorne**

Postal: Mill House Racing, Cropthorne, Pershore, Worcs
Contacts: **PHONE 01386 861020 MOBILE 07770 472431 FAX 01386 861628
EMAIL a.w.carroll@btconnect.com WEBSITE www.awcarroll.co.uk**

1 **AFFAIRE D'HONNEUR (FR),** 9, ch g Shirocco (GER)—Affaire de Moeurs (FR) **South Yorkshire Racing**
2 **AQUA LIBRE,** 7, b m Aqlaam—Be Free **Mrs D. Hopkins**
3 **BALTIC PRINCE (IRE),** 10, b g Baltic King—Brunswick **Mr A. Mills**
4 **BE FAIR,** 4, b g Kyllachy—Going For Gold **Surefire Racing & Partner**
5 **BE MY SEA (IRE),** 9, b g Sea The Stars (IRE)—Bitooh **L. T. Cheshire**
6 **BEAU GESTE (IRE),** 4, b g Lilbourne Lad (IRE)—Valbonne (IRE) **Mr A. W. Carroll**
7 **BLACK BUBLE (FR),** 7, b g Valanour (IRE)—Miss Bubble Rose (FR) **Northway Lodge Racing**
8 **BOLD DECISION,** 4, b g Zoffany (IRE)—Poly Pomona
9 **BOOM THE GROOM (IRE),** 9, b g Kodiac—Ecco Mi (IRE) **Mr B. J. Millen**
10 **BROTHER IN ARMS (IRE),** 6, b g Kodiac—Cool Cousin (IRE) **Cover Point Racing**
11 **CAFE SYDNEY (IRE),** 4, ch f Foxwedge (AUS)—Carafe **Contubernium Racing**
12 **CHETAN,** 8, b g Alfred Nobel (IRE)—Island Music (IRE) **L Judd T Stamp J Hardcastle R Miles**
13 **CLASHANISKA (IRE),** 4, b g Dark Angel (IRE)—Spirit Watch (IRE) **Mr A. W. Carroll**
14 **CLEARLY CAPABLE (IRE),** 11, b g Bienamado (USA)—Spout Road (IRE) **Mr J. Tucker**
15 **CREATIVE TALENT (IRE),** 8, br g Mastercraftsman (IRE)—Pitrizzia **The Rebelle Boys**
16 **DE VEGAS KID (IRE),** 6, ch g Lope de Vega (IRE)—Fravolina (USA) **The Rebelle Boys**
17 **DESERT SOUND,** 4, b f Kayf Tara—Princess Sabaah (IRE) **Mr D. Boocock**
18 **DOC SPORTELLO (IRE),** 8, b g Majestic Missile (IRE)—Queen of Silk (IRE) **Mr W. G. Nixon**
19 **EESHA SAYS (IRE),** 5, b m Fast Company (IRE)—Admire The View (IRE) **Mr A. W. Carroll**
20 **ESSAKA (IRE),** 8, b g Equiano (FR)—Dream Vision (USA) **Mrs J. Carrington**
21 **FALCON CLIFFS (IRE),** 6, b m Canford Cliffs (IRE)—Circle (IRE) **Mr A A Byrne & Mr Mark Wellbelove**
22 **FIELDSMAN (USA),** 8, b g Hard Spun (USA)—R Charlie's Angel (USA) **SF Racing Club**
23 **FLY THE NEST (IRE),** 4, b g Kodiac—Queen Wasp (IRE) **Mr B. J. Millen**
24 **FORESEE (GER),** 7, b g Sea The Stars (IRE)—Four Roses (IRE) **Millen & Cooke**
25 **FRENCH KISS (IRE),** 5, b g French Fifteen (FR)—Ms Cordelia (USA) **CCCP Syndicate**
26 **GLOBAL STYLE (IRE),** 5, b g Nathaniel (IRE)—Danaskaya (IRE) **Curry House Corner & Partner**
27 **GOLD STANDARD (IRE),** 4, ch g Casamento (IRE)—Goldplated (IRE) **Mr J. M. Wall**
28 **GOLDEN WOLF (IRE),** 6, b br g Big Bad Bob (IRE)—Jeunesse Doree (IRE) **The Risk Takers Partnership**
29 **HENRY CROFT,** 7, b g Dubawi (IRE)—Karen's Caper (USA) **Mr B. J. Millen**
30 **ILHABELA FACT,** 6, b gr h High Chaparral (IRE)—Ilhabela (IRE) **Cooke & Millen**
31 **IRIS'S SPIRIT,** 4, b f Sayif (IRE)—Dubawi's Spirit (IRE) **Mill House Racing Syndicate**
32 **KNOCKABOUT QUEEN,** 4, b f Sixties Icon—Rough Courte (IRE) **Mr J. Tucker**
33 **LADY CYLLA,** 5, b m Malinas (GER)—Lady Samantha **Mrs T. P. James**
34 **LAST PAGE,** 5, b g Pastoral Pursuits—No Page (IRE) **Harvey Lawrence Ltd**
35 **LATENT HEAT (IRE),** 4, b g Papal Bull—Taziria (SWI) **Mr J. M. Wall**
36 **LAYLA'S DREAM,** 4, b f Assertive—Layla's Oasis **Lady Whent**
37 **LONG CALL,** 7, b g Authorized (IRE)—Gacequita (URU) **Mr A. A. Byrne**
38 **MADRINHO (IRE),** 7, ch g Frozen Power (IRE)—Perfectly Clear (USA) **Mr A. Mills**
39 **MAN OF THE NORTH,** 7, b g And Beyond (IRE)—Latin Beauty (IRE) **Last Day Racing Partnership**
40 **MISTER DEPENDABLE (IRE),** 4, ro g Alhebayeb (IRE)—Caerella (IRE) **Mrs A. M. O'Sullivan**
41 **MISTER MUSIC,** 11, b g Singspiel (IRE)—Sierra **Mr A Sergent & Partner**
42 **MUSEE D'ORSAY (IRE),** 4, b g Showcasing—Da's Wish (IRE) **The Rebelle Boys**
43 **NELSON RIVER,** 5, b g Mount Nelson—I Say (IRE) **CCCP Syndicate**
44 **OEIL DE TIGRE (FR),** 9, b g Footstepsinthesand—Suerte **Mr A. W. Carroll**

MR TONY CARROLL - continued

45 **OH SO NICE**, 4, b f Kyllachy—Femme de Fer **Wedgwood Estates**
46 **ONEBABA (IRE)**, 4, ch g No Nay Never (USA)—Enharmonic (USA) **Shropshire Wolves**
47 **OUR MAN IN HAVANA**, 5, b g Havana Gold (IRE)—Auntie Kathryn (IRE) **D. J. Oseman**
48 **PEGGOTTY**, 4, ch f Assertive—Level Pegging (IRE) **Lady Whent**
49 **PILOT WINGS (IRE)**, 5, b g Epaulette (AUS)—Intaglia (GER) **Green lighting Ltd**
50 **POETIC FORCE (IRE)**, 6, ch g Lope de Vega (IRE)—Obligada (IRE) **Mr S. Barton**
51 **POUR LA VICTOIRE (IRE)**, 10, b g Antonius Pius (USA)—Lady Lucia (IRE) **Curry House Corner & Partner**
52 **PRAIRIE TOWN (IRE)**, 9, b g High Chaparral (IRE)—Lake Baino **Cooke & Millen**
53 **PROTON (IRE)**, 4, b g Slade Power (IRE)—Singing Bird (IRE) **The Risk Takers Partnership**
54 **RECON MISSION (IRE)**, 4, b c Kodiac—Ermine Ruby **Mr B. J. Millen**
55 **RED ALERT**, 6, b g Sleeping Indian—Red Sovereign **Mr A. A. Byrne**
56 **RIVER DART (IRE)**, 8, ch g Dutch Art—Sky Galaxy (USA) **Mr B. J. Millen**
57 **ROSE HIP**, 5, b m Acclamation—Poppy Seed **Lady Whent**
58 **ROUDRAPOUR (FR)**, 5, gr g Redoute's Choice (AUS)—Rosanara (FR) **Three Counties Racing**
59 **SCRAFTON**, 5, b g Leporello (IRE)—Some Diva **Mrs P. J. Clark**
60 **SECOND COLLECTION**, 4, b f Delegator—Quelle Affaire **Mr A. A. Byrne**
61 **SHOWU**, 4, b f Showcasing—Travelling **Longview Stud & Bloodstock Ltd**
62 **SILENT ATTACK**, 7, b g Dream Ahead (USA)—Chanterelle (FR) **South Yorkshire Racing**
63 **SILVERTURNSTOGOLD**, 5, ch g Equiano (FR)—Saharan Song (IRE) **Mr A. A. Byrne**
64 **SIR MAGNUM**, 5, ch g Sakhee (USA)—Queen of Heaven (USA) **Wedgewood Estates**
65 **SNOW LEOPARD (IRE)**, 4, gr g Mount Nelson—La Gandilie (FR) **CCCP Syndicate**
66 **SOCIAL CITY**, 4, b g Cityscape—Society Rose **H. M. W. Clifford**
67 **SUGAR PLUM FAIRY**, 5, ch m Halling (USA)—Atyaab **Wedgewood Estates**
68 **TELEKINETIC**, 5, b m Champs Elysees—Kinetix **Six Pack**
69 **TEMUR KHAN**, 5, br g Dansili—Slink **Mrs H. Hogben**
70 **THUNDEROAD**, 4, b g Street Sense (USA)—Royal Crystal (USA) **Mrs L Hunt & Mrs K Campbell**
71 **TONI'S A STAR**, 8, b m Avonbridge—Canina **A Star Recruitment Limited**
72 **TOP BOY**, 10, b g Exceed And Excel (AUS)—Injaaz **Mrs S. A. Bowen**
73 **UNDER CURFEW**, 4, ch g Stimulation (IRE)—Thicket **Mr M. J. Wellbelove**
74 **UPAVON**, 10, b g Avonbridge—Blaina **Mr D. Morgan and Mr K. J. Parris**
75 **URBAN HIGHWAY (IRE)**, 4, b g Kodiac—Viking Fair **Millen & Partner**
76 **VIVE LE ROI (IRE)**, 9, b g Robin des Pres (FR)—Cappard View (IRE) **Surefire Racing**
77 **WILEY POST**, 7, b g Kyllachy—Orange Pip **Lady Whent**
78 **WINDSORLOT (IRE)**, 7, ch g Windsor Knot (IRE)—Majestic Jenny (IRE) **SF Racing Club**

THREE-YEAR-OLDS

79 B g Due Diligence (USA)—Audrey Brown
80 **BEZZAS LAD (IRE)**, b g Society Rock (IRE)—Red Rosanna **Peter Sumner & Noel Berrisford**
81 **CHERISH (FR)**, b f Hunter's Light (IRE)—Agent Kensington **Wedgewood Estates**
82 **CORA BAY**, b f Cable Bay (IRE)—Musicora **Mr A Sergent & Partner**
83 **HARBOUR PROJECT**, b g Harbour Watch (IRE)—Quelle Affaire **Mr A. A. Byrne**
84 **HOT HOT HOT**, ch f Hot Streak (IRE)—Just Emma **Mr A. A. Byrne**
85 **KONDRATIEV WAVE (IRE)**, ch c Dragon Pulse (IRE)—Right Reason (IRE) **Mr B. J. Millen**
86 **LUSCIFER**, b g Heeraat (IRE)—Nut (IRE) **Mr Balraj Singh & Mr Robert C Smith**
87 **POP DANCER (IRE)**, b g Kodiac—Pop Art (IRE) **Mr B. J. Millen**
88 **SIR I'LL CHANCE IT (IRE)**, b g Sir Prancealot (IRE)—Doris Marie (IRE) **Mr A. W. Carroll**
89 **WINNETKA (IRE)**, ch g Camacho—Little Audio (IRE) **Mr A. W. Carroll**

TWO-YEAR-OLDS

90 B c 11/03 Epaulette (AUS)—Dunbrody (FR) (Jeune Homme (USA)) (2000)

Other Owners: Mr J. A. Barber, Mr N. Berrisford, Mr D. R. Blake, Mr A. A. Byrne, Mrs K. Campbell, Mr A. W. Carroll, Mr M. S. Cooke, Curry House Corner, Mr J. R. Daniell, Mrs L. Hunt, Mr J. Lawrence, Mr B. J. Millen, Mr R. J. Millen, Mr D. S. G. Morgan, Mr K. J. Parris, Mr A. W. Sergent, Mr B. Singh, Mr R. C. Smith, Mr P. J. Sumner, Surefire Racing, Mr A. N. Waters, Mr M. J. Wellbelove.

Flat Jockey: George Downing. **NH Jockey:** Lee Edwards. **Conditional Jockey:** Josh Hamer.

90 MR TONY CARSON, Newmarket
Postal: **Cedar Lodge Racing Stables, Hamilton Road, Newmarket, Suffolk, CB8 0NQ**
Contacts: **MOBILE 07837 601867**
WORK EMAIL tcarsonracing@gmail.com **INSTAGRAM** tcarsonracing

1 **CAINHOE STAR,** 7, ch g Pivotal—Celeste **Hugh & Mindi Byrne & W H Carson**
2 **CITY DIVA,** 5, b m Cityscape—Divea **W. F. H. Carson**
3 **DENABLE,** 4, b g Champs Elysees—Surprise (IRE) **Mr C. T. Dennett**
4 **DISTANT UNIVERSE,** 5, b m Universal (IRE)—Distant Florin **Mr C. T. Dennett**
5 **DOLLY MCQUEEN,** 4, b f Canford Cliffs (IRE)—Caterina de Medici (FR) **Rita's Racing**
6 **FRICKA,** 7, b m Sulamani (IRE)—Distant Florin **Mr C. T. Dennett**
7 **GULLAND ROCK,** 9, b g Exceed And Excel (AUS)—Sacre Coeur **Mr A. T. Carson**
8 **PIANISSIMO,** 4, b g Teofilo (IRE)—Perfect Note **Mr C. Butler**
9 **RASAASY (IRE),** 4, b g Cape Cross (IRE)—Drops (IRE) **Mr C. Butler**

THREE-YEAR-OLDS
10 **DAME DENALI,** b f Casamento (IRE)—Doric Lady **Dennett Cameron Francis Hart**
11 **ESCAPE TO OZ,** ch f Cityscape—Munchkin **Mr A. T. Carson**
12 B f Sir Percy—Laraib (IRE) **Mr C. T. Dennett**
13 **SHE'S ON THE EDGE (IRE),** b f Canford Cliffs (IRE)—Tea Cup **Mr A. T. Carson**
14 **SUKIE TWO,** ch f Harbour Watch (IRE)—Sula Two **Mr R. W. Prince**

TWO-YEAR-OLDS
15 **POY,** b c 15/05 Sepoy (AUS)—Sail Home (Mizzen Mast (USA)) **Mr P. Foster**

Other Owners: Mr H. M. Byrne, Mrs M. D. Byrne, W. F. H. Carson.

Flat Jockey: William Carson. **Amateur Jockey:** Mr Graham Carson.

91 MR LEE CARTER, Epsom
Postal: **The Old Yard, Clear Height Stables, Epsom, Surrey, KT18 5LB**
Contacts: **PHONE 01372 740878 MOBILE 07539 354819 FAX 01372 740898**
EMAIL leecarterracing@aol.co.uk **WEBSITE** www.leecarterracing.com

1 **ALRAMZ,** 4, b g Intello (GER)—Rewaaya (IRE) **Clear Racing**
2 **CLIFF FACE (IRE),** 7, b m Canford Cliffs (IRE)—Kotdiji **Mr J. J. Smith**
3 **COME ON TIER (FR),** 5, b g Kendargent (FR)—Milwaukee (FR) **Mr J. J. Smith**
4 **COMEONFEELTHEFORCE (IRE),** 4, b f Slade Power (IRE)—Balladiene (IRE) **Ewell Never Know**
5 **CUBAN SPIRIT,** 5, b g Harbour Watch (IRE)—Madam Mojito (USA) **Mr J. J. Smith**
6 **DI MATTEO,** 4, b f Bated Breath—Pantile **The Emily Charlotte Partnership**
7 **FAIRY FAST (IRE),** 4, b f Requinto (IRE)—Fairy Trader (IRE) **Only One Bid Partnership**
8 **FUWAIRT (IRE),** 8, b g Arcano (IRE)—Safiya Song (IRE) **Peter Clarke Racing Partners**
9 **GERRY THE GLOVER (IRE),** 8, b g Approve—Umlani (IRE) **Mr J. J. Smith**
10 **GLADDEN (IRE),** 5, ch m Teofilo (IRE)—Ballantrae (IRE) **Ewell Never Know**
11 **GOLD CLUB,** 9, b g Multiplex—Oceana Blue **Tattenham Corner Racing IV**
12 **HOLIDAY MAGIC (IRE),** 9, gr g Dark Angel (IRE)—Win Cash (IRE) **The Emily Charlotte Partnership**
13 **ISLAY MIST,** 4, ch f Coach House (IRE)—Amary (IRE) **Mr J. J. Smith**
14 **JONNYSIMPSON (IRE),** 5, gr m Zebedee—Applauding (IRE) **Mr L. A. Carter**
15 **MAAZEL (IRE),** 6, b g Elzaam (AUS)—Laylati (IRE) **Mr J. J. Smith**
16 **REBECKE (IRE),** 4, b f Camacho—Ibecke **Kestonracingclub**
17 **SALEH (IRE),** 7, b g Iffraaj—Pellinore (USA) **Only One Bid Partnership**
18 **SAVITAR (IRE),** 5, b g Shamardal—Foofaraw (USA) **Tattenham Corner Racing IV**
19 **SHYRON,** 9, b g Byron—Coconut Shy **Mr J. J. Smith**
20 **TERRI RULES (IRE),** 5, b m Camacho—Hawaiian Storm **Kestonracingclub**
21 **THE WARRIOR (IRE),** 8, b g Exceed And Excel (AUS)—Aymara **Kestonracingclub**
22 **TREBLE CLEF,** 5, b g Helmet (AUS)—Musical Key **Mrs K. T. Carter**

92 MR BEN CASE, Banbury
Postal: **Wardington Gate Farm, Edgcote, Banbury, Oxfordshire, OX17 1AG**
Contacts: **PHONE 01295 750959 MOBILE 07808 061223 FAX 01295 758840**
EMAIL info@bencaseracing.com WEBSITE www.bencaseracing.com

1 BATTLE OF PAVIA (IRE), 4, b g Milan—First Battle (IRE) **Lady Jane Grosvenor**
2 BOSTON T PARTY, 5, b g Declaration of War (USA)—Sri Kandi **Case Racing Partnership**
3 CODED MESSAGE, 7, b m Oscar (IRE)—Ring Back (IRE) **Wardington Hopefuls**
4 CROCO BAY (IRE), 13, b g Croco Rouge (IRE)—April Thistle (IRE) **Lady Jane Grosvenor**
5 DASH OF BLUE, 5, b g Great Pretender (IRE)—Madame Bleue **Bluebuyu**
6 DORADO DOLLAR (IRE), 6, ch g Golden Lariat (USA)—Stability Treaty (IRE) **P Murray**
7 FADE AND DIE, 4, ch g Gentlewave (IRE)—Ring Back (IRE) **D. P. Walsh**
8 FELTON BELLEVUE (FR), 5, b g Kap Rock (FR)—Sister du Berlais (FR) **Mr B. I. Case**
9 FERN HILL (IRE), 5, b g Dylan Thomas (IRE)—Water Rock **Cross Foran Harrison**
10 5, b g Mahler—Finallyfree (IRE) **Mrs S. R. Bailey**
11 FOURTOUT (FR), 5, b g Honolulu (IRE)—Madisone Fool (FR) **Wardington Hopefuls**
12 GAZETTE BOURGEOISE (FR), 4, b f Spanish Moon (USA)—Jasmine (FR) **Mr A. H. Harvey**
13 GRACEFUL LEGEND, 9, b m Midnight Legend—Clover Green (IRE) **Mr B. I. Case**
14 HUGO'S REFLECTION (IRE), 8, b g Robin des Champs (FR)—Dawn Court **Case Racing Partnership**
15 KILBREW BOY (IRE), 7, b g Stowaway—Bean Ki Moon (IRE) **Lady Jane Grosvenor**
16 KINGS TEMPTATION, 8, b g King's Theatre (IRE)—Temptation (FR) **Lady Jane Grosvenor**
17 LEVASSEUR, 6, b g Black Sam Bellamy (IRE)—Tiger Line **Mrs L. R. Lovell**
18 4, Br g Yeats (IRE)—Made In Kk (IRE) **Lady Jane Grosvenor**
19 MEGABOOST (IRE), 7, b m Court Cave—Sweetasanu (IRE) **Mr T W Moore & Mrs Wendy Moore**
20 MIDNIGHTREFLECTION, 5, b m Midnight Legend—Hymn To Love (FR) **Case Racing Partnership & Anita J Lush**
21 4, B f Leading Light (IRE)—Nechtan (IRE) **Mr A. H. Harvey**
22 PRINCESS ROXY, 7, ch m Midnight Legend—Royal Roxy (IRE) **Mr A. H. Harvey**
23 PULP FICTION (IRE), 8, b g Robin des Champs (FR)—Bean Ki Moon (IRE) **N. S. Hutley**
24 SHANTY ALLEY, 6, b g Shantou (USA)—Alexander Road (IRE) **Jerry Wright Adam Lucock Patricia Murray**
25 SHEILA TANIST (IRE), 7, b m Court Cave (IRE)—Douglas Park (IRE) **Case Racing Partnership**
26 SILENT ENCORE (IRE), 8, ch g Curtain Time (IRE)—What Can I Say (IRE) **North & South Racing Partnership**
27 4, Ch f Imperial Monarch (IRE)—Stein Castle (IRE) **L. A. Garfield**
28 WISECRACKER, 7, br g Sageburg (IRE)—Folie Lointaine (FR) **Lady Jane Grosvenor**

THREE-YEAR-OLDS
29 CLEVER GIRL (IRE), ch f Intello (GER)—Bertie's Best **Mrs A. D. Bourne**

Other Owners: Mr M. Batchelor, Bluebuyu, Case Racing Partnership, Mr R. Cross, Mrs S. P. Foran, Mr J. E. Harrison, Mr A. W. Lucock, Mr T. W. Moore, Mrs W. M. D. Moore, Miss P Murray, J. Wright.

NH Jockey: Daryl Jacob, Kielan Woods. **Amateur Jockey:** Charlie Case.

93 MR PATRICK CHAMINGS, Basingstoke
Postal: **Inhurst Farm Stables, Baughurst, Tadley, Hampshire, RG26 5JS**
Contacts: **PHONE 0118 981 4494 MOBILE 07831 360970 FAX 0118 982 0454**
EMAIL chamingsracing@talk21.com

1 CHARLES MOLSON, 9, b g Monsieur Bond (IRE)—Arculinge **Trolley Action**
2 DOURADO (IRE), 6, b h Dark Angel (IRE)—Skehana (IRE) **Mrs B. C. Wickens**
3 EMERALD FOX, 5, b m Foxwedge (AUS)—Roshina (IRE) **Jackie Cornwell & David Henery**
4 GHEPARDO, 5, b m Havana Gold (IRE)—Clincher **The Foxford House Partnership**
5 HAABIS (USA), 7, b g Super Saver (USA)—Raise Fee (USA) **The Foxford House Partnership**
6 HARBOUR QUAY, 6, b g Foxwedge (AUS)—Whatcameoverme (USA) **Jackie Cornwell & David Henery**
7 HARBOUR TIMES (IRE), 4, br f Harbour Watch (IRE)—Elegant Times (IRE) **Shirley Symonds & Fred Camis**
8 HARLEQUIN ROSE (IRE), 6, ch m Dutch Art—Miss Chaussini (IRE) **G E Bassett & P R Chamings**
9 JE M'EN FICHE, 4, b f Rock of Gibraltar (IRE)—Katya Kabanova **Wedgewood Estates**
10 LUCKY LOU (IRE), 4, b f Most Improved (IRE)—Bessie Lou (IRE) **Lamb & Willis**
11 MISS ICON, 6, b m Sixties Icon—Pretty Miss **Shirley Symonds Fred Camis P Chamings**

MR PATRICK CHAMINGS - continued

12 **MISTER FREEZE (IRE)**, 6, ch g Frozen Power (IRE)—Beacon of Hope (IRE) **G N Hunt, G E Bassett**
13 **SEABORN (IRE)**, 6, b g Born To Sea (IRE)—Next To The Top **Mr I. Beach**
14 **SPANISH STAR (IRE)**, 5, b g Requinto (IRE)—Rancho Star (IRE) **Shirley Symonds & Fred Camis**
15 **VINCENZO COCCOTTI (USA)**, 8, gr ro g Speightstown (USA)—Ocean Colors (USA) **Mr D. F. Henery**
16 **WILD DANCER**, 7, b m Mawatheeq (USA)—Pretty Miss **The Foxford House Partnership**

THREE-YEAR-OLDS

17 **FOUND DOUT**, b f Outstrip—Foundation Filly **Symonds, Camis and Davison**
18 **GUILTY PARTY (IRE)**, b f Lawman (FR)—Coolree Marj (IRE) **Mrs R. Lyon & Mr P. R. Chamings**
19 **MIDNIGHT WELCOME**, b f Fast Company (IRE)—Eleventh Hour (IRE) **Mrs K Meredith and Partners**

Other Owners: Mr G. E. Bassett, F. D. Camis, Mr P.R. Chamings, Mrs J. A. Cornwell, Mr D. F. Henery, Mr G. N. Hunt, Mr R. S. Lamb, Mrs R. Lyon, Mrs S. A. Symonds, Mr D. Willis.

Assistant Trainer: Phillippa Chamings.

---

94 **MR MICK CHANNON, West Ilsley**
Postal: **West Ilsley Stables, West Ilsley, Newbury, Berkshire, RG20 7AE**
Contacts: **PHONE 01635 281166 FAX 01635 281177**
EMAIL mick@mick-channon.co.uk WEBSITE www.mickchannon.tv

1 **AIR FORCE AMY**, 4, ch f Sixties Icon—Madame Hoi (IRE)
2 **BARBILL (IRE)**, 4, b g Zebedee—Fiuise (IRE) **Mrs S. G. Bunney**
3 **BEHOLDEN**, 4, b c Cacique (IRE)—Pure Joy
4 **CERTAIN LAD**, 4, b g Clodovil (IRE)—Chelsey Jayne (IRE) **Mr C. R. Hirst**
5 **CHAIRMANOFTHEBOARD (IRE)**, 4, b g Slade Power (IRE)—
Bound Copy (USA) **David Kilburn, David Hudd & Chris Wright**
6 **CITY WANDERER (IRE)**, 4, b g Kodiac—Viletta (GER) **George Materna & Roger Badley**
7 **DANCING JO**, 4, b g Mazameer (IRE)—Remix (IRE) **R E F Ten**
8 **EQUIPPED**, 4, b f Equiano (FR)—Marjong **Mr J. L. Marsden**
9 **FANNIE BY GASLIGHT**, 5, b m Sixties Icon—Inffiraaj (IRE) **Aston Bloodstock**
10 **HATS OFF TO LARRY**, 4, b g Sixties Icon—Highland Jig **Mr T. P. Radford**
11 **HOLD THE NOTE (IRE)**, 6, b g Jeremy (USA)—Keys Hope (IRE) **Mr T. P. Radford**
12 4, B g Shirocco (GER)—Holly Baloo (IRE) **The Tailenders**
13 **KOEMAN**, 6, b g Dutch Art—Angelic Note (IRE) **Peter Taplin & Susan Bunney**
14 **LORD HOWARD (IRE)**, 4, b g Havana Gold—Lady Gabrielle (IRE) **M. R. Channon**
15 **MISTER WHITAKER (IRE)**, 8, b g Court Cave (IRE)—Benbradagh Vard (IRE) **Mr T. P. Radford**
16 **POUCOR**, 5, b g Pour Moi (IRE)—Corinium (IRE) **Mr & Mrs D. D. Clee**
17 **QUIRKY GERTIE (IRE)**, 4, b f Fast Company (IRE)—Acushladear (IRE) **The Endless Folly Partnership**
18 **SADLER'S SOUL (USA)**, 4, b f Revolutionary (USA)—Sadler's Secretary (IRE) **Mr C. R. Hirst**
19 **SEVERANCE**, 4, b g Nathaniel (IRE)—Decorative (IRE) **The Megsons**
20 **SOCIETY GUEST (IRE)**, 4, b f Society Rock (IRE)—Bronze Baby (USA) **John Guest Racing Ltd**
21 **STORTING**, 4, b g Iffraaj—Stella Point (IRE) **Jon & Julia Aisbitt**
22 **VALENTINO SUNRISE**, 4, b g Sixties Icon—Leleyf (IRE) **P. Taplin**
23 **WESTBROOK BERTIE**, 5, b g Sixties Icon—Evanesce **The Further Folly Partnership 1**

THREE-YEAR-OLDS

24 B f Gleneagles (IRE)—Al Manaal
25 **ALENH**, b gr c Al Kazeem—Enaitch (IRE) **Mr & Mrs D. D. Clee**
26 **ANYONEWHOHADAHEART**, b f Sixties Icon—Bridie Ffrench **M. R. Channon**
27 **AWEEMAWEH (IRE)**, ch c Bungle Inthejungle—Grotta Del Fauno (IRE) **Six or Sticks**
28 **BARTAT**, b f Heeraat (IRE)—Pacches (IRE) **The Wentworth Amigos**
29 **BENTLEY WOOD**, b c Sixties Icon—Dozen (FR) **M. R. Channon**
30 **BLAIRLOGIE**, b g Roderic O'Connor (IRE)—Desert Morning (IRE) **Mr W H Carson & Partner**
31 **BRING THE MONEY (IRE)**, b g Anjaal—Princess Banu **Mrs T. Burns**
32 **BROWN EYED GIRL**, b f Sixties Icon—Fading Away **P. Taplin**
33 **BRUNEL'S BOY**, b g Dutch Art—Hot Secret **Mr R. O'Rourke**

MR MICK CHANNON - continued

34 **BUNGLE BEE (IRE)**, b f Bungle Inthejungle—Ajig Dancer **Mrs T. Burns**
35 **CRAZY LOVE**, b f Sixties Icon—Follow The Faith **M. R. Channon**
36 **DALANIJUJO (IRE)**, ch f Night of Thunder (IRE)—Kiss From A Rose **Mr C. R. Hirst**
37 **DECEPTION VALLEY (IRE)**, b g Slade Power (IRE)—Sahaayef (IRE)
38 **DECORA (IRE)**, ch f Conduit (IRE)—Grevillea (IRE) **Mr N. J. Hitchins**
39 **DONNA RAY**, b f Sixties Icon—Fiumicino **Stoneham Park Stud**
40 **GALAHAD THREEPWOOD**, b c Nathaniel (IRE)—Tesary **The Megsons & Partner**
41 **GLEEDS GIRL**, ch f Equiano (FR)—Linda (FR) **Trojan Way & Partner**
42 **HEAVENTREE (IRE)**, b f Fame And Glory—Savanna Days (IRE) **Jon & Julia Aisbitt**
43 Br g Footstepsinthesand—High Society Girl (IRE)
44 **HUNDRED ISLES (IRE)**, b g Fastnet Rock (AUS)—Gallic Star (IRE) **Jon & Julia Aisbitt**
45 **INDIAN CREAK (IRE)**, b c Camacho—Ushindi (IRE) **Peter Taplin & Susan Bunney**
46 Ch f Anjaal—Indiannie Moon **Mrs T. Burns**
47 **INYAMAZANE (IRE)**, b f Requinto (IRE)—Yasmeena (USA) **Mr C. R. Hirst**
48 **JUNGLE CAPERS (IRE)**, b g Bungle Inthejungle—Kidmeforever **Mr Chrisoper Wright & Mr W H Carson**
49 **KALEIDOSCOPIC**, b f Le Havre (IRE)—Riot of Colour
50 **LIGHTNING BLUE**, b f Harbour Watch (IRE)—Blue Beacon **M. R. Channon**
51 B f Camelot—Mare Imbrium (USA) **Barry Walters Farms**
52 **MILLTOWN STAR**, b c Roderic O'Connor (IRE)—Hail Shower (IRE) **Hunscote Stud Limited & Partner**
53 B g Captain Gerrard (IRE)—Natalie Jay
54 **OKSANA ASTANKOVA**, b f Cable Bay (IRE)—Royal Ffanci **Hunscote Stud Limited**
55 **OUR LAD**, br g Brazen Beau (AUS)—Our Gal **Peter Taplin & Susan Bunney**
56 **POPE GREGORY**, gr g Gregorian (IRE)—La Gifted
57 **PRINCESS LAHAR**, b f Australia—Lady Lahar **Barry Walters Farms**
58 **QUEEN LAHAR**, b br f Gleneagles (IRE)—Miss Lahar **Barry Walters Farms**
59 **QUEEN OF SILCA**, b f Kingman—Silca Chiave **Aldridge Racing Partnership & Partner**
60 **RAINS OF CASTAMERE**, ch g Harbour Watch (IRE)—Shrimpton **M. R. Channon**
61 **RALLY DRIVER**, b g Gregorian (IRE)—Exentricity **Barry Walters Farms & Partner**
62 **RHYME SCHEME (IRE)**, b f Poet's Voice—Tidal Moon **Jon & Julia Aisbitt**
63 **SHE STRIDES ON**, ch f Paco Boy (IRE)—Pose (IRE) **Samscorp**
64 **SINGLE (IRE)**, ch f Nathaniel (IRE)—Solita (USA) **M. R. Channon**
65 **SLY MINX**, b f Sixties Icon—Tanojin (IRE) **Stoneham Park Stud**
66 **SOME PICTURE (IRE)**, b f Kodiac—Windy Lane **Mr J. Turner**
67 **STRAWBERRY HIND (IRE)**, b f Kodiac—Fonseca (IRE) **Tails Partnership**
68 **TALKING ABOUT YOU**, b f Sixties Icon—Ificaniwill (IRE) **M. R. Channon**
69 **TUCKER'S GIRL**, b f Sixties Icon—Saona Island **Mr D Trundell**
70 **VITARE (IRE)**, b g Sidestep (AUS)—Question (USA) **Box 41**
71 **WALKONBY**, ch f Sixties Icon—Shadows Ofthenight (IRE) **M. R. Channon**
72 B f Sixties Icon—Wansdyke Lass **Stoneham Park Stud**
73 **WIGHTMAN (IRE)**, b g Anjaal—Defensive Boast (USA) **M. R. Channon**
74 **WILLIAMWILBERFORCE**, b c Dream Ahead (USA)—Isabella Bird **Jon & Julia Aisbitt**
75 **WINE FLIGHT**, b f Gregorian (IRE)—Amahoro **Dave & Gill Hedley**

TWO-YEAR-OLDS

76 **ADACE**, b f 18/03 Adaay (IRE)—Marjong (Mount Nelson) **Mr J. L. Marsden**
77 Gr c 26/03 Outstrip—Alpha Spirit (Sixties Icon) (571)
78 B f 14/04 Gregorian (IRE)—Altona (IRE) (Redback) **Bastian Family I**
79 B f 16/03 Harbour Watch (IRE)—Amahoro (Sixties Icon) **Dave & Gill Hedley**
80 **AMY BEACH (IRE)**, b f 29/01 New Approach (IRE)—Isabella Bird (Invincible Spirit (IRE)) **Jon & Julia Aisbitt**
81 B c 25/02 Vadamos (FR)—Ballet of Doha (IRE) (Zebedee) (10000) **Six or Sticks 2020**
82 Ch f 09/03 Captain Gerrard (IRE)—Blakeshall Rose (Tobougg (IRE)) **Bastian Family**
83 B f 27/03 Sixties Icon—Bridie Ffrench (Bahamian Bounty)
84 **CHATTRI**, b c 22/03 Sepoy (AUS)—Sandreamer (IRE) (Oasis Dream) **Jon & Julia Aisbitt**
85 B c 22/03 Dragon Pulse (IRE)—Clenaghcastle Lady (IRE) (Acclamation) (28000)
86 B f 29/04 Swiss Spirit—Crazee Diamond (Rock of Gibraltar (IRE))
87 B gr c 27/01 Sir Prancealot (IRE)—Danamight (IRE) (Danetime (IRE)) (40000) **Six or Sticks 2020**
88 Ch f 25/03 Sixties Icon—Dozen (FR) (Mastercraftsman (IRE))
89 B c 23/01 Helmet (AUS)—Early Start (Arcano (IRE)) (5000)
90 Ch c 27/03 Sepoy (AUS)—Effie B (Sixties Icon) (571) **Bastian Family**

MR MICK CHANNON - continued

91 Gr f 08/03 Sixties Icon—El Che (Winker Watson) **Mr Peter Taplin & Partner**
92 B f 09/04 Captain Gerrard (IRE)—Evanesce (Lujain (USA)) (2380) **Dave & Gill Hedley**
93 B f 19/02 Sixties Icon—Follow The Faith (Piccolo)
94 FOLLY BEACH, b f 09/04 Golden Horn—Vive Ma Fille (GER) (Doyen (IRE)) **Mr J. M. Mitchell**
95 B c 24/05 Sixties Icon—Good Morning Lady (Compton Place)
96 B f 06/04 Sixties Icon—Hi Note (Acclamation)
97 HIROMICHI (FR), gr c 09/02 Dabirsim (FR)—Pachelbelle (FR) (Anabaa (USA)) **Jon & Julia Aisbitt**
98 B f 26/02 Sixties Icon—Ificaniwill (IRE) (Mastercraftsman (IRE))
99 Ch c 16/04 Bated Breath—In Your Time (Dalakhani (IRE)) (33333) **Hunscote Stud Limited & Partner**
100 B c 28/04 Bungle Inthejungle—Inffiraaj (IRE) (Iffraaj) (12857)
101 JANIE JONES, ch f 13/04 Le Havre (IRE)—Coquet (Sir Percy) (120000) **The Megsons**
102 B f 03/03 Cityscape—Just Violet (Sixties Icon) **Eternal Folly Partnership 1**
103 B c 10/03 Exceed And Excel (AUS)—Lady Lahar (Fraam) (52000) **John & Zoe Webster**
104 MAJESTIC (IRE), b c 09/03 Conduit (IRE)—Grevillea (IRE) (Admiralofthefleet (USA)) **Mr N. J. Hitchins**
105 B c 07/03 Sixties Icon—Rough Courte (IRE) (Clodovil (IRE))
106 B c 06/04 Twilight Son—Royal Ffanci (Royal Applause) (95238) **Hunscote Stud Limited**
107 B f 14/03 Requinto (IRE)—Sandy Times (IRE) (Footstepsinthesand)
108 B c 24/05 Sixties Icon—Saona Island (Bahamian Bounty) (571)
109 SAULIRE STAR (IRE), b f 26/02 Awtaad (IRE)—Gallic Star (IRE) (Galileo (IRE)) **Jon & Julia Aisbitt**
110 B c 19/03 Sixties Icon—Siri (Atlantic Sport (USA)) **Dave & Gill Hedley**
111 SOPHIGGLIA, gr f 29/04 Sixties Icon—
                                Myladyjane (IRE) (Mastercraftsman (IRE)) **Nick & Olga Dhandsa, John & Zoe Webster**
112 B c 08/03 Kodi Bear (IRE)—Subtle Affair (IRE) (Barathea (IRE)) (24882)
113 B c 26/02 Dandy Man (IRE)—Surava (Big Bad Bob (IRE)) (17142)
114 B f 13/03 Cityscape—Symboline (Royal Applause)
115 B f 29/04 Sixties Icon—Tanojin (IRE) (Thousand Words) **Stoneham Park Stud**
116 Br c 31/03 Fountain of Youth (IRE)—Vilnius (Imperial Dancer) (3809)
117 Ch f 31/03 Sixties Icon—Winkaway (Winker Watson) (571) **P. Taplin**
118 B f 27/02 Sixties Icon—Zaatar (IRE) (Fast Company (IRE)) (571)
119 B f 19/02 Kodiac—Zarafa (Fraam) (42000)

Other Owners: Mr K Al-Mudhaf, Mr M Al-Qatami, Barry Walters Farms, Bastian Family, Mr G Black, Mrs S. G. Bunney, M. R. Channon, Mr A Heaney, Hunscote Stud Limited, Insignia Racing, Mrs A Jones, Mr A. S. L. Leader, Mrs N Lee, Mrs S Magnier, Mr Mills-Webb, Mr W Mula, Mr A Prickett, Mrs C Prickett, Mr T. P. Radford, Stoneham Park Stud, P. Taplin, The Megsons, Mr P Trant, Mr A Tuckerman.

Assistant Trainer: Jack Channon, Paul Morkan.

---

95 **MR MICHAEL CHAPMAN, Market Rasen**
Postal: **Woodlands Racing Stables, Woodlands Lane, Willingham Road, Market Rasen, Lincolnshire, LN8 3RE**
Contacts: **PHONE 01673 843663 MOBILE 07971 940087**
EMAIL woodlands.stables@btconnect.com WEBSITE www.woodlandsracingstables.co.uk

1 GLACIER FOX, 5, ch g Foxwedge (AUS)—Beat Seven **Mrs M. M. Chapman**
2 L'ES FREMANTLE (FR), 9, b g Orpen (USA)—Grand Design **Mr G. Nolan**
3 LUDUAMF (IRE), 6, ch g Tamayuz—Aphorism **Mrs M. M. Chapman**
4 MONZINO (USA), 12, b br g More Than Ready (USA)—Tasso's Magic Roo (USA) **Mrs M. M. Chapman**
5 NOLANS HOTSPUR (IRE), 8, b g Bushranger (IRE)—Cayambe (IRE) **Mr G. Nolan**
6 PORT LAIRGE, 10, b g Pastoral Pursuits—Stylish Clare (IRE) **Mrs M. M. Chapman**
7 THE SOCIETY MAN (IRE), 13, ch g Moscow Society (USA)—Redruth (IRE) **Mrs M. M. Chapman**
8 VOLCANIC JACK (IRE), 12, b g Kodiac—Rosaria Panatta (IRE) **Mrs M. M. Chapman**

Assistant Trainer: Mrs M. Chapman.

96 **MR RYAN CHAPMAN, St Columb**
Postal: Trembleath Farm, St. Columb, Cornwall, TR9 6DP

1 **DOYEN EXPRESS (IRE)**, 6, b m Doyen (IRE)—Crimson Bow (GER) **Mr R. G. Chapman**
2 **PERUVIEN BLEU (FR)**, 8, b br g Fuisse (FR)—Edelmira (FR) **Mr R. G. Chapman**
3 **SUPREME SOVIET (IRE)**, 6, b g Sholokhov (IRE)—Bay Pearl (FR) **Mr R. G. Chapman**

---

97 **MR FABRICE CHAPPET, Chantilly**
Postal: 29 Avenue de Joinville, 60500 Chantilly, France
Contacts: PHONE +33 3 44 21 03 00
EMAIL chappet-secretariat@orange.fr WEBSITE www.chappetracing.com

1 **AL ARESH (FR)**, 4, b c Footstepsinthesand—Itasca (FR) **Al Shaqab Racing**
2 **AL MALHOUF**, 5, ch h Dutch Art—Lady Eclair (IRE) **S. B. Al Kuwari**
3 **ALWAAB (FR)**, 4, b c Toronado (IRE)—Lady Gorgeous **S. B. Al Kuwari**
4 **AQUASTAR (IRE)**, 4, b g Sea The Stars (IRE)—Chiosina (IRE) **F. J. Carmichael**
5 **ATTIRANCE (FR)**, 4, b f Slickly (FR)—Gracieuse (IRE) **L. Mineo**
6 **BLISS FOR EVER (FR)**, 4, b c Slickly (FR)—Marital Bliss (FR) **H. de Pracomtal**
7 **CELESTISSIME (FR)**, 4, b f Camelot—Keegsquaw (IRE) **A. Curty**
8 **GLYSANDRINE (IRE)**, 4, b f Dabirsim (FR)—Gloomy Sunday (FR) **Ecurie Normandie Pur Sang**
9 **HONGBAO (FR)**, 4, ch g Literato (FR)—Bairgaine (FR) **F. Chappet**
10 **INATTENDU (FR)**, 4, b c Anodin (IRE)—Suama (FR) **F. Chappet**
11 **INTELLOGENT (FR)**, 5, ch h Intello (GER)—Nuit Polaire (IRE) **F. J. Carmichael**
12 **KEN COLT (IRE)**, 5, b g Kendargent (FR)—Velvet Revolver (IRE) **Roy Racing Ltd**
13 **KILFRUSH MEMORIES (FR)**, 4, b c Shakespearean (IRE)—Elusive Lily **S. Vidal**
14 **LITTLE FOLLY (FR)**, 4, b f Literato (FR)—Folle Dingue (FR) **X. Doumen**
15 **NOXARENO (GER)**, 4, b c Maxios—Nobilissima (GER) **Ecurie Normandie Pur Sang**
16 **PRETTY BOY (IRE)**, 4, b c Siyouni (FR)—Fast And Pretty (IRE) **S. B. Al Kuwari**
17 **REY PELAYO (FR)**, 4, b c Wootton Bassett—Darkova (USA) **Haras d'Etreham**
18 **ROC ANGEL (FR)**, 6, ch g Rock of Gibraltar (IRE)—Forewarned (IRE) **A. Gilibert**
19 **SALMON PLEASE (FR)**, 4, gr c Rajsaman (FR)—Midnight Flash (IRE) **H. de Pracomtal**
20 **SAN HUBERTO (IRE)**, 4, b c Speightstown (USA)—Sediciosa (USA) **M. Lagasse**
21 **SKYWARD (FR)**, 4, b c Camelot—Shakeyourbody (USA) **J. Messara**
22 **YSSINGEAUX (FR)**, 4, b g Dabirsim (FR)—Lovely Best (FR) **A. Gilibert**

THREE-YEAR-OLDS

23 **ALYSHKA (FR)**, b f Anodin (IRE)—Cosquillas (IRE) **A. Jathiere**
24 **ANNALYSE (FR)**, b f Olympic Glory (IRE)—Lily of The Lake (FR) **A. G. Kavanagh**
25 **APRIL FOOLS (IRE)**, b br f Gleneagles (IRE)—Elitiste (IRE) **F. Bianco**
26 **AVYON (FR)**, b f American Post—Airline **Bloodstock Agency Ltd**
27 **BAVARIA BABY (FR)**, b f Dabirsim (FR)—Baiadera (GER) **Ecurie Normandie Pur Sang**
28 **BE MY DAY (FR)**, b c Zebedee—Gloomy Sunday (FR) **Ecurie Normandie Pur Sang**
29 **BEDWYR**, b c Siyouni (FR)—Rumored (USA) **Al Shaqab Racing**
30 **BERNIE'S STAR (FR)**, b f Iffraaj—Bernie's Moon (USA) **R. Shaykhutdinov**
31 **CELESTIN (FR)**, b c Dabirsim (FR)—Celestoville (FR) **Ecurie Normandie Pur Sang**
32 **CHAMAILLE IRE**, b f Lawman (FR)—Babacora (FR) **A. Gilibert**
33 **DIGRESSION (IRE)**, ch f Gleneagles (IRE)—Daltiana (FR) **A. Gilibert**
34 **DREAM WORKS (FR)**, gr c Wootton Bassett—Sablionniere (FR) **Ecurie J. L. Bouchard**
35 **FORZA SEDACA (FR)**, b c Anodin (IRE)—Bella Vento **O. J. McDowell**
36 **FRANKEL'S MAGIC (FR)**, b f Frankel—Global Magic **R. Shaykhutdinov**
37 **GOLD TRIP (FR)**, b c Outstrip—Sarvana (FR) **Ecurie J. L. Bouchard**
38 **HEIR (FR)**, bl c Pedro The Great (USA)—Mofa Bere (FR) **L. Powell**
39 **HURRICANE IVOR (IRE)**, b c Ivawood (IRE)—Quickstep Queen **F. J. Carmichael**
40 **INSTRUIT**, b c Intello (GER)—Stumpy **A. Gilibert**
41 **JAMILYA (FR)**, gr f Kingman—Jane Eyre **R. Shaykhutdinov**
42 **JARNAC (FR)**, b f Siyouni (FR)—Optica (FR) **H. de Pracomtal**
43 **JUST LADY (FR)**, b f Dabirsim (FR)—Simply Lady (FR) **Ecurie Normandie Pur Sang**
44 **KAPSALIANA (FR)**, b f Wootton Bassett—Age of Refinement (IRE) **Ecurie Vivaldi**

MR FABRICE CHAPPET - continued

45 **KING PACHA (IRE)**, b c Acclamation—Regina Mundi (IRE) **NBH Racing**
46 **KRAQUANTE**, b f Bated Breath—Desert Image **Ecurie Vivaldi**
47 **LIGHT IN THE DARK (FR)**, b f Dark Angel (IRE)—Wonderous Light (IRE) **R. Shaykhutdinov**
48 **MA DECLARATION (IRE)**, ch f Declaration of War (USA)—Night Song **A. Gilibert**
49 **MAGEVA**, b f Wootton Bassett—Melilot (FR) **A. Gilibert**
50 **MOON DREAM (FR)**, b c Dream Ahead (USA)—Lune Rose **Ecurie Vivaldi**
51 **MOON SPIRIT**, b c Charm Spirit (IRE)—Full Snow Moon (USA) **L. Disaro**
52 **NEGUS**, ch c Le Havre (IRE)—Abyssinie (IRE) **Al Shaqab Racing**
53 **NEHOU (FR)**, b c Rajsaman (FR)—Noce (FR) **G. Augustin-Normand**
54 **NIKOFOTO**, b c Olympic Glory (IRE)—Jeu de Vivre (IRE) **Al Shaqab Racing**
55 **PICOSA CITY (IRE)**, b f Temple City (USA)—Chiquita Picosa (USA) **Ecurie J. L. Bouchard**
56 **PISANELLO (IRE)**, b c Raven's Pass (USA)—Painting (IRE) **Haras d'Etreham**
57 **PORCELAINE (IRE)**, b f Kodiac—Zut Alors (IRE) **A. M. Hayes**
58 **RACING GLORY (IRE)**, b c Zebedee—Glorious Adventure (IRE) **Ecurie Normandie Pur Sang**
59 **ROLLEVILLE (FR)**, ch f Rock of Gibraltar (IRE)—Racemate **G. Augustin-Normand**
60 **ROYAUMONT (FR)**, b g Dabirsim (FR)—Rosie Thomas (IRE) **A. Gilibert**
61 **SAN FABRIZIO (FR)**, b c Siyouni (FR)—Ponte Sanangelo (FR) **H. Guy**
62 **SECRET TIME (GER)**, b f Camacho—Song of Time (IRE) **G. Algranti**
63 **SPEAK OF THE DEVIL (FR)**, b f Wootton Bassett—Moranda (FR) **R. Shaykhutdinov**
64 **STONIA (FR)**, gr f Kendargent (FR)—Little Stone (FR) **G. Pariente**
65 **STORMACOMING (IRE)**, b f Stormy River (FR)—Kingdom Come (FR) **Mulungu Bloodstock**
66 **SUPERSTITIOUS (FR)**, b f Olympic Glory (IRE)—Superstition (FR) **R. Simmons**
67 B f Zoffany (IRE)—Sweet Dreams Baby (IRE) **A. Gilibert**
68 **TOGETHER APART**, b f Teofilo (IRE)—Holly Polly (GER) **A. Gilibert**
69 **TRES SPECIALE**, ch f Siyouni (FR)—Special Gift (IRE) **Ballylinch Stud**
70 **VALPARAISO**, b c Muhtathir—Suama (FR) **A. Gilibert**
71 **WIND SPIRIT (FR)**, b c Charm Spirit (IRE)—Alpine Rose **C. Marzocco**
72 **WING AND A PRAYER (FR)**, gr f Charm Spirit (IRE)—Atlantic Light **C.N. Wright**
73 **ZACCAPA (FR)**, b f Muhaarar—Soudanaise (IRE) **Ecurie J. L. Bouchard**
74 **ZADAR (FR)**, bl f Wootton Bassett—Zanyeva (IRE) **Riviera Equine**
75 **ZAHONY (FR)**, b f Lawman (FR)—Zardaka (IRE) **San Paolo Agri Stud**

TWO-YEAR-OLDS

76 B f 20/04 Siyouni (FR)—Acatama (Efisio) **Aleyrion Bloodstock**
77 B c 16/02 Toronado (IRE)—Al Hazmiia (IRE) (Zamindar (USA)) **Al Shaqab Racing**
78 B f 11/02 Le Havre (IRE)—Al Thakhira (Dubawi) **Al Shaqab Racing**
79 **AMBRE SOLEIL (FR)**, b f 23/01 Dabirsim (FR)—
　　　　　　　　　　　Ambre Doree (FR) (Rio de La Plata (USA)) **Ecurie Normandie Pur Sang**
80 B f 17/02 Muhaarar—Attractive Lady (Teofilo (IRE))
81 **BAVARIA EXPRESS (FR)**, b f 04/02 Dabirsim (FR)—Baiadera (GER) (Tertullian (USA)) **Ecurie Normandie Pur Sang**
82 **BEL ARISTO (FR)**, b c 25/03 New Approach (IRE)—Baroness Daniela (Tiger Hill (IRE)) (68640) **A. Gilibert**
83 B f 21/04 Siyouni (FR)—Changing Skies (IRE) (Sadler's Wells (USA)) **Al Shaqab Racing**
84 **COLORADO SAND (IRE)**, b f 02/04 Footstepsinthesand—
　　　　　　　　　　　Cindy Bould (High Chaparral (IRE)) **Ecurie Normandie Pur Sang**
85 B c 20/02 The Gurkha—Daltania (FR) (Selkirk (USA)) **A. Gilibert**
86 B c 25/04 Dariyan (FR)—Dilag (IRE) (Almutawakel) **C.N. Wright**
87 B c 10/04 Frankel—Dubai Rose (Dubai Destination (USA)) **H. Saito**
88 B c 06/04 Wootton Bassett—Accalmie (Invincible Spirit) **H. Saito**
89 B c 07/02 Fastnet Rock—Engage (IRE) (Pour Moi) **Ecurie Ades Hazan**
90 B c 19/03 Exosphere (AUS)—Excellent Girl (Exceed And Excel (AUS)) **Aleyrion Bloodstock**
91 B c 01/02 War Front (USA)—Fresh Air (IRE) (Montjeu (IRE)) **Haras d'Etreham**
92 B c 09/02 Sea The Moon (GER)—Gagarina (FR) (Galileo (IRE)) **R. Shaykhutdinov**
93 **GALACTICA (FR)**, b c 24/02 Dabirsim (FR)—Garmerita (Poliglote) **Ecurie Normandie Pur Sang**
94 **GIRL ON THE MOON**, b f 17/04 Wootton Bassett—
　　　　　　　　　　　Tempera Noire (FR) (Miesque's Son (USA)) (115830) **J.E. Dubois**
95 B f 05/03 Siyouni (FR)—Global Magic (Lando) **R. Shaykhutdinov**
96 B c 28/04 New Bay—High Limits (IRE) (High Chaparral (IRE)) **C. Marzocco**
97 **KAPANI (FR)**, bl c 07/04 Soldier Hollow—Oceanie (FR) (Dansili) **Hubert Meraud**
98 B c 08/05 Dragon Pulse—Kingdome Come (King's Best (USA)) **H. de Pracomtal**

MR FABRICE CHAPPET - continued

99 **MAHTHOUF (IRE)**, b c 18/02 Zoffany (IRE)—Last Jewel (IRE) (Invincible Spirit (IRE)) (60060) **S. B. Al Kuwari**
100 B c 30/04 Kodiac—Mambo Light (USA) (Kingmambo (USA)) **Ecurie J. L. Bouchard**
101 **MARIE (IRE)**, b c 27/05 Dabirsim (FR)—Moujah (FR) (Whipper (USA)) **Ecurie Normandie Pur Sang**
102 B f 03/05 Scissor Kick (AUS)—Minza (FR) (Zamindar (USA)) **Haras d'Etreham**
103 **MON AMOUR (IRE)**, b f 08/02 Kodi Bear (IRE)—Monspa (Monsun (GER)) (15444) **Ecurie Normandie Pur Sang**
104 **MORE JOY (FR)**, b f 07/05 Morandi—La Joie (Montjeu (IRE)) **H. de Pracomtal**
105 Ch f 20/04 Tamayuz—Ocean Talent (Aptitude)
106 **OK BOOMER (IRE)**, b f 24/04 Slade Power (IRE)—Pinaruh (FR) (Iffraaj) (55770)
107 **OMNIA MUNDA MUNDIS**, b f 21/03 Australia—Regina Mundi (IRE) (Montjeu (IRE)) (163020) **San Paolo Agri Stud**
108 Ch f 05/03 Karakontie (JPN)—Passing By (Raven's Pass (USA))
109 **PRINCE LANCELOT**, b c 13/02 Sir Prancealot (IRE)—Rainbow Vale (FR) (Moss Vale (IRE)) (77220) **A. Gilibert**
110 B c 12/02 Quality Road (USA)—Russian Symbol (IRE) (Danehill Dancer (USA)) **A. Gilibert**
111 B f 08/04 Olympic Glory (IRE)—Sandy Light (IRE) (Footstepsinthesand) **D. Malingue**
112 **SAQR (FR)**, b c 01/01 Dutch Art—Varega (FR) (Danehill Dancer (IRE)) (41184) **S. B. Al Kuwari**
113 **SECOND TO NONE (IRE)**, b c 04/05 Zoffany (IRE)—Magic America (High Yield) **Ecurie J. L. Bouchard**
114 **SENTILLY (FR)**, b f 21/01 Air Chief Marshal (IRE)—Sainte Adresse (Elusive City (USA)) **G. Augustin-Normand**
115 **SILENCE**, b c 24/02 Olympic Glory (IRE)—Sailor Moon (Tiger Hill (IRE)) **Ecurie des Monceaux**
116 **SIR OLAF (IRE)**, b c 06/05 Le Havre (IRE)—
                          Sunday Nectar (IRE) (Footstepsinthesand) (15444) **Ecurie Normandie Pur Sang**
117 **SIYOUNOW (IRE)**, ch f 27/02 Siyouni (FR)—Alta Lilea (IRE) (Galileo (IRE)) (60060)
118 B br f 17/04 No Nay Never (USA)—Sleek Gold (Dansili) **K. M. Al Attiyah**
119 **SMALL FIRES (FR)**, b c 03/05 Dabirsim (FR)—
                          Silent Sunday (IRE) (Testa Rossa (AUS)) (21450) **Ecurie Normandie Pur Sang**
120 **STEADYMAN (FR)**, b c 17/03 Kingman—Gooseley Chope (FR) (Indian Rocket) (579150) **F. J. Carmichael**
121 **TEA DANCE**, b f 11/04 Adaay (IRE)—Galaktea (IRE) (Statue of Liberty (USA)) **A. Gilibert, R. Simmons**
122 **TOURBE (FR)**, b f 20/04 Wootton Bassett—Pestagua (Lawman (FR)) **Ecurie des Dragons**
123 B f 03/04 Wootton Bassett—Vega Sicilia (FR) (Elusive City (USA))
124 **WATCH HIM (FR)**, b c 13/03 Elvstroem (AUS)—Watchful (IRE) (Galileo (IRE)) (85800) **A. Gilibert**
125 **ZVOLENSKA (FR)**, ch f 07/04 No Nay Never—Sea Of Blue (Fastnet Rock) **A. Jathiere**

Other Owners: K. M. Al Attiyah, F. Chappet, A. Curty, Meridian International, P. Nataf, M. Al Attiya, J. Messara.

---

98   MRS JANE CHAPPLE-HYAM, Newmarket
Postal: **Abington Place Racing Stables, 44 Bury Road, Newmarket, Suffolk, CB8 7BT**
Contacts: **PHONE 07899 000555 MOBILE 07899 000555 FAX 01638 661335**
EMAIL **janechapplehyam@hotmail.co.uk, janechapplehyamracing@outlook.com**

1 **AMBASSADORIAL (USA)**, 6, b g Elusive Quality (USA)—Tactfully (IRE) **Ms J. F. Chapple-Hyam**
2 **AQUARIUM**, 5, ch h Leroidesanimaux (BRZ)—Caribana **Alsharq racing**
3 **AZETS**, 4, b g Dubawi (IRE)—Nashmiah (IRE) **Alsharq racing**
4 **BLOWING DIXIE**, 4, b g Dubawi (IRE)—Time Control **Mr M. Alenezi**
5 **BRIDGEWATER BAY (IRE)**, 4, ch g Footstepsinthesand—Mexican Milly (IRE) **Suzanne & Nigel Williams**
6 **BULLINGTON BOY (IRE)**, 4, b g Canford Cliffs (IRE)—Borgia Gold (IRE) **Ms J. F. Chapple-Hyam**
7 **CIRCUS COUTURE (IRE)**, 8, ch g Intikhab (USA)—Bois Joli (IRE) **Ms J. F. Chapple-Hyam**
8 **DALGARNO (FR)**, 7, b g Sea The Stars (IRE)—Jakonda (USA) **Mrs F. J. Carmichael**
9 **EMOJIE**, 6, b g Captain Gerrard (IRE)—Striking Pose (IRE) **Jakes Family**
10 **EXTRODINAIR**, 5, b g Captain Gerrard (IRE)—Mindfulness **Jakes Family**
11 **FLAUNT IT (IRE)**, 4, b f Mukhadram—Labisa (IRE) **Mrs F. J. Carmichael**
12 **FRENCH RIVIERA (FR)**, 5, b m Intello (GER)—Ecume du Jour (FR) **Mr C. M. Humber**
13 **MAID MILLIE**, 4, b f Dream Ahead (USA)—Maid A Million **Ms J. F. Chapple-Hyam**
14 **MELBURNIAN**, 4, b g Hallucinate (USA)—Bedouin Bride (USA) **Ms J. F. Chapple-Hyam**
15 **MIRABAI**, 4, ch f Poet's Voice—Classical Flair **T Brudenell J Chapple-Hyam P Barrett**
16 **MOCHALOV**, 5, b g Denounce—Awesome Asset (USA) **Jane Chapple-Hyam & Essex Racing Club**
17 **REINE DE VITESSE (FR)**, 4, b f Wootton Bassett—Vitesse Superieure **Johnstone Partnership**
18 **STAMFORD RAFFLES**, 7, b g Champs Elysees—Romantic Retreat **Ms J. F. Chapple-Hyam**
19 **SUNG CHOI BAO**, 4, b f Casamento (IRE)—Six Diamonds **Ms J. F. Chapple-Hyam**
20 **SUZI'S CONNOISSEUR**, 9, b g Art Connoisseur (IRE)—Suzi Spends (IRE) **Ms J. F. Chapple-Hyam**

MRS JANE CHAPPLE-HYAM - continued

21 **TO BE WILD (IRE)**, 7, br g Big Bad Bob (IRE)—Fire Up **Mrs F. J. Carmichael**
22 **UBER COOL (IRE)**, 6, b g Born To Sea (IRE)—My Uptown Girl **Fiona Carmichael & Jane Chapple-hyam**
23 **VIVA GLORIA (GER)**, 5, b gr m Reliable Man—Vive La Reine (GER) **Mrs C Hains**

THREE-YEAR-OLDS

24 **CHARES (GER)**, ch c Ivawood (IRE)—Coco Demure (IRE) **Mr Y H Yue**
25 **COMMANDER OF WAR**, b g War Command (USA)—Pianola (USA) **Look Partnership**
26 **FLIGHT PATH**, br gr g Mukhadram—Tipping Over (IRE) **Tipping Over**
27 **LINCOLN BLUE**, b c Bated Breath—Garden Row (IRE) **Mr G. W. Y. Li**
28 **LINCOLN BRIGHT (IRE)**, b g Lope de Vega (IRE)—Night Fairy (IRE) **Mr G. W. Y. Li**
29 **MASTER ROCCO (IRE)**, ch g Dawn Approach (IRE)—Mama Rocco **Mrs A Cantillon & Jane Chapple-hyam**
30 **MUMS THE LAW**, b f Lawman (FR)—Tell Mum **Mums The Law Syndicate**
31 **MY DORRIS (IRE)**, b f Uncle Mo (USA)—Cherokee (USA) **Mr D. Brennan**
32 **ULTRA VIOLET**, b f Gleneagles (IRE)—Rive Gauche **Mr C. M. Humber**

TWO-YEAR-OLDS

33 **EX GRATIA**, b f 03/05 Exceed And Excel (AUS)—Beta (Selkirk (USA)) **Miss K Rausing**
34 **MANDARIN DUCK**, b c 19/05 Fascinating Rock (IRE)—
Foreign Language (USA) (Distant View (USA)) **Ms J. F. Chapple-Hyam**
35 **REINE DU BAL**, b f 09/02 Mukhadram—She's Gorgeous (IRE) (Acclamation) **Johnstone Partnership**
36 Ch c 25/03 Exceed And Excel (AUS)—Tingleo (Galileo (IRE)) (52000) **Mr G. W. Y. Li**

Other Owners: Mr S. Brewster, Mrs A. J. Brudenell, Mrs A. Cantillon, Mrs F. J. Carmichael, Ms J. F. Chapple-Hyam, Essex Racing Club, Mr M. Harniman, Mr J. C. Jakes, Mr T. M. A. Jakes, Mr H. A. Johnstone, Mr J. W. Johnstone, Mrs Zara Johnstone, Mrs J. P. Root, Mr R. B. Root, Mr N. Williams, Mrs S. E. Williams, Ms E. J. Youngman.

Assistant Trainer: Abi Harrison.

Flat Jockey: Tim Clark. **Apprentice Jockey:** Jay Mackay.

---

99 MR PETER CHAPPLE-HYAM, Newmarket
Postal: St Gatien Stables, All Saints Road, Newmarket, Suffolk, CB8 8HJ

1 **ANNAKONDA (IRE)**, 4, b f Morpheus—Royal Esteem **Mr W. J. S. Prosser**
2 **DEJA (FR)**, 5, b g Youmzain (IRE)—Atarfe (IRE) **Phoenix Thoroughbred Limited**
3 **LYNCHPIN (IRE)**, 4, b c Camacho—River Bounty **Mr W. J. S. Prosser**
4 **MARTINENGO (IRE)**, 5, b g Elusive Pimpernel (USA)—Albiatra (USA) **Eledy SRL**
5 **MIA MENTO (IRE)**, 4, b f Casamento (IRE)—Mia Divina **Phoenix Thoroughbred Limited**
6 **MITIGATOR**, 4, b g Delegator—Snake Skin **Mr W. J. S. Prosser**
7 **OCEAN TEMPTRESS**, 6, b m Equiano (FR)—Ipsa Loquitur **Mr W. J. S. Prosser**
8 **REFORMED CHARACTER (IRE)**, 4, b c Zoffany (IRE)—Sallysaysso (IRE) **Mr W. J. S. Prosser**

THREE-YEAR-OLDS

9 **ANANYA**, ch f Sepoy (AUS)—Whatizzit **Mr W. J. S. Prosser**
10 **ATLAS FLAME (IRE)**, b g Toronado (IRE)—Petite Nymphe **Woodcote Stud Ltd**
11 **BHARANI STAR (GER)**, ch f Sea The Stars (IRE)—Bay of Islands (FR) **Phoenix Thoroughbred Limited**
12 **CANBERRA (IRE)**, ch c Australia—San Sicharia (IRE) **Phoenix Thoroughbred Limited**
13 **CHATEAU PEAPOD**, b f Coach House (IRE)—Dash of Lime **Mr W. J. S. Prosser**
14 **LENNY THE LION**, ch g Lethal Force (IRE)—Agony And Ecstasy **Mr W. J. S. Prosser**
15 **MAXIMIZE**, b f Garswood—Dazzling View (USA) **Mr W. J. S. Prosser**
16 **MDINA**, b f Mukhadram—Inchberry **Star Pointe Ltd**
17 **UNION SPIRIT**, b br g Outstrip—Nouvelle Lune **Mr W Prosser & Star Pointe Ltd**

TWO-YEAR-OLDS

18 B c 13/05 Iffraaj—Annie The Doc (Nayef (USA)) (171600) **Phoenix Thoroughbred Limited**
19 B c 20/02 Kodiac—Soul Searcher (IRE) (Motivator) (137280) **Phoenix Thoroughbred Limited**
20 B f 17/02 Zoffany (IRE)—Thought Is Free (Cadeaux Genereux) **Mrs F. H. Hay**

Other Owners: Mr W. J. S. Prosser, Star Pointe Ltd.

100 MR PETER CHARALAMBOUS, Newmarket
Postal: **30 Newmarket Road,Cheveley, Suffolk, CB8 9EQ**
Contacts: **PHONE 07921 858421**
EMAIL camalotracing@btinternet.com

1 **EXMOOR BEAST**, 4, ch g Sepoy (AUS)—Junket **GG Thoroughbreds V**
2 4, B g Aussie Rules (USA)—Gala Rose **Front Runner Racing - I**
3 **THE GREY GOAT (IRE)**, 4, gr g Zebedee—Empress Charlotte **GG Thoroughbreds II**
4 **THEYDON BOXER**, 5, b g Piccolo—Angel of Fashion (IRE) **pcracing.co.uk**
5 **THEYDON SPIRIT**, 5, ch g Piccolo—Ela Gorrie Mou **pcracing.co.uk**

TWO-YEAR-OLDS
6 Ch c 22/03 Equiano (FR)—Boonga Roogeta (Tobougg (IRE)) (3500) **pcracing.co.uk**

101 MR ROGER CHARLTON, Beckhampton
Postal: **Beckhampton House, Marlborough, Wiltshire, SN8 1QR**
Contacts: **PHONE 01672 539533 MOBILE 07710 784511**
EMAIL office@beckhamptonstables.com WEBSITE www.rogercharlton.com

1 **ASPETAR (FR)**, 5, b g Al Kazeem—Bella Qatara (IRE) **H.H. Sheikh Mohammed bin Khalifa Al-Thani**
2 **BLUE MIST**, 5, ch g Makfi—Namaskar **K. Abdullah**
3 **CASUAL REPLY**, 4, b f Frankel—Passing Parade **Merry Fox Stud Limited**
4 **COCHISE**, 4, b g Intello (GER)—Ship's Biscuit **P. Newton**
5 **EXTRA ELUSIVE**, 5, ch g Mastercraftsman (IRE)—Nessina (USA) **Mr I. H. Al Sagar**
6 **FIELDS OF DREAMS**, 4, b g Champs Elysees—Dylanesque **Mr F. McAleavy**
7 **FORBIDDEN PLANET**, 5, b h Pivotal—Aiming **Kingwood Stud Management Co Ltd**
8 **HEADMAN**, 4, b c Kingman—Deliberate **K. Abdullah**
9 **IMPERIUM (IRE)**, 4, ch g Frankel—Ramruma (USA) **Weston Brook Farm & Bromfield**
10 **IN DEMAND (IRE)**, 5, b g Dalakhani (IRE)—Fleur de Cactus (IRE) **The Yes Men**
11 **MAKZEEM**, 7, b g Makfi—Kazeem **D. J. Deer**
12 **MYSTIQUESTAR (IRE)**, 4, b f Sea The Stars (IRE)—Magique (IRE) **Miss Y. M. G. Jacques**
13 **OSCAR'S RIDGE (IRE)**, 5, b g Galileo (IRE)—Posterity (IRE) **Merry Fox Stud Limited**
14 **QARASU (IRE)**, 4, br g Le Havre (IRE)—Bella Qatara (IRE) **H.H. Sheikh Mohammed bin Khalifa Al-Thani**
15 **TEMPUS**, 4, b c Kingman—Passage of Time **K. Abdullah**
16 **TRUE DESTINY**, 5, ch g Mastercraftsman (IRE)—Holy Dazzle **Exors of the Late Sultan Ahmad Shah**
17 **WITHHOLD**, 7, b g Champs Elysees—Coming Back **Mr A. G. Bloom**
18 **YOUNG MERLIN (IRE)**, 4, b g Camelot—Zelloof **Daniel MacAuliffe & Anoj Don**

THREE-YEAR-OLDS
19 **ADONIS BLUE (IRE)**, b g Helmet (AUS)—Blue Butterfly **Beckhampton Racing**
20 **AMIR KABIR**, b g Mukhadram—Victory Garden **Dr Jamal Ahmadzadeh & Mrs D Swinburn**
21 **BENGAL**, b f Footstepsinthesand—Desert Tigress (USA) **The Hon N. P. V. J. Rothschild**
22 **BULLFINCH**, b c Kodiac—Thistle Bird **The Hon N. P. V. J. Rothschild**
23 **CAMPARI**, b g Due Diligence (USA)—Spritzeria **D.Macauliffe, Anoj Don & Partner**
24 **CINNABAR**, b f Al Kazeem—Moonlight Rhapsody (IRE) **Mr J Stewart & Mrs B Milton**
25 **CODE OF CONDUCT**, b c Siyouni (FR)—Sequence (IRE) **Her Majesty The Queen**
26 **CONSCIOUS**, b c Oasis Dream—Deliberate **K. Abdullah**
27 **DANCING APPROACH**, b f Camelot—Dream Approach (IRE) **Fishdance Ltd**
28 **DANCING HARRY (IRE)**, b c Camelot—Poisson d'Or **Fishdance Ltd**
29 **DUE CARE**, gr f Due Diligence (USA)—Dolly Colman (IRE) **Hot To Trot Racing Vi**
30 **EVENING SUN**, b c Muhaarar—Fiery Sunset **Her Majesty The Queen**
31 **GAZELLE**, b f Al Kazeem—Perfect Practice **Dr Bridget Drew & D H Caslon**
32 B f Gleneagles (IRE)—Happy Holly (IRE) **Hunscote Stud Limited**
33 **HEXAGON (IRE)**, b g Acclamation—Somerset Falls (UAE) **Owners Group 032**
34 **IBIZA**, b f Sepoy (AUS)—Hi Calypso (IRE) **P. Newton**
35 B f Dansili—Introspective **B. E. Nielsen**
36 **ITS A GIVEN**, ch f Bated Breath—Emergency **K. Abdullah**

MR ROGER CHARLTON - continued

37 **IVADREAM**, b g Ivawood (IRE)—Midnight Fling **Mr S. Emmet & Miss R. Emmet**
38 B f Oasis Dream—Kazeem **D. J. Deer**
39 **LOUGANINI**, ch g Zoffany (IRE)—Princess Loulou (IRE) **Mr I. H. Al Sagar**
40 **MAKRAM (IRE)**, b g Make Believe—Spontaneous (IRE) **Mr M. Al-Qatami & Mr K. M. Al-Mudhaf**
41 **MAURIMO**, b f Kingman—Lynnwood Chase (USA) **Miranda Beaufort & Partners**
42 **MEGANS APPROACH**, b f Dawn Approach (IRE)—Bristol Fashion **Nick Bradley Racing 6**
43 **MERSIN**, b c Invincible Spirit (IRE)—Ferevia (IRE) **H.H. Sheikh Mohammed bin Khalifa Al-Thani**
44 **MOSEY (IRE)**, ch f Dream Ahead (USA)—Mince **The Hon N. P. V. J. Rothschild**
45 **NIGHT RANGER**, br g Dansili—Sleep Walk **K. Abdullah**
46 **NITRO EXPRESS**, b c Dubawi (IRE)—Flotilla (FR) **H.H. Sheikh Mohammed bin Khalifa Al-Thani**
47 **PENMAEN SPIRIT (IRE)**, b f Kingman—Penmaen (IRE) **D. J. Deer**
48 **POCKET SQUARE**, ch f Night of Thunder (IRE)—Shared Account **K. Abdullah**
49 **QUADRILATERAL**, ch f Frankel—Nimble Thimble (USA) **K. Abdullah**
50 B c Sea The Stars (IRE)—Rainbow Dancing **Clipper Logistics**
51 **SCARLET RUBY**, b f Al Kazeem—Monisha (FR) **D. J. Deer**
52 **SELECTO**, b c Paco Boy (IRE)—Telescopic **Mr Daniel Hunt & Mrs Eileen Markham**
53 **SMOKEY BEAR (IRE)**, b c Kodiac—Shamankiyna (FR) **de Zoete, Inglett & Jones**
54 **STANLEY STANLEY**, b f Camelot—Seaham Hall **Mrs S. A. J. Kinsella**
55 **STRIKING APPROACH**, b c New Approach (IRE)—Nazli (IRE) **Mr I. H. Al Sagar**
56 **SURE I'M YOUR MAN (IRE)**, b g Sea The Moon (GER)—All Hallows (IRE) **Mr & Mrs Paul & Clare Rooney**
57 **TACITLY**, b f Dubawi (IRE)—Timepiece **K. Abdullah**
58 **TAMARIS (IRE)**, br c Dansili—Fleur de Cactus (IRE) **H.H. Sheikh Mohammed bin Khalifa Al-Thani**
59 **TAMBOURINE GIRL**, b f Cable Bay (IRE)—Triton Dance (IRE) **Owners Group 041**
60 **ULTIMATE AIM**, b f Pivotal—Aiming **Mr & Mrs David Brown**
61 **WIN O'CLOCK**, ch c Australia—Gee Kel (IRE) **Kingwood Stud Management Co Ltd**
62 **WREN**, b f Raven's Pass (USA)—Magical Romance (IRE) **The Hon N. P. V. J. Rothschild**

TWO-YEAR-OLDS

63 **AETHELBURGA**, b f 26/01 Cityscape—Sweet Pilgrim (Talkin Man (CAN)) **Sandy Hames**
64 **AMALFI BAY**, b c 14/03 Lope de Vega (IRE)—Affinity (Sadler's Wells (USA)) **Elite Racing Club**
65 **BARN OWL**, b c 05/03 Frankel—Thistle Bird (Selkirk (USA)) **The Hon N. P. V. J. Rothschild**
66 **BEHELD**, ch f 21/02 Frankel—Tendu (Oasis Dream) **K. Abdullah**
67 **BOLTAWAY**, ch c 24/02 Dubawi (IRE)—Proviso (Dansili) **K. Abdullah**
68 B f 24/03 Showcasing—Comeback Queen (Nayef (USA)) **Kingwood Stud Management Co Ltd**
69 **DESERT PIONEER**, b c 04/04 Dubawi (IRE)—Lady Wingshot (IRE) (Lawman (FR)) (100000) **Mr I. H. Al Sagar**
70 **DOLPHIN**, b f 04/03 Sea The Stars (IRE)—Dolma (FR) (Marchand de Sable (USA)) **Lady Bamford**
71 Br c 11/04 Harzand (IRE)—Donatia (Shamardal (USA)) (35000)
72 **DORTE (IRE)**, b f 27/01 Dubawi (IRE)—Gretchen (Galileo (IRE)) **Normandie Stud Ltd**
73 **ELVIC**, b f 16/03 Siyouni (FR)—Magical Romance (Barathea (IRE))
74 **ENCOURAGE**, b c 07/03 Iffraaj—Good Hope (Cape Cross (IRE)) **Her Majesty The Queen**
75 B f 18/02 Mastercraftsman (IRE)—Estrela (Authorized (IRE)) **Seasons Holidays**
76 B f 09/04 Oasis Dream—Ferevia (IRE) (Motivator) **H.H. Sheikh Mohammed bin Khalifa Al-Thani**
77 B c 09/04 Invincible Spirit (IRE)—
                    Fleur de Cactus (IRE) (Montjeu (IRE)) **H.H. Sheikh Mohammed bin Khalifa Al-Thani**
78 Ch f 19/04 The Gurkha (IRE)—Healing Music (FR) (Kheleyf (USA)) (80000) **Mildmay Racing**
79 **HER WAY**, b c 11/03 Harzand (IRE)—Its In The Air (IRE) (Whipper (USA)) (35000) **P Inglett, de Zoete, Milln**
80 **IN THE BREEZE**, b c 11/03 Harzand (IRE)—Its In The Air (IRE) (Whipper (USA)) (35000) **P Inglett, de Zoete, Milln**
81 **JUMBY BREEZE**, b f 29/01 Dubawi (IRE)—Annabelle's Charm (IRE) (Indian Ridge) **Merry Fox Stud Limited**
82 **KEEPER**, b c 19/04 Frankel—Portodora (USA) (Kingmambo (USA)) **K. Abdullah**
83 **LASSIE (IRE)**, b f 07/04 Gleneagles (IRE)—Ship's Biscuit (Tiger Hill (IRE)) **P. Newton**
84 **LOVE IS YOU (IRE)**, b f 26/03 Kingman—Fallen For You (Dansili) **Normandie Stud Ltd**
85 **LOVING KISS (IRE)**, b f 25/02 Le Havre (IRE)—Loving Things (Pivotal) **Normandie Stud Ltd**
86 **LUCID DREAMER**, gr f 24/02 Dansili—Sleep Walk (Oasis Dream) **K. Abdullah**
87 **LUDISIA**, b f 22/02 Frankel—African Rose (Observatory (USA)) **K. Abdullah**
88 B c 21/03 Galileo (IRE)—Melito (AUS) (Redoute's Choice (AUS)) (140000) **Brook Farm Bloodstock**
89 **NAJEEBA**, gr f 21/03 Dansili—Rose of Miracles (Dalakhani (IRE)) (60000) **Mr I. H. Al Sagar**
90 B c 29/04 Intello (GER)—Nantes (GER) (Night Shift (USA)) (42900) **Mr Mohammed Jaber**
91 **NASSIMA**, b f 22/04 Fastnet Rock (AUS)—Soon (IRE) (Galileo (IRE)) **Mr I. H. Al Sagar**
92 **ONE DAY**, b f 22/03 Adaay (IRE)—Pelican Key (IRE) (Mujadil (USA)) (32000) **Andrew Bengough & Mindy Hammond**

MR ROGER CHARLTON - continued

93   B f 03/04 Frankel—Palimony (IRE) (Oasis Dream) (110000) **Nick Bradley Racing & Partners**
94   **QUILTED,** b f 19/04 Frankel—Nimble Thimble (USA) (Mizzen Mast (USA)) **K. Abdullah**
95   Ch f 18/02 Australia—Rosie Probert (Dylan Thomas (IRE)) **Seasons Holidays**
96   B f 16/05 Frankel—Royal Secrets (IRE) (Highest Honor (FR)) **Mr Mohammed Jaber**
97   **SALIGO BAY (IRE),** b c 21/03 New Bay—
                          Glorification (Champs Elysees) (300000) **Ballylinch Stud, P Inglett & N Jones**
98   B c 27/03 Dubawi (IRE)—Samba Brazil (GER) (Teofilo (IRE)) **H.H. Sheikh Mohammed bin Khalifa Al-Thani**
99   **SAND IN MY SHOES (FR),** b c 23/03 Mastercraftsman (IRE)—Suquia (GER) (Mount Nelson) (36894)
100 Ch c 09/02 Shamardal (USA)—Sooraah (Dubawi (IRE)) **Mr Mohammed Jaber**
101 Ch c 22/02 Dawn Approach (IRE)—Step Sequence (Nayef (USA)) (30000) **Brook Farm Bloodstock**
102 B c 03/05 Soldier Hollow—Tarap (IRE) (Myboycharlie (IRE)) **H.H. Sheikh Mohammed bin Khalifa Al-Thani**
103 B f 08/04 Paco Boy—Telescopic **Dan Hunt & Partners**
104 **TIME INTERVAL,** b c 18/03 Adaay (IRE)—Kuriosa (IRE) (Rip Van Winkle (IRE)) (34000) **P Inglett, de Zoete, Milln**
105 **VICTORY ROLL,** b c 06/02 Charm Spirit—Passing Parade (Cape Cross (IRE)) **Merry Fox Stud Limited**
106 B f 27/03 Invincible Spirit—Vorda (FR) (Orpen (USA)) **H.H. Sheikh Mohammed bin Khalifa Al-Thani**
107 **WITHOUT REVENGE,** b c 29/01 Muhaarar—
                          La Dorotea (IRE) (Lope de Vega (IRE)) (70000) **Carter, Dean, Gerber, Inglett**
108 B c 20/04 Muhaarar—Wittgenstein (IRE) (Shamardal (USA)) (65000) **Mr Mohammed Jaber**
109 **WORTHWHILE,** b f 27/03 Al Kazeem—Salutare (IRE) (Sadler's Wells (USA)) **Turf Club & Whatton Manor Stud**

Assistant Trainer: Harry Charlton, **Pupil Assistant:** Ben James.

Flat Jockey: Adam McNamara, Jason Watson. **Apprentice Jockey:** Thomas Greatrex.

---

102 **MR HARRY CHISMAN, Stow-on-the-Wold**
Postal: **25 Coachmans Court, Station Road, Moreton-In-Marsh, Gloucestershire, GL56 0DE**
Contacts: **PHONE 07787 516723**
WEBSITE www.harrychisman.co.uk

1   **ALL RILED UP,** 12, b m Dr Massini (IRE)—Martha Reilly (IRE) **P Baker D Wood M Flint**
2   **FOYLESIDEVIEW (IRE),** 8, b g Dark Angel (IRE)—Showerproof **P Baker W Summers**
3   **LEGENDOIRE (IRE),** 6, b g Fast Company (IRE)—Last Shaambles (IRE) **Mr H. J. Chisman**

Other Owners: Mr P. M. Baker, Mr H. J. Chisman, Mr M. J. Flint, Miss W. Summers, D. C. Wood.

Assistant Trainer: G. Charles-Jones.

Flat Jockey: Robert Havlin. **NH Jockey:** Tom O'Brien, Sean Quinlan. **Conditional Jockey:** Daniel Hiskett.
Amateur Jockey: Mr Paddy Berkins.

---

103 **MR NICOLAS CLEMENT, Chantilly**
Postal: **37, Avenue de Joinville, 60500 Chantilly, France**
Contacts: **PHONE +33 3 44 57 59 60 MOBILE +33 6 07 23 46 40**
EMAIL office@nicolasclement.com WEBSITE www.nicolasclement.com

1   **DANS LA LUNE (FR),** 4, b f Le Havre (IRE)—Wevanella (FR)
2   **DEADLINE DIVA,** 5, b m Frankel—Hurry Home Hillary (USA)
3   **EPHEMERAL (IRE),** 4, b f Footstepsinthesand—Mycenae
4   **KIWIANA,** 4, b f Kodiac—Redskin Dancer (IRE)
5   **MENTHE PASTILLE (FR),** 4, b f Style Vendome (FR)—Age of Refinement (IRE)
6   **NO TINC POR,** 4, b f Authorized (IRE)—Tierceville (IRE)
7   **RELIABLE SON (FR),** 4, b c Reliable Man—Hot Fudge (SWE)
8   **STAKING (FR),** 5, b g Stormy River (FR)—Shaking
9   **WONDERMENT (IRE),** 4, b f Camelot—Wiwilia

MR NICOLAS CLEMENT - continued

THREE-YEAR-OLDS

10 **AIGUIERE D'ARGENT (FR),** b g Excebloration (IRE)—Plaisanciere (FR)
11 **AMBRE (FR),** b f Dabirsim (FR)—Teoris (IRE)
12 **ASSIGNED (IRE),** b f Camelot—Entrust (NZ)
13 **BAY VIEW (IRE),** b f Power—Bristol Bay (IRE)
14 **BEAUTE POUR TOI,** b f Camelot—Grain de Beaute (IRE)
15 **CONTE DE FEE,** ch f Sea The Stars (IRE)—Padmini
16 **CONTROL TOWER,** b f Youmzain (IRE)—La Tour Rouge
17 **COUNTESS DE VEGA (IRE),** ch f Lope de Vega (IRE)—Pure Symmetry (USA)
18 **DEMETER (GER),** b f Soldier Hollow—Douala
19 **ES VEDRA (FR),** b f Dutch Art—Faithful One (IRE)
20 **FIERCE RIVAL,** b c Olympic Glory (IRE)—Cheam Ksah (IRE)
21 **FITZCARRALDO,** ch c Makfi—Sapfo (FR)
22 **FOREARMED,** ch f Born To Sea (IRE)—Forewarned (IRE)
23 **GLAMOUREUSE,** b f Intello (GER)—La Pedrera (IRE)
24 **GLOBALE VILLE,** b f Le Havre (IRE)—Global Wand (GER)
25 **HAGWAAT (FR),** b f Le Havre (IRE)—Timepecker (IRE)
26 **HAVANA BOUND,** ch f Havana Gold (IRE)—Exceedingly Rare (IRE)
27 **HOLLYWOOD (FR),** b f Style Vendome (FR)—Lady Wood (FR)
28 **JUKEBOX DANCER (FR),** b f Muhaarar—Waldjagd
29 **KALANI,** b f Wootton Bassett—On The Line (FR)
30 **MER BLANCHE,** b f Oasis Dream—Aigue Marine
31 **MINSTER (IRE),** ch g Mastercraftsman (IRE)—Mycenae
32 **NOW WE KNOW (FR),** gr c Kendargent (FR)—Now Forever (GER)
33 **PARIS BEAUTY,** b f Gleneagles (IRE)—Nuit Polaire (IRE)
34 **PRINCESS KAGUYA (IRE),** b f Frankel—Guaranda
35 **PRIVATE ROMANCE (IRE),** ch f Siyouni (FR)—Private Eye (FR)
36 **PUNTARELLE (FR),** b f Zoffany (IRE)—Astrologie (FR)
37 **SALOCIN (FR),** ch g Lope de Vega (IRE)—Alkania
38 B f Style Vendome (FR)—Shaking
39 **STYLE SETTER,** b f Style Vendome (FR)—Almaardiyah (IRE)
40 **TIGER TOUCH (USA),** b c American Pharoah (USA)—Osaila (IRE)
41 **TOPKAPI (FR),** b f Golden Horn—Top Toss (IRE)
42 **TRAPISTA (FR),** b f Golden Horn—Quezon Sun (GER)
43 **TRESORELLA (FR),** b f Intello (GER)—Treasure (FR)
44 **WHISKEY LULLABY,** b f Intello (GER)—Colonialiste (IRE)

TWO-YEAR-OLDS

45 **BENI KHIAR (FR),** b c 03/02 Amaron—Elea (GER) (Lord of England)
46 **CAPRICE DES DIEUX (FR),** b c 07/02 Declaration of War—Neko (FR) (Dansili)
47 B f 06/04 Camelot—Dijlah (Linamix (FR))
48 **EUTHYDIKOS (FR),** bl c 15/01 Goken (FR)—Teth (Dansili)
49 Ch f 28/04 Siyouni (FR)—Extreme Green (Motivator)
50 **HOPISSIME (FR),** b f 14/02 Camelot—Baino Hope (FR) (Jeremy (USA))
51 B c 07/03 Toronado (IRE)—Ideechic (FR) (Chichicastenango (FR))
52 B f 09/03 Showcasing—Idle Tears (Selkirk (USA))
53 **JANULIS (FR),** b c 12/04 Toronado (IRE)—Leen (IRE) (Danehill Dancer (IRE))
54 **LILY FOR EVER (FR),** b f 02/05 Dariyan (FR)—Golden Lily (FR) (Dolphin Street (FR))
55 B f 08/04 Kitten's Joy (USA)—Nominative (USA) (Johar (USA))
56 B c 21/03 Le Havre (IRE)—Now Forever (GER) (Tiger Hill (IRE))
57 B f 15/04 Camelot—Swift Action (IRE) (Invincible Spirit (IRE))
58 **WILDWOOD (FR),** b br f 01/05 Maxios—Walayta (GER) (Oasis Dream)

Flat Jockey: Laura Grosso, Sebastien Maillot, Stephane Pasquier. **Apprentice Jockey:** Thomas Truillier.

104 MR TOM CLOVER, Newmarket
Postal: **Kremlin House Stables, Fordham Road, Newmarket, Suffolk, CB8 7AQ**
Contacts: **PHONE 07795 834960, 01638 660055**
EMAIL thomaspwclover@gmail.com WEBSITE www.tomcloverracing.com

1 **BALGAIR**, 6, ch g Foxwedge (AUS)—Glencal
2 **CELSIUS (IRE)**, 4, ch g Dragon Pulse (IRE)—Grecian Artisan (IRE) **J. Collins, C. Fahy & S. Piper**
3 **CHENG GONG**, 4, b g Archipenko (USA)—Kinetica **R & S Marchant, D Fawdon & G Jarvis**
4 **CRIMEWAVE (IRE)**, 4, b g Teofilo (IRE)—Crossover **Mr T. P. Clover, Mr A. R. Elliott**
5 **DARING GUEST (IRE)**, 6, b g Fast Company (IRE)—Balm **Mrs G. A. S. Jarvis**
6 **HOLBROOK PARK**, 10, b g Midnight Legend—Viciana **Mrs B. M. Chamberlain**
7 **HOLY KINGDOM (IRE)**, 4, gr c Australia—Cable (USA) **Mr T. P. Clover, Mr A. R. Elliott**
8 **HUNNI**, 5, b m Captain Gerrard (IRE)—Lady O Malley (IRE) **Mr T. P. Clover, Mrs G. A. S. Jarvis**
9 **MONSIEUR LAMBRAYS**, 4, b g Champs Elysees—Windermere Island **K. A. Dasmal**
10 **RAJMAN**, 4, ch c Zoffany (IRE)—Mutheera **Mr R. S. Matharu**
11 **RITCHIE VALENS (IRE)**, 4, ch g Helmet (AUS)—Miss Cape (IRE) **Dr O. Rangabashyam**

THREE-YEAR-OLDS
12 **ALIANNE**, b f Worthadd (IRE)—Alboretta **Miss K. Rausing**
13 **BROUGHTON SUNPEARL**, b f Swiss Spirit—Sunpearl **Broughton Thermal Insulations**
14 **BROUGHTONS GOLD**, bl gr g Lethal Force (IRE)—Broughtons Jewel (IRE) **Broughton Thermal Insulations**
15 **CRAIGBURN**, b g Casamento (IRE)—Craighall **Mrs G. A. S. Jarvis**
16 **EAGLESGLEN**, b g Gleneagles (IRE)—Coquet **Mr T. P. Clover, Mr A. R. Elliott**
17 B f Bated Breath—Eventfull Meet (IRE) **B Keane & S Nugent**
18 **GRAND CANAL (IRE)**, b c Australia—Loreto (IRE) **Mr P. Chau**
19 **I HAD A DREAM**, b f Dream Ahead (USA)—Grandmas Dream **Mr T. P. Clover, Mrs J. I. Clover**
20 **MACHINE GUN (IRE)**, b c Dark Angel (IRE)—Artistic Jewel (IRE) **Mr T. P. Clover, Mr A. R. Elliott**
21 **RAJGURU**, ch c Dutch Art—Gakalina (IRE) **Mr R. S. Matharu**
22 **ROGUE ASSASSIN (IRE)**, ch g Iffraaj—Zahrat Narjis **Mr T. P. Clover, Mr A. R. Elliott**
23 **RUSPER'S LAD**, b c Brazen Beau (AUS)—Camelopardalis **Ben Spiers & Adam Signy**
24 **SUPERIOR MOMENT (IRE)**, b c Pivotal—Superior Charm (USA) **Mr A. A. Albuainain**
25 **SURRAJAH (IRE)**, b c Camelot—Sharaarah (IRE) **Raj Matharu & Suresh Sivagnanam**
26 **WISE EAGLE (IRE)**, ch g Free Eagle (IRE)—
                  Best Be Careful (IRE) **Mr T. P. Clover, Ms J. C. Finucane, York Thoroughbred Racing-Best Be Careful**

TWO-YEAR-OLDS
27 Ch c 25/02 Australia—Became (USA) (Giant's Causeway (USA)) (55769) **H Moorhead, C Fahy & J Collins**
28 **FAHRENHEIT (IRE)**, ch f 17/02 Dragon Pulse (IRE)—
                  Grecian Artisan (IRE) (Mastercraftsman (IRE)) (20952) **H Moorhead, C Fahy & J Collins**
29 **FAIRY DUST (IRE)**, b f 15/03 Gregorian (IRE)—Dreaming Lady (IRE) (Dream Ahead (USA)) (12000)
30 B c 22/03 Sepoy (AUS)—Lamps of Heaven (IRE) (Invincible Spirit (IRE)) (6666) **Mrs J. I. Clover**
31 B c 16/02 Power—Pretty Darling (IRE) (Le Havre (IRE)) (19047) **F H Lee & T Clover**
32 **RAJMEISTER**, b c 05/02 Showcasing—Brilliant Sunshine (Pivotal) (27500) **Mr R. S. Matharu**
33 **ROGUE POWER**, b c 12/02 Pivotal—Strawberry Sorbet (Street Cry (IRE)) (35000) **Mr T. P. Clover, Mr A. R. Elliott**
34 **THE GUVNOR (IRE)**, b c 14/05 Frankel—
                  Eva's Request (IRE) (Soviet Star (USA)) (75000) **Mr T. P. Clover, Mr A. R. Elliott**
35 B c 01/04 The Gurkha (IRE)—Wood Chorus (Singspiel (IRE)) (16000) **Mr T. P. Clover**

Other Owners: Mrs J. I. Clover, Mr T. P. Clover, Mr D. Fawdon, Mrs G. A. S. Jarvis, Mr B. A. Keane, Mr F. H. Lee, Mr R. P. Marchant, Mr S. Marchant, Mr R. S. Matharu, Newmarket Racing Club, Mr S. Nugent, Mr A. Signy, Mr S. Sivagnanam, Mr B. P. J. Spiers, The Hunni Partnership, The Rogues Gallery Two, The Shimplingthorne Syndicate, York Thoroughbred Racing & Partners.

105 MR KEN CLUTTERBUCK, Newmarket
Postal: **Pond House Stables, Church Lane, Exning, Newmarket, Suffolk, CB8 7HF**
Contacts: **PHONE 07868 605995**
EMAIL kennethclutterbuck123@outlook.com

1 **COLOURFIELD (IRE),** 5, b m Makfi—Rainbow Desert (USA) **K. F. Clutterbuck**
2 4, Ch f Toronado (IRE)—Impertinent
3 **SIGNSEALDELIVERED,** 6, b g Mawatheeq (USA)—Confluence **C. V. Lines**

THREE-YEAR-OLDS

4 B g Harbour Watch (IRE)—Impertinent **K. F. Clutterbuck**

106 MR DENIS COAKLEY, West Ilsley
Postal: **Keeper's Stables, West Ilsley, Newbury, Berkshire, RG20 7AH**
Contacts: **PHONE 01635 281622 MOBILE 07768 658056**
EMAIL racing@deniscoakley.com WEBSITE www.deniscoakley.com

1 **BARTIMAEUS (IRE),** 4, b g Nathaniel (IRE)—Zora Seas (IRE) **West Ilsley Racing**
2 **GIVEPEACEACHANCE,** 5, b m Declaration of War (USA)—Mount Crystal (IRE) **Chris van Hoorn Racing**
3 **POWER HOME (IRE),** 6, ch m Power—Ascendancy **Poachers' Dozen**
4 **ROCKSTAR MAX (GER),** 4, b g Maxios—Remote Romance (USA) **Melbourne 10 Racing & Mr R Barnes**
5 **SARI MAREIS,** 4, b f Toronado (IRE)—Fanny May **Chris van Hoorn Racing**
6 **SHEILA'S SHOWCASE,** 4, b g Showcasing—Loreto Rose **R. J. Styles**
7 **SHEILA'S SPIRIT,** 4, b g Swiss Spirit—Velma Kelly **Mrs B. Coakley**
8 **SONNETINA,** 4, b f Poet's Voice—Tebee's Oasis **The Good Mixers**
9 **STAR COMMAND (IRE),** 4, b f War Command (USA)—Megaspiel **Bramble Syndicate**
10 **SWEET CHARITY,** 5, b m Mount Nelson—Fanny May **Chris van Hoorn Racing**
11 **TIAR NA NOG (IRE),** 8, b m Ask—Carmencita **Mrs U. M. Loughrey**

THREE-YEAR-OLDS

12 **CARMENERE,** ch f Dawn Approach (IRE)—Sacred Aspect (IRE) **Sparkling Partners**
13 Ch g Mastercraftsman (IRE)—Firey Red (IRE)
14 **MY SHEILA (IRE),** b f Australia—Dorothy B (IRE) **R. J. Styles**
15 **PARTY ISLAND (IRE),** ch g Tagula (IRE)—Pretty Demanding (IRE) **Mr T. A. Killoran**

TWO-YEAR-OLDS

16 B c 15/03 Adaay (IRE)—Atwix (Sakhee (USA)) (5500)
17 **BOBBY KENNEDY,** b c 14/04 Bobby's Kitten (USA)—
All Annalena (IRE) (Dubai Destination (USA)) (6666) **Ms I. Coakley**
18 B c 02/03 Free Eagle (IRE)—Fasten Up (Fastnet Rock (AUS)) (8000) **Keeper's 12**
19 B f 09/05 Cable Bay (IRE)—La Concorde (FR) (Sadler's Wells (USA)) (6000)
20 **LISDARRAGH,** b c 13/03 Hit It A Bomb (USA)—Thewholeshebang (USA) (In Summation (USA)) (15000)
21 **NELL QUICKLY (IRE),** b f 26/03 The Gurkha (IRE)—
Burke's Rock (Cape Cross (IRE)) (70000) **Chris van Hoorn Racing**

Other Owners: Mr R. J. Barnes, Mrs C. J. Barratt, Mr I. J. Barratt, Melbourne 10 Racing, Miss A. D. Swift, Mr C. T. Van Hoorn.

107 MR PAUL COLE, Whatcombe
Postal: **Whatcombe Estate, Whatcombe, Wantage, Oxfordshire, OX12 9NW**
Contacts: **PHONE 01488 638433**
EMAIL admin@paulcole.co.uk **WEBSITE** www.paulcole.co.uk

1 **ARCTIC SEA**, 6, b br g Oasis Dream—Rainbow Dancing **P. F. I. Cole Ltd**
2 **CELTIC CLASSIC (IRE)**, 4, b g Cacique (IRE)—Dabtiyra (IRE) **P. F. I. Cole Ltd**
3 **DUKE OF HAZZARD (FR)**, 4, b c Lope de Vega (IRE)—With Your Spirit (FR) **Mrs Fitri Hay**
4 **HIGH COMMISSIONER (IRE)**, 4, ch g Australia—Winesong (IRE) **Mrs Fitri Hay**
5 **MAJESTIC DAWN (IRE)**, 4, ch c Dawn Approach (IRE)—Jolie Chanson (FR) **Mr C. S. Norman, Mrs J. Green**
6 **MEDIEVAL (IRE)**, 6, b g Kodiac—Quickstyx **Mrs Fitri Hay**
7 **MERCENARY ROSE (IRE)**, 4, b f Sepoy (AUS)—Hulcote Rose (IRE) **Mr F. P. Stella**
8 **QUEMONDA**, 4, ch f Mount Nelson—Quesada (IRE) **Mrs E. A. Bass**
9 **RIVER DAWN**, 4, ch g Dawn Approach (IRE)—Echo River (USA) **P. F. I. Cole Ltd**
10 **ROTHERWICK (IRE)**, 8, ch g Starspangledbanner (AUS)—Pivotalia (IRE) **P. F. I. Cole Ltd**
11 **SANDYMAN**, 5, b g Footstepsinthesand—Quiz Mistress **The Fairy Story Partnership**
12 **SHIR KHAN**, 4, ch g Leroidesanimaux (BRZ)—Sterling Sound (USA) **Mr P. F. I. Cole**

THREE-YEAR-OLDS
13 **ATLANTIC CROSSING (IRE)**, b c Mukhadram—Ghizlaan (USA) **Christopher Wright & David Kilburn**
14 **CELTIC ART (FR)**, ch c Mastercraftsman (IRE)—Irish Song (FR) **Mrs Fitri Hay**
15 **CHARLEMAINE (IRE)**, b c War Command (USA)—Newyearresolution (USA) **P. F. I. Cole Ltd**
16 **DARK PHOENIX (IRE)**, gr c Camacho—Alba Verde **P. F. I. Cole Ltd**
17 **GLENGOWAN (IRE)**, b f Kingman—Pink Damsel (IRE) **Mrs Fitri Hay**
18 **HIGHLAND CHIEF (IRE)**, b c Gleneagles (IRE)—Pink Symphony **Mrs Fitri Hay**
19 **IVATHEENGINE (IRE)**, br g Ivawood (IRE)—Sharp Applause (IRE) **Mr F. P. Stella**
20 **JAZZ PARTY**, b c New Approach (IRE)—Harlem Dancer **Mr C. Shiacolas**
21 **LIN CHONG**, b c Muhaarar—Reroute (IRE) **Hurun Racing**
22 **MASTER SPY (IRE)**, gr g Mastercraftsman (IRE)—Stealth Bolt (USA) **Arbib, Robinson & Tabet**
23 **MIDNIGHT TRAVELLER (IRE)**, b c Mukhadram—Springlike (IRE) **Pjl Snook Wright Asprey & Wilcock**
24 **MILLIONAIRE WALTZ**, b c Heeraat (IRE)—Radio Gaga **P. F. I. Cole Ltd**
25 **THE FIRST KING (IRE)**, b g War Command (USA)—Rochitta (USA) **Mr P. F. I. Cole**

TWO-YEAR-OLDS
26 B f 16/02 Manduro (GER)—Aztec Queen (Holy Roman Emperor (IRE)) (7722) **The Fairy Story Partnership**
27 B c 24/02 Gleneagles (IRE)—Ballybacka Lady (IRE) (Hurricane Run (IRE)) (120120) **Mrs Fitri Hay**
28 Gr ro f 23/02 Tamayuz—Comfort In Sound (USA) (War Front (USA)) **Mr C. N. Wright**
29 **GENERAL LEE**, b c 03/04 Lope de Vega (IRE)—Hall Hee (IRE) (Invincible Spirit (IRE)) (90000) **Mrs Fitri Hay**
30 **GORDONSTOUN**, b c 12/05 Gleneagles (IRE)—Elusive Girl (IRE) (Elusive City (USA)) (15000)
31 B c 27/04 Pearl Secret—Hulcote Rose (IRE) (Rock of Gibraltar (IRE))
32 **IMPERIAL DAWN**, b c 15/03 Dawn Approach (IRE)—
                 Miss Lahar (Clodovil (IRE)) (42000) **C S Norman, Max Wallace-Jones, J. Edgedale**
33 B f 31/01 Gleneagles (IRE)—Mirage (IRE) (Oasis Dream) **Mrs Fitri Hay**
34 B f 17/04 Dawn Approach (IRE)—Nancy Star (IRE) (Bushranger (IRE)) (9523) **Mr D. Vakilgilani**
35 B c 25/04 Bated Breath—Poulaine Bleue (Bertolini (USA)) (14000)
36 **RAW HIDE (IRE)**, b c 20/03 War Command (USA)—Tioga Pass (High Chaparral (IRE)) **The Fairy Story Partnership**
37 **SERENHILL**, gr f 26/01 Kingston Hill—Seramindar (Zamindar (USA)) **The Fairy Story Partnership**
38 **STRICTLY SPICY**, b c 12/02 Nathaniel (IRE)—Spicy Dal (Dalakhani (IRE)) **Sir Martyn Arbib**
39 **WANTAGE (IRE)**, b c 16/05 Camelot—
                 Lucy Cavendish (USA) (Elusive Quality (USA)) (50000) **Mr C. S. Norman, The Wantage Syndicate**
40 B f 18/04 American Pharoah (USA)—Winnie Dixie (USA) (Dixie Union (USA)) **Mrs Fitri Hay**
41 **ZHANG FEI**, b c 03/04 Camelot—
                 Mambomiss (FR) (Mastercraftsman (IRE)) (42900) **Mr C. S. Norman, Hurun Racing, Sophie Magnier**

Other Owners: Sir Martyn Arbib, Miss Emily Charlotte Asprey, Mrs C. E. S. Baker, Mr G. Baker, Cobra Bloodstock, Mr O. N. I. Cole, Mr J. W. Edgedale, Mrs F. H. Hay, Mr Daniel Jefferies, D. Kilburn, Mr Tom Magnier, Mr C S Norman & the Wantage Syndicate, Mr Lee Green, Mr C. S. Norman, P.F. I. Cole Ltd, Mr J. Piggott, Mr A. H. Robinson, Mr C. Shiacolas, Mrs V. M. Snook, Mr J. A. Tabet, The Fairy Story Partnership, Mr M. Wallace-Jones, Mr N. Wilcock, Mr C. N. Wright.

Assistant Trainer: Mr Oliver Cole, Mr Alistair Lidderdale.

108 **MR TJADE COLLIER, Wilsden**
Postal: **Salter Royd House, Shay Lane, Wilsden, Bradford, West Yorkshire, BD15 0DJ**
Contacts: **PHONE 01535 271445**
EMAIL tjade331@icloud.com

1 **BLUE HAWAII (IRE),** 5, b m Jeremy (USA)—Luanna (IRE) **R. Banks & J. Sheard**
2 **LADRONNE (FR),** 6, b g Linda's Lad—Worldeta (FR) **Mrs V. J. Walker**
3 **MIDNIGHT ANTICS (IRE),** 6, b m Midnight Legend—Toungara (FR) **Mrs V. J. Walker**
4 **PAT CARROT (IRE),** 7, b g Germany (USA)—Gevity **Mrs V. J. Walker**
5 4, Ch f Shantou (USA)—Toubeera
6 **VIVA JEZ VEGAS (IRE),** 5, b m Jeremy (USA)—New Vega (FR) **R. Banks & J. Sheard**

Other Owners: Mr R. Banks, Mr J. N. Sheard.

109 **MR PAUL COLLINS, Saltburn-By-The-Sea**
Postal: **1 Longthwaite Close, Skelton-In-Cleveland, Saltburn-By-The-Sea, Cleveland, TS12 2WP**
Contacts: **MOBILE 07779 794684**

1 **REBELJUSTFORKICKS,** 4, b f Yorgunnabelucky (USA)—Willow Burn Wisp **Ms R. E. Taylor**
2 **SOLID STRIKE,** 12, b g Sir Harry Lewis (USA)—Solid Land (FR) **Mr P. Collins**

110 **MR STUART COLTHERD, Selkirk**
Postal: **Clarilawmuir Farm, Selkirk, Selkirkshire, TD7 4QA**
Contacts: **PHONE 01750 21251 MOBILE 07801 398199 FAX 01750 21251**
EMAIL wscoltherd@gmail.com

1 **ACHILL ROAD BOY (IRE),** 11, b g Morozov (USA)—Presenting Katie (IRE) **Farming Army Newitt Flannigan Findlater**
2 **ARCHI'S AFFAIRE,** 6, ch g Archipenko (USA)—Affaire d'Amour **D. Neale**
3 **ARD CHROS (IRE),** 8, b g Publisher (USA)—Threecrossmammies (IRE) **Coltherd McDougal**
4 **ASH PARK (IRE),** 12, b g Milan—Distant Gale (IRE) **Coltherd McDougal**
5 **CAPTAIN REDBEARD (IRE),** 11, ch g Bach (IRE)—Diesel Dancer (IRE) **W. S. Coltherd**
6 **CASIMIR DU CLOS (FR),** 8, b g Blue Bresil (FR)—Cyrienne du Maine (FR) **Newitt Flannigan Scott Gillie Swinton**
7 **CHANCEANOTHERFIVE (IRE),** 8, b g Dubai Destination (USA)—Ryhall (IRE) **Mr R. McCulloch**
8 **DEQUALL,** 4, ch g Zoffany (IRE)—Bark (IRE) **W. S. Coltherd**
9 **FELIX MENDELSSOHN (IRE),** 9, b g Galileo (IRE)—Ice Queen (IRE) **Shire Dreamers**
10 **GET HELP (IRE),** 7, b g Gold Well—Present Abbey (IRE) **Robertson,Gillie,Tawse,Knaggs,Ferguson**
11 **GRAYSTOWN (IRE),** 8, b g Well Chosen—Temple Girl (IRE) **The Farming Army**
12 **LONGTYMEGONE (IRE),** 10, b g Portrait Gallery (USA)—Katie O'Toole (IRE) **W. S. Coltherd**
13 **MAID O'MALLEY,** 7, b m Black Sam Bellamy (IRE)—Jolie (IRE) **W. S. Coltherd**
14 **MILL ISLAND (IRE),** 6, ch g Sholokhov (IRE)—Blueanna (IRE) **W. S. Coltherd**
15 **MILLY ON AIR,** 4, ro f Proclamation (IRE)—Lady Counsellor
16 **MRS VONN (IRE),** 8, b m Scorpion (IRE)—Mrs Ritchie **Mercer Campbell Stanners**
17 **POOKIE PEKAN (IRE),** 7, b g Putra Pekan—Shii-Take's Girl **W. S. Coltherd**
18 **RIDETHEWAVES,** 4, b f Gentlewave (IRE)—Julia Too
19 **ST BASIL,** 7, gr g Geordieland (FR)—Wibble Wobble **Mr J L & Mrs H R Gledson**
20 **WARENDORF (FR),** 7, b g Speedmaster (GER)—Hyllisia (FR) **Howard Coltherd Flannigan Newitt**
21 **WHEELBAHRI,** 6, b g Bahri (USA)—Midlem Melody **W. S. Coltherd**

Other Owners: Mr D. T. Campbell, W. S. Coltherd, Mr T. Ferguson, Mr G. Findlater, Mr I. R. Flannigan, Mr R. Flannigan, Mr E. Gillie, Mrs H. R. Gledson, J. L. Gledson, Mr D. A. Gray, Mr G. P. Howard, Mr D. Knaggs, Mr G. McDougal, Mr K. Mercer, Mrs S. C. Newitt, Mr D. Reive, Mr B. A. Robertson, Mr M. J. Scott, Mr M. Stanners, Mr S. Swinton, Mrs S. Tawse, The Farming Army.

Conditional Jockey: Sam Coltherd.

111 MR SEAN CONWAY, Lutterworth
Postal: **Home Farm, Shawell Lane, Cotesbach, Lutterworth, Leicestershire, LE17 4HR**
Contacts: **MOBILE 07879 066901**

1 **BAMBI DU NOYER (FR),** 9, b br g Sageburg (IRE)—Zouk Wood (USA) **Mr S. Conway**
2 **BEFOREYPUSHDACHAIR (IRE),** 6, b g Garuda (IRE)—No Ones Oscar (IRE) **Mr S. Conway**
3 **DEFINITE WARRIOR (IRE),** 7, b g Definite Article—Waist Deep (IRE) **Mr S. Conway**
4 **DOLLY DUPREE,** 4, b f Poet's Voice—Meddle **Mr S. Conway**
5 **ISIDOR BONHEUR YES (FR),** 6, b g Sageburg (IRE)—Isarnixe (GER) **Mr S. Conway**
6 **KYMATA,** 6, b m Sulamani (IRE)—Miss Annabell (IRE) **Mr S. Conway**
7 **LITTLE SAINT (IRE),** 5, b g Morozov (USA)—Matinee Show (IRE) **Mr S. Conway**
8 4, B g Sakhee (USA)—Narima (GER) **Mr S. Conway**
9 **NOT ANOTHER BAY (IRE),** 5, b m Carlotamix (FR)—Smile Sweetly (IRE) **Mr S. Conway**
10 **OLIVER'S ISLAND (IRE),** 8, b g Milan—Leading Rank (IRE) **Mr S. Conway**

Amateur Jockey: Mr Philip Armson.

112 MRS SUSAN CORBETT, Otterburn
Postal: **Girsonfield, Otterburn, Newcastle upon Tyne, Tyne and Wear, NE19 1NT**
Contacts: **PHONE 01830 520771 MOBILE 07713 651215 FAX 01830 520771**
EMAIL girsonfield@outlook.com WEBSITE www.girsonfield.co.uk

1 **AHEAD OF THE CURVE (FR),** 8, b g Ballingarry (IRE)—Jasla (FR) **Mr T. H. J. Green**
2 **DEVOUR (IRE),** 7, b g Milan—Marble Desire (IRE) **Girsonfield Racing Club**
3 **GORGEOUS GOBOLINA,** 4, b f Captain Gerrard (IRE)—Gorgeous Goblin (IRE) **Mr S. Humphries**
4 **GOWANBUSTER,** 5, b g Bahri (USA)—Aahgowangowan (IRE) **Hassle-Free Racing**
5 **GREY EXPECTATIONS,** 4, gr f Proclamation (IRE)—Linns Heir **Mr T. H. J. Green**
6 **HARLEYS MAX,** 11, b g Winged Love (IRE)—Researcher **Girsonfield Racing Club**
7 **HEARTASIA (IRE),** 7, b m Danehill Dancer (IRE)—Big Heart **The Winning Tipster Racing Club**
8 **HEATHERLEA (IRE),** 6, b m Germany (USA)—Betsy Babe (IRE) **Girsonfield Racing Club**
9 **HILLS OF CONNEMARA (IRE),** 8, gr m Tikkanen (USA)—Desirable Rhythm (IRE) **Mr F. W. W. Chapman**
10 **LET'S SWAY,** 6, b m Authorized (IRE)—Let's Dance (IRE) **Castle View Racing**
11 **MACARDLE (IRE),** 7, b g Beneficial—Monavale (IRE) **Mr L. P. Richards**
12 **MY BROWN EYED GIRL,** 7, b m Ferrule (IRE)—Chalosse **Mr G. Satchwell**
13 **ORLAS ABBEY,** 5, b m Multiplex—Evelith Abbey (IRE) **Mrs S. Corbett**
14 **OUR PROMISE,** 6, ch m Malinas (GER)—Hello My Lovely **The 3 Wise Men**
15 **PENTELITUBBY,** 5, ch g Kutub (IRE)—Penteli **Mr W. F. Corbett**
16 **PRINCESS AVERY (IRE),** 6, b m Yeats (IRE)—Bobs Article (IRE) **Mr F. W. W. Chapman**
17 **REDESDALE REBEL,** 4, ch g Mayson—Jubilee **The Redesdale Rebels**
18 **REIVERS LODGE,** 8, b m Black Sam Bellamy (IRE)—Crystal Princess (IRE) **Mr F. W. W. Chapman**
19 **SATIS HOUSE,** 8, b m Bahri (USA)—Ex Mill Lady **Castle View Racing**
20 **SKIPTHESCALES (IRE),** 8, b g Winged Love (IRE)—Waterland Gale (IRE) **Mr L. P. Richards**
21 **SUTTON WAY,** 8, b m Bahri (USA)—Kates Own **J. B. Wharf**
22 **THANKQ,** 5, b m Proclamation (IRE)—Turbo Linn **Mr T. H. J. Green**
23 **TOOYOU,** 5, gr m Proclamation (IRE)—Lady Counsellor **The Nelson Racing Partnership**
24 **WOR VERGE,** 7, b g Virtual—Hanover Gate **The Goodfellow Partnership**

THREE-YEAR-OLDS

25 **GOWANLASSIE,** ch f Mayson—Gowanharry (IRE) **Hassle-Free Racing**
26 **LES'S LEGACY,** b g Kutub (IRE)—Morning With Ivan (IRE) **Mr L. P. Richards**

TWO-YEAR-OLDS

27 Ch f 23/03 Cityscape—First Harmony (First Trump) (761)
28 Ch f 09/03 Ruler of The World (IRE)—Ogaritmo (Manduro (GER))

Other Owners: Mr D. J. Clarke, Mr M. D. Foden, Mr I. Galletley, Mr T. H. J. Green, Mr S. Humphries, Mr L. Waugh.

Assistant Trainer: Mr J. Corbett, **Yard Sponsor:** Finnies Heavy Haulage.

NH Jockey: James Corbett.

113 MR JOHN CORNWALL, Melton Mowbray
Postal: **April Cottage, Pasture Lane, Hose, Melton Mowbray, Leicestershire, LE14 4LB**
Contacts: **PHONE 01664 444453 MOBILE 07939 557091 FAX 01664 444754**
EMAIL johncornwall7@gmail.com

1 LESKINFERE (IRE), 7, b g Darsi (FR)—Taipans Girl (IRE) **Mr J. R. Cornwall**
2 THE JUGOPOLIST (IRE), 13, b g Oscar (IRE)—Chance My Native (IRE) **Mr J. R. Cornwall**
3 TORRENT DES MOTTES (FR), 9, gr g Montmartre (FR)—Wavy (FR) **Mr J. R. Cornwall**

114 MR JAKE COULSON, Heaton
Postal: **Bent End Farm, Bearda Hill Racing, Heaton, Macclesfield, Cheshire, SK11 0SJ**
Contacts: **MOBILE 07460 471492**
EMAIL beardahillracing@gmail.com

1 CHAPATI (FR), 6, b gr g Fragrant Mix (IRE)—Bessouba (FR) **Mr N. Carter**
2 4, B g Sir Percy—Clifton Encore (USA) **Mr K. Dove**
3 EMPRESARIO (IRE), 11, ch g Hurricane Run (IRE)—La Stravaganza (USA) **Mr N. Carter**
4 GOLD PATROL (IRE), 12, b g Gold Well—One Love (IRE) **Mr N. Carter**
5 ROB ROYAL (FR), 8, gr g Rob Roy (USA)—Royale Trophy (FR) **Mr N. Carter**

Assistant Trainer: Sarah Carter.

115 MISS JACQUELINE COWARD, Sheriff Hutton
Postal: **Low Moor Farm, Dalby, Dalby, Yorkshire, YO60 6PF**
Contacts: **PHONE 01653 628995**

1 COVIGLIA (IRE), 6, gr g Invincible Spirit (IRE)—Bright Snow (USA) **Mr John Blackburn Racing**
2 TAPIS LIBRE, 12, b g Librettist (USA)—Stella Manuela (FR) **The Laura Mason Syndicate**

Other Owners: Mr J. N. Blackburn, M. W. Easterby.

116 MR ROBERT COWELL, Newmarket
Postal: **Bottisham Heath Stud, Six Mile Bottom, Newmarket, Suffolk, CB8 0TT**
Contacts: **PHONE 01638 570330 MOBILE 07785 512463**
EMAIL robert@robertcowellracing.co.uk WEBSITE www.robertcowellracing.co.uk

1 ALJADY (FR), 5, b g Bated Breath—No Truth (IRE) **Mrs M. J. Morley**
2 BECKER, 5, b g Delegator—Mosa Mine **Mrs Morley, R Penney & A Rix**
3 BHANGRA, 4, br f Showcasing—Soundwave **Manor Farm Stud (Rutland)**
4 BLUE DE VEGA (GER), 7, b g Lope de Vega (IRE)—Burning Heights (GER) **Mrs M. J. Morley**
5 COWBOY SOLDIER (IRE), 5, b g Kodiac—Urgele (FR) **Mrs F. H. Hay**
6 DIAMOND DOUGAL (IRE), 5, b g Zebedee—Blue Saphire **Mrs M. J. Morley**
7 ENCORE D'OR, 8, b g Oasis Dream—Entente Cordiale (IRE) **Mrs Morley, G Johnson & Newsells Park Stud**
8 ERISSIMUS MAXIMUS (FR), 6, b g Holy Roman Emperor (IRE)—Tegan (IRE) **Mrs M. J. Morley**
9 GOOD ANSWER, 4, b g Iffraaj—Cool Question **Mr J. Sargeant**
10 GRANDFATHER TOM, 5, b g Kheleyf (USA)—Kassuta **Mr J. Sargeant**
11 GREEN DOOR (IRE), 9, b g Camacho—Inourhearts (IRE) **Bottisham Heath Stud**
12 GRISONS (FR), 4, b c Iffraaj—Fig Roll **Mr T. W. Morley**
13 INDIAN TINKER, 11, b g Sleeping Indian—Breakfast Creek **Bottisham Heath Stud**
14 JUMIRA BRIDGE, 4, b g Invincible Spirit (IRE)—Zykina **Mrs M. J. Morley**
15 MISS GRADENKO, 4, b f Foxwedge (AUS)—Instructress **Bottisham Heath Stud**
16 RAUCOUS, 7, b g Dream Ahead (USA)—Shyrl **Mr T. W. Morley**
17 REEVES, 4, b g Tamayuz—Mania (IRE) **Mr T. W. Morley**

MR ROBERT COWELL - continued

18 **ROCKET ACTION**, 4, gr g Toronado (IRE)—Winning Express (IRE) **Mr R. Ng**
19 **SAVALAS (IRE)**, 5, gr g Zebedee—Tap The Dot (IRE) **Mrs M. J. Morley**
20 **SOCIETY STAR**, 4, b f Society Rock (IRE)—Clapperboard **Mr W. J. S. Prosser**
21 **SWELL SONG**, 4, ch f Kyllachy—Racina **Mr I. A. Southcott**
22 **TOMSHALFBROTHER**, 4, b g Sir Percy—Kassuta **Mr J. Sargeant**
23 **WARSAW ROAD (IRE)**, 6, ch g Zebedee—Warda **Mrs M. J. Morley**
24 **WONDROUS SCENE (IRE)**, 4, b f Acclamation—Rock Exhibition **Mr R. Ng**

THREE-YEAR-OLDS

25 **ARJU (USA)**, b br f Karakontie (JPN)—War Clan (USA) **Mrs F. H. Hay**
26 **COCONUT SUGAR (IRE)**, b f Gutaifan (IRE)—Murrieta **Mr N. Simpson**
27 **EXCITING DAYS (USA)**, b br g Blame (USA)—Whenthetimeisright (USA) **K. A. Dasmal**
28 **GMASHA**, ch f Intrinsic—She's So Pretty (IRE) **Malih L. Al Basti**
29 **ISHVARA**, b f Dutch Art—Cloud's End **Manor Farm Stud & Mr J. E. Rose**
30 **KRAFLA (USA)**, b f Trappe Shot (USA)—Lexi Morgan **Mr T. W. Morley**
31 **LEG IT LENNY (IRE)**, b g Baltic King—El Morocco (USA) **The Tigers Racing Syndicate**
32 **LOTTIE MARIE**, ch f Intello (GER)—Heavenly Dawn **Cheveley Park Stud Limited**
33 **MOMENTUM SWING**, br g Dark Angel (IRE)—Winning Express (IRE) **Mr R. Ng**
34 **PEACEFUL DREAM**, ch f Dream Ahead (USA)—Path of Peace **Hot To Trot Racing & D Tunmore**
35 **ROYAL APPOINTMENT**, b c Pivotal—Royal Seal **Cheveley Park Stud Limited**
36 **SUR MER**, b f Equiano (FR)—Miss Villefranche **Mr T. W. Morley**
37 **SWEET TALKED**, ch f Poet's Voice—Most Tempting **Bottisham Heath Stud**
38 **TAKE IT THUNDER (IRE)**, b c Night of Thunder (IRE)—Al Nassa (USA) **Mr N. Al Habtoor**
39 **TASTE THE NECTAR (USA)**, ch f More Than Ready (USA)—Alb (USA) **Mr T. W. Morley**
40 **TELL ME THUNDER (IRE)**, ch c Night of Thunder (IRE)—International Love (IRE) **Mr N. Al Habtoor**

TWO-YEAR-OLDS

41 B br c 11/02 Violence (USA)—Battle Axe (USA) (War Front (USA)) **Mr T. W. Morley**
42 B br c 19/03 Super Saver (USA)—Beat to Quarters (USA) (War Front (USA)) **K. A. Dasmal**
43 B c 18/02 Kantharos (USA)—Bellarada (USA) (Rockport Harbor (USA)) **Mr T. W. Morley**
44 Ch c 04/02 Distorted Humor (USA)—Everything Sweet (USA) (Bluegrass Cat (USA)) **Mrs F. H. Hay**
45 B f 30/01 Brazen Beau (AUS)—Falsify (Compton Place) **Bottisham Heath Stud**
46 **FAUSTUS**, b c 19/02 Mayson—Israfel (Dark Angel (IRE)) (14000) **Mrs J. Hadida**
47 **ISLE OF LISMORE (IRE)**, b c 08/03 Zebedee—Spring Bouquet (IRE) (King's Best (USA)) (15000) **Mr P. S. Ryan**
48 **K REX (USA)**, b br c 10/03 Speightster (USA)—Chasing Lightning (USA) (Belong To Me (USA)) **K. A. Dasmal**
49 B f 31/01 Congrats (USA)—Lemon Splash (CAN) (Lemon Drop Kid (USA)) **Mr T. W. Morley**
50 B c 30/03 Brazen Beau (AUS)—Most Tempting (Showcasing) **Bottisham Heath Stud**
51 B f 03/03 Palace (USA)—Quiet Sunshine (USA) (Real Quiet (USA)) **Mr T. W. Morley**
52 B f 12/01 Brazen Beau (AUS)—Sciacca (IRE) (Royal Applause) **Bottisham Heath Stud**
53 B br c 07/02 Fed Biz (USA)—The Right Bird (USA) (Birdstone (USA)) **Mr T. W. Morley**
54 B c 21/01 Showcasing—Weisse Socken (IRE) (Acclamation) (55000) **K. A. Dasmal**

Other Owners: Mr R. S. Hoskins, Hot To Trot Racing 1, Mr G. M. C. Johnson, Manor Farm Stud (Rutland), Mrs M. J. Morley, Newsells Park Stud Limited, Mr R. C. Penney, Mr A. J. Rix, J. E. Rose, Mr D. Tunmore.

Assistant Trainer: Mr Ross Studholme.

MR CLIVE COX, Hungerford
Postal: **Beechdown Farm, Sheepdrove Road, Lambourn, Hungerford, Berkshire, RG17 7UN**
Contacts: **WORK** 01488 73072 **MOBILE** 07740 630521
EMAIL clive@clivecox.com **WEBSITE** www.clivecox.com

1 **BOBBY WHEELER (IRE)**, 7, b g Pivotal—Regal Rose **Mr P. N. Ridgers**
2 **DARGEL (IRE)**, 4, b g Dark Angel (IRE)—Lady Duxyana **Mr T. H. S. Fox**
3 **GETCHAGETCHAGETCHA**, 4, b g Champs Elysees—Paella (IRE) **Mr & Mrs Paul & Clare Rooney**
4 **GLOBAL PROSPECTOR (USA)**, 4, b br c Scat Daddy (USA)—Alegendinmyownmind **Dr J. Hon**
5 **JUST THE MAN (FR)**, 4, b ro g Rajsaman (FR)—Yachtclubgenoa (IRE) **Mr & Mrs Paul & Clare Rooney**

MR CLIVE COX - continued

6 **KING'S SLIPPER**, 5, b g Leroidesanimaux (BRZ)—Last Slipper **D B Clark & A R Bentall**
7 **KITCARINA (FR)**, 5, b m Shamardal (USA)—Kitcat (GER) **Windmill Racing - Kitcarina**
8 **KONCHEK**, 4, bl g Lethal Force (IRE)—Soar **AlMohamediya Racing**
9 **LETHAL LUNCH**, 5, gr g Lethal Force (IRE)—Pin Cushion **The Rat Pack Partnership 2017**
10 **LETHAL MISSILE (IRE)**, 4, b g Lethal Force (IRE)—Lostintheclouds **B Allen, G Hill & N Wagland**
11 **LITTLE MISS LILLY**, 5, b m Lethal Force (IRE)—Malilla (IRE) **Clive Cox Racing Ltd**
12 **LITTLE PALAVER**, 8, b g Showcasing—Little Nymph **Mr T. H. S. Fox**
13 **LOUIE DE PALMA**, 8, b g Pastoral Pursuits—Tahirah **Mr P. N. Ridgers**
14 **MEGHAN SPARKLE (IRE)**, 4, b f Showcasing—Poppet's Lovein **Mr P. N. Ridgers**
15 **NOBLE FOX**, 4, b g Foxwedge (AUS)—Woolfall Rose **Cox's Foxes**
16 **PERFECT REFUGE**, 5, gr m Champs Elysees—Perfect Haven **Hants & Herts**
17 **PERFECT SHOWDANCE**, 4, ch f Showcasing—Perfect Star **Mildmay Racing**
18 **SHADES OF BLUE (IRE)**, 4, br f Kodiac—Enjoyable (IRE) **Miss Alison Jones**
19 **SNAZZY JAZZY (IRE)**, 5, b h Red Jazz (USA)—Bulrushes **Mrs O. A. Shaw**
20 **TIS MARVELLOUS**, 6, b g Harbour Watch (IRE)—Mythicism **Miss J. Deadman & Mr S. Barrow**
21 **WISE COUNSEL**, 4, b g Invincible Spirit (IRE)—Noozhah **Clipper Group Holdings Ltd**

THREE-YEAR-OLDS

22 **ABLE GRACE (IRE)**, b f No Nay Never (USA)—Sanadaat **Ms C. LI**
23 **AMARSANAA**, gr f Dream Ahead (USA)—Nullarbor Sky (IRE) **AlMohamediya Racing**
24 **BAYAR**, b c Bated Breath—So Belle **AlMohamediya Racing**
25 **CAN'T STOP NOW (IRE)**, ch g Starspangledbanner (AUS)—Sorry Woman (FR) **Mr & Mrs Paul & Clare Rooney**
26 **COMPANY MINX (IRE)**, gr f Fast Company (IRE)—Ice Haven (IRE) **Mrs O. A. Shaw**
27 **DANCE FEVER (IRE)**, b c Sir Prancealot (IRE)—Silk Fan (IRE) **Kennet Valley Thoroughbreds VIII**
28 **ENDOWMENT**, b f Garswood—Inheritance **Cheveley Park Stud Limited**
29 **FIREPOWER (FR)**, b g Starspangledbanner (AUS)—Torentosa (FR) **Mrs M. E. Morgan**
30 **GOLDEN HORDE (IRE)**, ch c Lethal Force (IRE)—Entreat **AlMohamediya Racing**
31 **GOOD TIME CHARLIE**, b g Due Diligence (USA)—Our Faye **Miss J. Deadman & Mr S. Barrow**
32 **HAND ON MY HEART**, ch f Iffraaj—Place In My Heart **Hot To Trot Racing V**
33 **IRISH ACCLAIM (IRE)**, b c Acclamation—Irish Cliff (IRE) **Mr & Mrs Paul & Clare Rooney**
34 **IT'S GOOD TO LAUGH (IRE)**, b g Tamayuz—London Plane (IRE) **Mr & Mrs Paul & Clare Rooney**
35 **JUST MAY**, br f Lethal Force (IRE)—Milly's Gift **Ken Lock Racing**
36 **KALFU**, b f Pivotal—Synergy (FR) **Mr A. L. Cohen**
37 **KEBEK KHAN (IRE)**, b g Acclamation—Vanity's Girl (IRE) **AlMohamediya Racing**
38 **KLOPP OF THE KOP (IRE)**, ch g Excelebration (IRE)—Avomcic (IRE) **Alderson Burke Francis**
39 **KNAPSACK (IRE)**, b f Nathaniel (IRE)—Packed House **Mrs Belinda Miles & Mrs Valda Burke**
40 **LADY FANDITHA (IRE)**, b f Kodiac—Lady Ro **Mr P. N. Ridgers**
41 **MAGICAL DRAGON (IRE)**, b c Dragon Pulse (IRE)—Place That Face **The Flame Throwers**
42 **MAHALA BAY**, b br g Fountain of Youth (IRE)—Catmint **Mr T. H. S. Fox**
43 **MIDNIGHT DRIFT**, b gr f Lethal Force (IRE)—Malilla (IRE) **Clive Cox Racing Ltd**
44 **NOTFORALONGTIME**, b c Paco Boy (IRE)—Punchy Lady **Mr & Mrs Paul & Clare Rooney**
45 **ORLAITH (IRE)**, b f Fastnet Rock (AUS)—Cmonbabylitemyfire (IRE) **Dragon Racing**
46 **PAWPAW**, b g Showcasing—Papaya (IRE) **China Horse Club International Limited**
47 **PERFECT OUTING**, gr f Outstrip—Makara **Mildmay Racing**
48 **PITCHCOMBE**, b g Lethal Force (IRE)—Emmuska **Mr A. G. Craddock**
49 **POSITIVE**, b c Dutch Art—Osipova **Mr Alan Spence**
50 **PRIZE FIGHTING**, b g Sepoy (AUS)—Street Fire (IRE) **Mr & Mrs P Hargreaves & Mr A Spence**
51 **RISK TAKER (IRE)**, ch g Lope de Vega (IRE)—What A Treasure (IRE) **Mr & Mrs Paul & Clare Rooney**
52 **RIVER NYMPH**, b c Cable Bay (IRE)—Little Nymph **Mr T. H. S. Fox**
53 **SHINE ON BRENDAN (IRE)**, b g Society Rock (IRE)—Something Magic **Mr & Mrs Paul & Clare Rooney**
54 **SOVEREIGN BEAUTY (IRE)**, b f Free Eagle (IRE)—Indian Maiden (IRE) **The Free Flyers**
55 **STAR IN THE MAKING**, b f Muhaarar—Lonely Ahead (USA) **Mr A D Spence & Mr M B Spence**
56 **STATION TO STATION**, b g Cacique (IRE)—Jubilant Queen **Alderson Burke Francis**
57 **STOWEMAN**, ch g Lethal Force (IRE)—Poetic Dancer **Mr A. G. Craddock**
58 **STREAMLINE**, b c Due Diligence (USA)—Ahwahnee **Mainline Racing**
59 **TIDAL RACER**, b g Heeraat (IRE)—Making Waves (IRE) **Mr T. H. S. Fox**
60 **TIGER ZONE (IRE)**, b g Society Rock (IRE)—Shalabina **Miss J. Deadman & Mr S. Barrow**
61 **TOMMY ROCK (IRE)**, gr c Society Rock (IRE)—Chiara Wells (IRE) **Mr P. N. Ridgers**
62 **TOP SECRET**, ch g Anjaal—Just Devine (IRE) **Carmel Stud**

63 TUSCAN OASIS (IRE), b f Oasis Dream—Sovana (IRE) **Mr James Egan**
64 VELETA, ch f Dutch Art—Barynya **Cheveley Park Stud Limited**
65 WILLY NILLY (IRE), b g Morpheus—Subtle Shimmer **Mr & Mrs Paul & Clare Rooney**
66 ZAMBEZI MAGIC, b g Zoffany (IRE)—Millestan (IRE) **D B Clark & A R Bentall**

TWO-YEAR-OLDS

67 Br c 31/03 Kodi Bear (IRE)—Arbeel (Royal Applause) (85800) **China Horse Club International Limited**
68 B c 09/02 Kodiac—Chibola (ARG) (Roy (USA)) (200000) **Mrs Marie McCartan**
69 CHURCHILL BAY, b c 17/02 The Last Lion (IRE)—Cape Cay (Cape Cross (IRE)) **Mr J C Smith**
70 B f 01/04 Muhaarar—Cloud's End (Dubawi (IRE)) (65000) **Mr Alan Spence**
71 Ch c 27/03 Lethal Force (IRE)—Dartrix (Dutch Art) (2857) **Clive Cox Racing Ltd**
72 B f 26/02 Fountain of Youth (IRE)—Dayville (USA) (Dayjur (USA)) (35500) **Mr P. N. Ridgers**
73 DILIGENT HARRY, b c 02/04 Due Diligence (USA)—Harryana To (Compton Place) (36190) **A Syndicate**
74 B f 01/02 Dark Angel (IRE)—Enjoyable (IRE) (Verglas (IRE)) (85800) **Tom & Clodagh Hassett**
75 Ch f 12/02 Night of Thunder (IRE)—Exempt (Exceed And Excel (AUS)) (110000) **Sheikh R. D. Al Maktoum**
76 Ch c 09/02 Mehmas (IRE)—Fataawy (IRE) (Invincible Spirit (IRE)) (19047) **AlMohamediya Racing**
77 FINAL FANTASY, ch f 18/04 Lethal Force (IRE)—Fantasize (Groom Dancer (USA)) **Cheveley Park Stud Limited**
78 FOREVER FORWARD (IRE), b c 16/04 Exceed And Excel (AUS)—
                    Teofilo's Princess (IRE) (Teofilo (IRE)) (105000) **Mr Simon Munir & Mr Isaac Souede**
79 FUNKY BEAR, b c 10/04 Kodi Bear (IRE)—Ice Haven (IRE) (Verglas (IRE)) **Mrs O. A. Shaw**
80 GET IT, b c 01/03 Twilight Son—Pine Ridge (Elusive City (USA)) (19047) **Mr A. L. Cohen**
81 B c 20/02 Pride of Dubai (AUS)—Golden Shine (Royal Applause) (64761) **Miss J. Deadman & Mr S. Barrow**
82 B c 15/04 Dark Angel (IRE)—Havin' A Good Time (IRE) (Jeremy (USA)) (77220) **Mr J. Goddard**
83 INVINCIBLE SOLDIER (IRE), b c 27/02 The Gurkha (IRE)—Guessing (USA) (Kingmambo (USA)) (13727)
84 ISABELLA SWAN, b f 13/02 Twilight Son—First Eclipse (IRE) (Fayruz) **Redgate Bloodstock**
85 B f 20/04 Mukhadram—Katy Nowaitee (Komaite (USA)) **The Kathryn Stud Limited**
86 B c 23/03 Lethal Force (IRE)—Lacing (Equiano (FR)) (50000) **Mr P. N. Ridgers**
87 Br f 06/02 Pivotal—Lyricist (Librettist (USA)) (38095) **The Kathryn Stud Limited**
88 B c 28/02 Kodi Bear (IRE)—Malilla (IRE) (Red Clubs (IRE)) (8000) **Clive Cox Racing Ltd**
89 B f 27/03 Oasis Dream—May Rose (IRE) (Lawman (FR)) (75000) **Mr A D Spence & Mr M B Spence**
90 B f 20/01 Kodi Bear (IRE)—Midnight Martini (Night Shift (USA)) (85714) **AlMohamediya Racing**
91 NIKULINA, ch f 10/03 Dutch Art—Osipova (Makfi) **Cheveley Park Stud Limited**
92 B c 20/02 Mehmas (IRE)—Oh Simple Thing (IRE) (Compton Place) (32380) **Miss J. Deadman & Mr S. Barrow**
93 PERHAPS TONIGHT (IRE), b f 04/04 Sir Prancealot (IRE)—
                                    Quiza (Major Cadeaux) (35238) **Mr P Stokes & Mr S Krase**
94 PINBALL WIZARD (IRE), b c 03/04 Dark Angel (IRE)—Alsalwa (IRE) (Nayef (USA)) (60000) **Mr Alan Spence**
95 B c 07/02 Territories (IRE)—Prequel (IRE) (Dark Angel (IRE)) (80000) **AlMohamediya Racing**
96 PRIDE OF ENGLAND, b c 07/02 Pride of Dubai (AUS)—
                                Weetles (High Chaparral (IRE)) (30000) **D B Clark & A R Bentall**
97 PROP FORWARD, b c 16/03 Iffraaj—My Propeller (IRE) (Holy Roman Emperor (IRE)) **Mr J C Smith**
98 B f 07/03 Twilight Son—Sacre Coeur (Compton Place) **Mainline Racing**
99 B f 07/02 Adaay (IRE)—Satsuma (Compton Place) (95238) **AlMohamediya Racing**
100 Ch c 24/01 Hot Streak (IRE)—Sciarra (Monsieur Bond (IRE)) (34285) **AlMohamediya Racing**
101 B c 15/04 Free Eagle (IRE)—Shauna's Princess (IRE) (Soviet Star (USA)) (70000) **A. Butler**
102 Ch f 21/03 Red Jazz (USA)—Silver Tide (USA) (Silver Hawk (USA)) (15444) **Mrs O. A. Shaw**
103 SPIRIT OF THE BAY, b f 03/04 Cable Bay (IRE)—Decorative (IRE) (Danehill Dancer (IRE)) (32604) **A Syndicate**
104 B c 14/03 Estidhkaar (IRE)—
                    Tatiana Romanova (USA) (Mr Greeley (USA)) (24024) **Mr Ken Ivory & Mr Ian Higginson**
105 TELL'EM NOWT, b c 12/04 Belardo (IRE)—Taleteller (USA) (Bernardini (USA)) (40000) **Mrs O. A. Shaw**
106 TIPOFTHETONGUE, b f 31/01 Due Diligence (USA)—
                            Tongue Twista (Stimulation (IRE)) (60000) **The Rat Pack Partnership 2017**
107 B c 28/03 Mehmas (IRE)—Triggers Broom (IRE) (Arcano (IRE)) (61904) **Mr J. Goddard**
108 VERBENA, b f 27/03 Lethal Force (IRE)—Red Bloom (Selkirk (USA)) **Cheveley Park Stud Limited**
109 WHISKEY 'N' CHIPS, b f 22/01 Dark Angel (IRE)—
                                Ensemble (FR) (Iron Mask (USA)) (75000) **Mr P Stokes & Mr S Krase**

Other Owners: P. S. Alderson, Miss B. Allen, Mr S. W. Barrow, Mr A. R. Bentall, Mr D. J. Burke, Mrs V. F. Burke, D. B. Clark, Clive Cox Racing Ltd, Mr C. G. Cox, Mrs T. L. Cox, Miss J. Deadman, Mr M. R. Francis, Mr I. C. Higginson, Mr G. I. Hill, K. T. Ivory, Ms B. Miles, S. E. Munir, Mr I. Souede, Mr Alan Spence, Mr M. B. Spence, Mr N. Wagland.

Flat Jockey: Hector Crouch, Adam Kirby. **Apprentice Jockey:** Imogen Carter, Amelia Glass.

118 **MR TONY COYLE, Norton**
Postal: **Long Row Stables, Beverley Road, Norton, Malton, North Yorkshire, YO17 9PJ**
Contacts: **MOBILE 07976 621425**
EMAIL tonycoyleracing@hotmail.co.uk

1 BROKEN SPEAR, 4, b g Pastoral Pursuits—My Pretty Girl **Morecool Racing**
2 FLOWER POWER, 9, br m Bollin Eric—Floral Rhapsody **Ms M. H. Matheson**
3 LITTLE PIPPIN, 7, b m Sir Percy—Lady Le Quesne (IRE) **Mr A. C. Coyle**
4 NEWGATE ANGEL, 4, b f Heeraat (IRE)—Rio's Girl **W. P. S. Johnson**
5 NEWGATE DUCHESS, 6, b m Haafhd—Arctic Queen **W. P. S. Johnson**

THREE-YEAR-OLDS

6 BORIS THE BRAVE, b g Universal (IRE)—Newgate Queen **W. P. S. Johnson**
7 FULL CIRCLE, b g Finsceal Fior (IRE)—Full Bloom **John & Heather Raw & Tony Coyle**
8 B f Kodiac—Geht Fasteur (IRE) **Mr A. C. Coyle**
9 Ch f Sleeping Indian—Rio's Girl **W. P. S. Johnson**
10 WOTS THE WIFI CODE, b g Fast Company (IRE)—Velvet Jaguar **Mrs M. Lingwood**

TWO-YEAR-OLDS

11 Ch f 01/01 French Navy—My Pretty Girl (Arakan (USA)) **David Bishop & Tony Coyle**
12 Ch f 15/04 Fast Company (IRE)—Spice It Up (Authorized (IRE)) (4761) **Mr A. C. Coyle**

Other Owners: Mr D. F. L. Bishop, Mr A. C. Coyle, Mrs H. B. Raw, Mr J. Raw.

Flat Jockey: Barry McHugh.

119 **MR RAY CRAGGS, Sedgefield**
Postal: **East Close Farm, Sedgefield, Stockton-On-Tees, Cleveland, TS21 3HW**
Contacts: **PHONE 01740 620239 FAX 01740 623476**

1 AMELIA R (IRE), 4, b f Zoffany (IRE)—Xaloc (IRE) **R. Craggs**
2 AMOURI CHIEF, 6, b g Sleeping Indian—Tour d'Amour (IRE) **R. Craggs**
3 AMOURI GLEAM, 5, b m Arabian Gleam—Tour d'Amour (IRE) **R. Craggs**
4 AMOURIE, 4, ch f Haafhd—Tour d'Amour (IRE) **R. Craggs**
5 CORAL QUEEN, 9, b m Desideratum—Queen's Lodge (IRE) **R. Craggs**
6 GALLEY CAT, 5, ch m Sleeping Indian—Celestial Welcome **R. Craggs**
7 GLASGON, 10, gr g Verglas (IRE)—Miss St Tropez **R. Craggs**
8 GRANNY ROZ, 6, b m Bahamian Bounty—Hulcote Rose (IRE) **R. Craggs**
9 PARK HOUSE, 11, b g Tillerman—Rasin Luck **R. Craggs**
10 QUAY QUEST, 6, ch g Shami—Quay Four (IRE) **R. Craggs**
11 TARA TIARA, 8, b m Kayf Tara—Royal Roxy (IRE) **R. Craggs**
12 WELL I NEVER, 8, b g Josr Algarhoud (IRE)—Tour d'Amour (IRE) **R. Craggs**

Assistant Trainer: Miss J N Craggs.

120 **MR PETER CRATE, Newdigate**
Postal: **Springfield Farm, Parkgate Road, Newdigate, Dorking, Surrey, RH5 5DZ**
Contacts: **MOBILE 07775 821560**
EMAIL peterdcrate@jandjfranks.com

1 MOMTATHIL, 4, b g Oasis Dream—Motmayza **P. D. Crate**
2 PINK ICEBURG (IRE), 4, b f Kodiac—Twinkling Ice (USA) **P. D. Crate**

THREE-YEAR-OLDS

3 SAND DIEGO (IRE), ch g Starspangledbanner (AUS)—Supreme Quest **P. D. Crate**
4 SAND JUNE, b f Piccolo—Alhufoof (USA) **P. D. Crate**

Flat Jockey: Shane Kelly. **Amateur Jockey:** Mr George Crate.

121

MR SIMON CRISFORD, Newmarket
Postal: **Gainsborough Stables, Hamilton Road, Newmarket, Suffolk, CB8 0TE**
Contacts: **PHONE 01638 662661**
EMAIL office@crisfordracing.com **TWITTER** @crisfordracing **INSTAGRAM** crisford_racing

1 **ARISTOCRATIC LADY (IRE)**, 4, b f Invincible Spirit (IRE)—Dubai Queen (USA)
2 **ASAD (IRE)**, 4, ch g Lope de Vega (IRE)—Venus de Milo (IRE)
3 **CAPE CAVALLI (IRE)**, 4, b g Cape Cross (IRE)—Matauri Pearl (IRE)
4 **CENTURY DREAM (IRE)**, 6, b h Cape Cross (IRE)—Salacia (IRE)
5 **DOUBLE KODIAC (IRE)**, 4, b g Kodiac—Via Lattea (IRE)
6 **EBBRAAM**, 4, b f Teofilo (IRE)—Oojooba
7 **EPIC HERO (FR)**, 4, b g Siyouni (FR)—Grace Lady (FR)
8 **JASH (IRE)**, 4, b c Kodiac—Miss Azeza
9 **MAYBE TODAY**, 5, b m Cacique (IRE)—Quiza Quiza Quiza
10 **MORDIN (IRE)**, 6, b g Invincible Spirit (IRE)—Bryanstown (IRE)
11 **NEESAAN**, 4, b f New Approach (IRE)—Red Dune (IRE)
12 **OSTILIO**, 5, ch h New Approach (IRE)—Reem Three
13 **OUTBOX**, 5, b g Frankel—Emirates Queen
14 **PERSIAN BEAUTY (IRE)**, 4, b f Dubawi (IRE)—Zeeba (IRE)
15 **RASTRELLI (FR)**, 5, b g Siyouni (FR)—Ponte di Legno (FR)
16 **RED MIST**, 5, b h Frankel—Red Dune (IRE)
17 **ROULSTON SCAR (IRE)**, 4, b g Lope de Vega (IRE)—Pussycat Lips (IRE)
18 **SAFFRAN (IRE)**, 4, b g Teofilo (IRE)—Oriental Step (IRE)

THREE-YEAR-OLDS

19 **A'ALI (IRE)**, b br c Society Rock (IRE)—Motion Lass
20 **A'SHAMARDI (IRE)**, b c Shamardal (USA)—Twilight Sky
21 **AADDEEY (IRE)**, b c New Approach (IRE)—Feedyah (USA)
22 **AFEEFAH (IRE)**, b f Dark Angel (IRE)—Soraaya (IRE)
23 **AL BADR**, b g Kodiac—Mitre Peak
24 **AL RAYA**, b f Siyouni (FR)—Fig Roll
25 **AL SHOMOOKH (IRE)**, gr f More Than Ready (USA)—Lismore (IRE)
26 **AMAAN**, b g Dawn Approach (IRE)—Qareenah (USA)
27 **ANJAH (IRE)**, b g Kodiac—Terhaab (USA)
28 **AQAAREB (IRE)**, b g Muhaarar—Vanishing Grey (IRE)
29 **ARIJ (IRE)**, b g Charm Spirit (IRE)—Aquarelliste (FR)
30 **BANNA**, b f Pivotal—Salacia (IRE)
31 **BE PREPARED**, b c Due Diligence (USA)—Chicklade
32 **BRIGHT VIEW (IRE)**, b f Siyouni (FR)—Quilting (USA)
33 **BURNING SUN (IRE)**, ch f Slade Power (IRE)—Crimson Year (USA)
34 **CASTING VOTE (IRE)**, br g New Approach (IRE)—Masarah (IRE)
35 **CORVAIR (IRE)**, b c Toronado (IRE)—Nagham (IRE)
36 **DEFENCE GIRL (USA)**, b f First Defence (USA)—Supposition
37 **FANTAIL**, b f Zoffany (IRE)—Red Fantasy (IRE)
38 **FAST SPIN (USA)**, b br f Hard Spun (USA)—Lacy (GER)
39 **FEMININE FELICITY**, b f Dawn Approach (IRE)—Emirates Holidays (USA)
40 **FESTIVE STAR**, b f Golden Horn—Festoso (IRE)
41 **FINELY TUNED (IRE)**, b g Gleneagles (IRE)—Turning Top (IRE)
42 **FINEST SOUND (IRE)**, b g Exceed And Excel (AUS)—Amplifier
43 **FLY TILL DAWN**, ch g Starspangledbanner (AUS)—Lorient
44 **FREEDOM FLYER (IRE)**, b c Invincible Spirit (IRE)—Liberating
45 **HEAD OF THE HOUSE (IRE)**, br g Dream Ahead (USA)—Rahlah
46 **HUNTSMAN'S CALL (IRE)**, b g Golden Horn—Fragrancy (IRE)
47 **KEY LOOK (IRE)**, ch f Dawn Approach (IRE)—Fashion Line (IRE)
48 **LABEEBB (IRE)**, b c Exceed And Excel (AUS)—Tazffin (IRE)
49 **LAST SURPRISE (IRE)**, ch f No Nay Never (USA)—Beta Tauri (USA)
50 **LATE ARRIVAL (IRE)**, b c Night of Thunder (IRE)—Powdermill
51 **LUNCIES**, gr c Iffraaj—Under The Rainbow
52 **MAESTRO STICK**, b c Frankel—Moon Sister (IRE)
53 **MAJESTIC JEWEL**, b f Kingman—Soryah (IRE)

MR SIMON CRISFORD - continued

54 **MAKE IT RAIN (IRE),** b f Night of Thunder (IRE)—Badalona
55 **MANAATIG,** b f Iffraaj—Dance Awhile (IRE)
56 **MOOLHIM (FR),** b c Siyouni (FR)—Melbourne Shuffle (USA)
57 **MY SENORITA (FR),** ch f Lope de Vega (IRE)—Copernica (IRE)
58 **MYSEVEN (IRE),** b f Golden Horn—Anaamil (IRE)
59 **NIGHT COLOURS (IRE),** b f Night of Thunder (IRE)—Many Colours
60 **OCEANS MEET,** b f Sea The Stars (IRE)—Elision (IRE)
61 **ONE IDEA,** gr gr c Dubawi (IRE)—Rose Diamond (IRE)
62 **PASSIONAL,** b f Footstepsinthesand—Cordial
63 **PERFECT FOCUS (IRE),** b c Acclamation—Tonle Sap (IRE)
64 **SAARYAA (IRE),** b f Dubawi (IRE)—Red Dune (IRE)
65 **SACRE BLEU,** b g Oasis Dream—Sand River (IRE)
66 Ch f Gleneagles (IRE)—Saturn Girl (IRE)
67 **TURQUOISE KINGDOM,** b c Dubawi (IRE)—Fallen For You
68 **WILL TO WIN (GER),** ch g Showcasing—Win For Life (GER)
69 **WISE GLORY (IRE),** b g Muhaarar—Bint Almukhtar (IRE)
70 **WITHOUT A FIGHT (IRE),** b g Teofilo (IRE)—Khor Sheed
71 **ZEYARAH (FR),** ch f Lope de Vega (IRE)—Starring Guest (IRE)

TWO-YEAR-OLDS

72 Ch c 28/04 Night of Thunder (IRE)—Alice Rose (IRE) (Manduro (GER)) (210000)
73 Gr c 08/02 Markaz (IRE)—Arsheef (USA) (Hard Spun (USA))
74 **ATACAMENA (IRE),** b f 10/03 Fast Company (IRE)—Emboss (IRE) (Cape Cross (IRE)) (65000)
75 B f 03/02 Kingman—Comic (IRE) (Be My Chief (USA)) (200000)
76 B f 02/05 Muhaarar—Daymooma (Pivotal)
77 B f 08/03 Exceed And Excel (AUS)—Different (Bahamian Bounty) (55000)
78 B c 31/01 Camelot—Dorothy B (IRE) (Fastnet Rock (AUS)) (135000)
79 **FIGURES,** b f 13/02 Fastnet Rock (AUS)—Gadfly (Galileo (IRE)) (200000)
80 B c 18/03 Myboycharlie (IRE)—Fontaine Margot (FR) (Ballingarry (IRE)) (42900)
81 B f 08/03 Kodiac—Intaglia (New Approach (IRE)) (150000)
82 B c 22/04 Adlerflug (GER)—Irika (GER) (Areion (GER))
83 B c 19/04 Sea The Stars (IRE)—Lilting (IRE) (Montjeu (IRE)) (55769)
84 **LINE OF DESCENT (IRE),** b c 04/04 Nathaniel—Joys of Spring (IRE) (Invincible Spirit (IRE))
85 Ch f 08/03 Night of Thunder (IRE)—Linet (IRE) (Oasis Dream) (60000)
86 B f 04/02 Kingman—Lustrous (Champs Elysees) (100000)
87 **MABDAA,** b c 14/05 Oasis Dream—Darajaat (USA) (Elusive Quality (USA))
88 B f 07/03 Acclamation—Marsh Daisy (Pivotal) (260000)
89 **MASTER OF COMBAT (IRE),** b c 07/03 Invincible Spirit (IRE)—Sharja Queen (Pivotal)
90 B f 16/01 New Approach (IRE)—Mazuna (IRE) (Cape Cross (IRE))
91 Ch f 18/04 Bated Breath—Mutheera (Oasis Dream) (20000)
92 B c 13/02 Siyouni (FR)—Nabaraat (USA) (War Front (USA))
93 B c 09/02 Kodiac—Nayfah (FR) (Falco (USA)) (160000)
94 **OPERATIC (IRE),** ch f 02/03 Showcasing—Dream Dana (IRE) (Dream Ahead (USA)) (66923)
95 B c 28/01 Fastnet Rock (AUS)—Private Paradise (IRE) (Galileo (IRE)) (105000)
96 B f 26/04 Dark Angel (IRE)—Raasefah (Pivotal)
97 B f 10/05 Shamardal (USA)—Red Dune (IRE) (Red Ransom (USA))
98 Ch c 11/02 Iffraaj—Rekdhat (IRE) (Shamardal (USA))
99 B c 02/02 Frankel—Rizeena (IRE) (Iffraaj)
100 **ROYAL HARMONY (IRE),** b f 28/01 Shamardal (USA)—Lady Of Dubai (Dubawi (IRE))
101 B f 01/03 Dubawi (IRE)—Sajjhaa (King's Best (USA))
102 **SARAY PRINCE (IRE),** ch c 01/02 Exceed And Excel (AUS)—Zabeel Princess (Dubawi (IRE))
103 B c 05/04 Lope de Vega (IRE)—Shemya (FR) (Dansili) (100000)
104 **SO IMPRESSED (IRE),** b f 01/05 Exceed And Excel (AUS)—Mundana (IRE) (King's Best (USA))
105 B c 07/05 Holy Roman Emperor (IRE)—South Sister (Sakhee (USA)) (64350)
106 B c 07/03 Shamardal (USA)—Special Guest (Dubawi (IRE))
107 B c 13/05 Dubawi (IRE)—Talmada (USA) (Cape Cross (IRE))
108 B c 13/03 Sepoy (AUS)—Tantshi (IRE) (Invincible Spirit (IRE))
109 B c 28/02 Camelot—Temptress (IRE) (Shirocco (GER)) (140000)
110 B c 04/03 Dubawi (IRE)—Yellow Rosebud (IRE) (Jeremy (USA))

122 MR ANDREW CROOK, Leyburn
Postal: Ashgill Stables (Yard 2), Tupgill Park, Coverham, Middleham, North Yorkshire, DL8 4TJ
Contacts: PHONE 01969 640303 MOBILE 07764 158899
EMAIL andycrookracing@gmail.com WEBSITE www.andrewcrookracing.co.uk

1 **ALONG CAME THEO (IRE)**, 10, b g Vertical Speed (FR)—Kachina (IRE) **The 100 Club**
2 **BAH LAMB**, 9, ch m Sakhee (USA)—Lucinda Lamb **Mrs D. S. Wilkinson**
3 **CRAKEHALL LAD (IRE)**, 9, ch g Manduro (GER)—My Uptown Girl **Mrs K. M. Savage**
4 **CYRANO STAR (FR)**, 8, gr g Martaline—Quezac du Boulay (FR) **Leeds Plywood & Doors Ltd**
5 **DONALD DUX (IRE)**, 6, b g Sholokhov (IRE)—Good Shine (IRE) **Mr D. Carter**
6 **EARLY BOY (FR)**, 9, b g Early March—Eclat de Rose (FR) **R. P. E. Berry**
7 **EMPORTEPARLAFOULE (FR)**, 6, gr g Smadoun (FR)—Sempiternelle (FR) **Mr D. Carter**
8 **HEY JAZZY LADY (IRE)**, 4, b f Red Jazz (USA)—First Bunting (IRE) **Miss M. Hodgson**
9 **HIGH ANXIETY**, 6, ch m Bated Breath—Odense (USA) **Mrs S. J. Beddis**
10 **JACARNO**, 8, ch g Lucarno (USA)—Sparkling Jewel **The 100 Club**
11 **JAGERBOND**, 4, ch g Monsieur Bond (IRE)—Velvet Jaguar **Mrs C. Hopper**
12 **K O KENNY**, 9, b g Apple Tree (FR)—Cool Island (IRE) **Mr K. Heilbron**
13 **LADY BABS**, 6, br m Malinas (GER)—Jontys'lass **Ashgill Stud**
14 **MONTELIMAR**, 5, b m Raven's Pass (USA)—Mascarene (USA) **Carl Chapman & Robert Parks**
15 **OUR CILLA**, 6, gr m Sixties Icon—Kinetix **The Newtown Partnership**
16 **PINKIE PIE (IRE)**, 4, b f Tagula (IRE)—Bidable **The 100 Club**
17 **RACEMAKER**, 6, b g Stimulation (IRE)—Sophies Heart **Mrs H. Sinclair**
18 **STITCH UP (IRE)**, 4, b g Milan—Be My Granny **Mr D. Carter**
19 **VESHENSKAYA (IRE)**, 5, b m Sholokhov (IRE)—Manorville (IRE) **Signify Partnership**
20 **ZARA'S UNIVERSE**, 4, b f Universal (IRE)—Jontys'lass **Mrs C Hopper & David Carter**

THREE-YEAR-OLDS
21 **TILTILYS ROCK (IRE)**, ch g Society Rock (IRE)—Tiltili (IRE) **Mr D. Carter**

Other Owners: R. P. E. Berry, Mr D. Carter, Mr C. Chapman, Miss A. M. Crook, Miss M. Hodgson, Mrs C. Hopper, Mr R. J. Parks, Mrs K. M. Savage, Mr J. A. Saxby, Mr E. Skeels, O. R. Weeks, Mr T. D. Wooldridge.

Assistant Trainer: Amy Crook.

Flat Jockey: Jason Hart, Kevin Stott. **NH Jockey:** Will Kennedy, Adam Nicol.

123 MR SEAN CURRAN, Swindon
Postal: Twelve Oaks, Lechlade Road, Highworth, Swindon, Wiltshire, SN6 7QR
Contacts: MOBILE 07774 146169

1 **ALL YOURS (FR)**, 9, ch g Halling (USA)—Fontaine Riant (FR) **Power Geneva Ltd**
2 **COUSIN RITA**, 8, b m Black Sam Bellamy (IRE)—Aunt Rita (IRE) **I. M. McGready**
3 **DOMAINE DE L'ISLE (FR)**, 7, b g Network (GER)—Gratiene de l'Isle (FR) **12 Oaks Racing**
4 **FREDDIE CORBITT (IRE)**, 6, ch g Sans Frontieres (IRE)—Thrilling Prospect (IRE) **12 Oaks Racing**
5 **GRIGGY (IRE)**, 4, b g Dandy Man (IRE)—Joint Destiny (IRE) **Power Geneva Ltd**
6 **HILLARY JOHN (IRE)**, 9, ch g Gamut (IRE)—Dar Dar Supreme **Mr P. Burns**
7 **IS IT OFF (IRE)**, 5, b g Clodovil (IRE)—French Doll (IRE) **Power Geneva Ltd**
8 **KING CRIMSON**, 8, ch g Captain Gerrard (IRE)—Elegant Lady **Power Geneva Ltd**
9 **SIEGE OF BOSTON (IRE)**, 7, ch g Starspangledbanner (AUS)—Milton of Campsie **Power Geneva Ltd**
10 **UNFORGIVING MINUTE**, 9, b g Cape Cross (IRE)—Ada River **Power Geneva Ltd**
11 **WORD OF HONOUR**, 4, b g Showcasing—Veiled Intrigue

Other Owners: Mr J. M. S. Curran, L. M. Power.

124 MISS REBECCA CURTIS, Newport
Postal: **Fforest Farm, Newport, Pembrokeshire, SA42 0UG**
Contacts: **PHONE 01348 811489 MOBILE 07970 710690**
EMAIL rebcurtis@hotmail.com

1 **ABSOLUTE POWER**, 9, b g Flemensfirth (USA)—Crystal Ballerina (IRE) **Mark Sherwood & Spencer Gammond**
2 **ANAX (IRE)**, 6, b g Oscar (IRE)—Limetree Leader (IRE) **Mr N. D. Morris**
3 **CUBAO (IRE)**, 6, b g Fame And Glory—Rematch (IRE) **Primus Partners**
4 **DALAMAN (IRE)**, 9, b g Duke of Marmalade (IRE)—Crimphill (IRE) **Diamond Racing Ltd**
5 **EASY WOOD (FR)**, 6, gr g Martaline—Ball of Wood (FR) **Beesley, McDermott, Smith, Trembath**
6 **FINANCIAL OUTCOME (IRE)**, 7, b g Financial Reward (IRE)—Catriona's Mare (IRE) **Ccorz Partners**
7 **GEORDIE DES CHAMPS (IRE)**, 9, br g Robin des Champs (FR)—Kilcoleman Lady (IRE) **Mr J. P. McManus**
8 **GETAWAY WITHIT (IRE)**, 5, ch g Getaway (GER)—Native Wood (IRE) **Relentless Dreamers Racing**
9 **JOE FARRELL (IRE)**, 11, b g Presenting—Luck of The Deise (IRE) **M Sherwood, N Morris & J Turner**
10 **JOUEUR BRESILIEN (FR)**, 8, b g Fuisse (FR)—Fille du Bresil (FR) **Inthewayboy Group**
11 **JUST A THOUGHT (IRE)**, 8, ch m Stowaway—Carrig Lucy (IRE) **Hyde, Outhart, Moran & Hill**
12 **LEGENDS GOLD (IRE)**, 6, b m Gold Well—Fu's Legend (IRE) **Lockett,Hyde,Mountford,Bishop&Outhart**
13 **LISNAGAR OSCAR (IRE)**, 7, b g Oscar (IRE)—Asta Belle (FR) **Racing For Fun**
14 **LISSITZKY (IRE)**, 5, b g Declaration of War (USA)—Tarfshi **Mr N. D. Morris**
15 **MINELLA BOBO (IRE)**, 7, gr g Oscar (IRE)—Line Kendie (FR) **Moran, Outhart, McDermott, Hyde & Hill**
16 4, B f Black Sam Bellamy (IRE)—Moonlight Music (IRE) **Mr M. A. Sherwood**
17 **OSCAR ASCHE (IRE)**, 6, b g Oscar (IRE)—
Boro Supreme (IRE) **Spencer Gammond, Jackie Rymer & Rob Farnham**
18 4, B g Frozen Power (IRE)—Perovskia (USA) **Miss R. Curtis**
19 **RELENTLESS DREAMER (IRE)**, 11, b g Kayf Tara—Full of Elegance (FR) **Mr N. D. Morris**
20 **RUTHLESS ARTICLE (IRE)**, 7, b g Definite Article—Lady Kamando **M Sherwood J Rymer R Farnham C Rymer**
21 **SPECIAL PRINCESS (IRE)**, 10, br m Cloudings (IRE)—Cockpit Rose (IRE) **Claire Lockett & Rebecca Curtis**
22 **SUMMER NAME (IRE)**, 8, b g Duke of Marmalade (IRE)—Summer's Eve **Miss R. Curtis**
23 **SUNSET SHOWDOWN (IRE)**, 7, b g Flemensfirth (USA)—Sunset Queen (IRE) **Mr J. P. McManus**
24 **WAYFINDER (IRE)**, 6, br g Shantou (USA)—Sibury (IRE) **The Wayfinders**

Other Owners: Mr M. A. Beesley, Mr D. J. Bishop, Mr A. R. Clerkson, Mr J. Conyers, Miss R. Curtis, Mr M. Davis, Mr R. A. Farnham, Fishlake Commercial Motors Ltd, Mr G. S. Gammond, Mr I. Glendenning, Mr N. Goulden, M. Hill, Mr K. Hopgood, Mr R. Hyde, Mr R. J. Line, Mrs C. M. Lockett, Mr D. P. McDermott, Mr B. Merrett, Ms J. A. Moran, Mr N. D. Morris, Mrs K. M. Mountford, Mr J. P. O'Reilly, Mr W. J. O'Reilly, A. J. Outhart, Mr D. Paish, Mr N. M. Roddis, Mr C. A. Rymer, Mr J. Rymer, Mrs J. Rymer, Mr M. A. Sherwood, Mr A. J. Smith, Mr A. Spencer, Mr C. R. Trembath, Mr J. Turner, D. C. Zeffman.

Assistant Trainer: Paul Sheldrake.

125 MISS HELEN CUTHBERT, Brampton
Postal: **Woodlands, Cowranbridge, How Mill, Brampton, Cumbria, CA8 9LH**
Contacts: **PHONE 01228 560822 MOBILE 07879 634494**
EMAIL cuthbertracing@gmail.com

1 **RED FOREVER**, 9, ch g Major Cadeaux—Spindara (IRE) **Mrs J. Cuthbert**
2 **YAIR HILL (IRE)**, 12, b g Selkirk (USA)—Conspiracy **Mrs J. Cuthbert**

126 MR PAUL D'ARCY, Newmarket
Postal: **Charnwood Stables, Hamilton Road, Newmarket, Suffolk, CB8 7JQ**
Contacts: **WORK 01638 662000 MOBILE 07768 807653**
WORK EMAIL pauldarcyracingltd@gmail.com WEBSITE www.pauldarcyracing.com FACEBOOK @
pauldarcyracing TWITTER @Pauldarcyracing INSTAGRAM pauldarcyracing

1 **ISLE OF INNISFREE (USA)**, 4, b c Scat Daddy (USA)—Dream The Blues (IRE) **C. M. Wilson**
2 **NAMPARA**, 5, b m Kyllachy—Nurai **Mr K. Snell**
3 **PASS THE VINO (IRE)**, 4, b g Power—Excellent Mariner (IRE) **Rowley Racing**
4 **ZEEBAD (IRE)**, 4, gr g Zebedee—Love Intrigue (IRE) **Mr P. W. D'Arcy**

MR PAUL D'ARCY - continued

THREE-YEAR-OLDS

5 **CHEAT (IRE)**, gr g Gutaifan (IRE)—Beguiler **Paul D'Arcy Racing Partnership**
6 **JUST NORMAN**, b g Sepoy (AUS)—Nurai **Mr K. Snell**
7 **LIGHT LILY**, ch f Iffraaj—Night Lily (IRE) **Mr K. Snell**
8 **SOPHAR SOGOOD (IRE)**, b g French Navy—Cloud Break **Mr A. N. Seymour**

TWO-YEAR-OLDS

9 B c 12/02 Helmet (AUS)—Meddle (Diktat) **Mr K. Snell**
10 **POWER ON (IRE)**, b c 24/02 Power—Intermittent (Cacique (IRE)) (18876) **Rowley Racing & Partners**

Assistant Trainer: Sue D'Arcy.

---

127 MR LUKE DACE, Billingshurst
Postal: **Copped Hall Farm and Stud, Okehurst House, Okehurst Lane, Billingshurst, West Sussex, RH14 9HR**
Contacts: **MOBILE 07949 401085 FAX 01403 612176**
EMAIL lukedace@yahoo.co.uk WEBSITE www.lukedace.co.uk

1 **RAVENOUS**, 9, b g Raven's Pass (USA)—Supereva (IRE) **Ian Farminer & Farminer Developments Ltd**
2 **TAUREAN STAR (IRE)**, 7, b g Elnadim (USA)—Marhaba **Mr I. W. Moss**

THREE-YEAR-OLDS

3 **BARBOUKHA**, b f Swiss Spirit—Brooksby **The Sussex Partnership**
4 **CALAMITY MAY**, ch f Helmet (AUS)—Romantic Retreat **Mrs E. A. Cyzer**

Other Owners: Mr I. E. J. Farminer, Farminer Developments Ltd.

Assistant Trainer: Mrs L Dace.

---

128 MR KEITH DALGLEISH, Carluke
Postal: **Belstane Racing Stables, Carluke, Lanarkshire, ML8 5HN**
Contacts: **PHONE 01555 773335**
EMAIL dalgleish.racing@outlook.com

1 **ALRIGHT SUNSHINE (IRE)**, 5, b g Casamento (IRE)—Miss Gibraltar **Mr & Mrs Paul & Clare Rooney**
2 **AMALFI DOUG (FR)**, 10, gr g Network (GER)—Queissa (FR) **The County Set (seven) & Partner**
3 **BEECHWOOD JUDE (FR)**, 4, b g War Command (USA)—Ponte Sanangelo (FR) **Middleham Park Racing LXXXIV**
4 **BLUESKYANDSUNSHINE (IRE)**, 5, b g Fame And Glory—Printing Polly (IRE) **Mr & Mrs Paul & Clare Rooney**
5 **BOSTON GEORGE (IRE)**, 4, b g Raven's Pass (USA)—Her Own Kind (JPN) **Weldspec Glasgow Limited**
6 **CABALLERO (IRE)**, 4, ch c Camacho—Dame d'Honneur (IRE) **Weldspec Glasgow Limited**
7 **CAUSTIC LOVE (IRE)**, 4, b f Fast Company (IRE)—Moss Top (IRE) **Weldspec Glasgow Limited**
8 **CHOOKIE DUNEDIN (IRE)**, 5, b g Epaulette (AUS)—Lady of Windsor (IRE) **Raeburn Brick Limited**
9 **CLIFF BAY (IRE)**, 6, b g Elzaam (AUS)—Lost Highway (IRE) **Mr J. K. McGarrity**
10 **CORTON LAD**, 10, b g Refuse To Bend (IRE)—Kelucia (IRE) **Mr J. J. Hutton**
11 **CORTON LASS**, 5, gr m Showcasing—Elbow Beach **Mr J. J. Hutton**
12 **DARK LOCHNAGAR (USA)**, 4, b c Australia—Virginia Waters (USA) **Weldspec Glasgow Limited**
13 **DESERT POINT (FR)**, 8, b g Le Havre (USA)—Bonne Mere (FR) **Straightline Bloodstock**
14 **DIAMONIQUE**, 4, b f Kyllachy—Al Joudha (FR) **Weldspec Glasgow Limited**
15 **DRAGON MOUNTAIN**, 5, b g Sir Percy—Rouge Dancer **Mr J S Morrison**
16 **EL HOMBRE**, 6, ch g Camacho—Nigella **Weldspec Glasgow Limited**
17 **EL PICADOR (IRE)**, 4, b g Dansili—West of Venus (USA) **Sir Ian & Ms Catriona Good**
18 **ELLE EST GRANDE (IRE)**, 6, b m Jeremy (USA)—Hester Hall (IRE) **The Gilbert's & Mr Campbell**
19 **EPONA**, 4, b f Epaulette (AUS)—Jackline **From the Front Racing & Partner**
20 **EURO IMPLOSION (IRE)**, 4, b g Battle of Marengo (IRE)—Mikes Baby (IRE) **Mr J S Morrison**

MR KEITH DALGLEISH - continued

21 **FOREVER A LADY (IRE)**, 7, b m Dark Angel (IRE)—Unicamp **Mr J. K. McGarry**
22 **FRIENDLY ADVICE (IRE)**, 4, ch g Orientor—Secret Advice **A. R. M. Galbraith**
23 **FUENTE**, 4, ch g Havana Gold (IRE)—Bounty Box **Mr K. W. Dalgleish**
24 **GENNADY (IRE)**, 6, b g Arakan (USA)—Topathistle (IRE) **Straightline Bloodstock**
25 **GLENGARRY**, 7, b g Monsieur Bond (IRE)—Lady McBeth (IRE) **Mrs J. M. MacPherson**
26 **GLORIOUS LADY (IRE)**, 6, b m Fame And Glory—Lady Secret (FR) **Straightline Bloodstock**
27 **GOLD OPERA (IRE)**, 11, b g Gold Well—Flute Opera (IRE) **Straightline Bloodstock**
28 **GOLDENCARD (IRE)**, 7, b g Golden Lariat (USA)—Flemensfirth Lady (IRE) **The Gilbert's & Mr Campbell**
29 **GOMETRA GINTY (IRE)**, 4, b f Morpheus—Silver Cache (USA) **Ken McGarrity & Partner**
30 **GRUMPY MCGRUMPFACE (IRE)**, 5, b g Arctic Cosmos (USA)—Celestial Spirit (IRE) **Straightline Bloodstock**
31 **HIGHWAY COMPANION (IRE)**, 6, b g Milan—Niffyrann (FR) **Weldspec Glasgow Limited**
32 **HOLLY FLIGHT (FR)**, 8, b m Walk In The Park (IRE)—Lover Flight (FR) **Mr M. Fennessy**
33 **HOME BEFORE DUSK**, 5, b g Medicean—Flylowflylong (IRE) **Mr G. R. Leckie**
34 **HOWZER BLACK (IRE)**, 4, b g Requinto (IRE)—Mattinata **Middleham Park Racing LXXVI**
35 **I'M TO BLAME (IRE)**, 7, b g Winged Love (IRE)—Swap Shop (IRE) **Mr & Mrs Paul & Clare Rooney**
36 **ICONIC CODE**, 5, ch m Sixties Icon—Silca Key **Sir Ian & Ms Catriona Good**
37 **INVISIONANDQMARTYN (IRE)**, 5, b g Arcadio (GER)—River Lass (IRE) **Mrs L. M. Hannity**
38 **IRON MIKE**, 4, gr g Gregorian—Regal Velvet **Weldspec Glasgow Limited**
39 **JACOB BLACK**, 9, b g Amadeus Wolf—First Eclipse (IRE) **Mr J. K. McGarry**
40 **LET ME BE (IRE)**, 4, b g Gale Force Ten—Peryzat (IRE) **Mr & Mrs Paul & Clare Rooney**
41 **MAULESDEN MAY (IRE)**, 7, b m Dark Angel (IRE)—Jemima's Art **The County Set (Two)**
42 **MI CAPRICHO (IRE)**, 5, b g Elzaam (AUS)—Mavemacullen (IRE) **Mr C. Jones**
43 **MONSIEUR CO (FR)**, 7, b g Turgeon (USA)—Cayras Style (FR) **The Gilbert's & Mr Campbell**
44 **MOVIN'ON UP (IRE)**, 5, b m Milan—Kalygarde (FR) **Straightline Bloodstock**
45 **NEVER BE ENOUGH**, 5, ch m Sir Percy—Camp Fire (IRE) **Straightline Bloodstock**
46 **NEWTOWN BOY (IRE)**, 7, b g Beneficial—Tanit Lady (IRE) **The Gilbert's & Mr Campbell**
47 **NORTHERN SOCIETY (IRE)**, 4, b f Camacho—La Estatua **John Kelly, John McNeill & Alan Johnston**
48 **OSCAR CLOUDS (IRE)**, 5, b g Oscar (IRE)—Bobbing Back (IRE) **Straightline Bloodstock**
49 **PENNY BLAK**, 7, ch g Black Sam Bellamy (IRE)—Pennys Pride (IRE) **Sir Ian & Ms Catriona Good**
50 **PHILIP'S WISH**, 4, b g Maxios—Queen's Dream (GER) **Two Goldfish & A Balloon**
51 **PLATINUMCARD (IRE)**, 5, b g Golden Lariat (USA)—Flemensfirth Lady (IRE) **Straightline Bloodstock**
52 **POUR ME A DRINK**, 4, ch g Nathaniel (IRE)—Euroceleb (IRE) **Mr & Mrs Paul & Clare Rooney**
53 **PRINCE KAYF**, 6, b g Kayf Tara—Annie's Answer (IRE) **Straightline Bloodstock**
54 **RAYMOND (IRE)**, 5, b g Tobougg (IRE)—Crack The Kicker (IRE) **Straightline Bloodstock**
55 **RED BOND (IRE)**, 4, b c Red Jazz (USA)—Faithfulbond (IRE) **Middleham Park Racing XXVII**
56 **ROMAN STONE (USA)**, 4, b g Noble Mission—Winendynme (USA) **Weldspec Glasgow Limited**
57 **SENOR LOMBARDY (IRE)**, 7, b g Milan—Killoughey Babe (IRE) **Straightline Bloodstock**
58 **SEPAL (USA)**, 7, b m Afleet Alex (USA)—Faraway Flower (USA) **Mrs C. E. Dods**
59 **SIDI ISMAEL (FR)**, 6, b g Great Pretender (IRE)—Tetouane (FR) **Straightline Bloodstock**
60 **SOLDIER'S MINUTE**, 5, b g Raven's Pass (USA)—Hadba (IRE) **Weldspec Glasgow Limited**
61 **SPORTING PRESS (IRE)**, 7, b g Flemensfirth (USA)—Rudy Renata (IRE) **Straightline Bloodstock**
62 **STARPLEX**, 10, b g Multiplex—Turtle Bay **Mr K. W. Dalgleish**
63 **SUMMER DAYDREAM (IRE)**, 4, b f Footstepsinthesand—Summer Dream (IRE) **Mr R. Docherty**
64 **TAXMEIFYOUCAN (IRE)**, 6, b g Beat Hollow—Accounting **Straightline Bloodstock**
65 **THREE CASTLES**, 4, b g Zoffany (IRE)—Fountain of Honour (IRE) **Mr J. K. McGarrity**
66 **UNIVERSAL GLEAM**, 5, b g Sir Percy—Mookhlesa **Weldspec Glasgow Limited**
67 **WARRIORS STORY**, 4, b g Midnight Legend—Samandara (FR) **Straightline Bloodstock**
68 **WHAT'S THE STORY**, 6, b g Harbour Watch (IRE)—Spring Fashion (IRE) **Weldspec Glasgow Limited**
69 **WOODSIDE WONDER**, 4, br g Camacho—Cambridge Duchess **Middleham Park Racing XIV**

THREE-YEAR-OLDS

70 **ABERAMA GOLD**, b c Heeraat (IRE)—Nigella **Weldspec Glasgow Limited**
71 **AMBER STORM (IRE)**, ch f Night of Thunder (IRE)—Doregan (IRE) **Cull, Gilbert, Huntingford & Mackenzie**
72 **ARTHUR'S SEAT (IRE)**, b f Champs Elysees—Sojitzen (FR) **Mr & Mrs Paul & Clare Rooney**
73 **AUTUMN COLOURS (USA)**, b br f Orb (USA)—Avaricity (USA) **Weldspec Glasgow Limited**
74 **BLACK STAR DANCING (USA)**, b g Lemon Drop Kid (USA)—Beautiful Cat (USA) **Weldspec Glasgow Limited**
75 **BRAINCHILD**, b f Dark Angel (IRE)—Impressible **Mr M. Fennessy**
76 **BREGUET BOY (IRE)**, br g Requinto (IRE)—Holly Hawk (IRE) **R. McNeill**
77 **BRINGITONBORIS (USA)**, gr g Distorted Humor (USA)—Miss Fontana (USA) **Mr J S Morrison & Partner**

MR KEITH DALGLEISH - continued

78 **BYE BYE EURO (IRE)**, ch f Dragon Pulse (IRE)—Miss Frime (IRE) **Mr J S Morrison**
79 B f Honor Code (USA)—Casual Smile **Weldspec Glasgow Limited**
80 **CELESTIAL WOOD (IRE)**, b g Ivawood (IRE)—Angelic Angie (IRE) **Teme Valley Partnership**
81 **CLAY REGAZZONI**, b g Due Diligence (USA)—Shifting Moon **Middleham Park Racing XXXVIII & Partner**
82 **FASHION ADVICE**, ch f Dandy Man (IRE)—Secret Advice **A. R. M. Galbraith**
83 **FINALLY MINE (USA)**, ch f Animal Kingdom (USA)—Midnight Music (IRE) **Weldspec Glasgow Limited**
84 **FUNKY DUNKY (IRE)**, b g Requinto (IRE)—Red Blanche (IRE) **Mr K. W. Dalgleish**
85 **GET BOOSTING**, b g Swiss Spirit—Inagh River **The Strattonites**
86 **GLASVEGAS (IRE)**, gr g Zebedee—Rejuvenation (IRE) **Weldspec Glasgow Limited**
87 **GOT THE T SHIRT**, ch g Casamento (IRE)—Lolamotion **Middleham Park Racing CXI & Partner**
88 **HANDLEBARS (IRE)**, br f Footstepsinthesand—Amodio (IRE) **Equus I**
89 **HUA MULAN (IRE)**, gr f Harbour Watch (IRE)—Ultimate Best **Weldspec Glasgow Limited**
90 **I CAN'T REMEMBER (IRE)**, b c Dragon Pulse (IRE)—Time Signal **Mr & Mrs Paul & Clare Rooney**
91 **RIVER OF KINGS (IRE)**, b g Kodiac—Esedra (IRE) **Ontoawinner 8 & Partner**
92 **THE WINE CELLAR (IRE)**, ch c Dragon Pulse (IRE)—Veronica Falls **Mr & Mrs Paul & Clare Rooney**
93 **VENTURA DESTINY (FR)**, gr f Outstrip—Medalha Milagrosa (USA) **Middleham Park Racing CXVIII & Partner**
94 **VENTURA FLAME (IRE)**, b f Dandy Man (IRE)—Kramer Drive (IRE) **Middleham Park Racing LXXXIII & Partner**
95 B f American Pharoah (USA)—Virginia Waters (USA) **Weldspec Glasgow Limited**
96 **VOLATILE ANALYST (USA)**, b c Distorted Humor (USA)—Gentle Caroline (USA) **A. F. O'Callaghan**
97 **YOUNEVERLETMEDOWN (IRE)**, br f Footstepsinthesand—Calorie **Equus I**

TWO-YEAR-OLDS

98 Gr f 09/04 Twilight Son—Alabastrine (Green Desert (USA)) (4289)
99 B f 05/04 Harzand (IRE)—Cailin Meidhreach (IRE) (Big Bad Bob (IRE))
100 **COOL DANDY (IRE)**, b f 16/03 Dandy Man (IRE)—
                                         Cool Express (IRE) (Holy Roman Emperor (IRE)) (7721) **Mr F. Brady**
101 **DENZIL'S LAUGHING (IRE)**, b c 09/03 Mehmas (IRE)—
                                         Question (Coronado's Quest (USA)) (26666) **Ontoawinner 8 & Partner**
102 Ch f 03/03 Hot Streak (IRE)—Fine Blend (IRE) (Sakhee's Secret) (25000)
103 B f 27/04 Holy Roman Emperor (IRE)—Gale Green (Galileo (IRE)) (24761)
104 B f 04/04 Camacho—La Estatua (Lope de Vega (IRE)) (4289)
105 Ch f 24/03 Buratino (IRE)—La Noe (Nayef (USA)) (4290)
106 B f 17/04 Belardo (IRE)—Light And Airy (Linamix (FR))
107 B c 28/02 Mayson—Resist (Rock of Gibraltar (IRE)) (19047)
108 Ch f 22/04 Dandy Man (IRE)—Spavento (IRE) (Verglas (IRE)) (4718)
109 B f 04/03 Markaz (IRE)—Sweet Sioux (Halling (USA)) (3002)
110 Ch c 15/03 Anjaal—Tamara Love (IRE) (Tamayuz) (8580)
111 B f 15/02 Camacho—Tip It On The Top (IRE) (War Chant (USA)) (22307)
112 Br f 15/05 Slade Power (IRE)—Wild Academy (IRE) (Royal Academy (USA)) (3860)

Other Owners: Mr S. Bridge, A. Cadger, Mr J. J. Campbell, Mr M. J. S. Cockburn, County Set Seven, Mr R. Cull, Mr K. W. Dalgleish, Mr R. Doak, Mr D. Duncan, Equus I, Mr S. Franks, From The Front Racing, Mr A. N. Gargan, Mrs K. E. Gilbert, Mr P. Gilbert, Richard & Katherine Gilbert, G. Godsman, Ms C. Good, Sir Ian Good, E. D. Haggart, Mr A. W. Henderson, Mr T. Huntingford, Mr A. Johnston, Keith Dalgleish Racing Limited, Mr J. Kelly, Mr J. S. Lessells, Mrs P. M. Mackenzie, Mr J. K. McGarrity, Mr J. McNeill, Mr J. M. Mcintyre, Mr M. G. Mellor, Middleham Park Racing CXI, Middleham Park Racing CXVIII, Middleham Park Racing LXXXIII, Middleham Park Racing XXXVIII, Mr J S Morrison, Mr N. J. O'Brien, Ontoawinner 8, T. S. Palin, M. Prince, Mr S. C. Reay, Mr A. Savage, A. W. Sinclair, Miss M. M. Smith, Mr P. B. Tann, Mr D. A. Walker.

Assistant Trainer: Kevin Dalgleish.

Conditional Jockey: Callum Bewley. **Apprentice Jockey:** Rowan Scott.

129 MR HENRY DALY, Ludlow
Postal: **Downton Hall Stables, Ludlow, Shropshire, SY8 3DX**
Contacts: WORK **01584 873688** MOBILE **07720 074544**
EMAIL **henry@henrydaly.co.uk** WEBSITE **www.henrydaly.co.uk**

1 **ACCORDING TO ALEX (FR)**, 5, gr g Al Namix (FR)—Go Lison (FR) **Sir W. J. A. Timpson**
2 **ATLANTA ABLAZE**, 9, b m Kayf Tara—Rocheflamme (FR) **The Last Man Standing**
3 **BELATRIX LESTRANGE**, 5, b m Malinas (GER)—Who's Afraid **The Henry Daly Racing Club**
4 **BIG HEARTED ARTHUR**, 4, br g Trans Island—Overthrow **H. D. J. Daly**
5 **BLACK TULIP**, 8, ch m Black Sam Bellamy (IRE)—Combe Florey **Hot To Trot Jumping & Mr B G Hellyer**
6 **BRETNEY (IRE)**, 5, b g Milan—Pearl Buttons **Mr T. J. Hemmings**
7 **CHILLI FILLI**, 7, ch m Presenting—Daprika (FR) **StrachanLewisGabbGrahamSalwey&Griffith**
8 **DON JUAN DU GOUET (FR)**, 7, b g Special Kaldoun (IRE)—Querida de Ferbet (FR) **The Henry Daly Racing Club**
9 4, B f Malinas (GER)—Even Flo **Mr J. F. Perriss**
10 **FAIR AND DANDY**, 7, gr m Fair Mix (IRE)—Ashnaya (FR) **Mrs H Plumbly J Trafford K Deane S Holme**
11 **FLASHJACK (IRE)**, 10, br g Soapy Danger—Open Miss **Mr Charles Whittaker & Belinda Clarke**
12 **FORTESCUE**, 6, b g Shirocco (GER)—Last of Her Line **T. F. F. Nixon**
13 **HEAD TO THE STARS**, 9, br g Kayf Tara—Sail By The Stars **T. F. F. Nixon**
14 **HONEST VIC (IRE)**, 7, b g Kalanisi (IRE)—Miss Vic Lovin (IRE) **Carole Daly & Partners**
15 **IT'S PROBABLY ME**, 5, b m Great Pretender (IRE)—Sting In The Gale **James and Jean Potter Ltd**
16 **JIMMY THE DIGGER**, 7, b g Black Sam Bellamy (IRE)—The Lyme Volunteer (IRE) **H. D. J. Daly**
17 **LAXEY (IRE)**, 6, b g Yeats (IRE)—Nerissa (IRE) **Mr T. J. Hemmings**
18 **LILY GLITTERS**, 4, b f Shirocco (GER)—Alegralil
19 **LIME DROP (FR)**, 4, ch f Martaline—Lady Drop (FR) **Mrs C. M. Graves**
20 **LYGON ROCK (IRE)**, 7, b g Robin des Champs (FR)—Cute Lass (IRE) **The MAMIT Racing Partnership**
21 **MILESHA (IRE)**, 5, b m Milan—Shameena (IRE) **Strachan,Corbet,Andrewes,Salwey,Griffith**
22 **MISS MASH**, 9, b m Multiplex—Shanxi Girl **Barlow, Brindley, Kent**
23 **MORE OVERDRAUGHT**, 5, b m Shirocco (GER)—No More Money **Mrs C. M. Graves**
24 **PETRONELLA MANNERS**, 7, b m Shirocco (GER)—Last of Her Line **T. F. F. Nixon**
25 **PRECIOUS ELEANOR (FR)**, 5, gr m Maresca Sorrento (FR)—Precious Lucy (FR) **Rocking Horse Racing**
26 **RAPPER**, 6, b g Scorpion (IRE)—Bling Noir (FR) **The Home Farm Partnership**
27 **ROCK ON TIGER (IRE)**, 5, gr g Alberto Giacometti (IRE)—
            Kennaaly (FR) **Michael O'Flynn,John O'Flynnjohn Nesbitt**
28 5, Br g Stowaway—Shop Dj (IRE) **Mr T. J. Hemmings**
29 **SPIDER'S BITE (IRE)**, 8, b g Scorpion (IRE)—Model Girl **Mr T. J. Hemmings**
30 **STONEY MOUNTAIN (IRE)**, 7, ch g Mountain High (IRE)—Cherry Pie (FR) **Mr T. J. Hemmings**
31 **TEME SPIRIT (IRE)**, 6, b m Sans Frontieres (IRE)—
            Newtown Dancer (IRE) **Strachanstoddartsalweygabbstaley&corbett**
32 **VICE ET VERTU (FR)**, 11, b g Network (GER)—Duchesse du Cochet (FR) **Neville Statham & Family**
33 **WHATMORE**, 8, b g Schiaparelli (GER)—Polymiss (FR) **Strachan, Lewis, Gabb, Graham & Inkin**
34 **WHOOPSEY**, 5, b m Presenting—Whoops A Daisy **Strachangabbsalweyinkingriffithgraham**
35 **WILDE SPIRIT (IRE)**, 6, b m Oscar (IRE)—Full of Spirit (IRE) **Ludlow Racing Partnership**
36 **YOYO (IRE)**, 5, br m Getaway (GER)—Norabelle (FR) **The Glazeley Partnership**

Other Owners: Mr E. W. E. Andrewes, Mr C. R. Arkwright, Sir J. Barlow, Mr J. R. Brindley, Mr H. M. Butler, Mrs B. Clarke, Mrs P. Corbett, Mrs C. M. Daly, H. D. J. Daly, Mrs K. M. Deane, Mr B. P. Evans, Mrs M. A. Gabb, Mr C. G. Gibbons, Mrs S. A. Graham, Mrs J. G. Griffith, Exors of the Late Mr C. M. Hamer, E. R. Hanbury, B. G. Hellyer, Mrs S. E. Holme, Mr R. S. Hoskins, Hot To Trot Jumping, Lady S. L. Inkin, R. Kent, Mr P. A. Lewington, Mrs S. M. Lewis, Mr J. O. Nesbitt, Mr J. O'Flynn, Mr M. O'Flynn, Mr R. A. Pilkington, Sir Thomas Pilkington, Mrs H. Plumbly, Mr G. C. Rowles, Mr H. Salwey, Mrs S. A. J. Staley, M. C. Stoddart, Mr M. Stokes, Mr R. A. Strachan, Mrs E. J. Trafford, Mr C. G. Whittaker, Mr M. D. Wiggin.

130 MR PHILLIP DANDO, Peterston-Super-Ely
Postal: **Springfield Court, Peterston-Super-Ely, Cardiff, South Glamorgan, CF5 6LG**
Contacts: **PHONE 01446 760012 MOBILE 07872 965395**

1 **BEAU HAZE**, 7, b g Black Sam Bellamy (IRE)—Bella Haze **P. C. Dando**
2 **DRIFTWOOD HAZE**, 12, b g Nomadic Way (USA)—Kristal Haze **P. C. Dando**
3 **HARRY HAZE**, 8, b g Dr Massini (IRE)—Gypsy Haze **Mr Phillip Dando & Mr Anthony Brown**
4 **IFANDABUT (IRE)**, 8, b g Scorpion (IRE)—Native Wonder (IRE) **The Gambling Cousins**

Other Owners: Mr H. A. Brown, P. C. Dando.

Assistant Trainer: Mrs Rebecca Davies.

131 MR VICTOR DARTNALL, Barnstaple
Postal: **Higher Shutscombe Farm, Charles, Brayford, Barnstaple, Devon, EX32 7PU**
Contacts: **PHONE 01598 710280 MOBILE 07974 374272 FAX 01598 710708**
EMAIL victordartnall@gmail.com WEBSITE www.victordartnallracing.com

1 **ADMIRAL'S SECRET**, 9, b g Kayf Tara—Bobs Bay (IRE) **The Whacko Partnership**
2 **ATJIMA (IRE)**, 5, b m Mahler—Qui Plus Est (FR)
3 **BINDON LANE**, 6, b g Arvico (FR)—Cuckoo Lane (IRE) **Mrs E. S. Weld**
4 4, B g Sans Frontieres (IRE)—Blue Article (IRE) **The First Shutscombe Syndicate**
5 **BOLVING (IRE)**, 9, b g Stowaway—Kiniohio (FR) **Mrs C. M. Barber**
6 **DANCING SHADOW (IRE)**, 11, br g Craigsteel—Be My Shadow (IRE) **The Dancing Shadows**
7 **FISHERMANS COVE (IRE)**, 6, b g Getaway (GER)—Toscar (IRE) **G. D. Hake**
8 **GET WISHING (IRE)**, 8, b g Getaway (GER)—Third Wish (IRE) **Edge Of Exmoor**
9 **HALDON HILL (IRE)**, 7, b g Mahler—Qui Plus Est (FR) **Mr J. P. McManus**
10 **HARTNOLL HERO (IRE)**, 4, br g Sageburg (IRE)—Skyra (IRE) **Mrs. S. De Wilde, Mr. B. Dallyn, Mrs. C. Carter**
11 **HOWARDIAN HILLS (IRE)**, 7, b g Vale of York (IRE)—Handsome Anna (IRE) **Mr V. R. A. Dartnall**
12 **MAHLER'S FIRST (IRE)**, 8, b g Mahler—Fridays Folly (IRE) **First Brayford Partnership**
13 **MINNIE ESCAPE**, 8, b m Getaway (GER)—Minnie Hill (IRE) **The Second Brayford Partnership**
14 **RIVER BRAY (IRE)**, 7, ch g Arakan (USA)—Cill Fhearga (IRE) **The River Bray Syndicate**
15 **RUN TO MILAN (IRE)**, 8, b g Milan (IRE)—Run Supreme (IRE) **Barber, Birchenhough, De Wilde**
16 **SWEET ADARE (IRE)**, 7, b m Getaway (GER)—The Adare Woman (IRE) **G. D. Hake**
17 **UT MAJEUR AULMES (FR)**, 12, ch g Northern Park (USA)—My Wish Aulmes (FR) **Mrs S. De Wilde**

Other Owners: Mrs C. M. Barber, Mrs K. Birchenhough, Ms C. Carter, Mr B. C. Dallyn, Mr V. R. A. Dartnall, Mrs S. De Wilde, Mr J. Edelman, Mrs S. M. Hall, Mr M. E. Nicholls, Mr M. W. Richards, Mr L. Singleton, A. P. Staple.

Assistant Trainer: G. A. Dartnall.

132 MR TOM DASCOMBE, Malpas
Postal: **Manor House Stables, Malpas, Cheshire, SY14 8AD**
Contacts: **PHONE 01948 820485 MOBILE 07973 511664 FAX 01948 820495**
EMAIL tom@manorhousestables.com WEBSITE www.manorhousestables.com

1 **ANGEL ALEXANDER (IRE)**, 4, ro g Dark Angel (IRE)—Majestic Alexander (IRE) **Birbeck Mound Trowbridge & Owen**
2 **ARCANADA (IRE)**, 7, ch g Arcano (IRE)—Bond Deal (IRE) **The Arcanada Partnership**
3 **CALDER PRINCE (IRE)**, 7, gr g Dark Angel (IRE)—Flame of Ireland (IRE) **Mr P. G. Birbeck**
4 **CASTING SPELLS**, 4, ch f Lope de Vega (IRE)—Ballymore Celebre (IRE) **Mr J. E. Dance**
5 **CHARLIE D (USA)**, 5, b g Animal Kingdom (USA)—Ocicat (USA) **Mr D. R. Passant & Mr T. Dascombe**
6 **EPAULEMENT (IRE)**, 5, b g Epaulette (AUS)—Little Whisper (IRE) **Deva Racing Epaulette Partnership**
7 **FANCY FOOTINGS (IRE)**, 4, b g Dandy Man (IRE)—Mystical Past (IRE) **Andrew Brown & Gemma Brown**
8 **FINOAH (IRE)**, 4, b g Kodiac—Burstingdalak (IRE) **Alan & Sue Cronshaw & Peter Birbeck**
9 **ICONIC CHOICE**, 4, ch f Sixties Icon—Adorable Choice (IRE) **Mr J. D. Brown**
10 **JACKSTAR (IRE)**, 4, gr g Dark Angel (IRE)—Starbright (IRE) **Mrs C. L. Ingram**
11 **JONAH JONES (IRE)**, 4, b c No Nay Never (USA)—Conniption (IRE) **Mr D. Ward**

MR TOM DASCOMBE - continued

12 **KACHY**, 7, b h Kyllachy—Dubai Bounty **Mr D. J. Lowe**
13 **MICKEY (IRE)**, 7, b g Zoffany (IRE)—Enchantment **Mrs Janet Lowe & Mr Tom Dascombe**
14 **RAJINSKY (IRE)**, 4, b g Zoffany (IRE)—Pink Moon (IRE) **Mr R. S. Matharu**
15 **REFLEKTOR (IRE)**, 7, ch g Bahamian Bounty—Baby Bunting **David Lowe & Miss Amber Lowe**
16 **SHA LA LA LA LEE**, 5, b g Helmet (AUS)—Shamara (IRE) **Nigel and Sharon Mather & Charles Ledigo**
17 **SHE CAN BOOGIE (IRE)**, 4, b f Dandy Man (IRE)—Disko (IRE) **Mike Nolan & Partner**
18 **WILD EDRIC**, 4, ch g Equiano (FR)—Lady Red Oak **Mr D. R. Passant**

THREE-YEAR-OLDS

19 **ANFIELD GIRL (IRE)**, b f Starspangledbanner (AUS)—Grivele (IRE) **Mr J. M. Kirkland**
20 **ANNIE JONES (IRE)**, b f Camelot—Conniption (IRE) **Mr D. Ward**
21 **BOOMER**, b f Kingman—Wall of Sound **Chasemore Farm LLP**
22 **BRAD THE BRIEF**, b c Dutch Art—Kenzadargent (FR) **Chasemore Farm LLP**
23 **BREATHALYZE (FR)**, b g Bated Breath—Laber Ildut (IRE) **More Turf Racing**
24 **BROOKSIDE BANNER (IRE)**, ch f Starspangledbanner (AUS)—Akrivi (IRE) **Mr S. Burns**
25 **CABARET PARISIENNE (USA)**, ch f Declaration of War (USA)—
Parisian Affair (USA) **Empire State Racing Partnership**
26 **DANA FOREVER (IRE)**, b f Requinto (IRE)—Positive Step (IRE) **Miss S. Y. D. Goh**
27 **DEEP END (IRE)**, b g Epaulette (AUS)—Party Feet (IRE) **The Big Easy Racing Syndicate**
28 **FILO'S FLYER (IRE)**, b f Teofilo (IRE)—Floating Along (IRE) **More Turf Racing**
29 **GENEVER DRAGON (IRE)**, b g Dragon Pulse (IRE)—Glen Ginnie (IRE) **Middleham Park Racing C & Barry Taylor**
30 **GIFTED RULER**, b c Muhaarar—Dubai Bounty **Mr D. R. Passant**
31 **GIRL FROM MARS (IRE)**, b f Make Believe—Miss Lucy Jane **Peter Birbeck & Rachel Dawson**
32 **GODFATHER (IRE)**, ch c Night of Thunder (IRE)—Aqlaam Vision **Miss S. Y. D. Goh**
33 **HE'S A KEEPER (IRE)**, gr g Brazen Beau (AUS)—Silver Grey (IRE) **Mr N. Canning**
34 **HIGH FLYING BIRD (FR)**, ro gr f Reliable Man—Supernova Heights (IRE) **The High Flying Bird Partnership**
35 **HOT AFFAIR**, b f Ivawood (IRE)—Romp **Clipper Group Holdings Ltd**
36 **KNOW NO LIMITS (IRE)**, b f Outstrip—Singing Field (USA) **Fdcholdings Hedges Nolan Rutherford**
37 B g Fountain of Youth (IRE)—La Rosiere (USA) **Empire State Racing Partnership**
38 **LOVABLE CHOICE**, ch f Sixties Icon—Adorable Choice (IRE) **Mr J. D. Brown**
39 **MANDIBLE (IRE)**, b g Dandy Man (IRE)—Mad About The Girl (IRE) **Owen Promotions Limited**
40 **MORISCO (IRE)**, b g Requinto (IRE)—Mattinata **Mrs C. L. Ingram**
41 **MR JONES AND ME**, b g Brazen Beau (AUS)—Posy Fossil (USA) **Mr R. Jones**
42 **PHUKET POWER (IRE)**, b g Kodiac—Brazilian Bride (IRE) **King Power Racing Co Ltd**
43 **POT OF PAINT**, b c New Approach (IRE)—Regency (JPN) **Mr D. R. Passant**
44 **QUICK RECAP (IRE)**, ch f No Nay Never (USA)—Princess Patsky (USA) **More Turf Racing**
45 **SERMON (IRE)**, gr g Dark Angel (IRE)—Kermana (IRE) **Highclere T'Bred Racing - David Hockney**
46 **SHEVCHENKO PARK (IRE)**, b g Epaulette (AUS)—Compton Girl **Nolan O'Halloran Satchell & Partner**
47 B f Golden Horn—Simonetta (IRE) **Mr D. Ward**
48 **URSULINA (IRE)**, b f Kodiac—Esterlina (IRE) **Chasemore Farm LLP**
49 **WELSH WAYNE (IRE)**, ch c Dragon Pulse (IRE)—Balaagha (USA) **Manor House Stables LLP**

TWO-YEAR-OLDS

50 **ADAAY DREAM**, b c 21/05 Adaay (IRE)—
Virtuality (USA) (Elusive Quality (USA)) (19047) **Faulkner, Joynson, Morris & Simpson**
51 **ARTORIOUS (IRE)**, ch c 08/03 New Bay—Sudu Queen (GER) (Invincible Spirit (IRE)) (52380) **Mr D. R. Passant**
52 **ASTRONOMIC CHOICE**, b c 21/02 Havana Gold (IRE)—
Adorable Choice (IRE) (Choisir (AUS)) (55238) **Mr J. D. Brown**
53 **BAKERSBOY**, b c 07/03 Oasis Dream—Dubai Bounty (Dubai Destination (USA)) (100000) **David Lowe & Partner**
54 B c 06/02 Gutaifan (IRE)—Bella Ophelia (IRE) (Baltic King) (48047) **Manor House Stables LLP**
55 B c 28/02 Bated Breath—Critical Path (IRE) (Noverre (USA)) (55238) **More Turf Racing**
56 Gr c 05/04 Dark Angel (IRE)—
Duchess Andorra (IRE) (Duke of Marmalade (IRE)) (77220) **Barry, Trowbridge & Empire State Racing**
57 B c 20/04 Equiano (FR)—Ellen (IRE) (Machiavellian (USA)) (24000) **Satchell Moran Solicitors**
58 Br c 11/01 Mehmas (IRE)—Faddwa (IRE) (Arcano (IRE)) (57142) **Manor House Stables LLP**
59 **FALCON BROOK**, b c 20/03 Heeraat (IRE)—
Sitting Pretty (IRE) (Compton Place) **Owen Promotions & Dooley Thoroughbreds**
60 **FANCY ANGEL (IRE)**, gr f 19/04 Dark Angel (IRE)—Vow (Motivator) (55769) **Andrew Brown & Gemma Brown**

MR TOM DASCOMBE - continued

61 GOLDEN ARMOUR, b c 24/04 Golden Horn—
Viola d'Amour (IRE) (Teofilo (IRE)) (90000) **Andrew Brown & Gemma Brown**
62 B f 18/03 Gleneagles (IRE)—Golden Glimmer (IRE) (Danehill Dancer (IRE)) **Chasemore Farm LLP**
63 GRACEFUL MOMENT (IRE), gr ro f 04/05 Fast Company (IRE)—
Silver Grey (IRE) (Chineur (FR)) (33333) **Deva Racing Himbleton Partnership**
64 HARMONY LIL (IRE), b f 16/01 Kodi Bear (IRE)—
Lil's Joy (IRE) (Lilbourne Lad (IRE)) (38609) **Sue Cronshaw & Karen Bennett**
65 B c 04/02 Muhaarar—I Am (IRE) (Galileo (IRE)) **Manor House Stables LLP**
66 JONQUERETS (FR), b c 16/02 Le Havre (IRE)—Jamboree (IRE) (Peintre Celebre (USA)) (44616) **Carswell Racing**
67 KODIAC BROWN BEAR (IRE), b c 13/03 Kodiac—
Olive Branch (IRE) (Arcano (IRE)) (55769) **Andrew Brown & Gemma Brown**
68 LAXTON LADD (IRE), b c 13/03 Iffraaj—Morning Frost (IRE) (Duke of Marmalade (IRE)) (42900) **More Turf Racing**
69 MIRAMICHI (IRE), b c 17/03 Markaz (IRE)—Mattinata (Tiger Hill (IRE)) (47619) **Mrs C. L. Ingram**
70 B c 12/03 Helmet (AUS)—Miramont (Iffraaj) (15000) **Three Chums Partnership**
71 B f 10/02 Nathaniel (IRE)—Parsnip (Zebedee) **Chasemore Farm LLP**
72 PAWS FOR THOUGHT (IRE), b c 20/03 Requinto (IRE)—
Kitty Softpaws (IRE) (Royal Applause) (23809) **Mrs C. A. Shaw**
73 Ch f 04/05 Proconsul—Raktina (Polish Precedent (USA))
74 ROCKETS RED GLARE (IRE), ch c 24/02 Starspangledbanner (AUS)—
Spirit of Paris (IRE) (Big Bad Bob (IRE)) (38610) **Mr D. J. Lowe**
75 SCARLET BEAR (IRE), b f 28/02 Kodi Bear (IRE)—Scarlet Plum (Pivotal) (28571) **Mr R. Jones**
76 B c 12/03 Fast Company (IRE)—Seren Devious (Dr Devious (IRE)) (42857) **Manor House Stables LLP**
77 SOLENT GATEWAY (IRE), b c 22/03 Awtaad (IRE)—Aoife Alainn (IRE) (Dr Fong (USA)) (59047) **Mr D. R. Passant**
78 SPIRIT OF SISRA (IRE), b f 30/04 Zoffany (IRE)—Tadris (USA) (Red Ransom (USA)) (19047) **SISRA Ltd**
79 B c 04/03 Acclamation—Thatsallimsaying (IRE) (Dandy Man (IRE)) (39468)
80 B f 01/05 Dandy Man (IRE)—Veiled Beauty (USA) (Royal Academy (USA)) **Chasemore Farm LLP**

Other Owners: Major P. W. F. Arkwright, Mrs Sandra G. E. Arkwright, Mr N. B. Attenborough, Mr D. J. Barry, Mrs K. V. Bennett, Mrs A. Biles, Mr P. G. Birbeck, A. W. Black, Mr A. Brown, Mrs G. Brown, Mr D. J. E. Carswell, Mr E. Carswell, Mr N. Clyne, Mr P. G. Cooke, Mr A. Cronshaw, Alan & Sue Cronshaw, Mrs S. P. Cronshaw, Mr T. G. Dascombe, Mrs R. L. Dawson, Mr J. Dooley, Mr M. Downes, Mr M. Edwards, Mrs M. Edwards, Edwards Elite Engineering Ltd, Empire State Racing Partnership, FDC Holdings Ltd, Mr J. A. Faulkner, Mr G. S. Goss, Mr A. P. Hamilton, Mrs S. Hedges, Mr R. K. Joynson, Mr C. Ledigo, Miss A. J. Lowe, Mr D. J. Lowe, Mrs J. Lowe, Manor House Stables LLP, Mr N. P. Mather, Mrs S. E. Mather, Mrs J. P. Melia, Mr T. J. Moran, Mr R. G. Morris, Mr S. N. Mound, M. F. Nolan, Mr M. O'Halloran, Mr M.J Owen, Owen Promotions Limited, Mr D. R. Passant, L. M. Rutherford, Mr M. Satchell, Mr P. Simpson, Mr W. Threlfall, K. P. Trowbridge, Keith & Mary Trowbridge, Mrs M. C. Trowbridge.

Assistant Trainer: Colin Gorman.

Flat Jockey: Richard Kingscote. **Apprentice Jockey:** Elisha Whittington. **Amateur Jockey:** Miss Alyson Deniel.

---

133 **MR TRISTAN DAVIDSON, Carlisle**
Postal: Bellmount, Laversdale, Irthington, Carlisle, Cumbria, CA6 4PS
Contacts: **MOBILE 07789 684290**

1 ASKGARMOR (IRE), 8, b g Ask—
Karmafair (IRE) **E G Tunstall, The Not Very Likely Lads, Mr Gary Etheridge, Mr G. G. Adamson, Mr J. Reay**
2 BARACALU (FR), 9, gr g Califet (FR)—Myagentry (FR) **J. T. Davidson**
3 BLAZING PORT (IRE), 5, b g Yeats (IRE)—Despute (IRE) **SprayClad UK**
4 CASUAL CAVALIER (IRE), 12, br g Presenting—Asklynn (IRE) **martingrayracing**
5 CRESSWELL QUEEN, 5, b m Brian Boru—Cresswell Willow (IRE) **J. T. Davidson**
6 GREENGAGE (IRE), 5, b m Choisir (AUS)—Empowermentofwomen (IRE) **J. T. Davidson**
7 HEAVENLY TALE (IRE), 4, b f Shamardal (USA)—Angels Story (IRE)
8 JUSTATENNER, 9, b g Northern Legend—Shelayly (IRE) **The Whartons**
9 NELSON ROAD (IRE), 7, b g Mount Nelson—Merciful (USA) **J. T. Davidson**
10 PADDYPLEX, 7, b g Multiplex—Turtle Bay **G & J Park**
11 PEARL OF QATAR, 4, gr f Footstepsinthesand—Musical Molly (IRE) **Beswick Brothers Bloodstock**
12 ROUSSIMOFF (IRE), 5, b g Yeats (IRE)—Baby Briggs (IRE) **SprayClad UK**

MR TRISTAN DAVIDSON - continued

13 **RUBENESQUE (IRE)**, 8, b m Getaway (GER)—Shouette (IRE) **Toby Noble & Andy Bell**
14 **SAXA VORD**, 4, b f Phoenix Reach (IRE)—Turtle Bay **G & J Park**
15 **SHAKA THE KING (IRE)**, 6, b g Yeats (IRE)—Kissantell (IRE)
16 **SOL DE MAYO**, 4, b g Dubawi (IRE)—Argentina (IRE) **SprayClad UK**
17 **THE DUTCHMAN (IRE)**, 10, b g King's Theatre (IRE)—Shivertimember (IRE) **SprayClad UK**

Other Owners: Mr A. Bell, Mr D. S. Hogg, Mr T. Noble, Mr G. Park, Miss J. Park, Qatar Racing Limited, Mr E. G. Tunstall, Mrs J. H. Wharton, Mr R. E. Wharton, Mr T. R. Wharton.

Conditional Jockey: Harry Reed.

134
MR JOHN DAVIES, Darlington
Postal: **Denton Grange, Piercebridge, Darlington, County Durham, DL2 3TZ**
Contacts: **PHONE 01325 374366 MOBILE 07746 292782**
EMAIL johndavieshorses@live.co.uk WEBSITE www.johndaviesracing.com

1 **ALFRED RICHARDSON**, 6, ch g Dapper—Vera Richardson (IRE) **K Kirkup & J Davies, J. J. Davies, K. Kirkup**
2 **CRIMSON SKIES (IRE)**, 5, ch m Declaration of War (USA)—Emily Blake (IRE) **The Red and White Stripes**
3 **HIGHJACKED**, 4, b g Dick Turpin (IRE)—Vera Richardson (IRE) **K Kirkup & J Davies, J. J. Davies, K. Kirkup**
4 **IM DAPPER TOO**, 9, b g Dapper—Lonely One **Mr C. W. Davies**
5 **MANGO CHUTNEY**, 7, b g Sleeping Indian—Crimson Topaz **The Red and White Stripes**
6 **MOUNT BARINA**, 5, b m Mount Nelson—Sambarina (IRE) **Ms D. Nicholson**
7 **MR COOL CASH**, 8, b g Firebreak—Cashleen (USA) **Mr I. Lawson**
8 **PETITIONER (IRE)**, 6, b g Dansili—Reflective (USA) **Mr C. J. Mooney**

THREE-YEAR-OLDS

9 Ch c Intrinsic—Angelic Kitten (IRE) **J. J. Davies**
10 B c Helmet (AUS)—Emily Blake (IRE) **Mr & Mrs R. Scott**
11 **FULL HOUSE**, b g Lethal Force (IRE)—Tamalain (USA) **Mr & Mrs R. Scott**
12 **OOH LA LAH**, b f Champs Elysees—Cameo Tiara (IRE) **Mr C. W. Davies**
13 Ch c Casamento (IRE)—Tamara Bay **Mr & Mrs R. Scott, J. J. Davies, Mr & Mrs R Scott & J Davies**

TWO-YEAR-OLDS

14 B f 09/02 Cannock Chase (USA)—La Hoofon (Mastercraftsman (IRE))
15 B g 12/03 Cannock Chase (USA)—Tsarina Louise (Red Ransom (USA)) (3809) **Ms D. Nicholson**
16 B c 08/05 Heeraat (IRE)—Vera Richardson (IRE) (Dutch Art) **K. Kirkup**
17 Ch f 12/05 Monsieur Bond (IRE)—Wedgewood Star (Bishop of Cashel) **Mr C. W. Davies**

Other Owners: J. J. Davies.

135
MISS SARAH-JAYNE DAVIES, Leominster
Postal: **The Upper Withers, Hundred Lane, Kimbolton, Leominster, Herefordshire, HR6 0HZ**
Contacts: **PHONE 01584 711138 MOBILE 07779 797079**
EMAIL amy@sjdracing.co.uk WEBSITE www.sjdracing.co.uk

1 **ACCESSALLAREAS (IRE)**, 15, ch g Swift Gulliver (IRE)—Arushgold (IRE) **Miss S. J. Davies**
2 **ARVICO'S LIGHT**, 6, b g Arvico (FR)—Miss Lightning **Pipannsue Partnership**
3 **CAMLAD KINGFISHER**, 8, ch g Sulamani (IRE)—Val de Fleurie (GER) **Mrs C. J. Davies**
4 **DAYS TO REMEMBER**, 4, b g Malinas (GER)—Top Totti **Mrs C. J. Davies**
5 **FAIR TO DREAM**, 7, b g Fair Mix (IRE)—Sahara's Dream **K. E. Stait**
6 **FUN DE NUIT (FR)**, 5, gr g Montmartre (FR)—Nuit de Volupte (FR) **Quadriga Racing**
7 **GENEVA BARRACKS (IRE)**, 8, br g Thewayyouare (USA)—Anna Kareena (IRE) **Miss S. J. Davies**
8 **HUME LOUGH**, 9, b g Teofilo (IRE)—Pink Cristal **Withers Winners**
9 **I'M BRIAN**, 4, b g Sepoy (AUS)—Emily Carr (IRE) **Miss S. J. Davies**
10 **KIMS DIAMOND (IRE)**, 6, b m Mountain High (IRE)—Accordion To Pat (IRE) **Mr T. J. Richards**

MISS SARAH-JAYNE DAVIES - continued

11 **LAST CHANCE PADDY (USA),** 6, gr g Paddy O'Prado (USA)—Mizzcan'tbewrong (USA) **Summertime Racing**
12 **METATRONS CUBE (IRE),** 5, b g Artie Schiller (USA)—Quiet Down (USA) **Michael & Lesley Wilkes**
13 **MURRAY MOUNT (IRE),** 10, b g Trans Island—Ash **Mr A. J. Gough**
14 **PEMBROKE HOUSE,** 13, gr g Terimon—Bon Coeur **Sarah-jayne Davies & Steve Mace**
15 **PERCY THROWER (IRE),** 6, ch g Sir Percy—Dayrose **Moorland Racing & Mark Hammond**
16 **ROYAL ACT,** 8, br g Royal Anthem (USA)—Native's Return (IRE) **Moorland Racing**
17 **SALAZAR (IRE),** 5, ch g Raven's Pass (USA)—Queen Padme (IRE) **Miss N. Thompson**
18 **SAM CHISOLM (IRE),** 7, br g Getaway (GER)—
                                      Undecided Hall (IRE) **Steve Mace, Paul Whilock & Mark Hammond**
19 **SECRET MELODY,** 7, b g Sakhee's Secret—Montjeu's Melody (IRE) **Moorland Racing & Mark Hammond**
20 **STORM GIRL,** 4, b f Paco Boy (IRE)—Evenstorm (USA) **Mr A. J. Gough**
21 **THEQUEENBEE (IRE),** 5, b m Stowaway—Accordeon Royale (IRE) **Michael & Lesley Wilkes**
22 **UPTON ENCORE,** 7, b g Kadastrof (FR)—Upton Adventure **Miss S. J. Davies**

Other Owners: Miss S. J. Davies, Mrs S. M. Davies, Mr M. J. Hammond, Mrs A. M. Mace, S. A. Mace, Moorland Racing, Mrs C. Tucker, Mr M. J. F. Tucker, Mrs P. Vaughan, Mrs B. Vincent, Mr J. F. Vincent, Mr P. R. Whilock, Mrs L. Wilkes, Mr M. H. A. Wilkes.

Racing Secretary: Amy Watkins.

NH Jockey: Lee Edwards. **Conditional Jockey:** Charlie Hammond.

---

136 MISS JO DAVIS, East Garston
Postal: **1 Parson Close Stables, School Lane, East Garston, Hungerford, Berkshire, RG17 7HR**
Contacts: **PHONE 01488 649977 MOBILE 07879 811535 FAX 01488 649977**
EMAIL davisjo_007@hotmail.com WEBSITE www.jodavisracing.com

1   **CAPELLIAN CRUSADER (IRE),** 11, b g Cape Cross (IRE)—Llia
2   4, B f Passing Glance—Eveon (IRE) **Maggie Davis & Jo Davis, Miss J. S. Davis, Mrs M. A. Davis**
3   **GALLIC DESTINY (IRE),** 9, b g Champs Elysees—Cross Your Fingers (USA) **Mrs P. M. Brown**
4   **INTO THE MIST,** 5, gr m Black Sam Bellamy (IRE)—Kullu Valley **The Ab Fab Patsy Partnership**
5   **IT'S FOR ALAN,** 7, b g Multiplex—Miss Keck **Tony Worth & Vic Bedley**
6   **JOHN BISCUIT (IRE),** 12, ch g Hawk Wing (USA)—Princess Magdalena **Mrs P. M. Brown**
7   **KEN'S WELL (IRE),** 9, b g Trans Island—Tiergarten (IRE) **Mrs P. M. Brown**
8   **MARMONT,** 7, ch g Winker Watson—Five Bells (IRE) **Miss J. S. Davis**
9   **MINIATURE DAFFODIL (IRE),** 5, b g Thewayyouare (USA)—Queen of Stars (USA) **TheseGirlsCan Racing Club**
10 **MR FITZROY (IRE),** 10, ch g Kyllachy—Reputable **Mrs P. M. Brown**
11 4, B f Epaulette (AUS)—No Frills (IRE) **Mrs P. M. Brown**
12 **SAGGAZZA,** 6, b g Schiaparelli (GER)—Wee Dinns (IRE) **Mrs P. M. Brown**
13 **THE BIG YIN,** 6, ch g Malinas (GER)—
                              Bright Spangle (IRE) **Maggie Davis & Jo Davis, Miss J. S. Davis, Mrs M. A. Davis**

Other Owners: Mr R. C. C. Baker, V. R. Bedley, Mrs S. L. Bender, Mrs P. M. Brown, Miss J. S. Davis, Mrs M. A. Davis, Mr A. G. Worth.

Assistant Trainer: Gregg Whitehead.

---

137 MISS ZOE DAVISON, East Grinstead
Postal: **Shovelstrode Racing Stables, Shovelstrode Lane, Ashurstwood, East Grinstead, West Sussex, RH19 3PN**
Contacts: **PHONE 01342 300319 MOBILE 07970 839357, 07812 007554**
EMAIL andy01031976@yahoo.co.uk WEBSITE www.shovelstroderacing.co.uk

1   **BLARNEY BATELEUR (IRE),** 7, b m Flemensfirth (USA)—Blarney Kestrel (IRE) **Miss S. Searle**
2   **BRANDY CROSS (IRE),** 6, b g Le Fou (IRE)—Glenquin (IRE) **Surefire Racing**
3   **BROTHER BENNETT (FR),** 10, gr g Martaline—La Gaminerie (FR) **The Secret Circle**

MISS ZOE DAVISON - continued

4 **CAGLIOSTRO (FR)**, 8, gr g Lord du Sud (FR)—Belle de Liziere (FR) **The Secret Circle Racing Club**
5 **CLONDAW ROBIN (IRE)**, 7, ch g Robin des Champs (FR)—Old Town Queen (IRE) **The Plum Merchants**
6 **DEVIOUS DICKS DAME**, 5, b m Dick Turpin (IRE)—Bridal White **The Secret Circle Racing Club**
7 **DYLANSEOGHAN (IRE)**, 11, b g Pierre—Sabbatical (IRE) **The Lump O'Clock Syndicate**
8 **FINNEGAN'S GARDEN (IRE)**, 11, b g Definite Article—Tri Folene (FR) **Mr K. Corke**
9 **GLORIOUS BORU (IRE)**, 9, b g Brian Boru—Sea Off The Gales (IRE) **Eventmasters Racing**
10 **GUSTAV (IRE)**, 10, b g Mahler—Pakaradyssa (FR) **The Plum Merchants**
11 **HARRY HAZARD**, 6, b g Schiaparelli (GER)—Eveon (IRE) **Mr A. Lewers**
12 **IMPULSIVE LEADER (IRE)**, 7, b m Westerner—Impulsive Ita (IRE) **Mr K. Corke**
13 **KILINAKIN (IRE)**, 10, ch g Definite Article—Topanberry (IRE) **The Lump O'Clock Syndicate**
14 **KING OF THE SHARKS (IRE)**, 7, b g Flemensfirth (USA)—Kings Rose (IRE) **Go Faster Syndicate**
15 **MON PETIT CHERI**, 4, b f Nayef (USA)—Mon Petit Diamant **Exors of the Late Mr R. Devereux**
16 **O'RAHILLY (IRE)**, 8, b g Aristotle (IRE)—Linoora (IRE) **The Lump Oclock the Secret Circle**
17 **OUR DOT'S BABY (IRE)**, 8, b m Helissio (FR)—Our Dot (IRE) **Mr D. Shaw**
18 **PETE'S CHOICE (IRE)**, 7, b br g Arcadio (GER)—Definite Design (IRE) **Jokulhlaup Syndicate**
19 **QUEEN AMONG KINGS (IRE)**, 6, b m Sans Frontieres (IRE)—Miss Legend (IRE) **Surefire Racing**
20 **RUACANA**, 11, b g Cape Cross (IRE)—Farrfesheena (USA) **Mr V. Lewis**
21 **SCRUTINISE**, 8, b g Intense Focus (USA)—Tetravella (IRE) **Mrs L. Bowtell**
22 **THE GAME IS A FOOT (IRE)**, 13, b g Oscar (IRE)—Cooksgrove Rosie (IRE) **The Secret Circle Racing Club**
23 **WATAR ALLSTAR (IRE)**, 6, ch g Watar (IRE)—All Star Lady (IRE) **Mr D. Shaw**
24 **YEATS BABY (IRE)**, 8, b m Yeats (IRE)—Cabo (FR) **Eventmasters Racing**

Other Owners: S. J. Clare, Miss Z. C. Davison, Mr A. J. Irvine, The Lump O'Clock Syndicate, The Secret Circle, Mr A. N. Waters.

Assistant Trainer: A. Irvine.

---

138 **MR ANTHONY DAY, Hinckley**
Postal: **Wolvey Fields Farm, Coalpit Lane, Wolvey, Hinckley, Leicestershire, LE10 3HD**

1 **GETTYSBURGH (IRE)**, 5, b m Presenting—Rhapsody In Blue (GER) **Mrs K. D. Day**
2 **LAVERTEEN (FR)**, 9, b g Laveron—Manson Teene (FR) **Mrs K. D. Day**
3 **MY ANCHOR**, 9, b g Mount Nelson—War Shanty **Mrs K. D. Day**
4 **STRIPE OF HONOUR (IRE)**, 7, b g Court Cave (IRE)—Miss Top (IRE) **Mrs K. D. Day**

---

139 **MR WILLIAM DE BEST-TURNER, Marlborough**
Postal: **Browns Farm, Marlborough, Wiltshire, SN8 4ND**
Contacts: **HOME 01249 813850 PHONE 01249 811944 MOBILE 07977 910779**
EMAIL debestracing@hotmail.co.uk

1 **CALGARY TIGER**, 5, b g Tiger Groom—Sachiko **W. de Best-Turner**
2 **NELSON'S HILL**, 10, b g Mount Nelson—Regal Step **Debestracing**
3 **PIXELATIT**, 5, b m Dream Eater (IRE)—Spartaculous **Debestracing**
4 **TIGER PRINT**, 5, b m Tiger Groom—Maylan (IRE) **Debestracing**

THREE-YEAR-OLDS

5 **MOLLY'S ANGEL**, ch f Arvico (FR)—Sterling Moll
6 **RUBY RUBLES**, b f Phenomena—Spartaculous **W. de Best-Turner**

Assistant Trainer: Mrs I. de Best.

140 MR ED DE GILES, Ledbury
Postal: **Lilly Hall Farm, Little Marcle, Ledbury, Herefordshire, HR8 2LD**
Contacts: **PHONE 01531 637369 MOBILE 07811 388345**
EMAIL ed@eddegilesracing.com WEBSITE www.eddegilesracing.com

1 **BACON'S REBELLION**, 4, b g Nathaniel (IRE)—Linda (FR) **Carrington & Cunningham**
2 **BOMBERO (IRE)**, 6, b g Dragon Pulse (IRE)—Mathool (IRE) **Woodham Walter Partnership**
3 **BORN TO FINISH (IRE)**, 7, b g Dark Angel (IRE)—Music Pearl (IRE) **Crowd Racing Partnership**
4 **CORRIDA DE TOROS (IRE)**, 4, b g Lope de Vega (IRE)—The Shrew **Mr Ali Mortazavi & Ms Sirma Dogan**
5 **DOUBLY BEAUTIFUL (IRE)**, 4, ch g Born To Sea (IRE)—Bella Bella (IRE) **Mr P. Inglett**
6 **FITZROVIA**, 5, br g Poet's Voice—Pompey Girl **Simon Treacher & Clarissa Casdagali**
7 **FRANCISCO BAY**, 4, b g Paco Boy (IRE)—Lucky Breeze (IRE) **Mr C. C. Shand Kydd & Partner**
8 **INCUS**, 7, b g Bertolini (USA)—Cloudchaser (IRE) **Tight Lines Partnership**
9 **MAERCHENGARTEN**, 4, b f Bated Breath—Kammaan **The LAM Partnership**
10 **MISTER MERLIN**, 4, gr g Dark Angel (IRE)—Rosehill Artist (IRE) **Mr P. Inglett**
11 **ORANGE SUIT (IRE)**, 5, b g Declaration of War (USA)—Guantanamera (IRE) **Tight Lines Partnership**
12 **OVERHAUGH STREET**, 7, b g Bahri (USA)—Bom Chicka Wah Wah (USA) **Sharron & Robert Colvin**
13 **ROAR (IRE)**, 6, b g Pour Moi (IRE)—Evening Rushour (IRE) **P Inglett, J Basquill & E Frost**
14 **SALSA VERDE (IRE)**, 5, b g Canford Cliffs (IRE)—Bridal Dance (IRE) **John Manser & Simon Treacher**
15 **SEXY BEAST**, 5, b g Teofilo (IRE)—Wadaat **Tight Lines Partnership**
16 **SWANTON BLUE (IRE)**, 7, b g Kodiac—Cabopino (IRE) **Mr E. B. de Giles**
17 **THE FURROWS END**, 4, bl g Proclamation (IRE)—Chalosse **Sharron & Robert Colvin**
18 **TREACHEROUS**, 6, b g Paco Boy (IRE)—Black Baroness **Woodham Walter Partnership**
19 **WIND IN MY SAILS**, 8, b g Footstepsinthesand—Dylanesque **Mr P. J. Manser**
20 4, B g Acclamation—Zamorano (IRE)
21 **ZLATAN (IRE)**, 7, b g Dark Angel (IRE)—Guard Hill (USA) **Casdagli & Partners**

THREE-YEAR-OLDS
22 **CHIFA (IRE)**, br g Gutaifan (IRE)—Inca Trail (USA) **Mr J. P. Carrington**
23 **LUCKY DRAW**, b f Roderic O'Connor (IRE)—Lucky Breeze (IRE) **Mr C. C. Shand Kydd & Partner**
24 **SOBRIQUET (IRE)**, ch f Night of Thunder (IRE)—Broadway Duchess (IRE) **The LAM Partnership**

TWO-YEAR-OLDS
25 Ch f 01/04 Kutub (IRE)—Chalosse (Doyoun) **R. Colvin**
26 **INSPIRING LOVE**, ch f 19/02 Cityscape—Miss Meticulous (Bahamian Bounty) **The LAM Partnership**
27 B f 06/03 Cityscape—Lucky Breeze (IRE) (Key of Luck (USA))
28 Ch c 25/02 Cityscape—Tijuca (IRE) (Captain Rio)

Other Owners: Mr J. M. Basquill, Mr J. P. Carrington, Mrs C. R. Casdagli, R. Colvin, Mrs S. Colvin, Ms A. P. M. Cunningham, Ms S. Dogan, Dr M. F. Ford, Mr E. H. M. Frost, Mr P. Inglett, Mr P. J. Manser, Mr A. Mortazavi, Ms L. M. Mulcahy, C. C. Shand Kydd, Mr S. Treacher, Mr E. B. de Giles.

141 MR GEOFFREY DEACON, Compton
Postal: **Hamilton Stables, Hockham Road, Compton, Newbury, Berkshire, RG20 6QJ**
Contacts: **MOBILE 07967 626757**
EMAIL geoffdeacon5@gmail.com WEBSITE www.geoffreydeacontraining.com

1 **CAPTAIN RYAN**, 9, b g Captain Gerrard (IRE)—Ryan's Quest (IRE) **Geoffrey Deacon Racing Crew**
2 **FROSTY TERN**, 4, gr f Aussie Rules (USA)—Frosty Welcome (USA) **Mr G. Deacon**
3 **HONEY BOO**, 7, ch m Tobougg (IRE)—Queen of The Bees (IRE) **Mrs S. A. Roe**
4 **ITSAKINDAMAGIC**, 6, b g Mount Nelson—Carsulae (IRE) **Hearty Racing**
5 4, B f Born To Sea (IRE)—Khajool (IRE) **Geoffrey Deacon Racing Crew**
6 **LA ROCA DEL FUEGO (IRE)**, 4, br g Rock of Gibraltar (IRE)—Reign (IRE) **Mr M. D. Drake**
7 **MISREAD**, 4, ch f Nayef (USA)—Widescreen (USA) **Compton Racing Club**
8 **NIGHT N GALE (IRE)**, 4, b f Gale Force Ten—Hadya (IRE) **Geoffrey Deacon Racing Crew**
9 **RAHMAH (IRE)**, 8, b g Vale of York (IRE)—Sweet Home Alabama (IRE) **Mr P. D. Cundell and Partner**
10 **WOGGLE (IRE)**, 5, ch m Camacho—Radio Wave **Hearty Racing**

MR GEOFFREY DEACON - continued

THREE-YEAR-OLDS
11 **APRICOT STAR (IRE)**, ch f Anjaal—Allegrissimo (IRE) **Allinc Property Services**
12 Gr f Fast Company (IRE)—Glastonberry **Mr A. Altazi**
13 **JUST ALBERT**, gr ro g Toronado (IRE)—Deire Na Sli (IRE) **Mr and Mrs Duckett**
14 **SAHHAB (USA)**, b f Declaration of War (USA)—Princess Consort (USA) **Mr A. Altazi**

TWO-YEAR-OLDS
15 Ch f 03/05 Havana Gold (IRE)—Victrix Ludorum (IRE) (Invincible Spirit (IRE)) (761)

Other Owners: P. D. Cundell, Mr G. Deacon.

Assistant Trainer: Sally Duckett.

142
MR DAVID DENNIS, Hanley Swan
Postal: Tyre Hill Racing Stables, Hanley Swan, Worcester, Worcestershire, WR8 0EQ
Contacts: PHONE 01684 310565 MOBILE 07867 974880
EMAIL david@daviddennistrainer.co.uk WEBSITE www.ddracing.co.uk

1 **ADAMS STAR (IRE)**, 5, b g Mahler—Pepelina (IRE) **The Adam's Star Syndicate**
2 **AUBIS PARK (FR)**, 5, b m Walk In The Park (IRE)—Aubisquinette (FR) **Prof L. P. Hardwick**
3 **AVOID DE MASTER (IRE)**, 6, b g Getaway (GER)—Tanit **Mrs J. Rees**
4 **BATHIVA (FR)**, 6, b g Spanish Moon (USA)—Thithia (FR) **Mrs J. Rees**
5 **BROKEN QUEST (IRE)**, 8, b g Ask—Broken Thought (IRE) **Wright Morgan Ltd & Partner**
6 **CYCLOP (IRE)**, 9, b g King's Theatre (IRE)—Tasmani (FR) **DD Racing & Professor L P Hardwick**
7 **DANECASE (IRE)**, 7, ch g Showcasing—Yding (IRE) **Professor L P Hardwick & Partner**
8 **DEAUVILLE DANCER (IRE)**, 9, b g Tamayuz—Mathool (IRE) **Mr G.Brandrick & Partner**
9 **DONATELLO MAIL (FR)**, 7, ch g Zambezi Sun—Kestrel Mail (FR) **Mrs J. Rees & Professor L P Hardwick**
10 **DONTCOUNTURCHIKENS (IRE)**, 6, b g Getaway (GER)—Stormy Breeze (IRE) **Clan McNeil**
11 **EMMARELLI**, 4, ch f Schiaparelli (GER)—Emmaslegend **Mrs E. C. Stewart**
12 **FILLYBUSTA (IRE)**, 5, b m Presenting—Aguida (IRE) **Mrs Emma Stewart & Partner**
13 **FINAL NUDGE (IRE)**, 11, b g Kayf Tara—Another Shot (IRE) **Mrs J. Rees**
14 **FLYING VERSE**, 8, b g Yeats (IRE)—Flight Sequence **Dr C. A. Barnett & Partner**
15 **FUNKY SENSATION**, 6, b g Black Sam Bellamy (IRE)—Sambara (IRE) **Mr G. Saville & Partner**
16 **HAHADI (IRE)**, 8, ch g Getaway (GER)—Derrygowna Lord (IRE) **Legacy Racing**
17 **HARDY ARTICOS (IRE)**, 5, b g Arctic Cosmos (USA)—Hardy Lamb (IRE) **D D Racing 3**
18 **INDY FIVE (IRE)**, 10, b g Vertical Speed (FR)—Beesplease (IRE) **The Dobbin Club**
19 **INNISFREE LAD (IRE)**, 8, b g Yeats (IRE)—Tasmani (FR) **Rees, Hardwick, Allum & Saville**
20 **JEREMY THE JINN (IRE)**, 5, br g Jeremy (USA)—Phantom Waters **Mrs J. Rees**
21 **JUST SO COOL (IRE)**, 9, gr g Acambaro (GER)—Lauras Dote (IRE) **Mr B. Vaughan & D D Racing 4**
22 **KINGFAST (IRE)**, 5, b g Fast Company (IRE)—Monarchy (IRE) **Mr G. Saville, Mr G. Brandrick & Partner**
23 **MARQUIS OF CARABAS (IRE)**, 10, b br g Hurricane Run (IRE)—Miss Otis Regrets (IRE) **Mrs J. Rees**
24 4, B f Getaway (GER)—Merry Missed (IRE) **Mrs J. Rees**
25 **MR WASHINGTON (IRE)**, 7, b g Vinnie Roe (IRE)—Anna Bird (IRE) **Mrs J. Hitchings**
26 **NIGHTBOATTOCLYRO (IRE)**, 6, ch g Sulamani (IRE)—Wychwoods Legend **Glastonburys & On the Gallops 1**
27 **NOTHING MAN (IRE)**, 6, b g Ask—Holly Gaga (IRE) **Mrs J. Rees**
28 4, B g Fame And Glory—Rose of Clare **Mrs J. Rees**
29 **SCHNABEL (IRE)**, 8, b g Ask—Velsatis (IRE) **Professor L P Hardwick & Partner**
30 **SWISSAL (IRE)**, 5, b g Swiss Spirit—Al Gharrafa **Mrs J. Rees**
31 **VEILED SECRET (IRE)**, 6, b g Teofilo (IRE)—Seven Veils (IRE) **Clan McNeil**
32 4, B g Tobougg (IRE)—Whistling Gypse (IRE) **Professor L P Hardwick & Partner**
33 **WILLIAMS OVERTURE (IRE)**, 5, b g Mahler—Venusorserena (IRE) **Taylormaid & Partner**
34 **ZEE MAN (FR)**, 6, b g Soldier of Fortune (IRE)—Sky High Flyer **Mr B. D. Vaughan**

Other Owners: Mr R. Allum, Mr G. J. E. Brandrick, D D Racing 4, Mr D. R. Dennis, Mr D. W. Doolittle, Miss T. A. Fulcher, Mrs A. J. Glastonbury, Mr K. J. Glastonbury, Kevin & Anne Glastonbury, Mr M. Glastonbury, Mr R. Glastonbury, J. R. Hall, Prof L. P. Hardwick, M. Hingley, Mr A. R. Hitchings, Mr J. McNeil, Mr P. J. McNeil, On The Gallops Racing Club, Mrs J. Rees, Mr G. A. S. Saville, Mrs E. C. Stewart, Taylormaid, Mr B. D. Vaughan.

143 MR TIM DENNIS, Bude
Postal: **Thorne Farm, Bude, Cornwall, EX23 0LU**

1 NEETSIDE (IRE), 8, b m Getaway (GER)—Lady Wagtail (IRE) **Mrs J. E. Dennis**

144 MR ROBIN DICKIN, Alcester
Postal: **Hill Farm, Park Lane, Great Alne, Alcester, Warwickshire, B49 6HS**
Contacts: **MOBILE 07979 518594, 07979 518593**
EMAIL **claire@robindickinracing.org.uk** WEBSITE **www.robindickinracing.org.uk**

1 ACHY BREAKY HEART (IRE), 6, b m Milan—Hazy Outlook (IRE) **N. J. Allen**
2 ALL IS GOOD (IRE), 8, b g Scorpion (IRE)—Peinture Rose (IRE) **The Tricksters & The Goodies**
3 ANTI COOL (IRE), 11, b g Heron Island (IRE)—Youngborogal (IRE) **Robin Dickin Racing Club**
4 BALLY LAGAN (IRE), 12, gr g Kalanisi (IRE)—Rose Palma (FR) **Park Lane Partnership**
5 BLACK KALAROSA (IRE), 6, br m Kalanisi (IRE)—Blackthorne Winter (IRE) **NHRE Racing Club**
6 BLAZING GOLD, 7, b m Fair Mix (IRE)—Playing With Fire (IRE) **Mrs A. L. Merry**
7 BOB MAXWELL (IRE), 6, b g Big Bad Bob (IRE)—Catching Stars (IRE) **Just 4 Fun**
8 CHEER'S DELBOY (IRE), 7, ch g Golan—Lindy Lou **Just 4 Fun**
9 DONTMINDDBOYS (IRE), 11, gr g Portrait Gallery (IRE)—Native Ocean (IRE) **Mrs C. M. Dickin**
10 GALACTIC POWER (IRE), 10, ch g Gamut (IRE)—Celtic Peace (IRE) **Robin Dickin Racing Club**
11 LARA TROT (IRE), 8, b m Scorpion (IRE)—Honour Own (IRE) **The Trotters**
12 MR PALMTREE (IRE), 7, gr g Robin des Pres (FR)—Mattys Joy (IRE) **The Cocoa Nuts & the Tricksters**
13 NOMINATION GAME (IRE), 9, b g Oscar (IRE)—Tiarella (IRE) **John Nicholls (Trading) Ltd**
14 ONEIDA TRIBE (IRE), 11, b g Turtle Island (IRE)—Glory Queen (IRE) **John Nicholls (Trading) Ltd**
15 PHOEBUS LESCRIBAA (FR), 8, b g Policy Maker (IRE)—Mia Lescribaa (FR) **Mr K. Elvins**
16 SECRET COURT (IRE), 6, b m Court Cave (IRE)—Tasanak (IRE) **The Point Of Attack Partnership**
17 SOME FINISH (IRE), 11, b g Kayf Tara—Kylie Kaprice (GER) **Mrs C Dickin & The Some Finish Partners**
18 SPARKY STOWAWAY (IRE), 8, b g Stowaway—Torose (IRE) **John Nicholls (Trading) Ltd**
19 TARA WELL (IRE), 10, b m Kayf Tara—Miss Baden (IRE) **Mrs C M Dickin & Miss H Turner**
20 THE LION MAN (IRE), 10, b g Let The Lion Roar—Just Smart (IRE) **Mrs M A Cooper & Mr J R Cooper**
21 THREE BULLET GATE (IRE), 7, b g Touch of Land (FR)—Brave Hope (IRE) **The Point Of Attack Partnership**
22 TWYCROSS WARRIOR, 8, b g Cockney Rebel (IRE)—Gaelic Roulette (IRE) **Graham & Lynn Knight**
23 VOCALISER (IRE), 8, b g Vocalised (USA)—Bring Back Matron (IRE) **The Songsters**

THREE-YEAR-OLDS
24 IT FITZ, gr g Havana Gold (IRE)—Crocus Rose **Cahill FitzGerald Bloodstock Ltd**
25 ROYAL BASSETT (FR), b g Wootton Bassett—Donna Roberta (GER) **The Bertie Allsorts**

Assistant Trainer: Claire Dickin.

NH Jockey: Jack Quinlan. **Conditional Jockey:** Ceris Biddle, Tabitha Worsley.

145 MR JOHN DIXON, Carlisle
Postal: **Moorend, Thursby, Carlisle, Cumbria, CA5 6QP**
Contacts: **PHONE 01228 711019**

1 BALLELA'S DREAM, 6, b m Josr Algarhoud (IRE)—Ballela Road (IRE) **Mrs S. F. Dixon**
2 CAPTAIN ZEBO (IRE), 8, b g Brian Boru—Waydale Hill **Mrs S. F. Dixon**
3 PISTOL (IRE), 11, b g High Chaparral (IRE)—Alinea (USA) **Mrs S. F. Dixon**
4 PRESENCE FELT (IRE), 12, br g Heron Island (IRE)—Faeroe Isle (IRE) **Mrs S. F. Dixon**

Amateur Jockey: Mr J. J. Dixon.

146 MR SCOTT DIXON, Retford

Postal: **Haygarth House Stud, Haygarth House, Babworth, Retford, Nottinghamshire, DN22 8ES**
Contacts: **PHONE 01777 869079, 01777 701818, 01777 869300 MOBILE 07976 267019**
FAX 01777 869326
EMAIL scottdixon1987@hotmail.com, mrsyvettedixon@gmail.com WEBSITE www.scottdixonracing.com

1 **BEST TAMAYUZ**, 9, ch g Tamayuz—Pink Ivory **Winning Connections Racing**
2 **BREAK THE SILENCE**, 6, b g Rip Van Winkle (IRE)—In A Silent Way (IRE) **Winning Connections Racing**
3 **CHAMPAGNE MONDAYS**, 4, ch g Milk It Mick—La Capriosa **The William A Robinson & Partners**
4 **COISTE BODHAR (IRE)**, 9, b g Camacho—Nortolixa (FR) **The William A Robinson & Partners**
5 **CROSSE FIRE**, 8, b g Monsieur Bond (IRE)—Watersilk (IRE) **Paul J Dixon, K Brennan & Darren Lucas**
6 **DARK SHOT**, 7, b g Acclamation—Dark Missile **Chappell Rose & Radford**
7 **EBITDA**, 6, b m Compton Place—Tipsy Girl **P. J. Dixon**
8 **FEEL THE THUNDER**, 4, b c Milk It Mick—Totally Trusted **P. J. Dixon**
9 **GIOGIOBBO**, 7, b h Bahamian Bounty—Legnani **ARC Racing Syndicate**
10 **HENRY THE SIXTH**, 4, b c Milk It Mick—Six Wives **Sexy Six Partnership**
11 **INN WITH THE GIN**, 4, b f Coach House (IRE)—Tipsy Girl **The William A Robinson & Partners**
12 **KRYSTALLITE**, 7, ch m Kheleyf (USA)—Chrystal Venture (IRE) **Paul J Dixon & The Chrystal Maze Ptn**
13 **LAKESKI**, 6, b m Sir Percy—Floating **ARC Racing Syndicate**
14 **LOVE RAT**, 5, b g Mawatheeq (USA)—Watersilk (IRE) **The Love Rat Partnership**
15 **PEARL NOIR**, 10, b g Milk It Mick—Cora Pearl (IRE) **Winning Connections Racing**
16 **PORT SOIF**, 6, b m Foxwedge (AUS)—Positivity **ARC Racing Club**
17 **RED DOUGLAS**, 6, ch g Sakhee (USA)—Chrystal Venture (IRE) **Paul J Dixon & The Chrystal Maze Ptn**
18 **SAMOVAR**, 5, b g Finjaan—Chrystal Venture (IRE) **P J Dixon,Chrystal Maze & Ashley Severn**
19 **SANS SOUCI BAY**, 6, b g Medicean—Cumana Bay **Chappell Rose & Radford**
20 **SAVANNAH BEAU**, 8, b m Major Cadeaux—Mancunian Way **P. J. Dixon**
21 **SIR GEOFFREY (IRE)**, 14, b g Captain Rio—Disarm (IRE) **Generalsirgeoffreyhowlett/Mrpaulj.Dixon**
22 **SOCIALITES RED**, 7, ch m Sakhee's Secret—Tipsy Girl **The William A Robinson & Partners**
23 **SOCIOLOGIST (FR)**, 5, ch g Society Rock (IRE)—Fabiola (GER) **Rob Massheder, A J Turton & Partners**
24 **SOLO HUNTER**, 9, b g Sleeping Indian—Night Owl **Rob Massheder, A J Turton & Partners**
25 **THUNDERBELL**, 6, ch m Haafhd—Trustthunder **P. J. Dixon**
26 **THUNDERCLOUD**, 5, gr m Aussie Rules (USA)—Trustthunder **P. J. Dixon**
27 **TILLY DEVINE**, 6, gr m Aussie Rules (USA)—Cora Pearl (IRE) **Winning Connections Racing**

THREE-YEAR-OLDS

28 **ALEX GRACIE**, b f Fountain of Youth (IRE)—Kyllarney **Middleham Park Racing LXIV**
29 **BLUE STREAK**, ch f Hot Streak (IRE)—Vivid Blue **The Cool Silk Partnership**
30 **ILSERENO**, gr f Lethal Force (IRE)—She's A Worldie (IRE) **Mr S. E. Chappell**
31 **PERTEMPS SIA (IRE)**, b f Canford Cliffs (IRE)—Sentimental (IRE)

TWO-YEAR-OLDS

32 B f 10/04 Fountain of Youth (IRE)—Kyllarney (Kyllachy)

Other Owners: Mr A. D. Baker, Mr K. Brennan, P. J. Dixon, General Sir G. H. W. Howlett, Mr D. R. Lucas, Mr R. Massheder, Mr A. Severn, The Chrystal Maze Partnership, Mr A. C. Timms, Mr A. Turton.

Assistant Trainer: Mr K. Locking.

Amateur Jockey: Mr Kevin Locking.

147 MR STEVEN DIXON, Salisbury

Postal: **Apple Tree Barn, Livery Road, Winterslow, Nr Salisbury, Wiltshire, SP5 1RJ**
Contacts: **PHONE 01980 862930 MOBILE 07771 963011**
EMAIL sarahjdixon@hotmail.co.uk

1 **I'LL BE YOUR CLOWN (IRE)**, 9, b g Aqlaam—Lady Avenger (IRE) **Mr S. D. Dixon**

Assistant Trainer: Mrs Sarah Dixon.

148 MRS ROSE DOBBIN, Alnwick

Postal: **South Hazelrigg Farm, Chatton, Alnwick, Northumberland, NE66 5RZ**
Contacts: **PHONE 01668 215151, 01668 215395 MOBILE 07969 993563 FAX 01668 215114**
EMAIL **hazelriggracing1@btconnect.com** WEBSITE **www.rosedobbinracing.co.uk**

1 **ARDGLASS STAR (IRE)**, 6, b g Arctic Cosmos (USA)—Verney Roe (IRE) **Straightline Bloodstock**
2 **ATTENTION PLEASE (IRE)**, 10, b g Kalanisi (IRE)—Dangerous Dolly (IRE) **Mr Ronnie Jacobs & Mrs Rose Dobbin**
3 **BAKO DE LA SAULAIE (FR)**, 9, b g Balko (FR)—Krickette (FR) **Mr & Mrs Duncan Davidson**
4 **BIGIRONONHISHIP (IRE)**, 9, b g Beneficial—Portobello Lady (IRE) **Mr & Mrs Duncan Davidson**
5 **BROADSTRUTHER (IRE)**, 5, b g Shantou (USA)—Accardi (IRE) **Mr & Mrs Duncan Davidson**
6 **CHOSEN FLAME (IRE)**, 8, b g Well Chosen—Flaming Misty (IRE) **S & G Soils Limited**
7 **CLASSICAL SOUND (IRE)**, 8, b g Mahler—Sovienne (IRE) **Hunter, Matterson & Dobbin**
8 **COOLE HALL (IRE)**, 8, b g Flemensfirth (USA)—Coole Assembly (IRE) **Mr & Mrs Duncan Davidson**
9 **DEFINITE WISDOM (IRE)**, 7, b g Definite Article—
                          Wisdom And Light (IRE) **M & M Edwardson, M Hunter & J Matterson**
10 **DO NOT DISTURB (IRE)**, 7, b g Mahler—Galbertstown Run (IRE) **Mr & Mrs Duncan Davidson**
11 **DOKTOR GLAZ (FR)**, 10, b g Mount Nelson—Deviolina (IRE) **Mr & Mrs D Davidson & The Friday Lions**
12 **ENZILLERYA (FR)**, 6, b g Anzillero (GER)—Trieste (FR) **Mr & Mrs Duncan Davidson**
13 **ESPOIR MORIVIERE (FR)**, 6, ch g Saddex—Sagesse Moriviere (FR) **Ray, Roberts & Dobbin**
14 **FAMOUS MOMENT (IRE)**, 5, b g Fame And Glory—Endless Moments (IRE) **Mr & Mrs Duncan Davidson**
15 **FINAL FLING (IRE)**, 9, b g Milan—Supreme Singer (IRE) **J. M. & Mrs M. R. Edwardson**
16 **GEORDIELANDGANGSTA**, 7, br g Geordieland (FR)—
                          Dunsfold Duchess (IRE) **Mr & Mrs Davidson, C Davidson & N James**
17 **GET WITH IT (IRE)**, 5, b g Getaway (GER)—Listening (IRE) **Mr & Mrs Duncan Davidson**
18 **HITMAN FRED (IRE)**, 7, b g Getaway (GER)—Garravagh Lass (IRE) **Mr & Mrs Duncan Davidson**
19 **HONOURABLE GENT (IRE)**, 12, b g Gentleman's Deal (IRE)—Gudasmum **Mr & Mrs Duncan Davidson**
20 **JACK DEVINE (IRE)**, 8, b g Kalanisi (IRE)—Sybil Says (IRE) **Mr & Mrs Duncan Davidson**
21 **JONNIESOFA (IRE)**, 10, b g Well Made (GER)—
                          Lucky Sarah (IRE) **Mr R & Mrs A The Late Mr A.Houghton & Partners**
22 **LAST ONE TO SHOW (IRE)**, 5, b g Arcadio (GER)—Garravagh Lass (IRE) **Mrs R. Dobbin**
23 **LE CHEVAL NOIR (IRE)**, 6, b g Le Fou (IRE)—Bonny Lass **Mr & Mrs Duncan Davidson**
24 **LE GAVROCHE (IRE)**, 7, b g Flemensfirth (USA)—Knockieran (IRE) **Mr. Ronnie Jacobs & Mr. Albert Roux**
25 **MISTER DON (IRE)**, 10, br g Presenting—Spring Flower (IRE) **Mr Ronnie Jacobs & Mrs Rose Dobbin**
26 **MONFASS (IRE)**, 9, b g Trans Island—Ajo Green (IRE) **Mrs Dobbin & The Dimhorns**
27 **OKAVANGO DELTA (IRE)**, 4, b g Ocovango—Court My Eye **One For the Road Flower**
28 **PERMISSION GRANTED (IRE)**, 8, b g Oscar (IRE)—Ask The Misses (IRE) **Jacobs, Dickson & Brown**
29 **PLANET NINE (IRE)**, 8, b g Flemensfirth (USA)—Old Moon (IRE) **Mr & Mrs Duncan Davidson**
30 **POLITENESS (FR)**, 11, b g Poliglote—Martiniquaise (FR) **Dickson, Brown & Dobbin**
31 **PURCELL'S BRIDGE (FR)**, 13, b g Trempolino (USA)—Theatrical Lady (USA) **Mrs R. Dobbin**
32 **RATH AN IUIR (IRE)**, 7, b g Flemensfirth (USA)—Amathea (IRE) **Mr & Mrs Duncan Davidson**
33 **ROMULUS DU DONJON (IRE)**, 9, gr g Stormy River (FR)—Spring Stroll (USA) **Jacobs, Ray & Roberts**
34 **SLANELOUGH (IRE)**, 8, b g Westerner—Tango Lady (IRE) **Miss J. Matterson & Mrs D. Davidson**
35 **SMUGGLER'S STASH (IRE)**, 10, ch g Stowaway—Sweetasanu (IRE) **The Friday Lions 2**
36 **SOME REIGN (IRE)**, 9, b g Kayf Tara—Bridge Love (FR) **Mr & Mrs Duncan Davidson**
37 **STYLE NELSON (FR)**, 5, b g Mount Nelson—Ana Style (FR) **Mr & Mrs Duncan Davidson**
38 **SWEET AS CANDY (IRE)**, 8, b g Morozov (USA)—Sweet Nancy (IRE) **Mr & Mrs Duncan Davidson**
39 **THE HOLLOW CHAP (IRE)**, 6, ch g Beat Hollow—An Banog (IRE) **Mr & Mrs Duncan Davidson**
40 **TROOPER TURNBULL (IRE)**, 6, b g Arcadio (GER)—Clover Pearl (IRE) **Hunter & McKie**
41 **VINTAGE GLEN (IRE)**, 8, b g Ask—Rare Vintage (IRE) **Mrs R. Dobbin**
42 **WILD POLLY (IRE)**, 6, ch m Mahler—Dalzenia (FR) **Mr & Mrs Duncan Davidson**
43 **WORCESTER PEARMAIN**, 10, b m Beat All (USA)—Granoski Gala **Mr & Mrs Duncan Davidson**

Other Owners: Mr E. R. Brown, Miss C. M. Davidson, D. H. Davidson, Mr & Mrs Duncan Davidson, Mrs S. K. Davidson, Mr J. L. Dickson, Mr L. Dimsdale, Mr A. G. Dobbin, Mrs R. Dobbin, J. M. Edwardson, J. M. & Mrs M. R. Edwardson, Mrs M. R. Edwardson, Mrs S. Helmont, Mr A. Houghton, Mrs A. M. Houghton, Mr R. Houghton, M. S. Hunter, Mr R. A. Jacobs, Mrs N. James, J. R. Jeffreys, Miss C. L. Jones, Miss J. G. K. Matterson, Mrs V. J. McKie, Mrs M. H. Ray, Mr R. Roberts, Mr A. H. Roux, Mr D. A. C. Spencer-Churchill.

Assistant Trainer: Tony Dobbin.

NH Jockey: Craig Nichol.

149 **MR ASHLEY DODGSON, Thirsk**
Postal: **Southerby House, Catton, Thirsk, North Yorkshire, YO7 4SQ**

1 **MR DEALER (IRE)**, 8, b g Mr Dinos (IRE)—Vera Glynn (IRE) **Mrs F. M. G. Dodgson**

150 **MR MICHAEL DODS, Darlington**
Postal: **Denton Hall Farm, Piercebridge, Darlington, County Durham, DL2 3TY**
Contacts: PHONE 01325 374270 MOBILE 07860 411590, 07773 290830 FAX 01325 374020
EMAIL dods@michaeldodsracing.co.uk WEBSITE www.michaeldodsracing.co.uk

1 **AMPLIFICATION (USA)**, 5, b g Lonhro (AUS)—Our Drama Queen (IRE) **Mr M. D. Pearson**
2 **ARCAVALLO (IRE)**, 5, ch g Arcano (IRE)—Pashmina (IRE) **Mr P Appleton & Mrs Anne Elliott**
3 **BILLY NO MATES (IRE)**, 4, b g Clodovil (IRE)—Sabaidee (IRE) **Mr J Sagar & Mr M Dods**
4 **BUMBLEDOM**, 4, br g Epaulette (AUS)—Miaplacidus (IRE) **Mr G Thompson & Mr M Dods**
5 **BYRON'S CHOICE**, 5, b g Poet's Voice—Byrony (IRE) **Mr Doug Graham & Mrs M Wynn-williams**
6 **CAMACHO CHIEF (IRE)**, 5, b g Camacho—Passage To India (IRE) **Davison & Drysdale**
7 **DAKOTA GOLD**, 6, b g Equiano (FR)—Joyeaux **Doug Graham & Ian Davison**
8 **DANCIN BOY**, 4, br g Gregorian (IRE)—La Gifted **Mr R. R. D. Saunders**
9 **DANIELSFLYER (IRE)**, 6, b g Dandy Man (IRE)—Warm Welcome **Elliott Brothers And Peacock**
10 **GALE FORCE MAYA**, 4, ch f Gale Force Ten—Parabola **Mr F. Lowe**
11 **GET KNOTTED (IRE)**, 8, ch g Windsor Knot (IRE)—Genuinely (IRE) **D. Neale**
12 **HEATH CHARNOCK**, 4, b c Showcasing—Bayleaf **Mr D. W. Armstrong**
13 **JAWWAAL**, 5, ch g Bahamian Bounty—Avenbury **Sekura Trade Frames Ltd**
14 **JOHN KIRKUP**, 5, ch g Assertive—Bikini **Mrs Suzanne Kirkup & Mr Kevin Kirkup**
15 **KOLOSSUS**, 4, ch g Assertive—Bikini **K. Kirkup**
16 **MUSTAQBAL (IRE)**, 8, b g Invincible Spirit (IRE)—Alshamatry (USA) **Denton Hall Racing Ltd**
17 **MYRMIDONS (IRE)**, 4, ch g Casamento (IRE)—Allegrissimo (IRE) **Mr D. Stone**
18 **PROUD ARCHI (IRE)**, 6, b g Archipenko (USA)—Baharah (USA) **Eagle Racing**
19 **QUE AMORO (IRE)**, 4, b f Es Que Love (IRE)—Onomatomania (USA) **Mr P Appleton & Mrs Anne Elliott**
20 **RUMSHAK (IRE)**, 5, ch g Arcano (IRE)—Scarlet Rosefinch **Mrs C. Dods & Mr D Stone**
21 **WAHOO**, 5, b g Stimulation (IRE)—Shohrah (IRE) **Mr J Blackburn & Mr A Turton**

THREE-YEAR-OLDS
22 **AMERICA FIRST (IRE)**, gr g Le Havre (IRE)—Aglaia (IRE) **Bardsley, Hyde & Tattersall**
23 **ARCH MOON**, b g Sea The Moon (GER)—Archduchess **Mr Allan Mcluckie & Mr M. J. K. Dods**
24 **BAY FILLY ROLLA**, b f Showcasing—Memoria **The Storm Again Syndicate**
25 **BIRDIE BOWERS (IRE)**, b g Bungle Inthejungle—Shamiya (IRE) **K. Kirkup**
26 **BOUNCING BOBBY (IRE)**, b g Raven's Pass (USA)—Silicon Star (FR) **D. Neale**
27 **BRUNCH**, b g Harbour Watch (IRE)—Granola **Mrs F. Denniff**
28 **CHALLET (IRE)**, b g Clodovil (IRE)—Eileenlilian **Dunham Trading Ltd**
29 **COLD LIGHT OF DAY**, gr f Sea The Moon (GER)—Frosty Welcome (USA) **Miss K. Rausing**
30 **COMMANCHE FALLS**, br g Lethal Force (IRE)—Joyeaux **Mr Doug Graham, Davison & Drysdale**
31 **DOUBLE D'S**, b g Archipenko (USA)—Florentia **Mr D Neale & Mr D Stone**
32 **EL NASERI (IRE)**, b c Battle of Marengo (IRE)—Dubaya **Rjh Ltd & D Stone**
33 **FOUR JACKS (IRE)**, b g Camacho—Taaluf (IRE) **Mr G Thompson & Mr M Dods**
34 **GOOD VIBES**, b f Due Diligence (USA)—Satsuma **Qatar Racing Limited**
35 **INDUCTIVE**, b g Canford Cliffs (IRE)—Princess Rose **T. A. Scothern**
36 **JOMONT (FR)**, b g Motivator—Sea Life (FR) **Mrs Teresa Blackett & M Dods**
37 B f Heeraat (IRE)—Magic Echo **D. C. Batey**
38 **MECCA'S HOT STEPS**, ch f Hot Streak (IRE)—Vintage Steps (IRE) **Mr David T J Metcalfe & Mr M J K Dods**
39 **PALO SANTO**, b g Due Diligence (USA)—Frequent **Mr P Appleton & Mrs Anne Elliott**
40 **PEARL STREAM**, b f Fountain of Youth (IRE)—Seaperle **Mrs C. E. Dods**
41 **PEERLESS PERCY (IRE)**, b g Sir Percy—Victoria Montoya **D. Neale**
42 **RAPID RUSSO (IRE)**, b g Coach House (IRE)—Rapid Recruit (IRE) **Dunham Trading & Carole Dods**
43 **ROAD RAGE (IRE)**, b g Requinto (IRE)—Grid Lock (IRE) **Merchants and Missionaries**
44 **ROARING DRAGON (IRE)**, ch g Dragon Pulse (IRE)—Salydora (FR) **Mr D. Stone**
45 **SHADOW LEADER**, b g Equiano (FR)—Midnight M **Merchants and Missionaries**

MR MICHAEL DODS - continued

46 **TOMBOLO (FR)**, b c Le Havre (IRE)—Sandbar **Merchants and Missionaries**
47 **TROUBADOR (IRE)**, gr g Poet's Voice—Eastern Destiny **Mr J Sagar & Mr S Lowthian**
48 **UNIFIER**, b g Showcasing—Miss Chicane **Brook Stud**
49 **WALLGATE**, ch c Iffraaj—Miss Meggy **Mr D. W. Armstrong**
50 **WHITE COPPER**, br gr,f Outstrip—Native Nickel (IRE) **The Storm Again Syndicate**

TWO-YEAR-OLDS

51 Ch c 27/03 Territories (IRE)—Amberley Heights (IRE) (Elnadim (USA)) (19047)
52 **BLOWING WIND (IRE)**, b c 27/03 Markaz (IRE)—Wojha (IRE) (Pivotal) (15000) **Merchants and Missionaries**
53 Gr f 04/04 Gregorian (IRE)—Blue Bahia (IRE) (Big Bad Bob (IRE)) (12869) **D. T. J. Metcalfe**
54 B f 31/03 Charm Spirit (IRE)—Clifton Dancer (Fraam) (20952) **Mr D. R. Graham**
55 Ch c 08/04 Footstepsinthesand—Coppertop (IRE) (Exceed And Excel (AUS)) (36035)
56 **DIAMOND HAZE (IRE)**, b c 24/03 Coulsty (IRE)—Cannot Give (USA) (Proud Citizen (USA)) (9438)
57 B f 15/03 Bungle Inthejungle—Dream Scenario (Araafa (IRE)) (7000) **Mrs T. Burns**
58 B f 15/02 Elzaam (AUS)—Dubaya (Dubawi (IRE)) (30029) **Rjh Ltd & D Stone**
59 B g 01/02 Sir Prancealot (IRE)—Fainleog (IRE) (Rock of Gibraltar (IRE)) (20000) **Mrs C. E. Dods**
60 **FIRST GREYED (IRE)**, gr c 07/02 Gutaifan (IRE)—Hidden Girl (IRE) (Tamayuz) (23000) **The Gorijeb Partnership**
61 **HEAR ME ROAR (IRE)**, b c 02/03 The Last Lion (IRE)—
                                        Dutch Heiress (Dutch Art) (26000) **Mr P Appleton & Mrs Anne Elliott**
62 B c 04/02 Al Kazeem—It's My Time (Green Desert (USA)) (35000) **Sekura Trade Frames Ltd**

Other Owners: Mr P. Appleton, Mr D. A. Bardsley, Mr J. N. Blackburn, Mrs T. Blackett, Mr Ian Davison, Mrs C. E. Dods, M. J. K. Dods, Mr A. Drysdale, Dunham Trading Ltd, Mrs A. E. Elliott, R. T. Goodes, Mr D. R. Graham, Mr J. B. Hart, Mr G. Hyde, K. Kirkup, Mrs S. Kirkup, Mr R. A. Little, Mr S. R. Lowthian, Mr A. McLuckie, D. T. J. Metcalfe, Mr R. I. Moffatt, D. Neale, Mrs S. Peacock, R J H Limited, D. G. Raffel, Mr J. Sagar, Mr S. R. Skinns, Mr B. Stewart, Mr D. Stone, Mr M. W. Syme, A. Tattersall, Mr G. C. Thompson, Mr A. Turton, D. Watts, Mrs M. Wynn-Williams.

Assistant Trainer: Carole Dods, **Head Lad:** Steve Alderson, David Dickenson.

Flat Jockey: Connor Beasley, Paul Mulrennan, Callum Rodriguez. **Apprentice Jockey:** Aidan Redpath. **Amateur Jockey:** Miss Chloe Dods, Miss Sophie Dods, Miss Rachel Taylor.

151
MR CONOR DORE, Frampton Fen
Postal: **Barford Farm, Swineshead Road, Frampton Fen, Boston, Lincolnshire, PE20 1SG**
Contacts: **PHONE 01775 822747 MOBILE 07984 609170**
EMAIL dores@supanet.com

1 **BIGHORN MOUNTAIN (IRE)**, 6, b g Arcadio (GER)—Dorcet'slast Stand (IRE) **Mrs J Lamley & Mr Mike Fitzsimmons**
2 **COLLODI (GER)**, 11, b g Konigstiger (GER)—Codera (GER) **A. N. Page**
3 **EYE OF THE STORM (IRE)**, 10, ch g Galileo (IRE)—Mohican Princess **A. N. Page**
4 **FARMER BOY (IRE)**, 7, b g Scorpion (IRE)—Absent Beauty (IRE) **A. N. Page**
5 **FLOTED (IRE)**, 4, br f Arctic Cosmos (USA)—Uimhir A Seacht (IRE) **Mrs J. W. Lamley**
6 **GRAND INQUISITOR**, 8, b g Dansili—Dusty Answer **A. N. Page**
7 **HURRICANE RITA (FR)**, 10, gr m Sagamix (FR)—Madonna da Rossi **Barford Farm**

Other Owners: Mr M. Fitzsimons, Mrs J. W. Lamley.

152
MR SIMON DOW, Epsom
Postal: **Clear Height Stable, Derby Stables Road, Epsom, Surrey, KT18 5LB**
Contacts: **PHONE 01372 721490 MOBILE 07860 800109**
EMAIL simon@simondow.co.uk WEBSITE www.simondow.co.uk TWITTER @SimonDowRacing

1 **CORAZON ESPINADO (IRE)**, 5, b h Iffraaj—Three Decades (IRE) **Mr R. J. Moss**
2 **DELCIA**, 4, b f Delegator—Fiducia **P. G. Jacobs**
3 **EMENEM**, 6, b g Sir Percy—Kahalah (IRE) **Mr R. J. Moss**
4 **MISS ENIGMA (IRE)**, 4, b f Kodiac—Mysteriousness (FR) **Sir Martyn Arbib & Everett Partnership**

MR SIMON DOW - continued

5 **MONT KIARA (FR)**, 7, b g Kendargent (FR)—Xaarienne **Mr C. G. J. Chua**
6 **MR SCARAMANGA**, 6, b h Sir Percy—Lulla **Mr R. J. Moss**
7 **MYTHICAL MADNESS**, 9, b g Dubawi (IRE)—Miss Delila (USA) **Mr C. G. J. Chua**
8 **PRINCE ROCK (IRE)**, 5, ch g Society Rock (IRE)—She's A Queen (IRE) **Mr M. McAllister**
9 **QUE QUIERES (USA)**, 4, b g Bernardini (USA)—Christine Daae (USA) **Mr R. J. Moss**
10 **RECUERDAME (USA)**, 4, b g The Factor (USA)—B R's Girl (USA) **Mr R. J. Moss**
11 **ROUNDABOUT MAGIC (IRE)**, 6, ch h Zebedee—Cayo Largo (IRE) **Six Mile Hill Racing**
12 **SPARKALOT**, 6, br g Bated Breath—Three Wrens (IRE) **R Moss, H Redknapp**
13 **SUBLIMINAL**, 5, b g Arcano (IRE)—Rare Virtue (USA) **Mr M. McAllister**
14 **TE AMO TE AMO**, 4, b g Kyllachy—Caption **Mr R. J. Moss**

THREE-YEAR-OLDS

15 **BEAT THE BREEZE**, gr c Outstrip—Tranquil Flight **Mr S. A. Caunce**
16 **CAFE MILANO**, b c Al Kazeem—Selka (FR) **Stoney's Bloodstock**
17 **CHICA DEL DIA**, b f Toronado (IRE)—Vezere (USA) **Mr R. J. Moss**
18 **HEADLEY GEORGE (IRE)**, b g Due Diligence (USA)—Silent Secret (IRE) **Mr M. J. Convey**
19 **HECTOR LOZA**, b c Kodiac—Queen Sarra **Mr R. J. Moss**
20 **MADAM HASHTAG**, b f Zebedee—Stinky Socks (IRE) **Mr N. J. Hawkins**
21 **MUNGO'S QUEST (IRE)**, ch g Sir Prancealot (IRE)—Sheila Blige **S. L. Dow**
22 **TALLEE (FR)**, b f Manduro (GER)—Western Hope (IRE) **Malcolm & Alicia Aldis**

TWO-YEAR-OLDS

23 **BLUE BERET**, ch f 24/03 Helmet (AUS)—Vivid Blue (Haafhd)
24 **PABLO DEL PUEBLO (IRE)**, b c 23/02 Kodiac—Solar Event (Galileo (IRE)) (100000) **Mr R. J. Moss**
25 B c 30/03 Le Havre (IRE)—Regatta (FR) (Layman) (USA) (140000) **Mr H. Redknapp**
26 **SOYUZ**, b c 24/04 Sea The Moon (GER)—Inchberry (Barathea (IRE)) **Hawkins Family & Star Pointe Ltd**
27 **TWENTYSHARESOFGREY**, bl gr f 25/03 Markaz (IRE)—
Carsulae (IRE) (Marju (IRE)) (5000) **The Fat Jockey Partnership**

Other Owners: Mrs A. Aldis, Mr M. S. Aldis, M. Arbib, Mr G. D. D. Everett, Mr M. M. Everett, Mr N. J. Hawkins, Mr R. J. Moss, Mr B Phillpott, Mr H. Redknapp, Star Pointe Ltd, Mr I. R. Steadman.

---

153 MR CHRIS DOWN, Cullompton
Postal: **Upton, Cullompton, Devon, EX15 1RA**
Contacts: **PHONE 01884 33097 MOBILE 07828 021232 FAX 01884 33097**
EMAIL cjdownracing@gmail.com

1 **ARCTIC FOOTPRINT**, 6, br m Blueprint (IRE)—Arctic Flow **Mrs H. R. Dunn**
2 **BOLLIN CASCADE**, 5, b m Bollin Eric—Cinnamon Hill **Mrs M. A. Barrett**
3 **BROADCLYST (IRE)**, 8, b g Ask—Broadcast **Mrs S. M. Trump**
4 **CHAMPAGNE IDEAS (IRE)**, 7, b g Acambaro (GER)—Charannah (IRE) **Upton Racing 2**
5 **COBRA ANGEL (IRE)**, 6, br m Flemensfirth (USA)—Lemon Cello (IRE) **Upton Racing 2**
6 **ESPRESSINO**, 6, b gr g Tikkanen (USA)—Mocha (FR) **Mrs S. M. Trump**
7 **FANFAN LA COLMINE (FR)**, 5, b g No Risk At All (FR)—Union Leto (FR) **Mr P. R. Carter**
8 **FOXY ACT**, 9, ch m Act One—Brown Fox (FR) **C. J. Down**
9 **GAELIC FLOW**, 9, ch g With The Flow (USA)—Gaelic Lime **The Jack High Racing Partnership**
10 **HAZY DREAM**, 4, b gr f Dream Eater (IRE)—Lily Potts
11 4, B f Passing Glance—La Marette
12 4, Gr f Dream Eater (IRE)—Lily Potts **C. J. Down**
13 **MAX FORTE (IRE)**, 10, br g Indian River (FR)—Brook Forte **P Holland,JT Measures,MA Kerr,V Holland**
14 **MIDNIGHT ANNIE**, 6, b m Arvico (FR)—Miss Midnight **John & Greer Norman**
15 **MINELLA MOJO (IRE)**, 8, b g King's Theatre (IRE)—On The Horizon (IRE) **Mrs J. Elliott**
16 **MR SOCIABLE**, 5, b g Geordieland (FR)—Secret Queen **Kittymore Racing**
17 **PAHASKA (GER)**, 7, b m Saddex—Pacific Sun (GER) **P Holland,JT Measures,MA Kerr,V Holland**
18 4, B c Dream Eater (IRE)—Russie With Love
19 **STARLIT NIGHT**, 8, b m Nayef (USA)—Perfect Night **C. J. Down**

MR CHRIS DOWN - continued

THREE-YEAR-OLDS

20 **BRYHER,** b g Dream Eater (IRE)—Angel Sprints **Miss V. M. Halloran**

Other Owners: Mrs J. Elliott, P. D. Holland, Mrs V. Holland, Ms M. A. Kerr, Mr D. Luscombe, Mrs H. M. Luscombe, Mr J. T. Measures, Miss E. M. Pearse.

NH Jockey: James Davies.

---

154 **MR CLIVE DREW, Rampton**
Postal: **Fox End Stables, 83 King Street, Rampton, Cambridgeshire, CB24 8QD**
Contacts: **PHONE 01954 250772 MOBILE 07917 718127**
EMAIL polly.drew@googlemail.com

1 **MAISON BRILLET (IRE),** 13, b g Pyrus (USA)—Stormchaser (IRE) **C. Drew**
2 **MONSIEUR ROYALE,** 10, ch g Monsieur Bond (IRE)—Bond Royale **C. Drew**

TWO-YEAR-OLDS

3 B c 21/02 Sixties Icon—Hallo Sexy (Halling (USA))
4 B c 18/03 Alhebayeb (IRE)—Ur Secret Is Safe (IRE) (Dylan Thomas (IRE)) (800)

Assistant Trainer: Miss Polly Drew.

---

155 **MR DAVID W. DRINKWATER, Redmarley**
Postal: **Chapel Farm, Chapel Lane, Redmarley, Gloucester, Gloucestershire, GL19 3JF**
Contacts: **PHONE 07766 011007, 07973 193771**
EMAIL drinkys35@outlook.com

1 **ASHPAN SAM,** 11, b g Firebreak—Sweet Patoopie **R Tudor Holdings Limited**
2 **DLTRIPLESEVEN (IRE),** 7, gr g Dark Angel (IRE)—Namu **R Tudor Holdings Limited**
3 **MAHNA MAHNA (IRE),** 6, b g Kodiac—Namu **R Tudor Holdings Limited**
4 **MISS DUSKY DIVA (IRE),** 8, gr m Verglas (IRE)—Dispol Veleta **R Tudor Holdings Limited**
5 **TABLE BLUFF (IRE),** 11, ch g Indian Haven—Double Deal **R Tudor Holdings Limited**

Assistant Trainer: Rachel Tudor.

---

156 **MR SAMUEL DRINKWATER, Strensham**
Postal: **The Granary, Twyning Road, Strensham, Worcester, Worcestershire, WR8 9LH**
Contacts: **MOBILE 07747 444633**
EMAIL samdrinkwater@gmail.com

1 **ANGELS ANTICS,** 7, b m Schiaparelli (GER)—Safari Run (IRE) **Mrs K. Drinkwater**
2 **BIGCHEXTOCASH (IRE),** 8, b g Stowaway—Monakeeba (IRE) **The Railway children**
3 **BILLY HICKS,** 9, b g Kayf Tara—Michelle's Ella (IRE) **P. Drinkwater**
4 **BUZZ DE TURCOING (FR),** 6, b g Maresca Sorrento (FR)—Panora Night (FR) **Prestbury Thoroughbreds**
5 **CHATELIER (FR),** 8, ch g Network (GER)—Elza III (FR) **The Lucky Seven**
6 4, b g Schiaparelli (GER)—Cottstown Gold (IRE)
7 **GALLIC GEORDIE,** 7, b g Geordieland (FR)—Je Ne Sais Plus (FR) **Glastonburys & On the Gallops 1**
8 **GENERAL CONSENSUS,** 8, br g Black Sam Bellamy (IRE)—Charlottes Webb (IRE) **Mrs K. Drinkwater**
9 **HELLO BOB,** 5, ch m Cityscape—Maid of Perth **Mrs J. Drinkwater**
10 **HIGGY HIGGINS (IRE),** 4, gr g Leading Light (IRE)—Fantasia Filly (FR) **Mick Coulson, Karen Drinkwater**
11 **HOWLING MILAN (IRE),** 6, b g Milan—Fantasia Filly (FR) **Strensham Stragglers**
12 **JEANS GENIE,** 5, b gr m Kayf Tara—Aberdeen Park **The Lucky Seven**

MR SAMUEL DRINKWATER - continued

13 **KICKONMYSON**, 4, b g Schiaparelli (GER)—Madam Min **The Cheltenham Boys Racing Club**
14 **LA FILLE FRANCAISE (FR)**, 7, b m Kapgarde (FR)—Pondimari (FR) **Mrs Louise Merry & Mrs Julia Venvell**
15 **PRAY FOR A RAINBOW**, 9, b g Rainbow High—Blackchurch Lass (IRE) **Glastonburys & On the Gallops 1**
16 **RUSSIAN SERVICE**, 8, b g Robin des Champs (FR)—Just Kate **Stephen Mattick & Mr D.P. Drinkwater**
17 **SERGEANT BRODY**, 9, ch g Black Sam Bellamy (IRE)—Ardent Bride **Mrs K. Drinkwater**
18 **SOME CAN DANCE (IRE)**, 7, b g Gold Well—Rocella (GER) **Richard Bailey & Mr D P Drinkwater**
19 **TOP DECISION (IRE)**, 7, ch g Beneficial—Great Decision (IRE) **Prestbury Thoroughbreds**

Other Owners: Mr R. E. Bailey, R. J. Clarke, Mr M. D. Coulson, Mr D. P. Drinkwater, Mrs K. Drinkwater, P. Drinkwater, Mrs A. J. Glastonbury, Mr K. J. Glastonbury, Kevin & Anne Glastonbury, Mr M. Glastonbury, Mr R. Glastonbury, Mr S. J. Mattick, Mrs A. L. Merry, On The Gallops Racing Club, Mrs J. C. Venvell

---

157
MISS JACKIE DU PLESSIS, Saltash
Postal: **Burell Farm, Longlands, Saltash, Cornwall, PL12 4QH**
Contacts: **PHONE 01752 842362 MOBILE 07970 871505**
EMAIL ziggerson@aol.com

1 **BOTUS FLEMING**, 5, ch g Tiger Groom—Chelsea Express **Miss J. M. du Plessis**
2 **CORNELIUS SOCKS (IRE)**, 10, b g Asian Heights—Delightful Choice (IRE) **Miss J. M. du Plessis**
3 **ERICAS LAD**, 9, b g Mutazayid (IRE)—Kingsmill Quay **Miss J. M. du Plessis**
4 **KINGSMILL GIN**, 7, b m Fair Mix (IRE)—Kingsmill Lake **Miss J. M. du Plessis**
5 **LADY KINGSMILL**, 9, b m Bandmaster (USA)—Kingsmill Lake **Miss J. M. du Plessis**
6 **LEGEND LADY**, 9, b m Midnight Legend—Aoninch **The Cornish Barmies**
7 **MARLEY FIRTH (IRE)**, 8, b g Flemensfirth (USA)—Merrill Gaye (IRE) **Surrey Racing & Miss J. Du Plessis**
8 **NIGHT GENERATION (GER)**, 8, ch g Sholokhov (IRE)—Night Woman (GER) **Jackie Du Plessis & Sarah Pridham**
9 **SEA DESTINATION (IRE)**, 9, b m Dubai Destination (USA)—Nautical Lady (IRE) **The Cornish Barmies**
10 **ST ERNEY**, 9, ch g Kadastrof (FR)—Ticket To The Moon **Miss J. M. du Plessis**
11 **THEATRE MIX**, 7, gr m Fair Mix (IRE)—Theatre Diva (IRE) **Miss J. M. du Plessis**
12 **VALENTINO**, 5, b g Sulamani (IRE)—Romance Dance **Mr Shane O Sullivan & Miss J Du Plessis**

Other Owners: Mr S. M. O'Sullivan, Miss S. Pridham, Surrey Racing Limited, Miss J. M. du Plessis.

158
MRS ANN DUFFIELD, Leyburn
Postal: **Sun Hill Racing Stables, Sun Hill Farm, Constable Burton, Leyburn, North Yorkshire, DL8 5RL**
Contacts: **PHONE 01677 450303 MOBILE 07802 496332 FAX 01677 450993**
EMAIL ann@annduffield.co.uk **WEBSITE** www.annduffield.co.uk

1 **ANTICIPATE (IRE)**, 5, b g Yeats (IRE)—Princess Minnie **Mr T Ingham & Partner**
2 **ARNOLD**, 6, b g Equiano (FR)—Azurinta (FR) **DJ & SA Shewring, F Fantoni**
3 **BIBBIDIBOBBIDIBOO (IRE)**, 5, b m Red Jazz (USA)—Provence **Ms J. F. Bianco**
4 **CUPPACOCO**, 5, b m Stimulation (IRE)—Glen Molly (IRE) **Mrs C. A. Gledhill**
5 **NINEPIN BOWLER**, 6, b g Rip Van Winkle (IRE)—Smooth As Silk (IRE) **Ramscove Ltd**
6 **RIPON SPA**, 4, b g Rock of Gibraltar (IRE)—Lady Lahar **Mr T. S. Ingham & Mrs Liz Ingham**
7 **ROYAL RESIDENCE**, 5, b g Epaulette (AUS)—Jubilant Queen **Mr T. S. Ingham & Mrs Liz Ingham**
8 **SEA STORM**, 4, ch f Monsieur Bond (IRE)—Chez Cherie **Mr R C Bond**
9 **TROOP**, 5, gr g Lethal Force (IRE)—Bendis (GER) **DJ & SA Shewring, L Patterson**
10 **UNCLE CHARLIE (IRE)**, 6, b g Vale of York (IRE)—Velvet Kiss (IRE) **Mr David Barker & Partner**
11 **YOU LITTLE BEAUTY**, 4, b f Stimulation (IRE)—Ziefhd **Mrs A. Duffield**

THREE-YEAR-OLDS
12 **CLOTHERHOLME (IRE)**, b c Sir Prancealot (IRE)—Giorgi (IRE) **Mr T Ingham & Partner**
13 **GAINSBORO GREY**, gr g Archipenko (USA)—Albacocca **Mr Ian Farrington & Partner**
14 **INSPIRING NORA**, b f Swiss Spirit—Annie Kenney **Mr David Barker & Partner**
15 **LADY NECTAR (IRE)**, b f Zebedee—Mitchelton (FR) **Mr T Ingham & Partner**
16 **QUERCUS (IRE)**, b g Nayef (USA)—Dufoof (IRE) **Mrs C. A. Gledhill**

MRS ANN DUFFIELD - continued

TWO-YEAR-OLDS
17 B f 21/04 Fountain of Youth (IRE)—Ambella (IRE) (Dark Angel (IRE)) (800) **Mr T. S. Ingham & Mrs Liz Ingham**
18 B c 12/04 Fountain of Youth (IRE)—Bravo (Indian Charlie (USA))
19 B f 19/02 Fountain of Youth (IRE)—Cuppatee (IRE) (Canford Cliffs (IRE))
20 B c 11/02 Fountain of Youth (IRE)—Dont Tell Nan (Major Cadeaux) (761)
21 B f 19/03 Toronado (IRE)—Forever's Girl (Monsieur Bond (IRE)) **Mr R C Bond**
22 B f 13/04 Fountain of Youth (IRE)—Say A Prayer (Indesatchel (IRE)) **Mr T. S. Ingham & Mrs Liz Ingham**
23 B f 21/04 Brazen Beau (AUS)—Shesastar (Bahamian Bounty) (10476) **Ms J. F. Bianco**

Other Owners: D. K. Barker, Mrs A. Duffield, Mr F. Fantoni, Mr I. J. Farrington, Mrs M. E. Ingham, Mr T. S. Ingham, Mr L. S. Patterson, Mr D. J. Shewring, Mrs S. A. Shewring.

---

159 | **MR BRENDAN W. DUKE, The Curragh**
Postal: **Fenway House, Pollardstown, Curragh, Co. Kildare, Ireland**
Contacts: **MOBILE +353 85 818 9724**
EMAIL brendanwduke@hotmail.com

1 **CLEMENCIA (IRE)**, 4, b g Pour Moi (IRE)—Cleofila (IRE) **Mrs Jackie Bolger**
2 **EARLY VOICE (IRE)**, 4, b g Vocalised (USA)—Maidin Moch (IRE) **Mrs Jackie Bolger**
3 4, B c So You Think (NZ)—I'm Sheikra (IRE) **Brendan W. Duke Racing**
4 **LEAGAN GAEILGE (IRE)**, 4, b f Vocalised (USA)—Feile Bride (IRE) **Mrs Jackie Bolger**
5 **PRIDE OF PIMLICO (IRE)**, 4, ch g Casamento (IRE)—Casina Valadier (IRE) **Martin Hayes & Peter Slezak**
6 **PUNCH BAG (IRE)**, 9, ch g Teofilo (IRE)—Heir Today (IRE) **Martin Hayes, Peter Slezak**
7 **VOCAL DUKE (IRE)**, 4, b g Vocalised (USA)—Heir Today (IRE) **Mrs Jackie Bolger**
8 **VOCAL QUEEN (IRE)**, 5, b m Vocalised (USA)—Silver Queen **Mrs Jackie Bolger**
9 **VOLATILE LADY (IRE)**, 5, b m Vocalised (USA)—Astralai (IRE) **Mrs Jackie Bolger**

THREE-YEAR-OLDS
10 **JOAN OF PIMLICO (IRE)**, b f Free Eagle (IRE)—Poplar Close (IRE) **Martin Hayes, Peter Slezak**
11 **MADE IN PIMLICO (IRE)**, ch c Dragon Pulse (IRE)—Runway Giant (USA) **The Fenway Syndicate**
12 **PIMLICO PUBLICAN (IRE)**, b g Raven's Pass (USA)—Brazilian Spirit (IRE) **Martin Hayes, Peter Slezak**
13 **SAPPHIRE PEARL (IRE)**, b f Ivawood (IRE)—Pearl Blue (IRE) **Brendan Duke and Friends Syndicate**

TWO-YEAR-OLDS
14 **DOCTOR BROWN BEAR (IRE)**, B c 22/03 Estidhkaar (IRE)—
                                       All In Clover (IRE) (Bahri (USA)) (4290) **Brendan W. Duke Racing**
15 B f 17/04 Markaz (IRE)—Liscoa (IRE) (Foxhound (USA)) (858) **Brendan W. Duke Racing**
16 B c 08/03 Parish Hall (IRE)—Odisha (USA) (Drosselmeyer (USA)) **Mrs Jackie Bolger**
17 B f 01/05 Vadamos (FR)—Red Blanche (IRE) (Red Clubs (IRE)) (1886) **Angela Duke and Friends Syndicate**
18 **ROOM FOR GLORY (IRE)**, b f 30/04 Fulbright—Remedy (Pivotal) **Ms Patricia Kern**

Flat Jockey: Rory Cleary, Kevin Manning, Ronan Whelan. **NH Jockey:** Andrew Lynch. **Apprentice Jockey:** Daniel Redmond.

---

160 | **MR IAN DUNCAN, Coylton**
Postal: **Sandhill Farm, Coylton, Ayr, Ayrshire, KA6 6HE**
Contacts: **PHONE 01292 571118 MOBILE 07731 473668 FAX 01292 571118**
EMAIL idracing@outlook.com

1 **ABRACH ROAD**, 5, ch g Supreme Sound—Belfast Central (IRE) **Mr A. J. R. Lilley**
2 4, B g Epaulette (AUS)—Deserted **Mr A. J. R. Lilley**
3 **FINAGHY AYR (IRE)**, 12, ch g Lahib (USA)—Ali Ankah (IRE) **I. A. Duncan**
4 **GARRON CRESCENT (IRE)**, 5, b g Rock of Gibraltar (IRE)—Ladood **Mr A. J. R. Lilley**
5 **IMPERIAL PRINCE (IRE)**, 11, b g Subtle Power (IRE)—Satco Rose (IRE) **Stephen Sinclair & Ian Duncan**
6 **JESSIEMAC (IRE)**, 6, br m Sholokhov (IRE)—All Our Blessings (IRE) **Alan & Barry Macdonald**

MR IAN DUNCAN - continued

7 **KING OF FASHION (IRE)**, 10, ch g Desert King (IRE)—French Fashion (IRE) **Dr S. Sinclair**
8 **MISS HAMDA (IRE)**, 6, gr m Mastercraftsman (IRE)—Erstwhile (FR) **Cedars Two**
9 **NO NO MAC (IRE)**, 11, b g Oscar (IRE)—Whatdoyouthinkmac (IRE) **Alan & Barry Macdonald**
10 **ORIENT SUNSET**, 6, ch m Orientor—Watch Closely Now (IRE) **I. A. Duncan**
11 **PORTSTORM**, 5, b g Shirocco (GER)—Viva Victoria **Gregg, Lilley, Davidson, Hammersley**
12 **STRONG ECONOMY (IRE)**, 8, ch g Sandmason—Odd Decision (IRE) **Alan & Barry Macdonald**

Other Owners: Mr C. Davidson, I. A. Duncan, Mr A. L. Gregg, Mr G. Hammersley, Mr A. J. R. Lilley, Dr S. Sinclair.

---

161 | **MR NIGEL DUNGER, Pulborough**
Postal: **17 Allfrey Plat, Pulborough, West Sussex, RH20 2BU**
Contacts: **PHONE** 07494 344167 **MOBILE** 07790 631962
EMAIL debdunger05@gmail.com

1 **HIER ENCORE (FR)**, 8, ch g Kentucky Dynamite (USA)—Hierarchie (FR) **N. A. Dunger**
2 **PRIDE OF PEMBERLEY (IRE)**, 8, ch g Flemensfirth (USA)—On Galley Head (IRE) **N. A. Dunger**

Assistant Trainer: Mrs D Dunger.

---

162 | **MR ED DUNLOP, Newmarket**
Postal: **La Grange Stables, Fordham Road, Newmarket, Suffolk, CB8 7AA**
Contacts: **PHONE** 01638 661998 **MOBILE** 07785 328537 **FAX** 01638 667394
EMAIL edunlop@eddunloppracing.co.uk **WEBSITE** www.edunlop.com

1 **ALTERNATIVE FACT**, 5, b g Dalakhani (IRE)—O Fourlunda
2 **AMAZING RED (IRE)**, 7, b g Teofilo (IRE)—Artisia (IRE)
3 **DARK RED (IRE)**, 8, gr g Dark Angel (IRE)—Essexford (IRE)
4 **GLOBAL ART**, 5, b g Dutch Art—Constant Dream
5 **GLOBAL DESTINATION (IRE)**, 4, b g Slade Power (IRE)—Silk Trail
6 **GLOBAL ROCK (FR)**, 4, b g Siyouni (FR)—Baino Rock (FR)
7 **GLOBAL WARNING**, 4, b g Poet's Voice—Persario
8 **GOTTARDO (IRE)**, 5, b g Choisir (AUS)—Chantarella (IRE)
9 **GRANDSCAPE**, 5, b g Lemon Drop Kid (USA)—Unnatural (USA)
10 **HELIAN (IRE)**, 4, b c Shamardal (USA)—Amathia (IRE)
11 **MARBELLA (IRE)**, 4, b f Invincible Spirit (IRE)—Gift From Heaven (IRE)
12 **MERCURY DIME (IRE)**, 4, ch f Teofilo (IRE)—Margravine (USA)
13 **RED SECRET (CAN)**, 4, b c Lemon Drop Kid (USA)—Parley (USA)
14 **RED VERDON (USA)**, 7, ch h Lemon Drop Kid (USA)—Porto Marmay (IRE)
15 **ROCA MAGICA**, 4, b f Garswood—Marigay's Magic
16 **SAN SEBASTIAN (IRE)**, 4, b g Iffraaj—Invincible Cara (IRE)
17 **SAY NOTHING**, 4, b f Nathaniel (IRE)—I Say (IRE)
18 **TORO DORADO**, 4, b g Toronado (IRE)—Rawoof (IRE)

THREE-YEAR-OLDS

19 **AFRICAN SUN (IRE)**, b c Teofilo (IRE)—Castle Cross (IRE)
20 **AHDAB (IRE)**, b c Shamardal (USA)—Habaayib
21 **ASDAF (IRE)**, b g Brazen Beau (AUS)—Eclaircie (IRE)
22 **AYSAR (IRE)**, b g Sir Prancealot (IRE)—Yajala
23 **BIANCA CASTAFIORE (FR)**, b f Dabirsim (FR)—Faviva (USA)
24 **BURANO BOY (IRE)**, gr c Footstepsinthesand—Ghost of A Girl (IRE)
25 **DAAFY (USA)**, b g The Factor (USA)—Ishraak (USA)
26 **DELAQUINN**, b g Roderic O'Connor (IRE)—Hector's Girl
27 **ENOSI (FR)**, ch g Champs Elysees—Frasque (USA)
28 **FEISTY GAL (IRE)**, b f Invincible Spirit (IRE)—Bobbie Soxer (IRE)
29 B c Kingman—Lady Linda (USA)

MR ED DUNLOP - continued

30 **LYRICAL,** gr f Poet's Voice—Reaching Ahead (USA)
31 **MAGNIFICIA (IRE),** b f Sir Prancealot (IRE)—Star Bonita (IRE)
32 **MASTER THE STARS (GER),** b c Sea The Stars (IRE)—Magma (GER)
33 **MAYSONG,** ch g Mayson—Aldeburgh Music (IRE)
34 **NAYWAY,** b g Nayef (USA)—Sharway Lady
35 **OWHATANIGHT,** gr c Night of Thunder (IRE)—White Wedding (IRE)
36 **PARIKARMA (IRE),** b f Canford Cliffs (IRE)—Pushkar
37 **PLUNKETT,** b c Gleneagles (IRE)—Araqella (IRE)
38 **RED CELEBRE (IRE),** ch c Teofilo (IRE)—Artisia (IRE)
39 **RED FOR ALL,** b c Muhaarar—All For Laura
40 **SORAMOND (GER),** b f Sea The Moon (GER)—St Aye (USA)
41 **SPANDAVIA (IRE),** ch f Showcasing—Bronte Sister (IRE)
42 **SPECULATION,** ch g Gleneagles (IRE)—Precious Dream (USA)
43 **TAKE ME TO THE SKY,** b g Tamayuz—Nassaakh
44 **TEN CHANTS,** gr g Gregorian (IRE)—Tenbridge
45 **VIRGIN SNOW,** b f Gleneagles (IRE)—Snow Fairy (IRE)
46 **ZENAIDA (IRE),** b f Kodiac—Constellation

TWO-YEAR-OLDS

47 B c 28/03 Siyouni (FR)—Aristotelicienne (IRE) (Acclamation) (190476)
48 **ARTHUR'S REALM (IRE),** b c 08/01 Camelot—Morning Line (FR) (Anabaa (USA)) (28000)
49 B c 20/02 Kodi Bear (IRE)—Atlas Silk (Dansili) (40000)
50 B c 18/04 Make Believe—Dew (IRE) (Whipper (USA)) (22000)
51 B f 17/04 Equiano (FR)—Edge of Love (Kyllachy) (5238)
52 Gr f 10/02 Free Eagle (IRE)—Evening Frost (IRE) (Invincible Spirit (IRE)) (62000)
53 B c 29/01 Wootton Bassett—Gift of Life (USA) (Kitten's Joy (USA)) (100000)
54 B f 27/03 Lope de Vega (IRE)—Horse Sense (IRE) (Canford Cliffs (IRE)) (100000)
55 **JOHN LEEPER (IRE),** b c 28/04 Frankel—Snow Fairy (IRE) (Intikhab (USA))
56 B f 26/02 Lethal Force (IRE)—Lydiate (IRE) (Acclamation) (30476)
57 **MAIDEN'S TOWER (IRE),** b br f 13/04 Golden Horn—Harlem Dancer (Dr Devious (IRE)) (75000)
58 B br c 24/03 Intello (GER)—Moonee Valley (FR) (Aqlaam) (32000)
59 **POTATO PARK,** gr f 10/03 Oasis Dream—Loch Ma Naire (IRE) (Galileo (IRE))
60 B f 31/03 Invincible Spirit (IRE)—Prima Luce (IRE) (Galileo (IRE)) (95000)
61 Ch c 01/04 New Approach (IRE)—Princess Cammie (IRE) (Camacho) (160000)
62 B f 31/03 Oasis Dream—Red Fantasy (IRE) (High Chaparral (IRE)) (70000)
63 Ch c 13/04 Sixties Icon—Royal Warranty (Sir Percy) (70000)
64 **SAMBORA GIRL,** b f 15/03 Farhh—Elis Eliz (IRE) (Lord Shanakill (USA)) (24761)
65 B c 29/03 Due Diligence (USA)—See You Later (Emarati (USA)) (12000)
66 B f 19/03 Shalaa (IRE)—Social Media (New Approach (IRE)) (110000)
67 **SOUND OF U A E (IRE),** b c 24/04 Champs Elysees—Sandbox Two (IRE) (Foxhound (USA))
68 B f 14/04 Iffraaj—Synergy (FR) (Victory Note (USA)) (70000)
69 B f 14/02 Harzand (IRE)—The Madding Crowd (Dansili) (32000)
70 Ch c 08/04 Lope de Vega (IRE)—Tributary (New Approach (IRE)) (120000)
71 B c 24/03 Dabirsim (FR)—Vallota (Polish Precedent (USA)) (21450)
72 **ZANKALA,** b f 07/04 Zoffany (IRE)—Sannkala (FR) (Medicean) (22000)

Owners: Mr Hamdan Al Maktoum, Ahmad Al Shaikh, Mr Austin Allison, Mrs June Allison, Anamoine Ltd, The Hon R J Arculli, Mr N. B. Attenborough, Mrs Jessica Ball, Mr & Mrs R Bourne, Mrs Emma Capon, Mr W. Cox, Mr R. P. Foden, Mr Andrew Gemmell, Mr T Henderson, Philippa Higgins, Mr Dennis Hill, Dr Johnny Hon, Exors of the Late Mr S. F. Hui, Ms Helian Jianru, Mr Ralph Marshall, Mr Patrick Milmo, Mr A. M. Mitchell, Mrs Georgina Newcombe, Mr Mark Newcombe, Mr Brian Plows, Mr Malcolm Plows, Mr David Roberts, Mrs Susan Roy, Mrs G. A. Rupert, Mrs C. L. Smith, Mrs Doreen M. Swinburn, Mr Christopher Symons, The Old Etonian Racing Syndicate II, The Serendipity Partnership, Mr Richard Tucker, Mr Paul Turner, Mr Andrew White, Mrs Julie White, Mr Ken Wilson, Windflower Overseas Holdings Inc, Mr Yin Yue.

Assistant Trainer: Jack Morland.

Apprentice Jockey: Sophie Smith.

163   MR HARRY DUNLOP, Lambourn
Postal: Frenchmans Lodge Stables, Upper Lambourn, Hungerford, Berkshire, RG17 8QW
Contacts: PHONE 01488 73584 MOBILE 07880 791895
EMAIL info@harrydunloracing.com WEBSITE www.harrydunloracing.com

1 **BRIGHTON PIER (GER)**, 4, ch g Farhh—Bearlita (GER) **Mrs S. M. Roy**
2 **CRANEUR**, 4, ch g Showcasing—Paris Winds (IRE) **Be Hopeful Partnership**
3 **FIGHTING IRISH (IRE)**, 5, b h Camelot—Quixotic **Daniel MacAuliffe & Anoj Don**
4 **FLAT STONE**, 4, ch g Champs Elysees—Something Exciting **Kingwood Stud Management Co Ltd**
5 **JACKFINBAR (FR)**, 5, b h Whipper (USA)—Anna Simona (GER) **Haven't A Pot**
6 **LEVANTER (FR)**, 4, b f Rock of Gibraltar (IRE)—Seasonal Cross **Malcolm & Alicia Aldis**
7 **NICE FELLA**, 4, b f Kodiac—Across The Galaxy **Kingwood Stud Management Co Ltd**

THREE-YEAR-OLDS
8 **ALIZES (FR)**, b f Hurricane Run (IRE)—Hungry Heart (IRE) **Trade Winds**
9 **ANGEL ON HIGH (IRE)**, b c Dark Angel (IRE)—Angel of The Gwaun (IRE) **Mr L. N. Jones**
10 **AQUASCAPE (IRE)**, br g Montmartre (FR)—Water Feature **Mr Erik Penser & Bloomsbury Stud**
11 **CAPTAIN HADDOCK (IRE)**, b c Make Believe—Kayd Kodaun (IRE) **Mrs Susan Roy & Partner**
12 **CASSIDY JO (IRE)**, b f Golden Horn—Roses For The Lady (IRE) **Mr L. N. Jones**
13 **EMPEROR ALLEY (IRE)**, b g Holy Roman Emperor (IRE)—
                                              Miss Topsy Turvy (IRE) **Windflower Overseas Holdings Inc**
14 **FIGHTING DON (FR)**, ch g Anodin (IRE)—Mazayyen **Daniel MacAuliffe & Anoj Don**
15 **GENTLEMAN AT ARMS (IRE)**, b g Reliable Man—Sworn Sold (GER) **Be Hopeful (2) & Fair Salinia Ltd**
16 **GOLDEN LIPS (IRE)**, b f Golden Horn—Lady Penko (FR) **Haven't A Pot & Ballylinch Stud**
17 **LEMON SONG (FR)**, b g Stormy River (FR)—Lemon Twist (IRE) **Hambro von Opel**
18 **LOST EMPIRE (IRE)**, b g Footstepsinthesand—Ballerina Rose **Mr L. N. Jones**
19 **PRIDE OF AMERICA (FR)**, b c American Post—Atarfe (IRE) **Haven't A Pot, D. Macauliffe & Anoj Don**
20 **RAGTIME SALLY**, b f Iffraaj—Honky Tonk Sally **FLSP & Mrs Maitland-Jones**
21 **RELATIVITY (FR)**, ch c Rio de La Plata (USA)—Relation (USA) **The Einstein Partnership**
22 **SAFFRON LANE**, b f Mukhadram—Sabreon **Velocity Racing**
23 **TRIXIE WATERBURY (IRE)**, b f Baltic King—Smart Bounty **The Megsons & Partner**
24 **VULCAN (IRE)**, b g Free Eagle (IRE)—Quixotic **The 2 Under Partnership**

TWO-YEAR-OLDS
25 **A DAY OF MISCHIEF**, b f 19/04 Adaay (IRE)—
                         Red Mischief (IRE) (Red Clubs (IRE)) **The Turf Club & The Red Mischief Partnership**
26 **BISCAY**, b c 20/02 Fastnet Rock—Hereawi (Dubawi (IRE)) **Mr J H Richmond-Watson**
27 **DREAM CHASER (IRE)**, b c 28/03 Dream Ahead (USA)—
                         Avodale (IRE) (Lawman (FR)) (16302) **Kirby, Gehring & Woodley**
28 **FIRST PIROUETTE (IRE)**, b f 25/03 Acclamation—Ballerina Rose (Duke of Marmalade (IRE)) **Mr L. N. Jones**
29 B c 16/02 Kodi Bear (IRE)—Hobby (Robellino (USA)) **Larksborough Stud Limited**
30 **HONOURS**, b f 07/04 Exceed And Excel (AUS)—Roses For The Lady (IRE) (Sadler's Wells (USA)) **Mr L. N. Jones**
31 B c 21/03 Make Believe—Lady Penko (FR) (Archipenko (USA)) (37751)
32 **MAXINE (IRE)**, b f 13/04 Maxios—Saltita (IRE) (Galileo (IRE)) (8580) **Friends of John Dunlop**
33 B c 15/03 Lawman (FR)—Megec Blis (IRE) (Soviet Star (USA)) (12000)
34 **ONENIGHTINMIAMI (FR)**, b c 29/05 Motivator—Highborne (FR) (Anabaa (USA)) (34320) **Mrs S. M. Roy**
35 B f 04/03 Kodiac—Orpha (New Approach (IRE)) (22000) **Haven't A Pot**
36 B f 19/04 Charming Thought—Precious Dream (USA) (Mr Greeley) (5714)
37 **QUELLE VITESSE (GER)**, b f 14/04 Golden Horn—
                         Queensberry (GER) (Tertullian (USA)) (5000) **Mr Erik Penser & Bloomsbury Stud**
38 **SEA OF CHARM (FR)**, b f 18/02 Charm Spirit (IRE)—Sea Meets Sky (FR) (Dansili) (12500) **Elwes, Cooper & Deal**
39 **THUNDER AHEAD**, b c 17/02 Dark Angel (IRE)—Champagne Time (IRE) (Oasis Dream) **Mr L. N. Jones**

Other Owners: Mrs S. Abbott, Mrs A. Aldis, Mr M. S. Aldis, Ballylinch Stud, Be Hopeful (2), Bloomsbury Stud, Mr R. Burkland, Mr W. S. Burkland, Mr M. J. Cross, Mr A. R. Culumbarapitiyage Don, Mr A. S. Dudgeon, Mrs C. A. M. Dunlop, H. J. L. Dunlop, Mr G. Freeman, Mr K. C. Freeman, Frenchmans Lodge Stables Partnership, Mr R. W. Gregson-Williams, Lady C. Guise, Mr R. Hambro, S. A. Hanson, Haven't A Pot, Haven't A Pot & Ballylinch Stud, Mr D. A. Kirby, Mr D. P. MacAuliffe, Daniel MacAuliffe & Anoj Don, Mrs J. F. Maitland-Jones, Mr A. P. Megson, Mrs J. Megson, Mr E. Mudge, E. Penser, Mr L. C. Reed, Mrs S. M. Roy, The Megsons, Westerberg, Mr D. A. Woodley.

164 MRS ALEXANDRA DUNN, Wellington
Postal: **The Gallops, West Buckland, Wellington, Somerset, TA21 9LE**
Contacts: MOBILE **07738 512924**
WEBSITE **www.alexandradunnracing.com**

1 **ARGUS (IRE)**, 8, b g Rip Van Winkle (IRE)—Steel Princess (IRE) **Helium Racing LTD**
2 **ARTOIS**, 4, gr g Mizzen Mast (USA)—Intercontinental **Golden Equinox & W.B.B.**
3 **AZARI**, 8, b g Azamour (IRE)—Atasari (IRE) **B.B.S. & Lot 51**
4 **BALLARD DOWN (IRE)**, 7, b g Canford Cliffs (IRE)—Mackenzie's Friend **West Buckland Bloodstock Ltd**
5 **BEAU KNIGHT**, 8, b g Sir Percy—Nicola Bella (IRE) **West Buckland Bloodstock Ltd**
6 **BORN TO REASON (IRE)**, 6, b g Born To Sea (IRE)—Laureldean Lady (IRE) **West Buckland Bloodstock Ltd**
7 **BROKE AWAY (IRE)**, 8, br m Stowaway—Not Broke Yet (IRE) **Mr D. R. Arthur**
8 **CHIAVARI (IRE)**, 6, b m Born To Sea (IRE)—Chiarezza (AUS) **Dave Arthur & W.B.B.**
9 **COMPTON ABBEY**, 6, b m Compton Place—Bolsena (USA) **Mr D. J. Fitzgerald**
10 **CROMWELL**, 4, b g Swiss Spirit—Brooksby **West Buckland Bloodstock Ltd**
11 **CRY WOLF**, 7, ch g Street Cry (IRE)—Love Charm **W.B.B. & G.J. Daly**
12 **DE LITTLE ENGINE (IRE)**, 6, ch g Power—Reveuse de Jour (IRE) **Golden Equinox Racing & Team Dunn**
13 **DELIVERANCE**, 5, b g Havana Gold (IRE)—Tentpole (USA) **Willow to Whip Syndicate**
14 **DELIVERING DREAMS**, 4, b g Oasis Dream—Delivery **Golden Equinox Racing**
15 **ENMESHING**, 7, ch g Mastercraftsman (IRE)—Yacht Club (USA) **The Crafty Six & W. B. B.**
16 **FRANK BRIDGE**, 7, b g Avonbridge—First Among Equals **Mr J. R. Dyer**
17 **GANG WARFARE**, 9, b g Medicean—Light Impact (IRE) **Gangbusters**
18 **HOLLANDER**, 6, ch g Dutch Art—Thrill **Helium Racing LTD**
19 6, B g Malinas (GER)—Holy Smoke
20 **HOW ABOUT IT (IRE)**, 11, b g Kayf Tara—Midnight Gift (IRE) **Mrs K. R. Smith-Maxwell**
21 **JUPITER**, 5, b g Finjaan—Medicea Sidera **Team Dunn & W.B.B.**
22 **KAPITALISTE (FR)**, 4, b g Intello (GER)—Kapitale (GER) **The Profile Partnership 2**
23 **MASQUE**, 4, b f Toronado (IRE)—Amarullah (FR) **D. F. Powell**
24 **MASTER MEAD**, 5, b g Malinas (GER)—Double Mead **Mrs K. R. Smith-Maxwell**
25 **MINELLA VOUCHER**, 9, b g King's Theatre (IRE)—All Rise (GER) **Blue Blood Syndications & W. B. B.**
26 **MOLAAHETH**, 4, b g Heeraat (IRE)—All Fur Coat **West Buckland Bloodstock Ltd**
27 **MR MINERALS**, 6, ch g Poet's Voice—River Song (USA) **Helium Racing LTD**
28 **NAHHAM (IRE)**, 5, b g Dawn Approach (IRE)—Anna's Rock (IRE) **Ms L. L. Clune**
29 **NEVER A WORD (USA)**, 6, br g Lonhro (AUS)—Janetstickettocats (USA) **West Buckland Bloodstock Ltd**
30 **PANATOS (FR)**, 5, b g Denon (USA)—Prairie Scilla (GER) **Helium Racing LTD**
31 **RAMBLOW**, 7, b m Notnowcato—Nsx **West Buckland Bloodstock Ltd**
32 **REGULATOR (IRE)**, 5, b g Acclamation—Rasana **Team Dunn & W.B.B.**
33 **RESHAAN (IRE)**, 5, b g Dark Angel (IRE)—Bluebell (IRE) **Ms L. L. Clune**
34 **SHELLEBEAU (IRE)**, 4, b f War Command (USA)—Attracted To You (IRE) **West Buckland Bloodstock Ltd**
35 **SOLOIST (IRE)**, 4, b f Camelot—Ayshea **Ms L. L. Clune**
36 **SPRING STEEL (IRE)**, 11, b g Dushyantor (USA)—Fieldtown (IRE) **A Game Pair**

MRS ALEXANDRA DUNN - continued

37 **THAHAB IFRAJ (IRE)**, 7, ch g Frozen Power (IRE)—Penny Rouge (IRE) **The Dunnitalls**
38 **THE BRITISH LION (IRE)**, 5, b g Power—Mala Mala (IRE) **Helium Racing LTD**
39 **THE EAGLE'S NEST (IRE)**, 6, ch g Lope de Vega (IRE)—Follow My Lead **Helium Racing LTD**
40 **TRUCKERS TANGLE (IRE)**, 8, b g Tajraasi (USA)—Lodge Tangle (IRE) **Blue Blood Syndications & W. B. B.**
41 **VENTURA BLUES**, 6, b br m Bated Breath—Salmon Rose (IRE) **Ms L. L. Clune**
42 **WESTERNER OCEAN (IRE)**, 8, gr m Westerner—Silver Proverb **Team Dunn**
43 **ZEYZOUN (FR)**, 6, b g Excelebration (IRE)—Zayanida (IRE) **West Buckland Bloodstock Ltd**

Other Owners: Mr D. R. Arthur, Mr C. Bennett, Mrs Y. Bennett, Blue Blood Syndications, G. J. Daly, Mrs A. Dunn, Mr D. J. Fitzgerald, Golden Equinox Racing, Lot 51, Team Dunn, The Crafty Six, The Profile Partnership, West Buckland Bloodstock Ltd, Mrs C. M. Wheatley, Mr T. Wheatley, Mr A. G. S. Wiltshire, Mr R. G. Wiltshire, Mr C. J. Woods

165 MRS CHRISTINE DUNNETT, Norwich
Postal: **College Farm, Hingham, Norwich, Norfolk, NR9 4PP**
Contacts: PHONE 01953 850596 MOBILE 07775 793523
EMAIL christine@christinedunnett.com WEBSITE www.christinedunnett.com

1 **DROP KICK MURPHI (IRE)**, 6, b g Sir Prancealot (IRE)—Rindiseyda (IRE) **Trevor & Ruth Milner**
2 **ED CUVEE**, 4, ch g Mazameer (IRE)—Flaming Telepath **Ed's Gang**
3 **FORGOTTEN GIRL**, 4, b f Sir Prancealot (IRE)—College Doll **College Farm Stud**
4 **KRAKA (IRE)**, 5, b g Dark Angel (IRE)—Manuelita Rose (ITY) **Team Kraka**
5 **MAZMERIZE**, 4, b g Mazameer (IRE)—Patience **Mr P. Amey**
6 **PATIENCEISAVIRTUE**, 5, b m Libranno—Patience **Mrs C. A. Dunnett**
7 **PENARTH PIER (IRE)**, 4, b f Dark Angel (IRE)—Waveband **Ron Spore & P D West**
8 **PERCY TOPLIS**, 5, b g Kheleyf (USA)—West Lorne (USA) **Mrs C. A. Dunnett**
9 **QUEEN OF BURGUNDY**, 4, b f Lethal Force (IRE)—Empress Adelaide **Trevor & Ruth Milner**
10 **SAY IF I CAN**, 5, b g Sayif (IRE)—Lily Le Braz **Mr P. D. West**
11 **SECRET TREATIES**, 4, b f Heeraat (IRE)—Honky Tonk Queen (USA) **Mr A. Machin & Mrs C. Dunnett**
12 **SHYARCH**, 6, b g Archipenko (USA)—Coconut Shy **Mr P. D. West**
13 **SHYJACK**, 5, ch g Archipenko (USA)—Coconut Shy **Mrs C. A. Dunnett**

THREE-YEAR-OLDS
14 **CUBAN**, b g Havana Gold (IRE)—Dignify (IRE) **Mr P. Eggett**
15 **KATES STAR**, b f Casamento (IRE)—Naady **Mrs M. E. Tuddenham**
16 **LAST DAYS OF MAY**, gr ro f Outstrip—Fenella Rose **Machin & Eggett**
17 **MOMENT OF PEACE**, b g Gregorian (IRE)—Penny's Pearl (IRE) **Machin, Milner, Sparkes & Dunnett**

TWO-YEAR-OLDS
18 B c 14/04 Lethal Force (IRE)—Barathea Dancer (IRE) (Barathea (IRE)) **Mr P. D. West**
19 B g 18/05 Swiss Spirit—Cultured Pride (IRE) (King's Best (USA)) (1000) **Mr P. D. West**
20 B g 12/04 Estidhkaar (IRE)—Hot Property (USA) (Thunder Gulch (USA)) **Mrs C. A. Dunnett**
21 **INSPECTOR BLAKE**, ch g 07/04 Helmet (AUS)—Shamara (IRE) (Spectrum (IRE)) (1000) **Mr P. Eggett**
22 **LUCAYAN**, gr f 12/04 Belardo (IRE)—Sandy Cay (USA) (Mizzen Mast (USA)) (6000) **Trevor & Ruth Milner**
23 **MAGNA OF ILLUSION**, b f 25/03 Estidhkaar (IRE)—Enterprising (Dansili) (800) **Mr A. S. Machin**
24 B c 10/05 Bobby's Kitten (USA)—Marigay's Magic (Rock of Gibraltar (IRE)) (2500) **Mr E. N. Sparkes**
25 B f 13/03 Epaulette (AUS)—No Nightmare (USA) (Lion Heart (USA)) **Mrs C. A. Dunnett**
26 B g 02/04 Brazen Beau (AUS)—Patience (Kyllachy) **Mr P. D. West**

Other Owners: Mr A. Brown, Mrs B. I. Brown, Mr M. R. Brown, Mr D. G. Burt, Mr F. G. Butler, Mrs C. A. Dunnett, Mr P. Eggett, Mr A. S. Machin, Miss S. Mauriello, Mrs R. L. Milner, Mr T. Milner, Mr G. R. Price, Mr E. N. Sparkes, R. C. Spore, Mr P. D. West.

166 MR SEAMUS DURACK, Upper Lambourn
Postal: **The Croft Stables, Upper Lambourn, Hungerford, Berkshire, RG17 8QH**
Contacts: PHONE 01488 491480 MOBILE 07770 537971
EMAIL sd.111@btinternet.com WEBSITE www.seamusdurack.com

1 **ALFREDO (IRE)**, 8, ch g Arcano (IRE)—Western Sky **Mr Stephen Tucker & Mr Keith Mcintosh**
2 **CAYIRLI (FR)**, 8, b g Medicean—Clarinda (FR) **S. P. Tucker**
3 **EXCELINTHEJUNGLE (IRE)**, 4, b g Bungle Inthejungle—Kannon **Egan Waste & Beddoes**
4 **FAST ART (IRE)**, 4, b g Fast Company (IRE)—Poulkovo (IRE) **Mr & Mrs A Archer & Mr & Mrs M Leonard**
5 **MAKAARIM**, 6, b g Tamayuz—Dubawi Cheetah (IRE) **Miss S. J. Beddoes**
6 **PARA MIO (IRE)**, 5, b g Pour Moi (IRE)—Malaspina (IRE) **Tucker Stafford & McCormack**
7 **PIPES OF PEACE (IRE)**, 6, b g Galileo (IRE)—Coachella **Egan Waste Services Ltd**
8 **SEAPORT**, 9, ch g Champs Elysees—Cochin (IRE) **Mrs Pao, Mr Stafford & Mr Tucker**
9 **THE SWAGMAN (USA)**, 6, ch g Galileo (IRE)—Ventura (IRE) **Clan McNeil**

THREE-YEAR-OLDS
10 **PHOENIX AQUILUS (IRE)**, b c Slade Power (IRE)—Permsiri (IRE) **Miss S. J. Beddoes**

Other Owners: Mr A. Archer, Mrs J. Archer, Miss S. J. Beddoes, Egan Waste Services Ltd, Mr M. A. Leonard, Mrs M. E. Leonard, E. McCormack, Mr K. R. McIntosh, Mr J. McNeil, Mr P. J. McNeil, Mrs A. Pao, Mr N. J. Stafford, S. P. Tucker.

Assistant Trainer: Sam Beddoes.

167 **MISS CLAIRE DYSON, Evesham**
Postal: **Froglands Stud Farm, Froglands Lane, Cleeve Prior, Evesham, Worcestershire, WR11 8LB**
Contacts: **PHONE 01789 774000, 07803 720183 FAX 01789 774000**
EMAIL cdyson@live.co.uk WEBSITE www.clairedysonracing.co.uk

1 **AMERICAN CRAFTSMAN (IRE)**, 6, gr g Mastercraftsman (IRE)—Quiet Mouse (USA) **Mr M. P. Dunphy**
2 **CAP'N (IRE)**, 9, b g Gamut (IRE)—Dawn Princess (IRE) **Ishtar**
3 **CHARLIE MON (IRE)**, 11, ch g Presenting—Prowler (IRE) **Mr R. M. Evans**
4 **CLASSIC TUNE**, 10, b g Scorpion (IRE)—Classic Fantasy **D. J. Dyson**
5 **JUSTGIVEMEAREASON (IRE)**, 6, b g September Storm (GER)—Almnadia (IRE) **Mr M. P. Dunphy**
6 **LINGER (IRE)**, 7, b g Cape Cross (IRE)—Await So **Equestrian Direct Ltd & Partner**
7 **MIDNIGHT OWLE**, 10, ch g Midnight Legend—Owlesbury Dream (IRE) **FSF Racing**
8 **MINELLA STYLE (IRE)**, 10, b g King's Theatre (IRE)—Rose of The Erne (IRE) **Mr G. T. Sainsbury**
9 **PASSAM**, 8, b g Black Sam Bellamy (IRE)—One Wild Night **FSF Racing**
10 **PERSIAN DELIGHT**, 10, b g Lucarno (USA)—Persian Walk (FR) **D. J. Dyson**
11 **SNEAKY FEELING (IRE)**, 8, b g Oscar (IRE)—Shuil Aris (IRE) **Mr G. T. Sainsbury**
12 **SPARKLING RIVER (IRE)**, 10, gr m Indian River (FR)—Full Deck (IRE) **Mr M. P. Dunphy**
13 **STILL A DREAM**, 7, b g Sulamani (IRE)—Owlesbury Dream (IRE) **FSF Racing**
14 **TODAY PLEASE (IRE)**, 10, b g Westerner—Casiana (GER) **Mr M. P. Dunphy**
15 **WHAT ABOUT US (IRE)**, 7, b g Dubai Destination (USA)—Serpentaria **Mr M. P. Dunphy**
16 **YORSEXYANDUKNOWIT (IRE)**, 7, ch m Curtain Time (IRE)—Mercy Mission **Mr M. P. Dunphy**

Other Owners: Miss C. Dyson, Equestrian Direct LTD.

NH Jockey: David Noonan. **Conditional Jockey:** Charlie Hammond.

168 **MR SIMON EARLE, Sutton Veny**
Postal: **The Lower Barn, The Beeches Farm, Deverill Road, Sutton Veny, Wiltshire, BA12 7BY**
Contacts: **PHONE 01985 840450 MOBILE 07850 350116 FAX 01985 840450**
EMAIL simonearleracing@btinternet.com WEBSITE www.simonearleracing.co.uk

1 **BIG TREE (IRE)**, 7, b g Scorpion (IRE)—Montecateno (IRE) **Mr K. M. Harris**
2 **BUBBLES ARCADE**, 8, b m Arkadian Hero (USA)—Alwariah **Mrs B. C. Tucker**
3 **CROWD OF STARS**, 6, b g Yeats (IRE)—On Yer Own **Mr O. P. Hoddinott**
4 **GOLDEN HOUR (USA)**, 6, b g Medaglia d'Oro (USA)—Morrow **R. L. Dacombe**
5 4, B g Franklins Gardens—It's Molly **Mrs R. Scott**
6 **KILKEASKIN MOLLY (IRE)**, 6, b br m Mountain High (IRE)—
Nicola's Girl (IRE) **Mrs P Bridel, Mr C Marment, Mr C Church**
7 6, B g Sakhee (USA)—Madame Mozaik (USA) **Mr S. A. Earle**
8 **SIXTH OF JUNE**, 6, b m Crosspeace (IRE)—Eccentricity **Mrs B. C. Tucker**
9 **WITCH FROM ROME**, 9, b g Holy Roman Emperor (IRE)—Spangle **Mr S. A. Earle**

Other Owners: Mrs P. L. Bridel, Mr C. Church, Mr S. A. Earle, Mr C. V. Marment, Mr Brian Thrift

169 **MR MICHAEL EASTERBY, Sheriff Hutton**
Postal: **New House Farm, Sheriff Hutton, York, North Yorkshire, YO60 6TN**
Contacts: **PHONE 01347 878368 MOBILE 07831 347481 FAX 01347 878204**
EMAIL enquiries@mickeasterby.co.uk WEBSITE www.mickeasterby-racing.co.uk

1 **ABWAB (IRE)**, 4, b g Teofilo (IRE)—Alaia (IRE) **J Blackburn L Vincent R Sheppard Winter**
2 **AIRGLOW (IRE)**, 5, b g Invincible Spirit (IRE)—Pearl Grey **Mr S Davis & Mr S Hull**
3 **ALBERT'S BACK**, 6, b g Champs Elysees—Neath **Golden Ratio & J Blackburn**
4 **ALDRETH**, 9, b g Champs Elysees—Rowan Flower (IRE) **Mr A. Morse & Stittenham Racing**
5 **ART OF DIPLOMACY**, 4, b g Archipenko (USA)—Rowlestone Express **Imperial Racing, J Blackburn & P Scott**
6 **BLACKWEST (FR)**, 4, ch g Montmartre (FR)—Mariner's Light (FR) **J Blackburn L Westwood Imperial Racing**
7 **BOREAS DUKE**, 4, b g Rip Van Winkle (IRE)—Amalina **Sheep As A Lamb Syndicate**

MR MICHAEL EASTERBY - continued

8 **BOWSON FRED**, 8, b g Monsieur Bond (IRE)—Bow Bridge **Mrs A. Jarvis**
9 **BREAKING RECORDS (IRE)**, 5, b g Kodiac—Querulous (USA) **Mr R Chapman**
10 **CAPTON**, 7, b g Cape Cross (IRE)—Flavian **The Irrational Group & Mr J Blackburn**
11 **CHOOSEY (IRE)**, 5, ch g Choisir (AUS)—Petit Chou (IRE) **K. Wreglesworth**
12 **CONISTON SPA (IRE)**, 5, b g Watar (IRE)—Mundi Blues (IRE) **Mr M. J. R. Bannister Racing**
13 **CONTRAST (IRE)**, 6, ch g Dutch Art—Israar **Mr A Saha Racing**
14 **COSMIC LANDSCAPE**, 5, b g Lawman (FR)—Dancingintheclouds (IRE) **E. A. Brook**
15 **DAHIK (IRE)**, 5, ch g Society Rock (IRE)—Bishop's Lake **Mr A. Saha**
16 **DESERT DREAM**, 6, b g Oasis Dream—Rosika **The Racing Emporium**
17 **DREAMS AND VISIONS (IRE)**, 4, b g Archipenko (USA)—Kibini **Imperial Racing, J Blackburn & P Scott**
18 **ELIGIBLE (IRE)**, 4, b g Dark Angel (IRE)—Secrets Away (IRE)
19 **ELYSIAN FLAME**, 4, ch g Champs Elysees—Combustible (IRE) **Mr J Blackburn & Imperial Racing P'ship**
20 **ENLIGHTEN**, 6, b g Kayf Tara—Rapturous **Mr N Bannister Racing**
21 **FLYMETOTHESTARS**, 7, b g Sea The Stars (IRE)—Precious Gem (IRE) **Middleham Park Racing**
22 **GAOLBREAKER (IRE)**, 4, ch g Getaway (GER)—Glaisdale **Mr N Wrigley, Mrs J Lukas & Mr B Guerin**
23 **GEORGE RIDSDALE**, 4, ch g Ruler of The World (IRE)—Cape Rising (IRE) **Mr J Blackburn & Imperial Racing P'ship**
24 **GULF OF POETS**, 8, b g Oasis Dream—Sandglass **Mr J Blackburn Mr A Pollock Mr A Turton**
25 **HARVEST DAY**, 5, b m Harbour Watch (IRE)—Miss Wells (IRE) **Mrs C E Mason & Partner**
26 **HO WHOLE DREAM (IRE)**, 4, ch g Pivotal—Dream Play (IRE) **Mr Alan Zheng & Stittenham Racing**
27 **INTO THE ZONE**, 4, b g New Approach (IRE)—Lady Zonda
28 **KINDLY**, 7, b m Kyllachy—Touching (IRE) **Mr M Blades, Mr S Hollings & Mr S Hull**
29 **LA RAV (IRE)**, 6, b g Footstepsinthesand—Swift Acclaim (IRE) **Mr B Hoggarth, Mr S Davis & Mr S Hull**
30 **MALDONADO (FR)**, 6, ch g Rio de La Plata (USA)—Spanish Winner (IRE) **Mr A. Saha**
31 **MANZIL (IRE)**, 5, ch g Bated Breath—Pointed Arch (IRE) **Imperial Blackburn Saha Sh Df & Sh**
32 **MARWARI (IRE)**, 4, b c Exceed And Excel (AUS)—Miss Polaris **Mr J Blackburn & Imperial Racing P'ship**
33 **MELGATE MAGIC**, 4, ch g Harbour Watch (IRE)—Corn Rigs **Mr B. Hoggarth**
34 **MELGATE MAJEURE**, 4, br g Lethal Force (IRE)—Ambrix (IRE) **Bernard Hoggarth Racing**
35 **NO BILLS**, 4, ch f Mayson—Brave Mave **Mr J. Munroe**
36 **NOVELTY SEEKER (IRE)**, 11, b g Street Sense (USA)—Nawaiet (USA) **Mr C. D. Sigsworth**
37 **QAWAMEES (IRE)**, 5, b g Exceed And Excel (AUS)—Jabhaat (USA) **The Irrational Group & Mr J Blackburn**
38 **QUICK LOOK**, 7, b g Kheleyf (USA)—Weqaar (USA) **Golden Ratio, Hull, Hollings & Winter**
39 **RAPID APPLAUSE**, 8, b g Royal Applause—Madam Ninette **Folwell Morse Mulryan & Cram**
40 **ROLLADICE**, 5, ch g Bated Breath—Selkirk Sky **A Pollock and J Blackburn**
41 **ROYCANO**, 10, ch g Lucarno (USA)—Royal Distant (USA) **Mr M. J. R. Bannister Racing**
42 **SAM'S GUNNER**, 7, ch g Black Sam Bellamy (IRE)—Falcon's Gunner **Falcon's Line Ltd**
43 **SASSIE (IRE)**, 5, b m Rip Van Winkle (IRE)—Star of Gibraltar **L Vincent, S Hull & S Hollings**
44 **SOCRU (IRE)**, 4, b g Kodiac—Hemaris (IRE) **Blackburn Lm Syn Cram Mb Sh & Sh**
45 **SOFT SUMMER RAIN**, 4, ch f Champs Elysees—Modern Art **Imperial Racing P'Ship & Mr J Blackburn**
46 **STAR ARCHER**, 6, b g Champs Elysees—Postale **Blackburn Hull & Pollock**
47 **SWISS KNIGHT**, 5, b g Oasis Dream—Swiss Diva **Mr A Pollock & Mr H Jones**
48 **THORNTON LE CLAY**, 4, b g Nathaniel (IRE)—Dance East **W. H. & Mrs J. A. Tinning & Mrs C Wallis**
49 **TORRID**, 9, ch g Three Valleys (USA)—Western Appeal (USA) **J Blackburn, Mrs A Bartram & S Hull**
50 **TOWN HEAD**, 7, ch g Archipenko (USA)—Forever Loved **Mr M. J. R. Bannister Racing**
51 **TURQUOISE FRIENDLY**, 4, b g Holy Roman Emperor (IRE)—Cry Freedom (IRE) **Mr A. H. L. Zheng**
52 **UNPLUGGED (IRE)**, 4, b g Alhebayeb (IRE)—Crown Light **Mr S Windle**
53 **WHERE'S JEFF**, 5, b g Haafhd—Piece of Magic **A G Pollock, Golden Ratio & J Sissons**

THREE-YEAR-OLDS

54 **BANKAWI**, b f Coach House (IRE)—Whitby (IRE) **South Bank Racing**
55 **CASILLI**, b f Cacique (IRE)—Lilli Marlane **Tinning, Wallis, Hollings & Hull**
56 **CASTLEHILL LAD**, ch g New Approach (IRE)—Sudfah (USA) **Mr A Stott & Mrs J Lukas**
57 Gr c Piccolo—Cherrycombe-Row **Mr H Easterby & Partners**
58 **COME ON LINDA**, b gr f Alhebayeb (IRE)—Friendship Is Love **Mrs L Folwell & South Bank Racing**
59 **COTTAM**, b c Harbour Watch (IRE)—Gadfly **The Racing Emporium**
60 B c Nathaniel (IRE)—Dreaming of Stella (IRE) **Golden Equinox Racing**
61 **EBONY ADAMS**, b f Fountain of Youth (IRE)—Mortitia **The Laura Mason Syndicate**
62 **EVORA KNIGHTS**, ch g Equiano (FR)—Ewenny **Evora Racing**
63 **I'M EASY**, b g Archipenko (USA)—Eminencia **Mr J Blackburn & Imperial Racing P'ship**
64 **IRISH EILEEN**, b f Coach House (IRE)—El Molino Blanco **David Scott Ltd, Mr P Cram & Mr H Cram**

MR MICHAEL EASTERBY - continued

65 **ITOJEH,** ch g Cityscape—Croeso Cariad **Mr J Blackburn Racing**
66 **KIRBY UNDERDALE,** b g Fastnet Rock (AUS)—Angelic Note (IRE) **The Sangster Family & J Sissons**
67 B c Archipenko (USA)—Medaille d'Or **Mr J Blackburn & Imperial Racing P'ship**
68 **MISS CHILLI,** gr ro f Monsieur Bond (IRE)—Poetic Verse **Mr J Blackburn Racing**
69 **NODDY SHUFFLE,** b g Heeraat (IRE)—Sophie'jo **Mr Charles Black & Mr Steve Hull**
70 **OH MARY OH MARY,** b f Mukhadram—How Fortunate **Mrs M. Kennell**
71 **REFUGE,** b g Harbour Watch (IRE)—Beldale Memory (IRE) **J Blackburn & Julia Lukas**
72 **RING OF GOLD,** b g Havana Gold (IRE)—Pitter Patter **Gay & Peter Hartley**
73 **ROCKET DANCER,** b g Toronado (IRE)—Opera Dancer **Mr S Hull & South Bank Racing**
74 **SAM'S CALL,** b c Finjaan—Winner's Call **Westy Partnership**
75 **SEA OF SHADOWS,** gr f Sea The Stars (IRE)—Pink Opaque **Mr T. W. M. Turner**
76 **SKYE DREAMING (FR),** b g Dabirsim (FR)—Madonna Incognito (USA) **Mr S Davis & Mr S Hull**
77 **STITTENHAM WOOD,** br g Garswood—Handsome Molly **Rosyground Stud Racing**
78 **VARDON FLYER,** b g Fountain of Youth (IRE)—Harryana To **S Hollings, S Hull & S Davis**
79 **WINTERBURN (IRE),** b g Fulbright—Kotdiji **J Blackburn & S Winter**

TWO-YEAR-OLDS

80 B g 23/03 Swiss Spirit—Bow Bridge (Bertolini (USA)) **Mrs A. Jarvis**
81 B c 17/04 Mayson—Delft (Dutch Art) (7619)
82 B c 05/03 Monsieur Bond (IRE)—El Molino Blanco (Royal Applause) (4761) **D. Scott**
83 B c 04/02 Bobby's Kitten (USA)—
            Eminencia (Sadler's Wells (USA)) (1904) **Mr J Blackburn & Imperial Racing P'ship**
84 Ch f 04/04 Outstrip—Hoof's So Lucky (Compton Place) **The Laura Mason Syndicate**
85 B c 23/03 Swiss Spirit—Kibenga (Oasis Dream) (4761) **The Laura Mason Syndicate**
86 Ch c 28/02 Bobby's Kitten (USA)—
            Medium of Exchange (USA) (Exchange Rate (USA)) (3000) **Mr J Blackburn & Imperial Racing P'ship**
87 B c 17/02 Charm Spirit (IRE)—Mrs Greeley (Mr Greeley (USA)) (8000) **M. W. Easterby**
88 B f 17/05 Eagle Top—Piece of Magic (Alflora (IRE)) (6666) **Mr A Pollock & Mr H Jones**
89 Ch f 21/05 Eagle Top—Poetic Verse (Byron) **Mr J Blackburn Racing**
90 B c 19/04 Slade Power (IRE)—Ramamara (IRE) (Trans Island) **The Racing Emporium**
91 B g 03/05 Battle of Marengo (IRE)—
            Rock Magic (IRE) (Rock of Gibraltar (IRE)) (5576) **Mr J Blackburn & Imperial Racing P'ship**
92 Gr c 27/04 Lethal Force (IRE)—Sacred Aspect (IRE) (Haafet (USA)) (3809) **Bernard Hoggarth Racing**
93 B f 22/03 Garswood—Sarah Berry (First Trump) (15000) **Strawberry Fields Stud**
94 B c 18/04 Charming Thought—Scented Garden (Zamindar (USA)) (4000) **E. A. Brook**
95 B c 11/05 Summer Front (USA)—Secret Dream (IRE) (Zafonic (USA)) (6500) **Mr A Stott**
96 Ch c 19/02 Al Kazeem—Selka (FR) (Selkirk (USA)) (5500) **Mr J Blackburn & Imperial Racing P'ship**
97 B c 07/03 Iffraaj—Short Affair (Singspiel (IRE)) (10000) **Mr A Saha Racing**
98 B c 16/02 Estidhkaar (IRE)—Singitta (Singspiel (IRE)) (9000) **Mr S Hull & South Bank Racing**
99 B f 17/04 Swiss Spirit—Spritzeria (Bigstone (IRE)) (13000) **Mr S Hull & South Bank Racing**
100 B grc 21/02 Lethal Force (IRE)—Thrill (Pivotal) (11428) **Mr B Hoggarth & Mr J Blackburn**
101 **TWO BROTHERS,** b g 10/03 Sir Percy—Blandish (USA) (Wild Again (USA)) **Thompson Brothers**
102 Ch c 10/04 Mehmas (IRE)—Western Sky (Barathea (IRE)) (10000) **Altitude Racing**
103 Gr g 16/03 Lawman (FR)—
            Whistling Straits (FR) (Dalakhani (IRE)) (13727) **Mr J Blackburn & Imperial Racing P'ship**
104 B f 04/04 Monsieur Bond (IRE)—Winner's Call (Indian Ridge) (7619)
105 B g 17/02 War Command (USA)—Zari (Azamour (IRE)) **Mr J Blackburn & Imperial Racing P'ship**

Other Owners: B Hoggarth & D Scott Pattern Makers Ltd, Mr M. J. R. Bannister, Mr N. W. A. Bannister, Mrs J. A. Bartram, Bearstone Stud Limited, Mr C. M. A. Black, Mr J. N. Blackburn, Mr M. A. Blades, Mr J. E. Bray, Mr R Chapman, Mr R Chapman, Mr R. Connolly, Mr H. Cram, Mr P. D. Cram, David Scott & Co (Pattern Makers) Ltd, Mr S. G. Davis, M. W. Easterby, Mr R. F. Elam, Mr D. A. Fielding, Mrs L. S. Folwell, Mr E. H. M. Frost, Mr A. G. Greenwood, Mr B. M. P. R. Guerin, Mr B. Hoggarth, Mr S. A. Hollings, S. Hull, Imperial Racing Partnership, Imperial Racing Partnership 2016, Mrs M. Kennell, The Laura Mason Syndicate, Mrs J. K. Lukas, Mrs C. E. Mason, Mr A. Morse, Mr & Mrs P H Hartley, Mr Charles Black & Mr S Hull, Mr L. Mulryan, Mr A. G. Pollock, Mr Evora Racing & Mr David Scott, Mr I. Robinson, Miss M. R. Robinson, Mr A. Saha, B. V. Sangster, D. Scott, Mr P. G. Scott, Mr R. Sheppard, J. H. Sissons, South Bank Racing, Stittenham Racing, Mr A. F. Stott, Miss M. L. Taylor, Mr J. A. Tinning, W. H. Tinning, Mr A. Turton, Mr L. J. Vincent, V Vincent, S Hull & S Hollings, Mrs C. M. Wallis, Mr L. J. Westwood, Mr S. A. Windle, Mr S. J. Winter, N. H. T. Wrigley, Mr A. H. L. Zheng.

MR MICHAEL EASTERBY - continued

Assistant Trainer: D. M. Easterby.

Flat Jockey: Nathan Evans, Paul Mulrennan, James Sullivan. **NH Jockey:** Harry Bannister. **Apprentice Jockey:** Ger O'Neill.
Amateur Jockey: Miss S. Brotherton, Miss Joanna Mason.

---

170 MR TIM EASTERBY, Malton
Postal: **Habton Grange, Great Habton, Malton, North Yorkshire, YO17 6TY**
Contacts: **PHONE 01653 668566 FAX 01653 668621**
EMAIL easterby@btconnect.com WEBSITE www.timeasterby.co.uk

1 **AASHEQ (IRE)**, 7, b g Dubawi (IRE)—Beach Bunny (IRE) **Ryedale Partners No 1**
2 **AFANDEM (IRE)**, 6, b g Vale of York (IRE)—Al Mahmeyah **Reality Partnerships XI**
3 **AIYA (IRE)**, 5, ch g Declaration of War (USA)—Flamingo Sea (USA) **King Power Racing Co Ltd**
4 **AL ERAYG (IRE)**, 7, b g Oasis Dream—Vallee des Reves (USA) **Reality Partnerships III**
5 **AMADEUS GREY (IRE)**, 4, gr g Zebedee—Benedicte (IRE) **Ontoawinner 10 & Partner**
6 **APPOINTED**, 6, b m Delegator—Celestial Harmony **Martyn Macleod Racing**
7 4, B f Garswood—Aroundthebay **Mr D. W. Armstrong**
8 **AUTUMN FLIGHT (IRE)**, 4, b g Dandy Man (IRE)—Swallow Falls (IRE) **Mr Ambrose Turnbull & Partner**
9 **BOLLIN ACE**, 9, b g Bollin Eric—Bollin Annabel **Ryedale Partners No 3**
10 **BOLLIN JOAN**, 5, b m Mount Nelson—Bollin Greta **N Arton, P Hebdon, R Taylor & Partner**
11 **BOLLIN TED**, 6, b g Haafhd—Bollin Greta **Mr Neil Arton & Partner**
12 **BOSSIPOP**, 7, ch g Assertive—Opopmil (IRE) **A. R. Turnbull**
13 **BREATHABLE**, 5, b g Bated Breath—Cassique Lady (IRE) **Mr B Guerin Mr J Westoll & Habton Farms**
14 **BROTHER MCGONAGALL**, 6, b r Equiano (FR)—Anatase **Reality Partnerships VI**
15 **BRUTALAB**, 4, b g Epaulette (AUS)—Kahalah (IRE) **Ontoawinner 10**
16 **CAWTHORNE LAD**, 4, ch g Coach House (IRE)—Upton Seas **E. A. Brook**
17 **CHICAGO MAY (IRE)**, 4, b f Charm Spirit (IRE)—Urgele (FR) **Mr L. Bond**
18 **CILLUIRID (IRE)**, 6, b g Arcadio (GER)—Garw Valley **Reality Partnerships IV**
19 **CONTREBASSE**, 5, b g Champs Elysees—Viola da Braccio (IRE) **The Harmonious Lot & Partner**
20 **COPPER KNIGHT (IRE)**, 6, b g Sir Prancealot (IRE)—Mystic Dream **Middleham Park, Ventura Racing 6 & Partner**
21 **COUNT D'ORSAY (IRE)**, 4, b g Dandy Man (IRE)—Deira (USA) **Mr Ambrose Turnbull & John Cruces**
22 **CUBA RUBA**, 4, b g Havana Gold (IRE)—Diksie Dancer **Reality Partnerships XIII**
23 **DANCE KING**, 10, ch g Danehill Dancer (IRE)—One So Wonderful **Habton Farms**
24 **DANZAN (IRE)**, 5, b g Lawman (FR)—Charanga **Reality Partnerships XVII**
25 **DARK JEDI (IRE)**, 4, b g Kodiac—Whitefall (USA) **Mr Evan M Sutherland & Partner**
26 **DEW POND**, 8, b g Motivator—Rutland Water (IRE) **Ryedale Partners No 9**
27 **DREAM HOUSE**, 4, b g Coach House (IRE)—Kummel Excess (IRE) **Ontoawinner, SDH Project Services Ltd 2**
28 **DREAMSELLER (IRE)**, 4, ch g Dream Ahead (USA)—Picture of Lily **Ryedale Partners No 2**
29 **DUKE OF YORKSHIRE**, 10, b g Duke of Marmalade (IRE)—Dame Edith (FR) **Habton Farms**
30 **EAST STREET REVUE**, 7, ch g Pastoral Pursuits—Revue Princess (IRE) **Mr S. A. Heley & Partner**
31 **EEH BAH GUM (IRE)**, 5, b g Dandy Man (IRE)—Moonline Dancer (FR) **Mr N. A. Rhodes**
32 **EURO FOU (IRE)**, 5, ch g Le Fou (IRE)—Euro Joy (IRE) **Habton Farms**
33 **EXCELLENT TIMES**, 5, b m Excelebration (IRE)—Al Janadeirya **Times Of Wigan Ltd**
34 **EXCESSABLE**, 7, ch g Sakhee's Secret—Kummel Excess (IRE) **Mr B Guerin & Habton Farms**
35 **FLYING PURSUIT**, 7, ch g Pastoral Pursuits—Choisette **Ontoawinner, M Hulin & Partner**
36 **FOX KASPER (IRE)**, 4, ch g Society Rock (IRE)—Easy Times **Mr B. Valentine**
37 **GARDEN OASIS**, 5, b g Excelebration (IRE)—Queen Arabella **Mr T. A. Scothern & Partner**
38 **GLENCADAM GLORY**, 6, b g Nathaniel (IRE)—Lady Grace (IRE) **MPR, Ventura Racing 15 & Partner**
39 **GOLDEN APOLLO**, 5, ch g Pivotal—Elan **Mr David Scott & Partner**
40 **GULLANE ONE (IRE)**, 5, ch g Dream Ahead (USA)—Shamsalmaidan (IRE) **Mount Pleasant Racing**
41 5, B g Desideratum—Gwyre (IRE) **Habton Farms**
42 **HAWK HIGH (IRE)**, 10, b g High Chaparral (IRE)—Septembers Hawk (IRE) **Mr T. J. Hemmings**
43 **HIGH MOON**, 5, b g Midnight Legend—Dizzy Frizzy **Mr T. J. Hemmings**
44 **HIGHWAYGREY**, 4, b g Dick Turpin (IRE)—Maybeagrey **Reality Partnerships VII**
45 **HILLWALKER**, 5, b g Foxwedge (AUS)—Dance A Daydream
46 **HYPERFOCUS (IRE)**, 6, b br g Intense Focus (USA)—Jouel (FR) **Ryedale Partners No 14**
47 **IWASTHEFUTUREONCE (IRE)**, 7, b g Fruits of Love (USA)—Ruthy Lukey (IRE) **Ryedale Partners No 11**

MR TIM EASTERBY - continued

48 **JEWEL MAKER (IRE)**, 5, b g Invincible Spirit (IRE)—Sapphire (IRE) **Reality Partnerships I**
49 **JUST HISS**, 7, b g Lawman (FR)—Feather Boa (IRE) **The Sandmoor Partnership**
50 **JUST MAGIC**, 4, ch g Sepoy (AUS)—Magic Music (IRE) **R. Bailey**
51 **KITTY'S COVE**, 5, b m High Chaparral (IRE)—Juniper Girl (IRE) **Mickley Stud & Partner**
52 **LADY CALCARIA**, 4, b f Mayson—Ride The Wind **Ontoawinner 10 & Partner**
53 **LADY SCATTERLEY (FR)**, 4, ch f No Nay Never (USA)—Camdara (FR) **Mrs T. Whatley**
54 **LOOK OUT LOUIS**, 4, b g Harbour Watch (IRE)—Perfect Act **Miss Victoria Watt & Partner**
55 **LULU BALOO**, 5, b m Schiaparelli (GER)—Tarabaloo **R. W. Metcalfe**
56 **MAC AILEY**, 4, ch g Firebreak—Rosabee (IRE) **Dubelem (Racing) Limited & Partner**
57 **MELTING (IRE)**, 5, b g Epaulette (AUS)—Ice On Fire **Reality Partnerships IX**
58 **MIDNIGHT MALIBU (IRE)**, 7, b m Poet's Voice—Midnight Martini **Mr D. A. West & Partner**
59 **MIKMAK**, 7, b g Makfi—Rakata (USA) **K J Racing**
60 **MILL RACE KING (IRE)**, 7, b g Scorpion (IRE)—Oso Special **Reality Partnerships IX**
61 **MISCHIEF MANAGED (IRE)**, 6, ch g Tagula (IRE)—Cape Clear **Dubelem (Racing) Limited**
62 **MOUNTAIN HAWK (IRE)**, 8, b g Mountain High (IRE)—Septembers Hawk (IRE) **Mr T. J. Hemmings**
63 **MR CARPENTER (IRE)**, 4, gr ro g Mastercraftsman (IRE)—Satwa Pearl **Mr B Valentine & Partner**
64 **MUKHAYYAM**, 8, b g Dark Angel (IRE)—Caster Sugar (USA) **Mr T. A. Scothern & Partner**
65 **MULTELLIE**, 8, b g Multiplex—Bollin Nellie **Mr David Scott & Partner**
66 **MUSIC SOCIETY (IRE)**, 5, gr g Society Rock (IRE)—Absolutely Cool (IRE) **R. Taylor & Mr P. Hebdon**
67 **MY REWARD**, 8, b g Rail Link—Tarot Card **Mr M. J. Macleod**
68 **NED'S ESCAPE (IRE)**, 5, b g Getaway (GER)—Ned's Joy (IRE) **Mr T. J. Hemmings**
69 **NEILETA**, 4, b g Epaulette (AUS)—Neila (GER) **Mr E. A. Brook & Partner**
70 **OBEE JO (IRE)**, 4, b g Kodiac—Malcha (IRE) **Mrs Joanne Boxcer & Partner**
71 **ORION'S BOW**, 9, ch g Pivotal—Heavenly Ray (USA) **Mr T. J. Swiers**
72 **PARYS MOUNTAIN (IRE)**, 6, gr g Dark Angel (IRE)—Muzdaan (IRE) **Reality Partnerships XII**
73 **PATTAYA**, 4, b f Poet's Voice—Talampaya (USA) **King Power Racing Co Ltd**
74 **PERFECT SWISS**, 4, b g Swiss Spirit—Perfect Practice **Mr Craig Wilson & Partner**
75 **POET'S DAWN**, 5, ch g Poet's Voice—Dudley Queen (IRE) **Mr Timothy O'Gram & Partner**
76 **PUPPETONASTRING**, 5, b m Sixties Icon—Valbuena (IRE) **Habton Farms**
77 **RANDY PIKE (IRE)**, 10, b g Mahler—Niamh's Leader (IRE) **Reality Partnerships II**
78 **REASSURANCE**, 5, b m Champs Elysees—Timely Words **Reality Partnerships VIII**
79 **REETH (IRE)**, 4, b g Kodiac—Tanouma (USA) **Jesmond Racing & Partner**
80 **REGAL MIRAGE (IRE)**, 6, ch g Aqlaam—Alzaroof (USA) **Ryedale Partners No 7**
81 **RELIGHT MY FIRE**, 10, ch g Firebreak—Making Music **J. Gill**
82 **RELKADAM (FR)**, 6, ch g Muhtathir—Gloirez (FR) **Ryedale Partners No 12**
83 **RUX RUXX (IRE)**, 5, b m Dark Angel (IRE)—Lady Duxyana **King Power Racing Co Ltd**
84 **SHERIFF GARRETT (IRE)**, 6, b g Lawman (FR)—Few Are Chosen (IRE) **Ontoawinner 10 & Partner 4**
85 **STAXTON**, 5, b g Equiano (FR)—Snake's Head **Ontoawinner 10 & Partner**
86 **STORM AHEAD (IRE)**, 7, b g Iffraaj—Loose Julie (IRE) **A. R. Turnbull**
87 **SUITCASE 'N' TAXI**, 6, br g Major Cadeaux—Finalize **Ontoawinner 10 & Partner 3**
88 **THE GREY ZEBEDEE**, 4, gr g Zebedee—Nippy (FR) **The Geordie Boys & Partner**
89 **TRAVEL LIGHTLY**, 5, b m Showcasing—Upton Seas **E. A. Brook**
90 **TRUE BLUE MOON (IRE)**, 5, gr g Holy Roman Emperor (IRE)—Fancy Intense **Mr B Valentine & Partner**
91 **UGO GREGORY**, 4, gr g Gregorian (IRE)—Raajis (IRE) **Mr F. Gillespie**
92 **UNCLE NORMAN (FR)**, 4, ch g Havana Gold (IRE)—Holy Moly (USA) **Mr J. R. Saville**
93 **VINTAGE BRUT**, 4, b g Dick Turpin (IRE)—Traditionelle **King Power Racing Co Ltd**
94 **VIVE LA DIFFERENCE (IRE)**, 6, b g Holy Roman Emperor (IRE)—Galaxie Sud (USA) **Ryedale Partners No 5**
95 **WELLS FARHH GO (IRE)**, 5, b h Farhh—Mowazana (IRE) **Mr S A Heley & Partner**

THREE-YEAR-OLDS

96 **AL JAWHRA (IRE)**, b f Holy Roman Emperor (IRE)—Mango Mischief (IRE) **Mr E. A. Al Afoo**
97 **ARAKA LI (IRE)**, b g Havana Gold (IRE)—Stylos Ecossais **Mr H. E. Alromaihi**
98 **ART POWER (IRE)**, gr c Dark Angel (IRE)—Evening Time (IRE) **King Power Racing Co Ltd**
99 **BOLLIN MARGARET**, b f Fountain of Youth (IRE)—Bollin Greta **Mr D B & Mrs C Lamplough & Partner**
100 **BOULEVARD BEAUTY (IRE)**, b f Champs Elysees—Astral Weeks **Reality Partnerships XV**
101 **BRAZEN POINT**, b c Brazen Beau (AUS)—Point of Control **Habton Farms**
102 B g Mazameer (IRE)—Cassique Lady (IRE) **Habton Farms**
103 **CASSY O (IRE)**, b g Camacho—Hawaajib (FR) **R. Taylor & Mr P. Hebdon**
104 **CHAMPAGNE ANGEL (IRE)**, gr f Dark Angel (IRE)—On High **Mr D. A. West & Partner**

MR TIM EASTERBY - continued

105 CHAMPAGNE FOUNTAIN, br f Fountain of Youth (IRE)—Bebe de Cham **Lovely Bubbly Racing**
106 CRESSBROOK, b g Fountain of Youth (IRE)—Penny Garcia **Mr J. F. Bowers**
107 CRUYFF TURN, ch g Dutch Art—Provenance **Aberdeen Park & Partner**
108 DANDY STORY (IRE), b f Dandy Man (IRE)—Storyline (IRE) **Mr Godfrey Horsford & Partner**
109 DANGEROFFIZZ (IRE), ch g Champs Elysees—Tingleo **Gremot Racing**
110 EMERALD SWALK (IRE), gr g Zebedee—Telegraphy (USA) **Mrs Joanne Boxcer & Partner**
111 FARHH TO GO, b g Farhh—Queen Aggie (IRE) **Mr S. A. Heley & Partner**
112 FAST DEAL, ch g Fast Company (IRE)—Maven **Mrs J Pallister & Partner**
113 FISHABLE, b c Dutch Art—Sweet Stream (ITY) **Mr B Guerin & Habton Farms**
114 GRAND PIANOLA, b g Firebreak—Grand Liaison **Mr J. C. Mowat**
115 HARBOUR MIST (IRE), b g Harbour Watch (IRE)—Ittasal **R. Taylor & Mr P. Hebdon**
116 HAYUPLASS, b f Showcasing—Music In Exile (USA) **Mr D B & Mrs C Lamplough & Partner**
117 HERBERT POCKET, b g Helmet (AUS)—Marysienka **Mr F. Gillespie**
118 IVA GO (IRE), b f Ivawood (IRE)—Enliven **Mr B Valentine & Partner**
119 IVA REFLECTION (IRE), b g Ivawood (IRE)—Mirror Image **Mr B Guerin & Habton Farms**
120 JERBOURG, b g Mayson—Tabrina (IRE) **Italia Keogh & Partner**
121 JOE'S WAY, b g Equiano (FR)—Nos Da **Ontoawinner 10 & Partner**
122 KILIG, b g Fountain of Youth (IRE)—Today's The Day **Mr J Ball, Mr A Hodkinson & Mr P Malley**
123 KNIGHTCAP, b f Sir Percy—Mookhlesa **Lovely Bubbly Racing**
124 KRABI, ro f Gutaifan (IRE)—Miskin Diamond **King Power Racing Co Ltd**
125 LAMPANG (IRE), b c Dandy Man (IRE)—Black Mascara (IRE) **King Power Racing Co Ltd**
126 LIBERTY POWER, b c Makfi—Liberty Chery **King Power Racing Co Ltd**
127 LITTLE TED, ch c Cityscape—Speedy Utmost Meg **Mr M. J. Macleod**
128 B g Poet's Voice—Magic Music (IRE) **R. Bailey**
129 MARINA GROVE (IRE), b f Kodiac—Charlie Em **Mr D. W. Armstrong**
130 B g Delegator—Maybeagrey **Reality Partnerships XIV**
131 MORE THAN LOVE, b g Kitten's Joy (USA)—He Loves Me More (USA) **Habton Farms**
132 MUKHTOON (IRE), b g Mukhadram—Umthoulah (IRE) **The Geordie Boys & Partner**
133 NEARLY A GONNA, g Helmet (AUS)—Clodova (IRE) **E. A. Brook**
134 NEW MAN, b g Equiano (FR)—Magic Myth (IRE) **Habton Farms**
135 NOBLE BERTIE (USA), ch g Noble Mission—Oxbow Lake (USA) **Mr J. R. Saville**
136 NODDYOLDER, b g Slade Power (IRE)—Shamardal Phantom (IRE) **Habton Farms**
137 NORTHERN CELT (IRE), b g Gutaifan (IRE)—Scent of Summer (USA) **Reality Partnerships**
138 PHOENIX APPROACH (IRE), b g Dawn Approach (IRE)—Purple Warrior (USA) **Mr Lee Bond & Partner**
139 RED HOT STREAK, b g Hot Streak (IRE)—Perfect Act **J.Joyce, J.H.Lofthouse & Partner**
140 B g Helmet (AUS)—Royal Circles **Habton Farms**
141 RUSALKA (IRE), b f Ivawood (IRE)—Song To The Moon (IRE) **Mr David F Powell & Partner**
142 SAN ROCH (FR), ch g Le Havre (IRE)—Four Green (FR) **Ryedale Partners No 13**
143 B g Mustajeeb—Shemriyna (IRE) **A. Ali**
144 SILVER SNIPER, b g Zebedee—Velvet Kiss (IRE) **David Lumley & Partner**
145 SIR CHARLES PUNCH, b g Sir Percy—Russian Punch **Habton Farms**
146 Ch g Shooting To Win (AUS)—Spirit of Success **Habton Farms**
147 STROXX (IRE), b g Camacho—Labisa (IRE) **Stroxx Partnership**
148 SUSHI POWER (IRE), b f No Nay Never (USA)—Bright And Clear **King Power Racing Co Ltd**
149 TEMPER TRAP, br g Slade Power (IRE)—Sloane Square **Ontoawinner 10 & Partner**
150 TOP BUCK (IRE), ch g Dandy Man (IRE)—Tip It On The Top (IRE) **Habton Farms**
151 TWO SOX, b g Nathaniel (IRE)—Anna Sophia (USA) **Mr D Whittaker & Partner**
152 Gr g Lethal Force (IRE)—Unasuming (IRE) **Habton Farms**
153 VINTAGE TIMES, b f Firebreak—Traditionelle **Ontoawinner 10 & Partner**
154 WADE'S MAGIC, br gr g Lethal Force (IRE)—Millika **Reality Partnerships XVI**
155 WADI AL SALAAM (IRE), b c Outstrip—Candy Banter (USA) **Mr E. A. Al Afoo**
156 WAR DEFENDER, b g War Command (USA)—Never Lose **Ryedale Partners No 15**
157 WILDBEAUTIFULTHING, b f Cityscape—Beautifulwildthing **Mr M. J. Macleod**

TWO-YEAR-OLDS

158 FOSSOS (IRE), b c 17/04 Dandy Man (IRE)—Beguiler (Refuse To Bend (IRE)) (23165) **Fossos**
159 B c 05/04 Dandy Man (IRE)—Lily's Rainbow (IRE) (Intikhab (USA)) (188760) **King Power Racing Co Ltd**
160 MAXIMUM RISK (IRE), b c 22/03 Twilight Son—
Hasty (IRE) (Invincible Spirit (IRE)) (19047) **Abbas Alalawi & Partner**

MR TIM EASTERBY - continued

161 B br c 20/02 Brazen Beau (AUS)—Midnight Fantasy (Oasis Dream) (12380) **Reality Partnerships XVIII**
162 B c 03/04 Pivotal—Musical Beat (IRE) (Acclamation) (40000) **D Scott & Co (Pattern Makers) Ltd & Partner**
163 B f 21/04 Make Believe—Though (IRE) (Dansili) (4000) **Ryedale Partners No 8**
164 B f 16/03 Bungle Inthejungle—Titian Saga (IRE) (Titus Livius (FR)) (77220) **King Power Racing Co Ltd**

Other Owners: Mr A. Alalawi, Mr N. F. Arton, Mr J. Ball, Mr L. Bond, Mrs J. Boxcer, Mr S. Bridge, E. A. Brook, J. Buzzeo, Mr J. Cruces, David Scott & Co (Pattern Makers) Ltd, Mr T. Denham, Dubelem (Racing) Limited, Mr G. Fox, M. A. Gemmell, A. J. Gompertz, Mr J. H. Green, Mrs K. E. Green, Mr B. M. P. R. Guerin, Habton Farms, Mr P. F. Hebdon, S. A. Heley, Mr A. S. Hodkinson, G. Horsford, Mr M. A. S. Hulin, Jesmond Racing, Prof J. Joyce, R. Kent, Miss I. Keogh, Mrs D. Lamplough, D. B. Lamplough, Mr J. H. Lofthouse, Mr David John Lumley, Mr M. J. Macleod, Mr P. Malley, Mr F. McBain, Middleham Park and Ventura Racing 15, Middleham Park and Ventura Racing 6, Mr P. H. Milmo, Mr J. E. Mott, Mrs J. M. Mott, Mr N. J. O'Brien, T. J. O'Gram, Ontoawinner 10, Ontoawinner, SDH Project Services Ltd, Mr W. M. Oxley, T. S. Palin, Mrs J. E. Pallister, D. F. Powell, M. Prince, Mr S. V. Rutter, T. A. Sochern, D. Scott, Mr J. F. Strain, Mr T. J. Strain, Mr E. M. Sutherland, Mr R. Taylor, The Geordie Boys, A. R. Turnbull, Mr B. Valentine, Miss V. Watt, D. A. West, Mr James Westoll, Mr D. J. Whittaker, Mr C. Wilson.

Flat Jockey: Rachel Richardson. **Amateur Jockey:** Mr W. Easterby.

MR BRIAN ECKLEY, Brecon
Postal: Closcedi Farm, Llanspyddid, Brecon, Powys, LD3 8NS
Contacts: PHONE 01874 622422 MOBILE 07891 445409
EMAIL brian.eckley@live.co.uk

1 BEACON FOX, 4, ch g Yorgunnabelucky (USA)—Sunsational Girl **B. J. Eckley**
2 4, B g Yorgunnabelucky (USA)—Classy Crewella **B. J. Eckley**
3 JAUNTY FREYJA, 5, b m Norse Dancer (IRE)—Jaunty Walk **B. J. Eckley**
4 4, B g Yorgunnabelucky (USA)—Jaunty Spirit **B. J. Eckley**
5 JAUNTY VIKING, 5, b g Norse Dancer (IRE)—Jaunty Spirit **B. J. Eckley**
6 LIBERTY BELLA, 6, b m Librettist (USA)—Classy Crewella **B. J. Eckley**
7 TIMEFORADANCE, 5, b g Norse Dancer (IRE)—Timeforagin **B. J. Eckley**
8 4, B g Yorgunnabelucky (USA)—Timeforagin **B. J. Eckley**

MR ROBERT EDDERY, Newmarket
Postal: Robert Eddery Racing Limited, Heyward Place Stables, Hamilton Road, Newmarket, Suffolk, CB8 7JQ
Contacts: PHONE 01638 428001 MOBILE 07938 898455
EMAIL info@robertedderyracing.com WEBSITE www.robbertedderyracing.com

1 COLWOOD, 6, ch g Champs Elysees—La Colline (GER) **Mr R. J. Creese**
2 COUNTRY'N'WESTERN (FR), 8, b g Samum (GER)—Cracking Melody **Mr C. R. Eddery**
3 ELSIE VIOLET (IRE), 4, ch f Gale Force Ten—Kuaicoss (IRE) **Mr S. Phillips**
4 FIERY BREATH, 5, br g Bated Breath—Sunset Kitty (USA) **Mr E. S. Phillips**
5 GEORGE THOMAS, 4, b g Heeraat (IRE)—Lexington Rose **Mr C. R. Eddery**
6 GRACEFUL LADY, 7, b m Sixties Icon—Leitzu (IRE) **Graham & Lynn Knight**
7 NATIVE SILVER, 4, gr g Olympic Glory (IRE)—Kendorova (IRE) **Pamela Aitken & Julia Rayment**
8 SEVENTII, 6, b m Medicean—Lowndes **Mr C. R. Eddery**
9 TIFFINDELL (IRE), 4, ch f Raven's Pass (USA)—Nadia **David Bannon & Robert Eddery**
10 TYNECASTLE PARK, 7, b g Sea The Stars (IRE)—So Silk **Mr C. R. Eddery**

THREE-YEAR-OLDS

11 EEVILYNN DREW, b c Epaulette (AUS)—Halicardia **Graham & Lynn Knight**

TWO-YEAR-OLDS

12 CECCO BRAVO, b c 06/03 Mukhadram—Flora Medici (Sir Percy) (800) **Robert's Rogues**

MR ROBERT EDDERY - continued

13 **CLASSY DAME (IRE)**, b f 28/03 Belardo (IRE)—
               Scholarly (Authorized (IRE)) (6006) **Graham & Lynn Knight, Mr R. J. Creese**
14 **LION FACE (IRE)**, b c 16/02 Animal Kingdom (USA)—Blue Enzian (USA) (Street Cry (IRE)) (9438) **Mr D. Bannon**

Other Owners: Mrs P. Aitken, Mr D. Bannon, Mr C. R. Eddery, Mrs J. M. Rayment.

Flat Jockey: Andrea Atzeni. **Apprentice Jockey:** Selma Grage. **Amateur Jockey:** Mr George Eddery.

---

173 **MR STUART EDMUNDS, Newport Pagnell**
Postal: **6 Fences Farm, Tyringham, Newport Pagnell, Buckinghamshire, MK16 9EN**
Contacts: **PHONE 01908 611369, 01908 611406 MOBILE 07778 782591 FAX 01908 611255**
EMAIL Trishandstu@aol.com

1 **A LITTLE CHAOS (IRE)**, 6, b m Yeats (IRE)—Marias Dream (IRE) **The Garratt Family**
2 **AIRGEAD SUAS (IRE)**, 7, b m Gold Well—Emmas' House (IRE) **The Holryale Partnership**
3 **BLACKFINCH**, 5, ch g Black Sam Bellamy (IRE)—Grassfinch **Exors of the Late Mr P. D. Robeson**
4 **BLUE BIKINI**, 4, b f Winged Love (IRE)—Bleu d'Avril (FR) **Nick Brown Racing**
5 **BRAN**, 5, b g Sakhee (USA)—Cup of Love (USA) **M. Kehoe**
6 **BUILDING BRIDGES**, 4, br c New Approach (IRE)—City On Sea (IRE) **Oaklands Racing & Bloodstock Ltd**
7 **CLASSIC BEN (IRE)**, 7, b g Beneficial—Dark Daisy (IRE) **The Lavendon Partnership**
8 **DEPUTY'S OSCAR (IRE)**, 7, b m Oscar (IRE)—Shesourpresent (IRE) **Horwood Harriers Partnership**
9 **DUNEFINCH**, 4, b g Dunaden (FR)—Grassfinch **Exors of the Late Mr P. D. Robeson**
10 **FIGARELLA BORGET (FR)**, 5, b m Network (GER)—Kashima (FR) **Nick Brown Racing**
11 **GO MILLIE GO (IRE)**, 7, b m Milan—Another Present (IRE) **The Chicheley Partnership**
12 **GOELETTE (FR)**, 4, b f Muhtathir—Tamara (FR) **Oaklands Racing & Bloodstock Ltd**
13 **GRAND LORD (FR)**, 4, gr g Lord du Sud (FR)—Toscane des Fleurs (FR) **Oaklands Racing & Bloodstock Ltd**
14 **HAVANA HERMANO (IRE)**, 6, b g Flemensfirth (USA)—Senorita Rumbalita **The Golf Victor Charlie Syndicate**
15 **HEPIJEU (FR)**, 9, b g Palace Episode (USA)—Helenjeu **Mr D. & Mrs H. Woodhall**
16 **HI HO SILVA LINING (IRE)**, 4, b br g Flemensfirth (USA)—Madame McGoldrick (IRE) **The Ivo Partnership**
17 **HOMETOWN BOY (IRE)**, 5, ch g Curtain Time (IRE)—Mercy Mission **The Garratt Family**
18 **LAND LEAGUE (IRE)**, 9, b g Touch of Land (FR)—Be My Sunset (IRE) **Nick Brown Racing**
19 **MARSH WREN**, 4, b f Schiaparelli (GER)—Carolina Wren **Exors of the Late Mr P. D. Robeson**
20 **MASKADA (FR)**, 4, b f Masked Marvel—Mandina (FR) **M. Kehoe**
21 **MEXICO (GER)**, 4, b g Sea The Moon (GER)—Mexicali (IRE) **Oaklands Racing & Bloodstock Ltd**
22 **MIDNIGHT MARY**, 4, b f Midnight Legend—Epee Celeste (FR) **Mr S A Richards & Louise Kemble**
23 **MISAPS**, 6, b m Schiaparelli (GER)—Fleurette **G. C. Hartigan**
24 **MOLLY CHILDERS (IRE)**, 8, b m Stowaway—Hushaby (IRE) **The Ravenstone Partnership**
25 **MY GIRL LOLLIPOP (IRE)**, 4, b f Mahler—Pop Princess **Mrs N. C. Kappler**
26 **NOW MCGINTY (IRE)**, 9, b g Stowaway—Western Whisper (IRE) **The Garratt Family**
27 **OUR BUBBA (IRE)**, 6, b g Scorpion (IRE)—Lady Marnay (IRE) **The Sharnbrook Partnership**
28 **PINE WARBLER**, 11, b g Pilsudski (IRE)—Cetti's Warbler **Exors of the Late Mr P. D. Robeson**
29 **PULL TOGETHER (IRE)**, 8, b g Curtain Time (IRE)—Whos To Know (IRE) **Oaklands Racing & Bloodstock Ltd**
30 **QUEENOHEARTS (IRE)**, 7, ch m Flemensfirth (USA)—Chars (IRE) **The Sherington Partnership**
31 **RED ROYALIST**, 6, b g Royal Applause—Scarlet Royal **Mrs R. L. Banks**
32 **ROWLAND WARD**, 4, b g Sea The Stars (IRE)—Honor Bound **Oaklands Racing & Bloodstock Ltd**
33 **THECLOCKISTICKING (IRE)**, 8, br g Gamut (IRE)—Curragheen (IRE) **Asphalt Reinforcement Services Ltd**
34 **VELVET VOICE**, 6, b m Azamour (IRE)—Battery Power **Sarabex**
35 **WHO'S THE BOSS (IRE)**, 5, b br m Oscar (IRE)—Final Episode (IRE) **Oaklands Racing & Bloodstock Ltd**
36 **WOLF OF WINDLESHAM (IRE)**, 8, ch g Mastercraftsman (IRE)—Al Amlah (USA) **M. W. Lawrence**
37 **YOUNG OFFENDER (IRE)**, 5, b g Rule of Law (USA)—Cayetina **Oaklands Racing & Bloodstock Ltd**

THREE-YEAR-OLDS

38 **HILLFINCH**, ch f Hillstar—Grassfinch **Exors of the Late Mr P. D. Robeson**

TWO-YEAR-OLDS

39 **SEDGE WREN**, b f 28/04 Blue Bresil (FR)—Carolina Wren (Sir Harry Lewis (USA)) **Exors of the Late Mr P. D. Robeson**
40 **TREEFINCH**, b f 12/04 Telescope (IRE)—Grassfinch (Generous (IRE)) **Exors of the Late Mr P. D. Robeson**

MR STUART EDMUNDS - continued

Other Owners: Ms L. M. Kemble, Mr S. A. Richards, D. M. Woodhall, Mrs H. C. L. Woodhall.

Assistant Trainer: Miss Harriet Edmunds.

---

174 **MR GORDON EDWARDS, Minehead**
Postal: **Summering, Wheddon Cross, Minehead, Somerset, TA24 7AT**
Contacts: **PHONE 01643 831549 MOBILE 07970 059297 FAX 01643 831549**
EMAIL angelaedwards549@gmail.com

1 **IN ARREARS (IRE)**, 8, b m Beneficial—Gullet Dawn (IRE) **G. F. Edwards**
2 **PRINCESS CAVE (IRE)**, 6, b m Court Cave (IRE)—Black Magic Baby (IRE) **G. F. Edwards**
3 **SHANANN STAR (IRE)**, 14, br m Anshan—Baile An Droichid (IRE) **G. F. Edwards**

Amateur Jockey: Mr D. Edwards.

---

175 **MR BRIAN ELLISON, Malton**
Postal: **Spring Cottage Stables, Langton Road, Norton, Malton, North Yorkshire, YO17 9PY**
Contacts: **PHONE 01653 690004 MOBILE 07785 747426 FAX 01653 690008**
EMAIL office@brianellisonracing.co.uk WEBSITE www.brianellisonracing.co.uk

1 **ALGAFFAAL (USA)**, 5, ch g Speightstown (USA)—Rockcide (USA) **Mr Ian & Tom Pallas & Mrs D F Robe**
2 **ANTICO LADY (IRE)**, 4, b f Dandy Man (IRE)—Former Drama (USA) **Julie & Keith Hanson**
3 **BALLYVIC BORU (IRE)**, 8, b g Brian Boru—Thedoublede (IRE) **Mr P J Martin & Partner**
4 **BARAWEEZ (IRE)**, 10, b g Cape Cross (IRE)—Aquarelle Bleue **A. Barnes**
5 **BARON DE MIDLETON (IRE)**, 7, b g Brian Boru—Present Climate (IRE) **Phil & Julie Martin**
6 **BARRYS JACK (IRE)**, 10, b g Well Chosen—Theatre Fool (IRE) **D Gilbert, M Lawrence, A Bruce**
7 **BIG JOE (IRE)**, 6, ch g Mahler—Some Bob Back (IRE) **Mr A. Barnes & C. N. Barnes**
8 **BORDEAUX BILL (IRE)**, 9, b g Craigsteel—Laura Croft (IRE) **Julie & Phil Martin**
9 **BURN SOME DUST (IRE)**, 5, b g Shirocco (GER)—Chilly Filly (IRE) **Mr Dan Gilbert**
10 **CHATEAU MARMONT (IRE)**, 7, b g Flemensfirth (USA)—Sliabh Geal Gcua (IRE) **Phil & Julie Martin**
11 **CONSTANTINE BAY**, 9, b g Kayl Tara—Alina Rheinberg (GER) **D Gilbert, M Lawrence, A Bruce**
12 **CORMIER (IRE)**, 4, b g Born To Sea (IRE)—Scotch Bonnet (IRE) **Mr Kristian Strangeway**
13 **CRACKDELOUST (FR)**, 8, b g Daramsar (FR)—Magic Rose (FR) **Phil & Julie Martin**
14 **DEFINITLY RED (IRE)**, 11, ch g Definite Article—The Red Wench (IRE) **Phil & Julie Martin**
15 **DESERT DAWN**, 4, b g Dawn Approach (IRE)—Camlet **Geoff & Sandra Turnbull**
16 **ELEVEN SEVEN TEN (IRE)**, 4, b g Gale Force Ten—Faanan Aldaar (IRE)
17 **FAIR STAR (IRE)**, 4, b g Sea The Stars (IRE)—Night Fairy (IRE) **D Gilbert, M Lawrence, A Bruce**
18 **FERRY ALL (FR)**, 5, ch g No Risk At All (FR)—Ohe Les Aulmes (FR) **Phil & Julie Martin**
19 **FOREST BIHAN (FR)**, 9, ch g Forestier (FR)—Katell Bihan (FR) **Phil & Julie Martin**
20 **GHADBBAAN**, 4, b g Intello (GER)—Rock Choir **Mr Kristian Strangeway**
21 **HANATI (IRE)**, 4, ch f Camacho—Royal Visit (IRE) **S & S Racing 2 & Partner**
22 **HARRY GEORGE (IRE)**, 6, br g Big Bad Bob (IRE)—Somva of Liberty (IRE) **A. Barnes**
23 **HIGHLAND SKY (IRE)**, 5, b g Camelot—Healing Music (FR) **Mr P. Boyle**
24 **HOOFLEPUFF (IRE)**, 4, b g Gale Force Ten—Hflah (IRE) **Mr Keith Brown**
25 **INSTANT REPLAY (IRE)**, 8, ch g Fruits of Love (USA)—Ding Dong Belle **Phil & Julie Martin**
26 **JUALS SPIRIT (IRE)**, 4, b f Raven's Pass (USA)—Bahama Spirit (IRE) **K & J Hanson & A Dawson**
27 **KEARNEY HILL (IRE)**, 5, b g Dylan Thomas (IRE)—Sunny Glen (IRE) **Julie & Phil Martin**
28 **LARGY MOUTH**, 5, b g Court Cave (IRE)—Leblon (IRE) **Mr D. J. Burke & Mr P Alderson**
29 **LITTLE JO**, 6, b g Major Cadeaux—Discoed **Mr T. Pallas**
30 **LITTLE LEGS**, 4, b f Captain Gerrard (IRE)—Livia Drusilla (IRE) **Brian Ellison Racing Club**
31 **LOPES DANCER (IRE)**, 8, b g Lope de Vega (IRE)—Ballet Dancer (IRE) **W. A. Bethell**
32 **LUCKY ROBIN (IRE)**, 8, ch g Mister Fotis (USA)—Bewilderment (IRE) **Brian Ellison Racing Club**
33 **MAJALAAT (IRE)**, 4, b g New Approach (IRE)—Fawaayed (IRE)
34 **MEDAKI ROC (IRE)**, 4, b g Shirocco (GER)—Sliabh Geal Gcua (IRE) **Mr P. Boyle**
35 **MR WHIPPED (IRE)**, 7, br g Beneficial—Dyrick Daybreak (IRE) **Phil & Julie Martin**

MR BRIAN ELLISON - continued

36 **NIETZSCHE,** 7, ch g Poet's Voice—Ganga (IRE) **D Gilbert, M Lawrence, A. Bruce, G. Wills**
37 **NORTHERN QUEEN (IRE),** 5, gr m Dark Angel (IRE)—
  Queen Bodicea (IRE) **Northern Water Services & Graham Lund**
38 **NORTHGATE LAD (IRE),** 8, gr g Dark Angel (IRE)—Canosa (IRE) **Julie & Phil Martin**
39 **PISTOL PARK (FR),** 9, b g Poliglote—Pistolera (GER) **Brian's Mates**
40 **QUICKLY DOES IT,** 4, b f Havana Gold (IRE)—Mylington Maid **Quickly Group Holdings Limited**
41 **ROBEAM (IRE),** 4, b g Helmet (AUS)—Secret Flame **Brian Ellison Racing Club**
42 **SAM'S ADVENTURE,** 8, b g Black Sam Bellamy (IRE)—My Adventure (IRE) **Julie & Phil Martin**
43 **SEA ME WIN (IRE),** 7, b g Sea The Stars (IRE)—Silk Trail **Miss Leanne Aspery**
44 **SEAMOUR (IRE),** 9, b g Azamour (IRE)—Chifney Rush (IRE) **Phil & Julie Martin**
45 **SHARP SUITED,** 5, b g Dansili—Appearance **D Gilbert, M Lawrence, A Bruce**
46 **SIANNES STAR (IRE),** 7, b g Arakan (USA)—Musical Madam (IRE) **Julie & Phil Martin**
47 **SNOOKERED (IRE),** 6, b g Born To Sea (IRE)—Secret Quest **Brian Ellison Racing Club**
48 **SWEET MARMALADE (IRE),** 5, b m Duke of Marmalade (IRE)—Lady Chaparral **Geoff & Sandra Turnbull**
49 **THE DANCING POET,** 4, ch g Poet's Voice—Caldy Dancer **Spring Cottage Syndicate**
50 **THE KING OF MAY (FR),** 6, b g High Rock (IRE)—Waltzing (IRE) **Phil & Julie Martin**
51 **THE MACKEM TORPEDO,** 4, b g Multiplex—Gagajulu **Mrs C. L. Ellison**
52 **TUPELO MISSISSIPPI (IRE),** 5, b g Yeats (IRE)—Misleain (IRE) **Phil & Julie Martin**
53 **URBAN LEGEND (IRE),** 6, b g Pasternak—Da Das Delight (IRE) **Mr P Boyle & Mr Brian Ellison**
54 **VICTORIANO (IRE),** 4, b g Teofilo (IRE)—Victorian Beauty (USA) **Mr Brian Ellison**
55 **WEAKFIELD (IRE),** 7, b g Court Cave (IRE)—Thats The Lot (IRE) **Phil & Julie Martin**
56 **WHISKEY AND WATER,** 4, b g Harbour Watch (IRE)—Bahamamia **D Gilbert, M Lawrence, A Bruce**
57 **WINDSOR AVENUE (IRE),** 8, b g Winged Love (IRE)—Zaffarella (IRE) **Phil & Julie Martin**

THREE-YEAR-OLDS

58 B g Nathaniel (IRE)—Bridle Belle **D Gilbert, M Lawrence, A Bruce**
59 **DAWN LANDING (IRE),** ch f Dawn Approach (IRE)—Landiora (FR) **Mr P. Boyle**
60 **EL JEFE (IRE),** b g Born To Sea (IRE)—Ros Mountain (IRE) **Mr Kristian Strangeway**
61 **FAST TRACK FLYER (IRE),** b f Free Eagle (IRE)—Chanter **Quickly Group Holdings Ltd & Partner**
62 **GRANDMA,** b f Mayson—Livia Drusilla (IRE) **Brian Ellison Racing Club**
63 **GREEN BOOK (FR),** b g Authorized (IRE)—Mantissa **Mr Kristian Strangeway**
64 **KATSONIS (IRE),** b g Ivawood (IRE)—Livadiya (IRE) **S & S Racing & Partner**
65 **MINI CHEDDA (IRE),** b g Camacho—Tizzy Lizzy (IRE)
66 **NORTHERN GRACE,** ch f Helmet (AUS)—Amelia Grace (IRE) **Northern Water Services & Brian Ellison**
67 B f Hallowed Crown (AUS)—Oasis Fire (IRE) **Mr Keith Brown**
68 **PADDY ELLIOTT (IRE),** b g French Navy—Siphon Melody (USA) **Mr E. Elliott**
69 **PALLAS DANCER (IRE),** b g War Command—Dance Card **Spring Cottage Syndicate 3**
70 **PUERTO SOL (IRE),** b g Camacho—Reina de Luz (IRE) **Mr Keith Brown**
71 **PUNXSUTAWNEY PHIL (IRE),** b g Shirocco (GER)—Chilly Filly (IRE) **Mr Dan Gilbert**
72 **RECLAIM VICTORY (IRE),** b f Helmet (AUS)—Doctor's Note **Quickly Group Holdings Ltd & Partner**
73 **STONE PRINCESS (IRE),** gr f Camacho—Stone Roses (IRE) **S & S Racing & Partner**
74 **THE MACKEM MISSILE (IRE),** ch f Society Rock (IRE)—Southern Barfly (USA) **Mrs C. L. Ellison**
75 **THE MACKEM ROCKET,** ch f Dandy Man (IRE)—Alice Girl (IRE) **Mrs C. L. Ellison**
76 **TYCHE,** b f Due Diligence (USA)—Szabo's Art **Spring Cottage Syndicate 3**
77 **VERY UNDECIDED (IRE),** b f Anjaal—Pescia (IRE)

TWO-YEAR-OLDS

78 **JIGS PRINCESS,** ch f 05/03 Mukhadram—
  Anna's Vision (IRE) (Invincible Spirit (IRE)) (7619) **Hughes Bros Construction LTD**
79 B f 17/03 Fast Company (IRE)—Mirabile Dictu (IRE) (King's Best (USA)) (28571) **Geoff & Sandra Turnbull**
80 **ANNIE FROM NAAS (IRE),** b f 27/03 Anjaal—Fitrah (IRE) **Mr Keith Brown**
81 B c 26/04 Exceed And Excel (AUS)—Perfect Fun (Marju (IRE)) (21450) **Mr T. Alderson**
82 **TANTASTIC,** b c 22/01 Mayson—Love Island (Acclamation) (20952) **Spring Cottage Syndicate 2**
83 **THE MOUSEN CHAMP,** b c 27/02 Buratino (IRE)—Show Willing (IRE) (Sir Prancealot (IRE)) (7619) **Spring Cottage Syndicate 2**
84 **TIBERIUS AUGUSTUS,** b c 14/03 Adaay (IRE)—
  Livia Drusilla (IRE) (Holy Roman Emperor (IRE)) **Brian Ellison Racing Club**
85 **TOMMY TITTLEMOUSE (IRE),** b c 13/04 Sir Prancealot (IRE)—
  French Doll (IRE) (Titus Livius (FR)) (20592) **Mrs L. Pallas**

MR BRIAN ELLISON - continued

Other Owners: P. S. Alderson, A. Barnes, C. N. Barnes, Mr P. Boyle, Mr P Boyle & Mr Brian Ellison, Mr A. Bruce, Mr D. J. Burke, Mr A. Dawson, Mr Brian Ellison, Mrs C. L. Ellison, Mr Dan Gilbert, Mrs J. Hanson, Mr K. Hanson, Mr S. T. Hoare, Mr M. Lawrence, Mr G. Lund, Mr N. P. Lyons, Mrs J. A. Martin, Mr P. J. Martin, Northern Water Services Limited, Quickly Group Holdings Limited, S and S Racing 2, Mr R. J. T. Smillie, Mr P. M. Stacey, Mr G. Wills.

Assistant Trainer: Jessica Bell.

Flat Jockey: Ben Robinson, Kieran Schofield. **NH Jockey:** Henry Brooke, Danny Cook, Brian Hughes, Sean Quinlan. **Apprentice Jockey:** Harry Russell.

---

176 MR DAVID ELSWORTH, Newmarket
Postal: Kings Yard, Egerton House Stables, Cambridge Road, Newmarket, Suffolk, CB8 0TH
Contacts: **PHONE 01638 665511 MOBILE 07540 750424 FAX 01638 665310**
EMAIL office@drcelsworth.com

1 **BRANCASTER (IRE)**, 6, ch g Casamento (IRE)—Makheelah **Mr D. R. C. Elsworth**
2 **DASH OF SPICE (IRE)**, 6, ch g Teofilio—Dashiba **J. C. Smith**
3 **DESERT SKYLINE (IRE)**, 6, ch g Tamayuz—Diamond Tango **C Benham/ D Whitford/ L Quinn/ K Quinn**
4 **ENTANGLING (IRE)**, 6, b g Fastnet Rock (AUS)—Question Times **Mr B. C. M. Wong**
5 **LADY DANCEALOT (IRE)**, 5, b m Sir Prancealot (IRE)—Mayorstone (IRE) **K. J. Quinn**
6 **MAKE HASTE SLOWLY**, 5, ch g Medicean—Skara Brae **Mr D. R. C. Elsworth**
7 **MASTER THE WORLD (IRE)**, 9, gr g Mastercraftsman (IRE)—Zadalla **K. Quinn/ C. Benham**
8 **NO NONSENSE**, 4, b f Cadeaux Genereux—Gift Of Music **J. C. Smith**
9 **RIPP ORF (IRE)**, 6, b g Rip Van Winkle—Barzah **C Benham/ D Whitford/ L Quinn/ K Quinn**
10 **SIR DANCEALOT (IRE)**, 6, b g Sir Prancealot (IRE)—
Majesty's Dancer (IRE) **C Benham/ D Whitford/ L Quinn/ K Quinn**
11 **WAIT FOR THE LORD**, 4, br f Bated Breath—Miss Moses **G. B. Partnership**

THREE-YEAR-OLDS
12 **BLUE SKYLINE (IRE)**, ch g Footstepsinthesand—Ballerina Blue **C Benham/ D Whitford/ L Quinn/ K Quinn**
13 **DOGGED**, b c Due Diligence (USA)—Bling Bling (IRE) **David Elsworth & Michael Elliott**
14 **END RESULT**, b f Nathaniel (IRE)—Daniella **B. A. Cooper**
15 **GLENCORA (IRE)**, b f Gleneagles (IRE)—Eleanora Duse (IRE) **B. A. Cooper**
16 **NORTH POINT**, b g Norse Dancer (IRE)—Cascades (IRE) **J. C. Smith**
17 **O'REILLY'S PASS**, b g Australia—Dynaglow (USA)
18 **OZGOOD (IRE)**, b c Australia—Anna Karenina (USA) **C Benham/ D Whitford/ L Quinn/ K Quinn**
19 **PRECISELY**, b f Al Kazeem—Easter Diva (IRE) **C Benham/ D Whitford/ L Quinn/ K Quinn**
20 **RED SHELLEY**, b f Sir Percy—Rouge Dancer **Mrs A Coughlan & Mr D Elsworth**
21 **ROMAN MELODY**, b g Holy Roman Emperor—Gift of Music (IRE) **J. C. Smith**
22 **STARSHIBA**, b c Acclamation—Dashiba **J. C. Smith**
23 **THANK YOU POWER (IRE)**, b c Camelot—Fraulein **King Power Racing Co Ltd**
24 **THE TURPINATOR (IRE)**, b c Canford Cliffs (IRE)—Bessichka **Mr J. D. Manley**
25 **TOM COLLINS**, br c Dubawi (IRE)—Cocktail Queen (IRE) **J. C. Smith**
26 **TRECCO BAY**, b f New Approach (IRE)—Porthcawl **Ten Green Bottles & Elsworth**

Other Owners: Mr J. Adams, Mr C. F. Benham, Mrs A. M. Coughlan, Mr M. D. Elliott, Mr D. R. C. Elsworth, G. B. Partnership, Mr A. M. H. Heald, M. G. H. Heald, K. J. Quinn, Mr L. M. Quinn, K. Quinn/ C. Benham, Ten Green Bottles Racing, Mr D. L. Whitford.

Amateur Jockey: Mr George Eddery.

177 **MISS SARA ENDER, Malton**
Postal: **Swallows Barn, East Heslerton, Malton, North Yorkshire, YO17 8RN**
Contacts: **MOBILE 07983 462314**
EMAIL **seeequineservices@hotmail.com** WEBSITE **www.nevilleender.wix.com/enderracing**

1 **DURLINGTON (FR)**, 7, ch g Montmartre (FR)—Dalyonne (FR) **Mr I. Ender**
2 **EVISCERATING (IRE)**, 8, gr g Court Cave (IRE)—Titanic Quarter (IRE) **Mr N. P. Ender**
3 **MOORLANDS MIST**, 13, gr g Fair Mix (IRE)—Sandford Springs (USA) **Mr N. P. Ender**
4 **MURCHISON RIVER**, 6, b g Medicean—Free Offer **Mr N. P. Ender**
5 **NORTHANDSOUTH (IRE)**, 10, ch g Spadoun (FR)—Ennel Lady (IRE) **Mr N. P. Ender**
6 **STONEFORD (IRE)**, 9, b g Beneficial—Hester Hall (IRE) **Mr N. P. Ender**
7 **SUNSTORM**, 5, ch g Medicean—Crimson Cloud **Mr N. P. Ender**
8 **WELLS GOLD (IRE)**, 9, b g Gold Well—Exit Baby (IRE) **Mr I. Ender**
9 **WHEREWOULDUGETIT (IRE)**, 6, b g Morozov (USA)—Matinee Show (IRE) **Mr N. P. Ender**

Assistant Trainer: Mr Neville Ender.

178 **MRS SAM ENGLAND, Guiseley**
Postal: **Brentwood, Manor Farm, Guiseley, Leeds, West Yorkshire, LS20 8EW**
Contacts: **MOBILE 07921 003155**

1 **ASK PADDY (IRE)**, 8, ch g Ask—Dalzenia (FR) **Mr J. E. Mott, Mr J. H. Green**
2 **BILLY RAY**, 5, b g Sixties Icon—Fiumicino
3 **BORODIN (IRE)**, 5, b g High Chaparral (IRE)—Songbird (IRE)
4 **CYBALKO (FR)**, 7, b g Balko (FR)—Cybertina (FR) **The Atkin Partnership**
5 **GATACRE STREET**, 8, b g Lucarno (USA)—Sherry Darling (IRE) **Worcester Racing Club**
6 **GOING MOBILE (IRE)**, 5, b g Arcano (IRE)—Next To The Top **Cragg Wood Racing**
7 **HONOURMISSION (FR)**, 6, b g Linda's Lad—Orabelle (FR) **Crowd Racing & Sam England**
8 **KING'S COINAGE (IRE)**, 6, b g Holy Roman Emperor (IRE)—Seducing (IRE) **Cragg Wood Racing**
9 **MAMOO**, 7, ch g Sir Percy—Meredith **Nmus**
10 **MANWELL (IRE)**, 10, b g Gold Well—Roborette (FR) **Sam England Racing Club**
11 **OKSANA**, 7, b m Midnight Legend—La Harde (FR) **Sam England Racing Club**
12 **PEACE APPROVED (IRE)**, 5, ch m Approve (IRE)—Over Rating
13 **RAASHDY (IRE)**, 7, b g Intikhab (USA)—Maghya (USA) **R. Naylor**
14 **RUKWA (FR)**, 6, b g Soldier Hollow—So Oder So (FR) **John Birtles, Gary Ellis , Gary Smith**
15 **TARA MILL (IRE)**, 7, b g Kalanisi (IRE)—Eileens Dream (IRE) **Simon & Angela Gillie**
16 **WELL SMITTEN (IRE)**, 8, b g Gold Well—The Dark One (IRE)
17 **WISHFULL DREAMING**, 9, ch g Alflora (IRE)—Poussetiere Deux (FR) **Mr J C England and Valerie Beattie**

Other Owners: Mr M. V. Atkinson, Mrs V. A. Beattie, Mr J. Birtles, Bonnet de Douche, Mrs J. E. Drake, Mr R. Drye, Mr G. Ellis, Mr J. C. England, Mrs S. A. England, Ms S. Fawcett, Mr G. Fox, Mrs A. Gillie, Mr S. P. Gillie, Gremot Racing 2, Mrs J. Holgate, Dr K. Howard, Mrs P. Howard, Mr C. McKenna, Mr G. Smith, The Flat Cappers, The Sandmoor Partnership 2, Miss H. Webster.

179 **MR JAMES EUSTACE, Newmarket**
Postal: **Park Lodge Stables, Park Lane, Newmarket, Suffolk, CB8 8AX**
Contacts: **PHONE 01638 664277 MOBILE 07802 243764 FAX 01638 664156**
EMAIL **jameseustace@tiscali.co.uk** WEBSITE **www.jameseustace.com**

1 **COVERHAM (IRE)**, 6, b g Bated Breath—Mark Too (IRE) **Blue Peter Racing 15**
2 **DIRECTORY**, 5, b g Oasis Dream—Minority **Blue Peter Racing 16**
3 **ENVOY**, 6, gr g Delegator—La Gessa **Mrs G. R. Eustace**
4 **GLENDUN (USA)**, 6, b g First Defence (USA)—La Mina (USA) **The MacDougall Two**
5 **HIGHFALUTING (IRE)**, 6, b g High Chaparral (IRE)—Walk On Water **Mr D. H. Batten**
6 **MENDOZA (IRE)**, 4, ch g Zebedee—Strange Magic (IRE) **The MacDougall Two**
7 **NEXT TRAIN'S GONE**, 7, b g Rail Link—Coh Sho No **Mr Harold Nass**
8 **PERIPHERIQUE**, 4, ch f Champs Elysees—Somersault **Rushby, Barma, Carstairs**

MR JAMES EUSTACE - continued

9 POSTIE, 4, b f Medicean—Postage Stampe **Mr Andrew McGladdery & Mrs James Eustace**
10 POTENZA (IRE), 4, b g Born To Sea (IRE)—Cranky Spanky (IRE) **The MacDougall Two**
11 REASONED (IRE), 4, ch f Intello (GER)—Do The Honours (IRE) **Park Lodge Racing**
12 SEE THE CITY (IRE), 6, b g Lawman (FR)—Cedar Sea (IRE) **The MacDougall Two**
13 SIBLE HEDINGHAM, 4, ch f Rip Van Winkle (IRE)—Emily Blake (IRE) **Mr & Mrs R Scott & Mrs James Eustace**
14 WITH CAUTION (IRE), 4, ch f Dandy Man (IRE)—Kitty Softpaws (IRE) **Harold Nass & David Ballheimer**

THREE-YEAR-OLDS

15 AMSBY, b g Sir Percy—Astrodiva **Judi Dench, Bryan Agar & Mystic Meg Ltd.**
16 ASTROGEM, b f Equiano (FR)—Astromancer (USA) **Mystic Meg Limited**
17 ASTROMAN, b c Garswood—Mega (IRE) **Mystic Meg Limited**
18 BLUE CABLE, b f Cable Bay (IRE)—Bahama Blue **J. C. Smith**
19 BREAK COVER, ch g Casamento (IRE)—Brushing **Sarabex**
20 FORT NELSON, b g Mount Nelson—Iron Butterfly **Mr. Harold Nass & Partner**
21 PEARLY REDD, b f Heeraat (IRE)—Lady O Malley (IRE) **Sherin & Rod Lloyd**
22 PILLARS OF EARTH, b g Nathaniel (IRE)—Aliena (IRE) **Four Winds Racing & Mr. S. Agodino**
23 TOPANTICIPATION, b f Mount Nelson—Topatoo **Mr M. P. Bowring & Mr R. Smith**
24 WINDY COVE, b f Lawman (FR)—Gale Green **Major M. G. Wyatt**

TWO-YEAR-OLDS

25 B c 20/02 Bated Breath—Azure Mist (Bahamian Bounty) **Mr David Noblett**
26 B c 16/03 Sixties Icon—Brushing (Medicean) **Sarabex**
27 GOOD COP, ch g 12/04 Helmet—Speed Cop (Cadeaux Genereux) **J. C. Smith**
28 HARSTON, b f 30/01 Harzand (IRE)—Time Crystal (IRE) (Sadler's Wells (USA)) **Major M. G. Wyatt**
29 NORDIC DASH, b c 24/03 Norse Dancer—Dashiba (Dashing Blade) **J. C. Smith**

Other Owners: Mr R. P. Abel, B. R. Agar, Mr S. Agodino, Mr D. F. Ballheimer, T. H. Barma, Mr G. N. Carstairs, Mrs B. J. Carter, C. Z. Curtis, Dame J. O. Dench, Mrs G. R. Eustace, Four Winds Racing Partnership, Mr A. C. Frost, Mrs J. A. Gibson, Mr S. J. Gibson, R. E. Lloyd, Mrs S. A. Lloyd, Mr A. J. McGladdery, Mrs E. A. Mear, Mr R. J. Mear, Mystic Meg Limited, H. D. Nass, Mr I. L. Rushby, Mrs P. M. Scott, Mr & Mrs R. Scott, R. Scott, Mrs K. J. Smith, Mr R. J. Uzupris.

---

180   **MR DAVID EVANS, Abergavenny**
Postal: **Ty Derlwyn Farm, Pandy, Abergavenny, Monmouthshire, NP7 8DR**
Contacts: **PHONE 07834 834775, 01873 890837 MOBILE 07860 668499 FAX 01873 890837**
EMAIL pdevansracing@btinternet.com WEBSITE www.pdevansracing.co.uk

1 AMOR FATI (IRE), 5, b g Zoffany (IRE)—Roman Love (IRE) **Mrs I. M. Folkes**
2 ATLETICO (IRE), 8, b g Kodiac—Queenofthefairies **Mr K McCabe & Mr P D Evans**
3 BOND ANGEL, 5, gr m Monsieur Bond (IRE)—Angel Grigio **M. W. Lawrence**
4 BROCKEY RISE (IRE), 5, ch g Zebedee—Age of Diplomacy **John Abbey & Emma Evans**
5 DERRY BOY, 4, b g Havana Gold (IRE)—Steppe By Steppe **Lynn Cullimore & Partner**
6 DISRUPTOR (FR), 4, ch g Siyouni (FR)—Ultradargent (FR) **Dave & Emma Evans**
7 ELEGANT LOVE, 4, b f Delegator—Lovellian **H. M. W. Clifford**
8 ESSENAITCH (IRE), 7, b g Zoffany (IRE)—Karlisse (IRE) **Spiers & Hartwell Ltd & Mrs E. Evans**
9 FIVEHUNDREDMILES (IRE), 7, b g The Carbon Unit (USA)—There's A Light (IRE) **Dave & Emma Evans**
10 HERM (IRE), 6, b g Bushranger (IRE)—School Holidays (USA) **T. H. Gallienne**
11 J'OUVERT (IRE), 4, b f Dawn Approach (IRE)—Areyaam (USA) **Mr S. W. Banks**
12 KASHID (USA), 5, b g Elusive Quality (USA)—Fiesta Lady (ARG) **Dave & Emma Evans**
13 KODILINE (IRE), 6, b g Kodiac—Kris Spring **Mr K. McCabe**
14 LIHOU, 4, ch g Mayson—Kodiac Island **T. H. Gallienne**
15 MEMORY HILL (IRE), 4, gr g Zebedee—Munaasaba (IRE) **Mrs I. M. Folkes**
16 MR TOP HAT, 5, b g Helmet (AUS)—Tut (IRE) **Mr B McCabe & Mrs E Evans**
17 PIKE CORNER CROSS (IRE), 8, b g Cape Cross—Smart Coco (USA) **John Abbey & Emma Evans**
18 SCOFFLAW, 6, b g Foxwedge (AUS)—Belle des Airs (IRE) **John Abbey & Emma Evans**
19 SEA FOX (IRE), 6, b g Kodiac—City Maiden (USA) **Eric Griffiths & P D Evans**
20 4, B f Heeraat (IRE)—Shallow Ground (IRE) **Mr R Kent & Mr D Mossop**
21 SMOKEY LANE (IRE), 6, ch g Zebedee—Masela (IRE) **Mrs E. Evans**

MR DAVID EVANS - continued

22 **SNOW OCEAN (IRE)**, 4, b g Exceed And Excel (AUS)—Callistan (IRE) **Shropshire Wolves 3**
23 **SUNSHINEANDBUBBLES**, 7, b m Multiplex—Dockside Strike **Amazing Racing**
24 **THE GROOVE**, 7, b g Azamour (IRE)—Dance East **Mr Stuart Morgan & Partner**
25 **TWPSYN (IRE)**, 4, b g Es Que Love (IRE)—Gold Blended (IRE) **Rob Emmanuelle, T Burns & P D Evans**

THREE-YEAR-OLDS

26 **A GO GO**, b f Heeraat (IRE)—Gagajulu **R. Kent**
27 **BARKING MAD**, b g Due Diligence (USA)—Jules (IRE) **Spiers & Hartwell Ltd & Mrs E. Evans**
28 **BIG BORIS (IRE)**, b g Baltic King—Cayambe (IRE) **Mrs E. Evans, P. D. Evans, Dave & Emma Evans**
29 **DARK OPTIMIST (IRE)**, b g Alhebayeb (IRE)—Luvmedo (IRE) **The United Optimists**
30 **HEER WE GO AGAIN**, b c Heeraat (IRE)—Madam Mojito (USA) **Power Geneva Ltd & Partner**
31 **ISOBAR WIND (IRE)**, b g Baltic King—Zeeoneandonly (IRE) **Mr E. R. Griffiths**
32 **LETS GO LUCKY**, ch f Yorgunnabelucky (USA)—Reset City **R. S. Brookhouse**
33 **LILI WEN FACH (IRE)**, gr f Gregorian (IRE)—Zuzinia (IRE) **Rob Emmanuelle, Lynn Cullimore & Partner**
34 **MABRE (IRE)**, gr c Make Believe—Slope **Mr P. G. Molony**
35 **MARBLE BAY (IRE)**, gr f Toronado (IRE)—Indian Dumaani **T. H. Gallienne**
36 **MICROSCOPIC (IRE)**, br f Intense Focus (USA)—Royal Esteem **Mrs I. M. Folkes**
37 **MR KODI (IRE)**, b g Kodiac—Khaimah **D. E. Edwards**
38 B f Dandy Man (IRE)—Tartufo Dolce (IRE) **Dave & Emma Evans**
39 **THE CHEROKEE KID (IRE)**, ch g Anjaal—Hazardous **Mrs I. M. Folkes**
40 **WHERE NEXT JO**, gr f Lethal Force (IRE)—Almunia (IRE) **Ne-Chance**
41 **ZULU ZANDER (IRE)**, b g Bungle Inthejungle—Fig Digliani (IRE) **Mr John Wilcox & P D Evans**

TWO-YEAR-OLDS

42 B c 05/03 Kodi Bear (IRE)—By The Edge (IRE) (Shinko Forest (IRE)) **H. M. W. Clifford**
43 Ch c 30/04 Dandy Man (IRE)—Dangerous Duo (IRE) (Intikhab (USA)) (17160) **Mr K. McCabe**
44 B f 01/04 Kodi Bear (IRE)—Englishwoman (Acclamation) (6476) **Dave & Emma Evans**
45 B c 09/04 Mayson—Fenella Rose (Compton Place) (9000) **T. H. Gallienne**
46 Gr c 11/04 Estidhkaar (IRE)—Karlinha (IRE) (Desert Style) (8580) **Mr K. McCabe**
47 **LADY ROSETA (IRE)**, b f 16/03 Dragon Pulse (IRE)—Dreamaway (IRE) (Oasis Dream) (18017) **Mr S. W. Banks**
48 B f 16/04 Coulsty (IRE)—Lady Spangles (IRE) (Starspangledbanner (AUS)) (3431)
49 B c 06/03 Clodovil (IRE)—Leading Actress (IRE) (Makfi) (27455) **Mr K. McCabe**
50 Bl ro f 16/04 Lethal Force (IRE)—Mylaporyours (IRE) (Jeremy (USA)) (4761)
51 B c 28/04 Dandy Man (IRE)—Platinum Darling (IRE) (Iffraaj) (2574)
52 B f 12/03 Dragon Pulse (IRE)—Red Savina (Exceed And Excel (AUS)) (1715) **Mr A. L. Al Zeer**
53 B f 20/03 Clodovil (IRE)—Rockahoolababy (IRE) (Kalanisi (IRE)) (2574) **Mr E. R. Griffiths**
54 B c 27/03 Prince of Lir (IRE)—Sapphire Lake (IRE) (Dandy Man (IRE)) (5148) **Mr E. R. Griffiths**
55 B f 28/04 Vadamos (FR)—Victoria Lodge (IRE) (Grand Lodge (USA)) (3432)

Other Owners: Mrs E. Evans, P.D. Evans, R. Kent, D. Mossop.

Assistant Trainer: Emma Evans.

Apprentice Jockey: Cameron Iles, Laura Pearson.

---

181 **MR JAMES EVANS**, Worcester
Postal: **Stone Farm, Broadwas, Worcester, Worcestershire, WR6 5NE**
Contacts: MOBILE **07813 166430**
EMAIL **herbie_evans@hotmail.com** WEBSITE **www.hjamesevans.co.uk**

1 **COMPADRE (IRE)**, 9, b g Yeats (IRE)—Jolivia (FR) **Mr B. W. Preece**
2 **CONNETABLE (FR)**, 8, b g Saint des Saints (FR)—Montbresia (FR) **Elegant Clutter & Mr S D Faiers**
3 **CROESO CYMRAEG**, 6, b g Dick Turpin (IRE)—Croeso Cusan **Richard Evans Bloodstock**
4 **FRENCH DE GUYE (FR)**, 5, gr g Lord du Sud (FR)—Kasibelle de Guye (FR) **Elegant Clutter & Mr S D Faiers**
5 **FRIENDSHIP BAY**, 16, b g Midnight Legend—Friendly Fairy **Mrs J. Evans**
6 **GALACTIC SPIRIT**, 5, ch g Dutch Art—Gino's Spirits **Mr B. W. Preece**
7 6, B m Passing Glance—Highlight Girl **Mr T. P. Hitchman**
8 **KENTUCKY KINGDOM (IRE)**, 4, b g Camacho—Venetian Rhapsody (IRE) **The Cheltenham Flyers**

MR JAMES EVANS - continued

9 **LORD GETAWAY (IRE)**, 8, b g Getaway (GER)—Terre d'Orient (FR) **Mr B. W. Preece**
10 **MALINDI BAY (FR)**, 7, b m Malinas (GER)—La Grande Villez (FR) **Mr S. D. Faiers**
11 **MOSSING**, 8, b m Passing Glance—Missy Moscow (IRE) **James Evans Racing & the Gmw Syndicate**
12 **NOBEL LEADER (IRE)**, 10, b g Afllora (IRE)—Ben Roseler (IRE) **Mr S. D. Faiers**
13 **OPTIMISTIC BIAS (IRE)**, 11, b g Sayarshan (FR)—Dashers Folly (IRE) **Elegant Clutter Ltd**
14 **PRINCE OF STEAL (IRE)**, 10, b g Craigsteel—Princess Gloria (IRE) **The Cheltenham Flyers**
15 **SANDS COVE (IRE)**, 13, b g Flemensfirth (USA)—Lillies Bordello (IRE) **James Evans & The Harlequins Racing**
16 **SHARAINA**, 6, b m Yorgunnabelucky (USA)—Sharbasia (IRE) **Mrs J. Evans**

Other Owners: Elegant Clutter Ltd, Mr H. J. Evans, Mrs J. Evans, Mr S. D. Faiers, Mr N. Goodger, Mr A. J. Pidgeon, Mr P. M. Smith, The GMW Syndicate, The Harlequins Racing.

Assistant Trainer: Mrs Jane Evans.

NH Jockey: Liam Treadwell. **Amateur Jockey:** Miss Emma Yardley.

---

182 MRS MARY EVANS, Haverfordwest
Postal: Hengoed, Clabeston Road, Haverfordwest, Dyfed, SA63 4QL
Contacts: **PHONE** 01437 731336

1 **ADIMELO (FR)**, 10, b br g Honolulu (IRE)—Meliflo (FR) **Mary & Billy Evans**
2 **HOLD COURT (IRE)**, 13, br g Court Cave (IRE)—Tipsy Miss (IRE) **Mary & Billy Evans**
3 **SHREWD TACTICS (IRE)**, 9, ch g Broadway Flyer (USA)—Taking My Time (IRE) **W. J. Evans**

Other Owners: Mrs M. Evans, W. J. Evans.

Assistant Trainer: W J Evans.

---

183 MRS NIKKI EVANS, Abergavenny
Postal: Penbiddle Farm, Penbidwal, Pandy, Abergavenny, Gwent, NP7 8EA
Contacts: **PHONE** 01873 890957 **MOBILE** 07977 753437
EMAIL penbiddleracing@gmail.com **WEBSITE** www.nikkievansracing.co.uk

1 **AGREEMENT (IRE)**, 10, b g Galileo (IRE)—Cozzene's Angel (USA) **Mrs N. S. Evans**
2 **AHEAD OF SCHEDULE (IRE)**, 5, ch g Shirocco (GER)—Colleen Bawn (FR) **Mr R. Singh**
3 **ALMONTASER (FR)**, 6, ch g Manduro (GER)—Mamitador **Melissa Barlow Nikki Evans**
4 **ATLANTIC SUNSHINE**, 5, b m Fight Club (GER)—Atlantic Lady (GER) **Nikki Evans Racing**
5 **CARNAGE**, 5, b g Holy Roman Emperor (IRE)—Sylvestris (IRE) **Mr J. Berry**
6 **CONNEMARA LASS (IRE)**, 7, b m Darsi (FR)—One Forward (IRE) **Jamie Knight Nikki Evans**
7 **CRIMSON PRINCESS**, 5, ch m Sayif (IRE)—Crimson Queen **Mr A. T. L. Clayton**
8 **JACKBLACK**, 8, b g Crosspeace (IRE)—Saharan Royal **Mrs N. S. Evans**
9 **JUKEBOX JUNIOR**, 4, gr g Jukebox Jury (IRE)—Street Fire (IRE) **Mrs M. E. Gittings-Watts**
10 **LATE SHIPMENT**, 9, b g Authorized (IRE)—Time Over **Mrs M. E. Gittings-Watts**
11 **MAROC**, 7, b g Rock of Gibraltar (IRE)—Zietory **Jamie Knight Melissa Barlow**
12 **MORE THAN LIKELY**, 4, b f Coach House (IRE)—Moss Likely (IRE) **Mr A. T. L. Clayton**
13 **SKYLARK LADY (IRE)**, 7, ch m Tamayuz—Allegrissimo (IRE) **Mrs M. E. Gittings-Watts**
14 **SUE BE IT (IRE)**, 9, b m Presenting—Runaround Sue (IRE) **Hanford's Chemist Ltd**
15 **TAKBEER (IRE)**, 8, b g Aqlaam—Precious Secret (IRE) **Mrs M. E. Gittings-Watts**
16 **TIME FOR CHAMPERS (IRE)**, 10, b m Robin des Champs (FR)—Someone Told Me (IRE) **Hanford's Chemist Ltd**
17 **TURNBURY**, 9, b g Azamour (IRE)—Scottish Heights (IRE) **Severn Bridge Racing**
18 **WATCHMAN (IRE)**, 6, b g Oasis Dream—Caphene **Tip of the Sword Racing**

THREE-YEAR-OLDS

19 **GIRL OF DREAMS**, b f Heeraat (IRE)—Princess of Rock **Tip of the Sword Racing**

Other Owners: Miss M. Barlow, Mrs L. Bodman, Mrs N. S. Evans, P. T. Evans, Mr M. Huntington, Mr J. Knight.

Assistant Trainer: Mr P. T. Evans.

184 MR JAMES EWART, Langholm
Postal: **James Ewart Racing Limited, Craig Farm, Westerkirk, Langholm, Dumfriesshire, DG13 0NZ**
Contacts: **PHONE 013873 70707 MOBILE 07786 995073**
EMAIL office@jeracing.co.uk WEBSITE www.jamesewartracing.com

1 **AQUITAINE BOY (FR),** 5, b g Walk In The Park (IRE)—Dolce Vita Yug **Mrs J. E. Dodd**
2 **ARISTO DU PLESSIS (FR),** 10, b g Voix du Nord (FR)—J'Aime (FR) **Mrs J. E. Dodd**
3 **ASCOT DE BRUYERE (FR),** 10, b br g Kapgarde (FR)—Quid de Neuville (FR) **The Steel Bonnets**
4 **BEAT BOX (FR),** 4, b g Cokoriko (FR)—Niemen (FR) **J. D. Gordon**
5 **BERING UPSUN,** 9, b g And Beyond (IRE)—Bering Up (IRE) **The Craig Farm Syndicate**
6 **BINGO D'OLIVATE (FR),** 9, b g Laverock (IRE)—Ombrelle de L'Orme (FR) **The Craig Farm Syndicate**
7 **BLACK PIRATE,** 8, b g Black Sam Bellamy (IRE)—Proper Posh **Leeds Plywood & Doors Ltd**
8 **BLUEFORTYTWO,** 7, gr g Overbury (IRE)—Celine Message **Leeds Plywood & Doors Ltd**
9 **BULLION (FR),** 7, ch g Full of Gold (FR)—Ryde (FR) **Mrs Hugh Fraser**
10 **CALIX DELAFAYETTE (FR),** 8, b g Caballo Raptor (CAN)—Obepinedelafayette (FR) **Mrs J. E. Dodd**
11 **CELLAR VIE,** 6, gr g Tikkanen (USA)—Branceilles (FR) **Ewart, Palmer & Percy**
12 **CHARMANT (FR),** 8, b g Balko (FR)—Ravissante (FR) **Mr A Phillips & Mr&Mrs Sperling**
13 **COCHISEE,** 6, gr g Tikkanen (USA)—Pocahontas (FR) **N. M. L. Ewart**
14 **DRENEK (FR),** 7, gr g Turgeon (USA)—Sireva (FR) **Mr James Westoll**
15 **DUNLY (FR),** 7, b g Gris de Gris (IRE)—Octavine du Meix (FR) **The Craig Farm Syndicate**
16 **EMPIRE DE MAULDE (FR),** 6, b g Spanish Moon (USA)—Ondine de Brejoux (FR) **Ewart, Murrills**
17 **ETTILA DE SIVOLA (FR),** 6, gr g Noroit (GER)—Wild Rose Bloom (FR) **Kesson,Phillips,Humbert,Ogilvie**
18 **FEETRONIE DE KERVI (FR),** 5, b m No Risk At All (FR)—Malandra **Mr N Ewart & Mrs Drew**
19 **FOR THREE (IRE),** 6, b g Pour Moi (IRE)—Asmaa (USA) **Craig Farm Syndicate,Percy,Palmer,Graham**
20 **FOSTERED PHIL (IRE),** 6, b g Arcadio (GER)—Knock Na Shee (IRE) **N. M. L. Ewart**
21 **FOXEY,** 5, b g Foxwedge (AUS)—Blue Lyric **Mr M. J. James**
22 **HONOURARY GIFT (IRE),** 7, b g City Honours (USA)—Zaffalong (IRE) **Phillips,Elliot,Carruthers,Drew,Palmer**
23 **I AM DANDY (IRE),** 5, b g Dandy Man (IRE)—Acushladear (IRE) **The Craig Farm Syndicate**
24 **INTO THE BREACH (FR),** 7, b g Al Namix (FR)—Arvicaya **The Craig Farm Syndicate**
25 **JASSAS (FR),** 8, ch g Fuisse (FR)—Sylverina (FR) **Mrs J. E. Dodd**
26 **KARISMATIK (FR),** 4, b g Kap Rock (FR)—Crack d'Emble (FR) **N. M. L. Ewart**
27 **KNOCKREA (IRE),** 13, b g Pierre—Glynn Cross (IRE) **The Craig Farm Syndicate**
28 **LAKE TAKAPUNA (IRE),** 9, b g Shantou (USA)—Close To Shore (IRE) **Ewart, Carruthers, Graham**
29 **MIATURK,** 6, b m Court Cave (IRE)—Azturk (FR) **N. M. L. Ewart**
30 **MUHTAMAR (FR),** 5, ch g Muhtathir—Martalina (FR) **Mrs J. E. Dodd**
31 **MULTIPEDE,** 8, b g Multiplex—Playful Lady **Mrs Hugh Fraser**
32 **NIKGARDE (FR),** 5, b g Kapgarde (FR)—Nikoline (FR) **Mrs J. E. Dodd**
33 **SAO MAXENCE (FR),** 7, b g Saint des Saints (FR)—Primadona (FR) **Mrs J. E. Dodd**
34 **THE BLAME GAME (IRE),** 6, b g Getaway (GER)—Tribal Princess (IRE) **J. D. Gordon**
35 **THE MAESTRO (IRE),** 6, b g Doyen (IRE)—Myown (IRE) **J. D. Gordon**
36 **TORTUGA BAY,** 6, b m Sulamani (IRE)—Empress of Light **Mrs Hugh Fraser**
37 **UN GUET APENS (FR),** 12, b g Enrique—Belisama (FR) **Drew, Percy, Carruthers & Graham**
38 **UNDISPUTED (FR),** 6, gr g Al Namix (FR)—Arvicaya **Mr M. J. James**

THREE-YEAR-OLDS
39 **IT'S ENOUGH,** b g Multiplex—High Meadow Girl **Mrs B. J. Ewart**

Other Owners: Exors of the Late Mr J. D. Allen, Mr R. Carruthers, Mrs L. J. Drew, Mr J. J. Elliot, Mr J. Ewart, N. M. L. Ewart, W. Graham, Mrs A. G. Humbert, Dr C. M. Kesson, Mr S. A. Murrills, Mr P. M. Ogilvie, Dr R. A. Palmer, Mrs J. D. Percy, Mr A. M. Phillips, Mr D. I. Rolinson, Mr R. E. Smith, Mrs J. Sperling, Mr N. A. Sperling, Mr D. R. Stanhope, The Craig Farm Syndicate.

Assistant Trainer: Briony Ewart.

185 **MR LES EYRE, Beverley**
Postal: Ivy House Stables, Main Street, Catwick, Beverley, North Humberside, HU17 5PJ
Contacts: **MOBILE 07864 677444**
EMAIL leseyreracing@hotmail.co.uk

1 **ALISIA R (IRE)**, 4, b f Holy Roman Emperor (IRE)—Shamrock Lady (IRE) **M Rozenbroek & J L Eyre**
2 **AMBER ROCK (USA)**, 4, b g Australia—Amber Isle (USA) **RP Racing Ltd**
3 **BUNGLE BILLY (IRE)**, 4, b g Bungle Inthejungle—Testa Unica (ITY) **Mr J. L. Eyre**
4 **COSMIC RAY**, 8, b g Phoenix Reach (IRE)—Beat Seven **Mrs M. A. Cooke**
5 **COTE D'AZUR**, 7, ch g Champs Elysees—Florentia **Billy Parker & Steven Parker**
6 **DAWAALEEB (USA)**, 6, b g Invincible Spirit (IRE)—Plaza (USA) **Billy Parker & Steven Parker**
7 **HIGHLY SPRUNG (IRE)**, 7, b g Zebedee—Miss Donovan **Mr A Turton & Dr V Webb**
8 **MORETTI (IRE)**, 5, b m Requinto (IRE)—Hassaya (IRE) **Mr J. L. Eyre**
9 **OLIVIA R (IRE)**, 4, ch f Excelebration (IRE)—Rozene (IRE) **Mr J. L. Eyre**
10 **QUEEN OF KALAHARI**, 5, b m Lethal Force (IRE)—Aromatherapy **Les Eyre Racing Partnership I**
11 **VALLEY OF FIRE**, 8, b g Firebreak—Charlie Girl **Billy Parker & Steven Parker**
12 **YORKSHIRE FLYER (IRE)**, 4, b g Cape Cross (IRE)—Moonlight Wish (IRE) **RP Racing Ltd**

THREE-YEAR-OLDS
13 **BIRKENHEAD**, b g Captain Gerrard (IRE)—Vilnius **Sunpak Racing**
14 **STRICTLY SANDRA (IRE)**, b f Iffraaj—Dance Club (IRE) **Sunpak Racing**
15 B f Champs Elysees—Veenwouden **Mr M. J. Rozenbroek**
16 **WILLIAM ALEXANDER**, b g Zoffany (IRE)—Xaloc (IRE) **Mr M. J. Rozenbroek**

TWO-YEAR-OLDS
17 **COSMIC STAR**, b grf 05/04 Charm Spirit (IRE)—Reaching Ahead (USA) (Mizzen Mast (USA)) (15000) **Melissa Cooke & Val Webb**
18 **JUST FRANK**, b c 22/03 Epaulette (AUS)—Mabinia (IRE) (Cape Cross (IRE)) (27000) **Billy Parker & Steven Parker**
19 B c 27/04 Clodovil (IRE)—Nafa (IRE) (Shamardal (USA)) (62000) **RP Racing Ltd**
20 Ch c 12/05 Toronado (IRE)—Xaloc (IRE) (Shirocco (GER)) **Mr M. J. Rozenbroek**

Other Owners: Mrs M. A. Cooke, Mr J. L. Eyre, Mr B. Parker, Mr S. Parker, Mr M. J. Rozenbroek, Mr A. Turton, Dr V. Webb.

Assistant Trainer: Tracy Johnson.

186 **MR RICHARD FAHEY, Malton**
Postal: RF Racing Ltd, Mews House, Musley Bank, Malton, North Yorkshire, YO17 6TD
Contacts: **PHONE 01653 698915 MOBILE 07713 478079 FAX 01653 699735**
EMAIL enquiries@richardfahey.com WEBSITE www.richardfahey.com

1 **ABSOLUTE DREAM (IRE)**, 4, ch g Dream Ahead (USA)—Absolute Diamond **S & G Clayton**
2 **ALLEN A DALE (IRE)**, 4, br g Kyllachy—Wood Chorus **Mr H. J. P. Farr**
3 **ANOTHER TOUCH**, 7, b g Arcano (IRE)—Alsalwa (IRE) **Nicholas Wrigley & Kevin Hart**
4 **BARONIAL PRIDE**, 4, b g Mayson—Trust Fund Babe (IRE) **Nick Bradley Racing 20 & Partner**
5 **BILLY BOND**, 8, b g Monsieur Bond (IRE)—Princess Cocoa (IRE) **Mr & Mrs P. Ashton**
6 **COSMIC LAW (IRE)**, 4, b g No Nay Never (USA)—Dhamma (USA) **Mr J. E. Dance**
7 **CROWNTHORPE**, 5, b g Monsieur Bond (IRE)—Normandy Maid **Richard Fahey Ebor Racing Club Ltd**
8 **DARTUM TEMPUS (IRE)**, 5, b g Arcadio (GER)—Vera Glynn (IRE) **Richard Fahey Ebor Racing Club Ltd**
9 **DEFENCE TREATY (IRE)**, 4, b g Dandy Man (IRE)—Just Like Ivy (CAN) **Mr R. A. Fahey**
10 **DELPH CRESCENT (IRE)**, 5, gr g Dark Angel (IRE)—Zut Alors (IRE) **Withernsea Thoroughbred Limited**
11 **DUBAI ACCLAIM (IRE)**, 5, b g Acclamation—Bahati (IRE) **S & G Clayton**
12 **ETERNAL ROMANTIC**, 4, ch g Nathaniel (IRE)—Romantic Settings **Mr Mel Roberts & Ms Nicola Meese 1**
13 **EVA MARIA**, 4, b f Sea The Stars (IRE)—Whazzat **W. J. and T. C. O. Gredley**
14 **FAIRY STORIES**, 4, b f Mayson—Fairy Shoes **Richard Fahey Ebor Racing Club Ltd**
15 **FIREWATER**, 4, ch g Monsieur Bond (IRE)—Spirit Na Heireann (IRE) **Mrs H. Steel**
16 **FOOL FOR YOU**, 5, b m Lawman (FR)—Bosphorus Queen (IRE) **Mr J. E. Dance**
17 **FOREST RANGER (IRE)**, 6, b g Lawman (FR)—Alava (IRE) **Mrs H. Steel**
18 **FURZIG**, 5, b g Monsieur Bond (IRE)—Princess Cocoa (IRE) **Mr & Mrs P. Ashton**

MR RICHARD FAHEY - continued

19 **GABRIAL THE SAINT (IRE)**, 5, ch g Society Rock (IRE)—Green Briar **Dr M. B. Q. S. Koukash**
20 **GABRIAL THE WIRE**, 4, b g Garswood—Nightunderthestars **Dr M. B. Q. S. Koukash**
21 **GABRIALS BOY**, 4, b g Paco Boy (IRE)—Statua (IRE) **Dr M. B. Q. S. Koukash**
22 **GALLIPOLI (IRE)**, 7, b g Compton Place—Altadena Lady (IRE) **P. Timmins**
23 **GEORGE BOWEN (IRE)**, 8, gr g Dark Angel (IRE)—Midnight Oasis **M. A. Scaife**
24 **GINGER MAX**, 4, b c Garswood—Miss Bunter **Withernsea Thoroughbred Ltd & Partner**
25 **HARRYJOEJOE**, 4, b g Iffraaj—Salutare (IRE) **Richard Fahey Ebor Racing Club Ltd**
26 **IFYOUCARESHARE**, 5, gr g Fair Mix (IRE)—Mobhi Boreen (IRE) **D&D Armstrong Limited**
27 **IT'LLCOMEIN (FR)**, 4, b g Wootton Bassett—L'Hommee (FR) **Middleham Park Racing LXXV & Partner**
28 **JAZZ HANDS (IRE)**, 4, b g Red Jazz (USA)—Ishimagic **Mr Mike Browne & Mrs Dee Howe**
29 **JUNGLE SECRET (IRE)**, 4, ch f Bungle Inthejungle—Secret Circle **The Secret O'Circle Syndicate**
30 **KENSINGTON ART**, 4, b g Dutch Art—Lady Luachmhar (IRE) **Mrs H. Steel**
31 **KINGSON (IRE)**, 4, b g Kingman—Gaditana **Mr & Mrs P Ashton & Partner**
32 **KNOWING GLANCE (IRE)**, 5, b g Kodiac—Shauna's Princess (IRE) **Posh John 11**
33 **LUCKY LUCKY MAN (IRE)**, 5, gr g Clodovil (IRE)—Regrette Rien (IRE) **The Musley Bank Partnership & Partner**
34 **LUIS VAZ DE TORRES (IRE)**, 8, b g Tagula (IRE)—Tekhania (IRE) **Lets Go Racing 1**
35 **METALLIC BLACK**, 4, br g Bated Breath—Silken Express (IRE) **Richard Fahey Ebor Racing Club Ltd**
36 **MR LUPTON (IRE)**, 7, ch g Elnadim (USA)—Chiloe Wigeon (IRE) **Mr N. D. Kershaw & Partner**
37 **MRS HOO (IRE)**, 4, b f Lawman (FR)—Wingspan (USA) **Richard Fahey Ebor Racing Club Ltd**
38 **ODDS ON OLI**, 5, b g Camelot—Red Blooded Woman (USA) **Richard Fahey Ebor Racing Club Ltd**
39 **PADDY POWER (IRE)**, 7, ch g Pivotal—Rag Top (IRE) **M Scaife & R A Fahey**
40 **PENWORTHAM (IRE)**, 7, b g Dandy Man (IRE)—Portofino Bay (IRE) **Dr M. B. Q. S. Koukash**
41 **REQUINTO DAWN (IRE)**, 5, br g Requinto (IRE)—Till Dawn (IRE) **The Phoenix Racing C.O. & Partner**
42 **RIGHT ACTION**, 6, b g Dandy Man (IRE)—Rockaby Baby (IRE) **Middleham Park Racing LVII & Partner**
43 **ROYAL COSMIC**, 6, b m Wootton Bassett—Cosmic Case **The Cosmic Cases**
44 **SHOW ME A SUNSET**, 4, b c Showcasing—Sunrise Star **The Cool Silk Partnership**
45 **SILVER DUST (IRE)**, 4, gr g Clodovil (IRE)—Silesian (IRE) **The Far Corner Partnership**
46 **SOCIETY QUEEN (IRE)**, 4, b f Society Rock (IRE)—Passion Fruit **Mrs H. Steel**
47 **SOCIETY RED**, 6, ch g Arcano (IRE)—Idonea (CAN) **Mr M. J. Macleod**
48 **SOOTABILITY (IRE)**, 4, br f Camelot—Balaagha (USA) **Mrs H. Steel**
49 **TADLEEL**, 5, b g Dark Angel (IRE)—Quelle Affaire **Mr R. A. Fahey**
50 **TORONADO QUEEN (IRE)**, 4, b f Toronado (IRE)—Queenofthenorth (IRE) **Richard Fahey Ebor Racing Club Ltd**
51 **VENTURA OCEAN (IRE)**, 4, b g Raven's Pass (USA)—Tranquil Spirit (IRE) **Middleham Park Racing XIX & Partner**
52 **WASNTEXPECTINGTHAT**, 4, b g Foxwedge (AUS)—Carsulae (IRE) **Good Bad Ugly & Deaf**
53 **WHATAGUY**, 4, ch g Mayson—La Fortunata **Mr R. A. Fahey**
54 **WINDSOR CROSS (IRE)**, 5, gr g Camacho—Lizzy's Township (USA) **Richard Fahey Ebor Racing Club Ltd**
55 **ZAP**, 5, b g Mayson—Moonglow
56 **ZIP**, 4, ro g Kyllachy—Flycatcher (IRE)

THREE-YEAR-OLDS

57 **A TOUCH OF LUCK (GER)**, b f Frankel—Aigrette Garzette (IRE) **P. D. Smith Holdings Ltd**
58 **AL RASMAH (IRE)**, b f Iffraaj—Oeuvre d'Art (IRE) **Sheikh J. D. Al Maktoum**
59 **ALBEN SPIRIT**, b g Camacho—Priti Fabulous (IRE) **Mr J. K. Shannon & Mr M. A. Scaife**
60 **ALENEVA (IRE)**, b f Kodiac—Peace Palace **Mr J. E. Dance**
61 **AMAYSMONT**, b g Mayson—Montjen (IRE) **Mr G. J. Paver**
62 **ANNA MARIA**, b f Invincible Spirit (IRE)—Nannina **Cheveley Park Stud Limited**
63 **ARAIFJAN**, ch c Kyllachy—Light Hearted **Sheikh A. H. F. M. A. Al Sabah**
64 **ASSAYER (IRE)**, b f Galileo (IRE)—Fix (NZ) **China Horse Club International Limited**
65 **ASSTECH (IRE)**, b g Ivawood (IRE)—Beyond Belief (IRE) **Assembly Techniques Syndicate**
66 **BANK HOLIDAY (IRE)**, ch f Ruler of The World (IRE)—Banco Suivi (IRE) **Farranamanagh & Partner**
67 **BARNES WALLIS (IRE)**, b g Canford Cliffs (IRE)—Next One **Havelock Racing 2**
68 **BENDY SPIRIT (IRE)**, b g Helmet (AUS)—Parakopi (IRE) **Mr A Tattersall & Partner**
69 **BETUSHKA (IRE)**, b f Archipenko (USA)—Wood Fairy **Mrs P. B. E. P. Farr**
70 **BOND'S BOY**, ch g Monsieur Bond (IRE)—Blades Girl **Crown Select**
71 **BRAVO FAISAL (IRE)**, b c Kodiac—Israar **Sheikh A. H. F. M. A. Al Sabah**
72 **CLOUDEA (IRE)**, gr f Clodovil (IRE)—Maria Luisa (IRE) **Richard Fahey Ebor Racing Club Ltd**
73 **CORNDAVON LAD (IRE)**, b g Camacho—Wild Ways **G. Murray**
74 **CUBAN AFFAIR**, b f Havana Gold—Cecily **Clipper Group Holdings Ltd**
75 **CUSTODIAN (IRE)**, b c Muhaarar—Zuhoor Baynoona (IRE) **Cheveley Park Stud Limited**

MR RICHARD FAHEY - continued

76 **DELICATE TOUCH (IRE)**, b f Dutch Art—Nigh (IRE) **N. H. T. Wrigley**
77 **DREAMING BLUE**, b g Showcasing—Got To Dream **Sheikh R. D. Al Maktoum**
78 **DUESENBERG (IRE)**, b g Elzaam (AUS)—Alabama Grace (IRE) **Mr A. J. Ryan**
79 **DYLAN DE VEGA**, ch g Poet's Voice—Colorada **Smarden Thoroughbreds**
80 **EASTWELL PARK**, ch f Medicean—Crimson Cloud **Richard Fahey Ebor Racing Club Ltd**
81 **EASY DESIRE**, ch f Outstrip—Dularame (IRE) **Richard Fahey Ebor Racing Club Ltd**
82 **EMBOLDEN (IRE)**, b c Kodiac—Sassy Gal (IRE) **Mr P. F. O'Callaghan**
83 **ENTRANCING**, br f Mayson—Hypnotize **Cheveley Park Stud Limited**
84 **EXCEPTIONAL**, b f Dutch Art—Expressive **Cheveley Park Stud Limited**
85 **FELICIA BLUE**, ch f Mayson—Diamond Blue **Mrs Jane Newett & Partner**
86 **FORTHELOVEOFGRAVY (IRE)**, gr g Dark Angel (IRE)—Maybe Now Baby (IRE) **Middleham Park Racing XXVI**
87 **FULL SECRET (IRE)**, b f Footstepsinthesand—Meadow **Sheikh A. H. F. M. A. Al Sabah**
88 **G FOR GABRIAL (IRE)**, gr g Gutaifan (IRE)—Cockney Rhyme **Dr M. B. Q. S. Koukash**
89 **GRACE AND VIRTUE (IRE)**, b f Iffraaj—Spiralling **Kaniz Bloodstock Investments Ltd**
90 **HARTSWOOD**, b g Garswood—Nihal (IRE) **Percy / Green Racing 2**
91 **HEAVENS OPEN**, b f Pivotal—Celeste **Cheveley Park Stud Limited**
92 **HURCLE (IRE)**, b c Exceed And Excel (AUS)—Switcher (IRE) **The Hurcle Syndicate**
93 **INNINGS**, b c Intello (GER)—Red Bloom **Cheveley Park Stud Limited**
94 **INTERNATIONAL LION**, ch c Kyllachy—Redskin Dancer (IRE) **P. D. Smith Holdings Ltd**
95 **INTERNATIONALANGEL (IRE)**, gr f Dark Angel (IRE)—Wrong Answer **P. D. Smith Holdings Ltd**
96 **INTERNATIONALTIGER**, b c Garswood—Elusive Sue (USA) **P. D. Smith Holdings Ltd**
97 **ITWOULDBERUDENOTTO**, b g Fountain of Youth—Jive **Good Bad Ugly & Deaf**
98 **KATELLI (IRE)**, br g Dragon Pulse (IRE)—Kateeva (IRE) **Middleham Park Racing III & Partner**
99 **KEY SPIRIT**, b g Pivotal—Perfect Spirit (IRE) **Mr John Rhodes & Peter Timmins**
100 **KIDDA**, gr g Gutaifan (IRE)—Lily Again **Nick Bradley Racing 36 & Partner**
101 **KITTEN'S DREAM**, b c Kitten's Joy (USA)—Strathnaver **Mr & Mrs J. D. Cotton**
102 **KUWAIT SHIELD**, ch g Kyllachy—Varnish **Sheikh A. H. F. M. A. Al Sabah**
103 **LADY CELIA**, b f Mayson—Fairy Shoes **Richard Fahey Ebor Racing Club Ltd**
104 **LAWAA (FR)**, b g Bated Breath—Smaisma (IRE) **Al Shaqab Racing UK Limited**
105 **LET HER LOOSE (IRE)**, ch f Mukhadram—Passionable **The Up For Anything Syndicate**
106 **LIBERATION POINT (IRE)**, b c Iffraaj—Botanique (IRE) **Clipper Group Holdings Ltd**
107 **LIKE SUGAR**, ch f Showcasing—Ivory Gala (FR) **Mr J. E. Dance**
108 **LOVERS CRY**, b br f Cityscape—Wizby **Mr J. E. Dance**
109 **MAJESTIC SANDS (IRE)**, b c Kodiac—La Grande Zoa (IRE) **The Cool Silk Partnership**
110 **MIGHTY SPIRIT (IRE)**, b f Acclamation—Majestic Alexander (IRE) **Mr J. E. Dance**
111 **MOON OF LOVE (IRE)**, b f Kodiac—Moon Club (IRE) **The Cool Silk Partnership**
112 **MOONLIGHT ECHO**, b f Kodiac—Dolphina (USA) **Titanium Racing Club**
113 **MR FUDGE**, ch g Anjaal—Clann Force **Richard Fahey Ebor Racing Club Ltd**
114 **MR GUS (IRE)**, b g Slade Power (IRE)—Perfect Venture **Ontoawinner 8 & Partner 4**
115 **MY KINDA DAY (IRE)**, b g Exceed And Excel (AUS)—Sound The Alarm **Peter Timmins & John Rhodes**
116 **MY SISTER JO**, b f Showcasing—Full Mandate (IRE) **Middleham Park Racing LXVI & Chris Liesack**
117 **NATIONAL LEAGUE (IRE)**, gr g Gutaifan (IRE)—Margarita (IRE) **Mr R. A. Fahey**
118 **RUBY SHIELD (USA)**, b f War Front (USA)—Ruby Tuesday (USA) **Mrs R. Henry**
119 **SANDS OF GIZA (FR)**, ch c Kheleyf (USA)—Kadiania (FR) **The Cool Silk Partnership**
120 **SAVAGE BEAUTY (IRE)**, b f Starspangledbanner (AUS)—Sister Sylvia **Ontoawinner 8 & Partner 4**
121 **SAY IT SIMPLE**, ch f Iffraaj—Nashama (USA) **W. J. and T. C. O. Gredley**
122 **SCHERZO**, b f Golden Horn—Labise (IRE) **W. J. and T. C. O. Gredley**
123 **SENDACARD**, br f Showcasing—Valentine Glory **Hot To Trot Racing 2 & Partners**
124 **SHOW ME SHOW ME**, b g Showcasing—Springing Baroness **Ontoawinner 8 & Partner 4**
125 **SILVER MISSION (IRE)**, gr g Dark Angel (IRE)—Miss Indigo **Mr H. Dalmook Al Maktoum**
126 **SIR HAVELOCK (IRE)**, br g Hallowed Crown (AUS)—Gemma's Pearl **Nick Bradley Racing 40 & Partner**
127 **SPIRIT DANCER**, b c Frankel—Queen's Dream (GER) **Done Ferguson Mason**
128 **SPIRIT OF THE SKY**, ch f Swiss Spirit—Clouds Rest **Racegoers Club Owners Group**
129 **STAR OF ST JAMES (GER)**, b g Equiano (FR)—Slight Advantage (IRE) **The Market Men**
130 **STAXTON HILL**, gr g Outstrip—Snake's Head **Ontoawinner 8 & Partner 4**
131 **STREET LIFE**, ch g Hot Streak (IRE)—Atheera (IRE) **Dr M. B. Q. S. Koukash**
132 **STRONG WOOD (IRE)**, b g Make Believe—Lake Moon **D & D Armstrong Ltd & Mr L Westwood**
133 **SUN CRYSTAL (IRE)**, ch f Exceed And Excel (AUS)—Takizada (IRE) **Mrs H. Steel**
134 **SWEET JOANNA (IRE)**, gr f Gutaifan (IRE)—Rugged Up (IRE) **Middleham Park, Ventura Racing 10 & Partner**

MR RICHARD FAHEY - continued

135 **TAKE THAT**, b g Iffraaj—Letterfromamerica (USA) **Morebrooke Limited**
136 **TORO STRIKE (USA)**, b c Toronado (IRE)—Scarlet Strike (USA) **Al Shaqab Racing UK Limited**
137 **UNAPOLOGETIC (IRE)**, b f Kodiac—Try Yes **Farranamanagh & Partner**
138 **UPSTATE NEW YORK (IRE)**, gr c No Nay Never—Mizayin (IRE) **Clipper Group Holdings Ltd**
139 **VENTURA EXPRESS**, ch c Mayson—Mail Express (IRE) **Middleham Park & Ventura Racing 16**
140 **VENTURA LIGHTNING (FR)**, gr c No Nay Never—
From This Day On (USA) **Middleham Park Racing LXXXI & Partner**
141 **VENTURA REBEL**, b c Pastoral Pursuits—Finalize **Mr A. Menahi**
142 **VICEREGENT**, b g Nathaniel (IRE)—Simply Shining (IRE) **Mrs H. Steel**
143 **WHAT IS LIFE (IRE)**, b f Iffraaj—Media Luna **Peter Timmins & John Rhodes**
144 **YOSHIMI (IRE)**, gr g Dream Ahead (USA)—Dawn Dew (GER) **Mrs Lauren Hart & Partner**

Trainer did not supply details of their two-year-olds.

Other Owners: Ontoawinner 9 & Partner 2, Aidan J Ryan & Partner, Sheikh J. D. Al Maktoum, Mr S. B. M. Al Qassimi, Sheikh A. H. F. M. A. Al Sabah, Mr T. Alderson, Mr P. Ashton, Mr & Mrs P. Ashton, Mrs S. Ashton, Bearstone Stud Limited, Mr D. Bowen, Mr N. Bradley, Mr S. D. Bradley, Mr S. Bridge, M. F. Browne, Mrs T. Burns, Cheveley Park Stud Limited, Mrs G. A. Clayton, Mr S. W. Clayton, A. E. Corbett, Mr M. Cressey, Crown Select, Mr G. D. Cuthbert, D&D Armstrong Limited, Mr T. Denham, Mr S. Ellis, Facility Solutions Management Limited, Mr R. A. Fahey, Farranamanagh, M. J. Feneron, Mrs H. J. Fitzsimons, G R Bailey Ltd (Baileys Horse Feeds), W. J. and T. C. O. Gredley, D. A. Green, K. Hart, Mrs L. Hart, R. J. Hart, Mr G. P. Henderson, Miss S. Holden, Mr D. Holgate, Mr R. S. Hoskins, Hot To Trot Racing 2, Mrs D. Howe, Mr K. W. Hubery, Mrs L. J. Huddlestone, Mr N. D. Kershaw, Mr S. A. Kershaw, Kevin Mercer & Partner, D. M. Knaggs, Dr M. B. Q. S. Koukash, M. A. Leatham, Let's Go Racing 2, L. Lillingston, Mr P. D. Macintosh, Mrs T. Marnane, Ms N. Meese, Mr K. J. Mercer, Merchant and Missionaries and Partner, Merchants and Missionaries, Middleham Park Racing (VII), Middleham Park Racing CVIII, Middleham Park Racing III, Middleham Park Racing LXXXI, Middleham Park Racing LXXXV, Middleham Park Racing XIX, Middleham Park and Ventura Racing 10, Mrs A. Morrissey, Mr M. Morrissey, Mrs Jane Newett & Partner, Mrs J. E. Newett, Nick Bradley Racing 20, Nick Bradley Racing 36, Nick Bradley Racing 40, Mr N. J. O'Brien, Ontoawinner 8, Ontoawinner 9, Mr J. R. Owen, P. D. Smith Holdings Ltd, T. S. Palin, Mr G. J. Paver, Peniaphobia Partnership, M. Prince, Mr J. Rhodes, Richard Fahey Ebor Racing Club Ltd, Mr M. Roberts, Mr Mel Roberts & Ms Nicola Meese, Run For Your Money, Mr A. J. Ryan, M. A. Scaife, J. K. Shannon, Smarden Thoroughbreds, Mr P. K. Spencer, Mrs H. Steel, Mr K. J. Strangeway, Mr R. Sutcliffe, A. Tattersall, Mr D. M. Tempest, The AAA Partnership, The Fairweather Foursome, The Knavesmire Partnership, The Phoenix Racing C.O., Mr P. P. Thorman, P. Timmins, Mr W. A. Tinkler, Mr C. J. Titcomb, Ventura Racing 16, Mr L. J. Westwood, Mr M. K. Williams, Withernsea Thoroughbred Limited, N. H. T. Wrigley, Mrs V. A. Wrigley, Z B Farming Renewables.

Assistant Trainer: Robin O'Ryan, Ben Stephens.

Flat Jockey: Jack Garritty, Tony Hamilton, Paul Hanagan, Paddy Mathers, Barry McHugh, David Nolan. **NH Jockey:** Jamie Hamilton, Brian Hughes. **Apprentice Jockey:** Sean Davis, Connor Murtagh.

---

187 **MR CHRIS FAIRHURST, Middleham**
Postal: Glasgow House, Middleham, Leyburn, North Yorkshire, DL8 4QG
Contacts: PHONE 01969 622039 MOBILE 07889 410840
EMAIL cfairhurst@tiscali.co.uk

1 **BENADALID**, 5, b g Assertive—Gambatte **Mrs S. France**
2 **FEEBI**, 4, b f Pour Moi (IRE)—Scorn (USA) **Mr A. Davies**
3 **FLORENZA**, 7, b m Haafhd—Danzatrice **980 Racing**
4 **KATY ROYAL**, 8, b m King's Theatre (IRE)—Water Stratford (IRE) **Hugh T. Redhead**
5 **RED TORNADO (FR)**, 8, ch g Dr Fong (USA)—Encircle (USA) **Richard III Partnership**
6 **SIXTIES STAR**, 6, b g Sixties Icon—Songbook **Mrs A. M. Leggett**
7 **THE ARMED MAN**, 7, b g Misu Bond (IRE)—Accamelia **Mrs C. Arnold**
8 **THE GINGERBREADMAN**, 5, b g Misu Bond (IRE)—Accamelia **Mrs C. Arnold**

THREE-YEAR-OLDS

9 **LASTING LEGACY**, gr f Lethal Force (IRE)—Araminte **Exors of the Late Mrs L. Peacock**
10 **MASHAM MOOR**, b g Music Master—Jane's Payoff (IRE) **Miss B. C. Duxbury**
11 **TOP ATTRACTION**, b g Fountain of Youth (IRE)—Symphonic Dancer (USA) **The PQD Partnership**
12 **VELMA**, b f Fast Company (IRE)—Valoria **Mr A. Davies**

MR CHRIS FAIRHURST - continued

TWO-YEAR-OLDS

13 **KAYLYN**, b f 01/04 Charm Spirit (IRE)—Dark Quest (Rainbow Quest (USA)) (3200) **Mr A. Davies**

Other Owners: Mr J. M. Tozer, Mr M. D. Tozer

188

MR JAMES R. FANSHAWE, Newmarket
Postal: **Pegasus Stables, Snailwell Road, Newmarket, Suffolk, CB8 7DJ**
Contacts: **PHONE 01638 664525 FAX 01638 664523**
EMAIL **james@jamesfanshawe.com** WEBSITE **www.jamesfanshawe.com, www.fredarcherracing.com**

1 **ARCHER'S DREAM (IRE)**, 4, b f Dream Ahead (USA)—
Badr Al Badoor (IRE) **Fred Archer Racing - Wheel of Fortune**
2 **AUDARYA (FR)**, 4, b f Wootton Bassett—Green Bananas (FR) **Mrs A. M. Swinburn**
3 **CANASTA**, 4, b f Charm Spirit (IRE)—Morzine **Elite Racing Club**
4 **CARNIVAL ROSE**, 4, b f Harbour Watch (IRE)—Gypsy Carnival **The Duchess of Sutherland**
5 **DURRELL**, 4, b g Animal Kingdom (USA)—Royal Order (USA) **Silver,Steed,Gambini & Venice Consulting**
6 **ENVISAGING (IRE)**, 6, b g Zoffany (IRE)—Star of Stars (IRE) **Fred Archer Racing - Ormonde**
7 **HARRY'S BAR**, 5, ch g Exceed And Excel (AUS)—Firenze **Jan & Peter Hopper**
8 **KIRSTENBOSCH**, 4, b f Mount Nelson—Kassiyra (IRE) **Fittocks Stud**
9 **KNOWING**, 4, b g Pour Moi (IRE)—Wedding Speech (IRE) **Mr G. Marney**
10 **LADY BERGAMOT (IRE)**, 6, gr m Mastercraftsman (IRE)—Mahima (FR) **Andrew & Julia Turner**
11 **MERCHANT OF VENICE**, 5, b g Bated Breath—Isola Verde **Mr & Mrs M. Morris & Mr & Mrs P. Hopper**
12 **NINE SPINNEY (IRE)**, 4, b g Lope de Vega (IRE)—Arkadina (IRE) **Merry Fox Stud Limited**
13 **OLYMPIC CONQUEROR (IRE)**, 4, b g Olympic Glory (IRE)—Queen's Conquer **The Cool Silk Partnership**
14 **PREENING**, 5, b m Dutch Art—Striving (IRE) **Cheveley Park Stud Limited**
15 **QATAR QUEEN**, 4, b f Kodiac—Alina (IRE) **Qatar Racing Limited**
16 **RAINING FIRE (IRE)**, 4, ch g Kitten's Joy (USA)—Flame of Hestia (IRE) **Merry Fox Stud Limited**
17 **SELINO**, 4, b g Champs Elysees—Air Kiss **Qatar Racing Limited**
18 **SERENADING**, 4, br f Iffraaj—Constant Dream **John E Rose & Manor Farm Stud**
19 **SINCERITY**, 4, b f Iffraaj—Affinity **Elite Racing Club**
20 **SKERRYVORE**, 4, ch g Toronado (IRE)—Succinct **Dr C. M. H. Wills**
21 **SLEEPING LION (USA)**, 5, ch g Teofilo (IRE)—Flame of Hestia (IRE) **Merry Fox Stud Limited**
22 **SPANISH ARCHER (FR)**, 5, b g Lope de Vega (IRE)—Parcelle Perdue (FR) **Fred Archer Racing - Iroquois**
23 **SWEET PROMISE**, 4, b f Intello (GER)—Penny Rose **Mr A. R. Boyd-Rochfort**
24 **THE PINTO KID (FR)**, 5, b g High Chaparral (IRE)—Lake Palace **Fred Archer Racing - Bruce**
25 **THE TIN MAN**, 8, b g Equiano (FR)—Persario **Fred Archer Racing - Ormonde**
26 **VIBRANCE**, 4, b f Nathaniel (IRE)—Park Crystal (IRE) **Cheveley Park Stud Limited**
27 **VISOR**, 5, b g Helmet (AUS)—Entitlement **Dr Catherine Wills & Frederik Tylicki**

THREE-YEAR-OLDS

28 **AMICABLE**, br gr f Dutch Art—Likeable **Helena Springfield Ltd**
29 **BOMB PROOF (IRE)**, br c Society Rock (IRE)—Chantaleen (FR) **Mr C Fox & Shalfleet Partnership**
30 **COBNUT (IRE)**, b g Kodiac—Macadamia (IRE) **Lord Vestey**
31 **COUSIN ROSAURA**, b f Nathaniel (IRE)—Czarna Roza **The Duchess of Sutherland**
32 **CROWN POWER (IRE)**, b f Camelot—Causeway Queen (IRE) **King Power Racing Co Ltd**
33 **ESTATE HOUSE (FR)**, b g Oasis Dream—Alsace Lorraine (IRE) **Merry Fox Stud Limited**
34 **FLOWER OF SCOTLAND**, b f Gleneagles (IRE)—Seal of Approval **T. R. G. Vestey**
35 **FLYING WEST**, b f Free Eagle (IRE)—West of The Moon **Cheveley Park Stud Limited**
36 **FUCHSIA**, b f Bated Breath—Esteemable **Mrs C. R. Philipson**
37 **GOLDEN DAWN (IRE)**, b f Golden Horn—Prima Luce **Miss P. F. O'Kelly**
38 **GREYCOAT**, gr c Lethal Force (IRE)—Scarlet Royal **Chris van Hoorn Racing**
39 **HI WAY**, b f Intrinsic—Sensible Way (USA) **Mr J. R. Fanshawe**
40 Ch g Lope de Vega (IRE)—Jam Jar **Mrs A. M. Swinburn**
41 B c Bated Breath—Kendal Mint **Clipper Logistics**
42 **KIMBERLEY**, b f Oasis Dream—Millennium Star (IRE) **Fittocks Stud**
43 **LA PUNTALINA (IRE)**, ch f Pivotal—Fondled **Mr C. Fox & Mr B. Wilson**

MR JAMES R. FANSHAWE - continued

44 **LADY ELEANOR,** ch f Iffraaj—Firenze **Jan & Peter Hopper**
45 **LONG HAIRED LOVER (IRE),** b f Night of Thunder (IRE)—
                  Love And Laughter (IRE) **D. Howden, N. Wheeler & D. Redvers**
46 **MAN OF LIGHT (FR),** ch g Manduro (GER)—Pilgrim of Grace (FR) **My Racing Manager Friends**
47 **MINORI (USA),** b f Blame (USA)—Zahrah (USA) **Dr J. P. Ryan**
48 **PENPAL (IRE),** b f Invincible Spirit (IRE)—French Friend (IRE) **Fred Archer Racing - Jannette**
49 **RAINBIRD,** gr f Oasis Dream—Pocket Watch **Mr S. A. Stuckey**
50 **ROZALIA,** b f Sir Percy—Lady Stardust **Somerton Sporting Club**
51 **SARAYAAT (IRE),** b f Exceed And Excel (AUS)—Stravina (GER) **Mr F. Nass**
52 **SECOND SLIP (IRE),** b g Lope de Vega (IRE)—Arkadina (IRE) **Merry Fox Stud Limited**
53 **SHELTERED,** b f Dutch Art—Cosseted **Cheveley Park Stud Limited**
54 **TILLY FRANKL,** b f Frankel—Ribbons **Fred Archer Racing - Lonely**
55 **TURN ON THE CHARM (FR),** b g Charm Spirit (IRE)—Shendaya (FR) **Fred Archer Racing - Paradox**
56 **VIOLA (IRE),** ch f Lope de Vega (IRE)—Sistine **Elite Racing Club**

TWO-YEAR-OLDS

57 **ARADENA (IRE),** b f 07/03 Helmet (AUS)—Air Kiss (Red Ransom (USA)) **Dr C. M. H. Wills**
58 B c 15/05 Free Eagle (IRE)—Badr Al Badoor (IRE) (Acclamation) (125000) **Fred Archer Racing - Galliard**
59 **BLUE ARTEMIS,** b f 26/01 Showcasing—
                  Azure Amour (IRE) (Azamour (IRE)) (72000) **Fred Archer Racing - Dutch Oven**
60 Ch c 24/04 Sea The Stars (IRE)—Brazilian Bride (IRE) (Pivotal) (110000) **Mr B. C. M. Wong**
61 **CEDAR'S STARS,** b f 08/02 Sea The Stars (IRE)—Instance (Invincible Spirit (IRE)) **Mr C. Fox & Mr B. Wilson**
62 **CRATHES CASTLE,** b c 06/05 Oasis Dream—Alyday (Kyllachy) (37000) **Mr A. R. Boyd-Rochfort**
63 **DEVILRY,** b f 11/02 Sea The Moon (GER)—Diablerette (Green Desert (USA)) **Miss K. Rausing**
64 B c 20/05 The Gurkha (IRE)—Don't Cry For Me (USA) (Street Cry (IRE)) (125000) **Mr B. C. M. Wong**
65 **DUTCH LIGHT,** ch f 05/04 Dutch Art—Regal Riband (Fantastic Light (USA)) **Cheveley Park Stud Limited**
66 B f 28/02 Le Havre (IRE)—Epic Emirates (Dubawi (IRE)) **Mr Hubert John Strecker**
67 Ch f 09/03 Twilight Son—Firenze (Efisio) (50000) **Sheikh Juma Dalmook Al Maktoum**
68 **GEMINGA,** b f 13/03 Awtaad—Starlet (Sea The Stars) **Lord Halifax**
69 **GRANNY MELBA,** b f 08/01 Australia—Spirit Raiser (IRE) (Invincible Spirit (IRE)) **The Hon William Vestey**
70 **GREEK FLAME (FR),** ch f 12/05 Siyouni—Flame Of Hestia (Giant's Causeway) **Merry Fox Stud Limited**
71 B f 14/04 Iffraaj—Isola Verde (Oasis Dream) **Mr & Mrs M. Morris & Mr & Mrs P. Hopper**
72 **JASMINE JOY (IRE),** b f 10/02 Lope De Vega—Pecking Order **Merry Fox Stud Limited**
73 **LAST PICASSO (IRE),** ch c 24/04 Lope de Vega (IRE)—
                  Alvee (IRE) (Key of Luck (USA)) (55000) **Merry Fox Stud Limited**
74 **LITTLE BY LITTLE,** ch f 17/03 Sixties Icon—Steppe By Steppe (Zamindar (USA)) **The Duchess of Sutherland**
75 B f 04/05 Kingman—Lonely Ahead (USA) (Rahy (USA)) (120000) **Mr Mohamed Obaida**
76 B f 23/03 Lope De Vega—Miss Dashwood (Dylan Thomas) **Helena Springfield Ltd**
77 **MURAU,** b c 22/03 Mukhadram—Entitlement (Authorized (IRE)) **Dr C. M. H. Wills**
78 B f 03/05 Equiano (FR)—Persario (Bishop of Cashel) (150000) **Hot To Trot Racing**
79 **PLACATED,** b f 16/02 Archipenko (USA)—Cosseted (Pivotal) **Cheveley Park Stud Limited**
80 Ch f 04/04 New Approach—Scribonia (Danehill) **Qatar Racing Limited**
81 B f 26/04 Muhaarar—Split Trois (FR) (Dubawi (IRE)) (10000) **Mr Mohamed Obaida**
82 **TWO TWO TIME,** ch f 02/03 Al Kazeem—Alla Breve (Dansili) **Cheveley Park Stud Limited**
83 **UPROAR,** b f 17/03 Sepoy (AUS)—Isis (USA) (Royal Academy (USA)) **Dr C. M. H. Wills**
84 B c 04/05 Kodiac—Victoria Montoya (High Chaparral) **Dragon Racing & Qatar Racing**

Other Owners: Mr Geoffrey Baber, Mrs Denise Beetles, Mr Graham Beetles, Mrs Mary Benjafield, Mr John Bodie, Mr Isidore Carivalis, Mr Alex Davidson, Mrs Olivia Davidson, Mr Robin Dowling, Mr Roy Eady, Mr Nigel Elwes, Mrs Georgia Fanshawe, Mrs Libby Fanshawe, Fittocks Stud, Mr Tony Francis, Mr Colin Gilbert, Mr Haydn Gott, Mr Robert Grove, Mr Terry Hart, Mr Dave King, Mrs Jenny King, Mr Mike King, Mrs Sarah King, Mr Arne Korsbakken, Mr Bill Lemon, Mr R. M. Levitt, Mr Niall Lynch, Mr Dan Marney, Mr Simon Massen, Mrs Lee Masters, Mrs Liz Meads, Mrs Joan Mitchell, Mr John Mitchell, Mrs Christine Munday, Mr Colin Munday, Mrs Tam Murray Thriepland, Mr Gordon Papworth, Mr Ian Pittaway, Mr Bill Rogerson, Mrs Pat Rowley, Mr Steve Rowley, Mr David Russell, Mr William Russell, Mr Ulf Ryden, Mrs Hermione Scrope, Mr Roger Shelton, Mr Nigel Smith, Mr Richard Stephens, Mr Rob Stevens, Mr David Tarrant, Mr Peter Tarrant, Mrs Gilly Thompson, Mr Adam Tjolle, Mrs Janet Walker, Dr C. M. H. Wills, Mrs Sue Wilson, Mr Peter Young.

Assistant Trainer: Kevin Philippart de Foy, **Pupil Assistant:** Tom Fanshawe.

189 MR JOHNNY FARRELLY, Midford
Postal: Upper Twinhoe Farm, Midford, Bath, Avon, BA2 8QX
Contacts: PHONE 01278 671782 MOBILE 07811 113363

1 ALI THE HUNTER (IRE), 7, ch m Papal Bull—Polish Spring (IRE) **Monday Boys Partnership**
2 AND THE NEW (IRE), 9, b g Kalanisi (IRE)—Wheredidthemoneygo (IRE) **Mr P. A. Randall**
3 AUTUMN GOLD, 7, ch m Apple Tree (FR)—Present Love (IRE) **Mr D. J. Adams**
4 BATHWICK BRAVE (IRE), 13, b g Westerner—Dorans Grove **Mr J. Farrelly**
5 BERMEO (IRE), 9, b g Definite Article—Miss Blueyes (IRE) **Mr R. E. Stuart-Jervis**
6 BIG PICTURE, 8, b g Recharge (IRE)—Just Jenny (IRE) **Donegal Mayo Association**
7 BLACK NOAH, 5, br g Big Bad Bob (IRE)—Frequently **Mrs G. Morgan**
8 BREFFNIBOYE (FR), 6, b g Sageburg (IRE)—Dawn Cat (USA) **F. A. Clegg**
9 CAPTAIN IVAN (IRE), 6, ch g Stowaway—Western Starlight (IRE) **Mr P. A. Randall**
10 CAPTAINS RUN (IRE), 8, ch g Curtain Time (IRE)—Sailors Run (IRE) **Mr P. M. Tosh**
11 CHANCE IT (IRE), 10, b g Tajraasi (USA)—Lafanta (IRE) **F. A. Clegg**
12 CROWN HILL (IRE), 10, b g Definite Article—Silver Prayer (IRE) **Hanford's Chemist Ltd**
13 DEJA BOUGG, 9, b m Tobougg (IRE)—La Riveraine (USA) **H. M. W. Clifford**
14 DOUBLY CLEVER (IRE), 8, ch g Iffraaj—Smartest (IRE) **Mrs G. Morgan**
15 FARCEUR DE MAULNE (FR), 5, b g Doctor Dino (FR)—Alize de La Prise (FR)
16 FOOL TO CRY (IRE), 7, ch m Fast Company (IRE)—Islandagore (IRE) **Mr J. Farrelly**
17 GASTARA, 5, b g Kayf Tara—Gaspaisie (FR) **Ms Gillian Metherell**
18 GINGILI, 10, b g Beat All (USA)—Gentian **Mr J. Farrelly**
19 GOLD MAN (IRE), 11, ch g Presenting—Mama Jaffa (IRE) **Mr Greenfingers Syndicate**
20 HAVANA RIVER (IRE), 7, b m Mahler—Dancingonthemoon (IRE) **Mr J. Farrelly**
21 HOW'S THE CRICKET (IRE), 5, b g Doyen (IRE)—Hayley Cometh (IRE) **Mr R. E. Stuart-Jervis**
22 KALASKADESEMILLEY, 9, b g Myboycharlie (IRE)—Congressional (IRE) **C. Cheesman**
23 LADY MAKFI (IRE), 8, b m Makfi—Dulcet Tones (IRE) **Mr J. McMahon**
24 LAKE SHORE DRIVE (IRE), 8, b g Thewayyouare (USA)—Labrusca **Mr P. M. Tosh**
25 LOVE THE LEADER (IRE), 12, b g Fruits of Love (USA)—Suelena (IRE) **Mr J. Farrelly**
26 MR LANDO, 11, b g Shirocco (GER)—Capitana (GER) **The Lansdowners**
27 NUMBERONEBEAUBOW, 5, ch m Norse Dancer (IRE)—Pull The Wool (IRE) **Mrs G. Morgan**
28 ORMSKIRK, 7, gr g Hellvelyn—River Song (USA) **Mrs G. Morgan**
29 OUTLAW JACK (IRE), 8, b g Mr Dinos (IRE)—Bonus Issue (IRE) **Mrs G. Morgan**
30 POLISHED ROCK (IRE), 10, ch g Rock of Gibraltar (IRE)—Where We Left Off **Mr J. McMahon**
31 SANDFORD CASTLE (IRE), 10, b g Norwich—Pegs Polly (IRE) **Live The Life**
32 SATOSHI (IRE), 6, b g Shirocco (GER)—Morar **Mr J. Farrelly**
33 SCARAMUCCI (IRE), 6, b g Sholokhov—Toppolesa (IRE) **Mr P. M. Tosh**
34 SEHAYLI (IRE), 7, b g Iffraaj—Quaich **Mr P. M. Tosh**
35 SPARKLING DAWN, 8, gr m Sulamani (IRE)—Clotted Cream (USA) **Live The Life - Atlas**
36 SPORTING BOY (IRE), 12, b g Barathea (IRE)—Sportsticketing (IRE) **H. M. W. Clifford**
37 TWILIGHT WAR (IRE), 5, b g Declaration of War (USA)—Special Assignment (IRE) **Fourth Time Lucky**
38 VALSE AU TAILLONS (FR), 7, b m Montmartre (FR)—Eyaelle (FR) **Hanford's Chemist Ltd**
39 WESTERN SUNRISE (IRE), 11, b m Westerner—Presenting Gayle (IRE) **Mr D. J. Adams**

190 MISS JULIA FEILDEN, Newmarket
Postal: Harraton Stud, Laceys Lane, Exning, Newmarket, Suffolk, CB8 7HW
Contacts: MOBILE 07974 817694
EMAIL juliafeilden@gmail.com WEBSITE www.juliafeildenracing.com

1 APPROVE THE DREAM (IRE), 4, ch g Approve—Jacquotte (IRE) **Harraton Hopefuls**
2 ENGRAVE, 4, gr f Dark Angel (IRE)—Hot Wired **Mrs C. T. Bushnell**
3 GAS MONKEY, 5, b g Cityscape—Bavarica **Newmarket Equine Tours Racing Club**
4 HIGHWAY ROBBERY, 4, gr g Dick Turpin (IRE)—Minty Fox **Mrs C. T. Bushnell**
5 LIMERICK LORD (IRE), 8, b g Lord Shanakill (USA)—Hollow Green (IRE) **Steve Clarke & Partner**
6 NEW EXPO (IRE), 4, ch g New Approach (IRE)—Anayid **Chris Cleevely & Partners**
7 NOBLE ACCOUNT, 4, b g Dansili—Illustrious Miss (USA) **Mrs C. T. Bushnell**
8 OUD METHA BRIDGE (IRE), 6, ch g Helmet (AUS)—Central Force **In It To Win Partnership**

MISS JULIA FEILDEN - continued

9 **PAINTBALL WIZARD (IRE)**, 4, ch g Mastercraftsman (IRE)—Dance Avenue (IRE) **Carol Bushnell & Partners**
10 **RAHA**, 4, b f Mukhadram—Cefira (USA) **Ahamed Farook & Julia Feilden**
11 **SEA SHACK**, 6, b g Equiano (FR)—Folly Bridge **Mr S. Claridge**
12 **SPANISH MANE (IRE)**, 5, b m Havana Gold (IRE)—Kiva **Stowstowquickquickstow Partnership**
13 **WAR EMPRESS (IRE)**, 4, b f War Command (USA)—Alice Rose (IRE) **Steve Clarke & Partner**
14 **WILSON (IRE)**, 5, b g Born To Sea (IRE)—Alkhawarah (USA) **Adrian Sparks & Partners**
15 **WINTER SNOWDROP (IRE)**, 4, gr f War Command (USA)—Morning Jewel (IRE) **Mrs C. T. Bushnell**

THREE-YEAR-OLDS

16 **ALIBABA**, b g Lawman (FR)—Fantasy In Blue **Ahamed Farook & Julia Feilden**
17 **DIVINE QUEEN**, b f Kingman—El Manati (IRE) **Good Company Partnership**
18 **MADAL BEE**, br g Fountain of Youth (IRE)—Charcoal **Mr S. Claridge**
19 **RIDE AND PREJUDICE**, b f Casamento (IRE)—Emma's Gift (IRE) **Newmarket Equine Tours Racing Club**
20 **VALLETTA SUNSET**, b g Casamento (IRE)—Sunset Kitty (USA) **Steve Clarke & Partners 3**

TWO-YEAR-OLDS

21 **FEN TIGER (IRE)**, b c 13/03 Vadamos (FR)—Three Knots (IRE) (Chineur (FR)) (30000) **Mrs C. T. Bushnell**
22 B f 13/05 Due Diligence (USA)—Rosa Luxemburg (Needwood Blade)
23 B f 24/04 Heeraat (IRE)—Sadiigah (Medicean) (800) **Mr J. W. Ford**
24 B f 16/05 Cannock Chase (USA)—The Ducking Stool (Where Or When (IRE)) **Newmarket Equine Tours Racing Club**
25 Gr c 14/04 Outstrip—Trixie Malone (Ishiguru (USA)) (11000)
26 B f 03/02 Hot Streak (IRE)—Vintage Steps (IRE) (Bahamian Bounty) (7000)

Other Owners: Mr S. J. Clarke, Mr C. R. Cleevely, Mr A. R. Farook, Miss J. D. Feilden, Mr C. M. Page, Mr A. K. Sparks, Mr O. A. Wideson.

Assistant Trainer: Ross Birkett.

Flat Jockey: Shelley Birkett. **Amateur Jockey:** Mr R. Birkett, Mr Sam Feilden.

---

191 | **MR ROGER FELL, Nawton**
Postal: **Arthington Barn House, Highfield Lane, Nawton, York, North Yorkshire, YO62 7TU**
Contacts: **PHONE 01439 770184**
EMAIL rogerfellracing@gmail.com **WEBSITE** www.rogerfell.co.uk

1 **AD LIBITUM**, 5, b g Elusive Quality (USA)—Sarmad (USA) **The Roses Partnership & R G Fell**
2 **ADMIRALITY**, 6, b g Mount Nelson—Dialma (USA) **Middleham Park Ventura Racing & Salthouse**
3 **AL OZZDI**, 5, b g Acclamation—Zibeling (IRE) **Northern Marking Ltd & Partners**
4 **CLUB WEXFORD (IRE)**, 9, b g Lawman (FR)—Masnada (IRE) **Mr C. J. Varley**
5 **COCKALORUM (IRE)**, 5, b g Cape Cross (IRE)—Opinionated (IRE) **H Dean & R Fell**
6 **DANDYS GOLD (IRE)**, 6, b m Dandy Man (IRE)—Proud Penny (IRE)
7 **DAPPER MAN (IRE)**, 6, b g Dandy Man (IRE)—Gist (IRE) **Colne Valley Racing & Partner**
8 **DOUBLE MARTINI (IRE)**, 4, ch c Mastercraftsman (IRE)—
Dusty Moon **Middleham Park, Ventura Racing & Partners**
9 **ELUSIVE HEIGHTS (IRE)**, 7, br g Elusive Pimpernel (USA)—
Berg Bahn (IRE) **Middleham Park Racing LXI & Partner 2**
10 **ERICH BLOCH (IRE)**, 4, b g Dandy Man (IRE)—Star Bonita (USA) **Swales & Fell**
11 **GLOBAL SPIRIT**, 5, b g Invincible Spirit (IRE)—Centime **Arthington Barn Racing**
12 **GRANDEE (IRE)**, 6, b g Lope de Vega (IRE)—Caravan of Dreams (IRE) **Nick Bradley Racing 16 & Sohi & Partner**
13 **GUARDIA SVIZZERA (IRE)**, 6, b g Holy Roman Emperor (IRE)—
Winged Harriet (IRE) **MPR, Ventura Racing 7 & Partner**
14 **HAROME (IRE)**, 6, ch g Bahamian Bounty—Clytha **Middleham Park Racing LXXI & Partner**
15 **KAPONO**, 4, b g Kuroshio (AUS)—Fair Maiden (JPN) **Mr S. M. Al Sabah**
16 **KUPA RIVER (IRE)**, 6, b g Big Bad Bob (IRE)—Lamanka Lass (USA) **Middleham Park Racing LXXII & Partner**
17 **MONTALVAN (IRE)**, 4, ch g Lope de Vega (IRE)—Shermeen (IRE) **Swales & Fell**
18 **MOTAWAAZY**, 4, b g Kingman—Shimah (USA) **Jane Greetham & Victoria Greetham**
19 **MULLIGATAWNY (IRE)**, 7, b g Lope de Vega (IRE)—Wild Whim (IRE) **Middleham Park Racing LI & Partner**
20 **MUNTADAB (IRE)**, 8, b g Invincible Spirit (IRE)—Chibola (ARG) **Fell & High Hopes Partnership**

MR ROGER FELL - continued

21 **MY BOY LEWIS (IRE),** 4, b g Dandy Man (IRE)—Flamelet (USA) **Fell & Salthouse**
22 **NAJASHEE (IRE),** 6, gr g Invincible Spirit (IRE)—Tonnara (IRE) **Swales & Fell**
23 **NAJIB (IRE),** 4, b g Invincible Spirit (IRE)—Angel's Tears **Mr D. M. Bainbridge**
24 **PIONEERING (IRE),** 6, b g Shamardal (USA)—Oregon Trail (USA) **Ebor Racing Club VI**
25 **PRESIDENTIAL (IRE),** 6, b g Invincible Spirit (IRE)—Poetical (IRE) **Nick Bradley Racing 3, Ian White & Partner**
26 **SMEATON (IRE),** 4, b g Sir Prancealot (IRE)—Sunny Harbor (IRE) **Mr R.G. Fell & Mr K Hamilton**
27 **TADAAWOL (IRE),** 7, b g Kyllachy—Bright Edge **Fell, Hamilton & Smeaton**
28 **TRICKY DICKY,** 7, b g Holy Roman Emperor (IRE)—Tricky Situation **Eight Gents & A Lady**
29 **WATHEER (IRE),** 5, ch g Leroidesanimaux (BRZ)—Sunset Shore **Middleham Park Racing CIII & Partner**
30 **YOLO AGAIN (IRE),** 4, b f Toronado (IRE)—Suite (IRE) **Nick Bradley Racing 12 & Partner**
31 **ZIHAAM,** 6, ch g Dutch Art—Hymnsheet **Nick Bradley Racing 29 & Partner**
32 **ZODIAKOS (IRE),** 7, b g Kodiac—Zonic **Mr C Varley & Mr R G Fell**
33 **ZYLAN (IRE),** 8, ch g Kyllachy—Belgique (IRE) **Mr R. G. Fell**

THREE-YEAR-OLDS

34 **BIG CITY,** b g Zoffany (IRE)—Anipa **Nick Bradley Racing 12 & Partners**
35 **COLD WAR STEVE,** ch g Lope de Vega (IRE)—Balamana (FR) **Nick Bradley Racing 12 & Partner**
36 **FANSURPER (IRE),** b g Gutaifan (IRE)—Twiggy's Girl (IRE) **Northern Marking Ltd**
37 **LA TRINIDAD,** b g Bated Breath—High Drama (IRE) **Mrs D. W. Davenport**
38 **SPANTIK,** b c Canford Cliffs (IRE)—Syrdarya **Mount Pleasant Racing & Partner**
39 **WHAT A BUSINESS (IRE),** b g Gregorian (IRE)—Lady Bee (IRE) **Mr S Greenhalgh & Northern Marking Ltd**

Other Owners: Armstrong Richardson & Co Ltd, P. Bamford, Mr J. M. Binns, Mr N. Bradley, Mr L. H. Christie, Colne Valley Racing, Mr H. T. H. Dean, Mr A. Denham, Mr T. Denham, Mr R. G. Fell, Mr A. Franks, S. Franks, Mr M. P. Glass, Mr S. Greenhalgh, Mrs J. Greetham, Miss V. Greetham, Mr K. Hamilton, Miss S. Holden, Mr N. E. M. Jones, Mr A. S. Kelvin, Mr P. M. Lockwood, Middleham Park Racing CIII, Middleham Park Racing LI, Middleham Park Racing LXI, Middleham Park Racing LXXI, Middleham Park Racing LXXII, Middleham Park Racing LXXIII, Middleham Park and Ventura Racing 6, Middleham Park and Ventura Racing 7, Mount Pleasant Racing, Nick Bradley Racing 12 & Sohi, Nick Bradley Racing 16, Nick Bradley Racing 29, Nick Bradley Racing 3, Northern Marking Ltd, T. S. Palin, M. Prince, Mr W. J. Salthouse, Mr R. J. Smeaton, Mr D. A. Swales, Mr M. Taylor, The Roses Partnership, Mr C. J. Varley, Mr I. K. White.

Assistant Trainer: Sean Murray.

Flat Jockey: Ben Curtis, Tony Hamilton. **Apprentice Jockey:** Keelan Baker, Ben Sanderson. **Amateur Jockey:** Ms Rosie Haworth, Ms Debra Hutchinson

---

192 **MR CHARLIE FELLOWES, Newmarket**
Postal: **Bedford House Stables, 7 Bury Road, Newmarket, Suffolk, CB8 7BX**
Contacts: **PHONE 01638 666948 MOBILE 07968 499596**
EMAIL **charlie@charliefellowesracing.co.uk WEBSITE www.charliefellowesracing.co.uk**

1 **ABE LINCOLN (USA),** 7, b h Discreet Cat (USA)—Truly Blushed (USA) **Mrs S. M. Roy**
2 **CAEN NA COILLE (USA),** 4, b br f Medaglia d'Oro (USA)—Strathnaver **Radley Racing Club**
3 **CAPLA JAIPUR,** 5, ch g Sepoy (AUS)—Parthenos **Joe Soiza & Mason Soiza**
4 **CARNWENNAN (IRE),** 5, b g Cacique (IRE)—Slieve **Mr K. F. V. Kong**
5 **CHIEFOFCHIEFS,** 7, b g Royal Applause—Danvers **M. L. Ayers**
6 **ESCALATOR,** 5, br g Cape Cross (IRE)—Sayyedati Symphony (USA) **Mr S. M. bel Obaida**
7 **EZZRAH,** 4, b g Garswood—Tessie **M. L. Ayers**
8 **FREEROLLING,** 5, ch g Exceed And Excel (AUS)—Overturned **Three Of A Kind**
9 **GOLDEN FORCE,** 4, b g Lethal Force (IRE)—Malilla (IRE) **A. M. Mitchell**
10 **HAVERLAND (IRE),** 5, b g Big Bad Bob (IRE)—Pivotal's Princess (IRE) **Mr G. Mills**
11 **JEREMIAH,** 5, ch g Kheleyf (USA)—Tessie **M. L. Ayers**
12 **KING OTTOKAR (FR),** 4, b c Motivator—Treasure (FR) **Mrs S. M. Roy**
13 **LADY DAUPHIN (IRE),** 4, b f Bungle Inthejungle—Chateau Dauphin (USA) **The Johnson's**
14 **LADY OF ARAN,** 5, b m Sir Prancealot (IRE)—
Tipperary Boutique (IRE) **Bengough, Fellowes, Horsford & Soiza**
15 **LORD HALIFAX (IRE),** 4, b g Famous Name—Neutral **Never So Bold - Aquino**

MR CHARLIE FELLOWES - continued

16 **MANKAYAN (IRE)**, 4, b g Intello (GER)—Angelic Note (IRE) **Dahab Racing**
17 **MAYFAIR POMPETTE (FR)**, 4, ch f Toronado (IRE)—Tipsy Me **Joe Soiza & Mason Soiza**
18 **MAYFAIR SPIRIT (IRE)**, 4, b g Charm Spirit (IRE)—Sassy Gal (IRE) **Mr J. Soiza**
19 **MOON SWIFT**, 4, b f Sea The Moon (GER)—Parisette **Mr & Mrs P. Homewood**
20 **PIRATE KING**, 5, br g Farhh—Generous Diana **Daniel MacAuliffe & Anoj Don**
21 **PRINCE OF ARRAN**, 7, b g Shirocco (GER)—Storming Sioux **Mr S. M. bel Obaida**
22 **RUDY LEWIS (IRE)**, 4, b g Excelebration (IRE)—Bless You **Mr A. S. F. Frost**
23 **RUM BABA**, 4, ch g New Approach (IRE)—Soft Centre **Normandie Stud Ltd**
24 **SMOKE ON THE WATER**, 4, ch g Iffraaj—Fullaah (IRE) **Miss Emily Asprey & Christopher Wright**

THREE-YEAR-OLDS

25 **ALAMORA**, gr f Gleneagles (IRE)—Mussoorie (FR) **A. E. Oppenheimer**
26 **AMARILLO STAR (IRE)**, ch c Society Rock (IRE)—Neutrina (IRE) **Lady De Ramsey**
27 **ANGLO SAXSON (IRE)**, ch g Starspangledbanner (AUS)—Obligada (IRE) **Daniel MacAuliffe & Anoj Don**
28 **ATAILOF TWO CITIES (IRE)**, b f Champs Elysees—Chelsea Morning (USA) **Mr C. N. Wright**
29 **BEAUTY CHOICE**, b g Bated Breath—Modesty's Way (USA) **Mr S. M. Kwok**
30 **BLOW YOUR HORN (IRE)**, b c Golden Horn—She's Complete (IRE) **A. E. Oppenheimer**
31 **BOASTY (IRE)**, b g Sir Prancealot (IRE)—Caffe Latte (IRE) **Sohi, Clark & Moore**
32 **BOMA GREEN**, b br c Iffraaj—Dubai Cyclone (USA) **Mrs S. M. Roy**
33 **BURNING (IRE)**, br c Gutaifan (IRE)—Rayon Rouge (IRE) **Mr M. B. Hughes**
34 **BYRON HILL (IRE)**, b c Kingston Hill—Gwen Lady Byron (IRE) **The St Gatien Stables Partnership**
35 **CONFOUNDING**, ch f Lethal Force (IRE)—Confusing **Gg Tbreds, Whatton Manor, Beetles & King**
36 B f Shamardal (USA)—Dubian To (IRE) **M. Obaida**
37 **DUEL IN THE SUN (IRE)**, ch c Sea The Stars (IRE)—Queen's Conquer **Mrs S. M. Roy**
38 B g Mayson—Height of Vanity (IRE)
39 **HELIAEBEL**, b f Camelot—Zamzama (IRE) **Mr P Hickman, Mr G Johns & Mr D King**
40 **HIGHLAND DREAMER (IRE)**, b f Gleneagles (IRE)—Seolan (IRE) **Mr D. Pearson**
41 **IMMORTAL BELOVED**, b f Gleneagles (IRE)—All's Forgotten (USA) **Lady Bamford**
42 **KING CARNEY**, ch c Australia—Petit Trianon **Mrs S. M. Roy**
43 **LONDON ARCH**, b c Fastnet Rock (AUS)—Mount Crystal (IRE) **Mr P Hickman, Mr G Johns & Mr D King**
44 **MADAME PELTIER (IRE)**, b f Exceed And Excel (AUS)—
⠀⠀⠀⠀⠀⠀⠀⠀⠀⠀⠀⠀⠀⠀⠀⠀⠀⠀⠀⠀Airline Hostess (IRE) **Mr P Hickman, Mr G Johns & Mr D King**
45 **ONASSIS (IRE)**, b f Dubawi (IRE)—Jacqueline Quest (IRE) **Triermore Stud & The Hon P. Stanley**
46 **PERFECT INCH**, ro f Dark Angel (IRE)—Inchina **Mr A E Oppenheimer & Ms A Oppenheimer**
47 **POET'S EYE**, b br f Poet's Voice—Monasata **Jck Partnership**
48 **PRINCE OF TIDES (IRE)**, b g New Approach (IRE)—Baby Houseman **Mrs S. M. Roy**
49 **RIVIERA BELLE**, b f Medaglia d'Oro (USA)—Eastern Belle **A. E. Oppenheimer**
50 Ch g Starspangledbanner (AUS)—Run of The Day **Mr D. R. J. King**
51 **SMALL PIANIST**, b c Kyllachy—Partly Sunny **Mr D. S. Lee**
52 **SOR HI HI**, b f Mukhadram—Miss Rimex (IRE) **Mr D. S. Lee**
53 **SOROS**, b g Teofilo (IRE)—Hana Lina **Mr P Hickman, Mr G Johns & Mr D King**
54 **STAR DREAMER**, b f Nathaniel (IRE)—Queen's Dream (IRE) **Mr A Simpson & Mrs S Roy**

TWO-YEAR-OLDS

55 B f 05/02 Siyouni (FR)—Akhmatova (Cape Cross) (IRE) (47000)
56 **ANGEL AMADEA**, gr f 05/04 Dark Angel (IRE)—Keene Dancer (Danehill Dancer (IRE)) (52380) **Mr G. Smith-Bernal**
57 B c 01/05 Sea The Stars (IRE)—Bibury (Royal Applause) (38000) **Dahab Racing**
58 **CABLE GUY**, b c 21/03 Cable Bay (IRE)—Diane's Choice (Komaite (USA))
59 **DEPUTY (IRE)**, b c 24/02 Lawman (FR)—
⠀⠀⠀⠀⠀⠀⠀⠀⠀⠀⠀⠀⠀⠀⠀⠀⠀⠀⠀⠀Finagle (IRE) (Azamour (IRE)) (31428) **Highclere T'Bred Racing - Philip Blacker**
60 **GEORGE SCOTT (IRE)**, b c 12/02 Zoffany (IRE)—African Plains (Oasis Dream) (20000) **Offthebridle Podcast**
61 **GOLDEN BEAR (IRE)**, b c 06/05 Kodiac—Golden Flower (Royal Applause) (100000) **Mrs S. M. Roy**
62 B f 26/04 Brazen Beau (AUS)—Her Honour (IRE) (Shamardal (USA)) **Mr D. R. J. King**
63 B c 05/05 New Bay—Lus Na Greine (IRE) (Pour Moi (IRE)) (42900)
64 Ch c 11/04 Night of Thunder (IRE)—Mathanora (IRE) (Anabaa (USA)) (85000) **M. Obaida**
65 B c 27/01 Vadamos (FR)—Peronism (USA) (Street Cry (IRE)) (60000) **M. Obaida**
66 **POCKETEER (IRE)**, b f 28/02 Adaay (IRE)—Dry Your Eyes (IRE) (Shamardal (USA)) (50000) **Mr G. Smith-Bernal**
67 Ch f 24/03 Casamento (IRE)—Pound Sterling (Champs Elysees)
68 B c 02/04 Asmar (IRE)—Qanateer (IRE) (Iffraaj) **Mrs V. Machen**

MR CHARLIE FELLOWES - continued

69 B gr f 04/05 Sixties Icon—Rose Cheval (USA) (Johannesburg (USA)) **Newmarket Racing Club**
70 B f 24/03 Pride of Dubai (AUS)—Run of The Day (Three Valleys (USA)) **Mr D. R. J. King**
71 B f 23/03 Gleneagles (IRE)—Seolan (IRE) (Alhaarth (IRE)) **Mr D. Pearson**
72 SHERRY BABY (IRE), b f 14/01 Nathaniel (IRE)—Disclose (Dansili) **Mrs S. M. Roy**
73 Ch c 09/02 Twilight Son—Signs And Signals (IRE) (Kodiac) (30476) **H.H. Shaikh Nasser Al Khalifa & Partner**
74 B c 26/04 Free Eagle (IRE)—Silirisa (FR) (Sillery (USA)) (25740)
75 TALLULAH (IRE), ch f 10/04 Sea The Stars (IRE)—Ninas Terz (GER) (Tertullian (USA)) (100000) **Mrs S. M. Roy**
76 B c 13/03 Charming Thought—Tessie (Tiger Hill (IRE)) **M. L. Ayers**
77 THE FIRST HURRAH (FR), b f 29/04 Muhaarar—Sweet Cecily (IRE) (Kodiac) (66666) **Mr G. Smith-Bernal**
78 B c 31/01 Pride of Dubai (AUS)—Timba (Oasis Dream) (23000) **Dahab Racing**
79 Ch c 05/02 Gleneagles (IRE)—Vendetta (IRE) (Fastnet Rock (AUS)) (51480) **Mrs S. M. Roy**
80 WANNABE SAFE (IRE), b f 28/02 Oasis Dream—Wannabe Posh (IRE) (Grand Lodge (USA)) **Normandie Stud Ltd**
81 Gr ro f 24/04 Twirling Candy (USA)—Winter Evening (USA) (Exchange Rate (USA)) (52083) **Mr C. N. Wright**
82 B c 04/04 Awtaad (IRE)—Ziria (IRE) (Danehill Dancer (IRE)) (23166)

Other Owners: H.H. Sheikh Nasser Al Khalifa, Miss Emily Charlotte Asprey, Mrs D. Beetles, Mr A. N. C. Bengough, Mr N. Clark, Mrs K. L. Day, Mr C. H. Fellowes, GG Thoroughbreds VI, Mr G. Gill, Mrs B. A. Hanbury, C. O. P. Hanbury, Mr P. J. Hickman, Mr P. E. Homewood, Mrs S. Homewood, G. Horsford, Mr G. Johns, Mr G. Johnson, Mr G. Johnson, Mr M. J. Johnson, Mr D. R. J. King, Mrs J. M. King, Marshall Farms Ltd, Mr C. Moore, Mr F. Nass, Ms A. Oppenheimer, A. E. Oppenheimer, Mrs C. E. Percival, Mr C. Pigram, P. D. Player, Mrs J. Rose, Mrs S. M. Roy, Alasdair Simpson, Mr K. Sohi, Mr J. Soiza, Mr M. R. Soiza, The Hon Mrs Frances Stanley, Triermore Stud, Mr C. N. Wright.

Flat Jockey: Stevie Donohoe. **Apprentice Jockey:** Aled Beech.

---

193   **MR JAMES FERGUSON, Newmarket**
Postal: **Saville House Stables, St Mary's Square, Newmarket, Suffolk, CB8 0HZ**
Contacts: **WORK 01638 599581 MOBILE 07826 889571**
WORK EMAIL james@jamesfergusonracing.com

1 ARABIAN KING, 4, ch g New Approach (IRE)—Barshiba (IRE) **The Gem Set**
2 JOHNNY REB, 4, b g Showcasing—Specific Dream
3 LEADER WRITER (FR), 8, b g Pivotal—Miss Emma May (IRE) **The Leader Writer Group**
4 THE RIGHT CHOICE (IRE), 5, ch g Choisir (AUS)—Expedience (USA) **Mrs M. Ferguson**
5 U S S MICHIGAN (USA), 4, gr g War Front (USA)—Photograph (USA) **Mr L. Williams**

THREE-YEAR-OLDS

6 MACK THE KNIFE (IRE), b g Australia—Kitty Matcham (IRE) **M. A. C. Buckley**
7 MYSTIC RIVER (IRE), b c Animal Kingdom (USA)—Harriet Tubman (USA) **M. A. C. Buckley**

TWO-YEAR-OLDS

8 B c 02/05 Invincible Spirit (IRE)—Cascading (Teofilo (IRE)) (125000)
9 B c 15/05 Teofilo (IRE)—Georgie Hyde (Yeats (IRE)) (60000)
10 B c 06/04 Vadamos (FR)—Good For Her (Rock of Gibraltar (IRE)) (45000)
11 B f 30/01 Iffraaj—Meeting Waters (Aqlaam) (28000)
12 B c 03/04 Camelot—Sapphire Waters (IRE) (Six Sense (JPN)) (62000)
13 B br c 03/04 Giant's Causeway—Sweet Shirley Mae (USA) (Broken Vow (USA)) **Mr J. P. Ferguson**
14 Ch c 16/05 Kitten's Joy (USA)—Trensa (USA) (Giant's Causeway (USA)) **Mr L. Williams**
15 B c 19/03 Frankel—Trophee (FR) (Mr Sidney (USA)) (200000)
16 B c 24/02 Charm Spirit (IRE)—Valonia (Three Valleys (USA)) (24761) **The Free Spirits**
17 B g 03/04 New Approach (IRE)—Vetlana (IRE) (Vale of York (IRE)) (26000)
18 Br f 22/02 Cable Bay (IRE)—Wosaita (Generous (IRE))
19 B f 05/04 Kodiac—Zallerina (Zamindar (USA)) (49523) **Glentree Pastoral Pty Ltd**

Head Girl: Aideen Marshall, **Travelling Head:** Alyson West.

194 MR DOMINIC FFRENCH DAVIS, Lambourn
Postal: **College House, 3 Oxford Street, Lambourn, Hungerford, Berkshire, RG17 8XP**
Contacts: **HOME 01488 72342 PHONE 01488 73675 MOBILE 07831 118764 FAX 01488 73675**
EMAIL ffrenchdavis@btinternet.com WEBSITE www.ffrenchdavis.com

1 **CHILL IN THE WOOD**, 11, br m Desert King (IRE)—Zaffaranni (IRE) **Mr D. G. Cramm**
2 **DISTANT APPLAUSE (IRE)**, 5, b g Acclamation—Spacecraft (USA) **S. J. Edwards**
3 **INDEED**, 5, b g Showcasing—Argumentative **Marchwood Aggregates**
4 **JAMES PARK WOODS (IRE)**, 4, b g Australia—Happy Holly (IRE) **D. J. S. Ffrench Davis**
5 **SNOWBIRD (IRE)**, 9, ch m Presenting—Blueanna (IRE)
6 **THEMATIC (USA)**, 4, b g Noble Mission—Gateway (USA) **Marchwood Aggregates**
7 **WHATTHEBUTLERSAW (IRE)**, 11, br g Arcadio (GER)—
                                    Phar From Men (IRE) **Mrs P Ffrench Davis & Mr D Ffrench Davis**

THREE-YEAR-OLDS
8 **BOY GEORGE**, b g Equiano (FR)—If I Were A Boy (IRE)
9 **CALL MY BLUFF (IRE)**, b c Make Believe—Ocean Bluff (IRE)
10 **EGYPSYAN CRACKAJAK**, b g Kutub (IRE)—Three Scoops **G. King Haulage Ltd**
11 **FORKED LIGHTNING**, b g Night of Thunder (IRE)—Darrfonah (IRE) **Mr Gary Black & Mr Paul Townend**
12 **JIM 'N' TOMIC (IRE)**, b g War Command (USA)—Anna David **The Agincourt Partnership**

TWO-YEAR-OLDS
13 **JUST A JEROBOAM**, b c 14/02 Bobby's Kitten (USA)—Isostatic (Champs Elysees)

Other Owners: Mr G. H. Black, D. J. S. Ffrench Davis, Mrs P. Ffrench Davis, Mr R. F. Haynes, The Ffrench Connection, Mr P. A. Townend.

Assistant Trainer: Ben Ffrench Davis.

NH Jockey: Mark Grant.

195 MR GUISEPPE FIERRO, Hednesford
Postal: **Brook House, Rawnsley Road, Hednesford, Cannock, Staffordshire, WS12 1RB**
Contacts: **PHONE 01543 879611 MOBILE 07976 321468**

1 **JUST LIKE BETH**, 12, b m Proclamation (IRE)—Just Beth **G. Fierro**
2 **LAFILIA (GER)**, 5, b m Teofilo (IRE)—Labrice **G. Fierro**
3 **LITTLE DOTTY**, 11, br m Erhaab (USA)—Marsh Marigold **G. Fierro**
4 **RAMBLING RIVER**, 9, b g Revoque (IRE)—Just Beth **G. Fierro**
5 **SUNDANCE BOY**, 11, gr g Proclamation (IRE)—Just Beth **G. Fierro**

Assistant Trainer: M Fierro.

196 MRS MARJORIE FIFE, Stillington
Postal: **White Thorn Farm, Stillington, Easingwold, York, YO61 1LT**
Contacts: **PHONE 01347 822012 MOBILE 07890 075217**
EMAIL wfife10416@aol.com

1 **ASTROSPEED (IRE)**, 5, ch g Choisir (AUS)—Angel Stevens (IRE) **Dragon Gate Development Limited**
2 **B FIFTY TWO (IRE)**, 11, br g Dark Angel (IRE)—Petite Maxine **Fat Badger Racing**
3 **BANKSEA**, 7, b g Lawman (FR)—Stars In Your Eyes **The Carlton Club**
4 **CLASSIC PURSUIT**, 9, b g Pastoral Pursuits—Snake's Head **Mrs M. Turner**
5 **DR RICHARD KIMBLE (IRE)**, 5, b g Lawman (FR)—Aoife Alainn (IRE) **Green Lane**
6 **FASCINATING SPIRIT (IRE)**, 5, b m Fastnet Rock (AUS)—Maryellen's Spirit (IRE) **Mr R. W. Fife**
7 **METAL EXCHANGE**, 4, b f Helmet (AUS)—Bochafina (FR) **Fat Badger Racing**
8 **MOUNTAIN RESCUE (IRE)**, 8, b g High Chaparral (IRE)—Amber Queen (IRE) **B. W. Parren**

MRS MARJORIE FIFE - continued

9 **PERCY (IRE)**, 6, gr g Kodiac—Bysshe **B. W. Parren**
10 **ROBOT BOY (IRE)**, 10, ch g Shamardal (USA)—Pivotal's Princess (IRE) **Mr R. W. Fife**
11 **TOR**, 6, ch g Orientor—Dance In The Sun **Mr I. Wilson**

THREE-YEAR-OLDS

12 **ELIXIR VITAE**, b f Fountain of Youth (IRE)—Just The Tonic
13 B c Hot Streak (IRE)—Lady Suesanne (IRE)

---

197 **MR TIM FITZGERALD, Malton**
Postal: **Norton Grange, Norton, Malton, North Yorkshire, YO17 9EA**
Contacts: **PHONE 01653 228456 MOBILE 07950 356437**
EMAIL fitzgeraldracing@hotmail.com

1 **FLAT TO THE MAX (FR)**, 5, b g Maxios—Another Name (USA) **Mr M. Pimlott**
2 **GLOBAL EXPRESS**, 4, ch g New Approach (IRE)—All For Laura **Koya Equine**
3 **HE'S MAGIC**, 9, b g Court Masterpiece—Lady Magician **Mrs M. Lingwood**
4 **LE MAHARAJAH (FR)**, 5, b g Cacique (IRE)—Sign of Life
5 **PUNJAB MAIL**, 4, b g Charm Spirit (IRE)—Harryana **Star Sports Bloodstock**
6 **STREETS OF MILAN (IRE)**, 9, b g Milan—Madame Jean (FR) **All For the Craic Partnership**

THREE-YEAR-OLDS

7 **DANCING GIRL (FR)**, ch f Style Vendome (FR)—Aljafliyah **De Zoete, Hoskins, Lewis & Nutting**
8 **GO WELL SPICY (IRE)**, gr f Gutaifan (IRE)—Best New Show (IRE) **Mr M. Pimlott**
9 **LOCKED N' LOADED**, b c Morpheus—La Roumegue (USA) **Star Sports Bloodstock**
10 **MAGIC TIMING**, b g Hot Streak (IRE)—Enchanted Princess **Mr M. Pimlott**

Other Owners: Mr S. M. De Zoete, Mr D. J. Haddrell, Mr R. S. Hoskins, Mr B. Keith, Mrs Rosemary F. Lewis, Mrs C. H. M. L. Nutting, Pearl Bloodstock Limited, Mr M. Pimlott.

---

198 **MR JOHN FLINT, Bridgend**
Postal: **Woodland Lodge, Waunbant Road, Kenfig Hill, Bridgend, Mid Glamorgan, CF33 6FF**
Contacts: **MOBILE 07581 428173 FAX 01656 744347**
EMAIL johnflint900@gmail.com WEBSITE www.johnflintracing.com

1 **AMATEUR (IRE)**, 7, ch g Giant's Causeway (USA)—Adja (IRE) **Burnham Plastering & Drylining Ltd**
2 **ARIAN (IRE)**, 8, b m King's Theatre (IRE)—Brave Betsy (IRE) **Mr D. M. Mathias**
3 **CAMERONSCAT**, 4, b f Cameron Highland (IRE)—French Quartet (IRE) **Team CH Racing**
4 **CARP KID (IRE)**, 5, b g Lope de Vega (IRE)—Homegrown (IRE) **JACK Racing**
5 **CILLIAN'S WELL (IRE)**, 10, b g Trans Island—Live A Lot (IRE) **Belly's Heroes**
6 **COURT DUTY (IRE)**, 8, b g Court Cave (IRE)—Easter Duties (IRE) **Davies & Price**
7 **DIAMOND SHOWER (IRE)**, 4, b f Clodovil (IRE)—Star Lodge **J. L. Flint**
8 **EDDIEMAURICE (IRE)**, 9, ch g Captain Rio—Annals **Mr D. M. Mathias**
9 **FIELD OF VISION (IRE)**, 7, b g Pastoral Pursuits—Grand Design **Paul Duffy, David Semmens, Viv Williams**
10 **GALILEO JADE (IRE)**, 4, b f Australia—Dusty In Memphis (USA) **Burnham Plastering & Drylining Ltd**
11 **GRAVITY WAVE (IRE)**, 6, br g Rip Van Winkle (IRE)—Phrase **Mr D. M. Mathias**
12 **I AM PLASTERED**, 5, b g Midnight Legend—One For Joules (IRE) **Burnham Plastering & Drylining Ltd**
13 **JUST CHAMPION**, 4, b g Dunaden (FR)—Koliakhova (FR) **Mr D. M. Mathias**
14 **JUST DYMOKE**, 4, b f Mount Nelson—Old Unit **Mr D. A. Poole**
15 **JUST RIGHT**, 5, ch m Medicean—Rightside **Mr D. M. Mathias**
16 **KATCHAR KISS**, 4, gr f Yorgunnabelucky (USA)—Ovilia (IRE) **Katchar Racing**
17 **LAC SACRE (FR)**, 11, b g Bering—Lady Glorieuse (FR) **Mr L. H. & Mrs T. Evans**
18 **LOVE AND BE LOVED**, 6, b m Lawman (FR)—Rightside **J. L. Flint**
19 **MAMA AFRICA (IRE)**, 6, br m Big Bad Bob—Colourpoint (USA) **Mr D. M. Mathias**
20 **MOREECE (IRE)**, 11, b g Chevalier (IRE)—Jumbo Romance (IRE) **Miss S. Embley**

MR JOHN FLINT - continued

21 **NATIVE SOLDIER (IRE)**, 6, b g Sepoy (AUS)—Electra Star **J. L. Flint**
22 **OUTER SPACE**, 9, b g Acclamation—Venoge (IRE) **J. L. Flint**
23 **SOMEONE YOU LOVE**, 4, b f Schiaparelli (GER)—Perjury
24 **THE WIRE FLYER**, 5, b g Champs Elysees—Good Morning Star (IRE) **Aled Evans & Tommy Williams**
25 **WINKLEMANN (IRE)**, 8, br g Rip Van Winkle (IRE)—Kykuit (IRE) **Mr D. M. Mathias**
26 **WITH PLEASURE**, 7, b g Poet's Voice—With Fascination (USA) **Burnham Plastering & Drylining Ltd**

Other Owners: Mr A. Evans, Mr L. H. Evans, Mrs T. Evans, Mr T. Williams.

Assistant Trainer: Mrs Martine Louise Flint, Rhys Flint.

---

199 **MR DAVID FLOOD, Hungerford**
Postal: **15 High Street, Chiseldon, Swindon, Wiltshire, SN4 0NG**
Contacts: **PHONE 07919 340619**
EMAIL davidflood1@hotmail.co.uk

1 **ACCREDITED**, 4, b f Archipenko (USA)—Saltpetre (IRE) **Mrs A. Cowley**
2 **BAZOOKA (IRE)**, 9, b g Camacho—Janadam (IRE) **Mrs A. Cowley**
3 **KENDERGARTEN KOP (IRE)**, 5, ch g Kendargent (FR)—Elsa T (IRE) **Mrs A. Cowley**
4 **PEDESTAL (IRE)**, 6, b g Invincible Spirit (IRE)—Ashley Hall (USA) **Mrs A. Cowley**
5 **STOPDWORLDNLETMEOF**, 6, b g Piccolo—Dilli Dancer **Royal Wootton Bassett Racing Limited**

THREE-YEAR-OLDS

6 **GLENCOE BOY (IRE)**, b g Gleneagles (IRE)—Eastern Appeal (IRE) **Mrs A. Cowley**
7 **LEO'S LUCKYMAN**, b g Cable Bay (IRE)—Atalis **Royal Wootton Bassett Racing Limited**
8 **MAJESTYK FIRE (IRE)**, ch g Ivawood (IRE)—Dream Impossible (IRE) **Mrs A. Cowley**
9 **ROYAL CHARMER**, b g Hallowed Crown (AUS)—Yaqootah (USA) **Mr Mr S Barton & Mr P Shields**
10 **TOOLMAKER**, b g Harbour Watch (IRE)—Calypso Dream (IRE) **Mrs Anne Cowley & Mr S J Barton**

Other Owners: Mr S. Barton, Mrs A. Cowley, Mr P. Shields.

---

200 **MR STEVE FLOOK, Leominster**
Postal: **The Granary Stables, Downwood Farm, Shobdon, Leominster, Herefordshire, HR6 9NH**
Contacts: **MOBILE 07811 511566**
EMAIL lwallace@btinternet.com

1 **CENTREOFEXCELLENCE (IRE)**, 9, b g Oscar (IRE)—Calm Approach (IRE) **Mrs P Corbett & Mrs A Thomas**
2 **CHAMPAGNE CASTLE (IRE)**, 4, b f Dragon Pulse (IRE)—Quiet Dream (USA) **T. J. Wardle**
3 **FLAMING CHARMER (IRE)**, 12, ch g Flemensfirth (USA)—Kates Charm (IRE) **Mr S. Price**
4 **GOLD HUNTER (IRE)**, 10, b g Invincible Spirit (IRE)—Goldthroat (IRE) **Chasing Charlie Syndicate**
6 **MR PEANUT**, 4, b g Aeroplane—Sumingasedit (IRE) **Chasing Charlie Syndicate**

TWO-YEAR-OLDS

7 **LIVING ON A DREAM**, b f 07/05 Swiss Spirit—Khafayif (USA) (Swain (IRE)) **S. M. Flook**

Other Owners: Mrs P. Corbett, Mrs A. P. Thomas.

Assistant Trainer: Lynn Wallace.

201 | MR TONY FORBES, Uttoxeter
Postal: **Hill House Farm, Poppits Lane, Stramshall, Uttoxeter, Staffordshire, ST14 5EX**
Contacts: **PHONE 01889 562722 MOBILE 07967 246571**
EMAIL tony@thimble.net

1 **BARCA (USA)**, 6, b g War Front (USA)—Magnificent Honour (USA) **Mr A. L. Forbes**
2 **NO ALARM (IRE)**, 8, b g Getaway (GER)—Chapanga (IRE) **Mr A. L. Forbes**
3 **TINGO IN THE TALE (IRE)**, 11, b g Oratorio (IRE)—Sunlit Skies **Mr A. L. Forbes**

Assistant Trainer: Mr Tim Eley.

202 | MRS PAM FORD, Hereford
Postal: **Stone House Stables, Preston Wynne, Hereford, Herefordshire, HR1 3PB**
Contacts: **PHONE 01432 820604 MOBILE 07733 152051**
EMAIL pam_ford@hotmail.co.uk

1 **APACHE CHIEF**, 12, b g Tikkanen (USA)—Dara's Course (IRE) **K. R. Ford**
2 **KING FRANK**, 7, b g Fantastic Spain (USA)—Elegant Accord (IRE) **K. R. Ford**
3 **TOMOROZ MAN (IRE)**, 8, b g Morozov (USA)—Outdoor Heather (IRE) **K. R. Ford**

Assistant Trainer: Mr K Ford.

203 | MRS RICHENDA FORD, Blandford Forum
Postal: **Garlands Farm, The Common, Okeford Fitzpaine, Blandford Forum, Dorset, DT11 0RT**
Contacts: **MOBILE 07800 634846**
WORK EMAIL Richendafordracing@gmail.com WEBSITE www.richendafordracing.co.uk

1 **DONT BE ROBIN (IRE)**, 8, b g Robin des Pres (FR)—Rainbow Times (IRE) **Mr & Mrs K. B. Snook**
2 **HURRY HENRY (IRE)**, 11, b g Blueprint (IRE)—Tower Princess (IRE) **Mr & Mrs K. B. Snook**
3 **KIRA'S STAR**, 4, b f Denounce—Choisirez (IRE) **Mr M. Enticott**
4 **LEAVE MY ALONE (IRE)**, 7, br m Getaway (GER)—Glenda King (IRE) **Mr & Mrs K. B. Snook**
5 **MONKEY HARRIS (IRE)**, 8, b g Oscar (IRE)—Benefit Ball (IRE) **Mr & Mrs K. B. Snook**
6 **SHANROE SMOOCH (IRE)**, 7, b g Ask—Lady Quesada (IRE) **Mr & Mrs K. B. Snook**
7 **SUSTAINABLE STAR (IRE)**, 9, gr g Winged Love (IRE)—Fooling Around (IRE) **Richenda Ford Racing Club**

Other Owners: K. B. Snook, Mrs M. Snook.

204 | MR BRIAN FORSEY, Taunton
Postal: **Three Oaks, Ash Priors, Taunton, Somerset, TA4 3NQ**
Contacts: **PHONE 01823 433914 MOBILE 07747 392760**
EMAIL forsey2001@yahoo.com

1 **BARISTA (IRE)**, 12, b g Titus Livius (FR)—Cappuccino (IRE) **Three Oaks Racing & Mrs P Bosley**
2 **BUTTERFIELD (IRE)**, 7, b g Fastnet Rock (AUS)—Cozzene's Angel (USA) **Mr Alan Stevens & Mr Brian Forsey**
3 **DROPZONE (USA)**, 11, b g Smart Strike (CAN)—Dalisay (IRE) **Mr Alan Stevens & Mr Brian Forsey**
4 **EDDIES PEARL (IRE)**, 10, b m Craigsteel—Florida Bay (IRE) **Mrs S. Smyth-Ribeiro**
5 **KERRY'S BOY (IRE)**, 7, b g Oscar (IRE)—Kerry's Girl (IRE) **Mr M. P. Ardley**
6 **RUNAIOCHT (IRE)**, 10, ch g Teofilo (IRE)—Julie Girl (USA) **Mrs C. E. E. Turner**

Other Owners: Mrs P. M. Bosley, B. Forsey, A. G. Stevens.

Assistant Trainer: Mrs Elizabeth Chatfield.

205 MISS SANDY FORSTER, Kelso
Postal: **Halterburn Head, Yetholm, Kelso, Roxburghshire, TD5 8PP**
Contacts: **PHONE 01573 420615 MOBILE 07976 587315, 07880 727877 FAX 01573 420615**
EMAIL clivestorey@btinternet.com

1 ASHJAN, 7, b g Medicean—Violet (IRE) **Dave Skeldon & Sandy Forster**
2 CHARLIE SNOW ANGEL, 11, b g Overbury (IRE)—Sister Seven (IRE) **C. Storey**
3 CLAUD AND GOLDIE (IRE), 11, ch g Portrait Gallery (IRE)—Glacial Jewel (IRE) **The Border Racers**
4 KITTY FISHER (IRE), 10, b m Scorpion (IRE)—Luck of The Deise (IRE) **Ms Allison Grant Long & Partner**
5 LASTIN' MEMORIES, 8, b g Overbury (IRE)—Dusky Dante (IRE) **Dave Skeldon & Sandy Forster**
6 LISSEN TO THE LADY (IRE), 6, b m Fame And Glory—Liss Rua (IRE) **Mr M. H. Walton**
7 LOWANBEHOLD (IRE), 13, gr g Cloudings (IRE)—Marble Quest (IRE) **C. Storey**
8 NETTLEBUSH (IRE), 10, br g Kalanisi (IRE)—Amber Gale (IRE) **Miss S. E. Forster, Mrs I. H. Thomson**
9 VEAUCE DE SIVOLA (FR), 11, b g Assessor (IRE)—Eva de Chalamont (FR) **P. Spottiswood**

Other Owners: Miss S. E. Forster, Ms A. G. Long, Mr D. A. Skeldon, C. Storey, Mrs I Thomson & Miss S Forster.

Assistant Trainer: C. Storey.

NH Jockey: Tommy Dowson. Conditional Jockey: Thomas Wilmott. Amateur Jockey: Miss J. Walton.

206 MISS JOANNE FOSTER, Ilkley
Postal: **Brookleigh Farm, Burley Road, Menston, Ilkley, West Yorkshire, LS29 6NS**
Contacts: **PHONE 07980 301808 MOBILE 07980 301808**
EMAIL info@jofosterracing.co.uk WEBSITE www.jofosterracing.co.uk

1 BROTHERLY COMPANY (IRE), 8, b g Fast Company (IRE)—Good Lady (IRE) **The Reign It In Partnership**
2 CANNY STYLE, 7, b m Canford Cliffs (IRE)—Stylish One (IRE) **Golden Syndicate & Mr P. Bentley**
3 CHASE THE WIND (IRE), 11, ch g Spadoun (FR)—Asfreeasthewind (IRE) **Mr J. Nixon**
4 DA VINCI HAND (IRE), 5, b g Champs Elysees—Thousandkissesdeep (IRE) **Mr J. Nixon**
5 DAY OF ROSES (IRE), 11, b g Acambaro (GER)—Dan's Choice (IRE) **Reign It In Again**
6 FRANKIE BALLOU (IRE), 11, br g Norwich—One Up (IRE) **The Yorkshire Racing Partnership**
7 GEORGE HASTINGS, 4, gr g Gregorian (IRE)—Pachanga **Mad For Fun & Partners (2)**
8 LAMMTURNER (IRE), 8, b m Brian Boru—Deploy Or Die (IRE) **Mr E. C. Wilkin**
9 LEOPARD (IRE), 6, b g Iffraaj—Appletreemagic (IRE) **Mad For Fun & Partners (2)**
10 MISDFLIGHT (IRE), 10, ch g Indian River (FR)—Jody's Girl (IRE) **P Williamson & J Foster**
11 SEAPOINT (IRE), 6, b m Footstepsinthesand—Genuinely (IRE) **Give It A Go Partners**
12 SIGURD (GER), 8, ch g Sholokhov (IRE)—Sky News (GER) **Mrs E. A. Verity**
13 TWO HOOTS (IRE), 9, gr g Tikkanen (USA)—Supreme Beneficial (IRE) **Reign It In 2**
14 WONDERFUL WOMAN (IRE), 6, ch m Ask—Green Sea **Greenwood, Collins & Foster**

Other Owners: Mr J. Batty, Mr P. V. Bentley, J. Berry, Ms J. Clark, Mr M. Collins, Mr W. M. Curtis, Mr D. B. Ellis, Mrs C. Finn, Miss J. E. Foster, P. Foster, Mrs J. Greenwood, Mr S. A. Hollings, Mr D. Liddle, Mr L. S. Musson, Mrs C. Potter, Mr M. J. Roche, Mr P. Thompson, J. Townson, Mr P. Williamson.

Assistant Trainer: P. Foster.

NH Jockey: Henry Brooke, Ryan Mania. Amateur Jockey: Miss Becky Smith.

207 MR JIMMY FOX, Marlborough
Postal: **Highlands Farm Stables, Herridge, Collingbourne Ducis, Marlborough, Wiltshire, SN8 3EG**
Contacts: **PHONE 01264 850218, 07931 724358 MOBILE 07702 880010**
EMAIL jcfoxtrainer@aol.com

1 ACT ACCORDINGLY, 7, gr g Sagamix (FR)—Anns Girl **Mrs J. A. Cleary**
2 BILLY STAR, 5, b g Sixties Icon—Appreciative **SP9 Racing Club**
3 CAPTAIN MARMALADE (IRE), 8, gr g Duke of Marmalade (IRE)—Elisium **Mrs S. J. Fox**
4 FRANKIE, 9, gr g Firebreak—Winterbourne **R. E. Kavanagh**

MR JIMMY FOX - continued

5 **GRACEFUL JAMES (IRE)**, 7, ch g Rock of Gibraltar (IRE)—Little Miss Gracie **Abacus Employment Services Ltd**
6 **GRACIOUS GEORGE (IRE)**, 10, b g Oratorio (IRE)—Little Miss Gracie **Highlands Farm Racing Partnership**
7 **MILLIE MAY**, 6, b m Sixties Icon—Maydream **The Dancing Partners**
8 **PURPLE PADDY**, 5, b g Swiss Spirit—Stunning In Purple (IRE) **Mrs B. A. Fuller**
9 **PURPLE TOMMY**, 4, ch g Assertive—Stunning In Purple (IRE) **Abacus Employment Services Ltd**
10 **SIONNACH RUA**, 5, ch m Foxwedge (AUS)—My Jeanie (IRE) **R. E. Kavanagh**

Other Owners: Mr D. S. Estall, Mrs E. Estall, Mrs S. J. Fox, Mrs B. A. Fuller.

Assistant Trainer: Sarah-Jane Fox.

208

MISS SUZZANNE FRANCE, Norton on Derwent
Postal: **Cheesecake Hill House, Highfield, Beverley Road, Norton on Derwent, North Yorkshire, YO17 9PJ**
Contacts: **PHONE 07904 117531 MOBILE 07904 117531 FAX 01653 691947**
EMAIL suzzanne@newstartracing.co.uk WEBSITE www.suzzannefranceracing.com, www.newstartracing.co.uk

1 **AD VITAM (IRE)**, 12, ch g Ad Valorem (USA)—Love Sonnet **Newstart Partnership**
2 **ARCHIVE (FR)**, 10, b g Sulamani (IRE)—Royale Dorothy (FR) **Newstart Partnership & Co**
3 **BILLY DYLAN (IRE)**, 5, b g Excelebration (IRE)—It's True (IRE) **Newstart Partnership**
4 **HE'S GUILTY (USA)**, 4, b br g Blame (USA)—She's Smashing (USA)
5 **LUATH**, 7, ch g Archipenko (USA)—Delaware Dancer (IRE) **Miss Kate Dobb & Mr Stuart Dobb**
6 **MOUNTAIN OF STARS**, 5, b g Equiano (FR)—Ivory Silk **Newstart Partnership**

THREE-YEAR-OLDS

7 **STAND FREE**, b f Helmet (AUS)—Ivory Silk **Miss Kate Dobb & Mr Stuart Dobb**

Other Owners: Miss K. M. Dobb, Mr S. Dobb, Miss Kate Dobb & Mr Stuart Dobb, Mrs P. France, Newstart Partnership.

Assistant Trainer: Mr Aaron James.

209

MR DEREK FRANKLAND, Brackley
Postal: **Springfields, Mixbury, Brackley, Northamptonshire, NN13 5RR**
Contacts: **MOBILE 07763 020406 FAX 01280 847334**
EMAIL dsfrankland@aol.com

1 **CANNY TOM (IRE)**, 10, b g Jimble (FR)—Tombazaan (IRE) **Mr D. S. Frankland & Mr D. J. Trott**
2 **JOINT ACCOUNT (IRE)**, 7, b g Jimble (FR)—Late Back (IRE) **Mr D. S. Frankland & Mr D. J. Trott**

Other Owners: D. S. Frankland, Mr D. J. Trott.

210

MR JAMES FROST, Buckfastleigh
Postal: **Hawson Stables, Buckfastleigh, Devon, TQ11 0HP**
Contacts: **HOME 01364 642332 PHONE 01364 642267 MOBILE 07860 220229 FAX 01364 643182**
EMAIL info@frostracingclub.co.uk

1 **ANTIDOTE (IRE)**, 4, gr g Dark Angel (IRE)—Mood Indigo (IRE) **Frost Racing Club**
2 **BOGOSS DU PERRET (FR)**, 9, b br g Malinas (GER)—Lady Paques (FR) **Mrs J. Bury**
3 **FALSE GETAWAY (IRE)**, 7, b m Getaway (GER)—False Messenger (IRE) **Mr T. Saye**
4 **FINDUSATGORCOMBE**, 8, b g Tobougg (IRE)—Seemma **Mr P. R. Meaden**
5 **GILLY GRACE**, 10, b m Morpeth—Miss Grace **Frost Racing Club**
6 **GOODGOLLYMISSJOLLY (IRE)**, 6, ch m Ask—Reconbustible (IRE) **Mr T. Symons**
7 **GORCOMBE'S RASCAL**, 7, b g Fantastic View (USA)—Seem of Gold **Mr P. R. Meaden**

MR JAMES FROST - continued

8 **JOHNOFGORCOMBE**, 6, b g Sakhee (USA)—Seem of Gold **Mr P. R. Meaden**
9 **KAPOUPAKAP (FR)**, 8, b m Kapgarde (FR)—Lily Valley (FR) **J. D. Frost**
10 **LEGEND OF ZORRO (IRE)**, 7, ch g Touch of Land (FR)—Wotaglen (IRE) **G. D. Thompson**
11 **MONET MOOR**, 11, b m Morpeth—Miracle Monarch **Frost Racing Club**
12 **NIAMH'S OSCAR (IRE)**, 8, b g Oscar (IRE)—High Park Lady (IRE) **The Flighty Five**
13 **OTTER LYNN**, 5, b m Alqaahir (USA)—Definite Lynn (IRE) **J. D. Frost**
14 **QUINTO**, 10, ch g Desideratum—Cruz Santa **Frost Racing Club**
15 **RULER RYDE**, 5, br g Alqaahir (USA)—Bobbies Ryde **Mr T. F. G. Marks**
16 **SILVER QUAY (IRE)**, 8, gr g Dark Angel (IRE)—She Runs (FR) **C & Mrs A Jones**
17 **THIS BREAC (IRE)**, 9, br g Carlo Bank (IRE)—De Breac (IRE) **Mr. Andrew Shepherd & Mr. Jimmy Frost**
18 **TREACYS JIM (IRE)**, 6, b g Milan—Bridge Hotel Lilly (IRE) **Mrs J. Bury**
19 **TRIPLE CHIEF (IRE)**, 9, b br g High Chaparral (IRE)—Trebles (IRE) **G. D. Thompson**
20 **TROED Y MELIN (IRE)**, 8, b g Craigsteel—Kissangel (IRE) **No Illusions Partnership**
21 **WHY SO KEEN BOB (IRE)**, 10, ch m Marienbard (IRE)—Bridge Hotel Katie (IRE) **J. D. Frost**

Other Owners: J. D. Frost, Mr C. Jones, Mrs J. A. Jones, Mr A. J. Shepherd.

Assistant Trainer: G. Frost.

NH Jockey: Bryony Frost.

---

211 **MR KEVIN FROST, Butterton**
Postal: **Butterton Racing Stables, Park Road, Butterton, Newcastle, Staffordshire, ST5 4DZ**
Contacts: **PHONE 07748 873092 MOBILE 07919 370081**
EMAIL info@kevinfrostracing.co.uk WEBSITE www.kevinfrostracing.co.uk

1 **ALL SET TO GO (IRE)**, 9, gr g Verglas (IRE)—Firecrest (IRE) **Total Asbestos Solutions Limiited**
2 **BILLIEBROOKEDIT (IRE)**, 5, ch g Dragon Pulse (IRE)—Klang (IRE) **Mr Matthew & Mrs Rachael Gavin**
3 **CALVINIST**, 7, b g Holy Roman Emperor (IRE)—Sharp Relief (IRE) **Mr M. G. Roberts**
4 **CHIEFTAIN'S CHOICE (IRE)**, 11, b g King's Theatre (IRE)—Fairy Native (IRE) **Curzon House Partnership & Friends**
5 **DOCUMENTING**, 7, b g Zamindar (USA)—Namaskar **Kevin Frost Racing Club & M.A. Humphreys**
6 **EARL OF BUNNACURRY (IRE)**, 6, b g Approve (IRE)—Bonkers **Mr M. J. Lynch**
7 **ENCHANTING ENYA (IRE)**, 5, ch m Champs Elysees—Miss Honorine (IRE) **Mr Matthew & Mrs Rachael Gavin**
8 **EPANEEMA (IRE)**, 5, b m Epaulette (AUS)—Taqqara (IRE) **Mr K. Frost**
9 **FRANCIS XAVIER (IRE)**, 6, b g High Chaparral (IRE)—Missionary Hymn (USA) **Curzon House Partnership**
10 **HART FELL**, 4, b g Nayef (USA)—Dumfriesshire **Total Asbestos Solutions Limiited**
11 **HELVETIAN**, 5, b g Swiss Spirit—Lucky Dip **Ms T. Keane**
12 **HOLY HYMN (IRE)**, 4, b g Holy Roman Emperor (IRE)—Missionary Hymn (USA) **Curzon House Partnership**
13 **HURRICANE DYLAN (IRE)**, 9, b g Brian Boru—Definetly Sarah (IRE) **Mr J. Stimpson**
14 **ICE CANYON**, 6, b g Raven's Pass (USA)—Picture Hat (USA) **Mr Derek & Mrs Marie Dean**
15 **MANFADH (IRE)**, 5, b g Iffraaj—Asiya (USA) **Mr Derek & Mrs Marie Dean**
16 **MY BROTHER MIKE (IRE)**, 6, b g Bated Breath—Coming Back **Mr J. Stimpson**
17 **MY TOWN CHICAGO (USA)**, 5, b g Medaglia d'Oro (USA)—Say You Will (IRE) **Mr J. Stimpson**
18 **PASTIME**, 6, b g Pastoral Pursuits—Piddies Pride (IRE) **Boston R. S. Ian Bennett**
19 **PERUVIAN SUMMER (IRE)**, 4, ch g Lope de Vega (IRE)—Need You Now (IRE) **Mr J. Stimpson**
20 **POPPOP (FR)**, 4, b g Great Pretender (IRE)—Bloody Sunday (FR) **Mr J. Stimpson**
21 **POPPY JAG (IRE)**, 5, b m Kodiac—Jacquelin Jag (IRE) **Curzon House Partnership**
22 **R BERNARD**, 4, b g Norse Dancer (IRE)—Channel Treat **Mr R. J. W. Broadley**
23 **RED SKY IN SPAIN**, 4, ch g Iffraaj—Adonesque (IRE) **Mr J. Stimpson**
24 **SNAFEE TIGER**, 4, ch g Dutch Art—Point of Control **Curzon House Partnership**
25 **STEAL THE SCENE (IRE)**, 8, b g Lord Shanakill (USA)—Namoos (USA) **Curzon House Partnership & Friends**
26 **STORM LIGHTNING**, 11, b g Exceed And Excel (AUS)—All For Laura **Law Abiding Citizens**
27 **TARBEYAH (IRE)**, 5, ch m Teofilo (IRE)—Shamtari (USA) **Mr K. Frost**
28 **THE THROSTLES**, 5, b g Poet's Voice—Stylish Dream (USA) **Kevin Frost Racing Club & Trisha Keane**

THREE-YEAR-OLDS

29 **APACHITO**, b g Fountain of Youth (IRE)—Apache Glory (USA) **Mr J. Stimpson**
30 **GYPSY TRAVELLER**, b g Alhebayeb (IRE)—Romany Gypsy **Mr K. Frost**

MR KEVIN FROST - continued

31 HACHERT, b g Lope de Vega (IRE)—Sense of Joy **Jonathan & Catherine Williams**
32 HALLOWED DREAM (IRE), b g Hallowed Crown (AUS)—Happy Wedding (IRE) **Curzon House Partnership**
33 MOONSHINE MO, b g Pastoral Pursuits—Topflight Princess **The Kevin Frost Racing Club**
34 REMEMBER ALWAYS, b g Fountain of Youth (IRE)—Rememberance Day **Mr J. Stimpson**
35 SCREECHING DRAGON (IRE), b g Tagula (IRE)—Array of Stars (IRE) **Mrs A. Frost**
36 TAZAMAN, ch g Mukhadram—Farletti **Mr D. Mead**
37 THE GREY BANDIT, bl g Gregorian (IRE)—Reel Cool **Mr J. Stimpson**

TWO-YEAR-OLDS

38 B c 20/03 Harbour Watch (IRE)—Dancing Primo (Primo Valentino (IRE))
39 B c 24/03 Pastoral Pursuits—Piddies Pride (IRE) (Indian Lodge (IRE)) **Boston R. S. Ian Bennett**

Other Owners: A. J. Banton, I. M. Bennett, Curzon House Partnership, D. Dean, Mrs M. Dean, Mrs A. Frost, Mr K. Frost, Mr M. Gavin, Mrs R. Gavin, Mr M. A. Humphreys, Mr H. Jones, Miss J. Jones, Ms T. Keane, P. R. Nodder, Mr A. Pitt, The Kevin Frost Racing Club, Mrs C. Williams, Mr J. Williams.

Flat Jockey: Rossa Ryan.

<table>
<tr><td>212</td><td>**MR HARRY FRY, Seaborough**
Postal: **Manor Farm, Seaborough, Beaminster, Dorset, DT8 3QY**
Contacts: **PHONE 01308 868192 FAX 01308 867512**
EMAIL info@harryfryracing.com WEBSITE www.harryfryracing.com</td></tr>
</table>

1 ACTING LASS (IRE), 9, b g King's Theatre (IRE)—Darrens Lass (IRE) **Nigel & Barbara Collison**
2 AIR HORSE ONE, 9, gr g Mountain High (IRE)—Whisky Rose (IRE) **The Dons**
3 ANY DRAMA (IRE), 9, b g Gamut (IRE)—Oak Lodge (IRE) **N. G. Cooper**
4 ART OF PAYROLL (GER), 11, b g Shirocco (GER)—Anna Maria (GER) **Bishopsgate Syndicate**
5 AS I SEE IT, 8, b g King's Theatre (IRE)—Chomba Womba (IRE) **Mrs D. J. Goodall**
6 ASK ME EARLY (IRE), 6, gr g Ask—Cotton Ali (IRE) **The Dare Family**
7 4, B g Maxios—Aujiang (GER)
8 AUTORISATION (FR), 5, b g Authorized (IRE)—Hold The Thought
9 BAGS GROOVE (IRE), 9, b g Oscar (IRE)—Golden Moment (IRE) **M. Pescod**
10 BLACK MISCHIEF, 8, b g Black Sam Bellamy (IRE)—Miss Mitch (IRE) **Tom Chadney and Friends**
11 BOOTHILL (IRE), 5, b br g Presenting—Oyster Pipit (IRE) **Brian & Sandy Lambert**
12 BULLIONAIRE (IRE), 7, b g Gold Well—Dontcallerthat (IRE) **Phil Fry & Charlie Walker -Osborne House**
13 BURROWS TREAT (FR), 4, b f Muhtathir—La Vie de Boitron (FR) **Mr M. Stenning**
14 CAPTAIN DRAKE (IRE), 7, b g Getaway (GER)—Julika (GER) **Gary Stevens & Brian & Sandy Lambert**
15 DALILA DU SEUIL (FR), 7, gr m Bachir (IRE)—Misery (FR) **Mr J. P. McManus**
16 DEFINITELYANOSCAR (IRE), 7, b m Oscar (IRE)—Bobs Article (IRE) **Jago & Taylor**
17 4, Ch g Muhtathir—Divine Cayras (FR) **Mrs C. Fry**
18 DRUMCLIFF (IRE), 9, b g Presenting—Dusty Too **Mr J. P. McManus**
19 4, B g Milan—Dubai Glory **C. C. Walker**
20 ENA BAIE (FR), 6, b m Crillon (FR)—Trema Baie (FR) **Mr J. P. McManus**
21 FEHILY (IRE), 5, b g Asian Heights—Leahs Joy (IRE) **Masterson Holdings Limited**
22 FISHKHOV (FR), 5, ch g Sholokhov (IRE)—Kavalle (FR)
23 FREDDIE DARLING (IRE), 5, b g Shantou (USA)—Baby Lenson (IRE) **Mr & Mrs Paul & Clare Rooney**
24 GAOT (FR), 4, b f Crillon (FR)—Truffe (FR) **Mr J. P. McManus**
25 GENTLEMAN KAP (FR), 4, b g Kapgarde (FR)—Sabubelle (FR) **Mr M. Stenning**
26 GEORGE VALENTINE (IRE), 5, b g George Vancouver (USA)—Yes My Love (FR) **A Holt, J Robinson, A Taylor**
27 GET BACK GET BACK (IRE), 5, b g Lord Shanakill (USA)—Bawaakeer (USA) **Get Back Get Back**
28 GOLD IN DOHA (FR), 4, b g Spanish Moon (USA)—Utah Bald (FR) **Mrs C. Fry**
29 GREEN DOLPHIN (IRE), 6, b g Oscar (IRE)—Shamrock Miss (IRE) **M. Pescod**
30 HELL'S KITCHEN, 9, b g Robin des Champs (FR)—Mille Et Une (FR) **Mr J. P. McManus**
31 HOLDBACKTHENIGHT, 4, ch g Leading Light (IRE)—Keyaza (IRE) **Mrs C. Fry**
32 HURRICANE MITCH (IRE), 5, b g Shirocco (GER)—Miss Mitch (IRE) **Tom Chadney and Friends**
33 IF THE CAP FITS (IRE), 8, b g Milan—Derravaragh Sayra (IRE) **Mr & Mrs Paul & Clare Rooney**
34 IMPERIAL ESPRIT (IRE), 6, b g Scorpion (IRE)—Shesourpresent (IRE) **Imperial Racing Partnership 2016**
35 ISHKHARA LADY, 6, b m Scorpion (IRE)—Loxhill Lady **The Horse Flys Partnership**
36 JEREMIAH JAMES (IRE), 6, b g Jeremy (USA)—Lougholly Native (IRE) **Dr Caroline Fry & Susie Dilhorne**

MR HARRY FRY - continued

37 **JOLLY'S CRACKED IT (FR)**, 11, b g Astarabad (USA)—Jolly Harbour **GDM Partnership**
38 6, B m Mount Nelson—Juno Mint
39 **JUST A STING (IRE)**, 8, b g Scorpion (IRE)—Shanann Lady (IRE) **Nigel & Barbara Collison**
40 **KING ROLAND (IRE)**, 6, br g Stowaway—Kiltiernan Robin (IRE) **Masterson Holdings Limited**
41 **LEGENDE DE MINUIT**, 6, br g Midnight Legend—Chilla Cilla **The Eyre Family**
42 **LIGHTLY SQUEEZE**, 6, b g Poet's Voice—Zuleika Dobson **J Davies, G Brown & P Govier**
43 **LITTERALE CI (FR)**, 7, b m Soldier of Fortune (IRE)—Cigalia **Mr J. P. McManus**
44 **LONDON EYE (USA)**, 4, ch c Australia—Circle of Life (USA)
45 4, Ch f Imperial Monarch (IRE)—Loxhill Lady
46 **MANTOVANI (FR)**, 5, b g High Chaparral (IRE)—Ripley (GER) **Mahon Racing**
47 **METIER (IRE)**, 4, b g Mastercraftsman (IRE)—We'll Go Walking (IRE) **G. C. Stevens**
48 **MIGHT I (IRE)**, 4, b g Fame And Glory—Our Honey (IRE) **Mrs C. Fry**
49 **MILLBANK FLYER (IRE)**, 5, b g Milan—The Last Bank (IRE) **The Jago Family Partnership**
50 **MILLE SUSSURRI (IRE)**, 5, b g Milan—Silent Whisper (IRE) **The Jago Family Partnership**
51 **MIND THE CRACK (IRE)**, 4, b g Jukebox Jury (IRE)—Mountain Melody (GER) **Mr & Mrs Paul & Clare Rooney**
52 **MISCHIEVOUS POPPY**, 4, b f So You Think (NZ)—Sinamay (USA) **Mr T. J. Hemmings**
53 **MISTY WHISKY**, 6, gr m Stowaway—Whisky Rose (IRE) **Distillery Stud**
54 **MOMELLA (IRE)**, 8, ch m Sholokhov (IRE)—Missing Link (IRE) **Holt, Clark, Macnabb, Nugent & Robinson**
55 **MR ONE MORE (IRE)**, 8, b g Asian Heights—Norah's Quay (IRE) **Mr J. P. McManus**
56 **MUY BIEN (IRE)**, 4, b g Cloudings (IRE)—Sari Rose (FR) **Mrs C. Fry**
57 **ONEFORTHEROADTOM**, 7, gr g Fair Mix (IRE)—Ifni du Luc (FR) **Mr J. P. McManus**
58 **OUTOFTHISWORLD (IRE)**, 7, b b m Shantou (USA)—Mystic Masie (IRE) **Chasing Gold Limited**
59 **OVER TO SAM**, 9, b g Black Sam Bellamy (IRE)—Lady Brig **The Jago Family Partnership**
60 **PADSTOW HARBOUR**, 5, ch m Malinas (GER)—Cherry Pie (IRE) **Mr T. J. Hemmings**
61 **PARSONS PLEASURE (FR)**, 4, gr c Planteur (IRE)—Netrebko (USA) **Mr R. J. Tompkins**
62 **PHOENIX WAY (IRE)**, 7, b g Stowaway—Arcuate **Mr J. P. McManus**
63 **POGO I AM**, 6, b m Passing Glance—Orbital Orchid **Sandie & David Newton**
64 **PURE BLISS**, 5, ch m Mount Nelson—Burton Ash **Jago & Allhusen**
65 **ROSEMARY RUSSET**, 8, b m Midnight Legend—Apple Days **Somerset Racing**
66 **RUFIO**, 6, b g Schiaparelli (GER)—Mole End **The Lost Boys**
67 **SAMARQUAND**, 6, b g Malinas (GER)—Samandara (FR) **Charlie Walker & Phil Fry -osborne House**
68 **SANDY MARASCHINO (IRE)**, 4, b g Milan—Diamond Smiles **Mrs C. Fry**
69 **SHALL WE GO NOW**, 7, b g Midnight Legend—Suave Shot **Noel Fehily Racing Syndicate - Shall We**
70 **SIR IVAN**, 10, b g Midnight Legend—Tisho **The Eyre Family**
71 **SKYLARK NINETEEN (IRE)**, 4, b br g Mahler—Florafern **Mrs C. Fry**
72 **SOUND WALL (IRE)**, 5, b g Milan—Wall of Silence (IRE) **C. C. Walker**
73 **THE BIG STING (IRE)**, 5, b g Scorpion (IRE)—Glory Queen (IRE) **Charlie Walker & Phil Fry -osborne House**
74 **THE JITTERBUG (IRE)**, 7, b g Sulamani (IRE)—She Likes To Boogy (IRE) **Twelfth Man Partnership 5**
75 5, B g Fame And Glory—Trabrega Bay (IRE)
76 **UNOWHATIMEANHARRY**, 12, b g Sir Harry Lewis (USA)—Red Nose Lady **Mr J. P. McManus**
77 **WHATAKNIGHT**, 11, b g Midnight Legend—What A Mover
78 **WHITE HART LADY (IRE)**, 6, b m Doyen (IRE)—Hats And Heels (IRE) **Chasing Gold Limited**
79 **WHITEHOTCHILLIFILI (IRE)**, 6, b m Milan—Mhuire Na Gale (IRE) **Chasing Gold Limited**
80 **WINNINGSEVERYTHING (IRE)**, 6, b g Flemensfirth (USA)—Baliya (IRE) **Mr & Mrs Paul & Clare Rooney**

TWO-YEAR-OLDS

81 B g 17/02 Mount Nelson—Vizean (IRE) (Medicean) (25000)

Other Owners: Mr N. C. Allhusen, G. S. Brown, Mrs S. Cameron, Mr D. Charlesworth, G. Charlesworth, Mr C. N. Clark, Mrs B. Collison, Mr N. Collison, Mr J. M. Dare, Mrs J. M. Dare, Mr J. Davies, Mr M. R. Dentten, Viscountess S. J. Dilhorne, Mrs C. A. Eyre, Mr C. G. S. Eyre, Mr H. Eyre, Miss R. E. Eyre, Dr C. E. Fry, R. P. Fry, Mr P. F. Govier, Mr A. G. Hipgrave, Mr A. Holt, Holt, Robinson, Macnabb, Clark, Weedon, Mr F. C. A. Jago, Mrs J. L. Jago, Miss M. L. A. Jago, Mr P. J. A. Jago, Mr I. N. Kingham, Mr B. Lambert, Mr I. Macnabb, Mr D. J. Mahon, Mr D. Newton, Mrs J. S. Newton, Mr J. O. Nugent, Mr D. A. Olver, Mr J. D. Robinson, Mr M. Smith, G. C. Stevens, Mr A. Taylor, Mr A. J. Taylor, Mr G. M. Thornton, C. C. Walker, Mr J. Weedon, Mr T. Wheatley.

Assistant Trainer: Ciara Fry, Mike Legg.

NH Jockey: Sean Bowen, Kieron Edgar. **Amateur Jockey:** Mr M. Legg, Mr M McIntyre.

213 **MISS CAROLINE FRYER, Wymondham**
Postal: Browick Hall Cottage, Browick Road, Wymondham, Norfolk, NR18 9RB
Contacts: PHONE 01953 601257 MOBILE 07768 056076
EMAIL caroline@carolinefryerracing.co.uk, c.fryer528@btinternet.com WEBSITE www.
carolinefryerracing.co.uk

1 **AMETHEA (IRE)**, 6, b m Yeats (IRE)—Moricana (GER) **C J Underwood & Caroline Fryer**
2 **BROOM TIP (IRE)**, 8, b g Flemensfirth (USA)—Norabelle (FR) **Mr N Gowing**
3 **DREAM DOC (IRE)**, 11, b m Dr Massini (IRE)—Storm Call **Miss C. Fryer**
4 **GOODNIGHT CHARLIE**, 10, gr m Midnight Legend—Over To Charlie **Miss C. Fryer**
5 **MERCERS COURT (IRE)**, 12, b g Court Cave (IRE)—Vikki's Dream (IRE) **Mrs S. Fryer**
6 **MOORSHOLME**, 8, b g Westerner—Royal Bride **C J Underwood & Caroline Fryer**
7 **RIDDLESTOWN (IRE)**, 13, b g Cloudings (IRE)—Gandi's Dream (IRE) **OAP Partnership**
8 **SCHAP**, 8, ch m Schiaparelli (GER)—Royal Keel **Miss C. Fryer**

Other Owners: Miss C. Fryer, C. J. Underwood.

214 **MR IVAN FURTADO, Newark**
Postal: The Old Stables, Averham Park Farm, Averham, Newark, Nottinghamshire, NG23 5RU
Contacts: MOBILE 07783 520746
EMAIL ivan.furtado@hotmail.co.uk

1 **BADAYEL (IRE)**, 4, ch g Havana Gold (IRE)—Raggiante (IRE) **Mr K. Sohi**
2 **BAYDAR**, 7, b g Rock of Gibraltar (IRE)—Splashdown **Mr K. Sohi**
3 **BROOKLYN BOY**, 4, b g Camelot—Tan Tan **Daniel MacAuliffe & Anoj Don**
4 **CAPTAIN DION**, 7, gr g Equiano (FR)—Bandanna **Daniel MacAuliffe & Anoj Don**
5 **CRAZY SPIN**, 4, b f Epaulette (AUS)—George's Gift **The Giggle Factor Partnership**
6 **DARALIMI (FR)**, 4, b g Siyouni (FR)—Daryaba (IRE) **J. L. Marriott**
7 **EESHA'S SMILE (IRE)**, 4, ch f Toronado (IRE)—Lamentation **Mr K. Sohi**
8 **EPIC CHALLENGE**, 5, b g Mastercraftsman (IRE)—Keep Dancing (IRE) **Robert Greenwood Racing**
9 **ETERNAL SUN**, 5, b m Mayson—Golden Dirham **Mrs S Nicholls Mrs R J Mitchell**
10 **FLY TRUE**, 7, b m Raven's Pass (USA)—Have Faith (IRE) **Stuart Dobb & Kate Dobb**
11 **FOLLOWTHESTARS (IRE)**, 4, b g Sea The Stars (IRE)—Penny Post (IRE) **J. L. Marriott**
12 **FOLLOWTHESTEPS (IRE)**, 5, b g Footstepsinthesand—Excellent Mariner (IRE) **J. L. Marriott**
13 **GHOST BUY (FR)**, 4, b g Orpen (USA)—Nantha (FR) **John Marriott & Giggle Factor**
14 **HEALING POWER**, 4, b g Kodiac—Loch Ma Naire (IRE) **Mr C. Hodgson**
15 **HECTOR'S HERE**, 4, b g Cityscape—L'Addition **John Marriott & Giggle Factor**
16 **INEXES**, 8, gr g Exceed And Excel (AUS)—Likeable **21st Century Racing**
17 **IRISH CHARM (FR)**, 6, b g Siyouni (FR)—Danclare (USA) **The Giggle Factor Partnership**
18 **JUNGLE SPEED (FR)**, 4, b g Bungle Inthejungle—Velvet Revolver (IRE) **Mr K. Sohi**
19 **JUNIORS DREAM (IRE)**, 4, gr g Holy Roman Emperor (IRE)—Lagoa (FR) **The Giggle Factor Partnership**
20 **KINGS HIGHWAY (IRE)**, 5, b g Shamardal (USA)—Bimini **A Graham - Bankruptcy Trustee M Stanley**
21 **KIRALEAH**, 4, b f Pastoral Pursuits—Jocasta Dawn **The Giggle Factor Partnership**
22 **LAITH ALAREEN**, 5, b g Invincible Spirit (IRE)—Bewitchment **21st Century Racing & Nigel Sennett**
23 **LAST SOLDIER (IRE)**, 4, b g Intello (GER)—Dream Girl **Mr C. Hodgson**
24 **LITTLE BUSTARD (IRE)**, 4, b f Roderic O'Connor (IRE)—Liturgy (IRE) **The Giggle Factor Partnership**
25 **LOOSE CHIPPINGS (IRE)**, 6, b g Rock of Gibraltar (IRE)—Karjera (IRE) **The Giggle Factor Partnership**
26 **MANDARIN (GER)**, 6, ch g Lope de Vega (IRE)—Margarita (GER) **Sohi & Sohi**
27 **MELISSA (FR)**, 4, ch f Evasive—Snow Jasmine (IRE) **J. L. Marriott**
28 5, Ch g Sixties Icon—Mistic Magic (USA) **Daniel MacAuliffe & Anoj Don**
29 **NETTLE PEGGY**, 4, b f Toronado (IRE)—Wise Melody **The Giggle Factor Partnership**
30 **PACT OF STEEL**, 5, ch g Declaration of War (USA)—She's My Dandy (IRE) **Daniel MacAuliffe & Anoj Don**
31 **PLACE PASDELOUP (FR)**, 4, b br f Motivator—Statia (IRE) **J. L. Marriott**
32 **SARTAJ (USA)**, 4, b br g Giant's Causeway (USA)—Sarkiyla (FR) **Mr K. Sohi**
33 **SAURON'S EYE**, 4, b g Delegator—Stylish Dream (USA) **The Giggle Factor Partnership**
34 **SPARKLEALOT (IRE)**, 4, b g Sir Prancealot (IRE)—Monsusu (IRE) **J. L. Marriott**
35 **STRAITOUTTACOMPTON**, 4, b g Compton Place—Red Mischief (IRE) **Golden Equinox Racing**
36 **SWORD EXCEED (GER)**, 6, b g Exceed And Excel (AUS)—Sword Roche (GER) **21st Century Racing & Nigel Sennett**

MR IVAN FURTADO - continued

37 TESTON (FR), 5, ch g Rio de La Plata (USA)—Tianshan (FR) **Daniel MacAuliffe & Anoj Don**
38 TRANCHEE (IRE), 4, b g War Front (USA)—Terrific (IRE) **Mr K. Sohi**

THREE-YEAR-OLDS

39 BALTIC STATE (IRE), b g Dandy Man (IRE)—Estonia **J. C. Fretwell**
40 BREADCRUMBS (FR), b br f Dabirsim (IRE)—Sister Agnes (IRE) **J. L. Marriott**
41 BROKEN RIFLE, b g Havana Gold (IRE)—Peace Concluded **J. C. Fretwell**
42 BYFORD (FR), b g Toronado (IRE)—Verba (FR) **Mr C. Hodgson**
43 CAPTAIN ST LUCIFER, b g Casamento (IRE)—Delaware Dancer (IRE) **Stuart Dobb & Kate Dobb**
44 EL AGRONOMO, b g Fast Company (IRE)—Deslaya (IRE)
45 FLASH TO BANG, b c Telescope (IRE)—Fangfoss Girls **Central Racing Ltd**
46 FULL STRENGTH, ch g Helmet (AUS)—Cafe Express (IRE) **The Giggle Factor Partnership**
47 HANDSOME YANK (USA), b br g Kitten's Joy (USA)—Upper East Sider (USA) **J. L. Marriott**
48 LADY DANDY (IRE), b f Dandy Man (IRE)—Rupa (IRE) **Ne Chance & Partner1**
49 LAST DATE, br g Music Master—Tanning **Mr E. P. Spain**
50 LOCO DEMPSEY (FR), b f Cityscape—L'Addition **The Giggle Factor Partnership**
51 Ch f Camacho—Lucky Date (IRE) **Tim & Miranda Johnson**
52 NOBLE DAWN (GER), ch f Dawn Approach (IRE)—Neuquen (IRE) **J. L. Marriott**
53 OCHRE RIU (IRE), ch g Tagula (IRE)—Raseel **From The Front Racing**
54 PRIDE OF PUNJAB, ch c Dawn Approach (IRE)—Learned Friend (GER) **Sohi & Sohi**
55 PURPLE EMPRESS, ch f Mayson—Purple Silk **Robert Greenwood Racing & Partner**
56 B f Mayson—Raajis (IRE) **The Giggle Factor Partnership**
57 RECALL IT ALL, b g Toronado (IRE)—Rotunda **The Giggle Factor Partnership**
58 SCUDAMORE (FR), ch g Dawn Approach (IRE)—Emirates Comfort (IRE) **Mr C. Hodgson**
59 STAY CALM (IRE), b g Epaulette (AUS)—Emerald Peace (IRE) **J. C. Fretwell**
60 VIVE AUDACTER, b f Canford Cliffs (IRE)—Sweet Serendipity **The Giggle Factor Partnership**
61 WALLS HAVE EARS (IRE), b f War Command (USA)—Shegotloose (USA) **The Giggle Factor Partnership**
62 B f Slade Power (IRE)—Weood (IRE) **The Giggle Factor Partnership**

TWO-YEAR-OLDS

63 Br f 24/03 Pride of Dubai (AUS)—Astrelle (IRE) (Makfi) (8000)
64 B c 30/01 Bated Breath—Astrodonna (Carnival Dancer) (3500)
65 B f 13/04 Charming Thought—Blissamore (Kyllachy) (1000)
66 B c 11/01 Gutaifan (IRE)—Crystal Quartz (IRE) (Rock of Gibraltar (IRE)) (1500)
67 Gr f 25/04 Havana Gold (IRE)—Daheeya (Daylami (IRE)) (1428)
68 Ch c 11/03 Sepoy (AUS)—Golden Dirham (Kheleyf (USA)) **Mrs S. E. Nicholls**
69 B f 18/02 Paco Boy (IRE)—Permasuri (IRE) (Sea The Stars (IRE))
70 B c 06/02 Fountain of Youth (IRE)—Russian Punch (Archipenko (USA)) (2857)
71 B gr f 26/02 Hellvelyn—Serena's Pride (Danbird (AUS)) (1904)
72 B f 03/03 Pride of Dubai (AUS)—Shegotloose (USA) (Dynaformer (USA)) (10000)
73 B f 30/01 Adaay (IRE)—Transvaal Sky (Avonbridge) (761)

Other Owners: 21st Century Racing, A. W. Catterall, Mrs B. Catterall, Miss K. M. Dobb, Mr S. Dobb, Mr R. J. Greenwood, Mr M. Hilton, Mr J. R. Holt, Mr N. N. Kane, J. L. Marriott, Mrs R. J. Mitchell, Ne-Chance, Mrs S. E. Nicholls, Robert Greenwood Racing, Mr N. P. Sennett, Mr J. Sohi, Mr K. Sohi, The Giggle Factor Partnership.

---

215 **MR JOHN GALLAGHER, Moreton-In-Marsh**
Postal: **Grove Farm, Chastleton, Moreton-In-Marsh, Gloucestershire, GL56 0SZ**
Contacts: PHONE **01608 674492** MOBILE **07780 972663**
EMAIL **john@gallagherracing.com** WEBSITE **www.gallagherracing.com**

1 BLUE BATTALION, 4, ch g Cityscape—Hollybell **Mr R. Little**
2 DOUBLE COFFEE, 4, b f Mawatheeq (USA)—Maimoona (IRE) **Mr K. L. Read**
3 GRAPE SODA, 4, b f Swiss Spirit—Namu **R Tudor Holdings Limited**
4 GREEN POWER, 5, b g Kheleyf (USA)—Hakuroa (IRE) **Nino's Partnership**
5 HOLD YOUR BREATH, 5, b m Bated Breath—Chittenden **Mr K. L. Read**
6 ILEY BOY, 6, b g Delegator—Menha **J & L Wetherald - M & M Glover**

MR JOHN GALLAGHER - continued

7 JUNOESQUE, 6, b m Virtual—Snake Skin **The Juniper Racing Club Ltd**
8 LOS CAMACHOS (IRE), 5, b g Camacho—Illuminise (IRE) **Steve & Mike Harris**
9 MAHUIKA, 4, b f Firebreak—Adweb **The Juniper Racing Club & Andrew Bell**
10 PURBECK HILLS (IRE), 4, b g Oasis Dream—Albisola (IRE) **Mr J. N. Greenley**
11 QUENCH DOLLY, 6, gr m Hellvelyn—Hollybell **John Gallagher**
12 RIVAS ROB ROY, 5, ch g Archipenko (USA)—Rivas Rhapsody (IRE) **Mr T. J. F. Smith**
13 SALLY HOPE, 4, ch f Coach House (IRE)—First Term **John Gallagher**
14 TOMAHAWK RIDGE (IRE), 4, gr g Alhebayeb (IRE)—Low Cut Affair (IRE) **Max Europe Limited**
15 WILDOMAR, 11, b g Kyllachy—Murrieta **Mr P. W. Hiatt**

THREE-YEAR-OLDS

16 HOT POPPY, ch f Hot Streak (IRE)—Columella **Hot Bucks Syndicate**
17 INTERCESSOR, b g Due Diligence (USA)—Miss Meticulous **The LAM Partnership**
18 LADY ILEY, b f Equiano (FR)—Hollybell **C. R. Marks (Banbury)**
19 SARAS HOPE, b g Swiss Spirit—Rivas Rhapsody (IRE) **Max Europe Limited**
20 TWELVE DIAMONDS (IRE), ch f Raven's Pass (USA)—Wardat Dubai

TWO-YEAR-OLDS

21 Ch f 27/04 Lethal Force (IRE)—Danehill Destiny (Danehill Dancer (IRE)) (23000) **The LAM Partnership**
22 Ch f 03/05 Equiano (FR)—Pusey Street Lady (Averti (IRE)) **John Gallagher**
23 Gr f 16/05 Hellvelyn—Pusey Street Vale (Moss Vale (IRE)) **C. R. Marks (Banbury)**
24 SILVER DIVA, gr f 30/03 Hellvelyn—Heartsong (Kheleyf (USA)) **J & L Wetherald - M & M Glover**

Other Owners: Mr A. Bell, Dr M. F. Ford, Ms M. E. Glover, M. P. Glover, Mr M. J. Harris, Mr S. J. Harris, Mrs B. A. Long, J. F. Long, Ms L. M. Mulcahy, The Juniper Racing Club Ltd, Mr J. A. Wetherald, Mrs L. T. Wetherald.

Assistant Trainer: Mrs R. J. Gallagher.

---

216 **MR THOMAS GALLAGHER, Borehamwood**
Postal: **5 Old Priory Park, Old London Road, St. Albans, Hertfordshire, AL1 1QF**

1 AH WELL (IRE), 8, b g Gold Well—Valentina Gaye (IRE) **Mr J. J. Reddington**
2 BEEPEECEE, 6, b g Henrythenavigator (USA)—Roedean (IRE) **Mr J. J. Reddington**
3 BOLAND'S MILL (IRE), 8, b g Winged Love (IRE)—Madam Rocher (IRE) **Mr J. J. Reddington**
4 BYRON GREEN (IRE), 8, b g Byron—Exit Stage Left (IRE) **Mr J. J. Reddington**
5 CARTRON (IRE), 4, b g Acclamation—Like A Dream (FR) **Mr J. J. Reddington**
6 DOM GARO CATELINE (FR), 7, b g Ungaro (GER)—Dame Jaune (FR) **Mr J. J. Reddington**
7 MOUNTAIN SO HIGH (IRE), 7, b g Mountain High (IRE)—Marigier (IRE) **Mr J. J. Reddington**
8 MR HARP (IRE), 7, b g Court Cave (IRE)—Chapel Wood Lady (IRE) **Mr J. J. Reddington**
9 POINTED SPEAR (IRE), 7, b g Dahjee (USA)—Exit Stage Left (IRE) **Mr J. J. Reddington**
10 5, Gr g Carlotamix (FR)—Whisky (IRE) **Mr J. J. Reddington**

---

217 **MRS ILKA GANSERA-LEVEQUE, Newmarket**
Postal: **Saint Wendreds, Hamilton Road, Newmarket, Suffolk, CB8 7JQ**
Contacts: **PHONE 01638 454973 MOBILE 07855 532072**
EMAIL office@gansera-leveque.com WEBSITE www.gansera-leveque.com

1 AWESOMEDUDE, 4, ch c Australia—Millevini (IRE) **Mr Y. L. A. Lee**
2 JUST ONCE, 4, b f Holy Roman Emperor (IRE)—Nur Jahan (IRE) **Mr I. Sze**
3 MYSTIC DRAGON, 4, ch f Intello (GER)—Portrait **Mr S. P Hussain**
4 RISING SEAS, 5, b g Mount Nelson—Puya **Mrs I. Gansera-Leveque**
5 4, B f Maxios—Tosca (GER)

MRS ILKA GANSERA-LEVEQUE - continued

THREE-YEAR-OLDS

 6 B c Exceed And Excel (AUS)—Ice Palace
 7 **IKIGAI**, b f Sayif (IRE)—Usem **Mrs I. Gansera-Leveque**
 8 **LONDON (GER)**, b f Lord of England (GER)—La Reine Noir (GER) **Quantum Leap Racing VI**
 9 **MELODIC THUNDER (FR)**, b f Night of Thunder (IRE)—Mystic Melody (IRE) **Joe Saumarez Smith & Partners**
10 **WENDREDA**, b f Casamento (IRE)—Zagarock **Mrs I. Gansera-Leveque**
11 B g Invincible Spirit (IRE)—Zotilla (IRE)

TWO-YEAR-OLDS

12 B f 04/05 Sir Percy—Acacalia (GER) (Ransom O'War (USA)) (17160)
13 B br f 01/04 Iffraaj—Badweia (USA) (Kingmambo (USA)) (26000)
14 **EDENS LAWN**, b f 24/03 Ruler of The World (IRE)—Jewelled (Fantastic Light (USA)) **M & M Franklin**
15 Br c 06/02 Slade Power (IRE)—La Pieta (AUS) (Redoute's Choice (AUS)) (25000)
16 B f 25/04 Mehmas (IRE)—Refuse To Give Up (IRE) (Refuse To Bend (IRE)) (32000)

Other Owners: Fergus Anstock, Mr J. J. Brummitt, Mr P. G. Buist, Mr M. Edwards, Mr M. Franklin, Mrs M. G. Franklin, Mr J. W. Saumarez Smith.

Assistant Trainer: Stephane Leveque.

218
MRS SUSAN GARDNER, Longdown
Postal: **Woodhayes Farm, Longdown, Exeter**
Contacts: **PHONE 01392 811213 MOBILE 07936 380492**
EMAIL woodhayesstudfarm@btinternet.com WEBSITE www.suegardnerracing.co.uk

 1 **BREDON HILL LAD**, 13, ch g Kirkwall—Persian Clover **Mr & Mrs R W & Mrs J M Mitchell**
 2 **CITY FLAME**, 4, b f Cityscape—High Drama (IRE) **Mr M. Vaughan**
 3 **ENDLESS FLIGHT (IRE)**, 6, b g Winged Love (IRE)—Lady Oakwell (IRE) **Mr D. V. Gardner**
 4 **HAVACUPPA**, 6, b m Dream Eater (IRE)—Darjeeling (IRE) **Mr D. V. Gardner**
 5 **HERE'S BINGO**, 7, b g With The Flow (USA)—Winter Scene (IRE) **P. A. Tylor**
 6 **HERE'S HERBIE**, 12, b g Classic Cliche (IRE)—Tyre Hill Lilly **Mr P. A. Tylor & Mr D V Gardner**
 7 **LIGHTONTHEWING (IRE)**, 5, b g Winged Love (IRE)—Neat 'n Nimble **Mr D. V. Gardner**
 8 **ROYAL MARTIAN**, 6, b g Schiaparelli (GER)—Queenoz (IRE) **Mr D. V. Gardner**
 9 **SIROP DE MENTHE (FR)**, 10, ch g Discover d'Auteuil (FR)—Jolie Menthe (FR) **Clear Racing & Partner**
10 **TEA TIME FRED**, 11, b g Kayf Tara—Darjeeling (IRE) **Mr D. V. Gardner**
11 **TEA TIME ON MARS**, 8, ch g Schiaparelli (GER)—Darjeeling (IRE) **Mrs B. Russell & Mr D. V. Gardner**
12 **THEBUDINPUNDIT**, 4, b g Multiplex—Buddug **Mr D. V. Gardner**
13 **TRANS EXPRESS (IRE)**, 10, br g Trans Island—Hazel Fastrack **Mr D. V. Gardner**
14 **WOULDUADAMANDEVEIT (IRE)**, 7, b g Stowaway—Figlette **Keith Harris & Tom Gardner**

Other Owners: Mr D. V. Gardner, Mr T. A. Gardner, Mr B. J. Greening, Mrs M. M. Greening, Mr K. T. Harris, Mrs J. M. Mitchell, R. W. Mitchell, Mrs B. A. Russell, P. A. Tylor.

Assistant Trainer: D. V. Gardner.

NH Jockey: Lucy Gardner, Micheal Nolan.

219
MRS ROSEMARY GASSON, Banbury
Postal: **Alkerton Grounds, Balscote, Banbury, Oxfordshire, OX15 6JS**
Contacts: **PHONE 01295 730248 MOBILE 07769 798430**
EMAIL arb@agf.myzen.co.uk

 1 **BIGNORM (IRE)**, 8, b g Mahler—Merry Heart **Mrs R. Gasson**
 2 **DESERT DE BRUYERE (FR)**, 7, b g Great Pretender (IRE)—Quid de Neuville (FR) **Mrs R. Gasson**
 3 **DRAGON KHAN (IRE)**, 11, b g Dr Fong (USA)—Desert Magic (IRE) **Mrs R. Gasson**
 4 **FREEDOM CHIMES**, 6, b g Champs Elysees—Ombre **Mrs R. Gasson**

MRS ROSEMARY GASSON - continued

5 **IRISH OCTAVE (IRE)**, 10, b g Gamut (IRE)—Fairytaleofnewyork (IRE) **Mrs R. Gasson**
6 **JUSTTHEGREY (IRE)**, 8, gr g Getaway (GER)—Line White (FR) **Mrs R. Gasson**
7 **MR MCGUINESS (IRE)**, 10, b g Kalanisi (IRE)—Maig Mandy (IRE) **Mrs R. Gasson**
8 **SCARTARE (IRE)**, 9, br g Trans Island—La Speziana (IRE) **Mrs R. Gasson**
9 **TAHAN (IRE)**, 5, b g Rock of Gibraltar (IRE)—Reehan (USA) **Mrs R. Gasson**

NH Jockey: Ben Poste.

---

220 **MR PAUL GEORGE, Crediton**
Postal: **Higher Eastington, Lapford, Crediton, Devon, EX17 6NE**
Contacts: **MOBILE 07733 171112**
EMAIL **paul.george1@icloud.com** WEBSITE **www.paulgeorgeracing.co.uk**

1 **BALLYCROSS**, 9, b g King's Theatre (IRE)—Ninna Nanna (FR) **P. J. H. George**
2 **BRINKLEYS KATIE**, 4, ch f New Approach (IRE)—Opera Gloves (IRE) **Eastington Racing**
3 **HALLE'S HARBOUR**, 4, ch f Harbour Watch (IRE)—Clifton Dancer **D. Boddy, E Foster & Karen George**
4 **I CAN SKIP TOO**, 6, b g Bollin Eric—April Attraction (FR) **Mrs J. Scrivens**
5 **LITTLE JESSTURE (IRE)**, 4, b f Dylan Thomas (IRE)—The Legislator (IRE) **Mr R. Butler**
6 **MARY LE BOW**, 9, b m Sir Percy—Bermondsey Girl **Mrs J. Scrivens**
7 **PIXIE LOC**, 5, gr m Lucarno (USA)—Ixora (IRE) **Mr R. Butler**
8 **PRINCESS WAY (IRE)**, 6, gr m Zebedee—Stef's Girl (IRE) **David Renfree & Paul George**
9 **SARASOTA (IRE)**, 5, b m Zoffany (IRE)—Saldenaera (GER) **Sherborne Utilities Ltd**
10 **SHERWOOD FORRESTER**, 4, b g Nayef (USA)—Panoptic **C Priestley & P George**
11 **THE AWESOME ALICE (IRE)**, 6, b m Mawatheeq (USA)—Amourallis (IRE) **The Black Type Partnership**

THREE-YEAR-OLDS

12 **ARTHALOT (IRE)**, b g Camelot—Annina (IRE) **Thethrillofitall**
13 **FULL SPECTRUM (IRE)**, b f Fulbright—With Colour **Fosnic Racing, A Senior, P George**
14 **LETHAL BLAST**, b f Lethal Force (IRE)—Having A Blast (USA) **Henacre Racing Club Ltd**
15 **SECRET EQUITY**, ch f Equiano (FR)—Secret Charge **Mr B. A. McGarrigle**
16 **ZIM BABY**, b f Roderic O'Connor (IRE)—Kenyan Cat **Fosnic Racing & Paul George**

TWO-YEAR-OLDS

17 B f 31/01 Markaz (IRE)—All Fur Coat (Multiplex) (2380)
18 B f 12/04 Outstrip—Another Name (USA) (Giant's Causeway (USA)) (858)
19 Br gr c 10/03 Outstrip—Anse Victorin (USA) (Mt Livermore (USA)) (2380)
20 Ch c 02/05 Havana Gold (IRE)—Ferayha (IRE) (Cape Cross (IRE))
21 Ch f 06/04 Bobby's Kitten (USA)—Freedom Reigns (IRE) (Jeremy (USA)) (9523)
22 B f 09/04 Alhebayeb (IRE)—Lady Gabrielle (IRE) (Dansili)
23 B c 24/03 Australia—Pennard (IRE) (High Chaparral (IRE)) (6500)
24 Ch f 07/03 Farhh—Poyle Sophie (Teofilo (IRE))
25 B c 22/01 Gleneagles (IRE)—Spice Trail (Champs Elysees) (2402)
26 B f 12/04 Kodi Bear (IRE)—Starfly (IRE) (Invincible Spirit (IRE)) (4118)
27 Ch f 24/03 Buratino (IRE)—Up At Dawn (Inchinor) (7722)

Other Owners: Mr D. Boddy, Fosnic Racing, Mr E. Foster, Miss K. M. George, P.J. H. George, Mr S. G. Nicholls, Mr C. Priestley, Mr D. W. Renfree, Mr A. Senior.

Assistant Trainer: Cassie Haughton.

Apprentice Jockey: Rhiain Ingram.

221 **MR TOM GEORGE, Slad**
Postal: **Down Farm, Slad, Stroud, Gloucestershire, GL6 7QE**
Contacts: **PHONE 01452 814267 MOBILE 07850 793483**
EMAIL tom@trgeorge.com WEBSITE www.tomgeorgeracing.co.uk

1 **ACTIVIAL (FR)**, 10, gr g Lord du Sud (FR)—Kissmirial (FR) **R. S. Brookhouse**
2 **AIR NAVIGATOR**, 9, b g Yeats (IRE)—Lox Lane (IRE) **Lady N. F. Cobham**
3 **ANOTHER STOWAWAY (IRE)**, 8, b g Stowaway—Another Pet (IRE) **H Stephen Smith & Family Gabbertas**
4 **AUSSIE BREEZE**, 4, ch f Australia—Terre du Vent (FR) **Mr S. W. Clarke**
5 **BABY KING (IRE)**, 11, b g Ivan Denisovich (IRE)—Burn Baby Burn (IRE) **About Two Weeks**
6 **BALLADAME (FR)**, 5, b m Ballingarry (IRE)—Summer (IRE) **Lord & Lady Harrington**
7 **BALLON ONABUDGET (FR)**, 7, b g Arcadio (GER)—Little Present (IRE) **The Little Faith Syndicate**
8 **BANISH (USA)**, 7, b g Smart Strike (CAN)—Beyond Our Reach (IRE) **Mr H. F. Birtles**
9 **BIG BRESIL**, 5, b g Blue Bresil (FR)—Cutielilou (FR) **R. S. Brookhouse**
10 **BIG NICK**, 7, b g Sea The Stars (IRE)—Adventure (USA) **R. S. Brookhouse**
11 **BLACK OP (IRE)**, 9, br g Sandmason—Afar Story (IRE) **R. S. Brookhouse**
12 **BOAGRIUS (IRE)**, 8, ch g Beneficial—Greenhall Rambler (IRE) **The MerseyClyde Partnership**
13 **BOYHOOD (IRE)**, 9, b g Oscar (IRE)—Glen Dubh (IRE) **H Stephen Smith & The Gabbertas Family**
14 **BRANDON HILL (IRE)**, 12, b g Beneficial—Annesbanker (IRE) **Mr N T Griffith & H M Haddock**
15 **BRAVENTARA**, 9, b m Kayf Tara—L'Aventure (FR) **Mr C. J. Harriman**
16 **BUCK'S BIN'S (FR)**, 6, b g Khalkevi (FR)—Buck's Bravo (FR) **R. S. Brookhouse**
17 **BUN DORAN (IRE)**, 9, b g Shantou (USA)—Village Queen (IRE) **Crossed Fingers Partnership**
18 **CAPTAIN BLACKPEARL**, 6, ch g Black Sam Bellamy (IRE)—
Bonne Anniversaire **R Foden T Keelan J Moynihan I Woodward**
19 **CASA ITALIA (FR)**, 6, b g No Risk At All (FR)—Gribouille Parcs (FR) **Tony, Judith, Sharon, Dermot & David**
20 **CELTIC RISING (IRE)**, 8, b g Curtain Time (IRE)—Supreme Dollar (IRE) **R. S. Brookhouse**
21 **CHAMPAGNE CITY**, 7, ch g Tobougg (IRE)—City of Angels **R. S. Brookhouse**
22 **CLEAR ON TOP (IRE)**, 4, b g Robin des Champs (FR)—Homelander (IRE) **Nelson, Bovington, Taylor, Delarocha**
23 **CLONDAW CASTLE (IRE)**, 8, b g Oscar (IRE)—Lohort Castle (IRE) **J French, D McDermott, S Nelson, T Syder**
24 **COME ON TEDDY (IRE)**, 6, b g Fame And Glory—Theatre View (IRE) **Mr N T Griffith & H M Haddock**
25 **CONNECT FOUR**, 6, b g Midnight Legend—Sovereignsflagship (IRE) **Simon Clarke & Sisters**
26 **COPPER WEST (IRE)**, 9, b g Westerner—Printing Copper (IRE) **The MerseyClyde Partnership**
27 **COTTUN (FR)**, 4, b g Le Havre (IRE)—Montebella (FR) **Sharon Nelson & Katya Taylor Delarocha**
28 **COUPDEBOL (FR)**, 5, gr g Rajsaman (FR)—Chance Bleue (FR) **Terry Warner & Tim Syder**
29 **CREALION (FR)**, 4, b g Creachadoir (IRE)—Lady La Lionne (FR) **S Nelson, T Keelan, H Polito, C Compton**
30 **DARLING DU LARGE (FR)**, 7, b m Kapgarde (FR)—Dissidente (FR) **Mr S. W. Clarke**
31 **DOCTOR DEX (IRE)**, 7, b g Oscar (IRE)—Larnalee (IRE) **Crossed Fingers Partnership**
32 **DOLLAR AND A DREAM (IRE)**, 11, b g Fruits of Love (USA)—Gorgeous Georgina (IRE) **Mr K. M. Bebbington**
33 **DOUBLE SHUFFLE (IRE)**, 10, b g Milan—Fiddlers Bar (IRE) **Crossed Fingers Partnership**
34 **ENEMY COAST AHEAD**, 6, br g Malinas (GER)—Penang Princess **McNeill Family Ltd**
35 **ESPOIR DE TEILLEE (FR)**, 8, b g Martaline—Belle de Lyphard (FR) **R. S. Brookhouse**
36 **FANFAN DU SEUIL (FR)**, 5, b g Racinger (FR)—Nina du Seuil (FR) **Crossed Fingers Partnership**
37 **FARO DE KERSER (FR)**, 5, b g Ungaro (GER)—Nuit de Kerser (FR) **The Twenty One Partnership**
38 **FEARLESS FRACAS (IRE)**, 6, b g Fracas (IRE)—Mayo Mystique (IRE) **R. S. Brookhouse**
39 4, B g Midnight Legend—Fentara **Chadney Keelan Knowles Moynihan Woodward**
40 **FONTLEY HOUSE (IRE)**, 8, ch g Getaway (GER)—Down Town Cork (IRE) **Colin Perry, Alan Waller & John Lawson**
41 **FORGOT TO ASK (IRE)**, 8, b g Ask—Lady Transcend (IRE) **Miss J. A. Hoskins**
42 **GLOBAL EFFECT (IRE)**, 5, b br g Presenting—Ella Watson (IRE) **S Nelson, R Blunt, K Delarocha, D Savell**
43 **GLOCKENSPIEL (IRE)**, 5, b g Teofilo (IRE)—Morning Bell **Mr D. W. Fox**
44 **GO ON BRYCEY LAD (FR)**, 4, b g Saddler Maker (IRE)—Lonita d'Airy (FR) **The MerseyClyde Partnership**
45 **GOD'S OWN (IRE)**, 12, b g Oscar (IRE)—Dantes Term (IRE) **Crossed Fingers Partnership**
46 **GOOD MAN JIM (FR)**, 7, gr g Martaline—Precious Lucy (FR)
47 **HOOLIGAN (IRE)**, 5, b g Aizavoski (IRE)—Victory Run (IRE) **O'Donohoe, Cavanagh, Robinson, Nelson**
48 **JOBESGREEN LAD**, 5, b g Passing Glance—Overnight Fame (IRE) **Mr R. T. Cornock**
49 **KAKAMORA**, 5, b g Great Pretender (IRE)—Roche d'Or **Mr T. D. J. Syder**
50 **KK LEXION (IRE)**, 9, b g Flemensfirth (USA)—Kiloradante (IRE) **Perry, Lawson, Waller, Rea, McDermott**
51 **LOOK ALIVE (IRE)**, 6, bl g Arakan (USA)—Itsafamilyaffair (IRE) **Mr N T Griffith & H M Haddock**
52 **LOUGHADERRA PRINCE (IRE)**, 11, b g Oscar (IRE)—Loughaderra Rose (IRE) **Mrs H. W. Polito**
53 **LYDIA VIOLET (IRE)**, 5, br m Kalanisi (IRE)—Anne Hathaway (IRE) **Chasing Gold Limited**
54 **MANOFTHEMOMENT (IRE)**, 6, b g Jeremy (USA)—Endless Ambition (IRE) **James Longley & Charles Tatnall**

MR TOM GEORGE - continued

55 **MASSINI MAN**, 7, b g Dr Massini (IRE)—Alleged To Rhyme (IRE) **Mrs E. A. Fletcher**
56 **MINELLA FOR ME (IRE)**, 10, b g King's Theatre (IRE)—Irish Mystics (IRE) **Mr S. W. Clarke**
57 **MOSAMBO (IRE)**, 5, b m Fame And Glory—Similan (IRE) **Somerset Racing**
58 **NOW LOOK AT ME (IRE)**, 6, ch g Shantou (USA)—Similan (IRE) **McNeill Family Ltd**
59 **OSCAR ROBERTSON (IRE)**, 6, b g Oscar (IRE)—Beaus Polly (IRE) **Crossed Fingers Partnership**
60 **OVERALL MAJORITY (IRE)**, 4, b g Sholokhov (IRE)—
                                     Liss Alainn (IRE) **S Nelson K Delarocha T Keelan J Edgedale**
61 **PETIT PALAIS**, 5, ch g Champs Elysees—Galicuix **Mr D. W. Fox**
62 **ROCK ON ROCCO (IRE)**, 6, b g Shirocco (GER)—Katalina **R. S. Brookhouse**
63 **SAY THE WORD**, 4, b g Authorized (IRE)—Soryah (IRE) **Silkword Racing Partnership**
64 **SEDDON (IRE)**, 7, b g Stowaway—Andreas Benefit (IRE) **McNeill Family Ltd**
65 **SEPTEMBER DAISY**, 5, b m September Storm (GER)—Alleged To Rhyme (IRE) **Mrs E. A. Fletcher**
66 **SINGLEFARMPAYMENT**, 10, b g Milan—Crevamoy (IRE) **Mr N T Griffith & H M Haddock**
67 **SLAP DASH HARRY (IRE)**, 5, b g Jeremy (USA)—Miss Vic Lovin (IRE) **Mr & Mrs Paul & Clare Rooney**
68 **SMUGGLER'S BLUES (IRE)**, 8, b g Yeats (IRE)—Rosy de Cyborg (FR) **Mr N T Griffith & H M Haddock**
69 **SPRINGFIELD FOX**, 7, gr g Sagamix (FR)—Marlbrook Fox **O'Donohoe, Cavanagh, Robinson, Nelson**
70 **STAMP YOUR FEET (IRE)**, 8, b g Galileo (IRE)—Nausicaa (USA) **Mr J. P. McManus**
71 **STOP THE WORLD (IRE)**, 7, b g Oscar (IRE)—Coolsilver (IRE) **McNeill Family Ltd**
72 **STRIKE IN MILAN (IRE)**, 8, b g Milan—Great Days (IRE) **R. S. Brookhouse**
73 **SUMKINDOFKING (IRE)**, 9, br g King's Theatre (IRE)—Shannon Rose (IRE) **Mr D. W. Fox**
74 **SUMMERVILLE BOY (IRE)**, 8, b g Sandmason—Suny House **R. S. Brookhouse**
75 **THE BIG BITE (IRE)**, 7, b g Scorpion (IRE)—Thanks Noel (IRE) **Mr N T Griffith & H M Haddock**
76 **THE BRASS MAN (IRE)**, 6, b g Milan—The Brass Lady (IRE) **S Nelson G Birrell K Delarocha D Savell**
77 **THE WORLDS END (IRE)**, 9, b g Stowaway—Bright Sprite (IRE) **McNeill Family Ltd**
78 **TRIBESMANS GLORY (IRE)**, 6, b g Jeremy (USA)—Benecash (IRE) **T Keelan,J Moynihan,S Nelson,D O'Donohoe**
79 **VALSEUR DU GRANVAL (FR)**, 11, b g Della Francesca (USA)—
                                     La Grande Vallee (FR) **D Thompson & The Magic Ten**
80 **WRITTENINTHESAND (IRE)**, 6, b g Milan—Sommer Sonnet (IRE) **Wilkin, Orr, Boileau & Douglas**
81 **ZOUTOISE (FR)**, 5, b m Enrique—Belle Yepa (FR) **Mr S. W. Clarke**

THREE-YEAR-OLDS

82 **BANNISTER (FR),** b g Olympic Glory (IRE)—Amou Daria (FR) **Mr T. George**
83 B f Passing Glance—Overnight Fame (IRE) **Mr R. T. Cornock**
84 B f Walk In The Park (IRE)—Toungara (FR) **Mr S. W. Clarke**

TWO-YEAR-OLDS

85 B c 19/03 Walk In The Park (IRE)—Toungara (FR) (Smadoun (FR)) **Mr S. W. Clarke**

Other Owners: Mrs E. G. A. Birrell, Mr R. J. Blunt, Mrs H. L. Boileau, Mr D. A. Bovington, R. S. Brookhouse, Mr P. R. Burslem, Mr J. P. Cavanagh, Mr S. W. Clarke, Mr C. B. Compton, Mr J. S. A. Douglas, Mr J. W. Edgedale, Mr J. M. Fawbert, Mr J. A. R. R. French, Mr J. M. Gabbertas, Mr R. K. Gabbertas, Mrs S. P Gabbertas, Mrs V. Gabbertas, Mrs J. Gerard-Pearse, Mr N. Griffith, Mrs H. M. Haddock, Countess A. Harrington, The Earl C. Harrington, Mrs S. A. Hayward, Mr T. J. Keelan, Mr J. B. Lawson, Mr J. T. C. Longley, Mrs M. E. MacGregor, Mr D. P. McDermott, Ms J. A. Moran, Mr J. Moynihan, Mrs S. C. Nelson, Mr D. J. O'Donohoe, Mrs S. Orr, Mr D. Osullivan, A. J. Outhart, Mr C. H. Perry, Mrs H. W. Polito, Mr David Rea, Ms V. Robinson, Mr D. A. Savell, H. S. Smith, Mr T. D. J. Syder, Mr C. R. S. Tatnall, Mr J. Taylor, Mrs K. Torres de la Rocha, A. M. Waller, J. T. Warner, Mr R. C. Wilkin, Mr N. Williamson.

Assistant Trainer: John Cullinan, Noel George, **Travelling Head:** Sarah Peacock, **Secretary:** Lauren Thompson.

NH Jockey: Jonathon Burke, Ciaran Gethings, Adrian Heskin. **Amateur Jockey:** Noel George.

222 **MR NICK GIFFORD, Findon**
Postal: **The Downs, Stable Lane, Findon, West Sussex, BN14 0RT**
Contacts: PHONE **01903 872226** MOBILE **07940 518077**
EMAIL **downs.stables@btconnect.com** WEBSITE **www.nickgiffordracing.co.uk**

1 4, B g Ocovango—A Long Way
2 **ALKA STEP (IRE)**, 9, gr g Alkaadhem—D'Bibbys Step (IRE) **Mr J E Burrows & Mrs V C Burrows**
3 4, B g Shirocco (GER)—Arctic Actress **Mrs R. E. Gifford**
4 **BELARGUS (FR)**, 5, b g Authorized (IRE)—Belga Wood (USA) **Mr J. P. McManus**
5 **CASTLEDHEM (IRE)**, 5, b g Alkaadhem—Castle Hope (IRE) **Paul & Louise Bowtell**
6 **CORAL LAD (IRE)**, 5, b g Shirocco (GER)—Gli Gli (IRE) **Project Mars Racing Partnership**
7 **DELTA ROSE (IRE)**, 6, br m Robin des Champs (FR)—Cruising Katie (IRE) **J. R. Hulme**
8 **DIDTHEYLEAVEUOUTTO (IRE)**, 7, ch g Presenting—Pretty Puttens (IRE) **Mr J. P. McManus**
9 **EL TORNADO (FR)**, 6, gr g Martaline—Okawanga Royale (FR) **Mr J. P. McManus**
10 **FAIRWAY FREDDY**, 7, b g Elusive Pimpernel (USA)—Silent Supreme (IRE) **New Gold Dream**
11 **FLIBINIGHT (IRE)**, 5, b m Getaway (GER)—Fern Bird (IRE) **The Ladybirds**
12 **FLY NUMBER ONE (IRE)**, 6, b g Oscar (IRE)—Kahysera **Mr The Brooks Family and J Kyle**
13 **GLEN ROCCO**, 9, ch g Shirocco (GER)—Adees Dancer **Kyle, Mason, Brooks, Ferguson & Stevens**
14 **HAWKERLAND (IRE)**, 7, b g Sea The Stars (IRE)—Zarara (USA) **The Willow & Bridle Partnership**
15 **ITSNOTWHATYOUTHINK (IRE)**, 5, b br g Westerner—Baladiva (IRE) **Mrs L Bowtell & Mrs S Cotty**
16 **JUNGLE PROSE (IRE)**, 5, b br m Yeats (IRE)—Spring Baloo (IRE) **Nick Gifford Racing Club**
17 **MYSTIC DREAMER (IRE)**, 6, b m Sans Frontieres (IRE)—Free Dreamer (IRE) **Nick Gifford Racing Club**
18 **NORTHERN POET (IRE)**, 5, b g Yeats (IRE)—Crowning Virtue (IRE) **The Hope Springs Syndicate**
19 **NOTRE AMI (IRE)**, 9, br g Kalanisi (IRE)—Shuilan (IRE) **The Morpheus Partnership**
20 **ODEN**, 6, ch g Lope de Vega (IRE)—Dashing (IRE) **Mrs S. Cotty**
21 **PADDY'S POEM**, 9, b g Proclamation (IRE)—Ashleys Petale (IRE) **Mrs T. J. Stone-Brown**
22 **ROSE OF AGHABOE (IRE)**, 7, b m Gold Well—Shillinglee Spring **The Rose Tinted Partnership**
23 **THE MIGHTY DON (IRE)**, 8, ch g Shantou (USA)—Flying Answer (IRE) **Golden Rose Partnership**
24 **THEO'S CHARM (IRE)**, 10, b g Presenting—Kates Charm (IRE) **Mr M. K. O'Shea**
25 **WOLFCATCHERJACK (IRE)**, 6, b g Lawman (FR)—Alleluia **Ne'er Do Wells V**

THREE-YEAR-OLDS
26 **LEGENDARY GRACE**, b f Multiplex—Fairyinthewind (IRE) **Mr R. J. Delnevo**

Other Owners: Mr A. T. Beer, Mrs S. A. Beer, Mr W. A. T. Beer, Mr J. P. M. Bowtell, Mrs L. Bowtell, Mr G. W. Brickwood, Mr G. F. Brooks, Mr J. E. Burrows, Mrs V. C. Burrows, Mr E. M. P Clark, Mrs S. Cotty, Mr D. Ellis, Sir A. Ferguson, Mr A. Goldsmith, Mr J. A. M. Johnson, Mr J. Kyle, G. A. Mason, Mr M. A. C. Rudd, Mr D. J. Stevens, Mr M. J. Tracey, Mr E. J. Williams, Mrs L. Wolfe.

NH Jockey: Leighton Aspell, James Davies.

MR NICK GIFFORD - continued

223 **MR MARK GILLARD, Sherborne**
Postal: **Hawkes Field Farm, Hilton, Blandford Forum, Dorset, DT11 0DN**
Contacts: PHONE **01258 881111** MOBILE **07970 700605**
EMAIL **office@markgillardracing.com** WEBSITE **www.markgillardracing.com**

1 **AVITHOS**, 10, b m Kayf Tara—Digyourheelsin (IRE) **Mr N. J. McMullan & Mr T. Winzer**
2 **EIGHTEENHUNDRED (IRE)**, 4, b g Battle of Marengo (IRE)—Kawaha (IRE) **Sherborne Utilities Ltd**
3 **FINISHER (USA)**, 5, b g Street Cry (IRE)—Morena (PER) **Mr V. Scott**
4 **JOHN BETJEMAN**, 4, b g Poet's Voice—A Great Beauty **Mr R. M. Rivers**
5 **KARL MARX (IRE)**, 10, b g Red Clubs (IRE)—Brillano (FR) **Mr S. Bartlett**
6 **KINGSTON MIMOSA**, 8, b g Kheleyf (USA)—Derartu (AUS) **Mr S. J. Garnett**
7 **NO NO CARDINAL (IRE)**, 11, ch g Touch of Land (FR)—Four Moons (IRE) **Mr T. J. C. Seegar**
8 **NO NO TONIC**, 6, b m Sulamani (IRE)—Karinga Madame (IRE) **Mr N. J. McMullan & Mr S. H. Bryant**
9 **PILANSBERG**, 8, b g Rail Link—Posteritas (USA) **Mr A. K. Hosie**
10 **POWERFUL SOCIETY (IRE)**, 5, b m Power—Society Gal (IRE) **Sherborne Utilities Ltd**

MR MARK GILLARD - continued

11 **TOP BEAK (IRE)**, 7, b g Lawman (FR)—Tree Tops **Sherborne Utilities Ltd**
12 **TOUCH SCREEN (IRE)**, 10, b g Touch of Land (FR)—Capard Lady (IRE) **Mrs Pippa Gillard**
13 **VANDERBILT (IRE)**, 6, ch g Intense Focus (USA)—Star of The West **Mr T. J. C. Seegar & Sherborne Utilities Ltd**

THREE-YEAR-OLDS

14 B f Casamento (IRE)—Enchanting Smile (FR) **Miss Kay Russell**

Other Owners: Mrs Pippa Gillard, Mr T. J. C. Seegar, Sherborne Utilities Ltd.

Assistant Trainer: Mrs Pippa Gillard, **Yard Sponsor:** Ascot Park Polo Club.

Conditional Jockey: Theo Gillard. **Amateur Jockey:** Mr Fergus Gillard.

224

MR JAMES GIVEN, Willoughton
Postal: **Mount House Stables, Long Lane, Willoughton, Gainsborough, Lincolnshire, DN21 5SQ**
Contacts: **PHONE 01427 667618 MOBILE 07801 100496 FAX 01427 667734**
EMAIL james@jamesgivenracing.com WEBSITE www.jamesgivenracing.com

1 **GINVINCIBLE**, 4, gr f Zebedee—Gone Sailing **Roy Tozer & Team Given 2**
2 **INDIANAPOLIS (IRE)**, 5, b h Galileo (IRE)—Adoration (USA) **Mr A. Owen**
3 **POPPY MAY (IRE)**, 6, b m Zoffany (IRE)—Lara Amelia (IRE) **Team Given 1**
4 **WAITAKI (IRE)**, 7, b m Invincible Spirit (IRE)—Bluebell Park (USA) **Mr D. Eiffe**

THREE-YEAR-OLDS

5 **CHALIS**, ch g Hot Streak (IRE)—Winners Chant (IRE) **Dachel Stud**
6 **D'ARCY SPICE**, b f Lethal Force (IRE)—Inyordreams **Apple Tree Stud**
7 **GREY EMINENCE**, gr g Outstrip—Laurena (GER) **Ron Spore & Exors Late Stephanie Oliver**
8 B f Mount Nelson—Katy Nowaitee **Team Given 3**
9 **MANY A STAR (IRE)**, ch c Starspangledbanner (AUS)—Many Hearts (USA) **Mrs L. P. Hobby**
10 **MONSARAZ**, b c Cityscape—Rattleyurjewellery **Mr P. Onslow**
11 B c Muhaarar—Passion Overflow (USA) **The Cool Silk Partnership**
12 **STONE SOLDIER**, ch c Mayson—La Adelita (IRE) **The Cool Silk Partnership**

TWO-YEAR-OLDS

13 B c 05/04 Fountain of Youth (IRE)—Mania (IRE) (Danehill (USA)) (4761) **Team Given 5**
14 **RATAFIA**, b c 23/04 Iffraaj—Aetna (Indesatchel (IRE)) (36000) **Ingram Racing**
15 B f 27/02 Slade Power (IRE)—Rose Kazan (IRE) (Teofilo (IRE)) **Bolton Grange**
16 **SPARKLING PERRY**, b f 30/03 Fountain of Youth (IRE)—Bebe de Cham (Tragic Role (USA)) **Lovely Bubbly Racing**
17 Ch f 21/03 Universal (IRE)—Tanaasub (IRE) (Lope de Vega (IRE)) **Dachel Stud**
18 B c 03/04 Bated Breath—Tarocchi (USA) (Affirmed (USA)) (3000) **Team Given 4**

225

MR JIM GOLDIE, Glasgow
Postal: **Libo Hill Farm, Uplawmoor, Glasgow, Lanarkshire, G78 4BA**
Contacts: **PHONE 01505 850212 MOBILE 07778 241522**
WEBSITE www.jimgoldieracing.com

1 **AYR POET**, 5, b g Poet's Voice—Jabbara (IRE) **W. M. Johnstone**
2 **BE PROUD (IRE)**, 4, b g Roderic O'Connor (IRE)—Agnista (IRE) **Gregg & O Shea**
3 5, Ch g Rock of Gibraltar (IRE)—Belle Rebelle (IRE)
4 **CALL ME GINGER**, 4, ch g Orientor—Primo Heights **Johnnie Delta Racing**
5 **COUNTY FAIR**, 6, b g Nayef (USA)—Village Fete **Mr & Mrs Raymond Anderson Green**
6 **DOON STAR**, 5, b m Sulamani (USA)—La Vecchia Scuola (IRE) **Mrs V. C. Macdonald**
7 **EUCHEN GLEN**, 7, b g Authorized (IRE)—Jabbara (IRE) **W. M. Johnstone**
8 **FIRLINFEU**, 5, b g New Approach (IRE)—Antara (GER) **Johnnie Delta Racing**
9 4, B g Orientor—Gargoyle Girl

MR JIM GOLDIE - continued

10 **GET OUT THE GATE (IRE)**, 7, b g Mahler—Chartani (IRE) **Mr J. Fyffe**
11 **GLENIFFER**, 4, b g Orientor—Glenlini **Johnnie Delta Racing**
12 **GLOBAL HUMOR (USA)**, 5, b g Distorted Humor (USA)—In Bloom (USA) **Johnnie Delta Racing**
13 **HUGOIGO**, 6, b g Sulamani (IRE)—Gargoyle Girl **Johnnie Delta Racing**
14 **INSURPLUS (IRE)**, 7, b g Bushranger (IRE)—Emly Express (IRE) **Mr D Renton & Mr J Goldie**
15 **JEFFREY HARRIS**, 5, b g Orientor—Theatrical Dancer **Mr & Mrs Philip C. Smith**
16 **JESSIE ALLAN (IRE)**, 9, b m Bushranger (IRE)—Ishimagic **Mr R. W. C. McLachlan**
17 **4**, B f Kayf Tara—La Vecchia Scuola (IRE) **The Reluctant Suitor's**
18 **LORD OF THE GLEN**, 5, b g Orientor—Glenlini **Johnnie Delta Racing**
19 **NEEDS TO BE SEEN (FR)**, 5, b g Motivator—Morning Line (FR) **Mr J Fyffe & Mr Gerry McGladery**
20 **ONE LAST HUG**, 5, b g Orientor—Gargoyle Girl **Mr James Callow & Mr J. S. Goldie**
21 **ORIENTAL LILLY**, 6, ch m Orientor—Eternal Instinct **Johnnie Delta Racing**
22 **PAMMI**, 5, b m Poet's Voice—Bright Girl (IRE) **Ayrshire Racing & Partner**
23 **PRIMO'S COMET**, 5, b g Orientor—Primo Heights **The Reluctant Suitor's**
24 **REMMY D (IRE)**, 5, b g Lawman (FR)—Evening Time (IRE) **Whitestonecliffe Racing Partnership**
25 **RIOJA DAY (IRE)**, 10, b g Red Clubs (IRE)—Dai E Dai (USA) **Mr J. S. Goldie**
26 **SARVI**, 5, br m Intello (GER)—Crystal Swan (IRE) **Johnnie Delta Racing**
27 **SCOTS SONNET**, 6, b g Poet's Voice—Jabbara (IRE) **Mr W. M. Johnstone & Mr J. S. Goldie**
28 **SIR CHAUVELIN**, 8, b g Authorized (IRE)—Jabbara (IRE) **Mr J. Fyffe, Mrs M. Craig, Mr G. Thomson**
29 **SISTER MIDNIGHT (IRE)**, 4, b f Dark Angel (IRE)—Yoga (IRE) **Mr J. Fyffe**
30 **SOUND OF IONA**, 4, ch f Orientor—Eternal Instinct **Mr & Mrs G Grant & the Reluctant Suitors**
31 **STAR CRACKER (IRE)**, 8, ch g Starspangledbanner (AUS)—Champagne Cracker **Mr G E Adams & Mr J S Goldie**
32 **TANNADICE PARK (IRE)**, 5, b m Shirocco (GER)—Catcherinscratcher (IRE) **Mrs S. Townshend**
33 **THEGLASGOWWARRIOR**, 6, b g Sir Percy—Sweet Cando (IRE) **Mrs L. B. K. Bone**
34 **TOMMY G**, 7, ch g Makfi—Primo Heights **Johnnie Delta Racing**
35 **WALKIN IN THE RAIN (IRE)**, 7, b g Darsi (FR)—Kyle Hill (IRE) **Musselburgh Lunch Club**

THREE-YEAR-OLDS

36 **CECI WELLS**, b f Orientor—Theatrical Dancer **Mr & Mrs Philip C. Smith**
37 Ch g Poet's Voice—Miss Anneliese (IRE) **W. M. Johnstone**
38 Ch c Casamento (IRE)—Spirit of The Sea (IRE) **W. M. Johnstone**
39 **SUMMER HEIGHTS**, b f Orientor—Primo Heights **Johnnie Delta Racing**

Other Owners: Mr G. Adams, Ayrshire Racing, Mr N. Boyle, Mr J. R. Callow, Mrs M. Craig, Mr J. Fyffe, Mrs D. I. Goldie, Mr J. S. Goldie, Mrs C. H. Grant, Mr G. R. Grant, Mr A. L. Gregg, W. M. Johnstone, Mr G. R. McGladery, Mr D. W. McIntyre, Mr G. P. O'Shea, D. C. Renton, Mrs J. W. Smith, Exors of the Late Mr P.C. Smith, The Reluctant Suitor's, G. M. Thomson, Mr G. T. Wallace.

Assistant Trainer: George Goldie, James Goldie.

Flat Jockey: P. J. McDonald. **Conditional Jockey:** Callum Bewley. **Apprentice Jockey:** Phil Dennis.

---

226 **MR STEVE GOLLINGS, Louth**
Postal: **Highfield House, Scamblesby, Louth, Lincolnshire, LN11 9XT**
Contacts: PHONE **01507 343213, 01507 343204 MOBILE 07860 218910**
EMAIL **stevegollings@aol.com** WEBSITE **www.stevegollings.com**

1 **ASPIRE TOWER (IRE)**, 4, b g Born To Sea (IRE)—Red Planet **North Yorkshire B'stock & B. McNeill**
2 **CAGED LIGHTNING (IRE)**, 10, b g Haatef (USA)—Rainbow Melody (IRE) **Northern Bloodstock Racing**
3 **COLONY QUEEN**, 4, b f Gregorian (IRE)—Queen Margrethe **David & Ros Chapman**
4 **HANDIWORK**, 10, ch g Motivator—Spinning Top **Mr C. A. Johnstone**
5 **MOLTEN LAVA (IRE)**, 8, b g Rock of Gibraltar (IRE)—Skehana (IRE) **David & Ros Chapman**
6 **NEVADA**, 7, gr g Proclamation (IRE)—La Columbina **Northern Bloodstock Racing**
7 **ROCOCO STYLE**, 7, b m Shirocco (GER)—Akdara (IRE) **Tensational**
8 **VENTURA GOLD (IRE)**, 5, b g Red Jazz (USA)—Desert Shine (IRE) **Mr R. C. Key**
9 **ZAMOYSKI**, 10, ch g Dutch Art—Speech **P Taiano, N Gollings, S Powell**

MR STEVE GOLLINGS - continued

THREE-YEAR-OLDS

10 NAT LOVE (IRE), b g Gregorian (IRE)—Chaguaramas (IRE) **David & Ros Chapman**

Other Owners: Mr G. Barot, Mrs B. Blair, Mr D. O. Chapman, Mrs R. M. H. Chapman, Miss N. J. Gollings, Mr B. McNeill, North Yorkshire Bloodstock Racing, Mr S. T. Powell, Mr P. G. Taiano.

Assistant Trainer: Mrs J M Gollings

227
MR CHRIS GORDON, Winchester
Postal: **Morestead Farm Stables, Morestead, Winchester, Hampshire, SO21 1JD**
Contacts: **PHONE 01962 712774 MOBILE 07713 082392 FAX 01962 712774**
EMAIL chrisgordon68@hotmail.co.uk WEBSITE www.chrisgordonracing.com

1 ALBERT HUCKLEBUCK (IRE), 4, b g Leading Light (IRE)—Queen of Cool (IRE) **Ms E. J. Southall**
2 ALKETIOS (GR), 9, b g Kavafi (IRE)—Mazea (IRE) **Chris Gordon Racing Club**
3 ANNUAL INVICTUS (IRE), 5, b g Mahler—Shantou Rose (IRE) **Mr T. M. Smith**
4 AZOR AHAI, 4, b g Sixties Icon—Good Morning Lady **Let's Be Lucky Racing 25**
5 BADDESLEY (IRE), 5, b g Presenting—Fox Theatre (IRE) **Mr Richard & Mrs Carol Cheshire**
6 BADDESLEY KNIGHT (IRE), 7, b g Doyen (IRE)—Grangeclare Rhythm (IRE) **Mr Richard & Mrs Carol Cheshire**
7 BADDESLEY PRINCE (IRE), 6, b g Doyen (IRE)—Norabella (IRE) **Mr Richard & Mrs Carol Cheshire**
8 BE DARING (IRE), 9, gr g Dom Alco (FR)—Quinine (FR) **Gilbert & Gamble**
9 COMMANCHE RED (IRE), 7, ch g Mahler—Auntie Bob **Mr Richard & Mrs Carol Cheshire**
10 COMMANDANT (IRE), 7, br g Presenting—Miss Nomer (IRE) **Mrs B. I. Chantler**
11 DON'T TELL KATE (IRE), 5, b m Winged Love (IRE)—Gill Hall Lady **Mrs K. Digweed**
12 FIZZLESTIX (FR), 8, b g Bonbon Rose (FR)—Skipnight **Mrs C. New**
13 FOXY MEGAN, 6, b m Indian Haven—Alexandra S (IRE) **Starting Gate Racing**
14 GO WHATEVER (IRE), 6, b g Gold Well—And Whatever Else (IRE) **A. C. Ward-Thomas**
15 4, B f Doyen (IRE)—Grangeclare Rhythm (IRE) **C. E. Gordon**
16 HAREFIELD (IRE), 7, b g Doyen (IRE)—Bobbi's Venture (IRE) **Mr A. Charity**
17 HIGHWAY ONE O ONE (IRE), 8, br g Stowaway—High Accord (IRE) **A. C. Ward-Thomas**
18 HIGHWAY ONE O TWO (IRE), 5, b br g Shirocco (GER)—Supreme Dreamer (IRE) **A. C. Ward-Thomas**
19 HIT THE HIGHWAY (IRE), 11, b g Pierre—Highway Belle (IRE) **Team ABC**
20 HORATIO STAR, 5, b g Mount Nelson—Star Entry **J. H. Widdows**
21 HOWLONGISAFOOT (IRE), 11, b g Beneficial—Miss Vic (IRE) **Mr D. S. Dennis**
22 INVINCIBLE CAVE (IRE), 7, b g Court Cave (IRE)—Bespoke Baby (IRE) **Mr D. S. Dennis**
23 ITSONLYROCKNROLL (IRE), 8, ch g Shantou (USA)—Compelled (IRE) **The Select Syndicate**
24 JIMMY, 7, ch g Norse Dancer (IRE)—Isintshelovely (IRE) **L. Gilbert**
25 4, B c Libertarian—Lady Eile (IRE) **Mr D. S. Dennis**
26 LORD BADDESLEY (IRE), 5, b br g Doyen (IRE)—Tropical Ocean (IRE) **Mr Richard & Mrs Carol Cheshire**
27 MELLOW BEN (IRE), 7, b g Beneficial—Mellowthemoonlight (IRE) **Broadsword Group Ltd**
28 MILNTHORPE (IRE), 5, b g Sans Frontieres (IRE)—Lady Nelson (IRE) **Mrs N. Morris**
29 MOROMAC (IRE), 6, b g Morozov (USA)—My Bay Lady **Chris Gordon Racing Club**
30 MOUNT WINDSOR (IRE), 5, b g Mountain High (IRE)—Mrs Bukay (IRE) **Party People**
31 4, Ch g Shirocco (GER)—Nodelay (IRE) **Mr D. S. Dennis**
32 ON THE SLOPES, 6, b g Librettist (USA)—Dalriath **Skill Scaffolding Ltd**
33 ONLY MONEY (IRE), 6, ch g Getaway (GER)—Kings Diva (IRE) **Ward-thomas & Dennis**
34 PEAKY, 6, b g Distant Peak (IRE)—Mount Hillaby (IRE) **Mrs B. M. Ansell**
35 PRES (IRE), 6, ch g Sans Frontieres (IRE)—Present Company (IRE) **The Pres Partnership**
36 PRESS YOUR LUCK (IRE), 5, b g Doyen (IRE)—Merry Gladness (IRE) **C. E. Gordon**
37 RAMORE WILL (IRE), 9, gr g Tikkanen (USA)—Gill Hall Lady **E. J. Farrant**
38 REALLYRADICAL (IRE), 7, b g Insatiable (USA)—Glenogra Cailin (IRE) **Mrs B. I. Chantler**
39 REMILUC (FR), 11, b g Mister Sacha (FR)—Markene de Durtal (FR) **Gilbert & Gamble**
40 SAMI BEAR, 4, b g Sulamani (IRE)—Dalriath **Mr F. A. Axel-Berg**
41 SHUT THE BOX (IRE), 6, ch g Doyen (IRE)—Bond Holder (IRE) **The Shut The Box Syndicate**
42 SKY FULL OF STARS (IRE), 10, b g Mahler—Gold Flo (IRE) **Gilbert & Gamble**
43 SMURPHY ENKI (FR), 5, b g Blue Bresil (FR)—Creme Veloutee (USA)
44 TARA BRIDGE, 12, b g Kayf Tara—Annie Greenlaw **B. J. Champion**

MR CHRIS GORDON - continued

45 **TELEGRAPH PLACE (IRE)**, 7, br g Yeats (IRE)—Sea Skate (USA) **L. Gilbert**
46 **THE TIN MINER (IRE)**, 9, br g Presenting—Sidalcea (IRE) **Mrs B. M. Ansell**
47 **TOP MAN (IRE)**, 6, b g Milan—Get In There (IRE) **Broadsword Group Ltd**
48 **TWOMINUTES TURKISH (IRE)**, 5, ch g Mahler—Kilbarry Cliche (IRE) **The Cabal**
49 **VICENZO MIO (FR)**, 10, b g Corri Piano (FR)—Sweet Valrose (FR) **Dennis,Gordon,Gamble**

Other Owners: Mrs C. L. Cheshire, Mr R. Cheshire, Mr D. S. Dennis, Mr J. M. Gamble, L. Gilbert, C. E. Gordon, A. C. Ward-Thomas.

Assistant Trainer: Jenny Gordon.

NH Jockey: Tom Cannon

228

MR JOHN GOSDEN, Newmarket
Postal: Clarehaven, Bury Road, Newmarket, Suffolk, CB8 7BY
Contacts: **PHONE** 01638 565400 **FAX** 01638 565401
EMAIL jhmg@johngosden.com

1 **ALRAJAA**, 4, b g Dubawi (IRE)—Ethaara
2 **BEATBOXER (USA)**, 4, b g Scat Daddy (USA)—Thmoruplathlesupay (USA)
3 **COURT HOUSE (IRE)**, 5, b g Dawn Approach (IRE)—Crossanza (IRE)
4 **CROSSED BATON**, 5, b g Dansili—Sacred Shield
5 **DUBAI WARRIOR**, 4, b c Dansili—Mahbooba (AUS)
6 **EL MISK**, 4, b c Dansili—Igugu (AUS)
7 **ENABLE**, 6, b m Nathaniel (IRE)—Concentric
8 **ENBIHAAR (IRE)**, 5, b m Redoute's Choice (AUS)—Chanterelle (FR)
9 **FANNY LOGAN (IRE)**, 4, b f Sea The Stars (IRE)—Linda Radlett (IRE)
10 **FIRST IN LINE**, 4, ch c New Approach (IRE)—Hidden Hope
11 **FOREST OF DEAN**, 4, b g Iffraaj—Forest Crown
12 **GLOBAL GIANT**, 5, b h Shamardal (USA)—Aniseed (IRE)
13 **GODHEAD**, 4, b c Charm Spirit (IRE)—Hello Glory
14 **GOOD TIDINGS (FR)**, 4, b br g Teofilo (IRE)—Nouvelle Bonne (FR)
15 **HARROVIAN**, 4, b g Leroidesanimaux (BRZ)—Alma Mater
16 **HUMANITARIAN (USA)**, 4, b g Noble Mission—Sharbat (USA)
17 **KESIA (IRE)**, 4, ch f Australia—Caserta
18 **KING OF COMEDY (IRE)**, 4, b c Kingman—Stage Presence (IRE)
19 **LOGICIAN**, 4, gr c Frankel—Scuffle
20 **LORD NORTH (IRE)**, 4, b g Dubawi (IRE)—Najoum (USA)
21 **MEHDAAYIH**, 4, b f Frankel—Sayyedati Symphony (USA)
22 **MILLICENT FAWCETT**, 4, b f Kingman—Mainstay
23 **NAZEEF**, 4, b f Invincible Spirit (IRE)—Handassa
24 **PROMISSORY (IRE)**, 4, b f Dubawi (IRE)—Seal of Approval
25 **ROYAL LINE**, 6, ch h Dubawi (IRE)—Melikah (IRE)
26 **SCENTASIA**, 4, b f Cape Cross (IRE)—Sweet Rose
27 **STAR CATCHER**, 4, b f Sea The Stars (IRE)—Lynnwood Chase (USA)
28 **STAR OF BENGAL**, 5, b h Oasis Dream—Stage Presence (IRE)
29 **STRADIVARIUS (IRE)**, 6, ch h Sea The Stars (IRE)—Private Life (FR)
30 **TEREBELLUM (IRE)**, 4, br f Sea The Stars (IRE)—Marvada (IRE)
31 **TURGENEV**, 4, b c Dubawi (IRE)—Tasaday (USA)
32 **WEEKENDER**, 6, b g Frankel—Very Good News (USA)
33 **YURI GAGARIN**, 4, ch g Sea The Moon (GER)—Soviet Terms

THREE-YEAR-OLDS

34 **AFRICAN DREAM**, b f Oasis Dream—Alsindi (IRE)
35 **AGREED**, b f Gleneagles (IRE)—Intrigued
36 **AL RUFAA (FR)**, b c Kingman—Clarmina (IRE)
37 **ALKHAT**, b c Oasis Dream—Yasmeen
38 **ALMIGHWAR**, b c Dubawi (IRE)—Taghrooda

MR JOHN GOSDEN - continued

39 **AMTIYAZ,** b c Frankel—Rose of Miracles
40 **ANASTARSIA (IRE),** b f Sea The Stars (IRE)—Aniseed (IRE)
41 **ANOINTED,** b f Invincible Spirit (IRE)—Sariska
42 **ASBAAGH (IRE),** b f Siyouni (FR)—Brynica (FR)
43 **ASWAAT,** b f Muhaarar—Hedaaya (IRE)
44 **ATIAAF,** b f Dubawi (IRE)—Maqaasid
45 **AUREUM (USA),** b f Medaglia d'Oro (USA)—Alina (USA)
46 **BAAQY (IRE),** b f Iffraaj—Natalisa (USA)
47 **BIRDWATCHER (USA),** b f Uncle Mo (USA)—Bizzy Caroline (USA)
48 **BIZZI LIZZI,** b f Muhaarar—Izzi Top
49 **BRACKISH,** b c Golden Horn—Delizia (IRE)
50 **BUBBLING UP (IRE),** br f Galileo (IRE)—Bufera (IRE)
51 **BYZANTIA,** b f Golden Horn—Hoyam
52 **CAPE PALACE,** b c Golden Horn—Mia Diletta
53 **CELESTRAN,** b c Dansili—Starscope
54 **CEMHAAN,** b c Muhaarar—Shalwa
55 **CHARMING ROSE,** b f Kingman—Sweet Rose
56 **CHEROKEE TRAIL (USA),** b c War Front (USA)—Moth (IRE)
57 **COLONIZE,** b c Empire Maker (USA)—Nayarra (IRE)
58 **CRESSIDA,** b f Dansili—Modern Look
59 **DAFINAH (IRE),** b f War Front (USA)—Spring In The Air (CAN)
60 **DARAIN,** b c Dubawi (IRE)—Dar Re Mi
61 **DAUNTLESS,** b g Dubawi (IRE)—Enticement
62 **DESERT FLYER,** b f Shamardal (USA)—White Moonstone (USA)
63 **DISCO FEVER,** b f Oasis Dream—Penelopa
64 **DONNYBROOK (IRE),** b f Invincible Spirit (IRE)—Mayhem (IRE)
65 **EDITH PIAF (IRE),** b f Le Havre (IRE)—Blissful Beat
66 **ENCIPHER,** b c Siyouni (FR)—Ennaya (FR)
67 **ENEMY,** b c Muhaarar—Prudenzia (IRE)
68 **FAISAL,** b c Golden Horn—Bella Lulu
69 **FARAMMAN,** b c Fastnet Rock (AUS)—Nessina (USA)
70 **FLATLEY,** ch g Kendargent (FR)—Premiere Danseuse
71 **FRANCONIA,** b f Frankel—Winter Sunrise
72 **FRANKLY DARLING,** b f Frankel—Hidden Hope
73 **GALLAGHER,** b c Oasis Dream—Azanara (IRE)
74 **GALSWORTHY,** b c Dansili—Gallipot
75 **GLAER,** b c Siyouni (FR)—Glorious Sight (IRE)
76 **GOLDEN RULES,** b c Golden Horn—Sinnamary (IRE)
77 **GRAND BAZAAR,** b c Golden Horn—Damaniyat Girl (USA)
78 **HALFWAYTOTHEMOON (IRE),** b f Sea The Stars (IRE)—Reflective (USA)
79 **HAQEEQY (IRE),** b c Lope de Vega (IRE)—Legal Lyric (IRE)
80 **HAWKISH,** b c Dansili—Rimth
81 **HIGH AMBITION,** b f Invincible Spirit (IRE)—High Heeled (IRE)
82 **HYPOTHETICAL (IRE),** ch c Lope de Vega (IRE)—Peut Etre (IRE)
83 **INDIE ANGEL (IRE),** gr f Dark Angel (IRE)—Indigo Lady
84 **INDIGO LAKE,** b c Frankel—Responsible
85 **INNOVATION,** b f Dubawi (IRE)—Free Verse
86 **IRIS BUD (USA),** b f War Front (USA)—Seta
87 **ISTIQRAAR (IRE),** b g Showcasing—City Image (IRE)
88 **JANE MARPLE,** b f Nathaniel (IRE)—Miss Pinkerton
89 **KING LEONIDAS,** b c Kingman—Reem (AUS)
90 **KING OF ARMS,** b c Kingman—Marika
91 **KURAMATA (IRE),** b c Australia—Blue Kimono (IRE)
92 **LADY ANDAZ (IRE),** b f Dark Angel (IRE)—Marvada (IRE)
93 **LAKE LUCERNE (USA),** b f Dubawi (IRE)—Round Pond (USA)
94 **LEAD SINGER (IRE),** b c Kingman—Boston Rocker (IRE)
95 **LEAFHOPPER (IRE),** gr f Dark Angel (IRE)—Layla Jamil (IRE)
96 **LIBRETTI (USA),** b f Noble Mission—Liberty Flag (USA)
97 **LIGHTNESS (IRE),** b f Shamardal (USA)—Serene Beauty (USA)

MR JOHN GOSDEN - continued

98 **LOQUACIOUS (IRE)**, b f Kodiac—Portentous
99 **LORDOFTHEHORIZON (FR)**, b br c Dansili—Astronomy Domine
100 **MAGICAL MORNING**, b c Muhaarar—The Lark
101 **MAJESTIC NOOR**, b f Frankel—Nouriya
102 **MARIA ROSA (USA)**, b f War Front (USA)—Seeking Gabrielle (USA)
103 **MISHRIFF (IRE)**, b c Make Believe—Contradict
104 **MISS YODA (GER)**, ch f Sea The Stars (IRE)—Monami (GER)
105 **MOOHAREEBA**, b f Invincible Spirit (IRE)—Mahbooba (AUS)
106 **MOONLIGHT IN PARIS (IRE)**, b f Camelot—Malayan Mist (IRE)
107 **MOSTLY**, b f Makfi—Montare (IRE)
108 **MY THOUGHT (IRE)**, b g Kodiac—Aricia (IRE)
109 **NASRAAWY (USA)**, ch c Kitten's Joy (USA)—Brushwork (USA)
110 **NOVA ROMA**, b c Golden Horn—Ragsah (IRE)
111 **OCEAN PEARL (IRE)**, b f Oasis Dream—Islington (IRE)
112 **ON GUARD**, b c Invincible Spirit (IRE)—Palitana (USA)
113 **OVER THE OCEAN**, b f Nathaniel (IRE)—Coral Wave (IRE)
114 **PALACE PIER**, b c Kingman—Beach Frolic
115 **PARADISE ON EARTH**, b f Invincible Spirit (IRE)—Rainbow Springs
116 **PERONISTA (IRE)**, b f Muhaarar—Evita
117 **PHAROAH KING (USA)**, b c American Pharoah (USA)—Dancing Trieste (USA)
118 **PITCHER'S POINT (USA)**, b br c Medaglia d'Oro (USA)—Hungry Island (USA)
119 **POCKET VETO (IRE)**, br f No Nay Never (USA)—Pivoina (IRE)
120 **PRISMATIC (IRE)**, b f Golden Horn—Teeky
121 **PROCEEDING (USA)**, b c Point of Entry (USA)—Vignette (USA)
122 **PROVEN (IRE)**, b c Gleneagles (IRE)—Bratislava
123 **RAVENTREE (IRE)**, b f Nathaniel (IRE)—Ethel
124 **RICETTA**, b f Camelot—Panzanella
125 **RIOT (IRE)**, b c Kingman—Alexander Queen (IRE)
126 **ROYAL MEWS (FR)**, ch c Siyouni (FR)—Queen Arabella
127 **RUN WILD (GER)**, ch f Amaron—Rondinay (FR)
128 **SHAREEFA**, gr f Shamardal (USA)—Qertaas (IRE)
129 **SHIMMERING (IRE)**, b f Lope de Vega (IRE)—Crysdal
130 **SUN BEAR**, b f Dubawi (IRE)—Great Heavens
131 **SUNRAY MAJOR**, b c Dubawi (IRE)—Zenda
132 **SWIFT VERDICT**, b c Dubawi (IRE)—Just The Judge (IRE)
133 **TAO TE CHING (IRE)**, b f Lope de Vega (IRE)—Albarouche
134 **TAQAREER (IRE)**, b f Frankel—Bethrah (IRE)
135 **TENBURY WELLS (USA)**, b c Medaglia d'Oro (USA)—Dayatthespa (USA)
136 **THEBIAN**, b c Kingman—Amarillo Starlight (IRE)
137 **TIEMPO VUELA**, b f Lope de Vega (IRE)—Tempest Fugit (IRE)
138 **TO NATHANIEL**, ch c Nathaniel (IRE)—Too The Stars (IRE)
139 **TORRICELLA**, b f Dubawi (IRE)—Taranto
140 **TSAR**, b c Kingman—Kilo Alpha
141 **TUSCAN GAZE (IRE)**, ch c Galileo (IRE)—Crystal Gaze (IRE)
142 **URS FISCHER (IRE)**, b c Pivotal—Amerique (IRE)
143 **URSA MINOR (IRE)**, b c Sea The Stars (IRE)—Kincob (USA)
144 **VERBOTEN (IRE)**, b gr c No Nay Never (USA)—Far Away Eyes (IRE)
145 **WALDKONIG**, b c Kingman—Waldlerche
146 **WASAAYEF (IRE)**, b f Kingman—Seagull (IRE)
147 **WOLFLET**, ch f Lope de Vega (IRE)—Martlet
148 **ZAHRATTY (IRE)**, b f Muhaarar—Beach Bunny (IRE)

Trainer did not supply details of their two-year-olds.

Flat Jockey: L. Dettori, Robert Havlin, Nicky Mackay, Kieran O'Neill.

229   MRS HARRIET GRAHAM, Jedburgh
Postal: **Strip End, Jedburgh, Roxburghshire, TD8 6NE**
Contacts: **PHONE 01835 840354 MOBILE 07843 380401**
EMAIL hgrahamracing@aol.com

1 **AYE RIGHT (IRE)**, 7, b g Yeats (IRE)—Gaybric (IRE) **Mr G. F. Adam**
2 **BANNOCKBURN (IRE)**, 4, b g Battle of Marengo (IRE)—Misrepresent (USA) **Mr M McGovern & Partner**
3 **DANCEWITHTHEWIND (IRE)**, 5, br g Jeremy (USA)—Sithgaoithe (IRE) **Mr G. F. Adam**
4 **MILLARVILLE (IRE)**, 7, b m Court Cave (IRE)—Portavoe (IRE) **Mr G. F. Adam**
5 4, B f Black Sam Bellamy (IRE)—Minimum **H G Racing**
6 **WEE GOLDIE**, 6, b g Gold Well—Presenteea (IRE) **Mr G. F. Adam**

Other Owners: Mr R. D. Graham, Mr M. J. McGovern.

Assistant Trainer: R D Graham.

Conditional Jockey: Callum Bewley, Tommy Dowson.

230   MR CHRIS GRANT, Billingham
Postal: **Low Burntoft Farm, Wolviston, Billingham, Cleveland, TS22 5PD**
Contacts: **PHONE 01740 644054 MOBILE 07860 577998**
EMAIL chrisgrantracing@gmail.com WEBSITE www.chrisgrantracing.co.uk

1 **ACDC (IRE)**, 10, b g King's Theatre (IRE)—Always Alert (IRE) **D&D Armstrong Limited**
2 5, Br g Malinas (GER)—Annie's Gift (IRE) **P. Nelson**
3 **ASK CAITLIN (IRE)**, 6, b m Ask—Bold Cailin (IRE) **Mrs H. N. Eubank**
4 **ASKMEWHY (IRE)**, 6, b g Ask—Grey Clouds **Mr T. J. Hemmings**
5 **BARFLY**, 6, gr g Fair Mix (IRE)—Just Smokie **D&D Armstrong Limited**
6 **BRAMPTON BILLY**, 4, b g Haafhd—May Clover **Miss S. J. Turner**
7 **BROADWAY BELLE**, 10, b m Lucarno (USA)—Theatre Belle **Mrs M Nicholas & Chris Grant**
8 **CASTLE ON A CLOUD (IRE)**, 9, b g Flemensfirth (USA)—Ifyoucouldseemenow (IRE) **C. Grant**
9 **CHEEKY CHES**, 5, ch g Sulamani (IRE)—Youamazeme **P. Nelson**
10 **DARIUS DES SOURCES (FR)**, 7, gr g Irish Wells (FR)—Lionata (FR) **D & D Armstrong Ltd & Mr L Westwood**
11 **DONNA'S DIAMOND (IRE)**, 11, gr g Cloudings (IRE)—Inish Bofin (IRE) **D&D Armstrong Limited**
12 **DRUMS OF WAR (IRE)**, 8, b g Youmzain (IRE)—Min Asl Wafi (IRE) **J. Wade**
13 4, B g Robin des Champs (FR)—Evening Rushour (IRE) **D. Mossop**
14 **FIERY MISSION (USA)**, 4, b g Noble Mission—Quickfire **Mr N. E. M. Jones**
15 **FLAKARNA**, 5, b m Lucarno (USA)—Flaybay **Miss A. P. Lee**
16 4, Ch g Proclamation (IRE)—Forsters Plantin
17 **GLEN BALLAGH (IRE)**, 5, b g Yeats (IRE)—Ballylough Lady (IRE) **Mr T. J. Hemmings**
18 **HEY BOB (IRE)**, 8, br g Big Bad Bob (IRE)—Bounty Star (IRE) **Miss Alison P. Lee & Mr Chris Grant**
19 **JACKS LAST HOPE**, 11, b g King's Theatre (IRE)—Ninna Nanna (FR) **Mr J. Kenny**
20 **JINKABELL**, 5, ch m Black Sam Bellamy (IRE)—Lady Jinks **Miss A. P. Lee**
21 **JINKAMAN**, 6, b g Black Sam Bellamy (IRE)—Lady Jinks **Miss A. P. Lee**
22 **JO CASHFLOW**, 6, b m Getaway (GER)—Mary Kate O'Brien **Mary Stone & Chris Grant**
23 **LYNDALE**, 5, b gr g Mountain High (IRE)—Grey Clouds **Mr T. J. Hemmings**
24 5, B m Oscar (IRE)—Micro Mission (IRE) **D&D Armstrong Limited**
25 **RED OCHRE**, 7, b g Virtual—Red Hibiscus **C. Grant**
26 **RED REMINDER**, 6, b m Mount Nelson—Red Hibiscus **Mrs H. N. Eubank**
27 4, Ch g Yorgunnabelucky (USA)—Shanxi Girl **Mickley Stud & Mr D. Mossop**
28 **SHOW AND GO (IRE)**, 11, b g Stowaway—Nooradeen (IRE) **Mr I. P. Crane**
29 **SIX ONE NINE (IRE)**, 5, b g Cloudings (IRE)—Indian Athlete (IRE) **D&D Armstrong Limited**
30 **SLANEMORE HILL (IRE)**, 8, br g Court Cave (IRE)—Goodonyou-Polly (IRE) **The Hon Mrs D. J. Faulkner**
31 **STORMY RECEPTION (IRE)**, 6, b m September Storm (GER)—Mandalus Lady (IRE) **Mrs S. Sunter**
32 **STRONG TEAM (IRE)**, 7, b g Exceed And Excel (AUS)—Star Blossom (USA) **C. Grant**
33 **THEATRE LEGEND**, 7, b g Midnight Legend—Theatre Belle **Division Bell Partnership**
34 **WINNINGTRY (IRE)**, 9, br g Flemensfirth (USA)—Jeruflo (IRE) **Mr T. J. Hemmings**
35 **ZAKETY ZAK**, 9, b g Overbury (IRE)—Jeanne d'Arc **Mr D. M. Wordsworth**

MR CHRIS GRANT - continued

Other Owners: D&D Armstrong Limited, C. Grant, R. Kent, Miss A. P. Lee, D. Mossop, Mrs M. Nicholas, Mrs M. S. Stone, Mr L. J. Westwood.

Assistant Trainer: Mrs S. Grant.

NH Jockey: Brian Hughes. **Conditional Jockey:** Callum Bewley.

231
MR JAMES GRASSICK, Cheltenham
Postal: **Dryfield Farm, Cleeve Hill, Cheltenham, Gloucestershire, GL54 5AG**
Contacts: **MOBILE 07976 779623**

1 **ISOBEL BLEU**, 5, b m Arvico (FR)—Appleppie Lady (IRE) **J. R. Grassick**
2 **LADY NATASHA (IRE)**, 7, b m Alfred Nobel (IRE)—Hot To Rock (IRE) **J. R. Grassick**
3 **VALENTINE MIST (IRE)**, 8, b m Vale of York (IRE)—Silvertine (IRE) **J. R. Grassick**
4 **VILLANEVE**, 5, b m Arvico (FR)—Pechaubar (FR) **J. R. Grassick**
5 **WAYWARD SUN (IRE)**, 9, b g Double Eclipse (IRE)—Mahonrun (IRE) **J. R. Grassick**

232
MR CARROLL GRAY, Bridgwater
Postal: **The Little Glen, Peartwater Road, Spaxton, Bridgwater, Somerset, TA5 1DG**
Contacts: **MOBILE 07989 768163**

1 **BELLAMY'S GREY**, 8, gr g Black Sam Bellamy (IRE)—Lambrini Queen **Riverdance Consortium 2**
2 **GENERAL GIRLING**, 13, b g General Gambul—Gold Charm **The Yeovilton Flyers**
3 **SEASEARCH**, 5, b g Passing Glance—Seaflower Reef (IRE) **Unity Farm Holiday Centre Ltd**
4 **VINNIE'S ICON (IRE)**, 6, b m Vinnie Roe (IRE)—Iconic Events (IRE) **Mr R. J. Napper & Mr S Reeves**

Other Owners: Mr R. J. Napper, Mr S. A. Reeves.

Assistant Trainer: Mrs C. M. L. Gray.

NH Jockey: Micheal Nolan.

233
MR WARREN GREATREX, Upper Lambourn
Postal: **Uplands, Upper Lambourn, Hungerford, Berkshire, RG17 8QH**
Contacts: **PHONE 01488 670279 MOBILE 07920 039114 FAX 01488 72193**
EMAIL info@wgreatrexracing.com WEBSITE www.wgreatrexracing.com

1 **ANOTHER EMOTION (FR)**, 8, gr g Turgeon (USA)—Line Perle (FR) **Mr Terry Warner & the McNeill Family**
2 **ANOTHER TUCO (IRE)**, 7, b g Westerner—Run And Dream (IRE) **Fitorfat Racing**
3 4, B g Leading Light (IRE)—Ask Sally (IRE)
4 **AUDACITY**, 4, ch g Pivotal—Carlanda (FR) **The Audacity Partnership**
5 **AURELLO**, 6, b m Kayf Tara—Haudello (FR) **Little Lodge Farm & Warren Greatrex**
6 **BAILARICO (IRE)**, 7, b g Dubawi (IRE)—Baila Me (GER) **Fitorfat Racing**
7 **BALLYBEGG (IRE)**, 5, b br g Mahler—Rebel Flyer (IRE) **Mr T. J. Hemmings**
8 **BEAUFORT (IRE)**, 4, b g Zoffany (IRE)—Change Course **Mr W. J. Greatrex**
9 **BLUBERRY HIGH (IRE)**, 6, b m Getaway (GER)—Blu Louisiana (GER) **Million in Mind Partnership**
10 **BOB MAHLER (IRE)**, 8, b g Mahler—Cooladurragh (IRE) **Bolingbroke, Bunch, Howard & Sutton**
11 **BOLD SOLDIER**, 5, b g Kayf Tara—Major Hoolihan **Alan & Andrew Turner**
12 **CALVARIO (FR)**, 5, gr g Falco (USA)—Ashkirya (FR) **Kate & Andrew Brooks**
13 **CRONK Y KNOX (IRE)**, 5, gr g Cloudings (IRE)—Exit Baby (IRE) **Mr T. J. Hemmings**
14 **DANCINGWITH STORMS (IRE)**, 6, ch g New Approach (IRE)—Mad About You (IRE) **Jadobry Management Ltd**
15 **DON'T ASK (IRE)**, 7, b g Ask—Outback Ivy (IRE) **Walters Plant Hire & Potter Group**
16 **DRUMLEE WATAR (IRE)**, 7, ch g Watar (IRE)—Dolly of Dublin (IRE) **Mr B. J. C. Drew**
17 **EARL OF HARROW**, 4, b g Sixties Icon—The Screamer (IRE) **Mr W. J. Greatrex**
18 **ECTOR (FR)**, 6, b g Coastal Path—Evane (FR) **Fitorfat Racing**
19 **ELEANOR GROVE (FR)**, 5, ch m Kapgarde (FR)—Dabaratsa (FR) **Kate & Andrew Brooks & Catherine Black**

MR WARREN GREATREX - continued

20 **ELLEON (FR)**, 5, b g Martaline—Ailette **The Spero & Batting Partnership**
21 4, B f Shirocco (GER)—Ellnando Queen **Mrs R. I. Vaughan**
22 **EMITOM (IRE)**, 6, b g Gold Well—Avenging Angel (IRE) **The Spero Partnership Ltd**
23 **ENCORE CHAMPS (IRE)**, 6, b g Robin des Champs (FR)—Dani California **Mr B. J. C. Drew**
24 **FRANKIE BABY (IRE)**, 5, b g Yeats (IRE)—Belsalsa (FR) **Jadobry Management Ltd**
25 **FULL SPES (FR)**, 4, gr g Al Namix (FR)—Full Passion (FR) **J & R Eynon, Majithia & Richards**
26 **GANGSTER (FR)**, 10, ch g Green Tune (USA)—Dahlia's Krissy (USA) **Jadobry Management Ltd**
27 4, B g Leading Light (IRE)—Generous Girl
28 **GO PHARISEE FLYER (FR)**, 4, b g Cokoriko (FR)—Rosalie Malta (FR) **Glassex Holdings Ltd**
29 **HEN (IRE)**, 4, b f Camelot—Lily of Kenmare (IRE) **Fitorfat Racing**
30 **HENSCHKE (IRE)**, 6, b g Mahler—Reserve The Right (IRE) **Mrs T. J. Stone-Brown**
31 **JAMMIN MASTERS (IRE)**, 9, b g Sinndar (IRE)—Zara Million (ITY) **No Dramas**
32 **JUST A SIP**, 5, b m Great Pretender (IRE)—One Gulp **Swanee River Partnership**
33 **KEEPER HILL (IRE)**, 9, b g Westerner—You Take Care (IRE) **McNeill Family Ltd**
34 **KEMBLE'S CASCADE (IRE)**, 5, b g Kalanisi (IRE)—Beauty Star (IRE) **Mr Awk Merriam & Mrs Henri Bayford**
35 **LA BAGUE AU ROI (FR)**, 9, b m Doctor Dino (FR)—

Alliance Royale (FR) **Mrs Julien Turner & Mr Andrew Merriam**
36 **LITTLE JACK**, 6, b g Malinas (GER)—Persian Forest **Jadobry Management Ltd**
37 **LUCY IN THE SKY (IRE)**, 4, b f Milan—Our Girl Lucy (IRE) **Lady Dulverton**
38 **MADAM MALINA**, 6, b m Malinas (GER)—Madam Jolie **Bolingbroke Da Mata Molony & Sutton**
39 **MAHLERVOUS (IRE)**, 7, b g Mahler—Brook Style (IRE) **The Marvellous Partnership**
40 **MANDALAYAN (IRE)**, 5, b g Arakan (USA)—Danza Nera (IRE) **Alan & Andrew Turner**
41 **MARTHA BRAE**, 5, b m Shirocco (GER)—Harringay **Mrs R. I. Vaughan**
42 **MASTER CARD**, 7, ch g Presenting—Subtilty **Shropshire Wanderers**
43 **MINELLA EXAMINER**, 7, b g Beat Hollow—Bold Fire **The Examiners**
44 **MISS HONEY RYDER (IRE)**, 7, b m Stowaway—Seesea (IRE) **The Albatross Club**
45 **MISSED APPROACH (IRE)**, 10, b g Golan (IRE)—Polly's Dream (IRE) **Alan & Andrew Turner**
46 **MULCAHYS HILL (IRE)**, 8, b g Brian Boru—Belsalsa (FR) **McNeill Family and Prodec Networks Ltd**
47 **NORTH STAR OSCAR (IRE)**, 6, b g Oscar (IRE)—North Star Poly (IRE) **The North Star Oscar Partnership**
48 **PICARA'S PROMISE**, 4, ch f Gentlewave (IRE)—Ambrosia's Promise (IRE) **The Spero Partnership Ltd**
49 **PORTRUSH TED (IRE)**, 8, b g Shantou (USA)—Village Queen **McNeill Family Ltd**
50 **PRINTING DOLLARS (IRE)**, 7, br m Doyen (IRE)—Printing Polly (IRE) **Mr R. B. Waley-Cohen**
51 **ROCCOWITHLOVE**, 6, b g Shirocco (GER)—Love Train (IRE) **Crimbourne Bloodstock**
52 **ROSE OF CIMARRON (IRE)**, 7, b m Westerner—Sharp Single (IRE)
53 **SARIM (IRE)**, 5, b g Declaration of War—Silver Star **Fitorfat Racing**
54 **SPEEDY CARGO (IRE)**, 7, b g Stowaway—Vics Miller (IRE) **N.W.A. Bannister & M.J.R. Bannister**
55 **STAR OF LANKA (IRE)**, 6, b g Zoffany (FR)—Indian Bounty **J & R Eynon, Little, Roberts, Dowley & Turner**
56 **SUNNY EXPRESS (IRE)**, 5, b g Jeremy (USA)—Golden Summer (IRE) **McNeill Family and Prodec Networks Ltd**
57 5, B m Kayf Tara—Sunshine Rays **Mr H. Redknapp**
58 **SYMPHONY HALL (IRE)**, 5, b g Mahler—Coumhall (IRE) **Mr L. A. Bolingbroke**
59 **TALKTOMENOW**, 6, b g Shirocco (GER)—Sweet Stormy (IRE) **Mr T. D. J. Syder**
60 **TRIO FOR RIO (IRE)**, 7, b br g Getaway (GER)—Rio Trio (IRE) **Mr T. J. Hemmings**
61 **WESTERN HALL (IRE)**, 8, b g Westerner—Seesea (IRE) **Albatross Club/Bryan Drew & Friends**
62 **WESTERN STARLET (IRE)**, 5, b g Westerner—Pepsi Starlet (FR) **Mrs J & Miss C Shipp & W Greatrex**
63 **YOUNG LIEUTENANT (IRE)**, 6, b g Robin des Champs (FR)—Be My Gesture (IRE) **Mrs S. M. Drysdale**

Other Owners: Mr M. J. R. Bannister, Mr N. W. A. Bannister, Mr T. J. Batting, Ms C. Black, Mr L. A. Bolingbroke, Mr A. L. Brooks, Mrs K. L. Brooks, Bryan Drew and Friends, Mrs P. M. Bunch, Mrs J. S. Chugg, Mr R. D. Chugg, Mr J. P. Da Mata, Mr K. J. Dowley, Mr B. J. C. Drew, Mrs J. M. Eynon, R. A. F. Eynon, Mrs Jill Eynon & Mr Robin Eynon, Fitorfat1 Racing, Mr T. R. Gittins, Glassex Holdings Ltd, Mr W. J. Greatrex, Mr M. W. Gregory, Mr M. Helyar, Mr G. P. Howard, Mr S. M. Little, Little Roberts Dowley & Turner, Mrs L. Majithia, Mr P. Martin, McNeill Family Ltd, A. W. K. Merriam, Ms H. J. Merriam, Mr P. Molony, Palatinate Thoroughbred Racing Limited, Mr C. M. Parker, Mrs M. Parker, Mr S. J. Piper, Mr N. Pogmore, Prodec Networks Ltd, Mr A. W. Richards, Mr D. A. Roberts, Mr S. R. Roper, Miss C. S. D. Shipp, Mrs J. Shipp, Sundorne Products (Llanidloes) Ltd, Mr C. J. Sutton, The Albatross Club, The Spero Partnership Ltd, Mr D. A. Turner, Mrs N. C. Turner, Walters Plant Hire Ltd, J. T. Warner, Mrs N. White, Mr S. Williams.

Assistant Trainer: Olly Kozak, **Head Lad:** Trigger Plunkett, Ian Yeates.

Flat Jockey: Edward Greatrex. **NH Jockey:** Harry Bannister, Adrian Heskin, Daryl Jacob, Richard Johnson, Gavin Sheehan. **Conditional Jockey:** Lee Cosgrove. **Apprentice Jockey:** Thomas Greatrex. **Amateur Jockey:** Mr Caoilin Quinn.

234 | **MR OLIVER GREENALL, Malpas**
Postal: **Stockton Hall Farm, Oldcastle, Malpas, Cheshire, SY14 7AE**
Contacts: **PHONE 01948 861207 MOBILE 07771 571000**
EMAIL ocg@stocktonhall.co.uk WEBSITE www.olivergreenall.co.uk

1 **ABSOLUTE JAFFA**, 5, ch m Lucarno (USA)—Reverse Swing **Astbury, Hewitt & Hockenhull**
2 **ACE VENTURA**, 5, b g Mayson—Ventura Highway **Hardscrabble**
3 **AKILAYA (IRE)**, 5, b m Getaway (GER)—Akilara (IRE) **The Ivy Syndicate**
4 **ARCTIC ROAD**, 7, b g Flemensfirth (USA)—Arctic Actress **Mr J. F. Wilson**
5 **ASKING QUESTIONS (IRE)**, 8, b g Ask—Just Sara (IRE) **Salmon Racing**
6 **AUTHORIZO (FR)**, 5, b g Authorized (IRE)—Street Lightning (FR) **The Deesiders**
7 **BLUE BALLERINA (IRE)**, 6, br m Fame And Glory—Peinture Rose (IRE) **P Nolan, T Nolan, P Norbury, P Daresbury**
8 **BOSSINEY BAY (IRE)**, 5, b m Camelot—Ursula Minor (IRE) **The Lucky Lovers Partnership**
9 **CAPTAIN REVELATION**, 8, ch g Captain Rio—Agony Aunt **Cheshire Racing**
10 **CAVE TOP (IRE)**, 8, b g Court Cave (IRE)—Cyrils Top Girl (IRE) **Lord Daresbury & Jocelyn Rosenburg**
11 **CAWTHORNE**, 6, b g Sulamani (IRE)—Kings Maiden (IRE) **Mr D. J. Astbury**
12 **CLONDAW PRETENDER**, 5, br g Great Pretender (FR)—Shropshire Girl **Dewhurst, Peavoy, Emdells & Daresbury**
13 **CONUNDRUM**, 4, ch g Sir Percy—Famusa **The Conundrum Partnership**
14 **COURT IN MATERA (IRE)**, 6, b g Court Cave (IRE)—
Orador Sur Glane (IRE) **Daresbury, Macechern, Hewitt & Lee Baldwin**
15 **EL BORRACHO (IRE)**, 5, br g Society Rock (IRE)—Flame of Hibernia (IRE) **Mr O. C. Greenall**
16 **EVANDER (IRE)**, 5, br g Arcadio (GER)—Blazing Belle (IRE) **Highclere TBred Racing - Henry Moore**
17 **FIRST MAN (IRE)**, 5, b g Lilbourne Lad (IRE)—Dos Lunas (IRE) **The Jockey Club Haydock Park Racing Club Ltd**
18 **FORT DE L'OCEAN (FR)**, 5, b g Racinger (FR)—Iconea (FR) **Hedgehoppers**
19 **FURIUS DE CIERGUES (FR)**, 5, b g Lord du Sud (FR)—Java de Ciergues (FR) **Brook & Daresbury**
20 **GAMESTERS ICON**, 5, b m Sixties Icon—Gamesters Lady **Gamesters Partnership**
21 **GOUET DES BRUYERES (FR)**, 4, bl g Policy Maker (IRE)—Innsbruck (IRE) **Mr O. C. Greenall**
22 **GRAND COUREUR (FR)**, 8, b br g Grand Couturier—Iris du Berlais (FR) **Mrs B. A. Bostock**
23 **JUST GOT TO GET ON**, 6, ch g Malinas (GER)—Just Cliquot **Mrs C. Swarbrick**
24 **KING GYPSY (IRE)**, 5, b br g Court Cave (IRE)—Be My Gypsy (IRE) **E. A. Brook**
25 **LATE ROMANTIC (IRE)**, 10, b g Mahler—Mere Gaye (IRE) **Spitalized Racing**
26 **LORD COUNTY (FR)**, 6, gr g Lord du Sud (FR)—County County (FR) **E. A. Brook**
27 **LUCKY LOVER BOY (IRE)**, 5, b g Teofilo (IRE)—Mayonga (IRE) **The Lucky Lovers Partnership**
28 **MI LADDO (IRE)**, 4, b g Lilbourne Lad (IRE)—Fritta Mista (IRE) **The Two Greys Syndicate**
29 **MIDNIGHT MOSS**, 8, ch g Midnight Legend—Brackenmoss (IRE) **Midnight Moss Partnership**
30 **MIGHTY MARVEL (IRE)**, 5, b g Morozov (USA)—Alphablend (IRE) **The Marvel Partnership**
31 **MISS DELIGHTED (IRE)**, 7, b m Getaway (GER)—Abhainn Ri (IRE) **Arkwrightblummichaelsononionsdaresbury**
32 **NO CRUISE YET**, 5, b g Passing Glance—Claradotnet **Rgm Partnership**
33 **NOBLE WARRIOR (IRE)**, 7, b g Vertical Speed (FR)—Everdane (IRE) **Mr M. S. Scott**
34 **RIDE THE MONKEY (IRE)**, 4, b g Bungle Inthejungle—Eileenlilian **Mr A. F. Anson**
35 **SEROSEVSKY (IRE)**, 7, b g Morozov (USA)—Be My Rainbow (IRE) **Salmon Racing**
36 **SHADY CHARACTER**, 7, b g Malinas (GER)—Shady Anne **Jocelyn Rosenberg & Roger Weatherby**
37 **STEEL YARD (IRE)**, 5, ch g Frozen Fire (GER)—Banphrionsa (IRE) **J. T. Guerriero**
38 **STRONG RESEMBLANCE (IRE)**, 9, b g Tikkanen (USA)—Shenamar (IRE) **Oliver's Army**
39 **TIM ROCCO (GER)**, 8, ch g Doyen (IRE)—Timbalada (GER) **The Tim Rocco Partnership**
40 **TOORSINAA (IRE)**, 4, b f Tamayuz—Maghya (IRE) **The Marvel Partnership**
41 **TOP OF THE ROCKS (IRE)**, 7, b g Rock of Gibraltar (IRE)—Runaway Top **Mr O. C. Greenall**
42 **TWOTWOTHREE (IRE)**, 7, b g Shantou (IRE)—Sibury (IRE) **Evason, Hewitt, Michaelson & Walsh**
43 **VANDEMERE (IRE)**, 5, b g Jeremy (USA)—Victoria Bridge (IRE) **Mr S. Burns**
44 **VEREINA**, 5, b m Universal (IRE)—Lady de La Vega (IRE) **Oliver Greenall Racing Club**
45 **WASASTYLEQUEEN**, 5, b m Schiaparelli (GER)—As Was **The Burling Family Ltd**
46 **ZALVADOS (FR)**, 7, ch g Soldier of Fortune (FR)—Zariyana (FR) **Mr D. C. Mercer**

Other Owners: Mrs Sandra G. E. Arkwright, Mr D. J. Astbury, Mrs J. L. Baldwin, Mr W. B. B. Blum Gentilomo, Mrs B. A. Bostock, E. A. Brook, Lord Daresbury, Mr K. J. Dodd, Mr S. Evason, Mr O. C. Greenall, R. J. Hewitt, P.D. Hockenhull, D. M. W. Hodgkiss, Mrs S. A. Hodgkiss, M. B. Jones, Mr M. H. Lampton, Gavin MacEchern, Mr G. Malanga, Exors of the Late Mr R. P. B. Michaelson, Mr R. J. Nicholas, Mr P. Nolan, Mr T. Nolan, C. P. Norbury, Mr J. D. Norbury, Mr A. W. Onions, Mrs J. P. Rosenberg, Mr D. B. Salmon, Mrs Lynn Salmon, Mr M. W. Salmon, Steven James Project Management Ltd, Mr S. M. Walsh, Mr R. N. Weatherby.

Assistant Trainer: J. Guerriero.

235 MR TOM GRETTON, Inkberrow

Postal: C/o Gretton & Co Ltd, Middle Bouts Farm, Bouts Lane, Inkberrow, Worcester
Contacts: PHONE 01386 792240 MOBILE 07866 116928 FAX 01386 792472
EMAIL tomgretton@hotmail.co.uk WEBSITE www.tomgrettonracing.com

1 BAGAN, 6, ch g Sulamani (IRE)—Aunt Rita (IRE) **Tom Gretton Racing Club**
2 BRING THE BACON, 5, b g Sulamani (IRE)—Grainne Ni Maille **Mr B. P. Keogh**
3 CABALLINE, 4, b f Motivator—Likelihood (USA) **Callling Le Cab Partnership**
4 INCERTAINE, 7, b m Milan—La Dame Brune (FR) **Not The Peloton Partnership**
5 KAUTO RIKO (FR), 9, b g Ballingarry (IRE)—Kauto Relstar (FR) **Mr & Mrs J.Dale & Partners**
6 LASSANA ANGEL, 6, b m High Chaparral (IRE)—Diara Angel (IRE) **Ownaracehorse Ltd & Mr T. R. Gretton**
7 LICKPENNY LARRY, 9, gr g Sagamix (FR)—Myriah (IRE) **Alan S Clarke & Ownaracehorse**
8 PAINTED CLIFFS (IRE), 7, b g Canford Cliffs (IRE)—Lulawin **Ownaracehorse Ltd**
9 SHAW'S DILEMMA, 6, bl m Sakhee (USA)—Donastrela (IRE) **Mr B. P. Keogh**
10 THENIGHTISYOUNG (IRE), 6, b g Gold Well—Larnalee (IRE) **Justonemore Partnership**
11 TROTTINETTE (FR), 5, ch m No Risk At All (FR)—Princesse Irena (FR) **Not The Peloton Partnership**
12 VIVA LA VEGA, 6, b m Sulamani (IRE)—Lady de La Vega (FR) **Edwards, Richards & Ray**

Other Owners: Mr F. J. Allen, Mr A. S. Clarke, Mrs J. S. Dale, Mr J. W. Dale, Ms C. A. C. Davis, Mr B. Dennehy, Mr J. P. Edwards, T. R. Gretton, Mr J. R. Hynes, Miss H. Lewis-Jones, Ownaracehorse Ltd, Mr G. C. Parkins, Mr I. Powell, Dr D. J. M. Ray, Mr T. Rees, Mr B. M. Williams, Mr D. J. Williams.

Assistant Trainer: Laura Gretton.

236 MR DAVID C. GRIFFITHS, Bawtry

Postal: Martin Hall farm, Martin Common, Bawtry, Doncaster, South Yorkshire, DN10 6DA
Contacts: PHONE 01302 714247 MOBILE 07816 924621
EMAIL davidgriffiths250@hotmail.com WEBSITE www.davidgriffithsracing.co.uk

1 ANGEL FORCE (IRE), 5, ch m Lethal Force (IRE)—Indian Angel **Mr P. Baker**
2 ARCHIMEDES (IRE), 7, b g Invincible Spirit (IRE)—Waveband **Ladies & The Tramps**
3 ARTHUR SHELBY, 4, ch g Arakan (USA)—Ambonnay **The Count On Arthur Racing Club & 1**
4 BAWTRY LADY, 4, b f Epaulette (AUS)—Precious Secret (IRE)
5 BLACK ISLE BOY (IRE), 6, b g Elzaam (AUS)—Shadow Mountain **Mr E. M. Sutherland**
6 DE BRUYNE HORSE, 5, b g Showcasing—Right Rave (IRE) **A.Turton, Rob Massheder, A.Rhodes & 1**
7 DORMIO, 4, b g Equiano (FR)—Diska (GER) **Cheshire Racing Partnership**
8 DUKE OF FIRENZE, 11, ch g Pivotal—Nannina **Adlam,Damary-Thompson,Wilson,Griffiths**
9 4, B c Epaulette (AUS)—Enchanted Dream
10 LEO MINOR (USA), 6, b g War Front (USA)—Kissed (IRE) **Wentdale Limited & Partner**
11 LUCKY BEGGAR (IRE), 10, gr g Verglas (IRE)—Lucky Clio (IRE) **Eros Bloodstock**
12 ORNATE, 7, b g Bahamian Bounty—Adorn **Kings Road Racing Partnership**
13 PEARL ACCLAIM (IRE), 10, b g Acclamation—With Colour
14 TAVENER, 8, b g Exceed And Excel (AUS)—Sea Chorus **The Dash & Brash Partnership**
15 TERUNTUM STAR (FR), 8, ch g Dutch Art—Seralia **Miss E. Shepherd**
16 WARRIOR'S VALLEY, 5, b g Mayson—Sand And Deliver **Miss E Shepherd, D Clarke & Eros**

THREE-YEAR-OLDS

17 DORCHA KNIGHT (IRE), gr c Make Believe—Stella River (FR) **Baker, Friend, Griffiths**
18 B g Phoenix Reach (IRE)—Lookalike

Other Owners: Mr J. P. Adlam, Mr P. Baker, Mr M. Burton, Mr D. J. Clarke, Miss H. A. Damary-Thompson, Mr G. Davidoff, Eros Bloodstock, Mr D. L. Friend, Mr D. C. Griffiths, Mrs S. E. Griffiths, Mr S. Humphries, Mr A. R. Lavender, Mr P. Lewis, Mr R. Massheder, Mr N. J. O'Brien, Mr A. Rhodes, Miss E. Shepherd, Mr J. Slater, The Count on Arthur Racing Club, Mr A. Turton, Wentdale Limited, Mr L. Wilson.

Assistant Trainer: Mrs S. E. Griffiths.

Flat Jockey: David Allan, Phil Dennis. **Amateur Jockey:** Mr Shaun Lee.

237 MRS DIANA GRISSELL, Robertsbridge
Postal: **Brightling Park, Robertsbridge, East Sussex, TN32 5HH**
Contacts: PHONE **01424 838241** MOBILE **07950 312610**
EMAIL **digrissell@aol.com** WEBSITE **www.brightlingpark.com**

1 **DOWNE MILKING LANE**, 6, b g Fair Mix (IRE)—
Downe Payment (IRE) **Gardie Grissell & Mrs E.A.Lynch, D. M. Grissell, Mrs E. E. A. Lynch**
2 **GRAYHAWK (IRE)**, 10, gr g Kalanisi (IRE)—Saddler Regal (IRE) **Mrs C. V. Wedmore**
3 **ISKRABOB**, 10, ch g Tobougg (IRE)—Honour Bolton **Mrs S. B. Bolton**
4 **JAPPELOUP (IRE)**, 11, b br g Presenting—Crackin' Liss (IRE) **Mrs D. M. Grissell**
5 **MILTON**, 8, br g Nomadic Way (USA)—Jesmund **Ms C. A. Lacey**

Other Owners: Mr J. B. Robinson.

Assistant Trainer: Paul Hacking.

NH Jockey: Marc Goldstein. **Amateur Jockey:** Mr O. Wedmore.

238 MR JOHN GROUCOTT, Much Wenlock
Postal: **Dairy Cottage, Bourton, Much Wenlock, Shropshire, TF13 6QD**
Contacts: PHONE **01746 785603**

1 **AGAINN DUL AGHAIDH**, 9, b g Black Sam Bellamy (IRE)—Star Ar Aghaidh (IRE) **The Wenlock Optimists**
2 **ALDERSON**, 7, b g Zamindar (USA)—Claradotnet **Mr G. D. Kendrick**
3 **BATTLEBRAVE (IRE)**, 7, b g Fracas (IRE)—Silly Mille (IRE) **Mrs B. Clarke**
4 **BATTLEFIELD (IRE)**, 8, b g Central Park (IRE)—Silly Mille (IRE) **Mrs B. Clarke**
5 **BATTLETANK (IRE)**, 7, b g Robin des Pres (FR)—Regal Brigade (IRE) **Mrs B. Clarke**
6 **BEST DIRECTOR (IRE)**, 12, b g Oscar (IRE)—Taneys Leader (IRE) **Mrs B. Clarke**
7 **EL SCORPIO (IRE)**, 8, b g Scorpion (IRE)—El Monica (IRE) **Mrs B. Clarke**
8 **HAPPY NEWS**, 7, gr m Fair Mix (IRE)—Welcome News **Mrs C. L. Shaw**
9 5, B m Scorpion (IRE)—Heather Feather (IRE)
10 **JESSIE LIGHTFOOT (IRE)**, 6, b m Yeats (IRE)—Needle Doll (IRE) **Mr E. C. Parkes**
11 **KAYF ANEDA**, 5, b m Kayf Tara—Aneda Rose (IRE)
12 **MAISIEBELLA**, 7, b m Black Sam Bellamy (IRE)—Lucylou **Mrs B. Clarke**
13 **MUSE OF FIRE (IRE)**, 6, b g Getaway (GER)—Maria Sophia **C. J. Tipton**
14 **NEWERA**, 8, ch g Makfi—Coming Home **Mr D. R. Passant**
15 **OVERAWED**, 9, b m Overbury (IRE)—Alleged To Rhyme **Mrs E. A. Fletcher**
16 **SHININSTAR (IRE)**, 11, b g Westerner—Shiny Button **Mrs B. Clarke**
17 **SIDSTEEL (IRE)**, 9, b g Craigsteel—Clare Hogan (IRE) **Mrs B. Clarke**
18 **STAR OF RORY (IRE)**, 6, b g Born To Sea (IRE)—Dame Alicia (IRE) **Mr D. R. Passant & Hefin Williams**
19 **THE TOOJUMPA**, 7, b m Midnight Legend—Sunnyland **Lord C. D. Harrison**
20 **TIFFANY'S CAT (IRE)**, 6, b m Fame And Glory—Simply Kitty (IRE)
21 **TRUCKERS HIGHWAY (IRE)**, 11, b g Rudimentary (USA)—Countessdee (IRE) **C. J. Tipton**

Other Owners: Mr D. R. Passant, Mr H. Williams.

239 MR RAE GUEST, Newmarket
Postal: **Chestnut Tree Stables, Hamilton Road, Newmarket, Suffolk, CB8 0NY**
Contacts: WORK **01638 661508** MOBILE **07711 301095**
EMAIL **raeguest@raeguest.com** WEBSITE **www.raeguest.com**

1 **ALASKAN BAY (IRE)**, 5, b m Kodiac—Party Appeal (USA) **Mr P. A. Sakal**
2 **CAPLA BERRY**, 4, b f Roderic O'Connor (IRE)—Salsa Brava (IRE) **G. F. L. Robinson**
3 **FASHIONESQUE (IRE)**, 4, b f Fast Company (IRE)—Featherlight **Miss V. Markowiak**
4 **FEN BREEZE**, 4, b f Bated Breath—Ruffled **Mr C. J. Murfitt**
5 **LAND OF WINTER (FR)**, 4, b g Camelot—Gaselee (USA) **Paul Smith & Rae Guest**
6 **ROMAN SPINNER**, 5, ch m Intikhab (USA)—Pompeia **Reprobates Too**

MR RAE GUEST - continued

7 **SQUELCH**, 4, b f Dark Angel (IRE)—Blancmange **Purple & Yellow**
8 **ZARRAR (IRE)**, 5, b g Thewayyouare (USA)—Featherlight **Miss V. Markowiak**

THREE-YEAR-OLDS

9 **ARAMIS GREY (IRE)**, gr f Gutaifan (IRE)—Sveva (IRE) **The Musketeers**
10 **ARRIVISTE**, b f Sea The Moon (GER)—Apparatchika **Miss K. Rausing**
11 **AUTUMN TRAIL**, b f Sixties Icon—Boleyna (USA) **Mr P. J. Smith**
12 **CITY ESCAPE (IRE)**, b f Cityscape—Lady Gabrielle (IRE) **Paul Smith & Rae Guest**
13 **CRY HAVOC (IRE)**, b f War Command (USA)—Na Zdorovie **The Musketeers**
14 **DREAMBOAT GIRL (IRE)**, b f Dream Ahead (USA)—Junia Tepzia (IRE) **The Storm Again Syndicate**
15 **MADISON AVENUE**, b f Golden Horn—Morzine **The Musketeers**
16 **MJOLNIR**, b c Dark Angel (IRE)—Minalisa **C. J. Mills**
17 **PERFORMANCE POET**, ch f Poet's Voice—Winifred Jo **Mr C. S. Joseph**
18 **POETS DANCE**, b f Poet's Voice—Whirly Dancer **Mrs J. E. Wallsgrove**
19 **ROSA GOLD**, b f Havana Gold (IRE)—Rosa Grace **Mr E. P. Duggan**
20 **ROSARDO SENORITA**, b f Requinto (IRE)—Poudretteite **Top Hat and Tails**
21 **SEA OF MARIA**, b f Sea The Stars (IRE)—Despatch **The Storm Again Syndicate**

TWO-YEAR-OLDS

22 B f 09/04 Helmet (AUS)—Alsaaden (Acclamation) **BB Thoroughbreds**
23 **BAHIA STAR**, b f 13/02 Twilight Son—Bahia Breeze (Mister Baileys) **BB Bloodstock**
24 **CAPE COLUMBUS**, b c 06/03 Acclamation—Cape Factor (IRE) (Oratorio (IRE)) (28000) **Mr D. J. Willis**
25 **EMPRESS MAKEDA (IRE)**, b f 22/02 Sea The Stars (IRE)—Sheba Five (USA) (Five Star Day (USA)) (120000) **Sonia M. Rogers & Anthony Rogers**
26 **JEWEL IN MY CROWN**, gr f 02/04 Mukhadram—Rosa Grace (Lomitas) **Mr E. P. Duggan**
27 **SALONNIERE**, b f 20/01 Sea The Moon (GER)—Stellaire (Archipenko (USA)) **Miss K. Rausing**
28 B br f 29/03 Kitten's Joy (USA)—Time Being (Zamindar (USA)) **Reiko Baum & Michael Baum**

Other Owners: Mr Michael Baum, Mrs R. Baum, R. T. Goodes, Mr R. Guest, D. G. Raffel, A. P. Rogers, Mrs S. M. Rogers, Mr P. J. Smith, Mr B. Stewart.

240	**MR RICHARD GUEST, Ingmanthorpe**

Postal: **Ingmanthorpe Racing Stables, Loshpot Lane, Ingmanthorpe, Wetherby, West Yorkshire, LS22 5HL**
Contacts: PHONE **07840 112303** MOBILE **07398 600270**
WORK EMAIL **enquiries@richardguestracing.co.uk** FACEBOOK **@richardguesthorseracing** TWITTER **@GuestRacing**

1 **AMBITIOUS ICARUS**, 11, b g Striking Ambition—Nesting Box **Mr C. J. Penney**
2 **BREATHOFFRESHAIR**, 6, b g Bated Breath—Stormy Weather **Mrs A. Kenny**
3 **EXCHEQUER (IRE)**, 9, ch g Exceed And Excel (AUS)—Tara's Force (IRE) **Mr J Toes & Mr J O'Loan**
4 **FOXRUSH TAKE TIME (FR)**, 5, b g Showcasing—Stranded **Mrs A. Kenny**
5 **ISNTSHESOMETHING**, 8, br m Assertive—Princess Almora **Mr C. J. Penney**
6 **LADY JOANNA VASSA (IRE)**, 7, ch m Equiano (FR)—Lady Natilda **Mrs A. Kenny**
7 **LASTMANLASTROUND (IRE)**, 7, b g Azamour (IRE)—Lastroseofsummer (IRE) **Mrs A. Kenny**
8 **LOUGH SALT (IRE)**, 9, b g Brian Boru—Castlehill Lady (IRE) **Mr J Toes & Mr J O'Loan**
9 **MY GIRL MAISIE (IRE)**, 6, b m Fast Company (IRE)—Queen Al Andalous (IRE) **Mrs A. Kenny**
10 **NO CIVIL JUSTICE**, 5, b g Milk It Mick—Flashing Floozie **Mrs A. Kenny**
11 **NOCIVILJUSTICEHERE**, 4, b f Lilbourne Lad (IRE)—Cameo Tiara (IRE) **Mrs A. Kenny**
12 **OUTLAW TORN (IRE)**, 11, ch g Iffraaj—Touch And Love (IRE) **Mr J Toes & Mr J O'Loan**
13 **TELLOVOI (IRE)**, 12, b g Indian Haven—Kloonlara (IRE) **Mrs A. Kenny**
14 **TREASURED COMPANY (IRE)**, 4, b g Fast Company (IRE)—Lady's Locket (IRE) **Mr C. J. Penney**
15 **UDONTDODOU**, 7, b g Fastnet Rock (AUS)—Forever Times **Mr C. J. Penney**
16 **WHATWOULDYOUKNOW (IRE)**, 5, b g Lope de Vega (IRE)—Holamo (IRE) **Dearing Plastics Ltd & Partner**

THREE-YEAR-OLDS

17 Pt c Angrove Spottedick—Charlemagne Diva **Mr C. J. Penney**

MR RICHARD GUEST - continued

TWO-YEAR-OLDS

18 B f 02/03 Finjaan—Modern Lady (Bertolini (USA)) **Mrs A. Kenny**

Other Owners: Dearing Plastics Ltd, Mr John O'Loan, Mr C. J. Penney, Mr J. Toes.

Assistant Trainer: Mr Chris Penney.

---

241 MS POLLY GUNDRY, Ottery St Mary
Postal: Holcombe Brook, Holcombe Lane, Ottery St Mary, Devon, EX11 1PH
Contacts: PHONE 01404 811181 MOBILE 07932 780621
EMAIL pollygundrytraining@live.co.uk WEBSITE www.pollygundrytraining.co.uk

1 BIG TIME FRANK (IRE), 9, b g Bienamado (USA)—Pure Spirit (IRE) **N Allen & P Bowler**
2 DAWSON CITY, 11, b g Midnight Legend—Running For Annie **Ian Payne & Kim Franklin**
3 DOODLE DANDY (IRE), 7, b m Starspangledbanner (AUS)—Grid Lock (IRE) **Mrs P. Walker**
4 HOLD ME TIGHT (IRE), 6, b g Zoffany (IRE)—All Embracing (IRE) **Mrs W. J. Jarrett**
5 MAGNETIC (IRE), 4, b g Alhebayeb (IRE)—Telltime (IRE) **Mrs W. J. Jarrett**
6 MAUNA KEA (IRE), 8, b g Mountain High (IRE)—The Bench (IRE) **Mr M. James**
7 MISS HARRIETT, 4, b f Arvico (FR)—Ivorsagoodun **Mr P. G. Gibbins**
8 SIR DYLAN, 11, b g Dylan Thomas (IRE)—Monteleone (IRE) **M James & S Jarrett**
9 SWINCOMBE SCORCHIO, 10, b g Scorpion (IRE)—Lady Felix **Holcombe Hopefuls**
10 4, B f Dunaden (FR)—Youngstar **Mr J. L. Lightfoot**

TWO-YEAR-OLDS

11 B f 14/04 Cannock Chase (USA)—Cheap N Chic (Primo Valentino (IRE)) **Mr M. James**
12 B f 13/05 Cannock Chase (USA)—Triplicity (Three Valleys (USA)) **Mr M. James**

Other Owners: Mr N. G. Allen, Mr P. O. Bowler, Miss K. M. Franklin, Mr M. James, Mr S. H. Jarrett, Mr I. T. Payne.

Assistant Trainer: Edward Walker.

NH Jockey: James Best, Nick Schofield. **Amateur Jockey:** Mr Josh Newman.

---

242 MR WILLIAM HAGGAS, Newmarket
Postal: Somerville Lodge, Fordham Road, Newmarket, Suffolk, CB8 7AA
Contacts: PHONE 01638 667013 MOBILE 07860 282281 FAX 01638 660534
EMAIL william@somerville-lodge.co.uk WEBSITE www.somerville-lodge.co.uk

1 ADDEYBB (IRE), 6, ch g Pivotal—Bush Cat (USA) **Sheikh Ahmed Al Maktoum**
2 AL MUFFRIH (IRE), 5, b g Sea The Stars (IRE)—Scarlet And Gold (IRE) **Sheikh Juma Dalmook Al Maktoum**
3 APLOMB (IRE), 4, b g Lope de Vega (IRE)—Mickleberry (IRE) **Mrs F. J. Carmichael**
4 COUNTRY, 4, b g Dubawi (IRE)—Birjand **Sheikh Ahmed Al Maktoum**
5 DAL HORRISGLE, 4, b g Nathaniel (IRE)—Dalvina **St Albans Bloodstock Limited**
6 DESERT CARAVAN, 4, b g Oasis Dream—Sequence (IRE) **Her Majesty The Queen**
7 DESERT ICON (FR), 4, b g Sea The Stars (IRE)—Plume Rose **Sheikh Juma Dalmook Al Maktoum**
8 FAYLAQ, 4, b c Dubawi (IRE)—Danedream (GER) **Mr Hamdan Al Maktoum**
9 GHAZIYAH, 4, gr f Galileo (IRE)—Fork Lightning (USA) **Sheikh Juma Dalmook Al Maktoum**
10 HAMISH, 4, b g Motivator—Tweed **Mr J. B. Haggas**
11 LUXOR, 4, b g Oasis Dream—Eminently **Highclere Tbred Racing -Highclere Castle**
12 MAJAALIS (FR), 4, b g Invincible Spirit (IRE)—High Surf (USA) **Mr Hamdan Al Maktoum**
13 MISS O CONNOR (IRE), 5, br m Roderic O'Connor (IRE)—Magadar (USA) **Lael Stable**
14 MOMKIN (IRE), 4, b c Bated Breath—Contradict **Prince A. A. Faisal**
15 MONICA SHERIFF, 4, b f Lawman (FR)—Require **The Duke of Devonshire**
16 MONTATHAM, 4, gr g Showcasing—Eastern Destiny **Mr Hamdan Al Maktoum**
17 MUBTASIMAH, 4, gr f Dark Angel (IRE)—Midnight Hush (FR) **Sheikh Juma Dalmook Al Maktoum**

MR WILLIAM HAGGAS - continued

18 **NAHAARR (IRE)**, 4, b c Dark Angel (IRE)—Charlotte Rua (IRE) **Sheikh Ahmed Al Maktoum**
19 **NICKLAUS**, 5, ch g Exceed And Excel (AUS)—Nianga (GER) **Highclere Thoroughbred Racing - Nicklaus**
20 **NKOSIKAZI**, 5, gr m Cape Cross (IRE)—Whatami **Olivia Hoare**
21 **ONE MASTER**, 6, b m Fastnet Rock (AUS)—Enticing (IRE) **Lael Stable**
22 **PABLO ESCOBARR (IRE)**, 4, b c Galileo (IRE)—Bewitched (IRE) **Mr H. A. Lootah**
23 **SEA OF FAITH (IRE)**, 4, b f Sea The Stars (IRE)—Jumooh **Sunderland Holding Inc.**
24 **SINJAARI (IRE)**, 4, b g Camelot—Heavenly Song (IRE) **Mohammed Jaber**
25 **SKARDU**, 4, ch c Shamardal (USA)—Diala (IRE) **Sheikh A. B. I. Al Khalifa**
26 **SPACE WALK**, 4, b g Galileo (IRE)—Memory (IRE) **Her Majesty The Queen**
27 **TWO BIDS**, 4, gr g Dalakhani (IRE)—Echelon **Sheikh Ahmed Al Maktoum**
28 **UMMALNAR**, 5, ch m Shamardal (USA)—Royal Secrets (IRE) **Mohammed Jaber**
29 **YOUNG RASCAL (FR)**, 5, b g Intello (GER)—Rock My Soul (IRE) **Mr B. Kantor**

THREE-YEAR-OLDS

30 **ABERFFRAW**, ch g Exceed And Excel (AUS)—Nahab **Julie & David R Martin & Dan Hall**
31 **AJYAALL (FR)**, b c Kingman—Lucrece **Sheikh Ahmed Al Maktoum**
32 **AL AADHIB (IRE)**, b c Kodiac—Lady Lucia (IRE) **Mr Hamdan Al Maktoum**
33 **AL AASY (IRE)**, b c Sea The Stars (IRE)—Kitcara **Mr Hamdan Al Maktoum**
34 **AL MUTHANNA (IRE)**, ch g Lope de Vega (IRE)—Saraha **Mr Hamdan Al Maktoum**
35 **AL QAASIM (IRE)**, ch g Free Eagle (IRE)—Nebraas **Mr Hamdan Al Maktoum**
36 **AL QAQAA (USA)**, b c War Front (USA)—Pin Up (IRE) **Mr Hamdan Al Maktoum**
37 **AL SALT (IRE)**, b c Mukhadram—Estedaama (IRE) **Mr Hamdan Al Maktoum**
38 **AL TARMAAH (IRE)**, b c Muhaarar—How's She Cuttin' (IRE) **Mr Hamdan Al Maktoum**
39 **AL ZARAQAAN**, br c Golden Horn—Asheerah **Mr Hamdan Al Maktoum**
40 **AMETIST**, ch g Dutch Art—Zykina **Cheveley Park Stud Limited**
41 **AVEBURY (IRE)**, b f Dark Angel (IRE)—Wiltshire Life (IRE) **Cheveley Park Stud Limited**
42 **AWARD SCHEME**, b f Siyouni (FR)—Queen's Prize **Her Majesty The Queen**
43 **BAARRIJ (IRE)**, b f Iffraaj—Modeyra **Sheikh Ahmed Al Maktoum**
44 **BLUE DAWN**, b f Oasis Dream—Blue Waltz **Fittocks Stud & Andrew Bengough**
45 **BOOSALA (IRE)**, b c Dawn Approach (IRE)—Zoowraa **Sheikh Ahmed Al Maktoum**
46 **BORN A KING**, b c Frankel—Fairwater (USA) **Mr F. M. Al Qahtani**
47 **BORN WITH PRIDE (IRE)**, b f Born To Sea (IRE)—Jumooh **Sunderland Holding Inc.**
48 **CHORAL WORK**, gr f Nathaniel (IRE)—Chapel Choir **Cheveley Park Stud Limited**
49 **COINCIDENCE**, b c Teofilo (IRE)—Off Chance **The Royal Ascot Racing Club**
50 **COLD FRONT**, b c Lope de Vega (IRE)—Cloud Line **Lael Stable**
51 **CONVICT**, ch c Australia—Tweed **Mr J. B. Haggas**
52 **COSA ORGA (IRE)**, b c Golden Horn—New Morning (IRE) **Lois Day & J L Day**
53 **CRAVED**, b c Kodiac—Enticing (IRE) **Lael Stable**
54 **DALHOUSIE**, b f Golden Horn—Dalvina **St Albans Bloodstock Limited**
55 **DANCIN INTHESTREET**, b f Muhaarar—Souvenir Delondres (FR) **Mr C. N. Wright**
56 **DHABYAH**, ch f Australia—Sola Gratia (IRE) **Al Wasmiyah Farm**
57 **DIVINE CONSENT**, b c Muhaarar—Cozy Maria (USA) **A. E. Oppenheimer**
58 **DOMINO DARLING**, b f Golden Horn—Disco Volante **A. E. Oppenheimer**
59 **DUCK AND VANISH**, b c Lope de Vega (IRE)—Froglet **Mr J. B. Haggas**
60 **DUSTY DREAM**, b f Dubawi (IRE)—Memory (IRE) **Her Majesty The Queen**
61 **FAVORITE MOON (GER)**, b c Sea The Moon (GER)—Favorite (GER) **Mr S. Suhail**
62 **FIRST KINGDOM (IRE)**, b f Frankel—Simple Magic (IRE) **Prince A. A. Faisal**
63 **FRENCH POLISH**, ch f New Approach (IRE)—French Dressing **Normandie Stud Ltd**
64 **FRUITION**, b g Oasis Dream—Ananas **Her Majesty The Queen**
65 **GRAND ROCK (IRE)**, b c Acclamation—Miss Gibralter **Mr H. A. Lootah**
66 **HERO OF THE HOUR**, b c Lord Kanaloa (JPN)—Ripples Maid **Qatar Racing Limited**
67 **ICE SPRITE**, ch f Zoffany (IRE)—Queen of Ice **Cheveley Park Stud Limited**
68 **ILARAAB (IRE)**, b c Wootton Bassett—Belova (IRE) **Sheikh Ahmed Al Maktoum**
69 **JAANEH**, b f Dubawi (IRE)—Ethaara **Mr Hamdan Al Maktoum**
70 **JOHAN**, b c Zoffany (IRE)—Sandreamer (IRE) **Jon & Julia Aisbitt**
71 **KEW PALACE**, b f Kingman—Shama (IRE) **Her Majesty The Queen**
72 **KING FAIRY (IRE)**, b c Australia—My Fairy (IRE) **Sunderland Holding Inc.**
73 **KING'S CASTLE (IRE)**, b c Camelot—Kikonga **Mr S. Suhail**
74 **KINSMAN**, ch c Exceed And Excel (AUS)—Peeress **Cheveley Park Stud Limited**

MR WILLIAM HAGGAS - continued

75 **LADY G (IRE)**, b f Golden Horn—Hikari (IRE) **Mr H. A. Lootah**
76 **LAMORNA**, b f Oasis Dream—Golden Laughter (USA) **Mr G. F. Smith-Bernal**
77 **LAWAHED (IRE)**, b f Invincible Spirit—Sajjhaa **Sheikh Ahmed Al Maktoum**
78 **LEAH**, ch f Le Havre (IRE)—Dolores **Normandie Stud Ltd**
79 **MANAAJIM (IRE)**, b f Muhaarar—Queenofthefairies **Mr Hamdan Al Maktoum**
80 **MIDRARR (IRE)**, b f Dubawi (IRE)—Oojooba **Sheikh Ahmed Al Maktoum**
81 **MR G**, b c Galileo (IRE)—Giofra **Mr H. A. Lootah**
82 **MY OBERON (IRE)**, b c Dubawi (IRE)—My Titania (IRE) **Sunderland Holding Inc.**
83 **NAJIMA (IRE)**, b f Camelot—Brown Diamond (IRE) **Sheikh Juma Dalmook Al Maktoum**
84 **NEW CHAPTER (IRE)**, b c Invincible Spirit (IRE)—Silk Sari **Fittocks Stud & Partners**
85 **NEW NUMBER**, b f Muhaarar—Ballymore Celebre (IRE) **Mr H. A. Lootah**
86 **OTI MA BOATI**, b f Iffraaj—Mania (IRE) **Lael Stable**
87 **PINK SANDS**, b f No Nay Never (USA)—First Breeze (USA) **Bermuda Racing Limited**
88 **PIRANESI (IRE)**, b g Zoffany (IRE)—Starship (IRE) **The Piranesi Partnership**
89 **POLAR APPEAL (IRE)**, b c Siyouni (FR)—Ultra Appeal (IRE) **China Horse Club International Limited**
90 **PORTRAY**, b g Dubawi (IRE)—Placidia (IRE) **Her Majesty The Queen**
91 **PRAISED**, ch f Pivotal—Suelita **Cheveley Park Stud Limited**
92 **PRETTY PICKLE (IRE)**, b f Born To Sea (IRE)—Onomatomania (USA) **Mr T. J. W. Bridge**
93 **QUEEN'S COURSE (IRE)**, b f Gleneagles (IRE)—Dingle View (IRE) **Clipper Group Holdings Ltd**
94 **RAOUFAH**, b f Shamardal (USA)—Alshadhia (IRE) **Mr Hamdan Al Maktoum**
95 **REASSURE**, b f Oasis Dream—Blhadawa (USA) **Sheikh Juma Dalmook Al Maktoum**
96 **RED MISSILE (IRE)**, b g Battle of Marengo (IRE)—Plym **Sheikh Juma Dalmook Al Maktoum**
97 **RED POPPY**, ch f Declaration of War (USA)—Valiant Girl **A. E. Oppenheimer**
98 **REEMANNIE**, b f Dubawi (IRE)—Royal Secrets (IRE) **Mohammed Jaber**
99 **ROBERTO ESCOBARR (IRE)**, b c Galileo (IRE)—Bewitched (IRE) **Mr H. A. Lootah**
100 **ROYAL HIDEAWAY (IRE)**, b c Kodiac—Alexander Youth (IRE) **Sheikh Hamed Dalmook Al Maktoum**
101 **SEA MOOD (FR)**, b f Siyouni (FR)—Upbeat Mood (USA) **Highclere T'Bred Racing - Ben Saunders**
102 **SEA OF STYLE (IRE)**, ch f Sea The Stars (IRE)—Mamonta **Sunderland Holding Inc.**
103 **SEA TROUT REACH (IRE)**, ch c Mukhadram—Caelica (IRE) **Mr T. J. W. Bridge**
104 **SUGGESTIVE (IRE)**, b f Zoffany (IRE)—Allez Y (IRE) **Highclere T'Bred Racing - Lt Scott Sears**
105 **SURF DANCER (IRE)**, b c Lope de Vega (IRE)—Beach Belle **China Horse Club/Ballylinch Stud**
106 **SURROUND (IRE)**, b f Iffraaj—Pussycat Lips (IRE) **Qatar Racing Limited**
107 **TAMMANI**, b c Make Believe—Gentle On My Mind (IRE) **Prince A. A. Faisal**
108 **THOWQ (IRE)**, b f Invincible Spirit (IRE)—Alaata (USA) **Mr Hamdan Al Maktoum**
109 **THRILL SEEKER (IRE)**, b c Invincible Spirit (IRE)—Galvaun (IRE) **Mrs Fiona Carmichael / Ballylinch Stud**
110 **TOMORROW'S DREAM (FR)**, b f Oasis Dream—Midnight Thoughts (USA) **Apple Tree Stud**
111 **VEGA'S ANGEL**, b f Lope de Vega (IRE)—Lily's Angel (IRE) **Cheveley Park Stud Limited**
112 **WEJDAN (FR)**, b f Dabirsim (FR)—War Bride (GER) **Mr M. S. Al Shahi**
113 **WITH THANKS (IRE)**, b f Camacho—Thanks (IRE) **Sheikh Rashid Dalmook Al Maktoum**
114 **ZOOHOOR (IRE)**, b f Dark Angel (IRE)—Vine Street (IRE) **Sheikh Ahmed Al Maktoum**

TWO-YEAR-OLDS

115 Gr c 14/05 Dark Angel (IRE)—Alaata (USA) (Smart Strike (CAN)) **Mr Hamdan Al Maktoum**
116 B c 01/03 Siyouni (FR)—America Nova (FR) (Verglas (IRE)) (800000) **Mr Hamdan Al Maktoum**
117 **ARAMAIC (IRE)**, b br c 25/04 Le Havre (IRE)—Middle Persia (Dalakhani (IRE)) (200000) **Al Adiyat Racing**
118 **BAAEED**, b c 08/04 Sea The Stars (IRE)—Aghareed (USA) (Kingmambo (USA)) **Mr Hamdan Al Maktoum**
119 B br f 05/02 Frankel—Bantu (Cape Cross (IRE)) **Stanley, Broughton & Sir Peter Vela**
120 Br f 17/02 Dandy Man (IRE)—Barqeyya (Shamardal (USA)) (42857) **Sheikh Juma Dalmook Al Maktoum**
121 **BASHKIROVA**, b f 05/03 Pivotal—Russian Finale (Dansili) **Cheveley Park Stud Limited**
122 **BELIEF**, b f 14/03 Le Havre (IRE)—Elysian (Galileo (IRE)) **Cheveley Park Stud Limited**
123 B f 13/02 Shamardal (USA)—Besharah (IRE) (Kodiac) **Sheikh Rashid Dalmook Al Maktoum**
124 B gr c 15/04 Dark Angel (IRE)—Best Terms (Exceed And Excel (AUS)) (425000) **Mr Hamdan Al Maktoum**
125 **BRECCIA**, b f 06/03 Intello (GER)—Rock Choir (Pivotal) **Cheveley Park Stud Limited**
126 Ch c 04/03 Territories—Broughtons Revival (Pivotal) (150000) **Mr Hamdan Al Maktoum**
127 Gr c 17/03 Sea The Stars (IRE)—Causa Proxima (FR) (Kendor (FR)) (150000) **Sheikh Ahmed Al Maktoum**
128 **CEDRIC MORRIS (IRE)**, b c 13/02 Fast Company (IRE)—
                     Big Boned (USA) (Street Sense (USA)) (77220) **Mr Richard Green**
129 B f 08/02 Fastnet Rock (AUS)—
                     Celestial Bow (IRE) (Raven's Pass (USA)) (62000) **Sheikh Juma Dalmook Al Maktoum**

MR WILLIAM HAGGAS - continued

130 **CHALK STREAM**, b c 08/02 Sea The Stars (IRE)—
Golden Stream (IRE) (Sadler's Wells (USA)) **Her Majesty The Queen**
131 **COMPANIONSHIP**, b f 04/03 Galileo (IRE)—Sweet Idea (AUS) (Snitzel (AUS)) **Her Majesty The Queen**
132 **CONSERVATOIRE**, ch f 16/03 Dutch Art—Piano (Azamour (IRE)) **Cheveley Park Stud Limited**
133 **CRISTAL CLERE (IRE)**, b c 01/05 Harzand (IRE)—
Lady Catherine (Bering) (40000) **G&MRobertsGreenSavidgeWhittal-Williams**
134 B c 08/02 Kingman—Dorcas Lane (Norse Dancer (IRE)) **Barnane Stud Ltd**
135 Br f 09/04 Dansili—El Manati (IRE) (Iffraaj) (380000) **Sheikh Rashid Dalmook Al Maktoum**
136 B f 29/04 Kodiac—Enticing (IRE) (Pivotal) **Lael Stable**
137 **ERSAAL**, b c 04/03 Golden Horn—Alshadhia (IRE) (Marju (IRE)) **Mr Hamdan Al Maktoum**
138 **FLEUR DE GUY**, b c 03/03 Muhaarar—Melody of Love (Haafhd) (48000) **Wrigleys & Wyatts**
139 Ch f 27/03 Sea The Stars (IRE)—Flower Market (Cadeaux Genereux) (400000) **Sunderland Holding Inc.**
140 Ch c 26/03 Frankel—French Dressing (Sea The Stars (IRE)) (350000) **Mr Hamdan Al Maktoum**
141 **GOLDEN MELODY (IRE)**, ch f 15/03 Belardo (IRE)—Chanter (Lomitas) (52000) **Ian & Christine Beard**
142 **GOOD AND PROPER**, b f 18/02 Dansili—Grace And Glory (IRE) (Montjeu (IRE)) **Coln Valley Stud**
143 **IDOL**, ch f 30/01 Pivotal—Hightime Heroine (IRE) (Danetime (IRE)) **Cheveley Park Stud Limited**
144 B c 08/04 Muhaarar—If So (Iffraaj) (100000) **Sheikh Ahmed Al Maktoum**
145 B f 27/02 Sea The Stars (IRE)—Jumooh (Monsun (GER)) (650000) **Sunderland Holding Inc.**
146 **KADUPUL (FR)**, b f 05/05 Dark Angel (IRE)—Cup Cake (IRE) (Singspiel (IRE)) **Al Wasmiyah Farm**
147 B f 29/03 Sea The Stars (IRE)—Kitcara (Shamardal (USA)) (500000) **Sunderland Holding Inc.**
148 **KOLISI (IRE)**, b c 24/02 Harzand (IRE)—Wild Step (GER) (Footstepsinthesand) (81509) **Mr G. F. Smith-Bernal**
149 Gr ro c 15/02 Shamardal (USA)—Lady Rosamunde (Maria's Mon (USA)) (500000) **Mr Hamdan Al Maktoum**
150 Ch c 09/04 Kitten's Joy (USA)—Lahudood (Singspiel (IRE)) **Mr Hamdan Al Maktoum**
151 **LIGHT REFRAIN**, b f 13/01 Frankel—Light Music (Elusive Quality (USA)) **Her Majesty The Queen**
152 **LILAC ROAD (IRE)**, ch f 14/02 Mastercraftsman (IRE)—Lavender Lane (IRE) (Shamardal (USA)) **Jon & Julia Aisbitt**
153 **LOCKERBIE**, ch f 01/05 New Approach (IRE)—Tweed (Sakhee (USA)) **Mr J. B. Haggas**
154 B c 15/02 Iffraaj—Lucelle (IRE) (High Chaparral (IRE)) (167310) **Mr Michael Buckley**
155 B f 09/03 Shamardal (USA)—Majeyda (USA) (Street Cry (IRE)) **Sheikh Ahmed Al Maktoum**
156 B c 24/04 Iffraaj—Mamma Morton (IRE) (Elnadim (USA)) (190000) **Sheikh Ahmed Al Maktoum**
157 **MARAAKIZ (IRE)**, b c 26/02 Muhaarar—Entisaar (AUS) (More Than Ready (USA)) **Mr Hamdan Al Maktoum**
158 Ch f 05/02 Shamardal (USA)—Mardie Gras (Galileo (IRE)) **Sheikh Juma Dalmook Al Maktoum**
159 B c 09/02 Kodiac—Margaret's Mission (IRE) (Shamardal (USA)) (120000) **Mrs J. M. T. Martin, D. R. Martin**
160 B f 04/03 Oasis Dream—Marmalady (AUS) (Duke of Marmalade (IRE)) **Barnane Stud Ltd**
161 **MARY CASSATT**, b f 15/02 Gutaifan (IRE)—Quite A Thing (Dutch Art) (75000) **Mr Richard Green**
162 B c 17/02 Muhaarar—Melbourne Memories (Sleeping Indian) (123809) **Mr Hamdan Al Maktoum**
163 B c 07/04 Kingman—Miss Plimsoll (USA) (Arch (USA)) (729300) **Mrs F. J. Carmichael**
164 Ch c 21/04 Night of Thunder (IRE)—
Mon Bijou (IRE) (Green Desert (USA)) (130000) **Sheikh Hamed Dalmook Al Maktoum**
165 B c 20/02 Pride of Dubai (AUS)—Mondelice (Montjeu (IRE)) (110000) **M. Obaida**
166 Gr ro f 24/02 Flintshire—Mortgage the House (USA) (Chester House (USA)) (107249) **Qatar Racing Limited**
167 **MUJTABA**, b c 30/04 Dubawi (IRE)—Majmu (AUS) (Redoute's Choice (AUS)) **Mr Hamdan Al Maktoum**
168 B f 04/04 Australia—My Fairy (IRE) (Sea The Stars (IRE)) **Sunderland Holding Inc.**
169 B f 19/04 Lope de Vega (IRE)—My Titania (IRE) (Sea The Stars (IRE)) **Sunderland Holding Inc.**
170 Br f 29/03 Awtaad (IRE)—Oasis Sunset (IRE) (Oasis Dream) (125000) **Mohammed Jaber**
171 B c 17/02 Kodiac—Online Alexander (IRE) (Acclamation) (185000) **Sheikh Ahmed Al Maktoum**
172 B c 21/03 Sea The Stars (IRE)—Oojooba (Monsun (GER)) **Sheikh Ahmed Al Maktoum**
173 B br c 01/03 Oasis Dream—Piccola Sissi (IRE) (Footstepsinthesand) (35000) **Mohammed Jaber**
174 Ch c 01/04 New Approach (IRE)—Praline (IRE) (Pivotal) (125000) **M. Obaida**
175 **PRIDE OF PRIORY**, b c 20/04 Pivotal—Millennium Star (IRE) (High Chaparral (IRE)) (60000) **Mr T. J. W. Bridge**
176 **REGIONAL**, b c 04/03 Territories (IRE)—Favulusa (Dansili) (120000) **Al Adiyat Racing**
177 **ROBIOLA (IRE)**, b c 25/03 Harzand (IRE)—
Weeping Wind (Oratorio (IRE)) (80000) **Mr Simon Munir & Mr Isaac Souede**
178 **SACRED**, b f 04/04 Exceed And Excel (AUS)—Sacre Caroline (USA) (Blame (USA)) **Cheveley Park Stud Limited**
179 Ch c 25/02 Dawn Approach (IRE)—Saraha (Dansili) **Mr Hamdan Al Maktoum**
180 **SECRET HAUNT**, b f 31/03 Dubawi (IRE)—Enticement (Montjeu (IRE)) **Her Majesty The Queen**
181 B f 18/01 Le Havre (IRE)—Selyl (Oasis Dream) (128700) **Sunderland Holding Inc.**
182 B br c 26/02 Siyouni (FR)—Sentaril (Danehill Dancer (IRE)) **Lael Stable**
183 B f 02/03 Galileo (IRE)—Sharp Susan (USA) (Touch Gold (USA)) **Cayton Park Stud Limited**

MR WILLIAM HAGGAS - continued

184 **SKYRUNNER (IRE)**, b c 26/03 Invincible Spirit (IRE)—
Maidservant (USA) (Seeking The Gold (USA)) (190000) **Mr G. F. Smith-Bernal**
185 **SKYTREE**, b f 04/02 Dark Angel (IRE)—
Tiptree (IRE) (Duke of Marmalade (IRE)) **Mr Mike Morris, Mrs Michelle Morris**
186 Br c 31/01 Fastnet Rock (AUS)—Soundstrings (Oasis Dream) **Lael Stable**
187 B c 16/04 Awtaad (IRE)—Soviet Terms (Soviet Star (USA)) (150000) **Mr Hamdan Al Maktoum**
188 B c 17/02 Frankel—Superstar Leo (IRE) (College Chapel) **Lael Stable**
189 **TARHIB (IRE)**, b f 14/03 Dark Angel (IRE)—Allez Alaia (IRE) (Pivotal) (1050000) **Mr Hamdan Al Maktoum**
190 Ch f 07/04 Sea The Stars (IRE)—Tayma (IRE) (Exceed And Excel (AUS)) **Sunderland Holding Inc.**
191 B f 18/02 Cable Bay (IRE)—Undress (IRE) (Dalakhani (IRE)) **Mr J. B. Haggas**
192 Ch c 26/04 Sea The Stars (IRE)—Valais Girl (Holy Roman Emperor (IRE)) **Sunderland Holding Inc.**
193 **VISALA**, b f 18/02 Exceed And Excel (AUS)—Visoliya (FR) (Nayef (USA)) **Miss Yvonne Jacques**
194 B f 03/04 Kodiac—Warda (Pivotal) (145000) **Sheikh Juma Dalmook Al Maktoum**
195 **B c 18/04 Oasis Dream—**
What A Picture (FR) (Peintre Celebre (USA)) (81509) **China Horse Club International Limited**
196 B f 16/04 New Approach (IRE)—White Dress (IRE) (Pivotal) (110000) **Sheikh Rashid Dalmook Al Maktoum**
197 **WINK OF AN EYE**, b c 09/02 Dubawi (IRE)—Momentary (Nayef (USA)) **Her Majesty The Queen**
198 B f 24/03 Kingman—Wonderstruck (IRE) (Sea The Stars (IRE)) **Lael Stable**
199 **ZENITH (IRE)**, gr c 07/02 Invincible Spirit (IRE)—
Freezy (IRE) (Dalakhani (IRE)) (120000) **Highclere Tbred Racing-Charlie Langton**

Other Owners: Sheikh Rashid Dalmook Al Maktoum, Mrs F. J. Carmichael, China Horse Club International Limited, D. R. Martin, Mrs J. M. T. Martin.

Assistant Trainer: Harry Eustace, Josh Hamer, Andy McIntyre.

Apprentice Jockey: Georgia Cox, Cieran Fallon, Gianluca Sanna.

---

243 | **MR ALEX HALES, Edgecote**
Postal: Trafford Bridge Stables, Edgecote, Banbury, Oxfordshire, OX17 1AG
Contacts: **PHONE** 01295 660131 **MOBILE** 07771 511652 **FAX** 01295 660128
EMAIL alex@alexhalesracing.co.uk **WEBSITE** www.alexhalesracing.co.uk

1 **ADSTANTES**, 4, b g Gregorian (IRE)—Flying Hi **Mr & Mrs Nigel Bailey & Paddy Durnin**
2 **BOURBON BEAUTY**, 5, b m Great Pretender (IRE)—It Doesn't Matter **Old Stoic Racing Club**
3 **CEARA BE (IRE)**, 7, b m Oscar (IRE)—Pearl's A Singer (IRE) **Mr P. J. Byrne**
4 **EMILY WEBB**, 5, b m Franklins Gardens—Lofaire (IRE) **Mr R Hunt & Mr T J Acott**
5 **ES QUE MAGIC (IRE)**, 4, b g Es Que Love (IRE)—Itzakindamagic (IRE) **Edging Ahead**
6 **FLORRIE KNOX (IRE)**, 7, gr g Gold Well—Miss Orphan (FR) **The Fortune Hunters**
7 **FLOW AWAY (IRE)**, 6, br m Stowaway—Water Rock **Mr N Rodway & Partner**
8 **FOR PLEASURE (IRE)**, 5, ch g Excelebration (IRE)—Darsan (IRE) **Premier Plastering (UK) Limited**
9 **HUNTSMAN SON (IRE)**, 10, b g Millenary—Daly Lady (IRE) **C. W. Booth**
10 **INDIAN NATIVE (IRE)**, 10, b m Oscar (IRE)—Roman Native (IRE) **C. W. Booth**
11 **JIMMI CHEW (IRE)**, 7, br g Jimble (FR)—Katie Baby (IRE) **Mr B. E. Brackenbury**
12 **JONJOELA (IRE)**, 9, b m Great Exhibition (USA)—Yorkshire Blade (IRE) **In The Pink Partnership**
13 **JUST MARVIN (IRE)**, 7, b g Atraf—Gailybay Ellen (IRE) **Mr S. Brown**
14 **KANKIN**, 4, ch g Archipenko (USA)—Touriga **Mr A. L. Cohen**
15 **LOVE THE WELL (IRE)**, 9, b g Fruits of Love (USA)—Junga Connection **Mr A. M. Hales**
16 **MARIA MAGDALENA (IRE)**, 4, b f Battle of Marengo (IRE)—Few Words **The Problem Solvers**
17 **METHAG (FR)**, 7, b m Pour Moi (IRE)—Kyria **The One For Us**
18 **MILLERS BANK**, 6, b g Passing Glance—It Doesn't Matter **Millers Bank Partnership**
19 **MOVE CLOSER (IRE)**, 6, b m Zafeen (FR)—Royale Sulawesie (FR) **Mr A. M. Hales**
20 **MUSICAL STARDUST**, 7, b m Passing Glance—Royal Musical **Mrs J. Way**
21 **PANKO (IRE)**, 7, b g Iffraaj—Engraving **S Mullaney, S Brown, D & V Jones**
22 **ROUGH NIGHT (IRE)**, 7, b g Doyen (IRE)—Sunny Bob (IRE) **Miss P. M. Morris**
23 **RUNNING WOLF (IRE)**, 9, b g Amadeus Wolf—Monet's Lady (IRE) **The Wolfgangers**
24 **SEA PRINCE**, 4, b g Born To Sea (IRE)—Briery (IRE) **The Sea Prince Racing Partnership**
25 **SEEUBACKINCOPPERS (IRE)**, 7, b m Oscar (IRE)—Foxtail (IRE) **The Copper Plated Partnership**

MR ALEX HALES - continued

26 **SHIROCCSMYWORLD (IRE),** 5, ch m Shirocco (GER)—Phillis Hill **Golden Equinox Racing**
27 **SITRON,** 5, b m Black Sam Bellamy (IRE)—Chilly Squaw (IRE) **Edging Ahead**
28 **SMOOTH STEPPER,** 11, b g Alflora (IRE)—Jazzy Refrain (IRE) **Mr B. E. Brackenbury**
29 **STACEY SUE (IRE),** 7, b m Robin des Champs (FR)—Antonia Hall (IRE) **The The Backburners**
30 **STEPOVER,** 9, b m Midnight Legend—Ring Back (IRE) **Mrs A. P. B. Allen**
31 **SWILLY SUNSET,** 7, b g Kyllachy—Spanish Springs (IRE) **In The Pink Partnership**
32 **TICKET TO L A (IRE),** 5, b m Westerner—In Bloom (IRE) **Golden Equinox Racing & Partner**
33 **ULTIMATUM DU ROY (FR),** 12, b g Brier Creek (USA)—La Fleur du Roy (FR) **Edging Ahead**

THREE-YEAR-OLDS
34 **GONE IN SIXTY,** b g Sixties Icon—Gib (IRE) **Golden Equinox Racing**
35 **HICONIC,** b f Sixties Icon—Hi Note **Golden Equinox Racing & Partner**
36 **NOW WE'RE TOURING (IRE),** b c Kingston Hill—Drumcliffe Dancer (IRE)

Other Owners: Mr T. J. Acott, Mr N. Bailey, Mrs S. Bailey, Mr C. Bennett, Mr S. Bocking, Mr P. Durnin, Golden Equinox Racing, Mr A. M. Hales, Mr C. R. B. Hunt, Mr N. Rodway, Mr C. J. Woods.

244

MR MICHAEL HALFORD, Kildare
Postal: **Copper Beech Stables, Doneaney, Kildangan Road, Kildare, Co. Kildare, Ireland**
Contacts: **PHONE +353 45 526 119 MOBILE +353 87 257 9204 FAX +353 45 526 157**
EMAIL info@michaelhalford.com WEBSITE www.michaelhalford.com

1 **ARCANEARS (IRE),** 5, b g Arcano (IRE)—Ondeafears (IRE) **Mrs Caroline Roper**
2 **BLUE WOOD (IRE),** 4, b c Requinto (IRE)—Talkin Kate (IRE) **CVK Syndicate**
3 **EQUITANT,** 5, ch g Equiano (FR)—Intrusion **Mr Nasir Askar**
4 **EYE OF THE DRAGON (IRE),** 4, b f Dragon Pulse (IRE)—Jiran (IRE) **Mr Evan Newell**
5 **GENTLE M'AM (IRE),** 4, b f Morpheus—Gentle Soul (IRE) **Mr Brian Gallivan**
6 **GOUGANE BARRA (USA),** 6, b br g First Defence (USA)—Beiramar (IRE) **Mr P Rooney**
7 **HAMARIYNA (IRE),** 4, b f Sea The Moon (GER)—Hanakiyya (IRE) **H. H. Aga Khan**
8 **KATIYMANN (IRE),** 8, b g Shamardal (USA)—Katiyra (IRE) **Mr P Rooney**
9 **LADY DE VESCI (IRE),** 7, ch m Approve (IRE)—La Bandola (GER) **Mr F Sommer**
10 **MASSIF CENTRAL (IRE),** 6, b g Arcano (IRE)—Melaaya (USA) **Mr P Rooney**
11 **MISS SNOSSYBOOTS (IRE),** 6, ch m Rip Van Winkle (IRE)—Nick's Nikita (IRE) **Mr N Hartery**
12 **PIANO SOLO (FR),** 4, b g Planteur (IRE)—Pianiste (FR) **Mr Huang Kai Wen**
13 **RAYOUNPOUR (IRE),** 4, b g Cape Cross (IRE)—Rayna (IRE) **Mr R McNally**
14 **SENDMYLOVETOYOU (IRE),** 4, b f Invincible Spirit (IRE)—Sendmylovetorose **Mr M Enright**
15 **SHAMIYAN (IRE),** 4, b g Lope de Vega (IRE)—Shamooda (IRE) **Mr R McNally**
16 **SIMSIR (IRE),** 4, b c Zoffany (IRE)—Simawa (IRE) **H. H. Aga Khan**
17 **SKY SEVEN (IRE),** 4, ch c Helmet (AUS)—Ready When You Are (IRE) **Mr Nasir Askar**
18 **SPELGA,** 4, b g Sir Percy—Emma's Gift (IRE) **Mr P Rooney**
19 **SURROUNDING (IRE),** 7, b m Lilbourne Lad (IRE)—Roundabout Girl (IRE) **Mr P E I Newell**
20 **TIRMIZI (FR),** 7, b g Sea The Stars (IRE)—Timabiyra (IRE) **Mr P Rooney**
21 **WAR DIARY,** 5, b g Declaration of War (USA)—Titivation **Mr P Rooney**
22 **WHEREWITHAL,** 4, b c Lope de Vega (IRE)—Banks Hill **Mr Fathi Egziama**
23 **WUFUD,** 5, b h Dubawi (IRE)—Tahrir (IRE) **Mr Fathi Egziama**

THREE-YEAR-OLDS
24 **AIRLIFT (IRE),** b c Clodovil (IRE)—Hattie Jacques **Copper Beech Racing Syndicate**
25 **ALATAR (IRE),** b c Ruler of The World (IRE)—Aliyfa (IRE) **H. H. Aga Khan**
26 **CARA KATHERINE (IRE),** b f Mastercraftsman (IRE)—Adeste **Mrs Pearl O'Rourke**
27 **COMRADERY (IRE),** b c Camacho—Shamardyh (IRE) **Copper Beech Racing Syndicate**
28 **DICEBOX (IRE),** ch c Teofilo (IRE)—Scatter Dice (IRE) **Godolphin**
29 **DILIYMI (IRE),** ch g Footstepsinthesand—Diylawa (IRE) **H. H. Aga Khan**
30 **FEMINISM (IRE),** ch f Shamardal (USA)—Modern Ideals **Godolphin**
31 **FINANS BAY (IRE),** b c Kodiac—Wrood (USA) **Mr N Hartery**
32 **HARAKANN (IRE),** b c Australia—Hanakiyya (IRE) **H. H. Aga Khan**
33 **HIEROGLYPHIC,** ch f Exceed And Excel (AUS)—Philae (USA) **Godolphin**

MR MICHAEL HALFORD - continued

34 **KADIYAMA (IRE)**, b f Born To Sea (IRE)—Kadayna (IRE) **H. H. Aga Khan**
35 **KALAPOUR (IRE)**, b c War Command (USA)—Kaladena (IRE) **H. H. Aga Khan**
36 **KALAYENA (IRE)**, gr f Mastercraftsman (IRE)—Kalabaya (IRE) **H. H. Aga Khan**
37 **KASMIYRA (IRE)**, b f Free Eagle (IRE)—Kastania (USA) **H. H. Aga Khan**
38 **KERANDI (IRE)**, ch c Champs Elysees—Kerisa (IRE) **H. H. Aga Khan**
39 **LADY BLAKENEY**, b f Shamardal (USA)—Pimpernel (IRE) **Godolphin**
40 **LITTMANN (IRE)**, b g Dandy Man (IRE)—Talitha Kum (IRE) **Copper Beech Racing Syndicate**
41 **LORD PARK (IRE)**, b c Tamayuz—Hammiya (IRE) **Mr Garrett Freyne**
42 B c Gleneagles (IRE)—Love Excelling (FR) **Mr John Connaughton**
43 **NAILA'S BABY (IRE)**, br f Bated Breath—Triple Sharp **Mr Taher Al Alawi**
44 **ORCHID GARDENS (IRE)**, b f Muhaarar—Lidanski (IRE) **Mrs W O'Leary**
45 **OVERTAKE**, gr g Outstrip—Winterbourne **Mr Ger McDonald**
46 **PLAYA DEL DUQUE (IRE)**, b f Dylan Thomas (IRE)—Playamongthestars (AUS) **Mr T Vaughan**
47 **RIDENZA (IRE)**, br f Sea The Stars (IRE)—Raydara (IRE) **H. H. Aga Khan**
48 **ROMAN TURBO (IRE)**, b c Holy Roman Emperor (IRE)—Swish (GER) **Mr Sammy Hon Kit Ma**
49 **ROYAL CASAMENTO (IRE)**, b g Casamento (IRE)—Royal Blue **Mr David O'Connell**
50 **SAMPERS SEVEN (IRE)**, b f Anjaal—Sampers (IRE) **Mr N Hartery**
51 **SATIN SLIPPER (IRE)**, b f Camacho—Slipper Orchid (IRE) **Mrs Caroline Roper**
52 **SIENNA LADY (IRE)**, b f Lope de Vega (IRE)—Paimpolaise (IRE) **Mr M Enright**
53 **SINAWANN (IRE)**, b c Kingman—Simawa (IRE) **H. H. Aga Khan**
54 **SINDHIA (IRE)**, b f Mastercraftsman (IRE)—Sinaniya (USA) **H. H. Aga Khan**
55 **SLIEVE BEARNAGH (IRE)**, b c Zoffany (IRE)—Angels Story (IRE) **Mr P Rooney**
56 **SORELLA D'ANGELO (IRE)**, b f Dark Angel (IRE)—Silca's Sister **Godolphin**
57 **STRIP LIGHT (IRE)**, ch g Outstrip—Quinine **Copper Beech Racing Syndicate**
58 **SYLVIA PLATH IRE**, ch f Poet's Voice—Speak Softly (JPN) **Godolphin**
59 **TEN WIN**, b c Heeraat (IRE)—Kallisima
60 **WITHBATEDBREATH (IRE)**, b c Bated Breath—Starlight Symphony (IRE)
61 **ZANAHIYR (IRE)**, ch c Nathaniel (IRE)—Zariyna (IRE) **H. H. Aga Khan**
62 **ZARZYNI (IRE)**, b g Siyouni (FR)—Zunera (IRE) **H. H. Aga Khan**

TWO-YEAR-OLDS

63 Ch c 04/05 Tamayuz—Abama Lady (CAN) (Mr Greeley (USA))
64 Gr c 05/05 Zoffany (IRE)—Callistan (IRE) (Galileo (IRE))
65 Ch c 01/04 Raven's Pass (USA)—City Vaults Girl (IRE) (Oratorio (IRE)) **Mr Nasir Askar**
66 **DIAMIL (IRE)**, b c 27/02 Awtaad (IRE)—Diylawa (IRE) (Mastercraftsman (IRE)) **H. H. Aga Khan**
67 **EBASARI (IRE)**, b c 03/02 Lope de Vega (IRE)—Ebayya (IRE) (Azamour (IRE)) **H. H. Aga Khan**
68 B f 11/02 Adaay (IRE)—Elmaam (Nayef (USA)) **Mr Nasir Askar**
69 B c 25/02 Exceed And Excel (AUS)—Ghany (IRE) (Lawman (FR))
70 B f 05/02 Footstepsinthesand—Hasanza (USA) (Mr Greeley (USA))
71 Br f 22/04 Le Havre (IRE)—Hazaraba (IRE) (Oasis Dream) **H. H. Aga Khan**
72 B f 28/02 Rock of Gibraltar (IRE)—High Society Girl (IRE) (Key of Luck (USA)) **Mr Nasir Askar**
73 **KAMARAZI (IRE)**, b c 13/02 Fast Company (IRE)—Karasiyra (IRE) (Alhaarth (IRE)) **H. H. Aga Khan**
74 Gr c 25/04 Free Eagle (IRE)—Kapera (IRE) (Linamix (FR))
75 B c 13/02 Starspangledbanner (AUS)—Karalara (IRE) (Shamardal (USA)) **H. H. Aga Khan**
76 **KARIYNA (IRE)**, b f 29/04 Olympic Glory (IRE)—Kerisa (IRE) (Azamour (IRE)) **H. H. Aga Khan**
77 Ch c 30/03 Al Kazeem—Kid Gloves (In The Wings) **Mr Nasir Askar**
78 B c 08/04 Elzaam (AUS)—Lady Conway (USA) (El Corredor (USA))
79 B c 26/04 Elzaam (AUS)—Love Note (USA) (Elusive Quality (USA))
80 Br c 10/04 Starspangledbanner (AUS)—Luminance (IRE) (Danehill Dancer (IRE))
81 Ch c 19/04 New Bay—Majestic Dancer (IRE) (Danehill Dancer (IRE))
82 **MAKE IT TURBO (IRE)**, b c 30/03 Make Believe—Royal Alchemist (Kingsinger (IRE)) **Mr Sammy Hon Kit Ma**
83 B c 30/01 Dark Angel (IRE)—Marenko (Exceed And Excel (AUS)) **Mr Nasir Askar**
84 **MAZYAD (IRE)**, b c 15/04 Fastnet Rock (AUS)—Masiyma (IRE) (Dalakhani (IRE)) **H. H. Aga Khan**
85 B c 06/03 Dandy Man (IRE)—Musaadaqa (IRE) (Tamayuz)
86 Ch c 27/04 Night of Thunder (IRE)—Pixie Belle (IRE) (Echo of Light) **Mr Nasir Askar**
87 B c 03/02 Cable Bay (IRE)—Positive Spin (Dalakhani (IRE))
88 **RAYAGARA (IRE)**, b f 28/01 Dark Angel (IRE)—Raydara (IRE) (Rock of Gibraltar (IRE)) **H. H. Aga Khan**
89 **RAZDAN (IRE)**, b c 19/02 Zoffany (IRE)—Rayna (IRE) (Selkirk (USA)) **H. H. Aga Khan**
90 **RILIYA (IRE)**, b f 21/02 Awtaad (IRE)—Riyaba (IRE) (Dalakhani (IRE)) **H. H. Aga Khan**

MR MICHAEL HALFORD - continued

91 B f 24/04 Gleneagles (IRE)—Rivers of Babylon (IRE) (Holy Roman Emperor (IRE)) **Mr Garrett Freyne**
92 B c 19/04 Rock of Gibraltar (IRE)—Roskeen (IRE) (Grand Lodge (USA)) **Mr Nasir Askar**
93 ROZIYNA (IRE), b f 11/02 Sea The Stars (IRE)—Rayisa (IRE) (Holy Roman Emperor (IRE)) **H. H. Aga Khan**
94 B c 20/04 Charm Spirit (IRE)—Sharp Relief (IRE) (Galileo (IRE))
95 SILAIYLI (IRE), b c 24/03 Olympic Glory (IRE)—Sinaniya (USA) (More Than Ready (USA)) **H. H. Aga Khan**
96 TASHKHAN (IRE), b c 15/02 Born To Sea (IRE)—Tarziyna (IRE) (Raven's Pass (USA)) **H. H. Aga Khan**
97 TURBO SPIRIT, b c 02/04 Charm Spirit (IRE)—Bijou A Moi (Rainbow Quest (USA)) **Mr Sammy Hon Kit Ma**
98 B c 23/03 Elzaam (AUS)—Well Done Me (IRE) (Moss Vale (IRE))
99 B f 24/03 Mehmas (IRE)—Wrood (USA) (Invasor (ARG)) **Pioneer Racing**
100 ZAYNUDIN (IRE), b c 11/03 Fastnet Rock (AUS)—Zanoubiya (IRE) (Dalakhani (IRE)) **H. H. Aga Khan**
101 ZURKHANA (IRE), b f 06/03 Helmet (AUS)—Zunera (IRE) (Invincible Spirit (IRE)) **H. H. Aga Khan**

Assistant Trainer: Fabian Burke.

Flat Jockey: Ross Coakley, Niall McCullagh, Ronan Whelan. **Apprentice Jockey:** Liam Browne, Adam Farraghar, Eamonn Fitzgerald. **Amateur Jockey:** Mr Evan Halford.

245

MRS DEBRA HAMER, Carmarthen
Postal: **Bryngors Uchaf, Nantycaws, Carmarthen, Dyfed, SA32 8EY**
Contacts: **HOME 01267 234585 MOBILE 07980 665274**
EMAIL hamerracing@hotmail.co.uk

1 CONSTANCE DE CHAMP (IRE), 6, b m Robin des Champs (FR)—Jamie's Darling (IRE) **Miss M. Peterson**
2 EMMPRESSIVE LADY (IRE), 5, b m Jeremy (USA)—Court Lexi (IRE) **Clear Racing**
3 FLEURY, 5, b m Brian Boru—Barfleur (IRE) **Mr S. F. Barlow**
4 HIDDEN CARGO (IRE), 8, b g Stowaway—All Heart **The Smith Swinburne Partnership**
5 JAC BROWN, 6, b g Multiplex—Do It On Dani **The Hamers**
6 LAYERTHORPE (IRE), 8, b bl g Vale of York (IRE)—Strobinia (IRE) **Mr C. A. Hanbury**
7 LOOKS LIKE POWER (IRE), 10, ch g Spadoun (FR)—Martovic (IRE) **Mr C. A. Hanbury**
8 MAGICAL MAN, 13, b br g Lahib (USA)—Majestic Di (IRE) **Mr C. A. Hanbury**
9 MANHATTAN MEAD, 10, ch g Central Park (IRE)—Honey Nut **Exors of the Late Mr G. Phillips**
10 OUT THE GLEN (IRE), 7, b g Millenary—Dicera (IRE) **Mrs J. M. Edmonds**
11 SADDLERS QUEST, 6, b m Dr Massini (IRE)—Lady Maranzi **Mrs D. A. Hamer**
12 TOBEFAIR, 10, b br g Central Park (IRE)—Nan **Down The Quay Club**

Other Owners: D. A. Smith, R. D. J. Swinburne.

Assistant Trainer: Mr M. P. Hamer.

246

MRS ALISON HAMILTON, Denholm
Postal: **Dykes Farm House, Denholm, Hawick, Roxburghshire, TD9 8TB**
Contacts: **PHONE 01450 870323 MOBILE 07885 477349**
EMAIL Alisonhamilton53@yahoo.com

1 BUTTEVANT LADY (IRE), 7, b m Presenting—Off She Goes (IRE) **J. P. G. Hamilton**
2 CHOIX DES ARMES (FR), 8, b g Saint des Saints (FR)—Kicka **J. P. G. Hamilton**
3 EXPRESS DES MOTTES (FR), 6, b g Network (GER)—Uzelle des Mottes (FR) **Mr & Mrs D S Byers & Jpg Hamilton**
4 GETAWAY KID (IRE), 8, ch g Getaway (GER)—Bambootcha (IRE) **J. P. G. Hamilton**
5 PAINTERS LAD (IRE), 9, b g Fruits of Love (USA)—Great Cullen (IRE) **J. P. G. Hamilton**
6 SANDHURST LAD (IRE), 9, b g Presenting—Off She Goes (IRE) **J. P. G. Hamilton**
7 SKYHILL (IRE), 7, b g Gold Well—Classic Mari (IRE) **Mr & Mrs D S Byers & Jpg Hamilton**
8 SUNSET MARQUIS (IRE), 9, b m Kayf Tara—Miss Abrahnovic (IRE) **J. P. G. Hamilton**
9 THE ICE FACTOR, 12, b g Iceman—Kiruna **J. P. G. Hamilton**
10 TOWERBURN (IRE), 11, b g Cloudings (IRE)—Lady Newmill (IRE) **J. P. G. Hamilton**
11 WAYUPINTHESKY (IRE), 13, gr g Cloudings (IRE)—Riancoir Alainn **J. P. G. Hamilton**

Other Owners: Mr & Mrs D. S. Byers, D. S. Byers, Mrs M. J. Byers, Mrs A. C. Hamilton, J. P. G. Hamilton.

Assistant Trainer: Mr G. Hamilton.

247 — MR ANDREW HAMILTON, Carluke
Postal: **Nellfield House, Braidwood, Carluke, Lanarkshire, ML8 4PP**
Contacts: **PHONE 01555 771502**

1 **ELYSIAN PRINCE**, 9, b g Champs Elysees—Trinkila (USA) **Mr A. B. Hamilton**
2 **GOLDSLINGER (FR)**, 8, b g Gold Away (IRE)—Singaporette (FR) **Mr A. B. Hamilton**
3 **LETEMGO (IRE)**, 12, b g Brian Boru—Leteminletemout (IRE) **Mr A. B. Hamilton**
4 **MAJOR DAVIS (FR)**, 8, b g Vision d'Etat (FR)—Majorica Sancta (FR) **Mr A. B. Hamilton**
5 **TUATHA DE DANNAN (IRE)**, 5, ch g Imperial Monarch (IRE)—Glenasheen (IRE) **Mr A. B. Hamilton**

248 — MRS ANN HAMILTON, Newcastle Upon Tyne
Postal: **Claywalls Farm, Capheaton, Newcastle Upon Tyne, Tyne and Wear, NE19 2BP**
Contacts: **PHONE 01830 530219 MOBILE 07704 670704**
EMAIL annhamilton1952@hotmail.com

1 **BAVINGTON BOB (IRE)**, 5, br g Court Cave (IRE)—Chocolate Silk (IRE) **Mr I. Hamilton**
2 **MISTER MANDURO (FR)**, 6, ch g Manduro (GER)—Semenova (FR) **Mr I. Hamilton**
3 **NUTS WELL**, 9, b g Dylan Thomas (IRE)—Renada **Mr I. Hamilton**
4 **POINT BREAK (IRE)**, 6, b g Westerner—Pertinent Point (IRE) **Mr I. Hamilton**
5 **RUNSWICK ROYAL (IRE)**, 11, ch g Excellent Art—Renada **Mr I. Hamilton**
6 **THE GAP (IRE)**, 5, b g Arcadio (GER)—Ballyorril Hill (IRE) **Mr I. Hamilton**

Assistant Trainer: Ian Hamilton.

249 — MR MICKY HAMMOND, Middleham
Postal: **Oakwood Stables, East Witton Road, Middleham, Leyburn, North Yorkshire, DL8 4PT**
Contacts: **PHONE 01969 625223 MOBILE 07808 572777**
EMAIL mickyhammondracing@hotmail.com WEBSITE www.mickyhammondracing.co.uk

1 **ALDERBROOK LAD (IRE)**, 14, ch g Alderbrook—Alone Tabankulu (IRE) **Ian Barran, Rita Butler & Gemma Hogg**
2 **APPLAUS (GER)**, 8, b g Tiger Hill (IRE)—All About Love (GER) **The Deckchair Syndicate**
3 **BALLYCRYSTAL (IRE)**, 9, b g Oscar (IRE)—Musical Madam (IRE) **M. D. Hammond, Mrs G. Hogg**
4 **BECKY THE THATCHER**, 7, b m Mastercraftsman (IRE)—Fairmont (IRE)
5 **BELLE O' THE DALES (FR)**, 4, b f Blue Bresil (FR)—Egery (FR)
6 **BLACK KETTLE (IRE)**, 10, b g Robin des Pres (FR)—Whistful Suzie (IRE)
7 **BLUE HUSSAR (IRE)**, 9, b g Montjeu (IRE)—Metaphor (USA) **Mr Richard Howard & Mr Ben Howard**
8 **BRICKADANK (IRE)**, 4, b g Cape Cross—Tralanza (IRE) **M. D. Hammond, Mrs G. Hogg**
9 **BURDIGALA (FR)**, 7, b g Way of Light (USA)—Tiara
10 **BURNAGE BOY (IRE)**, 4, b g Footstepsinthesand—Speedi Mouse **JFW Properties Limited**
11 **CALIPTION**, 8, gr g Fair Mix (IRE)—Sheriff's Falcon (IRE) **The Cheltenham Trail**
12 **CANFORD THOMPSON**, 7, b g Canford Cliffs (IRE)—
Sadie Thompson (IRE) **Ian Barran, Rita Butler & Gemma Hogg**
13 **COCKNEY BEAU (FR)**, 5, gr g Cockney Rebel (IRE)—Salsa Melody (FR) **M. D. Hammond, Mr J. Cain**
14 **COMMANDING SPIRIT (IRE)**, 8, ch g Presenting—
Park Athlete (IRE) **M. D. Hammond, Mrs Jennifer Hill & Mrs Samantha Toomes**
15 **CONVIVIAL**, 5, b m Mount Nelson—Vino **Grange Park Racing XV1**
16 **CORNERSTONE LAD**, 6, b g Delegator—Chapel Corner (IRE) **Mrs B. M. Lofthouse**
17 **CRASH HELMET**, 5, b g Helmet (AUS)—Hot Secret **M. D. Hammond, Mrs G. Hogg**
18 **DADDYJACKS SPECIAL (FR)**, 4, gr g Spirit One (FR)—Great Way (FR)
19 **DAKOTA GREY**, 9, gr g Fair Mix (IRE)—Miss Sassi **M. D. Hammond, Mrs A. Kane**
20 **DONTDELAY (IRE)**, 10, b g Indian Danehill (IRE)—Garden Heaven (IRE) **M. D. Hammond, Mrs G. Hogg**
21 **DRAGONS WILL RISE (IRE)**, 4, b g Dragon Pulse (IRE)—Jaldini (IRE) **M. D. Hammond, Mrs G. Hogg**
22 **ENFIN PHIL (FR)**, 6, ch g No Risk At All (FR)—Nheyranne (FR) **Randall Orchard & Partners**
23 **EX S'ELANCE (FR)**, 6, b g Saddex—Pampa Brune (FR) **The Fifty Fifty Partnership**
24 **EXCALIBUR (POL)**, 7, gr g Youmzain (IRE)—Electra Deelites **The Golden Cuckoo**
25 **FORTIA**, 6, b m Nathaniel (IRE)—Veenwouden **M. D. Hammond, Mr S. Sutton**
26 **FOSTER'SISLAND**, 5, b g Trans Island—Mrs Eff

MR MICKY HAMMOND - continued

27 **FRANKELIO (FR)**, 5, b g Frankel—Restiadargent (FR) **Forty Forty Twenty**
28 **FRANKSTER (FR)**, 7, b g Equiano (FR)—Milwaukee (FR) **The Cobb Family**
29 **GRAND DU NORD (FR)**, 4, b g Montmartre (FR)—Vanille d'Ainay (FR) **Middleham Park Racing & Mr S Nicols**
30 **GRANGE RANGER (IRE)**, 8, b g Kalanisi (IRE)—Grangeclare Flight (IRE) **Mrs G. Hogg**
31 **HIGH NOON (IRE)**, 8, b g Westerner—Seymourswift **Mr N. Pietrzyk**
32 **ILAYA (FR)**, 6, gr m Kapgarde (FR)—Tour Magic (FR) **The Golden Cuckoo**
33 **INDIAN VISION (IRE)**, 6, ch g Iffraaj—Sweet Fairnando **The Futurists**
34 **IRV (IRE)**, 4, ch g Zoffany (IRE)—Marion Antoinette (IRE)
35 **IT'S ALL ABOUT ME (IRE)**, 8, b m King's Theatre (IRE)—Annie Spectrim (IRE) **M. D. Hammond, Mrs G. Hogg**
36 **JUSTFORJAMES (IRE)**, 11, b g Dr Massini (IRE)—Over The Road (IRE) **M. D. Hammond, Mrs G. Hogg**
37 **KISUMU**, 8, b g High Chaparral (IRE)—Arum Lily (USA)
38 **KNOCKNAMONA (IRE)**, 9, b g Trans Island—Faraday Lady (IRE) **M. D. Hammond, Mrs G. Hogg**
39 **LATE DATE (IRE)**, 9, b g Oscar (IRE)—Regents Ballerina (IRE) **County Set Six & Partner**
40 **LUCOU (FR)**, 4, b g Axxos (GER)—Winnor (FR) **A Walsh, J Hill, S Toomes**
41 **MAC CENNETIG (IRE)**, 8, b g Brian Boru—Buslane (IRE) **Mrs B. M. Lofthouse**
42 **MAISON D'OR (IRE)**, 6, b g Galileo (IRE)—Thai Haku (IRE)
43 **MARVELLOUS JOE (IRE)**, 5, b g Mahler—Marvellous Dream (FR) **M. D. Hammond, J. Buzzeo**
44 **NOMOUNTAINHIENOUGH (IRE)**, 5, b g Mountain High (IRE)—Nohabodder (IRE) **M. D. Hammond, Mrs G. Hogg**
45 **ONLYFOOLSOWNHORSES (IRE)**, 9, br g Presenting—Lizzy Langtry (IRE)
46 **PADDLING (FR)**, 9, b g Walk In The Park (IRE)—Sea Mamaille (FR) **Masters Of The Hall 2**
47 **PERCY B SHELLEY**, 6, ch g Archipenko (USA)—Oshiponga **M. D. Hammond, Mrs G. Hogg**
48 **QUOTELINE DIRECT**, 7, ch g Sir Percy—Queen's Pudding (IRE)
49 **RADDLE AND HUM (IRE)**, 6, b m Milan—Gaybric (IRE)
50 **ROCKLIFFE**, 7, b g Notnowcato—Hope Island (IRE) **Rm&t, S Toomes, J Hill & Partners**
51 **RORY AND ME (FR)**, 5, b g Shamardal (USA)—Rosawa (FR) **Mr Richard Howard & Mr Ben Howard**
52 **ROXYFET (FR)**, 10, b g Califet (FR)—Roxalamour (FR) **M. D. Hammond, Mr S. Sutton**
53 **RUSSIAN ROYALE**, 10, b m Royal Applause—Russian Ruby (FR) **M. D. Hammond, Mrs G. Hogg**
54 **SAUCY SALLY (IRE)**, 5, b m Declaration of War (USA)—Ardere (USA) **Mr S & Mrs D Everard, A Smith & O Weeks**
55 **SCHIEHALLION MUNRO**, 7, ch g Schiaparelli (GER)—Mrs Fawlty
56 **SILVER TASSIE (IRE)**, 12, b g Shantou (USA)—Silver Castor (FRA)
57 **SIR RUNS A LOT**, 8, b g Sir Percy—Monjouet (IRE) **R M & T Holdings Limited & Oakwood**
58 **SQUARE VIVIANI (FR)**, 9, b g Satri (IRE)—Idria (GER) **Stephen Sugden & Ryder Sugden**
59 **STORMIN NORMAN**, 5, b g Sir Percy—Roses
60 **STRIKE WEST (IRE)**, 8, b g Westerner—Fuel Queen (IRE) **R. P. E. Berry, O. R. Weeks**
61 **SWINTON DIAMOND (IRE)**, 9, b g Dubai Destination (USA)—Absent Beauty (IRE)
62 **THE PINE MARTIN (IRE)**, 10, br g Kalanisi (IRE)—Regal Holly
63 **THE RETRIEVER (IRE)**, 5, ch g Shamardal (USA)—Silent Secret (IRE)
64 **THE RUTLAND REBEL (IRE)**, 4, b g Delegator—Do Disturb (IRE)
65 **THE VERY THING (IRE)**, 6, b g Getaway (GER)—Katie Quinn (IRE)
66 **TRIMMERS LANE (IRE)**, 10, b g Publisher (USA)—Kilcormac Glow (IRE) **M. D. Hammond**
67 6, B m Bahri (USA)—Waverbeck (IRE)
68 **WHO'S THE GUV'NOR (IRE)**, 6, b g Gold Well—Clamit Brook (IRE) **Mr & Mrs I P Earnshaw**

THREE-YEAR-OLDS

69 **COUNTESS OLIVIA (IRE)**, ch f Ruler of The World (IRE)—Twelfth Night (IRE)
70 **JUST JEAN (IRE)**, b f Society Rock (IRE)—Yashila (IRE) **Mr & Mrs P. Chapman**
71 **MICK (IRE)**, b g Makfi—Sereza (IRE)

Other Owners: A & S Associates, I. J. Barran, Mr C. Buckingham, Mrs L. K. Buckingham, Mrs M. A. Butler, Mr Joe Buzzeo & Partner, Mrs J. Chapman, Mr P. W. Chapman, Cheerleader Racing, Mrs J. Cobb, Mr S. J. M. Cobb, Mr R. Doak, Mr & Mrs I P Earnshaw, Mr I. P. Earnshaw, Mrs J. Earnshaw, Mrs D. S. Everard, Mr S. M. Everard, Mr S. M. & Mrs. D. S. Everard, G. Godsman, M. D. Hammond, Mr D. A. Harrison, Mrs R. Hetherington, Mrs J. Hill, Mr J. A. Hill, Mrs G. Hogg, Horizon, Mr B. R. Howard, Mr R. M. Howard, J4J Properties Limited, Mr M. Kent, Mr D. Lees, I. M. Lynch, M.H.O.G., Mr R. Manners, McGoldrick Racing, Mrs D. J. Merson, Middleham Park Racing XXIII, Mr Samuel Sutton & Partners, Mr G. Newton, Mr S. Nicols, G. R. Orchard, T. S. Palin, Mr J. Pettit, M. Prince, R M & T Holdings Limited, R M & T Holdings Limited & Partners, Raypasha, Mr J. Reid, Mr N. J. Rust, Mr A. Savage, A. W. Sinclair, Mr A. Smith, Still Game Associates, Straightline Bloodstock, Mr P. Sugden, Mr S. Sugden, Stephen Sugden & Ryder Sugden, Tasker-Brown & Partners, Mr J. E. Tennant, Tennant, Lynch,Sharpe and Boston, The Cheltenham Trail & Proform Racing, The Faiseur De Miracle Partnership, The Golden Cuckoo, The Monday Club, The Multi-Taskers, The Oakwood Nobels, The Rat Pack Racing Club, Lady S. Toomes, Mr D. Walpole, Mr A. Walsh, O. R. Weeks.

MR MICKY HAMMOND - continued

Assistant Trainer: Mrs G. Hogg.

NH Jockey: Alain Cawley, Joe Colliver. **Conditional Jockey:** Billy Garritty, Aidan Macdonald, Emma Smith Chaston. **Amateur Jockey:** Miss R. Smith, James Waggott.

---

250 **MR GARY HANMER, Tattenhall**
Postal: **Church Farm, Harthill Lane, Harthill, Tattenhall, Chester, Cheshire, CH3 9LQ**
Contacts: **MOBILE 07737 181165**

1 **ARCTIC VALLEY (IRE),** 6, b g Arctic Cosmos (USA)—Grangevalley Gold (IRE) **The Ed-chester Partnership**
2 **DEE STAR (IRE),** 7, b g Shantou (USA)—Alicias Lady (IRE) **The Deeside Partnership**
3 **FUSIONFORCE (IRE),** 13, b g Overbury (IRE)—Seviot **Mr S. P. Edkins**
4 **HIGH COUNSEL (IRE),** 11, br g Presenting—The Bench (IRE) **Herongate Racers**
5 **ISTHEBAROPEN,** 7, b m Grape Tree Road—Seviot **Mr G. Evans**
6 **KNOCKNAGOSHEL (IRE),** 7, b g Kalanisi (IRE)—Granny Clark (IRE) **Knock Knock Syndicate**
7 **LOCH GARMAN ARIS (IRE),** 10, b g Jammaal—See Em Aime (IRE) **Exors of Late George Brookes & Family**
8 **O CEALLAIGH (IRE),** 11, b g Westerner—Hirayna **Mr G. Evans**
9 **O'GRADY'S BOY (IRE),** 9, b g Kalanisi (IRE)—Jemima Jay (IRE) **The Deeside Partnership**
10 **OSCAR NOMINATION (IRE),** 8, b g Getaway (GER)—Nightofthe Oscars (IRE) **The Deeside Partnership**
11 **PACKETTOTHERAFTERS (IRE),** 11, b g Craigsteel—Darazari River (IRE) **The Tunstall Green Partnership**
12 **STEEL WAVE (IRE),** 10, br g Craigsteel—Musical Waves (IRE) **The Tunstall Green Partnership**
13 **WBEE (IRE),** 5, b g Yeats (IRE)—Consultation (IRE) **Mrs M. D. Ritson**
14 **WHAT A LAUGH,** 15, b g Kayf Tara—Just For A Laugh **Mr S. P. Edkins**

THREE-YEAR-OLDS

15 **DEE EIRE,** bl f Gentlewave (IRE)—Kahipiroska (FR) **The Deeside Partnership**

Other Owners: Mr S. P. Edkins, M. E. Green, Mr N. P. Tunstall, Mr G. J. Winchester.

---

251 **MR RICHARD HANNON, Marlborough**
Postal: **Herridge Racing Stables, Herridge, Collingbourne Ducis, Wiltshire, SN8 3EG**
Contacts: **PHONE 01264 850254 FAX 01264 850076**
EMAIL kevin@richardhannonracing.co.uk WEBSITE www.richardhannonracing.co.uk

1 **ANNA NERIUM,** 5, ch m Dubawi (IRE)—Anna Oleanda (IRE)
2 **BEAT LE BON (FR),** 4, b c Wootton Bassett—Frida La Blonde (FR)
3 **BILLESDON BROOK,** 5, ch m Champs Elysees—Coplow
4 **BOITRON (FR),** 4, b c Le Havre (IRE)—Belliflore (FR)
5 **BRIAN EPSTEIN (IRE),** 4, b c Dark Angel (IRE)—Jewel In The Sand (IRE)
6 **BURIDAN (FR),** 5, b g Choisir (AUS)—Lady McKell (IRE)
7 **DRAGON SUN,** 4, ch g Pivotal—Moon Sister (IRE)
8 **EMBOUR (IRE),** 5, b g Acclamation—Carpet Lady (IRE)
9 **FLOATING ARTIST,** 4, b c Nathaniel (IRE)—Miss Kenton (IRE)
10 **FOX CHAMPION (IRE),** 4, b c Kodiac—Folegandros Island (FR)
11 **FOX POWER (IRE),** 4, gr c Dark Angel (IRE)—Zenella
12 **HAAYEM (FR),** 4, b g Olympic Glory (IRE)—Almaardiyah (IRE)
13 **IN THE COVE (IRE),** 4, b c Footstepsinthesand—Vatrouchka (USA)
14 **KING OF CHANGE,** 4, b c Farhh—Salacia (IRE)
15 **KUWAIT CURRENCY (USA),** 4, ch g Kitten's Joy (USA)—Thebignbadestbunny (USA)
16 **MAGICAL WISH (IRE),** 4, br g Heeraat (IRE)—Tomintoul Magic (IRE)
17 **MONTYS INN (IRE),** 4, b g Kodiac—Bailonguera (ARG)
18 **MORDRED (IRE),** 4, b c Camelot—Endure (IRE)
19 **OH THIS IS US (IRE),** 7, b h Acclamation—Shamwari Lodge (IRE)
20 **OUZO,** 4, b c Charm Spirit (IRE)—Miss Meltemi (IRE)

MR RICHARD HANNON - continued

21 **POSTED,** 4, b f Kingman—Time Away (IRE)
22 **QAYSAR (FR),** 5, b g Choisir (AUS)—Coco Demure (IRE)
23 **RAYMOND TUSK (IRE),** 5, b h High Chaparral (IRE)—Dancing Shoes (IRE)
24 **ROBINSON CRUSOE (IRE),** 5, b g Footstepsinthesand—Corrozal (GER)
25 **STAR TERMS,** 4, ch f Sea The Stars (IRE)—Best Terms
26 **TABARRAK (IRE),** 7, b g Acclamation—Bahati (IRE)
27 **TYPHOON TEN (IRE),** 4, b g Slade Power (IRE)—Cake (IRE)
28 **URBAN ICON,** 4, b c Cityscape—Fauran (IRE)
29 **WALKINTHESAND (IRE),** 4, b c Footstepsinthesand—Masseera (IRE)
30 **WAR GLORY (IRE),** 7, b g Canford Cliffs (IRE)—Attracted To You (IRE)
31 **WATAN,** 4, ch c Toronado (IRE)—Shotgun Gulch (USA)
32 **WEDDING DATE,** 4, b f Dandy Man (IRE)—Fiancee (IRE)

THREE-YEAR-OLDS

33 **AFRO BLUE (IRE),** b c Oasis Dream—Najraan
34 **AJAX TAVERN,** b g Canford Cliffs (IRE)—Gimme Some Lovin (IRE)
35 **AL DAWODIYA (IRE),** b f Gutaifan (IRE)—Lillebonne (FR)
36 **AL GAIYA (FR),** b f Olympic Glory (IRE)—Lathah (IRE)
37 **AL HAAMY (IRE),** b c Shamardal (USA)—Sharedah (IRE)
38 **AL MADHAR (FR),** b c Siyouni (FR)—Phiz (GER)
39 **AL MUHAAJIR (IRE),** ch g Tamayuz—Lemon Rock
40 **AL NAMIR (IRE),** b c Shamardal (USA)—Rayaheen
41 **ALJALELA (FR),** b f Golden Horn—Shahah
42 **ALWAYS FEARLESS (IRE),** ch g Camacho—Zenella
43 **ASTON SMOKEY JOE (IRE),** ch c Zebedee—Smokey Ryder
44 **BIG WING (IRE),** b c Free Eagle (IRE)—Orafinitis (IRE)
45 **BRUISA,** ch f Sepoy (AUS)—Coplow
46 **CAPALL (IRE),** b c Zoffany (IRE)—Dress Rehearsal (IRE)
47 Ch f Farhh—Chocolate Hills (FR)
48 **CITYZEN SERG (IRE),** b c Raven's Pass (USA)—Summer Dream (IRE)
49 **CLOAK OF SPIRITS (IRE),** b f Invincible Spirit (IRE)—Pivotique
50 **COUNT OF AMAZONIA (IRE),** b c Lope de Vega (IRE)—Queen Myrine (IRE)
51 **CRISIS,** b c Cable Bay (IRE)—Alzahran
52 **DARK LADY,** gr grf Dark Angel (IRE)—Ladyship
53 **DESERT PALMS,** b c Oasis Dream—Be My Gal
54 **DOLLA DOLLA BILL (IRE),** b c Epaulette (AUS)—My Uptown Girl
55 **ELEGANT ERIN (IRE),** b f Dandy Man (IRE)—Eriniya (IRE)
56 **EXHIBIT (IRE),** b f Showcasing—Timely
57 **EXTINCTION (USA),** b br g Street Sense (USA)—Black Tunic (USA)
58 **FLOWER OF THUNDER (IRE),** b f Night of Thunder (IRE)—Flower Fairy (USA)
59 **FLY FALCON (IRE),** b c Free Eagle (IRE)—Regalline (USA)
60 **FROMNOWON (IRE),** b f Showcasing—Jeanie Johnston (IRE)
61 **FROZEN WATERS (IRE),** ch c No Nay Never (USA)—Whitefall (USA)
62 **GOLD DESERT,** ch c Mastercraftsman (IRE)—Tendency (USA)
63 **GOOD JOB POWER (IRE),** b c Acclamation—Thousandfold (USA)
64 **GRANDE RUMORE,** ch f Night of Thunder (IRE)—Silent Serenade
65 **GRINLING (IRE),** b c Mastercraftsman (IRE)—Gravitation
66 **HADDAD (IRE),** b c Gutaifan (IRE)—Alyaafel
67 **INTREPID ITALIAN,** b c Havana Gold (IRE)—Pizzarra
68 **JAMAHEERY (IRE),** b f Kodiac—Ambiguous
69 **JEN'S FELLA (FR),** b g Zoffany (IRE)—Heliocentric (FR)
70 **JEN'S LAD (IRE),** b g Dandy Man (IRE)—Strawberry Queen
71 **JUNVIEVE (FR),** b f Orpen (USA)—Tengeline (FR)
72 **KATZOFF (IRE),** b c Mastercraftsman (IRE)—Loved (IRE)
73 **KEEP IT BRIEF,** b c Muhaarar—Brevity (USA)
74 **KUWAIT DIRECTION (IRE),** b c Kodiac—Open Verse (USA)
75 **LEXINGTON DASH (FR),** b c Siyouni (FR)—Mythical Border (USA)
76 **LEXINGTON FORCE (FR),** b c Dabirsim (FR)—Fox Force Five (IRE)
77 **LEXINGTON REBEL (FR),** b c Dabirsim (FR)—Silent Sunday (IRE)

MR RICHARD HANNON - continued

78 **LEXINGTON STORM (IRE),** br c Dream Ahead (USA)—Body Beautiful (IRE)
79 **LOST EDEN (IRE),** b c Sea The Stars (IRE)—Ghostflower (IRE)
80 **LOVE LOVE,** b f Kodiac—Perfect Blessings (IRE)
81 **LOVE POWERFUL (IRE),** b f Gutaifan (IRE)—Montefino (IRE)
82 **LYRIC GOLD,** b c Dubawi (IRE)—The Sound of Music (IRE)
83 **MAFIA POWER,** b c Gleneagles (IRE)—Rivara
84 **MAKEEN,** b c Dubawi (IRE)—Estidraaj (USA)
85 **MAMBO NIGHTS (IRE),** b c Havana Gold (IRE)—Inez
86 **MAN OF THE NIGHT (FR),** b c Night of Thunder (IRE)—Mandheera (USA)
87 **MANIGORDO (USA),** b br c Kitten's Joy (USA)—Cutting Edge (USA)
88 **MARK OF GOLD,** b c Golden Horn—Polly's Mark (IRE)
89 **MIRAZ (IRE),** b c Kodiac—Summer Blues (USA)
90 **MORE THAN A PRINCE,** b c Oasis Dream—La Petite Reine
91 **MUMS TIPPLE (IRE),** ch c Footstepsinthesand—Colomone Cross (IRE)
92 **MYSTERY POWER (IRE),** b c No Nay Never (USA)—Gems
93 **NO SHOW (IRE),** ch c Showcasing—Innocent Air
94 **NOONDAY GUN,** gr c Dubawi (IRE)—Sky Lantern (IRE)
95 **NORTHERN SUN (IRE),** b c Showcasing—Solstice
96 **NUGGET,** b c Siyouni (FR)—Gemstone (IRE)
97 **OCASIO CORTEZ (IRE),** gr ro f Gutaifan (IRE)—Novel Fun (IRE)
98 **OH PURPLE REIGN (IRE),** b c Sir Prancealot (IRE)—Warda
99 **ORCZY (IRE),** b c Sir Percy—Maria Kristina (FR)
100 **PARTRIDGE (IRE),** b f Zoffany (IRE)—Lasilia (IRE)
101 **PHOTOGRAPH (IRE),** b c Kodiac—Supreme Occasion (IRE)
102 **PRINCE CASPIAN,** b c Muhaarar—Riskit Fora Biskit (IRE)
103 **PUMMEL (IRE),** ch f Lethal Force (IRE)—Catopuma (USA)
104 **RAPIDASH,** b f Dark Angel (IRE)—Lottie Dod (IRE)
105 **ROCKY DREAMS,** b c Muhaarar—Mrs Greeley
106 **RUBY POWER (IRE),** b f Kodiac—Coquette Rouge (IRE)
107 **SEADANCE,** b c Harbour Watch (IRE)—Sand Dancer (IRE)
108 **SEPARATE,** b f Cable Bay (IRE)—Miss Moses (USA)
109 **SESAME BIRAH (IRE),** b f Gregorian (IRE)—Limousine
110 **SHAMMAH (IRE),** b f Frankel—Biscaya Bay
111 **SKY POWER (IRE),** b c Fastnet Rock (AUS)—Dame Blanche (IRE)
112 **SNOWBALL JACKSON,** br c No Nay Never (USA)—Emeralds Spirit (IRE)
113 **SPIRITS HIGH (FR),** b f Dabirsim (FR)—Mamusella (IRE)
114 **SRI SENE POWER (IRE),** b f Dark Angel (IRE)—Fanciful Dancer
115 **SUN POWER (FR),** b g Night of Thunder (IRE)—Sparkling Smile (IRE)
116 **SUNSET SEEKER (IRE),** b g Harbour Watch (IRE)—Lucina
117 **TAHITIAN PRINCE (FR),** b c Siyouni (FR)—Tehamana (FR)
118 **THANIELLE (FR),** b f Nathaniel (IRE)—Tingling (USA)
119 **THE CINCINNATI KID (FR),** b c Charm Spirit (IRE)—Tocopilla (FR)
120 **THE SEVENTH DAY (IRE),** b c Siyouni (FR)—Mad Existence (IRE)
121 **THEOTHERSIDE (IRE),** br f Dandy Man (IRE)—New Magic (IRE)
122 **THREAT (IRE),** ch c Footstepsinthesand—Flare of Firelight (USA)
123 **TODAY POWER (IRE),** b g Dark Angel (IRE)—Todegica
124 **TOP CLASS ANGEL (IRE),** b f Dark Angel (IRE)—Expensive Date
125 **TOTAL PERFECTION (IRE),** br c Fountain of Youth (IRE)—Day By Day
126 **VENTURA BOUNTY (FR),** b c Dabirsim (FR)—Amazing Bounty (FR)
127 **WELL PREPARED,** b c Due Diligence (USA)—Amazed
128 **WHISPER NOT,** b c Poet's Voice—Poyle Meg
129 **WILD THUNDER (IRE),** b c Night of Thunder (IRE)—Shama's Song (IRE)
130 **WILLA,** b f Dutch Art—Holberg Suite
131 **WIN WIN POWER (IRE),** b c Exceed And Excel (AUS)—Spesialta
132 **WINTER HALO (IRE),** b f Dark Angel (IRE)—Snowy Peak
133 **ZIGGLE POPS,** ch c Zoffany (IRE)—Loch Ma Naire (IRE)

MR RICHARD HANNON - continued

TWO-YEAR-OLDS

134 B f 29/03 Kingman—Alamarie (FR) (Acclamation) (210000)

135 B c 17/02 Kodiac—Alkhawarah (USA) (Intidab (USA)) (80000)

136 B f 17/04 Starspangledbanner (AUS)—Aloisi (Kalanisi (IRE)) (85000)

137 B f 17/03 No Nay Never (USA)—Along The Shore (IRE) (Dylan Thomas (IRE)) (180000)

138 B c 18/03 Fast Company (IRE)—Alternanthera (Nayef (USA)) (110000)

139 BABAJAN (IRE), b c 26/03 Acclamation—Alerted (USA) (First Defence (USA)) (76190)

140 B c 13/03 Archipenko (USA)—Barnezet (GR) (Invincible Spirit (IRE))

141 BE MY BEAU, b c 22/04 Brazen Beau (AUS)—Sylvestris (IRE) (Arch (USA))

142 B c 23/03 Footstepsinthesand—Beal Ban (IRE) (Daggers Drawn (USA)) (95238)

143 Ch c 15/04 Equiano (FR)—Bedouin Dancer (IRE) (Pivotal) (87619)

144 BEIJING BILLY (IRE), b c 30/03 Shanghai Bobby (USA)—Rag And Bone (CAN) (Street Cry (IRE))

145 BELLA NOTTE, ch f 18/02 Twilight Son—Fair Value (IRE) (Compton Place)

146 BILLY MILL, b c 12/03 Adaay (IRE)—Phantom Spirit (Invincible Spirit (IRE)) (42857)

147 Gr ro c 15/03 Dark Angel (IRE)—Bint Almukhtar (IRE) (Halling (USA))

148 Ch c 10/03 Zoffany (IRE)—Bright Sapphire (IRE) (Galileo (IRE)) (85800)

149 Ch f 19/03 Zoffany (IRE)—Broadway Duchess (IRE) (New Approach (IRE)) (38610)

150 B c 01/04 Canford Cliffs (IRE)—Cake (IRE) (Acclamation)

151 CANDACE, b f 13/04 Dutch Art—Oasis Mirage (Oasis Dream)

152 CARAMELISED, b c 03/03 Dansili—Caster Sugar (USA) (Cozzene (USA)) (75000)

153 B c 22/02 Territories (IRE)—Cephalonie (USA) (Kris S (USA)) (110000)

154 B c 13/04 Footstepsinthesand—Challow Hills (USA) (Woodman (USA)) (35238)

155 B f 03/05 Showcasing—Chase The Lady (USA) (Atticus (USA)) (82000)

156 CHINDIT (IRE), b c 05/03 Wootton Bassett—Always A Dream (Oasis Dream) (65000)

157 CIRRUS, ch f 04/03 Starspangledbanner (AUS)—Callendula (Halling (USA)) (38095)

158 B br c 03/02 Cable Bay (IRE)—Coin A Phrase (Dubawi (IRE)) (150000)

159 COLLINSBAY, b c 16/02 Cable Bay (IRE)—Kinematic (Kyllachy)

160 Ch c 26/01 Pearl Secret—Concentration (IRE) (Mind Games) (28571)

161 CONIGER (IRE), b f 31/05 Coulsty (IRE)—Macadamia (IRE) (Classic Cliche (IRE))

162 CRITICAL (FR), b c 23/02 No Nay Never (USA)—Maid To Believe (Galileo (IRE)) (270000)

163 DESERT ROSE, b f 12/03 Showcasing—Park Law (IRE) (Fasliyev (USA)) (200000)

164 B c 11/05 Night of Thunder (IRE)—Dream Day (Oasis Dream) (92000)

165 Ch c 09/05 Night of Thunder (IRE)—Dust Flicker (Suave Dancer (USA)) (85800)

166 Ch f 05/04 The Last Lion (IRE)—Dutch Courage (Dutch Art) (78935)

167 ELOQUENT ARTHUR, b c 20/02 Sir Prancealot (IRE)—Ambriel (IRE) (Dark Angel (IRE))

168 EMINENT HIPSTER (IRE), b c 28/02 Make Believe—Organza (Pour Moi (IRE)) (70000)

169 EMMA OF NORMANDY (IRE), b f 02/03 The Last Lion (IRE)—Saxon Princess (IRE) (Dalakhani (IRE)) (19047)

170 ESCAPE, ch c 27/04 Territories (IRE)—Fen Guest (Woodborough (USA)) (77000)

171 FANCY MAN (IRE), b c 20/03 Pride of Dubai (AUS)—Fancy (IRE) (Galileo (IRE)) (25740)

172 FASHION, b f 04/02 Lope de Vega (IRE)—All The Rage (Dubawi (IRE))

173 B c 05/04 Cityscape—Firebelly (Nicolotte) (24000)

174 B c 19/02 Prince of Lir (IRE)—Folegandros Island (FR) (Red Rocks (IRE)) (260000)

175 FOUNTAIN CROSS, b c 22/03 Muhaarar—Infamous Angel (Exceed And Excel (AUS))

176 B c 23/01 Gleneagles (IRE)—Gadwa (Oasis Dream) (75000)

177 Ch c 02/03 Buratino (IRE)—Gin Twist (Invincible Spirit (IRE)) (28571)

178 GLEAMING WAVE, b f 14/04 Siyouni (FR)—Merletta (Raven's Pass (USA))

179 B c 19/03 Fascinating Rock (IRE)—Golden Shadow (IRE) (Selkirk (USA)) (85800)

180 GUSTAV HOLST (IRE), b c 03/05 Sea The Stars (IRE)—Scarlet And Gold (IRE) (Peintre Celebre (USA)) (77220)

181 HAFEZ (IRE), br c 18/01 Dark Angel (IRE)—Stellar Path (FR) (Astronomer Royal (USA)) (400000)

182 B c 20/03 Muhaarar—Handbell (IRE) (Acclamation)

183 HAPPY ROMANCE (IRE), b f 12/03 Dandy Man (IRE)—Rugged Up (IRE) (Marju (IRE)) (23809)

184 B c 27/03 Footstepsinthesand—Inis Boffin (Danehill Dancer (IRE))

185 Br f 28/02 Shalaa (IRE)—Inez (Dai Jin) (260000)

186 B c 27/03 Footstepsinthesand—Inis Boffin (Danehill Dancer (IRE)) (240240)

187 KEEP RIGHT ON (IRE), b c 11/04 Acclamation—Khalice (Bahamian Bounty) (24761)

188 Ch c 01/05 Footstepsinthesand—Keeper's Ring (USA) (Street Cry (IRE)) (27000)

189 B c 10/04 Awtaad (IRE)—Kesara (Sadler's Wells (USA)) (70000)

190 KUZNETSOVA, b f 31/01 Shalaa (IRE)—Vesnina (Sea The Stars (IRE)) (100000)

191 B c 10/02 Showcasing—Lady Estella (IRE) (Equiano (FR)) (155000)

192 B c 16/03 Adaay (IRE)—Lamentation (Singspiel (IRE)) (48000)

MR RICHARD HANNON - continued

193 B f 26/02 Footstepsinthesand—Liberty Sky (IRE) (Rip Van Winkle (IRE)) (28571)
194 B c 17/02 Mehmas (IRE)—Looks Great (New Approach (IRE)) (47619)
195 B c 06/03 New Approach (IRE)—Meet Me Halfway (Exceed And Excel (AUS)) (60000)
196 MESOPOTAMIA, b c 28/03 Kodiac—Arabian Beauty (IRE) (Shamardal (USA)) (65000)
197 B c 28/02 Pride of Dubai (AUS)—Michael's Song (IRE) (Refuse To Bend (IRE)) (47000)
198 B c 10/02 Acclamation—Midnight Oasis (Oasis Dream) (90476)
199 B br c 07/03 Charm Spirit (IRE)—Miss Meltemi (IRE) (Miswaki Tern (USA)) (15238)
200 MISTER SPEEDY (FR), bl c 22/01 Lawman (FR)—Cherita (IRE) (Rip Van Winkle (IRE)) (42900)
201 MOJO STAR (IRE), b c 08/04 Sea The Stars (IRE)—Galley (Zamindar (USA)) (220000)
202 B f 12/02 Bated Breath—Moqla (Teofilo (IRE))
203 B c 03/04 Twilight Son—Mrs Mogg (Green Desert (USA)) (60000)
204 MUMMY BEAR (IRE), br f 06/02 Kodi Bear (IRE)—Shortmile Lady (IRE) (Arcano (IRE)) (38095)
205 Gr f 01/03 Frankel—Natagora (FR) (Divine Light (JPN))
206 B c 09/02 Nathaniel (IRE)—Notary (Lawman (FR)) (70000)
207 B f 24/02 Vadamos (FR)—Open Verse (USA) (Black Minnaloushe (USA)) (42900)
208 B f 20/02 Bated Breath—Out of The Dark (IRE) (Kyllachy) (10000)
209 Gr f 24/04 Dark Angel (IRE)—Pickle (Piccolo) (72000)
210 Ch f 24/02 Slade Power (IRE)—Pivotique (Pivotal)
211 B c 13/03 Myboycharlie (IRE)—Plebeya (IRE) (Dubawi (IRE)) (12870)
212 B c 08/04 Oasis Dream—Pure Line (Zamindar (USA)) (50000)
213 QUEEN OF ASIA (IRE), b f 24/04 Exceed And Excel (AUS)—Alumni (Selkirk (USA)) (98669)
214 Br gr c 11/03 Gutaifan (IRE)—Relay (Clodovil (IRE)) (12012)
215 B c 30/03 Mehmas (IRE)—Ripalong (IRE) (Revoque (IRE)) (78095)
216 RIVER ALWEN (IRE), gr c 02/04 Dark Angel (IRE)—Intense Pink (Pivotal) (124409)
217 Gr c 30/04 Dubawi (IRE)—Rose Diamond (IRE) (Daylami (IRE))
218 B c 14/03 Twilight Son—Roslea Lady (IRE) (Alhaarth (IRE)) (59047)
219 B f 17/02 Cable Bay (IRE)—Royal Whisper (Royal Applause) (38095)
220 SAFE PASSAGE, b f 23/02 Paco Boy (IRE)—Daring Aim (Daylami (IRE))
221 B f 25/02 Golden Horn—Salacia (IRE) (Echo of Light)
222 SAUNTON (IRE), b c 14/04 Footstepsinthesand—Camellia Japonica (IRE) (Zoffany (IRE)) (58000)
223 B f 01/03 Toronado (IRE)—Sefaat (Haatef (USA))
224 B c 01/03 Havana Gold (IRE)—Semayyel (IRE) (Green Desert (USA)) (38095)
225 B c 31/03 Mehmas (IRE)—Senadora (GER) (Tertullian (USA)) (25000)
226 SHADY COVE, b c 12/04 Cable Bay (IRE)—Clapperboard (Royal Applause) (20952)
227 SHANGHAI ROCK, b c 03/02 Dark Angel (IRE)—Red Lady (IRE) (Dutch Art) (125000)
228 Ch f 06/02 Toronado (IRE)—Shdedah (IRE) (Dragon Pulse (IRE)) (25740)
229 B f 16/01 Cable Bay (IRE)—Shine (Exceed And Excel (AUS)) (80952)
230 SIR RUMI (IRE), ch c 09/03 Gleneagles (IRE)—Reine des Plages (IRE) (Danehill Dancer (IRE)) (137280)
231 B c 14/02 Acclamation—Sliabh Luachra (IRE) (High Chaparral (IRE)) (95238)
232 B f 03/04 Shalaa (IRE)—Snowy Amour (IRE) (Azamour (IRE)) (43809)
233 B c 16/04 Twilight Son—Spangle (Galileo (IRE)) (32000)
234 B c 28/01 Iffraaj—Sparring Queen (USA) (War Front (USA)) (120000)
235 Ch f 21/02 Frankel—Sweepstake (IRE) (Acclamation) (429000)
236 B c 29/01 Kingman—Sweet Acclaim (IRE) (Acclamation)
237 B f 07/05 Kodiac—Teodelight (IRE) (Teofilo (IRE)) (100000)
238 B f 19/04 Dark Angel (IRE)—The Hermitage (IRE) (Kheleyf (USA)) (377520)
239 B f 07/02 Dansili—Top Model (IRE) (Dubawi (IRE))
240 TRIBUTE TO JADE, b f 14/03 Acclamation—Magic Florence (IRE) (Zebedee) (78095)
241 B c 26/01 Maxios—Trimurti (USA) (Harlan's Holiday (USA)) (25714)
242 B c 06/03 Awtaad (IRE)—Venetian Beauty (USA) (Lear Fan (USA)) (300000)
243 B f 02/02 Territories (IRE)—Vintage Molly (Mount Nelson) (68640)
244 B f 24/03 Dark Angel (IRE)—War Effort (USA) (War Front (USA)) (55000)
245 B c 08/03 Markaz (IRE)—Wishing Chair (USA) (Giant's Causeway (USA)) (24761)
246 B c 07/04 Acclamation—Xema (Danehill (USA)) (68571)
247 B c 18/04 Estidhkaar (IRE)—Yasmin Satine (IRE) (Key of Luck (USA)) (47619)
248 B f 10/05 Night of Thunder (IRE)—Zarabaya (IRE) (Doyoun) (47189)
249 B f 18/02 Acclamation—Zigarra (Halling (USA)) (75000)

Flat Jockey: Pat Dobbs, Hollie Doyle, Sean Levey, Tom Marquand, Rossa Ryan. **Apprentice Jockey:** Luke Catton, Mark Crehan, Thore Hammer Hansen.

252 MR GEOFFREY HARKER, Thirsk
Postal: **Stockhill Green, York Rd, Thirkelby, Thirsk, North Yorkshire, YO7 3AS**
Contacts: **PHONE 01845 501117 MOBILE 07803 116412, 07930 125544**
EMAIL **gandjhome@aol.com** WEBSITE **www.geoffharkerracing.com**

1 **ELDELBAR (SPA)**, 6, ch g Footstepsinthesand—Malinche **The Twelve Minimum Racing Club**
2 **EXTRASOLAR**, 10, b g Exceed And Excel (AUS)—Amicable Terms **The Twelve Minimum Partnership**
3 **RANGEFIELD EXPRESS (IRE)**, 4, b g Born To Sea (IRE)—Bogini (IRE) **Cloud 9 Racing & Phil Harker**
4 **SCOTTISH SUMMIT (IRE)**, 7, b g Shamardal (USA)—Scottish Stage (IRE) **T Banerjee,N Mather,P Downes & G Harker**
5 **WENTWORTH FALLS**, 8, gr g Dansili—Strawberry Morn (CAN) **The Fall Guys Club**
6 **WHITEHALL**, 5, b g Dansili—Majestic Roi (USA) **P. I. Harker**

Other Owners: Dr A. T. Banerjee, Cloud 9 Racing, Mr P. Downes, Mr G. A. Harker, P. I. Harker, Mr D. M. Mather.

Assistant Trainer: Jenny Harker.

NH Jockey: W. T. Kennedy.

253 MR RICHARD HARPER, Kings Sutton
Postal: **Home Farm, Kings Sutton, Banbury, Oxfordshire, OX17 3RS**
Contacts: **PHONE 01295 810997 MOBILE 07970 223481**
EMAIL **richard@harpersfarm.co.uk**

1 **JUST SKITTLES**, 12, b g Storming Home—Miss Roberto (IRE) **R. C. Harper**
2 **THOMAS BLOSSOM (IRE)**, 10, b g Dylan Thomas (IRE)—Woman Secret (IRE) **R. C. Harper**

Assistant Trainer: C. Harper.

254 MRS JESSICA HARRINGTON, Kildare
Postal: **Commonstown Stud, Moone, Co. Kildare, Ireland**
Contacts: **PHONE +353 59 862 4153 MOBILE +353 87 256 6129**
EMAIL **jessica@jessicaharringtonracing.com** WEBSITE **www.jessicaharringtonracing.com**

1 **ABOVE AND BEYOND (FR)**, 5, gr g Al Namix (FR)—Comohio (FR) **Robcour**
2 **ANNIE KATE**, 5, b m Califet—Spartan Girl **The Flyers Syndicate**
3 **ASHDALE BOB (IRE)**, 5, b g Shantou (USA)—Ceol Rua (IRE) **Diarmuid Horgan**
4 **BARRINGTON COURT**, 6, ch m Mastercraftsman—Arabian Hideway **Mr J P McManus**
5 **BELLA REGINA**, 4, b f Bungleinthejungle—Alarme Belle **J Hennessy Claire Jennings Derek Hogan**
6 **BELLAKRIS (USA)**, 4, br f Scat Daddy (USA)—Akris Queen (USA) **Sally Rowley-Williams**
7 **CALLING TIME (IRE)**, 4, b f Camelot—
                           Timeless Call (IRE) **Diana Cooper, P K Cooper and Ronchalon Ireland Partnership**
8 **CAMPHOR (IRE)**, 4, b f Camelot—Paraphernalia **Dermot Brennan and OTI Racing**
9 **CHAMPAGNE IZZY**, 4, b c Doyen—Johnsons Coat **Champagne Izzy Partnership**
10 **CHARCOR (IRE)**, 6, b g Choisir (AUS)—Sanadaat **Mr John O'Hagan**
11 **CONRON (IRE)**, 6, b g Mastercraftsman (IRE)—Numbers Game **Mr John O'Hagan**
12 **CROSSHILL (IRE)**, 5, b g Sholokhov—Rathvawn Belle **Ronnie Bartlett and David Hodgkiss**
13 **DANDJIRA**, 5, b m Sinndar—Darjana **Lakeside Syndicate**
14 **DISCORDANTLY (IRE)**, 6, b g Salutino (GER)—Collinstown Queen (IRE) **Odd Fellows**
15 **EARL OF DESMOND**, 5, ch g Beneficial—Gemini Lucy (IRE) **Basil Holian**
16 **EMILY MOON (IRE)**, 6, b m Beneficial—Wood Lily (IRE) **Mr Philip Myerscough**
17 **ENVIOUS EDITOR (IRE)**, 6, b br g Aizavoski (IRE)—Moll The Rol (IRE) **Robcour**
18 **ESTIJMAAM (IRE)**, 5, b m Raven's Pass—Merayaat **Mount Temple Three Racing Syndicate**
19 **EVER PRESENT**, 4, br g Elusive Pimpernel—Persian Memories **Anamoine Ltd**
20 **EXIT POLL (IRE)**, 6, b g Elusive Pimpernel (USA)—Carolobrian (IRE) **Bernadine Mulryan**
21 **EXULTATION (IRE)**, 6, b g Secret Singer—Nanny **Mrs A Frost**
22 **FANCY FEAT (IRE)**, 4, b f Rajj (IRE)—Royal Jelly **Mr Jim Nicholson**
23 **FLASH GORDON (IRE)**, 4, b c Kodiac—Oasis Sunset (IRE) **Ms Fiona Carmichael**

MRS JESSICA HARRINGTON - continued

24 **GAMBLING MISTRESS**, 6, br m Big Bad Bob—Gambling Spirit **River Racing Partnership**
25 **GEORGETTE FUN (IRE)**, 4, b f Cokoriko—More Fun **Basil Holian**
26 **GIN ON LIME**, 4, b f Dr Dino—Quiche Lorraine **Robcour**
27 **GOD KNOWS WHY (IRE)**, 5, b g Oscar (IRE)—Ballys Baby (IRE) **Joe Doyle**
28 **GOLD DES BOIS**, 6, ch h Full Of Gold—Equatoriale **Robcour**
29 **GOT TRUMPED**, 5, ch g Thewayyouare (USA)—Madam President **David Reid Scott**
30 **HELIERS BAY (IRE)**, 6, ch m Flemensfirth (USA)—Now Its My Turn (IRE) **The Flyers Syndicate**
31 **HOTEL DU NORD (FR)**, 7, b g Voix du Nord (FR)—Iu Mi Nao (IRE) **Matt Booth and Jared Sullivan**
32 **I'M SO BUSY (IRE)**, 5, gr g Carlotamix—Ballcrina Girl **Kate Harrington**
33 **INSTANT RETURN**, 4, b g Elzaam—Instant Memories **Brian Millar**
34 **JANUARY JETS**, 6, b h Presenting—Poetic's Girl **Robcour**
35 **JELONA (IRE)**, 5, b m Milan—Jeree (IRE) **Mr Gerard McGrath**
36 **JETT (IRE)**, 9, b g Flemensfirth (USA)—La Noire (IRE) **Mr Gerard McGrath**
37 **JETZ (IRE)**, 8, b g Flemensfirth (USA)—Miss Squiff (IRE) **Mr Gerard McGrath**
38 **JUNGLE JUNCTION (IRE)**, 5, br g Elusive Pimpernel (USA)—Consignia (IRE) **Mrs A Frost and Mrs G Galvin**
39 **LEO DE FURY (IRE)**, 4, ch c Australia—Attire **Mr Zhang Yuesheng**
40 **LIFETIME AMBITION**, 5, b g Kapgarde—Jeanquiri **Jim Mulcahy**
41 **LYNWOOD GOLD (IRE)**, 5, gr ro g Mastercraftsman (IRE)—Witch of Fife (USA) **Robcour**
42 **MAGIC OF LIGHT (IRE)**, 9, b m Flemensfirth (USA)—Quest of Passion (FR) **Ann & Alan Potts Ltd**
43 **MIGHTY MEGGSIE (IRE)**, 4, b f Arakan—Angel Loez **Mr P Quelly**
44 **MOONSHINE BAY (IRE)**, 7, b g Milan—Chantoue Royale (FR) **Ann & Alan Potts Ltd**
45 **MOROSINI (FR)**, 5, b g Martaline—Iris du Berlais (FR) **Mr J P McManus**
46 **MR HENDRICKS**, 6, b g Milan—Coming Home **David Reid Scott**
47 **NEVERUSHACON (IRE)**, 9, b g Echo of Light—Lily Beth (IRE) **David Reid Scott**
48 **NJORD (IRE)**, 4, b g Roderic O'Connor—Rosalind Franklin **A Blessing In Disguise Partnership**
49 **NOT MANY LEFT (IRE)**, 7, b g Oscar (IRE)—Lasado (IRE) **Robcour**
50 5, B m Yeats—On The Prairie **Dash Racing/Kate Harrington/Steve Kemble**
51 **ONLY HUMAN (IRE)**, 7, b g Invincible Spirit—Liscune **Michael Cooke**
52 **PAPAL PEARL (IRE)**, 5, b m Doyen (IRE)—Johnsons Coat (IRE) **Joe Doyle**
53 **PEPPERONI PETE**, 4, b g Zoffany—Zaafran **A Blessing In Disguise Partnership**
54 **PERES ET FILS (IRE)**, 6, br g Stowaway—Allthewhile (IRE) **Lynch Bages, Samac Ltd and Robcour**
55 **POLISHED STEEL (IRE)**, 6, b g Jeremy (USA)—Chaperoned (IRE) **Mr Joe O'Flaherty**
56 **PORT STANLEY**, 6, b g Papal Bull—Prairie Moonlight **Jim Mulcahy**
57 **PRESS CONFERENCE (IRE)**, 7, b g Getaway (GER)—Beautiful Tune (FR) **Robcour**
58 **RAPID RESPONSE (FR)**, 6, br m Network (GER)—La Grande Villez (FR) **Ann & Alan Potts Ltd**
59 **ROBIN DES SIVOLA (IRE)**, 6, b m Robin des Champs (FR)—Falcons Gift (IRE) **Jim Mulcahy**
60 **ROCK THE WORLD (IRE)**, 12, b g Orpen (USA)—Sue N Win (IRE) **Mr J P McManus**
61 **SERENISA**, 4, gr f Kayf Tara—Sisella **Dash Racing**
62 **SILVER SHEEN (IRE)**, 6, b g Sulamani—Silver Gypsy **John Turner**
63 **SIZING POTTSIE (FR)**, 6, b g Kapgarde (FR)—Line Salsa (FR) **Ann & Alan Potts Ltd**
65 **SONNENKONIG (IRE)**, 5, ch g Dream Well—Sigune Pierji **Kate Harrington**
66 **STILL STANDING (IRE)**, 5, ch h Mastercraftsman (IRE)—

Il Palazzo (USA) **Danny Durkan/Liam Durkan/ Neil Durkan**
67 **SUPASUNDAE**, 10, b g Galileo (IRE)—Distinctive Look (IRE) **Ann & Alan Potts Ltd**
68 **TAURAN SHAMAN (IRE)**, 4, b c Shamardal—Danelissima **Mr Zhang Yuesheng**
69 **THE GABBY CABBY (IRE)**, 5, b g Stowaway—Coca's Lady (IRE) **Neil Durkan, Liam Durkan and Danny Durkan**
70 **THEGOAHEADMAN (IRE)**, 6, br g Jeremy (USA)—Little Luv (IRE) **Rainbow Gems Syndicate**
71 **WHAT NEXT (IRE)**, 5, b m Scorpion—Espresso Lady **Multinational Syndicate**
72 **WHERETHEWINDSBLOW**, 5, b g Shirocco—Forever Present **Mr Philip Myerscough**
73 **WHISPERINTHEBREEZE**, 7, gr ro g Kayf Tara—Silver Spinner **Ann & Alan Potts Ltd**
74 **WINGIN A PRAYER (IRE)**, 5, b g Winged Love—Toubliss **Rainbow Gems Syndicate**
75 **WINTER GREY**, 5, gr g Al Namix—Royale Malinelle **Commonstown Racing Stables**

THREE-YEAR-OLDS

76 **AESOP (IRE)**, b c Make Believe—Sadima **Ms AH Marshall**
77 **ALBIGNA (IRE)**, ch f Zoffany (IRE)—Freedonia **Niarchos Family**
78 **ALLEZ ALLEZ ALLEZ (IRE)**, b f Invincible Spirit (IRE)—Growling (IRE) **Carmel Acheson**
79 **ALPINE STAR (IRE)**, ch f Sea The Moon (GER)—Alpha Lupi (IRE) **Niarchos Family**
80 **AUNT BEE (IRE)**, b f Australia—English Ballet **David Reid Scott and Richmond Bloodstock**

MRS JESSICA HARRINGTON - continued

81 BELLA BRAZIL, b f Clodavil—Daanaat **Peter Savill**
82 BETWEEN HILLS (IRE), b c Hot Streak—Breedj **P K Cooper**
83 BIG WHITE CHIEF (USA), b c War Front—Kissed **Mr Zhang Yuesheng**
84 BUT YOU SAID (IRE), b f No Nay Never (USA)—San Macchia **Carmel Acheson**
85 CAYENNE PEPPER, ch f Australia—Muwakaba **Jon S. Kelly**
86 CELESTIAL OBJECT, b f Galileo—Sea Siren **Newtown Anner Stud Farm Ltd**
87 CHASING THE DAWN, b f Acclamation—Urban Daydream (IRE) **Peter Savill**
88 CHILDERS, b c Mastercraftsman—Excellent Mariner **P K Cooper**
89 COOL VIXEN (IRE), b f Dandy Man—Cool Tarifa **Mr Vimal Khosla**
90 ELITE LEGION (IRE), b f War Command—Sonnig Rose **Mr Zhang Yuesheng**
91 FLOR DE LA LUNA, b f Sea The Moon—Fresa **Kirsten Rausing**
92 FOR THE TREES, b f Ivawood—

Siesta Time **Suzi Prichard-Jones, Commonstown Racing Stables and Russell Jones**
93 FREE SOLO (IRE), ch c Showcasing—Amuser (IRE) **Niarchos Family**
94 GIBSON DESERT, b c Australia—Namaadhej (USA) **Alpha Racing**
95 GOLD MAZE (IRE), b c Golden Horn—Astonishing **The Long Wait Partnership**
96 B f Kitten's Joy—Granny Franny **Newtown Anner Stud Farm Ltd**
97 GRIZZLY (IRE), b c Kodiac—Savannah Poppy (IRE) **Alpha Racing**
98 HINT OF STARS (IRE), ch c Sea The Stars (IRE)—Rosenreihe (IRE) **Jon S. Kelly**
99 IN THE PRESENT (USA), b f Karakontie (JPN)—Dreams of Fire (USA) **Flaxman Stables Ireland Ltd**
100 IRISH MASTER (IRE), gr ro c Mastercraftsman (IRE)—Selva Real **Jon S. Kelly**
101 JUNGLE COVE, gr c Mastercraftsman—Purple Glow **Millhouse LLC**
102 JUSTINA, b f Holy Roman Emperor—Mary McPhee **Peter Vela and Jeremy Gompertz and Richmond Bloodstock**
103 KATIE BO KAT, b f Muhaarar—Infamous Angel **Alpha Racing**
104 B f Fastnet Rock—Lady Bones **Newtown Anner Stud Farm Ltd**
105 LADY TASMANIA, b f Australia—Nimboo (USA) **Mr Vimal Khosla**
106 Ch c Lope De Vega—Louve Nationale **Ballylinch Stud**
107 Ch g Tamayuz—Martagon Lily **Mr Joe O'Flaherty**
108 MAUD GONNE SPIRIT (IRE), ch f Intello—Bari **Ms Olivia Hoare**
109 MENTE HERMOSA, b f Gleneagles—Que Puntual **Frank Fahy**
110 MILLISLE, ch f Starspangledbanner—Green Castle **Stonethorn Stud Farm Ltd**
111 MUTINY (IRE), ch f Sepoy (AUS)—Lashkaal **Its All About The Girls**
112 MYKONOS (IRE), b c Galileo—Acoma **Mr Zhang Yuesheng**
113 OCEAN MONARCH (IRE), b c Bungle Inthejungle—Spinning Ruby **Alpha Racing**
114 ONE VOICE, b f Poet's Voice—Zaaqya **J Hennessy, Robcour and Commonstown Racing Stables**
115 PAPER BEAR, b c Kodiac—Roger Sez **Millhouse LLC**
116 PATTLE REEF (IRE), b f Fastnet Rock—Chatifa **Mr Zhang Yuesheng**
117 PIXEL POWER, b f Dream Ahead—Polly Perkins **Mr Vimal Khosla**
118 PROTAGONIST (IRE), b c Wootton Bassett—Sagariya **M Buckley**
119 PSYCHE, b c Lope De Vega—Ode to Psyche **The Long Wait Partnership**
120 PUNITA AURORA, ch f Sepoy (AUS)—Wojha (IRE) **Alpha Racing**
121 PYRAMID ROCK (IRE), b f Fastnet Rock—Marie Celeste **Mr Zhang Yuesheng**
122 ROCKET SCIENCE (IRE), b f Fastnet Rock—Hairy Rocket **Ms AH Marshall**
123 ROYAL FREE HOTEL, gr f Mastercraftsman—Marigold Hotel **Newtown Anner Stud Farm Ltd**
124 SERENE SPIRIT (IRE), gr f Dark Angel—One Spirit **Ms AH Marshall**
125 SHONA MEA, b f Dragon Pulse—Weekend Getaway **Mr Pat Harty**
126 SILENCE PLEASE (IRE), b f Gleneagles—Crazy Volume **Gary Barber and Team Valor International LLC**
127 SOPHELANKA, b f Kyllachy—Attachee De Presse **Roddy Ryan**
128 ST CLERANS (IRE), b f Golden Horn—Discreet Brief **Frank Fahy**
129 THE TRUANT (IRE), b g Mastercraftsman—Invincible Cara **Anamoine Ltd**
130 TOORA LOORA, ch f Nathaniel (IRE)—Victoria Regina (IRE) **Jon S. Kelly**
131 UNKNOWN PLEASURES (IRE), b f Zoffany (IRE)—Three Mysteries (IRE) **Niarchos Family**
132 VALERIA MESSALINA (IRE), b f Holy Roman Emperor—Arty Crafty **Airlie Stud**
133 WAR CABINET (IRE), b c Galileo—Simply Perfect **Mr Zhang Yuesheng**
134 WATERVILLE LADY (IRE), b f Starspangledbanner—Sheer Delight **Kate Harrington**
135 YA BEAUTY, b f Muhaarar—Long Face (USA) **Alpha Racing**
136 YA YA BABY (IRE), b f Hallowed Crown (AUS)—Standout (FR) **Its All About The Girls**
137 YULONG MAGICREEF (IRE), b g Fastnet Rock—Lindikhaya **Mr Zhang Yuesheng**
138 YULONG MONEYREEF (IRE), b c Fastnet Rock—On A Pedestal **Mr Zhang Yuesheng**

MRS JESSICA HARRINGTON - continued

139 **YULONG PEARLISLAND (IRE),** b c Fastnet Rock—Cochabamba **Mr Zhang Yuesheng**
140 **YULONG TRANSCEND (IRE),** ch c Exceed and Excel—Causeway Lass **Mr Zhang Yuesheng**
141 **YULONG VOICE,** br g Poet's Voice—Daraiyna **Mr Zhang Yuesheng**

TWO-YEAR-OLDS

142 **ALICE KITTY,** ch f 13/02 Bobby's Kitten—Classic Legend (Galileo) **P K Cooper**
143 B f 22/03 Invincible Spirit—Ashley Hall (Maria's Moon) **Epona Bloodstock**
144 B f 08/03 Footstepsinthesand—Bayan Kasirga (Aussie Rules) **Mr Zhang Yuesheng**
145 B f 30/01 Australia—Bewitched (Dansili) **Robert Scarborough and Carradale**
146 B f 08/04 The Last Lion—Biaraafa (Araafa) **Mr Zhang Yuesheng**
147 B f 07/04 Showcasing—Boo Boo Bear (Almutawakel) **PK Cooper and Richie Galway**
148 B f 24/03 Fastnet Rock—Butterfly Blue (Saddler's Wells) **D Nagle and Roncon**
149 B f 04/04 Australia—Crafty (Manhatten Rain) **Alpha Racing**
150 **CYCLADIC (IRE),** b f 30/01 Fastnet Rock—Peloponnese (Montjeu) **Niarchos Family**
151 **DACESA (IRE),** ch f 11/04 Tamayuz—Duchesse (Duke Of Marmalade) **Suzi Prichard-Jones, Commonstown Racing Stables and Russell Jones**
152 B f 27/02 New Bay—Elltaaf (Invincible Spirit) **Its All About The Girls**
153 **EQUILOVE,** b f 27/02 Equiano—Arosha (Cape Cross) **G Byrne**
154 B f 01/05 Mount Nelson—Espresso Lady (Shantou) **Commonstown Racing Stables**
155 B f 08/03 Showcasing—Eyeshine (Dubawi) **Flaxman Stables Ireland Ltd and Mr W Farish**
156 B f 18/04 New Bay—Fashion Statement (Rainbow Quest) **Peter Savill**
157 Ch f 03/04 Havana Gold—Frequently (Dansili)
158 **GIULIANA (GER),** b f 27/01 Muhaarar—Golden Whip (Seattle Dancer) **Bespoke Bloodstock/Commonstown Racing Stables/Richie Galway**
159 B c 15/03 Showcasing—Greenisland (Fasliyev) **Stonethorn Stud Farm Ltd**
160 **ISABELLA AUGUSTA,** b f 05/02 Tamayuz—Heart's Desire (Royal Applause) **Its All About The Girls**
161 B c 22/02 Frankel—Kenzadargent (Kendargent) **Westward Bloodstock Ltd**
162 **KOREA (IRE),** b f 19/04 Galileo—Miss Childrey (Dr Fong) **Westerberg Ltd**
163 B c 19/02 Awtaad—La Negra (Dark Angel) **Millhouse LLC**
164 **LIGHT OF MY EYES,** b f 24/05 Frankel—Divine Proportions (Kingmambo) **Flaxman Stables Ireland Ltd**
165 **LOS ANDES,** b c 06/04 Karakontie—Candy Kitty (Lemon Drop Kid (USA)) **Flaxman Stables Ireland Ltd**
166 B f 24/02 Awtaad—Magi Noire (Marju) **Commonstown Racing Stables**
167 **MALAYSIAN (IRE),** ch f 24/02 Pride Of Dubai—Booker (Mastercraftsman) **P K Cooper**
168 B f 13/02 Acclamation—Mary McPhee (Mafki) **Michael Hernon and Cormac Flynn**
169 B f 30/01 Australia—Midnight Mystic (Fastnet Rock) **Shane Foley/Richie Galway/Ben McElory**
170 Ch f 01/03 Siyouni—Montalcino (Big Bad Bob) **Ben Sangster**
171 **NO SPEAK ALEXANDER (IRE),** b f 14/04 Shaala—Rapacity Alexander (Dandy Man) **Noel O'Callaghan/Paul O'Callaghan/ Charles O'Callaghan**
172 B f 20/03 Le Harve—Oh Goodness Me (Galileo) **Mr Robert Scarborough**
173 Ch f 14/02 Seathestars—Padmini (Tiger Hill)
174 B f 24/02 Ifraaj—Photophore (Clodovil) **Alpha Racing**
175 Ch f 08/03 Buratino—Pivka (Pivotal) **Bespoke Bloodstock/Commonstown Racing Stables/Richie Galway**
176 B c 26/03 Kodiac—Plum Sugar (Footstepsinthesand) **Yulong Investments Australia PTY Ltd**
177 Ch f 01/02 Mehmas—Private Alexander (Footstepsinthesand) **Peter Savill**
178 **PROVOCATEUSE (IRE),** b f 11/04 Pride Of Dubai—Malicieuse (Galileo) **Niarchos Family**
179 B c 27/02 Lope De Vega—Queen Of Carthage (Cape Cross) **Yulong Investments Australia PTY Ltd**
180 B c 12/02 Australia—Queenscliff (Danehill Dancer) **Yulong Investments Australia PTY Ltd**
181 B f 18/02 Kodiac—Ramone (Marju) **Alpha Racing**
182 B f 11/03 Camelot—Red Avis (Exceed and Excel) **Alpha Racing**
183 **RED COGNAC (IRE),** b f 23/03 Kodiac—Coquette Rouge (Croco Rouge) **The Long Wait Partnership**
184 **ROSES BLUE (IRE),** b f 28/02 Kodiac—Sweet Irish (Shamardal) **Moyglare Stud Farm Ltd**
185 Ch f 08/02 Sepoy (AUS)—Sablerose (Dubawi) **Chryss O'Reilly**
186 B c 24/03 Zoffany—Sarawati (Haafhd) **Mr Zhang Yuesheng**
187 B c 10/02 Lope De Vega—Seas Of Wells (Dansili) **Alpha Racing**
188 Ch f 16/03 Starspangledbanner—So Dandy (Oratorio) **Alpha Racing**
189 B f 06/04 Muhaarar—Soul Of Houdini (Dansili) **Alpha Racing**
190 **STREET KID,** ch c 15/05 Street Boss—Brushed Gold (Touch Gold) **Jon S. Kelly**
191 B c 03/04 Holyromanemperor—Two Days In Paris (Dansili) **Alpha Racing**
192 **UNBROKEN,** b f 14/01 Ifraaj—Abend (Sea The Stars) **Jon S. Kelly**

MRS JESSICA HARRINGTON - continued

193 VALLE DE LA LUNA, b f 13/03 Galileo—Fiesolana (Aussie Rules) **Flaxman Stables Ireland Ltd**
194 B c 12/03 Zoffany—Wild Child (Galileo) **Sally Rowley-Williams**
195 B f 17/03 Pride Of Dubai—Zaafran (Singspiel) **A Blessing In Disguise Partnership**

Other Owners: Anamoine Ltd, Commonstown Racing Stables, Course Investment Corporation, Robcour, Westerwood Global Ltd, Westward Bloodstock Ltd, Yulong Investments Australia PTY Ltd, Barton Stud Jane Marsh Naseby Bloodstock, Jim Cockburn, Frank Dunne, Niarchos Family, A Frost, Bespoke Bloodstock Ltd/Richie Galway/RJB Bloodstock Ltd, Barton Stud Jane Marsh Naseby Bloodstock, Westward Bloodstock Ltd, Commonstown Racing Stables Mr Russell Jones Mrs PK Cooper, Kate Harrington and Robert Power, Roderic Ryan, Commonstown Racing Stables/Mr Russell Jones/Mrs PK Cooper, Commonstown Racing Stables/Shane Foley/Richie Galway, Mount Temple Three Racing Syndicate.

Assistant Trainer: Miss Kate Harrington, Eamonn Leigh.

MISS GRACE HARRIS, Shirenewton
Postal: **White House, Shirenewton, Chepstow, Gwent, NP16 6AQ**
Contacts: **MOBILE 07912 359425**
EMAIL gracehariss90@gmail.com WEBSITE www.graceharrisracing.com

1 **AIR OF YORK (IRE),** 8, b g Vale of York (IRE)—State Secret **Mrs L. A. Cullimore**
2 **ASKING A LOT (IRE),** 7, ch m Ask—Millbrook Marble (IRE) **Mrs S. M. Maine**
3 **BOUTAN,** 7, gr m Tobougg (IRE)—High Tan **Mrs S. M. Maine**
4 **BUNGEE JUMP (IRE),** 5, b m Canford Cliffs (IRE)—Starchy **Mr Ronald Davies & Mrs Candida Davies**
5 **COX BAZAR (FR),** 6, b g Nombre Premier—Dame de Montlebeau (FR) **Grace Harris Racing**
6 **FAINT HOPE,** 8, ch g Midnight Legend—Rhinestone Ruby **Mrs Elaine Tate & Partner**
7 **FIELD EXHIBITION (IRE),** 10, b m Great Exhibition (IRE)—Leefield Rose (IRE) **Mr C. Johnston**
8 **GRAMS AND OUNCES,** 13, b g Royal Applause—Ashdown Princess (IRE) **Grace Harris Racing**
9 **HALF NELSON,** 5, ch g Mount Nelson—Maria Antonia (IRE) **Jonathan Thomas & Partner**
10 **JACKE IS BACK (IRE),** 5, b g Planteur (IRE)—Black Jack Lady (IRE) **J. Thomas, D. Lawton & Associates**
11 **KARAKORAM,** 5, b g Excelebration (IRE)—Portrait **Grace Harris Racing**
12 **LITTLE ANXIOUS,** 4, ch f Coach House (IRE)—Allmost Inti **R Matthews, D Matthews & Associates**
13 **NEARLY FAMOUS,** 7, b m Rip Van Winkle (IRE)—Ermena **Brendon Sabin & Partner**
14 **PROFILE PICTURE (IRE),** 6, b g Sans Frontieres (IRE)—Sehoya (IRE) **R Matthews, D Matthews & Associates**
15 **ROXZANE,** 4, b f Aeroplane—Winspiel **Mrs V. James**
16 **SEARCHING (IRE),** 8, ro g Mastercraftsman (IRE)—Miracolia (IRE) **Mr C. Johnston**
17 **SIMON THE GREAT,** 7, b g Great Palm (USA)—Miss Royello **V C James, C R Cox, B Hussain**
18 **SUNVISOR (IRE),** 4, ch g Helmet (AUS)—Island Sunset (IRE) **Grace Harris Racing**
19 **TALLY'S SON,** 6, b g Assertive—Talamahana **Paul & Ann de Weck**
20 **THE GARRISON (IRE),** 6, b g Arakan (USA)—Kerry Lily (IRE) **Mrs V. James**

THREE-YEAR-OLDS

21 **DEREK LE GRAND,** b g Mukhadram—Duo de Choc (IRE) **Mrs V. James**
22 **PORT NOIR,** bl f Harbour Watch (IRE)—Cocabana **Mrs V. James**
23 **TWENTYONERED,** br g Due Diligence (USA)—Eve **Mrs S. M. Tucker**

Other Owners: Mr C. R. Cox, Mrs C. M. Davies, Mr R. I. D. Davies, Mrs A. De Weck, Grace Harris Racing, Miss G. Harris, Ms M. Harris, Mr B. Hussain, Mrs V. James, Mrs D. L. S. Lawton, Mr D. Matthews, Mr R. Matthews, Riverwood Racing, Mr B. Sabin, Mrs E. Tate, Mr J. P. Thomas, P. L. de Weck.

Assistant Trainer: Michelle Harris.

NH Jockey: Liam Heard.

256 MR MILTON HARRIS, Warminster
Postal: **The Beeches, Deverill Road, Sutton Veny, Warminster, Wiltshire, BA12 7BY**
Contacts: **MOBILE 07879 634308**

1 **AINTREE MY DREAM (FR)**, 10, b br g Saint des Saints (FR)—Pretty Melodie (FR) **Mrs S. E. Brown**
2 **ALCOCK AND BROWN (IRE)**, 8, b g Oasis Dream—Heart Stopping (USA) **Emdells Limited**
3 **AMERICAN LIFE (FR)**, 13, b br g American Post—Poplife (FR) **American Life Partnership**
4 **AWAY FOR SLATES (IRE)**, 10, b g Arcadio (GER)—Rumi **Mrs Anthea Williams & Partner**
5 **CANNIE LAD**, 5, b g Haafhd—So Cannie **Only Horses and Fools**
6 **DISCREET HERO (IRE)**, 7, ch g Siyouni (FR)—Alfaguara (USA) **Mr M. Harris**
7 **FLYING FOCUS (IRE)**, 5, b g The Carbon Unit (USA)—Cat Belling (IRE) **L Turland and A Smith**
8 **IF KARL'S BERG DID**, 5, b g Fame And Glory—Mayberry **Air-water Treatments Ltd**
9 **JACAMAR (GER)**, 5, b g Maxios—Juvena (GER) **Pegasus Bloodstock Limited**
10 **JACKSON HILL (IRE)**, 6, b g Jeremy (USA)—Definite Leader (IRE) **The Jackson 8**
11 **JANUS (IRE)**, 5, br g Rock of Gibraltar (IRE)—Jardina (GER) **Pegasus Bloodstock Limited**
12 **KING'S PROCTOR (IRE)**, 5, b g Cape Cross (IRE)—Alimony (IRE) **Air-water Treatments Ltd**
13 **LOS CERRITOS (SWI)**, 8, ch g Dr Fong (USA)—La Coruna (SWI) **Emdells Limited**
14 **MAGIC RIVER (IRE)**, 9, ch g Indian River (FR)—All Magic (IRE) **Emdells Limited**
15 4, B g Masterofthehorse (IRE)—Martha's Way
16 **NOT GOING OUT (IRE)**, 6, ch g Doyen (IRE)—Alannico **Ruth Nelmes & Milton Harris**
17 **PRESENTING YEATS (IRE)**, 4, b g Yeats (IRE)—Va'vite (IRE) **Mrs D. Dewbery**
18 **QUARRY WIZARD (IRE)**, 10, b g Trans Island—Hazel Green (IRE) **Mrs D. J. Brown & Mrs D. Dewbery**
19 **RWANDA**, 4, b c New Approach (IRE)—Bantu
20 4, B f Heeraat (IRE)—So Cannie
21 **SONGO (IRE)**, 4, b g Most Improved (IRE)—Sacre Fleur (IRE)
22 **STIMULATING SONG**, 5, ch g Stimulation (IRE)—Choral Singer **Pegasus Bloodstock & Mr A. Harrison**
23 **SUFI**, 6, ch g Pivotal—Basanti (USA) **Mr J. F. Pearl**
24 **TECHNOLOGICAL**, 5, gr g Universal (IRE)—Qeethara (USA) **Air-water Treatments Ltd**
25 **THE LACEMAKER**, 6, b m Dutch Art—Sospel **Mrs D. C. Scott**
26 **WASEEM FARIS (IRE)**, 11, b g Exceed And Excel (AUS)—Kissing Time **Mr M. Harris**
27 **WETANWINDY**, 5, br g Watar (IRE)—Tinkwood (IRE) **Mr M. Harris**
28 4, B f Milan—Zoeys Dream (IRE)

THREE-YEAR-OLDS
29 **GLOBAL AGREEMENT**, ch g Mayson—Amicable Terms **Charlie Holding, Emdells & Partners**
30 Ch c Harbour Watch (IRE)—La Palma
31 B c Yeats (IRE)—Va'vite (IRE)

TWO-YEAR-OLDS
32 B f 17/04 Heeraat (IRE)—Amicable Terms (Royal Applause) (7142)
33 B c 20/03 Monsieur Bond (IRE)—Choral Singer (Daylami (IRE))

Other Owners: Mrs S. E. Brown, Charlie Holding Limited, Emdells Limited, Mr J. G. Giddings, Mr M. Harris, Mr A. Harrison, Mr J. P Naylor, Mrs R. E. Nelmes, Pegasus Bloodstock Limited, Mr A. G. Smith, L. R. Turland, Mrs A. M. Williams, Mrs L. Winrow-Campbell.

257 MR RONALD HARRIS, Chepstow
Postal: **Ridge House Stables, Earlswood, Chepstow, Monmouthshire, NP16 6AN**
Contacts: **PHONE 01291 641689 MOBILE 07831 770899 FAX 01291 641258**
EMAIL ridgehousestables.ltd@btinternet.com WEBSITE www.ronharrisracing.co.uk

1 **ARIZONA SNOW**, 8, b g Phoenix Reach (IRE)—Calgary **Ridge House Stables Ltd**
2 **BROADHAVEN DREAM (IRE)**, 4, b g Dream Ahead (USA)—Queen Grace (IRE) **M Doocey, S Doocey & P J Doocey**
3 **BROADHAVEN HONEY (IRE)**, 6, b m Harbour Watch (IRE)—Honeymead (IRE) **M Doocey, S Doocey & P J Doocey**
4 **BROTHER BENTLEY**, 4, gr g Hellvelyn—Lady Mango (IRE) **Ridge House Stables Ltd**
5 **CASTANEA**, 8, ch g Pivotal—Invitee **Ridge House Stables Ltd**
6 **CLEVEDON (IRE)**, 4, br g Bungle Inthejungle—Sandy Smile (IRE) **J. A. Gent**

MR RONALD HARRIS - continued

7 **COUNTRY ROSE (IRE)**, 4, b f Bungle Inthejungle—Fitrah (IRE) **Mrs J. Jarrett**
8 **DIAMOND VINE (IRE)**, 12, b g Diamond Green (FR)—Glasnas Giant **Ridge House Stables Ltd**
9 **DRUMSHANBO DESTINY (FR)**, 4, ch g Nathaniel (IRE)—Lacy Sunday (USA) **Mr David N.Reynolds & Mr Chris Watkins**
10 **ELZAAM'S DREAM (IRE)**, 4, b f Elzaam (AUS)—Alinda (IRE) **Ridge House Stables Ltd**
11 **EQUALLY FAST**, 8, b g Equiano (FR)—Fabulously Fast (USA) **Mr S. Bell**
12 **EYE OF THE WATER (IRE)**, 4, b g Lilbourne Lad (IRE)—Desert Location **Mr M. E. Wright**
13 **FANTASY JUSTIFIER (IRE)**, 9, b g Arakan (USA)—Grandel **Ridge House Stables Ltd**
14 **FETHIYE BOY**, 6, br g Pastoral Pursuits—Ocean Blaze **Ridge House Stables Ltd**
15 **GLAM'SELLE**, 6, b m Elnadim (USA)—Town And Gown **Robert & Nina Bailey**
16 **LADY MANGO (IRE)**, 12, ch m Bahamian Bounty—Opera
17 **MAJESTIC HERO (IRE)**, 8, b g Majestic Missile (IRE)—Xena (IRE) **Mrs Jackie Jarrett & Ridge House Stables**
18 **MONETA**, 4, b f Kodiac—Money Note **H. M. W. Clifford**
19 **PEACE SEEKER**, 12, b g Oasis Dream—Mina **Ridge House Stables Ltd**
20 **POWERFUL DREAM (IRE)**, 7, b m Frozen Power (IRE)—Noble View (USA) **Ridge House Stables Ltd**
21 **RECTORY ROAD**, 4, b g Paco Boy (IRE)—Caerlonore (IRE) **Mr S. R. Middleton**
22 **RUPERTCAMBELLBLACK (IRE)**, 6, b g Canford Cliffs (IRE)—Negotiate **Ridge House Stables Ltd**
23 **SECRET POTION**, 6, b g Stimulation (IRE)—Fiancee (IRE) **RHS Ltd, Mr R Fox, Mr P Charter**
24 **TANACANDO (FR)**, 8, b g Ballingarry (IRE)—Tamaziya (IRE) **Flat Out Shinton Racing**
25 **TEXAN NOMAD**, 8, ch g Nomadic Way (USA)—Texas Belle (IRE) **Mr J. W. Miles**
26 **THE DALEY EXPRESS (IRE)**, 6, b g Elzaam (AUS)—Seraphina (IRE) **The W.H.O. Society**
27 **THEGREYVTRAIN**, 4, gr f Coach House (IRE)—Debutante Blues (USA) **Ridge House Stables Ltd**
28 **UNION ROSE**, 8, b g Stimulation (IRE)—Dot Hill **Mr D. A. Evans**
29 **VIOLA PARK**, 6, b g Aqlaam—Violette **Mr John & Margaret Hatherell & RHS Ltd**

THREE-YEAR-OLDS

30 **DON'T STOP DANCING (IRE)**, ch c Anjaal—Elayoon (USA) **Mr J. McCoy**
31 **GLAMOROUS FORCE**, b g Lethal Force (IRE)—Glamorous Spirit (IRE) **M Doocey, S Doocey & P J Doocey**
32 **I'M WATCHING YOU**, ch g Harbour Watch (IRE)—Victrix Ludorum (IRE) **Mr J. McCoy**
33 **MAYFLOWER LADY (IRE)**, b f Bungle Inthejungle—Disc Play **Mrs J. Jarrett**
34 **SACRED LEGACY (IRE)**, ch g Zebedee—Sacred Love (IRE) **Rhs Limited & Mr Peter Charter**
35 **SARAH'S VERSE**, b f Poet's Voice—Sancai (USA)
36 **SHAUN'S DELIGHT (IRE)**, ch g Camacho—Leopard Hunt (USA) **Mr S. R. Middleton**
37 **THE FITZPIERS LION (IRE)**, gr g Gutaifan (IRE)—Miss Mary **Mr M. E. Wright**
38 **WE'RE REUNITED (IRE)**, b g Kodiac—Caelis **H. M. W. Clifford**

Other Owners: Mrs J. H. Bailey, R. M. Bailey, P. F. Charter, Mr M. A. Doocey, Mr P. J. Doocey, Mr S. Doocey, Mr R. S. Fox, Mrs M. E. Hatherell, Mr R. A. J. Hatherell, Mrs J. Jarrett, Ridge House Stables Ltd, Mr D. A. Shinton, Mr J. D. Shinton.

Flat Jockey: Luke Morris.

 MR SHAUN HARRIS, Worksop
Postal: Pinewood Stables, Carburton, Worksop, Nottinghamshire, S80 3BT
Contacts: **PHONE** 01909 470936 **MOBILE** 07761 395596
EMAIL shaunharrisracing@yahoo.com **WEBSITE** www.shaunharrisracing.co.uk

1 **ALI STAR BERT**, 4, b g Phoenix Reach (IRE)—Clumber Pursuits **Notts Racing, S A Harris & Miss H Ward**
2 **APRIL RISING**, 5, b br m Dick Turpin (IRE)—Tomintoul Star **Arrathorne Racing Club**
3 **DOLPHIN VILLAGE (IRE)**, 10, b g Cape Cross (IRE)—Reform Act (USA) **Nottinghamshire Racing**
4 **HARBOUR SUNRISE**, 5, b m Harbour Watch (IRE)—Nairobi (FR) **Mr C. Harris**
5 **HEAR THE CHIMES**, 11, b g Midnight Legend—Severn Air **Miss G. H. Ward**
6 **ORBIT OF IOLITE**, 4, ch g Sun Central (IRE)—Blue Clumber **Miss G. H. Ward**
7 **QUICK MONET (IRE)**, 7, b g Excellent Art—Clinging Vine (USA) **J. Morris**
8 **SAVLAD**, 5, b g Delegator—Dubai Legend **D. & S. L. Tanker Transport Limited**
9 **SON OF BEAUTY (IRE)**, 4, b g Vocalised (USA)—Sunset Beauty (IRE) **Notts Racing, S A Harris & Miss H Ward**
10 **SUPREME DREAM**, 4, b f Captain Gerrard (IRE)—Sweet Lily Pea (USA) **Mr S. Firth**

Other Owners: Miss G. H. Ward.

Assistant Trainer: Miss G. H. Ward.

259 MISS LISA HARRISON, Wigton

Postal: **Cobble Hall, Aldoth, Nr Silloth, Cumbria, CA7 4NE**
Contacts: **PHONE 016973 61753 MOBILE 07725 535554 FAX 016973 42250**
EMAIL **lisa@daharrison.co.uk**

1 **GREEN ZONE (IRE)**, 9, b g Bushranger (IRE)—Incense **T Hunter & D A Harrison Racing**
2 **INSTINGTIVE (IRE)**, 9, b g Scorpion (IRE)—Fully Focused (IRE) **D A Harrison & Abbadis Racing & Thompson**
3 **MILEVA ROLLER**, 8, b m Multiplex—Alikat (IRE) **D A Harrison Racing**
4 **MUWALLA**, 13, b g Bahri (USA)—Easy Sunshine (IRE) **Bell Bridge Racing**
5 **SOLWAY AVA**, 7, b m Overbury (IRE)—Solway Sunset
6 **SOLWAY BERRY**, 9, b m Overbury (IRE)—Solway Rose **D A Harrison Racing**
7 **SOLWAY LARK**, 9, b g Beat All (USA)—Solway Larkin (IRE) **F Crone& D A Harrison Racing**
8 **SOLWAY MOLLY**, 5, b m Trans Island—Solway Sunset **D A Harrison Racing**
9 **SOLWAY SPIRIT**, 7, b g Overbury (IRE)—Notadandy
10 **SONG OF THE NIGHT**, 9, b g Mahler—Pollys Attic (IRE) **Mr & Mrs Batey & D A Harrison Racing**

Other Owners: Abbadis Racing Club, Mrs A. E. Batey, Mr K. D. Batey, Mrs F. H. Crone, D A Harrison Racing, Mr D. Gillespie, Mr J. D. Graves, Miss L. Harrison, Mr R. A. Harrison, Mr W. H. Harrison, Mr T. Hunter, R. E. Jackson, Mr K. V. Thompson.

MISS LISA HARRISON - continued

260 MR BEN HASLAM, Middleham
Postal: **Castle Barn Cottage, Castle Hill, Middleham, Leyburn, North Yorkshire, DL8 4QW**
Contacts: **PHONE 01969 624351 MOBILE 07764 411660**
EMAIL **office@benhaslamracing.com** WEBSITE **www.benhaslamracing.com**

1 4, B br g Yeats (IRE)—Beaus Polly (IRE)
2 **BLACK KRAKEN**, 4, b g Battle of Marengo (IRE)—Stereo Love (FR) **Mr D. Shapiro & Mr B. M. R. Haslam**
3 **BLAZING DREAMS (IRE)**, 4, b g Morpheus—Pure Folly (IRE) **Simon King & Partner**
4 **BLINDINGLY (GER)**, 5, br g Shamardal (USA)—Boccassini (GER) **Mrs C. Barclay**
5 **CALEVADE (IRE)**, 4, gr g Gregorian (IRE)—Avoidance (USA) **D Shapiro, Mrs Anne Haslam & Partners**
6 **CALL THE COPS (IRE)**, 11, b g Presenting—Ballygill Heights (IRE)
7 **CASH AGAIN (IRE)**, 8, br g Great Pretender (IRE)—Jeu de Lune (FR) **Mrs C. Barclay**
8 **DEMI SANG (FR)**, 7, b g Gris de Gris (IRE)—Morvandelle (FR) **Mr J. P. McManus**
9 **DEPUTY STAR**, 4, b g Epaulette (AUS)—Starkat **Norcroft Park Stud**
10 **EPEIUS (IRE)**, 7, b g Arakan (USA)—Gilda Lilly (USA) **Ben Haslam Racing Syndicate**
11 **EVER SO MUCH (IRE)**, 11, b g Westerner—Masaalstruck (IRE) **Mr J. P. McManus**
12 **FOREVER MINE**, 4, ch f Iffraaj—Best Regards (IRE) **Brightwalton Bloodstock Limited**
13 **FORTAMOUR (IRE)**, 4, b g Es Que Love (IRE)—Kathy Sun (IRE) **Mrs C Barclay & P Wood**
14 **FUNKADELIC**, 5, ch g Dandy Man (IRE)—Cape Elizabeth (IRE) **South Yorkshire Racing & M T Buckley**
15 **GAMEFACE (IRE)**, 6, b g Oscar (IRE)—Queensland Bay **Mr J. P. McManus**
16 **INCA GOLD (IRE)**, 6, b g Galileo (IRE)—Queen of France (USA) **Mr J. P. McManus**
17 **LADY SHANAWELL (IRE)**, 4, ch f Lord Shanakill (USA)—Lukes Well (IRE) **Blue Lion Racing IX**
18 **LASKADINE (IRE)**, 5, b m Martaline—Laskadoun (FR) **Mr J. P. McManus**
19 **LORD CAPRIO (IRE)**, 5, b g Lord Shanakill (USA)—Azzurra du Caprio (IRE) **Blue Lion Racing IX**
20 **MANAMITE (FR)**, 7, b g Kentucky Dynamite (USA)—Masaya (SWI) **Mr J. P. McManus**
21 **MELODY OF SCOTLAND (FR)**, 6, b m Youmzain (IRE)—This Melody (FR) **Mr J. P. McManus**
22 **NATALEENA (IRE)**, 4, b f Nathaniel (IRE)—Hayyona **Shapiro,Milner,Rees,Nicol,Feeney & Adams**
23 **PINARELLA (IRE)**, 4, ch f Kendargent (FR)—Ponte di Legno (FR) **R Brinkley, K Nicol & B Haslam**
24 **PRANCING OSCAR (IRE)**, 6, b g Sir Prancealot (IRE)—Beguiler **Mr R. R. Brinkley**
25 **PROTEK DES FLOS (FR)**, 8, b g Protektor (GER)—Flore de Chantenay (FR) **Mr J. P. McManus**
26 **REY LOOPY (IRE)**, 6, b g Lope de Vega (IRE)—Al Basar (USA) **Mr Daniel Shapiro & Mrs C Barclay**
27 **RITCHIE STAR (IRE)**, 4, b g Lilbourne Lad (IRE)—Array of Stars (IRE) **Mr R. Tocher**
28 **RIVER FROST**, 8, b g Silver Frost—River Test **Mr J. P. McManus**
29 **ROCK ON FRUITY (IRE)**, 11, b g Fruits of Love (USA)—Sancta Miria (IRE) **Mr J. P. McManus**
30 **SANDRET (IRE)**, 4, b g Zebedee—Sava Sunset (IRE) **Mrs C Barclay & Ben Haslam Racing Synd**
31 **SCOOP THE POT (IRE)**, 10, b g Mahler—Miss Brecknell (IRE) **Mr J. P. McManus**
32 **SOLO SAXOPHONE (IRE)**, 6, b g Frankel—Society Hostess (USA) **Golden Equinox Racing**

MR BEN HASLAM - continued

33 **THE BULL (IRE)**, 5, ch g Camacho—Zarara (USA) **Ben Haslam Racing Synd & Linda McGarry**
34 **UPONASTAR (IRE)**, 4, b f Zebedee—Eponastone (IRE) **Mr S. P. King**

THREE-YEAR-OLDS

35 **AIDEN'S REWARD (IRE)**, b g Dandy Man (IRE)—Bonne **Mrs C Barclay & Mr D Wood**
36 **APPLES ACRE (IRE)**, ch f No Nay Never (USA)—Matron **Mr R. R. Brinkley**
37 **AUCKLAND LODGE (IRE)**, ch f Dandy Man (IRE)—Proud Maria (IRE) **The Auckland Lodge Partnership**
38 **CASTLEHILL RETREAT**, ch g Casamento (IRE)—Ansina (USA) **Middleham Park Xx, Mrs C Barclay & J Pak**
39 **COCK A HOOP (IRE)**, ch f Ivawood (IRE)—Dancing With Stars (IRE) **D. Howden, N. Wheeler & D. Redvers**
40 **COPPERLIGHT (IRE)**, b g Poet's Voice—Delighted (IRE) **Mr R Brinkley & Mr R Catling**
41 **DOMINIC'S GREY**, gr c Sepoy (AUS)—Batik (IRE) **Mr R. R. Brinkley**
42 **DREAM GAME**, bl f Brazen Beau (AUS)—Dreamily (IRE) **Ms S. J. Humber**
43 **EMILY'S DELIGHT (IRE)**, ch f Anjaal—Masela (IRE) **Mrs C. Barclay**
44 **FAIRY RING**, b f Casamento (IRE)—Fairy Steps **Ms S. J. Humber**
45 **MARENGO SALLY (IRE)**, b f Battle of Marengo (IRE)—Saldenaera (GER) **South Yorkshire Racing & C Cleevely**
46 **PHOENIX STRIKE**, b c Casamento (IRE)—Promise You **Mr D. Shapiro**
47 **RODDY RANSOM**, b g Roderic O'Connor (IRE)—Midnight Ransom **Ms S. J. Humber**
48 **THREE DRAGONS**, ch g Sakhee (USA)—Three Heart's **Ms S. J. Humber**

TWO-YEAR-OLDS

49 B br c 29/04 Lawman (FR)—Curious Lashes (IRE) (Footstepsinthesand) (19733)
50 B c 16/03 Dandy Man (IRE)—Fonnie (IRE)—Baratehea (IRE) (15443)
51 B c 20/02 Estidhkaar (IRE)—Fuaigh Mor (IRE) (Dubai Destination (USA)) (31745)
52 Ch c 24/03 Hot Streak (IRE)—High Drama (IRE) (High Chaparral (IRE)) (18875)
53 B f 19/04 Helmet (AUS)—Holy Grail (IRE) (Canford Cliffs (IRE))
54 **MACHO PRIDE (IRE)**, b c 19/04 Camacho—
                          Proud Maria (IRE) (Medicean) (55769) **The Auckland Lodge Partnership**
55 **MAEVE'S MEMORY (IRE)**, b f 10/05 Kodiac—Startori (Vettori (IRE)) (17160) **The Auckland Lodge Partnership**
56 B c 24/03 Fast Company (IRE)—Shama's Song (IRE) (Teofilo (IRE)) (52380)
57 Ch f 19/02 Starspangledbanner (AUS)—Sunbula (USA) (Singspiel (IRE)) (10295)

Other Owners: Mr P. Adams, Mrs C. Barclay, Ben Haslam Racing Syndicate, Mr R. R. Brinkley, Mr M. T. Buckley, Mr R. J. Catling, Mr C. R. Cleevely, Mr E. A. Dupont, Mrs J. M. Feeney, Mr J. S. Feeney, Mrs A. M. C. Haslam, Mr B. M. R. Haslam, Mr D. Howden, Mr S. P. King, Mrs L. McGarry, Middleham Park Racing XX, Mrs S. V. Milner, Mr K. Nicol, T. S. Palin, M. Prince, Mr D. Redvers, Mr M. Rees, Mr D. Shapiro, South Yorkshire Racing, Mr W. N. Standeven, Mr N. C. T. Wheeler, Mr D. Wood, Mr P G. Wood.

Assistant Trainer: Alice Haslam.

261	**MR NIGEL HAWKE**, Tiverton Postal: **Thorne Farm, Stoodleigh, Tiverton, Devon, EX16 9QG** Contacts: **PHONE 01884 881666 MOBILE 07769 295839** **EMAIL nigel@thornefarmracingltd.co.uk WEBSITE www.nigelhawkethornefarmracing.co.uk**

1 **A NEW SIEGE (IRE)**, 5, ch m New Approach (IRE)—Arminta (USA) **Atlantic Friends Racing**
2 **ALMINAR (IRE)**, 7, b g Arakan (USA)—Classic Magic (IRE) **Mr M. J. Phillips**
3 **BALLYMAGROARTY BOY (IRE)**, 7, b g Milan—Glazed Storm (IRE) **Nigel Hawke Racing Club & Partners**
4 **BELLA BEAU (IRE)**, 5, b m Jeremy (USA)—Bella Patrice (IRE) **Mr M. J. Phillips**
5 **CALIN DU BRIZAIS (FR)**, 9, b g Loup Solitaire (USA)—Caline du Brizais (FR) **Mrs K. Hawke**
6 **CAMRON DE CHAILLAC (FR)**, 8, br g Laverock (IRE)—Hadeel **Mr R. Lane**
7 **CIDER KILT (IRE)**, 4, b g Yeats (IRE)—Royal Nora (IRE) **Atlantic Friends Racing**
8 **CLONMONARCH (IRE)**, 5, b g Imperial Monarch (IRE)—Grancore Girl (IRE) **Mr R. Lane**
9 **CROSSFIREHURRICANE**, 6, b m Malinas (GER)—Leroy's Sister (FR) **Thorne Farm Racing Limited**
10 **DAWN TROUPER (IRE)**, 5, b g Dawn Approach (IRE)—Dance Troupe **Mr R. Lane**
11 **DEAUVILLE CRYSTAL (FR)**, 7, b m Raven's Pass (USA)—Top Crystal (IRE) **Mrs K. Hawke & Mr W. Simms**
12 **EUROWORK (FR)**, 6, bl g Network (GER)—Nandina (FR) **R. J. & Mrs J. A. Peake**
13 **FLINTS LEGACY**, 8, gr m Sagamix (FR)—Luneray (FR) **Flints Legacy Partnership**

MR NIGEL HAWKE - continued

14 **GEORDIE WASHINGTON (IRE)**, 4, b br g Sageburg (IRE)—Rathturtin Brief (IRE) **Atlantic Friends Racing**
15 **GLOBAL GODDESS (IRE)**, 4, b f Morpheus---Church Mice (IRE) **Mr P Madgwick, Sc Browne & Thorne Farm**
16 **GREYBOUGG**, 11, gr g Tobougg (IRE)—Kildee Lass **Capps, Smith & Partner**
17 **GUARDIA TOP (FR)**, 4, b f Top Trip—Jour de Chance (FR) **Mr Terence Wood & Partners**
18 **GWENNOLINE (FR)**, 4, gr f Balko (FR)—Ugoline (FR) **Thorne Farm Racing Limited**
19 **HARTLAND QUAY (IRE)**, 5, b gr g Arcadio (GER)—Regents Ballerina (IRE) **Mr Richard Weeks & Partner**
20 **HEART OF KERNOW (IRE)**, 8, b g Fruits of Love (USA)—Rathturtin Brief (IRE) **Mrs K. Hawke & Mr W. Simms**
21 **INNERPICKLE**, 6, b g Pour Moi (IRE)—Bay Swallow (IRE) **Ms C. Sellar-Elliott**
22 **JOHANOS (FR)**, 9, ch g Limnos (JPN)—Madame Johann (FR) **Mark Phillips, Mrs Pumphrey & Partners**
23 **KAPITALL**, 5, b m Kapgarde (FR)—Doubly Guest **Mr R Weeks & Jimmy & Toots Partnership**
24 **KENDELU (IRE)**, 5, b g Yeats (IRE)—Supreme Baloo (IRE) **Ken & Della Neilson & Partners**
25 **LAMH AR LAMH (IRE)**, 6, ch m Teofilo (IRE)—Tintreach (CAN) **Mrs M. J. Martin**
26 **LE MUSEE (FR)**, 7, b g Galileo (IRE)—Delicieuse Lady **Mrs K Hawke, W Simms & Dragonfly Racing**
27 **LEVEL OF INTENSITY (IRE)**, 6, b g Intense Focus (USA)—Teofolina (FR) **Milltown Racing & Partner**
28 **LORD BALLIM (FR)**, 10, ch g Balko (FR)—Lady Pauline (FR) **MrJeffW.Hall,MrsK.Hawke,MrWilliamSimms**
29 **MALINA OCARINA**, 5, b m Malinas (GER)—Ocarina Davis (FR) **Mr & Mrs C Glover**
30 **MEAD VALE**, 7, ch g Schiaparelli (GER)—Devon Peasant **Meadvale Syndicate**
31 **NIKAP (FR)**, 6, b m Kapgarde (FR)—Nika Glitters (FR) **Kapinhand**
32 **NOVUS ADITUS (IRE)**, 4, b g Teofilo (IRE)—Novel Approach (IRE) **Atlantic Friends Racing**
33 **OURO BRANCO (FR)**, 7, b g Kapgarde (FR)—Dolce Vita Yug **Pearce Bros & Partner**
34 **PEARL ROYALE (IRE)**, 8, b m Robin des Champs (FR)—Dartmeet (IRE) **Mr M. J. Phillips**
35 **POLA CHANCE (FR)**, 4, gr f Boris de Deauville (IRE)—

                                         Take A Chance (FR) **Smith Evans Bevan Browne Thorne Farm**
36 **PUXTON PARK**, 5, ch g Geordieland (FR)—Catherine Medici **Mr J A Vowles & Partners**
37 **REPETITIO (IRE)**, 4, b g Pour Moi (IRE)—Fionnuar (IRE) **Atlantic Friends Racing**
38 **SOME DETAIL (IRE)**, 6, b g Getaway (GER)—You Should Know Me (IRE) **Milltown Racing**
39 **SPEREDEK (FR)**, 9, b br g Kapgarde (FR)—Sendamagic (FR) **Kapinhand**
40 **SPERONIMO (FR)**, 8, b g Diamond Green (FR)—Sepita (FR) **Pearce Bros Partnership**
41 **TANRUDY (IRE)**, 6, b g Presenting—Come In Moscow (IRE) **Mark J Phillips & Mrs A B Walker**
42 **THE BOOLA BEE (IRE)**, 7, b m Arcadio (GER)—Hy Kate (IRE) **Mr R. Lane**
43 **VERBITUDE (IRE)**, 5, b g Vocalised (USA)—Bring Back Matron (IRE) **John White & Anne Underhill**
44 **WISE GARDEN (FR)**, 5, b m Kapgarde (FR)—Fabulous Wisdom (FR) **Kapinhand**

Other Owners: M. J. Bevan, Mrs K. M. Brain, Mr S. C. Browne, Mr M. G. Capps, Mr P. A. Docker, Mr S. A. Evans, Mr F. G. Flanagan, Mr C. S. Glover, Mrs K. J. Glover, Mr J. H. Gumbley, Mr J. W. Hall, Mrs K. Hawke, Mr N. J. Hawke, Mrs D. Hill, Mr T. B. James, Mrs H. M. Jefferies, Jimmy & Toots Partnership, Mr P. Madgwick, Milltown Racing, Mr K. Neilson, Mrs J. Peake, Mr R. Peake, Mr D. A. Pearce, Mr M. J. Phillips, Mrs M. M. R. Pumphrey, Mr W. J. Simms, Mrs D. E. Smith, The Nigel Hawke Racing Club, Thorne Farm Racing Limited, Mrs A. Underhill, Mr J. A. Vowles, Mrs A. B. Walker, R. J. Weeks, Mr A. J. White, Mr S. W. H. Winfield, Mr T. Wood.

Assistant Trainer: Edward Buckley, Katherine Hawke.

NH Jockey: Sean Bowen, Tom Cannon, Danny Cook, David Noonan. **Conditional Jockey:** Tom Buckley. **Amateur Jockey:** Mr Kieran Buckley.

---

262 | **MR MICHAEL HAWKER, Chippenham**
Postal: **Battens Farm, Allington, Chippenham, Wiltshire, SN14 6LT**

1 **BETTY BATTENS**, 7, ch m Tobougg (IRE)—Where's My Slave (IRE) **Mr M. R. E. Hawker**
2 **LEMONADE DRINKER**, 7, gr g Fair Mix (IRE)—Sheknowsyouknow **Mr M. R. E. Hawker**
3 **MORTENS LEAM**, 8, b g Sulamani (IRE)—Bonnet's Pieces **Mr M. R. E. Hawker**
4 5, B g Scorpion (IRE)—Sheknowsyouknow
5 **SPOTTY DOG**, 5, ch g Sixties Icon—Where's My Slave (IRE) **Mr M. R. E. Hawker**

263 MR RICHARD HAWKER, Frome
Postal: **Rode Farm, Rode, Bath, Somerset, BA11 6QQ**
Contacts: **PHONE 01373 831479**

1 **FIELD MASTER (IRE)**, 7, b g Doyen (IRE)—West Hill Rose (IRE) **The Rode Farm Racing Club**
2 **GENTLEMAN FARMER**, 8, ch g Tobougg (IRE)—Sweet Shooter **R. G. B. Hawker**
3 **JANESLITTLEVOICE**, 6, ch m Jelani (IRE)—Janes Allweather **Miss J. Nicholls**
4 **KILCREA BRIDGE**, 9, b g Kayf Tara—Ballyhoo (IRE) **Mr W. Rowles**
5 **MAGNUM (IRE)**, 7, gr g Lawman (FR)—Coventina (IRE) **Mr W. Rowles**
6 **PARLOUR MAID**, 9, gr m Dr Massini (IRE)—Charliebob **Rolling Aces**
7 **SUPER SNIPE**, 9, b g Kayf Tara—Sea Snipe **Mrs L. J. C. Tylor**

264 MR JONATHAN HAYNES, Brampton
Postal: **Cleugh Head, Low Row, Brampton, Cumbria, CA8 2JB**
Contacts: **PHONE 016977 46253 MOBILE 07771 511471**

1 **BEYONDTHEFLAME**, 10, b m And Beyond (IRE)—Flame of Zara **J. C. Haynes**
2 **DOROTHY'S FLAME**, 8, ch m Black Sam Bellamy (IRE)—Flame of Zara **J. C. Haynes**

265 MISS GAIL HAYWOOD, Moretonhampstead
Postal: **Stacombe Farm, Doccombe, Moretonhampstead, Newton Abbot, Devon, TQ13 8SS**
Contacts: **PHONE 01647 440826**
EMAIL gail@gghracing.com WEBSITE www.gghracing.com

1 **AMOUR D'OR**, 9, b m Winged Love (IRE)—Diletia **Haywood's Heroes**
2 **CHICA RAPIDA**, 8, ch m Paco Boy (IRE)—Tora Bora **Mrs J. Bland**
3 **DANCING GREY**, 7, gr m Dream Eater (IRE)—State of Grace **Mrs J B Floyd-walker & Mrs J Oliver**
4 **HIJA**, 9, b m Avonbridge—Pantita **Haywood's Heroes**
5 **HOOPER'S LEGEND**, 9, b g Midnight Legend—Norton Sapphire **Mr R. Harding**
6 **MIDNIGHT SAPPHIRE**, 10, ch m Midnight Legend—Norton Sapphire **Mr R. Harding**
7 **RICHARDOFDOCCOMBE (IRE)**, 14, b g Heron Island (IRE)—Strike Again (IRE) **Phillip & Mary Creese**
8 **RUSSIAN'S LEGACY**, 10, b m Kayf Tara—Ruby Star (IRE) **Phillip & Mary Creese**
9 **SECRET PALACE**, 8, ch m Pastoral Pursuits—Some Sunny Day **Phillip & Mary Creese**
10 **WOOKEY HOLE (IRE)**, 8, b g Court Cave (IRE)—Marguerite Bay (IRE) **Ms N. Dunford**
11 **ZULU**, 6, b g Cockney Rebel (IRE)—Pantita **The Young Warriors**

Other Owners: Mr P. V. Creese, Mrs S. M. Creese, Mrs J. B. Floyd-Walker, Miss G. G. Haywood, Ms V. O'Sullivan, Mrs J. Oliver.

NH Jockey: David Noonan. **Conditional Jockey:** Kieron Edgar. **Amateur Jockey:** Miss Sioned Whittle.

266 MR COLIN HEARD, Boscastle
Postal: **Lower Pennycrocker Farm, Boscastle, Cornwall, PL35 0BY**
Contacts: **PHONE 01840 250613**
EMAIL colin.heard@yahoo.com

1 **SAM MIGUEL**, 4, b g Black Sam Bellamy (IRE)—Solid Land (FR) **Mrs K. Heard**

267 MR PETER HEDGER, Hook

Postal: **PCF Racing, Peaked Croft Farm, Chalky Lane, Dogmersfield, Hook, Hampshire, RG27 8TG**
Contacts: **PHONE 023 9246 3161 MOBILE 07860 209448**
EMAIL hedgerlaura@hotmail.com

Licence will switch to SIMON HODGSON in Spring 2020 pending BHA approval

1 **C'EST NO MOUR (GER)**, 7, b g Champs Elysees—C'Est L'Amour (GER) **Mr P. R. Hedger & P C F Racing Ltd**
2 **CONTINUUM**, 11, b br g Dansili—Clepsydra **P C F Racing Ltd**
3 **MR MAC**, 6, b g Makfi—Veronica Franco **P C F Racing Ltd**
4 **SILENT ECHO**, 6, b g Oasis Dream—Quiet **P C F Racing Ltd**
5 **TOTAL COMMITMENT (IRE)**, 4, b g Exceed And Excel (AUS)—Crysdal **P C F Racing Ltd**
6 **TRALEE HILLS**, 6, gr ro g Mount Nelson—Distant Waters **P C F Racing Ltd**

THREE-YEAR-OLDS

7 **FINAIR**, b f Finjaan—Afro **P C F Racing Ltd**
8 **HELETA**, b f Helmet (AUS)—Juno Moneta (IRE) **P C F Racing Ltd**
9 **MEDBURN STAR**, b f Telescope (IRE)—Tiegs (IRE) **Mr Eddie Evans**
10 B g Kayf Tara—No Pushover **P C F Racing Ltd**

TWO-YEAR-OLDS

11 **TWILIGHT MADNESS**, ch c 27/01 Twilight Son—Rhal (IRE) (Rahy (USA)) **Mr P. R. Hedger & P C F Racing Ltd**

Other Owners: P. R. Hedger, P C F Racing Ltd.

Flat Jockey: Charles Bishop. **NH Jockey:** Leighton Aspell.

---

268 MR NICKY HENDERSON, Lambourn

Postal: **Seven Barrows, Lambourn, Hungerford, Berkshire, RG17 8UH**
Contacts: **PHONE 01488 72259 MOBILE 07774 608168**
EMAIL njh@njhenderson.com

1 **ADJALI (GER)**, 5, b g Kamsin (GER)—Anabasis (GER) **Mr Simon Munir & Mr Isaac Souede**
2 **ALLART (IRE)**, 6, b g Shantou (USA)—The Adare Woman (IRE) **R. A. Bartlett**
3 **ALTIOR (IRE)**, 10, b g High Chaparral (IRE)—Monte Solaro (IRE) **Mrs P. J. Pugh**
4 **ANGELS BREATH (IRE)**, 6, gr g Shantou (USA)—Mystic Masie (IRE) **Walters Plant Hire & Ronnie Bartlett**
5 **ARCADIAN PEARL (IRE)**, 5, br g Arcadio (GER)—Grangeclare Pearl (IRE) **Biddestone Racing XVII**
6 **ARTURUS (IRE)**, 5, b g Camelot—Scandisk (IRE) **Mr J. Turner**
7 **AT POETS CROSS (IRE)**, 4, b g Yeats (IRE)—At The Pound Cross (IRE) **HP Racing At Poets Cross**
8 **BALMUICK (IRE)**, 4, br g So You Think (NZ)—Full of Love (IRE) **T. Barr**
9 **BARBADOS BLUE (IRE)**, 6, b m Getaway—Buck's Blue (FR) **Crimbourne Bloodstock**
10 **BEFORE MIDNIGHT**, 7, ch g Midnight Legend—Lady Samantha **Walters Plant Hire & Potter Group**
11 **BEWARE THE BEAR (IRE)**, 10, b g Shantou (USA)—Native Bid (IRE) **G. B. Barlow**
12 **BEYONDTHESTORM (IRE)**, 7, b g Flemensfirth (USA)—Blue Gale (IRE) **Cheveley Park Stud Limited**
13 **BIRCHDALE (IRE)**, 6, b g Jeremy (USA)—Onewayortheother (IRE) **Mr J. P. McManus**
14 **BLAIRGOWRIE (IRE)**, 4, b g Yeats (IRE)—Gaye Preskina (IRE) **T. Barr**
15 **BOLD RECORD (IRE)**, 6, b g Fame And Glory—Shop Dj (IRE) **R. M. Kirkland**
16 **BOND'S LOVER (IRE)**, 6, gr m Flemensfirth (USA)—Courageuse (FR) **Mrs B. A. Hanbury**
17 **BOTHWELL BRIDGE (IRE)**, 5, b g Stowaway—Raise The Issue (IRE) **T. Barr**
18 **BRAIN POWER (IRE)**, 9, b g Kalanisi (IRE)—Blonde Ambition (IRE)
19 **BRAVE EAGLE (IRE)**, 8, b g Yeats (IRE)—Sinful Pleasure (IRE) **R. M. Kirkland**
20 **BURBANK (IRE)**, 8, b g Yeats (IRE)—Spring Swoon (FR) **Mr T. J. Hemmings**
21 **BURROWS EDGE (FR)**, 7, b g Martaline—La Vie de Boitron (FR)
22 **BUTTSBURY LADY**, 5, b m Great Pretender (IRE)—Ceilidh Royal **Mrs R. H. Brown**
23 **BUVEUR D'AIR (FR)**, 9, b g Crillon (FR)—History (FR) **Mr J. P. McManus**
24 **BUZZ (FR)**, 6, gr g Motivator—Tiysha (IRE) **Thurloe for Royal Marsden Cancer Charity**
25 **CALL ME LORD (FR)**, 7, b br g Slickly (FR)—Sosa (GER) **Mr Simon Munir & Mr Isaac Souede**
26 **CAPTAIN WOODIE (IRE)**, 8, b g Presenting—Lasado (IRE) **Middleham Park Racing LXXX**
27 **CARIBEAN BOY (FR)**, 6, gr g Myboycharlie (IRE)—Caribena (FR) **Mr Simon Munir & Mr Isaac Souede**

MR NICKY HENDERSON - continued

28 **CASABLANCA MIX (FR)**, 8, ch m Shirocco (GER)—Latitude (FR) **E. R. Hanbury**

29 **CASCOVA (IRE)**, 5, b g Casamento (IRE)—Sina Cova (IRE) **Chelsea Thoroughbreds - Cascova**

30 **CHAMP (IRE)**, 8, b g King's Theatre (IRE)—China Sky (IRE) **Mr J. P. McManus**

31 **CHAMPAGNE MYSTERY (IRE)**, 6, b g Shantou (USA)—Spanker **Mr T. J. Hemmings**

32 **CHAMPAGNE PLATINUM (IRE)**, 6, gr g Stowaway—Saffron Holly (IRE) **Mr J. P. McManus**

33 **CHANTRY HOUSE (IRE)**, 6, br g Yeats (IRE)—The Last Bank (IRE) **Mr J. P. McManus**

34 **CHASAMAX (IRE)**, 5, b g Jeremy (IRE)—Peratus (IRE) **International Plywood (Importers) Ltd**

35 **CHIVES**, 6, b g Sulamani (IRE)—Ceilidh Royal **Mrs R. H. Brown**

36 **COLONIAL DREAMS (IRE)**, 8, b g Westerner—Dochas Supreme (IRE) **C. N. Barnes**

37 **CORRANY (IRE)**, 6, br g Court Cave (IRE)—Time For An Audit **Mr T. J. Hemmings**

38 **COUNTISTER (FR)**, 8, b m Smadoun (FR)—Tistairly (FR) **Mr J. P. McManus**

39 **CRAIGNEICHE (IRE)**, 6, br g Flemensfirth (USA)—Itsalark (IRE) **R. M. Kirkland**

40 **DAME DE COMPAGNIE (FR)**, 7, b m Lucarno (USA)—Programmee (FR) **Mr J. P. McManus**

41 **DAPHNE DU CLOS (FR)**, 7, b m Spanish Moon (USA)—Katarina du Clos (FR) **Sullivan Bloodstock Limited**

42 **DIABLO DE ROUHET (FR)**, 7, b g Great Pretender (IRE)—

Querelle d'Estruval (FR) **Business Moves Group & David White**

43 **DIAMOND RIVER (IRE)**, 5, ch g Imperial Monarch (IRE)—River Clyde (IRE) **Jockey Club Ownership (SW 2018)**

44 **DIVINE SPEAR (IRE)**, 9, b g Oscar (IRE)—Testaway (IRE) **Middleham Park Racing LXII**

45 **DOCTE DINA (FR)**, 6, ch m Doctor Dino (FR)—Artofmen (FR) **Walters Plant Hire & Potter Group**

46 **DOWNTOWN GETAWAY (IRE)**, 7, b g Getaway (GER)—Shang A Lang (IRE) **T. F. P.**

47 **DRAGON D'ESTRUVAL (FR)**, 7, b g Enrique—Rose d'Estruval (FR) **Mr Simon Munir & Mr Isaac Souede**

48 **DREAM DU GRAND VAL (FR)**, 7, b g Puit d'Or (IRE)—Apple Mille (FR) **Mr T. J. Hemmings**

49 **DU DESTIN (FR)**, 7, gr g Fuisse (FR)—Parenthese (FR) **Middleham Park Racing V**

50 **DUKE OF CHALFONT (FR)**, 4, b g Alianthus (GER)—Bonne Mere (FR) **Mr A. Speelman & Mr M. Speelman**

51 **EL KALDOUN (FR)**, 6, b g Special Kaldoun (IRE)—Kermesse d'Estruval (FR) **Middleham Park Racing CIV**

52 **ELUSIVE BELLE (IRE)**, 6, b m Elusive Pimpernel (USA)—Soviet Belle (IRE) **Mr R. B. Waley-Cohen**

53 **EPATANTE (FR)**, 6, b m No Risk At All (FR)—Kadjara (FR) **Mr J. P. McManus**

54 **FALCO BLITZ (IRE)**, 6, b g Falco (USA)—Ignited **Axom LXXVII**

55 **FANTASTIC LADY (FR)**, 5, b m Network (GER)—Latitude (FR) **E. R. Hanbury**

56 **FAROUK DE CHENEAU (FR)**, 5, b g Day Flight—Kardamone (FR) **Owners Group 049**

57 **FATHER JOHN (FR)**, 5, b g Secret Singer (FR)—Oudette (FR) **Middleham Park Racing XI**

58 **FELONY (IRE)**, 5, b g Getaway (GER)—Sparkling Gem (IRE) **Highclere Thoroughbred Racing - Getaway**

59 **FIRESTEP (IRE)**, 4, b g Mahler—Springinherstep (IRE) **Mr C. B. J. Dingwall**

60 **FIX SUN (FR)**, 5, b g Al Namix (FR)—Quelly Bruere (FR) **Mr Simon Munir & Mr Isaac Souede**

61 **FLINTEUR SACRE (FR)**, 5, b g Network (GER)—Fatima III (FR) **Mr J. P. McManus**

62 **FLORESSA (FR)**, 5, b m Poligiote—Dona Rez (FR) **Just Four Men**

63 **FOLLOW THE BEAR (IRE)**, 8, b g King's Theatre (IRE)—Mrs Dempsey (IRE) **G. B. Barlow**

64 **FOX'S SOCKS (FR)**, 5, br g Crillon (FR)—Queva de Sarti (FR) **Mr J. Palmer-Brown**

65 **FRANCE DE REVE (FR)**, 5, gr m Lord du Sud (FR)—Kyrielle de Reve (FR) **Mr J. P. McManus**

66 **FRASER ISLAND (IRE)**, 4, ch g Australia—Ponty Acclaim (IRE) **Mr Alan Spence**

67 **FRED (FR)**, 5, b br g Cokoriko (FR)—Veribelle (FR) **Mr Simon Munir & Mr Isaac Souede**

68 **FUGITIVES DRIFT (IRE)**, 5, b g Yeats (IRE)—Shebeganit (IRE) **HP Racing Fugitives Drift**

69 **FUSIL RAFFLES (FR)**, 5, b g Saint des Saints (FR)—Tali des Obeaux (FR) **Mr Simon Munir & Mr Isaac Souede**

70 **GALAN DES PLANCHES (FR)**, 4, b g Crillon (FR)—Quaty des Planches (FR) **Seven Barrows Limited**

71 **GIANTS TABLE**, 5, br g Great Pretender (IRE)—Bold Fire **Lady C. Bamford & Miss A. Bamford**

72 **GLOBAL SOCIETY**, 5, b g Shirocco (GER)—Oligarch Society (IRE) **Mr J. L. Lightfoot**

73 **GLYNN (IRE)**, 6, b g Winged Love (IRE)—Barnish River (IRE) **Owners Group 039**

74 **GO CHIQUE (FR)**, 4, b f Crillon (FR)—Similaresisoldofa (FR) **Middleham Park Racing CX**

75 **GOLD PRESENT (IRE)**, 10, b g Presenting—Ouro Preto **Mr & Mrs J. D. Cotton**

76 **GRAN LUNA (FR)**, 4, b f Spanish Moon (USA)—Coppena (FR)

77 **GRAND MOGUL (IRE)**, 6, b g Presenting—Oligarch Society (IRE) **Mrs B. A. Hanbury**

78 **GRAND ROI (FR)**, 4, b g Spanish Moon (USA)—Ultra d'Anjou (FR) **Million in Mind Partnership**

79 **GUNNERY (FR)**, 7, ch g Le Havre (IRE)—Loup The Loup (FR) **Mrs F. H. Hay**

80 **HAMILTON'S FANTASY**, 5, b m Mount Nelson—Romantic Dream **Her Majesty The Queen**

81 **HAUL AWAY (IRE)**, 7, b g Stowaway—Lisacul Queen (IRE) **R. M. Kirkland**

82 **HIJACK (IRE)**, 5, b g Fame And Glory—Etolle Margot (FR) **Highclere Thoroughbred Racing - Fame**

83 **HOMER (FR)**, 4, b g Sea The Stars (IRE)—Synchronic (IRE) **Mr Simon Munir & Mr Isaac Souede**

84 **HOOPER**, 4, b g Rip Van Winkle (IRE)—Earth Amber **Pump & Plant Services Ltd**

85 **IGOR**, 7, b g Presenting—Stravinsky Dance **MHankin CNoell MenHolding RWaley-Cohen**

MR NICKY HENDERSON - continued

86 **INDIAN GLORY (IRE)**, 5, b m Fame And Glory—Real Papoose (IRE) **International Plywood (Importers) Ltd**
87 **IT SURE IS (IRE)**, 5, b g Shirocco (GER)—Stay At Home Mum (IRE) **Mrs M. Donnelly**
88 **ITALIAN LEGEND (IRE)**, 5, b br g Fame And Glory—Alannico **R. M. Kirkland**
89 **ITALIAN SUMMER**, 5, br m Milan—Midsummer Magic **Her Majesty The Queen**
90 **JACK SHARP (IRE)**, 5, b br g Scorpion (IRE)—That's Amazing (IRE) **Walters Plant Hire & Potter Group**
91 **JANIKA (FR)**, 7, b g Saddler Maker (IRE)—Majaka (IRE) **Mr Simon Munir & Mr Isaac Souede**
92 **JEN'S BOY**, 6, b g Malinas (GER)—Friendly Craic (IRE) **Middleham Park Racing CV**
93 **KAYMAR**, 5, b g Kayf Tara—Suave Shot **Trevor & Linda Marlow**
94 **KEEN ON**, 6, b g Kayf Tara—Romantic Dream **Her Majesty The Queen**
95 **KINGS RYDE**, 8, b g King's Theatre (IRE)—Ryde Back **Miss R. C. Tregaskes**
96 **KNOWN (IRE)**, 6, b g Fame And Glory—Aasleagh Lady (IRE) **The Rose & Thistle Partnership**
97 **L'AMI SERGE (IRE)**, 10, b g King's Theatre (IRE)—La Zingarella (IRE) **Mr Simon Munir & Mr Isaac Souede**
98 **LAUGHING LUIS**, 6, b g Authorized (IRE)—Leitzu (IRE) **J. C. Sillett**
99 **LECALE'S ARTICLE (IRE)**, 6, b g Malinas (GER)—Brookville (IRE) **Mrs M. Donnelly**
100 **LILLY PEDLAR**, 5, b m Yeats (IRE)—Mathine (FR) **Hot To Trot Jumping**
101 **LOVEHERANDLEAVEHER (IRE)**, 8, b br m Winged Love (IRE)—Rowdy Exit (IRE) **Mr Alan Spence**
102 **LUST FOR GLORY (IRE)**, 7, b m Getaway (GER)—Maisie Presenting (IRE) **Annabel Waley-cohen & Family**
103 **MAJOR STING (IRE)**, 4, b g Scorpion (IRE)—Suzababe (IRE) **The SMBs**
104 **MARIE'S ROCK (IRE)**, 5, b br m Milan—By The Hour (IRE) **Middleham Park Racing XLII**
105 **MEADOWSWEET (IRE)**, 4, b f Getaway (GER)—My Viking Bay (IRE) **Lady Tennant**
106 **MIGHT BITE (IRE)**, 11, b g Scorpion (IRE)—Knotted Midge (IRE) **The Knot Again Partnership**
107 **MILL GREEN**, 8, b g Black Sam Bellamy (IRE)—Ceilidh Royal **Mrs R. H. Brown**
108 **MISS FARAGE (IRE)**, 5, b m Sans Frontieres (IRE)—Maid of Might (IRE) **Turf Club 2018**
109 **MISS FISHER (IRE)**, 4, ch f Libertarian—That's Amazing (IRE) **James and Jean Potter Ltd**
110 **MISTER COFFEY (IRE)**, 5, b g Authorized (IRE)—Mamitador **Lady C. Bamford & Miss A. Bamford**
111 **MISTER FISHER (IRE)**, 6, b g Jeremy (USA)—That's Amazing (IRE) **James & Jean Potter**
112 **MONBEG LEGEND**, 10, b g Midnight Legend—Reverse Swing **Eventmasters Racing**
113 **MONTE CRISTO (FR)**, 4, b g Montmartre (FR)—Rylara des Brosses (FR) **Mr Simon Munir & Mr Isaac Souede**
114 **MORNING VICAR (IRE)**, 7, b g Beneficial—Mary's Little Vic (IRE) **The Parishioners**
115 **MOT A MOT (FR)**, 4, gr g Martaline—Gaily Zest (USA) **Walters Plant Hire & Potter Group**
116 **MY WHIRLWIND (IRE)**, 5, b m Stowaway—Garranlea Maree (IRE) **Mr J. P. McManus**
117 **NEVER ADAPT (FR)**, 5, ch m Anabaa Blue—She Hates Me (IRE) **Mr J. P. McManus**
118 **O CONNELL STREET (IRE)**, 6, b g Fame And Glory—Victorine (IRE) **Magniers'/ Mrs P Shanahan/justin Carthy**
119 **OK CORRAL (IRE)**, 10, b g Mahler—Accola (IRE) **Mr J. P. McManus**
120 **ON THE BLIND SIDE (IRE)**, 8, b g Stowaway—Such A Set Up (IRE) **Mr Alan Spence**
121 **PALLADIUM**, 4, ch g Champs Elysees—Galicuix **A. Meade, G. Van Geest, E. Kelvin-hughes**
122 **PARIS DIXIE**, 5, b m Champs Elysees—Last of The Dixies **Owners Group 037**
123 **PARISIAN BLUE**, 4, b br f Getaway (GER)—Another Evening (IRE) **Crimbourne Bloodstock**
124 **PENTLAND HILLS (IRE)**, 5, b g Motivator—Elle Galante (GER) **Owners Group 031**
125 **PIPESMOKER (FR)**, 5, b g Authorized (IRE)—Pisa (GER) **Lady Dulverton**
126 **PISTOL WHIPPED (IRE)**, 6, b g Beneficial—Holiday Time (IRE) **Mr A. Speelman & Mr M. Speelman**
127 **POST WAR**, 9, b g Nayef (USA)—Antebellum (FR) **The Duke Of Bedford & Dr Jerome Poupel**
128 **PRECIOUS CARGO (IRE)**, 7, b g Yeats (IRE)—Kilbarry Classic (IRE) **T. Barr**
129 **PYM (IRE)**, 7, b g Stowaway—Liss Rua (IRE) **Mrs P. J. Pugh**
130 **RATHHILL (IRE)**, 7, b g Getaway (GER)—Bella Venezia (IRE) **Mr J. P. McManus**
131 **ROYAL REEL (IRE)**, 7, ch g Shirocco (GER)—Close Harmony **Mrs R. H. Brown**
132 **ROYAL RUBY**, 8, b g Yeats (IRE)—Close Harmony **Mrs R. H. Brown**
133 **SANTINI**, 8, b g Milan—Tinagoodnight (FR) **Mr & Mrs R. G. Kelvin-Hughes**
134 **SCARPIA (IRE)**, 6, ch g Sans Frontieres (IRE)—Bunglasha Lady (IRE) **Mrs T. J. Stone-Brown**
135 **SETTIE HILL (USA)**, 7, b g Cape Blanco (IRE)—Claire Soleil (USA) **Michael Buckley & Lord Vestey**
136 **SHISHKIN (IRE)**, 6, b g Sholokhov—Labarynth (IRE) **Mrs M. Donnelly**
137 **SIR SHOLOKHOV (IRE)**, 5, b g Sholokhov (IRE)—Menepresents (IRE) **Mr Simon Munir & Mr Isaac Souede**
138 **SLEIGHT OF HAND (IRE)**, 6, b g Kalanisi (IRE)—Katariya (IRE) **Michael Buckley & Mark Blandford**
139 **SON OF CAMAS (IRE)**, 5, ch g Creachadoir (IRE)—Camas (FR) **Sullivan Bloodstock Limited**
140 **SOUL EMOTION (IRE)**, 7, b g Martaline—Second Emotion (FR) **Mr & Mrs J. D. Cotton**
141 **STAITHES (IRE)**, 5, b g Watar (IRE)—Corlea (IRE) **The Titanic Ten**
142 **STEAL A MARCH**, 5, b g Mount Nelson—Side Step **Her Majesty The Queen**
143 **STORM OF INTRIGUE (IRE)**, 8, b g Oscar (IRE)—Storminoora (IRE) **Mr Oscar Singh & Miss Priya Purewal**
144 **STYLE DE GARDE (FR)**, 6, b g Kapgarde (FR)—Anowe de Jelois (FR) **Highclere Thoroughbred Racing - Style**

MR NICKY HENDERSON - continued

145 **SUNRISE RUBY (IRE)**, 6, ch m Sholokhov (IRE)—Maryota (FR) **Blunt, Breslin, Duffy, Slattery**
146 **SUNSHADE**, 7, b m Sulamani (IRE)—Spring Flight **Her Majesty The Queen**
147 **SURF WALK (IRE)**, 5, b g Born To Sea (IRE)—Meon Mix **Mr A. Speelman & Mr M. Speelman**
148 **TEMPLE HIGH**, 5, b m Sulamani (IRE)—Uppermost **James and Jean Potter Ltd**
149 **THE CASHEL MAN (IRE)**, 8, b g High Chaparral (IRE)—Hadarama (IRE) **Mrs F. H. Hay**
150 **THEINVAL (FR)**, 10, b g Smadoun (FR)—Kinevees (FR) **Mr & Mrs Sandy Orr**
151 **TIMBERMAN (FR)**, 5, b g Califet (FR)—Millrock Lady (IRE) **Mr J. Turner**
152 **TIME FLIES BY (IRE)**, 5, ch g Getaway (GER)—What A Mewsment (IRE) **Mr J. P. McManus**
153 **TOMBEE DU CIEL (FR)**, 4, b f Zanzibari (USA)—In Caso di Neve (FR) **Mr Simon Munir & Mr Isaac Souede**
154 **TOP NOTCH (FR)**, 9, b g Poliglote—Topira (FR) **Mr Simon Munir & Mr Isaac Souede**
155 **TOROLIGHT**, 4, b g Toronado (IRE)—Tuscan Light **Canter Banter Racing**
156 **VALTOR (FR)**, 11, b g Nidor (FR)—Jossca (FR) **Mr Simon Munir & Mr Isaac Souede**
157 **VEGAS BLUE (IRE)**, 5, b m Getaway (GER)—Bella Venezia (IRE) **Crimbourne Bloodstock**
158 **VERDANA BLUE (IRE)**, 8, b m Getaway (GER)—Blue Gallery (IRE) **Mrs D. A. Tabor**
159 **VERSATILITY**, 6, b g Yeats (IRE)—Stravinsky Dance **The Barrow Boys 2**
160 **VOYAGE DE RETOUR (IRE)**, 8, b g Craigsteel—Taipers (IRE) **Mrs E. A. Bingley**
161 **WELSH SAINT (IRE)**, 6, b g Saint des Saints (FR)—Minirose (FR) **Walters Plant Hire & Potter Group**
162 **WENYERREADYFREDDIE (IRE)**, 9, ch g Beneficial—Ware It Vic (IRE) **Mr M. Landau & Mr J. Lightfoot**
163 **WHATSWRONGWITHYOU (IRE)**, 9, ch g Bienamado (USA)—Greenfield Noora (IRE) **5 Hertford Street Racing Club**
164 **WHITLOCK**, 5, ch g Dutch Art—Barynya **Lady Lloyd-Webber**
165 **WILLIAM HENRY (IRE)**, 10, b g King's Theatre (IRE)—Cincuenta (IRE) **Walters Plant Hire Ltd**
166 **WITH DISCRETION (IRE)**, 9, b m Tiger Hill (IRE)—Discreet **Bloomsbury Stud**

Other Owners: R. A. Bartlett, Bloomsbury Stud, Mr J. L. Lightfoot, Mrs S. Magnier, Mr R. B. Waley-Cohen, Walters Plant Hire Ltd.

NH Jockey: James Bowen, Aidan Coleman, Nico De Boinville, Barry Geraghty, Jeremiah McGrath. **Conditional Jockey:** Joe Anderson, Alfie Jordan.

---

269 **MR PAUL HENDERSON, Whitsbury**
Postal: **1 Manor Farm Cottage, Whitsbury, Fordingbridge, Hampshire, SP6 3QP**
Contacts: **PHONE 01725 518113 MOBILE 07958 482213 FAX 01725 518113**
EMAIL phendersonracing@gmail.com

1 **ABBEY STREET (IRE)**, 9, b g Asian Heights—Cnocbui Cailin (IRE) **Mr and Mrs J Baigent**
2 **AMRON KALI (IRE)**, 10, b m Kalanisi (IRE)—Glacial Snowboard (IRE) **Mareildar Racing Part 1**
3 **BIG MAN CLARENCE (IRE)**, 9, b g Golden Tornado (IRE)—Glens Lady (IRE) **Pittville Park**
4 **BRIDGETS CROSS**, 7, b m Getaway (GER)—Kallisti (IRE) **Turbanators**
5 **CRAFTY CODGER (IRE)**, 9, ch g Mastercraftsman (IRE)—Rainbow Melody (IRE) **Mr C. Clark**
6 **CROSSLEY TENDER**, 7, b g Sulamani (IRE)—Slow Starter (IRE) **Hawkings Harding Pearson Pyatt Willis**
7 **DOITFORTHEVILLAGE (IRE)**, 11, b g Turtle Island (IRE)—Last Chance Lady (IRE) **The Rockbourne Partnership**
8 **DUARIGLE (IRE)**, 8, ch g Dubai Destination (USA)—Silver Valley (IRE) **A Pearson E Hawkings M Jenner P Scope**
9 **FETHARD FLYER (IRE)**, 8, b g Brian Boru—Strylea (IRE) **J. P. Duffy**
10 **FOR CARMEL (IRE)**, 10, b g Mr Dinos (IRE)—Bobalena (IRE) **Miss J. Patten**
11 **HATCHET JACK (IRE)**, 8, b g Black Sam Bellamy (IRE)—
                          Identity Parade (IRE) **A J Pearson, Mark Jenner, Ed Hawkings**
12 4, Ch g Gentleware (IRE)—Kylenoe Fairy (IRE) **Mr E. J. Hawkings**
13 **LARCADIO (IRE)**, 7, b g Arcadio (GER)—Le Ciel (IRE) **The Rockbourne Partnership**
14 **LISRONAGH STONE (IRE)**, 7, b g Arcadio (GER)—From Above (IRE) **Table 8**
15 **MAASAI WARRIOR (IRE)**, 5, b g Lovelace—No Case (IRE) **A Pearson E Hawkings M Jenner P Scope**
16 **MEGALODON (IRE)**, 7, b g Getaway (GER)—Fitzgrey (IRE) **Hawkings Finch Harding Stubbs Willis**
17 **MINELLA TWEET (IRE)**, 12, b g King's Theatre (IRE)—Cara Mhaith (IRE) **Michael & Tracie Willis**
18 **MR SCAFF (IRE)**, 6, br g Vocalised (USA)—Nancy Rock (IRE) **M R Scaffolding Services Ltd**
19 **MR STUBBS (IRE)**, 9, b g Robin des Pres (FR)—Crystal Stream (IRE) **Turbanators**
20 **OUR NEST EGG (IRE)**, 7, b m Scorpion (IRE) Little Nest Egg (IRE) **The Two Hats Syndicate**
21 **POLAR LIGHT**, 5, b m Norse Dancer (IRE)—Dimelight **J. P. Duffy**
22 **RING MINELLA (IRE)**, 9, b g King's Theatre (IRE)—Ring of Water (USA) **NHRE Racing Club**
23 **SHAW'S CROSS (IRE)**, 8, b g Mr Dinos (IRE)—Capparoe Cross (IRE) **Mareildar Racing Part 1**
24 **TED BACH (IRE)**, 9, b g Bach (IRE)—Rose Tanner (IRE) **Pittville Park**

MR PAUL HENDERSON - continued

25 **THE GRANSON (IRE),** 8, b g Jeremy (USA)—Kimberely Bay (IRE) **John Finch & Mike & Tracie Willis**
26 **TRUCKERS CAILIN (IRE),** 7, b m Curtain Time (IRE)—Truckers Lady (IRE) **Mr M. Day**
27 **UN BEAU ROMAN (FR),** 12, bl g Roman Saddle (IRE)—Koukie (FR) **Mr J. H. W. Finch**

Other Owners: Mr J. H. W. Finch, Mr B. C. Harding, Mr E. J. Hawkings, Mr M. E. Jenner, Mr A. Pearson, Mr J. Pyatt, Mr P. T. Scope, Mr T. J. Stubbs, Mr M. R. Willis, Mrs T. J. Willis.

270	**MR MICHAEL HERRINGTON, Thirsk**

Postal: **Garbutt Farm, Cold Kirby, Thirsk, North Yorkshire, YO7 2HJ**
Contacts: **MOBILE 07855 396858**
EMAIL info@michaelherringtonracing.co.uk WEBSITE www.michaelherringtonracing.co.uk

1 **ANIF (IRE),** 6, b g Cape Cross (IRE)—Cadenza (FR) **Stuart Herrington & Peter Forster**
2 **ARCHIPPOS,** 7, b g Archipenko (USA)—Sparkling Clear **Stuart Herrington & Peter Forster**
3 **BARBAROSA (IRE),** 4, br g Holy Roman Emperor (IRE)—Snow Scene (IRE) **Mrs H. J. Lloyd-Herrington**
4 **BAY OF NAPLES (IRE),** 4, b g Exceed And Excel (AUS)—Copperbeech (IRE) **Mrs S. E. Lloyd**
5 **CIMETTA,** 5, b m Lucarno (USA)—Nobratinetta (FR) **Reveley Farms**
6 **EDESSANN (IRE),** 4, ch g Lope de Vega (IRE)—Edelmira (IRE) **Mrs H. J. Lloyd-Herrington**
7 **GLORIOUS CHARMER,** 4, b g Charm Spirit (IRE)—Fantacise **Flash Figs Racing**
8 **HEAVENLY RAINBOW (IRE),** 4, b g Havana Gold (IRE)—China Pink **Mrs H. J. Lloyd-Herrington**
9 **JAN VAN HOOF (IRE),** 9, b g Dutch Art—Cosenza **Mrs H. J. Lloyd-Herrington**
10 **KIPLIN,** 5, b g Desideratum—Another Paris **Mr J. D. Spensley & Mrs M. A. Spensley**
11 **KOMMANDER KIRKUP,** 9, ch g Assertive—Bikini **Mrs H. Lloyd-herrington & S. Herrington**
12 **LADY ALAVESA,** 5, b m Westlake—Matilda Peace **Mrs S. E. Lloyd**
13 **MAHARASHTRA,** 4, ch g Schiaparelli (GER)—Khandala (IRE) **Mrs H. J. Lloyd-Herrington**
14 **STEELRIVER (IRE),** 10, b g Iffraaj—Numerus Clausus (FR) **Mrs H. J. Lloyd-Herrington**
15 **STREET POET (IRE),** 7, b g Poet's Voice—Street Star (USA) **Mrs H. J. Lloyd-Herrington**
16 **THAAYER,** 5, b g Helmet (AUS)—Sakhya (IRE) **The Racing Brothers**
17 **THE GAME OF LIFE,** 5, b g Oasis Dream—Velvet Star (IRE) **Mrs H. J. Lloyd-Herrington**

Other Owners: Mr P. D. Forster, Mr J. S. Herrington, Mrs H. J. Lloyd-Herrington, Mr S. Roberts, Mr P. Slater, Mr J. D. Spensley, Mrs M. A. Spensley.

Assistant Trainer: Helen Lloyd-Herrington.

271	**MRS LAWNEY HILL, Aston Rowant**

Postal: **Woodway Farm, Aston Rowant, Watlington, Oxford, OX49 5SJ**
Contacts: **PHONE 01844 353051 MOBILE 07769 862648**
EMAIL lawney@lawneyhill.co.uk WEBSITE www.lawneyhill.co.uk

1 **CLONDAW WESTIE (IRE),** 9, b g Westerner—You're A Native (IRE) **Mrs D. M. Caudwell**
2 **HOT TO TROT,** 6, b m Brian Boru—Commanche Token (IRE) **Mr Martin Redman**
3 **MYSPACENOTYOURS,** 5, b m Dr Massini (IRE)—Home By Midnight **Mr Martin Redman**
4 **SHIMBA HILLS,** 9, b g Sixties Icon—Search Party **Mr A. Hill**
5 **VELVET COGNAC,** 12, b g Grape Tree Road—Scandalous Affair **Mr A. Hill**

272 MR CHARLES HILLS, Lambourn

Postal: **Wetherdown House, Lambourn, Hungerford, Berkshire, RG17 8UB**
Contacts: **PHONE 01488 71548 FAX 01488 72823**
EMAIL info@charleshills.co.uk WEBSITE www.charleshills.com

1   **A MOMENTOFMADNESS**, 7, b g Elnadim (USA)—Royal Blush **Tony Wechsler & Ann Plummer**
2   **AFAAK**, 6, b g Oasis Dream—Ghanaati (USA) **Mr Hamdan Al Maktoum**
3   **BATTAASH (IRE)**, 6, b g Dark Angel (IRE)—Anna Law (IRE) **Mr Hamdan Al Maktoum**
4   **BIN DAAHIR**, 5, b g Exceed And Excel (AUS)—Beach Frolic **Mr Hamdan Al Maktoum**
5   **BREATH OF AIR**, 4, b g Bated Breath—Western Appeal (USA) **Mr K. Abdullah**
6   **BRUSHWORK**, 4, b g Kyllachy—Miss Elegance **Mr K. Abdullah**
7   **CAESONIA**, 4, ch f Garswood—Agrippina **Mrs Fiona Williams**
8   **EQUILATERAL**, 5, b g Equiano (FR)—Tarentaise **Mr K. Abdullah**
9   **GARRUS (IRE)**, 4, gr c Acclamation—Queen of Power (IRE) **Mrs Susan Roy**
10 **HIGH CHANGE (IRE)**, 5, b g High Chaparral (IRE)—Small Change (IRE) **B. W. Hills**
11 **KHAADEM (IRE)**, 4, br c Dark Angel (IRE)—White Daffodil (IRE) **Mr Hamdan Al Maktoum**
12 **MAGICAL MEMORY (IRE)**, 8, gr g Zebedee—Marasem **Kennet Valley Thoroughbreds I**
13 **MAY SONIC**, 4, b g Mayson—Aromatherapy **Hills Angels**
14 **MONYA (IRE)**, 4, gr f Dark Angel (IRE)—Bridal Dance (IRE) **Mr Hamdan Al Maktoum**
15 **MOTAGALLY**, 4, b g Swiss Spirit—Gilt Linked **Mr Hamdan Al Maktoum**
16 **POGO (IRE)**, 4, b c Zebedee—Cute **Gary & Linnet Woodward**
17 **REWAAYAT**, 5, br g Pivotal—Rufoof **Mr Hamdan Al Maktoum**
18 **SPOOF**, 5, b g Poet's Voice—Filona (IRE) **Gary & Linnet Woodward**
19 **VINDOLANDA**, 4, ch f Nathaniel (IRE)—Cartimandua **Mrs Fiona Williams**
20 **VITRUVIUS**, 4, b c Zoffany (IRE)—Domitia **Mrs Fiona Williams**

THREE-YEAR-OLDS

21 **ALPIN KING (IRE)**, b c Free Eagle (IRE)—Rosa's Cantina (IRE) **Mrs Fitri Hay**
22 **ALREHB (USA)**, gr c War Front (USA)—Tahrir (IRE) **Mr Hamdan Al Maktoum**
23 **AT EASE**, b f Oasis Dream—Jostle (USA) **Mr K. Abdullah**
24 **BAASHIR (IRE)**, b c Muhaarar—Eshaadeh (USA) **Mr Hamdan Al Maktoum**
25 **BADRAH (USA)**, ch f Kitten's Joy (USA)—Aqsaam (USA) **Mr Hamdan Al Maktoum**
26 **BADRI**, b c Dark Angel (IRE)—Penny Drops **Mr Hamdan Al Maktoum**
27 **BARRAAQAH (IRE)**, ch f Kitten's Joy (USA)—Bluebell (IRE) **Mr Hamdan Al Maktoum**
28 **BRING HIM HOME (FR)**, ch c Le Havre (USA)—Unaided **Mrs Susan Roy**
29 **BUHTURI (IRE)**, ch g Raven's Pass (USA)—Moon's Whisper (USA) **Mr Hamdan Al Maktoum**
30 **CABLE SPEED (IRE)**, b c Cable Bay (IRE)—Hear My Cry (USA) **Dragon Gate**
31 **CABOT CLIFFS (IRE)**, ch c Gleneagles (IRE)—Hallouella **Mr M Tabor, Mr D Smith & Mrs J Magnier**
32 **COTAI AGAIN (IRE)**, b g Kodiac—Incessant (IRE) **Kangyu Int. Racing (HK) Ltd & Mr F Ma**
33 B c Cacique (IRE)—Domitia **Mrs Fiona Williams**
34 **DULAS (IRE)**, b c Raven's Pass (USA)—Petit Calva (FR) **Julie Martin & David R. Martin & Partner**
35 **ETERNAL SECRET**, b f Muhaarar—Walk On Bye (IRE) **Mrs Susan Roy**
36 **FANTASY BELIEVER (IRE)**, b c Make Believe—Avizare (IRE) **The Fantasy Believer Syndicate**
37 **FAVOURED DESTINY (USA)**, b f Noble Mission—Faraway Flower (USA) **Mr K. Abdullah**
38 **FLEETING PRINCE (IRE)**, b c No Nay Never (USA)—My Sweet Georgia (IRE) **Mrs Susan Roy**
39 **FLIPPA THE STRIPPA (IRE)**, gr f Outstrip—Celsius Degre (IRE) **Mr Christopher Wright**
40 **GAELIC KINGDOM (IRE)**, b g Gleneagles (IRE)—Impressionist Art (USA) **Mrs Fitri Hay**
41 **GINNIANO (IRE)**, b f Equiano (FR)—Guinnevre (IRE) **Mr J. Acheson**
42 **GIUSEPPE CASSIOLI**, b c Bated Breath—Olympic Medal **Mr P. K. Siu**
43 **GLORIOUS RIO (IRE)**, b g Gutaifan (IRE)—Renaissance Rio (IRE) **Kangyu International Racing (HK) Limited**
44 **GLORIOUS ZOFF (IRE)**, b g Zoffany (IRE)—Ardbrae Lady **Kangyu International Racing (HK) Limited**
45 **GLORY DAB (FR)**, b g Dabirsim (FR)—Aziali **Kangyu International Racing (HK) Limited**
46 **HAIDA GWAII (IRE)**, b f Zoffany (IRE)—Briolette (IRE) **International Plywood (Importers) Ltd**
47 **KING'S KNIGHT (IRE)**, b c Dark Angel (IRE)—Oatcake **Mr Ziad A. Galadari**
48 **MISS VILLANELLE**, b f Ivawood (IRE)—Parabola **Mr J H Widdows & Partners**
49 Ch g Bated Breath—Movementneverlies **Mrs Fitri Hay**
50 **MR WILTON (IRE)**, b c Raven's Pass (USA)—Full Moon Fever (IRE) **Mrs Fitri Hay**
51 **NEW ZEALANDER**, b g Australia—Dalasyla (IRE) **Sir P Vela, Triermore, P Stanley**
52 **PERSUASION (IRE)**, b c Acclamation—Effervesce (IRE) **Mrs Susan Roy**
53 **QUIET NIGHT (IRE)**, b f Dark Angel (IRE)—Pindrop **B. W. Hills**

MR CHARLES HILLS - continued

54 **RAAJIN**, b g Raven's Pass (USA)—Atab (IRE) **Mr Hamdan Al Maktoum**
55 **RONDO (USA)**, b c Twirling Candy (USA)—Short Dance (USA) **Mr K. Abdullah**
56 **ROYAL COMMANDO (IRE)**, b c No Nay Never (USA)—Online Alexander (IRE) **Mr Ziad A. Galadari**
57 **SEA THE GLORY**, b g Sea The Stars (IRE)—Full), (IRE) **Kangyu Int. Racing (HK) Ltd & Mr F Ma**
58 **SHATHA (USA)**, b f Muhaarar—Lear's Princess (USA) **Mr Hamdan Al Maktoum**
59 **SHURAFFA (IRE)**, b f Shamardal (USA)—Shamtari (IRE) **Mr Hamdan Al Maktoum**
60 **SMART CONNECTION (IRE)**, b c Dutch Art—Endless Love (IRE) **Mrs Susan Roy**
61 **SPUROFTHEMOMENT**, b f Brazen Beau (AUS)—Royal Blush **Tony Wechsler & Ann Plummer**
62 **SWELL SWILLY (IRE)**, ch g Australia—Wewantitall **Mr John C Grant & Partner**
63 **TAAMEEN**, ch c Showcasing—Puzzling **Mr Hamdan Al Maktoum**
64 **TAMEEMAH**, b f Dawn Approach (IRE)—Reyaadah **Mr Hamdan Al Maktoum**
65 **TILSIT (USA)**, b c First Defence (USA)—Multilingual **Mr K. Abdullah**
66 **TOMMY DE VITO**, b c Dandy Man (IRE)—Rohlindi **Chelsea Thoroughbreds - Goodfellas**
67 **TRIPLE GLORY**, b f Cable Bay (IRE)—Triple Star **Kangyu International Racing (HK) Limited**
68 **TURAATH**, b f Oasis Dream—Fadhayyil (IRE) **Mr Hamdan Al Maktoum**
69 **VIVIDLY**, b f Charm Spirit (IRE)—Zero Gravity **Mr K. Abdullah**
70 **YOU'RE SO VAIN (IRE)**, ch f Australia—Iffraaj Pink (IRE) **Mrs Fitri Hay**

TWO-YEAR-OLDS

71 B f 13/03 Exceed And Excel (AUS)—Adhwaa (Oasis Dream)
72 **ALTAAYSHSH (IRE)**, b f 22/01 Dark Angel (IRE)—Anna Law (IRE) (Lawman (FR))
73 **AMLWCH (IRE)**, b c 19/03 Muhaarar—Nations Alexander (IRE) (Dark Angel (IRE))
74 B f 07/02 Cable Bay (IRE)—Angels Wings (IRE) (Dark Angel (IRE)) (100000)
75 B f 14/04 Hard Spun (USA)—Anne of Kiev (IRE) (Oasis Dream) (51480)
76 **ARTHUR CONAN DOYLE**, b c 12/04 Oasis Dream—Secret Keeper (New Approach (IRE)) (49523)
77 B c 01/04 Mustajeeb—Atab (IRE) (New Approach (IRE))
78 B c 22/01 Kodi Bear (IRE)—Coup de Main (IRE) (Oasis Dream) (32000)
79 B c 15/03 Estidhkaar (IRE)—Cumbfree (IRE) (Footstepsinthesand) (60000)
80 B c 07/03 Footstepsinthesand—Dance On The Hill (IRE) (Danehill Dancer (IRE)) (32000)
81 **DIAMOND FIFE**, b f 23/04 Excelebration (IRE)—Chelsea Morning (USA) (Giant's Causeway (USA))
82 **DISCOTEQUE (IRE)**, b f 07/03 Acclamation—Party For Ever (IRE) (Iffraaj)
83 B c 10/03 Gleneagles (IRE)—Endless Love (IRE) (Dubai Destination (USA))
84 Ch f 12/03 Dutch Art—Finishingthethat (Sixties Icon)
85 B c 26/04 Exceed And Excel (AUS)—Garra Molly (IRE) (Nayef (USA)) (62000)
86 B c 29/03 Invincible Spirit (IRE)—Ghanaati (USA) (Giant's Causeway (USA))
87 B c 10/03 Muhaarar—Heho (Dansili) (50000)
88 **IBIZA ROCKS**, gr c 10/04 Dark Angel (IRE)—The Thrill Is Gone (Bahamian Bounty) (70000)
89 **IL BANDITO (IRE)**, b c 30/01 Acclamation—Molly Dolly (IRE) (Exceed And Excel (AUS)) (154440)
90 B f 31/03 Muhaarar—Inyordreams (Teofilo (IRE)) (78000)
91 B c 13/04 Shalaa (IRE)—Las Brisas (Shamardal (USA)) (38095)
92 **LE ROI LION (ITY)**, b c 10/03 Camacho—Delia Eria (IRE) (Zamindar (USA)) (38609)
93 **MENAI BRIDGE**, b c 05/04 Cable Bay (IRE)—Sonnellino (Singspiel (IRE)) (25740)
94 Br c 03/03 Dark Angel (IRE)—Misdaqeya (Red Ransom (USA))
95 **MOBARHIN (IRE)**, b c 09/04 Muhaarar—Fadhayyil (IRE) (Tamayuz)
96 **MOQADAMA (IRE)**, b f 16/02 Dark Angel (IRE)—White Daffodil (IRE) (Footstepsinthesand) (390000)
97 **MORAWETH (USA)**, ch c 29/03 Speightstown—Istiraaha (Tapit (USA))
98 **MUJBAR**, b c 12/03 Muhaarar—Madany (IRE) (Acclamation)
99 B c 27/02 Equiano (FR)—Penny Drops (Invincible Spirit (IRE)) (47619)
100 **PONTIUS (IRE)**, b c 24/04 No Nay Never (USA)—Sacrament (IRE) (Acclamation) (70000)
101 Ch f 05/05 Starspangledbanner (AUS)—Private Dancer (FR) (Green Tune (USA))
102 B f 25/03 Kodiac—Qawaasem (IRE) (Shamardal (USA))
103 Br c 23/01 Dark Angel (IRE)—Relation Alexander (IRE) (Dandy Man (IRE)) (138095)
104 **RHOSCOLYN**, b c 14/03 Territories (IRE)—Zeyran (IRE) (Galileo (IRE)) (75000)
105 B g 13/03 Showcasing—Royal Confidence (Royal Applause)
106 B f 09/04 Iffraaj—Royal Empress (IRE) (Holy Roman Emperor (IRE)) (67000)
107 **ROYAL MUSKETEER**, b c 04/03 Acclamation—Queen's Pearl (IRE) (Exceed And Excel (AUS))
108 B c 12/04 Invincible Spirit (IRE)—Rufoof (Zamindar (USA))
109 **SARATOGA GOLD**, ch c 27/03 Mayson—Lady Sylvia (Haafhd)
110 Gr f 27/04 Dark Angel (IRE)—Shawka (Oasis Dream)

MR CHARLES HILLS - continued

111 B c 19/01 Starspangledbanner (AUS)—Sorry Woman (FR) (Ivan Denisovich)
112 Gr f 16/02 Starspangledbanner (AUS)—Sparkling (IRE) (Dark Angel (IRE)) (42900)
113 B f 02/03 Muhaarar—Spirit Of Winning (Invincible Spirit (IRE))
114 B c 30/03 Dawn Approach (IRE)—Stylish One (IRE) (Invincible Spirit (IRE)) (55000)
115 B f 31/03 Oasis Dream—Super Sleuth (IRE) (Selkirk (USA)) (42000)
116 B c 12/02 Equiano (FR)—Terse (Dansili)
117 B c 17/03 Acclamation—Thakerah (IRE) (New Approach (IRE)) (64349)
118 **THE ATTORNEY (IRE),** b c 05/05 Kodiac—Next Trial (IRE) (Hard Spun (USA)) (100000)
119 B c 18/03 Markaz (IRE)—Wardat Dubai (Mawatheeq)
120 **WHITE LADY (IRE),** b f 03/03 Dark Angel (IRE)—Wiltshire Life (IRE) (Camacho) (68640)
121 Ch c 01/03 Belardo (IRE)—You're Back (USA) (Street Cry (IRE)) (135000)
122 B c 19/02 Mukhadram—Zaakhir (IRE) (Raven's Pass (USA))

Other Owners: Mr N. N. Browne, Chelsea Thoroughbreds ltd - Sherlock Holmes, John Dance, Mr Jeremy Gompertz, Mr Dan Hall, Martin Hughes, Mr D M James, David J Keast, Kennet Valley Thoroughbreds II, Michael Kerr-Dineen, Mr Paul McNamara, Mr Robin Millar, A O'Callaghan, J Allison, P Hills, Mrs Mary-Anne Parker.

Assistant Trainer: Joe Herbert, Jamie Insole.

Apprentice Jockey: Owen Lewis.

273	**MR MARK HOAD, Lewes**

Postal: **Windmill Lodge Stables, Spital Road, Lewes, East Sussex, BN7 1LS**
Contacts: **PHONE 01273 480691, 01273 477124 MOBILE 07742 446168 FAX 01273 477124**
EMAIL markhoad@aol.com

1 CHUTZPAH (IRE), 4, b g Alhebayeb (IRE)—Cheeky Weeky **Mrs K. B. Tester**
2 HEY HO LET'S GO, 4, b c Dream Ahead (USA)—Lookslikeanangel **Mrs K. B. Tester**
3 HURRICANE ALERT, 8, b g Showcasing—Raggle Taggle (IRE) **Mr M. R. Baldry**
4 SEA'S ARIA (IRE), 9, b g Sea The Stars (IRE)—Speed Song **Mrs K. B. Tester**

THREE-YEAR-OLDS

5 BROUGHTONS COMPASS, b g Henrythenavigator (USA)—Sayrianna **Broughton Thermal Insulations**
6 COTEAUX DU LAYON, b g Gregorian (IRE)—Jocasta Dawn **R. P. C. Hoad**

274	**MR PHILIP HOBBS, Minehead**

Postal: **Sandhill, Bilbrook, Minehead, Somerset, TA24 6HA**
Contacts: **PHONE 01984 640366 MOBILE 07860 729795 FAX 01984 641124**
EMAIL pjhobbs@pjhobbs.com WEBSITE www.pjhobbs.com

1 ALLENBY (IRE), 5, b g Presenting—Raya Light (IRE) **Mrs D. L. Whateley**
2 AT ITS OWN EXPENSE (IRE), 6, ch g Arakan (USA)—Blow A Gasket (IRE) **South Meadow Racing I**
3 AWAKE AT MIDNIGHT, 8, b g Midnight Legend—Wakeful **Mrs S. L. Lloyd-Baker**
4 BALLOTIN (FR), 9, b g Enrique—Orphee de Vonnas (FR) **David Maxwell Racing Limited**
5 BARBROOK STAR (IRE), 8, b g Getaway (GER)—Fille de Robin (FR) **Mrs B. A. Hitchcock**
6 BEAU DU BRIZAIS (FR), 8, gr g Kapgarde (FR)—Belle du Brizais (FR) **Mrs C. Skan**
7 BIG SHARK (IRE), 6, b g Vinnie Roe (IRE)—Castlelost (IRE) **Mrs C Walsh & Eden Valley Chancers**
8 5, Ch h Arakan (USA)—Blow A Gasket (IRE) **Mrs L. R. Lovell**
9 BROTHER TEDD, 11, gr g Kayf Tara—Neltina **Scrase Farms**
10 CALL SIMON (IRE), 5, b g Fame And Glory—All My Judges **Bradley Partnership**
11 CAPE MILANO (IRE), 5, b br g Milan—Shatani (IRE) **Mrs J. A. S. Luff**
12 CHEF D'EQUIPE (FR), 8, b g Presenting—Millesimee (FR) **David Maxwell Racing Limited**
13 COTSWOLD WAY (IRE), 7, b g Stowaway—Rosies All The Way **Miss I. D. Du Pre**
14 CROOKS PEAK, 7, b g Arcadio (GER)—Ballcrina Girl (IRE) **Mr C. A. H. Tilley**
15 DARK EPISODE (IRE), 6, b g Getaway (GER)—No Moore Bills **Louisville Syndicate Elite**

MR PHILIP HOBBS - continued

16 **DEFI DU SEUIL (FR)**, 7, b g Voix du Nord (FR)—Quarvine du Seuil (FR) **Mr J. P. McManus**
17 **DEISE ABA (IRE)**, 7, b g Mahler—Kit Massini (IRE) **Mr T. J. Hemmings**
18 **DEMOPOLIS (FR)**, 6, b g Poliglote—Princess Demut (GER) **Mr J. P. McManus**
19 **DIPLOMATE SIVOLA (FR)**, 7, ch g Noroit (GER)—None de Sivola (FR) **David Maxwell Racing Limited**
20 **DOLPHIN SQUARE (IRE)**, 6, b g Shantou (USA)—Carrig Eden Lass (IRE) **David Maxwell Racing Limited**
21 **DOSTAL PHIL (FR)**, 7, b g Coastal Path—Quiphile (FR) **Mr J. P. McManus**
22 **EARTH LORD (IRE)**, 4, ch g Mahler—Glebe Beauty (IRE) **R. M. Penny**
23 **EARTH MOOR (IRE)**, 6, ch g Ask—Merrylas (IRE) **Mrs C. E. Penny**
24 **EBONY GALE**, 6, br g Shirocco (GER)—Glenora Gale (IRE) **Mrs J. A. S. Luff**
25 **ECU DE LA NOVERIE (FR)**, 6, b g Linda's Lad—Quat'sous d'Or (FR) **David Maxwell Racing Limited**
26 **ESPION (FR)**, 6, ch g Coastal Path—Toutamie (FR) **Mr Michael & Mrs Norma Tuckey**
27 **ET APRES THOU (FR)**, 6, b g Network (GER)—Lady Thou (FR) **Dr V. M. G. Ferguson**
28 **EVERGLOW**, 5, br g Presenting—Cent Prime **Mr P. A. Munnelly**
29 **EVIDENCE DE THAIX (FR)**, 6, b m Network (GER)—Nacre de Thaix (FR) **Mr J. P. McManus**
30 **FEUILLE DE CHENE (FR)**, 5, b m Montmartre (FR)—Haldiana (FR) **Mr J. P. McManus**
31 **FILOU DES ISSARDS (FR)**, 5, ch g Network (GER)—Rapiere (FR) **S & G Soils Limited**
32 **FLINCK (IRE)**, 6, b g Fame And Glory—Princess Supreme (IRE) **R. A. Bartlett**
33 **FLYING TIGER (IRE)**, 7, bl g Soldier of Fortune (IRE)—Ma Preference (FR) **The Macaroni Beach Society**
34 **FOR LANGY (FR)**, 5, b g Day Flight—Jubilee II (FR) **David Maxwell Racing Limited**
35 **FOREVER DES LONG (FR)**, 5, b g Blue Bresil (FR)—Fetuque Du Moulin (FR) **Taunton Racecourse Owners Club**
36 **FROM THE HEART (IRE)**, 6, b g Jeremy—Zephyr Lilly (IRE) **Mr R. Whitehorn**
37 **GALA BALL (IRE)**, 10, b g Flemensfirth (USA)—Nuit des Chartreux (FR) **R. & Mrs J. E. Gibbs**
38 **GARDE LA VICTOIRE (FR)**, 11, b g Kapgarde (FR)—Next Victory (FR) **Mrs D. L. Whateley**
39 **GAVROCHEKA (FR)**, 4, b f Spanish Moon (USA)—Troika (FR) **Mr J. P. McManus**
40 **GELBOE DE CHANAY (FR)**, 4, b f Rail Link—Rose Celebre (FR) **Mr J. P. McManus**
41 **GLENTRUAN (IRE)**, 5, b g Getaway (GER)—Mac Idol (IRE) **Mr T. J. Hemmings**
42 **GOLDEN SOVEREIGN (IRE)**, 6, b g Gold Well—Fugal Maid (IRE) **Mr L. Quinn**
43 **GOSHEVEN (IRE)**, 7, b g Presenting—Fair Choice (IRE) **The Grocer Syndicate**
44 **GUERNESEY (FR)**, 4, gr g Martaline—Myrtille Jersey (FR) **J. T. Warner**
45 **GUMBALL (FR)**, 6, gr g No Risk At All (FR)—Good Time Girl (FR) **J. T. Warner**
46 **HALLOWEEN HARRY (IRE)**, 7, b g Wareed (IRE)—Leteminletemout (IRE) **Mr S. P. Marsh**
47 **HONORARY COLONEL (IRE)**, 4, b g Ocovango—Mushagak (IRE) **Mr A. E. Peterson**
48 **HORSE FORCE ONE (IRE)**, 9, b g Kalanisi (IRE)—Oilpainting (IRE) **Govier & Brown**
49 **IMPERIAL PRESENCE (IRE)**, 9, ch g Presenting—Penneyrose Bay **Sir Christopher & Lady Wates**
50 **JATILUWIH (IRE)**, 6, ch g Linda's Lad—Jaune de Beaufai (FR) **David Maxwell Racing Limited**
51 **JERRYSBACK (IRE)**, 8, b g Jeremy (USA)—Get A Few Bob Back (IRE) **Mr J. P. McManus**
52 **KALOOKI (GER)**, 6, b g Martaline—Karuma (GER) **Mr A. L. Cohen**
53 **KATIES ESCAPE (IRE)**, 5, ch m Getaway (GER)—Katies Pet (IRE) **The Philip Hobbs Racing Partnership**
54 **KAYF ADVENTURE**, 9, b g Kayf Tara—My Adventure (IRE) **Louisville Syndicate**
55 **KEEP MOVING (FR)**, 8, b g Linda's Lad—Keeping Gold (FR) **The Country Side**
56 **KEEP ROLLING (IRE)**, 7, ch g Mahler—Kayles Castle (IRE) **Mick Fitzgerald Racing Club**
57 **KEEP WONDERING (IRE)**, 6, b g Scorpion (IRE)—Supreme Touch (IRE) **Andy Bell & Fergus Lyons**
58 **LARKBARROW LAD**, 7, b g Kayf Tara—Follow My Leader (IRE) **The Englands and Heywoods**
59 **LE LIGERIEN (FR)**, 7, b g Turgeon (USA)—Etoile de Loir (FR) **D. R. Churches**
60 **LITTLE RIVER BAY (IRE)**, 5, b m Shirocco (GER)—Penneyrose Bay **Sir Christopher & Lady Wates**
61 **LONGSHANKS (IRE)**, 6, b g Scorpion (IRE)—Cash A Lawn (IRE) **Unity Farm Holiday Centre Ltd**
62 **LUTTRELL LAD (IRE)**, 4, b g Beat Hollow—Fairly Definite (IRE) **Owners for Owners Luttrell Lad**
63 **MAJESTIC TOUCH (IRE)**, 9, br g Kalanisi (IRE)—Alexander Divine **N. R. A. Sutton**
64 **MASTER WORK (FR)**, 7, b g Network (GER)—Mascarpone (FR) **Mr B K Peppiatt & Mr D R Peppiatt**
65 **MASTERS LEGACY (IRE)**, 5, br g Getaway (GER)—Gently Go (IRE) **Mrs P. M. Bosley**
66 **MCNAMARAS BAND (IRE)**, 7, b g Getaway (GER)—Katies Pet (IRE) **Tim Syder & Dominic Burke**
67 **MELEKHOV (IRE)**, 6, b g Sholokhov (IRE)—Yorkshire Girl (IRE) **Owners For Owners: Melekhov**
68 **MIDNIGHT GLORY**, 8, b m Midnight Legend—Land of Glory **Mrs L. R. Lovell**
69 **MUSICAL SLAVE (IRE)**, 7, b g Getaway (GER)—Inghwung **Mr J. P. McManus**
70 **NO COMMENT**, 9, br g Kayf Tara—Dizzy Frizzy **Mr J. P. McManus**
71 **NO STRANGERS HERE (IRE)**, 6, b br g Yeats—Just A Super Mare (IRE) **The Juwireya Partnership**
72 **OAKLEY (IRE)**, 7, b g Oscar (IRE)—Tirolean Dance (IRE) **Mr T. D. J. Syder**
73 **OFF THE PLANET (IRE)**, 5, ch g Presenting—Kings Diva (IRE) **Mr & Mrs Paul & Clare Rooney**
74 **OLLY GOLLY**, 7, gr g Kapgarde (FR)—As You Leave (FR) **F. R. Jarvey**

MR PHILIP HOBBS - continued

75 **ONE FOR YOU (IRE)**, 5, b g Yeats (IRE)—Tempest Belle (IRE) **Mr & Mrs Paul & Clare Rooney**
76 **PILEON (IRE)**, 6, b g Yeats (IRE)—Heath Heaven **Mr Tim Syder & Martin St Quinton**
77 **POINTED AND SHARP (IRE)**, 8, b g Scorpion (IRE)—Leamybe (IRE) **Tony Staple & George Giles**
78 **POL CROCAN (IRE)**, 5, br g Shirocco (GER)—She's All That (IRE) **Mrs C. Skan**
79 **POTTERS VENTURE (IRE)**, 6, b g Arcadio (GER)—Starventure (IRE) **Mr A. E. Peterson**
80 **PRESUMING ED (IRE)**, 5, b g Westerner—Maracana (IRE) **Louisville Syndicate II**
81 **RAGNAR**, 4, b g Toronado (IRE)—Inner Sea (USA) **Lydia's Boys**
82 **RAVEN COURT (IRE)**, 6, b g Court Cave (IRE)—Lady Kate Ellen (IRE) **Mr T. J. Hemmings**
83 **REIKERS ISLAND (IRE)**, 7, b g Yeats (IRE)—Moricana (GER) **The Hon J. R. Drummond**
84 **ROCK THE KASBAH (IRE)**, 10, ch g Shirocco (GER)—Impudent (IRE) **Mrs D. L. Whateley**
85 **ROLLING DYLAN (IRE)**, 9, ch g Indian River (FR)—Easter Saturday (IRE) **Miss I. D. Du Pre**
86 **SAMBURU SHUJAA (FR)**, 7, b g Poliglote—Girelle (FR) **R. & Mrs J. E. Gibbs**
87 **SANDY BOY (IRE)**, 6, b g Tajraasi (USA)—Annienoora (IRE) **Mrs B. A. Hitchcock**
88 **SAUCY POEM (IRE)**, 5, b m Yeats (IRE)—Saucy Present (IRE) **Hot To Trot Racing**
89 **SHANTOU SUNSET**, 6, ch m Shantou (USA)—Kingara **The Philip Hobbs Racing Partnership**
90 **SINGAPORE SAGA**, 5, b m Midnight Legend—Kim Tian Road (IRE) **Mr D. J. Burke**
91 **SMARTY WILD**, 6, b g Fair Mix (IRE)—Blaeberry **Mr Michael & Mrs Norma Tuckey**
92 **SPORTING JOHN (IRE)**, 5, b br g Getaway (GER)—Wild Spell (IRE) **Mr J. P. McManus**
93 **SPRINGTOWN LAKE (IRE)**, 8, b g Gamut (IRE)—Sprightly Gal (IRE) **Mr T. D. J. Syder**
94 **ST BARTS (IRE)**, 6, b g High Chaparral (IRE)—Lindeman (IRE) **Mr & Mrs R. G. Kelvin-Hughes**
95 **STEELY ADDITION (IRE)**, 8, b g Craigsteel—Blond's Addition (IRE) **Step By Step**
96 **STERNRUBIN (GER)**, 9, b g Authorized (IRE)—Sworn Mum (GER) **J. T. Warner**
97 **STORM FORCE BEN (IRE)**, 6, b g Fame And Glory—Torduff Storm (IRE) **Dr V. M. G. Ferguson**
98 **STRONG PURSUIT (IRE)**, 10, ch g Flemensfirth (USA)—Loughaderra (IRE) **Mr T. D. J. Syder**
99 **SURTITLE (IRE)**, 4, b g Presenting—Annabaloo (IRE) **Mrs V. F. Burke**
100 **TEN SIXTY (IRE)**, 10, br g Presenting—Senora Snoopy (IRE) **Mr A. L. Cohen**
101 **THYME HILL**, 6, b g Kayf Tara—Rosita Bay **The Englands and Heywoods**
102 **TIDAL FLOW**, 7, b g Black Sam Bellamy (IRE)—Mrs Philip **Brocade Racing**
103 **TRUCKERS PASS (IRE)**, 6, br g Kalanisi (IRE)—Lady Knightess (IRE) **Brocade Racing**
104 **TRUCKIN AWAY (IRE)**, 7, br g Getaway (IRE)—Simons Girl (IRE) **Brocade Racing**
105 **UMNDENI (FR)**, 6, b br g Balko (FR)—Marie Royale (FR) **St Quinton, D.L. Whateley & Syder**
106 **VANGO DE VAIGE (FR)**, 7, b g Great Pretender (IRE)—Yellow Park (FR) **M. Short**
107 **WAR SOUND**, 11, b g Kayf Tara—Come The Dawn **The Englands and Heywoods**
108 **WESTEND STORY (IRE)**, 9, b g Westerner—Sarahall (IRE) **Mick Fitzgerald Racing Club**
109 **WHATSTHECRAICJACK**, 7, gr g Crosspeace (IRE)—Maid of Silver **Mike & Jordan Ford**
110 **WILDFIRE WARRIOR (IRE)**, 5, b g Flemensfirth (USA)—Lady of Fortune (IRE) **Mrs D. L. Whateley**
111 **WINTER GETAWAY (IRE)**, 7, b m Getaway (GER)—Galzig (IRE) **The Kingpins**
112 **ZANZA (IRE)**, 6, b g Arcadio (GER)—What A Bleu (IRE) **Louisville Syndicate Elite**
113 **ZIZANEUR (FR)**, 5, b g Planteur (IRE)—Zitana (FR) **David Maxwell Racing Limited**
114 **ZOFFEE**, 4, b g Zoffany (IRE)—Mount Crystal (IRE) **Mr A. E. Peterson**

Other Owners: Mr A. J. Bell, Mrs T. Bell, Blythe Stables LLP, Mrs A. E. M. Broom, Mr G. R. Broom, Mrs J. L. Buckingham, Mr K. Buckle, Mr D. J. Burke, Mr J. P. Cooper, R. W. Devlin, Miss I. D. Du Pre, Eden Valley Chancers, Mr A. D. England, Mrs E. England, Mr J. M. R. Ford, Mr M. W. Ford, H. R. Gibbs, Mrs J. E. Gibbs, Mr G. R. Giles, Mr A. H. Heywood, Mr A. S. Heywood, Mrs C. Lyons, Mr F. Lyons, Fergus & Caroline Lyons, B. K. Peppiatt, D. R. Peppiatt, Mrs L. J. Roper, N. C. Savery, Exors of the Late Mrs J. E. Scrase, Mr J. M. Scrase, Mr N. D. Scrase, Mr M. G. St Quinton, A. P. Staple, Step By Step Supporting Independence Ltd, Mr T. D. J. Syder, Mr D. W. Symondson, M. J. Tuckey, Mrs N. Tuckey, C. J. M. Walker, Mrs C. J. Walsh, Sir Christopher Wates, Lady G. F. Wates, Mrs D. L. Whateley.

Assistant Trainer: Johnson White.

NH Jockey: Richard Johnson, Micheal Nolan, Tom O'Brien. **Conditional Jockey:** Sean Houlihan, Ben Jones.
Amateur Jockey: Mr Tom Doggrell, Mr Stefan Kirwan, Mr David Maxwell, Mr Nathan Vergne.

275 MISS CLARE HOBSON, Royston
Postal: **The Woolpack, London Road, Reed, Royston, Hertfordshire, SG8 8BB**
Contacts: **MOBILE 07966 734889**
EMAIL clarehobsonracing@gmail.com

1 **4**, B f Champs Elysees—A Lulu Ofa Menifee (USA) **Mr G. Molen**
2 **BRIGHT SAFFRON**, 5, ch m Champs Elysees—Mercy Pecksniff **Smith's Wapping Partnership**
3 **BULLSEMPIRE (IRE)**, 7, b g Papal Bull—Satanella (IRE) **The Fox and Duck syndicate**
4 **DHARMA RAIN (IRE)**, 5, b m High Chaparral (IRE)—Crazy Volume (IRE) **Mr B. White**
5 **FOXY SINGER (FR)**, 5, b m Secret Singer (FR)—Newport (FR) **Mr H. R. Hobson**
6 **JIMMY MAC**, 4, b g Malinas (GER)—Flo The Machine (IRE)
7 **4**, B g Ask—Kayfs Fancy (IRE)
8 **KING CNUT (FR)**, 6, ch g Kentucky Dynamite (USA)—Makadane **Mr H. R. Hobson**
9 **LOST ON YOU**, 5, b m Lord Shanakill (USA)—If Or When (IRE) **Greg Molen & Harry Hobson**
10 **MR NICE GUY (IRE)**, 4, b g Nathaniel (IRE)—Three Choirs (IRE) **Mr L. Brooks**
11 **OLDABBEY BRIDGE (IRE)**, 6, b g Morozov (USA)—Jacks Joy (IRE) **Mrs R. E. Hobson**
12 **THE TURFACCOUNTANT (IRE)**, 4, b g Ask—Kayfs Fancy (IRE)
13 **UNCLE O**, 6, gr g Fair Mix (IRE)—Clever Liz **The Fox and Duck syndicate**

Other Owners: Mr H. R. Hobson, Mr G. Molen.

Assistant Trainer: Harry Hobson.

276 MR RICHARD HOBSON, Little Rissington
Postal: **Bobble Barn Farm, Little Rissington, Cheltenham, Gloucestershire, GL54 2NE**
Contacts: **PHONE 01451 820535 MOBILE 07939 155843**
EMAIL hobson.r1@sky.com WEBSITE www.richardhobsonracing.co.uk

1 **ALLYSSON MONTERG (FR)**, 10, b g Network (GER)—Mellyssa (FR) **Mr D. W. Fox**
2 **CHIC NAME (FR)**, 8, b g Nickname (FR)—Vuelta Al Ruedo (FR) **The Boom Syndicate**
3 **DEFI SACRE (FR)**, 7, b g Network (GER)—Iowa Sacree (FR) **Mr R. I. H. Wills**
4 **DISCKO DES PLAGES (FR)**, 7, b g Balko (FR)—Lady des Plages (FR) **Mr G. C. Farr**
5 **ECHO WATT (FR)**, 6, gr g Fragrant Mix (IRE)—Roxane du Bois (FR) **The Boom Syndicate**
6 **EUREU DU BOULAY (FR)**, 6, b g Della Francesca (USA)—Idole du Boulay (FR) **Mr N. Allen & Mr R. Hobson**
7 **FANZIO (FR)**, 5, b g Day Flight—Tu L'As Eu (FR) **Mr N. Allen & Mr R. Hobson**
8 **IBIS DU RHEU (FR)**, 9, b g Blue Bresil (FR)—Dona du Rheu (FR) **Mr D. W. Fox**
9 **LORD DU MESNIL (FR)**, 7, b g Saint des Saints (FR)—Ladies Choice (FR) **P. Porter**
10 **PETIVILLE (FR)**, 8, gr g Montmartre (FR)—Aegle (IRE) **Mr R. H. Hobson**
11 **RAMONEX (GER)**, 9, b g Saddex—Ramondia (GER) **Mr R. H. Hobson**
12 **VALADOM (FR)**, 11, gr g Dadarissime (FR)—Laurana (FR) **Mr R. H. Hobson**
13 **WHO'S MY JOCKEY (IRE)**, 7, b g Yeats (IRE)—Scandisk (IRE) **Carl Hinchy & Mark Scott**

Other Owners: N. J. Allen, Mr C. S. Hinchy, Mr R. H. Hobson, Mr M. S. Scott.

Assistant Trainer: Shirley Jane Becker, **Head Lad:** Dawson Lees.

NH Jockey: James Bowen, Danny Cook. **Conditional Jockey:** Jordan Nailor, Paul O'Brien.

277 MR JOHN HODGE, Cumnock
Postal: **Corbie Lodge, Muirdyke Farm, Cumnock, Ayrshire, KA18 2SG**

1 **POYLE GEORGE TWO**, 5, b g Sepoy (AUS)—Poyle Dee Dee **Turf Talk Racing Club**
2 **REAVER (IRE)**, 7, b g Sabiango (GER)—Mattinata **Turf Talk Racing Club**

278 MR RON HODGES, Somerton
Postal: **Little Orchard, George Street, Charlton Adam, Somerton, Somerset, TA11 7AS**
Contacts: **PHONE 01458 223922 MOBILE 07770 625846**
EMAIL **mandyhodges@btconnect.com**

1 BEQUEST, 4, b f Equiano (FR)—Bandanna **Exors of the Late Miss R. J. Dobson**
2 DAYTIME AHEAD (IRE), 9, gr m Daylami (IRE)—Bright Times Ahead (IRE) **Mrs Jan Dare, R J Hodges**
3 DREAMS OF GLORY, 12, ch g Resplendent Glory (IRE)—Pip's Dream **P. E. Axon**
4 HERE'S TWO, 7, b m Hellvelyn—There's Two (IRE) **K Corcoran, C E Weare, R J Hodges**
5 MAJESTIC MERLIN, 5, b g Midnight Legend—Posh Emily **J.L & P Frampton A.M Midgley R.J Hodges**
6 MET BY MOONLIGHT, 6, b m Sakhee's Secret—Starlight Walk **P. E. Axon**
7 MISTER MUSICMASTER, 11, b g Amadeus Wolf—Misty Eyed (IRE) **R. J. Hodges**

Other Owners: K. J. Corcoran, Mrs J. M. Dare, J. L. Frampton, Mr P. S. Frampton, John Frampton & Paul Frampton, R. J. Hodges, A. M. Midgley, Mr C. E. Weare.

279 MR HENRY HOGARTH, Stillington
Postal: **New Grange Farm, Stillington, York**
Contacts: **PHONE 01347 811168 MOBILE 07788 777044 FAX 01347 811168**
EMAIL **harryhogarth@ymail.com**

1 BOSS DES MOTTES (FR), 9, b g Califet (FR)—Puszta des Mottes (FR) **Hogarth Racing**
2 GOLDRAPPER (IRE), 7, b g Gold Well—Mrs Bukay (IRE) **Hogarth Racing**
3 GRAND ENTERPRISE, 10, b g Fair Mix (IRE)—Miss Chinchilla **Hogarth Racing**
4 GRIS DE PRON (FR), 7, b g Gris de Gris (IRE)—Say Say (FR) **Hogarth Racing**
5 HATTONS HILL (IRE), 11, b g Pierre—Cluain Chaoin (IRE) **Hogarth Racing**
6 JACK LAMB, 8, gr g Sulamani (IRE)—Charlotte Lamb **Hogarth Racing**
7 KAMIL (GER), 7, ch g Sholokhov (IRE)—Kastoria (GER) **Hogarth Racing**
8 KILCULLEN LADY (IRE), 10, b m Scorpion (IRE)—Glittering Star (IRE) **Hogarth Racing**
9 MANCE RAYDER (IRE), 7, b g Flemensfirth (USA)—J'Y Viens (FR) **Hogarth Racing**
10 THE BLACK SQUIRREL (IRE), 7, br g Craigsteel—Terra Lucida (IRE) **Hogarth Racing**
11 WOOD EMERY (FR), 8, b g Califet (FR)—Take Emery (FR) **Hogarth Racing**

Other Owners: Mr H. P. Hogarth, J. Hogarth, J. L. Hogarth, P. H. Hogarth.

Assistant Trainer: Russ Garritty.

NH Jockey: Jamie Hamilton. Conditional Jockey: Billy Garritty. Amateur Jockey: Miss Emma Todd.

280 MISS SARAH HOLLINSHEAD, Upper Longdon
Postal: **Lodge Farm, Upper Longdon, Rugeley, Staffordshire, WS15 1QF**
Contacts: **PHONE 01543 490298**

1 CASTLEREA TESS, 7, ch m Pastoral Pursuits—Zartwyda (IRE) **Mr John Graham & Sarah Hollinshead**
2 FINAL ATTACK (IRE), 9, b g Cape Cross (IRE)—Northern Melody (IRE) **N. Chapman**
3 GMS PRINCE, 5, b g Kayf Tara—Zartwyda (IRE) **Graham Brothers Racing Partnership**
4 GMS PRINCESS, 4, b f Albaasil (IRE)—Zartwyda (IRE) **Graham Brothers Racing Partnership**
5 HEAD HIGH (IRE), 7, gr g Mastercraftsman (IRE)—Elisium **Mrs M Moore & Sarah Hollinshead**
6 JENNY REN, 5, b m Multiplex—Cherished Love (IRE) **Mr J. Gould**
7 LETHAL LOOK, 4, gr g Lethal Force (IRE)—Look Here's Dee **S. L. Edwards**
8 LOOKFORARAINBOW, 7, b g Rainbow High—Look Here's May **The Giddy Gang**
9 PIPA COIN, 11, b m Grape Tree Road—Andy Coin **Mr R. J. R. Moseley**
10 PUSH AHEAD (IRE), 11, br g Flemensfirth (USA)—Candle Massini (IRE) **Miss S. A. Hollinshead**
11 SINNDARELLA (IRE), 4, b f Fast Company (IRE)—Alafzara (IRE) **Mr J. A. Ashley**
12 UNCLE BERNIE (IRE), 10, gr g Aussie Rules (USA)—Alwiyda (USA) **Miss S. A. Hollinshead**
13 WILLETT, 4, br g Avonbridge—Madame Elizabeth **David Lockwood & Fred Lockwood**
14 ZENAFIRE, 11, b g Firebreak—Zen Garden **Mr R. J. R. Moseley**

MISS SARAH HOLLINSHEAD - continued

THREE-YEAR-OLDS

15 **CAPPELLA FELLA (IRE)**, b g Cappella Sansevero—Almatlaie (USA) **Mr R. Robinson & Ms S. Hollinshead**
16 **DIAMOND JILL (IRE)**, b f Footstepsinthesand—Sindiyma (IRE) **Mr J. A. Ashley**

Other Owners: Mr J. R. Graham, Miss S. A. Hollinshead, Mr A. Lawrence, Mrs M. A. Moore, R. Robinson.

---

281 | **MRS STEPH HOLLINSHEAD, Rugeley**
Postal: **Deva House, Bardy Lane, Upper Longdon, Rugeley, Staffordshire, WS15 4LJ**
Contacts: **PHONE 01543 493656 MOBILE 07791 385335**
EMAIL steph_hollinshead@hotmail.co.uk WEBSITE www.stephhollinsheadracing.com

1 **BUMBLEKITE**, 4, ch f Nayef (USA)—Harriet's Girl **Ray Bailey and Steph Hollinshead**
2 **GREGORY THE GREAT**, 4, b g Heeraat (IRE)—Word Perfect **Mr N. S. Sweeney**
3 **JUST A MINUTE**, 5, b m Poet's Voice—Inaminute (IRE) **R. Bailey**
4 **LA VOIX MAGIQUE**, 4, ch f Poet's Voice—Inaminute (IRE) **R. Bailey**
5 **LADY MUK**, 4, b f Mukhadram—Green Poppy **Mrs D. A. Hodson**
6 **SNOOKER JIM**, 5, b g Holy Roman Emperor (IRE)—Lucia de Medici **Mrs D. A. Hodson**
7 **THE GOLDEN CUE**, 5, ch g Zebedee—Khafayif (USA) **The Golden Cue Partnership**
8 **TIDAL POINT (IRE)**, 4, br g Sea The Moon (GER)—Centred (IRE) **Sleeve It Ltd**
9 **TIZWOTITIZ**, 4, b g Finjaan—Girl of The Rain (IRE) **Mrs S. C. Hawkins**

THREE-YEAR-OLDS

10 **AL SIMMO**, b f Al Kazeem—Magic Destiny **R. Bailey**
11 **CARRIAGE CLOCK**, b f Coach House (IRE)—Circadian Rhythm **M Johnson & S C Hawkins**
12 **DREAM ISLE (IRE)**, b g Tagula (IRE)—Desert Location **M Johnson & S C Hawkins**
13 B g Roderic O'Connor (IRE)—Inner Sea (USA)
14 **PUSHOVER**, gr f Hellvelyn—Soft Touch (IRE) **Chapel Stud Ltd & Loughshore Racing Synd**
15 **RACY STACEY**, ch f Fast Company (IRE)—Stilettoesinthemud (IRE) **Mr A. C. Gray**
16 **THE RED WITCH**, b f Cable Bay (IRE)—Lady Macduff (IRE) **Mrs D. A. Hodson**
17 **YUKON THUNDER**, ch g Night of Thunder (IRE)—Yukon Girl (IRE) **K Meredith & S C Hawkins**

TWO-YEAR-OLDS

18 B f 09/04 Pearl Secret—Jules (IRE) (Danehill (USA)) (5714) **J.Howlett, S.Hughes, G. Rowley**
19 **VELOCISTAR (IRE)**, b f 25/03 Starspangledbanner (AUS)—
Mahsooba (USA) (Hard Spun (USA)) (10000) **Sleeve It Ltd**

Other Owners: R. Bailey, Bucklands Farm & Stud Ltd, Mr K. Close, Mrs S. C. Hawkins, Mrs J. E. Howlett, Mr S. Hughes, M. A. N. Johnson, Loughshore Racing Syndicate, Mr C. K. M. Martland, K. S. Meredith, Mr G. T. Rowley, Mr R. Wildman.

Assistant Trainer: Adam Hawkins.

---

282 | **MR JOHN HOLT, Peckleton**
Postal: **Hall Farm, Church Road, Peckleton, Leicester, LE9 7RA**
Contacts: **PHONE 01455 821972 MOBILE 07850 321059**
EMAIL hallfarmracing@btconnect.com WEBSITE www.hallfarmracing.co.uk

1 **GLYDER**, 6, b m Camacho—Blades Princess **Jobsworth Racing 1**
2 **LADY MONICA**, 4, b f Bated Breath—Sina (GER) **Mr M. Hollier**
3 **MOCEAD CAPPALL**, 5, b m Captain Gerrard (IRE)—All Fur Coat **J R Holt & Greg Lynch**
4 **NOMADRUSH**, 10, b m Nomadic Way (USA)—Tanguero (IRE) **Mrs C. M. Tyler**
5 **NUMBER THEORY**, 12, b g Halling (USA)—Numanthia (IRE) **Mr M. S. Fonseka**
6 **TIGERINMYTANK**, 4, b f Heeraat (IRE)—Tiger Cub **J. R. Holt**
7 **VICKY CRISTINA (IRE)**, 5, b m Arcano (IRE)—And Again (USA) **Cleartherm Glass Sealed Units Ltd & J Holt**

MR JOHN HOLT - continued

THREE-YEAR-OLDS

8 **HERRING BAY**, b f Heeraat (IRE)—Hikkaduwa **Mr M. S. Fonseka**
9 B f Sir Percy—Lady Bling **J. R. Holt**
10 **MISTRY GIRL**, b f Cable Bay (IRE)—Goodie Twosues **Mr M. Bresland**
11 B f Clodovil (IRE)—Puerto Oro (IRE)
12 B g Casamento (IRE)—Sina (GER) **J. R. Holt**
13 **WHITE FACE (IRE)**, b f Cappella Sansevero—Annellis (UAE) **J. R. Holt**

Other Owners: Cleartherm Glass Sealed Units Ltd, Mr A. A. Ford, Mr M. P. Gavin, J. R. Holt, Jobsworth Racing, Mr M. G. Lynch.

Assistant Trainer: Jessica Holt.

Apprentice Jockey: Megan Ellingworth

---

283 MR ANTHONY HONEYBALL, Beaminster
Postal: **Potwell Farm, Mosterton, Beaminster, Dorset, DT8 3HG**
Contacts: **PHONE 01308 867452 MOBILE 07815 898569**
EMAIL anthony@ajhoneyballracing.co.uk **WEBSITE** www.ajhoneyballracing.co.uk

1 **ACEY MILAN (IRE)**, 6, b g Milan—Strong Wishes (IRE) **Owners For Owners: Acey Milan**
2 **AVOIR DE SOINS (IRE)**, 6, ch g Flemensfirth (USA)—Garranlea Maree (IRE) **Richard & Shirl Smith**
3 **BELLE DE MANECH (FR)**, 4, gr f Vision d'Etat (FR)—Noor Forever (FR) **Mr M. R. Chapman**
4 **BLEUE AWAY (IRE)**, 6, b m Getaway (GER)—Majorite Bleue (FR) **Potwell Racing Syndicate I**
5 **BOB BACKUS (IRE)**, 5, b g Milan—Boro Bee (IRE) **Decimus Racing IV**
6 **COQUELICOT (IRE)**, 4, b br f Soldier of Fortune (IRE)—Moscow Nights (IRE) **Geegeez.co.uk PA**
7 **DEJA VUE (IRE)**, 6, b m Fame And Glory—Westgrove Berry (IRE) **Axom LXXVI**
8 **DON LAMI (FR)**, 7, ch g Honolulu (IRE)—Toutamie (FR) **Les Amis De Don**
9 **DUHALLOW GESTURE (IRE)**, 8, b m King's Theatre (IRE)—Rare Gesture (IRE) **Galveston Partners**
10 **ENNISTOWN**, 10, b g Authorized (IRE)—Saoirse Abu (USA) **Jones, Kelly & Whittle**
11 **FANFARON DINO (FR)**, 5, gr g Doctor Dino (FR)—Kadjara (FR) **Mr J. P. McManus**
12 **GUSTAVIAN (IRE)**, 5, b g Mahler—Grange Oscar (IRE) **Decimus Racing I**
13 **HIDEAWAY VIC (IRE)**, 7, b g Stowaway—Cailin Vic Mo Cri (IRE) **Michael & Angela Bone**
14 **JEPECK (IRE)**, 11, b g Westerner—Jenny's Jewel (IRE) **Mr J. M. Pike**
15 **KAYF SERA SERA**, 5, b m Kayf Tara—Fernello **Kingswood Stud Limited (Hants)**
16 **KID COMMANDO**, 6, b g Robin des Champs (FR)—Banjaxed Girl **Chapman, Hanger, Kingston & Langford**
17 **KILCONNY BRIDGE (IRE)**, 6, b m Stowaway—Wattle Bridge (IRE) **Potwell Racing Syndicate I**
18 **LE COEUR NET (FR)**, 8, ch g Network (GER)—Silverwood (FR) **Wessex Racing Club**
19 **LILY THE PINK**, 6, b m Malinas (GER)—Carrigeen Queen (IRE) **Wessex Racing Club**
20 **MARILYN MONROE (IRE)**, 7, b m Scorpion (IRE)—Go On Eileen (IRE) **Some Like It Hot**
21 **MIDNIGHT CALLISTO**, 5, br m Midnight Legend—Carrigeen Queen (IRE) **Ms G. S. Langford**
22 **MIDNIGHT TUNE**, 9, b m Midnight Legend—Harmonic Motion (IRE) **The Park Homes Syndicate**
23 **MILAN IN MAY (IRE)**, 5, gr g Milan—Nina Fontenail (FR) **Richard & Shirl Smith**
24 **MONT SEGUR (FR)**, 5, ch g French Fifteen (FR)—Vie de Reine (FR) **Men Of Stone**
25 **MYSTICAL KNIGHT**, 11, b g Kayf Tara—Dark Diva **Geegeez.co.uk PA**
26 **NOCTURNAL MYTH**, 7, b g Midnight Legend—Gan On **The Night Shifters**
27 **PRECIOUS**, 4, b f Midnight Legend—Carrigeen Queen (IRE) **Mr P. R. Cartwright**
28 **PURE VISION (IRE)**, 9, b g Milan—Distillery Lane (IRE) **Mr J. P. McManus**
29 **REGAL ENCORE (IRE)**, 12, b g King's Theatre (IRE)—Go On Eileen (IRE) **Mr J. P. McManus**
30 **REPRESENTED (IRE)**, 7, b g Presenting—Lunar Path (IRE) **One Small Step**
31 **SAM BROWN**, 8, b g Black Sam Bellamy (IRE)—Cream Cracker **Mr T. C. Frost**
32 **SHAPIRO**, 7, b m Schiaparelli (GER)—Lady Turk (FR) **Burley, Buckingham, Chapman & Cobbett**
33 **SOJOURN (IRE)**, 7, b g Getaway (GER)—Toscar (IRE) **Jon & Jacqueline Hughes**
34 **SULLY D'OC AA (FR)**, 6, b g Konig Turf (GER)—Samarra d'Oc (FR) **Mr J. P. McManus**
35 **TEMPLAR (IRE)**, 5, b g Jeremy (USA)—Gaye Steel (IRE) **Ms G. S. Langford**
36 **VICTORS SERENADE (IRE)**, 15, b g Old Vic—Dantes Serenade (IRE) **Michael & Angela Bone**
37 **WAGNER (IRE)**, 5, b g Mahler—Astalanda (FR) **Potwell Racing Syndicate I**
38 **WINDANCE (IRE)**, 5, b g Shirocco (GER)—Maca Rince (IRE) **Decimus Racing III**
39 **WINDSWEPT GIRL (IRE)**, 5, ch m Getaway (GER)—Chicago Vic (IRE) **Geegeez.co.uk PA**
40 **WORLD OF DREAMS (IRE)**, 4, b g Kayf Tara—Rose of The World (IRE) **Atlantic Racing & R. W. Huggins**

MR ANTHONY HONEYBALL - continued

THREE-YEAR-OLDS

41 **UNBRIDLED LIGHT (FR)**, ch f Hunter's Light (IRE)—Polysheba (FR) **R W Huggins & Atlantic Racing**

Other Owners: Atlantic Racing Limited, Mrs A. P. Bone, Mr M. J. Bone, Mrs J. L. Buckingham, Mr J. Burley, Mr A. J. Chapman, Mr M. R. Chapman, Mr C. R. Cobbett, N. M. Hanger, Mr R. W. Huggins, Mr E. J. Hughes, Mrs J. Hughes, M. B. Jones, N. R. Kelly, Mr H. Kingston, Ms G. S. Langford, M. C. Pipe, Mr R. S. Smith, Mrs S. A. Smith, Mr J. S. Whittle.

Assistant Trainer: Rachael Honeyball.

NH Jockey: Aidan Coleman, David Noonan. **Conditional Jockey:** Rex Dingle.

---

284 **MS GEORGIE HOWELL, Tenbury Wells**
Postal: Woodstock bower farm, Broadheath, Tenbury Wells, Worcestershire, WR15 8QN
Contacts: PHONE 07968 864433
EMAIL georgie@drill-service.co.uk

1 **BETTERLATETHANNEVA (IRE)**, 9, b m Albano (IRE)—Acqua Pesante (IRE) **Ms G. P. C. Howell**
2 **BLACK LIGHTNING (IRE)**, 7, br g Whitmore's Conn (USA)—Annie May (IRE)
3 **DR KEENAN (IRE)**, 7, ch g Mahler—Dr Doocey (IRE) **Ms G. P. C. Howell**
4 **LET IT ROLL**, 6, b m Brian Boru—Branston Lily **Ms G. P. C. Howell**
5 **PIERLOW (IRE)**, 11, ch g Double Eclipse (IRE)—Dooleys Daughter (IRE) **Ms G. P. C. Howell**
6 **POETIC PRESENCE (IRE)**, 10, b m Presenting—Johnston's Crest (IRE) **Ms G. P. C. Howell**
7 **PUPPET WARRIOR**, 8, ch g Black Sam Bellamy (IRE)—Rakajack
8 **TOAD**, 7, b g Shirocco (GER)—One Gulp **Ms G. P. C. Howell**

---

285 **MRS DEBBIE HUGHES, Porth**
Postal: Tyr Heol Farm, Pantybrad, Tonyrefail, Rhondda, Mid Glamorgan, CF39 8HX
EMAIL dimots@btinternet.com

1 **BORN TO FROLIC (IRE)**, 5, b g Born To Sea (IRE)—Desert Frolic (IRE) **Mrs D. J. Hughes**
2 **BOSPHORUS PRINCE (IRE)**, 8, b g Hurricane Run (IRE)—Bosphorus Queen (IRE) **Mrs D. J. Hughes**
3 **CALL HIM ANYTHING**, 6, b g Mount Nelson—Focosa (ITY) **Mrs D. J. Hughes**
4 **DANCING LILLY**, 5, ch m Sir Percy—Bhima **Mrs D. J. Hughes**
5 7, B m Mount Nelson—Focosa (ITY) **Mrs D. J. Hughes**
6 **IGNIGHT**, 9, ch g Compton Place—Time Clash **Mrs D. J. Hughes**
7 **INSPIRE**, 8, gr m Hellvelyn—Time Clash **Mrs D. J. Hughes**
8 **JAZZAMEER**, 5, ch m Mazameer (IRE)—Jinks And Co **Mrs D. J. Hughes**
9 **LESS OF THAT (IRE)**, 6, b m Canford Cliffs (IRE)—Night Glimmer (IRE) **Mrs D. J. Hughes**
10 **LOVELY ACCLAMATION (IRE)**, 6, b m Acclamation—Titova **Mrs D. J. Hughes**
11 **MAJOR ASSAULT**, 7, b g Kyllachy—Night Premiere (IRE) **Mrs D. J. Hughes**
12 **NATTY DRESSER (IRE)**, 5, b g Dandy Man (IRE)—Parlour **Mrs D. J. Hughes**
13 **PICC AN ANGEL**, 4, b f Piccolo—Bhima **Mrs D. J. Hughes**
14 **PICC AND GO**, 7, b m Piccolo—Just Down The Road (IRE) **Mrs D. J. Hughes**
15 **STOP N START**, 8, ch m Piccolo—Dim Ots **Mrs D. J. Hughes**
16 5, Ch g Indian Haven—Time Clash **Mrs D. J. Hughes**

THREE-YEAR-OLDS

17 **FREEZING (IRE)**, b gr g Kingston Hill—Gimli's Treasure (IRE) **Mrs D. J. Hughes**
18 **GIVEN (IRE)**, b f Ivawood (IRE)—Annacurra (IRE) **Mrs D. J. Hughes**
19 Ch g Indian Haven—Time Clash **Mrs D. J. Hughes**
20 **YOLO ARIS**, b f Mukhadram—Hard Walnut (IRE) **Mrs D. J. Hughes**

TWO-YEAR-OLDS

21 B c 28/03 Moohaajim (IRE)—Somerset Falls (UAE) (Red Ransom (USA)) (3431) **Mrs D. J. Hughes**

286 MR RICHARD HUGHES, Upper Lambourn
Postal: Weathercock House, Upper Lambourn, Hungerford, Berkshire, RG17 8QT
Contacts: PHONE 01488 71198 MOBILE 07768 894828
EMAIL office@richardhughesracing.co.uk WEBSITE www.richardhughesracing.co.uk

1 BALLYLEMON (IRE), 4, b g Champs Elysees—Athreyaa Graham Doyle & Hazel Lawrence
2 CALLING THE WIND (IRE), 4, b g Authorized (IRE)—Al Jasrah (IRE) Mrs J. A. Wakefield
3 CHARLIE ARTHUR (IRE), 4, b g Slade Power (IRE)—Musical Bar (IRE) L Turland and A Smith
4 KATH'S LUSTRE, 5, b m Dick Turpin (IRE)—It's Dubai Dolly Mr Merv Cox
5 LE BATEAU, 4, b g Le Havre (IRE)—Bugie d'Amore Mr Danny Waters
6 PRINCE OF ROME (IRE), 4, gr c Lethal Force (IRE)—Garraun (IRE) Richard Hughes Racing Club
7 PTARMIGAN RIDGE, 6, b g Kyllachy—Joshua's Princess Mr M. A. Williams
8 PUDS, 5, br m Bated Breath—Missy Wassie Gal (USA) Mr N. Martin
9 SOGHAN (IRE), 6, br g Cape Cross (IRE)—Quiet Dream (USA) The Queens
10 TOP BREEZE (IRE), 4, b g Gale Force Ten—Shamarlane Life's A Breeze

THREE-YEAR-OLDS
11 BERMUDA SCHWARTZ, gr g Outstrip—Almaviva (IRE) Mr A. G. Smith
12 BLACKCASTLE STORM, bl c Showcasing—How High The Sky (IRE) Mrs J A Wakefield & Partners
13 BO TAIFAN (IRE), gr c Gutaifan (IRE)—Scarlet Rosefinch Mr Jaber Abdullah
14 BRENNER PASS, b c Raven's Pass (USA)—Bold Bidder Sir David Seale
15 BRENTFORD HOPE, b c Camelot—Miss Raven (IRE) Bernardine & Sean Mulryan
16 BRUNEL CHARM, b c Charm Spirit (IRE)—Manyara Mr J Langridge & Mr R Lane
17 CASPIAN QUEEN (IRE), b f Sepoy (AUS)—Rhythm Excel Mr Davood Vakilgilani
18 DAKOTA MOON (IRE), b g Shamardal (USA)—Moon Over Water (IRE) The Dakota Partnership
19 DARK KRIS (IRE), b g Dark Angel (IRE)—My Spirit (IRE) Mr M Rayner & Mr D Waters
20 DROMARA KING, ch c Mayson—Spirit Na Heireann (IRE) Mr B. McNicholas
21 I'M DIGBY (IRE), gr ro g Gutaifan (IRE)—Lathaat Mrs Philip Snow & Partners
22 ITSALLABOUTLUCK (IRE), b g Kodiac—Lucky (IRE) Mrs J. Williamson
23 KARIBANA (IRE), b c Hallowed Crown (AUS)—Queen Wasp (IRE) M Clarke, P Munnelly & D Waters
24 LADY LYNETTA (IRE), b f Tamayuz—Cristal Fashion (IRE) Mr Khalifa Dasmal
25 LIFE MATTERS (USA), ch c Candy Ride (ARG)—Moon Catcher (USA) Mr M Clarke & Mr R Rexton
26 MACKELLY (IRE), b g Ivawood—Last Gold (FR) M&O Construction & Civil Engineering Ltd
27 MAORI KNIGHT (IRE), b c Camelot—Chatham Islands (USA) White Beech Farm
28 MAZIKEEN, b f Dunkerque (FR)—Salome (FR) Mrs J. Bloomfield
29 MISTER SNOWDON, gr g Lethal Force (IRE)—Welsh Cake M. J. Caddy
30 OLD NEWS, b c Dutch Art—Queen's Charter The Queens
31 PUNTING (IRE), ch f Power—Lakatoi Mr M. H. Dixon
32 QUEEN OF ALL, b f Mukhadram—Dhuyoof (IRE) Mr Jaber Abdullah
33 RATHAGAN, b c Kyllachy—Ardessie Mr K Lawrence & Mr P Merritt
34 SIR OLIVER (IRE), b g Dark Angel (IRE)—Folga Mr Danny Waters
35 SO I TOLD YOU (IRE), b f Gleneagles (IRE)—Nocturne (GER) Flaxman Stables Ireland Ltd
36 SUMMERONSEVENHILLS (USA), b br c Summer Front (USA)—
     Iboughtheranyway (USA) Frank Deely & John McGarry
37 TAFISH (IRE), b g War Command (USA)—Zigarra Mr Jaber Abdullah
38 TWICE AS LIKELY, b f Tamayuz—Xaphania Ms H. N. Pinniger
39 WADDAT, b c Kodiac—Luminous Gold Mr N. Martin

TWO-YEAR-OLDS
40 ANJAALETTA (IRE), ch f 16/02 Anjaal—Shawhill (Dr Fong (USA)) (8571) B Galloway & H Pinniger
41 AUSSIE STORMER (IRE), b c 22/02 Mehmas (IRE)—
     Stormy Clouds (IRE) (Sir Prancealot (IRE)) (47619) P Cook & K Lawrence
42 BEASTIE BOY (IRE), b c 04/04 Dandy Man (IRE)—
     Gwyllion (USA) (Red Ransom (USA)) (51480) P Cook & K Lawrence
43 BONNIE LAD, ch c 30/03 Havana Gold—Bonnie Grey (Hellvelyn) (10476) BPC, Taylor & Young
44 B c 26/04 Showcasing—Canada Water (Dansili) (60060) The High Flyers
45 Ch c 25/02 Tamayuz—Coachhouse Lady (USA) (Rahy (USA)) (16190) Mr Jaber Abdullah
46 B c 08/04 Footstepsinthesand—Crimson Sunrise (IRE) (Holy Roman Emperor (IRE)) (75000) Mrs J. A. Wakefield
47 B c 10/03 Kodiac—Elektra Marino (Mount Nelson) (59047) Mrs J. A. Wakefield
48 KATH'S TOYBOY, b c 11/02 Gregorian (IRE)—It's Dubai Dolly (Dubai Destination (USA)) (3333) Mr Merv Cox

MR RICHARD HUGHES - continued

49 **LIKELY SUCCESSOR**, b f 05/03 Equiano (FR)—
　　　　　　　　　　　Classic Vision (Classic Cliche (IRE)) (3333) **H Pinniger & Peter Cook**
50 **MISS DIAMOND (IRE)**, ch f 12/03 No Nay Never (USA)—
　　　　　　Twinkling Ice (USA) (Elusive Quality (USA)) (61775) **Galloway,Lawrence,Merritt & Mrs Blake**
51 **MISS TIKI**, ch f 01/05 Zoffany (IRE)—Teeky (Daylami (IRE)) (50000) **The Lakota Partnership & Mrs Janie Blake**
52 **NAMASTE (IRE)**, b f 10/02 Mastercraftsman (IRE)—Satopanth (Medicean) **Niarchos Family**
53 **NELSON GAY (IRE)**, b c 09/02 Mehmas (IRE)—
　　　　　　　　Rublevka Star (USA) (Elusive Quality (USA)) (15238) **Mr R Gander & Partner**
54 Ch c 08/04 Kendargent (FR)—New River (USA) (Montjeu (IRE)) (4285) **The New River Partnership**
55 Ch c 09/02 Flintshire—No Panic (USA) (Henrythenavigator (USA)) (30000) **The Caledonians**
56 B br f 01/01 Swiss Spirit—Presto Levanter (Rock of Gibraltar) **Mrs Dawn Fleming**
57 Br c 15/02 Vadamos (FR)—Risk A Look (Observatory) (36035) **Clarke, Devine, Jeffries & Peters**
58 Gr c 15/04 Oasis Dream—Ronaldsay (Kirkwall) (38000) **Clarke, Jeffries, Lawrence & Wakefield, Mr J. Jeffries**
59 **SCENT OF AMBER**, br f 26/04 Flintshire—Miss Atomic Bomb (Intikhab (USA)) (52000) **Mr Khalifa Dasmal**
60 **SCHWARTZ (IRE)**, b c 07/03 Kodiac—Easy Times (Nayef (USA)) (75000) **Mr A. G. Smith**
61 B c 21/02 Starspangledbanner (AUS)—Shirley Blade (IRE) (Dylan Thomas (IRE)) (140000) **Mr Davood Vakilgilani**
62 B c 21/03 Acclamation—Spotlight (Dr Fong (USA)) (19047) **Mr Jaber Abdullah**
63 B f 25/01 Kodiac—Stor Mo Chroi (IRE) (Montjeu (IRE)) (50000) **H Rosenblatt & D Thorpe**
64 B br c 01/01 Camelot—Trail Of Tears (Exceed and Excel) **Bernardine & Sean Mulryan**
65 Br c 23/01 Showcasing—Zora Seas (IRE) (Marju (IRE)) (110000) **The Heffer Syndicate & Mr P Merritt**

Other Owners: Mrs J. A. Blake, Mr S. Blight, Mr R. G. W. Brown, Mr D. A. Campbell, D. G. Churston, Mr M. Clarke, Mr P. D. Conway, Mr P. Cook, Mrs E. Dadswell, Mr F. Deely, Mr R. J. Dellar, J. T. Devine, Mr G. J. Doyle, Mr I. Forster, Mr B. S. Galloway, R. A. Gander, Mr S. A. Geraghty, R. E. Greatorex, Mr R. Hannon, Mr Richard Hughes, Mr J. Jeffries, Mr R. Lane, Mr J. L. Langridge, Miss H. M. Lawrence, Mr K. Lawrence, Mr E. Malone, Mr J. J. McGarry, Mr P. D. Merritt, Mrs B. Mulryan, Mr S. Mulryan, Mr P. A. Munnelly, Mr P. Peters, Ms H. N. Pinniger, Mr M. S. P. Rayner, Mr R. J. Rexton, Mr D. W. Rogers, Ms F. E. Rogers, Mr H. Rosenblatt, Mr A. G. Smith, Mr R. C. Snedden, Mr N. Taylor, Ms D. Thomson, Mr D. A. Thorpe, Mr G. P. Triefus, L. R. Turland, Mrs J. A. Wakefield, Mr Danny Waters, Mrs F. P. Young.

Assistant Trainer: Patrick McEwan.

Apprentice Jockey: Tyler Heard, Finley Marsh, George Rooke, Angus Villiers.

287　　**MRS SARAH HUMPHREY, West Wratting**
Postal: Yen Hall Farm, West Wratting, Cambridge, Cambridgeshire, CB21 5LP
Contacts: **PHONE** 01223 291445 **MOBILE** 07798 702484
EMAIL sarah@yenhallfarm.com **WEBSITE** www.sarahhumphrey.co.uk

1 **ARCADIAN SEA (IRE)**, 6, b g Born To Sea (IRE)—Drombeg Dawn (IRE) **Yen Hall Farm Racing**
2 **BENNY FLIES HIGH (IRE)**, 4, br g Jet Away—Money Money Money **Hook Lane Syndicate**
3 **BRECON HILL (IRE)**, 7, b g Arcano (IRE)—Bryanstown Girl (IRE) **The Brecon Hill Partnership**
4 **CALL ME TJ**, 6, b g Mawatheeq (USA)—Silver Lily (IRE) **Silver Lily Bloodstock**
5 **DREAMBOAT DAVE (IRE)**, 4, b g Morpheus—Gatamalata (IRE) **The Old Eatonians**
6 **GRAINEYHILL (IRE)**, 9, b g Craigsteel—Inca Hill (IRE)
7 **IRISH SOVEREIGN (IRE)**, 5, b g Getaway (GER)—Magdoodle (IRE)
8 4, Ch f Nayef (USA)—Kompete
9 **LEGEND TO BE**, 10, b g Midnight Legend—Pentasilea **Mrs S. J. Humphrey**
10 **LOCAL SHOW (IRE)**, 12, br g Oscar (IRE)—Loughaderra Rose (IRE) **Mrs S. J. Humphrey**
11 **MISSHIROCCO (IRE)**, 5, b m Shirocco (GER)—Academy Miss (IRE) **Yen Hall Farm Racing**
12 **PARSONAL (IRE)**, 7, b g Oscar (IRE)—Rith Ar Aghaidh (IRE) **The Friday Lunch Club**
13 **RUMBLE B (IRE)**, 6, b g Presenting—John's Eliza (IRE) **The Pheasant Plotters**
14 **STONEBRIGG LEGEND**, 8, b m Midnight Legend—Forget The Ref (IRE) **Yen Hall Farm Racing**
15 **STOWAWAY MAGIC (IRE)**, 9, b g Stowaway—Irish Mystics (IRE) **The Friday Lunch Club**
16 **THE HAPPY CHAPPY (IRE)**, 9, b g Flemensfirth (USA)—Native Design (IRE) **The Happy Folders**
17 **VIRNON**, 9, b g Virtual—Freedom Song **Mr M. J. Pearce**

MRS SARAH HUMPHREY - continued

THREE-YEAR-OLDS
18 Ch g Casamento—Little Annie

TWO-YEAR-OLDS
19 B f 03/05 Clovis du Berlais (FR)—Call At Midnight (Midnight Legend) **Mrs S. J. Humphrey, Mr A R Humphrey**
20 B f 24/03 Toronado (IRE)—Kensington Gardens (Oasis Dream) **Mr M. J. Pearce**
21 Ch c 17/05 Mighty—Kompete (Komaite (USA)) **Mr M. J. Pearce**
22 **NAYON,** b c 08/04 Nayef (USA)—Freedom Song (Singspiel (IRE)) **Mr M. J. Pearce**

Other Owners: Dr R. C. Britton, Mr A. Eaton, Mr L Greenlees, Mrs S H Greenlees, Mrs S. J. Humphrey, Mr D. F. Nott, Mrs J Reece, Mrs E. Reid, Mr C. Sheen, Mr G. A. Thomas, Mr J Thomas, Mrs L Thomas.

Assistant Trainer: Mr A. R. Humphrey.

NH Jockey: Sean Bowen, Aidan Coleman, Daryl Jacob, Nick Scholfield. **Conditional Jockey:** Alexander Thorne. **Amateur Jockey:** Mr W. Humphrey.

---

288 MR KEVIN HUNTER, Natland
Postal: **Larkrigg, Natland, Cumbria, LA9 7QS**
Contacts: **PHONE 015395 60243**

1 **DAVID JOHN,** 9, b g Overbury (IRE)—Molly's Secret **J. K. Hunter**

---

289 MISS LAURA HURLEY, Tiverton
Postal: **Ringstone Stables, Oakford, Tiverton, Devon, EX16 9EU**
Contacts: **MOBILE 07999 693322**
EMAIL lauramhurley@hotmail.com

1 **CANDYMAN CAN (IRE),** 10, b g Holy Roman Emperor (IRE)—Palwina (FR) **Mrs R. E. Hurley**
2 **CATCHIN TIME (IRE),** 12, b g Chineur (FR)—Lady Dane (IRE) **Mrs R. E. Hurley**
3 **DARSI ROSE (IRE),** 7, b g Darsi (FR)—Win A Rose (IRE) **Mrs R. E. Hurley**
4 **OPERA BUFFA (IRE),** 7, b m Exceed And Excel (AUS)—Dubai Opera (USA) **Mrs R. E. Hurley**

---

290 MR ROGER INGRAM, Epsom
Postal: **Wendover Stables, Burgh Heath Road, Epsom, Surrey, KT17 4LX**
Contacts: **PHONE 01372 749157, 01372 748505 MOBILE 07773 665980, 07715 993911**
FAX 01372 748505
EMAIL roger.ingram.racing@virgin.net WEBSITE www.rogeringramracing.com

1 **ALBADR (USA),** 4, b g The Factor (USA)—Shawahid (USA) **Mr O. S. Harris**
2 **ARGENT BLEU,** 5, b g Steele Tango (USA)—Silver Marizah (IRE) **Mr R. Ingram**
3 **CHARLIE ALPHA,** 6, b g Dandy Man (IRE)—Maroussess Rock **Mr P. J. Burton**
4 **CRISTAL PALLAS CAT (IRE),** 5, b g Kodiac—Flower of Kent (USA) **Mr K. Tollick**
5 **DUKES MEADOW,** 9, b g Pastoral Pursuits—Figura **The Stargazers**
6 **JUST AN IDEA (IRE),** 6, b g Lilbourne Lad (IRE)—Emreliya (IRE) **Miss C. Swift**
7 **MISS POLLYANNA (IRE),** 4, ch f Helmet (AUS)—Ivy Batty (IRE) **Mrs Cathy Hallam & Wendover Racing**
8 **STAY IN THE LIGHT,** 5, b m Showcasing—Starlight Walk **Mr M. F. Cruse**
9 **YAGOOD (IRE),** 4, ch g Teofilo (IRE)—Tabassum (IRE) **Mr O. S. Harris**

THREE-YEAR-OLDS
10 **MAZEKINE,** b f Mukhadram—Dea Caelestis (FR) **Jeremy Scott & Wendover Racing**
11 **NO SUCH LUCK (IRE),** b g Tamayuz—Laftah (IRE) **Mr M. F. Cruse**
12 Br b f Heeratt—Silver Marizah **Mr P. J. Burton**

MR ROGER INGRAM - continued

Other Owners: Mrs C. E. Hallam, Mr R. Ingram, Mrs S. Ingram, Mr J. Scott.

Assistant Trainer: Sharon Ingram.

Apprentice Jockey: Rhiain Ingram.

---

291 MR DEAN IVORY, Radlett
Postal: **Harper Lodge Farm, Harper Lane, Radlett, Hertfordshire, WD7 7HU**
Contacts: **PHONE 01923 855337 MOBILE 07785 118658 FAX 01923 852470**
EMAIL deanivoryracing@gmail.com WEBSITE www.deanivoryracing.co.uk

1 **ARCHDEACON**, 4, b g Archipenko (USA)—Akdarena **K T Ivory & Michael Yarrow**
2 **BADENSCOTH**, 6, b g Foxwedge (AUS)—Twice Upon A Time **P. J. Skinner**
3 **BRUYERE (FR)**, 4, b f Exceed And Excel (AUS)—Pale Mimosa (IRE) **Heather & Michael Yarrow**
4 **CHARMING KID**, 4, b g Charm Spirit (IRE)—Child Bride (USA) **The Cool Silk Partnership**
5 **CLASSIC CHARM**, 5, b m Rip Van Winkle (IRE)—Classic Lass **Mrs G. Thomas**
6 **CLASSIC STAR**, 4, b g Sea The Moon (GER)—Classic Lass **Radlett Racing**
7 **DADDY'S DAUGHTER (CAN)**, 5, b m Scat Daddy (USA)—Golden Stripe (CAN) **Heather & Michael Yarrow**
8 **DOR'S DIAMOND**, 4, gr g Gregorian (IRE)—Primavera **Mrs D. A. Carter**
9 **DOR'S LAW**, 7, b m Lawman (FR)—Law of Chance **Mrs D. A. Carter**
10 **DROMISKIN**, 4, b f Dunaden (FR)—Ceilidh Band **Mr W. J. Reilly**
11 **ELJADDAAF (IRE)**, 9, b g Shamardal (USA)—Almansoora (USA) **Wentdale Ltd & Mrs L A Ivory**
12 **FANCY FLYER**, 4, b g Archipenko (USA)—Lucky Flyer **Radlett Racing**
13 **FANTASTIC FLYER**, 5, br m Harbour Watch (IRE)—Lucky Flyer **Mr M. McGuinness**
14 **FIGHTING TEMERAIRE (IRE)**, 7, b g Invincible Spirit (IRE)—Hot Ticket (IRE) **Michael & Heather Yarrow**
15 **FLAMING SPEAR (IRE)**, 8, ch g Lope de Vega (IRE)—Elshamms **Mr Tony Bloom**
16 **GREGORIAN GIRL**, 4, b f Gregorian (IRE)—Jackie's Opera (FR) **Skipsey, Franks & Roper & Mr A Chapman**
17 **JACK LOUIE**, 4, ch g Mazameer (IRE)—Fleetwood Nix **Mr R. Beadle**
18 **KADRIZZI (FR)**, 7, ch g Hurricane Cat (USA)—Kadiania (FR) **Mr A Chapman & Wentdale Limited**
19 **KERRERA**, 7, ch m Champs Elysees—Questa Nova **Mrs G. Thomas**
20 **LANCELOT DU LAC (ITY)**, 10, b g Shamardal (USA)—Dodie Mae (USA) **Michael & Heather Yarrow**
21 **LAURENTIA (IRE)**, 4, b f Iffraaj—Brynica (FR) **Doolan, Edwards & Hayes**
22 **LIBRISA BREEZE**, 8, gr g Mount Nelson—Bruxcalina (FR) **Mr Tony Bloom**
23 **LOTHARIO**, 6, gr g Dark Angel (IRE)—Kisses For Me (IRE) **Michael & Heather Yarrow**
24 **NEZAR (IRE)**, 9, ch g Mastercraftsman (IRE)—Teddy Bears Picnic **Mrs D. A. Carter**
25 **NICKY BABY (IRE)**, 6, gr g Dark Angel (IRE)—Moon Club (IRE) **Mrs D. A. Carter**
26 **ONE COOL DADDY (USA)**, 5, b g Scat Daddy (USA)—Coup (USA) **Michael & Heather Yarrow**
27 **OVERBECK (IRE)**, 5, b g Camelot—Brigid (USA) **Mr D. K. Ivory**
28 **PLEDGE OF HONOUR**, 4, b g Shamardal (USA)—Lura (USA) **Mr D. K. Ivory**
29 **RED COSSACK (CAN)**, 9, ch g Rebellion—Locata (USA) **Mrs G. Thomas**
30 **SANDY HEARTBEAT**, 4, ch f Compton Place—Vitta's Touch (USA) **It's Your Lucky Day**
31 **SIR PRIZE**, 5, b g Sir Percy—Three Sugars (AUS) **Michael & Heather Yarrow**
32 **SOARING SPIRITS (IRE)**, 10, ch g Tamayuz—Follow My Lead **Mrs D. A. Carter**
33 **SPRING ROMANCE (IRE)**, 5, b br g Zebedee—Love And Devotion **Solario Racing (Berkhamsted)**
34 **STAKE ACCLAIM (IRE)**, 8, b g Acclamation—Golden Legacy (IRE) **Mr M. J. Yarrow**
35 **TANGRAMM**, 8, b br g Sakhee's Secret—Tripti (IRE) **Mr R. Beadle**
36 **TROPICS (USA)**, 12, ch g Speightstown—Taj Aire (USA) **Mr D. K. Ivory**
37 **TRUST ME (IRE)**, 4, b g Shamardal (USA)—Punita (USA) **Mr D. K. Ivory, K. T. Ivory**
38 **VILLETTE (IRE)**, 6, b m Sixties Icon—Spinning Lucy (IRE) **Mr D. K. Ivory**
39 **YIMOU (IRE)**, 5, b br g Kodiac—Heroine Chic (IRE) **Mr A. L. Cohen**

THREE-YEAR-OLDS

40 **ALSUKAR**, b f Brazen Beau (AUS)—Three Sugars (AUS) **K T Ivory & Mrs Valerie Hubbard**
41 **BILLY BUTTON (IRE)**, b c Coach House (IRE)—Ojai (IRE) **Mr A. L. Cohen**
42 **DANCINGINTHEWOODS**, b c Garswood—Pachanga **Solario Racing (Berkhamsted)**
43 **DORS TOYBOY (IRE)**, gr g Dark Angel (IRE)—Rathaath (IRE) **Mrs D. A. Carter**
44 **DOVER LIGHT**, ch g Sir Prancealot (IRE)—Miss Mediator (USA) **K T Ivory & Mrs Valerie Hubbard**

MR DEAN IVORY - continued

45 **FLASHY FLYER,** ch f Helmet (AUS)—Lucky Flyer **Graceland Stud**
46 **GRANDBOB,** b c Fountain of Youth (IRE)—Miss Lesley **Mr R. Beadle**
47 **KELLY B,** b f Equiano (FR)—Primavera **Mr R. Beadle**
48 **MADAMES GIRL (IRE),** ch f Rock of Gibraltar (IRE)—Miss Madame (IRE) **Radlett Racing**
49 **MIRAKUHL,** b f Fast Company (IRE)—Four Miracles **Skipsey,Franks & Co & Richard Farleigh**
50 **ONE ALC (FR),** b g Wootton Bassett—Caspian Breeze (USA)
51 **ROCK OF REDMOND (IRE),** b f Rock of Gibraltar (IRE)—Classic Lass **Mr S. J. Redmond**

TWO-YEAR-OLDS

52 **HOT CHESNUT,** ch f 02/03 Camacho—Hot Ticket (IRE) (Selkirk (USA)) **Heather & Michael Yarrow**
53 Bl c 21/05 Heeraat (IRE)—Miss Lesley (Needwood Blade)
54 B f 20/02 Wootton Bassett—Nickels And Dimes (IRE) (Teofilo (IRE)) (18000)
55 **NO INQUESTS,** b c 10/05 Dandy Man (IRE)—Ojai (IRE) (Big Bad Bob (IRE)) (12380) **Mr A. L. Cohen**

Assistant Trainer: Chris Scally.

Apprentice Jockey: Luke Bacon.

---

292 MISS TINA JACKSON, Loftus
Postal: **Tick Hill Farm, Liverton, Loftus, Saltburn, Cleveland, TS13 4TG**
Contacts: **PHONE 01287 644952 MOBILE 07774 106906**

1 **BLACK OPIUM,** 6, b m Black Sam Bellamy (IRE)—Fragrant Rose **Mr H. L. Thompson**
2 **GLACEON (IRE),** 5, b m Zoffany (IRE)—Ihtiraam (IRE) **Peter Jeffers & Howard Thompson**
3 **GRIMTHORPE,** 9, ch g Alflora (IRE)—Sally Scally **Mr H. L. Thompson**
4 **HAVANA BAY,** 4, b g Havana Gold (IRE)—Bisou **Mr H. L. Thompson**
5 **IVORS INVOLVEMENT (IRE),** 8, b g Amadeus Wolf—Summer Spice (IRE) **Mr H. L. Thompson**
6 **JAMIH,** 5, ch g Intello (GER)—Hannda (IRE) **Peter Jeffers & Howard Thompson**
7 **JAMIL (IRE),** 5, b g Dansili—Havant **Peter Jeffers & Howard Thompson**
8 **JAN DE HEEM,** 10, ch g Dutch Art—Shasta **H L Thompson & D Tucker**
9 **KHITAAMY (IRE),** 6, b g Approve (IRE)—Halliwell House **Peter Jeffers & Howard Thompson**
10 **MADAM SCULLY,** 7, ch m Flying Legend (USA)—Sally Scally **Mr H. L. Thompson**
11 **MR WIGGINS,** 8, ch g Alflora (IRE)—Winnie Wild **Miss T. Jackson**
12 **POINT OF WOODS,** 7, b g Showcasing—Romantic Myth **Mr H. L. Thompson**
13 **PURPLE HARRY,** 12, gr g Sir Harry Lewis (USA)—Ellfiedick **Mr H. L. Thompson**
14 **ROSY RYAN (IRE),** 10, b m Tagula (IRE)—Khaydariya (IRE) **Mr H. L. Thompson**
15 **SNITCH (IRE),** 6, b g Witness Box (USA)—Kind Oscar (IRE) **Mr H. L. Thompson**
16 **SORY,** 13, b g Sakhee (USA)—Rule Britannia **Mr H. L. Thompson**
17 **THOMAS CRANMER (USA),** 6, b g Hard Spun (USA)—House of Grace (USA) **Peter Jeffers & Howard Thompson**
18 **WALLACE,** 7, gr m Fair Mix (IRE)—Winnie Wild **Miss T. Jackson**
19 **YOUNOSO,** 9, b g Alflora (IRE)—Teeno Nell **Mr H. L. Thompson**

TWO-YEAR-OLDS

20 B f 13/03 Lethal Force (IRE)—Postulant (Kyllachy) (8000) **Peter Jeffers & Howard Thompson**
21 Ch f 18/02 Camacho—Smoken Rosa (USA) (Smoke Glacken (USA)) (14000) **Peter Jeffers & Howard Thompson**

Other Owners: Mr P. Jeffers, Mr H. L. Thompson, Mr D. Tucker.

---

293 MISS HANNAH JAMES, Malvern
Postal: **The Merries Farm, Rye Street, Birtsmorton, Malvern, Worcestershire, WR13 6AS**

1 **EMMAS DILEMMA (IRE),** 8, b m Gold Well—Emmas Island (IRE) **Miss H. L. James**
2 **MOTUEKA (IRE),** 8, b g King's Theatre (IRE)—Tchouina (FR) **Miss H. L. James**

294 MR LEE JAMES, Malton
Postal: **Cheesecake Hill Stables, Norton, Malton, North Yorkshire, YO17 9PJ**
Contacts: **PHONE 01653 699466 MOBILE 07732 556322**

1 **CRASHING WAVES**, 10, b m Dubai Destination (USA)—Palisandra (USA) **Mrs C. Lloyd James**
2 **ICONIC FIGURE (IRE)**, 7, b g Approve (IRE)—Tough Chic (IRE) **L. R. James**
3 **JACKMAN**, 6, gr g Aussie Rules (USA)—Fit To Burst **Mr Ian Johnson & Partner**
4 **MA PETIT LUMIER**, 10, b g Echo of Light—Alisdanza **L. R. James**

THREE-YEAR-OLDS

5 **GOLD VENTURE (IRE)**, ch f Dandy Man (IRE)—Monroe **Mrs C. Lloyd James**

Other Owners: Mr I Johnson, Mrs C. Lloyd James.

Assistant Trainer: Carol James.

295 MR IAIN JARDINE, Carrutherstown
Postal: **Hetlandhill Farm, Carrutherstown, Dumfries, Dumfriesshire, DG1 4JX**
Contacts: **PHONE 01387 840347 MOBILE 07738 351232**
WORK EMAIL office@iainjardineracing.com WEBSITE www.iainjardineracing.com

1 **ANIMORE**, 7, b m Sulamani (IRE)—More Likely **Mrs A. F. Tullie**
2 **CAMILE (IRE)**, 7, b m Captain Rio—Heroic Performer (IRE) **Mr I Jardine & Partner**
3 **CEDAR HILL (IRE)**, 6, br b g Frammassone (IRE)—Dayamen **Mr J. Fyffe**
4 **CLEARANCE**, 6, b g Authorized (IRE)—Four Miracles **Kildonan Gold Racing 2, Brown, Jardine**
5 **COLOUR CONTRAST (IRE)**, 7, b g Rock of Gibraltar (IRE)—Colour Coordinated (IRE) **Kildonan Gold Racing**
6 **COOL MIX**, 8, gr g Fair Mix (IRE)—Lucylou (IRE) **D&D Armstrong Limited**
7 **DIVINE GIFT (IRE)**, 4, b g Nathaniel (IRE)—Souter's Sister (IRE) **Owners Group 047**
8 **EQUIDAE**, 5, ch h Equiano (FR)—Dularame (IRE) **Jardine & Shannon**
9 **EVOLUTIONARY (IRE)**, 4, b f Morpheus—Lilium **Bruce & Susan Jones**
10 **FIVE HELMETS (IRE)**, 4, b g Helmet (AUS)—Sweet Home Alabama (IRE) **Mr B. P. Keogh**
11 **FLOOD DEFENCE (IRE)**, 6, b m Harbour Watch (IRE)—Krynica (USA) **Let's Be Lucky Racing 20**
12 **FLOWERY (IRE)**, 8, b g Millenary—Dato Vic (IRE) **Mr I. Jardine**
13 **FRAME RATE**, 5, b g Arcano (IRE)—Miss Gaudy (USA) **The Dregs Of Humanity & Partner**
14 **GLORY FIGHTER**, 4, b g Kyllachy—Isola Verde **Mr Kenneth MacPherson**
15 **ISHEBAYORGREY (IRE)**, 8, gr g Clodovil (IRE)—Superjet (IRE) **Iain Jardine Racing Club**
16 **JABBAAR**, 7, ch g Medicean—Echelon **Let's Be Lucky Racing 11**
17 **KARASHENI (IRE)**, 4, ch g Poet's Voice—Karasiyra (IRE) **Linden Lads & Stephen Brown**
18 **KEEP THE RIVER**, 6, b m Scorpion (IRE)—River Alder **Kitchens Plus, Friel, Morrison & Jardine**
19 **L'INGANNO FELICE (FR)**, 10, br g Librettist (USA)—Final Overture (FR) **Mr A. Dawson & Mrs K. Campbell**
20 **LASTOFTHECOSMICS**, 5, b g Shirocco (GER)—Cosmic Case **The Cosmic Cases**
21 **LOMU (IRE)**, 6, ch g Dandy Man (IRE)—Miss Me **S. J. Macdonald**
22 **MEARING**, 5, b g Aussie Rules (USA)—Director's Dream (IRE) **Let's Be Lucky Racing 14**
23 **MERRICOURT (IRE)**, 4, gr g Mizzen Mast (USA)—Elite **Mr A. McLuckie**
24 **NAKEETA**, 9, b g Sixties Icon—Easy Red (IRE) **Alex & Janet Card & Mr D Wagner**
25 **NEWMARKET WARRIOR (IRE)**, 9, b g Dalakhani (IRE)—Heavens Peak **Ms S A Booth & Partner**
26 **NIGHT OF GLORY**, 6, b g Sea The Stars (IRE)—Kesara **Alba-eire Syndicate & Mr Iain Jardine**
27 **NUBOUGH (IRE)**, 4, b g Kodiac—Qawaasem (IRE) **Mrs V. C. Macdonald**
28 **NYOUFSEA**, 5, gr g Fair Mix (IRE)—Just Smokie **D&D Armstrong Limited**
29 4, Ch g Leading Light (IRE)—O What A Girl (IRE)
30 **PUMBLECHOOK**, 7, b g Champs Elysees—Chiang Mai (IRE) **Mr I. Jardine**
31 **RIVER ICON**, 8, b m Sixties Icon—River Alder **Mr M Friel & Mr T Reid**
32 **SHE'SASUPERMACK (IRE)**, 7, b m Arakan (USA)—Castleknock (IRE) **Mrs C Brown & Mr Michael Wares**
33 **SIOUX FRONTIER (IRE)**, 5, b g Excelebration (IRE)—Sioux Rising (IRE) **Let's Be Lucky Racing 23**
34 **SMART LASS (IRE)**, 5, b m Casamento (IRE)—Smart Ass (IRE) **Mr G. R. McGladery**
35 **SO SATISFIED**, 9, b g Aqlaam—Pirouetting **Wharton, Nixon, Jardine**
36 **SOMETHING BREWING (FR)**, 6, gr g Clodovil (IRE)—Talwin (IRE) **Mrs C Brown & Mr Michael Wares**

MR IAIN JARDINE - continued

38 **SPIRIT OF LUND (IRE)**, 4, b g Fast Company (IRE)—Kyrielle **Mr R. D. Rainey**
39 **STONE THE CROWS**, 6, b g Cape Cross (IRE)—Stars In Your Eyes **Mr R. D. Rainey**
40 **TARAMANDA**, 5, b m Kayf Tara—Millagros (IRE) **J. A. Cringan**
41 **THE DELRAY MUNKY**, 8, b m Overbury (IRE)—Delray Beach (FR) **The Twelve Munkys**
42 **TITUS BOLT (IRE)**, 11, b g Titus Livius (FR)—Megan's Bay **I. G. M. Dalgleish**
43 **TOKARAMORE**, 8, b m Sulamani (IRE)—More Likely **Mrs A. F. Tullie**
44 **TOMORROW'S ANGEL**, 5, ch m Teofilo (IRE)—Funday **Adamson, Etheridge & Jardine**
45 **TRADITIONAL DANCER (IRE)**, 8, b g Danehill Dancer (IRE)—Cote Quest (USA) **I. G. M. Dalgleish**
46 **WHISPERING WATERS (IRE)**, 7, b m Mahler—Eventide **Mr I Jardine & Co**

THREE-YEAR-OLDS

47 **ALIX JAMES**, b g Acclamation—Tout Va Bien (IRE) **James Property Ltd**
48 B f Showcasing—Dancing Moon (IRE) **Mr I. Jardine**
49 **GOLDEN SANDBANKS**, b c Havana Gold (IRE)—Serrenia (IRE) **Mr J Fyffe & Mr D Pryde**
50 **JORGIE (FR)**, ch c George Vancouver (USA)—Capannacce (IRE) **Mr J Fyffe & Mr D Pryde**
51 **JUMP THE GUN (IRE)**, b g Make Believe—Sound of Guns **Ballylinch Stud & Partner**
52 **JUNGLE ROCK (IRE)**, ch g Bungle Inthejungle—Green Vision (IRE) **Mr G. B. Davidson**
53 **LARA SILVIA**, ch f Casamento (IRE)—Idyllic Star (IRE)
54 **MARTIN'S BRIG (IRE)**, b c Equiano (FR)—Weeza (IRE) **Mr James Fyffe & Mr Scott Fyffe**
55 B g Acclamation—Quantum (IRE) **Mrs J. M. MacPherson**

TWO-YEAR-OLDS

56 Ch c 20/04 Camacho—Eclaircie (IRE) (Thunder Gulch (USA)) (6500) **Mr J Hay, Mr F Steele & Mr I Jardine**
57 **ELECTRIC ANGEL**, b f 31/01 Markaz (IRE)—All Fur Coat (Multiplex) (2380) **Let's Be Lucky Racing 11**
58 **HAVANA PARTY**, ch c 02/05 Havana Gold (IRE)—Ferayha (IRE) (Cape Cross (IRE)) **Let's Be Lucky Racing 11**
59 **HAVEYOUMISSEDME**, b c 05/02 Helmet (AUS)—Haydn's Lass (Sir Percy) (4290)
60 **HAZALOU**, ch c 20/02 Nathaniel (IRE)—Solar Magic (Pivotal) (45000) **Mr I. C. Jones**
61 Gr c 19/03 Nathaniel (IRE)—In The Soup (USA) (Alphabet Soup (USA)) (21449) **Castle Racing Scotland**
62 **INNSE GALL**, b c 04/02 Toronado (IRE)—Reaf (In The Wings) (85714) **C. H. McGhie**
63 **PUSH FOR SIXTY**, bl c 16/04 Sixties Icon—Push Me (IRE) (Verglas (IRE))
64 Ch c 04/05 Dandy Man (IRE)—Que Sera Sera (Dansili) **Mr B. P. Keogh**
65 B c 13/02 Bobby's Kitten (USA)—Rocknrollbaby (IRE) (Fastnet Rock (AUS))
66 **THE BRAVEST (GER)**, ro c 11/01 Jukebox Jury (IRE)—

Thunderstruck (GER) (Silvano (GER)) (20000) **Ballylinch Stud**
67 B c 10/02 The Last Lion (IRE)—Throne (Royal Applause) (26666) **Mr James Fyffe & Mr Scott Fyffe**
68 Ch c 07/04 Intello (GER)—Wo de Xin (Shamardal (USA)) (17160) **Mr G. R. McGladery**

Other Owners: Mr G. G. Adamson, Mr R. M. S. Allison, Ballylinch Stud, Miss S. A. Booth, Mrs C. Brown, Mr S. Brown, Mr C. A. Burness, Mr P. Byrne, Mrs K. Campbell, Mr A. M. Card, Alex & Janet Card, Mrs J. A. Card, A. Dawson, Mr J. Doherty, Mr Gary Etheridge, Mr M. Friel, Mr J. Fyffe, Mr S. Fyffe, Mr R. J. Goodfellow, Mr J. A. Hay, Mr I. Jardine, Mr B. Jones, Mrs S. Jones, Kitchens Plus Ltd, Mr D. I. B. Livingstone, Mr A. Manson, Mr B. Melrose, Mr R. Morrison, Mr D. E. T. Nicholson, G. R. S. Nixon, Mr J. A. Osborne, D. G. Pryde, Mr C. T. Reid, Mr N. Shannon, Mr F. T. Steele, The Dregs Of Humanity, Mr D. R. Wagner, Mr M. P. Wares, Mr R. E. Wharton.

Flat Jockey: Jamie Gormley. **NH Jockey:** Conor O'Farrell. **Conditional Jockey:** Bruce Lynn.

---

296 MR WILLIAM JARVIS, Newmarket
Postal: **Phantom House Stables, Fordham Road, Newmarket, Suffolk, CB8 7AA**
Contacts: **HOME 01638 662677 PHONE 01638 669873 FAX 01638 667328**
EMAIL mail@williamjarvis.com WEBSITE www.williamjarvis.com

1 **ARIGATO**, 5, b g Poet's Voice—Xtrasensory **Ms E. L. Banks**
2 **COLD SNAP (IRE)**, 7, b g Medicean—Shivering **P. C. J. Dalby & R. D. Schuster**
3 **GHOST QUEEN**, 4, gr f Mukhadram—Deire Na Sli (IRE) **The Raceology Partnership**
4 **HINDAAM (USA)**, 4, b f Arch (USA)—Saraama (USA) **Mrs L. M. Shanahan**
5 **LADY BOWTHORPE**, 4, b f Nathaniel (IRE)—Maglietta Fina (IRE) **Ms E. L. Banks**
6 **MICHAELS CHOICE**, 4, b g War Command (USA)—Todber **The Music Makers 2**

MR WILLIAM JARVIS - continued

7 **QUEEN CONSTANTINE (GER)**, 4, b f Holy Roman Emperor (IRE)—Quilita (GER) **Mr K. J. Hickman**
8 **THOUGHTFULLY (IRE)**, 4, b f Acclamation—Lovely Thought **Ms E. L. Banks**
9 **WIMPOLE HALL**, 7, b g Canford Cliffs (IRE)—Sparkling Eyes **Mr W. Jarvis**

THREE-YEAR-OLDS

10 **ARMY BOY**, b g Brazen Beau (AUS)—Wait It Out (USA) **The Raceology Partnership**
11 **HO LENG LUI**, b f Hot Streak (IRE)—Sparkling Eyes **Dr J. Walker**
12 **HOT AS (IRE)**, b f Hot Streak (IRE)—Rate **Mr K. J. Hickman**
13 **INVENTUS**, b g Brazen Beau (AUS)—Pearl Earing (IRE) **The Raceology Partnership**
14 **ONE NIGHT STAND**, b g Swiss Spirit—Tipsy Girl **David Batten & Partners**
15 **SERAPHINITE (IRE)**, gr f Gutaifan (IRE)—Eilasha **The Raceology Partnership**
16 **SHOOT THE MOON (IRE)**, b g Lawman (FR)—Luna Moon **P. C. J. Dalby & R. D. Schuster**
17 **UNCLE SID**, b g Free Eagle (IRE)—Paisley **Mr D. Robinson**
18 **VITELLIO SCARPIA**, b g Lawman (FR)—Madame Vestris (IRE) **R. C. C. Villers**
19 **WANNABE BETSY (IRE)**, b f Siyouni (FR)—Wannabe Special **Ms E. L. Banks**

TWO-YEAR-OLDS

20 **BERYL THE PERIL (IRE)**, ch f 19/02 Dandy Man (IRE)—
    Lady of Rohan (Pivotal) (58000) **P. C. J. Dalby & R. D. Schuster**
21 **CONTEMPT**, b c 15/04 Oasis Dream—Familliarity (Nayef (USA)) (50000) **The Music Makers**
22 B f 01/02 Kodiac—Diaminda (IRE) (Diamond Green (FR)) (60000) **Ms E. L. Banks**
23 **DUKE OF VERONA (IRE)**, br gr c 28/04 Belardo (IRE)—Somewhere (IRE) (Dalakhani (IRE)) (25000) **R. C. C. Villers**
24 **HUMAN ACTION**, b c 31/03 Twilight Son—Modify (New Approach (IRE)) (26000) **Dr J. Walker**
25 B f 02/04 Markaz (IRE)—Our Joy (IRE) (Kodiac) (62000) **Ms E. L. Banks**
26 B g 31/03 Brazen Beau (AUS)—Pearl Earing (IRE) (Excellent Art) **The Raceology Partnership**
27 **PORFIN (IRE)**, b c 01/02 Belardo (IRE)—Tropical Mist (Marju (IRE)) (40000) **Mr N. P. R. W. Warnock**

Other Owners: Mr D. H. Batten, Mr R. S. Hoskins, Mr P. P. Thorman.

Assistant Trainer: James Toller.

Apprentice Jockey: Gai Boni.

297

MISS RUTH JEFFERSON, Malton
Postal: **Newstead Stables, Beverley Road, Norton, Malton, North Yorkshire, YO17 9PJ**
Contacts: **PHONE 01653 697225 MOBILE 07976 568152**
WEBSITE www.ruthjefferson.co.uk

1 **BALLY CONOR (IRE)**, 7, b g Presenting—Soliya (FR) **Drew & Ailsa Russell**
2 **BLACK EBONY (IRE)**, 6, b g Malinas (GER)—Our Ethel **The Mount Fawcus Partnership**
3 **BLOSSOMING FORTH (IRE)**, 5, b m Flemensfirth (USA)—Blossom Trix (IRE) **The Mount Fawcus Partnership**
4 **BRINKHILL (IRE)**, 5, b m Shirocco (GER)—Banningham Blaze
5 **BUSTER VALENTINE (IRE)**, 7, b g Ask—Femme du Noir (IRE) **The Mount Fawcus Partnership**
6 **CLONDAW CAITLIN (IRE)**, 5, b m Court Cave (IRE)—Kilmessan (IRE) **Drew & Ailsa Russell**
7 **CYRUS KEEP (IRE)**, 7, b g Doyen (IRE)—Overbranch **Ruth Jefferson Racing Club**
8 **DOUBLE W'S (IRE)**, 10, ch g Fruits of Love (USA)—Zaffre (IRE) **Wharton & Wilson**
9 **DUBAI ANGEL (IRE)**, 9, b g Dubai Destination (USA)—Just Another Penny (IRE) **Mrs D. W. Davenport**
10 5, Ch g Le Fou (IRE)—Fleeting Arrow (IRE) **Miss N. R. Jefferson**
11 **FLEMENS FLEUR (IRE)**, 4, ch f Flemensfirth (USA)—Blossom Trix (IRE) **The Mount Fawcus Partnership**
12 **FLINT HILL**, 4, ch g Excelebration (IRE)—Modify **Miss N. R. Jefferson**
13 **JAMPOT EDDIE**, 6, ch g Sulamani (IRE)—Thenford Lass (IRE) **Mrs I C Straker & Steven Key**
14 **LEMON T**, 7, gr g Sulamani (IRE)—Altogether Now (IRE) **Newstead Racing Partnership**
15 **MASTER ALAN**, 5, b g Norse Dancer (IRE)—Overbranch **Mrs I C Straker & Steven Key**
16 **MEGA YEATS (IRE)**, 6, br m Yeats (IRE)—Mega Mum (IRE) **The Mount Fawcus Partnership**
17 **NORTHERN SOUL**, 7, ch g Presenting—Our Ethel **The Northern Triangle**
18 **ONWARD ROUTE (IRE)**, 6, b g Yeats (IRE)—Just Stunning (IRE) **Mr R. Collins**
19 **RAECIUS FELIX (IRE)**, 6, ch g Stowaway—Dances With Waves (IRE) **Mr R. Collins**
20 5, B g Sholokhov (IRE)—Reevolesa (IRE) **Miss N. R. Jefferson**

MISS RUTH JEFFERSON - continued

21 **RETURN TICKET (IRE)**, 7, b g Getaway (GER)—Capelvenere (IRE) **Mr R. Collins**
22 **ROBYN PUD (IRE)**, 6, b m Kalanisi (IRE)—Quit The Noise (IRE) **Derek Gennard & Gillian Gennard**
23 **SECRETE STREAM (IRE)**, 11, ch g Fruits of Love (USA)—Bonny River (IRE) **Mr A. R. Dixon**
24 **SHEPHERD'S BIGHT (IRE)**, 8, b g Court Cave (IRE)—Orador Sur Glane (IRE) **Mrs S. M. Wood**
25 **SIR JIM (IRE)**, 5, b g Shirocco (GER)—Stick Together **Derek Gennard & Gillian Gennard**
26 **TAYZAR**, 9, b g Kayf Tara—Matilda Too (IRE) **C. D. Carr**
27 **TEMPLE MAN**, 8, b g Sulamani (IRE)—Altogether Now (IRE) **Mrs I C Straker & Steven Key**
28 **WAITING PATIENTLY (IRE)**, 9, b g Flemensfirth (USA)—Rossavon (IRE) **Mr R. Collins**

THREE-YEAR-OLDS

29 B f Telescope (IRE)—Ancora (IRE)
30 B f Telescope (IRE)—En Reve

Other Owners: D. Gennard, Mrs G. Gennard, Mr S. Key, Mrs A. Russell, A. J. R. Russell, Mrs R. A. Straker, Mr R. M. Wharton, Mr J. H. Wilson.

Amateur Jockey: Mr Aiden Blakemore.

---

298 **MR D J JEFFREYS, Stow-on-the-Wold**
Postal: **Mount Pleasant Farm, Oddington Road, Stow-on-the-Wold, Gloucestershire, GL54 1JJ**
Contacts: PHONE 07917 714687
EMAIL djjeffreys15@hotmail.co.uk

1 **AUGHNACURRA KING (IRE)**, 7, ch g Tajraasi (USA)—Cracking Kate (IRE) **Mark E Smith & Jaykayjay Pals Ak**
2 **BOOMTIME BANKER (IRE)**, 6, b m Kalanisi (IRE)—Tiger Tiffney (IRE)
3 **DUBAI OUTLAW (IRE)**, 7, b g Dubai Destination (USA)—Lady Outlaw (IRE) **Mr D. Jeffreys**
4 **ENEMENEMYNEMO (IRE)**, 5, b g Lakeshore Road (USA)—Portobello Sunrise (IRE)
5 **GEROLAMO CARDANO**, 4, b g Motivator—Dark Quest **Mr M. E. Smith**
6 **GETAMAN (IRE)**, 7, b g Getaway (GER)—Zingarella's Joy (IRE) **Mrs A. Landale**
7 **GO HARD OR GO HOME (IRE)**, 7, b g Scorpion (IRE)—Site Eile (IRE) **Mr D. Jeffreys**
8 **ISLE ROAD (IRE)**, 11, b g Heron Island (IRE)—Corries Rein (IRE) **Mr D. Jeffreys**
9 **JETSTREAM (IRE)**, 5, b g Galileo (IRE)—Bewitched (IRE) **Mr M. E. Smith**
10 **KAYLEN'S MISCHIEF**, 7, ch g Doyen (IRE)—Pusey Street Girl **Mr M. E. Smith**
11 **KILDIMO (IRE)**, 5, b br g Stowaway—Beananti (IRE) **Mr M. E. Smith**
12 **LIVELY CITIZEN (IRE)**, 5, b g Frammassone—Acinorev (IRE) **Mark E Smith,Brake Horse Power Syndicate**
13 **LOTTIE DENO**, 4, b f Havana Gold (IRE)—Rapid Revalation (USA) **Mrs A. Landale**
14 **MODULUS**, 11, b g Motivator—Wild Academy (IRE) **Mr M. E. Smith**
15 **PETRASTAR**, 5, b g Passing Glance—Petrarchick (USA) **Exors of the Late Mr P. G. Horrocks**
16 **PETRUCCI (IRE)**, 8, b g Azamour (IRE)—Spring Symphony (IRE) **16.10 Fakenham**
17 **TREE OF LIBERTY (IRE)**, 8, ch g Stowaway—The Wrens Nest (IRE) **Mr M. E. Smith**
18 **ZARA HOPE (IRE)**, 9, b m Stowaway—Agua Caliente (IRE) **Mr M. E. Smith**

Other Owners: Mr A. T. Chatwin, Mr M. E. Smith, The Brake Horse Power Syndicate, The JayKayJay PALS AK Syndicate.

---

299 **MR J. R. JENKINS, Royston**
Postal: **Kings Ride, Therfield Heath, Royston, Hertfordshire, SG8 9NN**
Contacts: PHONE 01763 241141, 01763 246611 MOBILE 07802 750855 FAX 01763 248223
EMAIL john@johnjenkinsracing.co.uk WEBSITE www.johnjenkinsracing.co.uk

1 **ACE CHEETAH (USA)**, 6, b g Kitten's Joy (USA)—Imagistic (USA) **The Ace Cheetah Partnership**
2 **ACE TIME**, 6, b g Sinndar (IRE)—Desert Run (IRE) **Mrs W. A. Jenkins**
3 **CARVELAS (IRE)**, 11, b g Cape Cross (IRE)—Caraiyma (IRE) **Crofters Racing Syndicate**
4 **CHAMPAGNE VINTAGE (IRE)**, 7, b g Stowaway—Ask My Granny (IRE) **Barry Silkman & Sarah Parker**
5 **CHLOELLIE**, 5, b m Delegator—Caramelita **Mrs Veronica Bullard & Mrs Wendy Jenkins**
6 **COOL ECHO**, 6, b m Mount Nelson—Ellcon (IRE) **Mr M. Turner**
7 **DALKADAM (FR)**, 9, gr g Martaline—Cadoudame (FR) **Mrs S. F. Hadida**

MR J. R. JENKINS - continued

8 **DOLLYWAGGON PIKE**, 6, b m Hellvelyn—Once Removed **Mrs W. A. Jenkins**
9 **DURATION (IRE)**, 5, b g Champs Elysees—Fringe **Mr B Dowling & Mr R Stevens**
10 **GRANNY FRANKHAM**, 7, b m Authorized (IRE)—Faldal
11 **MAYKIR**, 4, b g Mayson—Kiruna **Mrs C. Goddard**
12 **MOBHAM (IRE)**, 5, b g Teofilo (IRE)—Elegant Beauty **Mrs Claire Goddard & Mr Robin Stevens**
13 **SAGA SPRINT (IRE)**, 7, b m Excellent Art—Queen of Malta (IRE) **Mr R. Stevens**
14 **SHERELLA**, 4, b f Delegator—Mediterranean Sea (IRE) **Mrs W. A. Jenkins**
15 **TILSWORTH EMERALD**, 5, b m Equiano (FR)—Tilsworth Charlie **Michael Ng**
16 **TILSWORTH LUKEY**, 7, b g Sixties Icon—Chara **Michael Ng & Phyllis Hutchins**
17 **TILSWORTH PRISCA**, 5, ch m Equiano (FR)—Ashwell Rose **Michael Ng**
18 **TILSWORTH ROSE**, 6, b m Pastoral Pursuits—Pallas **Michael Ng**
19 **TILSWORTH SAMMY**, 5, b g Mount Nelson—Chara **Michael Ng**
20 **WALLY'S WISDOM**, 8, b g Dutch Art—Faldal **Mr Royston Cooper**
21 **WHALEWEIGH STATION**, 9, b g Zamindar (USA)—Looby Loo **Mr J. Melo**
22 **WINALOTWITHALITTLE (IRE)**, 4, ch f Frozen Power (IRE)—Easy Going **Mr A. J. Taylor**
23 **ZAHIRAH**, 6, b m Mullionmileanhour (IRE)—Numanthia (IRE) **Mr F. Qadir**
24 **ZAHRAANI**, 5, b g Mount Nelson—Mediterranean Sea (IRE) **Mr F. Qadir**

THREE-YEAR-OLDS

25 B f Cappella Sansevero—Mediterranean Sea (IRE) **Mrs W. A. Jenkins**
26 **MIGHTY ENDEAVOUR**, b g Heeraat (IRE)—Magic By Bell **Mr M. Turner**
27 **NADIA'S SPIRIT (IRE)**, b g Ivawood (IRE)—Lilakiya (IRE) **Mr Q. Khan**
28 **SIR RODNEYREDBLOOD**, ch g Roderic O'Connor (IRE)—Red Blooded Woman (USA) **Mrs C. Goddard**
29 B f Fast Company (IRE)—Teyateyaneng (IRE) **Mr Mohammad Al-Khayarin**

TWO-YEAR-OLDS

30 B g 13/04 Equiano (FR)—Bella Beguine (Komaite (USA)) **Mr M. Turner**
31 **CARMELA SOPRANO**, bl f 25/02 Hellvelyn—Caramelita (Deportivo) **Golden Equinox Racing**
32 **COPPER KITTEN**, ch f 27/02 Bobby's Kitten (USA)—Night Haven (Night Shift (USA)) (2857) **Mrs C. Goddard**
33 **JOE PROUD**, b c 04/05 Sepoy (AUS)—Irrational (Kyllachy) (10000) **Mrs Irene Hampson**

Other Owners: Mrs V. Bullard, B. S. P. Dowling, Mrs C. Goddard, Mrs P. E. E. Hutchins, Mrs W. A. Jenkins, Michael Ng, Miss S. L. Parker, Mr J. Sales, B. Silkman, Mr R. Stevens, Mr Andy Taylor.

---

300 **MRS LINDA JEWELL, Maidstone**
Postal: **Southfield Stables, South Lane, Sutton Valence, Maidstone, Kent, ME17 3AZ**
Contacts: **PHONE 01622 842788 MOBILE 07856 686657**
EMAIL lindajewell@hotmail.com **WEBSITE** www.lindajewellracing.co.uk

1 **BREDEN (IRE)**, 10, b g Shamardal (USA)—Perfect Touch (USA) **The Breden Racing Partnership**
2 **CALYPSO JACK (IRE)**, 7, ch g Papal Bull—Miss Barbados (IRE) **Mr H J Jarvis & Mrs P Jarvis**
3 **CLONUSKER LADY (IRE)**, 5, b m Papal Bull—Goodthyne Miss (IRE) **Valence Racing Too**
4 **COCKNEY SEAGULL (IRE)**, 7, br g Watar (IRE)—Acountry Lane (IRE) **CS Partnership**
5 **DEEWHY (IRE)**, 7, b g Papal Bull—Chanteuse de Rue (IRE) **Mr D. N. Yeadon**
6 **EBONY BELLE (IRE)**, 4, b f Tough As Nails (IRE)—Ebonywood (USA) **Valence Racing**
7 **HAB SAB (IRE)**, 8, b g Papal Bull—Tamburello (IRE) **Mrs P. Reynolds**
8 **HUMBLE MARY**, 5, ch m Watar (IRE)—She's Humble (IRE) **Mr H J Jarvis & Mrs P Jarvis**
9 **ICONIC FLIGHT**, 5, b g Sixties Icon—Sabreflight **Valence Racing**
10 **INVINCIBLE SEA (IRE)**, 4, b f Born To Sea (IRE)—Melaaya (USA) **Mr T. Betteridge**
11 **MAB DAB (IRE)**, 9, b g Papal Bull—Pret A Porter (UAE) **Mr T. Betteridge**
12 **MERYEMS WAY (IRE)**, 4, b f Tough As Nails (IRE)—Anne-Lise **Valence Racing**
13 **MR JACK (IRE)**, 8, ch g Papal Bull—Miss Barbados (IRE) **The Breden Racing Partnership**
14 **MRS JACK (IRE)**, 6, ch m Papal Bull—Miss Barbados (IRE) **Mr R. Dean**
15 4, B f Elzaam (AUS)—Pret A Porter (UAE)
16 **ROYAL CONCORDE (IRE)**, 9, br g Kalanisi (IRE)—Talinas Rose (IRE) **Mr R. B. Morton**
17 4, B c Arcadio (GER)—Tash McGarry (IRE)
18 **TOOR GENERAL (IRE)**, 9, ch g Kaieteur (USA)—Alexander Euro **Mr R. Churcher**

MR J. R. JENKINS - continued

19 **UALLRIGHTHARRY (IRE)**, 8, b g Craigsteel—Enchanted Valley (IRE) **Mrs S. M. Stanier**
20 **URBAN SCENE**, 4, b f Cityscape—Fashionable Gal (IRE) **Mr J. C. Webb**

THREE-YEAR-OLDS
21 **HEER ME**, b f Heeraat (IRE)—Push Me (IRE) **Alex & Janet Card**

Other Owners: Mr C. G. Benford, Mr C. M. Couldrey, Mr M. G. Fitzjohn, Mrs S. M. Fitzjohn, Mrs A. P. Giggins, Mr W. Giggins, Miss S. E. Haughton, Mr B. J. Hensman, H. J. Jarvis, Mrs P Jarvis, Mr K. Pinder, Mr J. J. Saxton.

Assistant Trainer: Karen Jewell.

Flat Jockey: Robert Havlin. **NH Jockey:** Tom Cannon, Brendan Powell. **Conditional Jockey:** Phillip Donovan. **Amateur Jockey:** Mr O Brophy.

---

301 **MR BRETT JOHNSON, Epsom**
Postal: **The Durdans Stables, Chalk Lane, Epsom, Surrey, KT18 7AX**
Contacts: **MOBILE 07768 697141**
EMAIL thedurdansstables@googlemail.com WEBSITE www.brjohnsonracing.co.uk

1 **BAY DUDE**, 5, b g Sulamani (IRE)—Sky Calling **Born to Run Racing**
2 **CAYUGA**, 11, b g Montjeu (IRE)—Ithaca (USA) **B. R. Johnson**
3 **DANGEROUS ENDS**, 6, b g Monsieur Bond—Stolen Glance **Mr C. Westley**
4 **EWELL SPRING**, 4, b f Captain Gerrard (IRE)—Hey Mambo **Taylor Anderson Racing**
5 **HERON (USA)**, 6, b g Quality Road (USA)—Dreamt **O1 Racing Partnership**
6 **LERRYN LASS (IRE)**, 4, b f Acclamation—Belts And Braces (IRE) **Miss G. Povilaviciute**
7 **PRIME APPROACH (IRE)**, 4, ch g Dawn Approach (IRE)—Remarkable Story **Mr C. Westley**
8 **RAKEMATIZ**, 6, ch g Pivotal—Regal Velvet **Mr C. Westley**
9 **RUN AFTER GENESIS (IRE)**, 4, gr g Archipenko (USA)—She Is Great (IRE) **Mr C. Westley**
10 **TRUE BELIEF (IRE)**, 4, b g Excelebration (IRE)—It's True (IRE) **Mr C. Westley**
11 **VIOLET'S LADS (IRE)**, 6, b m Myboycharlie (IRE)—Cape Violet (IRE) **The Savy Group**

THREE-YEAR-OLDS
12 **ANISOPTERA (IRE)**, ch f Casamento (IRE)—Dragonera **Tann & Mr N Jarvis**
13 **BAY MAY**, b f Helmet (AUS)—Ceilidh Band
14 **LITTLE FLOOZIE**, b f Brazen Beau (AUS)—Sweet Wind Music **Omni Colour Presentations Ltd**
15 **STOPNSEARCH**, b g War Command (USA)—Secret Suspect **Omni Colour Presentations Ltd**
16 **TREPIDATION**, b g Bated Breath—True Pleasure (IRE) **Tann & Mr N Jarvis**

Other Owners: Mr M. Cumins, Mr N. Hale, Mr S. Hills, Mr N. A. Jarvis, Mr G. Peck, Mrs S. Rutherford, Mr G. Tann, Mr B. D. Townsend, Miss L. Wilde.

Assistant Trainer: Vanessa Johnson.

---

302 **MR KENNY JOHNSON, Newcastle Upon Tyne**
Postal: **Grange Farm, Newburn, Newcastle Upon Tyne, Tyne and Wear, NE15 8QA**
Contacts: **PHONE 01388 721813, 0191 267 4464 MOBILE 07774 131121**
EMAIL kennyjohnson68@hotmail.co.uk WEBSITE www.johnsonracing.co.uk

1 **BENARTY HILL (IRE)**, 10, b g September Storm (GER)—Crossmacahilly (IRE) **John Caldow & Kenny Johnson**
2 **CAIRNSHILL (IRE)**, 9, gr g Tikkanen (USA)—Illikeyou (IRE) **Jewitt/carter Thompson & Gardiner**
3 **CONNERYS HILL (IRE)**, 7, b g Stowaway—Hillmar (IRE) **John Caldow & Kenny Johnson**
4 **CRYOGENICS (IRE)**, 6, b g Frozen Power (IRE)—New Blossom (IRE) **Mr L Armstrong & Partner**
5 **HARD KNOCKS (IRE)**, 10, b g Turtle Island (IRE)—Celtic Tigress (IRE) **Mr Robert C. Whitelock/Mr Kenny Johnson**
6 **KING GOLAN (IRE)**, 9, b g Golan (IRE)—Crimson Bow (GER) **Blacklock & Partners**
7 **ON WE GO (IRE)**, 7, b m Robin des Pres (FR)—Clan Music (IRE) **Kenny Johnson & Mrs K Elliott**
8 **SWEET FLORA (IRE)**, 6, b m Arcadio (GER)—Country Flora **Mr Robert C. Whitelock/Mr Kenny Johnson**

MR KENNY JOHNSON - continued

Other Owners: J. L. Armstrong, Mr I. M. Blacklock, Mr J. R. Caldow, Mr A. Carter, Carter Thompson Associates, Mrs K. Elliott, Mr R. W. Gardiner, Mr R. W. Jewitt, Mr K. Johnson, Mr S. Thompson, R. C. Whitelock.

Conditional Jockey: Callum Bewley, Tommy Dowson, Kane Yeoman.

303	**MRS SUSAN JOHNSON, Madley**

Postal: **Carwardine Farm, Madley, Hereford**
Contacts: **PHONE 01981 250214 FAX 01981 251538**

1 **THE LAST BRIDGE,** 13, b g Milan—Celtic Bridge **I. K. Johnson**

NH Jockey: Richard Johnson.

304	**MISS EVE JOHNSON HOUGHTON, Blewbury**

Postal: **Woodway, Blewbury, Didcot, Oxfordshire, OX11 9EZ**
Contacts: **HOME 01235 850500 PHONE 01235 850480 MOBILE 07721 622700 FAX 01235 851045**
EMAIL Eve@JohnsonHoughton.com WEBSITE www.JohnsonHoughton.com

1 **ACCIDENTAL AGENT,** 6, b g Delegator—Roodle **Mrs R. F. Johnson Houghton**
2 **AFRICAN SHOWGIRL,** 7, ch m Showcasing—Georgie The Fourth (IRE) **Miss Vanda Ohlidalova**
3 **BELLA VITA,** 4, gr f Aussie Rules (USA)—Garabelle (IRE) **John & Heather Raw**
4 **BUCKINGHAM (IRE),** 4, gr g Clodovil (IRE)—Lizzy's Township (USA) **The Buckingham Partnership**
5 **CLUBORA (USA),** 4, b f Medaglia d'Oro (USA)—Middle Club **Clubora Team**
6 **FEARLESS WARRIOR (FR),** 4, ch g Sea The Stars (IRE)—Mambo Light (USA) **Mr H Frost**
7 **GAMBON (GER),** 4, b g Dutch Art—Guajara (GER) **Mr A. J. Pye-Jeary**
8 **GIN PALACE,** 4, b g Swiss Spirit—Regal Curtsy **Mrs Zara Campbell-Harris**
9 **GIVINITSUM (SAF),** 5, b g Lateral—Fine Hope (SAF) **Mr N. Cheng**
10 **GORING (GER),** 8, b g Areion (GER)—Globuli (GER) **Mr G. C. Stevens**
11 **HEDGING (IRE),** 6, gr ro g Mastercraftsman (IRE)—Privet (IRE) **Eden Racing Club**
12 **HYANNA,** 5, b m Champs Elysees—Highly Spiced **Mr G. C. Vibert**
13 **ICE AGE (IRE),** 7, b g Frozen Power (IRE)—Incendio **Eden Racing III**
14 **KIRKLAND FOREVER,** 6, ch m Sakhee (USA)—Maystock **Mrs M Fairbairn & Mr P Dean**
15 **KWELA,** 4, b f Kodiac—Funday **Mr & Mrs James Blyth Currie**
16 **LADY ELYSIA,** 4, ch f Champs Elysees—Lost In Lucca **The Nigel Bennett Partnership**
17 **MADAME TANTZY,** 4, b f Champs Elysees—Roodle **Mrs R. F. Johnson Houghton**
18 **MISS ELSA,** 4, b f Frozen Power (IRE)—Support Fund (IRE) **Eden Racing Club**
19 **MY STYLE (IRE),** 4, gr g Holy Roman Emperor (IRE)—
That's My Style **The Hon Mrs J. M. The Corbett & Mr C. Wright**
20 **OUTLANE,** 5, b m Camelot—Batik (IRE) **Aston House Stud**
21 **SOMETHINGABOUTJACK (IRE),** 4, br c No Nay Never (USA)—City Dazzler (IRE) **Ms E. Chivers & Merlin Racing**
22 **TIN HAT (IRE),** 4, ch g Helmet (AUS)—Precautionary **Eden Racing IV**

THREE-YEAR-OLDS

23 **ALEZAN,** ch f Dawn Approach (IRE)—Sarinda **Mr M. Middleton-Heath**
24 **ALLEZ SOPHIA (IRE),** b f Kingman—Allez Alaia (IRE) **Mr Trevor C Stewart**
25 **ARIARIA (IRE),** b f Clodovil (IRE)—Some Site (IRE) **The Buckingham Partnership II**
26 **BEALACH (IRE),** b c New Approach (IRE)—Samya **Mick and Janice Mariscotti**
27 **BILLHILLY (IRE),** b c Sea The Stars (IRE)—Boccassini (GER) **K. A. Dasmal**
28 **BUTO,** ch g Nathaniel (IRE)—Mea Parvitas (IRE) **Eden Racing Club**
29 **CAPTAIN CLARET,** b g Medicean—Shirazz **Mrs S. J. Doyle**
30 **COOL KNIGHT (IRE),** gr g Dragon Pulse (IRE)—Primrose Gate (IRE) **Arthur, Blake, Davis & Wyer**
31 **COSMIC POWER (IRE),** br g Power—Dhamma (USA) **McNamee Hewitt Harding Rice**
32 **FALDETTA,** b f Helmet (AUS)—Perfect Cover (IRE) **Mrs M. E. Slade & Partner**
33 **FOLIE D'AMOUR,** b f Nathaniel (IRE)—Rock Follies **J Cross, M Duckham, L Godfrey, P Wollaston**

MISS EVE JOHNSON HOUGHTON - continued

34 **FORGETFUL AGENT,** ch g Anjaal—Bronze Star **Miss E Asprey**
35 **GO BOB GO (IRE),** b g Big Bad Bob (IRE)—Fire Up **Mr G. J. Owen**
36 **GRACEFUL MAGIC,** gr f Gutaifan (IRE)—Magic Escapade (IRE) **The Kimber Family**
37 **HIGH CLASS AFFAIR (IRE),** ch f Zebedee—Acushladear (IRE) **Elaine Chivers Racing**
38 **HMS PRESIDENT (IRE),** b c Excelebration (IRE)—Dance Hall Girl (IRE) **HP Racing HMS President**
39 **KASHMIRELLA (IRE),** ch f Camacho—Pashmina (IRE) **Kennet Valley Thoroughbreds XII**
40 **KEPALA,** gr f Mastercraftsman (IRE)—Kebaya **Aston House Stud**
41 **MISS MATTERHORN,** b f Swiss Spirit—Support Fund (IRE) **The Ascot Colts & Fillies Club**
42 **NOBLE MASQUERADE,** b g Sir Percy—Moi Aussi (USA) **HP Racing Noble Masquerade**
43 **OCHO GRANDE (IRE),** b g Tamayuz—Soul Custody (CAN) **Rogate Racing**
44 **ON THE BRIGHTSIDE (IRE),** ch g Anjaal—Kardyls Hope (IRE) **Eden Racing**
45 **PUNCHBOWL FLYER (IRE),** b g Dream Ahead (USA)—All On Red (IRE) **The Punch Bunch**
46 **RIDGEWAY (FR),** b g Outstrip—Bocca Bianca (GER) **Miss E. A. Johnson Houghton**
47 **ROODICA,** b f Due Diligence (USA)—Roodle **Mrs Rf Johnson Houghton& Ascot Revellers**
48 **SABLET,** b f Fulbright—Garabelle (IRE) **Raw, Reeve & Wollaston**
49 **SHADOW GLEN,** b g Gleneagles (IRE)—Milady **D. J. Deer**
50 **SPECIAL SECRET,** b f Kodiac—Love's Secret **Mr H Frost**
51 **SPINACIA (IRE),** b f Charm Spirit (IRE)—Spinola (FR) **Mrs C. Vigors**
52 **SWORD BEACH (IRE),** ch g Ivawood (IRE)—Sleeping Princess (IRE) **HP Racing Sword Beach**
53 **ZULU GIRL,** b f Lethal Force (IRE)—Upskittled **Trish & Colin Fletcher-Hall**

TWO-YEAR-OLDS

54 **BATINDI,** b f 23/04 Bated Breath—Rohlindi (Red Ransom) **Mrs C. Vigors**
55 **BHUBEZI,** ch c 01/03 Starspangledbannor (AUS)—
             Lulani (IRE) (Royal Applause) (38095) **Mr & Mrs James Blyth Currie**
56 **COCO BEAR (IRE),** br c 22/04 Kodi Bear (IRE)—
             House of Roses (New Approach (IRE)) (14285) **Trish & Colin Fletcher-Hall**
57 **COLDSTREAM,** b c 23/02 Australia—Balandra (Medicean) **Aston House Stud**
58 **DANVILLE,** b c 28/01 Muhaarar—Faustinatheyounger (IRE) (Antonius Pius (USA)) (30000) **Viscount Astor**
59 **DARK ILLUSION,** bc 10/02 Equiano (FR)—Magic Escapade (IRE) (Azamour (IRE)) (19047) **The Kimber Family**
60 **DARK SHIFT,** gr c 01/04 Dark Angel (IRE)—Mosuo (IRE) (Oasis Dream) (50000) **Mr H Frost**
61 **ENDURING,** b c 05/02 Coulsty (IRE)—Yearbook (Byron) (9523) **Mr M. Middleton-Heath**
62 **FLAME OF FREEDOM,** b f 31/03 Dragon Pulse (IRE)—
             Catalan (IRE) (Duke of Marmalade (IRE)) (11154) **Mr & Mrs Nicholas Johnston**
63 **HOLLYANNA,** b f 20/04 Havana Gold (IRE)—Highly Spiced (Cadeaux Genereux) (14285) **Mr G. C. Vibert**
64 **JUMBY (IRE),** b c 17/05 New Bay—Sound of Guns (Acclamation) (45000) **Anthony Pye-Jeary & David Ian**
65 **MARSELAN (IRE),** b c 15/03 Awtaad (IRE)—
             Monclaire (GER) (Sholokhov (IRE)) (53000) **Mick and Janice Mariscotti**
66 **MOUNT OLYMPUS,** b c 07/03 Olympic Glory (IRE)—Ile Rouge (Red Ransom) **HP Racing Mount Olympus**
67 Ch f 03/04 Dragon Pulse (IRE)—Multi Grain (Sir Percy) (5714)
68 **PERCY WILLIS,** b g 24/03 Sir Percy—Peace Lily (Dansili) (2380) **Mrs R. F. Johnson Houghton**
69 **PERCY'S LAD,** ch c 28/04 Sir Percy—Victory Garden (New Approach (IRE)) (34000) **JD Partnership**
70 B f 26/03 Charming Thought—Roodle (Xaar) **Mrs R. F. Johnson Houghton**
71 **SANKALPA,** b f 23/02 Zoffany (IRE)—Partita (Montjeu (IRE)) **Aston House Stud**
72 **SCHILTHORN,** b c 10/03 Swiss Spirit—Wall of Light (Zamindar (USA)) (8571) **The Mighty Mouse Partnership**
73 **STIGWOOD (IRE),** b c 19/04 Kodiac—
             Time Honoured (Sadler's Wells (USA)) (42000) **Anthony Pye-Jeary & David Ian**
74 B c 06/02 Equiano (FR)—Stylos Ecossais (Aqlaam) (28571) **H.H. Shaikh Nasser Al Khalifa & Partner**
75 **TATTOO,** b f 16/03 Equiano (FR)—Belvoir Diva (Exceed And Excel (AUS)) (10476) **Mrs J. E. O'Halloran**
76 **TEMPLE LOCK,** b c 25/03 Pivotal—Graduation (Lomitas) **Mr G. C. Stevens**
77 **THE PRINCES POET,** b c 04/03 Brazen Beau (AUS)—Poesy (Poet's Voice) **HP Racing The Princes Poet**
78 **TIPSY LAIRD,** b c 02/04 Gleneagles (IRE)—
             Lady Eclair (IRE) (Danehill Dancer (IRE)) (82000) **Mr & Mrs Nicholas Johnston**
79 **UNCLE DICK,** b g 23/04 Toronado (IRE)—
             Golden Waters (Dubai Destination (USA)) (571) **Mrs R. F. Johnson Houghton**
80 B c 23/03 Holy Roman Emperor (IRE)—Xinji (IRE) (Xaar) (26666)

MISS EVE JOHNSON HOUGHTON - continued

Other Owners: H.H. Sheikh Nasser Al Khalifa, H. R. F. Arthur, Mr M. Bird, Mr D. S. Blake, Mrs H. D. Blyth Currie, Mr J. M. Blyth Currie, Mr J. A. Bryan, Mr R. J. Bryan, Mr P. A. Buckley, Mr A. J. Carter, Miss C. I. Chivers, Ms E. C. Chivers, Ms L. D. Chivers, The Hon Mrs C. Corbett, Mr G. Cosburn, Mr J. C. Cross, Mr S. J. Davis, Steve Davis & Miss E Johnson Houghton, P. Dean, Mr M. R. Duckham, Mrs M. Fairbairn, Mr C. M. Fletcher, Mr L. R. A. Godfrey, Lionel Godfrey & Peter Wollaston, Mr M. W. Gregory, Mrs P. A. Hall, Mr R. Harding, Mr L. N. Hewitt, Miss E. A. Johnson Houghton, Mrs R. F. Johnson Houghton, Mr N. Johnston, Mrs S. Johnston, Mr C. Jones, Mr H. F. Kearns, Mr D. Lane, Mrs J. M. Mariscotti, Mr M. G. Mariscotti, Mr B. P. McNamee, Mrs J. A. McWilliam, Mrs A. J. Middis, Mr F. Nass, Mrs H. B. Raw, Mr J. Raw, Mr R. K. Reeve, Mrs E. R. Rice, Mrs H. I. Slade, The Ascot Revellers, The Stewkley Shindiggers Partnership, Mr D. L. Thomas, J. R. Wallis, Mr P. R. Wollaston, Mr C. N. Wright, Mr A. P. Wyer.

Apprentice Jockey: Georgia Dobie.

305	**MR MARK JOHNSTON, Middleham**

Postal: **Kingsley Park, Middleham, Leyburn, North Yorkshire, DL8 4QZ**
Contacts: **PHONE 01969 622237 FAX 01969 622484**
EMAIL info@johnston.racing WEBSITE www.johnston.racing

1 **ANYONECANHAVEITALL,** 4, b g Nathaniel (IRE)—Floriade (IRE) **Mr G. J. Freyne**
2 **ARCTIC SOUND,** 4, b c Poet's Voice—Polar Circle (USA) **Mr S. B. M. Al Qassimi**
3 **ASDAA (IRE),** 4, b g Dutch Art—Danseuse de Reve (IRE) **Owners Group 045**
4 **BLOWN BY WIND,** 4, b c Invincible Spirit (IRE)—Discourse (USA) **Sheikh Hamdan Bin Mohammed Al Maktoum**
5 **CAPE COAST,** 6, b g Cape Cross (IRE)—Famusa **Ali Saeed**
6 **CAPLIN,** 4, b g Cape Cross (IRE)—Party Line **S. R. Counsell**
7 **CARDSHARP,** 5, b g Lonhro (AUS)—Pure Illusion (IRE) **Sheikh Hamdan Bin Mohammed Al Maktoum**
8 **COMMUNIQUE (IRE),** 5, ch h Casamento (IRE)—
    Midnight Line (USA) **Sheikh Hamdan Bin Mohammed Al Maktoum**
9 **COUNTRY STAR,** 4, b f Iffraaj—Honky Tonk Sally **Mr S. R. Bin Ghadayer**
10 **CUCKOO CLOCK,** 4, ch f Pivotal—Betimes **Sheikh Hamdan Bin Mohammed Al Maktoum**
11 **DARK VISION (IRE),** 4, b c Dream Ahead (USA)—Black Dahlia **Godolphin Management Company Ltd**
12 **DEEP INTRIGUE,** 4, gr c Dark Angel (IRE)—Abbakova (IRE) **Clipper Group Holdings Ltd**
13 **ELARQAM,** 5, b h Frankel—Attraction **Hamdan bin Rashid Al Maktoum**
14 **FIRE FIGHTING (IRE),** 9, b g Soldier of Fortune (IRE)—Savoie (FR) **Mr Alan Spence**
15 **GRENADIER GUARD (IRE),** 4, ch g Australia—Another Storm (USA) **Mr J. A. Barson**
16 **HOCHFELD (IRE),** 6, b g Cape Cross (IRE)—What A Charm (IRE) **Sheikh Hamdan Bin Mohammed Al Maktoum**
17 **KING'S ADVICE,** 6, ch h Frankel—Queen's Logic (IRE) **Mr Saeed Jaber**
18 **MARIE'S DIAMOND (IRE),** 4, b br c Footstepsinthesand—Sindiyma (IRE) **Middleham Park Racing LXXXVI**
19 **MASHAM STAR (IRE),** 6, b g Lawman (FR)—Croisiere (USA) **3 Batterhams and a Reay**
20 **MILDENBERGER,** 5, b b Teofilo (IRE)—Belle Josephine **Sheikh Hamdan Bin Mohammed Al Maktoum**
21 **MOUNTAIN RULER,** 4, ch g Ruler of The World (IRE)—Regal Fairy (IRE) **East Layton Stud Ltd**
22 **NAYEF ROAD (IRE),** 4, ch c Galileo (IRE)—Rose Bonheur **M. Obaida**
23 **ROCHESTER HOUSE (IRE),** 4, ch g Galileo (IRE)—Kalla **John Brown & Megan Dennis**
24 **ROYAL BIG NIGHT (USA),** 4, ch c Distorted Humor (USA)—Tamboz (USA) **Kingsley Park 19 - Ready To Run**
25 **SIR RON PRIESTLEY (IRE),** 4, ch c Australia—Reckoning (IRE) **P. Dean**
26 **SKY DEFENDER,** 4, b c Farhh—Al Mahmeyah **Mr H. R. Bin Ghedayer**
27 **SMILE A MILE (IRE),** 4, ch g Slade Power (IRE)—Bergamask (USA) **Sheikh Hamdan Bin Mohammed Al Maktoum**
28 **SNOW SPACE (IRE),** 4, b c Shamardal (USA)—Alpine Storm (IRE) **Sheikh Hamdan Bin Mohammed Al Maktoum**
29 **STAR OF THE EAST (IRE),** 4, b g Cape Cross (IRE)—Serenity Star **Sheikh Hamdan Bin Mohammed Al Maktoum**
30 **SUMMER MOON,** 4, ch g Sea The Moon (GER)—Songerie **The Originals**
31 **THAI TERRIER (USA),** 4, b g Kitten's Joy (USA)—Perfect Agility (USA) **Mr C. R. Hirst**
32 **THE TRADER (IRE),** 4, gr g Mastercraftsman (IRE)—Chinese White (IRE) **Ali Saeed**
33 **THEMAXWECAN (IRE),** 4, b c Maxios—Psychometry (FR) **D. C. Livingston**
34 **VALE OF KENT (IRE),** 5, b g Kodiac—Red Vale (IRE) **Sheikh Hamdan Bin Mohammed Al Maktoum**
35 **VIVID DIAMOND (IRE),** 4, b f Cape Cross (IRE)—Pretty Diamond (IRE) **Cayton Park Stud Limited**
36 **WEST END CHARMER (IRE),** 4, b c Nathaniel (IRE)—Solar Midnight (USA) **Mr M. McHale**

MR MARK JOHNSTON - continued

THREE-YEAR-OLDS

37 **AFRICAN SWIFT (USA)**, ch f Distorted Humor (USA)—
Sahara Wind (USA) **Sheikh Hamdan Bin Mohammed Al Maktoum**
38 **ALLGOLD (IRE)**, br c Golden Horn—Liber Nauticus (IRE) **Mrs J. E. Newett**
39 **ALMQVIST**, b c Kingman—Alvarita **Miss K. Rausing**
40 **ARTILLERY**, b c Brazen Beau (AUS)—Malpas Missile (IRE) **Kingsley Park 14**
41 **AUCHTERARDER (IRE)**, b f Gleneagles (IRE)—Crossover **Kingsley Park 11**
42 B f New Approach (IRE)—Autumn Lily (USA) **Sheikh Hamdan Bin Mohammed Al Maktoum**
43 **AVENTURIERE**, b f Archipenko (USA)—Lady Jane Digby **Miss K. Rausing**
44 **BAILEYS PRINCESS**, b f Kingman—Posteritas (USA) **G R Bailey Ltd (Baileys Horse Feeds)**
45 **BATALHA**, b g Henrythenavigator (USA)—Lamentation **N Browne,I Boyce, S Frosell & S Richards**
46 **BEECHWOOD JIM BOB (IRE)**, bl c Footstepsinthesand—Clodovina (IRE) **Middleham Park & Ventura Racing 12**
47 **BLAKE'S VISION (IRE)**, b c Slade Power (IRE)—Shirley Blake (IRE) **Kingsley Park 13**
48 **BONDI SANDS (IRE)**, b g Australia—Thai Haku (IRE) **China Horse Club International Limited**
49 B f Sea The Stars (IRE)—Cat O' Nine Tails **Mr Mohammed Jaber**
50 **CLOG MAKER (IRE)**, b c Dark Angel (IRE)—Utrecht **Sheikh Hamdan Bin Mohammed Al Maktoum**
51 **COGNAC (IRE)**, b c Invincible Spirit (IRE)—Rose de France (IRE) **China Horse Club/Ballylinch Stud**
52 **COTTONOPOLIS**, b c Ruler of The World (IRE)—Jamboree Girl **W. T. Whittle**
53 **COUNTRY OF POETS (IRE)**, ch c Shamardal (USA)—
Villarrica (USA) **Sheikh Hamdan Bin Mohammed Al Maktoum**
54 **DA VINCI (IRE)**, b c Golden Horn—What A Picture (IRE) **Brown, Hathorns & Partner**
55 **DARK HEART**, b c Nathaniel (IRE)—Danehill Dreamer (USA) **T T Bloodstocks**
56 **DARK REGARD**, br f Dark Angel (IRE)—Best Regards (IRE) **Mr J. E. Dance**
57 **DESERT SAFARI (IRE)**, b c Slade Power (IRE)—Risen Sun **Sheikh Hamdan Bin Mohammed Al Maktoum**
58 **DONTASKMEAGAIN (USA)**, ch c Karakontie (JPN)—Al Beedaa (USA) **Crone Stud Farms Ltd**
59 **DREAM KART (IRE)**, b f Dream Ahead (USA)—Kartiste (IRE) **John O'Connor & Partner**
60 **DREAM WITH ME (IRE)**, b c Frankel—Where (IRE) **Mr S. Suhail**
61 **DUTCH DECOY**, ch g Dutch Art—The Terrier **Owners Group 045**
62 **ETON COLLEGE (IRE)**, b c Invincible Spirit (IRE)—
Windsor County (USA) **Sheikh Hamdan Bin Mohammed Al Maktoum**
63 **EXPENSIVE DIRHAM**, ch f Dubawi (IRE)—Hush Money (CHI) **Sheikh Hamdan Bin Mohammed Al Maktoum**
64 **FESTIVAL DAY**, b f Dubawi (IRE)—Ama (USA) **Sheikh Hamdan Bin Mohammed Al Maktoum**
65 **FLASHING APPROACH (IRE)**, b c New Approach (IRE)—Flashing Green **Mr C. R. Hirst**
66 **FLYLIKEANEAGLE (IRE)**, b g Free Eagle (IRE)—Dulcian (IRE) **Barbara & Alick Richmond Racing**
67 **FRED**, ch g Frankel—Deirdre **The Burke Family**
68 **GLENTIES (USA)**, b c Karakontie (JPN)—Candy Kitty (USA) **Mr M. Doyle**
69 **GOBI SUNSET**, b c Oasis Dream—Dark Promise **N Browne,I Boyce, S Frosell & S Richards**
70 **GOLD RIBBON**, b f Golden Horn—Chan Tong (BRZ) **Sheikh Hamdan Bin Mohammed Al Maktoum**
71 **GOLD SOUK (IRE)**, b c Casamento (IRE)—Dubai Sunrise (USA) **Sheikh Hamdan Bin Mohammed Al Maktoum**
72 **GOLD ZABEEL (IRE)**, b c Shamardal (USA)—Elshabakiya (IRE) **Jaber Abdullah**
73 **GOLDEN FOUNTAIN (IRE)**, br c Fountain of Youth (IRE)—Art of Gold **Kingsley Park 11**
74 **GOLDEN TIMES (SWI)**, ch f Lord of England (GER)—Ange Doree (FR) **M. W. Graff**
75 **HA'PENNY BRIDGE (IRE)**, ch f Tamayuz—Diminish (IRE) **Mr A D Spence & Mr M B Spence**
76 **HADEED**, ch g Shamardal (USA)—Shurfah (USA) **Hamdan bin Rashid Al Maktoum**
77 **HATHEEM (IRE)**, ch g New Approach (IRE)—Alonsoa (IRE) **Hamdan bin Rashid Al Maktoum**
78 **HOMESPIN (USA)**, ch c Speightstown (USA)—
Vaguely Familiar (USA) **Sheikh Hamdan Bin Mohammed Al Maktoum**
79 **HUBOOR (IRE)**, b f More Than Ready (USA)—Glorification **Hamdan bin Rashid Al Maktoum**
80 **HURAIZ (IRE)**, ch c Sepoy (AUS)—Samaah (IRE) **Hamdan bin Rashid Al Maktoum**
81 **I SPIED**, ch c Australia—Super Sleuth (IRE) **Jaber Abdullah**
82 **IFFRAAZ (IRE)**, b c Iffraaj—Zofzig (USA) **Sheikh Hamdan Bin Mohammed Al Maktoum**
83 **JM JACKSON (IRE)**, b br f No Nay Never (USA)—Kawn **MPS Racing Ltd**
84 **JUSTIFIED**, br g Authorized (IRE)—Caribbean Dancer (USA) **Mr H. C. Hart**
85 **KING FAN**, b c Kingman—Forever Times **Mr H. A. Lootah**
86 **KING'S CAPER**, br c New Approach (IRE)—Karen's Caper (USA) **Kingsley Park 13**
87 **KINGBROOK**, br gr c Kingman—Warling (USA) **R. S. Brookhouse**
88 **LION TOWER (IRE)**, b c Exceed And Excel (AUS)—Memorial (AUS) **Sheikh Hamdan Bin Mohammed Al Maktoum**
89 **MAKYON (IRE)**, b c Make Believe—Mise (IRE) **The Makyowners**

MR MARK JOHNSTON - continued

90 **MERAAS,** b c Oasis Dream—Rehn's Nest (IRE) **Mr S. M. Bel Obaida**
91 **MESMERIC (GER),** b c Casamento (IRE)—Mambo Rhythm **Kingsley Park 14**
92 **MISTY GREY (IRE),** gr c Dark Angel (IRE)—Chinese White (IRE) **Barbara & Alick Richmond**
93 **MONOSKI (USA),** b c Street Boss (USA)—Wipe Out (USA) **Sheikh Hamdan Bin Mohammed Al Maktoum**
94 **MORNING SHADOW,** ch f New Approach (IRE)—Elle Shade **Sheikh Hamdan Bin Mohammed Al Maktoum**
95 **MOTION,** b f Invincible Spirit (IRE)—Attraction **Exors of the Late Duke of G. D. Roxburghe**
96 **MOUNTAIN BRAVE,** b f Sepoy (AUS)—Plucky **East Layton Stud & James Lambert**
97 **MOUNTAIN DREAMS (USA),** b br f Temple City (USA)—
 Pico Duarte (USA) **Sheikh Hamdan Bin Mohammed Al Maktoum**
98 **MRS BOUQUET,** b f Toronado (IRE)—Riva Royale **Mr G. J. Freyne**
99 **MY GIRL MAGGIE,** b f Camelot—African Plains **Mr & Mrs Paul & Clare Rooney**
100 **NETIQUETTE,** ch f Archipenko (USA)—Nimiety **Miss K. Rausing**
101 **OLD HARBOUR,** ch c Dawn Approach (IRE)—Dunnes River (USA) **Sheikh Hamdan Bin Mohammed Al Maktoum**
102 Ch g Night of Thunder (IRE)—Oud Metha **Mr Mohammed Jaber**
103 **OVERWRITE (IRE),** ro c Zebedee—Negotiate **Sheikh Hamdan Bin Mohammed Al Maktoum**
104 **PEACE TREATY (IRE),** b f War Command (USA)—Naomh Geileis (USA) **Mrs Christine E Budden & Partners**
105 B c Night of Thunder (IRE)—Pencarrow **Rabbah Racing**
106 **PERFECT ROSE,** b f Oasis Dream—Maid To Perfection **Mrs J. E. Newett**
107 **PRAXEOLOGY (IRE),** b g Dark Angel (IRE)—Hartstown House (IRE) **Dr J. Walker**
108 **PRETTY LADY (IRE),** b f Es Que Love (IRE)—Quality Love (USA) **Crone Stud Farms Ltd**
109 Ch f Starspangledbanner (AUS)—Prianca (GER) **Mr P Monaghan**
110 **QUANTUM DAWN (IRE),** ch c Dawn Approach (IRE)—Shanooan (USA) **Kingsley Park 13**
111 **QUEEN GAMRAH,** b f Toronado (IRE)—Rainbow's Edge **Jaber Abdullah**
112 **RAFFLE PRIZE (IRE),** b f Slade Power (IRE)—Summer Fete (IRE) **Sheikh Hamdan Bin Mohammed Al Maktoum**
113 **REQUIEMS DREAM (IRE),** ch f Dream Ahead (USA)—Kerrys Requiem (IRE) **Robert Bradley & Carl Chapman**
114 **ROBERT GUISCARD (IRE),** b g Exceed And Excel (AUS)—Beneventa **Kingsley Park 19 - Ready To Run**
115 **ROSE OF KILDARE (IRE),** b f Make Believe—Cruck Realta **Kingsley Park 14**
116 **SALAMANCA SCHOOL (FR),** b c Rock of Gibraltar (IRE)—Princess Sofia (UAE) **Dr J. Walker**
117 **SEA OF MARMOON,** b c Golden Horn—Sibling Honour **Sheikh Hamdan Bin Mohammed Al Maktoum**
118 **SEASONY (IRE),** b c Siyouni (FR)—Rosie Cotton (IRE) **Mr H. A. Lootah**
119 **SERENGETI STAR,** b f Teofilo (IRE)—Shawanda (IRE) **Sheikh Hamdan Bin Mohammed Al Maktoum**
120 **STREAK LIGHTNING (IRE),** ch c Night of Thunder (IRE)—Emreliya (IRE) **Kennet Valley Thoroughbreds XIII**
121 **STRIDING EDGE (IRE),** b c Canford Cliffs (IRE)—Assault On Rome (USA) **Mrs Christine E Budden & Partners**
122 **SUBJECTIVIST,** b c Teofilo (IRE)—Reckoning (IRE) **Dr J. Walker**
123 **THE WEED MACHINE (IRE),** b c Kodiac—Noahs Ark (IRE) **P. D. Savill**
124 **THUNDEROUS (IRE),** b c Night of Thunder (IRE)—Souviens Toi **Highclere T'bred Racing - George Stubbs**
125 **TOO HARD TO HOLD (IRE),** b g Camacho—Bilderberg (IRE) **Mr G. J. Freyne**
126 **TRINITY GIRL,** b f Teofilo (IRE)—Micaela's Moon (USA) **Tactful Finance Limited**
127 **TRUE BELIEVER (IRE),** b f Make Believe—Laviniad (IRE) **Ballylinch Stud**
128 **TRUMPET MAN,** b c Golden Horn—Concordia **Sheikh Hamdan Bin Mohammed Al Maktoum**
129 **TULIP FIELDS,** b f Golden Horn—Vituisa **Sheikh Hamdan Bin Mohammed Al Maktoum**
130 **VINCITOMNIA (FR),** b br f Invincible Spirit (IRE)—Tales of Valour (IRE) **Miss K. Rausing**
131 **VISINARI (FR),** gr c Dark Angel (IRE)—Visinada (IRE) **Mr R. Ferguson**
132 **WADACRE GIGOLO,** ch g Makfi—Glenreef **Wadacre Stud**
133 **WARNE'S ARMY,** b f Fast Company (IRE)—Euro Empire (USA) **DGA Racing Limited**
134 **WARRANTY (FR),** b g Authorized (IRE)—Ballymena Lassie **Highclere T'bred Racing - JMW Turner**
135 **WEST END GIRL,** b f Golden Horn—Free Rein **Mr A D Spence & Mr M B Spence**
136 **ZABEEL CHAMPION,** b c Poet's Voice—Stars In Your Eyes **Jaber Abdullah**

TWO-YEAR-OLDS

137 B c 02/05 Free Eagle (IRE)—Agnetha (GER) (Big Shuffle (USA)) (18000) **Kingsley Park 16**
138 B f 22/03 Gleneagles (IRE)—Al Janadeirya (Oasis Dream) **Times Of Wigan Ltd**
139 Ch f 01/02 Sea The Stars (IRE)—Alamode (Sir Percy) (68640) **Miss K. Rausing**
140 **ALLEGRANZA,** b f 20/01 Bobby's Kitten—Alboretta (Hernando (FR)) **Miss K. Rausing**
141 **ANNANDALE (IRE),** ch c 24/01 Australia—Fountain of Honour (IRE) (Sadler's Wells (USA)) **W. M. Johnstone**
142 Ch f 05/04 Pivotal—Baileys Jubilee (Bahamian Bounty) **G R Bailey Ltd (Baileys Horse Feeds)**
143 **BEVERAGE (IRE),** b f 04/03 Alhebayeb (IRE)—Flood Plain (Orpen (USA)) **Mr S Ronan**
144 B f 08/02 The Last Lion (IRE)—Bitooh (Diktat) (10000) **Sheikh J. D. Al Maktoum**
145 B c 26/05 Night of Thunder (IRE)—Cairncross (IRE) (Cape Cross (IRE)) **Rabbah Racing**

MR MARK JOHNSTON - continued

146 B c 01/04 Frankel—Cape Dollar (IRE) (Cape Cross (IRE)) **Mr S. Suhail**
147 B c 13/04 The Gurkha (IRE)—Celtic Filly (IRE) (Footstepsinthesand) **Mr M. B. H. K. Al Attiya**
148 B c 06/02 Farhh—Chaquiras (USA) (Seeking The Gold (USA)) **Sheikh Hamdan Bin Mohammed Al Maktoum**
149 **CHICA BONITA,** b f 02/02 Lope de Vega (IRE)—
                                                        Hundi (IRE) (Fastnet Rock (AUS)) (82000) **Paul & Charles O'Callaghan**
150 B c 25/02 Belardo (IRE)—City Chic (USA) (Street Cry (IRE)) **Sheikh Hamdan Bin Mohammed Al Maktoum**
151 B f 08/04 Muhaarar—Clarietta (Shamardal (USA)) (50000) **Mr A D Spence & Mr M B Spence**
152 Ch c 21/02 Iffraaj—Coral Mist (Bahamian Bounty) (34285) **Rob Ferguson & Gary Pemberton**
153 **COUPE DE CHAMPAGNE (GER),** ch f 14/05 Gleneagles (IRE)—
                                                        Capichera (GER) (Shirocco (GER)) (15000) **Kingsley Park 17**
154 Ch c 22/04 Mastercraftsman (IRE)—Cranky Spanky (IRE) (Spectrum (IRE)) (17160) **Kingsley Park 18**
155 B f 10/04 Awtaad (IRE)—Dayrose (Daylami (IRE)) (45000) **Mr H. A. Lootah**
156 **DECODING (IRE),** b f 23/03 Dawn Approach (IRE)—
                                                        Khazina (USA) (Kingmambo (USA)) (16000) **Tactful Finance Limited & Partner**
157 B c 01/02 Gleneagles (IRE)—Defrost My Heart (IRE) (Fastnet Rock (AUS)) (64349) **Mr M. B. H. K. Al Attiya**
158 B c 20/04 Oasis Dream—Desert Sage (Selkirk (USA)) (52000) **Sheikh Hamdan Bin Mohammed Al Maktoum**
159 B c 25/04 Cannock Chase (USA)—Dreaming Beauty (Oasis Dream) **Mr S. Suhail**
160 B f 04/04 Exceed And Excel (AUS)—
                                                        Dubai Sunrise (USA) (Seeking The Gold (USA)) **Sheikh Hamdan Bin Mohammed Al Maktoum**
161 Ch c 01/02 Showcasing—Duchess Dora (IRE) (Tagula (IRE)) (100000) **Mr S. Suhail**
162 **EPIC PASS (IRE),** b c 25/01 Awtaad (IRE)—Kanes Pass (IRE) (Clodovil (IRE)) (30000) **Teme Valley 2**
163 B c 16/02 Golden Horn—First Blush (IRE) (Pivotal) **Sheikh Hamdan Bin Mohammed Al Maktoum**
164 B c 01/02 Golden Horn—
                                                        Flame of Gibraltar (IRE) (Rock of Gibraltar (IRE)) **Sheikh Hamdan Bin Mohammed Al Maktoum**
165 **GEAR UP (IRE),** b c 08/03 Teofilo (IRE)—Gearanai (USA) (Toccet (USA)) (44615) **Teme Valley 2**
166 **GLEN AGAIN (IRE),** b c 06/04 Gleneagles (IRE)—Four Eleven (CAN) (Arch (USA)) (42000) **Teme Valley 2**
167 B c 13/05 Dawn Approach (IRE)—Gold Bubbles (IRE) (Street Cry (IRE)) (12000) **Gallop Racing**
168 B f 04/03 Kodiac—Goldcrest (Assertive) (32380) **Cliff Stud**
169 B c 10/04 Awtaad (IRE)—Great Hope (IRE) (Halling (USA)) (52000) **C. C. Buckley**
170 **HARLEM SOUL,** ch c 23/02 Frankel—Giants Play (USA) (Giant's Causeway (USA)) (130000) **Teme Valley 2**
171 B c 25/04 Bobby's Kitten (USA)—Heading North (Teofilo (IRE)) (11154) **Kingsley Park 18**
172 **HIGH PEAK (IRE),** b c 03/05 Fascinating Rock (IRE)—
                                                        Expectation (IRE) (Night Shift (USA)) (8000) **Atlantic Racing & R. W. Huggins**
173 **HOME AND DRY (IRE),** ch c 05/04 Sea The Stars (IRE)—
                                                        Pale Mimosa (IRE) (Singspiel (IRE)) (100000) **Barbara & Alick Richmond**
174 **IMMACULATE,** b f 10/04 Invincible Spirit (IRE)—
                                                        Coquette Noire (IRE) (Holy Roman Emperor (IRE)) (82000) **Highclere T'Bred Racing - Juliet Cursham**
175 B c 19/04 Lawman (FR)—Jo Bo Bo (IRE) (Whipper (USA)) (12012) **Kingsley Park 15**
176 B c 11/02 Bernardini (USA)—Joyful Hope (Shamardal (USA)) (30000) **The Originals**
177 **JULIE JOHNSTON,** b f 07/03 Acclamation—
                                                        Jeanie Johnston (IRE) (One Cool Cat (USA)) (3809) **Robert Bradley & Carl Chapman**
178 B c 29/04 Awtaad (IRE)—Katla (IRE) (Majestic Missile (IRE)) (100000) **Mr H. A. Lootah**
179 **KING ZAIN (IRE),** b c 08/03 Kingman—Shreyas (IRE) (Dalakhani (IRE)) (81509) **Jaber Abdullah**
180 **KINGS PRINCE,** b c 05/02 Kingman—Dynaforce (USA) (Dynaformer (USA)) (75000) **Crone Stud Farms Ltd**
181 B c 28/02 Frankel—Lacily (USA) (Elusive Quality (USA)) **Sheikh Hamdan Bin Mohammed Al Maktoum**
182 **LADY ARIELLA,** b f 22/01 Dawn Approach (IRE)—
                                                        Perfectly Spirited (Invincible Spirit (IRE)) (15000) **Tactful Finance & J Barnett**
183 Ch c 02/05 Zoffany (IRE)—Lady Pimpernel (Sir Percy) (22000) **Kingsley Park 15**
184 Gr c 26/01 Kendargent (FR)—Lady's Secret (IRE) (Alzao (USA)) (13728) **Kingsley Park 17**
185 **LADYWOOD (IRE),** b f 06/04 Dark Angel (IRE)—Beneventa (Most Welcome) (67000) **Mr J. A. Barson**
186 B c 14/02 Exceed And Excel (AUS)—Landela (Alhaarth (IRE)) (140000) **Hamdan bin Rashid Al Maktoum**
187 B c 14/01 Dansili—Lavender And Lace (Barathea (IRE)) (30000) **Rob Ferguson & Gary Pemberton**
188 **LOVE IS GOLDEN (IRE),** b c 30/05 Golden Horn—
                                                        Holy Moon (IRE) (Hernando (FR)) (175000) **Crone Stud Farms Ltd**
189 **LOVE OF ZOFFANY (IRE),** ch c 20/02 Zoffany (IRE)—
                                                        Ithaca (USA) (Distant View (USA)) (38609) **Crone Stud Farms Ltd**
190 B c 09/04 Dark Angel (IRE)—Maid To Dream (Oasis Dream) (115000) **Hamdan bin Rashid Al Maktoum**
191 B c 15/02 Raven's Pass (USA)—
                                                        Malmoosa (IRE) (Shamardal (USA)) (75000) **Sheikh Hamdan Bin Mohammed Al Maktoum**

MR MARK JOHNSTON - continued

192 B c 02/04 Toronado (IRE)—Mambo Halo (USA) (Southern Halo (USA)) (17000) **Kingsley Park 16**
193 Ch f 26/01 Helmet (AUS)—Mambo Paradise (Makfi) (22000) **Around The World Partnership**
194 Ch c 24/03 Shamardal (USA)—Mehronissa (Iffraaj) (500000) **Mr S. R. Bin Ghadayer**
195 B f 09/02 Muhaarar—Memoria (Teofilo (IRE)) (42857) **Hamdan bin Rashid Al Maktoum**
196 B f 17/02 The Gurkha (IRE)—Missisipi Star (IRE) (Mujahid (USA)) **G R Bailey Ltd (Baileys Horse Feeds)**
197 B f 31/03 Fascinating Rock (IRE)—Mood Indigo (IRE) (Indian Ridge) (19734) **P. D. Savill**
198 B c 13/03 Muhaarar—Muteela (Dansili) **Hamdan bin Rashid Al Maktoum**
199 MYRTLE MACLAGAN (IRE), b f 27/04 Australia—
        Fifer (IRE) (Soviet Star (USA)) (42000) **N Browne,I Boyce, S Fresell & S Richards**
200 B c 03/04 Fastnet Rock (AUS)—Mzyoon (IRE) (Galileo (IRE)) **Mr H. A. Lootah**
201 B f 26/03 Teofilo (IRE)—Nafura (Dubawi (IRE)) **Sheikh Hamdan Bin Mohammed Al Maktoum**
202 B f 25/03 Night of Thunder (IRE)—
        Namhroodah (IRE) (Sea The Stars (IRE)) (200000) **Hamdan bin Rashid Al Maktoum**
203 Ch f 25/03 Exceleberation (IRE)—Naomh Geileis (USA) (Grand Slam (USA)) **Mrs Christine E Budden & Partners**
204 NIGHT MOMENT (GER), b c 10/05 Amaron—Noble Lady (GER) (Sholokhov (IRE)) (12870) **Kingsley Park 16**
205 B c 22/04 Kodiac—Noahs Ark (IRE) (Charnwood Forest (IRE)) (52000) **Mr R. Walker**
206 B c 05/04 Camelot—Opera Fan (FR) (Cape Cross (IRE)) (50000) **Jaber Abdullah**
207 OUTBACK BOY, ch c 29/04 Australia—Permission Slip (IRE) (Authorized (IRE)) (25740) **Teme Valley 2**
208 PARTY SPIRIT, ch f 18/04 Night of Thunder (IRE)—Party Line (Montjeu (IRE)) (16000) **S. R. Counsell**
209 B f 13/02 Footstepsinthesand—Parvenue (FR) (Ezzoud (IRE)) (17000) **Kingsley Park 15**
210 B c 26/04 Iffraaj—Peacoat (Doyen (IRE)) (15000) **Kingsley Park 17**
211 B f 02/04 Kodiac—Pelerin (IRE) (Shamardal (USA)) **Newsells Park Stud Limited**
212 B c 28/04 Authorized (IRE)—Pencarrow (Green Desert (USA)) **Rabbah Racing**
213 B f 04/04 Iffraaj—Pietrafiore (IRE) (Dubawi (IRE)) **Sheikh Hamdan Bin Mohammed Al Maktoum**
214 B f 11/02 Golden Horn—Pivotting (Pivotal) (70000) **Sheikh A. H. F. M. A. Al Sabah**
215 B f 05/03 Iffraaj—Policoro (IRE) (Pivotal) **Sheikh Hamdan Bin Mohammed Al Maktoum**
216 B c 26/02 New Approach (IRE)—Posteritas (USA) (Lear Fan (USA)) (80000) **G R Bailey Ltd (Baileys Horse Feeds)**
217 B c 18/03 Wootton Bassett—Praise Dancing (IRE) (Blame (USA)) (98670) **H.H. Shaikh Nasser Al Khalifa & Partner**
218 Ch c 21/04 Sea The Stars (IRE)—
        Pretty Diamond (IRE) (Hurricane Run (IRE)) (500000) **Hamdan bin Rashid Al Maktoum**
219 B c 15/01 Dark Angel (IRE)—Priceless Jewel (Selkirk (USA)) (52380) **Mr J. E. Dance**
220 B f 07/04 Cannock Chase (USA)—Prime Run (Dansili) **Mr S. Suhail**
221 B f 16/04 Holy Roman Emperor (IRE)—Prufrock (IRE) (Roderic O'Connor (IRE)) (12011) **Mr O Brennan**
222 REAMS OF LOVE, b c 04/04 Frankel—Night of Light (IRE) (Sea The Stars (IRE)) (68640) **Crone Stud Farms Ltd**
223 B f 01/04 Muhaarar—Reckoning (IRE) (Danehill Dancer (IRE)) (100000) **Dr J. Walker**
224 B c 22/03 Night of Thunder (IRE)—Redinha (Dansili) (110000) **Hamdan bin Rashid Al Maktoum**
225 B c 30/04 Dubawi (IRE)—Rehn's Nest (IRE) (Authorized (IRE)) **Mr S. M. Bel Obaida**
226 B f 27/04 Violence (USA)—Renesmee (USA) (Giant's Causeway (USA)) (72930) **Al Wasmiyah Stud**
227 B c 22/02 Exceed And Excel (AUS)—Risen Sun (Shamardal (USA)) **Sheikh Hamdan Bin Mohammed Al Maktoum**
228 B br c 13/03 Dragon Pulse (IRE)—
        Rock Follies (Rock of Gibraltar (IRE)) (40000) **H.H. Shaikh Nasser Al Khalifa & Partner**
229 Ch c 17/02 The Last Lion (IRE)—Romie's Kastett (GER) (Halling (USA)) (21000) **Mr J. D. Abell**
230 Ch f 26/02 Frankel—Rose Bonheur (Danehill Dancer (IRE)) (185000) **M. Obaida**
231 B c 15/02 Fast Company (IRE)—Roseraie (IRE) (Lawman (FR)) (30000) **Mr H. A. Lootah**
232 Ch c 30/03 New Approach (IRE)—
        Safe House (Exceed And Excel (AUS)) (40000) **Sheikh Hamdan Bin Mohammed Al Maktoum**
233 Ch c 16/03 Helmet (AUS)—Salsa Steps (USA) (Giant's Causeway (USA)) (24761) **Mr J. D. Abell**
234 SANDS OF TIME, b f 20/03 Bobby's Kitten (USA)—Starlit Sands (Oasis Dream) **Miss K. Rausing**
235 SEA THE SHELLS, b c 06/02 Sea The Stars (IRE)—Seychelloise (Pivotal) (40000) **Teme Valley 2**
236 B c 31/05 Galileo (IRE)—Sent From Heaven (IRE) (Footstepsinthesand) (80000) **Crone Stud Farms Ltd**
237 B c 07/03 Sea The Stars (IRE)—Sharna's Crown (IRE) (New Approach (IRE)) **Mr H. A. Lootah**
238 SHE GOT THE LOOK (IRE), b f 09/04 Camelot—Jessie Jane (IRE) (Dylan Thomas (IRE)) (21449) **M. W. Graff**
239 Gr ro c 14/02 Cairo Prince (USA)—Shovalla (USA) (Ghostzapper (USA)) **Mr H. A. Lootah**
240 B c 04/01 Iffraaj—Silent Moment (USA) (Giant's Causeway (USA)) **Sheikh Hamdan Bin Mohammed Al Maktoum**
241 B f 30/04 Exceed And Excel (AUS)—Silkwood (Singspiel (IRE)) (42000) **Miss D Finkler, A Herd, Dr P Holloway 1**
242 SIMPLY AMAZING, b c 24/03 Epaulette (AUS)—
        Chrisscross (IRE) (Cape Cross (IRE)) (30000) **Tactful Finance Limited**
243 SIR JOHN BOWDLER (IRE), b c 30/03 Exceed And Excel (AUS)—
        Gotta Have Her (USA) (Royal Academy (USA)) (50000) **P. Dean**

MR MARK JOHNSTON - continued

244 B c 11/05 Toronado (IRE)—Sitara (Salse (USA)) (25000) **Rob Ferguson & Gary Pemberton**
245 B f 08/02 Shamardal (USA)—
    Spinning Cloud (USA) (Street Cry (IRE)) **Sheikh Hamdan Bin Mohammed Al Maktoum**
246 B f 06/03 Dansili—St Francis Wood (USA) (Irish River (FR)) **Aynsford Holdings LLC**
247 STATE OF BLISS (IRE), b c 16/04 Gleneagles (IRE)—
    Crystal Valkyrie (IRE) (Danehill (USA)) (68640) **Barbara & Alick Richmond**
248 B f 04/03 Iffraaj—Street Fire (IRE) (Street Cry (IRE)) **Mr A.D. Spence & Mr & Mrs P.Hargreaves**
249 Gr ro c 27/03 Sepoy (AUS)—Sudfah (USA) (Unbridled's Song (USA))
250 B f 09/03 New Bay—This Is The Day (Footstepsinthesand) (20000) **John O'Connor & Partner**
251 B c 10/03 Exceed And Excel (AUS)—Tussie Mussie (Royal Applause) (20000) **Ali Saeed**
252 B c 03/03 Showcasing—Ultradargent (FR) (Kendargent (FR)) (13728) **Kingsley Park 18**
253 B c 30/03 Oasis Dream—Wake Up Call (Noverre (USA)) (45714) **Hamdan bin Rashid Al Maktoum**
254 B f 28/01 Zoffany (IRE)—We Are Ninety (IRE) (Thewayyouare (USA)) (24023) **Jaber Abdullah**
255 B f 30/01 Bobby's Kitten (USA)—Wholesome (USA) (Lemon Drop Kid (USA)) **Lech Racing Ltd**
256 WISE JUDGEMENT (IRE), b f 16/04 Lope de Vega (IRE)—Discreet Brief (IRE) (Darshaan) **A. P. Rogers**
257 WOOTTON CREEK, b f 03/02 Wootton Bassett—
    Tuileries (Cape Cross (IRE)) (58000) **Sheikh Hamdan Bin Mohammed Al Maktoum**
258 B c 18/05 Frankel—You'll Be Mine (USA) (Kingmambo (USA)) (280000) **M. Obaida**
259 B c 12/02 Dubawi (IRE)—Zara (BRZ) (Redattore (BRZ)) **Sheikh Hamdan Bin Mohammed Al Maktoum**
260 Ch c 07/05 Galileo (IRE)—Zouzou (AUS) (Redoute's Choice (AUS)) **Matsumoto/Orpendale/Chelston/Wynatt**

Other Owners: Ballylinch Stud, Mr J. M. Brown, John Brown & Megan Dennis, China Horse Club International Limited, East Layton Stud Ltd, Mr R. Ferguson, Miss D Finkler Mr A Herd & Dr P Holloway, Johnston Racing Limited, Kingsley Park Owners Club, Barbara & Alick Richmond, Mr Alan Spence, Tactful Finance Limited.

Assistant Trainer: Jock Bennett, Charlie Johnston, Deirdre Johnston.

Flat Jockey: Joe Fanning, P. J. McDonald, Franny Norton. **Apprentice Jockey:** Andrew Breslin, Oliver Stammers.

306	**MR ALAN JONES, Timberscombe**

Postal: **East Harwood Farm, Timberscombe, Minehead, Somerset, TA24 7UE**
Contacts: **MOBILE 07901 505064 FAX 01633 680232**
EMAIL heritageracing@btconnect.com WEBSITE www.alanjonesracing.co.uk

 1 5, B h Arvico (FR)—A Nun With A Gun (IRE)
 2 DUHALLOW LAD (IRE), 8, b g Papal Bull—Macca Luna (IRE) **Burnham Plastering & Drylining Ltd**
 3 7, B g Craigsteel—Glenair Lucy (IRE)
 4 I'M NOTAPARTYGIRL, 7, b m Arvico (FR)—Lady Shirley Hunt **Mr A. E. Jones**
 5 JACK'S A LEGEND, 5, b g Midnight Legend—Dancing Emily (IRE) **Burnham Plastering & Drylining Ltd**
 6 LADY AVERY (IRE), 8, b m Westerner—Bobs Article (IRE) **Burnham Plastering & Drylining Ltd**
 7 MISSMEBUTLETMEGO, 10, b g With The Flow (USA)—Bay Bianca (IRE) **Mr A. E. Jones**
 8 ON THE METER (IRE), 6, b br g Eastern Anthem (IRE)—Party Belle **Premier Plastering (UK) Limited**
 9 POKARI (FR), 8, ch g Bonbon Rose (FR)—Pokara (FR) **Mr A. E. Jones**
10 STAND BY ME (FR), 10, b g Dream Well (FR)—In Love New (FR) **Mr A. E. Jones**
11 TIQUER (FR), 12, b g Equerry (USA)—Tirenna (FR) **Burnham Plastering & Drylining Ltd**
12 TRICKS AND TRAILS (IRE), 7, b g Flemensfirth (USA)—Loughaneala (IRE) **Premier Plastering (UK) Limited**
13 VETONCALL (IRE), 8, b g Well Chosen—Miss Audacious (IRE) **Burnham Plastering & Drylining Ltd**

THREE-YEAR-OLDS

14 COCARDIER (FR), b c My Risk (FR)—Tamaline (FR) **Mr A. E. Jones**
15 LADY EXCALIBUR (IRE), b f Camelot—Market Forces **Burnham Plastering & Drylining Ltd**
16 B c Bollin Eric—Rest And Be (IRE)

TWO-YEAR-OLDS

17 B g 17/05 Clovis du Berlais (FR)—Dancing Emily (IRE) (Anshan)

Assistant Trainer: Miss A. Bartelink.

NH Jockey: Paddy Brennan, Richard Johnson, Tom O'Brien.

307 MRS FIONA KEHOE, Leighton Buzzard
Postal: **The Croft Farm, Wing Road, Stewkley, Leighton Buzzard, Bedfordshire, LU7 0JB**
Contacts: PHONE **07795 096908**
EMAIL **f.kehoe@btinternet.com**

1 ALWAYS ABLE (IRE), 5, b m Stowaway—Twotrailerparkgirl (IRE) **M. Kehoe**
2 TABLE MOUNTAIN (FR), 6, b g Mountain Town (USA)—Kandariya (FR) **M. Kehoe**

308 MR MARTIN KEIGHLEY, Moreton-In-Marsh
Postal: **Condicote Stables, Luckley, Longborough, Moreton-In-Marsh, Gloucestershire, GL56 0RD**
Contacts: MOBILE **07767 472547**
EMAIL **keighleyracing@btinternet.com** WEBSITE **www.martinkeighley.com**

1 BACK ON THE LASH, 6, b g Malinas (GER)—Giovanna **M Boothright G Lovett P Deffains**
2 BE THANKFUL, 5, ch m Helmet (AUS)—Be Joyful (IRE)
3 BEN BUIE (IRE), 6, br g Presenting—Change of Plan (IRE) **Owners for Owners Ben Buie**
4 BENEAGLES (IRE), 8, b g Milan—Liss Rua (IRE) **Lady Horn-Smith & Godfrey Wilson**
5 BIG NASTY, 7, b g Black Sam Bellamy (IRE)—Hello My Lovely **Peel Racing Syndicate**
6 BLACK PANTHER (IRE), 4, br g Nayef (USA)—Amjaad **Keighley Racing Limited**
7 BLACK PRINCE (FR), 6, b g Falco (USA)—Thamara (USA) **Martin Keighley Racing Partnership 6**
8 BOBBLE EMERALD (IRE), 12, ch g Rudimentary (USA)—Aunt Emeralds (IRE) **D Bishop, C Bowkley & M Parker**
9 BRILLARE MOMENTO (IRE), 9, b m Milan—Sunshine Leader (IRE) **Mr O. F. Ryan**
10 CAPITAL FORCE (IRE), 9, b g Kayf Tara—Watson River (IRE) **Mr J. Abernethy**
11 CAPRICIA (IRE), 5, b m Mahler—Bobset Leader (IRE) **Martin Keighley Racing Partnership 5**
12 CHEQUERED VIEW, 7, b m Passing Glance—Blue Plaid **H.R.H. The Princess Royal**
13 CITY NEVER SLEEPS (IRE), 8, b g Central Park—Goodnightmrskelly (IRE) **Martin Keighley Racing Club**
14 COTSWOLD PRINCE (IRE), 5, b g Elzaam (AUS)—Kalinjara (IRE) **Martin Keighley Racing Partnership 3**
15 DEBDEN BANK, 6, b g Cacique (IRE)—Rose Row **Tyrone Hanlon & Mark Boothright**
16 DREAMSUNDERMYFEET (IRE), 5, br g Yeats (IRE)—Change of Plan (IRE) **Owners for Owners Dreamers**
17 ECLAT DES MOTTES (FR), 6, b g Poliglote—Sun des Mottes (FR)
18 ENFORCEMENT (IRE), 5, b g Lawman (FR)—Elodie **Martin Keighley Racing Club**
19 FORECAST, 8, ch g Observatory (USA)—New Orchid (USA) **The The Tenovus Partnership**
20 GOLD MOUNTAIN (IRE), 10, b g Gold Well—La Belle de Serk (FR) **James Burley & Jon Hughes**
21 KAZONTHERAZZ, 4, b f Kayf Tara—Giovanna **The Meagher Family**
22 LORD CONDI (IRE), 7, ch g Papal Bull—Wings To Soar (USA) **Owners for Owners Lord Condi**
23 LUCKY CIRCLE, 4, b f Yorgunnabelucky (USA)—Circle of Angels **The Lucky Circle**
24 MISS ANTIPOVA, 8, b m Pasternak—Herballistic **Batsford Stud Racing Club**
25 MOZZARO (IRE), 5, b g Morozov (USA)—Baraza (IRE) **Owners for Owners Mozzaro**
26 PINNACLE PEAK, 5, b g Passing Glance—Giovanna **M Boothright & G Lovett**
27 RAVING BONKERS, 7, ch g Notnowcato—Harriet's Girl **What In Heavens Partnership**
28 REVE, 6, b g Nathaniel (IRE)—Rouge (FR) **Mr O. F. Ryan**
29 ROBSAM (IRE), 5, b g Mahler—Silver Set (IRE) **Mr M. Capp**
30 RUN A RIG, 5, ch m Black Sam Bellamy (IRE)—Somethinaboutmolly (IRE) **Mrs Z. A. E. Tindall**
31 SAMTARA, 6, b g Kayf Tara—Aunt Harriet **Mr & Mrs R. Allsop**
32 SARASOTA STAR (IRE), 4, gr ro g Zebedee—Riviera Rose (IRE) **Torben Dal & Jon Hughes**
33 SOLSTICE STAR, 10, b g Kayf Tara—Clover Green (IRE) **Foxtrot Racing: Solstice Star**
34 TEN PAST MIDNIGHT, 4, b g Midnight Legend—Thornton Alice
35 WITNESS PROTECTION (IRE), 7, b g Witness Box (USA)—Queen's Exit **Foxtrot Racing Witness Protection**
36 WORLD WAR (IRE), 6, ch g Galileo (IRE)—Jacqueline Quest (IRE) **Mrs L. Jones**

THREE-YEAR-OLDS
37 DUKE OF LUCKLEY (IRE), b g Mahler—Emily's Princess (IRE)

TWO-YEAR-OLDS
38 Br g 20/05 Califet (FR)—Clondalee (IRE) (Presenting)
39 B g 31/03 Sans Frontieres (IRE)—Killoughey Babe (IRE) (Alderbrook)
40 B g 20/03 Sans Frontieres (IRE)—Seana Ghael (IRE) (Oscar (IRE))

MR MARTIN KEIGHLEY - continued

Other Owners: Mr D. Abraham, Mrs J. Abraham, Mr R. Allsop, Mrs Y. E. Allsop, D. Bishop, M. Boothright, Mr C. Bowkley, Mr J. Burley, Mr A. J. A. Cole, Mr T. Dal, Mr P. Deffains, Mr J. M. Gibbs, Mr N. J. Guttridge, Mr T. Hanlon, Lady E. Horn-Smith, Mr E. J. Hughes, Mr G. P. A. Lovett, Mr A. S. Martin, Mr M. D. Parker, Mr S. C. Prowting, Mr J. E. S. Tufts, G. A. Wilson.

Assistant Trainer: Miss Hollie Watts, **Racing Secretary:** Mrs Belinda Keighley, **Yard Sponsor:** Mr Neil Lloyd FBC Manby Bowdler.

Conditional Jockey: Patrick Cowley.

---

309 MR SHAUN KEIGHTLEY, Newmarket
Postal: **Flat 1, Harraton Court Stables, Church Lane, Exning, Newmarket, Suffolk, CB8 7HF**

1 **ALONSO CANO (IRE),** 5, b g High Chaparral (IRE)—Awjila **Mrs C. C. Regalado-Gonzalez**
2 **CANIMAR,** 5, b m Havana Gold (IRE)—Acquifer **Simon Lockyer & Tim Clark**
3 **CATAPULT,** 5, b g Equiano (FR)—Alectrona (FR) **Mr S. Lockyer**
4 **ELUSIF (IRE),** 5, b g Elusive Quality (USA)—Appealing (IRE) **Simon Lockyer & Tim Clark**
5 **GENERAL ALLENBY,** 6, b g Medicean—Cat Hunter **Mr S. Lockyer**
6 **IMAGE OF THE MOON,** 4, b f Mukhadram—Hamsat Elqamar **Simon Lockyer & Tim Clark**
7 **JOHN JOINER,** 8, b g Captain Gerrard (IRE)—Nigella
8 **JUAN DE VALDES,** 4, br gr c Exceed And Excel (AUS)—Vayasa (FR) **Mrs C. C. Regalado-Gonzalez**
9 **MAISIE MOO,** 4, b f Swiss Spirit—Al Hawa (USA) **Simon Lockyer & Tim Clark**
10 **MASKED IDENTITY,** 5, b g Intello (GER)—Red Bloom **D. S. Lovatt**
11 **RAIL DANCER,** 8, b g Rail Link—Mara Dancer **Mr S. Lockyer**
12 **SAN CARLOS,** 4, b c Havana Gold (IRE)—Ittasal **Mrs C. C. Regalado-Gonzalez**
13 **SECRATARIO (FR),** 5, ch g Kendargent (FR)—Amoa (USA) **D. S. Lovatt**
14 **TROUBLE SHOOTER (IRE),** 4, b g Delegator—Khibraat **Mr S. Lockyer**
15 **TYRSAL (IRE),** 9, b g Jeremy (USA)—Blanchelande (IRE) **Mr S. Lockyer**
16 **VOLUNTEER,** 7, b g Aqlaam—Blaenavon **Mr S. Lockyer**
17 **WATERPROOF,** 4, b g Pour Moi (IRE)—Laughing Water (IRE) **R. C. Tooth**

THREE-YEAR-OLDS

18 **ALPINE MISTRAL (IRE),** b f Gale Force Ten—Snowtime (IRE) **Empire State Racing Partnership**
19 **ANGELIC FLAME (IRE),** b f Anjaal—Miss Inferno (IRE) **Simon Lockyer & Tim Clark**
20 B c Fountain of Youth (IRE)—Cards
21 B f Mayson—Catfish (IRE)
22 **CELTIC MIST (IRE),** ch f Camacho—Celtic Heroine (IRE) **Mr S. Lockyer**
23 **CHELSEA SHOWCASE,** b f Showcasing—Lunarian **Mr S. Lockyer**
24 Gr f Casamento (IRE)—Distant Waters
25 **LILKIAN,** ch g Sepoy (AUS)—Janie Runaway (IRE) **D. S. Lovatt**
26 **MAYSON MOUNT,** b c Mayson—Epernay **R. C. Tooth**
27 **MERCHANTS BREATH,** b c Bated Breath—Wiki Tiki **Mr S. Lockyer**
28 B f Fast Company (IRE)—Mylington Light
29 **ROSINA ROSE,** b f Heeraat (IRE)—Aquasulis (IRE) **Hever Stud Farm Ltd**
30 B c Gregorian (IRE)—Shambodia (IRE)
31 B f Society Rock (IRE)—Tifariti (USA) **R. C. Tooth**
32 **TYGER BAY,** b c Cable Bay (IRE)—Ribbon Royale **Mrs S. M. Tucker**
33 **VICTORIA JANE,** b f No Nay Never (USA)—Madhaaq (IRE) **Hever Stud Farm Ltd**
34 B f Slade Power (IRE)—Winterwell (USA) **D. S. Lovatt**

Other Owners: Mr T. M. Clarke, Mr S. Lockyer.

310 MR CHRISTOPHER KELLETT, Lathom
Postal: **6 Canal Cottages, Ring O Bells Lane, Lathom, Ormskirk, Lancashire, L40 5TF**
Contacts: **PHONE 01704 643775 MOBILE 07966 097989**
EMAIL CNKellett@outlook.com WEBSITE www.chriskellettracing.co.uk

1 **ARGENT KNIGHT**, 10, gr g Sir Percy—Tussah **Blythe Stables LLP**
2 **BEGOODTOYOURSELF (IRE)**, 5, b g Getaway (GER)—Loreley (IRE) **Blythe Stables LLP**
3 **BLISTERING BARNEY (IRE)**, 4, b g Sir Prancealot (IRE)—Eternal View (IRE) **Andy Bell & Fergus Lyons**
4 **CARLOW BOY (IRE)**, 4, b g Elzaam (AUS)—Whitershadeofpale (IRE) **Andy Bell & Fergus Lyons**
5 **CLONDAW STORM (IRE)**, 6, gr g September Storm (GER)—Oh So Smart (IRE) **Blythe Stables LLP**
6 **DECONSO**, 4, b g Dandy Man (IRE)—Tranquil Flight **Andy Bell & Fergus Lyons**
7 **DORETTE (FR)**, 7, b m Kingsalsa (USA)—Ombrelle (FR) **Blythe Stables LLP**
8 **SHOWSHUTAI**, 4, b g Showcasing—Sleeper **Andy Bell & Fergus Lyons**

Other Owners: Mr A. J. Bell, Mrs T. Bell, Blythe Stables LLP, Mrs C. Lyons, Mr F. Lyons, Fergus & Caroline Lyons.

311 MISS GAY KELLEWAY, Newmarket
Postal: **Trainer did not wish details of their string to appear**

312 MRS STEF KENIRY, Middleham
Postal: **Barry Keniry Racing, Warwick Lodge, North Road, Middleham, North Yorkshire, DL8 4PB**

1 **BLOW BY BLOW (IRE)**, 9, ch g Robin des Champs (FR)—Shean Rose (IRE) **The Strattonites**
2 **DANGEROUS GROUND (IRE)**, 6, b m High Chaparral (IRE)—Laurentina **Mrs S. J. Keniry**
3 **DURBANVILLE**, 8, b g Black Sam Bellamy (IRE)—Kealshore Lass **Mrs S. J. Keniry**
4 **HERMANUS (IRE)**, 8, ch m Golan (IRE)—Almost Trumps **Mrs S. J. Keniry**
5 **ICARIO (FR)**, 7, ch g Soldier of Fortune (IRE)—Indianapolis (GER) **Mr D. R. Gilbert**
7 4, B g Malinas (GER)—Lily Lenor (IRE) **Dan Gilbert & Kristian Strangeway**
8 **LIVA (IRE)**, 5, ch g Champs Elysees—Resistance Heroine **Mr D. R. Gilbert**
9 **MACS BLESSINGS (IRE)**, 4, b g Society Rock (IRE)—Lear's Crown (USA) **Central Racing Ltd & Stef Keniry**
10 **MAMDOOD (IRE)**, 6, gr g Clodovil (IRE)—Fact **Mrs S. J. Keniry**
11 **OLD SALT (IRE)**, 8, b g Craigsteel—Andrea Gale (IRE) **Mrs J. Keys**
12 **OSCAR CEREMONY (IRE)**, 9, b g Oscar (IRE)—Native Singer (IRE) **Ms J. Matthews**
13 **PEGGY'S ANGEL**, 5, b m Captain Gerrard (IRE)—Dora's Sister (IRE) **Mrs J. Keys**
14 **SPIRIT OF SARWAN (IRE)**, 6, b g Elzaam (AUS)—Hidden Heart (USA) **Mrs S. J. Keniry**

THREE-YEAR-OLDS

15 **JEAN MARY**, ch f Cityscape—Ananda Kanda (USA) **Mr K. J. Strangeway**
16 **ROSE BANDIT (IRE)**, b f Requinto (IRE)—Poppy's Rose **Russell Provan & James McLaughlin**

TWO-YEAR-OLDS

17 Gr f 22/02 Gutaifan (IRE)—On High (Exceed And Excel (AUS)) (4761) **Mr R. Provan**

Other Owners: Central Racing Ltd, Mr D. R. Gilbert, Mrs S. J. Keniry, Mr J. McLaughlin, Mr R. Provan, Mr K. J. Strangeway.

313 MR NICK KENT, Brigg
Postal: **Newstead House, Newstead Priory, Cadney Road, Brigg, Lincolnshire, DN20 9HP**
Contacts: **PHONE 01652 650628 MOBILE 07710 644428**
EMAIL nick@nickkent.co.uk WEBSITE www.nickkent.co.uk

1 **BOWIE (IRE)**, 13, br g Pelder (IRE)—La Fenice (IRE) **Cynthia Commons, Marina Kent, Nick Kent**
2 **CATLIN**, 5, b m Bollin Eric—Linen Line **Cynthia Commons, Nick Kent**
3 **DUFFY ALLEN (FR)**, 7, b g Lucarno (USA)—Parade (FR) **Mrs M Pinney, N Kent**
4 4, B f Fair Mix (IRE)—Just Smokie **Mr J. N. Kent**

MR NICK KENT - continued

5 **MICK MAESTRO (FR)**, 7, b br g Air Chief Marshal (IRE)—Mick Maya (FR) **Crossed Fingers Partnership**
6 **OREGON GOLD (FR)**, 7, b g Confuchias (IRE)—Gold Wine (FR) **Newstead Priory Racing Club**
7 **PICKNICK PARK**, 8, b g Sulamani (IRE)—Eva's Edge (IRE) **Mr Andy Parkin, Nick Kent**
8 **REVEREND JACOBS**, 6, b g Nathaniel (IRE)—Light Impact (IRE) **Crossed Fingers Partnership**
9 **WHO'S IN THE BOX (IRE)**, 6, b g Witness Box (USA)—See The Clouds **Mr Andy Parkin, Nick Kent**

THREE-YEAR-OLDS

10 B c Multiplex—Linen Line **Mr J. N. Kent**
11 B f Universal (IRE)—Saaboog **Mrs M. E. Kent**

TWO-YEAR-OLDS

12 B g 02/04 Gentlewave (IRE)—Celtic Sixpence (IRE) (Celtic Swing)

Other Owners: Miss C. Commons, Mr J. M. Fawbert, Mr J. N. Kent, Mrs M. E. Kent, Mr A. R. P. Parkin, Mrs M. A. Pinney, Mr N. Williamson.

Assistant Trainer: Mrs Jane Kent.

NH Jockey: Adam Wedge.

---

314 MR LEONARD KERR, Irvine
Postal: **Annick Lodge, Irvine, Ayrshire, KA11 2AN**

1 **CONS AMIGO (IRE)**, 7, b g Blueprint (IRE)—Consproblem (IRE) **Mr A Kerr Mr L Kerr**
2 **HAVANA JACK (IRE)**, 10, b g Westerner—Hackler Poitin (IRE) **Mr A Kerr Mr L Kerr**
3 **MISTERMOONBOY (IRE)**, 6, ch g Mister Fotis (USA)—Sister Moon (IRE) **Mr A Kerr Mr L Kerr**
4 **SWORD OF FATE (IRE)**, 7, b g Beneficial—Beann Ard (IRE) **Mr A Kerr Mr L Kerr**

Other Owners: Mr A. M. Kerr, Mr L. B. Kerr.

---

315 MR ALAN KING, Barbury Castle
Postal: **Barbury Castle Stables, Wroughton, Wiltshire, SN4 0QZ**
Contacts: **PHONE 01793 815009 MOBILE 07973 461233 FAX 01793 845080**
EMAIL alan@alanking.biz WEBSITE www.alankingracing.co.uk

1 **ALSA MIX (FR)**, 8, gr m Al Namix (FR)—Lady Tsana (FR) **Mrs J. A. Watts**
2 **ARKYN (FR)**, 5, ch g Champs Elysees—Fever Fever (USA) **Mr J. A. Law**
3 **AWEEDRAM (IRE)**, 4, ch g Mukhadram—Invitee **McNeill Family & Niall Farrell**
4 **AZZERTI (FR)**, 8, b g Voix du Nord (FR)—Zalagarry (FR) **McNeill Family and Prodec Networks Ltd**
5 **BALLYWOOD (FR)**, 6, b g Ballingarry (IRE)—Miss Hollywood (FR) **Highclere Thoroughbred Racing -Ballywood**
6 **BASTIEN (FR)**, 9, b br g Panoramic—Que du Charmil (FR) **The Sandy Lodge Syndicate**
7 **BERINGER**, 5, b g Sea The Stars (IRE)—Edaraat (USA) **L Field, B Cognet, N Farrell, J Spack**
8 **BIG CHIEF BENNY (IRE)**, 9, ch g Beneficial—Be Airlie (IRE) **Oitavos Partnership**
9 **BLACKO (FR)**, 4, gr g Balko (FR)—Ascella (FR) **Apple Tree Stud**
10 **BLAME IT ON SALLY (IRE)**, 4, b g Canford Cliffs (IRE)—Sliding Scale **Owners Group 053**
11 **BLISTERING BOB**, 5, b g Big Bad Bob (IRE)—Kristalette (IRE) **Bex Design & Print Ltd**
12 **BOARD OF TRADE**, 9, ch g Black Sam Bellamy (IRE)—Realms of Gold (USA) **Ian Payne & Kim Franklin**
13 **BURREN WALK**, 4, ch m Lucarno (USA)—Persian Walk (FR) **Mr D. J. Barry**
14 4, B f Mount Nelson—Burton Ash **Mrs S. Lee & Mr E. Lee**
15 4, B g Passing Glance—Call Me A Legend **Pitchall Stud Partnership**
16 **CANELO (IRE)**, 7, ch g Mahler—Nobody's Darling (IRE) **Mr J. P. McManus**
17 **CHICAGO DOLL**, 4, ch f Cityscape—Crooked Wood (USA) **Hunscote Stud Limited**
18 **CHICAGO GUY**, 4, ch c Cityscape—Hail Shower (IRE) **Hunscote Stud Limited**
19 **CHOSEN PATH (IRE)**, 7, b g Well Chosen—Karsulu (IRE) **McNeill Family and Prodec Networks Ltd**
20 **COEUR DE LION**, 7, b g Pour Moi (IRE)—Hora **The Barbury Boys**
21 **COLDITZ CASTLE (IRE)**, 6, ch g Getaway (GER)—Stowaway Sue (IRE) **Charles Dingwall & Tony Morris**

MR ALAN KING - continued

22 **COLOURS OF MY LIFE (IRE)**, 5, b m Arcadio (GER)—Lough Roe Lady (IRE) **Mr C. B. J. Dingwall**
23 **COSMEAPOLITAN**, 7, b g Mawatheeq (USA)—Cosmea **The Barbury Lions 4**
24 **DEYRANN DE CARJAC (FR)**, 7, b g Balko (FR)—Queyrann (FR) **Mr J. A. Law**
25 **DIDONATO (IRE)**, 5, b m Milan—Dream Lass (IRE) **Mr S. Smith**
26 **DINGO DOLLAR (IRE)**, 8, ch g Golden Lariat (USA)—
Social Society (IRE) **M Warren J Holmes R Kidner & J Wright**
27 **DINO VELVET (FR)**, 7, b g Naaqoos—Matgil (FR) **McNeill Family & Niall Farrell**
28 **EDWARDSTONE**, 6, b g Kayf Tara—Nothingtoloose (IRE) **Robert Abrey & Ian Thurtle**
29 **ELGIN**, 8, b g Duke of Marmalade (IRE)—China Tea (USA) **Elite Racing Club**
30 **ELYSEES (IRE)**, 5, ch g Champs Elysees—Queen of Tara (IRE) **Elysees Partnership**
31 **ES PERFECTO (IRE)**, 5, ch g Shirocco (GER)—Shadow Dearg (IRE) **Mrs E. A. Prowting**
32 **ESCAPABILITY (IRE)**, 5, b g Exceleration (IRE)—Brief Escapade (IRE) **S Love, H & C Barrett & D Gibbon**
33 **EYES RIGHT**, 5, b m Passing Glance—Call Me A Star **S Richardson & Exors Late Charles Hamer**
34 **FAIRY ROSE**, 4, b f Martaline—Valleyofthedolls **Rose Tinted Glasses**
35 **FIBONACCI**, 6, ch g Galileo (IRE)—Tereschenko (USA) **Mrs E. A. Prowting**
36 **FIDUX (FR)**, 7, b g Fine Grain (JPN)—Folle Tempete (FR) **AXOM LXVIII**
37 4, b f Flemensfirth (USA)—Forever Present (IRE) **Netherfield House Stud**
38 **FORGETTHESMALLTALK (IRE)**, 8, b g Flemensfirth (USA)—
Mylane du Charmil (FR) **Tim Leadbeater & Barry Winfield**
39 **FRATERNEL (FR)**, 5, b g Kap Rock (FR)—Valence (FR) **Mr T. D. J. Syder**
40 **FUSEAU (FR)**, 5, b g Barastraight—Monepopee (FR) **Michael Rembaum & Michael Tuckey**
41 **GAVI DI GAVI (IRE)**, 5, b g Camacho—Blossom Deary (IRE) **Alan King, Mr N. Farrell**
42 **GIVING BACK**, 6, br gr m Midnight Legend—Giving **Pitchall Stud Partnership & Mrs Pat Toye**
43 **GIVING GLANCES**, 5, b m Passing Glance—Giving **Pitchall Stud Partnership**
44 **GLASHA'S PEAK**, 6, b m Flemensfirth (USA)—Peggies Run **Sir Christopher Wates**
45 **GOOD MAN PAT (IRE)**, 7, b g Gold Well—Basically Supreme (IRE) **Mr D. J. S. Sewell**
46 **GRISBI DE BERCE (FR)**, 4, b g Tin Horse (IRE)—Volupia de Berce (FR) **Charles Dingwall & Alan King**
47 **GROSVENOR COURT**, 4, b g Shirocco (GER)—Hurricane Milly (IRE) **John J. Murray & Niall Farrell**
48 **GROUP STAGE (GER)**, 4, b g Maxios—Good Hope (GER) **McNeill Family & Niall Farrell**
49 **HACKSAW RIDGE (IRE)**, 5, b g Stowaway—Erins Lass (IRE) **Incipe Partnership**
50 **HARAMBE**, 7, br g Malinas (GER)—Crystal Princess (IRE) **Niall Farrell & Friends**
51 **HARROWBY**, 4, b g Gentlewave (IRE)—Cutielilou (FR) **The Harrowby Partnership**
52 **HEART OF A LION (IRE)**, 5, b g Yeats—Lady Secret (FR) **Mr J. P. McManus**
53 **HOSTILE**, 6, ch g Malinas (GER)—Skew **Alan King**
54 **HOTTER THAN HELL (FR)**, 6, ch m No Risk At All (FR)—Ombrelle (FR) **The Devil's Advocates**
55 **INN THE BULL (GER)**, 7, ch g Lope de Vega (IRE)—Ile Rousse **Loose Cannon Racing**
56 **INNER DRIVE (IRE)**, 12, b g Heron Island (IRE)—Hingis (IRE) **McNeill Family & A King**
57 **ISOLATE (FR)**, 4, b g Maxios—Unaided **Noel Fehily Racing - Isolate**
58 **JABOTICABA (FR)**, 6, ch g Muhtathir—Janiceinwonderland (FR) **Owners Group 025**
59 **JAY BEE WHY (IRE)**, 5, b g Yeats—Lady Bernie (IRE) **David J S Sewell & Tim Leadbeater**
60 **JERMININE GREEN (IRE)**, 6, b m Jeremy (USA)—Minnie Maguire (IRE) **Alan King**
61 **JUNDERSTAND**, 5, ch m Champs Elysees—Sienna Sunset (IRE) **R. Bailey**
62 **JUST IN TIME**, 6, b g Exceleration (IRE)—Flying Finish (FR) **HP Racing Just In Time**
63 **KARASTANI**, 4, gr f Dalakhani (IRE)—Karasta (IRE) **Mr M. J. Rembaum**
64 **KINGS ROYAL HUSSAR (FR)**, 4, b g Zebedee—Ile Rouge **HP Racing Kings Royal Hussar**
65 **KISMAT**, 5, b m Sepoy (AUS)—Magic Destiny **R. Bailey**
66 **KOZIER (GER)**, 6, ch g Muhtathir—Kasumi (GER) **Loose Cannon Racing**
67 5, Br g Great Pretender (GER)—L'Aventure (FR) **Mr C. J. Harriman**
68 **LABEL DES OBEAUX (FR)**, 9, b g Saddler Maker (IRE)—La Bessiere (FR) **David Sewell & Terry Warner**
69 **LEXINGTON LAW (IRE)**, 7, b g Lawman (FR)—Tus Nua (IRE) **Middleham Park Racing XXXIX**
70 **LISP (IRE)**, 6, ch g Poet's Voice—Hora **Mr & Mrs R. G. Kelvin-Hughes**
71 **LORD LAMINGTON**, 4, b g Australia—Lady Eclair (IRE) **Netherfield House Stud**
72 **LOVERBOY (FR)**, 9, b g Winged Love (IRE)—Tartan Belle **Mrs J. S. S. Page**
73 **MADIBA PASSION (FR)**, 6, b g Al Namix (FR)—Birsheba (IRE) **Mr P. V. Mendoza**
74 **MAHLERMADE (IRE)**, 7, ch g Mahler—Double Concerto (IRE) **The Lesser Lights**
75 **MAJOR DUNDEE (IRE)**, 5, b g Scorpion (IRE)—Be My Granny **Mr T. J. Hemmings**
76 **MANOR PARK**, 5, b g Medicean—Jadeel **McNeill Family & Niall Farrell**
77 **MATTIE ROSS**, 4, b f Champs Elysees—Ommadawn (IRE) **L & J Perkins, N. Freeman, R & P Scott**
78 **MERRY YARN (IRE)**, 4, ch g Galileo (IRE)—Posterity (IRE) **Merry Fox Stud Limited**

MR ALAN KING - continued

79 **MESSIRE DES OBEAUX (FR)**, 8, b g Saddler Maker (IRE)—
Madame Lys (FR) **Mr Simon Munir & Mr Isaac Souede**
80 **METHUSALAR (IRE)**, 4, b g Sholokhov (IRE)—Pixie Dust (IRE) **Top Brass Partnership**
81 **MIDNIGHT GINGER**, 4, ch f Midnight Legend—Calamintha **Pitchall Stud Partnership**
82 **MIDNIGHT GLANCE**, 5, b g Passing Glance—Magical Legend **R. H. Kerswell**
83 **MIDNIGHT MAESTRO**, 8, b g Midnight Legend—Calamintha **Mr J. P. McManus**
84 **MIDNIGHTREFERENDUM**, 7, b m Midnight Legend—Forget The Ref (IRE) **Robert Abrey & Ian Thurtle**
85 **MIDNIGHTS' GIFT**, 4, gr f Midnight Legend—Giving **Pitchall Stud Partnership**
86 **MILLSTONE**, 6, b g Alkaased (USA)—Stoney Path **Mrs S. C. Welch**
87 **MR PUMBLECHOOK**, 6, b g Midnight Legend—Definitely Pip (IRE) **Mr D. J. S. Sewell**
88 **MYSTICAL CLOUDS (IRE)**, 7, gr g Cloudings (IRE)—Silent Valley **Mr T. J. Hemmings**
89 **NEARLY PERFECTION (IRE)**, 4, b f Camacho—Leenavesta (USA) **Judy & Jamie Magee**
90 **NEBUCHADNEZZAR (FR)**, 5, b g Planteur (IRE)—Trexana **Top Brass 2**
91 **NED PEPPER (IRE)**, 4, b g Intello (GER)—Storyland (USA) **Mr & Mrs R. Scott**
92 **NINA THE TERRIER**, 4, b f Milan—Shees A Dante (IRE) **Mr C. B. J. Dingwall**
93 **NOBBY**, 6, b g Authorized (IRE)—Magic Music (IRE) **R. Bailey**
94 **NOTACHANCE (IRE)**, 6, b g Mahler—Ballybrowney Hall (IRE) **David J S Sewell & Tim Leadbeater**
95 **ON TO VICTORY**, 6, b g Rock of Gibraltar (IRE)—Clouds of Magellan (USA) **HP Racing On To Victory**
96 **OUTONPATROL (IRE)**, 6, gr m Stowaway—Burnt Oil Babe (IRE) **McNeill Family & Niall Farrell**
97 **PECKINPAH (IRE)**, 4, ch g Excelebration (IRE)—Melodrama (IRE) **Coupland, Gemmell, Hues & Sullivan**
98 **PERFECT HARMONY (IRE)**, 8, b g Definite Article—Brandam Supreme (IRE) **Mrs E. A. Prowting**
99 **PERFECT PREDATOR**, 5, b g Passing Glance—Cosmea **Kingston Stud**
100 **POTTERMAN**, 7, b g Sulamani (IRE)—Polly Potter **James and Jean Potter Ltd**
101 **PRODUCTION**, 4, b g Oasis Dream—Pure Excellence **The Royal Ascot Racing Club**
102 **RAINBOW DREAMER**, 7, b g Aqlaam—Zamhrear **The Maple Street Partnership**
103 **REBEL ROYAL (IRE)**, 7, b g Getaway (GER)—Molly Duffy (IRE) **Jerry Wright,Martin Walker & Tony Hughes**
104 **RIDEAU CANAL (IRE)**, 5, b g Robin des Champs (FR)—Miss Vinnie (IRE) **Farrell Field Sigler Lawson**
105 **ROSCOE TARA**, 5, b g Kayf Tara—Aunt Harriet **Mr & Mrs R. Allsop**
106 **ROYAL PRETENDER (FR)**, 4, b g Great Pretender (IRE)—Robinia Directa (GER) **Mrs C. Skan**
107 **SAN RUMOLDO**, 5, ch g Malinas (GER)—Ancora (IRE) **Mr J. P. McManus**
108 **SANTON (IRE)**, 5, b g Scorpion (IRE)—Nutmeg Tune (IRE) **Mr T. J. Hemmings**
109 **SCARLET DRAGON**, 7, b g Sir Percy—Welsh Angel **HP Racing Scarlet Dragon**
110 **SCEAU ROYAL (FR)**, 8, b g Doctor Dino (FR)—Sandside (FR) **Mr Simon Munir & Mr Isaac Souede**
111 **SENIOR CITIZEN**, 7, b g Tobougg (IRE)—Mothers Help **McNeill Family Ltd**
112 **SEPHTON**, 4, b g Shamardal (USA)—Honour **The Barbury Lions 4**
113 **SHESHOON SONNY (FR)**, 5, b g Youmzain (IRE)—Minnie's Mystery (FR) **McNeill Family & Niall Farrell**
114 **SMITH'S BAY**, 7, b g Midnight Legend—Takotna (IRE) **Ian Payne & Kim Franklin**
115 **STOCKBURN (IRE)**, 7, b g Scorpion (IRE)—Hayabusa **Godfrey Keirle & Alan King**
116 **SULA ISLAND**, 6, ch m Sulamani (IRE)—Cosmea **Alan King**
117 **TALKISCHEAP (IRE)**, 8, b g Getaway (GER)—Carrigmoorna Oak (IRE) **Mr C. B. J. Dingwall**
118 **THE CULL BANK (IRE)**, 6, b m Yeats (IRE)—Creme d'Arblay (IRE) **Mrs J. A. Watts**
119 **THE DEVILS DROP (IRE)**, 7, b g Court Cave (IRE)—Concernforkillen (IRE) **Mr D. M. Mason**
120 **THE GLANCING QUEEN (IRE)**, 6, b m Jeremy (USA)—Glancing (IRE) **Dingwall, Farrell, Hornsey & Murray**
121 **THE KICKING QUEEN (IRE)**, 4, b f Beat Hollow—Shivermetimber (IRE) **Mr & Mrs C. Harris**
122 **THE OLYMPIAN (IRE)**, 4, ch g Olympic Glory (IRE)—Basira (FR) **Mr J. P. McManus**
123 4, B f Kalanisi (IRE)—The Pirate's Queen (IRE) **Apple Tree Stud**
124 **THE TOURARD MAN (IRE)**, 14, b g Shantou (USA)—Small Iron **Mr & Mrs F Bell,N Farrell, A Marsh**
125 **THE UNIT (IRE)**, 9, b g Gold Well—Sovana (FR) **International Plywood (Importers) Ltd**
126 5, B m Sixties Icon—Tidal Run **Mr W. A. Harrison-Allan**
127 **TIMOTEO (FR)**, 7, b g Diamond Green (FR)—Goldnella (FR) **Million in Mind Partnership**
128 **TREMWEDGE**, 4, b g Foxwedge (AUS)—Tremelo Pointe (IRE) **LJP Racing**
129 **TRONADA**, 4, b f Toronado (IRE)—Manbaa (USA) **The Barbury Lions 4**
130 **TRUESHAN (FR)**, 4, b g Planteur (IRE)—Shao Line (FR) **Barbury Lions 5**
131 **VALDEZ**, 13, ch g Doyen (IRE)—Skew **Riverdee Stable**
132 **VALLERES (FR)**, 5, b g Coastal Path—Duchesse Pierji (FR) **S. E. Munir, Mr I. Souede**
133 **WAR CHIEF**, 6, ch g Aqlaam—My Colleen (USA) **Andrews Farrell King McNeill Sullivan**
134 **WAR PRINCESS (IRE)**, 4, b f War Command (USA)—Starlight Princess (IRE) **Judy & Jamie Magee**
135 **WHO DARES WINS (IRE)**, 8, b g Jeremy (USA)—Savignano **HP Racing Who Dares Wins**
136 **WILDE BLUE YONDER (IRE)**, 11, b g Oscar (IRE)—Blue Gallery (IRE) **Maybe Only Fools Have Horses**

MR ALAN KING - continued

137 **WILLIAM H BONNEY**, 9, b g Midnight Legend—Calamintha **Mr & Mrs R. Scott**
138 **WYNN HOUSE**, 5, ch m Presenting—Glorious Twelfth (IRE) **Mr J. R. D. Anton**
139 **Y FYN DUW A FYDD**, 5, b m Nathaniel (IRE)—Dignify (IRE) **R. Mathew**

THREE-YEAR-OLDS

140 **ALARGEDRAM (IRE)**, ch g Lope de Vega (IRE)—Myrica **McNeill Family & Niall Farrell**
141 **CHINESE WHISPERER (FR)**, b c Poet's Voice—Shanghai Noon (FR) **Barbury Lions 5**
142 **DANKING**, b g Dansili—Time Saved **Niall Farrell & Ian Dodds-smith**
143 **DUKE OF CONDICOTE**, b g No Nay Never (USA)—Duchess of Gazeley (IRE) **Jamie Magee, A Bromley & A King**
144 **ENCASHMENT**, b f Casamento (IRE)—Burton Ash **Mrs S. Lee & Mr E. Lee**
145 **HER INDOORS (IRE)**, b f Raven's Pass (USA)—Superfonic (FR) **McNeill Family & Niall Farrell**
146 **INCHICORE (IRE)**, b f Galileo (IRE)—Luas Line (IRE) **Apple Tree Stud**
147 B g Worthadd (IRE)—Khibraat **Wayne Clifford & Ian Gosden**
148 **KINGS CREEK (IRE)**, b g Elusive Quality (USA)—Nunavik (IRE) **Alan King**
149 **LORD NEIDIN**, br c Outstrip—Cosmea **Ron Sullivan & Kingston Stud**
150 **MAGNIFICAT (IRE)**, b c Dandy Man (IRE)—Retrato (USA) **The Maple Street Partnership**
151 B f Kingston Hill—Mayolynn (USA) **Mr & Mrs R. Scott**
152 **MIDNIGHTS LEGACY**, b c Midnight Legend—Giving **Pitchall Stud Partnership**
153 **PARTY POTENTIAL (USA)**, b g Congrats (USA)—Lil Miss Richie (USA) **The Legends Partnership**
154 **SON OF RED (IRE)**, b c French Navy—Tarziyma (IRE) **Ian Gosden & Richard House**
155 **TREMOR (IRE)**, ch g Intello (GER)—Shake The Moon (GER) **Elysees Partnership**
156 **TRITONIC**, ch c Sea The Moon (GER)—Selenography **McNeill Family & Mr Ian Dale**

Other Owners: Mr R. Abrey, Mr R. Allsop, Mrs Y. E. Allsop, Mrs P. Andrews, Mr C. M. A. Aston, R. K. Aston, Mr C. Barrett, Mrs H. A. Barrett, Mr F. D. Bell, Mrs H. L. Bell, A. R. Bromley, Mr N. S. G. Bunter, Miss C. Burke, H. M. W. Clifford, Mr B. R. Cognet, Mr A. P. Coupland, Mr W. I. C. Dale, Mr C. B. J. Dingwall, Mr I. Dodds-Smith, Mr N. Farrell, Mrs L. H. Field, Miss K. M. Franklin, Mr A. Gemmell, D. H. Gibbon, Mr I. F. Gosden, Exors of the Late Mr C. M. Hamer, Mrs C. A. Harris, Mr C. I. K. Harris, Mr D. F. Hill, Mr D. Holmes, J. Holmes, Mrs K. Holmes, J. Hornsey, Mr R. House, Mr D. Hues, Mr A. P. Hughes, Incipe Partnership, G. F. Keirle, Mr R. A. Kidner, Alan King, Kingston Stud, L Field, N Farrell, B Cognet & King, Mr M. S. Lawson, Mr E. T. D. Leadbeater, Mr W. P. Ledward, Mr E. Lee, Mrs S. M. Lee, S. Love, Mrs J Magee, Mr J. Magee, Mr A. R. W. Marsh, McNeill Family Ltd, Mr A. A. Morris, S. E. Munir, Mr J. J. Murray, John J. Murray & Niall Farrell, Mr P. Nolan, Mr T. Nolan, Mr I. T. Payne, Pitchall Stud Partnership, Prodec Networks Ltd, Mr M. J. Rembaum, Mrs S. Richardson, Mr S. J. Rogers, Mr D. J. S. Sewell, Mr J. Sigler, Mr I. Souede, Mrs J. A. Spack, Mr R. T. Sullivan, Mr A. L. Tappin, Mr I. R. Thurtle, Mrs P. J. Toye, M. J. Tuckey, Mr M. S. Walker, J. T. Warner, Mr M. K. Warren, B. Winfield, J. Wright.

Assistant Trainer: Dan Horsford, Olly Stevens, **Pupil Assistant:** Robin Smith, **Yard Sponsor:** HARE HARE.

NH Jockey: Tom Bellamy, Tom Cannon. **Conditional Jockey:** Alexander Thorne. **Amateur Jockey:** Max Browne, Georgia King, William Thirlby.

---

316 MR NEIL KING, Marlborough
Postal: **Upper Herdswick Farm, Burderop, Wroughton, Swindon, Wiltshire, SN4 0QH**
Contacts: **PHONE** 01793 845011 **MOBILE** 07880 702325 **FAX** 01793 845011
EMAIL neil@neil-king.co.uk **WEBSITE** www.neil-king.co.uk

1 **BALAGAN**, 5, b g Great Pretender (IRE)—Lovely Origny (FR) **Mr A. L. Cohen**
2 **BIG MEADOW (IRE)**, 9, b g Marienbard (IRE)—Lakyle Lady (IRE) **The Ridgeway Racing For Fun Partnership**
3 **BOULTING FOR GLORY (IRE)**, 5, b g Fame And Glory—Westgrove Berry (IRE) **C. Boultbee-Brooks**
4 **BRANDON CASTLE**, 8, b g Dylan Thomas (IRE)—Chelsey Jayne (IRE) **Mr I. A. Low & Mr J. S. English**
5 **CANYON CITY**, 7, b g Authorized (IRE)—Colorado Dawn **A Whyte, J Bone, D Nott & B Smith**
6 **CUBSWIN (IRE)**, 6, b m Zamindar (USA)—Moonlight Rhapsody (IRE) **Mr D Caldwell & Mr K Lawrence**
7 **DANCING DORIS**, 5, b m Malinas (GER)—Peggies Run **Mr P. M. H. Beadles**
8 5, b g Westerner—Evella (IRE) **Mrs H. M. Buckle**
9 **FARNE (IRE)**, 6, b m Stowaway—Bonnies Island (IRE) **Blyth Currie & Royle**
10 **FFORBIDDEN LOVE**, 6, b m Fastnet Rock (AUS)—Trinkila (USA) **Mr D. S. Lee**
11 **FLINTROCK (GER)**, 5, br g Sinndar (IRE)—Four Roses (IRE) **Mr G. C. B. Brook**
12 **FUNWAY MONARCH (IRE)**, 5, b g Imperial Monarch (IRE)—Mount Radhwa (IRE) **Mr R Bothway**

MR NEIL KING - continued

13 **GATEWAY TO EUROPE**, 6, b g Trans Island—Polly Doodle **A Whyte, K Loads & G Stevenson**
14 4, B f Malinas (GER)—Haveyoubeen (IRE)
15 **I HOPE STAR (IRE)**, 4, b g Casamento (IRE)—Bint Nayef (IRE) **Stellar Racing**
16 **IROLIN JACK**, 5, b g Bollin Eric—Aoninch **Milsom Baker Racing & Royle**
17 **KEYBOARD JOAN (IRE)**, 6, b m Jeremy (USA)—Kilcrea Present (IRE) **The Ridgeway Racing For Fun Partnership**
18 **LIL ROCKEFELLER (USA)**, 9, ch g Hard Spun (USA)—Layounne (USA) **Davies Smith Govier & Brown**
19 **MARIENSTAR (IRE)**, 9, b m Marienbard (IRE)—Starofdonickmore (IRE) **Kevin Taylor & Garry Ambrose**
20 **MILANSBAR (IRE)**, 13, b g Milan—Ardenbar **Mr Neil King**
21 **MR WOOLLEY**, 6, b g Shirocco (GER)—Evella (IRE) **Mrs H. M. Buckle**
22 **MYPLACEATMIDNIGHT**, 8, b g Midnight Legend—Zahra's Place **Mrs H. M. Buckle**
23 **NAUTICAL TWILIGHT**, 10, gr m Proclamation (IRE)—Anabranch **Dr T. Fielding**
24 **NEARLY PERFECT**, 6, b g Malinas (GER)—The Lyme Volunteer (IRE) **Mr P. M. H. Beadles**
25 **NORDANO (GER)**, 4, ch g Jukebox Jury (IRE)—Navajo Queen (GER) **A Whyte, T Messom & D Nott**
26 **OH LAND ABLOOM (IRE)**, 10, b g King's Theatre (IRE)—Talinas Rose (IRE) **Milsom Baker Racing**
27 **ONEMOREFORTHEROAD**, 5, b g Yorgunnabelucky (USA)—Vinomore **Miss D. Wallis**
28 **PARISIAN AFFAIR**, 5, b m Champs Elysees—Tricolla (USA) **Mr D. S. Lee**
29 **PERFECT MYTH**, 6, b m Midnight Legend—Perfect Silence **Richard Vines & David Nott**
30 **PETITE JACK**, 7, ch g Champs Elysees—Pilcomayo (IRE) **Mr W. Burn**
31 **PRINCETON ROYALE (IRE)**, 11, br g Royal Anthem (USA)—Shelikesitstraight (IRE) **D Nott, P Beadles, R Clarke**
32 **REGULATION (IRE)**, 11, br g Danehill Dancer (IRE)—
                                   Source of Life (IRE) **The Ridgeway Racing For Fun Partnership**
33 **REMEMBER THE MAN (IRE)**, 7, b g Dalakhani (IRE)—Perfect Hedge **Poynton Harrod Smith & Darlington**
34 **SACKETT**, 9, b g Midnight Legend—Gloriana **Woodward, Laurie & Smith**
35 **SILENT STEPS (IRE)**, 9, b m Milan—
                    Taking Silk (IRE) **Mr Neil King, The Silent Steps Partnership, Mrs D. J. Hagenbuch, Mr D. A. Sutton**
36 4, B f Shirocco (GER)—Storm In Front (IRE)
37 **TAMBURA**, 10, b m Tamure (IRE)—Singing Cottage **Mrs A. E. Maundrell**
38 **THE KNOT IS TIED (IRE)**, 5, b g Casamento (IRE)—Really Polish (USA) **Ken Lawrence & Roy Mousley**
39 **THEMANFROM MINELLA (IRE)**, 11, b g Shantou (USA)—Bobormy (IRE) **Mrs C. Kendrick**
40 **VENTURA MAGIC**, 5, b g Mount Nelson—Elle Desert (GER) **The Ridgeway Racing For Fun Partnership**
41 **VERY INTENSE (IRE)**, 9, b g Intense Focus (USA)—Astralai (IRE) **Woodenco**
42 **WILLIE BUTLER (IRE)**, 6, b g Yeats (IRE)—Belsalsa (FR) **Mr P. M. H. Beadles**

Other Owners: Mr T. P. Andrews, Mr S. R. Baker, Mr P. M. H. Beadles, Mr B. Bell, Mrs H. D. Blyth Currie, Mr J. Bone, G. S. Brown, Mr D. R. Caldwell, A. Carr, Mr N. J. Catterwell, Mr R. Clarke, Mr P. J. Darlington, Mr J. Davies, Mr J. S. English, Mr P. Govier, Mr P. F. Govier, Govier & Brown, Mr M. Harrod, Mrs C. Kendrick, N. King, Mr Neil King, Mr R. Laurie, Mr K. F. J. Loads, I. A. Low, Mr T. J. Messom, Mr G. Milsom, Milsom Baker Racing, Mr R. Mousley, Mr D. F. Nott, Mr B. Poynton, Mrs H. M. Royle, Mr A. J. Smith, Mr D. P. Smith, Mrs G. S. Smith, Mr R. W. Smith, Mr G. E. Stevenson, Mrs P. M. F. Sturgis, Mr K. A. Taylor, R. J. Vines, Mr A. A. Whyte, Mr B. Woodward.

Racing Secretary: Oriana-Jane Baines.

Flat Jockey: Ben Curtis, Luke Morris. **NH Jockey:** Bryony Frost.

---

317 **MR PHILIP KIRBY, Richmond**
Postal: **Green Oaks Farm, East Appleton, Richmond, North Yorkshire, DL10 7QE**
Contacts: PHONE **01748 517337** MOBILE **07984 403558**
EMAIL **pkirbyracing@gmail.com** WEBSITE **www.philipkirbyracing.co.uk**

1 **ABINGTON PARK**, 5, br g Passing Glance—Epicurean **Red Cap Racing & Clearabee Ltd**
2 **ADELPHI PRINCE**, 7, b g Schiaparelli (GER)—Cailin Na Ri (IRE) **Barry and Virginia Brown**
3 **ADELPHI REBEL**, 6, br g Kayf Tara—Cailin Na Ri (IRE) **Barry and Virginia Brown**
4 **ALSVINDER**, 7, b h Footstepsinthesand—Notting Hill (BRZ) **Alan Fairhurst & David Fairhurst**
5 **ANIKNAM (FR)**, 10, b g Nickname (FR)—Kelle Home (FR) **Mr P. A. Kirby**
6 **ANOTHER THEATRE (IRE)**, 7, b m Shantou (USA)—
                                   Whats Another One (IRE) **The Vacuum Pouch Company Limited**
7 **ARTHUR MAC (IRE)**, 7, ch g Getaway (GER)—Orchardstown Moss (IRE) **The Vacuum Pouch Company Limited**
8 **AUTONOMY**, 4, b g Dansili—Funsie (FR) **Mr P. A. Kirby, Hambleton Racing Ltd XXXIV**

MR PHILIP KIRBY - continued

9 **BAHKIT (IRE)**, 6, b g Intikhab (USA)—Pink Moon (IRE) **Mrs J. Porter**
10 **BERTIE BLAKE (IRE)**, 7, b g Beneficial—Diandrina **The Kirby Club Partnership**
11 **BIG EARS (IRE)**, 4, b f Yeats (IRE)—Theleze (FR) **Mrs J. A. Darling**
12 **DARES TO DREAM (IRE)**, 6, br m Beneficial—Miss McGoldrick (IRE) **Ashley & Sue Clark & Clearabee Ltd**
13 **DECEMBER SECOND (IRE)**, 6, b br g Teofilo (IRE)—Bulbul (IRE) **Mr D. R. Platt**
14 **DESARAY GIRL (FR)**, 5, gr m Montmartre (FR)—Feria To Bitch (FR) **Resdev Ltd**
15 **DIEU BENISSE (FR)**, 7, b m Blue Bresil (FR)—Flowerfull (FR) **The Gathering & J Matthews**
16 **DUBH DES CHAMPS (IRE)**, 8, br g Robin des Champs (FR)—Aneda Dubh (IRE) **The Des Champs Partnership**
17 **EN MEME TEMPS (FR)**, 6, b g Saddler Maker (IRE)—Lady Reine (FR) **Hope Eden Racing Limited**
18 **EPSOM DES MOTTES (FR)**, 6, b g Maresca Sorrento (FR)—Nellyssa Bleu (FR) **David Barlow & Lyn Rutherford**
19 **FABRICATION**, 5, b g Scorpion (IRE)—Pickworth (IRE) **Mrs J. Sivills**
20 **FADING ICON**, 5, b m Sixties Icon—Fading Away **Quench Racing Partnership**
21 **FASTERKHANI**, 4, b g Fast Company (IRE)—Musikhani **M Hodgson, R Parks & C Chapman**
22 **FILLE D'AVIGNON (IRE)**, 5, br m Getaway (GER)—Site-Leader (IRE) **The Topspec II Partnership**
23 **GET REAL (IRE)**, 6, br g Getaway (GER)—Viva Forever (FR) **The Vacuum Pouch Company Limited**
24 **GONN AWAY (IRE)**, 8, b m Mahler—Supreme Call (IRE) **Ramscove Ltd**
25 **GORDALAN**, 4, b g Foxwedge (AUS)—Mad Annie (USA) **Buckingham Flooring**
26 **HANGARD**, 8, b g Black Sam Bellamy (IRE)—Empress of Light **Mr D. C. Blake**
27 **ICE GALLEY (IRE)**, 7, br g Galileo (IRE)—Ice Queen (IRE) **Mr P. A. Kirby**
28 **ICE PYRAMID (IRE)**, 5, ch g New Approach (IRE)—Coolnagree (IRE) **Bill Fraser & Adrian Pritchard**
29 **ICONIC BELLE**, 6, ch m Sixties Icon—Five Bells (IRE) **Jowsey, Bainbridge, Cornforth & Everson**
30 **IMAJORBLUSH**, 4, ch g Mukhadram—Winter Dress **Zoe Hassall & George Hassall**
31 **JURISTE (IRE)**, 6, b g Lawman (FR)—Green Lassy (FR) **Mrs J. Porter**
32 **KANGAROO VALLEY (USA)**, 4, b g Australia—Dundalk Dust (USA) **The Vacuum Pouch Company Limited**
33 **KEITH'S GIRL (IRE)**, 5, ch m Golden Tornado (IRE)—Good Girl Rosie (IRE) **Mr P. A. Kirby**
34 **LADY BUTTONS**, 10, b m Beneficial—Lady Chapp (IRE) **Mrs J. Sivills**
35 **LADY CAMELOT (IRE)**, 5, b m Camelot—Queen Jock (USA) **The Ploughmen Syndicate**
36 **LADY KYRIA (IRE)**, 6, b m Holy Roman Emperor (IRE)—Segesta (IRE) **Hope Eden Racing Limited**
37 **LITTLE BRUCE (IRE)**, 8, b g Yeats (IRE)—Lady Rolfe (IRE) **The Gps Partnership**
38 **LORD BUTTONS**, 4, b g Presenting—Lady Chapp (IRE) **Mrs J. Sivills**
39 **LORD ROCCOCO (FR)**, 5, b g Shirocco (GER)—Lady Chloe **The Roccoco Partnership**
40 **LOUIS' VAC POUCH (IRE)**, 8, b g Oscar (IRE)—Coming Home (FR) **The Vacuum Pouch Company Limited**
41 **LUCKY ICON (IRE)**, 6, b g Sixties Icon—Sauterelle (USA) **Mrs J. Sivills**
42 **MADEEH**, 4, b c Oasis Dream—Ashaaqah (IRE) **Harbour Rose Partnership**
43 **MAN OF VERVE (IRE)**, 6, b g Dandy Man (IRE)—She's Our Rock (IRE) **A Jowsey & R Bainbridge**
44 **MASTER NEWTON (IRE)**, 5, gr g Mastercraftsman (IRE)—French Friend (IRE) **Cornforth, Barlow & Rutherford**
45 **MCGARRY (IRE)**, 6, b g Mahler—Little Pearl (IRE) **The Vacuum Pouch Company Limited**
46 **MIDNIGHT LEGACY (IRE)**, 6, b m Getaway (GER)—Lady of The Hall (IRE) **Hambleton Racing Ltd XXXIV**
47 **MILADYGRACE (IRE)**, 5, b m Universal (IRE)—Milan Athlete (IRE) **Sedbergh Lads Club**
48 **MILANVERA (IRE)**, 6, b m Milan—Sorivera **Mr A. Anderson**
49 **MISSCARLETT (IRE)**, 6, b m Red Rocks (IRE)—Coimbra (USA) **Mrs J. Porter**
50 **MR CARBONATOR**, 5, b g Bated Breath—Diamond Lass (IRE) **Alan Fairhurst & David Fairhurst**
51 **MY STRONG MAN (IRE)**, 4, b g Authorized (IRE)—Lady Chloe **The Platinum Partnership**
52 **NICELY INDEED (IRE)**, 10, b g Marienbard (IRE)—Rare Dollar (IRE) **Jowsey, Bainbridge & McKeown**
53 **NIVEN (IRE)**, 7, b g Elusive Pimpernel (USA)—Ginger Lily (IRE) **John Birtles & Bill Allan**
54 **OAK VINTAGE (IRE)**, 10, b g Fruits of Love (USA)—Brandam Supreme (IRE) **Mrs J. Porter**
55 **PENNINE CROSS**, 5, b g Shirocco (GER)—Gaspara (FR) **The Well Oiled Partnership**
56 **PULLMAN BROWN (USA)**, 8, b g Big Brown (USA)—Touch Too Much (USA) **Mr P. A. Kirby**
57 **RAIFF (IRE)**, 4, b g Shamardal (USA)—Estiqaama (USA) **Mr D. R. Platt**
58 **RAVENSCAR (IRE)**, 4, b f Helmet (AUS)—Cry Pearl (USA) **Mr J. A. Hall**
59 **RAYNA'S WORLD (IRE)**, 5, b m Poet's Voice—Salmon Rose (IRE) **Ace Bloodstock & Rayna Fitzgerald**
60 **RED DRAGONESS (IRE)**, 4, ch f Dragon Pulse (IRE)—Salydora (FR) **Roofing Consultants Group**
61 **ROBIN DES CHAPP (IRE)**, 5, b g Robin des Champs (FR)—Lady Chapp (IRE) **The Pinnacleplus Partnership**
62 **ROBINCOLLETTE (IRE)**, 6, br m Robin des Champs (FR)—Western Cowgirl (IRE) **The Yorkshire Puddings**
63 **ROMEO BROWN**, 6, br g Yeats (IRE)—Santia **McGoldrick Racing 5 & Birrafun**
64 **SAKHEE'S CITY (IRE)**, 9, b g Sakhee (USA)—A Lulu Ofa Menifee (USA) **Mrs J. Sivills**
65 **SHINE BABY SHINE**, 6, b m Aqlaam—Rosewood Belle (USA) **David Gray & P Kirby**
66 **SHOW PROMISE**, 6, b g Josr Algarhoud (IRE)—Show Potential (IRE) **The Philip Kirby Racing Partnership**
67 **SIENA MIA**, 5, b m Bated Breath—Serenata Mia **Mrs H. I. S. Calzini**

MR PHILIP KIRBY - continued

68 **SINCERELY RESDEV**, 5, br g Rock of Gibraltar (IRE)—Sincerely **Resdev Ltd**
69 5, B m Teofilo (IRE)—Skid (IRE) **Ace Bloodstock Ltd**
70 **STARGAZER (IRE)**, 7, b g Canford Cliffs (IRE)—Star Ruby (IRE) **Zoe Hassall & George Hassall & P Kirby**
71 **SUGGESTION**, 8, gr g Dansili—Jibboom (USA) **Red Cap Racing 1**
72 **TEKIBLUE DE L'ORME (FR)**, 7, b g Blue Bresil (FR)—Tekila de l'Orme (FR) **Mr W. S. Patterson**
73 **THE RESDEV WAY**, 7, b g Multiplex—Lady Duxyana **Resdev Ltd**
74 **THEFLICKERINGLIGHT (IRE)**, 6, b m Flemensfirth (USA)—Turtle Lamp (IRE) **The Yorkshire Puddings**
75 **TOP VILLE BEN (IRE)**, 8, b g Beneficial—Great Decision (IRE) **Harbour Rose Partnership**
76 **TWO THIRTY YEAT (IRE)**, 5, b m Yeats (IRE)—Aneda Dubh (IRE) **Mr P. Bryan**
77 **WEMYSS POINT**, 8, b g Champs Elysees—Wemyss Bay **The Green Oaks Partnership**
78 **WHOSHOTTHESHERIFF (IRE)**, 6, b g Dylan Thomas (IRE)—Dame Foraine (FR) **Hambleton Racing Ltd XXXIV**
79 **WINFOLA (FR)**, 6, gr m Motivator—Romance Bere (FR) **The Silver Linings Partnership**
80 **WYE AYE**, 5, b g Shirocco (GER)—A Media Luz (FR) **The Well Oiled Partnership**
81 **ZIG ZAG (IRE)**, 7, b g Zoffany (IRE)—Le Montrachet **Mr & Mrs R G Capstick**

THREE-YEAR-OLDS

82 **BURROWS SEESIDE (FR)**, b g Sidestep (AUS)—See Your Dream **Mrs J. Morgan, Mrs C. J. Casterton**
83 **GOWANLAD**, b c Mayson—Aahgowangowan (IRE) **Hassle-Free Racing**
84 **HARCANA LE DUN (FR)**, gr g Spanish Moon (USA)—Uranus Le Dun (FR) **FDC Holdings Ltd**
85 **QUEEN OF ROCK (IRE)**, b f Ruler of The World (IRE)—Lady Gibraltar **Buckingham Flooring**

Other Owners: Ace Bloodstock Ltd, Mr W. Allan, Mrs R. A. Bainbridge, Mr D. Barlow, Mr S. Beach, The Birrafun Partnership, Mr J. Birtles, Mr K. Bourke, Mrs K. L. Capstick, R. G. Capstick, Mr D. Cassidy, Mr C. Chapman, Mr A. G. Clark, Mrs S. M. Clark, Clearabee Limited, Mr B. J. Connolly, Mr J. Cornforth, Mr B. Costello, Mr B. H. Dolan, Mr B. R. Everson, Mr A. Fairhurst, Mr D. H. Fairhurst, Mrs R. Fitzgerald, Mr M. D. Foden, W. R. Fraser, Mr I. Galletley, Mr D. W. Gray, Mr R. Hamilton, Mr G. A. Hassall, Mr N. A. D. Hassall, Mrs Z. L. Hassall, Miss M. Hodgson, Mr A. Jowsey, Mr P. A. Kirby, Mrs P. R. Kirby, Mr R. J. Longley, Sir I. Magee, Mr J. Matthews, Mr J. McInerney, Mrs D. L. McKeown, Mr R. J. Parks, Mr A. Pritchard, Ramscove Ltd, Mr C. Reboul, Mr G. J. Reboul, Red Cap Racing, Mr W. G. Rolfe, L. M. Rutherford, D. F. Smith, Mr N. Smith, Mr M. C. P. Suddards, The Gathering, The Vacuum Pouch Company Limited, Mr L. Waugh.

Assistant Trainer: Simon Olley.

NH Jockey: Thomas Dowson, Adam Nicol. **Apprentice Jockey:** Nick Barratt-Atkin. **Amateur Jockey:** Mr Henry Newcombe.

---

318 **MR SYLVESTER KIRK, Upper Lambourn**
Postal: **Cedar Lodge Stables, Upper Lambourn, Hungerford, Berkshire, RG17 8QT**
Contacts: **PHONE 01488 73215 MOBILE 07768 855261**
EMAIL info@sylvesterkirkracing.co.uk WEBSITE www.sylvesterkirkracing.co.uk

1 **BENNY AND THE JETS (IRE)**, 4, ch g Showcasing—Orange Pip **Deauville Daze Partnership**
2 **BUBBLE AND SQUEAK**, 5, b m Mastercraftsman (IRE)—
                                    Comeback Queen **Chris Wright,Holly Wright,Chloe Forsyth**
3 **DISTURBING BEAUTY**, 4, b f Mazameer (IRE)—Deftera Fantutte (IRE) **Mr Y. Mustafa**
4 **GAWDAWPALIN (IRE)**, 7, b g Holy Roman Emperor (IRE)—Dirtybirdie **Mr H. Balasuriya**
5 **HTILOMINLO**, 4, b c Zoffany (IRE)—Haven's Wave (IRE) **Mr H. Balasuriya**
6 **IRENE MAY (IRE)**, 4, b f Moohaajim (IRE)—Poker Hospital **Mr N. Simpson**
7 **KODIAK ATTACK (IRE)**, 4, b g Kodiac—Good Clodora (IRE) **Mrs J. A. Fowler**
8 **NECOLETA**, 4, b f Intello (GER)—Ellbeedee (IRE) **Miss Alison Jones**
9 **ROYAL DANCER**, 4, b g Norse Dancer (IRE)—King's Siren (IRE) **Mr G. Dolan**
10 **SALOUEN (IRE)**, 6, b h Canford Cliffs (IRE)—Gali Gal (IRE) **Mr H. Balasuriya**
11 **SASHENKA (GER)**, 4, b f Maxios—Sarabia (GER) **N. Pickett**
12 **THREE LITTLE BIRDS**, 5, b m Dandy Man (IRE)—Oilinda **Miss A. J. Rawding**

THREE-YEAR-OLDS

13 **AMATHUS (IRE)**, b c Anjaal—Effigie (IRE) **Mr Y. Mustafa**
14 **CRISEYDE**, b f Brazen Beau (AUS)—Flemish School **N. Pickett**
15 **KNOCK KNOCK (IRE)**, br g Slade Power (IRE)—Knock Stars (IRE) **Angela Clifford & Partner**

MR SYLVESTER KIRK - continued

16 **LAFONTAINE (FR),** b f Canford Cliffs (IRE)—Moma Lee **Homebred Racing**
17 **MOULMEIN,** ch c Australia—Natty Bumppo (IRE) **Mr H. Balasuriya**
18 **MUST BE AN ANGEL (IRE),** gr f Dark Angel (IRE)—Lapis Blue (IRE) **Mrs J. A. Fowler**
19 **PAINT IT BLACK,** b g Iffraaj—Sister Ship **Deauville Daze Partnership 1**
20 **PRAIRIE MOPPINS (USA),** gr ro f Creative Cause (USA)—Saratta (USA) **Mr C. N. Wright**
21 **RHINESTONE BLUE (IRE),** ch g Gleneagles (IRE)—Bora Blues **The Fat Lads Syndicate**
22 **RICH GIRL (IRE),** b f Gutaifan (IRE)—Queenofthenorth (IRE) **Mr R. Clothier & Miss J. Gray**
23 **ROCKIN' N RAVEN,** b g Raven's Pass (USA)—Solva **Mrs J. A. Fowler**
24 **SYDNEY SIREN,** ch f Australia—King's Siren (IRE) **J. C. Smith**
25 **WILFY,** br g Kyllachy—Close To The Edge (IRE) **Marchwood Recycling Ltd**

TWO-YEAR-OLDS

26 B f 05/04 Territories (IRE)—Alzanti (USA) (Arch (USA)) (15443) **Mr C. N. Wright**
27 **EAUX DE VIE,** b f 19/03 Swiss Spirit—Delagoa Bay (IRE) (Encosta de Lago (AUS)) **Homebred Racing**
28 **FIVE RINGS,** ch c 28/01 The Gurkha (IRE)—Olympic Runner (Exceed And Excel (AUS)) **J. C. Smith**
29 **FREE DANCER,** ch c 18/04 Iffraaj—Opera Dancer (Norse Dancer (IRE)) **J. C. Smith**
30 **HONEYDEW (IRE),** ch f 14/04 Dandy Man (IRE)—
                                                           Leenavesta (USA) (Arch (USA)) (17160) **Mr Neil Simpson & Partners**
31 Ch f 31/03 Outstrip—Jaiyana (Dansili) **Mr R. Clothier & Miss J. Gray**
32 B f 22/03 The Gurkha (IRE)—Katiyra (IRE) (Peintre Celebre (USA))
33 B f 19/05 Camelot—Lady Babooshka (Cape Cross (IRE)) (24023) **Mrs S McKeever**
34 Br f 14/04 Twilight Son—Lead a Merry Dance (Bertolini) **Miss A. J. Rawding**
35 B f 05/03 Estidhkaar (IRE)—Little Oz (IRE) (Red Ransom (USA)) (3500) **Mr R. Clothier & Miss J. Gray**
36 B c 15/04 Twilight Son—Peace Concluded (Bertolini (USA)) (12000) **Fairway Racing**
37 **SEATTLE ROCK,** b f 08/05 Fastnet Rock (AUS)—Snoqualmie Girl (IRE) (Montjeu (IRE)) **J. C. Smith**
38 **SHADES OF RED,** b f 20/02 Acclamation—Marisol (IRE) (Teofilo (IRE)) (100000) **Miss Alison Jones**
39 B c 20/02 Zoffany (IRE)—Soft Ice (IRE) (Kingmambo (USA)) (42900)
40 **STUDY THE STARS,** b c 16/03 Due Diligence (USA)—Celestial Bay (Septieme Ciel (USA)) **Homebred Racing**
41 B br f 13/03 Gutaifan (IRE)—Yes Margot (IRE) (Clodovil (IRE)) (3860)

Other Owners: R. J. Brennan, Ms A. Clifford, Mr R. W. Clothier, Mr R. Clothier & Miss J. Gray, Mr P. Crowley, Deauville Daze Partnership, Ms C. Forsyth, Miss J. F. Gray, Mr N. Hayes, Mr M. V. Hill, Mr N. Hughes, S. A. Kirk, Mr P. T. O Brien, Mr N. Simpson, The Old Enough To Know Better Partners, Mr A. W. Wilson, Mr C. N. Wright, Miss H. E. Wright.

Assistant Trainer: Fanny Kirk.

---

319 MR STUART KITTOW, Cullompton
Postal: **Haynefield Farm, Blackborough, Cullompton, Devon, EX15 2JD**
Contacts: **HOME** 01823 680183 **MOBILE** 07714 218921 **FAX** 01823 680601
EMAIL stuartkittowracing@hotmail.com **WEBSITE** www.stuartkittowracing.com

1 **BEYOND EQUAL,** 5, b g Kheleyf (USA)—Samasana (IRE) **Stuart Wood & Partner**
2 **DORA'S FIELD (IRE),** 7, b m Rip Van Winkle (IRE)—Rydal Mount (IRE) **R. S. E. Gifford**
3 **EVERLASTING SEA,** 6, b m Harbour Watch (IRE)—Doliouchka **R. S. E. Gifford**
4 **FREDDY FANATAPAN,** 5, b g Nathaniel (IRE)—Pan Galactic (USA) **Dr G. S. Plastow**
5 **GLOWETH,** 5, b m Pastoral Pursuits—Dancing Storm **M. E. Harris**
6 **HOWABOUTRIGHTNOW (IRE),** 5, b g Where Or When (IRE)—Suelena (IRE) **The Howaboutrightnow Partnership**
7 **INCENTIVE,** 6, b m Stimulation (IRE)—Folly Drove **W. S. Kittow**
8 **MAD ENDEAVOUR,** 9, b g Muhtathir—Capefly **R. S. E. Gifford**
9 **SPIRIT OF ISHY,** 5, b m Hellvelyn—Our Piccadilly **Mrs G. R. Shire**
10 **TIBBIE DUNBAR,** 4, b f Poet's Voice—Gold Approach **Mr J. R. Urquhart**
11 **YOUKAN (IRE),** 5, b g Choisir (AUS)—Ellikan (IRE) **Mrs L. M. Francis**

THREE-YEAR-OLDS

12 **CROWDED EXPRESS,** b g Fast Company (IRE)—Dilys **Cushing, Boswell, Ingham & Kittow**
13 **GHERKIN,** b g Coach House (IRE)—Our Piccadilly (IRE) **Mrs G. R. Shire**
14 **MABEL JANE,** b f Champs Elysees—Sabaweeya **Dr Belinda J. Blouin**

MR STUART KITTOW - continued

15 **NEWTON JACK,** b g Fast Company (IRE)—Jackline **Newton Barn Racing**
16 **SIEMPRE RAPIDO,** b c Outstrip—Cape Mystery **Mr T. J. Malone**
17 B g Fast Company (IRE)—Sister Guru **D. R. Tucker**
18 **WINANDER,** b g Ruler of The World (IRE)—Rydal Mount (IRE) **R. S. E. Gifford**
19 **WISHING GATE,** b g Holy Roman Emperor (IRE)—Quiff **R. S. E. Gifford**

TWO-YEAR-OLDS

20 B g 19/03 Power—Dilgura (Ishiguru (USA))
21 **KEN'S BOY,** b c 02/03 Coach House (IRE)—Plauseabella (Royal Applause) **Mrs G. R. Shire**
22 B gr g 22/02 Outstrip—Suzy Wong (Auction House (USA)) (2857) **Mrs P. J. Pengelly**
23 B c 09/03 Swiss Spirit—Yat Ding Yau (FR) (Air Chief Marshal (IRE)) (4761) **W. S. Kittow**

Assistant Trainer: Mrs Judy Kittow.

Flat Jockey: Rob Hornby. **NH Jockey:** David Noonan, Tom Scudamore.

---

320 **MR WILLIAM KNIGHT, Angmering**
Postal: **Lower Coombe Racing Stables, Angmering Park, Littlehampton, West Sussex, BN16 4EX**
Contacts: **PHONE 01903 871188 MOBILE 07770 720828 FAX 01903 871184**
EMAIL william@wknightracing.co.uk WEBSITE www.wknightracing.co.uk

1 **AUTHOR'S DREAM,** 7, gr g Authorized (IRE)—Spring Dream (IRE) **Mr & Mrs Conroy**
2 **GAVLAR,** 9, b g Gentlewave (IRE)—Shawhill **Canisbay Bloodstock**
3 **HUDDLE,** 4, gr f Aussie Rules (USA)—Purest **Mr & Mrs N. Welby**
4 **KINGSTON KURRAJONG,** 7, b g Authorized (IRE)—Kingston Acacia **Canisbay Bloodstock**
5 **NOBLE GIFT,** 10, ch g Cadeaux Genereux—Noble Penny **Canisbay Bloodstock**
6 **SEINESATIONAL,** 5, b g Champs Elysees—Kibara **One Day Rodney Partnership**
7 **SHIFTING GOLD (IRE),** 4, b f Fast Company (IRE)—Elusive Gold (IRE) **Mrs Joanna Farrant & Partner**
8 **SIR BUSKER (IRE),** 4, b g Sir Prancealot (IRE)—Street Kitty (IRE) **Kennet Valley Thoroughbreds Xi Racing**
9 **SOTO SIZZLER,** 5, b g Mastercraftsman (IRE)—Jalousie (IRE) **I. J. Heseltine**
10 **UNIT OF ASSESSMENT (IRE),** 6, b g Dragon Pulse (IRE)—Before The Storm **Mr A. Hetherton**
11 **VELVET MORN (IRE),** 5, b m Epaulette (AUS)—El Soprano (IRE) **Mrs S. K. Hartley**

THREE-YEAR-OLDS

12 **ALDRICH BAY (IRE),** b g Xtension (IRE)—Sail With The Wind **Mr Y. O. Wong**
13 **COMMIT NO NUISANCE (IRE),** ch c Ivawood (IRE)—Free Lance (IRE) **G. C. Stevens**
14 **DASHING SPIRIT (IRE),** b g Sir Prancealot (IRE)—Gwyllion (USA) **Angmering Park Thoroughbreds I**
15 **DATA ROOM,** b f Due Diligence (USA)—Purest **Mr & Mrs N. Welby**
16 **GOODWOOD REBEL (IRE),** b g Dandy Man (IRE)—
                              Our Valkyrie (IRE) **Goodwood Racehorse Owners Group Limited**
17 **HARLEQUIN,** b g Swiss Spirit—Falcon In Flight **R. L. Page**
18 **HENLEY PARK,** ch g Paco Boy (IRE)—Sunny Afternoon **Mrs S. A. Windus**
19 **KALIMOTXO,** b f Equiano (FR)—Royal Ivy **Canisbay Bloodstock**
20 B g Kyllachy—Keep The Secret **Mr & Mrs N. Welby**
21 **MR NUTHERPUTT (IRE),** b g Camacho—Right After Moyne (IRE) **Seabrook Miller**
22 **PEARL BEACH,** b f Footstepsinthesand—Western Pearl **Mr & Mrs N. Welby**
23 B g Mukhadram—Plover **Canisbay Bloodstock**
24 **PROGRESSIVE RATING,** br c Bated Breath—Foxtrot Alpha (IRE) **Mr P Chan & Mr A Hetherton**
25 **QUARRY BAY (IRE),** b g Ivawood (IRE)—Sandbox Two (IRE) **Mr Y. O. Wong**
26 **SELSEY SIZZLER,** b g Nathaniel (IRE)—Heho **Mr I. J. Heseltine & Mr P Winkworth**
27 **SIGNAL TWENTY NINE,** gr g Gregorian—Beacon Lady **Chasemore Farm & Mr J Dwyer**
28 **SPANISH KISS,** ch c Lope de Vega (IRE)—Kissable (IRE) **Kennet Valley Thoroughbreds XIV**

TWO-YEAR-OLDS

29 B c 04/02 Dragon Pulse (IRE)—Before The Storm (Sadler's Wells (USA)) (11000)
30 B f 21/02 Siyouni (FR)—Clotilde (Dubawi (IRE)) **Chasemore Farm LLP**
31 B f 03/05 Swiss Spirit—Falcon In Flight (Shamardal (USA)) **R. L. Page**

MR WILLIAM KNIGHT - continued

32 **FOXTROT SIZZLER (GER)**, b c 16/02 Pride of Dubai (AUS)—Firedance (GER) (Lomitas) (42000) **I. J. Heseltine**
33 **GOODWOOD GLEN**, b c 05/04 Territories—Bonnie Brae **Goodwood Racehorse Owners Group Limited**
34 Ch g 28/02 Power—Kekova (Montjeu (IRE)) **Mr T. G. Roddick**
35 **PROGRESSIVE EZ (IRE)**, b c 17/03 Gutaifan (IRE)—
　　　　　　　　　　　　　　　　Cuilaphuca (IRE) (Danetime (IRE)) (9867) **Progressive Racing & Partner**
36 B f 11/04 Swiss Spirit—Stylistik (Sakhee's Secret) **R. L. Page**
37 B c 05/03 Belardo (IRE)—Teide Lady (Nashwan (USA)) (50000) **Kennet Valley Thoroughbreds IV**
38 **VISIONS OF GLORY (IRE)**, ch c 21/01 The Last Lion (IRE)—Aunt Julia (In The Wings) (28000) **Tom Earl & Apt Vi**

Other Owners: A. W. Black, Mrs J. E. Black, Mr P. Chan, Chasemore Farm LLP, Mr N. A. Coster, J. Dwyer, Mr T. E. Earl, Mrs J. D. Farrant, I. J. Heseltine, Mr A. Hetherton, Mr R. S. Hoskins, Kennet Valley Thoroughbreds XI, R. F. Kilby, Mrs E. J. J. Knight, W. J. Knight, Mrs M. E. A. Miller, Progressive Racing, Mr M. A. C. Rudd, Mr J. F. Seabrook, Miss M. E. Stopher, Mr L. A. Stoten, Mr M. J. Tracey, P. L. Winkworth.

Assistant Trainer: Kayleigh Flower.

---

321 **MR DANIEL KUBLER**, Upper Lambourn
Postal: **Sarsen Farm, Upper Lambourn, Hungerford, Berkshire, RG17 8RG**
Contacts: **MOBILE 07984 287254**
EMAIL daniel@kublerracing.com WEBSITE www.kublerracing.com

1 **ACT OF BRAVERY**, 5, b g Invincible Spirit (IRE)—Mama Quilla (USA) **Mr & Mrs G. Middlebrook**
2 **BRUTE FORCE**, 4, ch g Paco Boy (IRE)—Free Falling **A.C. Entertainment Technologies Limited**
3 **CASTELO (IRE)**, 4, b f Casamento (IRE)—Fortress **Diskovery Partnership V**
4 **CHAMOMILE**, 4, b f Teofilo (IRE)—Al Joza **Mr & Mrs G. Middlebrook**
5 **CHITRA**, 4, b f Sea The Moon (GER)—Persian Star **Mr & Mrs G. Middlebrook**
6 **FRONSAC**, 5, ch g Frankel—Riberac **Mr & Mrs G. Middlebrook**
7 **KING'S COUNSEL**, 4, b g Camelot—Love Everlasting **Mr & Mrs G. Middlebrook**
8 **OUTRAGE**, 8, ch g Exceed And Excel (AUS)—Ludynosa (USA) **Capture the Moment Vi**
9 **SENECA CHIEF**, 6, b g Invincible Spirit (IRE)—Albertine Rose **Mr & Mrs G. Middlebrook**
10 **ZEPHYRINA (IRE)**, 4, b f Big Bad Bob (IRE)—Western Sky **Mr P. J. H. Whitten**

THREE-YEAR-OLDS

11 **DON'T TELL CLAIRE**, ro f Gutaifan (IRE)—Avenbury **Mr A. Stonehill**
12 **HYDRAULIC**, b c Golden Horn—Dorcas Lane **D Blunt & G Middlebrook**
13 **RIVER SPRITE**, b f Swiss Spirit—Camp Riverside (USA) **Diskovery Partnership VII**
14 **SAIGON SUZI**, b f Sir Percy—Cio Cio San (IRE)
15 **SALSA DIP (IRE)**, b g Camacho—Baltic Dip (IRE) **Capture The Moment III**
16 **SECRET ACQUISITION**, b f Sea The Moon (GER)—Maria Letizia

TWO-YEAR-OLDS

17 B f 21/01 Charming Thought—Albertine Rose (Namid)
18 B br f 20/03 Kodi Bear (IRE)—Always The Lady (Halling (USA)) (10725) **Diskovery VIII**
19 B f 19/05 Fountain of Youth (IRE)—Dance of Light (USA) (Sadler's Wells (USA))
20 B c 20/04 New Bay—Distinctive (Tobougg (IRE)) **Mr & Mrs G. Middlebrook**
21 B c 23/03 Dark Angel (IRE)—Ducissa (Exceed And Excel (AUS)) (50000)
22 **EXCLUSIVELY YOURS**, b f 25/04 Gleneagles (IRE)—Acquainted (Shamardal (USA)) **Mr & Mrs G. Middlebrook**
23 B f 22/02 Belardo (IRE)—Intrigue (Fastnet Rock (AUS)) (9438)
24 B f 05/05 Fast Company (IRE)—Jubilant Lady (USA) (Aptitude (USA)) (50000)
25 B f 20/03 Paco Boy (IRE)—La Donacella (Sir Percy) **Ms V. O'Sullivan**
26 B f 15/04 Shalaa (IRE)—Lady Francesca (Montjeu (IRE)) (32000) **Mr & Mrs G. Middlebrook**
27 **MUSTAVIM**, ch c 14/03 Mustajeeb—Erebis (Green Desert (USA)) **Peter Onslow**
28 **NANTOSUELTA (IRE)**, b f 29/04 Kodiac—
　　　　　　　　　　　　Dearest Daisy (Forzando) (34320) **Crowd, New Image Contracts & Partners**
29 B c 11/01 Pivotal—Nibbling (IRE) (Invincible Spirit (IRE)) (92000) **Capture the Moment Vii**
30 B c 17/02 Vadamos (FR)—Of Course Darling (Dalakhani (IRE)) (13728) **Capture the Moment & Crowd Racing**
31 B c 11/03 Muhaarar—Oui Say Oui (IRE) (Royal Applause) (35000) **Capture The Moment III**

MR DANIEL KUBLER - continued

32 B f 11/02 Territories (IRE)—Penny Rose (Danehill Dancer (IRE)) (12000)
33 B c 31/01 Kyllachy—Penny's Gift (Tobougg (IRE))

Other Owners: A.C. Entertainment Technologies Limited, Mr D. Agate, Mr A. G. Bell, Mrs Y. Blunt, Crowd Racing Partnership, Mrs Fiona Denniff, Mr M. Ebert, Mr R. Lord, Mr C. McKenna, Mr & Mrs G. Middlebrook, Miss M. A. Thompson, Mr T Weech, Mr K Widdicks.

Assistant Trainer: Claire Kubler.

---

322 **MR TOM LACEY,** Woolhope
Postal: **Sapness Farm, Woolhope, Herefordshire, HR1 4RG**
Contacts: **MOBILE 07768 398604**
EMAIL tom@cottagefield.co.uk WEBSITE www.cottagefield.co.uk

1 ADRIMEL (FR), 5, b br g Tirwanako (FR)—Irise De Gene (FR) Lady Bamford, Miss A. C. Bamford
2 CAPAC (IRE), 5, ch g Aizavoski (IRE)—Wigwam Mam (IRE) Mr D. W. Macauley
3 CHRISTOPHER ROBIN (IRE), 5, b g Camelot—Iowa Falls Ford Associated Racing Team
4 CONINGSBY, 7, ch g Midnight Legend—Motcombe (IRE) Lady N. F. Cobham
5 DORKING BOY, 6, ch g Schiaparelli (GER)—Megasue Galloping On The South Downs Partnership
6 DORKING COCK (IRE), 6, b g Winged Love (IRE)—Kiss Jolie (FR) Galloping On The South Downs Partnership
7 EQUUS AMADEUS (IRE), 7, b g Beat Hollow—Charade (IRE) Galloping On The South Downs Partnership
8 FAIR KATE, 6, b m Fair Mix (IRE)—Silver Kate (IRE) Galloping On The South Downs Partnership
9 FLASHING GLANCE, 7, b g Passing Glance—Don And Gerry (IRE) Barrett, Meredith, Panniers, Wilde
10 FLOATING ROCK (GER), 5, b g It's Gino (GER)—Fly Osoria (GER) Lee Bolingbroke & Len Attrill
11 GINFLIX (FR), 4, b c Al Namix (FR)—Une Tournee (FR) Mr J. P. McManus
12 GLORY AND FORTUNE (IRE), 5, b g Fame And Glory—Night Heron (IRE) Mr J. Hinds
13 HUNTING PERCIVAL, 5, b g Sir Percy—Motcombe (IRE) Lady N. F. Cobham
14 JOHNBB (IRE), 6, b g Stowaway—Flemins Evening (IRE) C. Boultbee-Brooks
15 KATESON, 7, gr g Black Sam Bellamy (IRE)—Silver Kate (IRE) DavidMRichardsandRobertsCWhittalWilliams
16 KIMBERLITE CANDY (IRE), 8, b g Flemensfirth (USA)—Mandys Native (IRE) Mr J. P. McManus
17 LAMANVER STORM, 5, b g Geordieland (FR)—Lamanver Homerun Dr D. Christensen
18 LE GRAND FROMAGE, 5, b g Kayf Tara—Megalex Galloping On The South Downs Partnership
19 4, B br g Fame And Glory—Liss Na Tintri (IRE) Mr Jerry Hinds & Mr Ashley Head
20 LOSSIEMOUTH, 5, b g Makfi—First Bloom (USA) Lady N. F. Cobham
21 MARTY TIME (FR), 4, gr g Martaline—Shahwarda (FR) Mr Jerry Hinds & Mr Ashley Head
22 NEVILLE'S CROSS (IRE), 5, b g Stowaway—Dancing Bird (IRE) Mr F Green & Mr J Chinn
23 NOCTE VOLATUS, 5, b g Midnight Legend—Aeronautica (IRE) Lady Cobham & Dauntsey Park, Miss V. C. Sturgis
24 OUTLAW JESSE JAMES, 5, b m Passing Glance—Don And Gerry (IRE) The Jesse James Posse
25 POLYDORA (IRE), 8, b g Milan—Mandysway (IRE) P. J. H. Wills & J. J. King
26 QUICK DRAW (IRE), 4, b g Getaway (GER)—Sept Verites (FR) Lady C. Bamford & Miss A. Bamford
27 RED NIKA (FR), 5, br g Denham Red (FR)—Nika Glitters (FR) Mr D. Kellett
28 SEBASTOPOL (IRE), 6, b g Fame And Glory—Knockcroghery (IRE) C. Boultbee-Brooks
29 SIR EGBERT, 7, b g Kayf Tara—Little Miss Flora Mrs E. M. F. Cadbury
30 SNAPDRAGON FIRE (IRE), 7, b g Getaway (GER)—Global Diamond (IRE) P J King & Son
31 SWIFT WING, 4, ch g Pivotal—Gull Wing (IRE) Lady Bamford
32 TEA CLIPPER (IRE), 5, b g Stowaway—A Plus Ma Puce (FR) Mr Jerry Hinds & Mr Ashley Head
33 THAIS TOIR (FR), 5, b g Diamond Boy (FR)—Scotland Act (FR) Mr J. Hinds
34 THOMAS PATRICK (IRE), 8, b g Winged Love (IRE)—Huncheon Siss (IRE) Mr D. Kellett
35 UNOHU, 5, b g Kayf Tara—Little Miss Flora Mr J. J. King
36 VADO FORTE (FR), 7, b g Walk In The Park (IRE)—Gloire (FR) Roberts, Churchward, Whittal-Williams
37 YOU NAME HIM, 4, b g Proclamation (IRE)—Scarlett O'Tara HFT Forklifts Limited

Other Owners: Mr L. R. Attrill, Miss A. C. Bamford, Lady Bamford, Lady C. Bamford & Miss A. Bamford, Mr P. L. Barrett, Mr L. A. Bolingbroke, Mr W. J. Chinn, Lady N. F. Cobham, F. M. Green, Mr A. J. Head, Mr J. Hinds, Mr J. J. King, Mrs V. C. King, Mr T. F. Lacey, Mr G. J. Meredith, Mr N. J. Panniers, D. M. Richards, G. A. Roberts, Roberts, Churchward, Whittal-Williams, Mr E. B. Whittal-Williams, Mr W. E. Wilde, Mr P. J. H. Wills.

NH Jockey: Richard Johnson. **Conditional Jockey:** Stan Sheppard. **Amateur Jockey:** Mr Tommie O'Brien.

323 **MR CARLOS LAFFON-PARIAS, Chantilly**
Postal: 38, Avenue du General Leclerc, 60500 Chantilly, France
EMAIL ecuries.laffon.parias@wanadoo.fr

1 **CARTES,** 4, ch c Sea The Moon (GER)—Kensington Gardens **Bering SL**
2 **CONTORTIONISTE,** 5, ch h Pivotal—Distortion **Wertheimer et Frere**
3 **CORANDO,** 4, b c Dark Angel (IRE)—Norway Cross **Al Shira'aa Farms SARL**
4 **ECOLO (FR),** 4, b c Invincible Spirit (IRE)—Never Green (IRE) **Wertheimer et Frere**
5 **FLAMBEUR (USA),** 4, gr g Mizzen Mast (USA)—Flamenba (USA) **Wertheimer et Frere**
6 **GWENDOLA,** 4, b f Oasis Dream—Gwenseb (FR) **Wertheimer et Frere**
7 **ILLA ALQMAR,** 4, ch f Lope de Vega (IRE)—Tebee **Al Shira'aa Farms SARL**
8 **MUTAMAKINA,** 4, b f Nathaniel (IRE)—Joshua's Princess **Al Shira'aa Farms SARL**
9 **PALOMBA (IRE),** 4, b f Lope de Vega (IRE)—Australienne (IRE) **Wertheimer et Frere**
10 **PRAXIAS (IRE),** 4, gr c Iffraaj—Pearl Earrine (FR)
11 **SHAMAN (IRE),** 4, ch c Shamardal (USA)—Only Green (IRE) **Wertheimer et Frere**
12 **SOSOFT (FR),** 4, b c Pivotal—Soft Lips **Wertheimer et Frere**
13 **STARIFIQUE (IRE),** 4, ch f Sea The Stars (IRE)—Sapphire Pendant (IRE) **Wertheimer et Frere**
14 **STARMANIAC,** 4, b c Sea The Stars (IRE)—Plumania **Wertheimer et Frere**
15 **VILLALAR (FR),** 4, b f Whipper (USA)—Highphar (FR) **SARL Darpat France**
16 **ZIYAD,** 5, b br g Rock of Gibraltar (IRE)—Arme Ancienne **Wertheimer et Frere**

THREE-YEAR-OLDS

17 **ALLUCINATION,** b f Lope de Vega (IRE)—Desertiste **Wertheimer et Frere**
18 **ANGELISSIMA (FR),** gr f Dark Angel (IRE)—Foreign Tune **Wertheimer et Frere**
19 **ARABIAN BELLE (IRE),** b f No Nay Never (USA)—Opera Fan (FR) **Al Shira'aa Farms SARL**
20 **ARGOLIS (FR),** ch f Outstrip—Aranka **Mrs Catherine Kairis**
21 B br f Kitten's Joy (USA)—Celestial Woods (USA) **Al Shira'aa Farms SARL**
22 **CELTRA (IRE),** b f Oasis Dream—Zantenda **Wertheimer et Frere**
23 **DILAR,** b f Makfi—Campanillas (IRE) **SARL Darpat France**
24 **ECRIVAIN (FR),** ch c Lope de Vega (IRE)—Sapphire Pendant (IRE) **Wertheimer et Frere**
25 **FEMINA (IRE),** b f Siyouni (FR)—Legerete (USA) **Wertheimer et Frere**
26 **FLAMING ROUGE (USA),** ch f Kitten's Joy (USA)—Chianti Red (USA) **Al Shira'aa Farms SARL**
27 Gr f Dark Angel (IRE)—Foreign Legionary (IRE) **Partnership**
28 **GADEA (IRE),** b f Dandy Man (IRE)—Madam Macie (IRE) **Loughtown Stud Ltd**
29 **GALAWI (IRE),** b c Dubawi (IRE)—Galikova (FR) **Wertheimer et Frere**
30 **HOPEFUL (FR),** b c Motivator—Monst (IRE) **Wertheimer et Frere**
31 **HUETOR (FR),** ch g Archipenko (USA)—Briviesca **SARL Darpat France**
32 **KATAFONIC (FR),** b c Iffraaj—Pitamore (USA) **Wertheimer et Frere**
33 **LADY GOLDFRAPP (IRE),** b f Gutaifan (IRE)—Supreme Seductress (IRE) **Al Shira'aa Farms SARL**
34 **LASY W (USA),** b c War Front (USA)—Zaftig (USA) **Wertheimer et Frere**
35 **LIPSINK (IRE),** b c Kodiac—Iron Lips **Wertheimer et Frere**
36 **MATELLO (IRE),** b c Intello (GER)—Mama Lulu (USA) **Wertheimer et Frere**
37 **METAPHORE (FR),** b f Intello (GER)—Never Green (IRE) **Wertheimer et Frere**
38 **MINX AT MIDNIGHT (IRE),** gr f Dark Angel (IRE)—Boastful (IRE) **Al Shira'aa Farms SARL**
39 **NAT KING,** b c Nathaniel (IRE)—Shivering **Loughtown Stud Ltd**
40 **PAPUA (FR),** b f Mastercraftsman (IRE)—Mydarshaan **Wertheimer et Frere**
41 **PIONEER OF THE SKY (USA),** b f Pioneerof the Nile (USA)—Graeme Six (USA) **Al Shira'aa Farms SARL**
42 **REVENTADOR (IRE),** b c Zoffany (IRE)—Frine (IRE) **Duc D'Alburquerque**
43 **RIGHT HAND,** b f Lope de Vega (IRE)—Balladeuse (FR) **Wertheimer et Frere**
44 **ROBLE,** b c Cable Bay (IRE)—Fanny May **Loughtown Stud Ltd**
45 **SEACHANGE (FR),** b f Siyouni (FR)—Ydillique (IRE) **Wertheimer et Frere**
46 **SEAMIA,** b f Sea The Stars (IRE)—Solemia (IRE) **Wertheimer et Frere**
47 **SILASTAR,** b c Sea The Stars (IRE)—Silasol (IRE) **Wertheimer et Frere**
48 **SITOUTVABIEN (FR),** b c Golden Horn—Sefroua (USA) **Riviera Equine S.A.R.L**
49 **STANZO,** b c Speightstown (USA)—Viva Rafaela (BRZ) **Wertheimer et Frere**
50 **TURKO BEACH (CAN),** ch f Hard Spun (USA)—Orchard Beach (CAN) **Al Shira'aa Farms SARL**
51 **TWIST (FR),** ch c Pivotal—Distortion **Wertheimer et Frere**

MR CARLOS LAFFON-PARIAS - continued

TWO-YEAR-OLDS

52 **ABSURDE**, b c 04/05 Fastnet Rock—Incroyable **Wertheimer et Frere**
53 Ch f 19/04 Archipenko—Aguafria **SARL Darpat France**
54 **ANSILIA (IRE)**, b f 28/01 Dansili—Incahoots (Oasis Dream) **Wertheimer et Frere**
55 B c 25/01 Anodin (IRE)—Aranka (Iffraaj) **Mrs Catherine Kairis**
56 B f 23/04 Myboycharlie—Briviesca **SARL Darpat France**
57 **EVER PINK (IRE)**, ch f 13/04 Anodin (IRE)—Never Green (IRE) (Halling (USA)) **Wertheimer et Frere**
58 **FRONTGATE (USA)**, b f 24/02 War Front (USA)—Oceanique (USA) (Forest Wildcat (USA)) **Wertheimer et Frere**
59 **GOLDISTYLE (IRE)**, ch f 13/02 Dubawi (IRE)—Goldikova (IRE) (Anabaa (USA)) **Wertheimer et Frere**
60 Ch f 24/04 Adlerflug—Highphar **SARL Darpat France**
61 **HYPOCONDRIAC (FR)**, b c 01/01 Mastercraftsman (IRE)—Tristesse (USA) (Broken Vow (USA)) **Wertheimer et Frere**
62 **KALAOS (IRE)**, gr c 16/04 Helmet (AUS)—Pale Pearl (IRE) (King's Best (USA)) (30888) **Tolmi Racing**
63 **KARKHOV (IRE)**, ch c 26/03 Lope de Vega (IRE)—Akrivi (IRE) (Tobougg (IRE)) **MR Alain Jathiere**
64 **KOLKA**, b f 15/03 Shalaa (IRE)—Satiriste (Shamardal (USA)) (223080) **MR Alain Jathiere**
65 **KYNISKA (FR)**, b f 01/01 Zoffany (IRE)—Kleo (GR) (Kavafi (IRE)) **MR Alain Jathiere**
66 B f 16/02 Siyouni—La Zubia **Al Shira'aa Farms SARL**
67 B f 17/03 Shalaa (IRE)—Naissance Royale **Al Shira'aa Farms SARL**
68 B f 30/04 Night of Thunder—Sally is the Boss **Bering SL**
69 Br f 05/02 Frankel—Secrete (FR) **Al Shira'aa Farms SARL**
70 **SEULOMONDE**, b c 19/04 Dubawi (IRE)—Solemia (IRE) (Poliglote) **Wertheimer et Frere**
71 **SOLANIA (IRE)**, b f 01/03 Zoffany (IRE)—Solilea (IRE) (Galileo (IRE)) **Wertheimer et Frere**
72 **SOUPIR**, b c 08/03 Deep Impact (JPN)—Sasparella (FR) (Shamardal (USA)) **Wertheimer et Frere**
73 **STAR OF SAINTS (FR)**, b f 01/01 Sea The Stars (IRE)—
　　　　　　　　　　　　　　　　　Shahnila (FR) (Elusive City (USA)) (205920) **Al Shira'aa Farms SARL**
74 **TASMANIA (FR)**, ch br f 22/04 Zoffany—Australienne **Wertheimer et Frere**
75 B g 15/03 Myboycharlie (IRE)—Tia Kia (IRE) **MR Mathieu Offenstadt**
76 **UNVEIL (IRE)**, b f 04/02 Showcasing—Soft Lips (Rahy (USA)) **Wertheimer et Frere**
77 **VANOUCHE**, b c 07/05 Invincible Spirit—Blarney Stone **Wertheimer et Frere**
78 **VIRTUOSITE (FR)**, b f 09/05 camelot—legerete **Wertheimer et Frere**
79 **WALLAROO (IRE)**, b c 18/02 Australia—Dancequest (IRE) (Dansili) **Wertheimer et Frere**
80 **WOOF (GER)**, b c 03/02 Zoffany—Wanderina **Wertheimer et Frere**
81 **ZILEO**, b c 25/03 Galileo (IRE)—Lady Zuzu (USA) (Dynaformer (USA)) **Wertheimer et Frere**

Other Owners: Al Shira'aa Farms SARL, Haras d'Etreham, Tolmi Racing.

324
MR NICK LAMPARD, Marlborough
Postal: **South Cottage, 2 The Crossroads, Clatford, Marlborough, Wiltshire, SN8 4EA**
Contacts: **PHONE 01672 861420**

1 **FOREST LORD**, 6, b g Native Ruler—La Belle Au Bois (IRE) **N. M. Lampard**
2 4, B g Gentlewave (IRE)—Goochypoochyprader **The Ivy**
3 **LOGAN'S CHOICE**, 5, b g Redoute's Choice (AUS)—Bright Morning (USA) **N. M. Lampard**
4 **MINMORE GREY (IRE)**, 11, gr g Primary (USA)—Hopeful Memory (IRE) **N. M. Lampard**
5 **RUBY TAYLOR**, 8, b m Passing Glance—Bold Rose **N. M. Lampard**
6 **SADMA**, 11, gr g Street Cry (IRE)—Blue Dress (USA) **N. M. Lampard**
7 **WESSINGTON PARK**, 5, b m Bollin Eric—Sanendd (IRE) **The Ivy**

325
MR JUSTIN LANDY, Leyburn
Postal: **2 Beckwood, Spennithorne, Leyburn, North Yorkshire, DL8 5FB**
EMAIL jlandyracing@hotmail.com

1 **CHEERS JD (IRE)**, 8, b g Westerner—Fair Present (IRE) **Ms C. Southerington**
2 **GEORGE GENTLY (FR)**, 7, b g Gentlewave (IRE)—Sindibad (USA) **Ms C. Southerington**
3 **MCCRACKENS GATE (IRE)**, 9, br g Robin des Pres (FR)—Be My Libby (IRE) **Miss C. Tinkler**
4 **MELDRUM LAD (IRE)**, 11, b g Fruits of Love (USA)—Meldrum Hall (IRE) **Mrs P. Southerington**

MR JUSTIN LANDY - continued

5 **MONTE ALBAN (IRE),** 7, ch g Soviet Star (USA)—Esee (IRE) **Mrs P. Southerington**
6 **SCHIAPARANNIE,** 8, b m Schiaparelli (GER)—Annie's Answer (IRE) **Miss C. Tinkler**
7 **SERIOUS MOOD (IRE),** 7, b g Scorpion (IRE)—Criaire Nouveau (IRE) **Ms C. Southerington**
8 **SHETLAND BUS (GER),** 7, ch g Sholokhov (IRE)—Shali Tori (FR) **Mrs P. Southerington**
9 **SUNNYHILL LAD (IRE),** 5, ch g Casamento (IRE)—Tereed Elhawa **Mr J. P. G. Landy**
10 **TRAPPER PEAK (IRE),** 11, b g Westerner—Banningham Blaze **Mr J. P. G. Landy**

326	**MR DAVID LANIGAN, Newmarket** Postal: **Rathmoy Stables, Hamilton Road, Newmarket, Suffolk, CB8 0GU** Contacts: **PHONE 01638 664063 MOBILE 07803 257864** **EMAIL david@laniganracing.co.uk WEBSITE www.laniganracing.co.uk**

1 **CITY OF LOVE,** 4, b f Exceed And Excel (AUS)—Heart's Content (IRE)
2 **GOLD ARCH,** 4, b g Archipenko (USA)—Goldrenched (IRE)

THREE-YEAR-OLDS

3 **BLUE EAGLE (IRE),** b f Free Eagle (IRE)—Satwa Pearl
4 **FRENCH MINSTREL (IRE),** b c Gutaifan (IRE)—C'Est Ma Souer (IRE)
5 **ISLAND HIDEAWAY,** b f Mukhadram—Interstella
6 **KING OF THE SOUTH (IRE),** b c Kingman—South Atlantic (USA)
7 **LONGSIDER (IRE),** b c Ruler of The World (IRE)—Lady Dettoria (FR)
8 **PRINCE OF EAGLES (IRE),** b c Free Eagle (IRE)—Sleeping Beauty (IRE)
9 **RENZIA (GER),** ch f Sea The Stars (IRE)—Rietondale (USA)
10 **SAY IT'S ME,** b f Shamardal (USA)—Say No Now (IRE)
11 **SHOWMOLINA,** b c Showcasing—Crossmolina (IRE)
12 **SILVER DESERT (IRE),** gr f Mastercraftsman (IRE)—Stars At Night (IRE)
13 **SONG AT TWILIGHT (IRE),** b f Zoffany (IRE)—Jasmine Blue (IRE)
14 **SPARKLING OR STILL (IRE),** b f Kendargent (FR)—West of Venus (USA)
15 **SPEED OF THOUGHT (IRE),** b c Shamardal (USA)—Arabian Comet (IRE)
16 **VENTURA STAR (IRE),** b c Gutaifan (IRE)—Galileo's Star (IRE)
17 **WITH PROMISE,** b c Shamardal (USA)—Magical Crown (USA)

TWO-YEAR-OLDS

18 B c 17/02 Exceed And Excel (AUS)—Aquatinta (GER) (Samum (GER)) (75000)
19 B f 22/03 Mastercraftsman (IRE)—Lemon Rock (Green Desert (USA)) (75000)
20 B f 23/01 Dubawi (IRE)—Meeznah (Dynaformer (USA)) (180000)
21 B c 28/03 Zoffany (IRE)—Najam (Singspiel (IRE)) (55000)
22 B c 09/04 Sea The Moon (GER)—Nota Bene (GER) (Slickly (FR)) (42000)
23 B c 16/02 Acclamation—Pearl Sea (IRE) (Elusive City (USA)) (57000)
24 B c 01/05 Kodiac—Sabaweeya (Street Cry (IRE)) (80000)
25 B c 16/04 Iffraaj—Say No Now (IRE) (Refuse To Bend (IRE)) (10000)

Owners: Mr A. Al Mansoori, S. Ali, Saif Ali & Saeed H. Altayer, Mr I. Black, Ms M. Delaney, Mr T. Denham, Mr J. Henry, Middleham Park Racing LXXIV, Middleham Park Racing LXXVII, Middleham Park Racing XCII, Middleham Park Xcii, M Delaney & I Black, Middleham Park and Ventura Racing 6, Middleham Park, Ventura, Delaney & Black, Niarchos Family, T. S. Palin, M. Prince, The 21st Century Farms Ltd.

327	**MISS EMMA LAVELLE, Marlborough** Postal: **Bonita Racing Stables, Ogbourne Maizey, Marlborough, Wiltshire, SN8 1RY** Contacts: **PHONE 01672 511544 MOBILE 07774 993998 FAX 01672 511544** **EMAIL info@emmalavelle.com WEBSITE www.emmalavelle.com**

1 **AURELIA OR (IRE),** 5, b m Shantou (USA)—Aibrean (IRE) **Dr A. R. Sharkey**
2 **BELLE EMPRESS,** 9, b m Black Sam Bellamy (IRE)—Empress of Light **Mighty Acorn Stables**
3 5, Ch h Vinnie Roe (IRE)—Bewildered (IRE) **The Bonhamie Partnership**

MISS EMMA LAVELLE - continued

4 **BLUSHING RED (FR)**, 6, ch g Le Havre (IRE)—Boliche **Richard Lavelle & John Crook**
5 **BOLD REASON (GER)**, 5, b g Invincible Spirit (IRE)—Bufera (IRE) **Mrs C. J. Djivanovic**
6 **BONNIE LASS**, 5, b m Great Pretender (IRE)—Princess Cara **Ms S. Flook**
7 **BOOMARANG**, 6, b g Passing Glance—Materiality **Bonita Racing Club**
8 **BOREHAM BILL (IRE)**, 8, b g Tikkanen (USA)—Crimond (IRE) **Mrs S. P. Foran**
9 **BUSTER THOMAS (IRE)**, 9, b g Westerner—Awesome Miracle (IRE) **Axom LXVII**
10 **CELTIC JOY (IRE)**, 7, b g Kayf Tara—No Time For Tears (IRE) **Hawksmoor Partnership**
11 **CLOSING CEREMONY (IRE)**, 11, b g Flemensfirth (USA)—Supreme Von Pres (IRE) **The High Altitude Partnership**
12 **DAGUENEAU (IRE)**, 5, b g Champs Elysees—Bright Enough **Mr A. Gemmell**
13 **DE RASHER COUNTER**, 8, b g Yeats (IRE)—Dedrunkmunky (IRE) **Makin' Bacon Partnership**
14 **DO YOU THINK**, 4, b f So You Think (NZ)—Leblon (IRE) **Bonita Racing Club**
15 **DOC PENFRO**, 8, b g Dr Massini (IRE)—Prescelli (IRE) **Doc Redemption**
16 **DOLLNAMIX (FR)**, 9, b g Al Namix (FR)—Sleeping Doll (FR) **GDM Partnership**
17 4, B g Milan—Down By The Sea (IRE) **GDM Partnership**
18 **DOWN THE HIGHWAY (IRE)**, 7, b g Duke of Marmalade (IRE)—Petit Moselle (IRE) **Thurloe 56**
19 **EASTERLY**, 4, b f Shirocco (GER)—Easter Dancer **Easter Racing Club**
20 **ECLAIR SURF (FR)**, 6, b g Califet (FR)—Matasurf (FR) **Tim Syder & Dominic Burke**
21 **ENNISCOFFEY OSCAR (IRE)**, 8, b g Oscar (IRE)—Enniscoffey (IRE) **The Pick 'N' Mix Partnership**
22 **FEDELTA (IRE)**, 6, b g Flemensfirth (USA)—Old Moon (IRE) **Mr T. J. Hemmings**
23 **FLEMCARA (IRE)**, 8, b g Flemensfirth (USA)—Cara Mara (IRE) **Andy & The Frisky Fillies**
24 **FLEMINGS (IRE)**, 6, b g Flemensfirth (USA)—How Is Things (IRE) **T. Syder & N. Mustoe**
25 **FLYING NUN (IRE)**, 5, b m Robin des Champs (FR)—Razzle (USA) **N. Mustoe & A. Gemmell**
26 4, B f Shirocco (GER)—Folie Dancer **J. R. Lavelle & Dr Mark Scott**
27 **FORTUNATE GEORGE (IRE)**, 10, b g Oscar (IRE)—Fine Fortune (IRE) **The George Inn Racing Syndicate**
28 **GOLD LINK (FR)**, 4, b g Rail Link—Une de Montot (FR) **Owners Group 057**
29 **GUNFLEET (IRE)**, 8, b g Oscar (IRE)—Lady Lincon (IRE) **Mrs P. J. Travis**
30 **HANG IN THERE (IRE)**, 6, b g Yeats (IRE)—Jaldemosa (FR) **Tim Syder & Andrew Gemmell**
31 **HAWK'S WELL (IRE)**, 6, b g Yeats (IRE)—Our Song **Mrs N. Turner & Mrs E. Fenton**
32 **HEAD FOR THE HILLS**, 5, b g Kayf Tara—Kate Hill Dancer (IRE) **Greenlands Racing Syndicate**
33 **HIGHLY PRIZED**, 7, b br g Manduro (GER)—Razzle (USA) **H.Pridham & D.Donoghue**
34 **HOI POLLOI (IRE)**, 5, b g Shantou (USA)—Backtothekingsnest (IRE) **N. Mustoe**
35 **IRISH PROPHECY (IRE)**, 7, b g Azamour (IRE)—Prophets Honor (FR) **N. Mustoe**
36 **JEMIMA P (IRE)**, 6, b m Jeremy (USA)—Peig Alainn (IRE) **The Three A's Syndicate**
37 **JOYRIDER (IRE)**, 8, b g Stowaway—Aileen Supreme (IRE) **N. Mustoe**
38 **JUBILYMPICS**, 8, b m Kapgarde (FR)—Pepite de Soleil (FR) **Caloona Racing**
39 **KILLER CLOWN (IRE)**, 6, b g Getaway (GER)—Our Soiree (IRE) **Mr T. D. J. Syder**
40 4, Ch g Presenting—Kon Tiky (FR) **Mr Will & Mrs Sarah Davies**
41 4, Br gr g Yeats (IRE)—Lady Sagamix (FR) **Kevin Lloyd & Nicky Turner**
42 **LET RIP (IRE)**, 6, b g Rip Van Winkle (IRE)—Al Ihsas (IRE) **P. G. Jacobs**
43 **LOCH ARTHUR**, 5, b g Arvico (FR)—China Rose
44 **MANOFTHEMOUNTAIN (IRE)**, 7, b g Mahler—Womanofthemountain (IRE) **P. G. Jacobs**
45 **MASTER MILLINER (IRE)**, 4, ch g Helmet (AUS)—Aqualina (IRE) **Mrs Jennifer Simpson Racing**
46 **MISTY BLOOM (IRE)**, 7, b m Yeats (IRE)—Misty Mountain (IRE) **Bonita Racing Club**
47 **NAMIB DANCER (IRE)**, 6, b g Westerner—Derriana (IRE) **Mr & Mrs W & Dr T Davies & Mrs T Grundy**
48 **OLD RASCALS (IRE)**, 7, b g Ask—Balleen Rose (IRE) **The Optimists**
49 **PAISLEY PARK (IRE)**, 8, b g Oscar (IRE)—Presenting Shares (IRE) **Mr A. Gemmell**
50 **PEMBERLEY (IRE)**, 7, b g Darsi (FR)—Eyebright (IRE) **Laurie Kimber & Partners**
51 **POTTERS VISION (IRE)**, 7, b m Getaway (GER)—Peripheral Vision (IRE) **James and Jean Potter Ltd**
52 **PRIVATE MALONE (IRE)**, 11, b g Darsi (FR)—Native Artist (IRE) **P.B. Mitford-slade & Miss Joanna Stevens**
53 **PROPHETS PRAYER (IRE)**, 6, b m Azamour (IRE)—Prophets Honor (FR) **N. Mustoe**
54 **RED ROOKIE**, 5, ch g Black Sam Bellamy (IRE)—Auction Belle **The Hawk Inn Syndicate 3**
55 **RUNSWICK BAY**, 5, b g Arvico (FR)—Chantal **The Hon J. R. Drummond**
56 **SAM BARTON**, 5, b g Black Sam Bellamy (IRE)—Bartons Bride (IRE) **Mr T. J. Hemmings**
57 **SHANG TANG (IRE)**, 6, b g Shantou (USA)—Ballyguider Bridge (IRE) **T. Syder & N. Mustoe**
58 **SHIROCCAN ROLL**, 6, b g Shirocco (GER)—Folie Dancer **J. R. Lavelle & Dr Mark Scott**
59 **SILENT ASSISTANT (IRE)**, 8, b g Sans Frontieres (IRE)—Monanig Lass (IRE) **Lavelle, Awdry & Williams**
60 **SMARTER**, 4, gr ro g Dark Angel (IRE)—Coquette Rouge (IRE) **H.Pridham & D.Donoghue**
61 **TARA NIECE**, 7, b m Kayf Tara—Pepite de Soleil (FR) **Caloona Racing**
62 **THE DOMINO EFFECT (IRE)**, 6, b g Oscar (IRE)—Lively Lass (IRE) **Mighty Acorn Stables**

63 **THE SWEENEY (IRE)**, 8, b g Oscar (IRE)—Banningham Blaze **N. Mustoe**
64 **THOOR CASTLE (IRE)**, 7, b m Yeats (IRE)—Valleya (FR) **Mr T. J. Hemmings**
65 **THUNDERSTRUCK (IRE)**, 6, b g Fame And Glory—Go Sandy Go (IRE) **Mr T. D. J. Syder**
66 **TIERRA VERDE**, 9, b m Josr Algarhoud (IRE)—La Corujera **Greenlands Racing Syndicate**
67 4, B g Califet (FR)—Touched By Angels (IRE) **N. Mustoe**
68 **VENDREDI TROIS (FR)**, 11, b g Shaanmer (IRE)—Legende Sacree (FR) **Awdry, Gemmell, Pomford & Williams**
69 **VIVA VITTORIA (IRE)**, 6, b m Stowaway—La Fisarmonica (IRE) **Mr & Mrs A Millett**
70 **VIXEN (IRE)**, 6, b m Kodiac—Radio Wave **Mrs Jennifer Simpson Racing**
71 **WATER WAGTAIL**, 13, b g Kahyasi—Kentford Grebe **D. I. Bare**
72 **ZARAFSHAN (IRE)**, 4, b c Shamardal (USA)—Zarshana (IRE) **Mr R. J. Lavelle**

THREE-YEAR-OLDS

73 **GREY FOX (IRE)**, gr c Gutaifan (IRE)—Boucheron **Mrs Jennifer Simpson Racing**

TWO-YEAR-OLDS

74 B c 18/02 Tagula (IRE)—April Green (FR) (Green Tune (USA)) **Caloona Racing**

Other Owners: Mr C. V. Awdry, Mr D. M. Bradshaw, Mr D. J. Burke, Mr D. Charlesworth, G. Charlesworth, Mr D. L. Coles, Mr J. R. Crook, Mrs S. C. Davies, Dr T. J. W. Davies, Mr W. P. L. Davies, Mr D. Donoghue, Mr J. B. Duffy, Mr S. W. Dunn, Mr A. Gemmell, Mrs T. A. Grundy, Mr R. S. Keck, Mr L. G. Kimber, Mr M. Kirkby, Miss I. G. Langton, Miss E. C. Lavelle, Mr J. R. Lavelle, Mr R. J. Lavelle, Mr K. A. Lloyd, Mr G. P MacIntosh, Mrs S. Metcalfe, Mr A. J. Millett, Mrs A. M. Millett, Mr J. H. Mills, P. B. Mitford-Slade, Mrs M. A. Moore, N. Mustoe, Mr P. Nicholls, Mr B. G. Pomford, Ms H. A. Pridham, Mr M. G. Roberts, K. P. Ryan, Dr M. J. Scott, Mrs J. I. Simpson, Mr W. H. Simpson, Mr J. Smee, Mr M. Smith, Miss J. Stevens, Mr T. D. J. Syder, Mrs N. C. Turner, Mrs V. A. Villers, Mr A. G. Weston, Exors of the Late Mr P. R. Weston, Mrs P. H. Williams.

Assistant Trainer: Barry Fenton.

---

328 **MR TOBY LAWES, Beare Green**
Postal: **Henfold House Cottage, Henfold Lane, Beare Green, Dorking, Surrey, RH5 4RW**
EMAIL **toby@tobylawesracing.com**

1 **ALKOPOP (GER)**, 6, gr g Jukebox Jury (IRE)—Alkeste (GER) **A. T. A. Wates**
2 **CHINA FLOWER (IRE)**, 5, b m Shantou (USA)—Erins Stage (IRE) **A. T. A. Wates**
3 **EYE OF AN EAGLE (FR)**, 7, b g Linda's Lad—Vie des Aigles (FR) **A. T. A. Wates**
4 **EYES UP (FR)**, 6, ch g Muhtathir—High Destiny (FR) **A. T. A. Wates**
5 **FEODORA**, 5, b m Kayf Tara—La Harde (FR) **Hot To Trot Jumping**
6 **GO FORRIT (IRE)**, 6, b g Jeremy (USA)—Ben Roseler (IRE) **A. T. A. Wates**
7 **KANNAPOLIS (IRE)**, 5, b g Makfi—Alta Definizione (IRE) **Henfold Harriers**
8 **KAP AUTEUIL (FR)**, 5, b g Kapgarde (FR)—Turboka (FR) **A. T. A. Wates**
9 **NASHVILLE NIPPER (IRE)**, 6, b g Millenary—Benfrasea (IRE) **The Beare With Us Partnership**
10 **OLD TIMES (IRE)**, 5, b m Doyen—La Belle Bleu (IRE)
11 **POTTLEREAGHEXPRESS (IRE)**, 7, b m Beneficial—Needle Doll (IRE) **The Beare With Us Partnership**
12 **QUEENS PRESENT (IRE)**, 9, ch m Presenting—Fairy Dawn (IRE) **A. T. A. Wates**
13 **SOLDIER TO FOLLOW**, 5, b g Soldier Hollow—Nota Bene (GER) **Mr A T A Wates & Mrs S Wates**
14 **TOP OF THE MORNING (IRE)**, 8, b g Kalanisi (IRE)—Lady of The Mill (IRE) **A. T. A. Wates**
15 **ZACONY REBEL (IRE)**, 5, b g Getaway (GER)—Bay Rebel (IRE) **Mr A T A Wates & Mrs S Wates**

Other Owners: A. T. A. Wates, Mrs S. M. Wates.

---

329 **MR BARRY LEAVY, Stoke-on-Trent**
Postal: **Cash Heath Farm, Cash Heath, Forsbrook, Stoke on Trent, ST11 9DE**
Contacts: PHONE **01782 398591** MOBILE **07540 806915**
EMAIL **lauraleavy@hotmail.co.uk** WEBSITE **www.leavyracing.co.uk**

1 **CARVELLE'S CUTTER**, 6, b m Kayf Tara—Debbie
2 **COME ON CHARLIE (FR)**, 8, b g Anzillero (GER)—End of Spring (FR) **May The Horse Be With You**
3 **GENERATOR CITY (IRE)**, 7, b g Primary (USA)—Sabbatical (IRE) **Mrs Amy Phillimore**
4 **GEORGIAN FIREBIRD**, 10, b m Firebreak—Skovshoved (IRE) **Mrs E. A. Wilson**

MR BARRY LEAVY - continued

    5 **HE'S A GOER (IRE)**, 6, b g Yeats (IRE)—Tessas Girl (IRE) **Here We Go Racing**
    6 **INFINITI (IRE)**, 7, b m Arcano (IRE)—Seraphina (IRE) **Mrs Susan Ashford and Partner**
    7 **JAXLIGHT**, 8, b m Lucarno (USA)—Jaxelle (FR)

THREE-YEAR-OLDS
    8 **THE SPOKEN PHRASE**, b c Poet's Voice—Dominike (ITY)

Other Owners: Mrs Debbie Hart, Mr B. Leavy, Mrs S. D. Williams-Ashford.

Assistant Trainer: Mrs L Leavy.

330
MISS KERRY LEE, Presteigne
Postal: **Bell House, Byton, Presteigne, Powys, LD8 2HS**
Contacts: **PHONE 01544 267672 MOBILE 07968 242663**
EMAIL kerry@kerrylee.co.uk WEBSITE www.kerrylee.co.uk

    1 **BRIGADIER BOB (IRE)**, 7, b g Excellent Art—Plausabelle **A & B Beard, C Davies S Harris M Hawkins**
    2 **DEMACHINE (IRE)**, 6, b g Flemensfirth (USA)—Dancingonthemoon (IRE) **West Coast Haulage Limited**
    3 **DESTINED TO SHINE (IRE)**, 8, b g Dubai Destination (USA)—Good Shine (IRE) **Campbell-mizen**
    4 **DO IT FOR THY SEN (IRE)**, 6, ch g Mountain High (IRE)—Ashlings Princess (IRE) **Campbell-Mizen & R L Baker**
    5 **EATON COLLINA (IRE)**, 5, b g Milan—Flowers On Sunday (IRE) **Mrs H. Watson**
    6 **EATON HILL (IRE)**, 8, b g Yeats (IRE)—Guilt Less (FR) **Mrs H. Watson**
    7 **FAY CE QUE VOUDRAS (IRE)**, 4, b f Getaway (GER)—Buck's Blue (FR) **W. Roseff**
    8 **FINANCIER**, 7, ch g Dubawi (IRE)—Desired **W. Roseff**
    9 **FIRSTCOAT (FR)**, 5, b g Lauro (GER)—Pepita d'Armor (FR) **Glass Half Full**
    10 **GOODTOKNOW**, 12, b g Presenting—Atlantic Jane **Macechern & Nolan**
    11 **HAPPY DIVA (IRE)**, 9, b m King's Theatre (IRE)—Megans Joy (IRE) **W. Roseff**
    12 **HENRI LE BON (IRE)**, 5, b g Sea The Stars (IRE)—Speed Song **W. Roseff**
    13 **ICE COOL CHAMPS (IRE)**, 9, ch g Robin des Champs (FR)—Last of Many (IRE) **West Coast Haulage Limited**
    14 **KINGS MONARCH**, 7, b g Schiaparelli (GER)—Monarch's View **Miss K. Lee**
    15 **KRIS SPIN (IRE)**, 12, br g Kris Kin (USA)—Auditing Empress (IRE) **Six To Five Against**
    16 **LET'S GETAWAY (IRE)**, 5, b g Getaway (GER)—Roxtown **James & Jean Potter**
    17 **MAGIC DANCER**, 8, b g Norse Dancer (IRE)—King's Siren (IRE) **The Magic Partnership**
    18 **NOT SURE (IRE)**, 4, br g Presenting—Pink Mist (IRE) **W. Roseff**
    19 **STORM CONTROL (IRE)**, 7, b g September Storm (GER)—Double Dream (IRE) **W. Roseff**
    20 **THE WELSH PADDIES (IRE)**, 8, b g Court Cave (IRE)—Masiana (IRE) **West Coast Haulage Limited**
    21 **TOP GAMBLE (IRE)**, 12, ch g Presenting—Zeferina (IRE) **Miss K. Lee**
    22 **TOWN PARKS (IRE)**, 9, b g Morozov (USA)—Outdoor Heather (IRE) **Mrs J. A. Beavan**
    23 **WEST COAST GLORY (IRE)**, 6, b m Fame And Glory—Turntofacethesun **West Coast Haulage Limited**

Other Owners: Mr R. L. Baker, A. C. Beard, B. M. Beard, Mr D. E. Campbell, Campbell-mizen, Mrs C. D. E. Davies, Mr G. T. Gilbert, Mr S. Harris, R. L. C. Hartley, Mr M. R. Hawkins, R. A. Lee, Gavin MacEchern, Mr P. J. Mizen, Mr P. Nolan, Mr P. T. G. Phillips, Lady H. S. Ripley, W. Roseff.

Assistant Trainer: Richard Lee.

NH Jockey: Richard Johnson, Jamie Moore. **Conditional Jockey:** Richard Patrick.

331
MRS SOPHIE LEECH, Westbury-on-Severn
Postal: **T/A Leech Racing Limited, Tudor Racing Stables, Elton Road, Elton, Newnham, Gloucester-shire, GL14 1JN**
Contacts: **PHONE 01452 760691 MOBILE 07775 874630**
EMAIL info@leechracing.co.uk WEBSITE www.leechracing.co.uk

    1 **ANTEROS (IRE)**, 12, b g Milan—Sovereign Star (IRE) **K. W. Bell**
    2 **APPLESANDPIERRES (IRE)**, 12, b g Pierre—Cluain Chaoin (IRE) **C. J. Leech**
    3 **BIRCH HILL (IRE)**, 10, b g Kalanisi (IRE)—Miss Compliance (IRE) **G. D. Thompson**

MRS SOPHIE LEECH - continued

 4 **BUONAROTTI BOY (IRE)**, 8, b g Galileo (IRE)—Funsie (FR) **Mr R. S. Liddington**
 5 **CHESTNUT PETE**, 5, ch g Native Ruler—Rabbit **Mike Harris Racing Club**
 6 **CLONDAW CIAN (IRE)**, 10, br g Gold Well—Cocktail Bar (IRE) **G. D. Thompson**
 7 **DAWN TREADER (IRE)**, 4, b g Siyouni (FR)—Miss Elena **Mr C. R. Leech**
 8 **DOTHRAKI RAIDER**, 9, b g Kayf Tara—French Spice **Mr M. J. Gorman**
 9 **FINNISTON FARM**, 5, b g Helmet (AUS)—Logic **Godel Technologies Europe Limited**
10 **GARO DE JUILLEY (FR)**, 8, b g Ungaro (GER)—Lucy de Juilley (FR) **G. D. Thompson**
11 **GENERAL BUX**, 9, b g Lucarno (USA)—Cadoutene (FR) **The Scoobyless Partnership**
12 **GRAPEVINE (IRE)**, 7, b g Lilbourne Lad (IRE)—High Vintage (IRE) **Mr J. T. Finch**
13 **GUSTAVE AITCH (FR)**, 4, b g Maxios—Alyssandre (IRE) **Finch Moran Stone Smith Hooton Pearson-S**
14 **HAZAMAR (IRE)**, 7, gr g Manduro (GER)—Hazarafa (IRE) **Mike Harris Racing Club & Partner**
15 **LIEUTENANT COLONEL**, 11, b g Kayf Tara—Agnese **G. D. Thompson**
16 **LIL LAZARUS (FR)**, 7, ch g Anabaa Blue—Santoria (FR) **C. J. Leech**
17 **LYSANDER BELLE (IRE)**, 4, b f Exceed And Excel (AUS)—Switcher (IRE) **Mike Harris Racing Club**
18 **MAN OF PLENTY**, 11, ch g Manduro (GER)—Credit-A-Plenty **G. D. Thompson**
19 **MEAGHER'S FLAG (IRE)**, 5, b g Teofilo (IRE)—Gearanai (IRE) **Finch Moran Lamb Smith Boyd-Bowman**
20 **MILROW (IRE)**, 7, b g Tamayuz—Cannikin (IRE) **John Cocks & Roger Liddington**
21 **MUJASSAM**, 8, ch g Kyllachy—Naizak (IRE) **Mr J. T. Finch**
22 **OLD HARRY ROCKS (IRE)**, 8, b g Milan—Miss Baden (IRE) **G. D. Thompson**
23 **SAXO JACK (FR)**, 10, b g King's Best (USA)—Gamma (FR) **Mike Harris Racing Club & Partner**
24 **SINFONIETTA (FR)**, 8, b g Sinndar (IRE)—Final Whistle (IRE) **Cheltenham Racing Club**
25 **SLEEP EASY**, 8, b g Rip Van Winkle (IRE)—Strictly Lambada **Mr J. T. Finch**
26 **STEPHANIE SUNSHINE (IRE)**, 7, b m Dubai Destination (USA)—Shyanne (IRE) **Mike Harris Racing Club**
27 **TAMARILLO GROVE (IRE)**, 13, b g Cape Cross (IRE)—Tamarillo **Cheltenham Racing Club**
28 **UTILITY (GER)**, 9, b g Yeats (IRE)—Ungarin (GER) **Mr J. T. Finch**
29 **VANITEUX (FR)**, 11, br g Voix du Nord (FR)—Expoville (FR) **Mr C. R. Leech**
30 **WE'VE GOT PAYET**, 6, b g Authorized (IRE)—Missoula (FR) **Mr Steve Ashley & Mr Gary Pettit**
31 **WEST WIZARD (FR)**, 11, b br g King's Theatre (IRE)—Queen's Diamond (GER) **J. O'Brien**
32 **YASIR (USA)**, 12, b g Dynaformer (USA)—Khazayin (USA) **Mike Harris Racing Club**
33 **ZERO TO HERO (IRE)**, 5, ch m Arakan (USA)—Blue Daze **Mr J. T. Finch**

Other Owners: Mr S. A. Ashley, Mr J. J. Cocks, A. D. I. Harris, Mr M. E. Harris, C. J. Leech, Mr R. S. Liddington, Mr G. Pettit.

Assistant Trainer: Christian Leech.

---

332 **MISS TRACEY LEESON, Towcester**
Postal: **Glebe Stables, Blakesley Heath Farm, Maidford, Northants, NN12 8HN**
Contacts: **MOBILE 07761 537672**
EMAIL traceyl31@hotmail.co.uk WEBSITE www.traceyleesonracing.co.uk

1 **LOUPGAROU (FR)**, 8, gr g Martaline—Jasminette Doree (FR) **Miss Tracey Leeson**
2 **MOLPEG (IRE)**, 7, b g Winged Love (IRE)—Do As Your Bid (IRE) **The Blakesley Racing Club**
3 **MOROVAL (IRE)**, 9, b g Morozov (USA)—Valerie Ellen (IRE) **The Blakesley Racing Club**
4 **RINGMOYLAN (IRE)**, 8, b g Mahler—La Speziana (IRE) **Buzzing Again Partnership**

---

333 **MRS SHEILA LEWIS, Brecon**
Postal: **Mill Service Station, Three Cocks, Brecon, Powys, LD3 0SL**
Contacts: **PHONE 01497 847081**
EMAIL sheilalewisracing1@gmail.com

1 **COTTON END (IRE)**, 6, gr m Scorpion (IRE)—Scartara (FR) **Mr G. Wilson**
2 **KNIGHT COMMANDER**, 7, br g Sir Percy—Jardin **W. B. R. Davies**
3 **STRAW FAN JACK**, 5, gr g Geordieland (FR)—Callerlilly **Mr G. Wilson**
4 **STUPID CUPID (IRE)**, 9, b m Beneficial—Supreme Arrow (IRE) **W. B. R. Davies**
5 **VOLCANO (FR)**, 6, gr g Martaline—Lyli Rose (FR) **W. B. R. Davies**
6 **WAY OF THE WORLD (IRE)**, 9, b g Flemensfirth (USA)—Night Heron (IRE) **W. B. R. Davies**

334 **MR NICK LITTMODEN, Newmarket**
Postal: **Inner Yard, Brickfield Stud, Cemetery Hill, Newmarket, Suffolk, CB8 7JH**
Contacts: **MOBILE 07770 964865**
EMAIL **nicklittmoden@icloud.com**

1 **BERRY POPPINS**, 6, b m Mawatheeq (USA)—Florie **Strawberry Fields Stud**
2 **BROUAINS (FR)**, 4, ch g Anodin (IRE)—Enzina **Mr G. F. Chesneaux & Mr Nick Littmoden**
3 **BY RAIL**, 6, br g Rail Link—Soldata (USA) **Mr G. F. Chesneaux & Mr Nick Littmoden**
4 **CAPLA CRUSADER**, 4, b g Archipenko (USA)—Desert Berry **Strawberry Fields Stud**
5 **CAPTAIN SPEAKING (FR)**, 5, ch g Linda's Lad—Hillflower (FR) **We Live In Norfolk Partnership**
6 **FIGEAC (FR)**, 6, gr g Kendargent (FR)—Faviva (USA) **Mr G. F. Chesneaux & Mr Nick Littmoden**
7 **FLEUR IRLANDAISE (FR)**, 5, b m No Risk At All (FR)—Orlandaise (FR) **G. Chesneaux N. Littmoden**
8 **GLUTNFORPUNISHMENT**, 4, b g Dawn Approach (IRE)—Oxsana **A. A. Goodman**
9 **GREY D'ARS (FR)**, 4, gr g Rajsaman (FR)—Prisenflag (FR) **R.Favarulo,G.Chesneaux,N.Littmoden**
10 **IMPERIL (FR)**, 4, b g No Risk At All (FR)—Irevoltar Has (FR) **Gerry Chesneaux ,Emma Littmoden**
11 **NOVERRE DANCER (IRE)**, 4, ch g Le Havre (IRE)—Irish Cliff (IRE) **Mr G. F. Chesneaux & Mr Nick Littmoden**
12 **ORIGINAL CHOICE (IRE)**, 6, ch g Dragon Pulse (IRE)—Belle Watling (IRE) **A. A. Goodman**
13 **STEELCRAFT**, 4, gr g Mastercraftsman (IRE)—Crystal Swan (IRE) **Steelcraft Partnership**

THREE-YEAR-OLDS

14 **ARABESCATO**, b gr g Outstrip—Cat Hunter **D. Cohen**
15 Ch g Helmet (AUS)—Betty Brook (IRE)
16 **SACHAMAK (FR)**, b c Makfi—Sachet (USA) **The Fearsome Five**
17 B g Tobougg (IRE)—Sarah Berry **Strawberry Fields Stud**

Other Owners: G. F. Chesneaux, Mr R. Favarulo, S. Hassiakos, Mr Andrew Highfield, Mrs E. Littmoden, N. P. Littmoden, Mrs H. R. Pearce, Mr S. J. A. Turner, Ms A. V. Wilson-Martin.

NH Jockey: Jack Quinlan. **Amateur Jockey:** Mr Martin Dunne.

335 **MR BERNARD LLEWELLYN, Bargoed**
Postal: **Ffynonau Duon Farm, Pentwyn, Fochriw, Bargoed, Mid Glamorgan, CF81 9NP**
Contacts: **PHONE 01685 841259 MOBILE 07960 151083, 07971 233473 FAX 01685 843838**
EMAIL **bernard.llewellyn@btopenworld.com**

1 **ARTY CAMPBELL (IRE)**, 10, b g Dylan Thomas (IRE)—Kincob (USA) **Mr Alex James & Mr B. J. Llewellyn**
2 **ASCOT DAY (FR)**, 6, ch g Soave (GER)—Allez Hongkong (GER) **Mr Michael Edwards & Partner**
3 **CAPTAIN AULMES (FR)**, 8, gr g Al Namix (FR)—Opaline des Aulmes (FR) **Smerdon Tree Services Ltd**
4 **EARTHLY (USA)**, 6, b g Spring At Last (USA)—Geographic (USA) **B. J. Llewellyn**
5 **FLANAGANS FIELD (IRE)**, 12, b g Araafa (IRE)—Zvezda (USA) **B. J. Llewellyn**
6 **GLOBAL THRILL**, 11, b g Big Shuffle (USA)—Goonda **Mr Alex James & Mr B. J. Llewellyn**
7 **GUARDIOLA (USA)**, 5, b g Lonhro (AUS)—Badalona **Mr Gethyn Mills & Mr B. J. Llewellyn**
8 **JESSE'S LADY**, 5, b m Malinas (GER)—Lets Run **Smerdon Tree Services Ltd**
9 **KAISAN**, 7, b g Rip Van Winkle (IRE)—Orinoco (IRE) **Smerdon Tree Services Ltd**
10 **MARENGO**, 9, gr g Verglas (IRE)—Cloudchaser (IRE) **Mrs Beth Williams**
11 **NABHAN (IRE)**, 8, b g Youmzain (IRE)—Danidh Dubai (IRE) **Mr Gethyn Mills & Mr B. J. Llewellyn**
12 **NEVER EQUALLED (IRE)**, 11, br g Brian Boru (IRE)—Broken Thought (IRE) **Miss I. G. Tompsett**
13 **NORAB (GER)**, 9, b g Galileo (IRE)—Night Woman (GER) **B. J. Llewellyn**
14 **PATRICIADPLASTERER (IRE)**, 6, b m Presenting—Coumhall (IRE) **PC Bloodstock**
15 **SHADOW'S GIRL**, 8, gr m Fair Mix (IRE)—Special Beat **G. Mills**
16 **TOMBSTONE (IRE)**, 10, ch g Robin des Champs (FR)—Connaught Hall (IRE) **PC Bloodstock**
17 **TRIPLE NICKLE (IRE)**, 4, b f So You Think (NZ)—Secret Shine (IRE) **Mr Alex James & Mr B. J. Llewellyn**
18 **VOLTAIC**, 4, ch g Power—Seramindar **B. J. Llewellyn**
19 **WARRIOR DISPLAY (IRE)**, 4, b g Dandy Man (IRE)—Clare Glen (IRE) **PC Bloodstock**

Other Owners: Mr M. V. Edwards, Mr A. James, B. J. Llewellyn, Mrs E. A. Llewellyn, G. Mills.

Assistant Trainer: J L Llewellyn.

Flat Jockey: Daniel Muscutt, David Probert. **Conditional Jockey:** Jordan Williams, Robert Williams.
Amateur Jockey: Miss Jessica Llewellyn.

336 MISS NATALIE LLOYD-BEAVIS, East Garston
Postal: **Parsonage Farm Stables, Newbury Road, East Garston, Hungerford, Berkshire, RG17 7ER**
Contacts: PHONE **01488 648347** MOBILE **07768 117656**
EMAIL nlbracing@gmail.com

1 DEFTERA LAD (IRE), 8, b g Fast Company (IRE)—Speedbird (USA) **Mr Y. Mustafa**
2 DOCTOR PARKES, 14, b g Diktat—Lucky Parkes **Parsonage Racing Partnership**
3 GENTLEMAN MOORE (IRE), 10, b g Royal Anthem (USA)—Near Dunleer (IRE) **Parsonage Racing Partnership**
4 MEGABUCKS (IRE), 9, b g Well Chosen—Clonmayo (IRE) **Parsonage Racing Partnership**
5 MY AMAZING ONE (IRE), 6, b g Casamento (IRE)—Lafite
6 NELL 'N' FLO (IRE), 4, b f Leading Light (IRE)—Bella's Bury **Miss N. A. Lloyd-Beavis**

NH Jockey: David Bass. **Apprentice Jockey:** Charlie Bennett.

337 MR JOHN E. LONG, Brighton
Postal: **Southdown Stables, Bear Road, Brighton, East Sussex, BN2 6AB**
Contacts: MOBILE **07815 186085, 07958 296945**
EMAIL winalot@aol.com

1 BIGDEAL (FR), 7, gr g Montmartre (FR)—Rauxa **S. E. Colville**
2 CATIVO RAGAZZO, 5, b g Multiplex—Sea Isle **M. J. Gibbs**
3 CHORAL MUSIC, 5, b m Equiano (FR)—Gospel Music **Mrs A. M. Sturges**
4 KINGMON'S BOY, 5, b g Denounce—Ela d'Argent (IRE) **Mr John King**
5 KNOCKOUT BLOW, 5, b g Lethal Force (IRE)—Elidore **S. E. Colville**
6 LIBBRETTA, 5, ch m Libranno—Dispol Katie **Mrs A. M. Sturges**
7 MAGICINTHEMAKING (USA), 6, br m Wildcat Heir (USA)—Love in Bloom (USA) **M. J. Gibbs, R. D. John**

THREE-YEAR-OLDS
8 Ch g Mazameer—Bermacha **M. J. Gibbs**

Other Owners: S. E. Colville, Miss M. B. Fernandes, Miss J. L. Pearson, Mr R. J. Pearson.

Assistant Trainer: Miss S Cassidy.

Flat Jockey: Hollie Doyle, Robert Havlin. **NH Jockey:** Mattie Batchelor. **Apprentice Jockey:** Ellie MacKenzie.

338 MR CHARLIE LONGSDON, Chipping Norton
Postal: **Hull Farm Stables, Stratford Road, Chipping Norton, Oxfordshire, OX7 5QF**
Contacts: WORK **01608 645556** MOBILE **07775 993263**
EMAIL info@charlielongsdonracing.com WEBSITE www.charlielongsdonracing.com

1 ALMAZHAR GARDE (FR), 5, ch g Kapgarde (FR)—Loin de Moi (FR) **Kate & Andrew Brooks**
2 BALLYDINE (IRE), 10, ch g Stowaway—Bealaha Essie (IRE) **Mr D. A. Halsall**
3 BEYOND THE CLOUDS, 7, ch g Peintre Celebre (USA)—Evening **Mr R. J. Aplin**
4 CARDIGAN BAY (FR), 7, b m Turtle Bowl (IRE)—Nan's Catch (FR) **Birch, Djivanovic & Doel**
5 CARLOW FARMER (IRE), 7, b g Stowaway—Supreme Fivestar (IRE) **Cracker Syndicate**
6 CASTLE ROBIN (IRE), 5, ch g Robin des Champs (FR)—Coco Opera (IRE) **Bradley Partnership**
7 CHAMPAGNE NOIR (IRE), 6, br g Stowaway—Prayuwin Drummer (IRE) **Mr T. J. Hemmings**
8 CHECKITOUT (IRE), 6, b g Salutino (GER)—Akasha (IRE) **Mills & Mason Partnership**
9 CONJURING TRICK, 5, b m Great Pretender (IRE)—Magic Score **Her Majesty The Queen**
10 DANDRIDGE, 11, ch g Doyen (IRE)—Arantxa **Mrs J. A. Wakefield**
11 DARIYA (USA), 5, b m Include (USA)—Dubai (IRE)
12 DIGER DAUDAIE (FR), 7, b g Tiger Groom—Stone Again (FR) **Mr & Mrs R. Perkins**
13 DO WANNA KNOW (IRE), 6, b g Frammassone (IRE)—Mille Et Une Nuits (FR) **Girls Allowed**
14 ECLAIR ON LINE (FR), 6, gr g Dream Well (FR)—Odeline (FR) **Eclair On Line Syndicate**
15 FANFARONADE (USA), 4, gr f Exchange Rate (USA)—Fanzine (USA) **Slater Stockwood Nicholson Partnership**
16 FORTH BRIDGE, 7, b g Bernardini (USA)—Sally Forth **Her Majesty The Queen**

MR CHARLIE LONGSDON - continued

17 FREETHINKER (IRE), 4, b g Libertarian—Supreme Magical **The Free Thinkers**
18 GLENCASSLEY (IRE), 5, b g Yeats (IRE)—Reseda (GER) **Mr G. Leon**
19 GLIMPSE OF GALA, 4, b f Passing Glance—Apple Days **The Tweed Clad Fossils**
20 HIGHWAY GIRL, 7, b m Kayf Tara—Whichway Girl **Mrs D. P. G. Flory**
21 HOOT AT MIDNIGHT, 5, b m Midnight Legend—Kahooting **Mr Neil Maltby, Mrs J Maltby**
22 ILLEGAL MODEL (IRE), 6, b g Stowaway—She's So Beautiful (IRE) **The Charlie Longsdon Racing Club**
23 INAWHILECROCODILE (IRE), 5, b m Robin des Champs (FR)—Charming Present (IRE) **Lady Dulverton**
24 JAMACHO, 6, ch g Camacho—Obsessive Secret (IRE) **Stratford Racecourse & Robert Aplin**
25 JAMBOULET (IRE), 5, b g Jammaal—Shesnotthefirst (IRE) **Kate & Andrew Brooks**
26 JENKINS (IRE), 8, b g Azamour (IRE)—Aladiyna (IRE) **Mrs J. A. Wakefield**
27 JET SET (IRE), 8, b m Getaway (GER)—Lavender Track (IRE) **Lady Dulverton**
28 JETTISON, 4, b f Malinas (GER)—Side Step **Her Majesty The Queen**
29 JUST YOUR TYPE (IRE), 8, br g Morozov (USA)—Enistar (IRE) **Mr T. Hanlon**
30 KAPSIZE (FR), 6, b g Kapgarde (FR)—Loin de Moi (FR) **Stirrups Racing**
31 LARGY NIGHTS (IRE), 6, b g Jeremy (USA)—Rowdy Nights (IRE) **Mrs J. A. Wakefield**
32 LEITH HILL LAD, 10, b g Kayf Tara—Leith Hill Star **Mr Neil Maltby, Mrs J Maltby**
33 LISDOONVARNA LAD (IRE), 8, br g Westerner—Socialite Girl **Five Saints Racing**
34 LOCAL AFFAIR, 4, ch f Teofilo (IRE)—Local Spirit (USA) **Slater Stockwood Nicholson Partnership**
35 LOCHINVER (IRE), 6, b g American Post—Golden Gleam (IRE) **Macechern & Thornton Family & C Walsh**
36 LOOSE CHIPS, 14, br g Sir Harry Lewis (USA)—Worlaby Rose **Barrels Of Courage**
37 LOUSE TALK (IRE), 8, b g Mahler—Foxy-Lady (IRE) **Pauling,Perkins,Kerwood,King&Williams**
38 MARY THE MERMAID, 5, b m Kayf Tara—Faith And Fortune **Mr & Mrs R. Perkins**
39 MISS MOLINARI, 6, b m Malinas (GER)—Maiden Voyage **Mr N. Davies**
40 MONTY'S AWARD (IRE), 8, b g Oscar (IRE)—Montys Miss (IRE) **Mr D. A. Halsall**
41 NIGHTFLY, 9, br m Midnight Legend—Whichway Girl **Mrs D. P. G. Flory**
42 NIGHTLINE, 10, b g Midnight Legend—Whichway Girl **Mrs D. P. G. Flory**
43 NO TRUMPS, 6, b m Black Sam Bellamy (IRE)—Magic Score **Her Majesty The Queen**
44 OLD JEROBOAM (IRE), 6, b g Jeremy (USA)—Old Line (USA) **Mr Matthew Roberts & Simon Jessel**
45 OUR PERCY (IRE), 8, b g Stowaway—Another Present (IRE) **Mr T. J. Hemmings**
46 OVERWORKDUNDERPAID (IRE), 7, b g Getaway (GER)—Another Whiparound (IRE) **Mrs J. A. Wakefield**
47 PETER'S PORTRAIT (IRE), 7, b g Portrait Gallery (IRE)—Fancyfacia (IRE) **Four Nags and a Horse**
48 PRESENT ENDEAVOUR (IRE), 5, ch g Presenting—Boragh Thyme (IRE) **The Endeavour Racing Syndicate**
49 RAINMAKER (IRE), 4, b f Yeats (IRE)—Rubichamps **Mrs P Scott**
50 SAINT DALINA (FR), 6, b m Saint des Saints (FR)—Dalina (FR) **Mr D. A. Halsall**
51 SCENE NOT HERD (IRE), 5, b g Aizavoski (IRE)—Jessaway (IRE) **Swanee River Partnership**
52 SHAH AN SHAH, 6, ch g Shirocco (GER)—Queen Soraya **Knowlton**
53 SHANROE IN MILAN (IRE), 8, b g Milan—Shanroe Scenario (IRE) **Mr D. M. Mason**
54 SNOW LEOPARDESS, 8, gr m Martaline—Queen Soraya **Mrs M. M. Fox-Pitt**
55 STATE VISION (FR), 6, b g Vision d'Etat (FR)—Dona Rez (FR) **Mr D. A. Halsall**
56 STORM GODDESS (IRE), 6, br m Oscar (IRE)—Afasheen (IRE) **Don Sebastiao Partnership**
57 STORMY MILAN (IRE), 7, b g Milan—Socialite Girl **Stormy Milan Syndicate**
58 TEENAGE DIRTBAG (IRE), 4, b g Fame And Glory—Tavadden (IRE) **The Saddleworth Players**
59 THE VOLLAN (IRE), 6, b g Scorpion (IRE)—Print It On Lips (IRE) **Mr M. S. Scott**
60 THINQUE TANK, 4, b g So You Think (NZ)—Azharia **Mrs M. M. Fox-Pitt**
61 TUFF TIMES (IRE), 9, b g Curtain Time (IRE)—Fly Bid (IRE) **Mrs S. M. Monkland**
62 VIVAS (FR), 9, b br g Davidoff (GER)—Laviras (FR) **Mr N. Davies**
63 WESTERN MILLER (IRE), 9, b g Westerner—Definite Miller (IRE) **The Pantechnicons IV**
64 WHAT ABOUT TIME (IRE), 6, br g Oscar (IRE)—Fennor Rose (IRE)
65 WILBERDRAGON, 10, b g Kayf Tara—Swaythe (USA) **Don Sebastiao Partnership**

Other Owners: Mr R. J. Aplin, Mr N. M. Birch, Mr A. L. Brooks, Mrs K. L. Brooks, Mrs C. J. Djivanovic, Mrs R. J. Doel, Mrs M. M. Fox-Pitt, Mr S. R. J. Jessel, Mr C. E. Longsdon, Gavin MacEchern, Mr D. M. Mason, F. J. Mills, W. R. Mills, Mrs R. S. Perkins, Kevin Place, Mrs J. Plumptre, E. M. G. Roberts, Sharp Rise Racing, The Hull Farm Syndicate, The Stratford-On-Avon Racecourse Company, Ltd, Mrs J. Thornton, Mrs C. J. Walsh.

Conditional Jockey: Tom Buckley, Paul O'Brien.

339 MR DAVID LOUGHNANE, Tern Hill
Postal: **Helshaw Grange, Warrant Road, Tern Hill, Shropshire**
Contacts: **MOBILE 07527 173197**
EMAIL info@daveloughnaneracing.com **WEBSITE** www.daveloughnaneracing.com

1 **ANOTHER APPROACH (FR)**, 4, b f Dawn Approach (IRE)—Marmoom Flower (IRE) **Compas Racing**
2 **BABY STEPS**, 4, b g Paco Boy (IRE)—Stepping Out (IRE) **Mr D. J. Lowe**
3 **BAHUTA ACHA**, 5, b g Captain Gerrard (IRE)—Rosein **Lancashire Lads Partnership**
4 **BURFORD BROWN**, 5, br g Swiss Spirit—Sareb (FR) **Mr K. Sohi**
5 **CANDELISA (IRE)**, 7, br g Dream Ahead (USA)—Vasilia **Mr M. Godfrey**
6 **CONCIERGE (IRE)**, 4, br g Society Rock (IRE)—Warm Welcome **Mr K. Sohi**
7 **CRITICAL THINKING (IRE)**, 6, b g Art Connoisseur (IRE)—Cookie Cutter (IRE) **Mr J. Rocke**
8 **DARANOVA (IRE)**, 6, b g Arctic Cosmos (USA)—Dara Supreme (IRE) **Mr C. F. Moore**
9 **FAYETTA**, 4, b f Champs Elysees—Starfan (USA) **Miss S. L. Hoyland**
10 **FIZZY FEET (IRE)**, 4, b f Footstepsinthesand—Champagne Mistress **D Lowe & S Hoyland**
11 **FRENCH TWIST**, 4, ch f Animal Kingdom (USA)—Braided (USA) **Miss S. L. Hoyland**
12 **GHAITH**, 5, b g Invincible Spirit (IRE)—Wild Mimosa (IRE) **Miss S. L. Hoyland**
13 **GINGER FOX**, 4, ch g Iffraaj—Rimth **Shughal Mela Racing**
14 **HIC BIBI**, 5, b m Cityscape—Real Me **Mr P. Onslow**
15 **HIDE YOUR HEART (IRE)**, 4, b f Bungle Inthejungle—Cookie Cutter (IRE) **Mr J. Rocke**
16 **I THINK SO (IRE)**, 5, b m So You Think (NZ)—Nawaashi **A. H. Bennett**
17 **JOMROK**, 4, b f Mukhadram—Shadow Dancing **Mr K. Sohi**
18 **KASER (IRE)**, 5, b g Invincible Spirit (IRE)—Lethal Quality (USA) **Lowe, Lewis & Hoyland**
19 **MAC JETES**, 4, b f Archipenko (USA)—Real Me **Mr P. Onslow**
20 **MANJAAM (IRE)**, 7, ch g Tamayuz—Priory Rock (IRE) **Sohi & Sohi**
21 **MILAN REEF (IRE)**, 5, br m Famous Name—Jagapaw (IRE) **Mr M. Godfrey**
22 **PLUMETTE**, 4, b f Compton Place—Belatorio (IRE) **Mr J. Rocke**
23 **RAVEN'S RAFT (IRE)**, 5, gr m Raven's Pass (USA)—Sea Drift (FR) **Mr J. Rocke**
24 **ROCKESBURY**, 5, b g Foxwedge (AUS)—Nellie Ellis (IRE) **Mr J. Rocke**
25 5, B m Multiplex—Sherry Darling (IRE) **Mr R. Hand**
26 **STRINGYBARK CREEK**, 6, b g Bushranger—Money Note **Miss S. L. Hoyland**
27 **THE MET**, 4, b g Gregorian (IRE)—Kasaila (IRE) **Mr K. Sohi**
28 **THIS GIRL**, 5, b m Nathaniel (IRE)—Fibou (USA) **Mr D. J. Lowe**
29 **WANAASAH**, 4, b f Cape Cross (IRE)—Eldalil **Mr K. Sohi**
30 **YELLOW TIGER (FR)**, 4, b g Wootton Bassett—Comnena **K Sohi and Partner**

THREE-YEAR-OLDS
31 **ABADIE**, b g Muhaarar—Sacre Coeur **Mr K. Sohi**
32 **CAPP IT ALL (IRE)**, b f Cappella Sansevero—Katy Daly (IRE) **Stonegrave Thoroughbreds**
33 **CROFTIE**, b g Lethal Force (IRE)—Llyn **Mr A. Gray**
34 **CUPID'S BEAU**, b g Brazen Beau (AUS)—Oilinda **Mr D. J. Lowe**
35 **DWYFRAN**, b f Multiplex—Buddug **Mr J. E. Lloyd**
36 **ELPHEBA (IRE)**, b f Anjaal—Broadway Musical (IRE) **Mr D. J. Lowe**
37 **FALACHO (IRE)**, b f Requinto (IRE)—Picabo (IRE) **T. E. Ford**
38 **KINGMANS SPIRIT (IRE)**, b f Kingman—Kaabari (USA) **D. J. Lowe, G. Dewhurst & A. Lewis**
39 **LAKEVIEW (IRE)**, b g Tagula (IRE)—Eye Catching **D Lowe & S Hoyland**
40 **MAX'S VOICE (IRE)**, b g Poet's Voice—Duljanah (IRE) **Miss S. L. Hoyland**
41 **ORANGE JUSTICE**, ch f Harbour Watch (IRE)—Jord (IRE) **Mr J. E. Lloyd**
43 **PULSE FICTION (IRE)**, ch f Dragon Pulse (IRE)—Alexia Reveuse (IRE) **Stonegrave Thoroughbreds**
44 **RICHARD R H B (IRE)**, b g Fulbright—Royal Interlude (IRE) **Peter R Ball & Gentech Products Ltd**
46 **ROSEINA'S VOICE**, b f Poet's Voice—Signorina Roseina **Lancashire Lads 2, Gentech & Hoyland**
47 **STORMY GIRL (IRE)**, ch f Night of Thunder (IRE)—Refusetolisten (IRE) **Stonegrave Thoroughbreds**
48 **TATTLETIME (USA)**, b f Orb (USA)—Miss Tattle Tale (USA) **The Something Syndicate & Partner**
49 **TRUMPETS CALL (IRE)**, ch g Anjaal—Yellow Trumpet **Mike and Eileen Newbould**
50 **UTOPIAN LAD (IRE)**, b g Society Rock (IRE)—Perfect Pose (IRE) **Mr M. Batters**
51 **WHEN COMES HERE (IRE)**, br g Lawman (FR)—Quads (IRE) **Mr K. Sohi**

TWO-YEAR-OLDS
52 B c 04/03 Pride of Dubai (AUS)—Chelsey Jayne (IRE) (Galileo (IRE)) (38095) **Mr K. Sohi**
53 Ch f 05/03 Dandy Man (IRE)—Cold Cold Woman (Machiavellian (USA)) (4289) **Mr K. Sohi**

MR DAVID LOUGHNANE - continued

54 B f 07/05 Muhaarar—Havergate (Dansili) (15000) **Lydonford Ltd**
55 KIM WEXLER (IRE), b f 05/04 Mehmas (IRE)—Foreplay (IRE) (Lujain (USA)) (7142) **Mr D. J. Lowe**
56 B c 04/04 Dabirsim (FR)—Little Shambles (Shamardal (USA)) (6434)
57 Gr f 09/03 Gutaifan (IRE)—Maracuja (Medicean) (9437)
58 Ch c 12/04 Twilight Son—Money Note (Librettist (USA)) (7619) **Miss S. L. Hoyland**
59 B f 13/03 Lethal Force (IRE)—Stepping Out (IRE) (Tagula (IRE)) **Mr D. J. Lowe**
60 B c 10/03 Kodi Bear (IRE)—Yellow Trumpet (Petong) (23165) **Mr K. Sohi**

Other Owners: Mr P. Ball, Mrs C. Brown, Mr G. Dewhurst, Gentech Products Ltd, Mr B. K. Haughey, Miss S. L. Hoyland, Mr M. Keating, Lancashire Lads Partnership 2, Mr A. Lewis, Mr D. J. Lowe, Mrs E. E. Newbould, Mr J. M. Newbould, Mr K. Samra, Mr J. Singh, Mr J. Sohi, Mr K. Sohi, The Something Syndicate, Capt J. H. Wilson

---

340   MR MARK LOUGHNANE, Kidderminster
Postal: **Rock Farm, Rock Cross, Rock, Kidderminster, Worcestershire, DY14 9SA**
Contacts: **MOBILE 07805 531021**

1 AUNT HELEN (USA), 4, b f Verrazano (USA)—London Bid (USA) **Mrs C. M. Loughnane**
2 BIG LACHIE, 6, b g Camacho—Ryan's Quest (IRE) **Big Lachie Syndicate**
3 BLUE MEDICI, 6, b g Medicean—Bluebelle **Mr L. A. Bellman**
4 BOYCHICK (IRE), 7, b g Holy Roman Emperor (IRE)—al Saqiya (USA) **Mr L. A. Bellman**
5 CHOCOLATE BOX (IRE), 6, b g Zoffany (IRE)—Chocolate Mauk (USA)
6 DESTINYS ROCK, 5, b m Zoffany (IRE)—Special Destiny **Ladies of Rock**
7 DREAM MAGIC (IRE), 6, b g Lord Shanakill (USA)—Pursuit of Passion **Ben Parish & Clare Loughnane**
8 EMBER'S GLOW, 6, ch g Sepoy (AUS)—Fading Light **T. D. Johnson**
9 FALMOUTH LIGHT (FR), 5, b g Cape Cross (IRE)—Wonderous Light (IRE) **Shropshire Wolves**
10 FRIDAY FIZZ (IRE), 4, b f Kodiac—Sugarhoneybaby (IRE) **Haven't A Pot & Lee Bolingbroke**
11 INNER CIRCLE (IRE), 6, b g Choisir (AUS)—Eternity Ring **Mrs C. M. Loughnane**
12 ITMAKESYOUTHINK, 6, b g So You Think (NZ)—Anbella (FR) **Mr R. M. Brilley**
13 LEO DAVINCI (USA), 4, b g Artie Schiller (USA)—Sweet Temper (USA) **Excel Racing**
14 LITTLE MISS KODI (IRE), 7, b m Kodiac—Sensasse (IRE)
15 LOOKING FOR CARL, 5, b g Lope de Vega (IRE)—Dam Beautiful **Excel Racing, R Gray & Partners**
16 MAGWADIRI (IRE), 6, b g Casamento (IRE)—Hankering (IRE) **Rock Racing Club**
17 MOXY MARES, 5, ch g Motivator—Privalova (IRE) **S. & A. Mares**
18 NANANITA (IRE), 4, b f War Command (USA)—Causeway Queen (IRE) **S. & A. Mares**
19 PONTBLYDDYN, 5, ch g Mount Nelson—Daring Damsel (IRE)
20 PRECIOUS MOMENTO (IRE), 5, ch g Casamento (IRE)—Precious Citizen (USA) **Haven't A Pot & Lee Bolingbroke**
21 PRECISION PRINCE (IRE), 4, b g Dragon Pulse (IRE)—Little Live Wire (IRE) **Precision Facades Ltd**
22 RED GUNNER, 6, b g Oasis Dream—Blue Maiden **2 Counties Racing**
23 REVOLUTIONARY MAN (IRE), 5, b g Exceed And Excel (AUS)—Bint Almukhtar (IRE) **Mr L. A. Bellman**
24 ROCK BOY GREY (IRE), 5, gr g Dark Angel (IRE)—Encore View **The Likely Lads**
25 ROLLER, 7, b g Rail Link—Buffering **Over The Moon Racing**
26 RUNNING CLOUD (IRE), 5, b g Cacique (IRE)—Nimbus Star **Mr A. Jordan**
27 SMILEY BAGEL (IRE), 7, b g Kyllachy—Epistoliere (IRE) **Mr L. A. Bellman**
28 TAKEONEFORTHETEAM, 5, b g Bahamian Bounty—Miss Bond (IRE) **S. & A. Mares**
29 TRIGGERED (IRE), 4, b g Dandy Man (IRE)—Triggers Broom (IRE) **S. & A. Mares**
30 UNIVERSAL EFFECT, 4, b f Universal (IRE)—Saaboog **S & A Mares & Precision Facades Ltd**
31 4, B f Ocovango—Wattrey

THREE-YEAR-OLDS

32 COME ON MY SON, b g Mayson—Slinky McVelvet **Excel Racing, R Gray & Partners**
33 CONTRACT KID (IRE), b g G Force (IRE)—Danamight (IRE)
34 DOCTOR NUNO, b g Due Diligence (USA)—Aubrietia **Shropshire Wolves**
35 FANTOM FORCE (IRE), br c Gutaifan (IRE)—Aja (IRE) **Excel Racing**
36 FEDORA FITS, ch f Helmet (AUS)—Lee Miller (IRE) **Mr R. J. Douglas**
37 FIACH STONEY (IRE), b g Urban Poet—Randall's Rebecca (IRE) **Mrs C. M. Loughnane**
38 HIGH MAINTENANCE, b f Due Diligence (USA)—Random **Ms A. Quinn**
39 KNOCKACURRA (IRE), b c Anjaal—Ohh Lala (IRE) **Mr D. Commins**

MR MARK LOUGHNANE - continued

40 **MR DIB DAB (FR)**, b c Dabirsim (FR)—Naan (IRE) **S. & A. Mares**
41 **MUMSBIRTHDAYGIRL (IRE)**, ch f Dandy Man (IRE)—Dutch Party **Mr R. M. Brilley**
42 **PRECISION STORM**, gr g Dragon Pulse (IRE)—Way To The Stars **Precision Facades Ltd**
43 **QASBAZ (IRE)**, b g Make Believe—Esuvia (IRE) **Mr L. A. Bellman**
44 **ROCK OF PENSAX (IRE)**, br g Society Rock (IRE)—China Pink **S. & A. Mares**
45 **SPRINGVALE LAD**, b c Archipenko (USA)—Combustible (IRE) **Mr M. Millichamp**

TWO-YEAR-OLDS

46 Ro c 28/03 Lethal Force (IRE)—Colourfilly (Compton Place) **Mr L. A. Bellman**
47 B c 06/01 Elzaam (AUS)—Fly By (Elusive Quality (USA)) (7722)
48 **MEANT TWO B (IRE)**, gr c 21/04 Markaz (IRE)—Sayrah (Sakhee (USA)) (6006) **Mr W. J. Fisher**
49 B c 05/02 Dragon Pulse (IRE)—Princess Aloof (IRE) (Big Bad Bob (IRE)) (21450)
50 B c 07/02 Fast Company (IRE)—Saffa Garden (IRE) (King's Best (USA)) (8571) **Mr L. A. Bellman**
51 Ch f 07/02 Stimulation (IRE)—Verus Delicia (IRE) (Chineur (FR)) **Mr R. M. Brilley**

Other Owners: Mr C. Austin, Mr L. A. Bolingbroke, Mr K. J. Breen, Dining Chairs Uk Ltd, Excel Racing, Excel Racing & Keith Breen Ii, Mr P Fisher, Mr G. Freeman, Mr K. C. Freeman, Mr R. J. Gray, Haven't A Pot, Mrs C. M. Loughnane, Mrs A. Mares, Mr S. Mares, S. & A. Mares, Mr B. M. Parish, Precision Facades Ltd, Racing Facades Syndicate, Rock Racing Club, The Likely Lads

---

341
MR SHAUN LYCETT, Witney
Postal: **Fairspear Racing Stables, Fairspear Road, Leafield, Witney, Oxfordshire, OX29 9NT**
Contacts: **PHONE 01451 824143 MOBILE 07788 100894**
EMAIL trainer@bourtonhillracing.co.uk WEBSITE www.bourtonhillracing.co.uk

1 **AUMERLE**, 8, b g Authorized (IRE)—Succinct **Mr P. Freeman**
2 **DON'T JUMP GEORGE (IRE)**, 5, b g Canford Cliffs (IRE)—My Sweet Georgia (IRE) **Mr J. Searchfield**
3 **EXCELLENT PUCK (IRE)**, 10, b g Excellent Art—Puck's Castle **Bourton Racing**
4 **HALLINGS COMET**, 11, ch g Halling (USA)—Landinium (ITY) **Lord J. Blyth**
5 **PARK PADDOCKS (IRE)**, 6, b g Sea The Stars (IRE)—Dream of The Hill (IRE) **Mr D. R. Gilbert**
6 **RELATIVE EASE**, 4, b f Sayif (IRE)—Shohrah (IRE) **L & M Atkins**
7 **SCOTSBROOK NIGHT**, 7, b m Midnight Legend—Won More Night **Mr P. E. T. Price**
8 **SCOTSBROOK RHULA**, 5, b m Native Ruler—Scots Brook Terror **Mr P. E. T. Price**
9 **THE KING'S STEED**, 7, b g Equiano (FR)—King's Siren (IRE) **D Gilbert, J Lancaster, G Wills**
10 **TIKANITE (IRE)**, 9, ch g Tikkanen (USA)—Scented Night (IRE) **L & M Atkins**
11 **TORCELLO (IRE)**, 6, ch g Born To Sea (IRE)—Islandagore (IRE) **Mr D. R. Gilbert**
12 **TROY DEE KNEE**, 8, b g Rainbow High—Matthew's Bridey **The Golden Boys Partnership**
13 **WEEKLY GOSSIP (IRE)**, 9, br g Kalanisi (IRE)—Mary's Little Vic (IRE) **L & M Atkins**

Other Owners: Mr L. Atkins, Mrs M. Atkins.

342
MR JOHN MACKIE, Church Broughton
Postal: **The Bungalow, Barton Blount, Church Broughton, Derby**
Contacts: **PHONE 01283 585603, 01283 585604 MOBILE 07799 145243 FAX 01283 585603**
EMAIL jmackieracing@gmail.com

1 4, B g Epaulette (AUS)—Avonrose **Mr A. P. Simmill**
2 **BALADIO (IRE)**, 4, ch f Iffraaj—Balamana (FR) **Derbyshire Racing III**
3 **BARTON KNOLL**, 8, b g Midnight Legend—Barton Flower **Mr S. W. Clarke**
4 **BEEANDBEE**, 5, ch m Black Sam Bellamy (IRE)—Shafts Chance (IRE) **Mr B. J. Baggott**
5 **BERTOG**, 5, ch g Sepoy (AUS)—Lucky Token (IRE) **Mr D. Ward**
6 **CUSTARD THE DRAGON**, 7, b g Kyllachy—Autumn Pearl **Derbyshire Racing**
7 **DUKE OF ALBA (IRE)**, 5, b g Lope de Vega (IRE)—Royal Alchemist **Allstars**
8 **FIRE JET (IRE)**, 7, ch m Ask—Lightning Jet **Ladas**
9 **HERMOCRATES (FR)**, 4, b g Farhh—Little Shambles **Mrs E. M. Mackie**
10 **HURRICANE ALI (IRE)**, 4, b g Alhebayeb (IRE)—Hurricane Irene (IRE) **Mr M. J. Fruhwald**

MR JOHN MACKIE - continued

11 **LONDON PROTOCOL (FR),** 7, ch g Muhtathir—Troiecat (FR) **NSU Leisure & Mrs Carolyn Seymour**
12 **LUNAR JET,** 6, ch g Ask—Lightning Jet **Ladas**
13 **MANY TALES,** 8, b g Multiplex—All Three Fables **Mrs E. M. Mackie**
14 **MONTENAY,** 4, b f So You Think (NZ)—Jivry **Eventmasters Racing**
15 **POLYPHONY (IRE),** 5, b m Power—Start The Music (IRE) **Eventmasters Racing**
16 **TURANGA LEELA,** 6, ch m Paco Boy (IRE)—Sunday Bess (JPN) **Eventmasters Racing**

THREE-YEAR-OLDS

17 B g Farhh—Avonrose **Mr A. P. Simmill**
18 **HEARTSTAR,** b f Heeraat (IRE)—Available (IRE) **Derbyshire Racing IV**
19 **RAINBOW JET (IRE),** b f Dream Ahead (USA)—Star Jet (IRE) **Ladas**

Other Owners: Mr C. Mullin, Mrs M. T. Mullin, NSU Leisure Ltd, Mrs C. Seymour.

343

MR PETER MADDISON, Skewsby
Postal: **5 West End Cottages, Skewsby, York, YO61 4SG**
Contacts: **PHONE 01347 888385**

1 **KINGS OWN,** 6, b g Distant Peak (IRE)—Phoebe Nullis **P. Maddison**
2 **THE SASKATOON,** 11, b g Desideratum—Skewsby Girl **P. Maddison**

Conditional Jockey: Jamie Hamilton.

344

MR MICHAEL MADGWICK, Denmead
Postal: **Forest Farm, Forest Road, Denmead, Waterlooville, Hampshire, PO7 6UA**
Contacts: **PHONE 023 9225 8313 MOBILE 07835 964969**

1 **ABUJA (IRE),** 4, b f Society Rock (IRE)—Liscoa (IRE) **P. Taplin**
2 **ACE COMBAT,** 5, b g Shamardal (USA)—Require **Los Leader**
3 **ARBUCKLE,** 4, b g Heeraat (IRE)—Attlongglast **Mrs L N Harmes & Mr J Lane**
4 **DONO DI DIO,** 5, b m Nathaniel (IRE)—Sweet Cecily (IRE) **Mr O. Lodge**
5 **ETHANDEXTER,** 5, ch g Alkaased (USA)—Miss Venice (IRE) **Sheepwash Syndicate**
6 **FAMILY FORTUNES,** 6, ch g Paco Boy (IRE)—Barawin (IRE) **Los Leader**
7 **HI THERE SILVER (IRE),** 6, gr g Clodovil (IRE)—Elaborate **Lane & Madgwick**
8 **MAQUISARD (FR),** 8, ch g Creachadoir (IRE)—Gioiosa Marea (IRE) **M. K. George**
9 **MARGIE'S CHOICE (GER),** 5, b m Redoute's Choice (AUS)—Margie's World (GER) **Mr G. Dixon**
10 **MISS RECYCLED,** 5, b m Royal Applause—Steel Free (IRE) **Recycled Products Limited**
11 **SING OUT LOUD (IRE),** 5, b g Vocalised (USA)—Tus Maith (IRE) **Mrs Susan Neville & Mr Mike George**
12 **STORMBOMBER (CAN),** 4, ch g Stormy Atlantic (USA)—Swanky Bubbles (CAN) **Mr T. Smith**
13 **TOMMYS GEAL,** 8, b m Halling (USA)—Steel Free (IRE) **Recycled Products Limited**
14 **VLANNON,** 5, b g Captain Gerrard (IRE)—Attlongglast **M Gannon, H Vlatas, M Willis, L N Harmes**
15 **WHERE'S TOM,** 5, b g Cape Cross (IRE)—Where's Susie **Recycled Products Limited**

THREE-YEAR-OLDS

16 **BILLESDON,** ch g Cappella Sansevero—Meebo (IRE) **Bond - Ellis Partnership**
17 **RESPLENDENT ROSE,** b f Heeraat (IRE)—Attlongglast **Mrs L. N. Harmes**

Other Owners: Mr M. J. Bond, Mr S. Bond, Mr J. Ellis, Mr M. Gannon, M. K. George, Mrs L. N. Harmes, Mr J. Lane, M. J. Madgwick, Mrs S. C. Neville, Mr W. R. Oliver, Mr T. Smith, Mr H. Vlatas, Mr M. Willis.

Assistant Trainer: David Madgwick.

Flat Jockey: Adam Kirby. **NH Jockey:** Marc Goldstein. **Amateur Jockey:** Mr Lance Madgwick.

345 **MRS HEATHER MAIN, Wantage**
Postal: **Kingston Common Farm, Kingston Lisle, Wantage, Oxfordshire, OX12 9QT**
Contacts: **MOBILE 01367 820124 FAX 07920 558860**
EMAIL heather.main@hotmail.com WEBSITE www.heathermainracing.com

1 **AL KOUT**, 6, gr g Oasis Dream—Honorlina (FR) **John Rylands & Wetumpka Racing**
2 **DAWRY (IRE)**, 4, b g Showcasing—May Day Queen (IRE) **Mr & Mrs D. R. Guest**
3 **GRATOT (FR)**, 5, br g Le Havre (IRE)—Absolute Lady (IRE) **D. M. Kerr**
4 **ISLAND BRAVE (IRE)**, 6, b h Zebedee—Tip the Scale (USA) **D. M. Kerr**
5 **KELIS (IRE)**, 4, ch f No Nay Never (USA)—Apple Spirit (USA) **Mr Donald Kerr & Wetumpka Racing**
6 **KESWICK**, 6, b g Dansili—Marywell **Main Murphy Partnership**
7 **LAPIDARY**, 4, b f Kodiac—Carved Emerald **Andrew Knott & Wetumpka Racing**
8 **MARSHAL DAN (IRE)**, 5, b g Lawman (FR)—Aunt Nicola **Coxwell Partnership**
9 **MEDORAS CHILDE**, 4, b f Nayef (USA)—Byroness **Mr & Mrs D. R. Guest**
10 **MERWEB (IRE)**, 5, gr g Shamardal (USA)—Ashley Hall (USA) **Mr Stuart Mercer & Mr John Gent**
11 **MOSTAWAA**, 4, ch g Poet's Voice—Mumtaza **The Haroldians**
12 **NUMITOR**, 6, gr g Schiaparelli (GER)—Just Popsy **Wetumpka Racing**
13 **PARA QUEEN (IRE)**, 4, b f Slade Power—Dancer's Leap **Don Knott & Wetumpka Racing**
14 **POLAR CLOUD**, 4, gr g Mount Nelson—Cloud Illusions (USA) **Wetumpka Racing**
15 **PRINCE LLYR (IRE)**, 4, b g Zoffany (IRE)—Zadalla **Llewelyn Yardley Runeckles**
16 **RAKE'S PROGRESS**, 6, b g Sir Percy—Cartoon **Coxwell Partnership**
17 **SONG OF THE ISLES (IRE)**, 4, ch f Tagula (IRE)—Musicology (USA) **Wetumpka Racing**

THREE-YEAR-OLDS
18 **CLOUD THUNDER**, gr g Poet's Voice—Cloud Illusions (USA) **Coxwell Partnership**
19 **COLONEL WHITEHEAD (IRE)**, b c Showcasing—Lady Brigid (IRE) **Mr. Andrew Tuck & Wetumpka Racing**
20 **ISLAND MEMORY**, b f Exceed And Excel (AUS)—Ya Latif (IRE) **D. M. Kerr**
21 **ISLAND NATION (IRE)**, ch g Ruler of The World (IRE)—Rethink **D. M. Kerr**
22 **ISLAND STORM (IRE)**, b c Anjaal—She's Neat (IRE) **Mr Donald Kerr & Wetumpka Racing**
23 **ISLAND WARRIOR (IRE)**, ch g Power—Light Sea (IRE) **D. M. Kerr**
24 **THOMAS PERCY**, b g Sir Percy—Cultured Pride (IRE) **Mrs Helen Adams & Hot to Trot Racing 1**
25 **TINDRUM**, ch g Mukhadram—Tinshu (IRE) **Llewelyn,Runeckles**

Other Owners: Mrs H. Adams, J. A. Gent, Mr D. R. Guest, Mr R. S. Hoskins, Hot To Trot Racing 1, D. M. Kerr, Mr A. Knott, Mr D. G. Knott, Sir J. A. Mactaggart, Mrs H. S. Main, J. P. M. Main, Mr S. M. Mercer, Mr J. M. C. Rylands, Mr M. R. Telfer, Mr A. Tuck, Wetumpka Racing.

---

346 **MR PHILLIP MAKIN, Easingwold**
Postal: **Well Close Farm, York Road, Easingwold, York, North Yorkshire, YO61 3EN**
Contacts: **PHONE 07968 045436**
EMAIL philmakin.21@hotmail.co.uk

1 **ALMURR (IRE)**, 4, b g Dandy Man (IRE)—Passion Planet (IRE) **P. J. Makin**
2 **COLONEL SLADE (IRE)**, 4, b g Dandy Man (IRE)—Sense of A Woman (USA) **P. J. Makin**
3 **FENNAAN (IRE)**, 5, br g Footstepsinthesand—Sanadaat **Mrs W. Burdett**
4 **GALLOWAY HILLS**, 5, b g Kyllachy—Bonnie Brae
5 **JUNGLE INTHEBUNGLE (IRE)**, 4, ch g Bungle Inthejungle—Princess Banu **Mrs T. Burns**
6 **LAHORE (USA)**, 6, br g Elusive Quality (USA)—Nayarra (IRE) **Mrs W. Burdett**
7 **MUHAJJAL**, 6, b g Cape Cross (IRE)—Muqantara (USA) **Let's Be Lucky Racing 22**
8 **MUTAWAFFER (IRE)**, 4, b g Kodiac—Golden Flower **P. J. Makin**
9 **STORM OVER (IRE)**, 6, b g Elnadim (USA)—Stormy View (USA) **P. J. Makin**
10 **SUAIMHNEACH (IRE)**, 4, b f Vocalised (USA)—Amhrasach (IRE)
11 **THREE CARD TRICK**, b g Piccolo—Card Games **Exors of the Late Mr G. Reed**
12 **VIVACIOUS SPIRIT**, 4, b g Charm Spirit (USA)—Buredyma **P. J. Makin**
13 **WESTERN DAWN (IRE)**, 4, b g Dawn Approach (IRE)—Yes Oh Yes (USA) **Let's Be Lucky Racing 24**

MR PHILLIP MAKIN - continued

THREE-YEAR-OLDS

14 Br g War Command (USA)—Attracted To You (IRE)
15 **BORSTAL BULL (IRE)**, ro g Hot Streak (IRE)—Acquaint (IRE) **Mrs W. Burdett**
16 **CARLA ERANGEY (IRE)**, b f Acclamation (IRE)—Watsdaplan (IRE) **Mrs W. Burdett**
17 **DANDE (IRE)**, b g Dandy Man (IRE)—Scarpe Rosse (IRE) **SYPS (UK) Ltd**
18 **HAVANA DAWN**, gr f Havana Gold (IRE)—Rock Ace (IRE) **SYPS (UK) Ltd**
19 **MUKHADRAM WAY**, b f Mukhadram—Mancunian Way
20 **PENMELLYN (IRE)**, b f Dark Angel (IRE)—Red Avis **Mrs W. Burdett**
21 **PENTEWAN**, b f Havana Gold (IRE)—Serena's Pride **Mrs W. Burdett**
22 **THE BELL CONDUCTOR (IRE)**, b g Dandy Man (IRE)—Saffian **Mrs W. Burdett**

---

347 MRS ALYSON MALZARD, Jersey
Postal: Les Etabl'yes, Grosnez Farm, St Ouen, JE3 2AD, Jersey
Contacts: MOBILE +44 7797 738128
EMAIL malzardracing@gmail.com

1 **BAL AMIE (FR)**, 6, b g Ballingarry (IRE)—Amie Roli (FR) **Mr Anthony Taylor**
2 **BARWICK**, 12, b g Beat Hollow—Tenpence **Mr Michael Watt**
3 **BOWL IMPERIAL**, 8, ch h Raven's Pass (USA)—Turtle Point (USA) **Mr P G Somers**
4 **FOURNI (IRE)**, 11, ch m Rakti—Eckbeag (USA) **Miss Joan Lowery**
5 **HARD TO HANDEL**, 8, b g Stimulation (IRE)—Melody Maker **Mr Matt Watkinson & Baroque Partnership**
6 **HONCHO**, 8, gr g Dark Angel (IRE)—Disco Lights **Sheik A'Leg Racing**
7 **ICE ROYAL (IRE)**, 7, b g Frozen Power (IRE)—Salford Princess (IRE) **Mr Anthony Taylor**
8 **ISLAND SONG (IRE)**, 6, b m Equiano (FR)—Fortuna Limit **Mr P G Somers**
9 **MENDACIOUS HARPY (IRE)**, 9, b m Dark Angel (IRE)—Idesia (IRE) **Malzard Racing**
10 **RELAXED BOY (FR)**, 7, b g Le Havre (IRE)—Joyce (GER) **Mr P G Somers**
11 **SAFIRA MENINA**, 8, b m Paco Boy (IRE)—Isla Azul (IRE) **Mr & Mrs Simon Harrison-White**
12 **TIMETODOCK**, 4, b g Harbour Watch (IRE)—Unwrapit (USA) **Mr Anthony Taylor**
13 **WINKLEVI (FR)**, 5, b g Maxios—Wild Star (IRE) **Mr & Mrs Trevor Gallienne**

THREE-YEAR-OLDS

14 **ALLEGRO JETE (FR)**, b g Style Vendome (FR)—Neuilly **Sheik A'Leg Racing**
15 **DARK MOONLIGHT (IRE)**, b g Kodiac—On Location (USA) **Malzard Racing**

NH Jockey: Mattie Batchelor. **Amateur Jockey:** Miss Victoria Malzard, Mr Freddie Tett.

---

348 MR CHARLIE MANN, Upper Lambourn
Postal: Neardown, Upper Lambourn, Hungerford, Berkshire, RG17 8QP
Contacts: PHONE 01488 71717, 01488 73118 MOBILE 07721 888333 FAX 01488 73223
EMAIL charlie@charliemann.info WEBSITE www.charliemannracing.com

1 **CAPONE (GER)**, 5, br g Nathaniel (IRE)—Codera (GER) **Mr B. Kerr**
2 **COMMIT OR QUIT (IRE)**, 5, ch g Tobougg (IRE)—Gail Borden (IRE) **Mrs John Thorneloe**
3 **FINANCIAL CONDUCT (IRE)**, 6, b g Harbour Watch (IRE)—Popolo (IRE) **The Steeple Chasers**
4 **FIXED RATE**, 7, b g Oasis Dream—Pretty Face **The Steeple Chasers**
5 **GLORVINA (IRE)**, 6, b m Dragon Pulse (IRE)—Hawk Dance (IRE) **Mr M. J. R. Bannister**
6 **IVILNOBLE (IRE)**, 7, b g Alfred Nobel (IRE)—Almutamore (IRE) **Mrs L. C. Taylor**
7 **JACK THUNDER (IRE)**, 6, b g Masterofthehorse (IRE)—Acqua Pesante (IRE) **Mr D. G. Christian**
8 **LEX TALIONIS (IRE)**, 7, b g Thewayyouare (USA)—Dawn Air (USA) **Mrs J. M. Mayo**
9 **LIKE THE SOUND (FR)**, 9, b g Soldier of Fortune (IRE)—Zalida (IRE) **STG Racing Partnership**
10 **MELSONBY**, 6, b m Multiplex—Oscar's Lady (IRE) **Mr R. C. Penney & Partner**
11 **MORNEY WING (IRE)**, 11, b g Antonius Pius (USA)—Tillan Fuwain (FR) **The Steeple Chasers**
12 **PERCY ALEXANDER**, 4, ch g Sir Percy—Rosy Alexander **C. J. Mann**
13 **PICKAMIX**, 9, gr g Sagamix (FR)—Star of Wonder (FR) **Racing Ventures 2014**

MR CHARLIE MANN - continued

14 **PRABENI**, 5, ch g Teofilo (IRE)—Nyarhini **The Neardowners**
15 **ROBADDAN (IRE)**, 6, ch g Flemensfirth (USA)—Tiarella (IRE) **Lady E. Mays-Smith**
16 **ROYALS AND REBELS (IRE)**, 10, b g Robin des Pres (FR)—Native Deal (IRE) **The Neardowners**
17 **SID HOODIE (IRE)**, 6, b m Rip Van Winkle (IRE)—Universe **Mr D. G. Christian**
18 **SONG OF THE SKY**, 7, ch m Rip Van Winkle (IRE)—Holy Moly (USA) **STG Racing Partnership**
19 **STREAM OF STARS**, 5, b g Sea The Stars (IRE)—Precious Gem (IRE) **S & R Frosell**
20 **THE DARLEY LAMA (IRE)**, 6, b g Carlotamix (FR)—Last Sunrise (IRE) **Mr J. D. Mayo**
21 **THE DUBAI WAY (IRE)**, 8, b g Dubai Destination (USA)—Britway Lady (IRE) **N.W.A. Bannister & M.J.R. Bannister**
22 **THE LION DANCER (IRE)**, 8, b g Let The Lion Roar—Shesadoll (IRE) **The 25 Club**
23 **THE OGLE GOGLE MAN (IRE)**, 8, b g Yeats (IRE)—Miss Otis Regrets (IRE) **The 25 Club**
24 **THORNDALE**, 5, b m Multiplex—Oscar's Lady (IRE) **Mr R. C. Penney & Partner**
25 **TOP UP THE FASHION (IRE)**, 6, b g Court Cave (IRE)—Aqua Breezer (IRE) **Mr Hunter & Mrs Taylor**
26 **TRAILBOSS (IRE)**, 5, b g High Chaparral (IRE)—Seeking Solace **Noel Fehily Racing Syndicate - Trailboss**
27 **VIOLETS GIRL**, 10, b m Black Sam Bellamy (IRE)—Sunshine Rays
28 **ZEN MASTER (IRE)**, 8, b g Shantou (USA)—Back Log (IRE) **The 25 Club**

Other Owners: Mr M. J. R. Bannister, Mr N. W. A. Bannister, Mr R. N. Frosell, Mrs S. P. B. Frosell, Miss S. R. Haynes, M. S. Hunter, Mr R. C. Penney, Mrs L. C. Taylor.

Assistant Trainer: Lilly Carson, **Head Lad:** Shaun Graham, **Racing Secretary:** Kate Mann.

---

349 ## MR GEORGE MARGARSON, Newmarket
Postal: **Graham Lodge, Birdcage Walk, Newmarket, Suffolk, CB8 0NE**
Contacts: **PHONE 01638 668043 MOBILE 07860 198303**
EMAIL george@georgemargarson.co.uk WEBSITE www.georgemargarson.co.uk

1 **BLAME CULTURE (USA)**, 5, b g Blame (USA)—Pearl In The Sand (IRE)
2 **CARIBBEAN SPRING (IRE)**, 7, b g Dark Angel (IRE)—Bogini (IRE)
3 **MODEL GUEST**, 4, ch f Showcasing—Looks All Right (IRE)
4 **PAINTED DREAM**, 4, b f Showcasing—Speed Date
5 **PROTECTED GUEST**, 5, b g Helmet (AUS)—Reem Star
6 **SPIRITED GUEST**, 4, b g Swiss Spirit—Choisette

THREE-YEAR-OLDS

7 **ALVEDA**, b f Archipenko (USA)—Alizadora
8 **HOT DATE**, b f Hot Streak (IRE)—Speed Date
9 **LUNA WISH**, b f Sea The Moon (GER)—Crystal Wish
10 **ROPEY GUEST**, b c Cable Bay (IRE)—Hadeeya
11 **SHYMAY**, b f Mayson—Coconut Shy

TWO-YEAR-OLDS

12 B f 02/04 New Approach (IRE)—Adhere (AUS) (Teofilo (IRE))
13 Ch c 06/03 Sepoy (AUS)—Haley Bop (IRE) (Dream Ahead (USA))
14 B c 18/03 Wootton Bassett—Starlite Jewel (Virtual)

Owners: Mr A. Al Mansoori, Mr F. G. Butler, Graham Lodge Partnership, Graham Lodge Partnership II, John Guest Racing Ltd, Mangiacapra, Hill, Hook Partnership, Miss K. Rausing, The Bean Club.

Assistant Trainer: Katie Margarson.

Apprentice Jockey: Miss Abbie Pierce. **Amateur Jockey:** Miss Rosie Margarson.

350 **MR ANDREW J. MARTIN, Chipping Norton**
Postal: Yew Tree Barn, Hook Norton Road, Swerford, Chipping Norton, Oxfordshire, OX7 4BF
Contacts: **PHONE 01608 737288**

1 **CAN YOU CALL**, 5, b g Passing Glance—Call Me A Legend **A. J. Martin**
2 **MIDNIGHT MUSTANG**, 13, b g Midnight Legend—Mustang Molly **A. J. Martin**
3 **MIDNIGHT POPSTAR**, 6, b m Midnight Legend—It's Missy Imp **A. J. Martin**
4 **MILITARIAN**, 10, b g Kayf Tara—Mille Et Une (FR) **A. J. Martin**
5 **SUNNY LEDGEND**, 15, b g Midnight Legend—Swordella **A. J. Martin**

351 **MISS NICKY MARTIN, Minehead**
Postal: Great Bradley, Withypool, Minehead, Somerset, TA24 7RS
Contacts: **PHONE 01643 831175 MOBILE 07980 269510**
EMAIL nickymartin3@hotmail.co.uk

1 **ALBEROBELLO (IRE)**, 12, b g Old Vic—Tourist Attraction (IRE) **Bradley Partnership**
2 **BALLYDUN OSCAR (IRE)**, 8, b g Oscar (IRE)—Calling Classy (IRE) **Bradley Partnership**
3 **BEAR GHYLLS (IRE)**, 5, br g Arcadio (GER)—Inch Princess (IRE) **Bradley Partnership**
4 **BRADLEY BROOK (IRE)**, 14, ch g Alderbrook—Mazza **Bradley Partnership**
5 **CAN YOU BELIEVE IT (IRE)**, 7, br g Oscar (IRE)—Cassilis (IRE) **Bradley Partnership**
6 **COLONEL CUSTARD (IRE)**, 7, ch g Mahler—Criaire Princess (IRE) **Bradley Partnership**
7 **CRAIC MAGIC (IRE)**, 5, b g Oscar (IRE)—Chantoue Royale (FR) **Bradley Partnership**
8 **CUCUMBER GIN (IRE)**, 6, b m Oscar (IRE)—Redwood Lady (IRE) **Bradley Partnership**
9 **FEVERTRE (IRE)**, 5, ch g Sans Frontieres (IRE)—Avoca Star (IRE) **Bradley Partnership**
10 **FISTON DE BAUNE (FR)**, 4, b g Spanish Moon (USA)—Java de Baune (FR) **Bradley Partnership**
11 4, B g Leading Light (IRE)—Hushed Up (IRE) **Bradley Partnership**
12 **JOG ON (IRE)**, 7, b g Definite Article—Azabu Juban (IRE) **Bradley Partnership**
13 **MERRY MILAN (IRE)**, 8, b g Milan—Timerry (IRE) **Bradley Partnership**
14 **MOLE TRAP**, 9, b m Kayf Tara—Fairly High (IRE) **Bradley Partnership**
15 **MY LAST OSCAR (IRE)**, 5, b g Oscar (IRE)—Power Again (GER) **Bradley Partnership**
16 **OZZIE THE OSCAR (IRE)**, 9, b g Oscar (IRE)—Private Official (IRE) **Bradley Partnership**
17 **PINEAPPLE RUSH**, 7, b m Kayf Tara—Celtic Native (IRE) **Bradley Partnership**
18 **PURE VODKA**, 7, b m Westerner—Fairly High (IRE) **Bradley Partnership**
19 **SONOFTHEKING (IRE)**, 12, b g King's Theatre (IRE)—Nikadora (FR) **Bradley Partnership**
20 **STEADY AWAY (IRE)**, 6, b g Fame And Glory—Inch Pride (IRE) **Bradley Partnership**
21 **SYKES (IRE)**, 11, b g Mountain High (IRE)—Our Trick (IRE) **Bradley Partnership**
22 **THE TWO AMIGOS**, 8, b g Midnight Legend—As Was **Bradley Partnership**
23 **VODKA ALL THE WAY (IRE)**, 8, b g Oscar (IRE)—Fully Focused (IRE) **Bradley Partnership**
24 **WRONG SHAPE BALL (IRE)**, 4, b g Mahler—Ask June (IRE) **Bradley Partnership**

352 **MR CHRISTOPHER MASON, Caerwent**
Postal: Whitehall Barn, Five Lanes, Caerwent, Newport, Monmouthshire, Np26 5pe
Contacts: **PHONE 01291 422172 MOBILE 07970 202050 FAX 01633 666690**
EMAIL cjmasonracing@yahoo.co.uk

1 **AQUADABRA (IRE)**, 5, b h Born To Sea (IRE)—Amazing Win (IRE) **Mr Brian Hicks**
2 **ATTY'S EDGE**, 4, b g Coach House (IRE)—Belle's Edge **International Plywood (Importers) Ltd**
3 **DEL'S EDGE**, 4, b f Harbour Watch (IRE)—Elidore **Mr S Bishop & Mr C Mason**
4 **DISEY'S EDGE**, 4, b f Harbour Watch (IRE)—Edge of Light **Int Plywood (Importers) Ltd & C Mason**
5 **EDGED OUT**, 10, b m Piccolo—Edge of Light **Mr Christopher and Annabelle Mason Racing**
6 **GILT EDGE**, 4, b f Havana Gold (IRE)—Bright Edge **Mr S Bishop & Mr C Mason**
7 **JAGANORY (IRE)**, 8, b h Dylan Thomas (IRE)—Jacquelin Jag (IRE) **Mr Brian Hicks**

MR CHRISTOPHER MASON - continued

THREE-YEAR-OLDS
8 EDGE OF THE BAY, b f Cable Bay (IRE)—Sharpened Edge **Mr S Bishop & Mr C Mason**
9 GLAMOROUS ANNA, b c Cable Bay (IRE)—Go Glamorous (IRE) **Robert & Nina Bailey**

TWO-YEAR-OLDS
10 B c 30/04 Mayson—Edge of Light (Xaar)
11 GLAMOROUS BREEZE, b f 12/03 Cable Bay (IRE)—Go Glamorous (IRE) (Elnadim (USA)) **Robert & Nina Bailey**

Other Owners: Mrs J. H. Bailey, R. M. Bailey, Mr S. Bishop, Mr Christopher and Annabelle Mason Racing, International Plywood (Importers) Ltd, C. J. Mason.

Assistant Trainer: Miss Evie Young.

---

353 **MRS JENNIFER MASON, Cirencester**
Postal: **Manor Farm, Ablington, Bibury, Cirencester, Gloucestershire, GL7 5NY**
Contacts: **PHONE 01285 740445 MOBILE 07974 262438**
EMAIL pwmason2002@yahoo.co.uk WEBSITE www.jennifermasonracing.com

1 BONANZA SAM, 7, ch g Black Sam Bellamy (IRE)—Double Hit **G. MacEchern family & Mr N Mills**
2 CALL ME SID, 8, b g Schiaparelli (GER)—Zolotaya **Mr N. G. Mills**
3 FRILLY FROCK (IRE), 6, b m Mahler—Killoughey Baby (IRE) **Mason Racing Club**
4 GALLERY EXHIBITION (IRE), 13, b g Portrait Gallery (IRE)—Good Hearted (IRE) **Mr P. W. Mason**
5 NINTH WAVE (IRE), 6, b g September Storm (GER)—Royale Pearl **The Garland and Disney Families**

Other Owners: Gavin MacEchern, Mr N. G. Mills.

Assistant Trainer: Mr Peter W. Mason.

Amateur Jockey: Mr Peter Mason.

---

354 **MISS JANE MATHIAS, Llancarfan**
Postal: **Crosstown, Llancarfan, Vale of Glamorgan, CF62 3AD**
Contacts: **MOBILE 07779 382727**

1 DEFINATELY VINNIE, 10, ch g Vinnie Roe (IRE)—Sohapara **Mrs S. E. Mathias**

---

355 **MR PHILIP MCBRIDE, Newmarket**
Postal: **Exeter House Stables, 33 Exeter Road, Newmarket, Suffolk, CB8 8LP**
Contacts: **PHONE 01638 667841 MOBILE 07929 265711**

1 BOND STREET BEAU, 5, ch g Dandy Man (IRE)—Loveleaves **P. J. McBride**
2 BROUGHTONS FLARE (IRE), 4, ch g Rip Van Winkle (IRE)—Purple Glow (IRE) **Broughton Thermal Insulations**
3 CAMACHESS (IRE), 4, b f Camacho—Heeby Jeeby **The Narc Partnership**
4 FOUNTAIN OF LIFE, 4, b g Garswood—Suerte Loca (IRE) **Mr Chris Budgett & Mr P J McBride**
5 MOLLY MAI, 4, b f Mayson—Handsome Molly **The Ten Fools & A Horse Partnership**
6 PRISCILLA'S DREAM, 5, ch m Bated Breath—Be Free **Mr C Massie & Mr Pj McBride**
7 SIMBA SAMBA, 4, b g Leroidesanimaux (BRZ)—Rouge Dancer **PM Racing & P J McBride**
8 VAMPISH, 5, b m Sir Percy—Falling Angel **P. J. McBride**
9 ZACK MAYO, 6, b g Air Chief Marshal (IRE)—White Wedding (IRE) **Mrs Sarah Hamilton & Mr Chris Budgett 1**

THREE-YEAR-OLDS
10 BLAUSEE (IRE), b f Swiss Spirit—Fire Line **Maelor Racing**
11 INTIMATE MOMENT, b f Mustajeeb—Firebelly **Pmracing (Uk) Ltd**

MR PHILIP MCBRIDE - continued

12 **POKER MASTER (IRE),** b g Sepoy (AUS)—Three Cards **Mr Ian Pattle & P J Mcbride**
13 **PRISCILLA'S STAR,** b f G Force (IRE)—Amalfi (IRE) **Mr C Massie & Mr Pj McBride**
14 **SHINING AITCH,** gr g Sepoy (AUS)—Light Shine **Mr Howard J. Cooke & Mr P. J. Mcbride**
15 **SPARKLING DIAMOND,** b f Cable Bay (IRE)—Read Federica **Mrs Jacqui Barrs & Mr P. J. Mcbride**

Other Owners: Mrs J. Barrs, Mr C. M. Budgett, Mr A. D. Bunce, Mr H. J. Cooke, N. L. Davies, Mrs S. Hamilton, Mr D. L. Jackson, Mr C. Massie, P. J. McBride, Mr I. J. Pattle, Pmracing (Uk) Ltd, Mr R. Wilson.

356

MR DONALD MCCAIN, Cholmondeley
Postal: **D McCain Racing Ltd, Bankhouse, Cholmondeley, Cheshire, SY14 8AL**
Contacts: **PHONE** 01829 720351, 01829 720352 **MOBILE** 07903 066194
EMAIL info@donaldmccain.co.uk **WEBSITE** www.donaldmccain.co.uk

1 **4,** Ch f Sea The Moon (GER)—A Media Luz (FR) **T. G. Leslie**
2 **AKENTRICK,** 4, b g Champs Elysees—Torcross **Mrs L. Middleton**
3 **AMELIA'S DANCE (IRE),** 5, ch m Flemensfirth (USA)—
                                            Madame McGoldrick (IRE) **Mr Simon Munir & Mr Isaac Souede**
4 **ARMATTIEKAN (IRE),** 6, b g Arakan (USA)—Serpentine Mine (IRE) **Clwydian International**
5 **ARTICHOKE HEART,** 5, b m Shantou (USA)—Seedless **R Kent & Partner**
6 **ARTISTIC STREAK,** 4, b f New Approach (IRE)—Artisti **David & Carol Shaw**
7 **AWAY AT DAWN (IRE),** 5, b g Getaway (GER)—Wings At Dawn (IRE)
8 **BALATA BAY,** 4, b c Kyllachy—Cumana Bay **Mrs S. K. McCain**
9 **BANNIXTOWN GLORY (IRE),** 6, b m Fame And Glory—Me Auld Segosha (IRE) **Miss C. McCracken**
10 **BANRION SCAIRP (IRE),** 7, b m Scorpion (IRE)—Pairtree **Donald McCain Racing Club**
11 **BEACH BREAK,** 6, b g Cacique (IRE)—Wemyss Bay **Mr G. E. Fitzpatrick**
12 **BIRD ON THE WIRE (FR),** 5, ch g Martaline—Titi Jolie (FR) **T. G. Leslie**
13 **BLAKENEY POINT,** 7, b g Sir Percy—Cartoon **T W Johnson & G Maxwell**
14 **BRIGHT SIDE OFLIFE (IRE),** 7, ch m Doyen (IRE)—Lough Lein Leader (IRE) **T. G. Leslie**
15 **BROTHER PAT,** 5, b g Muhtathir—Comtesse du Sud (IRE) **The Coyne Family**
16 **BUCK CASSIDY (IRE),** 4, b g Shantou (USA)—River Rouge (IRE) **The Blue Nuns**
17 **CARRY ON,** 5, b g Footstepsinthesand—Evening **T. G. Leslie**
18 **CHELSEA FLYER (IRE),** 9, b g Westerner—Aktress (IRE) **Horse Watchers 1**
19 **CHELSEA'S BOY (IRE),** 7, gr g Rip Van Winkle (IRE)—St Roch (IRE) **Hale Racing Limited**
20 **CHTI BALKO (FR),** 8, br g Balko (FR)—Ina Scoop (FR) **Mr D. Carrington**
21 **CHUVELO (IRE),** 5, b g Milan—Bargante (IRE) **T. G. Leslie**
22 **COMMENTATOR,** 5, ch g Presenting—Grande Terre (IRE) **Mr & Mrs G. Calder**
23 **COURT DISMISSED (IRE),** 10, b g Court Cave (IRE)—Carramanagh Lady (IRE) **D. R. McCain**
24 **COURT JURADO (IRE),** 6, b g Court Cave (IRE)—Glen Eile (IRE) **David & Carol Shaw**
25 **COUSIN OSCAR (IRE),** 8, b g Oscar (IRE)—On The Jetty (IRE) **T. G. Leslie**
26 **CRAIG STAR (IRE),** 10, b g Craigsteel—Different Dee (IRE) **Hale Racing Limited**
27 **DEAR SIRE (FR),** 8, gr g Al Namix (FR)—Polismith (FR) **Green Day Racing**
28 **DEVITO'SREDROBIN (IRE),** 7, b m Robin des Champs (FR)—
                                      Koko Rose (IRE) **Bart Ryan-Beswick & Peel Bloodstock**
29 **ESME SHELBY (IRE),** 5, b m Arctic Cosmos (USA)—Kyle Again (IRE)
30 **FEDERICI,** 11, b g Overbury (IRE)—Vado Via **Mrs C Strang Steel 1**
31 **FIN AND GAME (IRE),** 8, b g Oscar (IRE)—Miss Cilla (IRE) **T. G. Leslie**
32 **FINGAL D'ARTHEL (FR),** 5, b g Cokoriko (FR)—La Fee d'Arthel (FR) **Mr Simon Munir & Mr Isaac Souede**
33 **FINISK RIVER,** 7, gr g Red Rocks (IRE)—Scopa d'Assi (IRE) **L. Buckley**
34 **GABRIEL OAK,** 4, b g Sir Percy—Maleficent **T. G. Leslie**
35 **GAELIK COAST (FR),** 6, br g Coastal Path—Gaelika (IRE) **T. G. Leslie**
36 **GARRIX DE LA SEE (FR),** 4, gr g Al Namix (FR)—Janita de La See (FR) **Miss C. McCracken**
37 **GET IN ROBIN (IRE),** 5, ch m Robin des Champs (FR)—Get In There (IRE) **T. G. Leslie**
38 **GLEBE AALIN (IRE),** 5, b br g Scorpion (IRE)—Glebe Dream (IRE) **Mr T. J. Hemmings**
39 **GOFFSBRIDGE GIRL (IRE),** 7, b m Touch of Land (FR)—The Bosses Mare (IRE) **Mr M. Kelly**
40 **GOOBINATOR (USA),** 4, ch g Noble Mission—Lilac Lilly (USA) **T. G. Leslie**
41 **GRAY DAY (IRE),** 9, gr g Daylami (USA)—Carrigeen Diamond (IRE) **Dr G. M. Thelwall Jones**
42 **GUILDHALL,** 4, b g Cityscape—Ecstasy **Mr J. M. Glews**

MR DONALD MCCAIN - continued

43 **HANDY HOLLOW (IRE)**, 7, ch g Beat Hollow—Hesperia **Donald McCain Racing Club**
44 **HART OF STEEL (IRE)**, 5, gr g Ask—Boberelle (IRE) **Mr N. Hartley**
45 **HEARTBREAK KID (IRE)**, 5, b g Getaway (GER)—Bella's Bury **T. G. Leslie**
46 **HENRY'S JOY (IRE)**, 7, b g Craigsteel—Shocona (IRE) **T. G. Leslie**
47 **KATACHENKO (IRE)**, 11, b g Kutub (IRE)—Karalee (IRE) **D. R. McCain**
48 **KHAMSIN MOOR (IRE)**, 5, b g Shirocco (GER)—Holme Rose **T. G. Leslie**
49 **KILLANE (IRE)**, 5, b g Cloudings (IRE)—Kilkylane (IRE) **Mr T. J. Hemmings**
50 **KING ORRY (IRE)**, 5, b g Oscar (IRE)—Deer Island Peg (IRE) **Mr T. J. Hemmings**
51 **KNOCK HOUSE (IRE)**, 11, ch g Old Vic—Lady's Gesture (IRE) **T. G. Leslie**
52 **KNOCKROBIN (IRE)**, 9, b br g Robin des Pres (FR)—Tudor Style (IRE) **Deva Racing Knockrobin Partnership**
53 **LADY TREMAINE (IRE)**, 5, b m Kalanisi (IRE)—
            Lough Lein Leader (IRE) **Mr D. Duncan, Duncan, Dunnington, Nicholls & Shaw**
54 **LAST GOLDEN TICKET (IRE)**, 5, b g Sholokhov (IRE)—Golden Flower (GER) **Owners Group 048**
55 **LI'L SEBASTIAN**, 4, gr g Aussie Rules (USA)—Granule **Tim & Miranda Johnson**
56 **LIGHTENING DANCE**, 6, b m Nathaniel (IRE)—Dance Lively (USA) **Tim & Miranda Johnson**
57 **LOFGREN**, 9, b g Multiplex—Sherry Darling (IRE) **Miss C. Lees-Jones**
58 **LOUGH DERG JEWEL (IRE)**, 9, b g Oscar (IRE)—River Valley Lady **Mrs A. E. Strang Steel**
59 **MACKENBERG (GER)**, 5, b g Jukebox Jury (IRE)—Mountain Melody (GER) **T. G. Leslie**
60 **MALPAS (IRE)**, 5, b g Milan—Skipping Along (IRE) **Mr T. J. Hemmings**
61 **MASTER MALACHY (IRE)**, 4, b g Mastercraftsman (IRE)—Stroke of Six (IRE) **T. G. Leslie**
62 **MIDDLEBROW (IRE)**, 9, b g Oscar (IRE)—O What A Girl (IRE) **Mrs S. K. McCain**
63 **MINELLA TRUMP (IRE)**, 6, b g Shantou (USA)—One Theatre (IRE) **T. G. Leslie**
64 4, B f Milan—Miss Cilla (IRE) **T. G. Leslie**
65 **MORRAMAN (IRE)**, 7, b g Gold Well—Casa Queen (IRE) **Richard & Holly Thomas**
66 **MOUNT MEWS (IRE)**, 9, b g Presenting—Kneeland Lass (IRE) **Mr T. J. Hemmings**
67 **MR MCGO (IRE)**, 9, b g Touch of Land (FR)—La Principal (IRE) **Mr J. M. Glews**
68 **NAVAJO PASS**, 4, b g Nathaniel (IRE)—Navajo Charm **T. G. Leslie**
69 **NAYATI (FR)**, 6, b g Spirit One (FR)—Smadouce (FR) **CP Racing**
70 **NEFYN BAY**, 11, b g Overbury (IRE)—So Cloudy **Tim & Miranda Johnson**
71 **NEFYN POINT**, 6, gr g Overbury (IRE)—So Cloudy **Tim & Miranda Johnson**
72 **O'HANRAHAN BRIDGE (IRE)**, 8, b g Gold Well—Greenacre Mandalay (IRE) **Mr M. Kelly**
73 **OCTOBER STORM**, 7, br g Shirocco (GER)—Cyber Star **Donald McCain Racing Club**
74 **OFCOURSEIWILL (IRE)**, 8, b g Publisher (USA)—Camden Princess (IRE) **Mr N. Hartley**
75 **ONTHEFRONTFOOT (IRE)**, 6, b g Shantou (USA)—On The Backfoot (IRE) **Duncan, Dunnington, Nicholls & Shaws**
76 **ORMESHER**, 5, b g Sir Percy—Marakabei **Sarah & Wayne Dale**
77 **OTTONIAN**, 6, ch g Dubawi (IRE)—Evil Empire (GER) **Nigel Dunnington & David Shaw**
78 **OUR RODNEY (IRE)**, 5, b g Canford Cliffs (IRE)—Sea Swell (USA) **Sarah & Wayne Dale 1**
79 **PARADISE RUN (IRE)**, 5, b m Fame And Glory—Azaban (IRE) **T. G. Leslie**
80 **PICHELOT (FR)**, 7, gr g Konig Turf (GER)—Haute Chartreuse (FR) **Mr Simon Munir & Mr Isaac Souede**
81 **PINCH OF GINGER (IRE)**, 9, ch g Golden Lariat (USA)—Espiritu Santo (IRE) **Miss C. McCracken**
82 **POGUE (IRE)**, 7, gr g Stowaway—Night Palm (IRE) **Mr J. Turner**
83 **PRESENTANDCOUNTING (IRE)**, 6, b g Presenting—Count On Me (IRE) **Mr J. Turner**
84 **PRINCE KHURRAM**, 10, b g Nayef (USA)—Saree **T. G. Leslie**
85 **PRINCESS MONONOKE (IRE)**, 9, b m Oscar (IRE)—Grande Solitaire (FR) **Donald McCain Racing Club**
86 **PULL GREEN (IRE)**, 5, b g Califet (FR)—Clogher Valley (IRE) **T. G. Leslie**
87 **QUART DE GARDE (FR)**, 5, b g Kapgarde (FR)—Wells Vision (GER) **Mr Simon Munir & Mr Isaac Souede**
88 **QUIDS IN (IRE)**, 7, b g Pour Moi (IRE)—Quixotic **Mrs I. I. Plumb**
89 **QUIK SHIFT (IRE)**, 6, b m Malinas (GER)—Kwaheri **D. R. McCain, R Kent & Partner, R. Kent**
90 **ROAD TO REWARD (IRE)**, 5, b g Gamut (IRE)—Lora Lady (IRE) **Birkdale Bloodstock**
91 4, B f Yorgunnabelucky (USA)—Rosie All Over
92 **SAME CIRCUS (IRE)**, 9, b m Brian Boru—Curragh Orpen (IRE) **Penketh & Sankey Jech Racing Club 1**
93 **SANDY STREET**, 4, b g Nayef (USA)—Apsara **Mr T. P. McMahon & Mr D. McMahon**
94 **SEE THE SEA (IRE)**, 6, b m Born To Sea (IRE)—Shahmina (IRE) **The Shinton Family 1**
95 **SHABBA DADA DO (IRE)**, 6, b m Jeremy (USA)—Koral Bay (IRE) **Beswick Brothers Bloodstock 1**
96 **SHALLOW RUN (IRE)**, 6, ch m Sholokhov (IRE)—Corrieann (IRE) **Mr E. Allen**
97 **SHANTALUZE (IRE)**, 8, b g Shantou (USA)—Nut Touluze (IRE) **Red Rum Racing**
98 **SHOCONA'S JOY (IRE)**, 6, b m Primary (USA)—Shocona (IRE) **Birkdale Bloodstock**
99 **SNOUGAR (IRE)**, 7, b g Arakan (USA)—Thorbella **Tim & Miranda Johnson**
100 **SONIC (IRE)**, 7, b g Vinnie Roe (IRE)—Bella's Bury **Special Piping Materials Ltd**

MR DONALD MCCAIN - continued

101 **SPIN THE COIN (IRE)**, 7, b g Witness Box (USA)—Kempinski (IRE) **Mrs S. C. Leslie**
102 **STEINKRAUS (IRE)**, 5, b g Jeremy (USA)—Red Fern (IRE) **Mr M. Pryde**
103 **SUBTLE QUEST (IRE)**, 6, b m Millenary—Subtle Hint (IRE) **Birkdale Bloodstock**
104 **SWASHBUCKLE**, 7, b g Dashing Blade—Inhibition **Mr M. J. Taylor**
105 **TAKINGITALLIN (IRE)**, 6, b m Fame And Glory—Gilt Benefit (IRE) **Mr G. E. Fitzpatrick**
106 **THE CATTLEJOBBER**, 8, b g Arvico (FR)—Stillhertoes **Mr N. Hartley**
107 **THE CON MAN (IRE)**, 7, b g Oscar (IRE)—Phillis Hill **T. G. Leslie**
108 **THE HERDS GARDEN**, 11, b g Multiplex—Hale Racing Limited & Mr D. Mccain Jnr
109 **THE SOME DANCE KID (IRE)**, 7, b g Shantou (USA)—River Rouge (IRE) **The Blue Nuns**
110 **THOMAS DO (IRE)**, 9, b g Flemensfirth (USA)—Loughaderra (IRE) **Deva Racing Persistence Partnership**
111 **TOTALLY REJECTED (IRE)**, 5, b g Mustameet (USA)—Boro Katie (IRE) **Four Counties**
112 **TWO BLONDES (IRE)**, 4, ch g Dragon Pulse (IRE)—Itaya (IRE) **Mr J. Turner**
113 **UBALTIQUE (FR)**, 12, b g Balko (FR)—Ode Antique (FR) **T. G. Leslie**
114 **UPSETTHEODDS (IRE)**, 8, b g Oscar (IRE)—Cruella de Vil **Clwydian Connections**
115 **VAL MOME (FR)**, 7, b g Turgeon (USA)—Valle Fleurie (FR) **Mr A. N. Brooke Rankin**
116 **WATCH AND LEARN**, 4, b f Havana Gold (IRE)—Charlecote (IRE) **Mrs B. E. McCain**
117 **WAZOWSKI**, 11, b g Overbury (IRE)—Malay **D. R. McCain**
118 5, Ch m Getaway (GER)—Whispers In Moscow (IRE) **Donald McCain Racing Club**
119 **WHITECHURCH (IRE)**, 6, br g Scorpion (IRE)—Flying Flame (IRE) **Mr T. J. Hemmings**
120 **WHITEOAK FLEUR**, 7, b m Black Sam Bellamy—Harringay **Mr B. J. Richardson**
121 **WINDING ROE (IRE)**, 6, ch g Vinnie Roe (IRE)—Brown Sheila (IRE) **Deva Racing & T.Fearn Winding Roe P'ship**
122 **WORD HAS IT (IRE)**, 6, b g Jeremy (USA)—Rathfeigh (IRE) **T. G. Leslie**
123 **YORVIK**, 6, b g Yeats (USA)—Overbranch **Mr & Mrs G. Calder, G. Calder, Mrs J. Calder**
124 **YOURACERT (IRE)**, 6, b g Multiplex—Calusa Crystal (FR) **Deva Racing Youracert 1**

Assistant Trainer: Adrian Lane.

NH Jockey: Henry Brooke, Brian Hughes, William Kennedy. **Conditional Jockey:** Jack Dinneen, Theo Gillard, Lorcan Murtagh.
Apprentice Jockey: Ella McCain. **Amateur Jockey:** Miss Abbie McCain.

---

357 **MR TIM MCCARTHY, Godstone**
Postal: **Nags Hall Farm, Oxted Road, Godstone, Surrey, RH9 8DB**
Contacts: **PHONE 01883 740379 MOBILE 07887 763062**
EMAIL tim@tdmccarthy.com

1 **UNDERSTORY (USA)**, 13, b g Forestry (USA)—Sha Tha (USA) **Homecroft Wealth Racing & T D McCarthy**
2 **W G GRACE (IRE)**, 5, b g Exceed And Excel (AUS)—Ownwan (USA) **Homecroft Wealth Racing & T D McCarthy**
3 **WATER THIEF (IRE)**, 8, b g Bellamy Road (USA)—Sometime (IRE) **Surrey Racing Club**
4 **WHITE TOWER (IRE)**, 6, b g Cape Cross (IRE)—Star Blossom (USA) **Surrey Racing Club**

Other Owners: Homecroft Wealth Racing, T. D. McCarthy, Mr B. Pettis, Mr S. J. Piper.

Assistant Trainer: Mrs C.V. McCarthy.

---

358 **MR PHIL MCENTEE, Newmarket**
Postal: **Racefield Stables, Carriageway, Hamilton Road, Newmarket, Suffolk, CB8 7JQ**
Contacts: **PHONE 01638 662092 MOBILE 07802 663256**
WORK EMAIL mcenteephil@yahoo.com

1 **BERNIE'S BOY**, 7, b g Lilbourne Lad (IRE)—Stoney Cove (IRE) **T. D. Johnson**
2 **CONTINGENCY FEE**, 5, b g Helmet (AUS)—Hearsay **Mr M. B. Hall**
3 **GLOBAL MELODY**, 5, b g Hellvelyn—Dash of Lime **T. D. Johnson**
4 **LONDON (FR)**, 7, b g Galileo (IRE)—Altana (USA) **T. D. Johnson**
5 **MARGARET J**, 4, gr f Bated Breath—Louverissa (IRE) **Mr S. Jakes**
6 **PEARL SPECTRE (USA)**, 9, ch g Street Cry (IRE)—Dark Sky (USA) **Mr S. Jakes**
7 **REDEMPTIVE**, 4, b f Royal Applause—Hope And Fortune (IRE) **Miss M. Bishop-Peck**

MR PHIL MCENTEE - continued

  8 **SONG OF SUMMER,** 5, ch m Choisir (AUS)—Height of Summer (IRE) **Mrs R. L. Baker**
  9 **SPLIT DOWN SOUTH,** 4, gr g Dark Angel (IRE)—Brown Eyed Honey **T. D. Johnson**
10 **SWISS VINNARE,** 6, b g Arabian Gleam—Matilda Peace **Mr S. Jakes**
11 **VALLEY BELLE (IRE),** 4, b f Slade Power (IRE)—Al Sharood **T. D. Johnson**

THREE-YEAR-OLDS
12 **COMEATCHOO (IRE),** b g Camacho—La Estatua **Mr S. Jakes**

TWO-YEAR-OLDS
13 **BAYTOWN POLLY,** b f 12/03 Pearl Secret—Portland Belle (IRE) (Fastnet Rock (AUS)) (800) **Miss R. B. McEntee**
14 Ch c 24/04 Sepoy (AUS)—Jimmy's Girl (IRE) (Equiano (FR)) (800) **Mr S. Jakes**
15 **YOUNG CHARLIE,** b g 20/02 Fountain of Youth (IRE)—Margrets Gift (Major Cadeaux) (1000) **Mr S. Jakes**

359
MR MURTY MCGRATH, Maidstone
Postal: **Galway Barn, Kiln Barn Road, East Malling, Kent, ME19 6BG**
Contacts: **PHONE 01732 840173 MOBILE 07818 098073**
EMAIL mjmcgrath@hotmail.com

1 **RAGSTONE ROAD (IRE),** 5, b g Kodiac—Greenflash **Gallagher Bloodstock Limited**
2 **SEI BELLA,** 6, b m Crosspeace (IRE)—Dizzy Whizz **M. McGrath**
3 **WHO WHAT WHEN,** 5, b m Champs Elysees—Freya Tricks **Mr R. P. Gallagher**
4 **WILD ANIMAL,** 4, b g Kingman—Epic Similie **Gallagher Bloodstock Limited**

THREE-YEAR-OLDS
5 **BOUBYAN (IRE),** ch g Sea The Stars (IRE)—Madhulika (FR) **Mr R. P. Gallagher**
6 **STEALTH COMMAND,** b g War Command (USA)—Akhila (IRE) **Mr R. P. Gallagher**

Assistant Trainer: Heidi McGrath.

360
MRS JEAN MCGREGOR, Milnathort
Postal: **Wester Tillyrie Steading, Milnathort, Kinross, KY13 0RW**
Contacts: **PHONE 01577 861792 MOBILE 07764 464299**
EMAIL purebred68@hotmail.co.uk

1 **BURLINGTON BERT (FR),** 9, b g Califet (FR)—Melhi Sun (FR) **The Good To Soft Firm**
2 **DIAMOND ROAD (IRE),** 6, b g Tikkanen (USA)—Silver Tassie (FR)
3 **GIAMAS,** 7, b g Bollin Eric—Ginger Brandy **Mrs D. Thomson**
4 **GO COMPLAIN,** 8, b m Mount Nelson—Trounce **Mrs J. C. McGregor**
5 **JACKOFHEARTS,** 12, b g Beat Hollow—Boutique **Mr S. Taylor**
6 **OSCAR BLUE (IRE),** 10, gr g Oscar (IRE)—Blossom Rose (IRE) **Tillyrie Racing Club**

NH Jockey: Henry Brooke, Sean Quinlan.

361
MR LUKE MCJANNET, Newmarket
Postal: **Heath View Stables, Hamilton Road, Newmarket, Suffolk, CB8 0NY**
Contacts: **PHONE 01638 664505**

1 **ACT OF MAGIC (IRE),** 4, b g Magician (IRE)—Davanti (IRE) **The Mojito Partnership**
2 **HIDEAWAY,** 4, b f Universal (IRE)—Loose Caboose (IRE) **Timms, Timms & McCabe**
3 **NOBLE GESTURE,** 5, b g Finjaan—Bexandella **Mr R W Reed & Mrs E J Reed**
4 **NORMANDY BLUE,** 5, ch g Le Havre (IRE)—Ballerina Blue (IRE) **Providence Racing**
5 **RED ARMOUR,** 4, b f Nayef (USA)—Ansina (USA) **Miss R. Dennis**

MR LUKE MCJANNET - continued

6 **RED SKYE DELIGHT (IRE)**, 4, gr f Clodovil (IRE)—Sole Bay **Miss R. Dennis**
7 **SAPPHIRE STAR**, 4, b f Firebreak—Diapason (IRE) **Mrs J. Degnan**
8 **SMUGGLERS CREEK (IRE)**, 6, b g Medicean—Crystany (IRE) **Mr A. McLuckie**
9 **SWEET AND DANDY (IRE)**, 5, b m Dandy Man (IRE)—Translator (IRE) **Miss R. Dennis**
10 **WILD FLOWER (IRE)**, 8, b m Approve (IRE)—Midsummernitedream (GER) **Miss R. Dennis**

THREE-YEAR-OLDS

11 **BAD ATTITUDE**, b c Canford Cliffs (IRE)—Cry Freedom (IRE) **Mr N. P. Hardy**
12 B g Helmet (AUS)—Daheeya **Hever Stud Farm Ltd**
13 **JANE VICTORIA**, ch f Helmet (AUS)—Winter Hey Lane (USA) **Hever Stud Farm Ltd**
14 Ch f Mukhadram—Pompeia **Hever Stud Farm Ltd**
15 B c Elzaam (AUS)—Translator (IRE)

TWO-YEAR-OLDS

16 **RED AMAPOLA**, b f 31/03 Marcel (IRE)—Si Belle (IRE) (Dalakhani (IRE)) (2000) **Miss R. Dennis**
17 **TAYLOR THE SAILOR**, ch c 13/04 New Approach (IRE)—Arwaah (IRE) (Dalakhani (IRE)) (7000) **Mr I. Collier**

Other Owners: Mr A. J. McCabe, Mr A. C. O Sullivan, Mrs C. E. O Sullivan, Mrs E. J. Reed, R. W. Reed, Mr A. C. Timms, Mr M. E. Timms.

362

MS KAREN MCLINTOCK, Newcastle Upon Tyne
Postal: **The Byerley Stud, Ingoe, Newcastle-Upon-Tyne, NE20 0SZ**
Contacts: **PHONE 01661 886356 MOBILE 07966 776710**
EMAIL karen.mclintock@equiname.co.uk WEBSITE www.karenmclintock.co.uk

1 **AVENUE OF STARS**, 7, b g Makfi—Clifton Dancer **Geoff Topham & Don Eddy**
2 **BIG LES (IRE)**, 5, b g Big Bad Bob (IRE)—Love Match **Stockdale Racing**
3 **BLACK FRIDAY**, 5, b g Equiano (IRE)—The Clan Macdonald **Miss S.A Booth & Don Eddy**
4 **DIODORUS (IRE)**, 6, b g Galileo (IRE)—Divine Proportions (USA) **Exors of the Late Mr G. Topham**
5 **DUBAWI FIFTY**, 7, b g Dubawi (IRE)—Plethora **Mr & Mrs Paul & Clare Rooney**
6 **EVERKYLLACHY (IRE)**, 6, br m Kyllachy—Superfonic (FR) **Ever Equine & Self Preservation Society**
7 **GOOD MAN (IRE)**, 7, ch g New Approach (IRE)—Garden City (FR) **Mr D. Eddy**
8 **GREY MIST**, 6, gr g Mastercraftsman (IRE)—Kekova **Brian Chicken & Equiname Ltd**
9 **GURKHA FRIEND**, 8, b g Showcasing—Parabola
10 **HIGH FORT (IRE)**, 5, b g Acclamation—Barracade (IRE) **Ian Clements & Don Eddy**
11 **PHANTASMAL**, 6, b g Pivotal—Asaawir **Mrs L. A. Ogilvie**
12 **TRINITY STAR (IRE)**, 9, gr g Kheleyf (USA)—Zamiyla (IRE) **Trinity Racing**
13 **URBAN SPIRIT (IRE)**, 6, b g Born To Sea (IRE)—Rose of Mooncoin (IRE) **Mr I. R. Clements & Dr L. G. Parry**
14 **WEATHER FRONT (USA)**, 7, ch g Stormy Atlantic (USA)—Kiswahili **Mr Ken Eales & Self Preservation Society**
15 **ZABEEL STAR (IRE)**, 8, ch g Arcano (IRE)—Deep Winter **The Self Preservation Society**

Other Owners: Miss S. A. Booth, B. Chicken, Mr I. R. Clements, Mr J. Cockcroft, Mr R. Cockcroft, Mr S. Cockcroft, Mr W. Cockcroft, Mr K. F. Eales, Mr D. Eddy, K. R. Elliott, Equiname Ltd, Ever Equine, Mr I. J. B. Gray, Dr L. G. Parry, The Self Preservation Society, Exors of the Late Mr G. Topham, Mr T. J. Whiting.

Assistant Trainer: Donald Eddy.

363

MR GRAEME MCPHERSON, Stow-On-The-Wold
Postal: **Martins Hill, Bledington Road, Stow-on-the-Wold, Gloucestershire, GL54 1JH**
Contacts: **PHONE 01451 830769 MOBILE 07815 887360**
EMAIL info@mcphersonracing.co.uk WEBSITE www.mcphersonracing.co.uk

1 **AJAY'S WAYS (IRE)**, 6, br g Stowaway—Beechfield Queen (IRE) **Burr & Dudwell Racing**
2 **ALEXANDER THE GREY**, 9, gr g Fair Mix (IRE)—Cadourova (FR) **Mr Howard Burdett/Mr Graeme P. Mcpherson**
3 **AMI DESBOIS (FR)**, 10, b g Dream Well (FR)—Baroya (FR) **The Reserved Judgment Partnership**
4 **ANDALEEP (IRE)**, 4, b g Siyouni (FR)—Oriental Magic (GER) **Finch Forbes and McPherson**

MR GRAEME MCPHERSON - continued

5 4, B f Shirocco (GER)—Ariels Serenade (IRE)
6 ASK BEN (IRE), 7, b g Ask—Decheekymonkey (IRE) **Mrs E. A. Prowting**
7 ASK HENRY (IRE), 7, b g Ask—Miss Muppet (IRE) **Turf Club 2018 & Graeme McPherson**
8 AVIEWTOSEA (IRE), 5, b g Where Or When (IRE)—Final Run (IRE)
9 4, B g Sholokhov (IRE)—Barrack Buster
10 BENTONS LAD, 9, br g Bollin Eric—Spirit of Ecstasy **The McPherson Racing Partnership**
11 BUDDING ROBIN, 7, b g Robin des Pres (FR)—Another Vodka (IRE) **Mr J. Chamberlain**
12 CALUM GILHOOLEY (IRE), 6, br g Kalanisi (IRE)—Honeyed (IRE) **Burr & Dudwell Racing**
13 CAPTAIN DINOSAUR (IRE), 7, b g Scorpion (IRE)—Fromrussiawithlove **Mr G. P. McPherson**
14 CAST IN GREY (IRE), 6, b g r m Fame And Glory—Derrinlanna (IRE) **Foxtrot Racing: Cast In Grey**
15 DAYDREAM AULMES (FR), 7, b g Linda's Lad—My Wish Aulmes (FR) **Ms S Howell & Partner**
16 4, B g Ask—Decheekymonkey (IRE) **Burr & Dudwell Racing**
17 DEHRADUN, 4, b g Australia—Ridafa (IRE) **Mrs L.Day, Mr H.Burdett & Mr G.McPherson**
18 DELIRIOUS LOVE (IRE), 8, b g Definite Article—Grangeclare Lark (IRE) **Wildcat Syndicate**
19 4, B g Fame And Glory—Derriana (IRE)
20 DERRICK D'ANJOU (IRE), 9, b g Double Eclipse (IRE)—Belle d'Anjou (FR) **The Odd Foxes**
21 DUBLIN FOUR (IRE), 6, ch g Arakan (USA)—Eluna **Fry & Mosvold**
22 ELK BRIDGE (IRE), 6, b m Dansant—Just Jodie (IRE) **Mrs E. A. Prowting**
23 ESSENDON (FR), 5, gr g Aussie Rules (USA)—Inhibition **Kingsclere Racing Club**
24 EXPLOITEUR (FR), 6, b br g Desir d'Un Soir (FR)—Sourya d'Airy (FR) **Shaw Racing Partnership 2**
25 EYEOFTHESCORPION (IRE), 6, b g Scorpion (IRE)—Shuil Sharp (IRE) **First With Mortgages Limited**
26 5, B g Aizavoski (IRE)—Faraday Lady (IRE) **Mr G. P. McPherson**
27 FLANN, 5, b g Brian Boru—Lady Karinga **Mr I. M. O'Doherty**
28 FLEETING VISIT, 7, b g Manduro (GER)—Short Affair **The FV Partnership**
29 FOLLOW THE SWALLOW (IRE), 12, b g Dr Massini (IRE)—Old Chapel (IRE) **Mrs Mary M Gwillam & Partner**
30 GALEA DU LIVET (FR), 4, b f Spanish Moon (USA)—Six Pack (FR)
31 HATTAAB, 7, b g Intikhab (USA)—Sundus (USA) **You Can Be Sure**
32 HELLO BUDDY (IRE), 6, ch g Salutino (GER)—Cotton Candy (IRE) **Mr J. Chamberlain**
33 HIGH WELLS, 6, b g High Chaparral (IRE)—Valencha **Mr G. P. McPherson**
34 HOMING STAR, 5, b m Harbour Watch (IRE)—Nightunderthestars **The Cotswold Stars**
35 IT'S FINE WINE, 7, b g Multiplex—Reem Two
36 JESSICA RABBIT, 6, b m Mawatheeq (USA)—Intersky High (USA) **The McPherson Racing Partnership**
37 KAYF BLANCO, 11, b g Kayf Tara—Land of Glory **Mrs L.Day, Mr H.Burdett & Mr G.McPherson**
38 LONDONIA, 8, gr g Paco Boy (IRE)—Snowdrops **The McPherson Racing Partnership**
39 LORD SCOUNDREL (IRE), 11, b g Presenting—Noble Choice **Mr G. P. McPherson**
40 MARBLE SANDS (FR), 4, gr g Martaline—Sans Rien (FR) **Mr D. L. Adams**
41 MISS KATNISS, 6, br m Kayf Tara—Kate Hill Dancer (IRE) **The McPherson Racing Partnership**
42 MISSTHECUDDLES (IRE), 6, b m Gold Well—Autumn Sky (IRE) **TyroneForSam**
43 MY CHARITY (IRE), 9, b g King's Theatre (IRE)—Benefit Ball (IRE) **Burr & Dudwell Racing**
44 NORMAN STANLEY (IRE), 8, b g Flemensfirth (USA)—Ballerina Laura (IRE) **Mr G. P. McPherson**
45 5, B g Oscar (IRE)—Notanotherone (IRE)
46 PASSING SHADOW, 6, b g Passing Glance—Peel Me A Grape **Mrs E. A. Prowting**
47 4, B f Fame And Glory—Prelude
48 RATFACEMCDOUGALL (IRE), 7, b g Robin des Champs (FR)—Milano Bay (IRE) **Mrs C. Kendrick**
49 SAMMYLOU (IRE), 7, b g Beneficial—Carrigeen Diamond (IRE) **DI Adams, Ja Adams & G McPherson**
50 SHADY GLEN (IRE), 11, br g Dr Massini (IRE)—Poppins (IRE) **Mrs Jill Phillips & Graeme McPherson**
51 SKIPTHECUDDLES (IRE), 9, b g Westerner—Autumn Sky (IRE) **TyroneForSam**
52 STYNES (IRE), 10, b g Aussie Rules (USA)—Magic Princess **The McPherson Racing Partnership**
53 TELSON BARLEY (IRE), 7, b g Scorpion (IRE)—El Monica (IRE) **Mrs L. Day**
54 THE DISTANT LADY (IRE), 6, b m Fracas (IRE)—Misty Native (IRE) **4 Left Footers & A Blewnose**
55 THUNDERSOCKSSUNDAE (IRE), 5, b g Yeats (IRE)—Roseabel (IRE) **4 Left Footers & A Blewnose**
56 TORQUAY, 7, b m Aqlaam—Torcross **Mr G. P. McPherson**
57 WILDE WATER (IRE), 6, b g Oscar (IRE)—Pay The Ferryman (IRE) **Mrs L. Day**
58 ZULU DAWN (IRE), 6, b g Fame And Glory—Maslam (IRE) **The Grand Cru Partnership**

Other Owners: Mr D. L. Adams, Mrs J. A. Adams, Mr H. Burdett, Mr A. N. Cheyne, Mr A. N. Clark, Mrs M. M. Gwillam, Ms S. A. Howell, Col A. J. E. Malcolm, Mr G. P. McPherson, Mrs J. D. Phillips, Turf Club 2018.

Assistant Trainer: Mick Finn, Jodie Mogford.

NH Jockey: Kielan Woods. **Conditional Jockey:** Tom Humphries. **Amateur Jockey:** Miss Lily Pinchin.

364

MR MARTYN MEADE, Manton
Postal: **Manton Estate Office, Manton, Wiltshire, SN8 4HB**
Contacts: **PHONE 01672 555000 MOBILE 07879 891811**
EMAIL mmeade@martynmeaderacing.com WEBSITE www.martynmeaderacing.com

1 **ASSUMING (IRE)**, 4, ch f Ruler of The World (IRE)—Bold Assumption **Mantonbury Stud**
2 **AXXELERATION**, 4, b f Monsieur Bond (IRE)—Tibesti **R. C. Bond**
3 **CADRE DU NOIR (USA)**, 4, b c War Front (USA)—Dynamic Feature (USA) **Phoenix Thoroughbred Limited**
4 **CONFIDING**, 4, b c Iffraaj—Entre Nous (IRE) **Manton Park Racing**
5 **CRACKLING (IRE)**, 4, b c Vale of York (IRE)—Almatlaie (USA) **Manton Park Racing**
6 **EBURY**, 4, ch c Iffraaj—Alabelle **Manton Park Racing**
7 **ENGROSSED (IRE)**, 4, ch f Tamayuz—Last Cry (FR) **Mantonbury Stud**
8 **FOX VARDY (USA)**, 4, b g Frankel—Dance With Another (IRE) **King Power Racing Co Ltd**
9 **FRILLY**, 4, ch f Frankel—Ladies Are Forever **Mrs Jane Newett 1**
10 **GRAYLING**, 4, b f Sea The Stars (IRE)—Silver Grey (IRE) **Mantonbury Stud**
11 **HEADLAND**, 4, b g Harbour Watch (IRE)—Bazzana **The Below Reeve Partnership**
12 **INFRASTRUCTURE**, 4, gr f Raven's Pass (USA)—Foundation Filly **Sefton Syndicate**
13 **LOVING GLANCE**, 4, b f Invincible Spirit (IRE)—Kissable (IRE) **Lordship Stud 1**
14 **LUMINATION**, 4, b g Toronado (IRE)—Sparkling Eyes **Manton Park Racing**
15 **LYZBETH (FR)**, 4, b f Zoffany (IRE)—Arcangela **Mantonbury Stud**
16 **MARLYN (IRE)**, 4, b f Exceed And Excel (AUS)—Myrine (IRE) **Mantonbury Stud**
17 **MONOGAMY**, 4, br gr f Poet's Voice—White Wedding (IRE) **Mantonbury Stud**
18 **OPPORTUNIST**, 4, b c Cape Cross (IRE)—Argent du Bois (USA) **Manton Park Racing**
19 **PEARL OF MANAMA (USA)**, 4, b br f Scat Daddy (USA)—Auction (IRE) **Phoenix Thoroughbred Limited**
20 **RISE HALL**, 5, b g Frankel—Forever Bond **R. C. Bond**
21 **TECHNICIAN (IRE)**, 4, gr c Mastercraftsman (IRE)—Arosa (IRE) **Team Valor 1**
22 **THEOULE (FR)**, 4, b br g Le Havre (IRE)—Santa Louisia **Manton Park Racing**

THREE-YEAR-OLDS

23 **ADDITIONAL (IRE)**, ch c Night of Thunder (IRE)—Aris (IRE) **Phoenix Thoroughbred Limited**
24 **ALBUM (IRE)**, gr c Clodovil (IRE)—Michael's Song (IRE) **Phoenix Thoroughbred Limited 1**
25 **ASPIRATION (IRE)**, b f Footstepsinthesand—Van de Cappelle (IRE) **Mantonbury Stud**
26 Ch c Free Eagle (IRE)—Badr Al Badoor (IRE) **Manton Park Racing**
27 B c Slade Power (IRE)—Bonfire Heart **Manton Park Racing**
28 **CLAREYBLUE (IRE)**, gr c Zebedee—Fancy Feathers (IRE) **Nick Bradley Racing - Mm41**
29 B br g New Approach (IRE)—Clear Voice (USA) **Manton Park Racing**
30 **COURTESY**, b f Uncle Mo (USA)—As Good As Gold (IRE) **Mantonbury Stud**
31 **DAWNING (IRE)**, ch f Iffraaj—Arabian Mirage **Mrs Paul Shanahan 1**
32 B c Cable Bay (IRE)—Euroceleb (IRE) **Manton Park Racing**
33 **GENTLY SPOKEN (IRE)**, b gr f Gutaifan (IRE)—Always Gentle (IRE) **Mrs B V Sangster 1**
34 **GOSSIP**, b f Exceed And Excel (AUS)—Al Sharood **Mantonbury Stud**
35 **OWNEY MADDEN**, b c Oasis Dream—Terre du Vent (FR) **Chelsea Thoroughbreds - Owney Madden 1**
36 Gr f Sea The Stars (IRE)—South Sister **Mantonbury Stud**
37 **SUBSIDIZE**, ch f Dandy Man (IRE)—Sheer Indulgence (FR) **Phoenix Thoroughbred Limited 1**
38 **SYCAMORE (IRE)**, b c Kingman—Scarborough Fair **Manton Park Racing**
39 **TENFOLD (IRE)**, b g Born To Sea (IRE)—Dear Dream (IRE) **Manton Park Racing**
40 Ch f Australia—Timeless Call (IRE) **Mantonbury Stud**
41 **VIADUCT**, b c Showcasing—Folly Bridge **Manton Park Racing**
42 **VISIBILITY (IRE)**, b g Raven's Pass (USA)—Cry Pearl (USA) **Manton Park Racing**

TWO-YEAR-OLDS

43 B br c 18/04 Flintshire—Ballade's Girl (USA) (Saint Ballado (CAN)) (78000) **Manton Park Racing**
44 B c 30/03 Shalaa (IRE)—Black Rodded (Bahamian Bounty) (61904) **Chelsea Thoroughbreds - Owney Madden 1**
45 B f 03/02 Footstepsinthesand—Bonfire Heart (Exceed And Excel (AUS)) (47619)
46 Ch f 16/02 Zoffany (IRE)—Connecting (Singspiel (IRE)) (15238)
47 B c 24/02 Kodiac—Dancing Jest (IRE) (Averti (IRE)) (120000)
48 Ch c 10/03 Mehmas (IRE)—Darsan (IRE) (Iffraaj) (19047)
49 Ch c 02/04 Zoffany (IRE)—Lake Nona (Authorized (IRE)) (30000)
50 B gr f 25/04 Mastercraftsman (IRE)—Lifting Me Higher (IRE) (Sea The Stars (IRE)) (40000)
51 B c 22/03 Galileo (IRE)—Modernstone (Duke of Marmalade (IRE)) (500000) **Ballylinch Stud**
52 B f 05/03 Kodiac—Pilates (IRE) (Shamardal (USA)) (57142)

MR MARTYN MEADE - continued

53 B c 21/03 Toronado (IRE)—Rock Cake (IRE) (Fastnet Rock (AUS))
54 B f 09/05 Galileo (IRE)—Sahara Sky (IRE) (Danehill (USA)) (150000)
55 B f 20/02 Belardo (IRE)—Semaral (IRE) (High Chaparral (IRE)) (30476)

Other Owners: Mr N. Bradley, Chelsea Thoroughbreds - Owney Madden, Chelsea Thoroughbreds Ltd, Mrs E. A. Harris, T. F. Harris, Miss S. Holden, Manton Park Racing, Mr F. M. Meade, Mrs J. E. Newett, Nick Bradley Racing 41, Phoenix Thoroughbred Limited, Mr T. J. Ramsden, Mrs L. O. Sangster, Mrs L. M. Shanahan, Team Valor LLC.

Assistant Trainer: Freddie Meade.

---

365 | **MR NOEL MEADE, Navan**
Postal: **Tu Va Stables, Castletown KP, Navan, Co Meath, C15 F384, Ireland**
Contacts: PHONE **+353 46 905 4197** MOBILE **+353 87 256 6039**
EMAIL **tuvastables@gmail.com** WEBSITE **www.noelmeade.com**

1 **ACTIVE FORCE (IRE)**, 7, br g Oscar (IRE)—Terracotta Queen (IRE)
2 **ARCH STANTON (IRE)**, 7, b g Jeremy (USA)—Half-Hitch (USA)
3 **ARGENTORATUM (IRE)**, 5, b g Mustameet—Connemara Rose
4 **ART OF AMERICA**, 5, br g American Post—Marigay's Magic
5 **BALLYHOT BOY (IRE)**, 5, b g Le Fou (IRE)—Esbeggi
6 **BARBARY MASTER**, 5, br g Presenting—Daisies Adventure
7 **BATTLE OF MIDWAY (IRE)**, 6, b g Mahler—Womanofthemountain (IRE)
8 **BEACON EDGE (IRE)**, 6, b g Doyen (IRE)—Laurel Gift (IRE)
9 **BEN THOMSON (IRE)**, 4, b g Famous Name—Essaoira Jewel
10 **BOMBAY BLUE (IRE)**, 6, b g Vocalised—Langfuhrina
11 **BRACE YOURSELF (IRE)**, 7, ch g Mahler—Angelica Garnett
12 **CALICOJACK (IRE)**, 8, b g Beneficial—Ballyoscar (IRE)
13 **CAP YORK (FR)**, 8, b g Ballingarry (IRE)—Robbe (FR)
14 **CAPTAIN MC (IRE)**, 5, b g Mahler—Deise Dreamer
15 **CARRIGEEN ROSE (IRE)**, 5, b m Jeremy (USA)—Carrigeen Kohleria (IRE)
16 **CASK MATE (IRE)**, 7, b g Kalanisi (IRE)—Littleton Liberty
17 **CHAMPAGNE DIVA**, 5, ch m Stowaway—Allys Bubble (IRE)
18 **CHARLIE SIRINGO**, 5, ch g Getaway (GER)—Drumderry (IRE)
19 **CHEROKEE BILL**, 9, b g Robin des Champs (FR)—Daizinni
20 **COCOHULABABY (IRE)**, 5, ch m Casamento—Rockahoolababy
21 **COOLBAWN LAD (IRE)**, 5, b g Imperial Monarch (IRE)—Hollygrove Bonnie (IRE)
22 **COSMO'S MOON (IRE)**, 7, b g Morozov (USA)—She's A Dreamer (IRE)
23 **DALY TIGER (FR)**, 7, b g Tiger Groom—Reine Tresor (FR)
24 **DAVY'S DILEMMA**, 6, b g Sixties Icon—Wandsyke Lass
25 **DE NAME ESCAPES ME (IRE)**, 10, ch g Vinnie Roe (IRE)—Heartlight (IRE)
26 **DEPLOYED (IRE)**, 6, b g Mahler—Brook Style (IRE)
27 **DEXTER TIGER (FR)**, 5, b g Saddex—Indian Tigress (IRE)
28 **DINARD ROSE (IRE)**, 4, b f Champs Elysees—Rose of Petra (IRE)
29 **DIOL KER (FR)**, 6, b g Martaline—Stiren Bleue (FR)
30 **DIS DONC (FR)**, 7, b g Kingsalsa (USA)—Skarina (FR)
31 **DON'T CROSS ME (FR)**, 4, b g Cape Cross—Sahool
32 4, B f Yeats—Down Ace
33 **DREAM CONTI (FR)**, 7, br g Lauro (GER)—Posterite (FR)
34 **EUROBOT**, 6, ch g Malinas (GER)—L'Aventure (FR)
35 **FACE THE ODDS (IRE)**, 5, b g Presenting—Miss Otis Regrets
36 **FANTASIA ROQUE (FR)**, 5, b m Blue Bresil—Bible Gun
37 **FARCEUR DU LARGE (FR)**, 5, b g Turgeon (USA)—Antagua (FR)
38 **FAUGUERNON (FR)**, 6, b g Martaline—I'm Right (USA)
39 **FIRST APPROACH (IRE)**, 7, b g Robin des Champs (FR)—Manhattan Babe (IRE)
40 **FLANKING MANEUVER (IRE)**, 5, b g Beat Hollow—Corskeagh Shadow
41 **FREE RANGER (IRE)**, 6, b g Lope de Vega (IRE)—Purple Tigress
42 **FUTURE PROOF (IRE)**, 5, b g Dream Ahead (USA)—Moraga (IRE)
43 **GAIUS DE MARCIGNY (FR)**, 4, gr g Legolas—Quety De Marcigny
44 **GHURBA (IRE)**, 6, b m Aqlaam—Mahaatheer (IRE)

MR NOEL MEADE - continued

45 **GIPSI JOE (FR)**, 4, gr g Montmartre—Island Du Frene
46 **GLINT IN HER EYE (IRE)**, 6, b m Presenting—Sharoose
47 **GOAHEADWITHTHEPLAN**, 5, b g Stowaway—Backandillo
48 **GUIDED BY YOU (IRE)**, 7, b g Getaway (GER)—Black Ouzel (IRE)
49 4, Ch g Ocovango—Had To Be Done
50 **HALF THE ODDS (IRE)**, 8, b m Flemensfirth (USA)—Technohead (IRE)
51 **HARRY ALONZO (IRE)**, 4, ch g Montmartre—Patrola
52 **HARVEST BOW (IRE)**, 4, b gr f Intikhab (USA)—Ghost of A Girl (IRE)
53 **HEISENBERG (IRE)**, 4, b g Milan—Native Idea
54 **HENRY BROWN (IRE)**, 5, b g Mahler—Blackeyedsue (IRE)
55 **HEROESANDVILLAINS**, 7, b gr g Beneficial—Keys Pride (IRE)
56 **HES A HARDY BLOKE (IRE)**, 5, b g Alzavoski—Talk Of Rain
57 **HIGHLAND CHARGE (IRE)**, 5, b g Fame And Glory—Full Of Birds
58 **HYPNOTICE FORCE**, 5, b m Lethal Force—Hip
59 **IAMASTARTOO (IRE)**, 7, ch m Well Chosen—Lobinstown Girl (IRE)
60 **ICE COLD SOUL (IRE)**, 10, b g Stowaway—Western Whisper
61 **IDAS BOY (IRE)**, 6, ch g Dubai Destination—Witness Express
62 **IFICUDIWUD (IRE)**, 7, b g Trans Island—Manucrin
63 **IMPATIENT PARTNER (IRE)**, 7, b g Gold Well—Madmoiselle Etoile (IRE)
64 **IN YOUR SHADOW (IRE)**, 6, gr g Stowaway—Classic Lin (FR)
65 **JAKOBY (IRE)**, 6, b g Frozen Fire (GER)—Morning Rise (GER)
66 **JERANDME (IRE)**, 6, b g Azamour—Estrelle
67 **JESSE EVANS (IRE)**, 4, b g So You Think—American Princess
68 **JESSICA'S BOY (IRE)**, 6, b g Court Cave (IRE)—Fathom Cross Lady (IRE)
69 **JOSHUA WEBB (IRE)**, 5, b g Flemensfirth (USA)—Lady of Appeal (IRE)
70 **KILLER MILLER (IRE)**, 11, b g Flemensfirth (USA)—Miss Brandywell (IRE)
71 **KILLER MODE (IRE)**, 5, b g Doyen—Cantou
72 4, B f Presenting—Kings Artist
73 **KIRWANS LANE (IRE)**, 7, ch g Excellent Art—Sosua (IRE)
74 **LAURA BULLION (IRE)**, 4, b f Canford Cliffs (IRE)—Vivachi (IRE)
76 **LIEUTENANT COMMAND (FR)**, 6, gr g Kendargent (FR)—Maternelle (FR)
77 **LIGNOU (FR)**, 5, b g Rajsaman (FR)—Lady Meydan (IRE)
78 **LILL SMITH (IRE)**, 7, b m Gold Well—Vivachi (IRE)
79 **LIVING'S BOY AN CO (FR)**, 5, b g Diamond Boy—Living Start
80 **MAGIC LADY (IRE)**, 6, b m Doyen—May's Magic
81 **MAJOR DESTINATION (IRE)**, 9, b g Dubai Destination (USA)—Clara Allen (IRE)
82 **MELLY AND ME (IRE)**, 7, b g Kalanisi (IRE)—College Daisy (IRE)
83 **MINELLA FAIR (IRE)**, 9, b g Flemensfirth (USA)—Bell Walks Run (IRE)
84 **MISS COGNAC**, 5, b m Flemensfirth (USA)—Miss Brandywell (IRE)
85 4, Br g Ocovango—Mistress Pope
86 **MOMUS (IRE)**, 7, b g Touch of Land (FR)—Accordion To Bob (IRE)
87 **MOYROSS**, 9, b g Kayf Tara—Dancing Dasi (IRE)
88 **NARCISSISTIC (IRE)**, 8, b g Robin des Champs (FR)—Night Therapy (IRE)
89 **NIGHT COMBAT (IRE)**, 5, b br g Presenting—Synthe Davis
90 **PART TIME FARMER (IRE)**, 4, b g Westerner—Sherin
91 **PAT'S PICK (IRE)**, 6, b g Shantou (USA)—Lady Lenson (IRE)
92 **PIENTA (USA)**, 5, b h Liaison (USA)—Belen (USA)
93 **POWERFUL TED (IRE)**, 5, b g Power—Haaf OK
94 **QUITE INCREDIBLE (IRE)**, 4, b g Shirocco—Daizinni
95 **RAGIN CAJUN (IRE)**, 7, b g Kalanisi (IRE)—Dipp In The Dark (IRE)
96 **RED GERRY (IRE)**, 4, b g Canford Cliffs (IRE)—Hollow Talk
97 **RED JACK (IRE)**, 7, b g Mahler—Hollygrove Bonnie (IRE)
98 **ROAD TO RESPECT (IRE)**, 9, ch g Gamut (IRE)—Lora Lady (IRE)
99 **ROSENCRANTZ (IRE)**, 6, b g Flemensfirth (USA)—Miss Brandywell (IRE)
100 **ROSGALME (IRE)**, 5, b g Mahler—Woodville Queen (IRE)
101 **RUSSIAN BILL (IRE)**, 10, b g Kalanisi (IRE)—Littleton Liberty
102 **SCHOOL BOY HOURS (IRE)**, 7, b g Presenting—Trinity Alley (IRE)
103 **SEEYOUINVINNYS (IRE)**, 6, b g Carlotamix (FR)—Deploy Or Die (IRE)
104 **SELLARBRIDGE (IRE)**, 5, b g Well Chosen—Dubai Petal (IRE)
105 **SHEISDIESEL**, 6, ch m Harbour Watch (IRE)—Rockme CockneyMR NOEL MEADE - continued

MR NOEL MEADE - continued

106 SIXSHOOTER (IRE), 5, ch g Well Chosen—Lobinstown Girl (IRE)
107 SNOW FALCON (IRE), 10, b g Presenting—Flocon de Neige (IRE)
108 STAR ADVENTURE (IRE), 6, b m Gold Well—Vivachi (IRE)
109 STEEL CABLE, 5, b g Well Chosen—Apache Rose (IRE)
110 SUPER FOLLO (FR), 8, b g Enrique—Summer Belle (FR)
111 THE CADDY ROSE (IRE), 6, br m Presenting—Las Princess (IRE)
112 THE RED MENACE (IRE), 6, ch g Mountain High (IRE)—Heather Sue (IRE)
113 THEDEVILSCOACHMAN (IRE), 4, br g Elusive Pimpernel—Hagawi
114 TOUT EST PERMIS (FR), 7, gr g Linda's Lad—Kadalbleue (FR)
115 TRAPPIST MONK (IRE), 7, b g Beneficial—Cush Jewel (IRE)
116 TRUMP LEGEND, 5, b g Mastercraftsman (IRE)—Minor Vamp (IRE)
117 UNION GAP (IRE), 5, b g Canford Cliffs (IRE)—Vivachi (IRE)
118 VALDIEU (FR), 7, b g Diamond Boy (FR)—Vamuna (FR)
119 VILLAGE MYSTIC (FR), 9, b g Saint Des Saints—Mistica
120 WESTERN FANCY (IRE), 6, b g Presenting—Noras Fancy
121 YOUNG TED (IRE), 6, b g Fame And Glory—Last of Many (IRE)
122 ZAMBEZIR (FR), 5, ch g Zambezi Sun—Lanciana (IRE)

THREE-YEAR-OLDS

123 BASS REEVES, b g Es Que Love (IRE)—Anazahl (USA)
124 BILL DOOLIN, b g Australia—Star Waves (IRE)
125 CHARLIE BASSETT (IRE), b g Lawman (FR)—Xinji (IRE)
126 CRASSUS (IRE), b c War Command—Buck Aspen
127 CROSSGUNS, b g Epaulette (AUS)—Maoin Dor (IRE)
128 CURIOUS BRIDE (IRE), b br f Excelebration—Padma
129 FANNIE PORTER, b f Tagula (IRE)—Eucharist (IRE)
130 HELVIC DREAM, b c Power—Rachevie (IRE)
131 JEFF KIDDER (IRE), b g Hallowed Crown (AUS)—Alpine
132 LAYFAYETTE (IRE), b c French Navy—Scala Romana
133 LUKE SHORT, b g Sayif (IRE)—Acclamare (IRE)
134 NATAHOOLABABY (IRE), b f Es Que Love—Rockahoolababy
135 PERRY OWENS (IRE), b g Free Eagle (IRE)—Peace Signal (USA)
136 QUICK QUICK (IRE), gr g Zebedee—Owega Dale

TWO-YEAR-OLDS

137 Gr c 14/04 Markaz—Avaselle (Ad Valorem)
138 Br g 06/03 Tagula—Big Bad Lily (Big Bad Bob)
139 B f 08/05 Requinto—Buck Aspen (Seeking The Gold)
140 B c 15/02 Charm Spirit—Cloud Line (Danehill Dancer)
141 B f 06/03 Alhebayeb—Glorious Melody (Dylan Thomas)
142 GREY ANGEL (IRE), ch gr f 23/02 Lethal Force—Ski Slope (Three Valleys)
143 Ch c 01/03 Farhh—Impetious (Inchinor)
144 B f 15/03 Marcel—Jersey Cream (Iffraaj)
145 Ch c 28/04 Dragon Pulse—Keilogue (Invincible Spirit)
146 B c 19/05 Dream Ahead—Loutka (Trempolino)
147 B c 01/04 Requinto—Lukes Well (Shirocco)
148 B c 23/04 Fast Company—Mindy (Zamindar)
149 B c 07/03 Dawn Approach—My Henrietta (Henrythenavigator)
150 SHEISBYBRID (IRE), gr f 29/04 Mastercraftsman—Empowermentofwomen (Manduro)
151 B f 28/03 Belardo—Sonning Rose (Hawk Wing)
152 B c 13/04 Tamayuz—Spring Crocus (Noverre)
153 B f 01/04 Sir Prancealot—Suburban Sky (Dandy Man)
154 B f 02/03 Dawn Approach—Thames Pageant (Dansili)

Owners: Gigginstown House Stud, High Spirits Racing Club, J. Hunt, Mrs P. Hunt, Laurelmore Partners, J. P. McManus, Mrs Derville Meade.

Assistant Trainer: Damien McGillick, Ted Walsh Jnr, **Head Man:** Paul Cullen, **Travelling Head:** Emma Connolly, **Racing Secretary:** Katie Daly.

NH Jockey: Sean Flanagan, Jonathan Moore. **Conditional Jockey:** Eoin Walsh. **Amateur Jockey:** Mr Jay Archdeacon, Mr Mark O'Hare.

366 | **MR BRIAN MEEHAN, Manton**
Postal: Trainer did not wish details of their string to appear

367 | **MR DAVID MENUISIER, Pulborough**
Postal: Shinco Racing Limited, Coombelands Racing Stables, Coombelands Lane, Pulborough, West Sussex, RH20 1BP
Contacts: MOBILE 07876 674095
WORK EMAIL david@dmhorseracing.com WEBSITE www.dmhorseracing.com
TWITTER @DavidMenuisier

1 **ARCHIMENTO**, 7, ch g Archipenko—Caribana
2 **ATALANTA'S BOY**, 5, b g Paco Boy (IRE)—Affirmatively **Mrs Monica Josefina Borton & Partner**
3 **CHAMP AYR**, 4, b g Champs Elysees—Rose Ayr **Mr W. F. N. Davis**
4 **CHIAVE DI VOLTA**, 5, ch g Intello (GER)—Silca Chiave **Mr C. A. Washbourn**
5 **DEAN STREET DOLL (IRE)**, 4, b f Oasis Dream—Soho Rose (IRE) **Mr C. A. Washbourn**
6 **DRAGONS VOICE**, 6, b g Poet's Voice—China **Heart of the South Racing 106**
7 **EDMOND DANTES (IRE)**, 4, gr g Alhebayeb (IRE)—Abhasana (IRE) **Mme C Head & Partner**
8 **HISTORY WRITER (IRE)**, 5, b g Canford Cliffs (IRE)—Abhasana (IRE) **Clive Washbourn & Partner**
9 **KALOOR**, 4, b g Nathaniel (IRE)—Blinking **Mr J. L. Day**
10 **MIGRATION (IRE)**, 4, b g Alhebayeb (IRE)—Caribbean Ace (IRE) **Gail Brown Racing (IX)**
11 **NUITS ST GEORGES (IRE)**, 5, ch g Mount Nelson—Twelfth Night (IRE) **Boy George Partnership**
12 **SIMPLETWISTOF FATE (USA)**, 4, b br f Quality Road (USA)—Element of Truth (USA) **Mr C. N. Wright**
13 **THUNDERING BLUE (USA)**, 7, gr ro g Exchange Rate (USA)—Relampago Azul (USA) **Mr C. A. Washbourn**

THREE-YEAR-OLDS

14 **ANDITSNONAYNEVER**, b c No Nay Never (USA)—Fantastisch (IRE) **Mrs M. C. Sweeney**
15 **FLYIN' SOLO**, b c Roderic O'Connor—Fille Good
16 **GYPSY WHISPER**, b f Helmet (AUS)—Secret Insider (USA) **Gail Brown Racing (A)**
17 **INTO FAITH (FR)**, b c Intello (GER)—Have Faith (IRE) **All for One Racing**
18 **LANVAL (IRE)**, b c Camelot—Flamingo Sea (USA) **Gail Brown Racing (XI)**
19 **LUIGI VAMPA (FR)**, b c Elvstroem (AUS)—Sunday Rose **Shinco Racing Limited**
20 **MY SILVER BEAR**, gr c Gregorian (IRE)—Torrecilla **Mrs S. The Frost, Mrs A.Hollis & Mr W.Kenny**
21 **POETIC LILLY**, b f Poet's Voice—Lilly Junior **Heart of the South Racing 116**
22 B c Toronado (IRE)—Russian Rhapsody **The Cromhall Stud**
23 **SAHARAN SHIMMER**, b c Oasis Dream—Come Touch The Sun (IRE) **Mr C. A. Washbourn**
24 **SHOULDERING (IRE)**, b f Epaulette (AUS)—Abhasana (IRE) **Clive Washbourn & Robert Wasey**
25 **WINTER REPRISE (FR)**, b c Intello (GER)—Winter Fashion (FR) **Mr C. A. Washbourn**
26 **WITCH HUNT (IRE)**, b c Lawman (FR)—Witches Brew (USA) **Gail Brown Racing (X)**
27 **WONDERFUL TONIGHT (FR)**, b br f Le Havre (IRE)—Salvation **Mr C. N. Wright**

TWO-YEAR-OLDS

28 B f 11/02 Havana Gold (IRE)—B Berry Brandy (USA) (Event of The Year (USA))
29 **BELLOCCIO**, gr c 29/01 Belardo (IRE)—Three Cards (Mastercraftsman (IRE)) (53196) **All for One Racing**
30 **CHATEAU D'IF**, b c 03/04 Intello (GER)—
Moonlight Cass (IRE) (Danehill Dancer (IRE)) (14586) **Shinco Racing Limited**
31 B c 01/03 Coulsty (IRE)—Daleside (Vale of York (IRE))
32 **DARK IMAGE**, b f 06/04 Awtaad (IRE)—Cool Kitten (IRE) (One Cool Cat (USA))
33 B c 08/03 Harzand (IRE)—Djumama (IRE) (Aussie Rules (USA)) (49764) **Australian Bloodstock & Mark Scott**
34 Ch c 16/05 New Approach (IRE)—Fullaah (IRE) (Shamardal (USA)) **Miss Emily Asprey & Christopher Wright**
35 B c 15/02 Pivotal—Idealist (Rip Van Winkle (IRE))
36 **KELMSCOTT (IRE)**, gr ro c 12/04 Mastercraftsman (IRE)—Zaya (GER) (Diktat) (60000) **Gail Brown Racing (XII)**
37 **LAMORNA COVE**, b f 14/03 Footstepsinthesand—Abbakova (IRE) (Dandy Man (IRE)) **Gail Brown Racing (B)**
38 B f 06/04 Le Havre (IRE)—Roger Sez (IRE) (Red Clubs (IRE))
39 B c 24/01 Vadamos (FR)—Selfara (Oasis Dream) (42857) **H.H. Shaikh Nasser Al Khalifa & Partner**
40 B f 12/03 Maxios—Shiramiyna (IRE) (Invincible Spirit (IRE)) (77220) **Mrs A. K. Oldfield**

MR DAVID MENUISIER - continued

Other Owners: H.H. Sheikh Nasser Al Khalifa, Mr S. A. Ashley, Miss Emily Charlotte Asprey, Australian Bloodstock, Chasemore Farm, Forever Optimists, Mrs S. Frost, Greens Racing, Mrs C. Head, Heart Of The South Racing, Mrs A. Hollis, Hot To Trot Racing, Mr W. Kenny, Mr J. J. Lancaster, Mr J. Lovett, Mrs M. J. Martinez-Borton, Mrs D. J. Merson, Mrs H Ringrose & Mrs D Thompson, Mr F. Nass, Pollards Stables, D. R. Price, Mrs W. J. Price, Mr Gordon Roddick, Mr M. L. L. Scott, Shinco Racing Limited, Mr R. G. Wasey, Mr C. A. Washbourn, Mr C. N. Wright.

---

368 | **MISS REBECCA MENZIES, Sedgefield**
Postal: **Howe Hills Farm, Sedgefield, Stockton-On-Tees, Cleveland, TS21 2HG**
Contacts: **MOBILE 07843 169217**
WORK EMAIL Rebecca@rebeccamenziesracing.co.uk WEBSITE www.rebeccamenziesracing.com
TWITTER @Rebeccaemenzies

1 **ALL HAIL CAESAR (IRE)**, 6, b g Nathaniel (IRE)—Ragiam (ITY) **The Top Silk Syndicate**
2 **ALPH (IRE)**, 6, b g Gold Well—She's Our Banker (IRE) **Mile High Racing**
3 **AREYOUWITHUS (IRE)**, 5, b g Watar (IRE)—Miss Sinnott (IRE) **J. Wade**
4 **BACKPACKER (IRE)**, 5, ch g Tobougg (IRE)—Oscars Vision (IRE) **J. Wade**
5 **BALLYCRYSTAL COURT (IRE)**, 8, b g Court Cave (IRE)—Monavale (IRE) **PMPro31 Ltd**
6 **BARNEY BULLET (IRE)**, 5, b g Havana Gold (IRE)—Lalinde **Marwood Racing**
7 **BREIZH ALKO (FR)**, 9, ch g Balko (FR)—Quisiera (FR) **Mr D. Parry**
8 6, Br m Le Fou (IRE)—Brienna (IRE) **Mrs Angela Bennett**
9 **CAPTAIN MOWBRAY**, 9, ch g Shami—Some Like It Hot **Rebecca Menzies Racing Partnerships**
10 **CELTIC ARTISAN (IRE)**, 9, ch g Dylan Thomas (IRE)—
Perfectly Clear (USA) **Rebecca Menzies Racing Partnerships**
11 **CHARMING DREAM (FR)**, 6, b g Dream Well (FR)—Changing Times (FR) **The Number 7 Club**
12 **COOL POSSIBILITY (IRE)**, 4, b g Dark Angel (IRE)—Pink Diva (IRE) **Jolly Boys Outing**
13 **DRAGON MALL (USA)**, 7, b g Blame (USA)—Petition the Lady (USA) **Mr & Mrs Ian Hall**
14 **DUTCH PURSUIT (IRE)**, 4, b g Canford Cliffs (IRE)—Dansili Dutch (IRE) **Riverside Racing Syndicate**
15 **ELUSIVE POPPY**, 5, b m Black Sam Bellamy (IRE)—Pelican Point **BumpersToJumpers 2**
16 4, B g Arcadio (GER)—Emma Jane (IRE) **J. Wade**
17 **FABIANSKI (IRE)**, 5, ch m Raven's Pass (USA)—Fabia (IRE) **Stoneleigh Racing**
18 **FAIR SHERIFF**, 6, gr m Fair Mix (IRE)—Sheriff's Falcon (IRE) **Falcon's Line Ltd**
19 **FALCONE DE BERSY (FR)**, 5, b g Maresca Sorrento (FR)—Tropulka God (FR) **J. Wade**
20 **GARDE FORESTIER (FR)**, 8, b g Forestier (FR)—Nette Rousse (FR) **J. Wade**
21 **HALCYON DAYS**, 11, b g Generous (IRE)—Indian Empress **Centaur Racing Club**
22 4, Ch g Gentlewave (IRE)—Himitas (FR) **Mr Pete Ingram**
23 **IM TOO GENEROUS**, 10, ch g Generous (IRE)—Something Major (IRE) **John Dance & Partner**
24 **ISLAND VILLA (IRE)**, 11, b g Turtle Island (IRE)—Violet Ville (IRE) **The Extra Time Partnership**
25 **LANDING NIGHT (IRE)**, 8, b g Kodiac—Night Delight (IRE) **Titanium Racing Club**
26 **LITTLE MEG**, 8, b m Josr Algarhoud (IRE)—Why The Big Paws
27 **LORD BRENDY**, 12, gr g Portrait Gallery (IRE)—Hervey Bay **Mrs R. A. Robson**
28 **MAID IN MANHATTAN (IRE)**, 6, b m Fame And Glory—Silly Goose (IRE) **Rebecca Menzies Racing Partnerships**
29 **MAJOR SNUGFIT**, 4, b g Ruler of The World (IRE)—Bridle Belle **Mr Adrian Greenwood, Mr Simon Windle**
30 **MY GALWAY GIRL (IRE)**, 6, b m Presenting—Our Lucky Venture (IRE) **For Sale**
31 **NADINE**, 5, b m Nathaniel (IRE)—Opening Ceremony (USA) **H. M. Hurst**
32 4, B g Well Chosen—Native Kin (IRE) **J. Wade**
33 **NORTONTHORPELEGEND (IRE)**, 10, b g Midnight Legend—Tanit **Miss M. D. Myco**
34 **PAIN AU CHOCOLAT (FR)**, 9, b g Enrique—Clair Chene (FR) **Mike and Eileen Newbould**
35 **PHANTOM ISLE**, 7, b g Teofilo (IRE)—Antillia **J. Wade**
36 **RAFFERTY'S RETURN**, 5, b g Schiaparelli (GER)—Duchess Theatre (IRE) **J. Wade**
37 **ROAD WARRIOR**, 6, gr g Fair Mix (IRE)—Mimi Equal **Mr N. Taylor**
38 **SCHALKE**, 5, b g Malinas (GER)—Prospero's Belle (IRE) **Sapphire Print Solutions Ltd**
39 **SCORCHED BREATH**, 4, b g Bated Breath—Danvers **Mr Joe Soiza**
40 **SCOTTISH ACCENT (IRE)**, 7, b g Golan (IRE)—Onthelongfinger (IRE) **Blacklock Simpson & Partner**
41 **SEARANGER (USA)**, 7, b g U S Ranger (USA)—
Baby Lets Cruise (USA) **Icm Racing, Kingmaker Racedays, Menzies**
42 **SET IN STONE (IRE)**, 6, b m Famous Name—Storminateacup (IRE) **Weight, Howe & Oliver**

MISS REBECCA MENZIES - continued

43 **SHE'S A DANCER (IRE)**, 5, b m Jeremy (USA)—Sugar Bullet (IRE) **J. Wade**
44 **SHINEDOWN (IRE)**, 5, b m Sholokhov (IRE)—Good Shine (IRE) **Centaur Racing Club**
45 **SKA RIDGE**, 8, b g Distant Peak (IRE)—Tandawizi **J. Wade**
46 **STORMBAY BOMBER (IRE)**, 11, b g September Storm (GER)—Top Tottie (IRE) **Mr P R Walker & Mr R Walker**
47 **SULAFAAT (IRE)**, 5, ch m Haatef (USA)—Elraabeya (CAN) **Mr J. A. Lister**
48 **TABOU BEACH BOY**, 4, b g Mukhadram—Illandrane (IRE) **J. Wade**
49 **TEELAR**, 6, b m Milan—Hervey Bay **Mrs R. A. Robson**
50 **THAT'S MY DUBAI (IRE)**, 7, b m Dubai Destination (USA)—Musical Accord (IRE) **Stoneleigh Racing**
51 **THE MEKON**, 5, b g Red Jazz (USA)—Date Mate (USA) **Marwood Racing**
52 **TOI STOREY (IRE)**, 7, b g Winged Love (IRE)—Where's Herself (IRE) **Liz Dixon & Shelagh Fagen 1**
53 **TOUGH REMEDY (IRE)**, 5, b g Tough As Nails (IRE)—Remediate (USA) **Titanium Racing Club**
54 **UKNOWMYMEANING (IRE)**, 6, ch g Touch of Land (FR)—Lucy Lodge (IRE) **The Extra Time Partnership**
55 **WAITING FOR RICHIE**, 7, b g Rail Link—Heart of Hearts **Love To Race Partnership**
56 **XPO UNIVERSEL (FR)**, 11, b g Poliglote—Xanadu Bliss (FR) **Club Racing Xpo Partnership**

THREE-YEAR-OLDS

57 **BAD RABBIT (IRE)**, b g Iffraaj—Bint Nayef (IRE) **Stonegrave Thoroughbreds**
58 B f Califet (FR)—Desert Moon (IRE) **Miss E. Hall**
59 **DUTCH SPIRIT**, gr f Most Improved (IRE)—Dansili Dutch (IRE) **Geoff & Sandra Turnbull**
60 B f Yeats (IRE)—Innishmore (IRE) **Miss E. Hall**
61 **JUST CALL ME ELLA**, ch f Iffraaj—Daughter Dawn (IRE) **H. M. Hurst**
62 **NITRIC BOLT**, b g Nathaniel (IRE)—Sandy Shaw **Miss R. E. A. Menzies**
63 **PRISSY MISSY (IRE)**, b f Gutaifan (IRE)—Maracuja **Stonegrave Thoroughbreds**
64 **RED TREBLE**, b f Iffraaj—Threetimesalady **Flying High**
65 **ROMAN'S EMPRESS (IRE)**, b f Holy Roman Emperor (IRE)—Dabtiyra (IRE) **Stonegrave Thoroughbreds**
66 **STORMY GIRL (IRE)**, b c Night of Thunder (IRE)—Refusetolisten (IRE) **Stonegrave Thoroughbreds**
67 **TRUMPETS CALL (IRE)**, b g Anjaal—Yellow Trumpet **Stonegrave Thoroughbreds**
68 **TWISTED DREAMS (USA)**, b br g Twirling Candy (USA)—Sweet Promises (USA) **Titanium Racing Club**
69 Ro gr f Authorized (IRE)—Zariziyna (IRE) **Stonegrave Thoroughbreds**

TWO-YEAR-OLDS

70 Bl c 17/04 Outstrip—Alluring Star (Gentleman's Deal (IRE)) **For Sale**
71 B f 05/02 Camacho—Dubai Sea (USA) (Street Sense (USA)) **Miss R. E. A. Menzies, For Sale**
72 Ch c 16/04 Sepoy (AUS)—How Fortunate (Haafhd) **E. A. Brook**
73 B f 01/03 Swiss Spirit—Pryers Princess (Medicean) (4761) **H. M. Hurst**

Other Owners: Mr I. M. Blacklock, Mr J. E. Dance, Ms D. Fields, Mr M. Gornall, Mr I. Harle, Mr P. J. Howe, ICM Racing, Kingmaker Racedays Club, Mr P. Lawrenson, Love To Race Partnership, Miss R. E. A. Menzies, Mrs E. E. Newbould, Mr J. M. Newbould, Mr R. G. Oliver, Mr I. Simpson, Major P. H. K. Steveney, Stonegrave Thoroughbreds, Mr P. R. Walker, Mr R. Walker, Mr A. C. Weight, Dr P. M. Weight.

Secretary: Mrs Emma Ramsden, **Business & Racing Manager:** Philip Lawrenson, **Yard Sponsor:** Bluegrass Horse Feeds.

Flat Jockey: Cam Hardie, PJ McDonald, Megan Nicholls. **NH Jockey:** Nathan Moscrop, Conor O'Farrell. **Conditional Jockey:** Kane Yeoman. **Amateur Jockey:** Miss Leah Cooper.

---

369 MR PHIL MIDDLETON, Aylesbury
Postal: **Dorton Place, Dorton Park Farm, Dorton, Aylesbury, Buckinghamshire, HP18 9NR**
Contacts: **PHONE** 01844 237503 **MOBILE** 07860 426607 **FAX** 01844 237503

1 **EVA'S DIVA (IRE)**, 6, b m Getaway (GER)—Shouette (IRE) **Mr P. W. Middleton**
2 **GOLAN FORTUNE (IRE)**, 8, b g Golan (IRE)—Ballyknock Alainn (IRE) **P Middleton, M Lowther**
3 **MAWLOOD (IRE)**, 4, b g Dawn Approach (IRE)—Kalaatah (USA) **P Middleton, M Lowther**
4 **SKEAPING**, 7, b g Excellent Art—Gale Green **Mr P. W. Middleton**
5 **SOPAT (IRE)**, 7, b m Gold Well—Silver Prayer (IRE) **Mr P. W. Middleton**

Other Owners: Mr M. Lowther, Mr P. W. Middleton.

370 | MR PAUL MIDGLEY, Westow

Postal: **The View, Sandfield Farm, Westow, York, North Yorkshire, YO60 7LS**
Contacts: **PHONE 01653 658790 MOBILE 07976 965220 FAX 01653 658790**
EMAIL ptmidley@aol.com WEBSITE www.ptmidgley.com

1 **AIRWAVES**, 4, b f Monsieur Bond (IRE)—Forever Bond
2 **BUCCANEERS VAULT (IRE)**, 8, gr g Aussie Rules (USA)—Heaven's Vault (IRE)
3 **BUNIANN (IRE)**, 4, b g Tamayuz—Darajaat (USA)
4 **DESERT ACE (IRE)**, 9, ch g Kheleyf (USA)—Champion Place
5 **FINAL VENTURE**, 8, b g Equiano (FR)—Sharplaw Venture
6 **GAMESOME (FR)**, 9, b g Rock of Gibraltar (IRE)—Hot Coal (USA)
7 **GOOD LUCK FOX (IRE)**, 4, b g Society Rock (IRE)—Violet Ballerina (IRE)
8 **GROUNDWORKER (IRE)**, 9, b g Tagula (IRE)—Notepad
9 **I AM A DREAMER**, 4, b g Dream Ahead (USA)—Alexander Ballet
10 **INDIAN SOUNDS (IRE)**, 4, b g Exceed And Excel (AUS)—Sarinda
11 **JAMES WATT (IRE)**, 4, b g Morpheus—Tomintoul Singer (IRE)
12 **JOHNNY CAVAGIN**, 11, b g Superior Premium—Beyond The Rainbow
13 **LINE OF REASON (IRE)**, 10, br g Kheleyf (USA)—Miss Party Line (USA)
14 **LONGROOM**, 8, b g Oasis Dream—Phantom Wind (USA)
15 **MANSHOOD (IRE)**, 7, b g Iffraaj—Thawrah (IRE)
16 **MERRY BANTER**, 6, b m Bated Breath—Merry Diva
17 **MILITIA**, 5, b g Equiano (FR)—Sweet As Honey
18 **MOSTAHEL**, 6, b g Acclamation—Entente Cordiale (IRE)
19 **MR ORANGE (IRE)**, 7, b g Paco Boy (IRE)—Shirley Blake (IRE)
20 **MUTAFARRID (IRE)**, 5, gr g Dark Angel (IRE)—Margarita (IRE)
21 **NIBRAS AGAIN (IRE)**, 6, b g Kyllachy—Regina
22 **ORVAR (IRE)**, 7, b g Dandy Man (IRE)—Roskeen (IRE)
23 **PATRICK (IRE)**, 8, b g Acclamation—Red Liason (IRE)
24 **PAVERS PRIDE**, 6, ch g Bahamian Bounty—Pride of Kinloch
25 **PUMAFLOR (IRE)**, 8, b g Aussie Rules (USA)—Krasotka (IRE)
26 **SALUTI (IRE)**, 6, b g Acclamation—Greek Easter (IRE)
27 **SAMBUCCA SPIRIT**, 4, b g Charm Spirit (IRE)—Hokkaido
28 **SPARK OF WAR (IRE)**, 5, b g Declaration of War (USA)—Acts of Grace (USA)
29 **TANASOQ (IRE)**, 7, b g Acclamation—Alexander Youth (IRE)
30 **TARBOOSH**, 7, b g Bahamian Bounty—Mullein
31 **THE DEFIANT**, 4, b g Morpheus—Killer Class
32 **VAN GERWEN**, 7, ch g Bahamian Bounty—Disco Ball
33 **WAR WHISPER (IRE)**, 7, b g Royal Applause—Featherweight (IRE)

THREE-YEAR-OLDS

34 **CECE CEYLON**, b f Iffraaj—Scent of Roses (IRE)
35 **IT'S NOT MY FAULT (IRE)**, b f Lawman (FR)—Paddy Again (IRE)

TWO-YEAR-OLDS

36 B f 20/01 Vadamos (FR)—Big Violett (IRE) (Haatef (USA)) (4718)
37 B g 02/03 Monsieur Bond (IRE)—Bond Artist (IRE) (Excellent Art)
38 B g 27/02 Mukhadram—Chance of Bubbles (IRE) (Exceed And Excel (AUS)) (11153)
39 Gr f 14/03 Gutaifan (IRE)—Cockaleekie (USA) (Alphabet Soup (USA)) (1886)

Owners: Mr C. Alton, Mr Colin Alton & Mr P. T. Midgley, Mr M. R. Baker, Mr J. M. Barker, Mr P Bateson, Mr J. Batty, A. Bell, Mr A. Bell & Mr P.T. Midgley, Mr A. B. Blackburn, Mrs G. I. Blackburn, Mr J. N. Blackburn, Mr J Blackburn & Mr A Turton, Blackburn Family, R. C. Bond, Mr R. Bradley, Mrs S. Bradley, R Bradley & M Hammond, Robert Bradley & P T Midgley, Sheila Bradley & P.T. Midgley, Mrs A. Brady, Mr F. Brady, Miss H. Brady, Mr J. Brady, Joe & Frank Brady, Miss R. Brady, Mr F Brady & Mr J S Morrison, Carl Chapman & Partner, Mr C. Chapman, Carl & Ryan Chapman, Mr R. Chapman, Chris Priestley & Partner, Dab Hand Racing, Mr D. B. Ellis, Mr M. K. Hammond, M Hammond & P T Midgley, Mr G. Hardy, M Hammond, Mad For Fun & Partners, D. Mann, Marwood Racing Limited, Mr P. T. Midgley, Mr T. W. Midgley, Mr J S Morrison, J. S. Morrison & Frank Brady, Mr G. J Paver, D. Pearson, Peedeetee Syndicate, Peedeetee Syndicate, Ta Stephenson & Twm, A. D. Pirie, Mr C. Priestley, Mr C. Priestley & Mr M. Hammond, Resdev Ltd, Sandfield Racing, Mr P. D. Simms, Slaters Arms Racing Club, Miss S. M. Smith, R. Standring, T. A. Stephenson, Taylor's Bloodstock Ltd, The Brady Girls, The Guys & Dolls & Sandfield Racing, The Guys & Dolls Syndicate, The Marina Partnership, The Slaters Arms & Marwood Racing, Mr H. Thornton, Mr H. Thornton & Mr D. Mann, Mr H. Thornton & Mr P.T. Midgley, Mr A. Turton, Mr A. D. Ward, Mr S. Wibberley.

Assistant Trainer: Mrs W. E. Midgley.

371 MR ROD MILLMAN, Cullompton
Postal: **The Paddocks, Dulford, Cullompton, Devon, EX15 2DX**
Contacts: **PHONE 01884 266620 MOBILE 07885 168447**
EMAIL rod.millman@ic24.net

1 **ARDIMENTO (IRE)**, 4, b g Roderic O'Connor (IRE)—Begin The Beguine (IRE) **Exors Late D Little The Links Partnership**
2 **BIOTIC**, 9, b g Aqlaam—Bramaputra (IRE) **Mrs B. Sumner & Mr B. R. Millman**
3 **CHAMPAGNE CHAMP**, 8, b g Champs Elysees—Maramba **Five Horses Ltd**
4 **CRYSTAL CASQUE**, 5, ch m Helmet (AUS)—Crystal Moments **The Dirham Partnership**
5 **DADDIES GIRL (IRE)**, 5, b m Elzaam (AUS)—La Cuvee **Daddies Girl Partnership**
6 **HANDYTALK (IRE)**, 7, b g Lilbourne Lad (IRE)—Dancing With Stars (IRE) **Cantay Racing**
7 **HAWRIDGE FLYER**, 6, b g Sir Percy—Strictly Lambada **E. J. S. Gadsden**
8 **HAWRIDGE STORM (IRE)**, 4, b g Intello (GER)—Aneedah (IRE) **E. J. S. Gadsden**
9 **MASTER GREY (IRE)**, 5, gr g Mastercraftsman (IRE)—Market Day **Exors Late D Little The Links Partnership**
10 **PUZZLE CACHE**, 6, b m Phoenix Reach (IRE)—Secret Queen **Kittymore Racing**
11 **RAGSTONE VIEW (IRE)**, 5, b g Requinto (IRE)—Highland Miss (USA) **Rioja Raiders 04**
12 **SINGING THE BLUES (IRE)**, 5, b g Sir Prancealot (IRE)—Atishoo (IRE) **Crown Connoisseurs**
13 **SIR PLATO (IRE)**, 6, b g Sir Prancealot (IRE)—Dessert Flower (IRE) **M.J. Tidball & B.R. Millman**
14 **SIR RODERIC (IRE)**, 7, b g Roderic O'Connor (IRE)—
Begin The Beguine (IRE) **Exors Late D Little The Links Partnership**

15 4, B f Camelot—Stellavera (FR)
16 **SUFFICIENT**, 4, gr f Showcasing—Good Enough (FR) **Whitsbury Manor Stud & Mrs M. E. Slade**
17 **SWEET PURSUIT**, 6, b m Pastoral Pursuits—Sugar Beet **Always Hopeful Partnership**
18 **TOTALLY COMMITTED**, 7, b g Invincible Spirit (IRE)—Zanzibar (IRE) **Millman Racing Club**

THREE-YEAR-OLDS

19 **ABLE KANE**, b g Due Diligence (USA)—Sugar Beet **Mr T. H. Chadney**
20 **BETTYS HOPE**, b f Anjaal—Miss Poppy **Millman Racing Club**
21 **HALLOWED CASTLE (IRE)**, b g Hallowed Crown (AUS)—Tagula Mon (IRE) **Hallowed Castle Partnership**
22 **KNIGHT'S GATE (IRE)**, ch g Sir Prancealot (IRE)—Porta Portese **The Knight's Gate Partnership**
23 **LOKAL HEROINE**, b f Leroierosanimaux (BRZ)—Lokaloka **J. L. Rowsell**
24 **MAGIC LUTE (FR)**, b g Motivator—Serenada (FR) **D. J. Deer**
25 **MAGICAL FORCE**, b f Lethal Force (IRE)—Mythical City (IRE) **Magical Avalon Partnership**
26 **MERCURIST**, b c Muhaarar—Xceedingly Xcited (IRE) **A. F. O'Callaghan**
27 **REGAL 'N BOLD**, b f Royal Anthem (USA)—Secret Queen **Kittymore Racing**
28 **ROCKINOVERTHEWORLD**, b f Ruler of The World (IRE)—Maramkova (IRE) **Kittymore Racing**
29 **STAYCEE**, ch f Bated Breath—Under Milk Wood **Mrs S. A. J. Kinsella**

TWO-YEAR-OLDS

30 B c 26/02 Holy Roman Emperor (IRE)—Club Tahiti (Hernando (FR)) **Mrs S. A. J. Kinsella**
31 **COPPERKIN**, ch g 26/03 Helmet (AUS)—Loulou (USA) (El Prado (IRE)) (5714) **Mr M J Watson & Deborah Collett**
32 **COUL KAT**, b c 10/02 Coulsty (IRE)—Katevan (IRE) (Heliostatic (IRE)) (14285)
33 **CRAZY LUCK**, b f 31/01 Twilight Son—Suerte Loca (IRE) (Peintre Celebre (USA)) (8571) **Crown Connoisseurs**
34 Br gr f 17/02 Gutaifan (IRE)—Dame Helen (Royal Applause) (7000) **JPM Racing I**
35 **DAYTADAY**, b f 22/02 Adaay (IRE)—Speed Date (Sakhee's Secret) **Whitsbury Manor Stud & Mrs M. E. Slade**
36 **FOUR ADAAY**, b f 29/01 Adaay (IRE)—Sonko (IRE) (Red Clubs (IRE)) (19047) **The Four Adaay Syndicate**
37 B f 21/03 Sayif (IRE)—Glen Molly (IRE) (Danetime (IRE)) (8000) **Exors Late D Little The Links Partnership**
38 B c 31/01 Hellvelyn—Glittering Prize (UAE) (Cadeaux Genereux) (4500) **Mr S. G. Lake**
39 **GREYCIOUS GIRL (IRE)**, gr f 09/04 Markaz (IRE)—
Cesca (IRE) (Fastnet Rock (AUS)) (1904) **Next Ones A Grey Partnership**
40 Ch f 03/05 Equiano (FR)—Kindia (IRE) (Cape Cross (IRE)) **Canisbay Bloodstock**
41 B f 24/02 Brazen Beau (AUS)—Lucky Token (USA) (Key of Luck (USA)) (4500) **Mr J.R. Millman**
42 B g 21/04 Charm Spirit (IRE)—Marlingford (Oasis Dream) **D. J. Deer**
43 **MOUNTAIN ASH**, b g 30/03 Sir Prancealot (IRE)—El Morocco (USA) (El Prado (IRE)) (11000)
44 B f 27/01 Twilight Son—Nicolosia (GER) (Dalakhani (IRE)) (2857) **Millman Racing Club**
45 B c 20/04 Adaay (IRE)—Ocean Bluff (IRE) (Dalakhani (IRE)) (8580) **Mainline Racing**
46 **ONARAGGATIP**, b c 11/05 Adaay (IRE)—Onlyyouknowme (IRE) (Martino Alonso (IRE)) (17142) **Crown Connoisseurs**
47 **PRIDE OF HAWRIDGE (IRE)**, b c 12/01 Vadamos (FR)—
Face The Storm (IRE) (Barathea (IRE)) (105000) **E. J. S. Gadsden**
48 B c 07/04 Equiano (FR)—Red Larkspur (IRE) (Red Clubs (IRE)) (12380) **Mr J Khan**

MR ROD MILLMAN - continued

49 B f 10/05 Garswood—Royal Ivy (Mujtahid (USA)) **Canisbay Bloodstock**
50 **SILENT FLAME,** b f 17/03 Al Kazeem—Burnt Fingers (IRE) (Kheleyf (USA)) (4000) **Miss G. J. Abbey**
51 **TOPTIME,** b g 25/01 Gregorian (IRE)—Dominance (Lilbourne Lad (IRE)) (15238) **Deborah Collett & M. J. Watson**
52 B c 12/02 Bated Breath—Under Milk Wood (Montjeu (IRE)) **Mrs S. A. J. Kinsella**

Other Owners: Mr J. F. A. Berry, Mr P. A. Brend, Mr S. J. Brown, Mr S. Calton, Mr N. A. Clark, Miss D. Collett, Mrs J. A. Daly, Mr R. W. Daly, Exors of the Late Mr K. L. Dare, Mr C. Demetriou, Mr A. S. P. Drake, Mr R. T. Ferris, Mr R. D. Gamlin, Mr P. C. W. Green, Mr R. Gudge, C. J. Harper, Mrs S. M. Langridge, Mr M. Leach, Mr D. Luscombe, Mrs H. M. Luscombe, B. R. Millman, Mrs L. S. Millman, Mr A. M. Nolan, Mr S. M. Perry, Mr C. H. Saunders, Mrs H. I. Slade, Mrs B. Sumner, Mr M. J. Tidball, Mr T. Tompkins, Mr M. J. Watson, Mr R. C. Watts.

Assistant Trainer: Mr James Millman, Louise Millman, Pat Millman.

Flat Jockey: Oisin Murphy. **Apprentice Jockey:** Oliver Searle. **Amateur Jockey:** Mr Pat Millman.

---

372 **MR RICHARD MITCHELL, Dorchester**
Postal: **East Hill Stables, Piddletrenthide, Dorchester, Dorset, DT2 7QY**
Contacts: **PHONE** 01300 348739 **MOBILE** 07775 843136
EMAIL easthillstables@tiscali.com

1 **BIG BOY BLUES (IRE),** 7, ch g Resplendent Cee (IRE)—Lovely Pride (IRE) **Mrs Robert Frosell & Mrs Andrew May**
2 **HENCHARD,** 9, b g Deltic (USA)—Kittenkat **Buck Hill**
3 **MILBERRY (IRE),** 9, b g Alflora (IRE)—Shuil Saoirse (IRE) **N. R. Mitchell**
4 **POUR UNE RAISON (FR),** 5, b br g Kapgarde (FR)—Got Aba (FR) **Mrs S. H. May**

Other Owners: Mr J. Boughey, Mrs S. P. B. Frosell, Mrs S. H. May, N. R. Mitchell.

Assistant Trainer: Mrs E. Mitchell.

---

373 **MR RICHARD MITFORD-SLADE, Norton Fitzwarren**
Postal: **Pontispool Farm, Allerford, Norton Fitzwarren, Taunton, Somerset, TA4 1BG**
Contacts: **PHONE** 01823 461196 **MOBILE** 07899 994420 **FAX** 01823 461508
EMAIL rms@pontispool.com

1 **APPLE MACK,** 7, b g Apple Tree (FR)—Allerford Annie (IRE) **R Mitford-Slade & Lucy Johnson**
2 **LAZY SUNDAY,** 6, b m Schiaparelli (GER)—Sari Rose (FR) **R Mitford-Slade & Lucy Johnson**
3 **MASTER TRADESMAN (IRE),** 9, ch g Marienbard (IRE)—Tobeornotobe (IRE) **R Mitford-Slade & Lucy Johnson**
4 **NORMANDY SOLDIER,** 6, b g Apple Tree (FR)—Primitive Quest **R Mitford-Slade & Lucy Johnson**
5 **SAMUEL JACKSON,** 8, b g Alflora (IRE)—Primitive Quest **R Mitford-Slade & Lucy Johnson**
6 **SECOND CAPTAIN (IRE),** 8, b g Stowaway—Coolanurequeen (IRE) **R. C. Mitford-Slade**

Other Owners: Mrs L. Fielding-Johnson, R. C. Mitford-Slade.

Assistant Trainer: Lucy Fielding-Johnson.

---

374 **MR JAMES MOFFATT, Cartmel**
Postal: **Pit Farm Racing Stables, Cartmel, Grange-Over-Sands, Cumbria, LA11 6PJ**
Contacts: **PHONE** 015395 33808 **MOBILE** 07767 367282 **FAX** 015395 36236
EMAIL jamesmoffatt@hotmail.co.uk **WEBSITE** www.jamesmoffatt.co.uk

1 **ALTRUISM (IRE),** 10, b g Authorized (IRE)—Bold Assumption **Mr V R Vyner-Brooks, Mr K Bowron**
2 **APTLY PUT (IRE),** 8, b br g Yeats (IRE)—Versatile Approach (IRE) **The Vilprano Partnership**
3 **BORUMA (IRE),** 10, b g Brian Boru—Itlallendintears (IRE) **The Running In Rail Partnership**
4 **DAGIAN (IRE),** 5, ch g Dawn Approach (IRE)—Hen Night (IRE) **Bowes Lodge Stables**
5 **GOLDEN TOWN (IRE),** 9, b g Invincible Spirit (IRE)—Princesse Dansante (IRE) **STM Racing**

MR JAMES MOFFATT - continued

6 **LADY BOWES**, 6, b m Malinas (GER)—Blazing Bay (IRE) **Bowes Lodge Stables**
7 **LOUGH KENT**, 11, b g Barathea (IRE)—King's Doll (IRE) **Hadwin, Moffatt, Green, Chamberlain Bros**
8 **MEGA DOUBLE (IRE)**, 6, b m Westerner—Distant Dreams (IRE) **Mr M. S. Scott**
9 **MINELLA CHARMER (IRE)**, 9, b g King's Theatre (IRE)—

Kim Hong (IRE) **Varlien Vyner-Brooks,Dave&Yvonne Simpson**
10 **MONDLICHT (USA)**, 10, b g Malibu Moon (USA)—Moonlight Cruise (USA) **Mr P. A. Holt**
11 **MORNING ROYALTY (IRE)**, 13, b g King's Theatre (IRE)—Portryan Native (IRE) **Mrs E. M. Milligan**
12 **NATIVE FIGHTER (IRE)**, 6, b g Lawman (FR)—Night of Magic (IRE) **Varlien Vyner-Brooks,Dave&Yvonne Simpson**
13 **NO HIDING PLACE (IRE)**, 7, b g Stowaway—Subtle Gem (IRE) **Racing in Furness**
14 **OAKMONT (FR)**, 7, ch g Turtle Bowl (IRE)—Onega Lake (IRE) **The Sheroot Partnership**
15 **SAINT JAMES**, 4, b g Universal (IRE)—Blazing Bay (IRE) **Bowes Lodge Stables**
16 **SHE GOT FAST (IRE)**, 5, b m Fastnet Rock (AUS)—Shegotloose (USA) **The Clock Tower Partnership**
17 **THE STEWARD (USA)**, 9, b g Street Cry (IRE)—Candlelight (USA) **Cartmel Six Pack**
18 **THINK AHEAD**, 9, b g Shamardal (USA)—Moonshadow **Mr V. R. Vyner-Brooks**
19 **TURTLE WARS (FR)**, 7, b g Turtle Bowl (IRE)—Forces Sweetheart **Dave & Yvonne Simpson & Mr Dennis Blyth**

Other Owners: Mr D. Blyth, Mr K. Bowron, Mr D. J. Simpson, Dave & Yvonne Simpson, Mrs Y. Simpson, Mr V. R. Vyner-Brooks, Mrs J. C. Wilson, Mr S. Wilson.

Assistant Trainer: Nadine Moffatt.

NH Jockey: Henry Brooke, Brian Hughes. **Conditional Jockey:** Charlotte Jones. **Apprentice Jockey:** Polly Steele.

---

375 | **MR ISMAIL MOHAMMED, Newmarket**
Postal: **Grange House Stables, Hamilton Road, Newmarket, Suffolk, CB8 0TE**
Contacts: **PHONE 01638 669074 MOBILE 07747 191606, 07766 570271**
EMAIL justina.stone@dubairacingclub.com

1 **AWAY HE GOES (IRE)**, 4, b c Farhh—Island Babe (USA) **Mr K. S. Sulaiman**
2 **BITHIAH (IRE)**, 4, b f Exceed And Excel (AUS)—Sharqawiyah **Mr I. Mohammed**
3 **BROWN HONEY**, 4, b f Farhh—Bronwen (IRE) **Mr A. A. Alameri**
4 **FANTASTIC BLUE**, 4, ch c Iffraaj—Blue Beacon **N. Mourad**
5 **GLENGLADE**, 5, b h Shamardal (USA)—Nantyglo **Mr I. Mohammed**
6 **GOOD EFFORT (IRE)**, 5, b h Shamardal (USA)—Magical Crown (USA) **Mr A. Al Mansoori**
7 **MASTER OF THE MOON**, 5, b g Sea The Stars (IRE)—Crystal Mountain (USA) **Mr A. Al Mansoori**
8 **NIBRAS POWER (IRE)**, 4, b f Slade Power (IRE)—Broadway Hit **Saif Ali & Saeed H. Altayer**
9 4, B c Dawn Approach (IRE)—Rainbow Desert (USA) **Saif Ali & Saeed H. Altayer**
10 **SINISTRY**, 4, b f Nathaniel (IRE)—Synergy (FR) **Mr I. Mohammed**
11 **WINGS OF DUBAI (IRE)**, 4, b f Dark Angel (IRE)—Aertex (IRE) **S. Ali**
12 **ZHUKOVSKY (IRE)**, 4, b g Zoffany (IRE)—Sea Paint (IRE) **Mr I. Mohammed**

THREE-YEAR-OLDS

13 **CORAZONADA (IRE)**, ch f Camacho—Giant Dancer (USA) **Mr M. Al Suboosi**
14 **KINGDOMFORAHORSE**, b c Sea The Stars (IRE)—Wosaita **Mr A. Al Mansoori**
15 **NABLAWYH (IRE)**, b f Acclamation—Simkana (IRE) **S. Ali**
16 **NIBRAS SHADOW (IRE)**, gr f Dark Angel (IRE)—Althea Rose (IRE) **S. H. Altayer**
17 **NIBRAS WISH (IRE)**, ch c Tamayuz—Viking Rose (IRE) **S. H. Altayer**
18 **NIGHT TIME GIRL**, ch f Night of Thunder (IRE)—Assabiyya (IRE) **Mr A. Al Mansoori**
19 **STAR APPROACH (IRE)**, ch c New Approach (IRE)—Starletina (IRE) **S. Ali**
20 **STORM AT DAWN (IRE)**, b f Dawn Approach (IRE)—Portland River (FR) **Mr A. Al Mansoori**
21 **VOLCANO BAY**, b f Universal (IRE)—Ras Shaikh (USA) **Mr A. Al Mansoori**
22 **WIN SMARTLY (IRE)**, b g Shooting To Win (AUS)—Quite Smart (IRE) **Mr A. Al Mansoori**
23 B f Shamardal (USA)—Zurigha (IRE) **S. H. Altayer**

TWO-YEAR-OLDS

24 B f 08/03 Due Diligence (USA)—Belatorio (IRE) (Oratorio (IRE)) (16000) **Mr I. Mohammed**
25 B c 08/04 Golden Horn—Counterclaim (Pivotal) (25000) **S. H. Altayer**
26 **DEMBE**, b c 20/03 Garswood—Disco Ball (Fantastic Light (USA)) (7000) **Mr A. Bintooq**

MR ISMAIL MOHAMMED - continued

27 B c 07/04 Mayson—Divine Power (Kyllachy) (17142) **S. H. Altayer**
28 EMSAKIT, br c 13/02 Bated Breath—Midnight Sky (Desert Prince (IRE)) (8000) **Mr A. Bintooq**
29 Ch c 20/04 Mayson—Fine Silk (USA) (Rahy (USA)) (7619) **S. H. Altayer**
30 Ch f 20/02 Bobby's Kitten (USA)—Flurry of Hands (IRE) (Acclamation) (16000) **Mr I. Mohammed**
31 MUFAWITH (IRE), b br c 02/04 No Nay Never (USA)—Contiguous (USA) (Danzig (USA)) (27000) **Mr A. Bintooq**
32 B c 06/04 Golden Horn—Nantyglo (Mark of Esteem (IRE)) (60000) **Mr I. Mohammed**
33 Ch c 01/05 Bobby's Kitten (USA)—Red Blooded Woman (USA) (Red Ransom (USA)) (5714) **S. H. Altayer**
34 B f 03/03 Fountain of Youth (IRE)—Symphonic Dancer (USA) (Smart Strike (CAN)) (2380) **S. H. Altayer**
35 B c 20/01 Golden Horn—Tunkwa (FR) (Gold Away (IRE)) **Mr A. Al Mansoori**
36 B c 17/01 Universal (IRE)—Winner's Wish (Clodovil (IRE)) **Mr A. Al Mansoori**
37 B c 09/02 Cable Bay (IRE)—Yensi (Doyen (IRE)) (20000) **S. H. Altayer**

Assistant Trainer: Mike Marshall.

---

376 | **MRS LAURA MONGAN, Epsom**
Postal: **Condover Stables, Langley Vale Road, Epsom, Surrey, KT18 6AP**
Contacts: **PHONE 01372 271494 MOBILE 07788 122942 FAX 01372 271494**
EMAIL ljmongan@hotmail.co.uk WEBSITE www.lauramongan.co.uk

1 ABLAZE, 6, ch m Arcano (IRE)—Angry Bark (USA) **Mrs P. J. Sheen**
2 BLACK MEDICK, 4, gr f Dark Angel (IRE)—Penny's Gift **Mrs P. J. Sheen**
3 BROGANS BAY (IRE), 5, b m Born To Sea (IRE)—Sister Sylvia **Mr J. Ayling**
4 DALE DOBACK, 5, b g Medicean—Emulate **Mrs L. J. Mongan**
5 GOLDEN NECTAR, 6, ch m Sakhee's Secret—Mildoura (FR) **Mrs P. J. Sheen**
6 GOUTEZ MOI (FR), 7, b g Dragon Dancer—Titi Jolie (FR) **Mrs P. J. Sheen**
7 IMPART, 6, b g Oasis Dream—Disclose **Charlie's Starrs & Laura Mongan**
8 MIDOURA, 4, b f Delegator—Mildoura (FR) **Mrs P. J. Sheen**
9 MILLIONS MEMORIES, 4, b g Zoffany (IRE)—Millestan (IRE) **Mrs P. J. Sheen**
10 MISS YEATS (IRE), 9, b m Yeats (IRE)—Mrs Wallensky (IRE) **Mrs P. J. Sheen**
11 MY BOY JAMES (IRE), 8, br g Getaway (GER)—Parkality (IRE) **Mrs P. J. Sheen**
12 NARJES, 6, b m Sepoy (AUS)—Dubai Sea (USA) **Mr P. R. Howell**
13 PASS CARD (IRE), 4, b f Authorized (IRE)—Dinaria (IRE) **Mrs P. J. Sheen**
14 RAMATUELLE, 4, ch f Champs Elysees—Florentia **Mrs L. J. Mongan**
15 RI AN RIAN (IRE), 7, b g Arcadio (GER)—Live A Lot (IRE) **Mrs P. J. Sheen**
16 SEA TIDE, 6, b m Champs Elysees—Change Course **Mrs P. J. Sheen**
17 SWEET NATURE (IRE), 5, b m Canford Cliffs (IRE)—High Figurine (IRE) **Mrs L Mongan & Mr R Murray**
18 YOUR CHOICE, 5, ch m Foxwedge (AUS)—Mildoura (FR) **Mrs P. J. Sheen**

Other Owners: Mr A. W. Bain, Mr S. W. Bain, Charlie's Starrs, Mrs L. J. Mongan, Mr R. Murray.

Assistant Trainer: Ian Mongan.

NH Jockey: Tom Cannon.

---

377 | **MR ARTHUR MOORE, Naas**
Postal: **Dereens, Caragh, Naas, Kildare, Ireland**
Contacts: **PHONE +353 45 876 292**
EMAIL arthurlmoore@eircom.net

1 AT YOUR EASE (IRE), 7, b g Scorpion (IRE)—Victoria Bridge (IRE) **Mr J. P. McManus**
2 BANNTOWN GIRL (IRE), 5, ch m Stowaway—Rinnce Moll (IRE) **B Hutchinson and M. B. Fitzpatrick**
3 BROSNA GEORGE (IRE), 9, b g Intikhab (USA)—Mrs St George (IRE) **R. G. Cullen and Tony Kilduff**
4 CONNARD (IRE), 7, b g Shantou (USA)—Sparkling Sword **R. Bartlett**
5 CROSSED MY MIND (IRE), 8, b g Beneficial—Coolvane (IRE) **Mr J. P. McManus**
6 FAG AN BEALACH (IRE), 6, br m Stowaway—Market Niche (IRE) **M. Beresford**
7 KING CON (FR), 5, ch g Rio de La Plata (USA)—Ionia (IRE) **Mrs A. L. T. Moore**

MR ARTHUR MOORE - continued

8 **ME TOO PLEASE (IRE)**, 4, b f Champs Elysees—Twilight Sky **Mrs A. L. T. Moore**
9 **MIDLAND MILLIE (IRE)**, 6, b m Kalanisi (IRE)—Cave Woman (IRE) **A. Trappe**
10 **PANI PROBLEM (FR)**, 5, ch g Muhtathir—Prodiga (FR) **Mrs A. L. T. Moore**
11 **SEA DUCOR**, 4, b g Sea The Moon (GER)—Swarm (IRE) **C. Jones**
12 **THE PRIESTS LEAP (IRE)**, 6, ch g Flemensfirth (USA)—Castlekelly Girl (IRE) **Dargle Equine Ltd**
13 **WHOWONTHETOSS (IRE)**, 4, b g Makfi—Sanaya (IRE) **Mrs A. L. T. Moore**

Assistant Trainer: J. D. Moore.

NH Jockey: Donagh Meyler.

---

378 MR GARY MOORE, Horsham
Postal: **Cisswood Racing Stables, Sandygate Lane, Lower Beeding, Horsham, West Sussex, RH13 6LR**
Contacts: **PHONE 01403 891912**
EMAIL info@garymooreracing.com

1 **A TOI PHIL (FR)**, 10, b g Day Flight—Lucidrile (FR) **Teme Valley 2**
2 **AGE OF WISDOM (FR)**, 7, ch g Pivotal—Learned Friend (GER) **The 1901 Partnership**
3 **AGENT OF FORTUNE**, 5, ch m Kheleyf (USA)—Royal Bloom (IRE) **Foreign Legion**
4 **AIGUILLE ROUGE (FR)**, 6, ch m Falco (USA)—Avanguardia (GER) **The Winning Hand**
5 **AIGUILLETTE**, 4, b g Epaulette (AUS)—Lucky Dice **Heart of the South Racing 108**
6 **ANTONY (FR)**, 10, b g Walk In The Park (IRE)—Melanie du Chenet (FR) **The Winning Hand**
7 **AR MEST (FR)**, 7, bl g Diamond Boy (FR)—Shabada (FR) **Galloping On The South Downs Partnership**
8 **AVORISK ET PERILS (FR)**, 5, b m No Risk At All (FR)—Pierre Azuree (FR) **Dedman Properties Limited**
9 **BAD BOY DU POULDU (FR)**, 9, b g Loup Solitaire (USA)—Wild Flush (USA) **Cocktail Racing Partnership**
10 **BALLINSLEA BRIDGE (IRE)**, 8, b g Pierre—Feelin' Looser (IRE) **Ashley, Carr, Duncan, Ives**
11 **BALLYDOYLE (GER)**, 5, b g Masterstroke (USA)—Best Tune **Mr N. J. Roach & Mr G. L. Moore**
12 **BAN SHOOF**, 7, b g Shirocco (GER)—Pasithea (IRE) **Mr Tommy Ware & Mr Bob Pettett**
13 **BARON ALCO (FR)**, 9, ch g Dom Alco (FR)—Paula (FR) **Mr J. K. Stone**
14 **BEAT THE JUDGE (IRE)**, 5, b g Canford Cliffs (IRE)—Charmingly (USA) **Mr E. P. Babington**
15 **BENATAR (FR)**, 8, b g Beneficial—Carrigeen Lily (IRE) **Mr A. J. Head**
16 **BENEVOLENTDICTATOR**, 6, ch g Schiaparelli (GER)—Kim Fontenail (FR) **The Knights Of Pleasure**
17 **BEYOND REDEMPTION (IRE)**, 6, b g Court Cave (IRE)—Hopeful Gleam (IRE) **Mr A. J. Head**
18 **BIGUNONTHEBALCONY**, 5, b g Fame And Glory—Zariyka (IRE) **Galloping On The South Downs Partnership**
19 **BLACK GERRY (IRE)**, 5, b g Westerner—Triptoshan (IRE) **Mrs M. Devine**
20 **BOTOX HAS (FR)**, 4, b g Dream Well (FR)—Bournie (FR) **Mr J. K. Stone**
21 **BRAMBLEDOWN**, 4, b g Canford Cliffs (IRE)—Pretty Flemingo (IRE) **E. A. Condon**
22 **BRIDLE LOANAN (IRE)**, 7, b g Getaway (GER)—Hanora O'Brien (IRE) **Mr A. J. Head**
23 **BRITANIO BELLO (FR)**, 9, b g Irish Wells (FR)—Tchi Tchi Bang Bang (FR) **Mr A. J. Head**
24 **BULLFROG (IRE)**, 7, b m Jeremy (USA)—Tramp Stamp (IRE) **Galloping On The South Downs Partnership**
25 **CALL OFF THE DOGS (IRE)**, 5, ch g Bienamado (USA)—
Lady Charmere (IRE) **Galloping On The South Downs Partnership**
26 **CAPRICORN PRINCE**, 4, ch g Garswood—Sakhee's Pearl **Mrs A. P. Wilkinson**
27 **CHAIN SMOKER**, 7, ch g Shantou (USA)—Handmemy Moneydown (IRE) **Mr David Leon & James Devine**
28 **CHEQUE EN BLANC (FR)**, 8, b br g Bernebeau (FR)—Necossaise (FR) **Mrs E. A. Kiernan**
29 **CRYSTAL LAD (FR)**, 8, ch g Kapgarde (FR)—Qrystale Mag (FR) **Mr C. E. Stedman**
30 **DAREBIN (GER)**, 8, ch g It's Gino (GER)—Delightful Sofie (GER) **Chris Stedman & Mark Albon**
31 **DARKEST DAY (IRE)**, 5, b g Aizavoski (IRE)—Dempseys Luck (IRE) **GG Thoroughbreds XIII**
32 **DEEBAJ (IRE)**, 8, br g Authorized (IRE)—Athreyaa **G. L. Moore**
33 **DELL ORO (FR)**, 7, b g Walk In The Park (IRE)—Kallistea (FR) **Galloping On The South Downs Partnership**
34 **DIABLE DE SIVOLA (FR)**, 7, b g Noroit (GER)—Grande Route (IRE) **Mr R. Forster**
35 **DIAKALI (FR)**, 11, gr g Sinndar (IRE)—Diasilixa (FR) **Mr Nick Peacock & Mr Gary Moore**
36 **DISTINGO (IRE)**, 7, b g Smart Strike (CAN)—Distinctive Look (IRE) **Alan Jamieson Site Services Ltd**
37 **DONNYTWOBUCKETS (IRE)**, 6, b g Jeremy (USA)—Manorville (USA) **Galloping On The South Downs Partnership**
38 **DORKING LAD (IRE)**, 9, b g Sholokhov (IRE)—Brookville (USA) **Galloping On The South Downs Partnership**
39 **DUCHESS OF AVON**, 5, ch m Dutch Art—Avon Lady **Caplin & Sheridan**
40 **EARLY DU LEMO (FR)**, 7, gr g Early March—Kiswa (FR) **Mr A. J. Head**

MR GARY MOORE - continued

41 **EDAM DU MESTIVEL (FR)**, 6, b g Al Namix (FR)—Quidam Rochelaise (FR) **Mr A. J. Head**
42 **EDITEUR DU GITE (FR)**, 6, b g Saddex—Malaga de St Sulpice (FR) **The Preston Family, Friends & T Jacobs**
43 **EL HAGEB ROSE (FR)**, 6, b g Coastal Path—Ile Rose (FR) **Galloping On The South Downs Partnership**
44 **ELISEZMOI (FR)**, 6, gr g Lord du Sud (FR)—Diva de La Borie (FR) **The Knights Of Pleasure**
45 **EPISODE (FR)**, 6, ch m Kotky Bleu (FR)—Morvandelle (FR) **Mr P. Hunt**
46 **ERAGON DE CHANAY (FR)**, 6, b g Racinger (FR)—Rose Celebre (FR) **Five Star Racing Group**
47 **ESPION DE SAFLO (FR)**, 6, b g Princeton (FR)—Neacoddes (FR) **Avery, Hodges, Moorhead, Collins & Prtnr**
48 **ESPRIT DE SOMOZA (FR)**, 6, b g Irish Wells (FR)—Topaze de Somoza (FR) **Mr R. Forster**
49 **ET MOI ALORS (FR)**, 6, b g Kap Rock (FR)—Qui L'Eut Cru (FR) **Mr A. J. Head**
50 **FIFTY BALL (FR)**, 5, b g Cokoriko (FR)—Voix de Montot (FR) **Mr S. Packham**
51 **FILLES DE FLEUR**, 4, gr ro f Gregorian (IRE)—Big Moza **Mr A Watson & Mr B Malyon**
52 **FIRST REVOLUTION (IRE)**, 6, b g Jeremy (USA)—Shaigino (IRE) **Mr D. Channon**
53 **FIX BAYONETS (IRE)**, 5, b g Yeats (IRE)—Grande Solitaire (IRE) **Galloping On The South Downs Partnership**
54 **FLAMINGER (FR)**, 5, gr g Racinger (FR)—Landalouse (FR) **Mrs E. H. Avery**
55 **FOXES FLYER (IRE)**, 4, b g Foxwedge (AUS)—Midnight Fling **Mr J. G. Jones**
56 **FULL BACK (FR)**, 5, b g Sinndar (IRE)—Quatre Bleue (FR) **Mr A. J. Head**
57 **FUME (IRE)**, 4, b g Frankel—Puff (IRE) **Mr E. P. Babington**
58 **FURIA D'OUDAIRIES (FR)**, 5, b m Hurricane Cat (USA)—Sonate d'Oudairies (FR) **Mr J. Terry**
59 **GENTLEMAN'S DREAM (FR)**, 8, b g Flemensfirth (USA)—Fair And Aisey (IRE) **Dedman Properties Limited**
60 **GLENO (IRE)**, 8, ch g Ask—Lwitikila **Crystal Racing Syndicate**
61 **GOLDEN BOY GREY (FR)**, 4, ch g Diamond Boy (FR)—Betwixt (IRE) **Mrs R. A. Arnold**
62 **GORHAM'S CAVE**, 6, b g Rock of Gibraltar (IRE)—Moiava (FR) **Mrs A. L. Lofts**
63 **GOSHEN (FR)**, 4, b g Authorized (IRE)—Hyde (FR) **Mr S. Packham**
64 **GOSSIPING**, 8, b g Dubawi (IRE)—Gossamer **A. Carr**
65 **GUGUSS COLLONGES (FR)**, 4, b g Secret Singer (IRE)—Une Collonges (FR)
66 **HIGH UP IN THE AIR (FR)**, 6, ch g Famous Name—You Got The Love **Mr P. T. Mott**
67 **HIT THE ROCKS (IRE)**, 5, br g Fast Company (IRE)—Skerries (IRE) **P Moorhead, H Moorhead, J Collins 1**
68 **HONORABLE (FR)**, 5, b g Lawman (FR)—Petite Noblesse (FR) **Mr C. E. Stedman**
69 **IBALLISTICVIN**, 7, b g Rail Link—Guntakal (IRE) **Mrs Arnold & Partner**
70 **ICONIC MUDDLE**, 7, gr g Sixties Icon—Spatham Rose **Saloop**
71 **IL RE DI NESSUNO (FR)**, 5, b g Sinndar (IRE)—Lady Elgar (IRE) **Mr Ashley Head & Mr Garry Dreher**
72 **IMPHAL**, 6, b g Nathaniel (IRE)—Navajo Rainbow **Mr N. J. Peacock**
73 **IN REM (FR)**, 5, b g Kapgarde (FR)—Etoile des Iles (FR) **Mr R. Forster**
74 **ISLA'S DREAM (IRE)**, 6, b m Notnowcato—Daghashah **Benham & Hook**
75 **IT'S GOT LEGS (IRE)**, 7, b g Getaway (GER)—Lady Cadia (IRE) **Galloping On The South Downs Partnership**
76 **JUMPING CATS**, 5, ch g Champs Elysees—Pivotal Drive (IRE) **Mr D. M. Thurlby**
77 **JUST IN A MUDDLE (IRE)**, 5, b g Finsceal Fior (IRE)—Just Josie **Saloop**
78 **KALAKAWA ENKI (FR)**, 6, b g Buck's Boum (FR)—Baba San Siro (FR) **Five Star Racing Group**
79 **KAPDAD (FR)**, 6, ch g Kapgarde (FR)—Reveries (FR) **G. L. Moore**
80 **KAVEMAN**, 8, b g Kayf Tara—Megalex **Galloping On The South Downs Partnership**
81 **KING ATHELSTAN (IRE)**, 5, b g Mayson—Ashtaroute (USA) **Caplin & Sheridan**
82 **KING COOL**, 9, b g King's Theatre (IRE)—Cool Spice **Mr P. T. Mott**
83 **KLOUD GATE (FR)**, 8, ch g Astronomer Royal (USA)—Talkata (IRE) **Hail Sargent Evans**
84 **KOST A COAT (FR)**, 5, b g Diamond Boy (FR)—Charming Princesse (FR) **Mrs R. A. Arnold**
85 **LADY MORPHEUS**, 4, b f Morpheus—Tatora **Mr P. B. Moorhead**
86 **LARRY**, 7, b g Midnight Legend—Gaspaisie (FR) **Galloping On The South Downs Partnership**
87 **LIGHT OF AIR (FR)**, 7, b g Youmzain (IRE)—Height of Vanity (IRE) **G. L. Moore**
88 **LUXFORD**, 6, b m Mullionmileanhour (IRE)—Dolly Parton (IRE) **Bush, Mair & Summers**
89 **MARMALADE DAY**, 4, ch f Mukhadram—Pink Stone (FR) **Miss Kim Bartlett**
90 **MICKEY BUCKMAN**, 7, b g Gleaming (IRE)—Mysaynoway **Mr & Mrs R Sage**
91 **MOTDEPAS (FR)**, 5, b g Davidoff (GER)—Singastar (FR) **Mr David Leon & James Devine**
92 **NEEDHAMS GAP (IRE)**, 6, br g Flemensfirth (USA)—Blue Maxi (IRE) **Collins, Moorhead, Michael & O'Sullivan**
93 **NEFF (GER)**, 5, b g Pastorius (GER)—Nouvelle Fortune (IRE) **Past The Post Racing**
94 **NOT ANOTHER MUDDLE**, 9, b g Kayf Tara—Spatham Rose **Saloop**
95 **PIONEERING (IRE)**, 6, b g Shamardal (USA)—Oregon Trail (USA) **Foreign Legion**
96 **PRIDE OF ANGELS**, 7, gr m Dark Angel (IRE)—Openness **Mr M. R. Baldry**
97 **QUIANA**, 5, b g Pour Moi (IRE)—Quisitor (IRE) **Shark Bay Racing & Mr G L Moore**
98 **QULOOB**, 6, b g New Approach (IRE)—Jadhwah **Heart of the South Racing 120**
99 **RAFIOT (USA)**, 4, b g Elusive Quality (USA)—Viva Rafaela (BRZ) **Mr B. Hepburn**

MR GARY MOORE - continued

100 REINATOR (FR), 4, b c Motivator—Vie de Reine (FR) **Mr C. E. Stedman**
101 RICHIDISH (FR), 5, b g Spanish Moon (USA)—Briere (FR) **Galloping On the South Downs & G L Moore**
102 RIGHT HAND OF GOD, 5, b g Norse Dancer (IRE)—Miss Sassi **Galloping On The South Downs Partnership**
103 ROBIN'S DREAM, 4, b g Kayf Tara—Sudden Light (IRE) **M&R Refurbishments Ltd**
104 ROCCO DU BERLAIS (IRE), 5, gr g Shirocco (GER)—Izzy du Berlais (IRE) **The Fourth Pillar Partnership**
105 RUBY YEATS, 9, b m Yeats (IRE)—Newbay Lady **Heart of the South Racing 122**
106 RYDAN (IRE), 9, ch g Intense Focus (USA)—Lough Mewin (IRE) **Jacobs Construction Ltd Partnership**
107 SAN PEDRO DE SENAM (FR), 7, br g Saint des Saints (FR)—Tetiaroa (FR) **Mrs Jane George & Mrs Helen Shelton**
108 SCARLET COUTURE, 7, b m Schiaparelli (GER)—Little Red Spider **Mr J. A. Jenkins**
109 SECRET ART (IRE), 10, ch g Excellent Art—Ivy Queen (IRE) **Excel Racing**
110 SLADE KING (IRE), 4, ch g Slade Power (IRE)—Lough Mewin (IRE) **Jacobs Construction Ltd Partnership**
111 SOPRAN THOR (FR), 5, b g Authorized (IRE)—Sopran Slam (IRE) **Galloping On The South Downs Partnership**
112 STORMINGIN (IRE), 7, gr g Clodovil (IRE)—Magadar (USA) **Mrs C. Reed**
113 SUSSEX RANGER (USA), 6, b g Hat Trick (JPN)—Purple (USA) **The Tongdean Partnership**
114 TAZKA (FR), 5, b m Network (GER)—Tazminya **B. Noakes & Baroness S. Noakes**
115 THAT'S A SHAME (IRE), 5, b g Arcadio (GER)—World of Ballet (IRE) **Galloping On The South Downs Partnership**
116 THE FLYING SOFA (IRE), 7, b g Sholokhov (IRE)—La Julie (IRE) **Galloping On The South Downs Partnership**
117 THE GRUMPER (IRE), 5, b g Scorpion (IRE)—Forgotten Lady (IRE) **Galloping On The South Downs Partnership**
118 THECHILDREN'STRUST (IRE), 5, br g Society Rock (IRE)—Estemaala (IRE) **Mr A. J. Head**
119 THOUNDER (FR), 6, ch g Hurricane Cat (USA)—Meldown (FR) **A. Head**
120 TOUCHTHESOUL (ITY), 5, b g Red Rocks (IRE)—Easy Hawk **The Soul Searchers**
121 TRAFALGAR BOY, 5, b g Mount Nelson—Aiaam Al Wafa (IRE) **Heart of the South Racing 114**
122 TRAFFIC FLUIDE (FR), 10, b g Astarabad (USA)—Petale Rouge (FR) **Galloping On The South Downs Partnership**
123 TWENTY TWENTY (IRE), 5, b g Henrythenavigator (USA)—Distinctive Look (IRE) **Mark Albon & Gary Moore**
124 VISION CLEAR (GER), 5, b g Soldier Hollow—Vive Madame (GER) **A. Head**
125 VORASHANN (FR), 4, b g Sinndar (IRE)—Visorama (IRE) **Jacobs Construction Ltd Partnership**
126 WAIKIKI WAVES (FR), 7, b g Alexandros—Lulabelle Spar (IRE) **Heart of the South Racing 119**
127 WHISTLER BOWL, 4, b f Mukhadram—Sablonne (USA) **Mr C. E. Stedman**
128 ZAMPERINI (IRE), 8, ch g Fast Company (IRE)—Lucky Date (IRE) **Mr R. E. Tillett**
129 ZHIGULI (IRE), 5, b g Flemensfirth (USA)—Grangeclare Flight (IRE) **Jonathan Muir, Derek Llambias & Friends**

THREE-YEAR-OLDS

130 BIG JIMBO, ch c Helmet (AUS)—Big Moza **Mr A Watson & Mr B Malyon**
131 CASA LOUPI, ch g Casamento (IRE)—Kameruka **Mrs V. Pritchard-Gordon**
132 CATH THE GREAT (IRE), b f War Command (USA)—Lady Marl **The Hon R. T. A. Goff**
133 DONALD LLEWELLYN, b c Pivotal—Rose Law **Mr C. E. Stedman**
134 ISAYALITTLEPRAYER, b f Nathaniel (IRE)—I Say (IRE) **Heart of the South Racing 117**
135 JUNKANOO, b c Epaulette (AUS)—Bahamian Music (IRE) **Jacobs Construction & Mr J Harley**
136 LETSCRACKON (IRE), b f Camacho—Laetoli (ITY) **Mrs C. Reed**
137 MOONDANCE, b f Mayson—Amontillado (IRE) **Shark Bay Racing Syndicate**
138 NIGHTSWIMMING, ch f Casamento (IRE)—Sonnellino **Mrs M. Parker**
139 NOTE BLEU, b c Camelot—Silent Music (IRE) **Mr C. E. Stedman**
140 PLATINUM PRINCE, gr g Harbour Watch (IRE)—Sakhee's Pearl **Mrs A. P. Wilkinson**
141 POETRY AND ART, br f Poet's Voice—Ashford Belle (IRE) **Mr R. Green**
142 POP THE CONFETTI (IRE), b f Acclamation—La Grande Elisa (IRE) **Mrs E Avery & Mr G L Moore**
143 PRINCE PERCY, b g Sir Percy—Crystal High **The Pride Of Sussex Partnership**
144 SCALLYWAGTAIL (IRE), br c Gutaifan (IRE)—Eminence Gift **Mrs E Avery & Mr G L Moore**
145 SILVER CLIFFS (IRE), b g Canford Cliffs (IRE)—Birdie Queen **The Golf Partnership**

TWO-YEAR-OLDS

146 B f 13/05 Dragon Pulse (IRE)—Gloved Hand (Royal Applause) (4290) **Mrs C. Reed**

Other Owners: Mrs M. Abey, Mr M. L. Albon, Mrs R. A. Arnold, Mr S. A. Ashley, Mrs E. H. Avery, Avery, Hodges, Moorhead & Collins, Mr H. Burch, Mr D. Caplin, A. Carr, Mr J. A. Collins, J. T. Devine, Mr G. C. Dreher, Mr M. Duncan, Mr D. L. Evans, G L Moore Racing, Galloping On The South Downs Partnership, Mrs J. George, Mr J. E. Hale, The Hon J. Hanham, J. E. Harley, Mr A. J. Head, Mr P. A. Herbert, Mr J. Hinds, Mr A. D. S. Hodges, Mr D. L. Ives, Jacobs Construction (Holdings) Limited, D. Leon, Mr D. Llambias, G. L. Moore, Mrs H. J. Moorhead, Mr J. Muir, C. B. Noakes, Baroness S. Noakes, P Moorhead, H Moorhead & J Collins, Mr N. J. Peacock, Mr R. Pettett, Mr N. J. Roach, Mr R. J. Sage, Mrs T. J. Sage, Mr R. D. Sargent, Mrs H. J. Shelton, Mr A. M. Sheridan, Mr C. E. Stedman, The Preston Family & Friends Ltd, Mr R. W. D. Trevelyan, Mr M. C. Waddingham, T. Ware, Miss C. A. Webb, Mr M. K. Webb.

MR GARY MOORE - continued

Assistant Trainer: David Wilson, Racing Secretary: Maria Workman.

Flat Jockey: Hector Crouch, Ryan Moore. NH Jockey: Jamie Moore, Joshua Moore. Conditional Jockey: Niall Houlihan. Apprentice Jockey: Rhys Clutterbuck, Louis Garoghan, Anna Gibson. Amateur Jockey: Miss Katy Brooks, Mr George Gorman, Miss Hayley Moore, Miss Elysia Vaughan.

---

379 **MR J. S. MOORE, Upper Lambourn**
Postal: Berkeley House Stables, Upper Lambourn, Hungerford, Berkshire, RG17 8QP
Contacts: PHONE 01488 73887 MOBILE 07860 811127, 07900 402856 FAX 01488 73997
EMAIL jsmoore.racing@btopenworld.com WEBSITE www.stanmooreracing.co.uk

1 **AULD BOY (USA)**, 4, b br g Speightstown (USA)—Ilikecandy (USA) **Tom Vaughan & Sara Moore**
2 **BROCKAGH CAILIN**, 5, b m Helmet (AUS)—Step Softly **Gridline Racing**
3 **CHAMPION BROGIE (IRE)**, 4, b g Alhebayeb (IRE)—Defensive Boast (USA) **Tom Vaughan & Sara Moore**
4 **DELTA BRAVO (IRE)**, 4, b f Mastercraftsman (IRE)—Rhiannon (IRE) **Eventmasters Racing & J S Moore**
5 **LAMBRISTO (IRE)**, 4, b c Bungle Inthejungle—Amodio (IRE) **Mrs Wendy Jarrett & J S Moore**
6 **UTHER PENDRAGON (IRE)**, 5, b g Dragon Pulse (IRE)—Unreal **Mrs Wendy Jarrett & J S Moore**

THREE-YEAR-OLDS

7 **BEGGARMAN**, ch g Toronado (IRE)—Let's Dance (IRE) **Howses Stud & J S Moore**
8 **BIRKIE QUEEN (IRE)**, br f Gutaifan (IRE)—The Oldladysays No (IRE) **Mrs S Gray, Mr Ian Gray & Sara Moore**
9 **BLUE SLATE (IRE)**, gr g Alhebayeb (IRE)—Hallbeck **The Moore The Merrier**
10 **BROWN EYES BLUE (IRE)**, b f Epaulette (AUS)—Union City Blues (IRE) **C Instone, K Badger & J S Moore**
11 **DANSE DE LA LUNE (IRE)**, ch f Anjaal—Mymoonlightdancer (IRE) **Mr Albert Conneally**
12 B f Bungle Inthejungle—Desert Alchemy (IRE)
13 **FACT OR FABLE (IRE)**, gr g Alhebayeb (IRE)—Unreal **Mrs Wendy Jarrett & J S Moore**
14 **GET THE LOOK (IRE)**, b f Brazen Beau (AUS)—Confidente (IRE) **J. S. Moore & Partner**
15 Ch g Mukhadram—Lovely Dancer (IRE)
16 **MR SHADY (IRE)**, gr g Elzaam (AUS)—Whitershadeofpale (IRE) **Enterprising Trio & Sara Moore**
17 **SARACEN STAR**, b f Make Believe—Singing Sky **The Pineapple Stud**
18 **SPARROW HAWK**, b f Free Eagle (IRE)—Calico Moon (USA) **Pineapple Stud & Sara Moore**
19 **TROUBLE**, b g Roderic O'Connor (IRE)—Caprella **Mrs Evelyn Yates, Tom Yates & J S Moore**
20 **XQUISITE (IRE)**, b f Xtension (IRE)—Make Amends (IRE) **Kieron Badger, Caroline Instone, S Moore**

TWO-YEAR-OLDS

21 **BOMB SQUAD (IRE)**, gr c 13/02 Lethal Force (IRE)—
                                    Dutch Destiny (Dutch Art) (2857) **Eventmasters Racing & J S Moore**
22 B f 19/04 Coulsty (IRE)—Eileenlilian (Authorized (IRE)) (800)
23 B c 21/04 Sir Prancealot (IRE)—Gatamalata (IRE) (Spartacus (IRE)) (1716)
24 B c 12/04 Sir Prancealot (IRE)—Krynica (USA) (Danzig (USA))
25 **LOLA B**, b f 30/03 Swiss Spirit—Garbo's Dream (IRE) (Arcano (IRE)) **Mrs Evelyn Yates, Tom Yates & J S Moore**
26 B f 27/03 Alhebayeb (IRE)—Ma Bella Paola (FR) (Naaqoos) **J. S. Moore & Partner**
27 B f 24/03 Epaulette (AUS)—Quick Chat (USA) (First Defence (USA))
28 B f 07/02 Estidhkaar (IRE)—She's A Minx (IRE) (Linamix (FR)) **J. S. Moore & Partner**
29 Ch f 18/02 Prince of Lir (IRE)—Tepeleni (Teofilo (IRE))
30 Ch f 24/04 Dragon Pulse (IRE)—The Burnham Mare (IRE) (Kodiac) (2857)
31 B c 16/05 Vadamos (FR)—Unfortunate (Komaite (USA)) **Mr Kieron Badger & J S Moore**
32 **WOODVIEW**, ch g 23/03 Ajaya—Spacecraft (USA) (Distant View (USA)) (11000)

Other Owners: Mr M. J. Ablett, Mrs R. Ablett, Mr K. P. Badger, Mrs E. R. Bickerton, Mr J. C. Bickerton, Enterprising Trio, Eventmasters Racing, Mr I. J. B. Gray, Mrs S. Gray, Mr P. J. Grimes, Howses Stud, Ms C. Instone, Mrs W. J. Jarrett, Mr E. McGlinchey, Mr N. J. McGlinchey, J. S. Moore, Mrs S. J. Moore, Mrs D. Sheasby, Mr E. J. N. Sheasby, The Pineapple Stud, Mr L. Tofts, Mr T. G. Vaughan.

Assistant Trainer: Mrs S. Moore, Racing Secretary: Miss Cathy Holding.

Apprentice Jockey: Miss Sophie Reed.

380 MISS KELLY MORGAN, Withcote
Postal: **Rose Cottage, Bridle Road, Withcote, Oakham, Leicestershire, LE15 8DP**
Contacts: **PHONE 01664 454904 MOBILE 07808 133324**
EMAIL **kellymorgan15@hotmail.com** WEBSITE **www.prestonlodgestud.com**

1 **CUBAN SUN**, 4, b f Havana Gold (IRE)—Sunseek **Mr J. R. Weatherby**
2 **PRESENTING MIRANDA**, 4, b f Malinas (GER)—Hunca Munca (IRE) **Mr J. R. Weatherby**
3 **RED INDIAN**, 8, b g Sulamani (IRE)—Rafiya **Mr J. R. Weatherby**
4 **TIMETOCHILL (IRE)**, 7, br m Scorpion (IRE)—Kilcoleman Lady (IRE) **Mr J. R. Weatherby**
5 **TOP WOOD (FR)**, 13, ch g Kotky Bleu (FR)—Heure Bleu (FR) **Mr J. R. Weatherby**
6 **UBETYA (IRE)**, 5, b g Le Fou (IRE)—Valentina Gaye (IRE) **Mr J. R. Weatherby**

381 MISS LAURA MORGAN, Waltham On The Wolds
Postal: **Foxfield Stud, Goadby Road, Waltham On The Wolds, Melton Mowbray, Leicestershire, LE14 4AG**
Contacts: **PHONE 01664 464571 MOBILE 07817 616622**
EMAIL **lauramorg@hotmail.co.uk**

1 **AGAINST ALL ODDS (FR)**, 5, b m Saint des Saints (FR)—Cue To Cue **Mr & Mrs W. J. Williams**
2 **ALKANADA (IRE)**, 5, b g Alkaadhem—Ellie Forte **Mrs A. M. Williams**
3 **ALYS ROCK (IRE)**, 11, gr m Medaaly—Rock Slide (IRE) **Miss L. Morgan**
4 4, B g Doyen (IRE)—Aphrodisias (FR) **Mr I. Guise**
5 **BEAUTIFUL BEN (IRE)**, 10, b g Beneficial—Almnadia (IRE) **A. Lyons**
6 **BIG PENNY (IRE)**, 8, b m Oscar (IRE)—Lady Marnay (IRE) **The Rann Family**
7 **CAKE DE L'ISLE (FR)**, 8, b g Fragrant Mix (IRE)—Taiga de L'Isle (FR) **Piece of Cake Partnership**
8 **CAVALRY SCOUT (IRE)**, 7, b br g Mahler—Yourfinalanswer (IRE) **Mrs M. J. Pepperdine**
9 **CLEM (IRE)**, 6, b m Malinas (GER)—Glorybe (GER) **The Rann Family**
10 **DAHILLS HILL (IRE)**, 8, br m Mahler—Whites Cross (IRE) **Laura Morgan Racing Club**
11 **DJARKEVI (FR)**, 7, b g Khalkevi (IRE)—Onvavoir (FR) **Mrs E. Holmes**
12 **GOLD FIELDS**, 6, b g Sakhee (USA)—Realms of Gold (USA) **Mrs M. J. Pepperdine**
13 **HAASAB (IRE)**, 7, b g Sakhee (USA)—Badweia (USA) **Roemex Ltd**
14 **HASANKEY (IRE)**, 4, gr g Mastercraftsman (IRE)—Haziyna (IRE) **The Hanky Panky Partnership**
15 **MOTARAABET**, 5, b g Dansili—Hawaafez **R. A. Jenkinson**
16 **PELICAN PIE**, 6, ch m Salutino (GER)—Pelican Point **Mrs E. Holmes**
17 **SKIPPING ON (IRE)**, 11, b g Westerner—Skipping Along (IRE) **Triumph In Mind**
18 **SOCIALIST AGENDA**, 4, ch g Sir Percy—Mercy Pecksniff **Miss L. Morgan**
19 **TAQWAA (IRE)**, 7, ch g Iffraaj—Hallowed Park (IRE) **Laura Morgan Racing Club**
20 **TARAS DAY**, 7, b m Kayf Tara—One of Those Days **Mrs H. M. Harvey**
21 **THOMAS TODD**, 10, b g Passing Glance—Miss Danbys **Burton, Copley & Todd**
22 **UISCE UR (IRE)**, 8, b m City Honours (USA)—Luna Fairy (IRE) **Launde Park Farm Partnership**
23 **WILL O'THE WEST (IRE)**, 9, b g Westerner—Simply Divine (IRE) **The Racing With Will Partnership**
24 **ZAKHAROVA**, 6, ch m Beat Hollow—Tcherina (IRE) **Mr & Mrs W. J. Williams**

Other Owners: Mr W. R. Bowler, Mr R. J. Burton, Mr M. Collie, Mr M. Copley, Mr I. Guise, Mr L. J. Heaver, Miss L. Morgan, Mr I. K. Pardy, Mrs M. J. Pepperdine, Mr G. P. D. Rann, Mrs L. E. Rann, Mr P. L. Read, Mr B. Ryan-Beswick, Miss L. Todd, Mrs A. M. Williams, Mrs M. Williams, W. J. Williams.

Assistant Trainer: Tom Morgan.

Amateur Jockey: Miss A. Peck.

382 MR MOUSE MORRIS, Fethard
Postal: **Everardsgrange, Fethard, Co. Tipperary, Ireland**
Contacts: **PHONE +353 52 613 1474 MOBILE +353 86 854 3010 FAX +353 52 613 1654**
EMAIL mouse@eircom.net

1 **BAILY GORSE (IRE)**, 6, b g Milan—Lillies Bordello (IRE) **Mr R. A. Scott**
2 **BAILY THUNDER (IRE)**, 6, ch g Yorgunnabelucky (USA)—Alikat (IRE) **Mr R. A. Scott**
3 **BARNEY STINSON (IRE)**, 4, b g Fame and Glory—Which Thistle
4 4, B f Milan—Benefit Ball
5 **BEYOND THE LAW (IRE)**, 8, b g Westerner—Thegoodwans Sister (IRE) **Exors of Alan & Anne Potts**
6 **CLONDAW BERTIE (IRE)**, 5, b g Thewayyouare (USA)—Female (IRE)
7 **FLYING COLUM (IRE)**, 5, b g Getaway—Curragheen
8 **FOXY JACKS (IRE)**, 6, b g Fame And Glory—Benefit Ball (IRE) **D. Desmond**
9 **FRENCH DYNAMITE (FR)**, 5, b r Kentucky Dynamite—Matnie
10 **FRIARY ROCK (FR)**, 5, b g Spanish Moon—Zenita Des Brosses
11 **GANDY MAN (IRE)**, 4, b g Arcadio—Topsham Belle
12 **GRAND GOSIER (FR)**, 5, b g Khalkevi—Teresa Moriniere
13 **INDIANA JONES (IRE)**, 4, b g Blue Bresil—Matnie
14 **L'INTEMPOREL (FR)**, 4, b g Saint Des Saints—Kpalime
15 **LARGY FIX (IRE)**, 5, ch g Notnowcato—Fix It Lady
16 4, B g Leading Light—Liss Ui Riain
17 **MISSISSIPPI WINE (IRE)**, 5, ch m Getaway—Tarrawarra
18 **MR LOMBARDI (IRE)**, 5, b g Milan—The Real Athlete
19 **NERO ROCK (IRE)**, 5, b g Shirocco—Gilt Benefit
20 **ROMAN ROCK (IRE)**, 6, b g Presenting—Native Idea (IRE) **M. O'Flynn, J. O'Flynn**
21 **SAMS PROFILE (IRE)**, 6, b g Black Sam Bellamy (IRE)—Lucylou (IRE) **M. O'Flynn, J. O'Flynn**
22 **SIZING JOSHUA (IRE)**, 7, b g Flemensfirth (USA)—Alleygrove Lass (IRE) **Exors of Alan & Anne Potts**
23 **THE LAST THROW (IRE)**, 4, b g Shirocco—Bridgequarter Girl
24 **THEBELLSOFSHANDON (IRE)**, 5, b g Fame and Glory—Western Cowgirl
25 **WHATSNOTOKNOW (IRE)**, 5, b g Mahler—Whos To Know (IRE) **A. R. Scott**

Other Owners: L.F Curtin, Mrs Trish Hyde, Mrs John Magnier, Sean O'Driscoll, Robcour, Room For One More Syndicate.

383 MR PATRICK MORRIS, Prescot
Postal: **Avenue House, George Hale Avenue, Knowsley Park, Prescot, Merseyside, L34 4AJ**
Contacts: **MOBILE 07545 425235**
EMAIL Patrickmorris76@yahoo.com

1 **BELL HEATHER (IRE)**, 7, b m Iffraaj—Burren Rose (USA) **Dr M. B. Q. S. Koukash**
2 **BRIAN THE SNAIL (IRE)**, 6, gr g Zebedee—Sweet Irish **Dr M. B. Q. S. Koukash**
3 **DARK DEVIL (IRE)**, 7, gr g Dark Angel (IRE)—Ride For Roses (IRE) **Dr M. B. Q. S. Koukash**
4 **GABRIAL THE DEVIL (IRE)**, 5, b g Epaulette (AUS)—Grasshoppergreen (IRE) **Dr M. B. Q. S. Koukash**
5 **GABRIAL THE ONE (IRE)**, 4, b g Zoffany (IRE)—Guilia **Dr M. B. Q. S. Koukash**
6 **GABRIAL THE TIGER (IRE)**, 8, b g Kodiac—Invincible **Dr M. B. Q. S. Koukash**
7 **HEART OF SOUL (IRE)**, 5, b g Makfi—Hadrian's Waltz (IRE) **Dr M. B. Q. S. Koukash**
8 **PACINO**, 4, b g Heeraat (IRE)—Ringtail (USA) **Dr M. B. Q. S. Koukash**
9 **POWERALLIED (IRE)**, 7, b g Camacho—Kaplinsky (IRE) **Dr M. B. Q. S. Koukash**
10 **RESHOUN (FR)**, 6, b g Shamardal (USA)—Radiyya (IRE) **Dr M. B. Q. S. Koukash**
11 **RESTORER**, 8, gr g Mastercraftsman (IRE)—Moon Empress (FR) **Dr M. B. Q. S. Koukash**
12 **SALAM ZAYED**, 4, b g Exceed And Excel (AUS)—Long Face (USA) **Dr M. B. Q. S. Koukash**
13 **SCOTTISH BLADE (IRE)**, 4, b c Exceed And Excel (AUS)—Hecuba **Dr S. Lane**
14 **SHABEEB (USA)**, 7, b g Smart Strike (CAN)—Sortita (GER) **Dr M. B. Q. S. Koukash**
15 **ZAMJAR**, 6, b g Exceed And Excel (AUS)—Cloud's End **Dr M. B. Q. S. Koukash**

THREE-YEAR-OLDS
16 **LEXI THE ONE (IRE)**, b f Dandy Man (IRE)—Garter Star **Dr M. B. Q. S. Koukash**

384

MR HUGHIE MORRISON, East Ilsley
Postal: Summerdown, East Ilsley, Newbury, Berkshire, RG20 7LB
Contacts: PHONE 01635 281678 MOBILE 07836 687799 FAX 01635 281746
EMAIL hughie@hughiemorrison.co.uk WEBSITE www.hughiemorrison.co.uk

1 **AFFAIR**, 6, b m Sakhee's Secret—Supato (USA) **H. Morrison**
2 **BELATED BREATH**, 5, ch m Bated Breath—Daffydowndilly **Lady Blyth**
3 **BORN LEADER (FR)**, 4, ch f Nathaniel (IRE)—Chieftess (IRE) **Thurloe Thoroughbreds XLVII & Partners**
4 **COUSIN KHEE**, 13, b g Sakhee (USA)—Cugina **Mrs M. D. W. Morrison**
5 **CRASTER (IRE)**, 4, b g Sea The Stars (IRE)—Coquet **Margadale, Scott, Kerr-Dineen**
6 **ENHANCED**, 4, ch g New Approach (IRE)—Complexion **Brightwalton Bloodstock Ltd**
7 **ESCAPE THE CITY**, 5, b m Cityscape—Jasmeno **MNC Racing**
8 4, B g Kayf Tara—Flirtatious **Mrs M. D. W. Morrison**
9 **FUN MAC (GER)**, 9, ch g Shirocco (GER)—Favorite (GER) **Mrs Angela McAlpine & Partners**
10 **LE BAOL (FR)**, 4, b g Orpen (USA)—La Teranga (FR) **Mr A. Kheir**
11 **LE DON DE VIE**, 4, b g Leroidesanimaux (BRZ)—Leaderene **Mr A. Kheir**
12 **MARIDADI**, 4, b f Beat Hollow—Mighty Splash **Mr D. H. Low**
13 **MISS AUSTEN (IRE)**, 5, b m Fame And Glory—Swap Shop (IRE) **L. A. Garfield**
14 **MOON OF BARODA**, 5, gr g Dubawi (IRE)—Millennium Star (IRE) **Tony Wechsler & Ann Plummer**
15 **MOUSEBIRD (IRE)**, 4, b f Zoffany (IRE)—Firecrest (IRE) **Sir Thomas Pilkington**
16 **NOT SO SLEEPY**, 8, ch g Beat Hollow—Papillon de Bronze (IRE) **Lady Blyth**
17 **OUR JESTER**, 4, b g Garswood—Cill Rialaig **Pangfield Racing V**
18 **REQUITED (IRE)**, 4, b g Requinto (IRE)—Joyfullness (USA) **H. Morrison**
19 **SCANNING**, 4, b g Pastoral Pursuits—Yonder **Mrs M. D. W. Morrison**
20 **TELECASTER**, 4, b c New Approach (IRE)—Shirocco Star **Castle Down Racing**
21 **THIRD WIND**, 6, b g Shirocco (GER)—Act Three **Mrs A. J. Hamilton-Fairley**
22 **URBAN ARTIST**, 5, ch m Cityscape—Cill Rialaig **Pangfield Racing V**

THREE-YEAR-OLDS

23 **CHIVALRY**, b g Camelot—Much Promise **Mr J L Rowsell & Mr M H Dixon**
24 **COQUETTE**, b f Champs Elysees—Tottie **Mr Julian Richmond-Watson**
25 **COSMIC PRINCESS**, b f Kingman—Galaxy Highflyer **Helena Springfield Ltd**
26 **CURTIZ**, b c Stimulation (IRE)—Supato (USA) **Julie Parkes**
27 **ELMETTO**, b f Helmet (AUS)—Italian Connection **Helena Springfield Ltd**
28 **EXCELFILLY**, b f Excelebration (IRE)—Respectfilly **The Fairy Story Partnership**
29 **FINAL ENCORE**, b g Dunaden (FR)—Act Three **Ann Plummer**
30 **KAVADI**, b f Siyouni (FR)—Ensemble (FR) **Michael Kerr-Dineen & Martin Hughes**
31 **KIPPS (IRE)**, gr c War Command (USA)—Sixpenny Sweets (IRE) **M Kerr-Dineen, M Hughes & W Eason**
32 **MASTER MALCOLM**, ch g Mastercraftsman (IRE)—Desert Sage **Mr Julian Richmond-Watson**
33 **MR POY**, ch c Sepoy (AUS)—Quiz Mistress **The Fairy Story Partnership**
34 **MYSTERY MAC (IRE)**, b c Le Havre (IRE)—Mishhar (IRE) **Mr Adrian McAlpine & Partners**
35 **OASIS SONG**, b f Oasis Dream—Wahylah (USA) **Mr T D Rootes & Mr O F Waller**
36 **QUAINT (IRE)**, b f Dandy Man (IRE)—Destiny's Kitten (IRE) **Caveat Emptor Partnership**
37 **QUICKTHORN**, b c Nathaniel (IRE)—Daffydowndilly **Lady Blyth**
38 **RAVENS ARK**, ch c Raven's Pass (USA)—Wonderful Desert **Beachview Corporation Ltd**
39 **ROMSEY**, b f Mukhadram—Broadlands **Mr A M B MacDonald-Buchanan, The End-R-Ways Partnership**
40 **ROYAL ASTRONOMER**, b g Telescope (IRE)—Regal Fairy (IRE) **Mr M.A. & Mrs J.E. Richards**
41 **SKY STORM**, ch f Night of Thunder (IRE)—Dinvar Diva **Brightwalton Bloodstock Ltd**
42 **SPOSABELLA (IRE)**, ch f Raven's Pass (USA)—Belanoiva (IRE) **Mr Simon Malcolm**
43 **STARCAT**, ch c Lope de Vega (IRE)—Purr Along **Michael Kerr-Dineen & Martin Hughes**
44 **SULOCHANA (IRE)**, br f Lope de Vega (IRE)—Yakshini (IRE) **Mr P. Brocklehurst**
45 **TREATY OF DINGLE**, b f Roderic O'Connor (IRE)—Josefa Goya **The TOD Partnership**
46 **VIZA**, b c Australia—Vizinga (FR) **Mrs C Swire,Mrs A Scott & Mr T Pickford**
47 **WHITEHAVEN (FR)**, bl g Le Havre (IRE)—Passion Blanche **P. C. J. Dalby & R. D. Schuster**
48 **WITH RESPECT (IRE)**, gr c Gutaifan (IRE)—More Respect (IRE) **Thurloe Thoroughbreds XLVIII**

TWO-YEAR-OLDS

49 B c 10/04 Charming Thought—Amanjena (Beat Hollow) **M. E. Wates**
50 **AURORA STAR (FR)**, b c 14/02 Harzand (IRE)—Maleficent (Azamour (IRE)) (22000) **Mr S. B. S. Ronaldson**
51 B f 16/02 Manduro (GER)—Aztec Queen (Holy Roman Emperor (IRE)) (7722) **The Fairy Story Partnership**

MR HUGHIE MORRISON - continued

52 B c 10/03 The Gurkha (IRE)—Best Regards (IRE) (Tamayuz) (17000) **Mr Tony Pickford, The Hon Mary Morrison,
Mr Roy Angliss, Mr Simon De Zoete, Mr Simon Malcolm**
53 B f 30/03 Equiano (FR)—Broadlands (Kheleyf (USA)) (55000) **Mr Tony Pickford, The Hon Mary Morrison,
Ms Deborah Collett, Mr Simon De Zoete**
54 CIDER APPLE, b f 21/02 Charm Spirit (IRE)—Golden Delicious (Cadeaux Genereux) **N. M. H. Jones**
55 B c 14/04 Kodiac—Fair Sailing (IRE) (Docksider (USA)) (115000) **Martin Hughes & Michael Kerr-Dineen**
56 FARRH SIGHTED, br f 08/03 Farhh—Respectfully (Mark of Esteem (IRE)) **The Fairy Story Partnership**
57 GWENHWYVAR (IRE), b f 11/03 Camelot—Quiz Mistress (Doyen (IRE)) **The Fairy Story Partnership**
58 B f 16/02 Iffraaj—
Jam Jar (Duke of Marmalade (IRE)) **Mr A M B MacDonald-Buchanan, The End-R-Ways Partnership**
59 KING OF CLUBS, b c 19/04 Intello (GER)—Queen Arabella (Medicean) **Castle Down Racing**
60 LEGENDARY DAY, b c 09/04 Adaay (IRE)—Dubai Legend (Cadeaux Genereux) (32000) **Mr A N Solomons**
61 MARSABIT (IRE), ch c 19/03 Mehmas (IRE)—Masela (IRE) (Medicean) (42000) **P. C. J. Dalby & R. D. Schuster**
62 B c 01/03 Awtaad (IRE)—Melodique (FR) (Falco (USA)) (30000) **Ms Marina Lund, Mr Adrian McAlpine**
63 MRS FITZHERBERT (IRE), b f 18/03 Kingman—
Stupendous Miss (USA) (Dynaformer (USA)) (120120) **Mrs Sonia Rogers**
64 B f 31/05 Adaay (IRE)—Pelagia (IRE) (Lycius (USA)) **Mr J Repard & Partners**
65 B f 17/04 Nathaniel (IRE)—Polar Circle (USA) (Royal Academy (USA)) **Mrs Ben Sangster**
66 ROOSTER, ch c 17/04 Showcasing—Slatey Hen (IRE) (Acclamation) (78000) **M. Kerr-Dineen, Mr M. B. Hughes**
67 B f 05/05 Dubawi (IRE)—Rosinka (IRE) (Soviet Star (USA)) (150000) **Mr A M B Macdonald-Buchanan & Partners**
68 B f 09/03 Camelot—Scarborough Fair (Pivotal) (30000) **Mr P. Brocklehurst**
69 Ch c 03/04 Helmet (AUS)—Sensationally (Montjeu (IRE)) **Castle Down Racing**
70 Gr c 19/04 Starspangledbanner (AUS)—
Sixpenny Sweets (IRE) (Dalakhani (IRE)) (47189) **Martin Hughes & Michael Kerr-Dineen**
71 SLEIGHT, b c 07/04 Showcasing—Magic (IRE) (Galileo (IRE)) **Martin Hughes & Michael Kerr-Dineen**
72 SURREY GOLD (IRE), b c 24/04 Golden Horn—Shemiyla (FR) (Dalakhani (IRE)) (37000) **Surrey Racing (SG)**
73 SWEEP THE STARS, b c 01/02 Iffraaj—Sweeping Up (Sea The Stars (IRE)) **Ben & Sir Martyn Arbib**
74 THUNDERCLAP (IRE), b c 13/05 Night of Thunder (IRE)—
Former Drama (USA) (Dynaformer (USA)) (70000) **Sir Thomas Pilkington, Mr R A Pilkington**
75 VINO VICTRIX, b c 07/03 Sir Percy—Valeria Victrix (IRE) (Dubawi (IRE)) (30000) **Dr J Wilson & Mr S Ronaldson**
76 B f 19/02 Bobby's Kitten (USA)—Wonderful Desert (Green Desert (USA)) (10000) **Helena Springfield Ltd**

Other Owners: Mr B. G. Arbib, M. Arbib, M. T. Bevan, M. H. Dixon, W. D. Eason, Mr M. B. Hughes, M. Kerr-Dineen, Mr Rod Lloyd, Mrs Sherin Lloyd, Mrs R. A. Luard, Lord Margadale, Mr Adrian McAlpine, Mrs M. D. W. Morrison, Mrs S. Read, Mrs J. Richards, Mr M. A. Richards, Mr S. B. S. Ronaldson, T. D. Rootes, J. L. Rowsell, Mr A. H. Scott, Mrs B. M. Scott, Selwood Bloodstock, O. F. Waller, Dr J. Wilson, Mr Richard Wright.

Flat Jockey: Charlie Bennett. **Amateur Jockey:** Mr Robert Pooles.

---

385   MR MOHAMED MOUBARAK, Newmarket
Postal: 3C Sunnyside, Park Lane, Newmarket, Suffolk, CB8 8AX
EMAIL Moubarak.mohammed17@gmail.com

1 FARD, 5, b g Dutch Art—Rose Blossom **Mr J. A. Alsabah**
2 RASHEEQ (IRE), 7, b g Vale of York (IRE)—Limber Up (IRE) **D. P. Fremel**
3 ROYAL DYNASTY, 4, b f Charm Spirit (IRE)—Millisecond **D. P. Fremel**
4 TEXTING, 4, b f Charm Spirit (IRE)—Dreamily (IRE) **Mr M. Y. Moubarak**

THREE-YEAR-OLDS
5 BANMI (IRE), b f Kodiac—Fingal Nights (IRE) **Mr J. A. Alsabah**
6 BY FAITH, b f Pastoral Pursuits—Shrewd Decision **D. P. Fremel**
7 ERDENE (USA), b f Midnight Lute (USA)—Lady of Akita (USA) **AlMohamediya Racing**
8 B f Shooting To Win (AUS)—High Regards (IRE) **Mr K. Kurt**
9 KENTUCKY HARDBOOT (IRE), ch g Starspangledbanner (AUS)—Fanditha (IRE) **D. P. Fremel**
10 LICIT (IRE), b f Poet's Voice—Deserted **Mr M. Y. Moubarak**
11 VANDAD (IRE), b c Dandy Man (IRE)—Ruby Girl (IRE) **Mr D. Vakilgilani**

MR MOHAMED MOUBARAK - continued

TWO-YEAR-OLDS

12 Ch c 16/01 Garswood—Friendship Is Love (Byron) (4000) **Mr D. Vakilgilani**
13 B f 05/05 Dawn Approach (IRE)—Ibiza Dream (Night Shift (USA)) **Mr D. Vakilgilani**
14 **MIND THAT JET (IRE),** b c 07/02 Kodiac—Rate (Galileo (IRE)) (135000) **Mr D. Vakilgilani**
15 B c 25/02 Anodin (IRE)—Mystic Melody (Montjeu (IRE)) (12380) **Mr D. Vakilgilani**
16 **NESS TA RAH,** br f 19/03 Cable Bay (IRE)—Point Perfect (Dansili) (20000) **Kevin O'Donnell & David Fremel**
17 **SARRDAR (IRE),** ch c 15/02 New Approach (IRE)—Coolnagree (IRE) (Dark Angel (IRE)) (120000) **Mr D. Vakilgilani**
18 Ch c 23/02 Helmet (AUS)—Self Centred (Medicean) (16000) **Mr D. Vakilgilani**

Other Owners: D. P. Fremel, Mr K. O'Donnell.

386
MR WILLIAM MUIR, Lambourn
Postal: **Linkslade, Wantage Road, Lambourn, Hungerford, Berkshire, RG17 8UG**
Contacts: HOME **01488 73748** PHONE **01488 73098** MOBILE **07831 457074** FAX **01488 73490**
EMAIL **william@williammuir.com** WEBSITE **www.williammuir.com**

1 **BLUE BEIRUT (IRE),** 4, b g Lilbourne Lad (IRE)—Ornellaia (IRE) **Mr J. M. O'Mulloy**
2 **CHIEF BRODY,** 9, b g Phoenix Reach (IRE)—Cherry Plum **Lucy Sandford & Richard Phillips**
3 **CUTTIN' EDGE (IRE),** 6, b g Rip Van Winkle (IRE)—How's She Cuttin' (IRE) **Purple & Lilac Racing**
4 **DATA PROTECTION,** 5, b g Foxwedge (AUS)—Midnight Sky **Muir Racing Partnership - Santa Anita**
5 **GENERAL ZOFF,** 5, b g Zoffany (IRE)—Aunt Julia **Purple & Lilac Racing X**
6 **GOLD AT MIDNIGHT,** 4, b f Havana Gold (IRE)—Midnight Ransom **Mr R. Haim**
7 **GURMIL,** 4, b g Mount Nelson—London Welsh **Perspicacious Punters Racing Club**
8 **HAMMY END (IRE),** 4, b g Mount Nelson—Northern Affair (IRE) **Mr J. M. O'Mulloy**
9 **HOLD STILL (IRE),** 4, b g Bated Breath—Effervesce (IRE) **Muir Racing Partnership - Saint Cloud**
10 **IMPRESSIONABLE,** 4, b f Exceed And Excel (AUS)—Appealing (IRE) **Miss Y. M. G. Jacques**
11 **ITS NICE TOBE NICE,** 4, b f Dalakhani (IRE)—Bright Halo (IRE) **It's Nice Tobe Nice**
12 **JACK'S POINT,** 4, b g Slade Power (IRE)—Electra Star **C. L. A. Edginton**
13 **JAMAICAN JILL,** 5, b m Teofilo (IRE)—Kahlua Kiss **M. J. Caddy**
14 **JAVELIN,** 5, ch m Lethal Force (IRE)—Amitola (IRE) **G O Leach & Mrs J M Leach**
15 **JUST HUBERT (IRE),** 4, b g Dunaden (FR)—La Tulipe (FR) **Foursome Thoroughbreds**
16 **LITTLE MISS DAISY,** 6, b m Arabian Gleam—Desert Liaison **Mrs J. M. Muir**
17 **LORNA COLE (IRE),** 4, gr f Lethal Force (IRE)—Suedehead **Mr J. M. O'Mulloy**
18 **NATTY NIGHT,** 4, b g Nathaniel (IRE)—Danehill Dreamer (USA) **Mr J. M. O'Mulloy**
19 **SO CLAIRE,** 4, br f Kyllachy—If So **Foursome Thoroughbreds**
20 **SWEET JEMIMA (USA),** 4, ch f More Than Ready (USA)—Sweet Nothings (USA) **C. L. A. Edginton**
21 **VIPIN (FR),** 5, b g Approve (IRE)—Heaven's Heart (IRE) **Mr J O'Mulloy & Mr K Jeffery**

THREE-YEAR-OLDS

22 **BEE MAGIC (IRE),** b g Zebedee—Star Port **Muir Racing Partnership - Leicester**
23 **EPIC ENDEAVOUR (IRE),** b g Epaulette (AUS)—Doubt (IRE) **Clarke, Edginton, Niven**
24 **FAR FROM A RUBY,** b f Farhh—Pretty Miss **Mr C. L. A. Edginton & Mr W. R. Muir**
25 **FINAL OPTION,** bl f Lethal Force (IRE)—If So **Foursome Thoroughbreds**
26 **HOWTONSTREET HARRY (IRE),** b g Anjaal—Kathy Sun (IRE) **Mr M. P. Graham**
27 **MOLINARI (IRE),** gr c Mastercraftsman (IRE)—Moon Empress (FR) **C. L. A. Edginton**
28 **NEWYORKSTATEOFMIND,** b g Brazen Beau (AUS)—Albany Rose (IRE) **Purple & Lilac Racing-Spotted Dog P'ship**
29 **PYLEDRIVER,** b c Harbour Watch (IRE)—La Pyle (FR) **Knox & Wells Limited & Mr R W Devlin**
30 **ROSES'S BOY (IRE),** br g Alhebayeb (IRE)—House of Roses **Mr A. Harman**
31 **SO SPECIAL,** gr f Lethal Force (IRE)—Secret Era **Carmel Stud**
32 **TIP TOP,** ch f Dream Ahead (USA)—Sweet Secret **Carmel Stud & G.O.Leach & Mrs J.M.Leach**

TWO-YEAR-OLDS

33 Gr c 24/03 Lethal Force (IRE)—Blaugrana (IRE) (Exceed And Excel (AUS)) (10000) **Mr J. M. O'Mulloy**
34 B c 16/01 Twilight Son—Cardrona (Selkirk (USA)) (32000) **Mr M. P. Graham**
35 B f 27/03 New Approach (IRE)—La Pyle (IRE) (Le Havre (IRE)) (35000) **Knox & Wells Limited & Mr R W Devlin**
36 **REINFORCER,** ch c 28/04 Lethal Force (IRE)—Heavenly Dawn (Pivotal) (35000) **Foursome Thoroughbreds**
37 B c 09/02 Adaay (IRE)—Secret Era (Cape Cross (IRE)) (20000) **Muir Racing Partnership - Flemington**

MR WILLIAM MUIR - continued

Other Owners: Mr P. A. Abberley, Carmel Stud, Mr G. Charles, Mr N. Clark, Mr D. G. Clarke, R. W. Devlin, C. L. A. Edginton, Mr M. P. Graham, Mr R. Haim, Mr K. Jeffery, Knox & Wells Limited, Mr G. O. Leach, Mrs J. M. Leach, Mrs S. Mercer, Mr C. Moore, Mrs M. E. Morgan, P. H. Morgan, W. R. Muir, Mr A. J. Niven, Mr J. M. O'Mulloy, Mr D. L. Quaintance, Mr P. D. Quaintance.

Assistant Trainer: Richard Phillips.

Flat Jockey: Martin Dwyer.

---

387 **MR CLIVE MULHALL, Scarcroft**
Postal: **Scarcroft Hall Farm, Thorner Lane, Scarcroft, Leeds, Yorkshire, LS14 3AQ**
Contacts: **HOME 0113 289 3095 MOBILE 07979 527675**
EMAIL clive@scarcrofthallracing.co.uk WEBSITE www.clivemulhallracing.co.uk

1 5, B m Desideratum—Alimure
2 **ANEEDH,** 10, b g Lucky Story (USA)—Seed Al Maha (USA) **Mrs C. M. Mulhall**
3 **BIGBADBOY (IRE),** 7, b g Big Bad Bob (IRE)—Elegantly (IRE) **Ms Y Featherstone & Mrs M Mulhall**
4 **LORD SERENDIPITY (IRE),** 8, gr g Lord Shanakill (USA)—Elitista (FR)
Other Owners: Ms Y. P. Featherstone, Mrs C. M. Mulhall.

---

388 **MR NEIL MULHOLLAND, Limpley Stoke**
Postal: **Conkwell Grange Stables, Conkwell, Limpley Stoke, Bath, Avon, BA2 7FD**
Contacts: **MOBILE 07739 258607**
EMAIL neil@neilmulhollandracing.com WEBSITE www.neilmulhollandracing.com

1 **ANGELA'S HOPE,** 5, b m Kayf Tara—Follow My Leader (IRE) **The Affordable Partnership**
2 **ASHLEY HOLLOW,** 6, b m Beat Hollow—Hazel Bank Lass (IRE) **Mrs A. C. Crofts**
3 **BALLYMILAN,** 5, b m Milan—Ballyhoo (IRE) **Heart Racing HR2**
4 **BOOTLEGGER (IRE),** 7, b g Kayf Tara—Sweetbitter (FR) **The Risk Takers Partnership**
5 **CAROLE'S DESTRIER,** 12, b g Kayf Tara—Barton May **Mrs C. Skipworth**
6 **CAROLINES CHARM (IRE),** 6, b g Masterofthehorse (IRE)—
Truckers Princess (IRE) **Jockey Club Ownership (SW 2018)**
7 **CESAR ET ROSALIE (FR),** 8, ch g Network (GER)—Regle de L'Art (FR) **Mrs J. M. Abbott**
8 **CHINWAG,** 5, b g Trans Island—Clohamon Gossip (IRE) **The Boot Inn Partnership**
9 **CHIRICO VALLIS (FR),** 8, b g Poliglote—Quora Vallis (FR) **Mr J. P. McManus**
10 **CODE OF LAW,** 6, ch g Papal Bull—Fyvie **The Affordable (3) Partnership**
11 **CONKWELL LEGEND,** 6, b g Midnight Legend—Gallimaufry **Mrs H. R. Cross & Mrs S. A. Keys**
12 **CREMANT (IRE),** 6, b g Getaway (GER)—Opera Season (IRE) **Mr P. M. Simmonds**
13 **DANDOLO DU GITE (FR),** 7, b g Khalkevi (IRE)—Lavande d'Eproniere (FR) **Equi ex Incertis Partners**
14 **DEAD RIGHT,** 8, b g Alflora (IRE)—April Queen **Mr J. P. McManus**
15 **DEPUTY JONES (IRE),** 7, b m Milan—Hudson Hope (IRE) **A. Carr**
16 **DOING FINE (IRE),** 12, b g Presenting—Howaya Pet (IRE) **Neil Mulholland Racing Club**
17 **DRAMATIC APPROACH (IRE),** 6, b m Flemensfirth (USA)—Sea Breeze Lady (IRE) **Mr Donald Bell & Partner**
18 **DREAM MACHINE (IRE),** 6, ch g Dream Ahead (USA)—Last Cry (FR) **D. M. Bell**
19 **DUBAI KEY (IRE),** 6, b g Dubai Destination (USA)—Diamond Key (IRE) **The Affordable Partnership**
20 **DYNAMIC KATE (IRE),** 4, br f Yeats (IRE)—Alverstone **BG Racing Partnership**
21 5, B g Califet (FR)—Essaoira Jewel (IRE) **Mr T. J. Abbott**
22 **EXELERATOR EXPRESS (FR),** 6, b g Poliglote—Reine de Lestrade (FR) **Walters Plant Hire & Potter Group**
23 **FERN OWL,** 8, ch g Nayef (USA)—Snow Goose **Mr J. Hobbs**
24 **FINGERONTHESWITCH (IRE),** 10, b g Beneficial—Houseoftherisinsun (IRE) **Cahill, Atwell & Crofts**
25 **FIRST QUEST (USA),** 6, b g First Defence (USA)—Dixie Quest (USA) **The Affordable (2) Partnership**
26 **FR HUMPHREY (IRE),** 12, ch g Carlo Bank (IRE)—An Realt Beag (IRE) **BG Racing Partnership**
27 **FRAU GEORGIA (IRE),** 6, b m Germany (USA)—Sumability (IRE) **Mr J. Henderson**
28 **FULL OF SURPRISES (FR),** 5, b m No Risk At All (FR)—Fontaine Riant (FR) **Mr J. P. McManus**
29 **GLENGAR (IRE),** 6, b g Stowaway—Accordeon Royale (IRE) **Equi ex Incertis Partners**

MR NEIL MULHOLLAND - continued

30 **GOLDEN EMBLEM (IRE),** 6, ch m Presenting—Merry Excuse (IRE) **Diamond Racing Ltd**
31 **GOLDENEYE VEE,** 5, b m Bollin Eric—Hazel Bank Lass (IRE) **Mrs A. C. Crofts**
32 **GREEN OR BLACK (IRE),** 8, gr m Zebedee—Boucheron **The Chosen Few**
33 **HARBOUR FORCE (FR),** 6, b g Harbour Watch (IRE)—Dam Beautiful **Mr D. B. Harris**
34 **HEAVEY,** 6, b g Trans Island—Clohamon Gossip (IRE) **Qdos Racing**
35 **HEREIA (IRE),** 4, b g Olympic Glory (IRE)—Rolled Gold (USA) **Mr O. S. Harris**
36 **HIDDEN DEPTHS (IRE),** 5, b g Dark Angel (IRE)—Liber Nauticus (IRE) **Neil Mulholland Racing Ltd**
37 **HYGROVE PERCY,** 7, ch g Sir Percy—Hygrove Welshlady (IRE) **G. P. and Miss S. J. Hayes**
38 **IMPULSIVE STAR (IRE),** 10, b g Busy Flight—Impulsive Ita (IRE) **Robert Waley-Cohen & Men Holding**
39 **INDIAN BRAVE (IRE),** 9, b g Definite Article—Fridays Folly (IRE) **J. J. Maguire**
40 **IRISH ODYSSEY (IRE),** 7, gr g Yeats (IRE)—Ma Furie (FR) **Mr A. G. Bloom**
41 **JOE WARBRICK,** 5, b g Universal (IRE)—Maori Legend **Mrs H. R. Cross**
42 **JUST HENNY,** 6, b m Midnight Legend—Exchanging Glances **Abbott & Bunch**
43 **KALONDRA (IRE),** 9, b g Spadoun (FR)—Mystic Vic (IRE) **Mr J. Henderson**
44 **KANSAS CITY CHIEF (IRE),** 11, b g Westerner—Badawi Street **Mr A. G. Bloom**
45 **LAKE BAIKAL (FR),** 6, gr g Martaline—La Curamalal (IRE) **Mr J. P. McManus**
46 **LAST ENCHANTMENT (IRE),** 5, b m Camelot—Illandrane (IRE) **Equi ex Incertis Partners**
47 **LEE SIDE LADY (IRE),** 10, ch m Mountain High (IRE)—Vicante (IRE) **The Affordable (2) Partnership**
48 **LIBBDAN (IRE),** 6, b m Oscar (IRE)—Benefique (IRE) **Mr Peter Gray & Jackie Abbott**
49 **LORD ACCORD (IRE),** 5, b g Yeats (IRE)—Cush Jewel (IRE) **Lynne & Angus Maclennan**
50 **LYRICAL BALLAD (IRE),** 4, gr f Dark Angel (IRE)—Iffraaj Pink (IRE) **Dajam Ltd**
51 **MAGICAL THOMAS,** 8, ch g Dylan Thomas (IRE)—Magical Cliche (USA) **G. P. and Miss S. J. Hayes**
52 **MALIBOO (IRE),** 7, b m Mahler—Aboo Lala (IRE) **Premier Care Management**
53 **MAN OF THE SEA (IRE),** 4, ch g Born To Sea (IRE)—Hurricane Lily (IRE) **Dajam Ltd**
54 **MASQUERADE BLING (IRE),** 6, b m Approve (IRE)—Mataji (IRE) **Neil Mulholland Racing Club**
55 **MASTER BURBIDGE,** 9, b g Pasternak—Silver Sequel **Dajam Ltd**
56 **MILKWOOD (IRE),** 6, b g Dylan Thomas (IRE)—Tropical Lake (IRE) **Ms J. Bridel**
57 **MILREU HAS (FR),** 5, b g Kapgarde (FR)—Miss Benedicte (FR) **Mr J. P. McManus**
58 **MIND YOUR BACK (IRE),** 7, b g Getaway (GER)—Local Hall (IRE) **Neil Mulholland Racing Ltd**
59 **MISS JEANNE MOON (IRE),** 6, b m Getaway (GER)—Moon Approach (IRE) **Mrs H. R. Cross & Mrs S. A. Keys**
60 **MOLLIANA,** 5, b m Olden Times—The Screamer (IRE) **Dajam Ltd**
61 **MOLLY CAREW,** 8, b m Midnight Legend—Moyliscar **Mrs H. R. Cross & Mrs S. A. Keys**
62 **MOUNT OLIVER (IRE),** 10, b g Mountain High (IRE)—Little Nancy (IRE) **BG Racing Partnership**
63 **MY BROTHER (IRE),** 7, b g Roderic O'Connor (IRE)—Victory Peak **BG Racing Partnership**
64 **NEACHELLS BRIDGE (IRE),** 8, ch g Getaway (GER)—Strawberry Lane (IRE) **Mr M. C. Creed**
65 **NIBLAWI (IRE),** 8, b g Vale of York (IRE)—Finnmark **Mr A. G. Bloom**
66 **NO HIDDEN CHARGES (IRE),** 7, b g Scorpion (IRE)—Soniadoir (IRE) **Stephen & Gloria Seymour**
67 **NOVIS ADVENTUS (IRE),** 8, b g New Approach (IRE)—Tiffed (USA) **The General Asphalte Company Ltd**
68 5, B h Rail Link—Ocean Transit (IRE) **Mr B. F. Mulholland**
69 **PANIA,** 6, b m Sakhee (USA)—Maori Legend **Happy Days Racing**
70 **PASSING OCEANS,** 6, gr g Passing Glance—Sherwood Rose (IRE) **Mr B. F. Mulholland**
71 **PELTWELL (IRE),** 7, b m Milan—Fast Finisher (IRE) **Mrs P. L. Bridel**
72 **PENNY POET (IRE),** 7, b m Intikhab (USA)—Mneme (FR) **The Boot Inn Partnership**
73 **PERCY POPS,** 6, ch g Getaway (GER)—Popsie Hall **Birchenhough, Dewilde, Dod**
74 **PRESENTING LUCINA (IRE),** 8, b m Presenting—Lucina (GER) **The Boot Inn Partnership**
75 **PRETTYLITTLETHING (IRE),** 10, b m Tajraasi (USA)—Cloncunny Girl (IRE) **Mr J. J. Brummitt**
76 **PRINCESS T,** 5, gr m Aussie Rules (USA)—Fairy Slipper **Harte Investments Ltd & Dajam Ltd**
77 **PUTTING GREEN,** 8, ch g Selkirk (USA)—Ryella (USA) **Mr A. G. Bloom**
78 **QUEEN'S MAGIC (IRE),** 8, b m Kalanisi (IRE)—Black Queen (IRE) **Wincanton Race Club**
79 **REFEREE,** 5, b g Dansili—Zulema **Stephen & Gloria Seymour**
80 **ROOKIE TRAINER (IRE),** 6, b g Gold Well—Crazy Falcon (IRE) **A Graham - Bankruptcy Trustee M Stanley**
81 **ROYAL ARCADE (IRE),** 5, b br g Arcadio (GER)—Miss Excitable (IRE)
82 **RUNASIMI RIVER,** 7, ch m Generous (IRE)—Zaffaranni (IRE) **Mrs G. A. Davies**
83 **SAINTE DOCTOR (FR),** 4, gr f Doctor Dino (FR)—Pakoonah **Mr J. P. McManus**
84 **SAMBELLA,** 5, ch m Black Sam Bellamy (IRE)—Chant de L'Aube (FR) **Mrs H. Dale-Staples**
85 **SANDYMOUNT ROSE (IRE),** 6, b m Yeats (IRE)—Ma Furie (FR) **Proudley & Whymark Partnership**
86 **SCARDURA (IRE),** 6, b g Stowaway—Sosua (IRE) **Mrs J. N. Cartwright**
87 **SHANTOU VILLAGE (IRE),** 10, b g Shantou (USA)—Village Queen (IRE) **Mrs J. Gerard-Pearse**
88 **SIMPLY SIN (IRE),** 5, b g Footstepsinthesand—Miss Sally (IRE) **Neil Mulholland Racing Ltd**

MR NEIL MULHOLLAND - continued

89 **SOLIGHOSTER (FR)**, 8, ch g Loup Solitaire (USA)—Miss Martine (FR) **The Colony Stable LLC & Dajam Ltd**
90 **SOUPY SOUPS (IRE)**, 9, ch g Stowaway—Near Dunleer (IRE) **Equi ex Incertis Partners**
91 **TANGO BOY (IRE)**, 7, ch g Flemensfirth (USA)—Hello Kitty (IRE) **Mr A. G. Bloom**
92 **TEMPLEROSS (IRE)**, 9, b g Presenting—Dame O'Neill (IRE) **Mr A. G. Bloom**
93 **TEST RIDE (IRE)**, 6, b g Rip Van Winkle (IRE)—Easter Fairy (USA) **The Affordable Partnership**
94 **THE DETAINEE**, 7, b g Aqlaam—Jakarta Jade (IRE) **Crowd Racing Partnership**
95 **THE TWISLER**, 8, b g Motivator—Panna **Mrs V. J. Hodsoll**
96 **THE WEASEL (IRE)**, 6, ch g Vinnie Roe (IRE)—Countess of Milan (IRE) **Neil Mulholland Racing Ltd**
97 **THE WICKET CHICKEN (IRE)**, 8, b m Milan—Soniadoir (IRE) **Dajam & Colm Hearne**
98 **THE YOUNG MASTER**, 11, b g Echo of Light—Fine Frenzy (IRE) **Mike Burbidge & The Old Masters**
99 **VANCOUVER**, 8, ch g Generous (IRE)—All Told (IRE) **J. J. Maguire**
100 **VEXILLUM (IRE)**, 11, br g Mujadil (USA)—Common Cause **Mr J. Heaney**
101 **VIKING RUBY**, 7, ch m Sulamani (IRE)—Viking Torch **Ms S. M. Exell**
102 **VIS A VIS**, 6, b g Dansili—Pretty Face **Ashley Carr, Eismark & Packham**
103 **WALT (IRE)**, 9, b g King's Theatre (IRE)—Allee Sarthoise (FR) **Mr P. M. Simmonds**
104 **WILLYEGOLASSIEGO**, 7, br m Kheleyf (USA)—Kryena **Mr J. Hobbs**

THREE-YEAR-OLDS

105 B f Free Eagle (IRE)—Al Kahina **Stephen & Gloria Seymour**
106 **ERIKA**, ch f Hot Streak (IRE)—Fame Is The Spur **Mrs H. R. Cross**
107 B f Norse Dancer (IRE)—Hazel Bank Lass (IRE) **Mrs A. C. Crofts**

Other Owners: Mrs J. M. Abbott, Mr T. J. Abbott, Mrs L. Atwell, D. M. Bell, Mrs K. Birchenhough, Sir M. F. Broughton, Mr S. W. Broughton, Mrs P. M. Bunch, Mr M. S. Burbidge, Mr M. G. Cahill, A. Carr, Colony Stable Llc, Mrs A. C. Crofts, Mrs H. R. Cross, Dajam Ltd, Mrs S. De Wilde, Mrs P. I. Dod, Mr E. Eismark, Miss J. A. Goddard, Mr P. Gray, Mr S. Harbour, Harte Investments Limited, Mr G. P. Hayes, Miss S. J. Hayes, Mr C. Hearne, Mrs S. A. Keys, Mr A. Maclennan, Mrs L. Maclennan, Mr S. Packham, Mr P. J. Proudley, Mrs G. P. Seymour, Mr S. G. Seymour, Sundorne Products (Llanidloes) Ltd, Mr J. N. Trueman, Mrs R. A. Turner, Mr R. F. Turner, Mr R. B. Waley-Cohen, Walters Plant Hire Ltd, Mr J. K. Whymark.

Assistant Trainer: Andrew Doyle.

NH Jockey: James Best, Robbie Dunne, Tom Scudamore, Sam Twiston-Davies. **Conditional Jockey:** Philip Donovan, Harry Reed. **Amateur Jockey:** Millie Wonnacott.

---

389 **MR LAWRENCE MULLANEY, Malton**
Postal: **Raikes Farm, Great Habton, Malton, North Yorkshire, YO17 6RX**
Contacts: **PHONE 01653 668595 MOBILE 07899 902565**
EMAIL nicolamullaney@yahoo.co.uk

1 **BEVERLEY BULLET**, 7, b g Makfi—Don't Tell Mary (IRE) **Mrs Jean Stapleton & Rob Wilson**
2 **BOBBA TEE**, 8, b g Rail Link—Trompette (USA) **David Furman & John Sugarman**
3 **GORGEOUS GENERAL**, 5, ch g Captain Gerrard (IRE)—Gorgeous Goblin (IRE) **Mr S. Humphries**
4 **HASILI FILLY**, 4, b f Zoffany (IRE)—Miss Marvellous (USA) **L. A. Mullaney**
5 **KYLLACHY WARRIOR (IRE)**, 4, gr g Kyllachy—Silver Act (IRE) **L. A. Mullaney**
6 **LORD OF THE ROCK (IRE)**, 8, b g Rock of Gibraltar (IRE)—La Sylphide **Mr & Mrs G. Turnbull**
7 **OUR LITTLE PONY**, 5, b m Bated Breath—Cracking Lass (IRE) **Mr J. R. Swift**

THREE-YEAR-OLDS

8 **CHENILLE (IRE)**, b f Nathaniel (IRE)—Camlet **Mr & Mrs G. Turnbull**
9 **HENET (IRE)**, b f Dream Ahead (USA)—Jen Jos Enigma (IRE) **Mr S Rimmer & Partners**
10 **JACK IS BACK**, b g Due Diligence (USA)—Rosa Luxemburg **R Massheder, C Napthine, A Turton & Ptnr**
11 **JAY ME LO (IRE)**, b f Equiano (FR)—Arabian Spell (IRE) **Ian Buckley James Lomas**

Other Owners: Ian Buckley, Mr D. E. Furman, Mr J. Lomas, Mr R. Massheder, L. A. Mullaney, Mr C. Napthine, Mr S. J. Rimmer, Mrs J. Stapleton, Mr J. B. Sugarman, Mr L. Taylor, Mr A. Turton, Mr R. J. Wilson.

390 **MR MICHAEL MULLINEAUX, Tarporley**
Postal: **Southley Farm, Alpraham, Tarporley, Cheshire, CW6 9JD**
Contacts: **PHONE 01829 261440 MOBILE 07753 650263 FAX 01829 261440**
EMAIL southlearacing@btinternet.com **WEBSITE** www.southleyfarm.co.uk

1 **ANTON DOLIN (IRE)**, 12, ch g Danehill Dancer (IRE)—Ski For Gold **S. A. Pritchard**
2 **BOB'S GIRL**, 5, b m Big Bad Bob (IRE)—Linda (FR) **S. A. Pritchard**
3 **DODGY BOB**, 7, b g Royal Applause—Rustam **M. Mullineaux**
4 **FAIR HIT**, 6, b g Fair Mix (IRE)—Double Hit **Dr G. M. Thelwall Jones**
5 **FOU DETOI (FR)**, 5, gr g Lord du Sud (FR)—Funkia (FR) **Mr H. Taylor**
6 **HES OUR ROBIN (IRE)**, 10, b g Robin des Pres (FR)—Poly Sandstorm (IRE) **Mrs C. S. Wilson**
7 **JACKSONFIRE**, 8, ch g Firebreak—Fitolini **Mr O. D. Knight**
8 **JEANE DE BELLVILLE**, 4, ch f Black Sam Bellamy (IRE)—Majeeda (IRE) **M. Mullineaux**
9 **MINTY JONES**, 11, b g Primo Valentino (IRE)—Reveur **P. Clacher**
10 **NO FRONTIERE (IRE)**, 6, ch m Sans Frontieres (IRE)—County Gate (IRE) **Mr L. Tomlinson**
11 **PEACHEY CARNEHAN**, 6, ch g Foxwedge (AUS)—Zubova **Mr K. Jones**
12 **POOR DUKE (IRE)**, 10, b g Bachelor Duke (USA)—Graze On Too (IRE) **M. Mullineaux**
13 **RED ALLURE**, 5, ch m Mayson—Lark In The Park (IRE) **Mia Racing**
14 **RED BRAE RAINY MAY**, 4, b g Lucarno (USA)—Breezy B's **Mrs C. S. Wilson**
15 **ROCK WARBLER (IRE)**, 7, ch g Raven's Pass (USA)—Rare Tern (IRE) **Mr R. A. Royle**
16 **SECRETINTHEPARK**, 10, ch g Sakhee's Secret—Lark In The Park (IRE) **Mia Racing**
17 **SOMEWHERE SECRET**, 6, ch g Sakhee's Secret—Lark In The Park (IRE) **Mia Racing**
18 8, Ch m Sulamani (IRE)—Sunny Parkes **M. Mullineaux**
19 **TEEPEE TIME**, 7, b m Compton Place—Deora De **Mr G. Cornes**
20 **VERY FIRST BLADE**, 11, b g Needwood Blade—Dispol Verity **Mr G. McCarthy**
21 **WE'VE GOT THE LOVE (IRE)**, 4, b f Charm Spirit (IRE)—Olympic Medal **S. A. Pritchard**

THREE-YEAR-OLDS

22 **SECRET IDENTITY**, b f Equiano (FR)—Onlyyouknowme (IRE) **Mr P. Ball**

TWO-YEAR-OLDS

23 **GIZZA JOB**, b f 08/04 Equiano (FR)—Masque Rose (Oasis Dream) (3000)

Other Owners: A. Tickle, Mrs I. M. Tickle, M. A. Tickle.

Assistant Trainer: Susan Mullineaux, Stuart Ross.

Amateur Jockey: Miss M. J. L. Mullineaux.

391 **MR SEAMUS MULLINS, Amesbury**
Postal: **Wilsford Stables, Wilsford-Cum-Lake, Amesbury, Salisbury, Wiltshire, SP4 7BL**
Contacts: **PHONE 01980 626344 MOBILE 07702 559634**
EMAIL info@jwmullins.co.uk **WEBSITE** www.seamusmullins.co.uk

1 **ARDBRUCE (IRE)**, 7, b g Scorpion (IRE)—An Bothar Ard (IRE) **Andrew Cocks & Tara Johnson**
2 **BARROWMOUNT (IRE)**, 4, b g Mountain High (IRE)—Nans Mare (IRE) **J. W. Mullins**
3 **BILL AND BARN (IRE)**, 9, br g Presenting—Forgotten Star (IRE) **Mr D Coles & Mr M Adams**
4 **CAP HORNER (FR)**, 8, gr g Apsis—Rapsodie Sea (FR) **J. W. Mullins**
5 **CHESTERFIELD (IRE)**, 10, ch g Pivotal—Antique (IRE) **The Rumble Racing Club**
6 **EN COEUR (FR)**, 6, b g Kap Rock (FR)—Fairyleap (FR) **Woodford Valley Racing**
7 **FENLONS COURT (IRE)**, 8, b g Court Cave (IRE)—Classic Note (IRE) **Mrs D. H. Potter**
8 **GRANITIC (IRE)**, 7, b g Court Cave (IRE)—Like A Miller (IRE) **Dr & Mrs John Millar**
9 **HEWN FROM GRANITE**, 5, b g Yeats (IRE)—Luccombe Chine **The Hopeful Partnership**
10 **I SEE YOU WELL (FR)**, 7, b g Air Chief Marshal (IRE)—
Bonne Mere (FR) **Philippa Downing, Clive Dunning & S Pitt**
11 **INSPIREUS (IRE)**, 7, b g Scorpion (IRE)—Miniconjou (IRE) **Geoff Barnett & Brian Edgeley**
12 **JARLATH**, 9, b g Norse Dancer (IRE)—Blue Lullaby (IRE) **Phoenix Bloodstock**
13 **KENTFORD HEIRESS**, 10, b m Midnight Legend—Kentford Duchess **D. I. Bare**
14 **KENTFORD MALLARD**, 7, b m Sulamani (IRE)—Kentford Grebe **D. I. Bare**

MR SEAMUS MULLINS - continued

15 **LYN'S SECRET (IRE)**, 5, ch m Sakhee's Secret—Blase Chevalier (IRE) **Mr C. Wilson**
16 4, B g Dylan Thomas (IRE)—Ma Baker (IRE) **Andrew Cocks & Tara Johnson**
17 **MAEBH (IRE)**, 6, b m Doyen (IRE)—South Queen Lady (IRE) **J. W. Mullins**
18 **MAHLER'S PROMISE (IRE)**, 5, b g Mahler—Loadsapromise (IRE) **The One More Sleep Racing Syndicate**
19 4, B g Dylan Thomas (IRE)—Miss Platinum (IRE) **Andrew Cocks & Tara Johnson**
20 **MOGESTIC (IRE)**, 11, b g Morozov (USA)—Crosschild (IRE) **Mrs J. C. Scorgie**
21 **MORODER (IRE)**, 6, b g Morozov (USA)—Another Tonto (IRE) **Mrs A. Leftley**
22 **MOSSY GLEN (IRE)**, 4, b f Shirocco (GER)—Golden Firth (IRE) **The Up The Glens Partnership**
23 **MRS MEADER**, 4, b f Cityscape—Bavarica **Nj Bloodstock**
24 4, B g Shirocco (GER)—Needed The Run (IRE) **Andrew Cocks & Tara Johnson**
25 **NELSON'S TOUCH**, 7, gr g Mount Nelson—Lady Friend **Mrs P. de W. Johnson**
26 **OBORNE LADY (IRE)**, 7, b m Watar (IRE)—Lady Shackleton (IRE) **Simon & Christine Prout**
27 **PLANTAGENET**, 8, b g Midnight Legend—Marsh Court **Mrs P. de W. Johnson**
28 **PLAYA BLANCA (IRE)**, 5, b g Zoffany (IRE)—Aiming Upwards **The Rumble Racing Club**
29 **POSTMAN (FR)**, 7, ch g American Post—Pepperjuice (GER) **Dr & Mrs John Millar**
30 5, B m Westerner—Put On Hold (IRE) **J. W. Mullins**
31 **ROMANOR**, 6, b g Holy Roman Emperor (IRE)—Salinia (IRE) **The Rumble Racing Club**
32 **SAKHEE'S CONQUEST**, 5, br g Sakhee's Secret—Another Conquest **Mr F G Matthews & Mr S Mullins**
33 **SHE'S GINA (GER)**, 7, b m It's Gino (GER)—Song of Night (GER) **Four Candles Partnership**
34 **SHELDON**, 4, ch g Shantou (USA)—Feabhra (IRE) **Andrew Cocks & Tara Johnson**
35 **SILVER NICKEL (IRE)**, 6, gr g Gold Well—Cooper's Rose (IRE) **Mrs D. H. Potter**
36 **SUMTIME**, 5, b m Doyen (IRE)—Seemarye **Roger & Rachel Jowett**
37 **SUNDIAL STORM**, 7, ch m Shantou (USA)—Shadow Line (FR) **J. W. Mullins**
38 **TARKS HILL**, 6, b m Brian Boru—Risky May **S Mullins Racing Club**
39 **THE PINK'N**, 4, gr g Dunaden (FR)—Lady Friend **Mrs P. de W. Johnson**
40 **THE RAVEN'S RETURN**, 7, b g Scorpion (IRE)—Mimis Bonnet (FR) **The Rumble Racing Club**
41 **TOMMIE BEAU (IRE)**, 5, b g Brian Boru—Bajan Girl (FR) **Andrew Cocks & Tara Johnson**
42 **UNIVERSAL SONG**, 4, ch f Universal (IRE)—Song of The Desert **D. Sutherland**
43 **WESTERBERRY (IRE)**, 8, b m Westerner—Casiana (GER) **S Mullins Racing Club**
44 **WHITE CHOCOLATE (IRE)**, 6, gr m Mastercraftsman (IRE)—Coco Demure (IRE) **The Rumble Racing Club**

THREE-YEAR-OLDS

45 **ARASUGAR (IRE)**, b f Arakan (USA)—Bahri Sugar (IRE) **J. W. Mullins**
46 **EDEBEZ (IRE)**, b g Zebedee—Silk City (IRE) **J. W. Mullins**
47 **INDYZEB (IRE)**, b f Zebedee—Indy Gal (IRE) **J. W. Mullins**

TWO-YEAR-OLDS

48 Br g 22/04 Mount Nelson—Lady Friend (Environment Friend) **J. W. Mullins**

Other Owners: Mr M. Adams, Mr G. Barnett, Mr N. Child, Mr D. J. Coles, Miss P. M. Downing, Mr C. R. Dunning, B. R. Edgeley, Miss S. Gorman, Mr R. Hall, Mr N. J. Johnston, Dr R. Jowett, Mrs R. A. Jowett, F. G. Matthews, Mrs J. D. Millar, Dr J. W. Millar, J. W. Mullins, C. I. C. Munro, Ms S. Pitt, Mrs C. A. Prout, Mr S. P. Prout, Mr A. Randle, D. Sutherland, Mr C. Wilson.

Assistant Trainer: Paul Attwater.

NH Jockey: Kevin Jones, Jeremiah McGrath, Daniel Sansom.

---

392 | MR WILLIAM P. MULLINS, Carlow
Postal: Closutton, Bagenalstown, Co. Carlow, Ireland
Contacts: PHONE +353 59 972 1786 MOBILE +353 87 256 4940 FAX +353 59 972 2709
EMAIL wpmullins@eircom.net WEBSITE www.wpmullins.com

1 **ACAPELLA BOURGEOIS (FR)**, 10, ch g Network (GER)—Jasmine (FR) **Slaneyville Syndicate**
2 **AIONE (FR)**, 7, b g Coastal Path—La Horquela (FR) **Mrs S Ricci**
3 **AL BOUM PHOTO (FR)**, 8, b g Buck's Boum (FR)—Al Gane (FR) **Mrs M. Donnelly**
4 **ALLAHO (FR)**, 6, b g No Risk At All (FR)—Idaho Falls (FR) **Cheveley Park Stud**
5 **ANDALUSA (FR)**, 5, gr m Martaline—Cadix (FR) **Lansdowne Partnership**
6 **ANNAMIX (FR)**, 7, gr g Martaline—Tashtiyana (IRE) **Mrs S Ricci**

MR WILLIAM P. MULLINS - continued

7 **ANTEY (GER)**, 7, b g Lord of England (GER)—Achinora **Mrs S. Ricci**

8 **APPRECIATE IT (IRE)**, 6, b g Jeremy (USA)—Sainte Baronne (FR) **Miss M A Masterson**

9 **ARAMON (GER)**, 7, b g Monsun (GER)—Aramina (GER) **Aramon Syndicate**

10 **ASK SUSAN (IRE)**, 8, b m Ask—Sitges (IRE) **Bowes Lodge Stables Partnership**

11 **ASTERION FORLONGE (FR)**, 6, gr g Coastal Path—Belle du Brizais (FR) **Mrs J Donnelly**

12 **AUTHORIZED ART (FR)**, 5, b g Authorized (IRE)—Rock Art (IRE) **Wicklow Bloodstock (Ireland) Ltd**

13 **BACARDYS (FR)**, 9, b br g Coastal Path—Oasice (FR) **Shanakiel Racing Syndicate**

14 **BACHASSON (FR)**, 9, gr g Voix du Nord (FR)—Belledonne (FR) **Edward O'Connell**

15 **BAMAKO MORIVIERE (FR)**, 9, b g Califet (FR)—Halladine (FR) **Mrs S. Ricci**

16 **BAPAUME (FR)**, 7, b g Turtle Bowl (IRE)—Brouhaha (FR) **Mrs S. Ricci**

17 **BELLOW MOME (FR)**, 9, b g Honolulu (GER)—Oll Mighty Fellow (FR) **Mrs Audrey Turley**

18 **BELLSHILL (IRE)**, 10, b g King's Theatre (IRE)—Fairy Native (IRE) **Andrea & Graham Wylie**

19 **BENIE DES DIEUX (FR)**, 9, b m Great Pretender (IRE)—Cana (FR) **Mrs S. Ricci**

20 **BERKSHIRE ROYAL**, 5, b g Sir Percy—Forest Express (AUS) **Mrs J M Mullins**

21 **BILLAWAY (IRE)**, 8, b g Well Chosen—Taipans Girl (IRE) **J Turner**

22 **BLACKBOW (IRE)**, 7, b g Stowaway—Rinnce Moll (IRE) **Roaringwater Syndicate**

23 **BLAZER (FR)**, 9, ch g Network (GER)—Juppelongue (FR) **J. P. McManus**

24 **BLAZING EMILY (IRE)**, 6, b m Presenting—Blazing Tempo (IRE) **Kenneth Alexander**

25 **BLEU BERRY (FR)**, 9, b g Special Kaldoun (IRE)—Somosierra (FR) **Mrs M. McMahon**

26 **BLUE LORD (FR)**, 5, b g Blue Bresil—Lorette (FR) **Simon Munir & Isaac Souede**

27 **BLUE SARI (FR)**, 5, b g Saddex—Blue Aster (FR) **John P. McManus**

28 **BONBON AU MIEL (FR)**, 9, b g Khalkevi (IRE)—Friandise II (FR) **Andrea & Graham Wylie**

29 **BRAHMA BULL (IRE)**, 9, ch g Presenting—Oligarch Society (IRE) **Mrs S. Ricci**

30 **BRONAGH'S BELLE (FR)**, 5, b m High Chaparral (IRE)—South Atlantic (USA) **Sean Sweeney**

31 **BUCK'S BILLIONAIRE (FR)**, 7, ch g Kapgarde (FR)—Buck's (FR) **Mrs J M Mullins**

32 **BUILDMEUPBUTTERCUP**, 6, ch m Sixties Icon—Eastern Paramour (IRE) **J. Turner**

33 **BURNING VICTORY (FR)**, 4, b f Nathaniel (IRE)—M'Oubliez Pas (USA) **Mrs Audrey Turley**

34 **BURROWS SAINT (FR)**, 7, b g Saint des Saints (FR)—La Bombonera (FR) **Mrs S. Ricci**

35 **CABARET QUEEN**, 8, b m King's Theatre (IRE)—La Dame Brune (FR) **Syndicates.Racing**

36 **CADMIUM (FR)**, 8, b g Early March—Mirquille (FR) **In Our Element Syndicate**

37 **CALIE DU MESNIL (FR)**, 8, b m Kapgarde (FR)—Perle du Mesnil (FR) **Andrea & Graham Wylie**

38 **CAPTAIN KANGAROO (IRE)**, 5, ch h Mastercraftsman (IRE)—
We Can Say It Now (AUS) **Kanga Racing & Brett Graham Syndicate**

39 **CAREFULLY SELECTED (IRE)**, 8, b g Well Chosen—Knockamullen Girl (IRE) **Miss M. A. Masterson**

40 **CASH BACK (FR)**, 8, b g Linda's Lad—Holding (FR) **Watch This Space Syndicate**

41 **CASTLEBAWN WEST (FR)**, 7, b g Westerner—Cooksgrove Lady (FR) **Mrs Rose Boyd Partnership**

42 **CHACUN POUR SOI (FR)**, 8, b g Policy Maker (IRE)—Kruscyna (FR) **Mrs S Ricci**

43 **CHEF DES OBEAUX (FR)**, 8, b g Saddler Maker (IRE)—O Dame de Gene (FR) **Sullivan Bloodstock Limited**

44 **CIEL DE NEIGE (FR)**, 5, b g Authorized (IRE)—In Caso di Neve (FR) **John P. McManus**

45 **CILAOS EMERY (FR)**, 8, b g Califet (FR)—Queissa (FR) **Luke McMahon**

46 **COLREEVY (IRE)**, 7, b m Flemensfirth (USA)—Poetics Girl (IRE) **Mrs N. Flynn**

47 **CONCERTISTA (FR)**, 6, ch m Nathaniel (IRE)—Zagzig **Simon Munir & Isaac Souede Partnership**

48 **CONTINGENCY**, 7, b m Champs Elysees—Cyclone Connie **Bowes Lodge Stables Partnership**

49 **COQUIN MANS (FR)**, 8, b br g Fragrant Mix (IRE)—Quississia Mans (FR) **Creighton Family**

50 **CRACK MOME (FR)**, 8, ch g Spanish Moon (USA)—Peche Mome (FR) **Andrea Wylie**

51 **CUT THE MUSTARD (FR)**, 8, br m Al Namix (FR)—Tadorna (FR) **Sullivan Bloodstock Limited**

52 **DANDY MAG (FR)**, 7, br g Special Kaldoun (IRE)—Naiade Mag (FR) **G Mercer/D Mercer/Mrs Caren Walsh**

53 **DEAL D'ESTRUVAL (FR)**, 7, b g Balko (FR)—Option d'Estruval (FR) **Mrs S. Ricci**

54 **DEFY DE MEE (FR)**, 7, b g Country Reel (USA)—Koeur de Mee (FR) **Defying The Odds Syndicate**

55 **DERBY (FR)**, 7, b g Policy Maker (IRE)—Blue Lane (FR) **Derby Survivors Syndicate**

56 **DIAMOND HILL (IRE)**, 7, b m Beat Hollow—Sixhills (FR) **Mrs A F Mee Partnership**

57 **DOLCITA (FR)**, 5, b m Saint des Saints (FR)—Orcantara (FR) **Sullivan Bloodstock Limited**

58 **DON'T TELL ALLEN (IRE)**, 5, b g Presenting—Liss Alainn (IRE) **John Joseph Flynn**

59 **DORRELLS PIERJI (FR)**, 7, br g Coastal Path—Playa Pierji (FR) **Sullivan Bloodstock Limited**

60 **DOUVAN (FR)**, 10, b g Walk In The Park (IRE)—Star Face (FR) **Mrs S. Ricci**

61 **DRACONIEN (FR)**, 7, br g Linda's Lad—Holding (FR) **Clipper Logistics Group Limited**

62 **DRURY (FR)**, 6, ch m Beat Hollow—China Sky (IRE) **Drury Tea & Coffee Limited**

63 **DUC DES GENIEVRES (FR)**, 7, gr g Buck's Boum (FR)—Lobelie (FR) **Sullivan Bloodstock Limited**

64 **DYSART DIAMOND (IRE)**, 5, ch m Shirocco (GER)—Dysart Dancer (IRE) **Eleanor Manning**

MR WILLIAM P. MULLINS - continued

65 **EASY GAME (FR)**, 6, b g Barastraight—Rule of The Game (FR) **Wicklow Bloodstock (Ireland) Ltd**
66 **ECHOES IN RAIN (FR)**, 4, b f Authorized (IRE)—Amarantine (FR) **Barnane Stud**
67 **EDEN FLIGHT (FR)**, 6, b g Great Pretender (IRE)—Traviata (FR) **Mrs S Ricci**
68 **EGLANTINE DU SEUIL (FR)**, 6, b m Saddler Maker (IRE)—Rixia du Seuil (FR) **Sullivan Bloodstock Limited**
69 **EGO DES MOTTES (FR)**, 6, b g Sunday Break (JPN)—Puszta des Mottes (FR) **John P. McManus**
70 **ELFILE (FR)**, 6, b m Saint des Saints (FR)—Rapide (FR) **Kenneth Alexander**
71 **ELIMAY (FR)**, 6, gr m Montmartre (FR)—Hyde (FR) **John P. McManus**
72 **ELITE CHARBONIERE (FR)**, 6, gr g Gris de Gris (IRE)—Star Folle Prail (FR) **Mrs S Ricci**
73 **ELIXIR D'AINAY (FR)**, 6, ch g Muhtathir—Perle du Bocage (FR) **John P. McManus**
74 **EN BETON (FR)**, 6, br g Network (GER)—Nee A Saint Voir (FR) **Cheveley Park Stud**
75 **ENERGUMENE (FR)**, 6, b g Denham Red (FR)—Olinight (FR) **Anthony Bloom**
76 **EQUILIBRIUM (FR)**, 6, b m Balko (FR)—Tacoma Gaugain (FR) **Mrs Rose Boyd**
77 **ET DITE (FR)**, 6, b m Limnos (JPN)—Truffe (FR) **Hammer & Trowel Syndicate**
78 **EXCHANGE RATE (GER)**, 8, b g Monsun (GER)—Erytheis (USA) **Mrs A. F. Mee**
79 **FABULOUS SAGA (FR)**, 8, b g Saint des Saints (FR)—Fabalina (FR) **Sullivan Bloodstock Limited**
80 **FAIS TON CHEMIN (FR)**, 5, b g Coastal Path—Tiree d'Affaire (FR) **M L Bloodstock**
81 **FAN DE BLUES (FR)**, 5, b g Poliglote—Tire En Touche (FR) **Simon Munir & Isaac Souede**
82 **FARID (FR)**, 5, b g Diamond Boy (FR)—Querrana de Sivola (FR) **John P. McManus**
83 **FAST BUCK (FR)**, 6, br g Kendargent (FR)—Juvenil Delinquent (USA) **Sullivan Bloodstock Limited**
84 **FAUGHEEN (IRE)**, 12, b g Germany (USA)—Miss Pickering (IRE) **Mrs S. Ricci**
85 **FENTA DES OBEAUX (FR)**, 5, b m Denham Red (FR)—Quenta des Obeaux (FR) **Jeremy Hancock Partnership**
86 **FERNY HOLLOW (IRE)**, 5, b br g Westerner—Mirazur (IRE) **Cheveley Park Stud**
87 **FILS SPIRITUEL (FR)**, 5, b g Presenting—Toque Rouge (FR) **Mrs J Donnelly**
88 **FIVE BAR BRIAN (IRE)**, 6, br g Elusive Pimpernel (USA)—
Vayenga (FR) **Beswick Brothers Bloodstock Partnership**
89 **FIVE O'CLOCK (FR)**, 5, b g Cokoriko (FR)—Rodika (FR) **Mrs S Ricci**
90 **FLY SMART (FR)**, 5, b g Day Flight—Abacab (FR) **Mrs S Ricci**
91 **FOOTPAD (FR)**, 8, b g Creachadoir (IRE)—Willamina (FR) **Mr Simon Munir**
92 **FOVEROS (FR)**, 5, b g Authorized (IRE)—Fanurio's Angel (FR) **Luke McMahon**
93 **FRANCIN (FR)**, 7, b g Air Chief Marshal (IRE)—Fulgence (FR) **Mrs S. Ricci**
94 **FRANCO DE PORT (FR)**, 5, b h Coastal Path—Ruth (FR) **Bruton Street IV Partnership**
95 **GENERAL COUNSEL (IRE)**, 7, b g Shantou (USA)—Josephine Cullen (IRE) **Clipper Logistics Group Limited**
96 **GETABIRD (IRE)**, 8, b g Getaway (GER)—Fern Bird (IRE) **Mrs S. Ricci**
97 **GETAREASON (IRE)**, 7, ch g Getaway (GER)—Simple Reason (IRE) **Sullivan Bloodstock Limited**
98 **GETAWAY GORGEOUS (IRE)**, 6, b m Getaway (GER)—Impudent (IRE) **Whitegrass Getaway Syndicate**
99 **GOLAZO (IRE)**, 7, b g Beat Hollow—Compelled (IRE) **David Manasseh**
100 **GOLDEN SPREAD**, 7, b g Duke of Marmalade (IRE)—Purely By Chance **Probus Racing & Ken Sharp Syndicate**
101 **GOOD THYNE TARA**, 10, b br m Kayf Tara—Good Thyne Mary (IRE) **N. G. King**
102 **GREAT FIELD (FR)**, 9, b g Great Pretender (IRE)—Eaton Lass (IRE) **John P. McManus**
103 **GREAT WHITE SHARK (FR)**, 6, gr m Le Havre (IRE)—Trip To Fame (FR) **Malcolm C. Denmark**
104 **GUARD OF HONOUR (IRE)**, 9, b g Galileo (IRE)—Queen of France (USA) **Syndicates.Racing**
105 **HARRIE (FR)**, 8, ch g Le Havre (IRE)—Honorable Love **Harrie/Brett Graham/Ken Sharp Syndicate**
106 **HOOK UP (FR)**, 4, b f No Risk At All (FR)—Mission Accomplie (FR) **Mrs S Ricci**
107 **HOPEFULLY (IRE)**, 5, b m Beat Hollow—Strina (IRE) **Joseph E Keeling**
108 **HYBERY (FR)**, 6, b g Centennial (IRE)—Zalagarry (FR) **Hybery Racing Syndicate**
109 **IFYOUCATCHMENOW (IRE)**, 7, b m Westerner—Ifyoucouldseemenow (IRE) **Coldunell Limited**
110 **JANIDIL (FR)**, 6, b g Indian Daffodil (IRE)—Janidouce (FR) **John P. McManus**
111 **JAZZAWAY (IRE)**, 5, b m Shantou (USA)—Backaway (IRE) **Whitegrass Racing Syndicate**
112 **JON SNOW (FR)**, 5, br g Le Havre (IRE)—Saroushka (FR) **Mrs S Ricci**
113 **KAATSKILL NAP (FR)**, 7, ch g Rip Van Winkle (IRE)—Last Cast (FR) **Anthony Bloom**
114 **KALANISI OG (IRE)**, 6, br m Kalanisi (IRE)—High Accord (IRE) **Lions Mouth Racing Club**
115 **KARL DER GROSSE (GER)**, 6, gr g Jukebox Jury (IRE)—Karsawina (GER) **Mrs S Ricci**
116 **KEMBOY (FR)**, 8, b g Voix du Nord (FR)—Vitora (FR) **Kemboy/Brett Graham/Ken Sharp Syndicate**
117 **KESSELRING**, 7, ch g New Approach (IRE)—Anna Oleanda (IRE) **Mrs S Ricci**
118 **KILLULTAGH BELLA (IRE)**, 5, b m Presenting—Killultagh Lady (IRE) **Mrs Rose Boyd**
119 **KILLULTAGH VIC (IRE)**, 11, b g Old Vic—Killultagh Dawn (IRE) **Mrs Rose Boyd**
120 **KISMET HARDY**, 7, ch g Mount Nelson—Quinzey's Best (IRE) **Mrs S Ricci**
121 **KLASSICAL DREAM (FR)**, 6, b g Dream Well (FR)—Klassical Way (FR) **Mrs Joanne Coleman**
122 **KOSHARI (FR)**, 8, br g Walk In The Park (IRE)—Honor May (FR) **Mrs S. Ricci**

MR WILLIAM P. MULLINS - continued

123 **LAMARCKISE (FR)**, 5, ch m Martaline—Shannongold (FR) **Mrs Joanne Coleman**
124 **LAURINA (FR)**, 7, b m Spanish Moon (USA)—Lamboghina (GER) **Sullivan Bloodstock Limited**
125 **LAWS OF SPIN (IRE)**, 7, b h Lawman (FR)—Spinning Well (IRE) **B. Hourihane**
126 **LEGAL SPIN (IRE)**, 5, b g Lawman (FR)—Spinning Well (IRE) **B Hourihane Partnership**
127 **LISTEN DEAR (IRE)**, 10, b m Robin des Champs (FR)—Crescendor (FR) **Syndicates.Racing**
128 **LITTLE NUGGET (IRE)**, 7, b m Daylami (IRE)—Grangeclare Gold (IRE) **Sunny Day Syndicate**
129 **LIVELOVELAUGH (IRE)**, 10, b g Beneficial—Another Evening (IRE) **Mrs S. Ricci**
130 **LORD ROYAL (FR)**, 5, gr g Lord du Sud (FR)—Tinoroyale **Paul Connell & Alan McGonnell**
131 **LOW SUN**, 7, b g Champs Elysees—Winter Solstice **Mrs S. Ricci**
132 **LUCKY ONE (FR)**, 5, br g Authorized (IRE)—Lady Anouchka (IRE) **Sullivan Bloodstock Limited**
133 **MAKITORIX (FR)**, 7, gr g Makfi—Goldamix (IRE) **Paul Connell & Alan McGonnell**
134 **MARAJMAN (FR)**, 6, gr g Rajsaman (FR)—Mascarpone (FR) **Roaringwater Syndicate**
135 **MAX DYNAMITE (FR)**, 10, b h Great Journey (JPN)—Mascara (GER) **Mrs S. Ricci**
136 **MAZE RUNNER (IRE)**, 5, b g Authorized (IRE)—Alice Rose (IRE) **Mrs J. M. Mullins**
137 **MELON**, 8, ch g Medicean—Night Teeny **Mrs J. Donnelly**
138 **MICRO MANAGE (IRE)**, 4, ch c Rip Van Winkle (IRE)—Lillebonne (FR) **Merriebelle Irish Farm Limited**
139 **MIN (FR)**, 9, b g Walk In The Park (IRE)—Phemyka (FR) **Mrs S. Ricci**
140 **MINELLA ENCORE (IRE)**, 8, b g King's Theatre (IRE)—Stashedaway (IRE) **David Bobbett**
141 **MISS PUNCH (IRE)**, 6, b m Yeats (IRE)—Coole Eile (IRE) **Blue Blood Racing Club**
142 **MISTER BLUE SKY (IRE)**, 6, gr g Royal Applause—Mujdeya **Shanakiel Racing Syndicate**
143 **MR ADJUDICATOR**, 6, b g Camacho—Attlongglast **David Bobbett**
144 **MT LEINSTER (IRE)**, 6, b g Beat Hollow—Sixhills (FR) **Roaringwater Syndicate**
145 **MY SISTER SARAH (IRE)**, 6, ch m Martaline—Reste Ren Or (IRE) **Barnane Stud**
146 **NESSUN DORMA (IRE)**, 7, b g Canford Cliffs (IRE)—Idle Chatter (IRE) **N. D. Kennelly Partnership**
147 **NEXT DESTINATION (IRE)**, 8, b g Dubai Destination (USA)—Liss Alainn (IRE) **Malcolm C. Denmark**
148 **ONTHEROPES (IRE)**, 6, b g Presenting—Dushion (IRE) **Cheveley Park Stud**
149 **ORION D'AUBRELLE (FR)**, 7, b g Saint des Saints (FR)—Erbalunga (FR) **Multi Nationals Syndicate**
150 **PENHILL**, 9, b g Mount Nelson—Serrenia (IRE) **Anthony Bloom**
151 **PLEASANT COMPANY (IRE)**, 12, b g Presenting—Katie Flame (IRE) **Malcolm C. Denmark**
152 **PONT AVAL (FR)**, 7, b m Soldier of Fortune (IRE)—Panzella (FR) **N G King**
153 **PONT AVEN (FR)**, 7, b g Doyen (IRE)—Behlaya (IRE) **Roderick Ryan Partnership**
154 **POWER OF PAUSE (IRE)**, 5, ch g Doyen (IRE)—Shady Pines (IRE) **Miss M A Masterson**
155 **PURPLE MOUNTAIN (IRE)**, 5, b m Beat Hollow—Bluemountainbeach (IRE) **Mrs A. F. Mee**
156 **QUARTZ DU RHEU (FR)**, 5, b g Konig Turf (GER)—Lady Akara (FR) **John P. McManus**
157 **REAL STEEL (FR)**, 7, gr g Loup Breton (IRE)—Kalimina (FR) **Sullivan Bloodstock Limited**
158 **REBEL OG (IRE)**, 7, br m Presenting—Oscar Rebel (IRE) **Lions Mouth Racing Club**
159 **REBELLITO (FR)**, 6, b g Montmartre (FR)—Saga d'Or (FR) **Mrs S Ricci**
160 **RHYME'N RHYTHM (IRE)**, 6, b m Yeats (IRE)—La Brave (FR) **Closutton Racing Club**
161 **RIO VIVAS (FR)**, 8, b g Voix du Nord (FR)—Rio Amata (GER) **Sullivan Bloodstock Limited**
162 **RIVEN LIGHT (IRE)**, 8, b g Raven's Pass (USA)—Vivacity **Mrs S. Ricci**
163 **ROBIN DE CARLOW**, 7, br m Robin des Champs (FR)—
　　　　　　　　　　　　　　　　　　La Reine de Riogh (IRE) **Catchherifyoucan & Brett Graham Syndicate**
164 **ROBIN DES FORET (IRE)**, 10, br g Robin des Pres (FR)—Omyn Supreme (IRE) **Byerley Racing Syndicate**
165 **ROYAL ILLUSION (IRE)**, 8, b m King's Theatre (IRE)—Spirit Run (IRE) **Ballylinch Stud**
166 **ROYAL RENDEZVOUS (IRE)**, 8, b g King's Theatre (IRE)—Novacella (FR) **Dr S P Fitzgerald**
167 **RUNRIZED (FR)**, 5, b g Authorized (IRE)—Courseulles (FR) **Clipper Logistics Group Limited**
168 **SAGLAWY (FR)**, 6, b g Youmzain (IRE)—Spasha **Sullivan Bloodstock Limited**
169 **SAINT ROI (FR)**, 5, b g Coastal Path—Sainte Vigne (FR) **John P. McManus**
170 **SALDIER (FR)**, 6, b g Soldier Hollow—Salve Evita **Mrs S Ricci**
171 **SALSARETTA (FR)**, 7, b m Kingsalsa (USA)—Kendoretta (FR) **Mrs S. Ricci**
172 **SANCTA SIMONA (FR)**, 7, b m Saddex—Desimona (GER) **John P. McManus**
173 **SAPPHIRE LADY (IRE)**, 8, b m Beneficial—Cloghoge Lady (IRE) **Anthony P. Butler**
174 **SATURNAS (FR)**, 9, b g Davidoff (GER)—Sayuri (GER) **Wicklow Bloodstock (Ireland) Ltd**
175 **SAYO**, 6, gr g Dalakhani (IRE)—Tiyi (FR) **Miss M A Masterson**
176 **SCAGLIETTI (IRE)**, 7, b m Beat Hollow—Cincuenta (IRE) **Michael F. Carroll Partnership**
177 **SCARPETA (FR)**, 7, b g Soldier of Fortune (IRE)—Sanada (IRE) **Thurloe Thoroughbreds Ireland Limited**
178 **SHANNING (IRE)**, 7, b m Spanish Moon (USA)—Idaho Falls (FR) **Lady In Waiting & Brett Graham Syndicate**
179 **SHARJAH (FR)**, 7, b g Doctor Dino (FR)—Saaryeh **Mrs S. Ricci**
180 **SMALL FARM (IRE)**, 8, b g Westerner—Eastertide (IRE) **Sullivan Bloodstock Limited**

MR WILLIAM P. MULLINS - continued

181 **SOME NECK (FR)**, 9, gr g Yeats (IRE)—Maternelle (FR) **Mrs S. Ricci**
182 **STATTLER (IRE)**, 5, br g Stowaway—Our Honey (IRE) **R. A. Bartlett**
183 **STONES AND ROSES (IRE)**, 6, b g Shantou (USA)—Compelled (IRE) **P. Reilly & C. Reilly**
184 **STORMY IRELAND (FR)**, 6, b m Motivator—Like A Storm (IRE) **Sullivan Bloodstock Limited**
185 **STRATUM**, 7, b g Dansili—Lunar Phase (IRE) **Anthony Bloom**
186 **SUINDA (IRE)**, 8, b m Mahler—Supreme Matriarch (IRE) **Luke McMahon**
187 **THE BIG GETAWAY (IRE)**, 6, b g Getaway (GER)—Saddlers Dawn (IRE) **Mrs J Donnelly**
188 **THE WEST AWAITS (IRE)**, 5, b m Flemensfirth (USA)—Lonesome Dove (IRE) **Mrs John Magnier**
189 **TIGER TAP TAP (GER)**, 5, ch g Jukebox Jury (IRE)—Tomato Finish (IRE) **Mrs S Ricci**
190 **TORNADO FLYER (IRE)**, 7, b g Flemensfirth (USA)—Mucho Macabi (IRE) **TFP Partnership**
191 **TOTAL RECALL (IRE)**, 11, b g Westerner—Augest Weekend (IRE) **Slaneyville Syndicate**
192 **TRUE SELF (IRE)**, 7, b m Oscar (IRE)—Good Thought (IRE) **Three Mile House Partnership, OTI Racing**
193 **UN DE SCEAUX (FR)**, 12, b g Denham Red (FR)—Hotesse de Sceaux (FR) **E. O'Connell**
194 **UNEXPECTED (FR)**, 6, br g Anzillero (GER)—Eaton Lass (IRE) **John P. McManus**
195 **URADEL (GER)**, 9, b g Kallisto (GER)—Unavita (GER) **Luke McMahon**
196 **URANO (FR)**, 12, b g Enrique—Neiland (FR) **Luke McMahon**
197 **VALLEY BREEZE (FR)**, 6, b g Sunday Break (JPN)—Valdemossa (FR) **Luke McMahon**
198 **VENT D'AUTOMNE (FR)**, 8, ch g Denham Red (FR)—Foret d'Automne (FR) **Andrea & Graham Wylie**
199 **VIS TA LOI (FR)**, 5, ch g Smadoun (FR)—Dicte Ta Loi (FR) **Creighton Family**
200 **VOIX DES TIEP (FR)**, 8, b br g Voix du Nord (FR)—Tiepataxe (FR) **OMG II Partnership**
201 **VOIX DU REVE (FR)**, 8, br g Voix du Nord (FR)—Pommbelle (FR) **Andrea & Graham Wylie**
202 **WHISKEY SOUR (IRE)**, 7, b h Jeremy (USA)—Swizzle Stick (IRE) **Luke McMahon**
203 **YORKHILL (IRE)**, 10, ch g Presenting—Lightning Breeze (IRE) **Andrea Wylie**
204 **YUKON LIL**, 6, b m Flemensfirth (USA)—Dare To Doubt **Mrs John Magnier**
205 **ZENON (IRE)**, 6, b g Galileo (IRE)—Jacqueline (IND) **Dreaming Cups Syndicate**
206 **ZOLA (IRE)**, 6, b m Court Cave (IRE)—Park Athlete (IRE) **Blue Blood Racing Club**

Other Owners: George Creighton, Mrs J. Donnelly, Mrs J M Mullins.

---

393 **MISS AMY MURPHY, Newmarket**
Postal: **Southgate Stables, Hamilton Road, Newmarket, Suffolk, CB8 0WY**
Contacts: PHONE **01638 429033** MOBILE **07711 992500**
EMAIL **info@amymurphyracing.com** WEBSITE **www.amymurphyracing.com**

1 **AMOR KETHLEY**, 4, b f Swiss Spirit—Nellie Ellis (IRE) **D. L. de Souza**
2 **ANGEL'S WHISPER (IRE)**, 5, gr m Dark Angel (IRE)—Tasheyaat **Box Clever Display & Shepherd Global**
3 **BEAR VALLEY (IRE)**, 6, b g Manduro (GER)—Shane (GER) **Miss A. L. Murphy**
4 **BLESSED TO EMPRESS (IRE)**, 5, b m Holy Roman Emperor (IRE)—Blessing Box **Empress Racing Partners**
5 **CAROLE'S TEMPLER**, 5, ch g Shirocco (GER)—Carole's Legacy **Mr P. Murphy**
6 4, B f Yeats (IRE)—Countess Comet (IRE) **The Rann Family**
7 **EASTER ERIC**, 6, b g Martaline—Easter Comet **Mr & Mrs S. C. Willes**
8 **EASTER ROCKET**, 6, b g Shirocco (GER)—Easter Legend **Mr & Mrs S. C. Willes**
9 **ESPRIT DE BAILEYS (FR)**, 8, b g Le Havre (IRE)—Lit (IRE) **G R Bailey Ltd (Baileys Horse Feeds)**
10 **HARMATTAN**, 5, ch m Shirocco (GER)—Bongo Fury (FR) **Charles Auld & Partner**
11 **HAWTHORN COTTAGE (IRE)**, 7, b m Gold Well—Miss Kilkeel (IRE) **Melbourne 10 Racing**
12 **JAMESSAINTPATRICK (IRE)**, 7, br g Stowaway—Cadia's Lady (IRE) **Melbourne 10 Racing**
13 **KALASHNIKOV (IRE)**, 7, br g Kalanisi (IRE)—Fairy Lane (IRE) **Mr P. Murphy**
14 **KENNOCHA (IRE)**, 4, b f Kodiac—Of Course Darling **Mr C.E. Dale & Mrs V. Knight**
15 **LAZARUS (IRE)**, 6, b g Zoffany (IRE)—Knysna (IRE) **Amy Murphy Racing Club**
16 **LEXI (FR)**, 5, b m Saint des Saints (FR)—Strawberry (IRE) **Miss A. L. Murphy**
17 **LILYPAD (IRE)**, 5, b m New Approach (IRE)—Vow **Miss A. L. Murphy**
18 **LOGAN ROCKS (IRE)**, 5, b g Yeats (IRE)—Countess Comet (IRE) **The Rann Family**
19 **MARLBOROUGH SOUNDS**, 5, b g Camelot—Wind Surf (USA) **Vitality Partnership**
20 **MERCIAN KNIGHT (IRE)**, 6, b g Saint des Saints (FR)—Carole's Legacy **Mr P. Murphy**
21 **MERCIAN PRINCE (IRE)**, 9, b g Midnight Legend—Bongo Fury (FR) **Mr P. Murphy**
22 **MINOGUE**, 4, b f Mukhadram—Melbourne Memories **M. P. Coleman & R. J. Coleman**
23 **NAPPING**, 7, b m Sleeping Indian—Vax Rapide **Eclipse Sports Racing Club**

MISS AMY MURPHY - continued

24 **PRIVATE MATTER**, 6, b g Mayson—Privacy Order **Paul Foster & Friends 2**
25 **REALLY SUPER**, 6, b m Cacique (IRE)—Sensationally **White Diamond Racing Partnership 1**
26 **REPONSE EXACTE (FR)**, 4, gr f Rajsaman (FR)—Barmaid (FR) **Mr David Howden & Mr David Redvers**
27 **ROARING FURY (IRE)**, 6, br m Sholokhov (IRE)—Bongo Fury (FR) **Charles Auld & Partner**
28 **ROCK ON BAILEYS**, 5, ch m Rock of Gibraltar (IRE)—Ring For Baileys **G R Bailey Ltd (Baileys Horse Feeds)**
29 **SEPRANI**, 6, b m Sepoy (AUS)—King's Guest (IRE) **Book 3 Partnership**
30 **TAKE IT DOWN UNDER**, 5, b g Oasis Dream—Roz **Miss A. L. Murphy**
31 **THAQAFFA (IRE)**, 7, b g Kodiac—Incense **The Champagne Club**
32 **THE ACCOUNTANT**, 5, ch g Dylan Thomas (IRE)—Glorybe (GER) **The Rann Family**
33 **THEGREATESTSHOWMAN**, 4, ch g Equiano (FR)—Conversational (IRE) **Miss A. L. Murphy**

THREE-YEAR-OLDS

34 **AL MAQAR (IRE)**, b f Make Believe—Tanouma (USA)
35 **ALBORKAN (FR)**, b c Joshua Tree (IRE)—Plaine Monceau (FR) **Mr M. Almahmoud**
36 **ALLEZ LOUISE (IRE)**, b f Acclamation—Dat Il Do **Mr P. Hollingsworth**
37 B f Nathaniel (IRE)—American Spirit (IRE) **D. L. de Souza**
38 **BAJA MOON (IRE)**, b c Equiano (FR)—Laguna Salada (IRE) **Mr J. Acheson**
39 **BLACKBERRY JACK (IRE)**, ch g Sir Percy—Ms Grande Corniche **Mr D. Osullivan**
40 **BREATH OF JOY**, b f Kodiac—Island Dreams (USA) **Mr I. H. Al Sagar**
41 **EARLY MORNING MIST (IRE)**, b br f Pour Moi (IRE)—Incense **Miss A. L. Murphy**
42 **EN FAMILLE**, b g Farhh—Poyle Caitlin (IRE) **Mr B. C. M. Wong**
43 B f Fame And Glory—Intent (IRE) **The Rann Family**
44 **ISOLDE (IRE)**, b f Camelot—Zanzibar Girl (USA) **Mr D. Osullivan**
45 **LADY STARK (IRE)**, b f Dandy Man (IRE)—Happy Go Lily **Daniel MacAuliffe & Anoj Don**
46 **LORD CHAPELFIELD**, b g Delegator—Diamond Vanessa (IRE) **Miss D L Wisbey & Mr R J Viney**
47 **LUCKY BEAU (IRE)**, b c Brazen Beau (AUS)—Lucky Legs (IRE) **Mr J. Acheson**
48 **MARGARETHA (IRE)**, b f Dawn Approach (IRE)—Hollow Green (IRE) **Sheila Tassell & Partner**
49 **NIRODHA (IRE)**, ch f Camacho—Ekagra **Daniel MacAuliffe & Anoj Don**
50 **PHILIPA VICTORIA**, b f Zoffany (IRE)—Lady Wingshot (IRE) **Mr I. H. Al Sagar**
51 **RUDAINA**, b f Dark Angel (IRE)—Bouyrin (IRE) **Mr I. H. Al Sagar**
52 **SAMILLE (IRE)**, b f Kodiac—Monicalew **Mick Jaselsky & Partner**
53 **SOIS REBELLE (FR)**, b f Dabirsim (FR)—Censure (FR) **Booth, Flatt, Foster**
54 **SOLDIER ON PARADE**, b g Dunaden (FR)—Litewska (IRE) **Qatar Racing Limited & Mr David Redvers**
55 **THUNDER KING (FR)**, b g Hunter's Light (IRE)—Lady McKell (IRE) **Daniel MacAuliffe & Anoj Don**
56 **TOPKAPI STAR**, b f Golden Horn—Burlesque Star (IRE) **Mr C. Johnston**
57 **TROUSER THE CASH (IRE)**, b f Starspangledbanner (AUS)—Bint Malyana (IRE) **A & P Braithwaite**

TWO-YEAR-OLDS

58 Ch c 07/04 Night of Thunder (IRE)—Millefiori (IRE) (Mastercraftsman (IRE)) (2000) **Miss A. L. Murphy**
59 B f 23/03 Sepoy (AUS)—Moment of Time (Rainbow Quest (USA)) (15000)
60 Ch c 22/03 Supplicant—My Inspiration (IRE) (Invincible Spirit (IRE)) **G R Bailey Ltd (Baileys Horse Feeds)**

Other Owners: Mr W. R. Asquith, Mr C. C. Auld, Mr P. Booth, Box Clever Display, Mr A. W. Braithwaite, Mrs P. J. Braithwaite, Mr S. J. Brown, Mr T. Castle, Mr M. P. Coleman, Mr R. J. Coleman, Mr C. E. Dale, Mr D. R. Flatt, Mr P. Foster, Mr R. S. Hoskins, Mr D. Howden, Mr M. Jaselsky, Mrs V. A. Knight, Mrs S. M. Langridge, Miss A. L. Murphy, Mr P. Murphy, P. Foster & Friends, Mrs A. Perkins, Qatar Racing Limited, R S Hoskins & Partners, Miss N. K. Rajani, Mr G. P. D. Rann, Mrs L. E. Rann, Mr D. Redvers, Mr G Ryan, Mr J. P. Ryan, Mrs C. G. Scott, Shepherd Global Ltd, Mrs S. C. Tassell, R. J. Viney, Mrs C. Wallace, White Diamond Racing Partnership, Mrs M. Willes, Mr S. C. Willes, Miss D. L. Wisbey.

394 MR MIKE MURPHY, Westoning
Postal: **Broadlands, Manor Park Stud, Westoning, Bedfordshire, MK45 5LA**
Contacts: **PHONE 01525 717305 MOBILE 07770 496103 FAX 01525 717305**
EMAIL **mmurphy@globalnet.co.uk** WEBSITE **www.mikemurphyracing.com**

1 **A PLACE TO DREAM**, 4, b g Compton Place—Phantasmagoria **Victoria Taylor & Family**
2 **AZZECCAGARBUGLI (IRE)**, 7, b g Kodiac—Consultant Stylist (IRE) **Ms A. D. Tibbett**
3 **BAMO MC**, 6, gr g Hellvelyn—Soft Touch (IRE)
4 **DANGLYDONTASK**, 9, b g Lucky Story (USA)—Strat's Quest **P. Banfield**
5 **DESERT FOX**, 6, b g Foxwedge—Snow Moccasin (IRE) **Rogerson, Lemon, Cooper & Arlotte**
6 **DUSTY DAMSEL**, 4, ch f Toronado (IRE)—Dusty Answer **The Calm Partnership**
7 **GARTH ROCKETT**, 6, b g Delegator—Leelu **P. Banfield**
8 **HAVANA SUNSET**, 4, b g Havana Gold—Sunset Kitty (USA) **The Sunsetters**
9 **LOUISIANA BEAT (IRE)**, 4, ch f Helmet (AUS)—Union City Blues (IRE) **Mr M. Murphy**
10 **MULZIM**, 6, b g Exceed And Excel (AUS)—Samaah (IRE) **Victoria Taylor & Family**
11 **RIO RONALDO (IRE)**, 8, b g Footstepsinthesand—Flanders (IRE)
12 **ROOF GARDEN**, 5, ch g Cityscape—Celebrity **Sarabex**
13 **VELVET VISION**, 5, b m Nathaniel (IRE)—Battery Power **Sarabex**
14 **VELVET VISTA**, 4, b f Sea The Moon (GER)—Battery Power **Sarabex**
15 **WOTADOLL**, 6, b br m Harbour Watch (IRE)—Rhapsilian **Mr D. C. Mead**
16 **YOUNG JOHN (IRE)**, 7, b g Acclamation—Carpet Lady (IRE) **Murphy, Cooper & East**

THREE-YEAR-OLDS
17 **BATTERSEA DUCHESS**, b f Youmzain (IRE)—
Duchessina (USA) **Mr Borgatti & Mr Moir, Mr M. Borgatti, Mr S. Moir**
18 **COSTELLO**, b g Makfi—Samba Chryss (IRE) **Mr E. W. d. C. Tillett**
19 **KYLLA LOOKS**, bl f Kyllachy—Love Your Looks
20 **LADY ESTA**, b f New Approach (IRE)—Esteemed Lady (IRE)
21 **ROCKETEER**, b g Equiano (FR)—Aalya (IRE) **Miss S. J. Ballinger**
22 **SEA THE SPIRIT**, b g Sea The Stars (IRE)—My Country (IRE) **The Good Spirit Partnership**
23 **SILVER GRACE (IRE)**, gr f Gutaifan (IRE)—Maybe Grace (IRE) **Mr Borgatti & Mr Moir, Mr M. Borgatti, Mr S. Moir**
24 **SPACESUIT**, b g Sea The Moon (GER)—Casaca **Ownaracehorse Ltd**

TWO-YEAR-OLDS
25 B f 16/03 Territories (IRE)—Clarentine (Dalakhani (IRE)) (48000)
26 B c 25/02 Awtaad (IRE)—Witnessed (Authorized (IRE)) (75000)

Other Owners: The Castaways, M&O Construction & Civil Engineering Ltd.

Assistant Trainer: Michael Keady.

395 MR OLLY MURPHY, Wilmcote
Postal: **Warren Chase Stables, Wilmcote, Stratford-Upon-Avon, Warwickshire, CV37 9XG**
Contacts: **PHONE 01789 613347**
EMAIL **office@ollymurphyracing.com** WEBSITE **www.ollymurphyracing.com**

1 **A PERFECT GIFT (IRE)**, 6, br m Presenting—Keyras Choice (IRE) **Mr M. J. D. Lambert**
2 **ADJUTANT**, 5, b g Champs Elysees—Jubilee **Ladies In Racing**
3 **AFRICAN DANCE (IRE)**, 5, br g Shirocco (GER)—Dani California **Noel & Valerie Moran**
4 **ALLAVINA**, 5, b m Getaway (GER)—One Cool Kate (IRE) **C. Boultbee-Brooks**
5 **ALPHA CARINAE (IRE)**, 5, ch m Robin des Champs (FR)—Annas Present (IRE) **Mr T. D. J. Syder**
6 **BEAU SANCY (FR)**, 8, b g Blue Bresil (FR)—Touquette (FR) **Tramore Tree**
7 **BLAZER'S MILL (IRE)**, 6, b g Westerner—Creation (IRE) **Mrs J. A. Wakefield**
8 **BON CALVADOS (FR)**, 6, b g Bonbon Rose (FR)—Lamorrese (FR) **Graeme Moore, Kate & Andrew Brooks**
9 **BREWIN'UPASTORM (IRE)**, 7, b g Milan—Daraheen Diamond (IRE) **Ms B. J. Abt**
10 **BUBBLES OF GOLD (IRE)**, 7, b g Gold Well—Bubble Bann (IRE) **Noel & Valerie Moran**
11 **CALIPSO COLLONGES (FR)**, 8, b g Crossharbour—Ivresse Collonges (FR) **The Black Horse Hotel Bridgnorth**
12 **CAPTAIN BIGGLES (IRE)**, 5, gr g Milan—Timon's Present **Mrs D. L. Whateley**

MR OLLY MURPHY - continued

13 **CELTIC TARA**, 6, b m Kayf Tara—Valdas Queen (GER) **A. P. Racing**

14 **CESAR DU GOUET (FR)**, 8, gr g Fragrant Mix (IRE)—Querida de Ferbet (FR) **FGD Limited**

15 **CHAMPAGNESUPEROVER (IRE)**, 5, b g Jeremy (USA)—
Meldrum Hall (IRE) **McNeill Family & Patrick&scott Bryceland**

16 **CHEZ HANS (IRE)**, 6, b g Aizavoski (IRE)—Hidden Reserve (IRE) **Ms B. J. Abt**

17 **COLLOONEY (IRE)**, 6, b g Yeats (IRE)—Amber Trix (IRE) **Mr J. P. McManus**

18 **COPPERLESS**, 5, b g Kayf Tara—Presenting Copper (IRE) **Aiden Murphy & Alan Peterson**

19 **CORINTO (IRE)**, 7, br g Flemensfirth (USA)—Fashion Target (IRE) **Mrs D. L. Whateley**

20 **CRAIGMOR (IRE)**, 8, b g Craigsteel—Twilight Princess (IRE) **Mr Peter. P. Elliott & Partners**

21 **DUBAI GUEST (IRE)**, 5, b g Dubai Destination (USA)—Formidable Guest **Oceana Racing**

22 **DUNDRUM WOOD (IRE)**, 6, b g Flemensfirth (USA)—Ruby Isabel (IRE) **Ms B. J. Abt**

23 **EAGLEHILL (FR)**, 6, gr g Blue Bresil (FR)—Ratina de Vaige (FR) **Mr J. P. McManus**

24 **ENCHANT ME**, 5, b m Great Pretender (IRE)—Mole End **The Farrow Flyers**

25 **ENDLESSLY (IRE)**, 5, b g Nathaniel (IRE)—What's Up Pussycat (IRE) **Mr R. Treacy**

26 **EROS (FR)**, 6, b g Diamond Boy (FR)—Madame Lys (FR) **Sullivan Bloodstock Limited**

27 **ETOILE REBELLE (FR)**, 5, gr g Walk In The Park (IRE)—Line Mexia (FR) **Sullivan Bloodstock Limited**

28 **EWOOD PARK (FR)**, 5, b g Shirocco (GER)—Windfola (FR) **McNeill Family Ltd**

29 **FEARLESS (IRE)**, 5, b g Arakan (USA)—La Spezia (IRE) **A Graham - Bankruptcy Trustee M Stanley**

30 **FIESOLE**, 8, b g Montjeu (IRE)—Forgotten Dreams (IRE) **LF Infrastructure Ltd**

31 **FINAWN BAWN (IRE)**, 7, b g Robin des Champs (FR)—Kayanti (IRE) **LF Infrastructure Ltd**

32 **FITZROY (IRE)**, 6, b g Fame And Glory—Forces of Destiny (IRE) **Tim Syder & Aiden Murphy**

33 **FIVETOTWELVE**, 6, b m Midnight Legend—To The Left (IRE) **Alan Marsh & Partner**

34 **FLETCH (FR)**, 5, b g Kayf Tara—Oeuvre Vive (FR) **Ms B. J. Abt**

35 **FOLLOW THAT**, 6, b m Malinas (GER)—Leading On **H. A. Murphy**

36 **FRESH NEW DAWN (IRE)**, 8, ch g Flemensfirth (USA)—Star Shuil (IRE) **Not For Friends Partnership**

37 **FUSIONICE (FR)**, 5, b g Coastal Path—Oasice (FR) **Mrs D. L. Whateley**

38 **GARRETTSTOWN (IRE)**, 7, b g Doyen (IRE)—Azur (IRE) **The Phillies Partnership**

39 **GENERAL CUSTARD**, 7, b g Shirocco (GER)—Diamant Noir **Syder, Whateley, Murphy, Burke**

40 **GETAWAY LUV (IRE)**, 5, b g Getaway (GER)—Ut Love (FR) **C. Boultbee-Brooks**

41 **GINISTRELLI (IRE)**, 4, b g Frankel—Guaranda **Mrs J. A. Wakefield**

42 **GRACES ORDER (IRE)**, 5, b m Mahler—Janebailey **Peaky Blinders**

43 **GRANDADS COTTAGE (IRE)**, 5, ch g Shantou (USA)—Sarah's Cottage (IRE) **Mr J. Hales**

44 **GUNSIGHT RIDGE**, 5, b g Midnight Legend—Grandma Griffiths **Mrs D. L. Whateley**

45 **HER DREAM (IRE)**, 8, b m Yeats (IRE)—High Benefit (IRE) **Miss L. J. Rogers**

46 **HERE COMES MCCOY (IRE)**, 5, br g Dylan Thomas (IRE)—Is It Here (IRE) **Mr C. J. Haughey**

47 **HERE COMES TRUBLE (IRE)**, 5, b g Flemensfirth (USA)—Old Moon (IRE) **Ms B. J. Abt**

48 **HIGHATE HILL (IRE)**, 6, b g Presenting—Lisrenny Lady **Patrick & Scott Bryceland**

49 **HIGHLAND BOBBY**, 5, b g Big Bad Bob (IRE)—Eolith **The Mighty Men**

50 **HOGAN (IRE)**, 4, b g Fame And Glory—Don't Be Upset (IRE) **Farrell Field Cognet Sigler**

51 **HUNTERS CALL (IRE)**, 10, b g Medaaly—Accordiontogelica (IRE) **Holloway,Clarke,Black**

52 **HURRICANE HERO (FR)**, 4, b g George Vancouver—Memoire (FR) **Sky's The Limit**

53 **HYPNOS (IRE)**, 4, b g Morpheus—Winter Song (IRE) **Mr O. J. Murphy**

54 **I K BRUNEL**, 6, b g Midnight Legend—Somethinaboutmolly (IRE) **McNeill Family and Prodec Networks Ltd**

55 **IT'S O KAY**, 7, b m Shirocco (GER)—Presenting Copper (IRE) **Aiden Murphy & Alan Peterson**

56 **ITCHY FEET (FR)**, 6, b g Cima de Triomphe (IRE)—Maeva Candas (FR) **Kate & Andrew Brooks**

57 **JETAWAY JOEY (IRE)**, 5, b g Getaway (GER)—Present Your Own (IRE) **Ms B. J. Abt**

58 **JONES WELL (IRE)**, 7, b g Gold Well—Mrs Jones (FR) **H. A. Murphy**

59 **KAPROYALE**, 5, gr g Kapgarde (FR)—As You Leave (FR) **Tommy Elphick & Mary Shalvey**

60 **KERRKENNY GOLD (IRE)**, 6, ch g Sans Frontieres (IRE)—Cailins Honour (IRE) **Kate & Andrew Brooks**

61 **KNOCKGRAFFON (IRE)**, 10, b g Flemensfirth (USA)—Gleaming Spire **Ms B. J. Abt**

62 **KRAZY PAVING**, 8, b g Kyllachy—Critical Path (IRE) **All The Kings Horses & Mr Aiden Murphy**

63 **LINELEE KING (FR)**, 5, gr g Martaline—Queen Lee (FR) **Mrs D. L. Whateley**

64 **MADE FOR YOU**, 5, b g Cape Cross (IRE)—Edallora (IRE) **Touchwood Racing**

65 **MARKOV (IRE)**, 10, b g Morozov (USA)—Willoughby Sue (IRE) **Mr A. R. W. Marsh**

66 **MIGHTY MEG**, 6, b m Malinas (GER)—Harry's Bride **The Mighty Men**

67 5, Ch m Shantou (USA)—Miss Denman (FR) **James and Jean Potter Ltd**

68 **MISTERCOBAR (FR)**, 8, b g Nicobar—Miss Decca (FR) **The Wayward Pilgrims**

69 **MIZEN MASTER (IRE)**, 7, b g Captain Rio—Nilassiba (FR) **H. A. Murphy**

70 **MON PORT (IRE)**, 8, b g Scorpion (IRE)—Sounds Charming (IRE) **J. T. Warner**

MR OLLY MURPHY - continued

71 **MONBEG ZENA (IRE)**, 8, ch m Flemensfirth (USA)—Mandys Gold (IRE) **Sullivan Bloodstock Limited**
72 **MOORE MARGAUX (IRE)**, 5, b g Flemensfirth (USA)—Omas Glen (IRE) **Graeme Moore, Kate & Andrew Brooks**
73 **NICKOLSON (FR)**, 6, b g No Risk At All (FR)—Incorrigible (FR) **Mr T. D. J. Syder**
74 **NOTRE PARI (IRE)**, 6, br g Jeremy (USA)—Glynn Approach (IRE) **Mr J. P. McManus**
75 **OSCAR ACADEMY (IRE)**, 7, b g Oscar (IRE)—Flaming Brandy (IRE) **Mr O. J. Murphy**
76 **OSCAR MAGUIRE (IRE)**, 7, b g Oscar (IRE)—Ballymaguirelass (IRE) **LF Infrastructure Ltd**
77 **OVERTHETOP (IRE)**, 6, br g Flemensfirth (USA)—Dawn Bid (IRE) **What the Elle**
78 **OXFORD BLU**, 6, b g Aqlaam—Blue Zealot (IRE) **geegeez.co.uk OM**
79 **PEACHEY (IRE)**, 6, b g Robin des Champs (FR)—Zita Hall (IRE) **Mrs D. L. Whateley**
80 **PERFECT MAN (IRE)**, 9, b g Morozov (USA)—Garrisker (IRE) **Holloway,Clarke,Black**
81 **PORT OF MARS (IRE)**, 6, b g Westerner—Sarahall (IRE) **Noel & Valerie Moran**
82 **PRESENCE OF MIND (IRE)**, 5, b g Presenting—Alleygrove Lass (IRE) **Noel & Valerie Moran**
83 **PROMPTING**, 4, br g Bated Breath—Enticing (IRE) **Mr R. Treacy**
84 **QUIVVY LOUGH (IRE)**, 6, b m Court Cave (IRE)—Quivvy Bridge (IRE) **Mr O. J. Murphy**
85 **REDEMPTORIST**, 5, b g Frozen Power (IRE)—Fly With Me (IRE)
86 **RIO QUINTO (FR)**, 7, b g Loup Breton (IRE)—Seal of Cause (IRE) **Mrs D. L. Whateley**
87 **ROCK ON TOMMY**, 5, gr g Fair Mix (IRE)—Little Carmela **Premier Thoroughbred Racing Ltd**
88 **SANGHA RIVER (IRE)**, 7, br g Arcadio (GER)—Hidden Reserve (IRE) **Ms B. J. Abt**
89 **SEA SISTER (IRE)**, 4, b f Born To Sea (IRE)—Campessa (IRE) **Mr H. Krebs**
90 **SEEMINGLY SO (IRE)**, 7, b g Dubai Destination (USA)—Jane Hall (IRE) **Emily Boultbee Brooks Racing**
91 **SKANDIBURG (FR)**, 6, b g Sageburg (IRE)—Skandia (FR) **Kate & Andrew Brooks**
92 **SMACKWATER JACK (IRE)**, 6, b g Flemensfirth (USA)—Malachy's Attic (IRE) **Par Four**
93 **SMART GETAWAY (IRE)**, 8, b m Getaway (GER)—Legendsofthefall (IRE) **Jacques Law P'ship & M Lyons**
94 **SOME BOY MCCOY (FR)**, 6, b g Enrique—Khaylama (IRE) **Mr C. J. Haughey**
95 **SPIRIT OF WATERLOO**, 6, b g Malinas (GER)—Warm Front **Salmon Racing**
96 **SPRINGVALE**, 5, b m Haafhd—Summervale (IRE) **A. Butler**
97 **ST GALLEN (IRE)**, 7, b g Majestic Missile (IRE)—Fly With Me (IRE) **Tommy Elphick & Mary Shalvey**
98 **ST LAWRENCE GAP (IRE)**, 8, ch g Tagula (IRE)—Kannon **Stephen R Hodgkinson & Partner**
99 **STRONG GLANCE**, 7, bl g Passing Glance—Strong Westerner (IRE) **Welfordgolf syndicate**
100 **SWAFFHAM BULBECK (IRE)**, 6, b g Jeremy (USA)—Ballygologue (IRE) **geegeez.co.uk OM**
101 **TAMAR BRIDGE (IRE)**, 5, b g Jeremy (USA)—Mise En Place **McNeill Family and Prodec Networks Ltd**
102 **THE BUTCHER SAID (IRE)**, 7, b g Robin des Champs (FR)—Georgina Valleya (IRE) **McNeill Family Ltd**
103 **THE WOLF (FR)**, 6, ch g Kapgarde (FR)—Ges (FR) **McNeill Family and Prodec Networks Ltd**
104 **THOMAS DARBY (IRE)**, 7, b g Beneficial—Silaoce (FR) **Mrs D. L. Whateley**
105 **THREE COUNTY'S (IRE)**, 9, b br g Beneficial—Pattern Queen (IRE) **Mr M. Fitzgerald**
106 **TIGERBYTHETAIL (IRE)**, 4, b g Yeats (IRE)—Talktothetail (IRE) **Ms B. J. Abt**
107 **TODD**, 10, b g Gentlewave (IRE)—Voice **Mrs A. L. M. Murphy**
108 **TOUR DE FRANCE**, 6, ch g Mount Nelson—Why Nee Amy **You Betta You Betta You Bet**
109 **VALENTINO DANCER**, 5, ch g Mastercraftsman (IRE)—Bertie's Best **Richard Hames & Alex Govorusa**
110 **VINNIE'S GETAWAY (IRE)**, 6, b g Getaway (GER)—Trixskin (IRE) **B McDonald, B Mellon & P McBride**
111 **WHAT WILL BE (IRE)**, 4, b g Thewayyouare (USA)—Gali Gal (USA) **The Dream Big Syndicate**
112 **WHATYA ON ABOUT**, 5, b g Schiaparelli (GER)—Grace Dieu **Ready Steady Go**
113 **WHISKEY IN THE JAR (IRE)**, 8, b g Oscar (IRE)—Baie Barbara (IRE) **Ms B. J. Abt**

Other Owners: All The Kings Horses, Mr S. T. Black, Boultbee Brooks Ltd, Miss E. Boultbee-Brooks, Mr A. L. Brooks, Mrs K. L. Brooks, Mr P. Bryceland, Mr S. Bryceland, Mrs V. F. Burke, Miss E. J. Clarke, Mr B. R. Cognet, Mr P. P. Elliott, Mr T. Elphick, Mr N. Farrell, Mrs L. H. Field, Mrs S. M. Gasch, Mr A. Govorusa, Mr J. R. Hales, Miss L. J. Hales, Mr R. D. A. Hames, Mr P. Henchoz, Mr S. R. Hodgkinson, Mr J. R. Holloway, Mrs A. C. Houldsworth, Mr D. Jacques, Jacques Law Partnership, Mr M. S. Lawson, Mr M. J. E. Lyons, Mr P. Maloney, Mr A. R. W. Marsh, Mr P. McBride, B. T. McDonald, McNeill Family Ltd, Mr B. H. Mellon, Mr G. Moore, Mr N. Moran, Mrs V. Moran, Mr M. Muldoon, Mrs A. L. M. Murphy, H. A. Murphy, Mr O. J. Murphy, Mr A. E. Peterson, Mr S. Powell, Prodec Networks Ltd, Mr B. Reynolds, Mr D. B. Salmon, Mrs Lynn Salmon, Mr M. M. W. Salmon, Ms M. Shalvey, Mr J. Sigler, Sky's The Limit 2, Mrs S. Stanley, Mr T. D. J. Syder, Mrs D. L. Whateley, Mrs M. G. Whittaker, Mrs S. C. Yarnold.

Assistant Trainer: Gerard Tumelty.

NH Jockey: Aidan Coleman, David England, Richard Johnson. **Conditional Jockey:** Fergus Gregory, Callum McKinnes, Lewis Stones. **Amateur Jockey:** Mr James King, Mr Luke Scott.

396   MR PAT MURPHY, Hungerford
Postal: **Glebe House, School Lane, East Garston, Hungerford, Berkshire, RG17 7HR**
Contacts: **PHONE 01488 648473**
EMAIL patgmurphy13@gmail.com

1 **GALTEE MOUNTAIN (IRE)**, 5, br g Mountain High (IRE)—Kings Queen (IRE) **P. G. Murphy**
2 **NESSFIELD BLUE**, 6, b g Kayf Tara—Bella Medici **Murphy & Chantler**

Other Owners: Mrs B. I. Chantler, P. G. Murphy.

397   MR BARRY MURTAGH, Carlisle
Postal: **Hurst Farm, Ivegill, Carlisle, Cumbria, CA4 0NL**
Contacts: **PHONE 017684 84649 MOBILE 07714 026741 FAX 017684 84744**
EMAIL suemurtagh7@gmail.com

1 **BAYMORE ROAD**, 6, b g Josr Algarhoud (IRE)—Animal Cracker **Hurst Farm Racing**
2 **BORDER VICTOR**, 8, b g Beat All (USA)—Sambara (IRE) **Mrs A. Stamper**
3 **CLONDAW BANKER (IRE)**, 11, b g Court Cave (IRE)—Freya Alex **A. R. White**
4 **ELIXER (IRE)**, 7, b g Oscar (IRE)—Sunny Native (IRE) **Hurst Farm Racing**
5 **ELUSIVE RED (IRE)**, 6, b g Elusive Pimpernel (USA)—Spin In The Wind (IRE) **Mrs S. A. Murtagh**
6 **FAST AND FRIENDLY (IRE)**, 6, b g September Storm (GER)—Merewood Lodge (IRE) **Famous Five Racing**
7 **GEYSER**, 4, b g Gale Force Ten—Popocatepetl (FR) **Mrs A. Stamper**
8 **PAPAGAYO (IRE)**, 8, b g Shirocco (GER)—Jomana (IRE) **M. A. Proudfoot**
9 **PEAK HILL**, 7, ch g Bahamian Bounty—River Naiad **Famous Five Racing**
10 **SAMTU (IRE)**, 9, b g Teofilo (IRE)—Samdaniya **A. R. White**
11 , B g Enrique—Staraba (FR) **Mrs S. A. Murtagh**
12 **SYMBOLIC STAR (IRE)**, 8, b g New Approach (IRE)—Epitome (IRE) **Mr G Fell & Mr R V Brass**
13 **TOMMY SHELBY (FR)**, 5, b g Dabirsim (FR)—Interior (USA) **Mrs S. A. Murtagh**

THREE-YEAR-OLDS

14 **CURTANA**, b f Saddler's Rock (IRE)—Lady Blade (IRE) **Mrs A. Stamper**

Other Owners: Mr R. V. Brass, Mr G. Fell.

Assistant Trainer: S A Murtagh.

Conditional Jockey: Lorcan Murtagh. **Apprentice Jockey:** Connor Murtagh.

398   DR JEREMY NAYLOR, Shrewton
Postal: **The Cleeve Stables, Elston, Shrewton, Salisbury, Wiltshire, SP3 4HL**
Contacts: **PHONE 01980 620804 MOBILE 07771 740126**
EMAIL info@jeremynaylor.com WEBSITE www.jeremynaylor.com

1 **CROUCHING HARRY (IRE)**, 11, b g Tiger Hill (IRE)—Catwalk Dreamer (IRE) **Mrs S. P. Elphick**
2 **FEARSOME FRED**, 11, b g Emperor Fountain—Ryewater Dream **Mrs S. P. Elphick**
3 **SEERAJ**, 5, b h Fastnet Rock (AUS)—Star On High (USA) **Dr J. R. J. Naylor**

399   MR JOHN NEEDHAM, Ludlow
Postal: **Gorsty Farm, Mary Knoll, Ludlow, Shropshire, SY8 2HD**
Contacts: **PHONE 01584 872112, 01584 874826 MOBILE 07811 451137 FAX 01584 873256**
EMAIL johnlneedham@btconnect.com

1 **DOWNTON FOX**, 12, b g Oscar (IRE)—Leinthall Fox **Miss J. C. L. Needham**
2 **MY FOXY LADY**, 8, br m Sagamix (FR)—Marlbrook Fox **Miss J. C. L. Needham**
3 **RIGHT ROYALS DAY**, 11, b m Beneficial—Just For A Laugh **Miss J. C. L. Needham**

MR JOHN NEEDHAM - continued

Assistant Trainer: J. Wall.

NH Jockey: Robbie Dunne, Richard Johnson, Jamie Moore.

400
MRS HELEN NELMES, Dorchester
Postal: **Warmwell Stables, 2 Church Cottages, Warmwell, Dorchester, Dorset, DT2 8HQ**
Contacts: **PHONE 01305 852254 MOBILE 07977 510318**
EMAIL warmwellstud@tiscali.co.uk WEBSITE www.warmwellstables.co.uk

1 ARC OF BUBBLES (IRE), 5, br g Arcadio (GER)—Bubble Bann (IRE) **Mr M. J. Hoskins**
2 GARRYDUFF CROSS (IRE), 10, b g Stowaway—Cooleycall (IRE) **K. A. Nelmes**
3 ITSABOUTIME (IRE), 10, gr g Whitmore's Conn (USA)—Blazing Love (IRE) **K. A. Nelmes**
4 KALMBEFORETHESTORM, 12, ch g Storming Home—Miss Honeypenny (IRE) **Warmwellcome Partnership**
5 KEEPYOURHEADUP, 9, b g Sir Percy—Sweet Lemon (IRE) **Mr K. Tyre**
6 LAOCH BEAG (IRE), 9, gr g King's Theatre (IRE)—Innocentines (FR) **KA Nelmes & LJ Burden**
7 MENAPIAN (IRE), 9, b br g Touch of Land (FR)—Mannequin (IRE) **T M W Partnership**
8 MERCHANT IN MILAN (IRE), 8, b g Milan—Azaban (IRE) **Mr L. J. Burden**
9 NORSE DA, 10, b g Norse Dancer (IRE)—End of An Error **T M W Partnership**
10 SERVEONTIME (IRE), 9, b g Echo of Light—Little Lovely (IRE) **K. A. Nelmes**

Other Owners: Mr L. J. Burden, K. A. Nelmes.

Assistant Trainer: K Nelmes.

Conditional Jockey: Conor Ring.

401
MR TONY NEWCOMBE, Barnstaple
Postal: **Lower Delworthy, Yarnscombe, Barnstaple, Devon, EX31 3LT**
Contacts: **PHONE 01271 858554 MOBILE 07785 297210**
EMAIL huntshawequineforest@talktalk.net

1 BUG BOY (IRE), 4, b g Big Bad Bob (IRE)—Velvetina (IRE) **Dr S. P. Hargreaves**
2 CARLA KOALA, 4, b f Kuroshio (AUS)—Bold Love **Joli Racing**
3 DON'T GIVE UP, 6, b h Dubawi (IRE)—Avongrove **Central Racing Ltd**
4 FIRST FLIGHT (IRE), 9, b g Invincible Spirit (IRE)—First of Many **Mr G. Darling**
5 KAY SERA, 12, b g Kayf Tara—Inflation **Mr N. P. Hardy**
6 LIGHTNING ATTACK, 4, b g Lethal Force—Afrodita (IRE) **Mr G. Darling**
7 LIIMARI, 7, b m Authorized (IRE)—Snow Polina (USA) **A. G. Newcombe**
8 LIPPY LADY (IRE), 4, b f Bungle Inthejungle—Sayrah **A. G. Newcombe**
9 PRINCELY, 5, b h Compton Place—Royal Award **Mr G. Darling**
10 SOVEREIGN STATE, 5, b g Compton Place—One Night In May (IRE) **R. Eagle**
11 TOMILY (IRE), 6, b g Canford Cliffs (IRE)—Cake (IRE) **Mr G. Darling**
12 WAR OF SUCCESSION, 6, b g Casamento (IRE)—Rohlindi **Dr S. P. Hargreaves**

THREE-YEAR-OLDS

13 AMAZON PRINCESS, b f War Command (USA)—Last Lahar **Joli Racing**
14 B c Cityscape—Makindi **Central Racing Ltd**
15 WRATH OF HECTOR, b c Mayson—Dutch Mistress **Central Racing Ltd**

Assistant Trainer: John Lovejoy.

DR RICHARD NEWLAND, Claines
402 Postal: **Linacres Farm, Egg Lane, Claines, Worcester, WR3 7SB**
Contacts: **PHONE 07956 196535**
EMAIL richard.newland1@btopenworld.com

1 **AARON LAD (IRE)**, 9, b g Daylami (IRE)—Borntobepampered **Off The Clock Partners & Dr RDP Newland**
2 **ABOLITIONIST (IRE)**, 12, b g Flemensfirth (USA)—All The Roses (IRE) **M Albon, J A Provan & C E Stedman**
3 **ARTISTIC LANGUAGE**, 4, b g Archipenko (USA)—Kiswahili **ValueRacingClub.co.uk**
4 **BBOLD (IRE)**, 6, b g Aizavoski (IRE)—Molly Be **BAA Management Ltd**
5 **BEAU BAY (FR)**, 9, b g Bernebeau (FR)—Slew Bay (FR) **Mr Peter Green & Dr R D P Newland**
6 **BENSON**, 5, b g Beat Hollow—Karla June **Pump & Plant Services Ltd**
7 **BIG G**, 5, b g Cityscape—Crazy (GER) **BAA Management Ltd**
8 **BOLTISSIME (FR)**, 5, b g Dawn Approach (IRE)—Be Yourself (FR) **M Albon & M P Tudor**
9 **BROUGHTONS ADMIRAL**, 6, b g Born To Sea (IRE)—Chanter **ValueRacingClub.co.uk**
10 **C'EST LE BONHEUR (FR)**, 8, b g Laveron—Joie de La Vie (FR) **J A Provan & Partner**
11 **CAID DU LIN (FR)**, 8, gr g Della Francesca (USA)—Asia du Lin (FR) **Foxtrot Racing**
12 **CAPTAIN TOM CAT (IRE)**, 5, b g Dylan Thomas (IRE)—Miss Molly Malone (IRE)
13 **CATAMARAN DU SEUIL (FR)**, 8, b g Network (GER)—Fleur du Tennis (FR) **Mr M. P. Tudor**
14 **CHEF DE TROUPE (FR)**, 7, b g Air Chief Marshal (IRE)—Tazminya **Mr C. E. Stedman**
15 **CLASSIC ESCAPE (IRE)**, 7, b g Golan (IRE)—Seana Ghael (IRE) **Dr R. D. P. Newland**
16 **CLEVER AS A FOX (IRE)**, 7, b g Gold Well—Inouette (IRE) **The Leicester Lads**
17 **COBALTIC (FR)**, 5, b br g Balko (FR)—Naiade de La Roque (FR) **The Three Amigos**
18 **COILLTE EILE (IRE)**, 7, b m Stowaway—Aughwilliam Lady (IRE) **Mr P K & Mrs A J Adams**
19 **COULONCES (FR)**, 5, b m Le Havre (IRE)—Talwin (IRE) **Mr P. Drinkwater**
20 **DANCING IN THE SKY (IRE)**, 7, b g Court Cave (IRE)—Agasaya (IRE) **Foxtrot Racing: Dancing In The Sky**
21 **DASHING PERK**, 9, b g Kayf Tara—Dashing Executive (IRE) **Mr P. Jenkins**
22 **DOUNYAPOUR (FR)**, 7, ch g Lope de Vega (IRE)—Diamond Tango (FR) **G Carstairs & R Marker**
23 **DUKE STREET (IRE)**, 8, b g Duke of Marmalade (IRE)—Act of The Pace (IRE) **Chris Stedman & Mark Albon**
24 **DUSTIN DES MOTTES (FR)**, 7, b g Kapgarde (FR)—Puszta des Mottes (FR) **Mr D. J. Smith**
25 **EMMA LAMB**, 6, b m Passing Glance—Lucinda Lamb **Doom Bar Beach Club**
26 **EMPLOYER (IRE)**, 5, b g Camelot—Close Regards (IRE)
27 **ENQARDE (FR)**, 6, b g Kapgarde (FR)—Usachaqa (FR) **Off The Clock Partners & Dr RDP Newland**
28 **EVITA DU MESNIL (FR)**, 6, gr m Gris de Gris (FR)—Perle du Mesnil (FR) **Foxtrot Racing Evita Du Mesnil**
29 **FLASH DE CLERVAL (FR)**, 5, b g Maresca Sorrento (FR)—Nonita de Clerval (FR) **ValueRacingClub.co.uk**
30 **FLEUR DU SEUIL (FR)**, 5, b m Youmzain (IRE)—Tulipe du Seuil (FR) **Mr M. P. Tudor**
31 **GARBANZO (IRE)**, 6, gr g Mastercraftsman (IRE)—Noble Fantasy (GER) **Mr C. E. Stedman**
32 **GOSPELUS (FR)**, 4, b g Rail Link—Precieuze (FR) **The Choirboys**
33 **HIGGS (IRE)**, 7, b g Scorpion (IRE)—Captain Supreme (IRE) **Pump & Plant Services Ltd**
34 **JIMMY RABBITTE (IRE)**, 7, b g Dubai Destination (USA)—Time To Act **P Jenkins & Partner**
35 **KATPOLI (FR)**, 5, b g Poliglote—Katkogarie (FR) **Mr C. E. Stedman**
36 **LE PATRIOTE (FR)**, 8, b g Poliglote—Sentosa (FR) **Canard Vert Racing Club**
37 **LEONCAVALLO (IRE)**, 8, br g Cape Cross (IRE)—Nafura **ValueRacingClub.co.uk**
38 **LITTLE RORY MAC (IRE)**, 6, b g Yeats (IRE)—Solar Quest (IRE) **The Vacuum Pouch Company Limited**
39 **LOVATO (GER)**, 8, br g Lauro (GER)—Larella (GER) **Plan B**
40 **MAKKA PAKKA (IRE)**, 7, b g Duke of Marmalade (IRE)—Betray **Ardroe Developments Ltd**
41 **MARINE ONE**, 6, b g Frankel—Marine Bleue (IRE) **Deva Racing Kingston**
42 **MASON JAR (FR)**, 6, ch g No Risk At All (FR)—Queen's Theatre (FR) **Foxtrot Racing Mason Jar**
43 **MAXENCHOP (FR)**, 5, b g Muhaymin (USA)—Gryffyn (FR) **Deva Racing Maxenchop**
44 **MCGROARTY (IRE)**, 9, b g Brian Boru—Uffizi (IRE) **Chris Stedman & Mark Albon**
45 **MISTER CHIANG**, 4, b g Archipenko (USA)—Robe Chinoise **Foxtrot Racing: Mister Chiang**
46 **MR CAFFREY**, 8, b g Duke of Marmalade (IRE)—Quest For Eternity (IRE) **R Trow, A P Barwell, C J Sanders**
47 **MR MULDOON (IRE)**, 7, ch g Rajj (IRE)—Miss Muldoon (IRE) **Foxtrot Racing Mr Muldoon**
48 **NET LOVE (FR)**, 6, b m Network (GER)—Droit d'Aimer (FR) **Mr C. E. Stedman**
49 **NORDICAN BLEUE (FR)**, 5, b m Anabaa Blue—Nordican Queen (FR) **Canard Vert Racing Club**
50 **ON THE WILD SIDE (IRE)**, 7, b g Robin des Champs (FR)—Clear Riposte (IRE) **M Albon & M P Tudor**
51 **OPERATIC EXPORT (IRE)**, 4, b f Vocalised (USA)—Teofolina (IRE) **J A Provan & Partner**
52 **OUR GIRL KATIE**, 5, ch m Shirocco (GER)—Our Girl Salley (IRE) **Miss F. Nimmo**
53 **POWDER PATH (FR)**, 5, b g Coastal Path—Powder Tremp (FR) **Foxtrot Racing: Powder Path**
54 **PURPLE KING (IRE)**, 6, ch g Lope de Vega (IRE)—Dixie Dance (IRE) **Foxtrot Racing Purple King**
55 **RED MIX (FR)**, 7, b g Al Namix (FR)—Fidelety (FR) **Brewers Racing Club**

DR RICHARD NEWLAND - continued

56 **RIKOBOY (FR)**, 4, b g Enrique—Dikanika (FR) **Mr D. J. Smith**
57 **ROSE SEA HAS (FR)**, 5, gr g Kapgarde (FR)—Vaibuscar Has (FR) **Mr Simon Munir & Mr Isaac Souede**
58 **ROSTELLO (FR)**, 5, ch g Fuisse (FR)—Rose d'Ete (FR) **Mrs D L Whateley & Dr R D P Newland**
59 **SOMETHINBOUTANGELA (IRE)**, 7, b m Milan—Cush Ramani (IRE) **Spur of the Moment & Partner**
60 **STAMINA CHOPE (FR)**, 4, ch f Muhaymin (USA)—My Virginia (FR) **Mr Paul Drinkwater/Dr R. D. P.Newland**
61 **STORM RISING (IRE)**, 7, b g Canford Cliffs (IRE)—Before The Storm **M Albon & M P Tudor**
62 **SUDDEN DESTINATION (IRE)**, 8, ch g Dubai Destination (USA)—
                                                       Sudden Approach (IRE) **Foxtrot NH Racing Syndicate**
63 **SWEETTOWATCH (IRE)**, 6, b m Fracas (IRE)—Molly's Mate (IRE) **Mr M. P. Tudor**
64 **TASTE THE FEAR (IRE)**, 5, b g Mores Wells—No Complaints But (IRE) **In It For Fun Partnership & Dr R Newland**
65 **THEO (IRE)**, 10, b g Westerner—Jemima Jay (IRE) **P Jenkins & Partner**
66 **URBANIST (IRE)**, 8, b g Black Sam Bellamy (IRE)—Sorcillera **Mr P. Drinkwater**
67 **VOSNE ROMANEE**, 9, ch g Arakan (USA)—Vento Del Oreno (FR) **Foxtrot NH Racing Partnership VI**
68 **WHATSDASTORY (IRE)**, 7, b m Beneficial—Supreme Contender (IRE) **Plan B**
69 **WHOSHOTWHO (IRE)**, 9, br g Beneficial—Inishbeg House (IRE) **Foxtrot Racing: Whoshotwho**
70 **YCCS PORTOCERVO (FR)**, 5, gr g Martaline—Griva (FR) **Mrs M C Litton & Mrs F D McInnes Skinner**

Other Owners: Mr D. Abraham, Mr M. L. Albon, Mr M. P. Ansell, Mr A. P. Barwell, Mr L. A. Bolingbroke, Mr G. N. Carstairs, Mr N. A. Clark, Mr A. S. P. Drake, Mr P. Drinkwater, Mr J. M. O. Evans, Foxtrot Racing Management Ltd, Mrs A. J. Gardiner, Mr P. K. Gardiner, Mr P. C. W. Green, In It For Fun, Mr P. Jenkins, Mrs P. J. Litton, R. J. T. Marker, Mrs F. D. McInnes Skinner, S. E. Munir, Mrs L. J. Newland, Dr R. D. P. Newland, C. G. Nicholl, Off The Clock Partners, Mr J. A. Provan, Mr C. J. Sanders, Mr I. Souede, Spur of the Moment, Mr C. E. Stedman, S. R. Trow, Mr M. P. Tudor, Mrs D. L. Whateley.

Assistant Trainer: Rod Trow.

Amateur Jockey: Mr T Weston.

---

403 **MISS ANNA NEWTON-SMITH, Jevington**
Postal: **Bull Pen Cottage, Jevington, Polegate, East Sussex, BN26 5QB**
Contacts: **PHONE 01323 488354 MOBILE 07970 914124**
EMAIL annanewtonsmith@gmail.com WEBSITE www.annanewtonsmith.co.uk

1 **BEET TOPPER (IRE)**, 7, b g Beat Hollow—What A Topper (IRE) **PPS Racing**
2 **BURGESS DREAM (IRE)**, 11, b g Spadoun (FR)—Ennel Lady (IRE) **The Beano Partnership**
3 **GORING ONE (IRE)**, 15, b g Broadway Flyer (USA)—Brigette's Secret **Mr G. E. Goring**
4 **MAID OF CAMELOT (IRE)**, 5, b m Camelot—Dea Mhein (IRE) **The Alice Partnership**

Assistant Trainer: Nicola Worley.

NH Jockey: Paddy Brennan, Charlie Deutsch, Jeremiah McGrath, David Noonan. **Conditional Jockey:** Rex Dingle.

---

404 **MR ADRIAN NICHOLLS, Sessay**
Postal: **The Ranch, Sessay, Thirsk, North Yorkshire, YO7 3ND**
Contacts: **PHONE 01845 597428**

1 **ABATE**, 4, br c Bated Breath—Red Kyte **The Never Say No Racing Club**
2 **ALAMEERY**, 4, b c Kingman—Zacheta **Golden Equinox Racing**
3 **SFUMATO**, 6, br g Bated Breath—Modern Look **J. A. Rattigan**
4 **SUPER FLORENCE (IRE)**, 5, gr m Zebedee—Top of The Ridge (IRE) **Mr M. J. Goggin**
5 **THE BIG HOUSE (IRE)**, 4, b g Coach House (IRE)—Tekhania (IRE) **Mr D. Stone**
6 **THE STALKING MOON (IRE)**, 6, b m Arcano (IRE)—Cornakill (USA) **Lycett Racing 100 Club**

THREE-YEAR-OLDS

7 **DANDIZETTE (IRE)**, ch f Dandy Man (IRE)—Interlacing **Northumbria Leisure Ltd**
8 **STRAWMAN (IRE)**, b c Starspangledbanner (AUS)—Youve Got A Friend (IRE) **The Strawman Partnership**
9 **ZAKHER ALAIN**, b c Sepoy (AUS)—Madame Mere (IRE) **Mr A. Nicholls**

MR ADRIAN NICHOLLS - continued

TWO-YEAR-OLDS

10 B f 25/01 Intrinsic—Blushes (FR) (Siyouni (FR)) **Malih L. Al Basti**
11 Gr f 10/03 Kodi Bear (IRE)—Bridal Path (Groom Dancer (USA)) (9437) **Mr D. Stone**
12 B c 13/02 Intrinsic—Lady Kyllar (Kyllachy) **Malih L. Al Basti**
13 B f 27/04 Mehmas (IRE)—Mistress of Rome (Holy Roman Emperor (IRE)) (5714) **Mr D. Stone**
14 B f 28/02 Bated Breath—Rapid Recruit (IRE) (Fast Company (IRE)) (14285) **Golden Equinox Racing**
15 B f 17/04 Belardo (IRE)—Toolentidhaar (USA) (Swain (IRE)) (10295) **Golden Equinox Racing**
16 WATCHTHISNOW (IRE), b c 16/04 Anjaal—Miss Megs (Croco Rouge (IRE)) **J. A. Rattigan**

Other Owners: Mr A. Nicholls, Mr K. Till.

405

MR PAUL NICHOLLS, Ditcheat
Postal: **Manor Farm Stables, Ditcheat, Shepton Mallet, Somerset, BA4 6RD**
Contacts: **PHONE 01749 860656 MOBILE 07977 270706**
EMAIL info@paulnichollsracing.com **WEBSITE** www.paulnichollsracing.com

1 ACCOMPLICE (FR), 6, gr g Network (GER)—Miss Vitoria (FR) **Mrs K. A. Stuart**
2 ADRIEN DU PONT (FR), 8, b g Califet (FR)—Santariyka (FR) **Mrs J. De La Hey**
3 ALCALA (FR), 10, gr g Turgeon (USA)—Pail Mel (FR) **Owners Group 016**
4 AMENON (FR), 5, b g Saint des Saints (FR)—La Couetrie (FR) **Mr & Mrs J. D. Cotton**
5 AMOUR DE NUIT (IRE), 8, b g Azamour (IRE)—Umthoulah (IRE) **Mr A. N. V. Williams**
6 ARCHIE BROWN (IRE), 6, br g Aizavoski (IRE)—Pure Beautiful (IRE) **Million in Mind Partnership**
7 AS DE MEE (FR), 10, b br g Kapgarde (FR)—Koeur de Mee (FR) **The Stewart Family & Judi Dench**
8 ASHUTOR (FR), 6, gr g Redoute's Choice (AUS)—Ashalanda (FR) **The Stewart Family**
9 ASK FOR GLORY (IRE), 6, b g Fame And Glory—Ask Helen (IRE) **Mr Colm Donlon & Mr & Mrs P. K. Barber**
10 ATHOLL STREET (IRE), 5, b g Jeremy (USA)—Allthewhile (IRE) **Mr T. J. Hemmings**
11 BAGAD BIHOUE (FR), 9, b g Nickname (FR)—Lann Bihouee (FR) **Owners Group 009**
12 BARBADOS BUCK'S (IRE), 5, b g Getaway (GER)—Buck's Blue (FR) **The Stewart Family**
13 BATHSHEBA BAY (FR), 5, br g Footstepsinthesand—Valamareha (IRE) **Mr M. F. Geoghegan**
14 BIRDS OF PREY (IRE), 6, b g Sir Prancealot (IRE)—Cute **Mrs K. A. Stuart**
15 BLACK CORTON (FR), 9, br g Laverock (IRE)—Pour Le Meilleur (FR) **The Brooks Family & J. Kyle**
16 BLACKJACK KENTUCKY (IRE), 7, b g Oscar (IRE)—My Name's Not Bin (IRE) **Owners Group 026**
17 BOB AND CO (FR), 9, b g Dom Alco (FR)—Outre Mer (FR) **David Maxwell Racing Limited**
18 BOB PEBBLE (IRE), 5, gr g Big Bad Bob (IRE)—Pebble In A Pool (IRE) **Old Gold Racing 1**
19 BRAQUEUR D'OR (FR), 9, b g Epalo (GER)—Hot d'Or (FR) **Corsellis & Seyfried**
20 BRAVEMANSGAME (FR), 5, b g Brave Mansonnien (FR)—Genifique (FR) **John Dance & Bryan Drew**
21 BRELAN D'AS (FR), 9, b g Crillon (FR)—Las de La Croix (FR) **Mr J. P. McManus**
22 BREWERS PROJECT (IRE), 6, b g Aizavoski (IRE)—Shaylee Wilde (IRE) **The Hon Mrs C. A. Townshend**
23 BROKEN HALO, 5, b g Kayf Tara—Miss Invincible **Giraffa Racing - BH**
24 CALVA D'AUGE (FR), 5, b g Air Chief Marshal (IRE)—Hill Ou Elle (FR) **Owners Group 040**
25 CAP DU MATHAN (FR), 5, b g Kapgarde (FR)—Nounjya du Mathan (FR) **The Stewart Family**
26 CAPELAND (FR), 8, b g Poliglote—Neiland (FR) **Mrs K. A. Stuart**
27 CAPTAIN CATTISTOCK, 7, b g Black Sam Bellamy (IRE)—Pearl Buttons **David Maxwell Racing Limited**
28 CASKO D'AIRY (FR), 8, b g Voix du Nord (FR)—Quaska d'Airy (FR) **G.Mason & Sir A. Ferguson**
29 CAT TIGER (FR), 6, b g Diamond Boy (FR)—Miss Canon (FR) **David Maxwell Racing Limited**
30 CELESTIAL FORCE (IRE), 5, b g Sea The Stars (IRE)—Aquarelle Bleue **Mr J. E. Dance**
31 CHANCE FINALE (FR), 6, b g Blue Bresil (FR)—Ballade Nordique (FR) **Tracey Bell & Caroline Lyons**
32 CHEZ HANS (GER), 4, b g Mamool (IRE)—Chandos Rose (IRE) **Owners Group 038**
33 CHRISTOPHER WOOD (IRE), 5, b g Fast Company (IRE)—Surf The Web (IRE) **Mrs S. A. J. Kinsella**
34 CILL ANNA (IRE), 5, b m Imperial Monarch (IRE)—Technohead (IRE) **The Stewart Family**
35 CLAN DES OBEAUX (FR), 8, b g Kapgarde (FR)—
                                                Nausicaa des Obeaux (FR) **Mr&Mrs P.K.Barber,G.Mason,Sir A Ferguson**
36 CLIFFS OF DOVER, 7, b g Canford Cliffs (IRE)—Basanti (USA) **Mr & Mrs J. D. Cotton**
37 CONFIRMATION BIAS (IRE), 5, b g Presenting—Bonnie Parker (IRE) **Mr C. A. Donlon**
38 COPAIN DE CLASSE (FR), 8, b g Enrique—Toque Rouge (FR) **The Stewart Family**
39 COUP DE PINCEAU (FR), 8, b g Buck's Boum (FR)—Castagnette III (FR) **Mr C. A. Donlon**
40 4, B g Getaway (GER)—Crossbar Lady (IRE) **Mr S. White**

MR PAUL NICHOLLS - continued

41 **CYRNAME (FR)**, 8, b g Nickname (FR)—Narquille (FR) **Mrs J. De La Hey**
42 **DAN MCGRUE (IRE)**, 8, b g Dansant—Aahsaypasty (IRE) **Mr&Mrs P.K.Barber, D. Bennett, D. Martin**
43 **DANNY KIRWAN (IRE)**, 7, b g Scorpion (IRE)—Sainte Baronne (FR) **Mrs J. De La Hey**
44 **DANNY WHIZZBANG (IRE)**, 7, b g Getaway (GER)—Lakil Princess (IRE) **Mrs A. Tincknell**
45 **DANSE IDOL (IRE)**, 7, b m Dansant—Screen Idol (IRE) **Highclere Thoroughbred Racing-Danse Idol**
46 **DARLING MALTAIX (FR)**, 7, b g Voix du Nord (FR)—Rosalie Malta (FR) **Mrs J. De La Hey**
47 **DENILIQUIN (IRE)**, 5, gr g Mastercraftsman (IRE)—Bernie's Moon (USA) **McNeill Family Ltd**
48 **DIAMOND GUY (FR)**, 7, b g Konig Turf (GER)—Unique Chance (FR) **Executors & Trustees of C G Roach Estate**
49 **DIEGO DU CHARMIL (FR)**, 8, b g Ballingarry (IRE)—Daramour (FR) **Mrs J. De La Hey**
50 **DOGON**, 5, b g Intello (GER)—Poppets Sweetlove **Middleham Park Racing LXXVIII& A&J Ryan**
51 **DOIN'WHATSHELIKES (IRE)**, 5, b m Presenting—Karkiyla (IRE) **The Brooks Family & J. Kyle**
52 **DOLOS (FR)**, 7, b g Kapgarde (FR)—Redowa (FR) **Mrs J. De La Hey**
53 **DORAH**, 4, b f Camelot—Rosie Probert **Mrs S. A. J. Kinsella**
54 **DR SANDERSON (IRE)**, 6, b g Jeremy (USA)—Guydus (IRE) **Mr J. P. McManus**
55 **DUC DE BOURBON (FR)**, 4, b g Buck's Boum—Astre Eria (FR) **Mr J. P. McManus**
56 **DYNAMITE DOLLARS (FR)**, 7, b br g Buck's Boum—Macadoun (FR) **Mr M. F. Geoghegan**
57 **EASYRUN DE VASSY (FR)**, 6, b g Muhtathir—Royale The Best (FR) **The Brooks Family & P.J. Vogt**
58 **ECCO**, 5, b g Maxios—Enjoy The Life **Mr C. A. Donlon**
59 **ELLARNA (FR)**, 6, b m Lucarno (USA)—Oeuvre d'Art (FR) **Axom LXIX**
60 **ENRILO (FR)**, 6, bl g Buck's Boum (FR)—Rock Treasure (FR) **Martin Broughton & Friends 4**
61 **ENVOYE SPECIAL (FR)**, 6, b g Coastal Path—Santa Bamba (FR) **Brooks, Kyle & Mason**
62 **ERITAGE (FR)**, 6, b g Martaline—Sauves La Reine (FR) **Mrs A. Tincknell**
63 **FAMOSO (IRE)**, 4, b g Fame And Glory—Mucho Macabi (IRE) **Mr P K Barber & Mr P J Vogt**
64 **FAVORITO BUCK'S (FR)**, 8, b g Buck's Boum (FR)—Sangrilla (FR) **Mrs J. De La Hey**
65 **FIDELIO VALLIS (FR)**, 5, b g Saint des Saints (FR)—Quora Vallis (FR) **Mr J. Hales**
66 **FLASH COLLONGES (FR)**, 5, b g Saddler Maker (IRE)—Prouesse Collonges (FR) **The Gi Gi Syndicate**
67 **FLASH DE TOUZAINE (FR)**, 5, b g Kapgarde (FR)—Narcisse de Touzaine (FR) **Mr S. White**
68 **FLEMENSTIDE (IRE)**, 5, b g Flemensfirth (USA)—Keep Face (IRE) **Mr P K Barber & Mr P J Vogt**
69 **FLIC OU VOYOU (FR)**, 6, b g Kapgarde (FR)—Hillflower (FR) **Mr C. A. Donlon**
70 **FORCE TEN (FR)**, 5, b g Al Namix (FR)—Quick Siren Mae (FR) **Owners Group 029**
71 **FRIEND OR FOE (FR)**, 5, b g Walk In The Park (IRE)—Mandchou (FR) **Gordon & Su Hall**
72 **FRODON (FR)**, 8, b g Nickname (FR)—Miss Country (FR) **Mr P. J. Vogt**
73 **GALA DE CORTON (FR)**, 4, b g Secret Singer (FR)—Pour Le Meilleur (FR) **Gordon & Su Hall**
74 **GELINO BELLO (FR)**, 4, b g Saint des Saints (FR)—Parade (FR) **Mr & Mrs J. D. Cotton**
75 **75**, B m Rail Link—Get Me Home (IRE) **M. C. Denmark**
76 **GET THE APPEAL (IRE)**, 6, b m Getaway (GER)—Lady Appeal (IRE) **Middleham Park Racing IX**
77 **GETAWAY TRUMP (IRE)**, 7, b g Getaway (GER)—Acinorev (IRE) **Owners Group 023**
78 **GIVE ME A COPPER (IRE)**, 10, ch g Presenting—
Copper Supreme (IRE) **Done, Ferguson, Mason, Nicholls & Wood**
79 **GLAJOU (FR)**, 4, b g Network (GER)—Toscane (FR) **Middleham Park Racing XLVIII**
80 **GLENLIVET (IRE)**, 5, b g Flemensfirth (USA)—Gleaming Spire **T. Barr**
81 **GOLDEN GIFT (IRE)**, 6, b g Gold Well—Five Star Present (IRE) **Mr&Mrs P.K.Barber,G.Mason,Sir A Ferguson**
82 **GRAND SANCY (FR)**, 6, b g Diamond Boy (FR)—La Courtille (FR) **Martin Broughton Racing Partners**
83 **GRAND SLAM (IRE)**, 6, b g Jeremy (USA)—Knockalane (IRE) **Mr J. P. McManus**
84 **GREANETEEN (FR)**, 6, b g Great Pretender (IRE)—Manson Teene (FR) **Mr C. M. Giles**
85 **GREAT GABLE (IRE)**, 4, b g Fame And Glory—Mistress Mole (IRE) **Owners Group 050**
86 **GREY GETAWAY (IRE)**, 6, gr g Getaway (GER)—Miss Greylands **Mr P. J. Vogt**
87 **GROOVY KIND (FR)**, 4, b f Masked Marvel—Toscane de Laroque (FR) **Owners Group 056**
88 **HIGHLAND HUNTER (IRE)**, 7, gr g Subtle Power (IRE)—Loughine Sparkle (IRE) **T. Barr**
89 **HUGOS OTHER HORSE**, 6, b g Gold Well—Wicked Crack (IRE) **The Stewart Family**
90 **IF YOU SAY RUN (IRE)**, 8, b m Mahler—De Lissa (IRE) **Highclere T'Bred Racing If You Say Run**
91 **IS A REAL CHAMP (IRE)**, 6, ch g Getaway (GER)—Siobhans Charm (IRE) **McNeill Family Ltd**
92 **JEREMY PASS (IRE)**, 5, b g Jeremy (USA)—Toulon Pass (IRE) **Mr J. E. Dance**
93 **KANDOO KID (FR)**, 4, gr g Kapgarde (FR)—Scarlett du Mesnil (FR) **Mr M. F. Geoghegan**
94 **KILMINGTON ROSE (IRE)**, 5, ch m Presenting—Robyn's Rose (IRE) **Mr Charles Pelham & Mr Henry Pelham**
95 **KING OF THE RING**, 4, b g Sepoy (AUS)—Anosti **Mason, Ferguson, Bolton & Gibson**
96 **KNAPPERS HILL (IRE)**, 4, b g Valirann (FR)—Brogella (IRE) **Mr P K Barber & Mr P J Vogt**
97 **KUMARA PLOUGH (IRE)**, 4, b g Milan—Back To Loughadera (IRE) **The Stewart Family**
98 **LIGHT IN THE SKY (FR)**, 4, b g Anodin (IRE)—Arsila (IRE) **Calala Island Syndicate**

MR PAUL NICHOLLS - continued

99   **LISA DE VASSY (FR)**, 5, b m Cokoriko (FR)—Mona Vassy (FR) **Mrs J. De La Hey**
100 **LOUGH DERG SPIRIT (IRE)**, 8, b g Westerner—Sno-Cat Lady (IRE) **The Stewart Family**
101 **LYDFORD LAD (IRE)**, 5, b g Yeats (IRE)—Shannon Rose (IRE) **Mr David Martin & Mr Paul Barber**
102 **LYONS (IRE)**, 4, ch g Australia—Light Quest (USA) **Martin Broughton & Friends 2**
103 **MAGIC SAINT (FR)**, 6, b g Saint des Saints (FR)—Magic Poline (FR) **Mr & Mrs J. D. Cotton**
104 **MALAYA (FR)**, 6, b m Martaline—Clarte d'Or (FR) **Mrs J. De La Hey**
105 **MASTER TOMMYTUCKER**, 9, b g Kayf Tara—No Need For Alarm **A. G. Fear**
106 **MCFABULOUS (IRE)**, 6, b g Milan—Rossavon (IRE) **Giraffa Racing**
107 **MERCY MERCY ME**, 8, b g Shirocco (GER)—Monsignorita (IRE) **M. C. Denmark**
108 **MICK PASTOR (FR)**, 4, b g Meshaheer (USA)—Mick Oceane (FR) **Mr J. P. McManus**
109 **MIRANDA (IRE)**, 5, b m Camelot—Great Artist (FR) **Owners Group 034**
110 **MOABIT (GER)**, 8, b g Azamour (IRE)—Moonlight Danceuse (IRE) **Owners Group 014**
111 **MONT DES AVALOIRS (FR)**, 7, b g Blue Bresil (FR)—Abu Dhabi (FR) **Mrs J. De La Hey**
112 **MONTYS MEDOC (IRE)**, 4, b g Westerner—Kilbarry Medoc (IRE) **Insurance Friends**
113 **MORTLACH**, 5, b g Yeats (IRE)—Belle Brook (IRE) **T. Barr**
114 **MR GLASS (IRE)**, 4, b g Sholokhov (IRE)—Maryota (FR) **Mr J. E. Dance**
115 **MY WAY (FR)**, 6, ch g Martaline—Royale Majesty (FR) **Richard&katherine Gilbert & Chris Giles**
116 **NIMIX DE JUILLEY (FR)**, 6, b g Al Namix (FR)—Halbina de Juilley (FR) **Mr J. P. McManus**
117 **NINEOHTWOONEOH (IRE)**, 6, b g Fame And Glory—Oscar's Beauty (IRE) **Mr J. P. McManus**
118 **NOT A NAIL (IRE)**, 6, b g Flemensfirth (USA)—Mandys Gold (IRE) **Mr C. A. Donlon**
119 **OLEG (GER)**, 5, gr g Kamsin (GER)—Dramraire Mist **Middleham Park Racing XII**
120 **ONETHREEFIVENOTOUT (FR)**, 4, b g Blue Bresil (FR)—Maralypha (FR) **The Stewart Family**
121 5, B g Robin des Champs (FR)—Onewayorotheother **M. C. Denmark**
122 **OSCARS MOONSHINE (IRE)**, 5, b g Oscar (IRE)—Scrapper Jack (IRE) **Mrs E. Lane**
123 **OSTUNI (FR)**, 7, b g Great Pretender (IRE)—Mamassita (FR) **B. N. Fulton**
124 4, B g Kayf Tara—Patsie Magern **Mr C. A. Donlon**
125 **PIC D'ORHY (FR)**, 5, b g Turgeon (USA)—Rose Candy (FR) **Mrs J. De La Hey**
126 **POLITOLOGUE (FR)**, 9, gr g Poliglote—Scarlet Row (FR) **Mr J. Hales**
127 **QUEL DESTIN (FR)**, 5, ch g Muhtathir—High Destiny (FR) **Martin Broughton & Friends**
128 **RED FORCE ONE**, 5, b g Lethal Force (IRE)—Dusty Red **Done Ferguson Mason**
129 **RED RISK (FR)**, 5, b g No Risk At All (FR)—Rolie de Vindecy (FR) **Middleham Park Racing Xliv & A&j Ryan**
130 **RHYTHM IS A DANCER,** 7, b g Norse Dancer (IRE)—Fascinatin Rhythm **Mr W. A. Harrison-Allan**
131 4, B c Yeats (IRE)—Rock The Baby (IRE) **M. C. Denmark**
132 **ROMAIN DE SENAM (FR)**, 8, b g Saint des Saints (FR)—Salvatrixe (FR) **Mr Chris Giles & Mr Dan Macdonald**
133 **SABRINA (FR)**, 5, b m Yeats (IRE)—En Vedette (FR) **Owners Group 030**
134 **SAINT DE REVE (FR)**, 6, b g Saint des Saints (FR)—Ty Mat (FR) **Mrs J. De La Hey**
135 **SAINT SONNET (FR)**, 5, b g Saint des Saints (FR)—Leprechaun Lady (FR) **Mr C. A. Donlon**
136 **SAINT XAVIER (FR)**, 8, b g Saint des Saints (FR)—Princesse Lucie (FR) **David Maxwell Racing Limited**
137 **SAINTEMILION (FR)**, 7, b g Diamond Green (FR)—Matakana (FR) **Mrs Kathy Stuart & Mr Terry Warner**
138 **SAMETEGAL (FR)**, 11, b g Saint des Saints (FR)—Loya Lescribaa (FR) **Mr & Mrs J. D. Cotton**
139 **SAN BENEDETO (FR)**, 9, ch g Layman (USA)—Cinco Baidy (FR) **Mr P. J. Vogt**
140 **SAO (FR)**, 6, b br g Great Pretender (IRE)—Miss Country (FR) **Mrs J. De La Hey**
141 **SCARAMANGA (IRE)**, 5, b g Mastercraftsman (IRE)—Herboriste **M. C. Denmark**
142 **SECRET INVESTOR**, 8, b g Kayf Tara—Silver Charmer **Hills of Ledbury Ltd**
143 **SECRET POTION (GER)**, 4, b g Dabirsim (FR)—Sola Gratia (IRE) **Mr A. N. V. Williams**
144 **SEELOTMOREBUSINESS (IRE)**, 5, b g Sholokhov (IRE)—Land of Pride (IRE) **The Stewart Family**
145 **SENDING LOVE (IRE)**, 7, b g Scorpion (IRE)—Dato Vic (IRE) **Sullivan Bloodstock Limited**
146 **SETTLE DOWN (FR)**, 5, b g Motivator—Zarafsha (IRE) **Rosecroft Partnership**
147 **SILVER FOREVER (IRE)**, 6, gr m Jeremy (USA)—Silver Prayer (FR) **Mr C. A. Donlon**
148 **SIR PSYCHO (FR)**, 4, b g Zoffany (IRE)—Open Book **Martin Broughton & Friends 3**
149 **SKATMAN (IRE)**, 5, br g Mustameet (USA)—Maid For Action (IRE) **Mr C. M. Giles**
150 **SOLDIER OF LOVE**, 7, b g Yeats (IRE)—Monsignorita (IRE) **M. C. Denmark**
151 **SOLO (FR)**, 4, b c Kapgarde (FR)—Flameche (FR) **Mrs J. De La Hey**
152 **SOUTHFIELD HARVEST**, 6, b g Kayf Tara—Chamoss Royale **Mrs A. B. Yeoman**
153 **SOUTHFIELD STONE**, 7, gr g Fair Mix (IRE)—Laureldean Belle (IRE) **Mrs Angela Hart & Mrs Angela Yeoman**
154 **SOUTHFIELD VIC (IRE)**, 11, ch g Old Vic—Chamoss Royale (FR) **Mrs A. B. Yeoman**
155 **STAGE STAR (IRE)**, 4, b g Fame And Glory—Sparky May **Owners Group 044**
156 **STARSKY (IRE)**, 6, b g Shantou (USA)—Lunar Star (IRE) **Miss Rachael Evans & Mr Matt Booth**
157 **STORM ARISING (IRE)**, 6, b g Yeats (IRE)—Ceol Rua (IRE) **Mr Barry Fulton & Mr Peter Hart**

MR PAUL NICHOLLS - continued

158 **STRATEGAM (FR)**, 4, gr g Sunday Break (JPN)—Our Ziga (FR) **David Maxwell Racing Limited**
159 **SWITCH HITTER (IRE)**, 5, b g Scorpion (IRE)—Country Time (IRE) **Hills of Ledbury Ltd**
160 **TAMAROC DU MATHAN (FR)**, 5, b g Poliglote—Thisbee du Mathan (FR) **Mrs J. De La Hey**
161 **A**, B g Flemensfirth (USA)—The Crown Jewel (IRE) **McNeill Family Ltd**
162 **THE GREATER GOOD**, 5, b g Tiger Groom—Our Kes (IRE) **Owners Group 043**
163 **THRAVE**, 5, b g Sir Percy—Feis Ceoil (IRE) **T. Barr**
164 **THREEUNDERTHRUFIVE (IRE)**, 5, b g Shantou (USA)—Didinas (FR) **McNeill Family Ltd**
165 **THYME WHITE (FR)**, 4, b g Anodin (IRE)—Jane (GER) **The Stewart Family**
166 **TIME TO TINKER (IRE)**, 5, br g Stowaway—Zuzka (IRE) **Mrs A. Tincknell**
167 **TOMMY SILVER (FR)**, 8, b g Silver Cross (FR)—Sainte Mante (FR) **Done, Ferguson, Mason & Wood**
168 **TOPOFTHEGAME (IRE)**, 8, ch g Flemensfirth (USA)—Derry Vale (IRE) **Mr Chris Giles & Mr&mrs P K Barber**
169 **TOUCH KICK (IRE)**, 9, b g Presenting—Bay Pearl (IRE) **Mr T. J. Hemmings**
170 **TREVELYN'S CORN (IRE)**, 7, b g Oscar (IRE)—Present Venture (IRE) **Mr C. M. Giles**
171 **TRUCKERS LODGE (IRE)**, 8, b g Westerner—Galeacord (IRE) **Gordon & Su Hall**
172 **WARRIORS TALE**, 11, b g Midnight Legend—Samandara (FR) **Mr T. J. Hemmings**
173 **4**, B g Sholokhov (IRE)—Watson River (IRE) **Mr C. A. Donlon**
174 **WESTHILL (IRE)**, 5, b g Westerner—Brogarais (IRE) **Hills of Ledbury Ltd**
175 **WHISKEY LULLABY (IRE)**, 5, b m Stowaway—Joie de Cotte (FR) **Highclere Thoroughbred Racing - Whiskey**
176 **WILD MAX (GER)**, 5, b g Maxios—Wildfahrte (GER) **Owners Group 036**
177 **WONDERFUL CHARM (FR)**, 12, b g Poliglote—Victoria Royale (FR) **RJH Geffen, Sir J Ritblat, R Waley-Cohen**
178 **WORTHY FARM (IRE)**, 7, b g Beneficial—Muckle Flugga (IRE) **YOLO**
179 **YALA ENKI (FR)**, 10, b br g Nickname (FR)—Cadiane (FR) **Hills of Ledbury Ltd**
180 **YOUNG BUCK (IRE)**, 6, b g Yeats (IRE)—Pepsi Starlet (IRE) **The Stewart Family**
181 **ZYON**, 6, gr g Martaline—Temptation (FR) **Mrs J. De La Hey**

THREE-YEAR-OLDS

182 **FROSTY LADY (IRE)**, gr f Silver Frost (IRE)—Beautiful Gem (FR) **Mr & Mrs J. D. Cotton**
183 **HARD FROST (FR)**, b g Silver Frost (IRE)—Lottie Belle (FR) **Mr & Mrs J. D. Cotton**
184 **HASHTAG BOUM (FR)**, b f Al Namix (FR)—Engagee (FR) **Mr C. A. Donlon**
185 B c Fame And Glory—Tabachines (FR) **Hills of Ledbury Ltd**

Other Owners: Mr R. J. Acock, Mr S. R. Aston, Mrs M. G. Barber, P. K. Barber, Mr J. Barnard, Mr A. J. Bell, Mrs T. Bell, Mr D. Bennett, Blythe Stables LLP, Mr J. F. Bolton, Mr M. Booth, Mr N. Brand, Mr G. F. Brooks, Lady J. M. Broughton, Sir M. F. Broughton, Mr S. W. Broughton, Mr A. P. Brown, Mrs J. C. Corsellis, Mr J. E. Dance, Dame J. O. Dench, Mr J. Diver, Mr P. E. Done, Mr C. A. Donlon, Mr B. J. C. Drew, Mr R. G. Eddy, Miss R. Evans, Sir A. Ferguson, B. N. Fulton, Mr R. J. H. Geffen, Mr A. Gibson, Mrs K. E. Gilbert, Mr R. P. Gilbert, Richard & Katherine Gilbert, Mr C. M. Giles, Mrs D. M. Gregory, Mr J. R. Hales, Miss L. J. Hales, Mr R. Hales, Mr G. A. Hall, Mrs S. L. Hall, Mr M. P. Hammond, Mrs A. R. Hart, Exors of the Late Mr P. L. Hart, Mr M. J. Holman, Mr J. H. Jackson, Mrs N. Jones, Mr J. Kyle, Mrs C. Lyons, Mr F. Lyons, Fergus & Caroline Lyons, Mr W. D. Macdonald, Mr P. D. Maddocks, Mr D. J. Martin, Marwyn Asset Management SPC, G. A. Mason, Mr B. J. McManus, Mrs M. E. Moody, P. F. Nicholls, Mr C. T. Pelham, Mr H. T. Pelham, Mr S. P. Price, Mr J. W. Randall, Sir J. H. Ritblat, Mr E. J. N. Seyfried, Miss Claire Simmonds, Mr B. D. Smith, Mr D. D. Stevenson, Mr A. Stewart, Mrs J. A. Stewart, Mrs K. A. Stuart, The Stewart Family, Mr D. J. Trembath, Mr P. J. Vogt, Mr R. B. Waley-Cohen, J. T. Warner, Mr R. J. Wood, Mrs A. B. Yeoman.

Assistant Trainer: Charlie Davies, Harry Derham, Natalie Parker.

NH Jockey: Sean Bowen, Harry Cobden, Bryony Frost, Katie O'Farrell, Sam Twiston-Davies. **Conditional Jockey:** Bryan Carver, Lorcan Williams. **Apprentice Jockey:** Megan Nicholls. **Amateur Jockey:** Mr Will Biddick, Mr Angus Cheleda, Mr Matt Hampton, Miss Natalie Parker, Miss Harriet Tucker.

---

406 | **MR PETER NIVEN**, Malton
Postal: **Clovafield, Barton-Le-Street, Malton, North Yorkshire, YO17 6PN**
Contacts: **PHONE 01653 628176 MOBILE 07860 260999 FAX 01653 627295**
EMAIL pruniven@btinternet.com WEBSITE www.peterniven.co.uk

1 **BRIAN BORANHA (IRE)**, 9, b g Brian Boru—Tapneiram (IRE) **Mrs K. J. Young**
2 **BROMANCE**, 7, b g Showcasing—Romantic Destiny **The SB Club**
3 **MALYSTIC**, 6, b g Malinas (GER)—Mystic Glen **Clova Syndicate & Mrs J A Niven**
4 5, B m Sulamani (IRE)—Mystic Glen

MR PETER NIVEN - continued

5 **PIXIEPOT**, 10, b m Alflora (IRE)—Folly Foster **The Rumpole Partnership**
6 **SIMPLY MANI**, 8, ch g Sulamani (IRE)—Simply Mystic **Mrs J A Niven & Angus Racing Club**
7 5, B m Sleeping Indian—Simply Mystic **Mrs J. A. Niven**
8 **STORM FORCE ONE**, 4, b f Schiaparelli (GER)—Force In The Wings (IRE) **Hedley, Little, Sharkey & Tomkins**
9 **WARRIOR'S SPIRIT (IRE)**, 6, b g Requinto (IRE)—Sandbox Two (IRE) **Mr David John Lumley**
10 **WICKLOW WARRIOR**, 5, b g Sleeping Indian—Vale of Clara (IRE) **Mr P. D. Niven**

THREE-YEAR-OLDS

11 B f Nayef (USA)—Rock Candy (IRE) **Hedley, Little, Sharkey & Tomkins**

Other Owners: Angus Racing Club, S. J. Bowett, Clova Syndicate, Mr B. W. Ewart, Mr C. R. Hedley, Mr K. J. Little, Mrs J. A. Niven, Mr M. W. G. Niven, Mr P. D. Niven, Mrs K. M. Richardson, Mr W. K. D. Sharkey, Ms L. P. Tomkins.

---

407 ### MRS LUCY NORMILE, Glenfarg
Postal: Duncrievie, Glenfarg, Perthshire, PH2 9PD
Contacts: PHONE 01577 830330 MOBILE 07721 454818 FAX 01577 830658
EMAIL lucy@normileracing.co.uk WEBSITE www.normileracing.co.uk

1 **CURRAMORE (IRE)**, 6, br g Arcadio (GER)—Beale Native (IRE) **Mrs F. E. Bocker**
2 **DOYEN BREED (IRE)**, 5, ch g Doyen (IRE)—Sweet Empire (IRE) **Carnaby, Gabellone & Thomson**
3 **GRANITE CITY DOC**, 7, b g Arabian Gleam—Hansomis (IRE) **Corsby Racing**
4 **KARINGO**, 13, ch g Karinga Bay—Wild Happening (GER) **Douglas Black & P A Carnaby**
5 **LEWA HOUSE**, 4, b g Yeats (IRE)—Primrose Time **Mrs F. M. Whitaker**
6 5, B g Westerner—Primrose Time **Mrs F. M. Whitaker**
7 **REMEMBER ROCKY**, 11, ch g Haafhd—Flower Market **The Silver Tops**
8 **ROYAL COUNTESS**, 4, b f Coach House (IRE)—Dont Tell Nan **Mr S. W. Dick**
9 **ROYAL REGENT**, 8, b g Urgent Request (IRE)—Royal Citadel (IRE) **Mr S. W. Dick**
10 **SON OF FEYAN (IRE)**, 9, ch g Nayef (USA)—Miss Penton **Mrs L. B. Normile**
11 **SPACE SAFARI (FR)**, 7, b g Kapgarde (FR)—Prodiga (FR) **Mrs F. E. Bocker**
12 **STORM NELSON (IRE)**, 7, b g Gold Well—Dabiyra (IRE) **Mrs F. E. Bocker**
13 **ZAMARKHAN (FR)**, 7, b g Great Journey (JPN)—Zannkiya **Mrs F. E. Bocker**

TWO-YEAR-OLDS

14 **AIGHEAR**, b f 03/04 Farhh—Kabjoy
15 **ROYAL PRINCESS**, b f 10/04 Fountain of Youth—Royal Citadel

Other Owners: Mr D. M. Black, Mr P. Carnaby, Miss P. A. Carnaby, Mr M. Gabellone, B. Thomson.

Assistant Trainer: Libby Brodie.

---

408 ### MR JOHN NORTON, Barnsley
Postal: Globe Farm, High Hoyland, Barnsley, South Yorkshire, S75 4BE
Contacts: PHONE 01226 387633 MOBILE 07970 212707
EMAIL johnrnorton@hotmail.com WEBSITE www.johnrnortonracehorsetrainer.co.uk

1 **ALJUNOOD (IRE)**, 6, br g Bated Breath—Ataraxy **Jaffa Racing Syndicate**
2 **ALNEEL (IRE)**, 6, ch g New Approach (IRE)—Almass (IRE) **J. R. Norton Ltd**
3 **BLACK MARKET (IRE)**, 6, b g Yeats (IRE)—Aneda Dubh (IRE) **Fellowship Of The Rose Partnership 2**
4 **MAGIC SHIP (IRE)**, 5, b g Kodiac—Baltic Belle (IRE) **J. R. Norton Ltd**
5 **MUFTAKKER**, 6, gr g Tamayuz—Qertaas (IRE) **Colin Holder Racing**
6 **NAASIK**, 7, b g Poet's Voice—Shemriyna (IRE) **J. R. Norton Ltd**
7 **SPY FI**, 6, b m Dick Turpin (IRE)—Sindarbella **J. R. Norton Ltd**

THREE-YEAR-OLDS

8 **BEN LILLY (IRE)**, b g Gleneagles (IRE)—Aristocratic Lady (USA) **Jack Thomas & Ben Thomas**

Other Owners: Fellowship Of The Rose Partnership, Mr C. Holder, J. R. Norton Ltd, Mr B. M. Thomas, Mr J. F. Thomas, Mr P. R. Woodcock-Jones.

409 **MR A. P. O'BRIEN, Ballydoyle**
Postal: **Ballydoyle Stables, Cashel, Co. Tipperary, Ireland**
Contacts: **PHONE +353 62 62615**
EMAIL racingoffice@ballydoyle.com

1 **ANTHONY VAN DYCK (IRE)**, 4, b c Galileo (IRE)—Believe'n'succeed (AUS)
2 **BROOME (IRE)**, 4, b c Australia—Sweepstake (IRE)
3 **CIRCUS MAXIMUS (IRE)**, 4, b c Galileo (IRE)—Duntle (IRE)
4 **DELPHINIA (IRE)**, 4, b f Galileo (IRE)—Again (IRE)
5 **FLEETING (IRE)**, 4, b f Zoffany (IRE)—Azafata (SPA)
6 **JAPAN**, 4, b c Galileo (IRE)—Shastye (IRE)
7 **KEW GARDENS (IRE)**, 5, b h Galileo (IRE)—Chelsea Rose (IRE)
8 **LANCASTER HOUSE (IRE)**, 4, b c Galileo (IRE)—Quiet Oasis (IRE)
9 **MAGIC WAND (IRE)**, 5, b m Galileo (IRE)—Prudenzia (IRE)
10 **MAGICAL (IRE)**, 5, b m Galileo (IRE)—Halfway To Heaven (IRE)
11 **MOUNT EVEREST (IRE)**, 4, b c Galileo (IRE)—Six Perfections (FR)
12 **SERGEI PROKOFIEV (CAN)**, 4, b c Scat Daddy (USA)—Orchard Beach (CAN)
13 **SIR DRAGONET (IRE)**, 4, b c Camelot—Sparrow (IRE)
14 **SOVEREIGN (IRE)**, 4, ch c Galileo (IRE)—Devoted To You (IRE)
15 **WESTERN AUSTRALIA (IRE)**, 4, ch c Australia—What A Treasure (IRE)
16 **YALE (USA)**, 4, b c Scat Daddy (USA)—Risky Rachel (USA)

THREE-YEAR-OLDS
17 **AMHRAN NA BHFIANN (IRE)**, b c Galileo (IRE)—Alluring Park (IRE)
18 **ARIZONA (IRE)**, b br c No Nay Never (USA)—Lady Ederle (USA)
19 **ARMORY (IRE)**, b c Galileo (IRE)—After (IRE)
20 **ARTHUR'S KINGDOM (IRE)**, b c Camelot—Madeira Mist (IRE)
21 **BATTLE OF LIEGE (USA)**, b c War Front (USA)—Liscanna (IRE)
22 **BLISSFUL (IRE)**, b f Galileo (IRE)—Massarra
23 **CELTIC HIGH KING (IRE)**, b c Galileo (IRE)—Homecoming Queen (IRE)
24 **CHOCTAW RIDGE (IRE)**, ch c Galileo (IRE)—Sharp Lisa (USA)
25 **CLASS ACT**, b f Galileo (IRE)—Saphira's Fire (IRE)
26 **CORMORANT (IRE)**, gr c Kingman—Shemya (FR)
27 **COVENTRY (IRE)**, b c Galileo (IRE)—Moonstone
28 **DARKEST (IRE)**, b f Dark Angel (IRE)—Kelsey Rose
29 **DAWN PATROL (IRE)**, b c Galileo (IRE)—Gwynn (IRE)
30 **DAWN RISING (IRE)**, b c Galileo (IRE)—Devoted To You (IRE)
31 **DELPHI (IRE)**, b c Galileo (IRE)—Bye Bye Birdie (IRE)
32 **DELTA DAWN (IRE)**, b c Galileo (IRE)—Fire Lily (IRE)
33 **DIAMOND RING (IRE)**, b f Fastnet Rock (AUS)—Sleeveless (USA)
34 **EDEN QUAY (IRE)**, b f No Nay Never (USA)—Seeking Solace
35 **ELFIN QUEEN (USA)**, ch f American Pharoah (USA)—Pretty 'n Smart (USA)
36 **ELIZABETHOFARAGON (IRE)**, ch f Galileo (IRE)—Beltisaal (FR)
37 **EMERALD GREEN**, b f Galileo (IRE)—Applauded (IRE)
38 **ENNISTYMON (IRE)**, b f Galileo (IRE)—Lahinch (IRE)
39 **ETOILE (USA)**, b f War Front (USA)—Gagnoa (IRE)
40 **EVENING PRIMROSE (IRE)**, ch f Galileo (IRE)—Weekend Strike (USA)
41 **FORT MYERS (USA)**, b c War Front (USA)—Marvellous (IRE)
42 **GAUNTLET (IRE)**, b c Galileo (IRE)—Danedrop (IRE)
43 **GREEK GLADIATOR (IRE)**, b c Galileo (IRE)—Danehurst (IRE)
44 **GRENADINE (IRE)**, b f Galileo (IRE)—Words (IRE)
45 **HEAVEN OF HEAVENS (IRE)**, b f Galileo (IRE)—Halfway To Heaven (IRE)
46 **HOLY ROMAN EMPRESS (IRE)**, b f American Pharoah (USA)—Damson (IRE)
47 **HONG KONG (USA)**, gr ro c American Pharoah (USA)—Mekko Hokte (USA)
48 **IBERIA (IRE)**, b c Galileo (IRE)—Beauty Bright (IRE)
49 **INNISFREE (IRE)**, b c Galileo (IRE)—Palace (IRE)
50 **KEATS (IRE)**, b c Galileo (IRE)—Airwave
51 **KING OF ATHENS (USA)**, b c War Front (USA)—Together Forever (IRE)
52 **KIPLING (IRE)**, b c Galileo (IRE)—La Traviata (USA)
53 **KNIGHT OF MALTA (USA)**, b c War Front (USA)—Was (IRE)

MR A. P. O'BRIEN - continued

54 **LABURNUM (IRE),** b f Galileo (IRE)—Secret Garden (IRE)
55 **LOPE Y FERNANDEZ (IRE),** b c Lope de Vega (IRE)—Black Dahlia
56 **LOUISIANA (IRE),** b c Galileo (IRE)—Chintz (IRE)
57 **LOVE (IRE),** ch f Galileo (IRE)—Pikaboo
58 **LOVE BRACELET (USA),** b f War Front (USA)—Bracelet (IRE)
59 **LOVE LOCKET (IRE),** b f No Nay Never (USA)—Starlet (IRE)
60 **LOVELIER (IRE),** ch f Galileo (IRE)—Laddies Poker Two (IRE)
61 **MEETING (IRE),** gr f Galileo (IRE)—Manderley (IRE)
62 **MEMORABILIS (IRE),** b c Galileo (IRE)—Sent From Heaven (IRE)
63 **MOGUL,** b c Galileo (IRE)—Shastye (IRE)
64 **MONARCH OF EGYPT (USA),** b c American Pharoah (USA)—Up (IRE)
65 **MONDAY MONDAY (IRE),** br gr f Galileo (IRE)—Miarixa (FR)
66 **MONUMENT VALLEY (IRE),** ch c Galileo (IRE)—Ikat (IRE)
67 **MR TAMBOURINE MAN (IRE),** b c Galileo (IRE)—Snow Queen (IRE)
68 **MYTHIC (IRE),** b f Australia—Jamrah (IRE)
69 **MYTHICAL (FR),** b c Camelot—Inchmina
70 **NAPA VALLEY (IRE),** b c Galileo (IRE)—Kheleyf's Silver (IRE)
71 **NEW WORLD TAPESTRY (USA),** b c War Front (USA)—Tapestry (IRE)
72 **NOBEL PRIZE (IRE),** b c Galileo (IRE)—Hveger (AUS)
73 **NUMEN (IRE),** ch c Galileo (IRE)—Divine Proportions (USA)
74 **OHIO STATE (USA),** b br c War Front (USA)—Misty For Me (IRE)
75 **ORDER OF AUSTRALIA (IRE),** b c Australia—Senta's Dream
76 **PALM BEACH (IRE),** b c Galileo (IRE)—Alta Anna (FR)
77 **PARADISO (IRE),** ch br c Galileo (IRE)—Meow (IRE)
78 **PASSION (IRE),** b f Galileo (IRE)—Dialafara (FR)
79 **PEACEFUL (IRE),** b br f Galileo (IRE)—Missvinski (USA)
80 **PENDANT (IRE),** b f Galileo (IRE)—Penchant
81 **PERSIA (IRE),** b br c Galileo (IRE)—Just Pretending (USA)
82 **PISTOLETTO (USA),** b c War Front (USA)—Lerici (USA)
83 **PRECIOUS MOMENTS (IRE),** b f Gleneagles (IRE)—Tarbela (IRE)
84 **PROSE (IRE),** b f Galileo (IRE)—Naples Bay (USA)
85 **RAMESSES THE GREAT (USA),** b br c Pioneerof the Nile (USA)—Mythical Bride (USA)
86 **ROYAL DORNOCH (IRE),** b c Gleneagles (IRE)—Bridal Dance (IRE)
87 **ROYAL LYTHAM (FR),** b c Gleneagles (IRE)—Gotlandia (FR)
88 **RUSSIAN EMPEROR (IRE),** b c Galileo (IRE)—Atlantic Jewel (AUS)
89 **SALSA (IRE),** b f Galileo (IRE)—Beauty Is Truth (IRE)
90 **SAN PEDRO (IRE),** b c Gleneagles (IRE)—Elle Woods (IRE)
91 **SANTIAGO (IRE),** b c Authorized (IRE)—Wadyhatta
92 **SATIN AND SILK (IRE),** b f Galileo (IRE)—Wildwood Flower (USA)
93 **SERPENTINE (IRE),** ch c Galileo (IRE)—Remember When (IRE)
94 **SHOSHONE WARRIOR (IRE),** b c Galileo (IRE)—Runway Dancer
95 **SILVER FOX (IRE),** b c Galileo (IRE)—Mystical Lady (IRE)
96 **SNOW (IRE),** ch f Galileo (IRE)—Chelsea Rose (IRE)
97 **SO WONDERFUL (USA),** b f War Front (USA)—Wonder of Wonders (USA)
98 **SOUTHERN HILLS (IRE),** ch c Gleneagles (IRE)—Remember You (IRE)
99 **ST JAMES'S SQUARE (USA),** b br c War Front (USA)—Streaming (USA)
100 **TANGO (IRE),** b f No Nay Never (USA)—Idle Chatter (IRE)
101 **TIGER MOTH (IRE),** b c Galileo (IRE)—Lesson In Humility (IRE)
102 **TORONTO (IRE),** b c Galileo (IRE)—Mrs Marsh
103 **UNITED FRONT (USA),** b c War Front (USA)—Shell House (IRE)
104 **VATICAN CITY (IRE),** ch c Galileo (IRE)—You'resothrilling (USA)
105 **VERMILION CLIFFS (IRE),** ch c Galileo (IRE)—Gilt Edge Girl
106 **VICTORY MARCH (IRE),** b c Zoffany (IRE)—Seatone (USA)
107 **WAR LEADER (USA),** b c War Front (USA)—Sun Shower (IRE)
108 **WICHITA (IRE),** b c No Nay Never (USA)—Lumiere Noire (FR)
109 **YANKEE STADIUM (IRE),** b c Galileo (IRE)—Switch (USA)
110 **YEAR OF THE TIGER (IRE),** b c Galileo (IRE)—Tiggy Wiggy (IRE)

MR A. P. O'BRIEN - continued

TWO-YEAR-OLDS

111 B c 06/01 Galileo (IRE)—Absolutelyfabulous (IRE) (Mozart (IRE))
112 B f 02/04 Galileo (IRE)—Acapulco (USA) (Scat Daddy (USA))
113 Ch c 22/02 Galileo (IRE)—After (IRE) (Danehill Dancer (IRE))
114 B f 11/05 Galileo (IRE)—Again (IRE) (Danehill Dancer (IRE))
115 B c 08/04 Galileo (IRE)—Alta Anna (FR) (Anabaa (USA))
116 B c 26/01 Camelot—Ambitious Lady (Anabaa (USA)) (180000)
117 B c 20/05 Australia—Anna Karenina (IRE) (Green Desert (USA))
118 B c 02/02 Frankel—Auld Alliance (IRE) (Montjeu (IRE)) (700000)
119 B f 02/01 Galileo (IRE)—Awesome Maria (USA) (Maria's Mon (USA))
120 B f 23/02 Fastnet Rock (AUS)—Ballydoyle (IRE) (Galileo (IRE))
121 B f 09/02 Deep Impact (JPN)—Best In The World (IRE) (Galileo (IRE))
122 B br c 07/02 American Pharoah (USA)—Bon Jovi Girl (USA) (Malibu Moon (USA)) (706845)
123 B c 02/04 Galileo (IRE)—Bridal Dance (IRE) (Danehill Dancer (IRE))
124 B c 18/03 Siyouni (FR)—Cabaret (IRE) (Galileo (IRE)) (1300000)
125 B f 16/02 Galileo (IRE)—Chartreuse (IRE) (Lawman (FR))
126 B c 10/04 No Nay Never (USA)—Chasing Ice (IRE) (Duke of Marmalade (IRE)) (257400)
127 Ch c 13/04 Galileo (IRE)—Chelsea Rose (IRE) (Desert King (IRE))
128 B f 30/01 American Pharoah (USA)—Cherry Hinton (Green Desert (USA))
129 B f 10/02 Galileo (IRE)—Chintz (IRE) (Danehill Dancer (IRE))
130 B c 18/02 War Front (USA)—Coolmore (IRE) (Galileo (IRE))
131 B c 23/02 Galileo (IRE)—Daldiyna (FR) (Dansili)
132 B c 06/03 Galileo (IRE)—Dialafara (FR) (Anabaa (USA))
133 B c 06/04 Galileo (IRE)—Discreet Marq (USA) (Discreet Cat (USA))
134 B c 29/01 Air Force Blue (USA)—Dream The Blues (IRE) (Oasis Dream)
135 Ch c 15/03 The Gurkha (IRE)—Euphrasia (IRE) (Windsor Knot (IRE)) (223080)
136 B f 24/01 Galileo (IRE)—Even Song (IRE) (Mastercraftsman (IRE))
137 B c 26/02 Deep Impact (JPN)—Fluff (IRE) (Galileo (IRE))
138 B c 10/05 War Front (USA)—Found (IRE) (Galileo (IRE))
139 B c 17/01 Camelot—Frequential (Dansili)
140 Ch c 27/03 Australia—Gems (Haafhd) (450449)
141 B f 25/04 Galileo (IRE)—Green Room (USA) (Theatrical) (2574001)
142 B c 28/01 No Nay Never (USA)—High Savannah (IRE) (High Chaparral (IRE)) (188760)
143 B c 11/02 American Pharoah (USA)—Imagine (IRE) (Sadler's Wells (USA))
144 B c 13/01 Galileo (IRE)—Inca Princess (IRE) (Holy Roman Emperor (IRE))
145 B br c 22/03 Uncle Mo (USA)—Irish Lights (AUS) (Fastnet Rock (AUS)) (483630)
146 B c 20/02 Galileo (IRE)—La Traviata (USA) (Johannesburg (USA))
147 Gr c 06/05 Galileo (IRE)—Laddies Poker Two (IRE) (Choisir (AUS))
148 B c 30/01 The Gurkha (IRE)—Larceny (IRE) (Cape Cross (IRE)) (450450)
149 B f 05/05 No Nay Never (USA)—Lesson In Life (Duke of Marmalade (IRE)) (214500)
150 B f 05/02 Galileo (IRE)—Lillie Langtry (IRE) (Danehill Dancer (IRE))
151 B f 24/04 Zoffany (IRE)—Many Colours (Green Desert (USA)) (128700)
152 Ch c 20/05 Air Force Blue (USA)—Marylebone (USA) (Unbridled's Song (USA))
153 Ch f 15/05 Galileo (IRE)—Massarra (Danehill (USA))
154 B f 22/04 War Front (USA)—Maybe (IRE) (Galileo (IRE))
155 B c 16/02 Galileo (IRE)—Mecca's Angel (IRE) (Dark Angel (IRE))
156 B c 08/04 Galileo (IRE)—Miarixa (FR) (Linamix (FR))
157 B f 31/03 War Front (USA)—Misty For Me (IRE) (Galileo (IRE))
158 B c 31/01 No Nay Never (USA)—Mixfeeling (IRE) (Red Ransom (USA)) (260000)
159 Ch f 08/04 Galileo (IRE)—Moonstone (Dalakhani (IRE))
160 B c 01/01 No Nay Never (USA)—Morello (IRE) (Commands (AUS))
161 B c 30/04 Uncle Mo (USA)—Mythical Bride (USA) (Street Cry (IRE)) (316220)
162 B c 10/02 No Nay Never (USA)—Nasty Storm (USA) (Gulch (USA))
163 B c 23/03 Gleneagles (IRE)—Obama Rule (IRE) (Danehill Dancer (IRE)) (145860)
164 B c 05/04 Kingman—One Last Dance (AUS) (Encosta de Lago (AUS)) (1800000)
165 B c 01/01 No Nay Never (USA)—Painting (IRE) (Peintre Celebre (USA)) (257400)
166 B c 18/05 Galileo (IRE)—Palace (IRE) (Fastnet Rock (AUS))
167 Ch f 13/02 American Pharoah (USA)—Paradise Playgirl (USA) (Speightstown (USA)) (133928)
168 B br c 21/02 Pioneerof the Nile (USA)—Party Starter (USA) (Medaglia d'Oro (USA)) (186011)

MR A. P. O'BRIEN - continued

169 B f 01/03 The Gurkha (IRE)—Pearl Grey (Gone West (USA)) (214500)
170 B f 09/03 American Pharoah (USA)—Peeping Fawn (USA) (Danehill (USA))
171 B f 08/03 Le Havre (IRE)—Phiz (GER) (Galileo (IRE)) (825000)
172 Ch c 18/05 Galileo (IRE)—Polished Gem (IRE) (Danehill (USA))
173 B f 08/05 Australia—Potion (Pivotal) (240240)
174 B c 16/02 American Pharoah (USA)—Rather Special (IRE) (Galileo (IRE))
175 B f 05/05 Galileo (IRE)—Red Evie (IRE) (Intikhab (USA))
176 Ch c 09/05 Galileo (IRE)—Remember When (IRE) (Danehill Dancer (IRE))
177 B c 14/03 Air Force Blue (USA)—Secret Charm (IRE) (Green Desert (USA)) (214500)
178 B f 12/03 Camelot—Senta's Dream (Danehill (USA))
179 B c 11/03 Kingman—Shamandar (FR) (Exceed And Excel (AUS)) (419047)
180 B c 11/03 Camelot—Simply A Star (IRE) (Giant's Causeway (USA))
181 B c 24/02 Camelot—Sparrow (IRE) (Oasis Dream)
182 B f 11/05 Galileo (IRE)—Sumora (IRE) (Danehill (USA))
183 B c 09/02 American Pharoah (USA)—Super Majesty (USA) (Super Saver (USA)) (595238)
184 **SWISS ACE**, b c 11/02 Kingman—Swiss Lake (USA) (Indian Ridge) (400000)
185 B c 08/02 War Front (USA)—Together Forever (IRE) (Galileo (IRE))
186 B c 01/04 Pioneerof the Nile (USA)—Up (IRE) (Galileo (IRE)) (744047)
187 B c 23/03 Camelot—Venus de Milo (IRE) (Duke of Marmalade (IRE))
188 B c 05/02 American Pharoah (USA)—Wading (USA) (Montjeu (IRE))
189 B f 20/04 Frankel—Wadyhatta (Cape Cross (IRE)) (850000)
190 Ch c 23/03 No Nay Never (USA)—Winning Sequence (FR) (Zafonic (USA)) (900000)
191 B f 04/02 Galileo (IRE)—You'resothrilling (USA) (Storm Cat (USA))

---

410 | MR DANIEL O'BRIEN, Tonbridge
Postal: **Knowles Bank, Capel, Tonbridge, Kent, TN11 0PU**
Contacts: **PHONE 01892 824072**

1 BOSTIN (IRE), 12, ch g Busy Flight—Bustingoutallover (USA) **D. C. O'Brien**
2 CABERNET D'ALENE (FR), 8, b g Day Flight—Haifa du Noyer (FR) **D. C. O'Brien**
3 CANTOR, 12, b g Iceman—Choir Mistress **D. C. O'Brien**
4 GOLD MERLION (IRE), 7, b m Alhaarth (IRE)—Sea of Time (USA) **D. C. O'Brien**

Assistant Trainer: Christopher O'Bryan.

NH Jockey: Mattie Batchelor, Sam Twiston-Davies.

---

411 | MR FERGAL O'BRIEN, Cheltenham
Postal: **Upper Yard, Grange Hill Farm, Naunton, Cheltenham, Gloucestershire, GL54 3AY**
Contacts: PHONE **01451 850538** MOBILE **07771 702829**
EMAIL admin@fergalobrienracing.com

1 4, B g Kayf Tara—Aeronautica (IRE) **Mrs C. Kendrick**
2 AGENT VALDEZ, 7, b m Arvico (FR)—Soleil Sauvage **The FOB Racing Partnership 6**
3 ASK A HONEY BEE (IRE), 6, b g Ask—Pure Honey (IRE) **Lewis, Lawson and Hope**
4 ASK DILLON (IRE), 7, b g Ask—Mum's Miracle (IRE) **4 The Fun Partnership**
5 AYE AYE CHARLIE, 8, b g Midnight Legend—Trial Trip **All Four One**
6 BALLYHOME (IRE), 9, b g Westerner—Nostra (FR) **A & K Ecofilm Ltd**
7 BELLE AMIS, 7, ch m Black Sam Bellamy (IRE)—Amaretto Rose **Peter Hockenhull & Don't Tell the Missus**
8 BENECHENKO (IRE), 8, br g Beneficial—Beann Ard (IRE) **Keeping The Dream Alive**
9 BENNY'S BRIDGE (IRE), 7, b g Beneficial—Wattle Bridge (IRE) **Biddestone Racing I**
10 BEYOND THE PALE (IRE), 5, b g Shirocco (GER)—Miss Mary Mac (IRE) **Mr F. M. O'Brien**
11 BLUE MONDAY (IRE), 7, b g Beneficial—Bradbury Baby (IRE) **The FOB Racing Partnership 5**
12 BOLD RED, 4, ch g Dunaden (FR)—Bold Tara **Mrs Anne Lee-Warner**
13 BRIEF AMBITION, 6, b g Yeats (IRE)—Kentucky Sky **C Coley, D Porter, H Redknapp, P Smith**
14 BUTTE MONTANA, 5, b g Presenting—My Cool Lady (IRE) **Mr T. Crowe**
15 CAGE OF FEAR (IRE), 6, b g Milan—Baile An Droichid (IRE) **Five Go Racing**

MR FERGAL O'BRIEN - continued

16 **CAP SOLEIL (FR)**, 7, b m Kapgarde (FR)—Move Again (FR) **Mrs S. A. Noott**
17 **CARROLLS MILAN (IRE)**, 7, b m Milan—Native Crystal (IRE) **The Gud Times Partnership**
18 **CHAMPAGNE WELL (IRE)**, 7, b g Gold Well—Perkanod (IRE) **The Bolly Champagne Crew**
19 **CITY DERBY (IRE)**, 4, ch g Ask—Reine d'Or (IRE) **Richard D A Hames & Walter O'Connor**
20 **COOL DESTINATION (IRE)**, 7, ch g Dubai Destination (USA)—
Coolafancy (IRE) **Nautilus, Mennell, Logan and Partner**
21 **COOLANLY (IRE)**, 8, b g Flemensfirth (USA)—La Fisarmonica (IRE) **Five Go Racing**
22 **COURTANDBOULD (IRE)**, 6, b g Court Cave (IRE)—Seaneen Mac Ri (IRE) **Craig & Laura Buckingham**
23 **CROSSGALESFAMEGAME (IRE)**, 6, b m Mahler—Fame Forever (IRE) **Walid Marzouk & Richard Rowland**
24 **DAN GUN (IRE)**, 6, b g Intikhab (USA)—Lady Magdalena (IRE) **Mr F. M. O'Brien**
25 **DE NAME EVADES ME (IRE)**, 8, b g Vinnie Roe (IRE)—Sound of The Crowd (IRE) **Brown Campbell James Foylan**
26 **DIAMOND FORT (IRE)**, 8, ch g Gamut (IRE)—Ellie Forte **D. J. Shorey**
27 **DIV INE TARA**, 5, b m Kayf Tara—Mid Div And Creep **Mrs K Exall & Mr G Molen**
28 **DREAMING OF GLORY (IRE)**, 4, b f Fame And Glory—Dream Function (IRE) **C. B. Brookes**
29 **FEEL THE PINCH**, 6, b g Librettist (USA)—Liqueur Rose **Miss S. Randell**
30 **FORTHEGREATERGOOD (IRE)**, 6, b m Yeats (IRE)—Feast Or Famine (IRE) **Mrs J. A. Watts**
31 **GENIAL HAWKSTONE (FR)**, 4, b f Cokoriko (FR)—Silane (FR) **Mrs S. A. Noott**
32 **GINO TRAIL (IRE)**, 13, br g Perugino (USA)—Borough Trail (IRE) **Mrs J. Smith**
33 **GLOBAL FAME (IRE)**, 6, b g Fame And Glory—Kinard True (IRE) **Chris Coley, Lord Vestey & ROA Arkle**
34 **GLOBAL TOUR (IRE)**, 7, b g Arakan (USA)—Galant Tour (USA) **Dr S. T. Gillson**
35 **GOLDEN TAIPAN (IRE)**, 6, b g Golden Lariat (USA)—Rose of Taipan (IRE) **Double Barrels Of Courage**
36 **GOOD AND HARDY (IRE)**, 7, b g Westerner—Kilganey Maid (IRE) **The Groovy Gang**
37 **GOODBYE DANCER (FR)**, 9, b g Dragon Dancer—Maribia Bella (FR) **Noel Fehily Racing Syndicate 01**
38 **GRAGELAGH GIRL (IRE)**, 9, b m Craigsteel—Smiths Lady (IRE) **C. S. J. Coley**
39 **HEAVENLY PROMISE (IRE)**, 9, ch m Presenting—Ambrosia's Promise (IRE) **Mr D. Brace**
40 **HIT THE BOTTLE**, 5, ch m Malinas (GER)—Ruby Magern **Mr F. M. O'Brien**
41 **HUNNY MOON**, 6, ch m Flemensfirth (USA)—No More Money **C. B. Brookes**
42 **HURRICANE HARVEY**, 6, b g Doyen (IRE)—Camp Fire (IRE) **Walid Marzouk & Richard Rowland**
43 **I'M WISER NOW (IRE)**, 6, b g Presenting—Reine Angevine (FR) **Mr J. C. Collett**
44 **IMPERIAL ALCAZAR (IRE)**, 6, b g Vinnie Roe (IRE)—Maddy's Supreme (IRE) **Imperial Racing Partnership 2016**
45 **IMPERIAL ELYSIAN (IRE)**, 6, ch g Kalanisi (IRE)—Diva Antonia (IRE) **Imperial Racing Partnership**
46 **JARVEYS PLATE (IRE)**, 7, ch g Getaway (GER)—She's Got To Go (IRE) **The Yes No Wait Sorries & Mr Chris Coley**
47 **KARL PHILIPPE (FR)**, 5, ch g Kentucky Dynamite (USA)—Kaer Gwell (FR) **Mr & Mrs Paul & Clare Rooney**
48 **LIES ABOUT MILAN (IRE)**, 9, b g Milan—The Millers Tale (IRE) **D. J. Shorey**
49 **LIOSDUIN BHEARNA (IRE)**, 7, b g Beneficial—Cloth Fair (IRE) **The FOB Racing Partnership 4**
50 **LORD OF THE ISLAND (IRE)**, 12, b g Heron Island (IRE)—Miss Morose (IRE) **The 'Lord Of The Island' Syndicate**
51 **LOUGH HAR (IRE)**, 6, b g Doyen (IRE)—Time To Act **Mr H. M. Posner**
52 **LUNGARNO PALACE (USA)**, 9, b g Henrythenavigator (USA)—Good Time Sally (USA) **Caveat Emptor Partnership**
53 **MERRY BERRY**, 4, b f Malinas (GER)—Mayberry **Miss S. Pilkington**
54 **MILANESE ROSE (IRE)**, 4, gr f Milan—Ma Furie (FR)
55 **MINELLA TARA (IRE)**, 5, b g Kayf Tara—Jolie Landaise (FR) **Graham & Alison Jelley**
56 **MOUNT BATUR (IRE)**, 7, ch g Mahler—Massini's Daughter (IRE) **Geoffrey & Donna Keeys**
57 **MRS HYDE (IRE)**, 7, b m Flemensfirth (USA)—Funny Times **The Jekyll**
58 **OCEAN COVE (IRE)**, 8, ch g Ask—Sand Eel (IRE) **The FOB Racing Partnership**
59 **OSCAR ROSE (IRE)**, 8, b m Oscar (IRE)—Ben Roseler (IRE) **Mrsk.Exall/Thegeneralasphaltecompanyltd**
60 **OSKI (IRE)**, 8, b g Oscar (IRE)—Mossville (FR) **Mrs C. Kendrick**
61 **PAINT THE DREAM**, 6, b g Brian Boru—Vineuil (FR) **Mr D. Brace**
62 **PEKING ROSE**, 5, br g Passing Glance—Miniature Rose **The Coln Valley Partnership**
63 **PERFECT CANDIDATE (IRE)**, 13, b g Winged Love (IRE)—Dansana (IRE) **ISL Recruitment**
64 **PETITE POWER (IRE)**, 11, b g Subtle Power (IRE)—Little Serena **P J King & Son**
65 **PHOENICIAN STAR (IRE)**, 5, ch g Mastercraftsman (IRE)—Place de L'Etoile (IRE) **The FOB Racing Partnership 2**
66 **POETIC RHYTHM (IRE)**, 9, b g Flemensfirth (USA)—
Sommer Sonnet (IRE) **The Yes No Wait Sorries & Mr Chris Coley**
67 **POLISH**, 5, b g Teofilo (IRE)—Polygon (USA) **Caveat Emptor Partnership**
68 **PRIDE OF LECALE (IRE)**, 9, b g Multiplex—Rock Gossip (IRE) **Noel Fehily Racing Syndicate 01**
69 **PROJECT MARS (IRE)**, 8, b g Presenting—Molly Massini (IRE) **The FOB Racing Partnership 9**
70 **PROPER TICKET (IRE)**, 7, b m Gold Well—Strand Lady (IRE) **The FOB Racing Partnership 8**
71 **QUANTUM OF SOLACE**, 10, b m Kayf Tara—Fashion House **007 Partnership**
72 **QUICK GRABIM (IRE)**, 8, b g Oscar (IRE)—Top Her Up (IRE) **Mrs G. S. Worcester**

MR FERGAL O'BRIEN - continued

73 **REBEL REBELLO (IRE)**, 4, ch g Flemensfirth (USA)—Bachello (IRE) **The Sandbaggers Club**
74 **RIGHT DESTINATION (IRE)**, 6, b g Dubai Destination (USA)—Sainte Careigne (FR) **C. S. J. Coley**
75 **ROBYNDZONE (IRE)**, 6, b g Frammassone (IRE)—Rebecca Susan **East India Racing**
76 **SAINTBURY LADY**, 6, b m Kayf Tara—Miss Flower Girl **Mr D. W. Pocock**
77 **SEE FOREVER (IRE)**, 6, gr m Stowaway—Flaming Poncho **Mr N. D. Wellington**
78 **SILVER HALLMARK**, 6, br gr g Shirocco (GER)—Gaye Sophie **Mr & Mrs William Rucker**
79 **STONER'S CHOICE**, 5, br g Great Pretender (IRE)—High Benefit (IRE) **Mrs C. Kendrick**
80 **TEMPLEPARK**, 7, b g Phoenix Reach (IRE)—Kenny's Dream **Mrs C. Kendrick**
81 **TEQUILA BLAZE**, 6, b m Sakhee (USA)—Miss Sassi **Ann Selsby, Chris Riley & Mike Wheeler**
82 **THEGALLANTWAY (IRE)**, 7, b g Stowaway—Imogens Fancy (IRE) **Caveat Emptor Partnership**
83 **TIME TO MOVE ON (IRE)**, 7, ch g Flemensfirth (USA)—Kapricia Speed (FR) **Mr & Mrs Paul & Clare Rooney**
84 **TOTTERDOWN**, 9, b g Pasternak—Yeldham Lady **Fairford Goes Racing**
85 **TRIOPAS (IRE)**, 8, b g Stowaway—Aine Dubh (IRE) **P J King & Son**
86 **TROUBLED SOUL (IRE)**, 11, ch m Definite Article—Dorrha Lass (IRE) **Mr F. M. O'Brien**
87 **UNE DE LA SENIERE (FR)**, 5, ch m Noroit (GER)—Smabelle (FR) **Millennium Racing Club**
88 **VERY LIVE (FR)**, 11, b g Secret Singer (FR)—Iona Will (FR) **Miss S. Randell**
89 4, B f Kayf Tara—West River (USA) **Blue StaRR Racing FOB**
90 **YAUTHYM (GER)**, 4, b f Authorized (IRE)—Ymlaen (IRE) **The Oakley Partnership**

THREE-YEAR-OLDS

91 Ch g Black Sam Bellamy (IRE)—Kansas City (FR) **Mr P. E. Smith**

Other Owners: Mr R. H. Beevor, Sir M. F. Broughton, Mr C. Buckingham, Mrs L. K. Buckingham, Mr D. J. Burke, C. S. J. Coley, Mr M. Costello, Don't Tell The Missus Partnership, Mrs K. G. Exall, Mr R. D. A. Hames, P.D. Hockenhull, Mrs A. D. Jelley, G. S. Jelley, Mrs N. Jones, Mrs S. H. Jones, Mrs C. M. Keeys, G. F. Keeys, Mr J. King, Mrs V. C. King, Mr J. B. Lawson, Mr W. Marzouk, Mr G. Molen, Mr W. O'Connor, Mr C. H. Plumb, Miss S. Randell, Dr R. N. Rowland, Mr N. J. Statham, The General Asphalte Company Ltd, The Yes No Wait Sorries, Mr M. A. W. Thompson, Mr M. K. Warren, Mrs R. B. Weaver, Mr R. Williams, T. C. Wilson.

Assistant Trainer: Sally Randell.

NH Jockey: Connor Brace, Paddy Brennan.

412

MR JEDD O'KEEFFE, Leyburn
Postal: **Highbeck Lodge, Brecongill, Coverham, Leyburn, North Yorkshire, DL8 7TJ**
Contacts: **PHONE 01969 640330 MOBILE 07710 476705**
EMAIL jedd@jeddokeefferacing.co.uk WEBSITE www.jeddokeefferacing.co.uk

1 **AEGEUS (USA)**, 4, b g First Defence (USA)—Supposition **Quantum**
2 **AIR RAID**, 5, b g Raven's Pass (USA)—Siren Sound **Caron & Paul Chapman**
3 **ARCHAEOLOGY**, 4, b g Charm Spirit (IRE)—Shuttle Mission **Quantum**
4 **BREANSKI**, 6, b g Delegator—Jubilee **Quantum**
5 **CALL ME FREDDIE**, 5, ch g Black Sam Bellamy (IRE)—Still Runs Deep **Caron & Paul Chapman**
6 **DEVIL'S ANGEL**, 4, gr g Dark Angel (IRE)—Rocking The Boat (IRE) **Mr J. E. Dance**
7 **ECHO (IRE)**, 5, b g Zoffany (IRE)—Aweebounce (IRE) **Miss S.E. Hall & Mr C. Platts**
8 **FAIRFIELD FERRATA**, 4, b f Kayf Tara—Via Ferrata (FR) **Mrs J. A. Darling**
9 **FLAVIUS TITUS**, 5, ch g Lethal Force (IRE)—Furbelow **Titanium Racing Club**
10 **GLORIOUS JEM**, 5, b g Helmet (AUS)—Polar Jem **Norcroft Park Stud**
11 **GROVEMAN**, 5, b g Holy Roman Emperor (IRE)—Raving Monsun **Quantum**
12 **INSTANT ATTRACTION (IRE)**, 9, b g Tagula (IRE)—Coup de Coeur (IRE) **J. E. D. O'Keeffe**
13 **IT HAD TO BE YOU**, 4, b g Frankel—Fallen For You **Normandie Stud Ltd**
14 **JEDHI**, 5, b m Big Bad Bob (IRE)—Capriolla **Quantum**
15 **KALL TO ALMS**, 4, b g Dick Turpin (IRE)—Lady Amakhala **Mrs S. Pearson**
16 **KIEFER**, 4, gr g Pour Moi (IRE)—Dali's Grey **Quantum**
17 **MIAH GRACE**, 5, b m Malinas (GER)—Silver Gypsy (IRE) **Caron & Paul Chapman**
18 **MISS LAMB**, 4, b f Passing Glance—Lucinda Lamb **Miss S. E. Hall**
19 **MOGSY (IRE)**, 4, br g Dandy Man (IRE)—Dictatrice (FR) **Quantum**
20 **MR SCRUMPY**, 6, b g Passing Glance—Apple Days **Mr H. M. Posner**

MR JEDD O'KEEFFE - continued

21 **ONLY SPOOFING (IRE)**, 6, b g Approve (IRE)—Golden Anthem (USA) **Mrs H Mannion Mr B Carter Mr F Durbin**
22 **ORBURSTOCK (IRE)**, 5, b g Millenary—Auction Girl (IRE) **The Ordynary Folk**
23 **PIEDITA (IRE)**, 6, b m Authorized (IRE)—Archina (IRE) **Stoneleigh Racing**
24 **RARE GROOVE (IRE)**, 5, ch h Lope de Vega (IRE)—Ascot Lady (IRE) **Mr J. E. Dance**
25 **REBEL STATE (IRE)**, 7, b g Zoffany (IRE)—Stately Princess **J. E. D. O'Keeffe**
26 **REMEMBER THE DAYS (IRE)**, 6, b g Kyllachy—Pointed Arch (IRE) **Ingham Racing Syndicate**
27 **SAISONS D'OR (IRE)**, 5, ro g Havana Gold (IRE)—Deux Saisons **The Fatalists**
28 **SAM SPINNER**, 8, b g Black Sam Bellamy (IRE)—Dawn Spinner **Caron & Paul Chapman**
29 **SEVEN FOR A POUND (USA)**, 4, b g Scat Daddy (USA)—Gimlet Witha Twist (USA) **Mr E. Broadwith**
30 **SOPHIA MARIA**, 4, b f Swiss Spirit—Malelane (IRE) **W A Tunstall & Son**
31 **SWEET DIME**, 4, b br f Toronado (IRE)—Rainbow's Edge **Miss S. E. Hall, Miss M. A. Thompson**
32 **TAVUS (IRE)**, 4, b g Pour Moi (IRE)—La Persiana **Quantum**
33 **THEATRO (IRE)**, 4, b f Camelot—Bogside Theatre (IRE) **Mr & Mrs G. Turnbull**
34 **TURN TO ROCK (IRE)**, 4, ch g Slade Power (IRE)—Pivotal's Princess (IRE) **Quantum**

THREE-YEAR-OLDS

35 **BALANCING ACT (IRE)**, ch f No Nay Never (USA)—My Lass **Mr J. E. Dance**
36 **BRASINGAMANBELLAMY**, b g Black Sam Bellamy (IRE)—Brasingaman Hifive **Mr R. Morgan**
37 **CONTINENTAL**, b f Acclamation—Swiss Kiss **Mr J. E. Dance**
38 **DREAM TOGETHER (IRE)**, ch g Dream Ahead (USA)—Shamsalmaidan (IRE) **The Fatalists**
39 **HIGH MOOR FLYER**, b f Pour Moi (IRE)—A Media Luz (FR) **Mrs J. A. Darling**
40 **ISOLA BELLA MAY (IRE)**, b f Free Eagle (USA)—Heart of Hearts **Mr B. McAllister & Mr A. Walker**
41 **KENDRED SOUL (IRE)**, ch f Kendargent (FR)—Champion Place **Yorkshire Owners Racing Club 1**
42 **ONLY ALONE (IRE)**, b f Starspangledbanner (AUS)—Only Together (IRE) **Mr & Mrs G. Turnbull**
43 Gr g Gutaifan (IRE)—Peace Talks **Mr K. Everitt**
44 **PHILOSOPHICAL**, ch g Mukhadram—Incarnation (IRE) **Highbeck Racing 5**
45 **QUEEN OF CAMELOT (IRE)**, b f Camelot—Bogside Theatre (IRE) **Mr & Mrs G. Turnbull**
46 **REGGINO (FR)**, b g Farhh—Musikhani **Mr J. E. Dance**
47 **SALSADA (IRE)**, ch f Mukhadram—Mokaraba **Mr & Mrs G. Turnbull**
48 **STRAIT OF HORMUZ (IRE)**, b g Sir Percy—Sliabh Luachra (IRE) **Quantum**
49 B f Free Eagle (IRE)—Tartessian (IRE) **Kildaragh Stud**
50 **UNBREAKABLE**, b c Stimulation (IRE)—Private Dancer (FR) **Mr J. E. Dance**
51 **WRITTEN BROADCAST (IRE)**, gr g Gutaifan (IRE)—Teeline (IRE) **Quantum**

TWO-YEAR-OLDS

52 B c 29/01 Bobby's Kitten (USA)—Aseela (IRE) (Teofilo (IRE)) **Mr & Mrs G. Turnbull**
53 **COLTON**, gr c 08/03 Lethal Force (IRE)—Lady Poppy (Kyllachy) **Mr T. S. Ingham & Mrs Liz Ingham**
54 B f 18/02 Mukhadram—Hazy Dancer (Oasis Dream) (25000) **Highbeck Racing 3**
55 Ch c 16/03 Bated Breath—Novellara (Sadler's Wells (USA)) (20000) **Highbeck Racing 2**
56 B f 27/01 Gutaifan (IRE)—Odyssee (FR) (Teofilo (IRE)) (15443) **Mr H. Alexander, Mr D. Powell**
57 B g 04/02 Helmet (AUS)—Random (Shamardal (USA)) (7619) **Highbeck Racing 4**
58 B c 11/04 Nathaniel (IRE)—Riot of Colour (Excellent Art) (11000) **Highbeck Racing 1**
59 B f 16/02 Acclamation—Shuttlecock (Dubawi (IRE)) **Mr & Mrs G. Turnbull**
60 B f 16/02 Flintshire—Spinamiss (IRE) (Lilbourne Lad (IRE)) (57142) **The City & Provincial Partnership**
61 B c 23/01 Sepoy (AUS)—Spirit of Sound (FR) (Invincible Spirit (IRE)) **The City & Provincial Partnership**
62 B c 28/03 War Command (USA)—Storming Sioux (Storming Home) **Mr & Mrs G. Turnbull**

Other Owners: Mr B. Carter, Mr D. G. Colledge, Mr F. C. Durbin, Mr M. Edwards, Mrs T. Edwards, Miss S. E. Hall, Highbeck Racing, Highbeck Racing 3, Mrs M. E. Ingham, Mr T. S. Ingham, Mrs H. Mannion, Mr B. McAllister, Mr M. D. Parker, Colin Platts, Titanium Racing, United We Stand, A. Walker.

Assistant Trainer: Tim Hogg, Leanne Kershaw.

Apprentice Jockey: Owen Payton.

413 MR DAVID O'MEARA, Upper Helmsley

Postal: Willow Farm, Upper Helmsley, York, Yorkshire, YO41 1JX
Contacts: PHONE 01759 372427 MOBILE 07747 825418
EMAIL info@davidomeara.co.uk WEBSITE www.davidomeara.co.uk

1 ABEL HANDY (IRE), 5, b g Arcano (IRE)—Belle Isle **Mr F. Gillespie**
2 AMJAADY (USA), 4, b g War Front (USA)—Prize Catch (USA) **Thoroughbred British Racing**
3 AMLIBA, 4, b f Mayson—Hisaronu (IRE) **Diamond Racing Ltd**
4 ANYTHINGTODAY (IRE), 6, b g Zoffany (IRE)—Corking (IRE) **Woodhurst Construction Ltd**
5 ARBALET (IRE), 4, gr g Dark Angel (IRE)—Miss Beatrix (IRE) **Withernsea Thoroughbred Limited**
6 ARECIBO (FR), 5, b g Invincible Spirit (IRE)—Oceanique (USA) **Mr George Turner & Clipper Logistics**
7 BALTIC BARON (IRE), 5, b g Shamardal (USA)—Born Wild (GER) **Mr & Mrs G. Turnbull**
8 BERYL THE PETAL (IRE), 4, b f Dandy Man (IRE)—
Pinewoods Lily (IRE) **N D Crummack Ltd & A Rhodes & Partner**
9 BETSEY TROTTER (IRE), 5, b m Camacho—Inourthoughts (IRE) **Mr F. Gillespie**
10 BLONDE WARRIOR (IRE), 4, ch g Zoffany (IRE)—Dame Blanche (IRE) **Mrs F. J. Carmichael**
11 COLD STARE (IRE), 5, b g Intense Focus (USA)—Ziria (IRE) **Middleham Park Racing XC**
12 CONFIDE, 4, b g Lope de Vega (IRE)—Confidential Lady **Cheveley Park Stud Limited**
13 CONSTANT, 4, ch g Dutch Art—West of The Moon **Gallop Racing**
14 COURTSIDE (FR), 5, ch g Siyouni (FR)—Memoire (FR) **Mr E. M. Sutherland**
15 CUSTOM CUT (IRE), 11, b g Notnowcato—Polished Gem (IRE) **Frank Gillespie & Pat Breslin**
16 DANCING RAVE, 4, b f Coach House (IRE)—Right Rave (IRE) **David Lumley & Partner**
17 ELECTOR, 5, b g Dansili—Enticement **Withernsea & Woodhurst Ltd**
18 ESCOBAR (IRE), 6, b g Famous Name—Saying Grace (IRE) **Withernsea Thoroughbred Limited**
19 FASTMAN (IRE), 4, br g Elzaam (AUS)—Manalisa (IRE) **Mr C. J. Miller**
20 FIRMAMENT, 8, b g Cape Cross (IRE)—Heaven Sent **Gallop Racing**
21 FLAMMARION (GER), 4, b g Sea The Moon (GER)—Favorite (GER) **Godolphin Management Company Ltd**
22 FRANKUUS (IRE), 6, gr g Frankel—Dookus (IRE) **Mr H. A. Lootah**
23 FUNNY MAN, 4, b g Distorted Humor (USA)—Midnight Thoughts (USA) **Apple Tree Stud**
24 GULLIVER, 6, b g Sayif (IRE)—Sweet Coincidence **Withernsea Thoroughbred Limited**
25 HARD SOLUTION, 4, ch g Showcasing—Copy-Cat **Rasio Cymru Racing 1 & Partner**
26 HIGHLAND ACCLAIM (IRE), 9, b g Acclamation—Emma's Star (ITY) **Mr E. M. Sutherland**
27 HORTZADAR (IRE), 5, b g Sepoy (AUS)—Clouds of Magellan (USA) **Akela Construction Ltd**
28 HUMBERT (IRE), 6, b g Kodiac—Fee Eria (FR) **Woodhurst Construction Ltd**
29 INGLEBY HOLLOW, 8, ch g Beat Hollow—Mistress Twister **Dave Scott & The Fallen Angels**
30 INTISAAB, 9, b g Elnadim (USA)—Katoom (IRE) **Mr S. M. Graham**
31 KING OF TONGA (IRE), 4, gr g Dark Angel (IRE)—Bronze Queen (IRE) **Middleham Park Racing LXV**
32 LAMLOOM (IRE), 6, b g Cape Cross (IRE)—Lulua (USA) **Mr H. R. Bin Ghedayer**
33 LAUBALI, 3, ch g Kyllachy—Different **Mrs F. Denniff**
34 LEODIS DREAM (IRE), 4, b g Dandy Man (IRE)—Paddy Again (IRE) **Andrew Kendall-jones I**
35 LIAMBA, 5, b m Equiano (IRE)—Hisaronu (IRE) **Diamond Racing Ltd**
36 LORD GLITTERS (FR), 7, gr ro g Whipper (USA)—Lady Glitters (FR) **Mr & Mrs G. Turnbull**
37 MARKAZI (FR), 6, gr g Dark Angel (IRE)—Marasima (IRE) **Thoroughbred British Racing**
38 MUSCIKA, 6, b g Kyllachy—Miss Villefranche **Gallop Racing & Dynast Racing**
39 NORDIC FIRE, 4, b g Dream Ahead (USA)—Nordic Spruce (USA) **Withernsea Thoroughbred & Kevin Bailey**
40 OLLIVANDER (IRE), 4, b g Heeraat (IRE)—Coy (IRE) **Diamond Racing & Partner 2**
41 ORBAAN, 5, b g Invincible Spirit (IRE)—Contradict **JCG Chua & CK Ong**
42 RGEEBEE, 4, b f Showcasing—Milford Sound **Rubix Properties**
43 SEGARELLI (IRE), 4, ch g Sea The Stars (IRE)—Samba Brazil (GER) **Northern Monkeys**
44 SHELIR (IRE), 4, b gr g Dark Angel (IRE)—Shelina (IRE) **Akela Construction Ltd**
45 SO BELOVED, 10, b g Dansili—Valencia **Thoroughbred British Racing**
46 STAR SHIELD, 5, b g Helmet (AUS)—Perfect Star **Middleham Park Racing XXIX**
47 STONIFIC (IRE), 7, b g Sea The Stars (IRE)—Sapphire Pendant (IRE) **Rasio Cymru 1 & Hurn Racing Club**
48 SUEDOIS (IRE), 9, b br g Le Havre (IRE)—Cup Cake (IRE) **Mr George Turner & Clipper Logistics**
49 SUMMERGHAND (IRE), 6, b g Lope de Vega (IRE)—Kate The Great **Mr H. R. Bin Ghedayer**
50 SUPERYACHT (IRE), 7, b g Fastnet Rock (AUS)—Olympienne (IRE) **Mrs D. E. H. Turner**
51 TABAAHY, 5, b g Kyllachy—Pious **Rasio Cymru Racing 1**
52 THREE SAINTS BAY (IRE), 5, b g Kodiac—Fiuise (IRE) **Mr G. J. Douglas**
53 TINANDALI (IRE), 4, b g Oasis Dream—Timarwa (IRE) **South Yorkshire Building Solutions Ltd**
54 TUKHOOM (IRE), 7, b g Acclamation—Carioca (IRE) **Mr R. B. Bremer**

MR DAVID O'MEARA - continued

55 **VENTURA ROYAL (IRE)**, 5, ch m Teofilo (IRE)—Ermine And Velvet **Middleham Park Racing CXVII**
56 **WAARIF (IRE)**, 7, b g Arcano (IRE)—Indian Belle (IRE) **Middleham Park Racing XLIX**
57 **WATCHABLE**, 10, ch g Pivotal—Irresistible **Hambleton XXXIX, P Bamford, Roses Partners**
58 **YOUNG FIRE (FR)**, 5, b g Fuisse (FR)—Young Majesty (USA) **Mr E. M. Sutherland**

THREE-YEAR-OLDS

59 **AUGUSTUS CAESAR (USA)**, ch c Speightstown (USA)—Endless Light **Mr P. J. Gallagher**
60 **DAZZLING DES (IRE)**, b g Brazen Beau (AUS)—Secret Liaison (IRE) **Mr E. M. Sutherland**
61 **DICK DATCHERY (IRE)**, b g Make Believe—Bayja (IRE) **Mr F. Gillespie**
62 **EAGLE COURT (IRE)**, b g Free Eagle (IRE)—Classic Remark (IRE) **Brook Farm Bloodstock**
63 **ESSENCE**, ch f Le Havre (IRE)—Entity **Cheveley Park Stud Limited**
64 **HOME FOR HALF PAST (IRE)**, b g Elusive Pimpernel (USA)—Spiritville (IRE) **N D Crummack Ltd**
65 **INFINITE GRACE**, ch f Sepoy (AUS)—Pepper Lane **Mr K. Nicholson**
66 **JOHN JASPER (USA)**, gr ro c Stormy Atlantic (USA)—Pooh Corner (USA) **Mr F. Gillespie**
67 **KILCONQUHAR**, b c Hallowed Crown (AUS)—Passing Stranger (IRE) **Mr N. Dalgarno**
68 **KING'S CHARISMA (IRE)**, b g Teofilo (IRE)—Bawaakeer (USA) **Mrs S. Holtby**
69 **KUMASI**, ch c New Approach (IRE)—Ghanaian (FR) **Cheveley Park Stud Limited**
70 **LADY MELODY (IRE)**, b f Kodiac—Hope And Faith (IRE) **G Brogan & Partner**
71 **MAHARG'S PRINCESS (IRE)**, ch f Night of Thunder (IRE)—Giveupyeraulsins (IRE) **Mr Stuart Graham & Partner**
72 **MANOLITH**, b g Dandy Man—Eolith **York Thoroughbred Racing**
73 **MANZO DURO (IRE)**, b g Slade Power (IRE)—Miss Cape (IRE) **The Pink Pot Partnership & Partner**
74 **MERRY MILLER (IRE)**, b g Camacho—Tender Surprise **Mr G. J. Douglas**
75 **MISCHIEF STAR**, b g Due Diligence (USA)—Red Mischief (IRE) **Three Men & A Trainer**
76 Ch f Monsieur Bond (IRE)—Moonwood **Gallop Racing**
77 **NORTHERN HOPE**, b g Equiano (FR)—Heading North **Great Northern Partnership & Partner**
78 **OLCAN**, b g Showcasing—Pickle **Akela Construction Ltd & Sarah O'Connell**
79 **OSO RAPIDO (IRE)**, b g Kodiac—Burke's Rock **Mr Kevin Bailey & Mr Gabriel Chrysanthou**
80 **PABLO HERNANDEZ**, b c Zoffany (IRE)—Miss Delila (USA) **Highbank Stud**
81 **PASSING NOD**, b g Zoffany (IRE)—Superstar Leo (IRE) **Mr R. Treacy**
82 **PERFECT PULSE (IRE)**, b f Dragon Pulse (IRE)—Asterism **Diamond Racing & Partner 2**
83 **RETURNOFTHEMAC (IRE)**, b g Swiss Spirit—Bibury
84 **RUBY WONDER**, b f Swiss Spirit—Nurse Gladys **A Turton, R Massheder, R Oliver**
85 **SCHUMLI**, b f Swiss Spirit—Noble Cause **Mr D. B. O'Meara**
86 **SEAS OF ELZAAM (IRE)**, b g Elzaam (AUS)—Ocean Sands (IRE) **York Thoroughbred Racing-Ocean Sands**
87 **THE TRENDY MAN (IRE)**, b g Dandy Man (IRE)—Nutshell **Trendy Ladies & Partner**
88 B g Born To Sea (IRE)—Valmari (IRE)
89 **YUKON (IRE)**, br c Lope de Vega (IRE)—Alegra **Sir R. Ogden C.B.E., LLD**

TWO-YEAR-OLDS

90 B c 25/03 Brazen Beau (AUS)—Absolutely Right (IRE) (Teofilo (IRE)) (10000) **Mr H. R. Bin Ghedayer**
91 B c 10/03 Dandy Man (IRE)—Be My Queen (IRE) (Sadler's Wells (USA)) (21450)
92 B c 02/02 Kodiac—Beatify (IRE) (Big Bad Bob (IRE)) **AlMohamediya Racing**
93 B c 08/03 Iffraaj—Brave Times (Exceed And Excel (AUS)) **Mr & Mrs G. Turnbull**
94 **BRAZEN BELLE**, b f 07/02 Brazen Beau (AUS)—Pepper Lane (Exceed And Excel (AUS)) (4761) **Mr K. Nicholson**
95 Gr c 28/03 Oasis Dream—Bruxcalina (FR) (Linamix (FR)) (27000)
96 Ch f 09/02 Helmet (AUS)—Caldy Dancer (IRE) (Soviet Star (USA)) (30000) **Mr M. Rashid**
97 B c 25/03 Intello (GER)—Capacious (Nayef (USA)) (55000)
98 B f 22/04 Alhebayeb (IRE)—Clytha (Mark of Esteem (IRE)) (8580)
99 B c 11/04 Elzaam (AUS)—Coconut Kisses (Bahamian Bounty) (8580)
100 B f 26/01 Kodi Bear (IRE)—Divert (IRE) (Averti (IRE)) (11428)
101 Ch c 10/02 Twilight Son—Evangelical (Dutch Art) (13728)
102 B c 19/02 Mehmas (IRE)—Fast Pick (IRE) (Fastnet Rock (AUS)) (17160)
103 B c 18/05 Havana Gold (IRE)—Hamloola (Red Ransom (USA)) (13727)
104 **HIGHLAND DANDY (IRE)**, br c 12/03 Dandy Man (IRE)—
Star Bonita (IRE) (Invincible Spirit (IRE)) (27619) **Mr E. M. Sutherland**
105 B f 07/04 Sepoy—Hoyamy (Dark Angel (IRE)) (11000) **Mr S. R. Bin Ghedayer**
106 **IMPERIAL EIGHT (IRE)**, b f 03/02 Lawman—Avomcic (Avonbridge) (21450)
107 B f 25/03 Rajsaman (FR)—Influence (FR) (Dansili) **Mrs C. Mitchell**
108 B c 04/02 Slade Power (IRE)—Khaleesi Wind (IRE) (Exceed And Excel (AUS)) (16000) **Mr H. R. Bin Ghedayer**

MR DAVID O'MEARA - continued

109 B c 06/04 Lawman (FR)—Kindu (Pivotal) (5000)
110 B f 13/02 Belardo (IRE)—Livius Lady (IRE) (Titus Livius (FR)) (30000)
111 LOCKET, b f 07/03 Bated Breath—Portraitofmylove (IRE) (Azamour (IRE)) **Cheveley Park Stud Limited**
112 B c 08/04 Requinto (IRE)—Love Thirty (Mister Baileys) (7292)
113 Ch c 07/02 Starspangledbanner (AUS)—Matron (Bahamian Bounty) **Mr N. J. Cable**
114 Gr c 04/01 Gutaifan (IRE)—Maybe Now Baby (IRE) (Kodiac) (9523)
115 B c 22/03 Authorized (IRE)—Millionaia (IRE) (Peintre Celebre (USA)) (51480) **Mrs S. Holtby**
116 B f 11/04 Slade Power (IRE)—Miss Cape (IRE) (Cape Cross (IRE)) (6864)
117 MY BEST FRIEND (IRE), b gr c 22/02 Gutaifan (IRE)—School Holidays (USA) (Harlan's Holiday (USA)) (38095)
118 NIGHT TERRORS (IRE), b c 07/02 Zoffany (IRE)—Dream of Tara (IRE) (Invincible Spirit (IRE)) (34320) **G. Murray**
119 B f 22/04 Make Believe—Paddy Again (IRE) (Moss Vale (IRE)) (36036)
120 Ch f 17/02 Territories (IRE)—Quadri (Polish Precedent (USA)) (9523)
121 RIPLEY ROSE, ch f 28/03 Sepoy (AUS)—Critical Speed (IRE) (Pivotal) (1904) **Mrs M. C. Hancock**
122 Ch f 16/04 Dutch Art—Romantic Settings (Mount Nelson) **Mr & Mrs G. Turnbull**
123 B f 04/04 Mayson—Rural Celebration (Pastoral Pursuits) (30000)
124 B f 23/04 Twilight Son—Spinatrix (Diktat) (28571)
125 B f 13/05 Awtaad (IRE)—Stravina (GER) (Platini (GER)) (12869) **Mr C. J. Miller**
126 SWING LOW, ch c 07/02 Mayson—Velvet Band (Verglas (IRE)) (23809)
127 THESETHINGSHAPPEN, b c 15/05 Siyouni (FR)—
National Day (IRE) (Barathea (IRE)) (20000) **Ray Treacy & Jason Reed**
128 B c 06/04 Gleneagles (IRE)—Toast of The Town (IRE) (Duke of Marmalade (IRE)) **Mr N. J. Cable**
129 B c 03/05 Make Believe—We'll Go Walking (IRE) (Authorized (IRE)) (17160)
130 B c 22/03 Fascinating Rock (IRE)—Why Now (Dansili) (49523) **Mr F. Gillespie**
131 B f 20/04 Helmet (AUS)—Ya Latif (IRE) (Iffraaj) (8000)

Other Owners: Akela Construction Ltd, Mrs P. M. A. Avison, Mr K. B. Bailey, Mr P. I. Baker, P. Bamford, Mr J. M. Binns, Mr P. Breslin, Mr G. Brogan, Mr P. A. Burgess, Mr G. Chrysanthou, Mr A. W. Clark, Clipper Group Holdings Ltd, Diamond Racing Ltd, Mr M. Dunn, Dynast Racing, Mr A. W. Ellis, Gallop Racing, Mr F. Gillespie, Mr S. M. Graham, Great Northern Partnership, Mr A. L. Gregg, Hambleton Racing Ltd, Hambleton Racing Ltd XXXIX, Hurn Racing Club, Mrs M. Ireland, Mrs I. M. Jessop, Mr J. J. Jones, Mr I. Kellett, Mr J. Kelly, Mr A. Kendall-Jones, J. K. S. Law, Mr David John Lumley, Mr R. Massheder, N D Crummack Ltd, Ms S. O'Connell, Mr D. B. O'Meara, Mr R. Oliver, Mr J. D. Pierce, Rasio Cymru Racing 1, Mr J. Reed, A. Rhodes, Mr D. Scott, Mr S. Stephens, The Fallen Angels, The Pink Pot Partnership LLP, The Roses Partnership, Mr R. Treacy, Trendy Ladies, Mr A. S. Trott, Mr G. D. Turner, Mr S. R. H. Turner, Mr A. Turton, Miss A. M. Walker, Mr R. Walker, Mr B. R. Warn, Willow Racing Partnership, Withernsea Thoroughbred Limited, Woodhurst Construction Ltd.

Assistant Trainer: Jason Kelly.

Flat Jockey: Daniel Tudhope. **Apprentice Jockey:** Conor McGovern.

414

MRS DANNI O'NEILL, North Fawley
Postal: **The Old Granary, North Fawley, Wantage, Oxfordshire, OX12 9NJ**
Contacts: **PHONE 01488 639350 MOBILE 07931 193790**
EMAIL danni@fawleyhousestud.com

1 BARDD (IRE), 8, b g Dylan Thomas (IRE)—Zarawa (IRE) **Fawley House Stud**
2 BISHOPSLOUGH (IRE), 12, b g Fruits of Love (USA)—Maid In Blue (IRE) **Fawley House Stud**
3 COMMANDER MILLER, 6, b g Shirocco (GER)—Milliegait **Fawley House Stud**
4 DREYFUS (FR), 9, ch g Notnowcato—Trauquebise (FR) **Fawley House Stud**
5 TALES OF THE TWEED (IRE), 8, b g Robin des Champs (FR)—Dancer Privado (IRE) **Fawley House Stud**

Other Owners: Mr R. H. McGrath, Mrs S. D. McGrath.

Assistant Trainer: Stephen O'Neill.

415

MR JOHN O'NEILL, Bicester
Postal: **Hall Farm, Stratton Audley, Nr Bicester, Oxfordshire, OX27 9BT**
Contacts: **PHONE 01869 277202 MOBILE 07785 394128**
EMAIL jgoneill4@gmail.com

1 CAPPARATTIN, 5, b g Universal (IRE)—Little Miss Prim **J. G. O'Neill**
2 FINULA (IRE), 8, b g Robin des Champs (FR)—Glens Ruby (IRE) **Mrs P. Taylor**
3 ONURBIKE, 12, b g Exit To Nowhere (USA)—Lay It Off (IRE) **J. G. O'Neill**
4 PHOENIX SONG, 7, b g Phoenix Reach (IRE)—Temple Heather **J. G. O'Neill**
5 SLEPTWITHMEBOOTSON, 5, b m Universal (IRE)—Temple Heather **Ms L. M. Keane**
6 W S GILBERT, 6, b g Librettist (USA)—Little Miss Prim **Ms L. M. Keane**

416

MR JONJO O'NEILL, Cheltenham
Postal: **Jackdaws Castle, Temple Guiting, Cheltenham, Gloucestershire, GL54 5XU**
Contacts: **PHONE 01386 584209**
EMAIL racingoffice@jonjooneillracing.com WEBSITE www.jonjooneillracing.com

1 ABOVE BOARD (IRE), 9, b g Mahler—Blackwater Babe (IRE) **Mr J. P. McManus**
2 ADICCI (IRE), 5, b g Shirocco (GER)—Lughnasa (IRE) **Mrs S. McAuley**
3 ANNIE MC (IRE), 6, b m Mahler—Classic Mari (IRE) **Coral Champions Club**
4 ANYWAYYOULOOKATIT (IRE), 7, b g Presenting—Whyalla (IRE) **Mr J. P. McManus**
5 APACHE CREEK (IRE), 5, ch g Shantou (USA)—Galshan (IRE) **Team Tuff**
6 ARRIVEDERCI (FR), 5, gr g Martaline—Etoile d'Ainay (FR) **Martin Broughton & Friends 1**
7 ASHFIELD PADDY (IRE), 6, b g Publisher (USA)—Thats Grace (IRE) **The Hon Mrs E. J. Wills**
8 AT FIRST GLANCE (IRE), 5, b m Stowaway—Mazza's Magic (IRE) **Mr A. Bound**
9 BEAN IN TROUBLE, 6, gr g Sulamani (IRE)—Bouncing Bean **Fanning, Griffith, Haddock**
10 BHUTAN (IRE), 7, gr g Galileo (IRE)—Ecology (USA) **Mr J. P. McManus**
11 CARYS' COMMODITY, 5, b g Fame And Glory—Native Sunrise (IRE) **Mrs F. H. Hay**
12 CHAMPAGNE WILDE (IRE), 5, b g Oscar (IRE)—Barloge Creek (IRE)
13 CLONDAW PROMISE (IRE), 6, b g Gold Well—Present Promise (IRE) **Highfields Farm Partnership**
14 CLOTH CAP (IRE), 8, b g Beneficial—Cloth Fair (IRE) **Mr T. J. Hemmings**
15 COBOLOBO (FR), 8, br g Maresca Sorrento (FR)—Nanou des Brosses (FR) **Anne, Harriet & Lucinda Bond**
16 COEUR AIMANT (FR), 5, b g Maresca Sorrento (FR)—Babet (FR) **Mr T O'Driscoll**
17 COEUR SEREIN (IRE), 6, b g Fame And Glory—Balvenie (IRE) **Mr A. T. S. Ralph**
18 COSTANTE VIA (IRE), 9, b m Milan—Spirit Rock (IRE) **Miss K. J. Holland**
19 DARSI IN THE PARK (IRE), 7, b g Darsi (FR)—Rock In The Park (IRE) **Mrs G. K. Smith**
20 DARTMOOR (FR), 5, b g Martaline—Danse du Soir (FR) **Mr D. J. Coles, Mr I F Gosden**
21 DEMON D'AUNOU (FR), 7, b g Martaline—Jimagine II (FR) **Mr J. P. McManus**
22 DESTIN D'AJONC (FR), 7, b g Martaline—Fleur d'Ajonc (FR) **Mr J. P. McManus**
23 DHOWIN (IRE), 6, b g Yeats (IRE)—On The Way Home (IRE) **Mr T. J. Hemmings**
24 DJANGO DJANGO (FR), 7, gr g Voix du Nord (FR)—Lady Jannina **Martin Broughton & Friends 5**
25 DREAM BERRY (FR), 9, b g Dream Well (FR)—Kalberry (FR) **Mr J. P. McManus**
26 EXTREME FORCE (IRE), 4, ch g Exceed And Excel (AUS)—Great Hope (IRE) **J. C. & S. R. Hitchins**
27 EY UP ROCKY, 7, b g Dylan Thomas (IRE)—Polo **Martyn & Elaine Booth**
28 FAST GETAWAY (IRE), 4, b g Getaway (GER)—Maddy's Supreme (IRE) **Martin Broughton Racing Partners 2**
29 FLEMINPORT (IRE), 7, b g Flemensfirth (USA)—Geek Chic (IRE) **Mr J. P. McManus**
30 FLIGHT DECK (IRE), 6, b g Getaway (GER)—Rate of Knots (IRE) **Mr J. P. McManus**
31 FOLKS ON THE HILL, 5, b g Black Sam Bellamy (IRE)—Any Pearl **Mr R. J. Stanton-Gleaves**
32 FRASCATO BELLO (FR), 5, ch g No Risk At All (FR)—Tchi Tchi Bang Bang (FR) **Mr P. Hickey**
33 FRISCO BAY (IRE), 5, b g Yeats (IRE)—Heath Heaven **Bassaire Cleanrooms Ltd.**
34 GARRY CLERMONT (FR), 5, b g Maresca Sorrento (FR)—Kalidria Beauchene (FR) **Mrs C. M. Walsh**
35 GENERATION GAP (IRE), 6, b g Olden Times—Kerso (IRE) **The Hon Mrs E. J. Wills**
36 GLOBAL ANCHOR (IRE), 6, b g Stowaway—Loreley (IRE) **E. A. Brook**
37 HANG TOUGH, 6, b g Geordieland (FR)—Allerford Lily **Tough Troop Partnership**
38 HENRY GONDOFF, 5, b g Great Pretender (IRE)—Mi Money
39 HEY JOE (IRE), 5, b g Oscar (IRE)—Jordrell (IRE) **J. C. & S. R. Hitchins**
40 HIS DREAM (IRE), 7, b g Yeats (IRE)—Rosa Muscosa (USA) **Jackdaws Racing**
41 I'DLIKETHEOPTION (IRE), 9, b g Presenting—Supreme Dreamer (IRE) **Mr J. P. McManus**

MR JONJO O'NEILL - continued

42 **JEREMEE (IRE)**, 5, b g Jeremy (USA)—Mary's Little Vic (IRE) **C. Boultbee-Brooks**
43 **JOLY MAKER (IRE)**, 6, b g Saddler Maker (IRE)—Joly Coeur (FR) **Mr J. P. McManus**
44 **KILBROOK (IRE)**, 5, b g Watar (IRE)—Daly Lady (IRE) **Mr D.J. Burke & Delancey**
45 **KNIGHT DESTROYER (IRE)**, 6, b g Dark Angel (IRE)—Do The Deal (IRE) **Mrs D. Carr**
46 **LITHIC (IRE)**, 9, b g Westerner—Acoola (IRE) **The Stone Composers**
47 **LOCK'S CORNER (IRE)**, 6, b g Gold Well—Last Century (IRE) **Mr J. P. McManus**
48 **LOVE THE DREAM (IRE)**, 5, b g Mahler—Norah's Quay (IRE) **The Number One Dream Team**
49 **LUNAR BABY (IRE)**, 5, b m Fame And Glory—Fiddlededee (IRE) **Mrs A. F. Bond**
50 **MANINTHESHADOWS (IRE)**, 5, ch g Well Chosen—Grannys Kitchen (IRE) **Mr A. Riley**
51 **MARCH IS ON (IRE)**, 7, b g Gold Well—Shannon Tiara (IRE) **Steve Killalea & Richard & Maralyn Seed**
52 **MAYPOLE CLASS (IRE)**, 6, b g Gold Well—
                                     Maypole Queen (IRE) **Delancey Real Estate Asset Management Limited**
53 **MERCUTIO ROCK (FR)**, 4, b g Maresca Sorrento (FR)—Mondovi (FR) **Mr Michael O'Flynn & Delancey**
54 **MEYER LANSKY (IRE)**, 5, b g Mahler—Sea Breeze Lady (IRE) **Delancey & Mr Michael O'Flynn**
55 **MINELLA BEAUTY (IRE)**, 5, b g Shirocco (GER)—Native Beauty (IRE) **Dydb Marketing Ltd. & Berys Connop**
56 **MINELLA ROCCO (IRE)**, 10, b g Shirocco (GER)—Petralona (USA) **Mr J. P. McManus**
57 **MORNING SPIRIT (IRE)**, 5, b g Milan—Morning Legend (IRE) **Mr P. Hickey**
58 **MUSTMEETALADY (IRE)**, 10, b g Mustameet (USA)—Ladymcgrath (IRE) **Mrs D. Carr**
59 **NOTAWORDOFALIE (IRE)**, 5, br m Presenting—Saddleeruppat (IRE) **Mr D Smith, Mrs J Magnier & Mr M Tabor**
60 **OATHKEEPER (IRE)**, 10, b g Oscar (IRE)—Lady Lamb (IRE) **Mr J. P. McManus**
61 **ON THE BANDWAGON (IRE)**, 5, b g Oscar (IRE)—Deep Supreme (IRE) **Mr A. F. Nolan**
62 **ORRISDALE (IRE)**, 6, b g Oscar (IRE)—Back To Loughadera (IRE) **Mr T. J. Hemmings**
63 **PAGERO (FR)**, 5, b g Nathaniel (IRE)—Pagera (FR) **Mr J. P. McManus**
64 **PALMERS HILL (IRE)**, 7, b g Gold Well—Tosca Shine (IRE) **Mr J. P. McManus**
65 **PAPA TANGO CHARLY (FR)**, 5, ch g No Risk At All (FR)—Chere Elenn (FR) **Mr M. J. Tedham**
66 **PENS MAN (IRE)**, 5, ch g Sholokhov (IRE)—Dudeen (IRE) **Castle Racing Scotland**
67 **PERFECT CITY (IRE)**, 5, b g Elusive City (USA)—Tall Perfection (USA) **Mrs F. H. Hay**
68 **PHOENIX ROCK (IRE)**, 8, br m Winged Love (USA)—Guillaume Rock (IRE) **Successio**
69 **PIGGY WINKLE (IRE)**, 6, b g Fame And Glory—Ar Muin Na Muice (IRE) **Mrs G. K. Smith**
70 **POP ROCKSTAR (IRE)**, 8, b br g Flemensfirth (USA)—Special Ballot (IRE) **Mrs L. Day**
71 **POP THE CORK (IRE)**, 4, b g Harbour Watch (IRE)—Gospel Music **Martyn & Elaine Booth**
72 **PREFONTAINE (IRE)**, 4, gr g Mastercraftsman (IRE)—Cochabamba (IRE) **Mr P. D. Smith**
73 **PRESENT CHIEF (IRE)**, 6, b g Presenting—Daizinni **Mr P. Hickey**
74 **PRINCE ESCALUS (IRE)**, 5, b g Jeremy (USA)—So You Said (IRE) **The As You Like It Syndicate**
75 **QUARENTA (IRE)**, 8, b br g Voix du Nord (FR)—Negresse de Cuta (FR) **Martin, Jocelyn & Steve Broughton**
76 **RABSKI (IRE)**, 4, b g Beat Hollow—Scarlet Feather (IRE) **Mrs S. McAuley**
77 **READY AND ABLE (IRE)**, 7, b g Flemensfirth (USA)—
                                     Gypsy Mo Chara (IRE) **Mr D Smith, Mrs J Magnier & Mr M Tabor**
78 **RED MAPLE (IRE)**, 4, b g Sholokhov (IRE)—Champagne Ruby (IRE) **Mr T. Cole**
79 **RUSSIAN INVASION (IRE)**, 5, b g Aizavoski (IRE)—Kerso (IRE) **Mr T. J. Hemmings**
80 **SEATON CAREW (IRE)**, 6, b m Getaway (GER)—Millys Gesture (IRE) **Jon & Julia Aisbitt**
81 **SERMANDO (FR)**, 6, ch g Fuisse (FR)—Josephjuliusjodie (IRE) **Mrs Jonjo O'Neill**
82 **SHANTOU'S MELODY**, 4, b g Shantou—Glens Melody
83 **SKY PIRATE**, 7, b g Midnight Legend—Dancingwithbubbles (IRE) **Lady C. Bamford & Miss A. Bamford**
84 **SKYLANNA BREEZE (IRE)**, 5, b g Primary (USA)—Waist Deep (IRE) **The Three Cabelleros**
85 **SOARING GLORY (IRE)**, 5, b g Fame And Glory—Hapeney (IRE) **Mr P. Hickey**
86 **STEADY THE SHIP (IRE)**, 4, ch g Ocovango—Vinnie's Princess (IRE) **Pitch Racing**
87 **SUCCESSOR (IRE)**, 7, b g Galileo (IRE)—Dame Again (AUS) **Mr J. P. McManus**
88 **TEDHAM (IRE)**, 6, b g Shirocco (GER)—Alegralil **Mr M. J. Tedham**
89 **TEGEREK (FR)**, 6, b g Mount Nelson—Takaniya (IRE) **Local Parking Security Limited**
90 **TERRY THE FISH (IRE)**, 8, b g Milan—Have More **Terry The Fishers**
91 **THATS THE TRUTH (IRE)**, 6, b m Darsi (FR)—Lucy Walters (IRE) **Bond Brewin Chapman Jackson**
92 **THE COMPOSEUR (IRE)**, 5, b g Mahler—Oscar's Reprieve (IRE) **London Design Group Limited**
93 **THE CRAFTY TOUCH (IRE)**, 7, ch m Touch of Land (FR)—Dicharachera **Ten Belles Partnership**
94 **THE MANUSCRIPT (IRE)**, 7, b g Mahler—Limavady (IRE) **The Valentine Partnership**
95 **THEME TUNE (IRE)**, 5, b g Fame And Glory—Supreme Melody (IRE) **Mr T. J. Hemmings**
96 **TIDAL WATCH (IRE)**, 6, b g Harbour Watch (IRE)—Najmati **Mrs D. Carr**
97 **TRANSPENNINE STAR (IRE)**, 7, ch g Mount Nelson—Brave Mave **Transpennine Partnership**
98 **UPTOWN LADY (IRE)**, 5, b m Milan—Lady Zephyr (IRE) **Recycling Pallet Services**

MR JONJO O'NEILL - continued

99 **WASDELL DUNDALK (FR),** 5, ch g Spirit One (FR)—Linda Queen (FR) **Mr M. J. Tedham**
100 **WHEN YOU'RE READY (IRE),** 6, gr g Malinas (GER)—Royale Wheeler (FR) **Local Parking Security Limited**
101 **YOUNG WOLF (IRE),** 7, b g Vinnie Roe (IRE)—Missy O'Brien (IRE) **Mrs G. K. Smith**

THREE-YEAR-OLDS
102 **HALF OF SEVEN,** b f Harbour Watch (IRE)—Neila (GER) **Mr D P Van Der Hoeven, Mr D G Pryde**
103 **IMPERIAL COMMAND (IRE),** b g War Command (USA)—
Acts Out Loud (USA) **Ms Thorley, Mrs Wills, Mrs McCallister**
104 **ITOLDYOUTOBACKIT (IRE),** ch c Ivawood (IRE)—Jawlaat (IRE) **Roll the Dice Racing**

TWO-YEAR-OLDS
105 **SOLDIEROFTHESTORM (IRE),** ch c 28/02 Soldier of Fortune (IRE)—Fiddlededee (IRE) (Beneficial) **Mr Tom Bond**

Other Owners: Mrs J. M. Aisbitt, J. R. Aisbitt, Miss A. C. Bamford, Lady Bamford, Mr J. Barnard, Mr N. J. Bate, Mrs A. F. Bond, Miss H. Bond, Miss L. Bond, Mrs E. Booth, Mr M. Booth, Mr N. Brand, Mr L. H. Brewin, Mr A. Brookes, Lady J. M. Broughton, Sir M. F. Broughton, Mr S. W. Broughton, Mr A. P. Brown, Mr D. J. Burke, Mr E. Chapman, Steve & Shirley Chick, Mr D J Coles, Mr D. J. Coles, Miss B. Connop, Mr G. Cook, DYDB Marketing Limited, Martin Dalton, Delancey Real Estate Asset Management Limited, Mr O. Fanning, Theo Goodin, Mr N. Griffith, Mrs H. M. Haddock, Mr T. C. B. Hale, Mrs S. Hall-Tinker, Mr M. P. Hammond, J. C. Hitchins, S. R. Hitchins, Mr T. Jackson, Mrs N. Jones, Mr D. Kehoe, Mr S. J. Killalea, London Design Group Limited, Mrs S. Magnier, Mrs C. McCallister, Tim Milvain, Mr M. O'Flynn, Mr J. O'Neill, Mrs J. S. T. O'Neill, Mr C. J. Pearce, Mr S. P. Perryman, David & Rosemary Sandy, Mrs M. L. Seed, Mr R. Seed, Claire Sellar-Elliott, Mr B. D. Smith, D. Smith, M. Tabor, The Commercial Flooring Company, Ms M. Thorley, Nathan Ware, Mrs R. B. Weaver, White Horse Telecom Ltd., The Hon Mr E. J. Wills.

NH Jockey: Alain Cawley, Adrian Heskin, Will Kennedy, Richie McLernon, Jonjo O'Neill Jr, Nick Scholfield, Gavin Sheehan.
Conditional Jockey: Edward Austin. **Amateur Jockey:** AJ O'Neill.

---

417 ## MR JOHN O'SHEA, Newnham-on-Severn
Postal: **The Stables, Bell House, Lumbars Lane, Newnham, Gloucestershire, GL14 1LH**
Contacts: **PHONE 01452 760835 MOBILE 07917 124717 FAX 01452 760233**
WEBSITE www.johnoshearacing.co.uk

1 **A BOOK OF INTRIGUE,** 7, b g Alflora (IRE)—Kahlua Cove **Mr Oscar Singh & Miss Priya Purewal**
2 **AGENT GIBBS,** 8, ch g Bertolini (USA)—Armada Grove **Mr P. G. Hart**
3 **BAY OF INTRIGUE,** 5, b g Sulamani (IRE)—Kahlua Cove **Mr Oscar Singh & Miss Priya Purewal**
4 **COUGAR KID (IRE),** 9, b g Yeats (IRE)—Western Skylark (IRE) **The Cross Racing Club**
5 **GENERAL BROOK (IRE),** 10, b g Westerner—Danse Grecque (IRE) **K. W. Bell**
6 **GET UP THEM STEPS,** 6, b g Excelebration (IRE)—Flag Day **The Cross Racing Club**
7 **JIMMY BELL,** 9, b g Tiger Hill (IRE)—Armada Grove **K. W. Bell**
8 **KINGLAMI,** 11, b g Kingsalsa (USA)—Red Japonica **Pete Smith & Phil Hart Racing**
9 **KNIGHT CRUSADER,** 8, b g Sir Percy—Lac Marmot (FR) **S. P. Bloodstock**
10 5, Ch g Black Sam Bellamy (IRE)—Lac Marmot (FR) **K. W. Bell**
11 **MAJOR VALENTINE,** 8, b g Major Cadeaux—Under My Spell **Mr P. Smith**
12 **MS INTRIGUE,** 5, b m Lucarno (USA)—Gemini June (IRE) **Mr Oscar Singh & Miss Priya Purewal**
13 **RICHIE VALENTINE,** 6, b g Native Ruler—Karmest **Mr N. G. H. Ayliffe**
14 **RIVER OF INTRIGUE (IRE),** 10, b g Indian River (FR)—Molly Hussey (IRE) **Mr Oscar Singh & Miss Priya Purewal**
15 **SHOW ME THE BUBBLY,** 4, b f Showcasing—Folly Bridge **The Cross Racing Club**
16 **SIMBIRSK,** 5, ch g Al Kazeem—Oulianovsk (IRE) **Mr S.G. Martin & the Cross Racing Club**
17 **SWIPER (IRE),** 4, b g Clodovil (IRE)—Hawk Dance (IRE) **The Cross Racing Club**

THREE-YEAR-OLDS
18 **IFFORCEDTOTELL,** b g Lethal Force (IRE)—Canukeepasecret **Mr S. P. Price**

Other Owners: Mr N. G. H. Ayliffe, Mrs S. Guest, S. G. Martin, Miss P. Purewal, Mr A. Singh, The Cross Racing Club.

Flat Jockey: Robert Havlin, Luke Morris.

418 MR HENRY OLIVER, Abberley

Postal: **Stable End, Worsley Racing Stables, Bank Lane, Abberley, Worcester, Worcestershire, WR6 6BQ**
Contacts: **PHONE 01299 890143 MOBILE 07701 068759**
EMAIL henryoliverracing@hotmail.co.uk WEBSITE www.henryoliverracing.co.uk

1 **ADMIRALS BAY (GER),** 4, b g Mount Nelson—Astragal **Roy & Louise Swinburne**
2 **AGAMEMMON (IRE),** 8, b g Getaway (GER)—Oscar Road (IRE) **Mr N T Griffith & H M Haddock**
3 **ANOTHER THEATRE (IRE),** 7, b m Shantou (USA)—Whats Another One (IRE) **The Vacuum Pouch Company Limited**
4 **ARTHUR MAC (IRE),** 7, ch g Getaway (GER)—Orchardstown Moss (IRE) **The Vacuum Pouch Company Limited**
5 **AVANTGARDIST (GER),** 6, ch g Campanologist (USA)—Avocette (GER) **Mr D. M. J. Lloyd**
6 **CATLOW (IRE),** 7, b g Let The Lion Roar—Jon Jon's Grace (IRE) **R. G. Whitehead**
7 **CORRI LINDO (FR),** 10, br g Corri Piano (FR)—Daresta (FR) **Mr H. J. Oliver**
8 **COURT GLORY (IRE),** 7, b m Court Cave (IRE)—Ad Gloria (IRE) **Ms S. A. Howell**
9 **DARLYN,** 7, b m Authorized (IRE)—Darariyna (IRE) **Best Foot Forward**
10 **DETATCHED (IRE),** 8, b g Beneficial—Witneses Daughter (IRE) **Catchtwentytwo,Andyfreight Holdingsltd**
11 **DR DES (IRE),** 9, b g Double Eclipse (IRE)—Dans Belle (IRE) **R. G. Whitehead**
12 **DR OAKLEY (IRE),** 6, ch g Le Fou (IRE)—Two Choices (IRE) **R. G. Whitehead**
13 **DUROUYN,** 6, b g Yeats (IRE)—Douryna **Martingrayracing2**
14 **FAIRY POL (IRE),** 7, b m Milan—Culmore Lady (IRE) **R. G. Whitehead**
15 **GENEROUS DAY (IRE),** 8, b g Daylami (IRE)—Our Pride **R. G. Whitehead**
16 **GET REAL (IRE),** 6, br g Getaway (GER)—Viva Forever (FR) **The Vacuum Pouch Company Limited**
17 **HARD TO FORGET (IRE),** 7, b g Gold Well—Raheen Na Hoon (IRE) **Inspire Racing Syndicate**
18 **HIJRAN (IRE),** 7, ch m Mastercraftsman (IRE)—Sunny Slope **Catchtwentytwo,Andyfreight Holdingsltd**
20 **KILFILUM CROSS (IRE),** 9, gr g Beneficial—Singh Street (IRE) **Andy Bell & Fergus Lyons**
21 **KILLARO BOY (IRE),** 11, ch g Mr Dinos (IRE)—Auburn Roilelet (IRE) **The H & H Partnership**
22 **MCGARRY (IRE),** 6, b g Mahler—Little Pearl (IRE) **The Vacuum Pouch Company Limited**
23 **MRSGREY (IRE),** 6, gr m Court Cave (IRE)—Caroline Fontenail (IRE) **Mr M. S. Hitchcroft**
24 **NICKNAME EXIT (FR),** 10, b g Nickname (FR)—Exit To Fire (FR) **Mr N T Griffith & H M Haddock**
25 **OZZY THOMAS (IRE),** 10, b g Gold Well—Bramble Leader (IRE) **Mr H. J. Oliver**
26 **SALLY CAN'T WAIT,** 7, b m Sulamani (IRE)—Kate Hill Dancer (IRE) **Ms S. A. Howell**
27 **SASTRUGA (IRE),** 7, b g Masterofthehorse (IRE)—Crimson Blue (IRE) **Ms S. A. Howell**
28 **TALKINGPICTURESTV,** 7, b m Flying Legend (USA)—Banoo (IRE) **Talking Pictures TV Limited**
29 **WAIHEKE,** 7, ch m Black Sam Bellamy (IRE)—Its Meant To Be **Mrs S. A. White**
30 **WESTERN CLIMATE (IRE),** 11, b g Westerner—Jo Peeks (IRE) **Mr D. M. J. Lloyd**
31 **WHATSMEANTTOBE,** 6, b g Fair Mix (IRE)—Its Meant To Be **Mrs S. A. White**
32 **ZARAZENA,** 5, b m Yeats (IRE)—Zarannda (IRE) **Best Foot Forward**

Other Owners: Andyfreight Holdings Limited, Mr A. J. Bell, Mrs T. Bell, Blythe Stables LLP, Catch Twenty Two, Mr I. M. Gray, Mr N. Griffith, Mrs H. M. Haddock, Mr M. S. Hitchcroft, Ms S. A. Howell, Mrs C. Lyons, Mr F. Lyons, Fergus & Caroline Lyons, Mr H. J. Oliver, martingrayracing.

Assistant Trainer: Heather Oliver.

Conditional Jockey: Jay Dixon.

419 MR JAMIE OSBORNE, Upper Lambourn

Postal: **The Old Malthouse, Upper Lambourn, Hungerford, Berkshire, RG17 8RG**
Contacts: **PHONE 01488 73139 MOBILE 07860 533422**
EMAIL info@jamieosborne.com WEBSITE www.jamieosborne.com

1 **BIG COUNTRY (IRE),** 7, b g High Chaparral (IRE)—Mount Eliza (IRE) **Melbourne 10 Racing**
2 **BRAINS (IRE),** 4, b g Dandy Man (IRE)—Pure Jazz (IRE) **The Judges & Partner**
3 **CLIFFS OF CAPRI,** 6, b g Canford Cliffs (IRE)—Shannon Spree **Melbourne 10 Racing**
4 **DREAM TODAY (IRE),** 5, b g Dream Ahead (USA)—Macheera (IRE) **Melbourne 10 Racing**
5 **DUKE DEBONAIR (IRE),** 4, b g Dream Ahead (USA)—Nurture (IRE) **Mrs H Allanson & Partner**
6 **JERSEY WONDER (IRE),** 4, ch g Zoffany (IRE)—Magena (USA) **Mr A. Taylor**

MR JAMIE OSBORNE - continued

7 MEKONG, 5, b g Frankel—Ship's Biscuit **Mr Khalid bin Mishref**
8 MURAAHIN, 5, ch g Teofilo (IRE)—Fatanah (IRE) **Melbourne 10 Racing**
9 ORION'S SHORE (IRE), 4, ch c Sea The Stars (IRE)—Bright Snow (USA) **Mr R Kinch & Partner**
10 RAISING SAND, 8, b g Oasis Dream—Balalaika **Nick Bradley Racing 22 & Partner**
11 USANECOLT (IRE), 4, b g Olympic Glory (IRE)—Never Busy (USA) **Homecroft Wealth Racing VIII**

THREE-YEAR-OLDS

12 **AMERICAN DREAMER,** b g Fountain of Youth (IRE)—Say A Prayer **Mr Lewis & Partner**
13 **CRIME OF PASSION (IRE),** b f Acclamation—Golden Shadow (IRE)
14 **DALT VILA (USA),** b c Street Boss (USA)—Nellie Bly (USA) **Merriebelle Irish Farm & Partner**
15 B c Lope de Vega (IRE)—Dazzle Dancer (USA) **Ballylinch Stud**
16 B c Dandy Man (IRE)—Elusive Bonus (IRE)
17 **EMTEN (IRE),** b f Bungle Inthejungle—Lucky Leigh **Melbourne 10 Racing**
18 **FORONCEINMYLIFE (IRE),** ch f Zoffany (IRE)—Kirinda (IRE) **Mrs L. M. Shanahan**
19 **GOOD EARTH (IRE),** b g Acclamation—Madhatten (IRE) **Mrs J A Wakefield & Partner**
20 **HALFACROWN (IRE),** b c Hallowed Crown (AUS)—Ava's World (IRE) **One More Coin Racing & Partner**
21 **HASHTAGMETOO (USA),** b f Declaration of War (USA)—Caribbean Princess (USA) **The Other Club**
22 **JERSEY GREY (FR),** gr g Rajsaman (FR)—Akoyama **Mr A. Taylor**
23 **JERSEY MASTER (IRE),** ch c Mastercraftsman (IRE)—Banquise (IRE) **Mr A. Taylor**
24 **LOOKTOTHELIGHT (USA),** b br c Mineshaft (USA)—Julie Napp (USA) **Merriebelle Irish Farm & Partner**
25 **MISS SLIGO (IRE),** b f New Approach (IRE)—Illandrane (IRE) **The Q Party**
26 **MISS THOUGHTFUL,** gr f Gutaifan (IRE)—Lovely Thought **The Q Party**
27 **MR ALCHEMY,** gr c Leroidesanimaux (BRZ)—Albaraka **The Q Party**
28 **MR BEAU BLUE,** br g Brazen Beau (AUS)—Precious Secret (IRE) **Mr & Mrs I. H. Bendelow**
29 **MR TERRY (IRE),** gr c Gutaifan (IRE)—Carallia (IRE) **The Q Party**
30 **MYKONOS ST JOHN,** b c Swiss Spirit—Royal Pardon **Mrs J A Wakefield & Partner**
31 **NICKS NOT WONDER,** b c Siyouni (FR)—Singuliere (IRE)
32 **PEAKED TOO SOON,** b g Iffraaj—Libys Dream (IRE) **The Joy of Six**
33 B c Brazen Beau (AUS)—Shy Appeal (IRE)
34 **SUNSHINE FUN (USA),** b f Bernardini (USA)—Claire Soleil (USA) **Phoenix Thoroughbred Limited**
35 **TINNAHALLA (IRE),** b g Starspangledbanner (AUS)—Bright Bank (IRE) **Mrs J A Wakefield & Partner**
36 **WEBUYANYHORSE,** gr g Gutaifan (IRE)—Hairicin (IRE) **Ennistown Stud**
37 **WENTWORTH AMIGO (IRE),** gr c Gutaifan (IRE)—Burning Dawn (USA) **Jacobs Construction (holdings) Ltd & Ptn**

TWO-YEAR-OLDS

38 Ch c 13/04 Zoffany (IRE)—Adventure Seeker (FR) (Bering) (47189) **M. A. C. Buckley**
39 Ch f 10/03 Zoffany (IRE)—Aja (IRE) (Excellent Art) (27456)
40 **ALVARINO,** b c 17/03 Bobby's Kitten (USA)—Alinstante (Archipenko (USA)) (1428) **Miss Kirsten Rausing**
41 B c 15/03 Estidhkaar (IRE)—Attracted To You (IRE) (Hurricane Run (IRE)) (47619) **Mr Ger Morrin**
42 B c 07/01 Zoffany (IRE)—Aurora Spring (IRE) (Power) (76190)
43 B c 18/03 Vadamos (FR)—Balamiyda (IRE) (Ashkalani (IRE)) (17160) **10 for 10 Partnership**
44 B f 16/04 Helmet (AUS)—Ballyalla (Mind Games) (12000) **10 for 10 Partnership**
45 B c 24/02 Sir Prancealot (IRE)—Beth (Deportivo) (20952) **10 for 10 Partnership**
46 B f 18/04 Gutaifan (IRE)—
Burning Dawn (USA) (Bernstein (USA)) (22308) **Jacobs Construction (holdings) Ltd & Ptn**
47 B f 14/04 Camelot—Civility Cat (USA) (Tale of The Cat (USA)) (34320) **The Other Club**
48 B c 25/03 Elzaam (AUS)—Cozzene's Pride (USA) (Cozzene) (30029)
49 B f 07/03 Lope de Vega (IRE)—Creme Anglaise (Motivator) (55000) **Hunscote Stud & Mr J O'Connor**
50 B f 30/04 The Gurkha (IRE)—Dream Role (Acclamation) (6005) **10 for 10 Partnership**
51 B c 03/02 Noble Mission—Dreamt (Oasis Dream) (77220)
52 B f 15/03 Dandy Man (IRE)—Ebony Street (USA) (Street Cry (IRE)) (16190) **The Judges & Partner**
53 Gr f 11/04 Gutaifan (IRE)—Ellasha (Shamardal (USA)) (28313) **10 for 10 Partnership**
54 B gr c 09/02 Lethal Force (IRE)—Exist (Exceed And Excel (AUS)) (30029) **Mr & Mrs I. H. Bendelow**
55 B c 21/02 Gutaifan (IRE)—Fanciful Dancer (Groom Dancer (USA)) (50000)
56 B f 03/03 Dark Angel (IRE)—Felcine (IRE) (Duke of Marmalade (IRE)) (107250) **Dargle Equine (UK) Ltd & Partner**
57 B c 14/05 The Gurkha (IRE)—Inkling (USA) (Seeking The Gold (USA)) (34320)
58 B c 11/03 Twilight Son—Jamboree Girl (Bahamian Bounty) (35000) **10 for 10 Partnership**
59 **JAMES' CHOICE (IRE),** b f 02/03 Ajaya—Forever More (IRE) (Galileo (IRE)) (25714) **Mr J. Lloyd-Townshend**
60 B f 01/03 Dandy Man (IRE)—Joyce Compton (IRE) (Tamayuz) (23166) **10 for 10 Partnership**

MR JAMIE OSBORNE - continued

61 B f 03/04 The Last Lion (IRE)—Last Lahar (Sixties Icon) (19000)
62 B c 19/04 Zoffany (IRE)—Layalee (IRE) (Lawman (FR)) (30887)
63 B c 30/04 Gutaifan (IRE)—Love In The Desert (Lemon Drop Kid (USA)) (34320)
64 B f 12/02 Coulsty (IRE)—Lucky Leigh (Piccolo) (40000)
65 Ch f 04/04 Mehmas (IRE)—My Lass (Elmaamul (USA)) (19047) **Gigginstown Stud**
66 B c 26/01 Camelot—Myrica (Dansili) (42900)
67 B f 11/04 Vadamos (FR)—Naqrah (IRE) (Haatef (USA)) (31745)
68 B c 09/04 Hot Streak (IRE)—News Desk (Cape Cross (IRE)) (11000) **10 for 10 Partnership**
69 B c 03/04 Nathaniel (IRE)—Pharadelle (Lope de Vega (IRE)) (35000)
70 B c 24/02 Gutaifan (IRE)—Pindrop (Exceed And Excel (AUS)) (15000) **10 for 10 Partnership**
71 B f 28/04 Coach House (IRE)—Queen Hermione (IRE) (Camacho) (571) **Dr David Chapman-Jones**
72 **ROCKSTAR BLONDE**, b f 07/03 Fascinating Rock (IRE)—
                                        Illegally Blonde (IRE) (Lawman (FR)) (1428) **Mrs and Mrs I Barratt**
73 Ch f 25/03 Zoffany (IRE)—Seatone (USA) (Mizzen Mast (USA)) (48000) **Mrs L. M. Shanahan**
74 B c 01/04 Zoffany (IRE)—Shahralasal (IRE) (Oasis Dream) (27455)
75 B f 01/04 Make Believe—Shifting (IRE) (Oratorio (IRE)) (18876) **10 for 10 Partnership**
76 B c 26/03 No Nay Never (USA)—
                              Starlight Princess (IRE) (Mastercraftsman (IRE)) (57142) **Mrs J A Wakefield & Partner**
77 B c 25/02 Zoffany (IRE)—Travelling (Dubai Destination (USA)) (30000)

Assistant Trainer: Jimmy McCarthy.

Flat Jockey: Dougie Costello, Nicola Currie. **Apprentice Jockey:** Saffie Osborne. **Amateur Jockey:** Miss Alexandra Bell, Mr Alex Ferguson.

---

420 **MISS EMMA OWEN, Nether Winchendon**
Postal: **Muskhill Farm, Nether Winchendon, Aylesbury, Buckinghamshire, HP18 0EB**
Contacts: **PHONE 01844 290282 MOBILE 07718 984799**
EMAIL emma.l.owen@hotmail.com

1 **AUSTIN FRIARS**, 8, b g New Approach (IRE)—My Luigia (IRE) **Miss E. L. Owen**
2 **BAHAMIAN HEIGHTS**, 9, b g Bahamian Bounty—Tahirah **Miss E. L. Owen**
3 **BALLESTEROS**, 11, ch g Tomba—Flamenco Dancer **Miss E. L. Owen**
4 **BORU'S BROOK (IRE)**, 12, b g Brian Boru—Collybrook Lady (IRE) **Miss E. L. Owen**
5 **DIVINE MESSENGER**, 6, b g Firebreak—Resentful Angel **Miss E. L. Owen**
6 **DUTIFUL SON (IRE)**, 10, b g Invincible Spirit (IRE)—Grecian Dancer **Miss E. L. Owen**
7 **FIREGUARD**, 7, b g Firebreak—Leaping Flame (USA) **Miss E. L. Owen**
8 **GUNNER MOYNE**, 8, b g Excellent Art—Maramkova (IRE) **H. G. Owen**
9 **HIGHER COURT (USA)**, 12, b g Shamardal (USA)—Nawaiet (USA) **Miss E. L. Owen**
10 **HIGHPLAINS DRIFTER (IRE)**, 9, b g High Chaparral (IRE)—Ghazeenah **Miss E. L. Owen**
11 **JOSHLEE (IRE)**, 6, b m Dark Angel (IRE)—Kay Es Jay (FR) **Miss E. L. Owen**
12 **LEGAL MIND**, 7, ch h Firebreak—La Sorrela (IRE) **Miss E. L. Owen**
13 **MILLDEAN BILLY (IRE)**, 4, b g Dandy Man (IRE)—Strawberriescream (IRE) **Miss E. L. Owen**
14 **MILLDEAN PANTHER**, 4, b g Mayson—Silver Halo **Miss E. L. Owen**
15 **MUSICAL COMEDY**, 9, b g Royal Applause—Spinning Top **Miss E. L. Owen**
16 **PEDDERY**, 4, b g Pastoral Pursuits—Resentful Angel **Miss E. L. Owen**
17 **RED HANRAHAN (IRE)**, 9, b g Yeats (IRE)—Monty's Sister (IRE) **Miss E. L. Owen**
18 **REIGNITE**, 5, b g Firebreak—Resentful Angel **Miss E. L. Owen**
19 **SEA THE WAVES**, 7, b g Canford Cliffs (IRE)—April (IRE) **Mr L. F. Daly**
20 **THE ARISTOCAT (IRE)**, 5, b m Kitten's Joy (USA)—Letters (FR) **Miss E. L. Owen**
21 **VERETA (IRE)**, 4, b f Dick Turpin (IRE)—Vera Lou (IRE) **Mr L. F. Daly**

---

421 **MR PATRICK OWENS, Newmarket**
Postal: **Trainer did not wish details of their string to appear**

422 **MR HUGO PALMER, Newmarket**
Postal: **Kremlin Cottage Stables, Snailwell Road, Newmarket, Suffolk, CB8 7DP**
Contacts: **PHONE 01638 669880 MOBILE 07824 887886 FAX 01638 666383**
EMAIL info@hugopalmer.com WEBSITE www.hugopalmer.com

1 **ALMUFTI**, 4, b g Toronado (IRE)—Green Tern (ITY) **Al Shaqab Racing UK Limited**
2 **CARAVAN OF HOPE (IRE)**, 4, b g Nathaniel (IRE)—Caravan of Dreams (IRE) **Dr A. Ridha**
3 **COLLIDE**, 5, b h Frankel—Scuffle **K. Abdullah**
4 **DEBBONAIR (IRE)**, 4, b g Slade Power (IRE)—Bryanstown Girl (IRE) **Commission Air Limited**
5 **DIAMOND OASIS**, 4, ch f Iffraaj—Belonging **Lady Manton & Partners Iii**
6 **EL GHAZWANI (IRE)**, 5, b h Cape Cross (IRE)—Almansoora (USA) **Mr H. R. Bin Ghedayer**
7 **GIFTED MASTER (IRE)**, 7, b g Kodiac—Shobobb **Dr A. Ridha**
8 **IRONCLAD**, 4, br g Dubawi (IRE)—Heat Haze **K. Abdullah**
9 **LEXINGTON FLAIR (FR)**, 5, b g Dabirsim (FR)—Kyleam **Middleham Park Racing XXVIII**
10 **OURS PUISSANT (IRE)**, 4, b g Kodiac—Lady Emly (IRE) **Mr Kevin Bailey & Mr Gabriel Chrysanthou**
11 **POWER OF STATES (IRE)**, 4, b g Lope de Vega (IRE)—Allegation (FR) **Dr A. Ridha**
12 **RACHEL ZANE (IRE)**, 4, b f Sea The Moon (GER)—Mark of An Angel (IRE) **FOMO Syndicate**
13 **RED OCTOBER (IRE)**, 4, ch g Dawn Approach (IRE)—Mamonta **Mrs Clodagh McStay & Partner**
14 **SIGLO SIX**, 4, ch g Havana Gold (IRE)—Yensi **John Livock & Nat Lacy**
15 **WHITE MOCHA (USA)**, 5, ch g Lope de Vega (IRE)—Lastroseofsummer (IRE) **Dr A. Ridha**

THREE-YEAR-OLDS

16 **ACQUITTED (IRE)**, b br c Night of Thunder (IRE)—Blameless (IRE) **John Livock & Nat Lacy**
17 **ANGEL OF DELIGHT (IRE)**, gr f Dark Angel (IRE)—Ventura Mist **Dr A. Ridha**
18 **ARTHUR'S COURT (IRE)**, b g Camelot—Logjam (IRE) **John Livock, Nat Lacy, Mrs M V Magnier**
19 **CHANKAYA**, ch c Dubawi (IRE)—Splashdown **Mr V. I. Araci**
20 **COASE**, b g Zoffany (IRE)—Sharnberry **Mr L. L. Lee**
21 **COLLETTE (IRE)**, ch f New Approach (IRE)—Shallow Lake (USA) **The Turf Club 2018 & Partners**
22 **COMBINE (IRE)**, b f Zoffany (IRE)—Unity (IRE) **Lady Manton & Partners 1**
23 **COMVIDA (IRE)**, b g Camacho—Savida (IRE) **East 11 Limited**
24 **CONVERTIBLE (IRE)**, b g Helmet (AUS)—Empress Ella (IRE) **Mr L. L. Lee**
25 **DEPOSE**, b f Kingman—Tested **K. Abdullah**
26 **DOUBLING DICE**, br g Teofilo (IRE)—Garanciere (FR) **Mr V. I. Araci**
27 **EAST OF EDEN (IRE)**, b f Exceed And Excel (AUS)—Allegation (FR) **T E Hyde, Mrs P Shanahan & Mrs T P Hyde**
28 **EASTERN SHERIFF**, b c Lawman (FR)—Abunai **Sheikh I. S. Al Khalifa**
29 **EMISSARY**, b c Kingman—Soviet Moon (IRE) **K. Abdullah**
30 **FALCONIDAE (IRE)**, b f Kodiac—Dhuma **Mr V. I. Araci**
31 **GIGI'S BEACH**, b g Oasis Dream—Clenor (IRE) **John Livock & Nat Lacy**
32 **GOLDEN PASS**, b f Golden Horn—Lovely Pass (IRE) **Dr A. Ridha**
33 **HAMISH MACBETH**, b g Due Diligence (USA)—Brick Tops **Hunscote Stud Ltd & Mrs Lynne Maclennan**
34 **HLAITAN**, b g Iffraaj—The Madding Crowd **Al Shaqab Racing UK Limited**
35 **HOT TOUCH**, ch f Hot Streak (IRE)—Stroll Patrol **Dr A. Ridha**
36 **IMRAHOR**, b c Kingman—She's Mine (IRE) **Mr V. I. Araci**
37 **KAITEN**, b g Gleneagles (IRE)—Caphene **Qatar Racing Limited**
38 **LOVER'S MOON (IRE)**, b f Make Believe—Night Fever (IRE) **Lovers Ladies**
39 **MONTAQEN (FR)**, b c Muhaarar—African Skies **Al Shaqab Racing UK Limited**
40 **NARRATE**, b f Dansili—Indication **K. Abdullah**
41 **OASIS JOY**, b f Oasis Dream—Pure Joy **K. Abdullah**
42 **POWERFUL BREEZE**, b f Iffraaj—Power of Light (IRE) **Dr A. Ridha**
43 **POWERTRAIN (IRE)**, ch g Zoffany (IRE)—Emerald Ring (IRE) **Sheikh I. S. Al Khalifa**
44 **RACHMANINOV (USA)**, b c Mizzen Mast (USA)—Solo Piano (USA) **K. Abdullah**
45 **ROCKET ROD (IRE)**, b c Australia (IRE)—Tessa Reef (IRE) **John Livock & Nat Lacy**
46 **SAVANNA GOLD (IRE)**, b g Havana Gold (IRE)—Prospera (IRE) **Mrs F. J. Carmichael**
47 **SHEILA (IRE)**, ch f Australia—Donnelly's Hollow (IRE) **Mr E. D. Tynan**
48 **SILENT PERFORMANCE (IRE)**, b f Zoffany (IRE)—Silent Thoughts (IRE) **Dr A. Ridha**
49 **STRAWBERRY ROCK (IRE)**, b g Rock of Gibraltar (IRE)—Strawberry Vodka **FOMO (Rock) Syndicate**
50 **SYSTEMIC**, b g Toronado (IRE)—Saskia's Dream **H Moorhead, C Fahy & J Collins**
51 **TIRITOMBA (IRE)**, b f Exceed And Excel (AUS)—Starry Messenger **Mr V. I. Araci**
52 B g Siyouni (IRE)—Titivation
53 **UNFORGETTABLE COLT**, ch c Sepoy (AUS)—Beautiful Filly **Dr A. Ridha**
54 **VINTAGE POLLY (IRE)**, br f Gutaifan (IRE)—Payphone **Mr R. W. Hill-Smith**

MR HUGO PALMER - continued

55 Ch g Zoffany (IRE)—Wandering Spirit (GER)
56 WARREN ROSE, b f Dansili—Chigun **Mr V. I. Araci**
57 ZORAN, b c Invincible Spirit (IRE)—Filia Regina **The Earl Of Derby**

TWO-YEAR-OLDS

58 Gr c 17/04 Mastercraftsman (IRE)—Atlantic Isle (GER) (Tamayuz)
59 B c 19/03 Charm Spirit (IRE)—Bounty Box (Bahamian Bounty) (45000) **Qatar Racing Limited**
60 BRUNNERA, b f 15/02 Dubawi (IRE)—Romantica (Galileo (IRE)) **K. Abdullah**
61 B c 06/05 Iffraaj—Catchline (USA) (Bertolini (USA)) **Dr A. Ridha**
62 B f 12/02 Australia—Chigun (Oasis Dream) **Mr V. I. Araci**
63 Gr ro f 24/02 Mehmas (IRE)—Crystal Snowflake (IRE) (Danehill Dancer (IRE)) (18875)
64 B c 17/02 Showcasing—Dam Beautiful (Sleeping Indian) (55770)
65 DANCING TO WIN, b f 15/04 Iffraaj—Smart Step (Montjeu (IRE)) (60000) **The HLS Partnership**
66 DANTORA, b c 10/02 Dansili—Rostova (USA) (Arch (USA)) **K. Abdullah**
67 ECOSSE, b f 18/03 Acclamation—Dumfriesshire (Oasis Dream) **K. Abdullah**
68 B f 05/04 Camelot—Elitiste (IRE) (Danehill Dancer (IRE)) **Sheikh I. S. Al Khalifa**
69 B c 17/04 Dubawi (IRE)—Filia Regina (Galileo (IRE)) **The Earl Of Derby**
70 B f 19/03 Australia—Fondly (IRE) (Dansili) (35000) **MPH O'Connor & Reinsurance Partners**
71 GLESGA GAL (IRE), ch f 14/03 Lope de Vega (IRE)—
                               Crystany (IRE) (Green Desert (USA)) (102960) **New Wave Racing & Partners**
72 HE DO, b c 23/04 Lawman (FR)—Dylanesque (Royal Applause) (10000) **T C O Gredley**
73 B f 02/03 Fastnet Rock (AUS)—
                       Heaven's Angel (IRE) (Henrythenavigator (USA)) (50000) **Mr H. Dalmook Al Maktoum**
74 B c 04/02 Sea The Stars (IRE)—Hot Sauce (IRE) (Peintre Celebre (USA)) (220000) **Mr J. W. Livock**
75 B br f 01/03 Iffraaj—Isobel Archer (Oasis Dream) (87000)
76 KIZOMBA, b f 13/03 Kodiac—Zulema (Shamardal (USA)) **K. Abdullah**
77 B c 23/04 Havana Gold (IRE)—Lara Amelia (IRE) (Ishiguru (USA)) (30030) **Mr L. L. Lee**
78 B c 11/03 Adaay (IRE)—Last Echo (IRE) (Whipper (USA)) (18000) **Kremlin Cottage IX**
79 B f 29/04 Australia—Love And Laughter (IRE) (Theatrical) (150000) **Qatar Racing Limited**
80 LOVELY BREEZE (IRE), b f 20/03 Sepoy (AUS)—Power of Light (IRE) (Echo of Light) **Dr A. Ridha**
81 Ch c 31/03 Shamardal (USA)—Lovely Pass (IRE) (Raven's Pass (USA)) **Dr A. Ridha**
82 B c 14/03 Kodiac—Lovely Surprise (IRE) (Shamardal (USA)) **Dr A. Ridha**
83 B c 28/02 Shalaa (IRE)—Mathool (IRE) (Alhaarth (IRE)) (70000) **Al Shaqab Racing UK Limited**
84 B c 17/01 Fast Company (IRE)—Natalisa (IRE) (Green Desert (USA)) **Kremlin Cottage IX**
85 NEW FORCE, ch c 30/03 New Approach (IRE)—Honky Tonk Sally (Dansili) (105000) **Sheikh I. S. Al Khalifa**
86 B f 06/02 Olympic Glory (IRE)—Ornelia Ruee (FR) (Sea The Stars (IRE)) (26598)
87 B f 24/03 Kodiac—Prance (IRE) (Danehill Dancer (IRE)) (120000) **Dr A. Ridha**
88 QUENELLE D'OR, b f 31/01 Golden Horn—Quenelle (Nayef (USA)) (55000) **Lady Derby & Lady Ritblat**
89 B f 04/02 Dawn Approach (IRE)—Race In Focus (IRE) (Vocalised) (952)
90 B f 15/04 Mukhadram—Royal Dalakhani (IRE) (Dalakhani (IRE)) (8000) **Kremlin Cottage IX**
91 Ch f 09/03 Sepoy (AUS)—Silver Games (IRE) (Verglas (IRE)) **Mr Chris Wright**
92 B c 07/02 Kodiac—Some Site (IRE) (Nayef (USA)) (75000) **Mr L. L. Lee**
93 B f 13/02 Charm Spirit (IRE)—Stroll Patrol (Mount Nelson) **Qatar Racing Limited**
94 Ch c 28/02 Starspangledbanner (AUS)—Via Lattea (IRE) (Teofilo (IRE)) (48906) **Middleham Park Racing LXXXVII**
95 B f 08/03 The Gurkha (IRE)—Wild Storm (Dubawi (IRE)) **Mr V. I. Araci**

Other Owners: Mr K. B. Bailey, Mr A. N. Cheyne, Mr G. Chrysanthou, Mr J. P. Ferguson, Hunscote Stud Limited, Mrs C. Hyde, T. Hyde, Mr N. Lacy, Mr J. W. Livock, Mrs L. Maclennan, Mrs E. Magnier, Exors of the Late Mr P. Magnier, Mrs S. Magnier, Col A. J. E. Malcolm, Lady Mary Manton, Mrs C. McStay, Mr M. J. McStay, Mr H. Palmer, Exors of the Late Duke of G. D. Roxburghe, Mrs L. M. Shanahan, Turf Club 2018.

---

423 **MR MARK PATTINSON, Epsom**
Postal: Flat 3, White House Stables, Tattenham Corner Road, Epsom, Surrey, KT18 5PP
Contacts: **MOBILE 07961 835401**

1 BRECQHOU ISLAND, 5, b g Pastoral Pursuits—Lihou Island **Mrs F A Veasey & G. B. Partnership**
2 GOLCONDA PRINCE (IRE), 6, b g Arcano (IRE)—Mujarah (IRE) **M I Pattinson Racing**

MR MARK PATTINSON - continued

3 **HIPPOLYTE BOUCHARD**, 4, b g Nayef (USA)—The Lady Lapwing **M I Pattinson Racing**
4 **MYKINDOFSUNSHINE (IRE)**, 4, gr g Zebedee—Silk Fan (IRE) **M I Pattinson Racing**
5 **OUR OYSTERCATCHER**, 6, br g Pastoral Pursuits—The Dark Eider **Mrs F A Veasey & G. B. Partnership**
6 **PERFECT SYMPHONY (IRE)**, 6, b g Dandy Man (IRE)—Fields of Joy (GER) **Lynne Stanbrook & Julian Power**
7 **THE PASTORAL BEAR**, 4, ch f Pastoral Pursuits—Torrecilla **Mrs S. Frost**
8 **TRUE COLORS**, 6, b g Sir Percy—Shesells Seashells **Smarden Thoroughbreds**

THREE-YEAR-OLDS

9 **BRONZE FLORIN**, b f Medicean—Copper Penny **Mrs F A Veasey & G. B. Partnership**

Other Owners: Mr S. D. Bradley, Mrs H. J. Fitzsimons, Mr A. M. H. Heald, M. G. H. Heald, Mr J. Power, Mrs L. C. Stanbrook, Mrs F. A. Veasey.

---

424 MR BEN PAULING, Bourton-on-the-Water
Postal: **Bourton Hill Farm, Bourton Hill, Bourton-On-The-Water, Cheltenham, Gloucestershire, GL54 2LF**
Contacts: **PHONE 01451 821252 MOBILE 07825 232888**
EMAIL ben@benpaulingracing.com **WEBSITE** www.benpaulingracing.com

1 **ANIGHTINLAMBOURN (IRE)**, 6, b m Gold Well—Madgehil (IRE) **The Megsons**
2 **APPLE ROCK (IRE)**, 6, b g Royal Anthem (USA)—Wayward Cove **Presumption in Favour Partnership**
3 **ARTEMISION**, 4, b g Gentlewave (IRE)—Miss Fahrenheit (IRE) **T K Racing Ltd**
4 **BANANA JOE (IRE)**, 6, b g Getaway (GER)—Rosetiepy (FR) **Slater Stockwood Nicholson Partnership**
5 **BANGERS AND CASH (IRE)**, 4, b g Fame And Glory—Cash Customer (IRE) **OAP II**
6 **BAXTER BASICS (IRE)**, 4, br g Getaway (GER)—Limekiln Lass (IRE) **Ardley, Bickmore & Pauling**
7 **BIG DIFFERENCE (IRE)**, 7, b g Presenting—Roque de Cyborg (IRE) **Mr M. Waters**
8 **BRAVE DANCING**, 6, b g Mount Nelson—Purring (USA) **Bruton Street**
9 **BRIGHT FORECAST (IRE)**, 6, b g Arcadio (GER)—Check The Forecast (IRE) **The Aldaniti Partnership**
10 **CAVOK (IRE)**, 8, b m Kayf Tara—Timon's Present **Mrs C. J. Zetter-Wells**
11 **CHESS PLAYER (IRE)**, 5, ch g No Risk At All (FR)—Merci Jandrer (FR) **Mrs Rachel Brodie & Mr John Brodie**
12 **CONCEAL (IRE)**, 5, ch g Stowaway—Babyshan (IRE) **Highclere Thoroughbred Racing - Stowaway**
13 **CURIO BAY (IRE)**, 4, b g Milan—Anna Magdalena (IRE) **Mrs Rachel Brodie & Mr John Brodie**
14 **DE BARLEY BASKET (IRE)**, 7, b g Alkaadhem—Lady Willmurt (IRE) **Mrs S N J Embiricos & Ms A Embiricos**
15 **DEL LA MAR ROCKET (IRE)**, 4, b g Fame And Glory—Pipe Lady (IRE) **Les de La Haye & Martin Mundy**
16 **DELAHAYE GOLD (IRE)**, 4, b g Ocovango—The Millers Tale (IRE) **Mr L. De la Haye**
17 **DELIRE D'ESTRUVAL (FR)**, 7, b g Youmzain (IRE)—Question d'Estruval (FR) **Mr Simon Munir & Mr Isaac Souede**
18 **EARL BIFFY BIFFEN (FR)**, 6, bl g Day Flight—Similaresisoldofa (FR) **The Megsons**
19 **EAU TOP (FR)**, 6, b g Barastraight—Monepopee (FR) **Mr O. Troup**
20 **ENCHANCIA (IRE)**, 6, b g Milan—Dancingwithbubbles (IRE) **The Ben Pauling Racing Club**
21 **EQUUS SECRETUS (IRE)**, 8, b g Brian Boru—Bodega Bay (IRE) **The Bourtoneers**
22 **ESPOIR DE LOIRE (FR)**, 6, b g Anabaa Blue—Grischa (FR) **Merriebelle Irish Farm Limited**
23 **FINE CASTING (IRE)**, 4, b g Shantou (USA)—Fine Fortune (IRE) **Mrs S. P. Davis**
24 **FOR LUCK (FR)**, 5, ch g Coastal Path—Isis de Sormain (FR) **The Bourtoneers**
25 **GENTLEMAN VALLEY (IRE)**, 4, b g Kapgarde (FR)—Richona (FR) **The Megsons**
26 **GERBOISE BORGET (FR)**, 5, b m Martaline—Ges (FR) **Mr J. P. McManus**
27 **GET PREPARED**, 5, b g Black Sam Bellamy (IRE)—Star Ar Aghaidh (IRE) **Mrs S. Pauling**
28 **GLOBAL CITIZEN (IRE)**, 8, b g Alkaadhem—Lady Willmurt (IRE) **The Megsons**
29 **GOWITHTHEFLOW (IRE)**, 7, b g Westerner—Maryiver (IRE) **Bruton Street**
30 **GRANNY'S SECRET (IRE)**, 6, b m Stowaway—Ask My Granny (IRE) **The Jp Girls**
31 **GUENA DES MOTTES (FR)**, 4, b g Soave (GER)—Sara de Flee (FR) **Mr Simon Munir & Mr Isaac Souede**
32 **HAWK WIND (IRE)**, 5, b g Dubai Destination (USA)—The Legislator (IRE) **The E Nicolson, V Embiricos & A Embiricos**
33 **HIDDEN GLEN (IRE)**, 7, ch g Stowaway—Gleanntan (IRE) **J Petit,C Skinner,R Sanders & J Tuttiett**
34 **HONOR GREY (IRE)**, 5, b g Flemensfirth (USA)—Rose Island **Mr & Mrs J Tuttiett**
35 **I'M SPELLBOUND (IRE)**, 4, b g Doyen (IRE)—Magic Park (IRE) **Mrs S. Pauling**
36 **IMPERIAL KNIGHT (IRE)**, 8, b g Mahler—And Whatever Else (IRE) **Middleham Park Racing LXXXIX**
37 **JOVIAL SPIRIT (IRE)**, 5, b g Doyen (IRE)—Banjo Davis (IRE) **Lost In 1936 Partnership**

MR BEN PAULING - continued

38 **KENNACK BAY (FR)**, 5, b g Balko (FR)—Nuance Tartare (FR)   **The Kennack Bay Partnership**
39 **KILDISART (IRE)**, 8, b g Dubai Destination (USA)—Princess Mairead (IRE)   **Mr Simon Munir & Mr Isaac Souede**
40 **KING ERIK**, 6, b g And Beyond (IRE)—Gretton   **The Pillar P Partnership**
41 **LADY CHUFFNELL (IRE)**, 6, b m Jeremy (USA)—Taraval (USA)   **The Megsons**
42 **LE BREUIL (FR)**, 8, ch g Anzillero (GER)—Slew Dancer   **Mrs E. A. Palmer**
43 **LE GRAND LION (FR)**, 4, gr g Turgeon (USA)—Grande Cavale (FR)   **The Lion Tamers**
44 **LEADING KNIGHT (IRE)**, 4, b g Leading Light (IRE)—Miss McGoldrick (IRE)   **Mr M. Jones**
45 **LEGAL EYES (IRE)**, 7, br g Court Cave (IRE)—Grass Tips (IRE)   **OAP Syndicate**
46 **LIFEISAHIGHWAY (IRE)**, 6, b g Court Cave (IRE)—Miss Top (IRE)
47 **LINENHALL (IRE)**, 8, ch g Stowaway—Option (IRE)   **Mrs E. L. Kendall**
48 **LITTLE RED DEVIL (IRE)**, 5, b m Cloudings (IRE)—Ardkilly Angel (IRE)   **The Three Legs Partnership**
49 **LOCH LAGGAN (IRE)**, 4, b g Sea The Stars (IRE)—Magic Sister   **Mr C. A. Washbourn**
50 **MALACHYS GIRL (IRE)**, 7, b m Darsi (FR)—Borleagh Princess (IRE)   **Mrs S. J. Lanz**
51 **MALINELLO**, 5, b g Malinas (GER)—Wyldello   **Mr M. Jones**
52 **MISS FLYING FOX**, 5, b br m Kayf Tara—Nile Cristale (FR)   **Mr M. Jones**
53 **MISTER WATSON**, 6, b g Mawatheeq (USA)—Island Odyssey   **Pump & Plant Services Ltd**
54 4, B g Leading Light (IRE)—Mrs Roberts   **Promanco Ltd**
55 **MYSTIC COURT (IRE)**, 7, b g Court Cave (IRE)—My Mystic Rose (IRE)   **Mystic Band of Brothers**
56 **NADAITAK**, 6, b g Teofilo (IRE)—Tanfidh   **The Megsons**
57 **NESTOR PARK (FR)**, 7, b g Walk In The Park (IRE)—Cila (FR)   **Mrs S. P. Davis**
58 **NORTHERN BOUND (IRE)**, 6, b g Fruits of Love (USA)—Noble Choice   **Mrs E. L. Kendall**
59 **NOT AT PRESENT (IRE)**, 5, b g Presenting—Anna Magdalena (IRE)   **Mrs Rachel Brodie & Mr John Brodie**
60 **NOW IS THE WINTER (IRE)**, 6, b g Fame And Glory—Supreme Melody (IRE)   **Broderick, Reddin, Brown & Whittle**
61 **OISTRAKH LE NOIR (FR)**, 6, b g Kentucky Dynamite (USA)—
                                                  Linares Noire (FR)   **Mr Simon Munir & Mr Isaac Souede**
62 **ON SPRINGS (IRE)**, 5, b g Mahler—Wild Fuchsia (IRE)   **Mrs S. Pauling**
63 **ONE TOUCH (IRE)**, 6, b g Court Cave (IRE)—Star Bui (IRE)   **Mr M. Jones**
64 **PENCREEK (FR)**, 7, ch g Konig Shuffle (GER)—Couture Fleurs (FR)   **Mrs G. S. Worcester**
65 **RAISE YOUR SHADES (IRE)**, 6, b g Morozov (USA)—Couleurs de Barra (IRE)   **Foxtrot Racing Raise Your Shades**
66 **RAVEN'S TOWER (USA)**, 10, b g Raven's Pass (USA)—Tizdubai (USA)   **Faithful Friends**
67 **RINTULLA (IRE)**, 6, ch g Tobougg (IRE)—The Millers Tale (IRE)   **McNeill Family Ltd**
68 **SEASIDE GIRL (IRE)**, 6, b m Mahler—Jade River (FR)   **Quevega Consulting LLP**
69 **SEBASTIAN BEACH**, 9, b g Yeats (IRE)—Night Club   **The Megsons**
70 **SHAKEM UP'ARRY (IRE)**, 6, b g Flemensfirth (USA)—Nun Better (IRE)   **Mr H. Redknapp**
71 **SHANROE TIC TEC (IRE)**, 8, b g Flemensfirth (USA)—Bonny Hall (IRE)   **Easy Going Racing**
72 **SLIPWAY (IRE)**, 5, b g Stowaway—Little Sioux (IRE)   **Mrs S. N. J. Embiricos**
73 **SOUTH MOUNTAIN (IRE)**, 4, b g Westerner—Maryiver (IRE)   **Bruton Street UK - III**
74 **SPECIAL BUDDY (IRE)**, 6, b g Robin des Pres (FR)—Annees d'Or (IRE)   **Fortnum Racing**
75 **STOKES (IRE)**, 5, b g Califet (FR)—Iktitafs Sister (IRE)   **Mrs S. Pauling**
76 **TEL'ART (FR)**, 6, gr g Montmartre (FR)—Textuelle (FR)   **Mr & Mrs J Tuttiett**
77 **THE CAPTAINS INN (IRE)**, 6, b g Flemensfirth (USA)—Killeen (IRE)   **The Megsons**
78 **THE COB (IRE)**, 6, b g Let The Lion Roar—Millenium Love (IRE)   **The Ben Pauling Racing Club**
79 **THE MACON LUGNATIC**, 6, b g Shirocco (GER)—Didbrook   **Genesis Racing Partnership II**
80 **TOBY MAGUIRE (IRE)**, 7, b g Darsi (FR)—Minnie Maguire (IRE)   **Charles Levinson & Alexia Robinson**
81 **TOWARDS THE DAWN**, 6, b g Midnight Legend—Wakeful   **Mrs S. L. Lloyd-Baker**
82 **TWIG**, 5, b g Sulamani (IRE)—Southern Exit   **Mr L. J. Strangman**
83 **UNAI (IRE)**, 5, b g Court Cave (IRE)—The Millers Tale (IRE)   **Mr Simon Munir & Mr Isaac Souede**
84 **WE RUN THE NIGHT (FR)**, 5, b g Sri Putra—Quatz Melody (FR)   **Mr Simon Munir & Mr Isaac Souede**
85 4, B g Kayf Tara—Wee Dinns (IRE)   **Mrs S. Pauling**
86 **WHATSUPWITHYOU (IRE)**, 6, b g Shantou (USA)—Whats Up Britta (IRE)   **Co-Foundations Ltd**
87 **WIRELESS OPERATOR (IRE)**, 5, b g Presenting—Princess Gaia (IRE)   **McNeill Family and Prodec Networks Ltd**
88 **YABASS (IRE)**, 5, ch g Lope de Vega (IRE)—Fresh Mint (IRE)   **The Ride The Lightning Partnership**
89 **YOUR DARLING (IRE)**, 5, b g Shirocco (GER)—Carries Darling   **Lord Vestey**
Other Owners: Mr M. P. Ardley, Mr A. R. Bickmore, Mrs B. A. Broderick, Mr J. W. Brodie, Mrs R. A. Brodie, Mr P Brown, Mr J. Byrne, Mr Charles E. Noell Esq, Mr L. De la Haye, Ms A. E. Embiricos, Mrs S. N. J. Embiricos, Mrs J. D. Farrant, Mr C. Fenwick, Mr M. D. Hankin, J H & N J Foxon Ltd, Mr S. L. Leach, Dr C. M. Levinson, McNeill Family Ltd, Mr M. Mundy, S. E. Munir, Mr E. D. Nicolson, Mr B. P. Pauling, Mr J. W. Petit, Prodec Networks Ltd, Mr S. D. Reddin, Ms A. Robinson, Mr R. D. Sanders, Mr C. A. L. Skinner, Mr I. Souede, Mrs A. J. Tuttiett, Mr J. E. Tuttiett, Mrs C. A. Waters, Mr J. S. Whittle.

MR BEN PAULING - continued

Assistant Trainer: Thomas David.

NH Jockey: David Bass, Nico De Boinville, Daryl Jacob. **Amateur Jockey:** Mr A. Rid.

---

425 **MR SIMON PEARCE, Newmarket**
Postal: **1 Whitegates, Newmarket, Suffolk, CB8 8DS**
Contacts: **PHONE 01638 664669**
EMAIL **spearceracing@hotmail.co.uk**

1 **ARABIAN OASIS,** 8, b g Oasis Dream—Love Divine **GG Bloodstock & Racing Club**
2 **BARTHOLOMEW J (IRE),** 6, ch g Fast Company (IRE)—Mana (IRE) **Jay Three Racing & Partners**
3 **CONQUERESS (IRE),** 6, ch m Dandy Man (IRE)—Sesmen **Game Of Chance**
4 **DYAGILEV,** 5, ch g Kheleyf (USA)—Dancemetothemoon **Killarney Glen & Lydia Pearce**
5 **FULL INTENTION,** 6, b g Showcasing—My Delirium **Killarney Glen & Lydia Pearce**
6 **NOBLE PEACE,** 7, b g Kyllachy—Peace Concluded **Killarney Glen**
7 **SEXY SECRET,** 9, b g Sakhee's Secret—Orange Walk (IRE) **Mrs L. S. Pearce**

THREE-YEAR-OLDS

8 **FRANKIE JAZZ,** b c Royal Applause—Pretty Kool **Killarney Glen**
9 **INFLAMED,** ch g New Approach (IRE)—Indignant **Howard Duff Racing (1)**
10 **LIL LISA (IRE),** b f Alhebayeb (IRE)—Mana (IRE) **A Partnership**

Other Owners: S. Andrews, Darren Burgess, Mr H. Crothers, Ben Davies, N. M. Hanger, J. Harrison, Jay Three Racing, Mr E. Jones, Killarney Glen, Steve Marriott, Jason Matthews, Mrs L. Matthews, Mrs L. S. Pearce, Steve & Karen Yallop.

---

426 **MR OLLIE PEARS, Malton**
Postal: **The Old Farmhouse, Beverley Road, Norton, Malton, North Yorkshire, YO17 9PJ**
Contacts: **PHONE 01653 690746 MOBILE 07760 197103**
EMAIL **info@olliepearsracing.co.uk WEBSITE www.olliepearsracing.co.uk**

1 **BILLYOAKES (IRE),** 8, b g Kodiac—Reality Check (IRE) **Keith West & Ollie Pears**
2 **CHRISTMAS NIGHT,** 5, ch g Compton Place—Night Haven **Ownaracehorse Ltd & Mr Ollie Pears**
3 **KROY,** 6, b g Sleeping Indian—Valley of The Moon (IRE) **Mrs S. A. Elsey**
4 **LETHAL GUEST,** 4, gr g Lethal Force (IRE)—Holberg Suite **NP Racing Syndicate**
5 **MOSAKHAR,** 4, b g Dawn Approach (IRE)—Min Banat Alreeh (IRE) **Mrs S. D. Pearson**
6 **PLACEBO EFFECT (IRE),** 5, b g Lilbourne Lad (IRE)—
Hawaiian Dream (IRE) **Timothy O'Gram, Keith West & Ollie Pears**
7 **ROARING RORY,** 7, ch g Sakhee's Secret—Barbieri (IRE) **Ownaracehorse Ltd & Mr Ollie Pears**
8 **SAPPHIRE JUBILEE,** 4, b f Lethal Force (IRE)—Queens Jubilee **Mrs S. D. Pearson**
9 **STRAIGHT ASH (IRE),** 5, gr g Zebedee—Blackangelheart (IRE) **NP Racing Syndicate**

THREE-YEAR-OLDS

10 **BELLA FIGLIA,** bl f Brazen Beau (AUS)—Powerfulstorm **Mr T O'Gram, Mrs P Moll & Mr R Marshall**
11 **BLITZLE,** gr f Toronado (IRE)—Kept Under Wraps (IRE) **Np Racing Syndicate & Ollie Pears**
12 **HARRY LOVE (IRE),** b g Lawman (FR)—Gimmick (IRE) **Ownaracehorse Ltd & Mr Ollie Pears**
13 **JACKATE,** b g Sleeping Indian—Anushka Noo Noo **Mr A. Caygill**
14 **PIVOTAL ART (IRE),** br g Dutch Art—Up Tempo **Mary Carter, Stuart Carter & Ollie Pears**
15 **SUSIE JAVEA,** b f Coach House (IRE)—Charlevoix (IRE) **Mr A. Caygill**
16 **WRIGHTIA (IRE),** gr f Mastercraftsman (IRE)—Gerika (FR) **T. Elsey**

TWO-YEAR-OLDS

17 **ALIVE WIRE,** b g 10/02 Swiss Spirit—Empress Livia (Paco Boy (IRE)) (1904) **Ownaracehorse Ltd & Mr Ollie Pears**
18 **CHRISTMAS MORNING (IRE),** b f 25/02 Vadamos (FR)—
Scottish Exile (IRE) (Ashkalani (IRE)) (3432) **Ownaracehorse Ltd & Mr Ollie Pears**

MR OLLIE PEARS - continued

19 **CROWN PRINCESS (IRE),** b f 06/05 Mehmas (IRE)—
                                    Al Hanyora (Teofilo (IRE)) (4761) **Ownaracehorse Ltd & Mr Ollie Pears**
20 B f 09/04 Charming Thought—Excellent Show (Exceed And Excel (AUS)) (4761) **O. J. Pears**
21 **FIND A PENNY,** b f 03/03 Charm Spirit (IRE)—
                                    Carnoustie (FR) (Acclamation) (2000) **Ownaracehorse Ltd & Mr Ollie Pears**
22 **FLISS FLOSS,** gr f 26/02 Lethal Force (IRE)—Raggle Taggle (IRE) (Tagula (IRE)) (2857) **Mr A. Caygill**
23 **LUCY RULES (IRE),** b f 25/04 Vadamos (FR)—Kodafine (IRE) (Kodiac) (7619) **Mr A. Caygill**
24 Ch g 30/04 Dandy Man (IRE)—Moving Waves (IRE) (Intense Focus (USA)) **O. J. Pears**
25 **NORTHERN CRACKER,** ch g 25/03 Monsieur Bond (IRE)—Bond Casino (Kyllachy) **Mr R. S. Marshall**
26 **READY FREDDIE GO (IRE),** b g 21/02 Swiss Spirit—
                                    Barbieri (IRE) (Encosta de Lago (AUS)) (2857) **Ownaracehorse Ltd & Mr Ollie Pears**
27 **RED HEADED TIGER,** b g 07/04 Coach House (IRE)—Spanish Gold (Vettori (IRE)) (4761) **NP Racing Syndicate**
28 **SUNSET KATIE,** b f 10/03 Twilight Son—Triple Star (Royal Applause) (3000) **Ownaracehorse Ltd & Mr Ollie Pears**

Other Owners: Mrs M. E. Carter, Mr S. J. Carter, Mr R. S. Marshall, Mrs P. E. Moll, NP Racing Syndicate, T. J. O'Gram, Ownaracehorse Ltd, O. J. Pears, Mrs N. Watson, K. C. West.

Assistant Trainer: Vicky Pears.

NH Jockey: Brian Hughes.

---

427 MISS LINDA PERRATT, East Kilbride
Postal: **North Allerton Farm, East Kilbride, Glasgow, Lanarkshire, G75 8RR**
Contacts: **PHONE 01355 303425 MOBILE 07931 306147**
EMAIL linda.perratt@btinternet.com

1 **CHINESE SPIRIT (IRE),** 6, gr g Clodovil (IRE)—In The Ribbons **Mr Y.C. Luk, Mr Sandy Jarvie & L Perratt**
2 **DARK CRYSTAL,** 9, b m Multiplex—Glitz (IRE) **Miss L. A. Perratt**
3 **INDIARO,** 4, b g Sleeping Indian—Cafe Express (IRE) **The Hon Miss H. Galbraith**
4 **LAOISE (USA),** 4, b f Noble Mission—Lilbourne Eliza (IRE) **Miss L. A. Perratt**
5 **LET RIGHT BE DONE,** 8, gr g Lawman (FR)—Cheerfully **Linda Perratt Racing Club**
6 **LUCKY VIOLET (IRE),** 8, b m Dandy Man (IRE)—Rashida **Miss L. A. Perratt**
7 **PALAVICINI RUN (IRE),** 7, ch m Palavicini (USA)—Dawn's Sharp Shot (IRE) **Ayr Racecourse Club**
8 **POPPING CORKS (IRE),** 4, b f Camacho—Shamardyh (IRE) **Mr B. A. Jordan**
9 **RETIREMENT BECKONS,** 5, b g Epaulette (AUS)—Mystical Ayr (IRE) **Miss L. A. Perratt**
10 **WAHWEI SPIRIT (IRE),** 5, b g Mustameet (USA)—La Belle de Serk (IRE) **Mr Peter Tsim & Miss Linda Perratt**

THREE-YEAR-OLDS

11 **BEIGNET (IRE),** b f Canford Cliffs (IRE)—Cake (IRE) **Miss L. A. Perratt**
12 **GRANDADS BEST GIRL,** b f Intrinsic—Mitchelland **Mrs A. E. Stark**
13 **HARD NUT (IRE),** b c Gutaifan (IRE)—With A Twist **Mr W. F. Perratt**

Other Owners: Mr A. Jarvie, Mr Y. C. Luk, Miss L. A. Perratt, P. Tsim.

Flat Jockey: Tom Eaves, P.J. McDonald. **Apprentice Jockey:** Leanne Ferguson.

---

428 MRS AMANDA PERRETT, Pulborough
Postal: **Coombelands Racing Stables, Pulborough, West Sussex, RH20 1BP**
Contacts: **PHONE 01798 873011 MOBILE 07803 088713**
EMAIL aperrett@coombelands-stables.com WEBSITE www.amandaperrett.com

1 **ALFIE SOLOMONS (IRE),** 4, b g Acclamation—Vastitas (IRE) **Alfie Solomons Partnership**
2 **ASTROMACHIA,** 5, b g Sea The Stars (IRE)—Fontley **John Connolly & Odile Griffith**
3 **COUNT OTTO (IRE),** 5, b g Sir Prancealot (IRE)—Dessert Flower (IRE) **Count Otto Partnership**
4 **DOUBLE LEGEND (IRE),** 5, b g Finsceal Fior—Damask Rose (IRE) **Dean Angell & Partner**
5 **DUTCH STORY,** 4, ch g Dutch Art—Shamandar (FR) **Mr & Mrs R Scott & Mr & Mrs D Bevan**
6 **FRONTISPIECE,** 6, b g Shamardal (USA)—Free Verse **The Frontispiece Partnership**

MRS AMANDA PERRETT - continued

7 **LAVENDER'S BLUE (IRE)**, 4, b f Sea The Stars (IRE)—Beatrice Aurore (IRE) **Benny Andersson**
8 **MANUCCI (IRE)**, 4, b g Nathaniel (IRE)—American Spirit (IRE) **John Connolly & Odile Griffith**
9 **MAZZURI (IRE)**, 5, ch m Raven's Pass (USA)—Essexford (IRE) **Mrs S. M. Conway**
10 **OPEN HANDED**, 5, b g Sakhee (USA)—Naemi (GER) **Mrs K. Meekins**
11 **OPEN WIDE (USA)**, 6, b br g Invincible Spirit (IRE)—Nunavik (IRE) **George Materna & John McInerney**
12 **PERCY'S PRINCE**, 4, b g Sir Percy—Attainable **Mrs A. M. Lewis**
13 **PLATITUDE**, 7, b g Dansili—Modesta **Mrs S. M. Conway**
14 **SAAHEQ**, 6, b g Invincible Spirit (IRE)—Brevity (USA) **Coombelands Racing Syndicate**
15 **TINTO**, 4, b g Compton Place—Amirah (IRE) **Mr D. M. James, Mr S. J. Jenkins, Mr M. F. Quigley**
16 **WORDISMYBOND**, 11, b g Monsieur Bond (IRE)—La Gessa **Bond Racing**
17 **YOU'RE HIRED**, 7, b g Dalakhani (IRE)—Heaven Sent **G. D. P. Materna**
18 **ZHUI FENG (IRE)**, 7, b g Invincible Spirit (IRE)—Es Que **John Connolly & Odile Griffith**
19 **ZUBA**, 4, b g Dubawi (IRE)—Purr Along **John Connolly & Odile Griffith**
20 **ZZORO (IRE)**, 7, br g Manduro (GER)—Krynica (USA) **Mrs S. M. Conway**

THREE-YEAR-OLDS

21 **AHORSECALLEDWANDA**, b f Music Master—Lady Mascot (IRE) **Mason Brown Partnership**
22 **ART FOR ART'S SAKE (IRE)**, ch g Dutch Art—Anayid **Mr R. J. B. Cheadle**
23 **AUDITORIA**, b f Gleneagles (IRE)—Authora (IRE) **Woodcote Stud Ltd**
24 **BEST ADDRESS (USA)**, b f City Zip—Preferential **K. Abdullah**
25 **COZONE**, b c Pour Moi (IRE)—Bella Nouf **John Connolly & Odile Griffith**
26 **DIAMOND RUBY**, b f Cable Bay (IRE)—Royal Confidence **Mrs Barbara James**
27 **FELDSPAR**, b g Champs Elysees—Novellara **K. Abdullah**
28 **GIFT OF YOUTH**, b g Fountain of Youth (IRE)—Margrets Gift **Gift Of Youth Partnership**
29 **MOOMBA (IRE)**, ch c Australia—Beatrice Aurore (IRE) **Benny Andersson**
30 **PENNY DIAMOND**, b f War Command (USA)—Penny Sixpence (FR) **Penny Diamond Partnership**
31 **PHOLAS**, b f Iffraaj—Scallop **K. Abdullah**
32 **POPULAIRE (FR)**, gr f Zebedee—Monspa **The Populaire Partnership**
33 **ROVERA (IRE)**, ch f No Nay Never (USA)—Minnie Hazel (IRE) **The The Rovera Partnership**
34 **RUBY RED EMPRESS (IRE)**, b f Holy Roman Emperor (IRE)—Rougette **Mr D. M. James**
35 **SAUCY ENCORE**, b f Showcasing—Saucy Minx (IRE) **Mr & Mrs F. Cotton and Mr & Mrs P. Conway**
36 **SUNS UP GUNS UP**, ch g Lope de Vega (IRE)—Strictly Silca **G. C. Stevens**
37 **TRANSITION**, b c Oasis Dream—Nancy O (IRE) **K. Abdullah**
38 **VERNIER**, ch g Nathaniel (IRE)—Tolerance (USA) **K. Abdullah**
39 **ZELLERATE (IRE)**, b g Gutaifan (IRE)—Ride For Roses (IRE) **Mr John E. Bodie & Partners**

TWO-YEAR-OLDS

40 B f 20/04 Oasis Dream—Authora (IRE) (Authorized (IRE)) **Woodcote Stud Ltd**
41 B c 10/04 Harzand (IRE)—Beatrice Aurore (IRE) (Danehill Dancer (IRE)) **Benny Andersson**
42 **EAGLE ONE**, b c 22/01 Gleneagles—Gloryette (Raven's Pass) **John Connolly & A D Spence**
43 **REBEL TERRITORY**, b c 23/02 Territories (IRE)—
    Saucy Minx (IRE) (Dylan Thomas (IRE)) **Mr & Mrs F. Cotton and Mr & Mrs P. Conway**
44 **SAYIFYOUWILL**, b f 20/04 Sayif (IRE)—
    Amirah (IRE) (Holy Roman Emperor (IRE)) (11000) **Mr Richard Cheadle & Partners**

Assistant Trainer: Mark Perrett.

---

429 **MR PAT PHELAN**, Epsom
Postal: **Ermyn Lodge, Shepherds Walk, Epsom, Surrey, KT18 6DF**
Contacts: **PHONE 01372 229014 MOBILE 07917 762781 FAX 01372 229001**
EMAIL pat.phelan@ermynlodge.com WEBSITE www.ermynlodge.com

1 **CRIMSON KISS (IRE)**, 4, ch f Sepoy (AUS)—Crimson Year (USA) **Mr P. J. Wheatley**
2 **DEVIZES**, 4, b g Dubawi (IRE)—Dalasyla (IRE) **Mr P. Bocking**
3 **DOTTIES DELIGHT**, 4, b f Archipenko (USA)—Auntie Dot Com **Mr A. Smith**
4 **EDE'S**, 4, b g Sir Percy—My Amalie (IRE)
5 **ERMYN'S EMERALD**, 8, b br g Alflora (IRE)—Emerald Project (IRE) **Ermyn Lodge Stud Limited**

MR PAT PHELAN - continued

6 **HACKBRIDGE**, 5, br g Archipenko (USA)—Famcred **Southdown Holdings Ltd**
7 **HATSAWAY (IRE)**, 9, b g Dubawi (IRE)—Scotch Bonnet (IRE) **P. P. Mclaughlin**
8 **KEEP IT COUNTRY TV**, 4, ch g Archipenko (USA)—Monda (USA) **Keep It Country**
9 **LEGEND OF FRANCE**, 7, ch m Flying Legend (USA)—Bonne Anniversaire **Ermyn Lodge Stud Limited**
10 **MAYTHEORSEBEWITHU (IRE)**, 5, b m Shirocco (GER)—Amoya (GER) **Mr A. Smith**
11 **MAZALTO (IRE)**, 7, b m Teofilo (IRE)—Mazaaya (USA) **Maginn Smith**
12 **MOONLIT SEA**, 4, b g Sea The Moon (GER)—Angeleno (IRE) **Mr J. F. Lang**
13 **PRESENCE PROCESS**, 6, b g Dansili—Loulwa (IRE) **Mr P. Bocking**
14 **REECELTIC**, 5, b g Champs Elysees—Sense of Pride **Celtic Contractors Limited**
15 **SETTLE PETAL**, 6, b m Peintre Celebre (USA)—Shall We Dance **I. W. Harfitt**
16 **SINGER IN THE SAND (IRE)**, 5, b m Footstepsinthesand—Village Singer (USA) **I. W. Harfitt**
17 **THE PREMIER CELTIC**, 7, b g Black Sam Bellamy (IRE)—Maria Antonia (IRE) **Celtic Contractors Limited**
18 **WE ARE ALL DOTTIE**, 4, b f Mayson—Young Dottie **Mr A. Smith**
19 **WESTERN RANGER (IRE)**, 5, b m Westerner—Ballyhindon Castle (IRE)
20 **WITCHES GLEN (IRE)**, 8, b m Helissio (FR)—Native Cheer (IRE) **Ermyn Lodge Stud Limited**

THREE-YEAR-OLDS

21 **DARK WHITE**, gr g Lethal Force (IRE)—Dark Skies (IRE) **Epsom Downers**
22 **EPSOM FAITHFULL**, b f Coach House (IRE)—La Fortunata **Epsom Racegoers No.2**
23 **HERRE DITTERY**, b br g Cable Bay (IRE)—Young Dottie **Mr A. Smith**
24 **ITSAJUNGLEOUTTHERE (IRE)**, b f Bungle Inthejungle—Dialing Tone (USA) **Mr P. Bocking**
25 **LADY BEAT**, b f Sir Percy—Keep To The Beat **Mr Paul Cox & Mr Liam Russell**
26 **PRINCESSE ANIMALE**, b f Leroidesanimaux (BRZ)—Isabella Beeton **Mr A. Smith**

Other Owners: Mr P. Cox, Mrs J. K. Lukas, Mr G. Maginn, Sir D. J. Prosser, Mr L. R. Russell, Mr A. Smith, Mr T. D. J. Syder.

Flat Jockey: J. F. Egan, Shane Kelly, Kieran O'Neill. **NH Jockey:** James Best, Josh Moore. **Conditional Jockey:** Sean Houlihan.
Apprentice Jockey: Paddy Bradley, Sophie Ralston.

---

430   **MR ALAN PHILLIPS, Callow End**
Postal: **Jennet Tree Farm, Kents Green, Callow End, Worcestershire, WR2 4UA**
Contacts: **PHONE 01905 831774 MOBILE 07870 112235**
EMAIL alan@alanphillipsracing.com WEBSITE www.alanphillipsracing.com

1 **BOHER LAD (IRE)**, 13, b g Gold Well—Shindeesharnick (IRE) **Miss R. L. Edwards**
2 4, Ch f Shantou (USA)—Couture Daisy (IRE)
3 **LINDA'S VEGA (FR)**, 8, b m Linda's Lad—Dal Kine (FR)
4 **MR FRANKIE**, 9, b g Sleeping Indian—Shes Minnie **The Guiting Knights**
5 **MR STANDFAST**, 7, b g Mullionmileanhour (IRE)—Phantom Ridge (IRE) **Miss R. L. Edwards**
6 4, Ch f Gentlewave (IRE)—Our Ethel
7 **RED INCA**, 12, ch g Pivotal—Magicalmysterykate (USA) **C. M. Rutledge**
8 **TARRONA**, 11, b g Kayf Tara—Lisrona (IRE) **Mr D. G. Redfern**
9 **THE MODEL COUNTY (IRE)**, 10, b m Robin des Champs (FR)—Ware It Vic (IRE) **Mr D. G. Redfern**
10 **WHY LIE (IRE)**, 9, b g Zagreb (USA)—Persian Avenue (IRE) **Miss R. L. Edwards**

Other Owners: Mr K. Brookes, Mr M. Edwards.

---

431   **MR RICHARD PHILLIPS, Moreton-in-Marsh**
Postal: **Adlestrop Stables, Adlestrop, Moreton-in-Marsh, Gloucestershire, GL56 0YN**
Contacts: **WORK 01608 658710 MOBILE 07774 832715**
EMAIL info@richardphillipsracing.com WEBSITE www.richardphillipsracing.com

1 **AVION**, 5, ch g Arvico (FR)—Tiger Line **Mrs S. C. Welch**
2 **BEAUTIFUL PEOPLE (FR)**, 9, b br m Early March—Night Fever (FR) **Beautiful People**
3 **BIG FIDDLE**, 7, b m Kayf Tara—Fiddling Again **Mrs E. C. Roberts**
4 **CELESTIAL MAGIC**, 8, b g Black Sam Bellamy (IRE)—Mighty Merlin **Mrs J. A. Watts**

MR RICHARD PHILLIPS - continued

5 **DANDY LASS (IRE)**, 4, b f Dandy Man (IRE)—El Mirage (IRE) **The Aspirationals**
6 **HIGHLAND SUN (IRE)**, 4, ch f Helmet (AUS)—Cintsa Sun (IRE) **W. D. S. Murdoch**
7 **IRON HORSE**, 9, b g Kayf Tara—What A Vintage (IRE) **The Someday's Here Racing Partnership**
8 **ISLANDRAY (IRE)**, 6, b g Milan—Dewasentah (IRE) **Carbine Of London Racing**
9 **J GAYE (IRE)**, 4, b f Canford Cliffs (IRE)—Ice Pie **S. F. Benton**
10 4, B f Leading Light (IRE)—Kapricia Speed (FR)
11 **LADY OF AUTHORITY**, 5, b m Kheleyf (USA)—Miss Authority **The Listeners**
12 **MADAME RITZ (IRE)**, 5, b m Canford Cliffs (IRE)—Sky Red **The Firebirds**
13 **MASTER VINTAGE**, 12, b g Kayf Tara—What A Vintage (IRE) **The Adlestrop Club**
14 **METHODTOTHEMAGIC (IRE)**, 5, b m Sans Frontieres (IRE)—
                                       Cindy's Fancy (IRE) **Dalziel Family, T White, J Inverdale**
15 **MIGHTY ELSA**, 7, b m Schiaparelli (GER)—Tiger Moss **Mr S. Smith**
16 **MINELLA WHISPER**, 9, b g Kayf Tara—Celtic Native (IRE) **Mrs E. A. Prowting**
17 **MRS BARNES (IRE)**, 7, b m Ask—Jills Oscar (IRE) **Mr & Mrs R. Scott**
18 **MUTHABIR (IRE)**, 10, b g Nayef (USA)—Northern Melody (IRE) **The Adlestrop Club**
19 **ORGANDI (FR)**, 8, br m Early March—Creme Pralinee (FR) **Beautiful People**
20 **OVER STATED (IRE)**, 8, b g Shantou (USA)—Mrs Gordi **Mr E. J. Ware**
21 **PICANHA**, 6, br g Malinas (GER)—Royal Bride **Mrs E. A. Prowting**
22 **POP MISTRESS (IRE)**, 4, ch f Sixties Icon—Mayolynn (USA) **Goodwood Owners Drinks Session**
23 **PRESENT FROM DUBAI (IRE)**, 7, b g Dubai Destination (USA)—Inch Promise (IRE) **Hopeful Travellers**
24 **ROUNDHEAD**, 5, ch g Helmet (AUS)—Blue Mistral (IRE) **Mr E. J. Ware**
25 **RUN ROSIE RUN**, 4, b f Native Ruler—No Compromise **Better Than Working**
26 **SHADOW WALKER (IRE)**, 6, b g Stowaway—Ilikeyou (IRE) **Mr C. Pocock**
27 **TIMETOBENEFIT (IRE)**, 9, b m Beneficial—Shokalocka Baby (IRE) **Mrs H. M. Nixseaman**
28 **TULANE (IRE)**, 5, br g Arcano (IRE)—Jeunesse Doree (IRE) **The Tulanes**

Other Owners: Ms K. Anderson, Mr R. S. Dalziel, Mrs S. J. Harvey, J. B. Inverdale, Mr T. White.

---

432 **MISS ELLA PICKARD, Umberleigh**
Postal: **Langridge Farm, Atherington, Umberleigh, Devon, EX37 9HP**
Contacts: **PHONE 07921 088893**
EMAIL ellapickard@outlook.com

1 **CINEVATOR (IRE)**, 13, b g Dr Massini (IRE)—Hurricane Bella (IRE) **Mr M. G. Tucker**
2 **DEEP INFERNO (IRE)**, 4, b br g Flemensfirth (USA)—Waist Deep (IRE)
3 **FLUTISTE (FR)**, 5, b g Secret Singer (FR)—Nanny (FR) **Mr M. G. Tucker**
4 **GETALEAD (IRE)**, 4, b g Getaway (GER)—Site-Leader (IRE) **Miss R. Pickard**
5 **GETAROUND (IRE)**, 5, gr g Getaway (GER)—Playing Around **Mr G. J. Wilson**
6 **LIGHTNING GOLD**, 5, ch m Black Sam Bellamy (IRE)—Santera (IRE) **Mr P. W. Gillbard**
7 **LUCKYJOHNHOBBS (IRE)**, 4, b g Milan—Hazlewood (IRE) **Mr G. J. Wilson**
8 **WHATABOUTWALT (IRE)**, 4, ch g Salutino (GER)—Cyclone Lorraine (IRE) **Miss R. Pickard**

---

433 **MISS IMOGEN PICKARD, Kingsland**
Postal: **The Granary, Sodgeley Farm, Kingsland, Leominster, Herefordshire, HR6 9PY**
Contacts: **PHONE 07884 437720**
EMAIL bundlepickardracing@yahoo.co.uk

1 **MISTER FIZZ**, 12, b g Sulamani (IRE)—Court Champagne **Bundle Pickard Racing Club**

434 **MR TIM PINFIELD, Upper Lambourn**
Postal: **Flemington Stables, Upper Lambourn, Hungerford, Berkshire, RG17 8QH**
EMAIL timpinfieldracing@hotmail.com

1 BAMBAJEE (FR), 7, b m Rock of Gibraltar (IRE)—Heaven's Dream (IRE) **Mrs G. A. Pinfield**
2 FREA, 4, b f Sea The Moon (GER)—Patronella (IRE) **Mr A. Altazi**
3 FREEDOM FIGHTER (IRE), 10, b g Danehill Dancer (IRE)—Rose of Petra (IRE) **Mr K. M. Pinfield**
4 MERAKI, 4, b g Heeraat (IRE)—Sound of Life (IRE) **Mr M. Eves**
5 ONEOVDEM, 6, ch g Yorgunnabelucky (USA)—Noor El Houdah (IRE) **Arion Equine Limited**
6 SIR THOMAS GRESHAM (IRE), 5, b h Dutch Art—Loquacity **Ladies who Lunch Syndicate**
7 WALKMAN (IRE), 4, b c War Command (USA)—Mooching Along (IRE) **Mr A. Altazi**
8 ZAYDANIDES (FR), 8, bl g American Post—Ouarzazate (IRE) **Ladies who Lunch Syndicate**

THREE-YEAR-OLDS
9 B f Cable Bay (IRE)—Ferayha (IRE)
10 B c Music Master—Gambatte
11 B c Requinto (IRE)—Medicean Bliss (IRE) **Mr M. Eves**
12 MEVAGISSEY COVE, b c Harbour Watch (IRE)—Shades of Silk **Happy Get Lucky Syndicate**
13 Ch c Assertive—Paris Sunrise (IRE)
14 B f Music Master—Sand And Deliver

435 **MR DAVID PIPE, Wellington**
Postal: **Pond House, Nicholashayne, Wellington, Somerset, TA21 9QY**
Contacts: PHONE 01884 840715 FAX 01884 841343
EMAIL david@davidpipe.com WEBSITE www.davidpipe.com

1 AIRTON, 7, b g Champs Elysees—Fly In Style **David Pipe Racing Club**
2 BRINKLEY (FR), 5, gr g Martaline—Royale Majesty (FR) **Brocade Racing**
3 BUSTER EDWARDS (IRE), 7, b g Kalanisi (IRE)—Hot Oscar (IRE) **Mr Jonathan Williams & Partner**
4 CHAMPERS ON ICE (IRE), 10, gr g Robin des Champs (FR)—Miss Nova **Prof C. Tisdall & Mr B. Drew**
5 COLLINGWOOD COURT (IRE), 6, b g Court Cave (IRE)—West Hill Rose (IRE) **City AM**
6 CROSSING LINES (IRE), 6, b g Jeremy (USA)—Coco Opera (IRE) **Middleham Park Racing CXVII**
7 DAKLONDIKE (IRE), 8, b g Gold Well—Strong Irish (IRE) **Prof C. Tisdall**
8 DELFACE (FR), 7, b g Della Francesca (USA)—Septieme Face (USA) **Pipe's Prospectors**
9 DELL' ARCA (IRE), 11, b g Sholokhov (IRE)—Daisy Belle (GER) **Prof C. Tisdall**
10 DROMINEER (IRE), 7, b g Oscar (IRE)—Aileen Supreme (IRE) **W. F. Frewen & M. C. Pipe**
11 DUC DE BEAUCHENE (FR), 7, b g Saddler Maker (IRE)—Quatia d'Angron (FR) **Mr J. P. McManus**
12 DUSKY HERCULES (IRE), 6, b g Shantou (USA)—Annalecky (IRE) **David Pipe Racing Club**
13 EAMON AN CNOIC (IRE), 9, b g Westerner—Nutmeg Tune (IRE) **The Angove Family**
14 EDEN DU HOUX (FR), 6, b g Irish Wells (FR)—Maralypha (FR) **Prof C. Tisdall**
15 EKAYBURG (FR), 6, b g Sageburg (IRE)—Kayseri (FR) **W. F. Frewen**
16 ELAN DE BALME (FR), 6, b g Cachet Noir (USA)—Jebarde Rederie (FR) **Prof C. Tisdall**
17 EXTRA MAG (FR), 6, b g Kapgarde (FR)—Qrystale Mag (FR) **The Angove Family**
18 FIRST LORD DE CUET (FR), 6, gr g Lord du Sud (FR)—Alyce (FR) **Potter, Pipe and Pete**
19 FLOU ARTSISTIQUE (FR), 5, b g Cokoriko (FR)—Castagnette III (FR) **Mr J. P. McManus**
20 FORT SUMMER (IRE), 5, b g Kalanisi (IRE)—Glen Ellie (IRE) **Two Hopes**
21 GABRIELLE DU SEUIL (FR), 4, b f Cokoriko (FR)—Marie du Seuil (FR)
22 GHOST SERGE (IRE), 5, gr g Zebedee—Cornakill (USA) **Mrs L. Webb**
23 GOLDEN JEFFREY (SWI), 7, b g Soldier Hollow—Ange Doree (FR) **Mrs Jo Tracey & Friends**
24 GRANGECLARE GLORY (IRE), 5, b g Fame And Glory—Annies Joy (IRE) **Prof C. Tisdall**
25 GREAT TEMPO (FR), 7, b g Great Pretender (IRE)—Prima Note (FR) **David Pipe Racing Club**
26 HUCCABY, 5, b g Arvico (FR)—Burrator **Somerset Racing**
27 HUGO 'N TAZ, 9, b g Kayf Tara—Ryde To Arms **ValueRacingClub.co.uk**
28 I'LLETYOUGONOW, 4, b f Bated Breath—Upskittled **Mrs J P E Cunningham & Mr G M Cunningham**
29 INDUNO (IRE), 6, b g Flemensfirth (USA)—Vast Consumption (IRE) **R. A. Bartlett**
30 INTO THE WOODS (IRE), 6, b g Milan—Wall of Silence (IRE) **Turner Webb**
31 ISRAEL CHAMP (IRE), 5, b g Milan—La Dariska (FR) **John White & Anne Underhill**

MR DAVID PIPE - continued

32 **JACBEQUICK,** 9, b g Calcutta—Toking N' Joken (IRE) **David Pipe Racing Club**
33 **JASMIN DES BORDES (FR),** 6, b g Great Pretender (IRE)—Queen des Bordes (FR) **John White & Anne Underhill**
34 **KEPAGGE (IRE),** 6, b g Getaway (GER)—Miracle Lady **Mrs S. J. Ling**
35 **KING'S MILLER (IRE),** 5, b g Stoovaway—Like A Miller (IRE) **The Angove Family**
36 **KING'S SOCKS (FR),** 8, b g King's Best (USA)—Alexandrina (GER) **Mr B. J. C. Drew**
37 **KNOW THE SCORE (IRE),** 7, b g Flemensfirth (USA)—Prairie Bell (IRE) **The Angove Family**
38 **LE GRAND ROCHER (FR),** 4, b g Saint des Saints (FR)—Belle du Roi (FR) **John White & Anne Underhill**
39 **LEGAL HISTORY (IRE),** 5, b g Lawman (FR)—Nina Celebre (IRE) **Middleham Park Racing XXXII & Partner 2**
40 **LITTLE RED LION (IRE),** 6, b g Sans Frontieres (IRE)—Rever Up (IRE) **David Pipe Racing Club**
41 **MAIN FACT (USA),** 7, b g Blame (USA)—Reflections **Munrowd's Partnership**
42 **MAKE ME A BELIEVER (IRE),** 5, br g Presenting—Kiltiernan Robin (IRE) **Prof. C. Tidsall & Jane Gerard-Pearse**
43 **MALANGEN (IRE),** 5, b g Born To Sea (IRE)—Lady's Locket (IRE) **Teddington CC Racing**
44 **MARTINHAL (IRE),** 5, b g Westerner—Gweedara (IRE) **Mrs L. Maclennan**
45 **MAX DO BRAZIL (FR),** 8, b g Blue Bresil (FR)—Lili Valley (FR) **Prof C. Tisdall & Mr B. Drew**
46 **MEEP MEEP MAG (IRE),** 6, b m Getaway (GER)—Deadly Pursuit (IRE) **Mr M. Lambert & Mrs R. White**
47 **MIDNIGHT MAGIC,** 8, b g Midnight Legend—Arctic Magic (IRE) **Midd Shire Racing**
48 **MISS M (IRE),** 6, b m Mastercraftsman (IRE)—Tintern **D. E. Pipe**
49 **MISS TYNTE (IRE),** 8, b m Mahler—Top Quality **N. Shutts**
50 **MR CLARKSON (IRE),** 8, b g Jeremy (USA)—Wynsleydale (USA) **Pipe's Prospectors**
51 **MRS MIGGINS (IRE),** 7, b m Presenting—Carrigeen Lunaria (IRE) **Mr Barry Wright & Mrs Rosemary White**
52 **NEW AGE DAWNING (IRE),** 6, ch g Stoovaway—Captain Supreme (IRE) **Brocade Racing**
53 **NIGHT EDITION (FR),** 4, b g Authorized (IRE)—Night Serenade (IRE) **Mr Mr Stuart & Simon Mercer & John Gent**
54 **NORDIC COMBINED (IRE),** 6, b g Haafhd—Chilly Filly (IRE) **Chris & David Stam**
55 **ORCHARD THIEVES (IRE),** 8, b g Ask—Ballycleary (IRE) **Brocade Racing**
56 **PANIC ATTACK (IRE),** 4, b f Canford Cliffs—Toto Corde Meo (IRE) **Mr B. Drew**
57 **PARICOLOR (FR),** 4, b g Orpen (USA)—Kadiana (IRE) **Mrs J P E Cunningham & Mr G M Cunningham**
58 **PERCY STREET,** 7, br g Sir Percy—Star of Gibraltar **Chris & David Stam**
59 **POKER PLAY (FR),** 7, ch g Martaline—Becquarette (FR) **The Angove Family**
60 **QUEEN ADELAIDE,** 5, b m Helmet (AUS)—Spunger **David Pipe & Partner**
61 **QUEENS CAVE (IRE),** 7, b m Court Cave (IRE)—Shuilan (IRE) **Mr K. Alexander**
62 **RAMSES DE TEILLEE (FR),** 8, gr g Martaline—Princesse d'Orton (FR) **John White & Anne Underhill**
63 **RATHLIN ROSE (IRE),** 12, b g Bonbon Rose (FR)—A Plus Ma Puce (FR) **Mr F. G. Wilson**
64 **REMASTERED,** 7, ch g Network (GER)—Cathodine Cayras (FR) **Brocade Racing**
65 **SEXY LOT (GER),** 4, b f Camelot—Saldennahe (GER) **Mr P. W. Garnsworthy**
66 **SHOOT TO FAME (IRE),** 6, b m Fame And Glory—Native Wood (IRE) **The Blue Ball Syndicate**
67 **STORY OF FRIENDS (FR),** 6, b g Kingsalsa (USA)—Royale Malinelle (FR) **Brocade Racing**
68 **STREAM LADY (IRE),** 7, b m Curtain Time (IRE)—Victory Queen (IRE) **G. D. Thompson**
69 **TAJ BADALANDABAD (IRE),** 10, ch g Shantou (USA)—Last Chance Lady (IRE) **W. F. Frewen**
70 **TEASER,** 5, b g Dansili—Tottie **The Willpower Partnership**
71 **THINKING (IRE),** 5, b g So You Think (NZ)—Laetoli (ITY) **N. Shutts**
72 **UMBRIGADO (IRE),** 6, br g Stowaway—Dame O'Neill (IRE) **John White & Anne Underhill**
73 **UN TEMPS POUR ELLE (FR),** 4, b f Cokoriko (FR)—Rougedespoir (FR) **Prof C. Tisdall & Mr B. Drew**
74 **VIEUX LION ROUGE (FR),** 11, ch g Sabiango (GER)—Indecise (FR) **Prof Caroline Tisdall & Mr John Gent**
75 **WHAT A MOMENT (IRE),** 10, b g Milan—Cuiloge Lady (IRE) **Bryan Drew & Steve Roper**
76 **YAA SALAAM (IRE),** 6, ch g Helmet (AUS)—Ya Hajar **Two Hopes**

Other Owners: Mrs A. E. M. Broom, Mr G. R. Broom, Mr G. M. Cunningham, Mrs J. P. E. Cunningham, Mr B. J. C. Drew, W. F. Frewen, J. A. Gent, Mrs J. Gerard-Pearse, Mr P. J. Green, The Hon Mrs D. Hulse, James & Jean Potter, Mr M. J. D. Lambert, Mr S. M. Mercer, Mr S. S. Mercer, Middleham Park Racing XXXII, B. G. Middleton, Mr M. A. Munrowd, Miss S. B. Munrowd, T. S. Palin, D. E. Pipe, M. C. Pipe, Mr J. E. Potter, Mrs M. J. Potter, M. Prince, Mr S. R. Roper, A. J. Shire, Dr C. Stam, Mr D. B. Stam, Prof C. Tisdall, Mrs J. Tracey, Mr P. Turner, Mrs A. Underhill, Mrs L. Webb, Mr A. J. White, Mrs R. E. White, Mr J. Williams, Mr B. Wright.

Assistant Trainer: Mr M. C. Pipe C.B.E.

NH Jockey: David Noonan, Tom Scudamore. **Amateur Jockey:** Mr Fergus Gillard.

436 MR CHARLES POGSON, Newark
Postal: Allamoor Farm, Mansfield Road, Farnsfield, Nottinghamshire, NG22 8HZ
Contacts: PHONE 01623 882275 MOBILE 07977 016155

1 ALLAMOOR BOY, 5, b g Kayf Tara—Candello P & P Wordingham, J Allott, C Pogson
2 BRIDEY'S LETTUCE (IRE), 8, b g Iffraaj—Its On The Air (IRE) C. T. Pogson
3 CUSHEEN BRIDGE (IRE), 12, b g Oscar (IRE)—One Hell Ofa Woman (IRE) Pete & Pauline Wordingham
4 DOUX PRETENDER (FR), 7, b g Great Pretender (IRE)—Lynnka (FR) C. T. Pogson
5 GETAWAY NORTH, 7, b g Getaway (GER)—Kings Equity (IRE) C. T. Pogson
6 MOIDORE, 11, b g Galileo (IRE)—Flash of Gold C. T. Pogson
7 MONDO CANE (IRE), 13, b g Beneficial—La Vita E Bella (FR) C. T. Pogson
8 OVERTOUGEORGE, 6, b g Overbury (IRE)—Captivating Tyna (IRE) C. T. Pogson
9 OVERTOUJAY, 10, b br g Overbury (IRE)—Ouh Jay Pete & Pauline Wordingham & Partner
10 QUASHA, 7, b m Black Sam Bellamy (IRE)—Gloriana Pete & Pauline Wordingham & Partner
11 ROLLERBALL ROCCO (IRE), 8, b g Ask—Jamica Ginger (IRE) Charles Pogson John Allott
12 SHADY OAKS (IRE), 7, b g Getaway (GER)—Naked Poser (IRE) Jjs Backers
13 WEST TO CROSSGALES (IRE), 9, b g Westerner—Mooreshill Bay (IRE) Pete & Pauline Wordingham & Partner

Other Owners: Mr J. Allott, M. T. Hughes, Pete & Pauline Wordingham, C. T. Pogson, Sotby Farming Company Limited, Mrs P. A. Wordingham, P. L. Wordingham.

Assistant Trainer: Adam Pogson.

NH Jockey: Adam Pogson.

---

437 MR JONATHAN PORTMAN, Upper Lambourn
Postal: Whitcoombe House Stables, Upper Lambourn, Hungerford, Berkshire, RG17 8RA
Contacts: PHONE 01488 73894 MOBILE 07798 824513
EMAIL jonathan@jonathanportmanracing.com WEBSITE www.jonathanportmanracing.com

1 ASHAZURI, 6, b m Dick Turpin (IRE)—Shesha Bear RWH Partnership
2 BALMORAL CASTLE, 11, b g Royal Applause—Mimiteh (USA) J. G. B. Portman
3 BROAD APPEAL, 6, ch g Medicean—Shy Appeal (IRE) J. G. B. Portman
4 DEVILS ROC, 4, gr f Lethal Force (IRE)—Ring For Baileys Roc Steady Partnership
5 ONEDOWNUNDER, 4, b g Aussie Rules (USA)—Saffron Fox M J Vandenberghe & Partners
6 ORIN SWIFT (IRE), 6, b g Dragon Pulse (IRE)—Hollow Green (IRE) Mr L. A. Bellman
7 POET'S MAGIC, 4, b f Poet's Voice—Magic Destiny R. Bailey
8 QUICK BREATH, 5, b g Bated Breath—Shy Appeal (IRE) Wood Street Syndicate
9 SPRING RUN, 4, ch f Nathaniel (IRE)—May Fox The Hon Mrs R. Pease
10 SWISS CHEER (FR), 4, b g Swiss Spirit—Happy Clapper Whitcoombe Park Racing
11 TOYBOX, 4, ch f Paco Boy (IRE)—Play Street Anthony Boswood & Mrs R Pease
12 WALK ON WALTER, 5, b g Footstepsinthesand—Hajmah (IRE) Mr P. V. Simpson

THREE-YEAR-OLDS
13 ANNIE QUICKSTEP (IRE), b c Epaulette (AUS)—Ragtime Dancer Fillies First
14 ARIETTA, b f Casamento (IRE)—Air Biscuit (IRE) Mrs Suzanne Williams & Partner
15 CLAN SPIRIT, b g Cable Bay (IRE)—Jessie's Spirit (IRE) Farraday Equine Partnership
16 DIVINE CONNECTION, b f Cable Bay (IRE)—Divine Power Turf Club 2018 & Partner 1
17 EVER AMBER (IRE), ch f Ivawood (IRE)—Much Faster (IRE) Berkeley Racing
18 GLORIOUS RETURN (IRE), ch g Camacho—Coming Back Kangyu International Racing (HK) Limited
19 GREATER LOVE, br f Brazen Beau (AUS)—Lovellian Mrs W Clifford
20 KING OF THE NORTH (IRE), b g Kodiac—Scotch Bonnet (IRE) Tony Wechsler & Ann Plummer
21 KOMMODITY KID (IRE), b g Kingston Hill—Sweetly Does It Mr L. A. Bellman
22 LADY MAGDA, b f Sir Percy—Alice's Dancer (IRE) Mr A. Chesterman
23 LETHAL TALENT, gr f Lethal Force (IRE)—Talent Spotter Whitcoombe Park Racing
24 B g Equiano (FR)—Miss Work of Art Absolute Solvents Ltd
25 NEVER SAID NOTHING (IRE), b g Hallowed Crown (AUS)—Semiquaver (IRE) Mr A. N. Brooke Rankin
26 ONE ABOVE (IRE), b f Dream Ahead (USA)—Walk On Water Bloomsbury Stud
27 PRETTY PACKET (FR), gr f Style Vendome (FR)—Costa Packet (IRE) Portlee Bloodstock

MR JONATHAN PORTMAN - continued

28 **RESTRICTED ACCESS**, b f Cable Bay (IRE)—Artistic Muse (IRE) **Mr and Mrs J Laws**
29 **ROCKMORE**, b g Mukhadram—Double Star **Mrs D. O. Joly**
30 **RUSSIAN RUMOUR (IRE)**, b f Make Believe—Russian Rave **Fillies First**
31 **SCHMOOZIE (IRE)**, b f Zoffany (IRE)—Steal The Show (NZ) **Bloomsbury Stud**
32 **SWEET REWARD (IRE)**, b g Acclamation—Dangle (IRE) **Mr A. Chesterman**
33 **THE BLUE BOWER (IRE)**, b f Morpheus—Blue Holly (IRE) **Mr A Sim**
34 **UP THE AISLE**, ch f Casamento (IRE)—Play Street **Anthony Boswood & Mrs R Pease**
35 **VILLANELLE**, b f Muhaarar—Station House (IRE) **Mascalls Stud**
36 **VISCHIO (IRE)**, b f Holy Roman Emperor (IRE)—Drifting Mist **Fillies First**

TWO-YEAR-OLDS

37 Ch c 24/04 French Navy—Alice's Dancer (IRE) (Clodovil (IRE)) **Old Stoic Racing Club**
38 Gr f 10/01 Hellvelyn—Arctic Moon (USA) (Raven's Pass (USA))
39 **BELAFONTE**, b c 27/04 Twilight Son—Scarlet Royal (Red Ransom (USA)) **Mr L. A. Bellman**
40 Gr f 21/03 Hellvelyn—Bellotta (Nayef (USA)) **Fillies First**
41 B f 21/04 Hot Streak (IRE)—Ebrah (Singspiel (IRE)) **Absolute Solvents Ltd**
42 B f 06/03 Adaay (IRE)—Fair Maiden (JPN) (Carnegie (IRE)) **Mrs M A Parker**
43 **FULL APPROVAL (IRE)**, b f 24/02 Mehmas (IRE)—Drifting Spirit (IRE) (Clodovil (IRE)) (14285) **Mr L. A. Bellman**
44 **HAVE TO HAVE**, b f 24/03 Havana Gold (IRE)—
　　　　　　　　　　　Having A Blast (USA) (Exchange Rate (USA)) (8000) **Mr A. N. Brooke Rankin**
45 **HELLAVAPACE**, gr f 13/04 Hellvelyn—Hasten (USA) (Lear Fan (USA))
46 **HESTERCOMBE**, b f 07/03 Hellvelyn—Heartsease (Pursuit of Love) **The Hon Mrs R. Pease**
47 B f 28/04 Pearl Secret—Jessie's Spirit (IRE) (Clodovil (IRE)) **Farraday Equine Partnership**
48 B c 02/03 Charming Thought—Keladora (USA) (Crafty Prospector (USA)) **Mr and Mrs J Laws**
49 B c 01/04 Havana Gold (IRE)—Lolamotion (Equiano (IRE)) **Whitcoombe Park Racing**
50 **MAJOR FORCE**, b c 08/02 Lethal Force (IRE)—Vesper (Kyllachy) (15000) **Whitcoombe Park Racing**
51 **MIA MIA**, b f 31/03 Charm Spirit (IRE)—Curly Come Home (Notnowcato) (10000) **M J Sinclair**
52 B c 16/04 Markaz (IRE)—Music Pearl (IRE) (Oratorio (IRE)) **Berkeley Racing**
53 **NEW HEIGHTS**, b f 17/03 Intello (GER)—How High The Sky (IRE) (Danehill Dancer (IRE)) (12000) **Simon Skinner**
54 **PENTREATH**, b c 01/04 Cable Bay (IRE)—Stresa (Pivotal) **Julie and David Martin**
55 **PEPPERCORN**, gr c 04/03 Lethal Force (IRE)—Tavy (Pivotal) **Mrs J Wigan**
56 B f 16/04 Cable Bay (IRE)—Shy Appeal (IRE) (Barathea (IRE)) **Berkeley Racing**
57 Ch f 22/04 Iffraaj—Station House (IRE) (Galileo (IRE)) **Mascalls Stud**
58 **STRIKE**, b c 02/04 Lethal Force (IRE)—Midnight Fling (Groom Dancer (USA)) **SA Emmet**
59 **SWALLOWDALE**, b f 19/02 Mukhadram—
　　　　　　　　　　　Windermere Island (Cadeaux Genereux) **CR Lambourne, M Forbes, D Losse**
60 B g 09/04 Sepoy (AUS)—Thiqa (IRE) (New Approach (IRE))
61 B c 25/04 Havana Gold (IRE)—Upskittled (Diktat)

Other Owners: Mr P Afia, Mr I Bath, A. R. Boswood, Mr D Brocklehurst, J. W. M. Brownlee, Mr & Mrs M. A. Burton, Mr F Camis, Mr A. N. Cheyne, G. F. Clark, Mr G Davies, Mr S Dawes, Mr S Dibb, Mr R Dollar, Miss R Emmet, Mr A Franklin, Mr C Hawkins, B. M. W. Hearn, Mrs S. J. Hearn, Mr J Hobson, Mr J Homan, Mr H Jones, Mr H Kimbell, Mr K Lau, Mr and Mrs J Laws, Col A. J. E. Malcolm, Mr S Mcphee, Mr C Nash, The Hon Mrs R. Pease, Portlee Bloodstock, J. G. B. Portman, Mr D Powell, Mr R Pritchard, Mr J Repard, M J Sinclair, Mr H Symmonds, Mrs A Tearne, Mr G Thomas, Mr P Tye, Whitcoombe Park Racing, Mr R White, Mr G Wickens.

Amateur Jockey: Mr J. Harding.

438	**MRS CAMILLA POULTON, Lewes**

Postal: **White Cottage, Stud Farm, Telscombe Village, Lewes, BN7 3HZ**
Contacts: PHONE **01273 300127**
EMAIL **camilla.poulton67@outlook.com**

1 **FRAMBOSIN BOY (IRE)**, 4, b g Finsceal Fior (IRE)—Formidable Guest **Miss V. Markowiak**
2 **HEMINGWAY (IRE)**, 6, ch g Dragon Pulse (IRE)—Degree of Honor (FR) **Mrs C. D. Poulton**
3 **INTO DEBT (IRE)**, 4, b g Paco Boy (IRE)—Katherine Parr **South Downs Racing**
4 **MILITRY DECORATION (IRE)**, 5, b g Epaulette (AUS)—Funcheon Vale (IRE) **Mrs C. D. Poulton**

MRS CAMILLA POULTON - continued

5 **MINELLA RISING (IRE)**, 8, b g King's Theatre (IRE)—Heltornic (IRE)
6 **NOBLE GLANCE**, 7, b m Schiaparelli (GER)—Ragdollianna **South Downs Racing**
7 **NORMAN THE RED**, 10, ch g Tobougg (IRE)—Linden Lime **Mr R. C. Moules**
8 **SASHCORD**, 4, b f Pour Moi (IRE)—Ms Cordelia (USA) **Mr J. N. Allen**

TWO-YEAR-OLDS

9 B c 03/06 Hallowed Crown (AUS)—Encore du Cristal (USA) (Quiet American (USA)) **P. S. Wardle**

Other Owners: Mrs C. D. Poulton, P. S. Wardle.

---

439 SIR MARK PRESCOTT BT, Newmarket

Postal: Heath House, Moulton Road, Newmarket, Suffolk, CB8 0DZ
Contacts: **PHONE** 01638 662117 **FAX** 01638 666572
EMAIL sirmark@heathhousestables.com **WEBSITE** www.heathhousestables.com
TWITTER @HeathHouseNkt

1 **BATTLE OF PARADISE (USA)**, 4, b g Declaration of War (USA)—
Garden of Eden (USA) **Charles C. Walker - Osborne House III**
2 **BRASSICA (IRE)**, 4, b f Australia—Lasilia (IRE) **Denford Stud**
3 **KODIAC PRIDE**, 4, b g Kodiac—Queen of Mean **Owners Group 046**
4 **LAND OF OZ**, 4, ch c Australia—Madame Defarge (IRE) **John Brown & Megan Dennis**
5 **MISS CELESTIAL (IRE)**, 4, b f Exceed And Excel (AUS)—Liber Nauticus (IRE) **John Pearce Racing Ltd**
6 **ROAD TO PARIS (IRE)**, 4, b g Champs Elysees—Alchemilla **Jones, Julian, Lee, Royle & Wicks**
7 **STARTER**, 4, b g Sea The Stars (IRE)—Froglet **Mr B. Haggas**
8 **THE GAME IS ON**, 4, b g Garswood—Paquerettza (FR) **Mr Timothy J. Rooney**

THREE-YEAR-OLDS

9 **ALPHABETICAL**, gr c Archipenko (USA)—Albanova **Tim Bunting - Osborne House III**
10 **ALPINISTA**, gr f Frankel—Alwilda **Miss K. Rausing**
11 **ANIMAL INSTINCT**, ch c Leroidesanimaux (BRZ)—Alea Iacta **G. Moore - Osborne House**
12 **ANNO LUCIS (IRE)**, gr g Mastercraftsman (IRE)—Summer's Eve **Attenborough,Casterton,Harenstam,JonesCG**
13 **BODYLINE (IRE)**, b c Australia—Eurirs (FR) **Tim Bunting - Osborne House IV**
14 **CAPLA CUBISTE**, b f Archipenko (USA)—Eurolink Artemis **Strawberry Fields Stud**
15 **CARIBENO**, ch c Archipenko (USA)—Cubanita **Charles C Walker - Osborne House IV**
16 **CEDAR CAGE**, b g Golden Horn—Faslen (USA) **Mr Paddy Barrett**
17 **CLIFF WIND**, gr f Invincible Spirit (IRE)—Fork Lightning (USA) **Denford Stud**
18 **ESCALADE (IRE)**, b f Canford Cliffs (IRE)—Sliding Scale **Mr & Mrs John Kelsey-Fry**
19 **FULL SPEIGHT (USA)**, ch g Speightstown (USA)—Athenian (IRE) **China Horse Club/Ballylinch Stud**
20 **GLEN FORCE (IRE)**, b c Gleneagles (IRE)—Lethal Quality (USA) **Mr G C Woodall & Partners**
21 **LANZEALOT**, b g Camelot—Blue Zealot (IRE) **Mrs Hoare, Mrs Hewins & Mr Castle**
22 **LE REVEUR (IRE)**, b g Dream Ahead (USA)—Don't Be **Mrs Olivia Hoare**
23 **LIMARO PROSPECT (IRE)**, b c Camacho—Ibecke **Mr R. Stedman**
24 **LISMORE (IRE)**, b f Zoffany (IRE)—Tecla (IRE) **Sonia M. Rogers & Anthony Rogers**
25 **MISS FRANGIPANI**, ch f Frankel—Miss Cap Estel **John Pearce Racing Ltd**
26 **PLEASURE GARDEN (USA)**, b g Union Rags (USA)—Garden of Eden (USA) **Charles C. Walker - Osborne House II**
27 **PRIVATE TREATY**, b f Pivotal—Between Us **Cheveley Park Stud**
28 **REVOLVER (IRE)**, b g Slade Power (IRE)—Swizzle Stick (IRE) **Ne'er Do Wells VI**
29 **SUNSET BREEZE**, b g Pivotal—Sunrise Star **Baxter, Gregson, Jenkins & Warman**
30 **TAIMA**, b f Make Believe—Highest **Denford Stud**
31 **TELL ME ALL**, b g Lope de Vega (IRE)—Confidential Lady **Cheveley Park Stud**
32 **THEHEARTNEVERLIES**, b g Oasis Dream—Albamara **Middleham Park Racing LIX**

TWO-YEAR-OLDS

33 **ALAGAPPA**, b f 05/05 Archipenko (USA)—Alma Mater (Sadler's Wells (USA)) **Miss K. Rausing**
34 **ALAMBRISTA**, ch f 28/04 Bobby's Kitten (USA)—Almiranta (Galileo (IRE)) **Miss K. Rausing**
35 B c 17/02 Exceed And Excel (AUS)—
Alchemilla (Dubai Destination (USA)) (180000) **H.H. SH Nasser Bin Hamad Al Khalifa**

SIR MARK PRESCOTT BT - continued

36 **ALERTA ROJA**, gr f 05/03 Golden Horn—Albaraka (Selkirk (USA)) **Miss K. Rausing**
37 **BELLOSA (IRE)**, b f 11/03 Awtaad (IRE)—Poole Belle (IRE) (Canford Cliffs (IRE)) (25740) **Sir Edmund Loder**
38 **BRYNELLO (FR)**, b c 17/03 Intello (GER)—Ellary (FR) **Middleham Park Racing XLV**
39 **CAPTAIN BONNY**, b f 25/02 Charm Spirit—Sea Pride **Bluehills Racing Limited**
40 **CHILL OUT (IRE)**, b f 14/03 Dark Angel (IRE)—Al Jasrah (IRE) (Shirocco (GER)) **Mt. Brilliant Farm & Ranch, LLC**
41 Ch f 24/03 Dragon Pulse (IRE)—Dancing Duchess (IRE) (Danehill Dancer (IRE)) (27000) **Mr Paddy Barrett**
42 **EAGLE'S REALM**, b c 17/03 Free Eagle (IRE)—Regal Realm (Medicean) (75000) **Cheveley Park Stud**
43 **FULL MARKS (IRE)**, b g 04/04 Markaz (IRE)—Zenella (Kyllachy) (50000) **W E Sturt - Osborne House**
44 **GAME PLAN**, gr f 09/04 Australia—Intrigued (Darshaan) **Denford Stud**
45 **HEAT AND DUST**, b f 21/04 Oasis Dream—Here To Eternity (USA) (Stormy Atlantic (USA)) **Miss K. Rausing**
46 **JACK BEAN**, b c 24/05 Golden Horn—Faslen (USA) (Fasliyev (USA)) (70000) **Mr Paddy Barrett**
47 **LINDWALL (IRE)**, ch c 06/04 Australia—
Cochabamba (IRE) (Hurricane Run (IRE)) (38000) **J Fishpool - Osborne House**
48 B c 19/05 Oasis Dream—Marika (Marju (IRE)) (40000) **Mrs Baxter, W Charnley, C Jenkins, P Lee**
49 **MEISTERZINGER (IRE)**, br g 30/03 Mastercraftsman (IRE)—
Zingeeyah (Singspiel (IRE)) (25740) **Budd,Greenwood,Gregson,Troubridge,Mailer**
50 B c 27/03 The Gurkha (IRE)—Merritt Island (Exceed And Excel (AUS)) **Mr & Mrs John Kelsey-Fry**
51 **MISS PALOMA**, b f 03/05 Sea The Moon (GER)—Miss Cap Estel (Hernando (FR)) **John Pearce Racing Ltd**
52 **POLAR ICE**, b c 04/03 Dansili—Queen of Ice (Selkirk (USA)) (120000) **Charles C. Walker - Osborne House**
53 **PREDOMINANT**, ch f 03/02 Dutch Art—Prominence **Cheveley Park Stud**
54 B c 13/03 Equiano (FR)—Primo Lady (Lucky Story (USA)) **Mr Malih L. Al Basti**
55 **PURRZEALOT**, b f 18/04 Bobby's Kitten—Blue Zealot (IRE) **Mrs Olivia Hoare & Mr J. M. Castle**
56 **REIVER LAW**, ch g 11/03 Archipenko (USA)—Cushat Law (IRE) (Montjeu (IRE)) **M & M Franklin**
57 **ROYAL PLEASURE (IRE)**, b c 19/02 Kingman—
Merry Jaunt (USA) (Street Sense (USA)) (110000) **Tim Bunting - Osborne House**
58 **SECRET BOX**, b c 21/02 Le Havre (IRE)—Red Box (Exceed And Excel (AUS)) **Cheveley Park Stud**
59 **SISU**, b f 23/03 Lawman (FR)—Salonmare (GER) (Manduro (GER)) (50000) **Lady Fairhaven & Erik Penser**
60 **SUMMER'S KNIGHT**, b c 11/04 Camelot—
Summer's Eve (Singspiel (IRE)) (40000) **P J McSwiney - Osborne House**
61 **THE TIDE TURNS**, ch c 14/02 Sea The Moon (GER)—
Red Roxanne (Rock of Gibraltar (IRE)) (30000) **Sir Mark Prescott Bt**
62 **YAGAN**, b c 09/03 Australia—Navajo Moon (IRE) (Danehill (USA)) (53195) **Middleham Park Racing L**

Other Owners: Mr N. Attenborough, Mr P. Bamford, Mr E. A. Baxter, Mrs J. Budd, Mr B. D. Burnet, Mr D. Casterton, Mr D. Ellis, Mr R. P. Fry, The Hon. R & G Greenwood, Mrs C. S. Gregson, Mr W. N. Greig, Mrs B. Harenstam, Irish National Stud, Mrs H. A. Jones, Mr P. M. Julian, Mr I. Mailer, Lady C. J. O'Reilly, Dr J. D. Royle, Mr M. A. C. Rudd, Mr M. J. Tracey, Sir T & Lady Troubridge, Mrs S. L. Warman, Mrs E. A. Wicks, Mr E. J. Williams.

Assistant Trainer: William Butler, **Pupil Assistant:** Tommy Lyon-Smith.

Flat Jockey: Luke Morris, Ryan Tate.

---

440 | **MISS KATY PRICE, Llanigon**
Postal: Willow Croft, Llanigon, Hay-On-Wye, Herefordshire, HR3 5PN
Contacts: PHONE 07976 820819
EMAIL katyprice2005@aol.com WEBSITE www.facebook.com/katypriceracing

1 **ALBERTO'S DREAM**, 11, b g Fantastic Spain (USA)—Molly's Folly **Wallys Dream Syndicate**
2 **CLONDAW RIGGER (IRE)**, 8, b g Stowaway—Daytona Lily (IRE) **Katy Price Racing Club**
3 **ECLAIR DES SABLONS (FR)**, 6, b g Noroit (GER)—Jolie Fabi (FR) **Mr N. Elliott**
4 **FARM THE ROCK (IRE)**, 9, b g Yeats (IRE)—Shades of Lavender (IRE) **Mr N. Elliott**
5 **HOLLOW PARK (IRE)**, 8, b m Flemensfirth (USA)—Love And Beauty (IRE) **Mr N. Elliott**
6 **ILLDOITTOMORROW**, 5, b g Norse Dancer (IRE)—Hearty Dove **Mr K. W. Price**
7 **ITSAMANSLIFE**, 7, b g Mahler—Medieval Banquet (IRE) **McLeish & Elliott**
8 **JENNYS DAY (IRE)**, 9, b g Daylami (IRE)—Jennys Oscar (IRE) **Mr N. Elliott**
9 **LUCCA LADY (IRE)**, 9, b m Milan—Trail Storm (IRE) **Making Hay**
10 **M' LADY MAY**, 6, ch m Phenomena—Lady Shirley Hunt **Miss E. Lewis**
11 **MINELLACELEBRATION (IRE)**, 10, b g King's Theatre (IRE)—Knocktartan (IRE) **Mr N. Elliott**

MISS KATY PRICE - continued

12 **OUT FOR JUSTICE (IRE)**, 7, b g Beneficial—Dustys Delight (IRE) **Alastair & Pippa McLeish**
13 **RATHNURE RANGER (IRE)**, 6, ch g Beneficial—Euro Magic (IRE) **Katy Price Racing Club**
14 **ROSEISAROSEISAROSE (IRE)**, 6, gr m Jeremy—Roses And Wine (IRE) **Alastair & Pippa McLeish**
15 **SEB'S SISTER (IRE)**, 5, b br m Arcadio (GER)—Knocktartan (IRE) **Peers Pleasure**
16 **TA DAAH**, 4, ch f Mount Nelson—Porcelain (IRE) **Mike Harris Racing Club**
17 **THROCKLEY**, 9, b g Passing Glance—Porcelain (IRE) **Mike Harris Racing Club**
18 **TRICKY CUSTOMER (IRE)**, 6, b g Aizavoski (IRE)—No More Chu Chu (IRE) **Out of Bounds & Katy Price**

Other Owners: Mr N. Elliott, A. D. I. Harris, Mr M. E. Harris, Katy Price Racing Club, Mr A. D. McLeish, Mrs P. J. McLeish, Out Of Bounds Racing Club, Miss K. J. Price.

---

441 **MR RICHARD PRICE, Hereford**
Postal: **Criftage Farm, Ullingswick, Hereford, Herefordshire, HR1 3JG**
Contacts: **PHONE 01432 820263 MOBILE 07929 200598**

1 **BELLEVARDE (IRE)**, 6, b m Kodiac—Pearl Mountain (IRE) **B. Veasey**
2 **BONJOUR STEVE**, 9, b g Bahamian Bounty—Anthea **B. Veasey**
3 **EASTERN LADY (IND)**, 7, ch m Dancing Forever (USA)—Oriental Lady (IRE) **K. Reece**
4 **FLIGHT TO NOWHERE**, 8, ch m Aeroplane—River Beauty **Mrs V. J. Morse**
5 **GRANDSTAND (IRE)**, 4, b g Kodiac—Lady Shanghai (IRE) **B. Veasey**
6 **HELLOFAGAME**, 5, b g Hellvelyn—Gracie's Games **Mr D. Prosser & Mr K. Warrington**
7 **INITIATIVE (IRE)**, 5, b g Excelebration (IRE)—Viking Fair **Mrs V. J. Morse**
8 **MAD BARRY**, 5, ch g Norse Dancer (IRE)—River Beauty **Mrs V. J. Morse**
9 **MEDICI MOON**, 6, ch g Medicean—Cockney Fire **The Cosimo Syndicate**
10 **OCEAN REACH**, 4, b f Phoenix Reach (IRE)—Ocean Transit (IRE) **Mr G E Amey & Mr D M Boddy**
11 **ROYAL BORN (IRE)**, 4, b g Born To Sea (IRE)—Albarouche **K. Reece**

Other Owners: Mr G. E. Amey, Mr D. Boddy, D. J. Prosser, K. A. Warrington.

Assistant Trainer: Jane Price.

---

442 **MR PETER PRITCHARD, Shipston-on-Stour**
Postal: **Upper Farm Lodge, Upper Farm, Whatcote, Shipston-On-Stour, Warwickshire, CV36 5EF**
Contacts: **MOBILE 07376 500499**
EMAIL pennypritch55@hotmail.co.uk

1 **EARCOMESALI**, 7, b m Passing Glance—Earcomesannie (IRE) **Mrs Alison Pritchard & Mr R W Stowe**
2 **FRANZ KLAMMER**, 8, b g Midnight Legend—Ski **Mr M. J. Miller**

Other Owners: Mrs A. D. Pritchard, Mr R. W. Stowe.

Assistant Trainer: Mrs E. Gardner.

NH Jockey: Tom Bellamy. **Conditional Jockey:** Charlie Hammond. **Amateur Jockey:** Claire Hardwick, Jordan Nailor.

---

443 **MR DENIS QUINN, Newmarket**
Postal: **Stockbridge Stables, 192 High Street, Newmarket, Suffolk, CB8 9AP**
Contacts: **MOBILE 07435 340008**

1 **GEORGE DRYDEN (IRE)**, 8, gr g Zebedee—Key To Fortune (GER) **Mr R. M. Grover**
2 4, B c Born To Sea (IRE)—Ice Rock (IRE)
3 **INTENSE STYLE (IRE)**, 8, ch g Intense Focus (USA)—Style Queen (IRE) **Miss C. McPhillips-Witt**
4 **JUAN HORSEPOWER**, 6, b g Foxwedge (AUS)—Elysee (IRE) **Miss C. McPhillips-Witt**
5 **STRICTLY ART (IRE)**, 7, b g Excellent Art—Sadinga (IRE) **Mr D. P. Quinn**

MR DENIS QUINN - continued

THREE-YEAR-OLDS

6 CASABLANCA KID (IRE), b c Worthadd (IRE)—Coill Cri (IRE) **Mr J. T. Mangan**
7 MRS MUNNELLY (IRE), b f Dandy Man (IRE)—Midnight Destiny (IRE) **Miss C. McPhillips-Witt**
8 NAVAJO EAGLE, b c Gleneagles (IRE)—Don't Forget Faith (USA) **Mr J. T. Mangan**
9 STAR OF ST LOUIS (FR), b c Style Vendome (FR)—Momix **Mr J. T. Mangan**

TWO-YEAR-OLDS

10 B c 30/03 Fountain of Youth (IRE)—So Discreet (Tragic Role (USA)) (2000)

444	**MR JOHN QUINN, Malton** Postal: **Bellwood Cottage Stables, Settrington, Malton, North Yorkshire, YO17 8NR** Contacts: **PHONE 01944 768370 MOBILE 07899 873304** EMAIL info@johnquinnracing.co.uk WEBSITE www.johnquinnracing.co.uk

1 AL KHERB, 5, b g Al Kazeem—Perfect Spirit (IRE) **Blackburn, Balfe & Partner**
2 AL SUIL EILE (FR), 4, gr g Alhebayeb (IRE)—Visual Element (USA) **Harmon, Bruton & Partner**
3 ALEXANDERTHEGREAT (FR), 5, b g Redoute's Choice (AUS)—Garota da Ipanema (FR) **The Top Silk Syndicate**
4 ASCOT WEEK (USA), 6, br g Lonhro (AUS)—Millenia **JJ Quinn Racing Ltd**
5 ASHINGTON, 5, b g Canford Cliffs (IRE)—Kadoma **Mr T. Alderson**
6 BODACIOUS NAME (IRE), 6, b g Famous Name—Nice Wee Girl (IRE) **JJ Quinn Racing Ltd**
7 BUGLER BOB (IRE), 4, ch g Dandy Man (IRE)—Callanish **Mr R. L. Houlton**
8 CAPTAIN JAMESON (IRE), 5, b g Camacho—Cross Section (USA) **The JAM Partnership**
9 CHEBSEY BEAU, 10, b g Multiplex—Chebsey Belle (IRE) **Kent, Greaves, Dawson**
10 CLEMENTO (IRE), 6, b g Canford Cliffs (IRE)—Street Style (IRE) **Blackburn, Balfe, Houlton**
11 4, Ch g Getaway (GER)—Collegeofknowledge **The Desperados 2**
12 DUSTY'S CHOICE (IRE), 5, gr g Elusive Pimpernel (USA)—Raheefa's Mix (IRE) **Mr & Mrs Paul & Clare Rooney**
13 EL ASTRONAUTE (IRE), 7, ch g Approve (IRE)—Drumcliffe Dancer (IRE) **Mr Ross Harmon Racing**
14 GEONICE (FR), 4, gr g Samum (GER)—Terenice (FR) **The Desperados 3**
15 INDIAN PURSUIT (IRE), 7, b g Compton Place—Church Melody **JJ Quinn Racing Ltd**
16 JE SUIS CHARLIE, 6, b g High Chaparral (IRE)—Fin **The JAM Partnership**
17 LOOK MY WAY, 6, b g Pour Moi (IRE)—Casual Glance **Drew & Ailsa Russell**
18 LORD RIDDIFORD (IRE), 5, gr g Zebedee—Beacon of Hope (IRE) **The JAM Partnership**
19 MR WAGYU (IRE), 5, ch g Choisir (AUS)—Lake Louise (IRE) **The New Century Partnership**
20 PROJECT BLUEBOOK (FR), 7, bl g Sinndar (IRE)—Apperella **Mr J. P. McManus**
21 SAFE VOYAGE (IRE), 7, b g Fast Company (IRE)—Shishangaan (IRE) **Mr R. Harmon**
22 SEA ART, 4, b g Born To Sea (IRE)—Kekova **JJ Quinn Racing Ltd**
23 SKEETAH, 4, b f Heeraat (IRE)—Skylla **The JAM Partnership**

THREE-YEAR-OLDS

24 BAL MAL (FR), b g The Wow Signal (IRE)—Nigwah (FR) **JJ Quinn Racing Ltd**
25 BUSINESS (FR), b c Siyouni (FR)—Mambo Mistress (USA) **Phoenix Thoroughbred Limited**
26 CHOCOLAAT HEER, b g Heeraat (IRE)—Calakanga **Richard Kent & Richard & Pam Dawson**
27 COASTAL MIST (IRE), gr g Gutaifan (IRE)—She's A Character **Hart Inn 1 & Partner**
28 COBRA EYE, b c Kodiac—Annie The Doc **Phoenix Thoroughbred Limited**
29 EBONY LEGEND, b f Camacho—Cross Section (USA) **The JAM Partnership**
30 FIRST IMPRESSION (IRE), b g Make Believe—Charmgoer (USA) **Blackburn, Fox, Mcwilliams & Pendelbury**
31 FRANKENSTELLA (IRE), b f Frankel—L'Ancresse (IRE) **Phoenix Thoroughbred Limited**
32 KEEP BUSY (IRE), b f Night of Thunder (IRE)—Look Busy (IRE) **Altitude Racing**
33 LIBERTY BEACH, b f Cable Bay (IRE)—Flirtinaskirt **Mr P. A. Wilkins**
34 LUCK ON SUNDAY (IRE), ch f Galileo (IRE)—Aleagueoftheirown (IRE) **Phoenix Thoroughbred Limited**
35 MAGNA MORALIA (IRE), gr g Gregorian (IRE)—Trentini (IRE) **The Desperados**
36 MELODY KING (IRE), b c Kodiac—Mekong Melody (IRE) **Phoenix Thoroughbred Limited**
37 MURITZ (IRE), ch f Free Eagle (IRE)—Super Saturday (IRE) **Mr W. Slattery**
38 MY DANDY DOC (IRE), b f Dandy Man (IRE)—Atishoo (IRE) **JJ Quinn Racing Ltd**
39 PARK LANE DANCER (IRE), br g Elzaam (AUS)—Greatest Dancer (IRE) **Simon Mulvany & Partner**

MR JOHN QUINN - continued

40 **PLYMOUTH ROCK (IRE)**, b g Starspangledbanner (AUS)—
Welcome Spring (IRE) **Tabor,Smith,Magnier & Shanahan**
41 **REBEL REDEMPTION**, gr g Lethal Force (IRE)—Tempting **The JAM Partnership**
42 **RECURRENT (IRE)**, b c Camacho—Night Sphere (IRE) **Phoenix Thoroughbred Limited**
43 **SARSANET (IRE)**, br f Kodiac—Duchess of Foxland (IRE) **Mr Ross Harmon & Partner**
44 **SHE'S EASYONTHEEYE (IRE)**, b f Kodiac—Bonnie Lesley (IRE) **The Odd One Out Partnership**
45 B g Heeraat (IRE)—Skylla
46 **TIME VOYAGE (IRE)**, b f Raven's Pass (USA)—Katherine Lee (IRE) **Honeycomb Stud Mr JO'Rourke & Mr G Fagan**
47 **TWIN PARADOX**, br br g Slade Power (IRE)—Malyana **Ross Harmon Racing & Partner**
48 **VALLETTA GOLD**, br gr f Gutaifan (IRE)—Anna Law (IRE) **Phoenix Thoroughbred Limited**
49 **VIRTUS AQUILA**, b g Gleneagles (IRE)—Sweet Coincidence **Mr Ross Harmon & Partner**
50 **WELL PLANTED (FR)**, b g Planteur (IRE)—Next Dream (FR) **Drew & Ailsa Russell**
51 **YUKON MISSION (IRE)**, b f Kodiac—Refuse To Give Up (IRE) **Phoenix Thoroughbred Limited**

TWO-YEAR-OLDS

52 B f 07/02 Kodiac—Asrafairy (IRE) (Zebedee) (80000)
53 B f 23/03 Charming Thought—Bint Aldar (Zoffany (IRE)) (9047) **Cufflinks & Cruise's**
54 **CHOSEN MARK (IRE)**, b c 05/03 The Last Lion (IRE)—
She's A Character (Invincible Spirit (IRE)) (19047) **A. Al Shaikh**
55 **EMIRATI DIRHAM (IRE)**, b c 31/03 Mehmas (IRE)—Golden Legacy (IRE) (Rossini (USA)) (38095) **A. Al Shaikh**
56 B c 13/03 Lethal Force (IRE)—Flycatcher (IRE) (Medicean) (14285) **MPS Racing Ltd**
57 B c 27/02 Territories (IRE)—Kotsi (IRE) (Nayef (USA)) **Phoenix Thoroughbred Limited**
58 **MISS NAY NEVER**, b f 12/02 No Nay Never (USA)—
Desert Sky (IRE) (Green Desert (USA)) (133333) **The Wild Rovers**
59 B f 19/04 The Gurkha (IRE)—Moore's Melody (IRE) (Marju (IRE)) (26000) **S & R Racing Partnership**
60 B f 08/04 Adaay (IRE)—Paella (IRE) (Oasis Dream) (19000) **Alchemy Bloodstock**
61 **VIRGINIA PLANE**, b f 25/02 Mehmas (IRE)—Flirtinaskirt (Avonbridge) **Mr P. A. Wilkins**
62 B c 13/02 Mayson—With Charm (USA) (Dubawi (IRE)) (14285) **Mrs Thompson Mrs Allen Adams & Cranston**

Other Owners: Mr D. E. Balfe, Mr J. N. Blackburn, Mr R. Blades, Mr J. Bruton, Mrs P. J. Dawson, Mr A. I. Derry, Mr J. I. Derry, Mr S. Furniss, Miss M. A. Greaves, Mr R. Harmon, Mr R. L. Houlton, JJ Quinn Racing Ltd, R. Kent, N. E. F. Luck, Mr R. Maddocks, Mrs S. Magnier, Mr S. Mulvany, Mrs S. Quinn, Mr S. A. T. Quinn, Mr M. Rapley, Mrs A. Russell, A. J. R. Russell, M. A. Scaife, Mrs L. M. Shanahan, D. Smith, M. Tabor.

Assistant Trainer: Sean Quinn.

Flat Jockey: Jason Hart. **Amateur Jockey:** Mr Kaine Wood.

---

445 **MR MICK QUINN, Newmarket**
Postal: 50 Edinburgh Road, Newmarket, Suffolk, CB8 0QF
Contacts: **PHONE** 01638 660017 **MOBILE** 07973 260054 **FAX** 01638 660017
EMAIL mickquinn2562@gmail.com

1 **COLONEL FRANK**, 6, b g Dutch Art—Loquacity **Mr K. F. C. Bruce**
2 **GREAT HALL**, 10, b g Halling (USA)—L'Affaire Monique **Mr M. Quinn**
3 **GREEK KODIAC (IRE)**, 4, b g Kodiac—Greek Easter (IRE) **Mr K. F. C. Bruce**
4 **INVINCIBLE LARNE (IRE)**, 4, b g Invincible Spirit (IRE)—Caphene **Mr K. F. C. Bruce**
5 **MRS DISCOMBE**, 4, b f Garswood—Dora's Sister (IRE) **Mr K. F. C. Bruce**
6 **PINK SHEETS (IRE)**, 6, b m Gold Well—Soft Skin (IRE) **Mr K. F. C. Bruce**
7 **PRINCESS HARLEY (IRE)**, 5, gr m Dark Angel (IRE)—Tonle Sap (IRE) **Mr K. F. C. Bruce**
8 **PRINCESS KEIRA**, 5, b m Acclamation—La Reine de Pearls (IRE) **Mr K. F. C. Bruce**
9 **THE NIGHT KING**, 5, b g Arcano—Semplicita (IRE) **Andy Viner, John Quorn, Mick Quinn**

THREE-YEAR-OLDS

10 B g Heeraat (IRE)—Anfield **Mr M. Quinn**
11 **EVENTFUL**, b f Oasis Dream—Spectacle **Mr K. F. C. Bruce**
12 **KELINDA DICE**, b f Hot Streak (IRE)—Dora's Sister (IRE) **Mr K. F. C. Bruce**
13 **PRINCESS SIYOUNI (IRE)**, b f Siyouni (FR)—Librettista (AUS) **Mr K. F. C. Bruce**

MR MICK QUINN - continued

14 **PURPLE POWER**, b br f Slade Power (IRE)—Peace Summit **Mr K. F. C. Bruce**
15 **RECALL THE SHOW**, ch c Showcasing—Rappel **Mr K. F. C. Bruce**

TWO-YEAR-OLDS

16 B f 08/02 Heeraat (IRE)—Icky Woo (Mark of Esteem (IRE)) **Mr K. F. C. Bruce**
17 **INVER PARK**, b c 13/03 Pivotal—Red Baton (Exceed And Excel (AUS)) (95000) **Mr K. F. C. Bruce**

Other Owners: Mr M. Quinn, J. E. Quorn, Mr A. Viner.

Assistant Trainer: Miss Karen Davies.

---

446 **MR ALASTAIR RALPH, Bridgnorth**
Postal: **Bynd Farm, Bynd Lane, Billingsley, Bridgnorth, Shropshire, WV16 6PQ**
Contacts: **WORK 01746 860807 PHONE 07912 184217**
WORK EMAIL info@alastairralphracing.co.uk WEBSITE www.alastairralphracing.co.uk

1 **AMANOFHISWORD (IRE)**, 5, gr g Mahler—Castle Lake (IRE) **B. Hawkins**
2 **BEAT STAR (IRE)**, 6, b g Beat Hollow—Bell Star (IRE) **Not The Turf Club**
3 **BILLINGSLEY (IRE)**, 8, b g Millenary—Retain That Magic (IRE) **Walters Plant Hire & Potter Group**
4 **BOB FORD (IRE)**, 13, b g Vinnie Roe (IRE)—Polar Lamb (IRE) **Only Fools Own Horses**
5 **BUTLER'S BRIEF (IRE)**, 5, b g Yeats (IRE)—She's On The Case (IRE) **You Can Be Sure**
6 **CALM AT SEA (IRE)**, 8, b m Gentlewave (IRE)—Belle Berry (FR) **James and Jean Potter Ltd**
7 **CHAMPAGNE MIST (IRE)**, 8, b g Stowaway—Valentines Misty (IRE) **Only Fools Own Horses**
8 **CHANCEUX (IRE)**, 4, b g Mahler—Granny Mc Cann (IRE) **Rskm Bloodstock**
9 **COMBER MILL (FR)**, 8, ch g Le Fou (IRE)—Kalistina (FR) **Rrrs Partnership**
10 **CUT THE CORNER (IRE)**, 12, br g Vinnie Roe (IRE)—Snipe Victory (IRE) **Mr Mike Fothergill**
11 **DAMUT I'M OUT (IRE)**, 10, b g Gamut (IRE)—Five Cents More (IRE) **Costello/Ralph Racing Partnership**
12 4, B g Dunaden (FR)—Dancing Emily (IRE) **Rskm Bloodstock**
13 **DRENAGH (IRE)**, 5, b g Kalanisi—Diva Antonia (IRE) **B. Hawkins**
14 **ENCOUNTER A GIANT (IRE)**, 8, b g Kalanisi—Sumability (IRE) **B. Hawkins**
15 **EVENSTEVENS (IRE)**, 5, b g Getaway (GER)—Native Diva (IRE) **Not The Turf Club**
16 **GENTLE RIVER**, 4, b g Gentlewave (IRE)—Absalom's Girl **Mr A. Ralph**
17 **GETAWAY TOTHEROCK (IRE)**, 7, b m Getaway (GER)—Theft **James, Archer, Ralph & Gentech**
18 **GIOVANNI ROYALE**, 4, ch g Schiaparelli (GER)—Benefique Royale **Mr Len Jakeman**
19 **GREEN ETOILE**, 4, ch g Nathaniel (IRE)—Myriades d'Etoiles (IRE) **Against All Odds Racing**
20 **GROOVEUR (FR)**, 4, b g Ballingarry (IRE)—Kelle Home (FR) **Prm Bloodstock**
21 **GUSTAVE MAHLER (IRE)**, 10, ch g Mahler—Kloetta (IRE) **Rc Jones & Mh Jones & Jc Jones**
22 **KABRIT (IRE)**, 5, ch g Mastercraftsman (IRE)—Twinkling Ice (USA) **Alastair Ralph Racing**
23 **KNICKERBOCKERGLORY (IRE)**, 4, b g Fame And Glory—The Brass Lady (IRE) **Prm Bloodstock**
24 **LADY SALLY (IRE)**, 6, b m Scorpion (IRE)—Broken Gale (IRE) **Mr A. Ralph**
25 **LUNAR LANDER (IRE)**, 4, b g Shirocco (GER)—Bean Ki Moon (IRE) **Prm Bloodstock**
26 **MASTER SUNRISE (IRE)**, 11, ch g Blueprint (IRE)—Aunty Dawn (IRE) **Mr M. H. Jones**
27 **MEMPHIS BLEEK**, 4, ch g Olympic Glory (IRE)—Party (IRE) **Only Fools Own Horses**
28 **MICK MONA (FR)**, 6, ro m Blue Bresil (FR)—Mick Toscane (FR) **The Burling Family Ltd**
29 **MIX OF CLOVER**, 6, b g Fair Mix (IRE)—Allforclover (IRE) **Miss S. Troughton**
30 **MUCHO TALENTO**, 4, b g Intello (GER)—Moiava (FR) **B. Hawkins**
31 **OLD PRIDE (IRE)**, 12, ch g Old Vic—Feel The Pride (IRE) **Mrs D Ralph & Mrs S Rimell**
32 **OUR ROCKSTAR (IRE)**, 6, b m Gold Well—Hazel Mist (IRE) **Strutting Cockerels Syndicate**
33 **QUEEN'S SOLDIER (GER)**, 4, b g Soldier Hollow—Queen Mum (GER) **B. Hawkins**
34 **RISK D'ARGENT (FR)**, 4, gr g My Risk (FR)—Villebruyere (FR) **Prm Bloodstock**
35 **SEYMOUR SOX**, 6, b g Multiplex—Seymour Chance **Mrs C J Black & Mrs Sue Briscoe**
36 **TAP TAP BOOM**, 6, ro g Foxwedge (AUS)—Exclusive Approval (USA) **Mr A. Ralph**
37 **TEMPURAN**, 11, b g Unbridled's Song (USA)—Tenderly (IRE) **Rrrs Partnership**
38 **TENNEWROW (IRE)**, 8, b m Stowaway—Silent Supreme (IRE) **Mr A. R. Bickmore**
39 **WHITE TURF (IRE)**, 5, gr g Clodovil (IRE)—Holda (IRE) **Only Fools Own Horses**
40 **YOUR BAND**, 5, b g Helmet (AUS)—Kampai **Only Fools & Cockerels**

MR ALASTAIR RALPH - continued

Other Owners: Mrs C. A. Archer, Mrs C. J. Black, Mrs S. Briscoe, Mrs M. P. Costello, Mr I. James, James, Archer & Ralph, Mr J. C. Jones, Mr M. H. Jones, Mr R. C. Jones, Mrs K. L. Maxwell, Mr B. Morgan, Only Fools Own Horses, Miss I. H. Pickard, Prm Bloodstock, Mr A. Ralph, Mrs D. J. Ralph, Mr R. D. Ralph, Mrs S. M. Rimell, Mr R. J. Simpson, Spiers & Hartwell Ltd, Strutting Cockerels Syndicate, Sundorne Products (Llanidloes) Ltd, Walters Plant Hire Ltd.

Assistant Trainer: Liam Treadwell, **Head Lad:** Callum Griffiths, **Secretary:** Bundle Pickard, **Yard Sponsor:** Planned Office Interiors Ltd.

NH Jockey: Lee Edwards, Liam Treadwell. **Conditional Jockey:** Tabitha Worsley. **Amateur Jockey:** Mr Alex Edwards, Mr Adam O'Shea.

---

447 | **MR TIM REED, Hexham**
Postal: Moss Kennels, Haydon Bridge, Hexham, Northumberland, NE47 6NL
Contacts: **PHONE 01434 344016 MOBILE 07703 270408**
EMAIL timreedracing@gmail.com

1 **BORDER BREAKER (IRE)**, 11, br g Indian Danehill (IRE)—Flying Answer (IRE) **Mr W. T. Reed**
2 **CARLINGFORD PRINCE (IRE)**, 11, ch g Definite Article—Castle Hope (IRE) **Mr W. T. Reed**
3 **INDIAN TEMPLE (IRE)**, 11, b g Indian River (FR)—Ballycraggan (IRE) **Mr J. K. Huddleston**
4 **LEVEROCK LASS (IRE)**, 7, b m Olden Times—Hazelhall Princess (IRE) **Beswick Brothers Bloodstock**
5 **WEAVE SOME MAGIC**, 5, b g Cityscape—Didbrook **Beswick Brothers Bloodstock**

Assistant Trainer: Mrs E. J. Reed.

Conditional Jockey: Harry Reed.

---

448 | **MR DAVID REES, Haverfordwest**
Postal: The Grove Yard, Clarbeston Road, Haverfordwest, Pembrokeshire, SA63 4SP
Contacts: **PHONE 01437 731308 MOBILE 07775 662463 FAX 01437 731551**
EMAIL davidreesfencing@lineone.net

1 **BENI LIGHT (FR)**, 9, b g Crossharbour—Or Light (FR) **Another Day Out**
2 **BUCK BRAVO (IRE)**, 8, b g Mahler—Damoiselle **D. A. Rees**
3 **CAVEAT EMPTOR (IRE)**, 7, b g Arcadio (GER)—Castle Supreme (IRE) **Miss R. R. I. Howells**
4 **DREAM BOLT (IRE)**, 12, ch g Urban Ocean (FR)—Riviera Dream (IRE) **Mr D A Rees & Mr N Adams**
5 **FLYING GARRY (FR)**, 5, gr g Ballingarry (IRE)—Quezac du Boulay (FR) **Harp Racing**
6 **GONE PLATINUM (IRE)**, 11, b g Mountain High (IRE)—Miss Platinum (IRE) **D. A. Rees**
7 **KARANNELLE (IRE)**, 5, b m Nathaniel (IRE)—Dance Lively (USA) **Eddie & Dai**
8 **KIERA ROYALE (IRE)**, 9, ch m Beneficial—Llancillo Lady (IRE) **D. A. Rees**
9 **MISTY MAI (IRE)**, 10, b m Westerner—Arcanum (IRE) **Eddie & Dai**
10 **ROBIN OF SHERWOOD (IRE)**, 7, b br g Robin des Pres (FR)—Galleta **West Is Best**
11 **STEEL NATIVE (IRE)**, 9, b g Craigsteel—Princess Gloria (IRE) **D. A. Rees**

Other Owners: Mr N. W. Adams, Miss A. Freeman, Mrs J. Mathias, Mr E. W. Morris, D. A. Rees, Mr J. E. Rees, Mr R. Williams.

---

449 | **MRS HELEN REES, Dorchester**
Postal: Distant Hills, Chalmington, Dorchester, Dorset, DT2 0HB
Contacts: **PHONE 07715 558289**
EMAIL helen-rees@live.co.uk

1 **BEYOND SUPREMACY (IRE)**, 8, b g Beneficial—Slaney Athlete (IRE) **Mrs H. E. Rees**
2 **SERJEANT PAINTER**, 5, b g Royal Applause—Szabo's Art **Mrs H. E. Rees**

450 MR SEAN REGAN, Middleham
Postal: **Low Beck, Coverham, Middleham, Leyburn, North Yorkshire, DL8 4TJ**
Contacts: **MOBILE 07866 437476**
EMAIL sean@seanreganracing.com WEBSITE www.seanreganracing.com

1 **CHEEKY RICCO**, 6, ch g Shirocco (GER)—Good Thinking **Miss M. Anderson**
2 **PROSECUTE (FR)**, 7, b g Lawman (FR)—Dissitation (IRE) **Mrs C. D. Taylor**
3 **SOUTHVIEW LADY**, 8, b m Misu Bond (IRE)—Salalah **S. Regan**
4 **TOM'S ANNA (IRE)**, 10, b m Antonius Pius (USA)—Vanilla Delight (IRE) **Mrs C. D. Taylor**

451 MRS LYDIA RICHARDS, Chichester
Postal: **Lynch Farm, Hares Lane, Funtington, Chichester, West Sussex, PO18 9LW**
Contacts: **PHONE 01243 574882 MOBILE 07803 199061**
EMAIL lydia.richards@sky.com

1 **CERTAINLY RED**, 6, ch g Midnight Legend—Venetian Lass **The Venetian Lad Partnership**
2 **CITY TOUR**, 4, b g Dutch Art—Privacy Order **Mrs E. F. J. Seal**
3 **GOLD DECREE (IRE)**, 8, b g Golan (IRE)—De Verdict (IRE) **Mrs L. Richards**
4 **GOOD NEWS**, 8, b g Midnight Legend—Venetian Lass **The Good News Partnership**
5 **MONSIEUR FOX**, 5, b g Foxwedge (AUS)—Demoiselle Bond **The Demoiselle Bond Partnership**
6 **MURHIB (IRE)**, 8, b g Sea The Stars (IRE)—Mood Swings (IRE) **The Murhib Partnership**
7 **RIFFT (IRE)**, 5, b g Iffraaj—Toquette (IRE) **Mrs L. Richards**
8 **ROYAL GOLDIE (IRE)**, 5, b m Havana Gold (IRE)—Dream Maker (IRE) **Mrs E. F. J. Seal**
9 **SMITH (IRE)**, 4, ch g Dawn Approach (IRE)—Alazeya (IRE) **Mrs L. Richards**
10 4, Gr ro f Alkaased (USA)—Venetian Lass

452 MR NICKY RICHARDS, Greystoke
Postal: **Rectory Farm, Greystoke, Penrith, Cumbria, CA11 0UJ**
Contacts: **HOME 017684 83160 PHONE 017684 83392 MOBILE 07771 906609 FAX 017684 83933**
EMAIL office@nickyrichardsracing.com WEBSITE www.nickyrichardsracing.com

1 **AMBEROSE**, 7, ch m Sulamani (IRE)—Miss Nellie (IRE) **Langdale Bloodstock**
2 **BERNARDELLI (IRE)**, 12, b g Golan (IRE)—Beautiful Blue (IRE) **Henriques & Lloyd-Bakers**
3 **BETTER GETALONG (IRE)**, 9, b g Gold Well—Arequipa (IRE) **Straightline Bloodstock**
4 **BIG BAD BEAR (IRE)**, 6, br g Jeremy (USA)—Our Polly (IRE) **Tor Side Racing**
5 **BOA ISLAND (IRE)**, 10, b g Trans Island—Eskimo Kiss (IRE) **Mr R. A. Clarke**
6 **CAIUS MARCIUS (IRE)**, 9, b g King's Theatre (IRE)—Ain't Misbehavin (IRE) **C. P. Norbury**
7 **CASTLE RUSHEN (IRE)**, 5, b g Fame And Glory—Rosie Suspect (IRE) **Mr T. J. Hemmings**
8 **CATHAL'S STAR**, 7, ch g Malinas (GER)—Hand Inn Glove **Charlie Doocey / Cathal Doocey**
9 **CHAPEL STILE (IRE)**, 8, b g Scorpion (IRE)—Peggy Cullen (IRE) **Langdale Bloodstock**
10 **CHATEAU ROBIN (IRE)**, 9, br g Robin des Pres (FR)—
               Bella With A Zee (IRE) **Mrs I. C. Sellars & Major & Mrs P. Arkwright**
11 **CHIDSWELL (IRE)**, 11, b g Gold Well—Manacured (IRE) **David & Nicky Robinson**
12 **COURT DREAMING (IRE)**, 7, b g Court Cave (IRE)—Louis's Teffia (IRE) **Dark Horse Racing Ltd**
13 **CULTRAM ABBEY**, 13, br g Fair Mix (IRE)—Kansas City (FR)
14 **DUKE OF NAVAN (IRE)**, 12, b br g Presenting—Greenfieldflyer (IRE) **David & Nicky Robinson**
15 **ELIOS D'OR (FR)**, 6, b g Puit d'Or (IRE)—Naker Mome (FR) **Langdale Bloodstock**
16 **FLY BY MILAN (IRE)**, 5, b g Milan—So Proper (IRE) **Langdale Bloodstock**
17 **GLENDUFF (IRE)**, 6, b g Gold Well—Last of The Bunch **Mr T. J. Hemmings**
18 **GLINGER FLAME (IRE)**, 8, ro g Daylami (IRE)—Titian Flame (IRE) **Mr James Westoll**
19 **GLITTERING LOVE (IRE)**, 8, b g Winged Love (IRE)—Glittering Image (IRE) **Mr & Mrs Paul & Clare Rooney**
20 **GUITAR PETE (IRE)**, 10, gr g Dark Angel (IRE)—Innishmore (IRE) **Mrs Pat Sloan**
21 **HEADSCARF LIL (IRE)**, 8, b m Getaway (GER)—Bleu Money (IRE) **Tarzan Bloodstock & Mr Oliver Brownlee**
22 **HIGHLAND GOLD**, 6, b m Yeats (IRE)—Crevamoy (IRE) **Distillery Stud**
23 **HOLME ABBEY**, 7, b g Fair Mix (IRE)—Brockwell Abbey **The Roper Family**

MR NICKY RICHARDS - continued

24 **IMADA (IRE)**, 10, br g Arcadio (GER)—Anck Su Namun (IRE) **Kenny & Laura Haughey**
25 **KAJAKI (IRE)**, 7, gr g Mastercraftsman (IRE)—No Quest (IRE) **Mr F. Gillespie**
26 **KITTY HALL (IRE)**, 6, b m Fame And Glory—Set In Her Ways (IRE) **Langdale Bloodstock**
27 **LANTY SLEA (IRE)**, 5, b g Beat Hollow—Catleen (IRE) **Langdale Bloodstock**
28 **LEGAL BEAGLE (IRE)**, 5, b g Rule of Law (USA)—
                                 Knockamullen Girl (IRE) **Mrs I. C. Sellars & Major & Mrs P. Arkwright**
29 **MAROWN (IRE)**, 6, b g Milan—Rosie Suspect (IRE) **Mr T. J. Hemmings**
30 **MAYO STAR (IRE)**, 8, b g Stowaway—Western Whisper (IRE) **Charlie Doocey / Cathal Doocey**
31 **MISS MILANO (IRE)**, 5, b m Milan—Dewasentah (IRE) **Tor Side Racing**
32 **MURVAGH BEACH (IRE)**, 5, ch g Doyen (IRE)—Magic Park (IRE) **David & Nicky Robinson**
33 **MY OLD GOLD (IRE)**, 10, b m Gold Well—Tenbo (IRE) **Tor Side Racing**
34 **NELLS SON**, 5, b h Trans Island—Miss Nellie (IRE) **Langdale Bloodstock**
35 **NO REGRETS (IRE)**, 6, b g Presenting—E Mac (IRE) **Straightline Bloodstock**
36 **NOTNOW SEAMUS**, 9, b g Notnowcato—Special Beat **Mr G. Houghton**
37 **ON A PROMISE (IRE)**, 8, gr g Definite Article—Silvers Promise (IRE) **Straightline Bloodstock**
38 **PETITE GANACHE (IRE)**, 8, ch g Presenting—Ain't Misbehavin (IRE) **Golden Dragon Racing**
39 **REIVERS LAD**, 9, b g Alflora (IRE)—Reivers Moon **Mr J. M. Stenhouse**
40 **RIBBLE VALLEY (IRE)**, 7, b g Westerner—Miss Greinton (GER) **D. Wesley-Yates**
41 **RUBYTWO**, 8, b m Sulamani (IRE)—Miss Nellie (IRE) **Langdale Bloodstock**
42 **SERIOUS EGO (GER)**, 7, b g Sholokhov (IRE)—Sunshine Story (IRE) **Kenny & Laura Haughey**
43 **SHE'S A ROCCA (IRE)**, 5, b m Shirocco (GER)—
                                 Hannigan's Lodger (IRE) **Mrs I. C. Sellars & Major & Mrs P. Arkwright**
44 **SIMPLY NED (IRE)**, 13, ch g Fruits of Love (USA)—Bishops Lass (IRE) **David & Nicky Robinson**
45 **SKIDDAW TARA**, 6, b g Kayf Tara—Bob Back's Lady (IRE) **J. R. Wills**
46 **SKIDDAW VALLEYS**, 8, ch g Three Valleys (USA)—Skiddaw Wolf **J. R. Wills**
47 **TAKINGRISKS (IRE)**, 11, b g Golden Tornado (IRE)—Downtown Rosie (IRE) **Mr F. Bird**
48 **UNCLE ALASTAIR**, 8, b g Midnight Legend—Cyd Charisse **Mr & Mrs Paul & Clare Rooney**
49 **UNCLE JONTY**, 8, b g Fruits of Love (USA)—Spend Accordingly (IRE) **Mr T. J. Hemmings**
50 **UNIVERSAL FOLLY**, 5, b g Universal (IRE)—Madam Jolie (IRE) **Tor Side Racing**
51 **WETLANDS (IRE)**, 5, b g Westerner—Un Jour D Ete (FR) **Mr T. J. Hemmings**

Other Owners: Mr R. F. Bennett, Mr A. Cartledge, Celtic Shamrock Racing, J. A. Dudgeon, Mrs R. L. Elliot, Mr N. T. Gallagher, M. Henriques, Miss R. K. Hill, R. Kent, Mrs E. M. Lloyd, Mr H. Lloyd-Baker, E. Q. Melville, Multiple Sclerosis Borders Racing Club, Mr E. C. Norris, Mr A. C. R. Stubbs, Mr A. Walker.

Assistant Trainer: Miss Joey Richards, Mr Harry Haynes.

NH Jockey: Ryan Day, Brian Hughes, Craig Nichol. **Conditional Jockey:** Danny McMenamin. **Amateur Jockey:** Mr Lyall Hodgins.

---

453   **MR JOHN DAVID RICHES, Pilling**
Postal: Moss Side Farm, Off Lancaster Road, Scronkey, Pilling, Lancashire, PR3 6SR
Contacts: **PHONE 01253 799190**
EMAIL jrracing@btinternet.com

1 **ANGEL EYES**, 5, b m Piccolo—Miacarla **J R Racing**
2 **PICKS PINTA**, 9, b g Piccolo—Past 'n' Present **J R Racing**
3 **TRULOVE**, 7, b m Piccolo—Snow Dancer (IRE) **J R Racing**

THREE-YEAR-OLDS

4 **MR GAMBINO**, b g Music Master—Snow Dancer (IRE) **J R Racing**
5 **RAIN CAP**, b g Fountain of Youth (IRE)—Rough Courte (IRE) **J R Racing**
6 **STORM MASTER**, b g Music Master—Miacarla **J R Racing**

Other Owners: J. D. Riches, Mrs L. Wohlers.

454 **MR MARK RIMELL, Witney**
Postal: Fairspear Equestrian Centre, Fairspear Road, Leafield, Witney, Oxfordshire, OX29 9NT
Contacts: PHONE 01993 878551 MOBILE 07778 648303, 07973 627054
EMAIL rimell@rimellracing.com WEBSITE www.rimellracing.com

1 DORTON GIRL, 6, gr m Geordieland (FR)—Cash Crisis (IRE) **Miss S. M. L. Parden**
2 ENDLESS ADVENTURE, 5, b g And Beyond (IRE)—Gulshique **Mrs C. Mackness**
3 I'M A STARMAN, 7, ch g Schiaparelli (GER)—Strathtay **M. G. Rimell**
4 KYLLACHY DRAGON (IRE), 5, b g Dragon Pulse (IRE)—Lafayette (GER) **M. G. Rimell**
5 MAGIC MIRROR, 7, b m Dutch Art—Balatoma (IRE) **Bill Wood & Mark Rimell**

Other Owners: M. G. Rimell, Mr W. J. Wood.

Assistant Trainer: Anne Rimell.

455 **MR DAVE ROBERTS, Kenley**
Postal: Leasowes Farm, Kenley, Shrewsbury, Shropshire, SY5 6NY
Contacts: PHONE 07854 550606

1 ADMAN SAM (IRE), 9, b g Black Sam Bellamy (IRE)—Koral Bay (FR) **Mr P. A. Downing**
2 BLUE RAMBLER, 10, b g Monsun (GER)—La Nuit Rose (FR) **Mr P. A. Downing**
3 CALIFORNIA SOUL (IRE), 9, b g Yeats (IRE)—Pointing North (USA)
4 4, B f Norse Dancer (IRE)—Cat Six (USA) **D. B. Roberts**
5 G'DAY AUSSIE, 7, b g Aussie Rules (USA)—Moi Aussi (USA) **Mr D. Bradbury**
6 LILY ASH (IRE), 7, b h Lilbourne Lad (IRE)—Ashdali (IRE)
7 RACING SPIRIT, 8, ch g Sir Percy—Suertuda (IRE) **D. B. Roberts**
8 SACKFULLOFDREAMS (IRE), 7, b g Rock of Gibraltar (IRE)—Nymphaea Alba (IRE) **D. B. Roberts**
9 TSUNDOKU (IRE), 9, ch m Medicean—Toberanthawn (IRE) **D. B. Roberts**
10 UNSAFE CONDUCT, 7, ch g Pasternak—Symbiosis **Mr D. Bradbury**
11 VIF ARGENT (FR), 11, b g Dom Alco (FR)—Formosa (FR) **D. B. Roberts**

THREE-YEAR-OLDS

12 CURRENT, b c Equiano (FR)—Updated (FR)

TWO-YEAR-OLDS

13 Ch c 07/05 Cannock Chase (USA)—Cat Six (USA) (Tale of The Cat (USA)) **D. B. Roberts**
14 B c 04/04 Bathyrhon (GER)—Russian Memories (FR) (Slickly (FR)) **Mr P. A. Downing**

456 **MR MIKE ROBERTS, Hailsham**
Postal: Summertree Farm, Bodle Street Green, Hailsham, East Sussex, BN27 4QT
Contacts: PHONE 01435 830231 MOBILE 07774 208040
EMAIL mike@summertree-racing.com

1 ANDAPA (FR), 6, br m Kapgarde (FR)—Daniety (FR) **M. J. Roberts**
2 CONCHITA (GER), 5, b m Zoffany (IRE)—Cross Check (IRE) **M. J. Roberts**
3 DREAM BAIE (FR), 7, b g Crillon (FR)—Montaraza (FR) **M. J. Roberts**
4 KING MURO, 10, b g Halling (USA)—Ushindi (IRE) **M. J. Roberts**
5 PERFECT MOMENT (IRE), 7, b m Milan—Faucon (FR) **M. J. Roberts**
6 PRONOUNCED (IRE), 6, b g Power—Le Montrachet **Mrs M. Martin**
7 VIA VOLUPTA, 10, b m Kayf Tara—Via Ferrata (FR) **M. J. Roberts**

Assistant Trainer: Marie Martin.

457 **MISS SARAH ROBINSON, Bridgwater**
Postal: **Newnham Farm, Shurton, Stogursey, Bridgwater, Somerset, TA5 1QG**
Contacts: **PHONE 01278 732357 MOBILE 07866 435197, 07518 785291 FAX 01278 732357**
EMAIL info@sarahrobinsonracing.co.uk WEBSITE www.sarahrobinsonracing.co.uk

1 **CONTROL ME (IRE)**, 6, b m Yeats (IRE)—Cullian **Neil & Simon Racing Partnership**
2 **DONT CALL ME DORIS**, 10, b m Franklins Gardens—Grove Dancer **Mr M. L. J. Fooks**
3 **GOULANES (IRE)**, 14, b g Mr Combustible (IRE)—Reboglane (IRE) **Mr B. Robinson**
4 **MARTHA'S DREAM**, 6, ch m Captain Gerrard (IRE)—Rose Bounty **Mr B. Robinson**
5 **MILLIE'S FLYING**, 7, b m Franklins Gardens—Grove Dancer **Mr M. L. J. Fooks**

Assistant Trainer: Mr B. Robinson, Mr R. J. Bailey.

NH Jockey: James Best. **Conditional Jockey:** Kieron Edgar, Dan Heskin. **Amateur Jockey:** Miss S. Robinson.

458 **MISS PAULINE ROBSON, Capheaton**
Postal: **Kidlaw Farm, Capheaton, Newcastle Upon Tyne, NE19 2AW**
Contacts: **PHONE 01830 530241 MOBILE 07814 708725, 07721 887489**
EMAIL pauline@prracing.co.uk

1 **BALLADEER**, 4, b g Poet's Voice—Diamond Run **Mr E. A. Elliott**
2 **BALLYDONAGH BOY (IRE)**, 6, b g Le Fou (IRE)—Hindi (FR) **It's a Bargain Syndicate**
3 **CASTLETOWN (FR)**, 8, gr g Poliglote—Message Personnel (FR) **Mr & Mrs Raymond Anderson Green**
4 **DIVINE PORT (USA)**, 10, b g Arch (USA)—Out of Reach **J. Wade**
5 **FAST SCENIC (FR)**, 5, b g Brave Mansonnien (FR)—Scenaria (IRE) **Mrs J. E. Dodd**
6 **GEORDIES DREAM**, 5, gr g Geordieland (FR)—Dream Leader (IRE) **J. Wade**
7 **KINGRULLAH (IRE)**, 5, b g Rule of Law (USA)—My Name's Not Bin (IRE) **J. Wade**
8 **MARTILA (FR)**, 8, b m Martaline—Paola Pierji (FR) **Mr & Mrs Raymond Anderson Green**
9 **SPECIAL PREP (IRE)**, 8, b g Brian Boru—Schindler's Dame (IRE) **Mr E. A. Elliott**
10 5, B g Kayf Tara—Special Trinket (IRE)
11 **STAY HUMBLE (IRE)**, 7, b g Beat Hollow—Rosy de Cyborg (FR) **D & D Armstrong Ltd & Mr L Westwood**

Other Owners: D&D Armstrong Limited, Mr L. J. Westwood.

Assistant Trainer: David Parker.

NH Jockey: Brian Hughes, Craig Nichol.

459 **MR RUSSELL ROSS, Consett**
Postal: **Rock Cottage Farm, 79 Iveston Lane, Consett, County Durham, DH8 7TB**

1 **JAZZY CARD (IRE)**, 4, ch f Red Jazz (USA)—Gilda Lilly (USA) **R. A. Ross**

THREE-YEAR-OLDS
2 **DOUGLAS FIR (IRE)**, b g Australia—Danehill Music (IRE) **R. A. Ross**

460 **MR BRIAN ROTHWELL, Malton**
Postal: **Old Post Office, Oswaldkirk, York, North Yorkshire, YO62 5XT**
Contacts: **PHONE 01439 788859 MOBILE 07969 968241**
EMAIL brian.rothwell1@googlemail.com

1 **FRESHFIELD FERRIS**, 4, b f Kuroshio (AUS)—Artistic Dawn (IRE) **B. S. Rothwell**
2 **GLORYELLA**, 4, b f Yorgunnabelucky (USA)—Ceiriog Valley **The Jelly Boys**
3 4, B f Heerat (IRE)—Lady Azamour (IRE) **B. S. Rothwell**
4 **ROSE MARMARA**, 7, ch m Exceed And Excel (AUS)—Show Rainbow **Mrs G. Sparks**

MR BRIAN ROTHWELL - continued

5 **SIRIUS STAR**, 11, b g Beat All (USA)—Miss Sirius **B. S. Rothwell**
6 **YASMIN FROM YORK**, 4, b f Sixties Icon—Bonnie Burnett (IRE) **Mrs G. Sparks**

THREE-YEAR-OLDS

7 **AETHON**, b f Multiplex—Bonnie Burnett (IRE) **Mr A. J. Sparks**
8 **ALLERTHORPE**, b g Casamento (IRE)—Shirocco Passion **S. P. Hudson**
9 **OUTOFTHEGLOOM**, b f Heeraat (IRE)—Srimenanti **Mr S. P. Hudson & Mr Brian Rothwell**
10 B g Helmet (AUS)—Skywards Miles (IRE) **B. S. Rothwell**
11 B c Pour Moi (IRE)—Yawail **B. S. Rothwell**

TWO-YEAR-OLDS

12 B c 12/03 Ruler of The World (IRE)—Artistic Dawn (IRE) (Excellent Art) **B. S. Rothwell**
13 B g 22/02 Mustajeeb—Byton (Byron) **S. P. Hudson**
14 B f 11/04 Power—Skywards Miles (IRE) (New Approach (IRE)) **B. S. Rothwell**
15 Gr c 07/04 Gregorian (IRE)—Symphony Star (IRE) (Amadeus Wolf) **B. S. Rothwell**
16 Ch c 10/04 Mustajeeb—Yawail (Medicean) **B. S. Rothwell**

Other Owners: Mr N. J. Brannan, S. P. Hudson, Mr A. R. Morgan, B. S. Rothwell.

---

461 MR RICHARD ROWE, Pulborough

Postal: **Ashleigh House Stables, Sullington Lane, Storrington, Pulborough, West Sussex, RH20 4AE**
Contacts: PHONE **01903 742871** MOBILE **07831 345636**
EMAIL **richard@richardroweracing.com** WEBSITE **www.richardrowe-racing.co.uk** FACEBOOK
RichardRoweRacehorseTrainer TWITTER **@rowe_racing**

1 **AZTEC DREAMS**, 7, b g Oasis Dream—Agathe Rare (IRE) **Captain Adrian Pratt & Lord Clinton**
2 **BANNIXTOWN BOY (IRE)**, 6, b g Oscar (IRE)—Lucky Loch (IRE)
3 **BATTLE ANTHEM (IRE)**, 9, b g Royal Anthem (USA)—Chika Boom (IRE) **R. Rowe**
4 **CELMA DES BOIS (FR)**, 8, b g Ballingarry (IRE)—Palafax (FR) **Encore Partnership V**
5 **COLONEL KEATING (IRE)**, 8, b g Yeats (IRE)—Jabroot (IRE) **Capt Adrian Pratt & Friends**
6 **DARK FLAME (IRE)**, 11, b g Gold Well—Glorys Flame (IRE) **The Encore Partnership III**
7 **DELGANY MONARCH (IRE)**, 5, ch g Imperial Monarch (IRE)—Naughty Marietta (IRE)
8 **DILLY THE PINK (IRE)**, 4, b f Thewayyouare (USA)—A Good Year (IRE) **Pink Birds**
9 **FLASHDANZA**, 5, ch g Sepoy (AUS)—Photo Flash (IRE) **B. H. Page**
10 **IDIDITFORYOOOO (IRE)**, 6, b g Fast Company (IRE)—Ann's Annie (IRE)
11 4, B g Paco Boy (IRE)—Miss Marauder **Mrs S. J. Doyle**
12 6, Ch g Black Sam Bellamy (IRE)—Miss Marauder **Mrs S. J. Doyle**
13 **MISTER MURCHAN (IRE)**, 7, b g Westerner—So Supreme (IRE) **The Battle Anthem Partnership**
14 **REMEMBER ME WELL (IRE)**, 7, b m Doyen (IRE)—Creidim (IRE) **Pink Birds**
15 **SOARLIKEANEAGLE (IRE)**, 8, b g Scorpion (IRE)—Wayward Cove **Capt A Pratt, Lord Clinton, P Anwyl-Harris**
16 **SUNDAY AT AUGUSTA (IRE)**, 7, b g Arakan (USA)—Alla Marcia (IRE) **Scott Parnell Limited**
17 **TATTLETALE (FR)**, 6, b g Linda's Lad—Barbarasse (FR) **Richard Rowe Racing Partnership**
18 **TRUCKERS TIME (IRE)**, 8, b g Curtain Time (IRE)—Truckers Lady (IRE) **Mr J. L. J. Butcher**
19 **TZAR DE L'ELFE (FR)**, 10, b g Satri (IRE)—Rue Tournefort (FR) **Lord Clinton & Captain Adrian Pratt**
20 **UP THE STRAIGHT (IRE)**, 6, b g Arcadio (GER)—Kings Artist (IRE) **The Forever Partnership**
21 **VITAL SIGN (IRE)**, 7, b g Let The Lion Roar—Grace N' Favour (IRE) **Winterfields Farm Ltd**
22 **WE'LLCWHATHAPPENS (IRE)**, 7, b m Court Cave (IRE)—Lost Prairie (IRE) **Mr D. Scott**

THREE-YEAR-OLDS

23 Ch g Medicean—Scarlette d'Or

Other Owners: Mr P. D. Anwyl-Harris, Mr R. W. Baker, Mr D. M. Bradshaw, Mrs H. C. G. Butcher, Mrs J. Case, Lord Clinton, Mr C. S. Coombe-Tennant, Mrs S. K. Coombe-Tennant, Dr C. Cowell, Mrs J. E. Debenham, K. L. Hunter, Capt A. Pratt, Mrs J. D. M. Sadler, Scott Parnell Limited, T. W. Wellard, Mr P. D. West, Mr P. R. Wilby, Winterfields Farm Ltd.

462 MISS MANDY ROWLAND, Lower Blidworth
Postal: **Kirkfields, Calverton Road, Lower Blidworth, Nottingham, Nottinghamshire, NG21 0NW**
Contacts: **PHONE 01623 794831 MOBILE 07768 224666**
EMAIL **kirkfieldsriding@hotmail.co.uk**

1 **BOOBOROWIE (IRE)**, 7, b br g Big Bad Bob (IRE)—Rejuvenation (IRE) **Miss M. E. Rowland**
2 **CHINA EXCELS**, 13, b g Exceed And Excel (AUS)—China Beauty **Miss M. E. Rowland**
3 **GO ANNIE GO**, 4, b f Es Que Love (IRE)—Make It Snappy **Miss M. E. Rowland**
4 **JAZZ LEGEND (USA)**, 7, b g Scat Daddy (USA)—Champion Ride (USA) **Miss M. E. Rowland**
5 **LET'S BE HAPPY (IRE)**, 6, gr m Mastercraftsman (IRE)—Corrozal (GER) **Miss M. E. Rowland**
6 **MABAADY**, 6, b g Bated Breath—Fifty (IRE) **Miss M. E. Rowland**

Assistant Trainer: Sarah Thomas.

Flat Jockey: Rob Hornby, Adam Kirby, Jimmy Quinn. **Apprentice Jockey:** William Cox.

463 MS LUCINDA RUSSELL, Kinross
Postal: **Arlary House Stables, Milnathort, Kinross, Tayside, KY13 9SJ**
Contacts: **PHONE 01577 865512 MOBILE 07970 645261 FAX 01577 861171**
EMAIL **lucindarussellracing@outlook.com** WEBSITE **www.lucindarussell.com**

1 **A LADIES MILAN (IRE)**, 6, b g Milan—Rag's Lady (IRE) **Dig In Racing**
2 **AIN'T MY FAULT (IRE)**, 7, b g Beneficial—Coolnasneachta (IRE) **Foresight Racing**
3 **ARIZONA BOUND (IRE)**, 8, b g Presenting—Loyal Gesture (IRE) **Mr P. J. S. Russell**
4 **AURORA THUNDER**, 6, b m Malinas (GER)—Ninna Nanna (FR) **Ailson Sparkle Ltd**
5 **BALRANALD (FR)**, 4, b g Mastercraftsman (IRE)—Shining Glory (GER) **Mr J. Fyffe**
6 **BEHINDTHELINES (IRE)**, 8, b g Milan—Sunset Leader (IRE) **London Scots for Doddie**
7 **BIALCO (FR)**, 9, gr g Dom Alco (FR)—Lacanale (FR) **The Vikings**
8 **BIG RIVER (IRE)**, 10, b g Milan—Call Kate (IRE) **Two Black Labs**
9 **BLAYDON (IRE)**, 7, b g Milan—Pretty Impressive (IRE) **Mrs S Russell & A M Russell**
10 **BLOORIEDOTCOM (IRE)**, 5, b g Holy Roman Emperor (IRE)—Peaceful Kingdom (USA) **Mutual Friends**
11 **BOLLINGERANDKRUG (IRE)**, 5, b g Getaway (GER)—Out Performer (IRE) **Ms D. Thomson**
12 **BOY'S ON TOUR (IRE)**, 8, b g Beneficial—Galant Tour (IRE) **Foresight Racing**
13 **BUDDHA SCHEME (IRE)**, 6, b g Milan—Benefit Scheme (IRE) **Mr G. R. McGladery**
14 **CABOY (FR)**, 8, b g Nidor (FR)—Cadouya Girl (FR) **Mr P. J. S. Russell**
15 **CALLE MALVA (IRE)**, 5, b m Getaway (GER)—Waydale Hill **The Falcon Partnership**
16 **CELTIC FLAMES (IRE)**, 10, gr g Celtic Swing—Don't Forget Shoka (IRE) **Mr W. T. Scott**
17 **CHANCEITON (IRE)**, 9, b g Vinnie Roe (IRE)—Lissnabrucka (IRE) **Mr P. J. S. Russell**
18 **CHARMIX (FR)**, 10, br g Laveron—Open Up (FR) **Mr J. Fyffe**
19 **COCKLE BAY (IRE)**, 8, b g Milan—Theredandthegreen (IRE) **The Kestrel Partnership**
20 **DESTINY IS ALL (IRE)**, 6, b g Prince Flori (GER)—Hearts Delight (IRE) **Mr J. R. Adam**
21 **DIAMOND STATE (FR)**, 4, b g Vision d'Etat (FR)—Wonderful Diamond (GER) **Mr G. R. McGladery**
22 **DR HOOVES**, 7, b g Yeats (IRE)—Sejour (IRE) **Mr G. R. McGladery**
23 **EEYORE (IRE)**, 6, b m Bernebeau (FR)—Nosika d'Airy (FR) **Mr & Mrs Raymond Anderson Green**
24 **EFFET SPECIAL (FR)**, 6, b g Network (GER)—Tisane (FR) **Brahms & Liszt**
25 **ELMONO (FR)**, 9, ch g Epalo (GER)—Monareva (FR) **Gerry And The Pacemakers**
26 **EMIRAT DE CATANA (FR)**, 6, b g Linda's Lad—Kolada (FR) **Kelso Lowflyers & Mr PJS Russell**
27 **EMISSAIRE (FR)**, 6, b g Kap Rock (FR)—Jacee (FR) **A Nicol & L S Russell**
28 **ENGLES ROCK (IRE)**, 4, b f Excelebration (IRE)—Lisa Gherardini (IRE) **Mrs H. Kelly**
29 **EXCHEQUER (FR)**, 4, gr g Equiano (FR)—Cumbrian Princess **Mr G. R. McGladery**
30 **EXIT TO WHERE (FR)**, 6, b r Kapgarde (FR)—Rapsodie Sea (FR) **Mr & Mrs Raymond Anderson Green**
31 **FLUTTER DOWN (FR)**, 5, b g Rob Roy (USA)—Florifere (FR) **Peter & Suzy Brown & Tony Evans**
32 **FONTCOMBEAU (FR)**, 4, ch g Kapgarde (FR)—La Ville Aux Dames (FR) **Mr P. J. S. Russell**
33 **FYFIN PATSY (IRE)**, 6, b m September Storm (GER)—Poshly Presented (IRE) **Fyfin Four**
34 **GEMOLOGIST (IRE)**, 5, b m Sir Percy—Tiffany Diamond (IRE) **Musselburgh Lunch Club**
35 **GRAND MORNING**, 8, b g Midnight Legend—Valentines Lady (IRE) **Mr J. P. McManus**
36 **GRIPPER**, 5, b g Thewayyouare (USA)—Hold On Tight (IRE) **The Phoenix Partnership**
37 **HAUL US IN (IRE)**, 8, br m Kalanisi (IRE)—Shuilan (IRE) **Mr & Mrs J. Morrison-Bell**

MS LUCINDA RUSSELL - continued

38 **ISLAND HEIGHTS (IRE)**, 11, b g Heron Island (IRE)—La Reina (IRE) **Mr G. R. McGladery**
39 **IZZY'S CHAMPION (IRE)**, 6, b g Gold Well—Native Crystal (IRE) **Mr & Mrs T. P. Winnell**
40 **KATALYSTIC (IRE)**, 9, br g Kalanisi (IRE)—Beltane Queen (IRE) **Mr R. B. H. Young**
41 **KELPIES MYTH**, 7, b g Dutch Art—Miss Respect **Bolton, McGladery, Duncan & Buchanan**
42 **LAST KING OF WALES**, 6, b g Crosspeace (IRE)—My Dancing Kin **Mr Michael & Lady Jane Kaplan**
43 **LE FRANK (IRE)**, 8, b g King's Theatre (IRE)—Dream Lass (IRE) **Smith, Fitzpatrick & Shiner**
44 **LOOKS LIKE MURT (IRE)**, 7, b g Well Chosen—Ninetypenceapound (IRE) **Mr J. R. Adam**
45 **LUCKY FLIGHT (FR)**, 6, b g Linda's Lad—Lili Flight (FR) **The Vikings**
46 **MAGNUM (DEN)**, 5, ch g Appel Au Maitre (FR)—Embattle (FR) **Mr M. Buskop**
47 **MANNOCHMORE**, 5, b g Dylan Thomas (IRE)—Loch Dhu (IRE) **Distillery Racing Club**
48 **MAX APPEAL (IRE)**, 5, b g Kayf Tara—Clairefontaine **One Team One Dream**
49 **METHODTOTHEMADNESS (IRE)**, 6, b m Gold Well—Odeeka (IRE) **Mrs S Russell & A M Russell**
50 **MIGHTY THUNDER**, 7, b g Malinas (GER)—Cool Island (IRE) **Allson Sparkle Ltd**
51 **MINT GOLD (IRE)**, 6, b g Gold Well—Lady Flyer (IRE) **Mrs S Russell & A M Russell**
52 **MISFITS (IRE)**, 9, b g Beneficial—Park Rose (IRE) **County Set Four & Keith Hunter**
53 **MISS BATTEN (IRE)**, 6, b m Vinnie Roe (IRE)—Awesome Miracle (IRE) **Mr P. J. S. Russell**
54 **MISSY MAY**, 6, b m Shantou (USA)—Oh So Beautiful (IRE) **G. S. Brown**
55 **MR TOASTIE**, 5, b g Brian Boru—Granary House **Major A. R. Trotter**
56 4, B g Sholokhov (IRE)—Odeeka (IRE) **Mr P. J. S. Russell**
57 **OFFTHESHOULDER (IRE)**, 6, b g Gold Well—Zafilly **Mr G. R. McGladery**
58 4, B g Shantou (USA)—Oh So Beautiful (IRE) **G. S. Brown**
59 **ONE FOR ARTHUR (IRE)**, 11, b g Milan—Nonnetia (FR) **Two Golf Widows**
60 **OPERATION OVERLORD (IRE)**, 5, b g Jeremy (USA)—Alfreeze **Mr J. P. McManus**
61 **ORDER OF THISTLE (IRE)**, 5, b g High Chaparral (IRE)—Law of The Jungle (IRE) **Mrs F. H. Hay**
62 **ORIONINVERNESS (IRE)**, 9, b g Brian Boru—Woodville Leader (IRE) **Tay Valley Chasers Racing Club**
63 **OTELLO MOOR (IRE)**, 5, b g Milan—Founding Daughter (IRE) **Mrs R. A. Stobart**
64 **PETITE RHAPSODY (IRE)**, 5, b g Shirocco (GER)—Peggy Cullen (IRE) **Mr P. J. S. Russell**
65 **PINSPOT**, 6, b g Presenting—Amber Cloud **Mr Michael & Lady Jane Kaplan**
66 **PRINCE DUNDEE (IRE)**, 7, b g Stowaway—Miss Dundee (IRE) **J W McNeill & County Set Three**
67 **RAPID RAIDER (IRE)**, 6, ch g Golden Lariat (USA)—Golden Court (IRE) **Mrs S Russell & A M Russell**
68 **REFER TO RORY**, 7, b m Great Palm (USA)—Royal Reference **Mrs E. Brockbank**
69 **RISING MARIENBARD (IRE)**, 8, b g Marienbard (IRE)—Dromkeen Wood **Mrs R. A. Stobart**
70 **RIVABODIVA (IRE)**, 10, ch m Flemensfirth (USA)—Sheebadiva (IRE) **Mrs S Russell & A M Russell**
71 **ROYAL RESERVE**, 7, b g Duke of Marmalade (IRE)—Lady Hawkfield (IRE) **London Scots for Doddie**
72 **RYALEX (IRE)**, 9, b g Arcadio (GER)—Lady Ramona (IRE) **County Set Five & Keith Hunter**
73 **SAINT FREULE (FR)**, 7, br g Saint des Saints—Topsy Blue (FR) **Mr K. Alexander**
74 **SHANROE STREET (IRE)**, 10, b g Mustameet (USA)—Zaffran Lady (IRE) **Netherfield House Stud**
75 **SIGNIFIANT (FR)**, 6, bl g Saint des Saints (FR)—Signature (FR) **Bolton, Moyles, Frame, Smart**
76 **SKY KHAN**, 11, b g Cape Cross (IRE)—Starlit Sky **The Ormello Way**
77 **SLAINTE MHOR (IRE)**, 6, b g Milan—Founding Daughter (IRE) **Mr P. J. S. Russell**
78 **SOUTHERN GIRL (IRE)**, 6, ch m Getaway (GER)—She's Got To Go (IRE) **Mr K. Alexander**
79 **SPARK OF MADNESS (FR)**, 4, b g Walk In The Park (IRE)—Prosopopee (FR) **Mrs S Russell & A M Russell**
80 **SPEAK OF THE DEVIL (IRE)**, 7, ch g Mahler—A Fine Romance (IRE) **The County Set & Mr P Russell & Friends**
81 **SUTTON MANOR (IRE)**, 9, b g Gold Well—Nighty Bless (IRE) **Mr P. J. S. Russell**
82 **TARSET HINNY (IRE)**, 5, ch m Presenting—Avondhu Lady (IRE) **Mr & Mrs J. Morrison-Bell**
83 **THE COMPELLER (IRE)**, 8, b g Lawman (FR)—Mark Too (IRE) **W M D Racing**
84 **THE ROAD HOME (IRE)**, 8, b g Oscar (IRE)—In Fact (IRE) **Mrs S Russell & A M Russell**
85 **THORPE (IRE)**, 10, b g Danehill Dancer (IRE)—Minkova (IRE) **Mr Michael & Lady Jane Kaplan**
86 **THUNDER IN MILAN (IRE)**, 4, b g Milan—Baby Briggs (IRE) **Allson Sparkle Ltd**
87 **TIMESAWAITING (IRE)**, 7, b g Arakan (USA)—Princess Nicole (IRE) **Goodtimes**
88 4, Ch f Leading Light (IRE)—Top Her Up (IRE) **Mrs H. Kelly**
89 **TOUCHEDBYANANGEL (IRE)**, 8, gr g Beneficial—Gray's Anatomy (IRE) **Tay Valley Chasers Racing Club**
90 **VENGEUR DE GUYE (FR)**, 11, b g Dom Alco (FR)—Mascotte de Guye (FR) **Brahms & Liszt**
91 **VINO'S CHOICE (IRE)**, 8, b g Kalanisi (IRE)—Ard's Pet (IRE) **A Bit of GG Fun**
92 **VOIX D'EAU (FR)**, 10, b g Voix du Nord (FR)—Eau de Chesne (FR) **Mr G. R. McGladery**
93 **WELL ABOVE PAR (IRE)**, 8, b g Gold Well—Glynn Glory (IRE) **The Eagle Partnership**
94 4, B c Dylan Thomas (IRE)—Zarata (IRE) **Mr P. J. S. Russell**

MS LUCINDA RUSSELL - continued

THREE-YEAR-OLDS
95 **BALLYARE**, b c Hot Streak (IRE)—Saddlers Bend (IRE) **Mrs H. Kelly**
96 **GREY WAR (IRE)**, gr f War Command (USA)—Lady Gray (IRE) **Mrs H. Kelly**
97 **HAUTE ESTIME (IRE)**, b f Walk In The Park (IRE)—Terre Haute (IRE) **Mr P. J. S. Russell**
98 **HECTOR MASTER (FR)**, b g Masterstroke (USA)—Queen Maresca (FR) **Mrs S Russell & A M Russell**
99 **NETYWELL (FR)**, b g Willywell (FR)—Netova (FR) **Mr P. J. S. Russell**
100 B g Sulamani (IRE)—Swift Getaway (IRE) **Mr P. J. S. Russell**
101 B f Getaway (GER)—The Toft **Mr P. J. S. Russell**

TWO-YEAR-OLDS
102 B c 12/04 Mayson—Infatuate (Dalakhani (IRE)) (8580) **Mrs H. Kelly**

Other Owners: Mr J. A. Aitkenhead, Mr W. M. Allan, Mr G. R. Brown, Mr P.R. Brown, Mrs S. Brown, Mrs Suzy Brown & Mr Peter R Brown, A. Cadger, County Set Four, Mr N. A. Crofts, Mr A. B. Cuthill, Mr C. Dempster, Mr E. W. Dempster, Mr R. Doak, Mr A. Evans, Mr M. J. Fitzpatrick, Mr A. T. Galloway, Gilbert McClung (Kelso) Ltd, G. Godsman, Mrs I. M. Grant, Mr J. Grant, E. D. Haggart, K. L. Hunter, Mr D. R. James, Mrs P James, Kelso Members Lowflyers Club, Mrs M Kennedy, Mr A. Kerr, Mrs C. J. Lamb, Mr R. M. Landale, Mrs Y. M. V. Learmonth, Ms A. M. MacInnes, Ms F. E. MacInnes, Ms S. C. Mackay, Mr G. R. McGladery, Mr J. W. McNeill, Mr M. G. Mellor, Mr J. Morrison-Bell, Mrs K. A. Morrison-Bell, Mr Peter J Russell & Friends, Mr A. G. Nicol, Mr A. M. Russell, Mr L. S. Russell, Mr P J. S. Russell, Mrs S. C. Russell, Mr A. Shiner, A. W. Sinclair, Miss M. M. Smith, Mr S. Smith, Ms P. Spours, The County Set, The County Set (Five), The County Set Three, Mr R. D. Thompson, Ms D. Thomson, Mr N. J. Turnbull, Mr G. T. Wallace, Mrs M. Winnell, Mr T. P Winnell.

Assistant Trainer: Jaimie Duff, Peter Scudamore, Jamie Turnbull.

NH Jockey: Derek Fox. **Conditional Jockey:** Blair Campbell, Stephen Mulqueen, Patrick Wadge, Thomas Willmott. **Amateur Jockey:** Miss Ailsa McClung, Mr Cameron Wadge.

464
MR JOHN RYAN, Newmarket
Postal: **Cadland Stables, Moulton Road, Newmarket, Suffolk, CB8 8DU**
Contacts: **PHONE 01638 664172 MOBILE 07739 801235**
EMAIL john.ryan@jryanracing.com WEBSITE www.jryanracing.com TWITTER @JohnRyanRacing

1 **BATTLE OF MARATHON (USA)**, 8, b g War Front (USA)—Sayedah (IRE) **Emma Ryan & Partner**
2 **BOOK OF INVASIONS (IRE)**, 5, ch g Declaration of War (USA)—Cedar Sea (IRE) **Mr G. R. McGladery**
3 **CATCH MY BREATH**, 4, ch g Bated Breath—Likeable **The Out of Puff Partnership**
4 **HIROSHIMA**, 4, b g Nathaniel (IRE)—Lisiere (IRE) **Mr G. F. Smith-Bernal**
5 **LOVELY LOU LOU**, 4, b f Sir Percy—Silver Linnet (IRE) **John Ryan Racing Partnership**
6 **MERHOOB (IRE)**, 8, b g Cape Cross (IRE)—Lady Slippers (IRE) **Mr G. R. McGladery**
7 **NORMAL NORMAN**, 6, ch g Shamardal (USA)—Ambria (GER) **Mr G. R. McGladery**
8 **PRINCESS FLORENCE (IRE)**, 4, gr f Zebedee—Villa Nova (IRE) **BB Thoroughbreds**
9 **SANDRIDGE LAD (IRE)**, 4, b g Equiano (FR)—Quixada (GER) **Mr J. F. Stocker**
10 **SEVENNA STAR (IRE)**, 5, b g Redoute's Choice (AUS)—Sevenna (FR) **Mr G. F. Smith-Bernal**
11 **SLEEPDANCER (IRE)**, 4, b g Rip Van Winkle (IRE)—Dancing Eclipse (IRE) **Mr G. R. McGladery**
12 **SPENNY'S LASS**, 5, br m Bated Breath—Midnight Hush (FR) **Mr M Firth & Mr J Ryan**

THREE-YEAR-OLDS
13 **DARK SIDE DIVISION**, b g Due Diligence (USA)—Belle of Honour (USA) **Mr M. M. Foulger**
14 **FLUTTERSHY**, ch f Roderic O'Connor (IRE)—Twilight Sparkle (IRE) **Mr G. R. McGladery**
15 **GODDESS OF FIRE**, b f Toronado (IRE)—Burnt Fingers (IRE) **Mr M. M. Foulger**
16 **HOMEGROWNALLIGATOR**, b g Poet's Voice—Samar Qand **Mr J. A. Thompson**
17 **JACK RYAN (IRE)**, b g Harbour Watch (IRE)—Anything (IRE) **Mr Gerry McGladery & Partner**
18 **SEA OF COOL (IRE)**, b g Sea The Stars (IRE)—Magh Meall **Mr J. B. Ryan**
19 B f Australia—This Is The Day **BB Thoroughbreds**

MR JOHN RYAN - continued

TWO-YEAR-OLDS

20 B f 06/04 Awtaad (IRE)—Flirty Thirty (IRE) (Big Bad Bob (IRE))
21 B f 17/04 Sepoy (AUS)—Plucky (Kyllachy)

Other Owners: DAS Racing Limited, Mr M. Firth, Mr G. R. McGladery, Mrs E. Ryan, Mr J. B. Ryan.

Apprentice Jockey: Darragh Keenan. **Amateur Jockey:** Miss Tia Phillips.

MR KEVIN RYAN, Hambleton
Postal: **Hambleton Lodge, Hambleton, Thirsk, North Yorkshire, YO7 2HA**
Contacts: **PHONE 01845 597010, 01845 597622 MOBILE 07768 016930 FAX 01845 597622**
EMAIL office@kevinryanracing.com WEBSITE www.kevinryanracing.com

1 ARMANDIHAN (IRE), 6, b g Zoffany (IRE)—Flying Flag (IRE) **CHH Racing**
2 BEA RYAN (IRE), 5, b m Dream Ahead (USA)—Kimola (IRE) **Mr Steve Ryan**
3 BIELSA (IRE), 5, b g Invincible Spirit (IRE)—Bourbon Ball (USA) **King Power Racing Co Ltd**
4 BIN MAKFI, 5, b g Makfi—Sayyedati Storm (USA) **Miss E J Butterworth & Partner**
5 BRANDO, 8, ch g Pivotal—Argent du Bois (USA) **Mrs A. Bailey**
6 CONGA, 4, ch f Footstepsinthesand—Palais Glide
7 DANDY'S BEANO (IRE), 5, ch m Dandy Man (IRE)—Hear My Cry (USA) **Hambleton Racing Ltd XLVII**
8 EMARAATY ANA, 4, b c Shamardal (USA)—Spirit of Dubai (USA) **Sheikh Mohammed Obaid Al Maktoum**
9 ENOUGH ALREADY, 4, b g Coach House (IRE)—Funny Enough **Sheikh Mohammed Obaid Al Maktoum**
10 GEORGE MALLORY, 4, b g Kingman—Rose Et Noire (IRE) **Mr F. Gillespie**
11 GLASS SLIPPERS, 4, b f Dream Ahead (USA)—Night Gypsy **Bearstone Stud Limited**
12 HELLO YOUMZAIN (FR), 4, b c Kodiac—Spasha **Haras d'Etreham and Cambridge Stud**
13 HEY JONESY (IRE), 5, b g Excelebration (IRE)—Fikrah **Pallister Racing**
14 JUSTANOTHERBOTTLE (IRE), 6, ch g Intense Focus (IRE)—Duchess K (IRE) **Mr Steve Ryan & Mr M J Tedham**
15 KNIGHTED (IRE), 5, b g Sir Prancealot (IRE)—Olympia Theatre **Highclere T'bred Racing- Nick Skelton**
16 LAST EMPIRE, 4, b f Pivotal—Final Dynasty **Clipper Logistics**
17 LAURIER (USA), 4, b br f Scat Daddy (USA)—Abundantly Blessed (USA) **Laurier Partners**
18 MAGICAL SPIRIT (IRE), 4, ch g Zebedee—La Dame de Fer (IRE) **Hambleton Racing Ltd XXXII**
19 MAJOR JUMBO, 6, gr g Zebedee—Gone Sailing **Mr T A Rahman**
20 PRINCES DES SABLES, 4, ch f Monsieur Bond (IRE)—Hopes N Dreams (IRE) **JCG Chua & CK Ong**
21 QUEEN JO JO, 4, gr f Gregorian (IRE)—River Song (USA) **Mr Roger Peel & Clipper Logistics**
22 QUEEN'S SARGENT (FR), 5, gr g Kendargent (FR)—Queen's Conquer **Mr Dave Stone**
23 RATHBONE, 4, b g Foxwedge (AUS)—Frequent **Mrs A. Bailey**
24 SALATEEN, 8, ch g Dutch Art—Amanda Carter **Sheikh Abdullah Almalek Alsabah**
25 SECRET VENTURE, 4, b g Kyllachy—Resort **Clipper Logistics**
26 SHAQWAR, 4, ch f Sea The Moon (GER)—Majestic Roi (USA) **Mr Jaber Abdullah**
27 SHARK (FR), 4, b g Siyouni (FR)—Sea Life (FR) **Hambleton Racing Ltd XXXV**
28 TAGUR (IRE), 6, ch g Tagula (IRE)—Westcote **Andy Turton & John Blackburn**
29 THE GREAT HEIR (FR), 4, b g Pedro The Great (USA)—Lady McKell (IRE) **Mr Dave Stone**
30 WILD HOPE, 4, b g Kingman—Wild Mimosa (IRE) **Hambleton Racing Ltd XLIV**
31 YOUSINI, 4, b g Siyouni (FR)—War Effort (USA) **Middleham Park Racing XXI**

THREE-YEAR-OLDS

32 A KNIGHT'S TALE, b c Sir Percy—Princess Aurora (USA) **Hambleton Racing Ltd XIVI & Partner**
33 ALIOSKI, b g Kodiac—Luluti (IRE) **Jack Berry & Partner**
34 ALWAATN SOUND (IRE), b c Shamardal (USA)—Lady of The Desert (USA) **Mr Jaber Abdullah**
35 ARABIAN MAIDEN, b f New Approach (IRE)—Spirit of Dubai (USA) **Sheikh Mohammed Obaid Al Maktoum**
36 ARROW OF GOLD (IRE), ch c Galileo (IRE)—Fleche d'Or **Sheikh Mohammed Obaid Al Maktoum**
37 B f Showcasing—Ballyalla **Clipper Logistics**
38 BARBARELLA (IRE), b f Hot Streak (IRE)—Acid **Mrs A. Bailey**
39 BLACK CASPIAN (IRE), b c Dark Angel (IRE)—Catch The Sea (IRE) **Sheikh Mohammed Obaid Al Maktoum**
40 BYLINE, b g Muhaarar—Lauren Louise **Highclere Thoroughbred Racing-LS Lowry 1**
41 CELESTIAL BLISS, b c Oasis Dream—La Pomme d'Amour **Guy Reed Racing**
42 CHARDONEIGH, b f Fountain of Youth (IRE)—Razzle (IRE) **Bearstone Stud Limited**

MR KEVIN RYAN - continued

43 **CLEVER TRICK**, b g Pivotal—Trick Or Treat **Mr P. Onslow**
44 **COAST OFALFUJAIRAH (IRE)**, br g Brazen Beau (AUS)—Khameela **Hambleton Racing Ltd XIVI & Partner**
45 **DILITHIUM (FR)**, b g Dabirsim (FR)—Lady Family (FR) **Mr Dave Stone**
46 **DIVINA GLORIA (FR)**, b f Dabirsim (FR)—Amouage (GER) **Sheikh Mohammed Obaid Al Maktoum**
47 **DREAM ACADEMY (IRE)**, b g Acclamation—Modello (IRE) **Academy Partners**
48 **DUBLIN ROCKER (IRE)**, b f No Nay Never (USA)—Rocking **Hambleton Racing Ltd XVIII**
49 **EVEAAJ (IRE)**, b f Iffraaj—Albaraari **Mr J. Matthews**
50 **GALADRIEL**, b f Dutch Art—Handbell (IRE) **Sheikh Mohammed Obaid Al Maktoum**
51 **GIFT OF KINGS**, b c Kingman—Indian Love Bird **Clipper Logistics**
52 **HART'S DREAM**, b g Poet's Voice—Angel Song **My Vein Clinic Syndicate**
53 **HISTORICAL**, b f New Approach (IRE)—Joys of Spring (IRE) **Sheikh Mohammed Obaid Al Maktoum**
54 **JAHRAWI (USA)**, b c Fed Biz (USA)—Honimiere (IRE) **Mr Mohammad Alsaeidi**
55 **JUAN ELCANO**, ch c Frankel—Whatami **Sheikh Mohammed Obaid Al Maktoum**
56 **LEOCH**, ch g Hot Streak (IRE)—Acquiesced (IRE) **Gordon Bulloch & Shaun Hardcastle**
57 **MAGICAL MOMENT (FR)**, b f Dubawi (IRE)—Maka (FR) **Magical Moment Partners**
58 **MAYSON QUEEN**, gr f Mayson—Special Queen (IRE) **Mr Jaber Abdullah**
59 **MIDNITE BRIDE**, b f Kodiac—Silkenveil (IRE) **Mr T A Rahman**
60 **MOONLIGHTING**, gr f Hot Streak (IRE)—Blue Moon **K&J Bloodstock Ltd**
61 **OAKENSHIELD (IRE)**, b c Invincible Spirit (IRE)—War Effort (USA) **Sheikh Mohammed Obaid Al Maktoum**
62 **QUEEN'S ORDER**, b f Delegator—Kirunavaara (IRE) **Clipper Logistics**
63 **REPARTEE (IRE)**, b c Invincible Spirit (IRE)—Pleasantry **Sheikh Mohammed Obaid Al Maktoum**
64 **REVIETTE (IRE)**, b f Kyllachy—Readyandaway (USA) **Highbank Stud**
65 **RHEA**, ch f Siyouni (FR)—Titian's Pride (USA) **Sheikh Mohammed Obaid Al Maktoum**
66 **ROMERO (IRE)**, b g Brazen Beau (AUS)—Out of Thanks (IRE) **Romero Partners**
67 **SALAM YA FAISAL (IRE)**, b g Dark Angel (IRE)—Age of Chivalry (IRE) **Sheikh Abdullah Almalek Alsabah**
68 **SHE CAN DANCE**, b f Acclamation—Corazon Canarias (FR) **Clipper Logistics**
69 **SOARING STAR (IRE)**, b g Starspangledbanner (AUS)—Peig (IRE) **Hambleton Racing Ltd XXV**
70 **SPIRITOFTHENORTH (FR)**, br g Bated Breath—Danlepordamsterdam (IRE) **Middleham Park Racing XLVI**
71 **STARS IN THE NIGHT (IRE)**, b f Starspangledbanner (AUS)—On The Dark Side (IRE) **Hambleton Racing Ltd XVI**
72 **SWITCHMAN (IRE)**, b c Lawman (FR)—Faraday Light (IRE) **Sheikh Mohammed Obaid Al Maktoum**
73 **THRONE HALL**, b c Kingman—Appearance **Sheikh Mohammed Obaid Al Maktoum**
74 **TREBLE TREBLE (IRE)**, b g Brazen Beau (AUS)—Sugar Blossom (IRE) **Mr B. T. McDonald**
75 **VEGA MAGIC (IRE)**, b c Lope de Vega (IRE)—Oriental Magic (GER) **Sheikh Mohammed Obaid Al Maktoum**
76 **VENTURA RASCAL**, b g Fountain of Youth—Choisette **Middleham Park Racing CVII**
77 **WESTERN HERO (IRE)**, b g Excelebration (IRE)—Kayak **Clipper Logistics**
78 **WILL SOMMERS**, b c Teofilo (IRE)—Dubai Queen (USA) **Sheikh Mohammed Obaid Al Maktoum**
79 **YORKSHIRE GOLD**, b c Muhaarar—Swift Campaign (IRE) **Sheikh Mohammed Obaid Al Maktoum**
80 **ZABEEL KING (IRE)**, b c Frankel—Vital Statistics **Sheikh Mohammed Obaid Al Maktoum**

TWO-YEAR-OLDS

81 B c 26/01 Invincible Spirit (IRE)—
　　　　　Angel Vision (IRE) (Oasis Dream) (280000) **Sheikh Mohammed Obaid Al Maktoum**
82 B c 24/03 Dark Angel (IRE)—
　　　　　Anthem Alexander (IRE) (Starspangledbanner (AUS)) (380000) **Sheikh Mohammed Obaid Al Maktoum**
83 **BEECHWOOD DONNA**, b f 28/02 Hot Streak (IRE)—
　　　　　Sabrewing (IRE) (Fast Company (IRE)) (16190) **Ontoawinner & Mrs J Ryan**
84 B f 13/03 Kodiac—Bobby Jane (Diktat) (76190) **Sheikh Abdullah Almalek Alsabah**
85 Ch c 03/03 Hot Streak (IRE)—Brown Eyed Honey (Elusive City (USA)) (26666) **Hambleton Racing Ltd XXIX**
86 B c 22/03 Kodiac—Candiland (IRE) (Shamardal (USA)) (55000)
87 B c 28/02 Paco Boy (IRE)—Danega (Galileo (IRE)) **Mr Jaber Abdullah**
88 Ch c 14/04 Buratino (IRE)—Endless Peace (IRE) (Russian Revival (USA)) (33333) **Hambleton Racing Ltd XXXVIII**
89 B c 07/04 Kodi Bear (IRE)—Fancy Vivid (IRE) (Galileo (IRE)) (71428) **Mrs A. Bailey**
90 B f 01/03 Exceed And Excel (AUS)—Hala Hala (IRE) (Invincible Spirit (IRE)) **Sultan Ali**
91 B c 09/02 Gleneagles (IRE)—Hooray (Invincible Spirit (IRE)) (200000) **Sheikh Mohammed Obaid Al Maktoum**
92 **INFANT HERCULES**, b c 24/03 Fountain of Youth (IRE)—
　　　　　Bay Tree (IRE) (Daylami (IRE)) (4761) **Riverside Racing Syndicate 2**
93 B f 24/02 Oasis Dream—La Napoule (Piccolo) **Guy Reed Racing**
94 B f 28/04 Toronado (IRE)—La Pomme d'Amour (Peintre Celebre (USA)) **Guy Reed Racing**
95 B c 07/03 Frankel—Lady of The Desert (USA) (Rahy (USA)) **Mr Jaber Abdullah**

MR KEVIN RYAN - continued

96 B c 21/03 Kodiac—Landmark (USA) (Arch (USA)) (525000) **Sheikh Mohammed Obaid Al Maktoum**
97 B c 15/02 Kingman—Martha Watson (IRE) (Dream Ahead (USA)) (550000) **Sheikh Mohammed Obaid Al Maktoum**
98 B c 16/03 Maxios—Monaco Show (FR) (Kheleyf (USA)) **Mr Jaber Abdullah**
99 Ch f 13/02 Mayson—Najim Al Thraya (FR) (Youmzain (IRE)) **Mr Jaber Abdullah**
100 B c 23/01 Kodi Bear (IRE)—Notte Illuminata (IRE) (Acclamation) (49523) **Highclere Thoroughbred Racing Ltd**
101 Ch f 21/03 Rio de La Plata (USA)—Queen's Logic (IRE) (Grand Lodge (USA)) **Mr Jaber Abdullah**
102 Br f 07/03 Camelot—Runway Dancer (Dansili) (105000) **Sultan Ali**
103 **SEACLUSION,** b f 20/05 Fountain of Youth (IRE)—On The Brink (Mind Games) **Bearstone Stud Limited**
104 B c 07/02 Dark Angel (IRE)—Shaden (IRE) (Kodiac) (210000) **Sheikh Mohammed Obaid Al Maktoum**
105 B f 01/03 Harbour Watch (IRE)—Signora Queen (FR) (Exceed And Excel (AUS)) **Mr Jaber Abdullah**
106 B c 08/05 Zoffany (IRE)—Sindirana (IRE) (Kalanisi (IRE)) (41000) **Hambleton Racing Ltd XXVII**
107 Ch c 10/05 Twilight Son—Soar (Danzero (AUS)) (130000) **Sheikh Mohammed Obaid Al Maktoum**
108 **TINY DANSER,** gr f 25/04 Markaz (IRE)—Aunt Nicola (Reel Buddy (USA)) **Bearstone Stud Limited**
109 **TWO COP BOP,** b c 07/02 Dutch Art—Rocking The Boat (IRE) (Zebedee) (28571) **Allan Kerr & Partner**
110 **UNCLE JUMBO,** gr c 22/03 Territories (IRE)—Gone Sailing (Mizzen Mast (USA)) (38095) **Mr T A Rahman**
111 Ch c 05/03 Shamardal (USA)—Why Not Queen (IRE) (Dubawi (IRE)) **Mr Jaber Abdullah**
112 B c 22/05 Dubawi (IRE)—
            Without You Babe (USA) (Lemon Drop Kid (USA)) (1000000) **Sheikh Mohammed Obaid Al Maktoum**

Other Owners: J. Berry, Mr J. N. Blackburn, Mr S. Bridge, Mr G. Bulloch, Miss E. Butterworth, Clipper Logistics, Mr B. N. Collier, Hambleton Racing Ltd, Hambleton Racing Ltd XLVI, Mr S. Hardcastle, A. C. Henson, Highclere Thoroughbred Racing Ltd, Mrs R. G. Hillen, Mr S. M. A. Hillen, B. E. Holland, Mr A. Holmes, Mrs A. J. Jackson, K&J Bloodstock Ltd, Mr A. Kerr, Mr N. J. O'Brien, Ontoawinner, Mrs A. H. Pallister, Mrs J. E. Pallister, Mr J. G. Pallister, Laurier Partners, Mr R. Peel, Mrs J. H. Ryan, Mr Steve Ryan, Mr M. J. Tedham, Mr S. R. H. Turner, Mr A. Turton.

Assistant Trainer: Adam Ryan.

Flat Jockey: Tom Eaves, Shane Gray, Kevin Stott. **Apprentice Jockey:** Miss Harriet Lees.

---

466 **MR AYTACH SADIK, Kidderminster**
Postal: **Wolverley Court Coach House, Wolverley, Kidderminster, Worcestershire, DY10 3RP**
Contacts: **PHONE 01562 852362 MOBILE 07803 040344**

1 **DOWNLOADTHEAPP (IRE),** 7, b g Definite Article—Chase A Dream (IRE) **A. M. Sadik**
2 **LOPE DE LOOP (IRE),** 5, b m Lope de Vega (IRE)—Patroller (USA) **A. M. Sadik**
3 **SUSSEX ROAD (IRE),** 10, b g Mahler—Rose Island **A. M. Sadik**
4 **THECORNISHBARRON (IRE),** 8, b g Bushranger (IRE)—Tripudium (IRE) **A. M. Sadik**

---

467 **MR GARY SANDERSON, Sheriff Hutton**
Postal: **Lilling Hall Farm, Sheriff Hutton, York, North Yorkshire, YO60 6RL**
Contacts: **PHONE 01904 468200 MOBILE 07950 622402**
EMAIL garysanderson.lhf@gmail.com WEBSITE lillinghallracing.wixsite.com

1 4, B c Passing Glance—Clipper Line (USA)
2 6, B m Champs Elysees—Leah's Pride
3 **MY BOY MONTY,** 4, b g Passing Glance—Sudden Impulse **Lilling Hall Racing**
4 6, B g Native Ruler—Pride of The Oaks
5 **WHIGWHAM,** 6, ch m Sleeping Indian—Normandy Maid **Lilling Hall Racing**

THREE-YEAR-OLDS

6 B f Passing Glance—Audley **Richard Mansfield & Sallie Wrath**
7 Ch f Burwaaz—Balinka **N N Woods, J S Reed, G Sanderson**

TWO-YEAR-OLDS

8 B f 02/03 Swiss Spirit—Lexi's Beauty (IRE) (Kheleyf (USA)) **Mr Peter Dodsworth**
9 B f 12/05 Tha'ir—Pride of The Oaks

MR GARY SANDERSON - continued

Other Owners: Dermot Fallon, Neil Francis, Mark Holdsworth, Steven Nellis, Teresa Nellis, Colin Smith, David Woods, Stuart Woods.

Assistant Trainer: Lynne Sanderson.

Flat Jockey: Cam Hardie. **Conditional Jockey:** Aiden Blakemore.

468
MR MALCOLM SAUNDERS, Wells
Postal: Blue Mountain Farm, Wells Hill Bottom, Haydon, Wells, Somerset, BA5 3EZ
Contacts: PHONE 01749 841011 MOBILE 07771 601035
EMAIL malcolm@malcolmsaunders.co.uk WEBSITE www.malcolmsaunders.co.uk

1 AMBERINE, 6, b m Equiano (FR)—Crimson Fern (IRE) M. S. Saunders
2 BLUEBELL TIME (IRE), 4, br f Coach House (IRE)—Matterofact (IRE) Mrs Ginny Nicholas & Mr M. S. Saunders
3 CORONATION COTTAGE, 6, b m Pastoral Pursuits—Avrilo Pat Hancock & Eric Jones
4 PASTFACT, 6, br g Pastoral Pursuits—Matterofact (IRE) Premier Conservatory Roofs
5 SCARLET RED, 5, b m Equiano (FR)—Crimson Fern (IRE) M. S. Saunders
6 SECRETFACT, 7, br g Sakhee's Secret—Matterofact (IRE) Premier Conservatory Roofs
7 TITUS SECRET, 8, ch g Sakhee's Secret—Crimson Fern (IRE) M. S. Saunders

THREE-YEAR-OLDS
8 CALYPSO DANSER, ch f Coach House (IRE)—Calypso Music Paul Nicholas / M S Saunders
9 DIAMOND COTTAGE, ch f Cappella Sansevero—Avrilo Pat Hancock & Eric Jones
10 LADY FLORENCE (IRE), b f Zebedee—Lady Caprice Paul Nicholas / M S Saunders
11 REDREDROBIN, b f Helmet (AUS)—Cape Rosie Paul Nicholas / M S Saunders

Other Owners: D. J. Collier, Mr P. K. Hancock, Mr E. W. Jones, Mr P. S. G. Nicholas, Mrs V. L. Nicholas, M. S. Saunders.

469
MRS DIANNE SAYER, Penrith
Postal: Town End Farm, Hackthorpe, Penrith, Cumbria, CA10 2HX
Contacts: PHONE 01931 712245 MOBILE 07980 295316

1 BAILEYS ARTIST, 5, ch g Zoffany (IRE)—Marasima (IRE) Mr G. H. Bell
2 BEENO (IRE), 11, b g Exit To Nowhere (USA)—Kay Theatre (IRE) Mrs Margaret Coppola & Mr Arthur Slack
3 CALLIOPE, 7, b m Poet's Voice—Costa Brava (IRE) Mr E. G. Tunstall
4 DETECTIVE, 4, b g Kingman—Promising Lead A. Slack
5 FRIGHTENED RABBIT (USA), 8, b g Hard Spun (USA)—Champagne Ending (USA) Mr R. A. Harrison
6 HOT GOSSIP (IRE), 6, b m Fast Company (IRE)—On The Make (IRE) Mr Dennis J. Coppola & Mrs Dianne Sayer
7 IOLANI (GER), 8, b g Sholokhov (IRE)—Imogen (IRE) SJD Racing & Dianne Sayer
8 JACKHAMMER (IRE), 6, b g Thewayyouare (USA)—Ask Annie (IRE) Mrs H. D. Sayer
9 JEU DE MOTS (FR), 7, b g Saint des Saints (FR)—Nanouska (GER) Mrs Margaret Coppola & Mr Arthur Slack
10 LEGALIZED, 6, br m Authorized (IRE)—Laurena (GER) Boom Racing
11 MILLIE THE MINX (IRE), 6, b m Medicean—Popocatepetl (FR) A. R. White
12 MY VALENTINO (IRE), 7, ch g Duke of Marmalade (IRE)—
                                          Nadwah (USA) Mr Dennis J. Coppola & Mrs Dianne Sayer
13 OCEANUS (IRE), 6, b g Born To Sea (IRE)—Alkhawarah (USA) Margaret Coppola & Dianne Sayer
14 REDARNA, 6, ch g Aqlaam—Curtains Graham Lund & Dianne Sayer
15 SIMUL AMICIS, 4, b f Hurricane Run (IRE)—Xaphania Graham Lund & Dianne Sayer
16 SIXTIES GLENARK, 7, b g Sixties Icon—Cashback Rose (IRE) Mrs M. R. Lewis
17 SUMMER LIGHTENING, 6, gr m Fair Mix (IRE)—Kristineau Messrs A & R Lyle
18 THE NAVIGATOR, 5, gr g Mastercraftsman (IRE)—Blessing (USA) Mr G. H. Bell
19 TICO TIMES (IRE), 7, br g Arcadio (GER)—Roomier (IRE) Mrs H. D. Sayer
20 TONTO'S SPIRIT, 8, b g Authorized (IRE)—Desert Royalty (IRE) A. Slack
21 WINGED MONARCH, 4, b g Kutub (IRE)—Primitive Tantrum

TWO-YEAR-OLDS
22 B g 09/04 Shirocco (GER)—Cool Baranca (GER) (Beat Hollow)

MRS DIANNE SAYER - continued

Other Owners: Mr D. J. Coppola, Mrs M. Coppola, Mr G. Lund, Mrs A. Lyle, Mr J. R. Lyle, R. Lyle, Mr S. Nicholson, S J D Racing, Mrs H. D. Sayer, A. Slack.

Assistant Trainer: Miss Joanna Sayer.

Amateur Jockey: Miss Liz Butterworth, Miss Emma Sayer.

---

470 DR JON SCARGILL, Newmarket
Postal: **Red House Stables, Hamilton Road, Newmarket, Suffolk, CB8 0TE**
Contacts: **PHONE 01638 667767 MOBILE 07785 350705**
EMAIL jdscargill@gmail.com **WEBSITE** www.jonscargill.co.uk

1 **ALABAMA DREAMING,** 4, gr f Foxwedge—Sweet Alabama **GB Horseracing**
2 **BILLIE BEANE,** 5, b m Sir Percy—Torver **Silent Partners**
3 **MISS FIRECRACKER (IRE),** 4, ch f Dragon Pulse (IRE)—Miss Otis **Theme Tune Partnership**
4 **MISSISSIPPI MISS,** 6, ch m Equiano (FR)—Junket **Silent Partners**
5 **MY PERFECT COUSIN,** 6, b g Showcasing—Torver **Mrs S. M. Scargill**

THREE-YEAR-OLDS
6 **DISARMING (IRE),** b f War Command (USA)—Gloved Hand **Dr Edna Robson & Partner**
7 **LOVE POEMS (IRE),** b f Camelot—Dansable (IRE) **Theme Tune Partnership**

TWO-YEAR-OLDS
8 Ch f 17/04 Al Kazeem—Greenery (IRE) (Green Desert)
9 B f 13/03 Slade Power—Publilia (Makfi)
10 B f 08/04 Nayef—Qualification (USA) (Afleet Alex)
11 B f 30/04 Mukhadram—Winter Dress (Haafhd)

Other Owners: Dr Edna Robson & Partner, Dr E. M. Robson, Mrs S. M. Scargill.

---

471 MR DERRICK SCOTT, Minehead
Postal: **East Lynch, Minehead, Somerset, TA24 8SS**
Contacts: **PHONE 01643 702430 FAX 01643 702430**

1 **ACTONETAKETWO,** 10, b m Act One—Temple Dancer **Mrs R. Scott**
2 **ROYBUOY,** 13, b g Royal Applause—Wavy Up (IRE) **Mrs R. Scott**

NH Jockey: James Best.

---

472 MR GEORGE SCOTT, Newmarket
Postal: **Saffron Stables, Hamilton Road, Newmarket, Suffolk, CB8 0NY**
Contacts: **MOBILE 07833 461294**
EMAIL george@georgescottracing.com **WEBSITE** www.georgescottracing.com

1 **COMIN' THROUGH (AUS),** 7, b g Fastnet Rock (AUS)—
Mica's Pride (AUS) **Breen, Walsh, Horncastle, Kilburn & Gut**
2 **CRANTOCK BAY,** 4, b g Havana Gold (IRE)—Orton Park (IRE) **Mr K. J. Breen**
3 **EARTH AND SKY (USA),** 4, b f Noble Mission—Youre So Sweet (USA) **Flaxman Stables Ireland Ltd**
4 **JACK THE TRUTH (IRE),** 6, ch g Dandy Man (IRE)—Friendly Heart (CAN) **Mr J. Stephenson**
5 **MOLL DAVIS (IRE),** 4, b f Kingman—Stupendous Miss (USA) **Sonia M. Rogers & Anthony Rogers**
6 **NARAK,** 4, ch f Dubawi (IRE)—Chachamaidee (IRE) **Mr R. A. H. Evans**
7 **PHOSPHORESCENCE (IRE),** 10, b g Sakhee (USA)—Eccentricity (USA) **Mr G. O. Scott**
8 **RELOADED (IRE),** 4, b g Excelebration (IRE)—Wooded Glade **Mr K. J. Breen**
9 **STRAWBERRY JACK,** 4, b g Foxwedge (AUS)—Strawberry Leaf **Mr J. Stephenson**

MR GEORGE SCOTT - continued

THREE-YEAR-OLDS

10 **AMAZING NEWS,** ch g Toronado (IRE)—Angelic Air **W. J. and T. C. O. Gredley**
11 **BILLY THE SQUID (IRE),** b g Requinto (IRE)—Edrea (FR) **Blue StaRR Racing**
12 **HONG KONG DRAGON,** ch g Harbour Watch (IRE)—Blue Maiden **The Black Dragon**
13 **JULIUS MAXIMUS (IRE),** b g Holy Roman Emperor (IRE)—Fine If (IRE) **Mr A. Al Mansoori**
14 **LUCKY LESLIE (IRE),** b g Camacho—Somewhere (IRE) **Simon Leslie & Partner**
15 **MISS MULLIGAN (IRE),** b f Gleneagles (IRE)—Banimpire (IRE) **Mr C. O. P. Hanbury**
16 **MUSIC THERAPIST (IRE),** gr g Zebedee—Provence **Mr Chris Wright, Ms Emma Banks & Partners**
17 **NOTION OF TIME (USA),** b f Into Mischief (USA)—Sea of Showers (USA) **Flaxman Stables Ireland Ltd**
18 **SARVAN,** gr g Lope de Vega (IRE)—Tequila Sunrise **Mr K Breen & Mr C Wright**
19 B f Declaration of War (USA)—Satulagi (USA) **Mr S. M. Al Sabah**
20 **SHOOT TO KILL (IRE),** b g Dandy Man (IRE)—Nancy Astor **Bartram,Kilburn & Ware**
21 **SOCIALIZE,** b g Kodiac—Sighora (IRE) **Mr F. Nass**
22 **STRONG POWER (IRE),** b g Kodiac—Soft Power (IRE) **K Breen,J Stephenson,M Lilley Et.,Al**
23 **TEACH (USA),** ch f Karakontie (JPN)—Twinkler (USA) **Flaxman Stables Ireland Ltd**

TWO-YEAR-OLDS

24 **BOLUDO (IRE),** b g 22/02 Belardo (IRE)—Virginia Celeste (IRE) (Galileo (IRE)) (20000) **Mr C. O. P. Hanbury**
25 **CABLE NEWS,** b f 11/02 Cable Bay (IRE)—Wemyss Bay (Sadler's Wells (USA)) **W. J. and T. C. O. Gredley**
26 **CHARLIE FELLOWES (IRE),** br c 02/04 Swiss Spirit—Filatelia (IRE) (Intikhab (USA)) (15444) **Offthebridle Podcast**
27 B f 28/02 Holy Roman Emperor (IRE)—
                         Chastushka (IRE) (Poet's Voice) (38095) **H.H. Shaikh Nasser Al Khalifa & Partner**
28 B f 17/03 Zoffany (IRE)—City On Sea (IRE) (Monsun (GER)) (15444) **S Leslie, Flaxman Stables Ire & Partner**
29 B f 08/04 Lope de Vega (IRE)—
                         Fifth Commandment (IRE) (Holy Roman Emperor (IRE)) (137280) **Ms Emma Banks & Mr John O'Connor**
30 B f 26/03 Bungle Inthejungle—Generous Heart (Sakhee's Secret) (30476) **Mr C. N. Wright**
31 **GEORGE PEABODY (IRE),** b c 13/04 Holy Roman Emperor (IRE)—
                         Swordhalf (Haafhd) (90000) **W. J. and T. C. O. Gredley**
32 **HOMEMADE JACK (IRE),** b c 04/03 War Command (USA)—
                         Love Intrigue (IRE) (Marju (IRE)) (14285) **Mr P Chau & Saffron Racing Ii**
33 B c 24/02 Camelot—Honey Hunter (IRE) (Shamardal (USA)) (25740) **Mr M. J. Lilley**
34 B br c 02/02 Mehmas (IRE)—Lady Mega (IRE) (Kodiac) (30029) **Al Rabban Racing & Partner Ii**
35 B f 19/03 Brazen Beau (AUS)—Moonlight Mystery (Pivotal) (57142) **H.H. Shaikh Nasser Al Khalifa & Partner**
36 B g 09/04 Belardo (IRE)—Pudding (IRE) (Bushranger (IRE)) (571) **Mr C. Woodhouse**
37 **PUNTA ARENAS (USA),** b c 20/02 Quality Road (USA)—
                         Absolute Crackers (IRE) (Giant's Causeway (USA)) **Flaxman Stables Ireland Ltd**
38 **RED CARPET QUEEN,** b f 10/02 Hot Streak (IRE)—Dark Reckoning (Equiano (FR)) (33333) **Ms L. Zissman**
39 Ch c 16/02 Territories (IRE)—Sell Out (Act One) (70000)
40 **SIMULATION THEORY (IRE),** ch c 07/03 Starspangledbanner (AUS)—
                         Barawin (IRE) (Hawk Wing (USA)) (30000) **Ms E. L. Banks**
41 Ch g 19/02 Sepoy (AUS)—Tears of The Sun (Mastercraftsman (IRE)) **Mildmay Racing**
42 Gr f 19/03 Iffraaj—Tequila Sunrise (Dansili) (11000) **The Grey Racehorse**
43 **TRIBUNA UFFIZI (IRE),** b c 14/01 Zoffany (IRE)—
                         Bunood (IRE) (Sadler's Wells (USA)) (35000) **Mr E Williams & Partner**
44 B c 02/03 Mayson—Vive Les Rouges (Acclamation) (34285) **H.H. Shaikh Nasser Al Khalifa & Partner**
45 **WALTER MITTY,** ro c 14/03 Lethal Force (IRE)—Furbelow (Pivotal) (75000) **W. J. and T. C. O. Gredley**
46 **WEST SUFFOLK,** b c 25/02 Make Believe—Wearing Wings (Sea The Stars (IRE)) (40000) **W. J. and T. C. O. Gredley**
47 **WHYZZAT,** b c 22/02 Dark Angel (IRE)—Whazzis (Desert Prince (IRE)) (160000) **W. J. and T. C. O. Gredley**
48 B c 11/04 Brazen Beau (AUS)—Wiki Tiki (Dixie Union (USA)) (9000) **Mr M. Bartram**

Other Owners: Mr H. A. Al Jehani, H.H. Sheikh Nasser Al Khalifa, Al Rabban Racing, Mr A. K. M. K. Al-Rabban, Ms E. L. Banks, Mr M. Bartram, Mr K. J. Breen, Mr P. Chau, Flaxman Stables Ireland Ltd, Miss M. Gut, Mr A. N. Horncastle, Mr W. A. Jackson-Stops, D. Kilburn, Mr S. Leslie, Mr M. J. Lilley, Mr F. Nass, A. F. O'Callaghan, Mr J. P. M. O'Connor, A. P. Rogers, Mrs S. M. Rogers, Saffron Racing Ii, Mr G. O. Scott, Mr J. Stephenson, Mr M. Walsh, Mr E. J. Ware, Mr E. W. B. Williams, Mr C. N. Wright.

Apprentice Jockey: Fletcher Yarham.

473 | **MR JEREMY SCOTT, Dulverton**
Postal: **Higher Holworthy Farm, Brompton Regis, Dulverton, Somerset, TA22 9NY**
Contacts: **PHONE 01398 371414 MOBILE 07709 279483**
EMAIL **holworthyfarm@yahoo.com**

1 **AKARDASHIAN (IRE),** 5, ch m Sans Frontieres (IRE)—Lady Taipan (IRE) **George & Glenda Giles**
2 **BALLYBOUGH NORA (IRE),** 7, b m Oscar (IRE)—Perspex Queen (IRE) **Pillhead House Partners**
3 **BANG ON (IRE),** 7, ch g Fracas (IRE)—Carramanagh Lady (IRE) **Cash For Honours**
4 **BELLEVARDE EXPRESS (IRE),** 5, b br m Shirocco (GER)—Senora Snoopy (IRE) **Kit James & Matt James**
5 **BLAZING SADDLES,** 5, b g High Chaparral (IRE)—Desert Sage **Mr J. P. Carrington**
6 **BONZA GIRL,** 7, b m Midnight Legend—Purple Patch **Mr G. T. Lever**
7 **BUSTER MOON (IRE),** 8, b g Darsi (FR)—Orinocco Blue (IRE) **The The Buster Moon Partnership**
8 **CHAMPAGNE COURT (IRE),** 7, b g Court Cave (IRE)—Lady Taipan (IRE) **Mr I F Gosden & Mr Dj Coles**
9 **CLONDAW DANCER (IRE),** 6, b g Big Bad Bob (IRE)—Berocco (IRE) **Friends From Insurance**
10 **DASHEL DRASHER,** 7, b g Passing Glance—So Long **Mrs B Tully & Mr R Lock**
11 **DEMON FOU (FR),** 7, b g Le Fou (IRE)—Nevka (FR) **Friends From Insurance**
12 **ELLENS WAY,** 8, b m Black Sam Bellamy (IRE)—Function Dreamer **Bet The Farm Partners**
13 **ESPALION (FR),** 6, b g Khalkevi (IRE)—Somosierra (FR) **Mr J. H. Frost**
14 **FANTASIA STORM (IRE),** 5, gr m Mahler—Fantasia Filly (IRE) **Govier & Brown**
15 **GARRANE (IRE),** 8, b g Tikkanen (USA)—Ballooley (IRE) **Friends From Insurance**
16 **GENERAL PROBUS,** 6, b br g Geordieland (FR)—Drop The Hammer **E G M Beard & R A Scott**
17 **GONNABEGOOD (IRE),** 9, b g Kutub (IRE)—Angels Flame (IRE) **The Free Spirits Partnership**
18 **GREENVIEW PARADISE (IRE),** 6, gr m Exchange Rate (USA)—Senza Rete (IRE) **Friends From Insurance**
19 **HEY BUD,** 7, b g Fair Mix (IRE)—Azione **Mr M. P. P. Brend**
20 **KELTUS,** 10, gr g Keltos (FR)—Regina d'Orthe (FR) **Fistral Beach Ltd**
21 **KERB LINE (IRE),** 7, b g Arcadio (GER)—Native Craft (IRE) **Langley's**
22 **KILCARA (IRE),** 7, b m Court Cave (IRE)—Easter Day (IRE) **London Erratics Racing Club**
23 **KISSESFORKATIE (IRE),** 6, b m Jeremy (USA)—Now Were Broke (IRE) **Derek Coles & Ian Gosden**
24 5, Ch g Fracas (IRE)—Minnie Turbo (IRE)
25 **NATIVE ROBIN (IRE),** 10, br g Robin des Pres (FR)—Homebird (IRE) **The Punchestown Syndicate**
26 **NELLA FANTASY,** 6, b m Arvico (FR)—Devon Peasant **Mrs A. E. Baker**
27 **NIFTY AT FIFTY (IRE),** 7, b g Gold Well—Tropical Sunset (IRE) **Mrs H. L. Stoneman**
28 **ORCHARDSTOWN CROSS (IRE),** 9, b g Westerner—Shang A Lang (IRE) **Mr J. H. Frost**
29 **PELORIC,** 5, ch g Intello (GER)—New Orchid (USA) **Wot No Coz**
30 **PURPLE JAZZ (IRE),** 5, b g Red Jazz (USA)—Breakmeheart (IRE) **The Barmy Men 3**
31 **RUBY WINE,** 4, b f Phenomena—Para Siempre **Trebles Holford Thoroughbreds**
32 **SEEANYTHINGYOULIKE (IRE),** 9, b g Fruits of Love (USA)—California Dreamin **Govier & Brown**
33 **SIENNA ROYALE (IRE),** 6, b m Sholokhov (IRE)—Dartmeet (IRE) **Air Cdre Hallam & Mrs Martin Hallam**
34 **SIZABLE SAM,** 5, ch g Black Sam Bellamy (IRE)—Halo Flora **Mrs C. C. Scott**
35 6, Ch m Geordieland (FR)—Sonoma (IRE) **Mr D. J. Coles**
36 **STORMY FLIGHT (IRE),** 6, gr g Cloudings (IRE)—Help Yourself (IRE) **Mr Ian Murray & Mr Dave Smith**
37 **TACTICAL MANOEUVRE (IRE),** 9, b g Marienbard (IRE)—Pride O'Fleet (IRE) **The Tacticians**
38 **TIKKINTHEBOX (IRE),** 8, b g Tikkanen (USA)—Surfing France (FR) **On A Mission**
39 **TUSCAN PEARL,** 5, b m Medicean—Western Pearl **Mr & Mrs N. Welby**
40 **TWO SAMS (IRE),** 7, b g Dubai Destination (USA)—Hello Louise (IRE) **Mr I. F. Gosden**
41 **UNISON (IRE),** 10, b g Jeremy (USA)—Easter Song (USA) **Mr J. P. Carrington**
42 **URTHEONETHATIWANT (IRE),** 7, ch g Shantou (USA)—Roberta Supreme (IRE) **The Barmy Men 4**
43 **WAVERING DOWN (IRE),** 5, b g Jeremy (USA)—Gortbofearna (IRE) **Mr J. H. Frost**

Other Owners: Mr E. G. M. Beard, Mr D. J. Coles, Mr V. P. Finn, Mrs G. D. Giles, Mr G. R. Giles, Mr I. F. Gosden, Mr P. Govier, Mr P. F. Govier, Mrs M. Hallam, Air Commodore M. R. Hallam, Mr S. Hill, Mr C. J. James, Mr M. J. James, Mr C. L. Keey, Mr R. J. Lock, Mr B. J. McManus, I. R. Murray, Mr R. A. Scott, David H. Smith, Mr M. J. Swallow, Mrs B. J. Tully.

Assistant Trainer: Camilla Scott.

NH Jockey: Matt Griffiths, Nick Scholfield. **Conditional Jockey:** Rob Hawker. **Amateur Jockey:** Miss V. Wade.

474 MISS KATIE SCOTT, Galashiels
Postal: **Stables Cottage, Millhaugh, Lindean, Galashiels, Scottish Borders**
Contacts: **MOBILE 07826 344577**

1 **CHAIN OF BEACONS**, 11, b g Midnight Legend—Millennium Girl **Simon & Angela Gillie**
2 **ELITE ICON**, 6, b g Sixties Icon—Sailing Days **Miss K. Scott**
3 **FLAMING GLORY (IRE)**, 6, b g Gold Well—Pearlsforthegirls **The Wee Guys**
4 **GETAWAY GERRY**, 6, b g Getaway (GER)—Loch Dhu (IRE) **Edward Cassie, Mark Hay & Murray Scott**
5 **KODIAC LASS (IRE)**, 4, b f Kodiac—Awwal Malika (USA) **Thistle racing club**
6 **NAPLES BAY**, 6, b g Kodiac—Trombe (FR) **Byrne Racing and Partners**
7 **ROBBEN RAINBOW**, 6, b g Delegator—Sally Can Wait **Edward Cassie & Katie Scott**
8 **ROCKLEY POINT**, 7, b g Canford Cliffs (IRE)—Statua (IRE) **The Vintage Flyers**
9 **SLADE STORM (IRE)**, 7, b g September Storm (GER)—Katie Kelly (IRE) **Mr E. Cassie**
10 **STONEY ROVER (IRE)**, 7, b g Scorpion (IRE)—Consultation (IRE) **Mr K. J. Telfer**
11 **TADASANA**, 4, b f Battle of Marengo (IRE)—Letters (FR) **Miss K. Scott**
12 **THAT'S YOUR LOTTIE**, 5, b m Imperial Monarch (IRE)—Caoba **The Jackson Partnership**
13 5, B m Fame And Glory—Twilight Eclipse (IRE)
14 **WESTERN LASS (IRE)**, 7, br m Westerner—Lady Roania (IRE) **Edward Cassie & Katie Scott**
15 **WESTERN SUPERNOVA**, 6, b m Westerner—Supreme Nova **Miss K. Scott**

THREE-YEAR-OLDS
16 **GWEEDORE**, b g Epaulette (AUS)—Ares Choix **Lamont Racing**
17 **NELLIE FRENCH (IRE)**, b f Dragon Pulse (IRE)—Texas Ruby (USA) **Mrs S. Scott**

TWO-YEAR-OLDS
18 B f 21/01 Equiano (FR)—Somersault (Pivotal) (6000)

Other Owners: Mr E. Cassie, Mrs A. Gillie, Mr S. P. Gillie, Mr M. W. Hay, Miss K. Scott, Mr W. M. Scott.

475 MR MICHAEL SCUDAMORE, Bromsash
Postal: **Ecclesswall Court, Bromsash, Nr. Ross-on-Wye, Herefordshire, HR9 7PP**
Contacts: **PHONE 01989 750844 MOBILE 07901 853520 FAX 01989 750281**
EMAIL michael.scu@btconnect.com WEBSITE www.michaelscudamoreracing.co.uk

1 **ALFIDA**, 5, b gr m Sulamani—Dissolve
2 **ASK HIMSELF (IRE)**, 6, ch g Ask—Wintry Day (IRE)
3 **BEE CROSSING**, 9, b m Fair Mix (IRE)—Indeed To Goodness (IRE)
4 **BELMONT JEWEL (IRE)**, 8, b m Westerner—Maddy's Supreme (IRE)
5 **CALTEX (FR)**, 8, bl g Network (GER)—Qomposita (FR)
6 **COPPER COIN**, 7, ch g Sulamani (IRE)—Silken Pearls
7 **COURT MASTER (IRE)**, 7, b g Court Cave (IRE)—Lusos Wonder (IRE)
8 **CZECH HER OUT (IRE)**, 6, b m Fame And Glory—Molly Hussey (IRE)
9 **DINSDALE**, 7, b g Cape Cross (IRE)—Emmy Award (IRE)
10 **DO YOUR JOB (IRE)**, 6, b g Fame And Glory—Full of Birds (FR)
11 **ENVOL DE LA COUR (FR)**, 6, b g Maresca Sorrento (FR)—Reveuse de La Cour (FR)
12 **FANCY SHAPES (IRE)**, 6, ch m Golden Lariat (USA)—Panglao Island (IRE)
13 **FANTASY SHIFT**, 5, b m Imperial Monarch (IRE)—Road Trip (IRE)
14 **HEAD HUNTER (IRE)**, 7, b g Rip Van Winkle (IRE)—Superfonic (FR)
15 **ISAAC WONDER (IRE)**, 5, b g Born To Sea (IRE)—Najaaba (USA)
16 **JOLYON**, 4, ch g Raven's Pass (USA)—Fleurissimo
17 **JUSTICE KNIGHT (IRE)**, 8, b g Raven's Pass (USA)—New Story (USA)
18 **KINGSWELL THEATRE**, 11, b g King's Theatre (IRE)—Cresswell Native (IRE)
19 **LADY MARWAH (IRE)**, 7, b m Iffraaj—Eyrecourt (IRE)
20 **LAWMAKING**, 9, b g Zamindar (USA)—Canada Water
21 **LET ME ENTERTAIN U**, 4, b g Saint des Saints (FR)—My Belle (FR)
22 **MAGS MELODY (IRE)**, 5, b m Shirocco (GER)—Supreme Serata (IRE)
23 **MONBEG AQUADUDE (IRE)**, 9, b g Flemensfirth (USA)—Mite Dash (IRE)
24 **MR CHUA (IRE)**, 4, b g Cape Cross (IRE)—Shama's Song (IRE)

MR MICHAEL SCUDAMORE - continued

25 **NADA TO PRADA**, 5, b m Kayf Tara—Ambrosia's Promise (IRE)
26 **NORTHERN BEAU (IRE)**, 7, b m Canford Cliffs (IRE)—View (IRE)
27 **PLENTY OF BUTTY (IRE)**, 7, b g Germany (USA)—Jump For Joy (IRE)
28 **QUIET SHY (FR)**, 5, b m Youmzain (IRE)—Quiet Queen
29 **ROBIN DES THEATRE (IRE)**, 5, b br m Robin des Champs (FR)—Shannon Theatre (IRE)
30 **ROLLERCOSTER (IRE)**, 8, b m Helissio (FR)—Full Deck (IRE)
31 **ROSIE AND MILLIE (IRE)**, 7, ch m Flemensfirth (USA)—Madgehil (IRE)
32 **SATURN 'N SILK (IRE)**, 5, b m Universal (IRE)—Manaphy (FR)
33 **SHATTERED GLASS (IRE)**, 6, b g Sholokhov (IRE)—Anns Present (IRE)
34 **SMITHS CROSS (IRE)**, 8, b g Westerner—Blue Supreme (IRE)
35 **SOME CHAOS (IRE)**, 9, b g Brian Boru (IRE)—Iruna Iris (IRE)
36 **SPEEDY BUCK (IRE)**, 7, b g Beat Hollow (GB)—Attymon Lill (IRE)
37 **SUMELIA (IRE)**, 5, ch m Sulamani (IRE)—Aimela (FR)
38 **SUNDAY SESSION (IRE)**, 6, b g Scorpion (IRE)—Casiana (GER)
39 **THE CRAZED MOON (IRE)**, 8, b m Yeats (IRE)—Rose Gallery (FR)
40 **THE DAWN MAN (IRE)**, 9, b g Milan—Calling Classy (IRE)
41 **THOR DE CERISY (FR)**, 6, b g Enrique—Midalisy (FR)
42 **UPTON ROAD (IRE)**, 6, b g Jeremy (USA)—Reynard's Glen (IRE)
43 **VOILA ERIC**, 8, b g Bollin Eric—Et Voila
44 **YORGONNAHEARMEROAR (IRE)**, 9, b g Scorpion (IRE)—Etoile Margot (FR)
45 **ZAYFIRE ARAMIS**, 11, ch g Zafeen (FR)—Kaylifa Aramis

THREE-YEAR-OLDS

46 **HORIZON BLEU (FR)**, b g Spanish Moon (USA)—Lili Bleue (FR)

Owners: Mr D. I. Alexander, Aramis Racing, Mr M. R. Blandford, Mr C. Breeze, Mr C. G. J. Chua, Mr D. E. Coltman, MR Mark Dunphy, Mrs B. V. Evans, Mr W. J. Fenn, Gabby Gajova and Friends, Mr R. R. Green, Having A Mare, Having A Mare I, Mr D. J. Lee, Mr A. Maclennan, Mrs L. Maclennan, Lynne & Angus Maclennan, Marchwood Aggregates, Having A Mare Mr WJ Fenn Mr DI Alexander, Mr A. Mason, Mason Scudamore Racing, Mr Mark Savidge Mr Richard Green, Mr J. J. Murray, Mrs J. M. Murray, Mr John J Murray & Mrs Lynne MacLennan, Ms I. Phipps Coltman, Mr S. Robson, Mr M. G. Savidge, Mark Savidge & Michael Scudamore, Mr M. Scudamore, Mrs M. L. Scudamore, Mrs L. J. Sluman, Mr P.E. Truscott, Mr P.E. Truscott & Mr M. Scudamore, WFenn LesleySluman DLee & Having a Mare, Wink N' A Drink.

Assistant Trainer: Mrs Marilyn Scudamore.

NH Jockey: Ben Poste, Brendan Powell, Tom Scudamore.

476
MR DEREK SHAW, Sproxton
Postal: **The Sidings, Saltby Road, Sproxton, Melton Mowbray, Leicestershire, LE14 4RA**
Contacts: **PHONE 01476 860578 MOBILE 07721 039645 FAX 01476 860578**
EMAIL mail@derekshawracing.com WEBSITE www.derekshawracing.com

1 **AMAZING AMAYA**, 5, b m New Approach (IRE)—Faslen (USA) **P. E. Barrett**
2 **ATYAAF**, 5, b g Invincible Spirit (IRE)—Eshaadeh (USA) **GB Civil Engineering (Leicester) LTD**
3 **DUBAI ELEGANCE**, 6, ch m Sepoy (AUS)—Some Sunny Day **Million Dreams Racing 1**
4 **DYNAMO WALT (IRE)**, 9, b g Acclamation—Cambara **Mr D. Shaw**
5 **FINAL LEGACY**, 4, b f Coach House (IRE)—Tartatartufata **Mrs L. J. Shaw**
6 **GO ON MY COCKER**, 4, b c Acclamation—Missisipi Star (IRE) **Mr A. Flint**
7 **HAMMER GUN (USA)**, 7, b g Smart Strike (CAN)—Caraboss **Mr A. Flint**
8 **HARBOUR VISION**, 5, gr g Harbour Watch (IRE)—Holy Nola (USA) **New Vision Bloodstock**
9 **HURRICANE HEIDI**, 4, gr f Kyllachy—The Manx Touch (IRE) **Mrs L. J. Shaw**
10 **ITS ALL CLOVER NOW (IRE)**, 5, b g Most Improved (IRE)—All In Clover (IRE) **Mr D. Shaw**
11 **LE MANEGE ENCHANTE (IRE)**, 7, gr g Zebedee—Beth **Mr N. P. Franklin**
12 **MOMTALIK (USA)**, 5, b g Point of Entry (USA)—Sacred Feather (USA) **GB Civil Engineering (Leicester) LTD**
13 **NAVETTE (USA)**, 4, b f Lemon Drop Kid (USA)—Winsili **Mr D. Shaw**
14 **POLARBROOK (IRE)**, 13, br g Alderbrook—Frozen Cello (IRE) **Mr J. R. Saville**
15 **PURELY PROSECCO**, 4, b f Poet's Voice—Nabat Sultan **Mrs L. J. Shaw**

MR DEREK SHAW - continued

16 **REMISSION**, 4, b g Epaulette (AUS)—Fenella Fudge **Mr D. Shaw**
17 **SAMPHIRE COAST**, 7, b g Fastnet Rock (AUS)—Faslen (USA) **P. E. Barrett**
18 **SING BERTIE (IRE)**, 4, b g Zebedee—Emirates Challenge (IRE) **Mr J. R. Saville**
19 **TINA TEASPOON**, 6, b m Kheleyf (USA)—Button Moon (IRE) **P. E. Barrett**
20 **ULYSSES (GER)**, 6, b g Sinndar (IRE)—Ungarin (GER) **Million Dreams Racing**
21 **WAFFLETON**, 4, gr f Epaulette (AUS)—Ming Meng (IRE) **P. E. Barrett**

THREE-YEAR-OLDS
22 **DUE A DIAMOND**, b f Due Diligence (USA)—Shaws Diamond (USA) **Mrs L. J. Shaw**
23 **LITTLEMISSATTITUDE**, b f Due Diligence (USA)—Lady Elalmadol (IRE) **Shawthing Racing Partnership (d Shaw)**
24 **NEROLI**, gr f Tamayuz—Ming Meng (IRE) **P. E. Barrett**
25 **SPEED DATING (FR)**, gr g Outstrip—Sign Your Name (GER) **Ownaracehorse & Lyndsey Shaw**
26 **THE KYLLACHY TOUCH**, gr c Kyllachy—The Manx Touch **Mrs L. J. Shaw**

Other Owners: Million Dreams Racing, Ownaracehorse Ltd, Mr I. D. Sellens, Mr D. Shaw, Mrs L. J. Shaw, Shawthing Racing Partnership.

Yard Sponsor: Grosvenor Contracts Leasing Ltd.

---

477 **MRS FIONA SHAW, Dorchester**
Postal: **Skippet Cottage, Bradford Peverell, Dorchester, Dorset, DT2 9SE**
Contacts: **PHONE 01305 889350 MOBILE 07970 370444**
EMAIL fiona.shaw05@gmail.com

1 **HIGHDAWN (IRE)**, 7, b m Alflora (IRE)—Wychnor Dawn (IRE) **John & Heather Snook**
2 **HOLLYWOOD KEN (IRE)**, 7, b g Arcano (IRE)—Third Dimension (FR) **Mr J. R. Dodington**
3 **HYMN AND A PRAYER**, 7, br g Eastern Anthem (IRE)—Kryssa **Mrs F. M. Shaw**
4 4, B f Kayf Tara—Ice Nelly (IRE) **Mrs F. M. Shaw**
5 **KIWI MYTH**, 8, b m Midnight Legend—Kiwi Katie **John & Heather Snook**
6 **SHOW ON THE ROAD**, 9, b g Flemensfirth (USA)—Roses of Picardy (IRE) **Mrs F. M. Shaw**
7 **THE MIGHTY ASH (IRE)**, 10, b g Arcadio (GER)—She's Got To Go (IRE) **Miss M. I. Macgregor**

Other Owners: Mrs H. A. Snook, J. W. Snook.

---

478 **MR MARK SHEARS, Newton Abbot**
Postal: **Lower Nattadon, Chagford, Newton Abbot, Devon, TQ13 8ER**
Contacts: **PHONE 01647 432356 MOBILE 07881 745314 FAX 01647 432356**
EMAIL markshearsracing@gmail.com

1 **JASPER JAY**, 7, b g Haafhd—Jenise (IRE) **Mr M. B. Shears**

Assistant Trainer: Miss K. Reynolds.

---

479 **MR MATT SHEPPARD, Ledbury**
Postal: **Home Farm Cottage, Eastnor, Ledbury, Herefordshire, HR8 1RD**
Contacts: **MOBILE 07770 625061 FAX 01531 634846**
EMAIL matthew.sheppard@cmail.co.uk

1 **ALL GOOD THINGS (IRE)**, 8, b g Dahjee (USA)—Material Lady (IRE) **Mrs N. Sheppard**
2 **GETAWAYTONEWBAY (IRE)**, 7, ch m Getaway (GER)—Boozy Lee (IRE) **Tony Scrivin & Lost In the Summer Wine**
3 **KESTREL VALLEY**, 6, b m Dr Massini (IRE)—Lady Karinga **Mrs J. M. Johnson**
4 **ROCK ON ROCKY**, 12, b g Overbury (IRE)—Tachometer (IRE) **Jan Johnson & Terry Harman**
5 **THE BAY BIRCH (IRE)**, 9, b m Beneficial—Tournant Vic (IRE) **Mr A. J. Scrivin**

MR MATT SHEPPARD - continued

Other Owners: Mr T. A. Harman, Mrs J. M. Johnson, R. A. Kujawa, Lost In The Summer Wine, Mr A. J. Scrivin, Mr P. R. W. Smith.

NH Jockey: Stan Sheppard.

---

480 **MR OLIVER SHERWOOD, Upper Lambourn**
Postal: **Rhonehurst House, Upper Lambourn, Hungerford, Berkshire, RG17 8RG**
Contacts: **PHONE 01488 71411 MOBILE 07979 591867 FAX 01488 72786**
EMAIL oliver.sherwood@virgin.net WEBSITE www.oliversherwood.co.uk

1 **A TIME TO SHINE (IRE)**, 5, b br g Malinas (GER)—Royal Bride **Tim Syder & Dominic Burke**
2 **ARCHIMENTO**, 7, ch g Archipenko (USA)—Caribana **Forever Optimists**
3 **BALLAQUANE (IRE)**, 5, b g Scorpion (IRE)—Barreenagh Beag (IRE) **Mr T. J. Hemmings**
4 **BAYAANAAT**, 4, ch g Dawn Approach (IRE)—Khothry (IRE) **Jeremy Dougall & Will Watt**
5 **BEMBRIDGE (IRE)**, 4, b g Westerner—Brotenstown (IRE) **Mr J. Palmer-Brown**
6 **BOOK OF GOLD (IRE)**, 8, b g Flemensfirth (USA)—Ballerina Queen (IRE) **Mr A Lousada & Mr A Kaplan**
7 **BRINGTHEHOUSEDOWN (IRE)**, 6, b g Royal Applause—Raskutani **Mrs S. Steele**
8 **BROUGHTONS BEAR (IRE)**, 4, b g Kodiac—Though (IRE) **Broughton Thermal Insulations**
9 **BROUGHTONS RHYTHM**, 11, b g Araafa (IRE)—Broughton Singer (IRE) **Broughton Thermal Insulations**
10 **BRUMMIE BOYS (IRE)**, 5, b g Flemensfirth (USA)—Bobs Article (IRE) **Mr Andrew Cohen & Mr Alan Kaplan**
11 **CASTLEGRACE ROSE (IRE)**, 5, b m Oscar (IRE)—Thunder Road (IRE) **Mr T. D. J. Syder**
12 **CERVARO MIX (FR)**, 6, gr g Al Namix (FR)—Semiramiss (FR) **Kate & Andrew Brooks**
13 **CILAOS GLACE (FR)**, 7, br g Voix du Nord (FR)—Miss Glacee (FR) **Heart of the South Racing 118**
14 **COSSACK DANCER**, 4, br g Sholokhov (IRE)—Lecon Benefique (IRE) **Valda Burke & Bryan Burrough**
15 **DOMINATEUR (FR)**, 7, b g Desir d'Un Soir (FR)—Sourya d'Airy (FR) **Kate & Andrew Brooks**
16 **DONLADD (IRE)**, 6, b g Cloudings (IRE)—Kentford Serotina **Mr T. J. Hemmings**
17 **FELIX D'AUTRY (FR)**, 6, b g Khalkevi (FR)—Hassaya (FR) **Lady Thompson & Julia Lukas**
18 **GOT AWAY (FR)**, 8, m American Post—Hideaway Girl **B McDonald & B Mellon**
19 **JERSEY BEAN (IRE)**, 7, b g Court Cave (IRE)—Jennifers Diary (IRE) **Mr A. Taylor**
20 **JERSEY LADY (FR)**, 4, ch f Martaline—La Bombonera (FR) **Mr A. Taylor**
21 **LADY IN HIDING (IRE)**, 6, br m Stowaway—Crackin' Liss (IRE) **A F Lousada & Mark Burton**
22 **LAURIE COME ON (IRE)**, 6, b g Robin des Champs (FR)—Seekayclaire (IRE) **Mr P. Mellett**
23 **LE BOULEVARDIER**, 4, b g Champs Elysees—Daffydowndilly **Lady Blyth**
24 **MAKETY**, 6, ch m Black Sam Bellamy (FR)—Mi Money **Mrs S. A. White**
25 **MANNING ESTATE (IRE)**, 6, b g Stowaway—Specifiedrisk (IRE) **Mr & Mrs Norman**
26 **MONKEY PUZZLE**, 8, ch g Sulamani (IRE)—Hunca Munca (IRE) **Melbourne 10 Racing**
27 **MR DORRELL SAGE (FR)**, 7, b g Sageburg (IRE)—Miss Breezy (FR) **The Three Fields**
28 **NO NO JULIET (IRE)**, 7, br m Scorpion (IRE)—Full Imperatrice (FR) **Don Sebastiao Partnership**
29 **NO NO MAESTRO (IRE)**, 5, b g Mahler—Maisey Down **Don Sebastiao Partnership**
30 **NORLEY (IRE)**, 5, b g Yeats (IRE)—No Moore Bills **Mr T. J. Hemmings**
31 **OCEAN DRIFTER (IRE)**, 5, b g Aizavoski (IRE)—Driftaway (IRE) **Mr T. D. J. Syder**
32 **OURVILLE'S MILLION (FR)**, 7, b g Sageburg (IRE)—Madeka (FR) **The Ivy Syndicate**
33 **PAPAGANA**, 7, b m Martaline—New Destiny (FR) **Mr D. J. Burke**
34 **PASEO**, 4, b g Champs Elysees—Posteritas (IRE) **The Daughters of Minella Partnership**
35 **PEUR DE RIEN (FR)**, 7, b g Kapgarde (FR)—Tango Princess (FR) **British Racing Club**
36 **PITON PETE (IRE)**, 9, b g Westerner—Glenair Lucy (IRE) **Mr P. Mellett**
37 **PONTRESINA (IRE)**, 7, b g Milan—Gilt Benefit (IRE) **Winterfields Farm Ltd, M Burton & H Cox**
38 **RAINBOW STORM (FR)**, 4, b g On Est Bien (FR)—Rainbow Oceane (FR)
39 **REPUBLICAN**, 5, b g Kayf Tara—Noun de La Thinte (FR) **Mr E. J. Ware**
40 **SAMMY BILL**, 7, b g Black Sam Bellamy (IRE)—Samrana (FR) **Mr T. J. Hemmings**
41 **SEASTON SPIRIT**, 7, b g Kayf Tara—Aphrodisias (FR) **Mr M. Fiddy**
42 **SEVARANO (IRE)**, 8, b g Shantou (USA)—Eva La Diva (IRE) **Mr T. D. J. Syder**
43 4, Gr g Montmartre (FR)—Seven Even (FR)
44 **SHAUGHNESSY**, 7, b g Shantou (USA)—Sudden Beat **Mr T. D. J. Syder**
45 **SOUTHERN SAM**, 6, b g Black Sam Bellamy (FR)—Pougatcheva (FR) **Mr T. D. J. Syder**
46 **SPICE WAR**, 5, b g Declaration of War (USA)—Blast Furnace (IRE) **Apiafi & Black**
47 **STORM KATIE**, 4, ch f Kapgarde (FR)—Stone Light (FR) **Andrew Brooks & Dominic Burke**

MR OLIVER SHERWOOD - continued

48 4, B g Walk In The Park (IRE)—Sublimissime (FR) **Heart of the South Racing 121**
49 TARADA, 7, br g Kayf Tara—Kerada (FR) **Mr T. J. Hemmings**
50 THE FRESH PRINCE (IRE), 10, b g Robin des Pres (FR)—Hayley Cometh (IRE) **Rhonehurst Raiders**
51 VENTURA DRAGON (IRE), 5, ch g Dragon Pulse (IRE)—Dancing Duchess (IRE) **Jeremy Dougall & Will Watt**
52 VINNIE THE HODDIE (IRE), 6, b g Vinnie Roe (IRE)—Blackwater Babe (IRE) **Five Guys & A Striker Syndicate**
53 WEST COAST FLYER, 7, b g Cape Cross (IRE)—La Felicita **A. Saeed**
54 WESTSTREET (IRE), 10, b g Westerner—Klipperstreet (IRE) **Weststreet Partnership**
55 WHEESHT (IRE), 6, b rm Scorpion (IRE)—Retain That Magic (IRE) **Million in Mind Partnership**
56 WORKING CLASS, 6, b g Bahri (USA)—Louise d'Arzens **Our Racing Club**

Other Owners: Mr J. Apiafi, Mr C. Austin, A. W. Black, Mr A. L. Brooks, Mrs K. L. Brooks, Mr D. J. Burke, Mrs V. F. Burke, B. R. H. Burrough, Mr M. A. Burton, Mr A. L. Cohen, Mr H. W. Cox, Mr J. M. Dougall, Mrs A. J. Green, D. M. W. Hodgkiss, Mrs S. A. Hodgkiss, Ms R. A. Jenner, Alan Kaplan, Mr A. F. Lousada, Mrs J. K. Lukas, B. T. McDonald, Mr B. H. Mellon, Mr R. R. Norman, Mrs S. D. Norman, Mr M. E. O'Hara, Mr O. M. C. Sherwood, Mr T. D. J. Syder, Lady Thompson, Mr W. S. Watt, Winter-fields Farm Ltd.

Assistant Trainer: Andy Llewellyn, **Head Lad:** Stefan Namesansky, **Secretary:** Emma Chugg.

NH Jockey: Leighton Aspell, Thomas Garner. **Amateur Jockey:** Harrison Beswick, Kai Lenihan.

---

481 ## MISS LYNN SIDDALL, Tadcaster
Postal: Stonebridge Farm, Colton, Tadcaster, North Yorkshire, LS24 8EP
Contacts: **PHONE 01904 744291 MOBILE 07778 216694, 07778 216692 FAX 01904 744291**

1 ALLSFINEANDANDY (IRE), 4, b g Dandy Man (IRE)—Swish Dancer (IRE) **Mr G. Kennington**
2 ASTROPHYSICS, 8, ch g Paco Boy (IRE)—Jodrell Bank (IRE) **Mr J. A. Kay**
3 BEVSBOY (IRE), 6, b g Elzaam (AUS)—Eurolink Sundance **Mr A. Longden**
4 ENCODED (IRE), 7, ch m Sakhee's Secret—Confidentiality (IRE) **Lynn Siddall Racing II**
5 FIRST OF NEVER (IRE), 14, b g Systematic—Never Promise (FR) **Lynn Siddall Racing II**
6 IN VINO VERITAS (IRE), 9, b g Art Connoisseur (IRE)—Robin **Mr J. A. Kay**
7 JAZZ MAGIC (IRE), 5, ch g Red Jazz (USA)—Caerella (IRE) **Mr J. A. Kay**
8 KYLLACHY CASTLE, 4, ch g Kyllachy—Amicable Terms **Mr G. Kennington**
9 MR CONUNDRUM, 7, b g Paco Boy (IRE)—Folly Drove **Lynn Siddall Racing II**
10 PADDY'S ROCK (IRE), 9, b g Whipper (USA)—Hedera (USA) **Mr J. A. Kay**
11 SERVO (IRE), 6, b g Power—Parade Scene (USA) **Mr J. A. Kay**
12 STAR OF VALOUR (IRE), 5, b g Invincible Spirit—Birthstone **Mr J. A. Kay**
13 YORKSHIREMAN (IRE), 10, b g Red Clubs (IRE)—Ossiana (IRE) **Jan Slater & Partners**

Other Owners: Miss L. C. Siddall, Miss J. M. Slater.

Assistant Trainer: Stephen Hackney.

---

482 ## MR OLIVER SIGNY, Lambourn
Postal: The Croft Stables, Upper Lambourn, Hungerford, Berkshire, RG17 8QH
EMAIL oliver@oliversignyracing.com

1 BE THE BEST (USA), 4, b g Declaration of War (USA)—Memories For Us (USA) **Adam Signy and Ben Spiers**
2 DREAM DE DREAM (IRE), 8, ch m Flemensfirth (USA)—Rudy Renata (FR) **LSRFC SALVPS**
3 DUISBURG (FR), 4, gr g Kendargent (FR)—Desca (GER) **I Barratt, A Signy & B Spiers**
4 ETAT MAJOR AULMES (FR), 6, b g Della Francesca (USA)—River Gold Aulmes (FR) **Mr & Mrs A. Signy**
5 FANCY A DANCE (IRE), 5, br g Arcadio (GER)—Fancy Fashion (IRE)
6 FRENCH PARADOXE (FR), 5, b g Day Flight—Sculture (FR) **Mick Fitzgerald Racing Club**
7 LUCINDA, 6, b m Kayf Tara—La Harde (FR)
8 RUSPER'S GIFT (IRE), 4, b g Requinto (IRE)—Cadescia (IRE) **Appletree Stud, M Gumienny & A Signy**
9 SOMETHING ROSIE (IRE), 6, b m Gold Well—Pakaradyssa (FR) **Mrs F. Kempe**

MR OLIVER SIGNY - continued

THREE-YEAR-OLDS
10 TWITTERING (IRE), b c Kodiac—Swallow Falls (IRE) **Oliver Signy Racing Club**

Other Owners: Little Lodge Farm.

Head Lad: Albert Ennis, **Racing Secretary:** Mrs Katherine Signy.

---

483 **MR DAVID SIMCOCK, Newmarket**
Postal: **The Office, Trillium Place, Birdcage Walk, Newmarket, Suffolk, CB8 0NE**
Contacts: **PHONE 01638 662968 MOBILE 07808 954109, 07702 851561 FAX 01638 663888**
EMAIL david@davidsimcock.co.uk WEBSITE www.davidsimcock.co.uk

1 **ALEMAGNA**, 4, b f Sea The Moon (GER)—Alta Moda
2 **ALMANIA (IRE)**, 4, b g Australia—Sent From Heaven (IRE)
3 **ALMOST MIDNIGHT**, 4, b g Siyouni (FR)—Late Night (GER)
4 **BLESS HIM (IRE)**, 6, b g Sea The Stars (IRE)—Happy Land (IRE)
5 **CLAP YOUR HANDS**, 4, b g Universal (IRE)—Woop Woop (IRE)
6 **DEAL A DOLLAR**, 4, b c Frankel—Cape Dollar (IRE)
7 **DESERT ENCOUNTER (IRE)**, 8, b g Halling (USA)—La Chicana (IRE)
8 **DESERT FRIEND (IRE)**, 4, ch g Universal (IRE)—Assabiyya (IRE)
9 **DURSTON**, 4, ch g Sea The Moon (GER)—Caribana
10 **FURIOUS**, 4, b f Oasis Dream—Noyelles (IRE)
11 **KASAMAN (FR)**, 4, b g Charm Spirit (IRE)—Kasatana (IRE)
12 **KITAABAAT**, 5, b g Dansili—Ausus (USA)
13 **LADY OF SHALOTT**, 5, b m Camelot—Silent Act (USA)
14 **MISS LATIN (IRE)**, 5, b m Galileo (IRE)—Breeze Hill (IRE)
15 **MOMENT OF HOPE (IRE)**, 4, b f Casamento (IRE)—Hikayati (IRE)
16 **NONIOS (IRE)**, 8, b g Oasis Dream—Young and Daring (IRE)
17 **OASIS FANTASY (IRE)**, 9, br g Oasis Dream—Cara Fantasy (IRE)
18 **PREJUDICE**, 4, ch g Dubawi (IRE)—Ever Rigg
19 **RAAKIB ALHAWA (IRE)**, 4, b c Kingman—Starlet (IRE)
20 **RANGALI ISLAND (IRE)**, 4, b c Camacho—Tender Surprise
21 **REGAL LILLY (IRE)**, 4, b f Iffraaj—Sweet Lilly
22 **SMART CHAMPION**, 5, b g Teofilo (IRE)—Soryah (IRE)
23 **SPANISH MISSION (USA)**, 4, b c Noble Mission—Limonar (IRE)
24 **ULTIMATE AVENUE (IRE)**, 6, b g Excelebration (IRE)—Dance Avenue (IRE)
25 **UNIVERSAL ORDER**, 4, ch g Universal (IRE)—My Order
26 **VEXED**, 4, b g Charm Spirit (IRE)—Kite Mark
27 **WOVEN**, 4, ch g Dutch Art—Regal Silk

THREE-YEAR-OLDS
28 **ALCHIMISTA**, b f Archipenko (USA)—Alta Moda
29 **AMIRA'S CROWN (USA)**, b f Big Brown (USA)—Regal's Encore (USA)
30 **ASIAN BEAU (USA)**, b br c Shanghai Bobby (USA)—Taro (USA)
31 **CALEDONIAN CRUSADE (IRE)**, gr g Gleneagles (IRE)—Convocate (USA)
32 **CARLOS FELIX (IRE)**, ch g Lope de Vega (IRE)—Quad's Melody (IRE)
33 **CLOSING SHOW**, br f Intello (GER)—Kamarinskaya (USA)
34 **DEPOSIT (IRE)**, b g Sea The Stars (IRE)—Interim Payment (USA)
35 **EASTERN GENERAL (IRE)**, b c Brazen Beau (AUS)—Celestial Empire (USA)
36 **EL SALVAJE**, b c Dutch Art—Crying Lightening (IRE)
37 **ELTHAM PALACE**, b f Invincible Spirit (IRE)—Moment In Time (IRE)
38 **END ZONE**, b g Dark Angel (IRE)—Brown Eyed Honey
39 **FIJI**, b c Muhaarar—Tropical Paradise (IRE)
40 **FLOAT (IRE)**, b f Nathaniel (IRE)—Honorine (IRE)
41 **FOLK DANCE**, b f Golden Horn—Folk Opera (IRE)
42 **GREGORY K (USA)**, b br c City Zip (USA)—Traffic Sister (USA)
43 **ILALLIQA (IRE)**, b f Muhaarar—Sun Bittern (USA)

MR DAVID SIMCOCK - continued

44 **INDIGO TIMES (IRE),** gr g Alhebayeb (IRE)—Easy Times
45 **ISPAHAN,** ch c Lope de Vega (IRE)—Elle Galante (GER)
46 **KING OF SPIES (USA),** b c Noble Mission—Fever's Gone (USA)
47 **MOHICAN HEIGHTS (IRE),** ch c Australia—Mohican Princess
48 **MORLAIX,** b g Mayson—Estemaala (IRE)
49 **ORIENTAL MYSTIQUE,** b f Kingman—Madame Chiang
50 **PALAMOS,** b f Blame (USA)—Qushchi
51 **PAX BRITANNICA (IRE),** b f Zoffany (IRE)—Athreyaa
52 **PAYCHECK,** ch f Raven's Pass (USA)—Fibou (USA)
53 **QUEEN OF THE WAVES,** b f Kingman—Marine Bleue (IRE)
54 **RESIG (USA),** ch c Tapiture (USA)—Golden Po (USA)
55 **RODRIGO DIAZ,** b g Golden Horn—Kitty Wells
56 **ROVANIEMI (IRE),** b c Oasis Dream—Landmark (USA)
57 **SHANGHAI TONG (USA),** b c Shanghai Bobby (USA)—Fashion House (USA)
58 **SUESTAR,** gr f Dark Angel (IRE)—Momentus (IRE)
59 **SURPRISE ENCOUNTER,** b f Iffraaj—Counterclaim
60 **TAMPERE (IRE),** b f Sea The Moon (GER)—Brigitta (IRE)
61 **TEPUI (USA),** b c Sky Mesa (USA)—Corleone (USA)
62 **TIGER CRUSADE (FR),** b c No Nay Never (USA)—Folle Allure (FR)
63 **TIME TO STRIKE (IRE),** b f Muhaarar—Up In Time
64 **YORKTOWN (IRE),** b c Free Eagle (IRE)—Bryanstown (IRE)

TWO-YEAR-OLDS

65 B c 25/03 No Nay Never (USA)—Aljumar (IRE) (Marju (IRE)) (155000)
66 B c 29/01 Lope de Vega (IRE)—Alpine Spirit (IRE) (Invincible Spirit (IRE)) (68640)
67 B c 03/05 Acclamation—Ardeola (GER) (Manduro (GER)) (77220)
68 **CLOVIS POINT (FR),** b c 26/01 Fastnet Rock (AUS)—Khaleesy (IRE) (Galileo (IRE)) (80000)
69 B c 20/03 Gleneagles (IRE)—Cubanita (Selkirk (USA)) (21000)
70 **DUBAI EMPEROR (IRE),** b c 17/04 Gleneagles (IRE)—Nateeja (IRE) (Shamardal (USA)) (32000)
71 **FOLK SONG,** b 30/03 Oasis Dream—Folk Opera (IRE) (Singspiel (IRE))
72 B c 21/02 Street Sense (USA)—Fortheloveofnell (IRE) (Galileo (IRE))
73 **FUTURE FORTUNE (IRE),** b br c 04/02 Vadamos (FR)—Allez Y (IRE) (Rip Van Winkle (IRE)) (55000)
74 B c 16/03 Quality Road (USA)—Hailey d'Oro (USA) (Medaglia d'Oro (USA))
75 B f 13/02 Fastnet Rock (AUS)—Heartless (New Approach (IRE)) (50000)
76 B c 19/03 Shalaa (IRE)—Inner Sea (USA) (Henrythenavigator (USA)) (9000)
77 B c 23/02 Kingman—Islington (Sadler's Wells (USA)) (150000)
78 B c 16/02 Kingman—Just Wood (FR) (Highest Honor (FR)) (220000)
79 B c 21/02 Sepoy (AUS)—Kahalah Fantasy (Authorized (IRE))
80 B br f 31/01 Honor Code (USA)—Keowee Clai (USA) (Cherokee Run (USA))
81 B f 17/04 Vadamos (FR)—La Chicana (IRE) (Invincible Spirit (IRE)) (145000)
82 B f 29/04 Invincible Spirit (IRE)—Lady Heidi (High Chaparral (IRE))
83 **LOWER STREET,** b f 22/04 Kingman—Upper Street (IRE) (Dansili)
84 B c 12/04 Pivotal—Madonna Dell'orto (Montjeu (IRE)) (180000)
85 Br c 19/05 Invincible Spirit (IRE)—Magic Mission (Machiavellian (USA)) (120000)
86 B c 04/04 Frankel—Moment In Time (IRE) (Tiger Hill (IRE))
87 B f 11/04 Shalaa (IRE)—Muhadathat (Showcasing) (90000)
88 B c 17/04 Kodiac—Multicolour Wave (IRE) (Rainbow Quest (USA)) (107249)
89 B f 29/01 Mukhadram—Musical Sands (Green Desert (USA)) (40000)
90 B c 05/02 Free Eagle (IRE)—Nans Joy (IRE) (In The Wings)
91 **ORIENTAL ART,** b c 27/02 Archipenko (USA)—Robe Chinoise (Robellino (USA)) (77000)
92 Ch c 05/02 Iffraaj—Pacifica Highway (USA) (Pulpit (USA)) (40000)
93 B f 11/02 Awtaad (IRE)—Pivotal's Princess (Pivotal) (42900)
94 Br gr c 26/03 Dark Angel (IRE)—Pure Excellence (Exceed And Excel (AUS))
95 **RANI OF JHANSI,** b f 20/03 Invincible Spirit (IRE)—Madame Chiang (Archipenko (USA))
96 B c 01/02 New Approach (IRE)—Royale Danehill (IRE) (Danehill (USA)) (130000)
97 B f 20/02 Muhaarar—Sospira (Cape Cross (IRE)) (10000)
98 B c 23/01 Awtaad (IRE)—Street Style (Rock of Gibraltar (IRE)) (100000)
99 B f 05/02 Galileo (IRE)—Terror (IRE) (Kodiac) (550000)
100 B br f 08/04 Sea The Stars (IRE)—Twilight Sky (Authorized (IRE)) (62000)

MR DAVID SIMCOCK - continued

101 B c 03/04 Dubawi (IRE)—Voleuse de Coeurs (IRE) (Teofilo (IRE)) (200000)
102 Ch c 10/05 Showcasing—Wahylah (IRE) (Shamardal (USA)) (120000)
103 Ch c 21/05 Galileo (IRE)—Withorwithoutyou (IRE) (Danehill (USA)) (200000)

Owners: Al Asayl Bloodstock Ltd, Malih L. Al Basti, Sheikh J. D. Al Maktoum, Mr A. Al Mansoori, M. Al Nabouda, Mr S. B. M. Al Qassimi, A. Al Shaikh, Mr S. J. A. Alharbi, Andrew Whitlock Racing Ltd, Australian Bloodstock, Mr W. Baker, Chola Dynasty, Mr C. F. Conroy, J. M. Cook, K. A. Dasmal, Khalifa Dasmal & Bryan Payne, Mr D. P. Duffy, El Catorce, Mr R. El Youssef, Mr E. Elhrari, Future, Mrs E. Grant, Mr S. P Grant, Mrs F. H. Hay, Highclere Thoroughbred Racing - Durston, Mr S. M. A. Hillen, Honorable Earle Mack & Team Valor Llc, Mr A. Howells, Mrs E. M. E. Irwin, Mrs Edward Irwin & Mrs John Magnier, Mr Jos & Mrs Jane Rodosthenous, Mr K. H. Kei, Khalifa Dasmal & Partners, Mr K. Lowe, Mrs M. Lowe, E. I. Mack, Mrs S. Magnier, Mrs J Magnier, Mr M Tabor & Mr D Smith, Mr A. Menahi, Millingbrook Racing, Millingbrook Racing & Partners, Mrs Fitri Hay & Partners 2, Never Say Die Partnership, Mr E. M. O'Connor, Mr C. C. Payne, Mr R. A. Pegum, Mr Pegum, Mr & Mrs Lowe & Mr & Mrs Grant, A. J. Perkins, Mr C. Pizarro, Mrs K. Pizarro, Qatar Racing Limited, Qatar Racing Ltd & Mr Kin Hung Kei, Qatar Racing Ltd & Partner, Qatar Racing Ltd & Sun Bloodstock Sarl, Quantum Leap Racing Xl, Quantum Leap Racing Xi & Partner, Miss K. Rausing, Mr J. Rodosthenous, Mrs J. Rodosthenous, Roldvale Ltd, Roldvale Ltd, Ed Ware & Partners, Mrs L. M. Shanahan, Mr D. M. I. Simcock, Mrs J. M. Simcock, Dr A. Sivananthan, Mrs K. Sivananthan, D. Smith, Speriamo Bloodstock Pty Ltd, St Albans Bloodstock Limited, St Albans Bloodstock Ltd & Associates, Mr S. Suhail, Sun Bloodstock SARL, Sun Bloodstock Sarl & Qatar Racing Ltd, M. Tabor, Talentschmiede Racing, Team Valor LLC, The Crepello Partnership, The John Cook & Partner, Tick Tock Partnership, Tony Perkins & Partners, Twenty Stars Partnership, Mr E. J. Ware, Major M. G. Wyatt, Mrs A. V. Yates, Mr D. Yates, Mr & Mrs D. Yates.

Assistant Trainer: Sam Goldsmith, Jack Jones.

Flat Jockey: Jamie Spencer. **Apprentice Jockey:** Poppy Bridgwater, Dylan Hogan.

---

484 MR DAN SKELTON, Alcester
Postal: **Lodge Hill, Shelfield Green, Shelfield, Alcester, Warwickshire, B49 6JR**
Contacts: PHONE **01789 336339**
EMAIL **office@danskeltonracing.com** WEBSITE **www.danskeltonracing.com**

1 **A LARGE ONE PLEASE (FR)**, 5, ch g Planteur (IRE)—Turtledove (FR) **Mr & Mrs Paul & Clare Rooney**
2 **ACCORDINGTOGINO (IRE)**, 7, ch g Perugino (USA)—Accordintomags (IRE) **Mrs Gill Duckworth & Mrs Pat Dry**
3 **ACROSS THE LINE (IRE)**, 5, b g Fame And Glory—
La Protagonista (IRE) **Mrs J & Mrs Mv Magnier & Mrs P Shanahan**
4 **AGGY WITH IT (IRE)**, 6, b m Presenting—Agathe du Berlais (FR) **Andy & Sharon Measham**
5 **AHEADFULLOFDREAMS (IRE)**, 7, b g Sandmason—Aphra Benn (IRE) **Mr I. Lawrence**
6 **ALLMANKIND**, 4, b g Sea The Moon (GER)—Wemyss Bay **W. J. and T. C. O. Gredley**
7 **ALNADAM (FR)**, 7, b g Poliglote—Rosadame (FR) **Mr B. J. C. Drew**
8 **AMOOLA GOLD (GER)**, 7, b g Mamool (IRE)—Aughamore Beauty (IRE) **Mr & Mrs Gordon Pink**
9 **ANTUNES**, 6, b g Nathaniel (IRE)—Aigrette Garzette (IRE) **Mr M. Adams**
10 **ANYTIME WILL DO (IRE)**, 7, b g Scorpion (IRE)—Pellerossa (IRE) **Surrey Racing (at)**
11 **ARDLETHEN (IRE)**, 7, ch g Arakan (USA)—Itsafamilyaffair (IRE) **Mike and Eileen Newbould**
12 **ASHOKA (IRE)**, 8, gr g Azamour (IRE)—Jinskys Gift (IRE) **Mr Frank McAleavy & Mr Ian McAleavy**
13 **ASHTOWN LAD (IRE)**, 6, b g Flemensfirth (USA)—Blossom Trix (IRE) **Mr & Mrs D. Yates**
14 **AZZURI**, 8, b g Azamour—Folly Lodge **The Blind Squirrels**
15 **BACKOFTHEENVELOPE (IRE)**, 5, b m Milan—Golden Firth (IRE) **Rio Gold Racing Club**
16 **BALLYCALLAN FAME (IRE)**, 5, b m Fame And Glory—Sallie's Secret (IRE) **C. W. Booth**
17 **BANDSMAN**, 9, b g Bandmaster (USA)—Soleil Sauvage **Mrs S. J. Faulks**
18 **BEAKSTOWN (IRE)**, 7, b g Stowaway—Midnight Reel (IRE) **Mr B. J. C. Drew**
19 **BENNYS KING (IRE)**, 9, b g Beneficial—Hellofaithful (IRE) **Mezzone Family**
20 **BLACK SAM BELLA**, 8, b m Black Sam Bellamy (IRE)—Newton Mo **Mrs J. A. Watts**
21 **BORN SURVIVOR (IRE)**, 9, b g King's Theatre (IRE)—
Bob's Flame (IRE) **Mrs G. Widdowson & Mrs R. Kelvin-Hughes**
22 **BOSS MAN FRED (IRE)**, 6, ch g Dubai Destination (USA)—Aboo Lala (IRE) **Masomo**
23 **CADZAND (IRE)**, 5, b g Stowaway—Queens Mark (IRE) **Chelsea Thoroughbreds - Cadzand**
24 **CALL ME CHRIS**, 6, b m Kayf Tara—I'm Delilah **Mr C. S. Johnston**
25 **CAPTAIN CHAOS (IRE)**, 9, ch g Golan—Times Have Changed (IRE) **Mike and Eileen Newbould**
26 **CH'TI DIAMOND (FR)**, 5, ch m Diamond Boy (FR)—Loralas (FR) **Yorton Racing**

MR DAN SKELTON - continued

27 **CH'TIBELLO (FR)**, 9, b g Sageburg (IRE)—Neicha (FR)   **The Can't Say No Partnership**
28 **CLONDAW ANCHOR (IRE)**, 7, gr g Stowaway—Masiana (IRE)   **Highclere Thoroughbred Racing - Anchor**
29 **COBRA DE MAI (FR)**, 8, b g Great Pretender (IRE)—Miria Galanda (FR)   **Norman Lake & Susan Carsberg**
30 **COOK THE BOOKS (IRE)**, 7, b g Stowaway—Greenhill Millie (IRE)   **Cathedral Plastics Limited**
31 **DESTRIER (FR)**, 7, b g Voix du Nord (FR)—Razia (FR)   **Three Celts**
32 **DIOMEDE DES MOTTES (FR)**, 7, ch g Kapgarde (FR)—Nellyssa Bleu (FR)   **Belbroughton Racing Club**
33 **DOG OF WAR (FR)**, 6, b g Soldier of Fortune (IRE)—Zainzana (FR)   **Mr C. A. Donlon**
34 **DURL ROCK (IRE)**, 5, b g Milan—Greenfieldflyer (IRE)   **Simon & Lisa Hobson**
35 **ELTON DES MOTTES (FR)**, 6, b g Maresca Sorrento (FR)—
                                                       Ouhetu des Mottes (FR)   **Horne, Hudson, Nolan & Ryans**
36 **EMMAS JOY (IRE)**, 7, b m Gold Well—Emma Jane (IRE)   **Julian Howl & Ian Tyrrell**
37 **EVER SO COOL (IRE)**, 5, b m Shantou (USA)—Cool Cool (FR)   **Bullen-smith & Faulks**
38 **FAIVOIR (FR)**, 5, b g Coastal Path—Qape Noir (FR)   **Mrs S. Lawrence**
39 **FALCON SUN (FR)**, 6, b g Falco (USA)—Pray For Sun (IRE)   **Mezzone Family**
40 **FERROBIN (IRE)**, 6, br g Robin des Champs (FR)—Fedaia (IRE)   **Three Celts**
41 **FIRAK (FR)**, 5, b g Fuisse (FR)—Nosika d'Airy (FR)   **Mr D. W. Fox**
42 **FLASH THE STEEL (IRE)**, 8, b br g Craigsteel—Anna's Melody (IRE)   **Mr J. J. Reilly**
43 **FLEGMATIK (FR)**, 5, ch g Fuisse (FR)—Crack d'Emble (FR)   **N. W. Lake**
44 **FRANKEUR (FR)**, 5, b g Khalkevi (IRE)—Razia (FR)   **Mr D. Hanafin**
45 **FRISSON COLLONGES (FR)**, 5, b g Coastal Path—Roxane Collonges (FR)   **Mr C. M. Giles**
46 **GET ON THE YAGER**, 10, b g Tamure (IRE)—Florentino   **Dick and Mandy Higgins**
47 **GETARIVER (IRE)**, 7, b m Getaway (GER)—Watson River (IRE)   **Mr & Mrs Gordon Pink**
48 **GETAWAY MAG (IRE)**, 6, b m Getaway (GER)—Aggies Girl (IRE)   **Mrs J. A. Watts**
49 **GLOBAL HARMONY (IRE)**, 5, b m Flemensfirth (USA)—Violin Davis (FR)   **Mrs S. Carsberg**
50 **GLOBAL RULER**, 8, b g Kalanisi (IRE)—Queen's Leader   **Mrs S. Carsberg**
51 **GO STEADY**, 8, b g Indian Danehill (IRE)—Pyleigh Lady   **Popham, Rogers**
52 **GORTROE JOE (IRE)**, 8, b g Beneficial—Rowlands Star (IRE)   **J. T. Warner**
53 **HALA PRINCESS (IRE)**, 5, br m Bernebeau (FR)—Aroka (FR)   **Craig & Laura Buckingham**
54 **HATCHER (IRE)**, 7, b g Doyen (IRE)—African Keys (IRE)   **P. H. Betts**
55 **HEAD LAD (FR)**, 7, b g Linda's Lad—Orabelle (FR)   **Capital Care Group Limited**
56 **HOMETOWN HERO (IRE)**, 5, b g Darsi (FR)—Kilcoltrim Society (IRE)
57 **HUMBLE HERO (IRE)**, 6, b g High Chaparral (IRE)—Alamouna (IRE)   **Notalotterry**
58 **IT CAN BE DONE (IRE)**, 4, gr f Sun Central (IRE)—Penang Princess   **Rio Gold Racing Club**
59 **KING D'ARGENT (FR)**, 5, ch g Kendargent (FR)—Ephigenie (IRE)   **Andrew Dick & John Stevenson**
60 **KNIGHT IN DUBAI (IRE)**, 7, b g Dubai Destination (USA)—Bobbies Storm (IRE)   **Mr & Mrs Ben Houghton**
61 **LANGER DAN (IRE)**, 4, b g Ocovango—What A Fashion (IRE)   **Mr C. A. Donlon**
62 **LEMON SHOULDER (IRE)**, 5, b g Dylan Thomas (IRE)—The Cookie Jar (IRE)   **Mr M. Fennessy**
63 **LEX ELEVEN (IRE)**, 5, b m Getaway (GER)—Sixofone (IRE)   **Mr Frank McAleavy & Mr Ian McAleavy**
64 **LONIMOSS BARELIERE (FR)**, 4, b g Palamoss (IRE)—Lonia Blue (FR)   **Mr N. Skelton**
65 **LOUGHAN (IRE)**, 5, b g Yeats (IRE)—Quiet Thought (IRE)   **Mr T. J. Hemmings**
66 **MAGELLAN**, 6, b g Sea The Stars (IRE)—Hector's Girl   **Mr & Mrs D. Yates**
67 **MAIRE BANRIGH (IRE)**, 8, b m King's Theatre (IRE)—La Marianne   **Mr J Hales & Mr J Diver**
68 **MARADA**, 5, ch m Martaline—Kerada (FR)   **Little Lodge Farm & Dan Skelton**
69 **MARRACUDJA (FR)**, 9, b g Martaline—Memorial (FR)   **Foxtrot Racing Marracudja**
70 **MIDNIGHT RIVER**, 5, ch g Midnight Legend—Well Connected   **Mr Frank McAleavy & Mr Ian McAleavy**
71 **MISSTREE SONG (IRE)**, 6, b m Librettist (USA)—Misstree Pitcher   **Mrs S. J. Faulks**
72 **MOHAAYED**, 8, b g Intikhab (USA)—Reyaada   **Mrs J. A. Watts**
73 **MOLLY OLLYS WISHES**, 6, b m Black Sam Bellamy (IRE)—September Moon   **West Mercia Fork Trucks Ltd**
74 **MONSIEUR D'ARQUE (IRE)**, 6, b g Muhtathir—Nervous Breakdown (FR)   **Mr I. Lawrence**
75 **MR LOVE (IRE)**, 8, b g Winged Love (IRE)—Bonny Rathlin (IRE)   **Mr B. H. Turner**
76 **MUILEAN NA MADOG (IRE)**, 9, b g Papal Bull—Truly Precious (IRE)
77 **NEW QUAY (IRE)**, 7, b g Mahler—Beg La Eile (IRE)   **Norman Lake & Susan Carsberg**
78 **NO GETAWAY (IRE)**, 7, ch g Getaway (GER)—Nonnetia (FR)   **Dick, Keenan, Sawer, Stevenson**
79 **NORTHOFTHEWALL (IRE)**, 6, b g Mahler—Sherchanceit (IRE)   **Winter Gold Racing**
80 **NOT THAT FUISSE (FR)**, 7, b g Fuisse (FR)—Edelmira (FR)   **Mr C. A. Donlon**
81 **NUBE NEGRA (SPA)**, 6, br g Dink (FR)—Manly Dream (FR)   **Mr T. Spraggett**
82 **OLDGRANGEWOOD**, 9, b g Central Park (IRE)—Top of The Class (IRE)   **Chris Giles & Sandra Giles**
83 **OLLY THE BRAVE**, 7, b g Black Sam Bellamy (IRE)—September Moon   **West Mercia Fork Trucks Ltd**
84 **ONE FOR BILLY**, 8, b g Midnight Legend—Saxona (IRE)   **Mr D. W. Fox**

MR DAN SKELTON - continued

85 **PERCY'S WORD,** 6, b g Sir Percy—Laverre (IRE) **Mezzone Family**
86 **PETER THE MAYO MAN (IRE),** 10, ch g Dylan Thomas (IRE)—Mommkin **Craig & Laura Buckingham**
87 **PROTEKTORAT (FR),** 5, b g Saint des Saints (FR)—Protektion (FR) **Sir A Ferguson G Mason J Hales & L Hales**
88 **PRUSSIA WITH LOVE,** 6, b m Presenting—Ruby Royale **Roxholme Racing**
89 **QUIET FLOW,** 5, b g Sholokhov (IRE)—Sardagna (FR) **Mr C. A. Donlon**
90 **RATOUTE YUTTY,** 7, b m Midnight Legend—Easibrook Jane **The Yes We Named Her Syndicate**
91 **REAL STONE,** 5, b g Arvico (FR)—Stoney Path **Mrs S. C. Welch**
92 **REDZOR (IRE),** 7, b g Shantou (USA)—Knockara One (IRE) **Bryan Drew & Steve Roper**
93 **RENWICK (IRE),** 7, b g Milan—Come In Moscow (IRE) **Mrs D. L. Whateley**
94 **RIGGS (IRE),** 5, b g Mahler—Cousin Kizzy (IRE) **Mr T. J. Hemmings**
95 **RIVER TYNE,** 5, b m Geordieland (FR)—Not Now Nellie **River Tyne Syndicate**
96 **ROBIN GOLD (IRE),** 7, b m Gold Well—One Song (IRE) **Rio Gold Racing Club**
97 **ROKSANA (IRE),** 8, b m Dubai Destination (USA)—Talktothetail (IRE) **Mrs S. J. Faulks**
98 **SCORCHED EARTH (IRE),** 4, ch g Zoffany (IRE)—How's She Cuttin' (IRE) **The Blind Squirrels**
99 **SEEUSOON (IRE),** 4, b g Sea The Moon (GER)—Village Fete **P. H. Betts**
100 **SHAN BLUE (IRE),** 6, b g Shantou (USA)—Lady Roberta (IRE) **Mr C. A. Donlon**
101 **SHANNON BRIDGE (IRE),** 7, ch g Flemensfirth (USA)—Bridgequarter Lady (IRE) **M Boothright G Lovett P Deffains**
102 **SOFIA'S ROCK (FR),** 6, b g Rock of Gibraltar (IRE)—Princess Sofia (UAE) **Mezzone Family 1**
103 **SOLOMON GREY (FR),** 8, gr g Sulamani (IRE)—Sardagna (FR) **Mrs S. J. Faulks**
104 **SOUTH SEAS (IRE),** 6, ch g Lope de Vega (IRE)—Let It Be Me (USA) **Mr & Mrs D. Yates**
105 **SOYOUTHINKSOAGAIN (IRE),** 5, b g So You Think (NZ)—Al Saqiya (USA) **Mr I. Lawrence**
106 **SPIRITOFTHEGAMES (IRE),** 8, b g Darsi (FR)—Lucy Walters (IRE) **N. W. Lake**
107 **SUPREMELY LUCKY (IRE),** 8, b g Milan—Lucky Supreme (IRE) **Mr M. Olden**
108 **TERRIERMAN (IRE),** 6, br g Getaway (GER)—Dibella (IRE) **Mr & Mrs Price & Mr Keith Loads**
109 **THE HOAX,** 5, br g Great Pretender (IRE)—Lily Potter **James and Jean Potter Ltd**
110 **THE MULCAIR (IRE),** 6, b g Flemensfirth (USA)—Black Lassie (IRE) **Mr D. W. Fox**
111 **THE ROSARY FLYER (IRE),** 5, b g Robin des Champs (FR)—
Present Gesture (IRE) **Mr Frank McAleavy & Mr Ian McAleavy**
112 **THIRD TIME LUCKI (IRE),** 5, br g Arcadio (GER)—Definite Valley (IRE) **Mike and Eileen Newbould**
113 **TOMMY RAPPER (IRE),** 9, b g Milan—Supreme Evening (IRE) **Judy Craymer & Nick Skelton**
114 **TWO TAFFS (IRE),** 10, b g Flemensfirth (USA)—Richs Mermaid (IRE) **Walters Plant Hire & Potter Group**
115 **VERY FIRST TIME,** 8, b g Champs Elysees—Like A Virgin (IRE) **The Can't Say No Partnership**
116 **VISION DU PUY (FR),** 5, b m Vision d'Etat (FR)—Fontaine Guerard (FR) **Mr J. P. McManus**
117 **WEST CORK,** 6, b g Midnight Legend—Calamintha **Mike and Eileen Newbould**
118 **WEST TO THE BRIDGE (IRE),** 7, b g Flemensfirth (USA)—Godlylady (IRE) **Mr P. J. Tierney**
119 **WHITE WALKER,** 5, gr g Dream Eater (IRE)—Soleil Sauvage **Winter Gold Racing**
120 **WILD ROMANCE (IRE),** 5, br m Kalanisi (IRE)—Aboo Lala (IRE)
121 **WILDE ABOUT OSCAR (IRE),** 5, b g Oscar (IRE)—Baie Barbara (IRE) **Mike and Eileen Newbould**

Other Owners: Mr D. Balchin, M. Boothright, Mr C. Buckingham, Mrs L. K. Buckingham, Mr P. P. J. Bullen-Smith, Mrs S. Carsberg, Mrs J. S. Chugg, Mr R. D. Chugg, Miss J. Craymer, Mr P. Deffains, Mr A. D. Dick, Mr J. Diver, Mr B. J. C. Drew, Mrs P. Dry, Mrs G. Duckworth, Mrs S. J. Faulks, Mrs L. Fellows, Sir A. Ferguson, Mrs A. E. Giles, Mr C. M. Giles, Mr J. B. Gilruth, Mr J. R. Hales, Miss L. J. Hales, Mrs A. J. Higgins, Mr P. B. R. Houghton, Mrs V. K. Houghton, Mr J. Howl, Johnston Racing Ltd, Mr K. D. Jones, N. W. Lake, K. F. J. Loads, Mr G. P. A. Lovett, Mrs E. Magnier, Mrs S. Magnier, G. A. Mason, Mr F. McAleavy, Mr I. McAleavy, Mr A. R. Measham, Mrs S. M. Measham, Mr G. G. Mezzone, Mr L. M. Mezzone, Mrs S. M. Mezzone, Mrs E. E. Newbould, Mr J. M. Newbould, Mr G. K. G. Pink, Mrs K. M. Pink, P. F. Popham, Mrs J. Price, Mr N. Price, Mr M. P. Rogers, Mr S. R. Roper, Mrs L. M. Shanahan, Mr D. N. Skelton, Mr N. Skelton, Mr J. M. Stevenson, Sundorne Products (Llanidloes) Ltd, Mr I. Tyrrell, Walters Plant Hire Ltd, Mrs A. V. Yates, Mr D. Yates.

Assistant Trainer: Sam Davies-Thomas, Tom Messenger, Nick Pearce.

NH Jockey: Bridget Andrews, Conor Shoemark, Harry Skelton. **Conditional Jockey:** William Marshall.
Amateur Jockey: Mr Murray Dodd, Mr Tristan Durrell.

485 MRS PAM SLY, Peterborough
Postal: **Singlecote, Thorney, Peterborough, Cambridgeshire, PE6 0PB**
Contacts: PHONE **01733 270212** MOBILE **07850 511267**
EMAIL **pamslyracing@btconnect.com**

1 **ACERTAIN CIRCUS**, 10, ch g Definite Article—Circus Rose **Mrs P. M. Sly**
2 **ALL MY LOVE (IRE)**, 8, b m Lord Shanakill (USA)—Afilla **D. L. Bayliss**
3 **DARK SPEC**, 5, b h Dark Angel (IRE)—Speciosa (IRE) **M. H. Sly, Dr T. Davies & Mrs P. Sly**
4 **DAZZLING DAN (IRE)**, 4, b g Dandy Man (IRE)—Scrumptious **Thorney Racing Partners**
5 **DRUMMOND WARRIOR (IRE)**, 4, b g Zoffany (IRE)—Ulanova (IRE) **Mr G. A. Libson & Mrs P. M. Sly**
6 **ESKENDASH (USA)**, 7, ch g Eskendereya (USA)—Daffaash (USA) **Boyle Racing**
7 **FRANSHAM**, 6, b g Sulamani (IRE)—Circus Rose **G. Libson, D. Bayliss, T. Davies & P. Sly**
8 **GAYTON**, 6, ch m Haafhd—Wistow **Mrs P. M. Sly**
9 **GENTLE ROSE**, 4, b f Gentlewave (USA)—Iconic Rose **The Stablemates**
10 **HAAFAPIECE**, 7, ch g Haafhd—Bonnet's Pieces **Mrs I. A. Coles**
11 **JOHN CLARE (IRE)**, 4, b g Poet's Voice—Specialty (IRE) **Michael H. Sly & Mrs Pam Sly**
12 **KEEPUP KEVIN**, 6, b g Haafhd—Black Salix (USA) **Mrs P. M. Sly**
13 **LIAM'S LASS (IRE)**, 4, b f Dandy Man (IRE)—Rupa (IRE) **Mrs P. M. Sly**
14 **RAINYDAY WOMAN**, 5, b m Kayf Tara—Wistow **Mrs P. M. Sly**
15 **SILKSTONE (IRE)**, 4, b g Alhebayeb (IRE)—Fine Silk (USA) **Pam's People**
16 **TAKEIT EASY**, 5, b g Malinas (GER)—Circus Rose **Mrs P. M. Sly**
17 **WELLAND**, 7, ch g Beat Hollow—Circus Rose **Mrs P. M. Sly**
18 **WITHAM**, 7, b m Beat Hollow—Wistow **Mrs P. M. Sly**
19 **XCITATIONS**, 5, b g Universal (IRE)—Bonnet's Pieces **G. Libson, D. Bayliss, T. Davies & P. Sly**
20 **ZAFARANAH (USA)**, 6, ch m Raven's Pass (USA)—Jiwen (CAN) **Pam's People**

THREE-YEAR-OLDS

21 **BELLICA**, b f War Command (USA)—Asteroidea **Michael H. Sly & Mrs Pam Sly**
22 **EILEENDOVER**, b f Canford Cliffs (IRE)—Specialty (IRE) **Michael H. Sly & Mrs Pam Sly**
23 **GROUSEMAN**, b g Kyllachy—Speciosa (IRE) **M. H. Sly, Dr T. Davies & Mrs P. Sly**

Other Owners: D. L. Bayliss, Mr P. J. J. Boyle, Mr S. Boyle, Dr T. J. W. Davies, Mr S. R. T. Jones, Mr G. A. Libson, M. H. S. Sly, Mrs P. M. Sly.

Assistant Trainer: Chris Scudder.

NH Jockey: Kielan Woods. **Amateur Jockey:** Miss Gina Andrews.

486 MR BRYAN SMART, Hambleton
Postal: **Hambleton House, Sutton Bank, Thirsk, North Yorkshire, YO7 2HA**
Contacts: PHONE **01845 597481** MOBILE **07748 634797** FAX **01845 597480**
EMAIL **office@bryansmart.plus.com** WEBSITE **www.bryansmart-racing.com**

1 **ALPHA DELPHINI (IRE)**, 9, b g Captain Gerrard (IRE)—Easy To Imagine (USA) **The Alpha Delphini Partnership**
2 **ANTAGONIZE**, 4, b g Epaulette (AUS)—Hakuraa (IRE) **Crossfields Racing**
3 **DEBAWTRY**, 5, b m Camacho—Maluk **Mrs Judith Hodgeson**
4 **FAIRY FALCON**, 5, ch m Sepoy (AUS)—Easy To Imagine (USA) **Branton Court Stud LLP**
5 **FENDALE**, 8, b g Exceed And Excel (AUS)—Adorn **Mr S. E. Chappell**
6 **FLINT SAID NO**, 4, gr g Harbour Watch (IRE)—Rock Ace (IRE) **Middleham Park Racing VIII**
7 **HELOVAPLAN (IRE)**, 6, b g Helmet (AUS)—Watsdaplan (IRE) **The Smart Set**
8 **KENTUCKYCONNECTION (USA)**, 7, b g Include—Youcanringmybell (USA) **Woodcock Electrical Limited**
9 **MIDNIGHT IN HAVANA**, 4, b g Havana Gold (IRE)—Eleventh Hour (IRE) **The Smart Set**
10 **MINA VELOUR**, 4, ch f Garswood—Ardessie **Mr Paul Sutherland**
11 **MYTHMAKER**, 8, b g Major Cadeaux—Mythicism **Crossfields Racing**
12 **NORTHERNPOWERHOUSE**, 4, b c Harbour Watch (IRE)—Mortitia **Mr Michael Moses & Mr Terry Moses**
13 **PALAZZO**, 4, b g Morpheus—Sweet Power **Mr B. Smart**
14 **PEPYS**, 6, b g Aqlaam—Generously Gifted **Mr P. Darling & Mrs A. Smith**
15 **RED PIKE**, 9, ch g Kheleyf—Fancy Feathers **Mr Tony Eyre, Mr Peter Watson**
16 **SIYAHAMBA (IRE)**, 6, ch g Helmet (AUS)—Kalabunga (IRE) **Mr B. Smart**

MR BRYAN SMART - continued

17 **SWISS CONNECTION**, 4, b g Swiss Spirit—Sofonisba **Woodcock Electrical Limited**
18 **TREVITHICK**, 5, b g Champs Elysees—New Choice (IRE) **Mrs P. A. Clark**
19 **WRENTHORPE**, 5, b g Hellvelyn—Milly-M **Dan Maltby Bloodstock Limited**
20 **YES YOU (IRE)**, 6, ch m Choisir (AUS)—Mexican Milly (IRE) **Taco Partners**

THREE-YEAR-OLDS

21 **ASTROZONE**, ch f Fast Company (IRE)—Rhal (IRE) **Crossfields Racing**
22 **AZTECA**, b f Fountain of Youth (IRE)—Irrational **Crossfields Racing**
23 **CHOCOHOLIC**, b g Due Diligence (USA)—Unwrapit (USA) **Crossfields Racing**
24 **DANCINGINTHESAND (IRE)**, b g Footstepsinthesand—Omanome (IRE) **The Smart Omanome Partnership**
25 **DUE A WIN**, b g Due Diligence (USA)—Malelane (IRE) **D. Blake,C. Dinsdale,S.McCay & M.Beadle**
26 **HURAA**, b f Brazen Beau (AUS)—Hakuraa (IRE) **Crossfields Racing**
27 **KISKADEE**, b f Mukhadram—Generously Gifted **Mr P. Darling & Mrs A. Smith**
28 **LUCAS**, b g Fountain of Youth (IRE)—Ice Mayden **J Ball & Partner**
29 **PROPER BEAU**, b g Brazen Beau (AUS)—Olivia Grace **Robert Ng, Michael & Terry Moses**
30 **REDZONE**, b g Sepoy (AUS)—Mythicism **Crossfields Racing & A. Welch & Partners**
31 **SLINGSHOT**, b f Due Diligence (USA)—Nizhoni (USA) **Crossfields Racing**
32 **SPEEDYMINING (IRE)**, b g Moohaajim (IRE)—Spacecraft (USA) **Middleham Park Racing I & Partner**

TWO-YEAR-OLDS

33 B c 13/02 Fountain of Youth (IRE)—Ayasha (Indesatchel (IRE)) (761) **Crossfields Racing**
34 **BILLIAN (IRE)**, b c 02/03 Mehmas (IRE)—
Truly Magnificent (USA) (Elusive Quality (USA)) (12380) **Bill Fraser & Adrian Pritchard**
35 B f 02/04 Mayson—Chinaconnection (IRE) (Dark Angel (IRE)) **Woodcock Electrical Limited**
36 Ch c 16/03 Mayson—Emblaze (Showcasing) (16190) **The Smart Emblaze Partnership**
37 B f 05/03 Fountain of Youth (IRE)—Equinox (Medicean) (761) **Crossfields Racing**
38 B f 01/01 Brazen Beau—Generously Gifted **Mrs P. A. Clark**
39 B f 08/02 Heeraat (IRE)—Hakuraa (IRE) (Elnadim (USA)) **Dan Maltby Bloodstock Limited**
40 B c 23/02 Casamento (IRE)—Last Dance (Sadler's Wells (USA)) (7142) **Mr B. Smart, Mrs Freda Moody**
41 B c 24/02 Dandy Man (IRE)—Moss Top (IRE) (Moss Vale (IRE)) (38000) **Mr Michael Moses & Mr Terry Moses**
42 B f 06/04 Cable Bay (IRE)—Musicora (Acclamation) (7619) **Ceffyl Racing**
43 **PENOMBRE**, b c 25/03 Twilight Son—Hayba (Invincible Spirit (IRE)) (25000) **The Unscrupulous Judges**
44 B f 05/03 Epaulette (AUS)—Sharqawiyah (Dubawi (IRE))
45 B f 29/03 Brazen Beau (AUS)—She's A Worldie (IRE) (Kodiac) (28571) **Mr S. Chappell & Partner**
46 B c 28/02 Equiano (FR)—Spontaneity (IRE) (Holy Roman Emperor (IRE)) (7142) **Crossfields Racing**
47 B f 01/03 Fountain of Youth (IRE)—Stocking (Acclamation) **Mr S. Chappell & Partner**
48 Gr c 30/03 Showcasing—Two In The Pink (IRE) (Clodovil (IRE)) (10000) **Michael & Terry Moses & Partner**

Other Owners: Mr M. G. Bullock, Mrs T. Bullock, Mr S. E. Chappell, Crossfields Racing, D. B. Elders, Mrs A. C. Hudson, Mrs Marie Matthews, Mr S. Chappell & Partner, R. A. Page, T. S. Palin, M. Prince, Mr B. Smart, Mr N. Williams, Mrs S. E. Williams.

Assistant Trainer: Kevin Edmunds, Victoria Smart, **Pupil Assistant:** Beth Smart.

Flat Jockey: Graham Lee.

 MR CHARLES SMITH, Temple Bruer
487 Postal: **6-7 Thompsons Bottom, Temple Bruer, Lincoln, Lincolnshire, LN5 0DE**
Contacts: **PHONE 01526 833245 MOBILE 07778 149188**

1 **ALPHA TAURI (USA)**, 14, b g Aldebaran (USA)—Seven Moons (JPN) **Mr J. R. Theaker**
2 **ATWAAR**, 4, b f Slade Power (IRE)—Musharakaat (IRE) **Mr M. J. Smeed**
3 **EJABAH (IRE)**, 6, b m Iffraaj—Relinquished **Mr N. J. Baines**
4 **ROBBIAN**, 9, b g Bertolini (USA)—Crathes **R. J. Lewin**

488 MR JULIAN SMITH, Tirley
Postal: Tirley Court, Tirley, Gloucester
Contacts: PHONE 01452 780461 MOBILE 07748 901175 FAX 01452 780461
EMAIL nicola.smith9156@o2.co.uk

1 CARO DES FLOS (FR), 8, b g Tiger Groom—Royale Marie (FR) Mrs J.A. Benson & Miss S.N. Benson
2 DIAMOND ROSE, 8, b m Sagamix (FR)—Swiss Rose Grand Jury Partnership
3 FINE BY HER, 4, b f Shirocco (GER)—High Benefit (IRE) Mrs J.A. Benson & Miss S.N. Benson
4 IONA DAYS (IRE), 15, br g Epistolaire (IRE)—Miss Best (FR) Mrs J.A. Benson & Miss S.N. Benson
5 MIDNIGHT SENSATION, 8, gr m Proclamation (IRE)—Midnight Ocean Exors of the Late Mr D. E. S. Smith
6 PENNIES AND POUNDS, 13, b m Sir Harry Lewis (USA)—Sense of Value Exors of the Late Mr D. E. S. Smith
7 THE RORY STORY (IRE), 9, b g Flemensfirth (USA)—Phardester (IRE) Exors of the Late Mr D. E. S. Smith

Other Owners: Mrs J. A. Benson, Miss S. N. Benson.

Assistant Trainer: Mrs Nicky Smith.

NH Jockey: Mark Grant, Sam Twiston-Davies. **Amateur Jockey:** Mr J. M. Ridley.

489 MR MARTIN SMITH, Newmarket
Postal: Stable Cottage, Calder Park, Hamilton Road, Newmarket, Suffolk, CB8 0NY
Contacts: MOBILE 07712 493589
WEBSITE www.martinsmithracing.com

1 AFFLUENCE (IRE), 5, b g Thewayyouare (USA)—Castalian Spring (IRE) The Affluence Partnership
2 ALEATORIC (IRE), 4, b g Dylan Thomas (IRE)—Castalian Spring (IRE) Mr Martin Smith & Mr Philip Brooks
3 BREAK THE RULES, 4, br f Aussie Rules (USA)—Fairy Slipper Mr Robert P Clarke & Partners
4 COOKUPASTORM (IRE), 4, b f Camacho—No Clubs (IRE) Mr Martin Smith & Mr Philip Brooks
5 FRIENDS DON'T ASK, 5, b g Champs Elysees—Kintyre Mr Robert P Clarke & Partners
6 HERRINGSWELL (FR), 5, b m Pour Moi (IRE)—Sovereign's Honour (USA) The Champagne Poppers
7 IN THE RED (IRE), 7, b g Elusive Pimpernel (USA)—Roses From Ridey (IRE) Sunville Rail Limited
8 MISTER TICKLE (IRE), 6, b g Morozov (USA)—Tatiana (IRE) Sunville Rail Limited
9 THREEFEETFROMGOLD (IRE), 4, ch g Helmet (AUS)—Lady Pitrizza (IRE) The Gold Partnership

THREE-YEAR-OLDS

10 HAPPY CRAF (ARG), ch f Mastercraftsman (IRE)—Alegre Roma (ARG) M B S Racing
11 LADY PENDRAGON, b f Camelot—Arthur's Girl Sunville Rail Limited
12 MASTER BAMBU (ARG), gr c Mastercraftsman (IRE)—Jane Bambu (ARG) M B S Racing

TWO-YEAR-OLDS

13 B c 07/05 Equiano (FR)—Inagh River (Fasliyev (USA)) (4000)
14 MORANI KALI, ch c 16/04 Charming Thought—Crystal Moments (Haafhd)
15 SPARK OF MAGIC, b br c 01/03 Equiano (FR)—Kawaii (Myboycharlie (IRE))

Other Owners: Mr J. Bridger, Mr P. Brooks, P. F. Charter, Mr R. P. Clarke, Mrs R. T. Rennie, Mr M. P. B. Smith, Mrs M. Smyth.

Apprentice Jockey: Jay Clark. **Amateur Jockey:** Mr Alex Teasdale.

490 MISS PAULA SMITH, Malton
Postal: Woodyard Barn, Ruffin Lane, Eddlethorpe, Malton, North Yorkshire, YO17 9QU
Contacts: PHONE 07760 247207
EMAIL Paulamsmith4@gmail.com

1 CARRIGMOORNA MATT (IRE), 9, b g Westerner—Carrigmorna Flyer (IRE) Miss P. M. Smith
2 DALLAS COWBOY (IRE), 10, b g Beneficial—Watson River (IRE) Miss P. M. Smith
3 MINSTREL SONG, 7, br g Dark Angel (IRE)—Sing Acapella (IRE) Miss P. M. Smith
4 MOLLY WHUPPIE, 7, br m Beat Hollow—Daisies Adventure (IRE) Miss P. M. Smith
5 RHYTHM OF SOUND (IRE), 10, ch g Mahler—Oscarvail (IRE) Miss P. M. Smith

491 **MR R. MIKE SMITH, Galston**
Postal: **West Loudoun Farm, Galston, Ayrshire, KA4 8PB**
Contacts: **PHONE 01563 822062 MOBILE 07711 692122**
EMAIL **mike@mikesmithracing.co.uk** WEBSITE **www.mikesmithracing.co.uk**

1 **AKAMANTO (IRE)**, 6, b g Cape Cross (IRE)—Allofus (IRE) **Reid Ross Smith**
2 **AN FEAR CIUIN (IRE)**, 9, b g Galileo (IRE)—Potion **P. Tsim**
3 **ARCHIES LAD**, 4, b g Lawman (FR)—Stirring Ballad **P. Tsim**
4 **ASTUTE BOY (IRE)**, 6, b g Arcano (IRE)—Spa **Mr R. M. Smith**
5 **BEAU ET SUBLIME (FR)**, 10, b g Saddler Maker (IRE)—Jolie Jouvencelle (FR) **Mr R. M. Smith**
6 **CALL ME MAIZIE (IRE)**, 5, b m Califet (FR)—Chevet Girl (IRE) **Spittal & Smith**
7 **CLAVIERE**, 4, b g Pivotal—Slatey Hen (IRE) **Mr R. M. Smith**
8 4, B g Arcadio (GER)—Detonante (FR) **Mr R. M. Smith**
9 **FARRAN DANCER (IRE)**, 7, b g Winged Love (IRE)—Fairylodge Scarlet (IRE) **Mr R. Cooper**
10 **FLYING MOON (GER)**, 4, b g Sea The Moon (GER)—Finity (USA) **West Loudoun Racing Club**
11 **FOUR KINGDOMS (IRE)**, 6, b g Lord Shanakill (USA)—Four Poorer (IRE) **Smith & Stewart**
12 **FOURTH OF JULY (IRE)**, 5, b g Salutino (GER)—Akasha (IRE) **Quigley & Smith**
13 **GEOGRAPHY TEACHER (IRE)**, 4, b g Bungle Inthejungle—Magical Bupers (IRE) **West Loudoun Racing Club**
14 **GLASSES UP (USA)**, 5, ch g English Channel (USA)—Hurricane Hallie (USA) **The Jolly Beggars**
15 **GO GUARANTOR**, 6, b g Medicean—Furbelow **The Guarantor Partnership**
16 **HAYMARKET**, 11, b g Singspiel (IRE)—Quickstyx **Mr A. M. Ross**
17 **HOPEFULL**, 10, br bl m Overbury (IRE)—Maryscross (IRE) **Mr R. M. Smith**
18 **LAS TUNAS (FR)**, 8, b br g Country Reel (USA)—Grey Winner (FR) **Spittal Family**
19 **LETHAL LAURA**, 4, ch f Lethal Force (IRE)—Laurena (GER) **Mr D. Orr**
20 **MILABELLA**, 4, b f Bated Breath—Miss Noble **Mr R. M. Smith**
21 **PICKING PEACHES (IRE)**, 5, b m Shantou (USA)—Detonante (FR) **Spittal & Smith**
22 **PUDDING CHARE (IRE)**, 6, b g Arcano (IRE)—Rosy Dudley (IRE) **Ayr Racecourse Club**
23 **RAEMOIR (FR)**, 5, gr g Rajsaman (FR)—Followeveryrainbow **North East Racehorses & Tony Whyte**
24 **REAL SMOOTH (IRE)**, 4, b g Teofilo (IRE)—Amber Silk (IRE) **Mr R. M. Smith**
25 **ROSEMAY (FR)**, 6, b m Mayson—Maine Rose **Dal Riata - A Barclay**
26 **STONE CROSSING (IRE)**, 4, gr f Rock of Gibraltar (IRE)—Livadream (IRE) **Burns Partnership**
27 4, B g Arcadio (GER)—Sumability (IRE) **Mr R. M. Smith**
28 **WEST DRIVE (IRE)**, 7, ch g Sea The Stars (IRE)—Fair Sailing (IRE) **P. Tsim**

THREE-YEAR-OLDS

29 **GARNOCK VALLEY**, b f Orientor—Midnight Bahia (IRE) **Mr A. J. Bogle**
30 B g Sepoy (AUS)—Just Like A Woman

TWO-YEAR-OLDS

31 **AUTUMN FLAME**, b f 12/04 Ruler of The World (IRE)—
Pesse (IRE) (Eagle Eyed (USA)) (4000) **Racing Connexions Ltd**

Other Owners: Mr A. Barclay, Mr G. W. B. Bryson, Dal Riata, Mr D. L. Dunbar, North East Racehorses, Mr D. Orr, Mr R. Quigley, Mr G. Reid, Mr A. M. Ross, Mr M. J. Russell, Mr R. M. Smith, Mr A. H. Spittal, Miss B. Spittal, Mr I. Stewart, Mr H. S. Watson, Mr A. G. Whyte.

492 **MR RALPH J. SMITH, Wiltshire**
Postal: **Westcourt Stables, Westcourt, Burbage, Marlborough, Wiltshire, SN8 3BW**
Contacts: **PHONE 07494 050859 MOBILE 07795 327003**
EMAIL **rjsmith.racing@hotmail.com** WEBSITE **www.rjsmithracing.com**

1 **DUHR (IRE)**, 6, b g Mawatheeq (USA)—Dijlah **Mr K. Old**
2 **FULL SUIT**, 6, gr m Dalakhani (IRE)—Perfect Hand **Clear Racing & Jayne Smith**
3 **MUZAAWEL**, 5, ch g New Approach (IRE)—Jilnaar (IRE) **The Steel Yard London**

THREE-YEAR-OLDS

4 **ON THE NOD**, b c Slade Power (IRE)—Marmaria (SPA) **The Steel Yard London**
5 **SIR GORDON**, br g Sixties Icon—Potternello (IRE) **Hoolabaloo Racing**

MR RALPH J. SMITH - continued

Other Owners: Clear Racing, Mr B. J. Greening, Mrs M. M. Greening, Homecroft Wealth Racing, Mr R. E. McVaddy, Mr K. Old, Mr B. Pettis, Mr S. J. Piper, Mrs J. C. Smith.

Assistant Trainer: Jayne Smith.

Amateur Jockey: Miss Ella Smith.

---

493 | **MRS SUE SMITH, Bingley**
Postal: **Craiglands Farm, High Eldwick, Bingley, West Yorkshire, BD16 3BE**
Contacts: **FAX** 01274 560626
WORK EMAIL office@craiglandsracing.co.uk WEBSITE www.suesmithracing.co.uk

1 **ABSOLUTELY DYLAN (IRE)**, 7, b g Scorpion (IRE)—Cash Customer (IRE) **Mr T. J. Hemmings**
2 **AIRE VALLEY LAD**, 6, b g Schiaparelli (GER)—Bonnie Rock (IRE) **Mrs S. J. Smith**
3 4, B g Midnight Legend—Autumm Spirit **Mrs S. J. Smith**
4 **BEAR THAT N MIND (IRE)**, 8, b g Mahler—Gibboghstown (IRE) **Mrs S. J. Smith**
5 **BLASTER YEATS**, 5, b g Yeats (IRE)—Jayjay Joules **McGoldrick Racing & Mr Gareth Plimley**
6 **BOBNDAVE (IRE)**, 8, b g Brian Boru—Sidblack (IRE) **Mrs S. J. Smith**
7 4, B g Yeats (IRE)—Bobnval (IRE) **Mrs S. J. Smith**
8 5, B g Schiaparelli (GER)—Bonnie Rock (IRE) **Mrs S. J. Smith**
9 **BURNING ISSUES (IRE)**, 13, b g Gold Well—Jillie James **Mrs S. J. Smith**
10 **BURROWS DIAMOND (FR)**, 5, b m Diamond Boy (FR)—La Vie de Boitron (FR)
11 **CAPTAIN MOIRETTE (FR)**, 8, gr g Kap Rock (FR)—Rahana Moirette (FR) **Mrs A. Clarke**
12 **CHESTERMAN (IRE)**, 8, b g Westerner—Cherry Pie (FR) **Mr T. J. Hemmings**
13 5, B g Paco Boy (IRE)—Colourways (IRE) **Mrs S. J. Smith**
14 **CRACKING FIND (IRE)**, 9, b g Robin des Pres (FR)—Crack The Kicker (IRE) **Mrs A. Ellis**
15 **FLAMBOYANT JOYAUX (FR)**, 5, b g Crossharbour—Merka (FR) **Formulated Polymer Products Ltd**
16 **FRIMEUR DE LANCRAY (FR)**, 5, b g Saddler Maker (IRE)—Jecyfly (FR) **Mrs A. Ellis**
17 **GETAWAY BAY (IRE)**, 8, b g Getaway (GER)—Wayward Star (IRE) **Mrs S. J. Smith**
18 **GOLDEN ROBIN (IRE)**, 6, br m Robin des Champs (FR)—Countess Eileen (IRE) **Mrs S. J. Smith**
19 **HILL SIXTEEN**, 7, b g Court Cave (IRE)—Chasers Chic **Mr T. J. Hemmings**
20 **I JUST KNOW (IRE)**, 10, b g Robin des Pres (FR)—Desperado Queen (IRE) **Mr C. M. Scholey**
21 4, B g Dunaden (FR)—I'm Delilah **Mrs S. J. Smith**
22 **INFORMATEUR (FR)**, 7, b g Maresca Sorrento (FR)—Isarella (GER) **Mrs J M Gray & Mr G R Orchard**
23 **ISKABEG LANE (IRE)**, 9, b g Westerner—Nosey Oscar (IRE) **Mrs S. J. Smith**
24 **JAYAAAH (IRE)**, 5, b g Yeats (IRE)—Nolans Legacy (IRE) **Mrs A. Ellis**
25 **JOKE DANCER**, 7, ch g Authorized (IRE)—Missy Dancer **Mrs A. Clarke**
26 **JUST GEORGIE**, 10, b g Kayf Tara—Just Kate **Mrs S. J. Smith**
27 **KAUTO D'AMOUR (FR)**, 5, b g Anabaa Blue—Kauto Luisa (FR) **Mrs S. J. Smith**
28 **LE DRAPEAU (FR)**, 8, ch g Satri (IRE)—La Bandera **A. D. Hollinrake**
29 **LOUGH DERG FARMER (IRE)**, 8, b g Presenting—Maryiver (IRE) **Mrs S. J. Smith**
30 **LOUGH LEGEND (IRE)**, 6, b g Watar (IRE)—Gibboghstown (IRE) **Broadway Racing Club 15**
31 **MACS GIFT (IRE)**, 8, b g Scorpion (IRE)—Gift Wrapped (IRE) **Mrs S. J. Smith**
32 **MANCINELLIE**, 5, ch g Schiaparelli (GER)—Shankhouse Wells (IRE) **Mrs S. J. Smith**
33 **MAXED OUT KING (IRE)**, 12, ch g Desert King (IRE)—Lady Max (IRE) **Mrs S. J. Smith**
34 **MIDNIGHT SHADOW**, 7, b g Midnight Legend—Holy Smoke **Mrs A. Clarke**
35 **MINELLA FIVEO (IRE)**, 12, b g Westerner—Autumn Sky (IRE) **Mrs S. J. Smith**
36 **MUTAWAASEL**, 8, b g Teofilo (IRE)—Muwakleh **Mrs S. J. Smith**
37 **NEVER UP (GER)**, 9, b g Danehill Dancer (IRE)—Never Green (IRE) **Mrs S. J. Smith**
38 **NORTH PARADE (IRE)**, 5, br g Dylan Thomas (IRE)—Retain That Magic (IRE) **Mrs S. J. Smith**
39 **OSCAR WILDE (IRE)**, 6, b g Oscar (IRE)—Deep Supreme (IRE) **Formulated Polymer Products Ltd**
40 4, Br g Sageburg (IRE)—Prairie Call (IRE) **Mrs S. J. Smith**
41 **RARE CLOUDS**, 6, b g Cloudings (IRE)—Rare Vintage (IRE) **Mr T. J. Hemmings**
42 **RAVENHILL ROAD (IRE)**, 9, ch g Exit To Nowhere (USA)—Zaffarella (IRE) **Phil & Julie Martin**
43 4, b g Schiaparelli (GER)—Roc Mirage **Mrs S. J. Smith**
44 **SCORCHIN**, 6, b g Multiplex—Lemon Queen (IRE) **Teme Valley 3**
45 **SEVEN ARCHES**, 5, b g Yeats (IRE)—Santia **Mrs S. J. Smith**

MRS SUE SMITH - continued

46 **SHARP RESPONSE (IRE)**, 9, b g Oscar (IRE)—Lambourne Lace (IRE) **Formulated Polymer Products Ltd**
47 4, B f Yeats (IRE)—She's On The Case (IRE) **A. D. Hollinrake**
48 **SILVA ECLIPSE**, 7, gr g Multiplex—Linen Line **Mrs S. J. Smith**
49 **SMALL PRESENT (IRE)**, 5, b g Presenting—Serpentaria **Mrs A. Clarke**
50 4, B f Darsi (FR)—The Farmers Sister (IRE) **Mrs S. J. Smith**
51 **THE PADDY PIE (IRE)**, 7, b g Beneficial—Salsita (FR) **J. Wade**
52 **THELONGWAYAROUND (IRE)**, 7, b g Fruits of Love (USA)—Brass Neck (IRE) **Mrs J. Morgan**
53 **TIKERTY TOK**, 9, gr g Tikkanen (USA)—Bonnie Rock (IRE) **Mrs S. J. Smith**
54 **TRESHNISH (FR)**, 7, ch g Gold Away (IRE)—Didn't I Tell You (IRE) **D G Pryde & D Van Der Hoeven**
55 **TUMBLING DICE**, 5, b g Lucarno (USA)—Arctic Ring **Mr D. Sutherland**
56 **VALENCE D'AUMONT (FR)**, 6, b g Sinndar (IRE)—Ice Ti (ITY) **Mrs J. Morgan**
57 **VERY PATIENT (IRE)**, 6, b g Mahler—Venusorserena (IRE) **J. Wade**
58 4, B f Midnight Legend—Very Special One (IRE) **Mrs S. J. Smith**
59 **VINTAGE CLOUDS (IRE)**, 10, gr g Cloudings (IRE)—Rare Vintage (IRE) **Mr T. J. Hemmings**
60 **WAITING FOREVER (IRE)**, 6, b g Witness Box (USA)—You Some Massini (IRE) **J. Wade**
61 **WAKANDA (IRE)**, 11, b g Westerner—Chanson Indienne (FR) **Mr C. M. Scholey**
62 **WHAT'S THE SCOOP (IRE)**, 10, ch g Presenting—Dame d'Harvard (USA) **Mrs S. J. Smith**
63 **WOLF RUN (IRE)**, 5, b br g Presenting—Our Pride **Mr G. R. Orchard & Mrs J. M. Gray**
64 **YEATS VENTURE (IRE)**, 5, b g Yeats (IRE)—Present Venture (IRE) **Mr T. J. Hemmings**

Other Owners: Mrs C. J. Casterton, Mr M. J. S. Cockburn, Mrs J. Conroy, J. Conroy, Mrs J. M. Gray, Mr R. J. Longley, Mrs J. A. Martin, Mr P. J. Martin, McGoldrick Racing, Mrs J. Morgan, G. R. Orchard, Mr A. M. Phillips, Mr G. J. Plimley, D. G. Pryde, Mrs S. J. Smith, Mr D. P. van der Hoeven.

Assistant Trainer: Ryan Clavin, **Travelling Head:** Reece Jarosiewicz, **Racing Secretary:** Rachel Swinden.

NH Jockey: Danny Cook. **Conditional Jockey:** Sam Coltherd, Bailey Sagar.

---

494 MISS SUZY SMITH, Lewes
Postal: **County Stables, The Old Racecourse, Lewes, East Sussex, BN7 1UR**
Contacts: **PHONE 01273 477173 MOBILE 07970 550828**
EMAIL suzy@suzysmithracing.co.uk WEBSITE www.suzysmithracing.co.uk FACEBOOK @ suzysmithracing

1 **ANIMAL (IRE)**, 4, b g Arcadio (GER)—Fantine (IRE)
2 **CLONDAW BISTO (IRE)**, 9, b g September Storm (GER)—Solo Venture (IRE) **Miss S. Smith**
3 **COUNTERACT**, 5, b g Dr Massini (IRE)—Aimigayle **Ms S. A. S. Palmer**
4 **CRACKER JAK (IRE)**, 6, b g September Storm (GER)—Princess Jaffa (IRE) **Mrs V. Palmer**
5 **DEBESTYMAN (IRE)**, 7, b g Mahler—Deise All Star (IRE) **The Plumpton Party**
6 **GETAWAY SUZY (IRE)**, 7, b m Getaway (GER)—Ashanti Dancer (IRE)
7 **INVICTA LAKE (IRE)**, 13, b b g Dr Massini (IRE)—Classic Material **The Invicta Partnership**
8 **LITTLE BOY BORU (IRE)**, 12, b g Brian Boru—How Is Things (IRE) **J Logan, D Harrison, T Loftus & S Smith**
9 **MADAME VOGUE**, 7, b m Multiplex—Roslin **Mr & Mrs R. Allsop**
10 **OSCARSMAN (IRE)**, 6, b g Oscar (IRE)—Ashwell Lady (IRE) **D Harrison J Logan J Rimmer & S Smith**
11 **ROSY WORLD**, 7, b m Shirocco (GER)—Material World **Kate Allisat & Chris Ames**
12 **STRIKE THE FLINT**, 6, b m Shirocco (GER)—Material World **Table For Six**
13 **VUE CAVALIERE (FR)**, 6, b m Spirit One (FR)—Grande Cavale (FR) **Mr G. Jones, Mr C. Ames & Mr D. Harrison**

THREE-YEAR-OLDS
14 **LIGHTNING BUG (IRE)**, b f Starspangledbanner (AUS)—Redinha **The Bright Lights**
15 B g Shirocco (GER)—Material World

Other Owners: Mrs K. H. Allisat, Mr R. Allsop, Mrs Y. E. Allsop, Mr C. B. Ames, Mr D. J. Harrison, Mr G. R. Jones, Mr T. H. Loftus, J. A. A. S. Logan, Mr J. Rimmer, Mr A. I. F. Sim, Miss S. Smith.

Assistant Trainer: Mr S E Gordon-Watson.

Flat Jockey: Jane Elliott, Luke Morris, Jason Watson. **NH Jockey:** Micheal Nolan, Tom O'Brien, Gavin Sheehan.

495 **MR GILES SMYLY, Broadway**
Postal: **Garden Cottage, Wormington Grange, Broadway, Worcestershire, WR12 7NJ**
Contacts: **PHONE 01386 584085 MOBILE 07747 035169 FAX 01386 584085**
EMAIL gilessmiler@aol.com WEBSITE www.smylyracing.co.uk

1 **BIG BANG DE LOIRE (FR)**, 9, b g Califet (FR)—Grischa (FR) **D. Maxwell**
2 **FENRIR BINDING**, 5, b g Norse Dancer (IRE)—Bethany Lewis **The Wolfpack**
3 **HENRY OLIVER (IRE)**, 12, b g Hasten To Add (USA)—Lisnabrin (IRE)

Assistant Trainer: Kim Smyly.

496 **MR JAMIE SNOWDEN, Lambourn**
Postal: **Folly House, Upper Lambourn Road, Lambourn, Hungerford, Berkshire, RG17 8QG**
Contacts: **PHONE 01488 72800 MOBILE 07779 497563**
EMAIL info@jamiesnowdenracing.co.uk WEBSITE www.jamiesnowdenracing.co.uk TWITTER @
jamiesnowden INSTAGRAM jamie_snowden

1 **ADRRASTOS (IRE)**, 8, b g Areion (GER)—Laren (GER) **Mrs K. Gunn**
2 **ALRIGHTJACK (IRE)**, 6, b g Stowaway—Brogella (IRE) **The GD Partnership**
3 **ANYTHINGFORLOVE**, 5, b m Black Sam Bellamy (IRE)—La Perrotine (FR) **Foxtrot Racing: Anythingforlove**
4 **ARBENNIG (IRE)**, 4, b br g Yeats (IRE)—Ultra Light (FR) **Richards, Stacey, Kirk & Fields**
5 **ASK ROBIN (IRE)**, 8, b g Robin des Champs (FR)—Ask June (IRE) **The Galloping Grannies**
6 **BARROWLANDS (IRE)**, 6, b g Stowaway—Badawi Street **Apache Star Racing**
7 **BATTLEOFTHESOMME (IRE)**, 7, b g Mountain High (IRE)—Shannon Pearl (IRE) **Mrs K. A. Buckett**
8 **BETWEEN THE WATERS (IRE)**, 9, ch g Indian River (FR)—Catch Ball **The Folly Partnership**
9 4, Ch g Dylan Thomas (IRE)—Bonny River (IRE) **Jamie Snowden Racing Club**
10 **BUCKO'S BOY**, 5, b g Midnight Legend—Buxom (IRE) **A. J. & Mrs J. Ward**
11 **CARNTOP**, 7, b g Dansili—Milford Sound **Foxtrot NH Racing Partnership**
12 **CARRIG COPPER (IRE)**, 6, b g Presenting—Copper Dusht (IRE) **Sir Chips Keswick**
13 **CHAPMANSHYPE (IRE)**, 6, b g Aizavoski (IRE)—Call Her Something (IRE) **The GD Partnership**
14 **CHARLIE GEORGE (IRE)**, 4, b g Presenting—Lareine d'Anjou (FR) **Sir Chips Keswick**
15 **COLLEGE OAK (IRE)**, 5, ch g Norse Dancer (IRE)—Katmai (IRE) **Radleian Society, L Lovell & P Stacey**
16 **COOLE WELL (IRE)**, 7, b g Gold Well—Bobs Lass (IRE) **Mrs C. Kendrick**
17 **DATSALRIGHTGINO (GER)**, 4, b g It's Gino (GER)—Delightful Sofie (GER) **The GD Partnership**
18 **DIDDLY DO**, 4, ch f Presenting—Lakaam **Mr E. J. M. Spurrier**
19 **DOUBLE TREASURE**, 9, b g King's Theatre—Double Red (IRE) **Mrs C. Kendrick**
20 **EARLY MORNING RAIN (FR)**, 6, gr m Martaline—Rosewater (GER) **Mrs J A Thomas & Heart Racing**
21 **EXOD'ELA (FR)**, 6, b g Saddler Maker (IRE)—Queen'ela (FR) **Duckworth Jordan Wright Cw Dellar Doel**
22 **FACT OF THE MATTER (IRE)**, 10, b g Brian Boru—Womanofthemountain (IRE) **The Sandylini Racing Partnership**
23 **FERALKAT**, 5, ch m Schiaparelli (GER)—Alikat (IRE)
24 **FLORAL BOUQUET**, 7, bl m Fair Mix (IRE)—Florarossa **The Picnic Party**
25 **FOOTLOOSE**, 6, b g Sulamani (IRE)—Altesse de Sou (FR) **Wiggin Robinson Wainwright Hill Davison**
26 **FORTUNATE FRED (FR)**, 5, b g Cokoriko (FR)—Rosalie Malta (FR) **Mr A. L. Brooks**
27 **FRANKADORE (IRE)**, 4, ch g Frankel—Adoration (USA) **Empire State Racing Partnership**
28 **GA LAW (FR)**, 4, b g Sinndar—Law (FR) **Wiggin Robinson Wainwright Hill Davison**
29 **HOGAN'S HEIGHT (IRE)**, 9, b g Indian River (FR)—Electre du Berlais (FR) **Foxtrot Racing: Hogan's Height**
30 **HOWDILYOUDO (IRE)**, 5, b m Presenting—Little Dil (IRE) **Chasing Gold Limited**
31 **INCLUDED**, 8, b m Champs Elysees—Cordoba **ValueRacingClub.co.uk**
32 **IRSKA (IRE)**, 6, b g Arcadio (GER)—Emmas' House (IRE) **ValueRacingClub.co.uk**
33 **KALAHARI QUEEN**, 7, br m Kalanisi (IRE)—Queen's Leader **The Cherry Pickers**
34 **KILTEALY BRIGGS (IRE)**, 6, b g Fame And Glory—Baby Briggs (IRE) **McNeill Family Ltd**
35 **LEADING EWE ON (IRE)**, 4, b f Leading Light (IRE)—April Thistle (IRE) **Sheep As A Lamb Syndicate**
36 **LEGENDS RYDE**, 5, ch m Midnight Legend—Ryde Back **AWTB Racing Partnership**
37 **LEMON HILL (IRE)**, 7, b m Ask—Rezoned (IRE) **Beswick Brothers Bloodstock**
38 **MIDNIGHT CHILL**, 8, b g Midnight Legend—Chilla Cilla **League Of Nations**
39 **MINELLA BEAT (IRE)**, 7, b g Beat Hollow—Tear Drops (IRE) **Sir Chips Keswick**
40 **MISS MAHMITE (IRE)**, 5, b m Mahler—Davids Delight (IRE) **Mrs J. A. Thomas & Ms K. J. Austin**
41 **MONBEG THEATRE (IRE)**, 11, b g King's Theatre (IRE)—Amberina (IRE) **Heather Pinniger & Lynda Lovell**
42 **MUSTANG ALPHA (IRE)**, 5, b g Stowaway—Tupia (FR) **Mrs C. Kendrick**

MR JAMIE SNOWDEN - continued

43 **NO ANXIETY (IRE)**, 4, ch g Presenting—Joanne One (IRE) **Sir Chips Keswick, S. E. Munir, Mr I. Souede**
44 **ONEOFTHESENIGHTS (IRE)**, 9, b m Milan—Alfreeze **Mr G. R. J. Jones**
45 **PACIFY**, 8, b g Paco Boy (IRE)—Supereva (IRE) **Duchess of Cornwall, Sir Chips Keswick**
46 **PISGAH PIKE (IRE)**, 5, br g Famous Name—Music On D Waters (IRE) **ValueRacingClub.co.uk**
47 **REDBRIDGE GOLD (IRE)**, 7, b m Gold Well—Marikala (IRE) **O'Connor, Coomes, Scholefield, Allen**
48 **REPRESENTING BOB (IRE)**, 4, ch g Presenting—Some Bob Back (IRE) **Beccle, Sperling, Allen & Hague**
49 **SAZERAK (IRE)**, 4, br f Sinndar—Toile d'auteuil (FR) **Mrs J A Thomas Mr S Fiddes & Mr J Beese**
50 **SOME DAY SOON (IRE)**, 7, b g Robin des Champs (FR)—
    Creative Approach (IRE) **Ogilvy, Shaw, Morley&the Racegoers Club**
51 **SOVEREIGN DUKE (GER)**, 5, b g Jukebox Jury (IRE)—Shadow Queen (GER) **One Too Many Partners**
52 **TAKEMEOUT FREDDIE (IRE)**, 6, ch g Doyen (IRE)—Me No Puppet **Mrs C. Kendrick**
53 **THE HONEYDIPPER (IRE)**, 5, b g Westerner—Ariesanne (IRE) **Jamie Snowden Racing Club**
54 **THEBANNERKINGREBEL (IRE)**, 7, b g Arakan (USA)—One Love (IRE) **Sir Chips Keswick**
55 **THISTLE DO NICELY (IRE)**, 6, b g Arcadio (GER)—April Thistle (IRE) **Appletree Stud, M Gumienny & A Signy**
56 **THOMAS MACDONAGH**, 7, b g Black Sam Bellamy (IRE)—
    Taqreem (IRE) **Sperling, Coomes, Davies, Hague, Collins**
57 **THREE WAYS**, 9, b g Flemensfirth (USA)—
    Serenique **Jamie Snowden Racing Club, We Accidentally Bought Another Horse**
58 **TIMCODA (IRE)**, 7, b g Milan—Sorelia (FR) **Mr P O'Leary & Mr P Mcginley, Mr P. O'Leary**
59 **TIMOSHENKO**, 5, ch g Archipenko (USA)—Nezhenka **Mr P. V. Mendoza**
60 **TINSMITH**, 5, gr ro g Mastercraftsman (IRE)—Catopuma (USA) **ValueRacingClub.co.uk**
61 **TRACTOR FRED (IRE)**, 6, br g Curtain Time (IRE)—Bonny Blackdoe (IRE) **Mrs K. A. Buckett**
62 **WINTER HOLIDAY**, 6, b m Dubai Destination (USA)—Tamara King (IRE) **Mr & Mrs R. H. F. Fuller**

Other Owners: Mr D. Abraham, Mrs J. Abraham, Accidentally Bought Another Horse, Jsrc, Miss B. Allen, Apple Tree Stud, Ms K. J. Austin, Miss R Bailey, Mr S. E. Beccle, Mr J. D. Beese, Mr S. Coomes, Cw Dellar Doel, Miss C. E. Davies, Mr G. Davison, Mrs R. Duckworth, Duckworth, Jordan, Wright, Mrs D. Dunkley, P.J. Dunkley, Mr S. J. Fiddes, Mr H. B. Fields, Mrs C. Fuller, R. H. F. Fuller, Mr M. S. Gumienny, Mr B. H. Hague, Heart Racing, Miss S. L. Hellyer, Mr M. Hill, Chips Keswick, Simon Munir, Isaac Souede, Mr J. C. Kirk, Mrs L. R. Lovell, Mr P. McGinley, Ms P. S. Mohabir, Mr A. M. Morley, Mr J. D. O'Connor, Dr M. M. Ogilvy, Mr A. M. Palk, Mr W. Palk, Ms H. N. Pinniger, Racegoers Club Owners Group, Mr A. Rice, Mr A. W. Richards, Mr N. R. Robinson, Mr A. Scholefield, W. G. C. Shaw, Mr A. Signy, Mr J. E. Snowden, Mrs L. E. Snowden, Mr N. A. Sperling, Mr P. A. Stacey, The Duchess Of Cornwall & Chips Keswick, The Radleian Society Racing Syndicate, Mrs J. A. Thomas, Mr M. J. Wainwright, Mr A. J. Ward, Mrs J. Ward, Mr D. P. Wiggin.

Assistant Trainer: Freddie Mitchell, **Head Girl:** Kate Robinson.

NH Jockey: Gavin Sheehan, Sam Twiston-Davies. **Conditional Jockey:** Page Fuller, Ben Hicks.

---

497 | **MR MIKE SOWERSBY, York**
Postal: **Southwold Farm, Goodmanham Wold, Market Weighton, York, East Yorkshire, YO43 3NA**
Contacts: **PHONE 01430 810534 MOBILE 07855 551056**

1 **AGENT LOUISE**, 12, b m Alflora (IRE)—Oso Special **Mr M. E. Sowersby/Mrs Carrie Zetter-Wells**
2 **ARBORETUM**, 12, b g Kayf Tara—Step Lively **Mrs J. M. Plummer**
3 **JACOBITE RISING (FR)**, 7, b g Rob Roy (USA)—Petillante Royale (FR) **T. J. Stubbins**
4 **KIWAYU**, 11, b g Medicean—Kibara **Mounted Games Association Syndicate**
5 **NO CEILING (IRE)**, 10, b g Turtle Island (IRE)—Pyrexie (FR) **Mrs Janet Cooper & Mr M. E. Sowersby**
6 **PENNY HILL (IRE)**, 6, b m Frammassone (IRE)—Mystical Megan (IRE) **Miss E. C. Forman**
7 **RECKLESS BEHAVIOR (IRE)**, 8, b g Gold Well—Wee Wallis **Miss E. C. Forman**
8 **RIDGEWAY PEARL**, 7, b m Malinas (GER)—Sparkling Jewel **R. D. Seldon**
9 **RIP VAN GO**, 6, b g Rip Van Winkle (IRE)—Thousandkissesdeep (IRE) **Mr Brian Valentine & Mr M. E. Sowersby**
10 **SIMPLY LUCKY (IRE)**, 11, b g Flemensfirth (USA)—Derrygowna Court (IRE) **The Southwold Set**
11 **SIZE MATTERS**, 6, b g Captain Gerrard (IRE)—Icky Woo **Janet Cooper/Gibson/Parkinson/Valentine**
12 **SMASHING LASS (IRE)**, 4, ch f Sir Prancealot (IRE)—Gilded Truffle (IRE) **J. Payne**
13 **STRATEGIC (IRE)**, 5, b g Kodiac—Run To Jane (IRE) **R. D. Seldon**
14 **SWEETEST SMILE (IRE)**, 5, b g Champs Elysees—Scorn (USA) **Janet Cooper/Gibson/Parkinson/Valentine**
15 **THAT MAN OF MINE (IRE)**, 8, ch g Thewayyouare (USA)—Do The Deal (IRE)
16 **TOMMYCOLE**, 5, b g Native Ruler—Tancred Miss **M. E. Sowersby**

MR MIKE SOWERSBY - continued

Other Owners: Mrs J. H. Cooper, Mr B. W. Gibson, Mr G. Parkinson, M. E. Sowersby, Mr B. Valentine, Mrs C. J. Zetter-Wells.

Assistant Trainer: Mary Sowersby.

Flat Jockey: Tom Eaves, James Sullivan. **NH Jockey:** Brian Hughes. **Conditional Jockey:** Adam Nichol, Gavin Sheehan.
Amateur Jockey: Mr Russell Lindsay.

498

MR JOHN SPEARING, Kinnersley
Postal: Kinnersley Racing Limited, Kinnersley Racing Stables, Kinnersley, Severn Stoke,
Worcestershire, WR8 9JR
Contacts: PHONE 01905 371054 MOBILE 07801 552922 FAX 01905 371054
EMAIL jlspearing@aol.com

1 A SURE WELCOME, 6, b g Pastoral Pursuits—Croeso Bach **Kinnersley Partnership 3**
2 A TOUCH OF SASS (IRE), 10, b m Mahler—Lwitikila **Miss C. J. Ive**
3 CAPTAIN SEDGWICK (IRE), 6, b m Approve (IRE)—Alinda (IRE) **Oakridge Racing**
4 COOL STRUTTER (IRE), 8, b g Kodiac—Cassava (IRE) **Kinnersley Partnership**
5 IT'S HOW WE ROLL (IRE), 6, b g Fastnet Rock (AUS)—Clodora (FR) **Kinnersley Partnership**
6 KEY TO THE WEST (IRE), 13, b g Westerner—Monte Solaro (IRE) **Miss R S Newell & Mr T P Morrissey**
7 LADY GWHINNYVERE (IRE), 6, b m Sir Prancealot (IRE)—Johar Jamal (IRE) **Mr J. L. Spearing**
8 LOST HISTORY (IRE), 7, b g Strategic Prince—Prelude **Mr J. J. Reilly**
9 PILLAR OF STEEL, 5, b m Shirocco (GER)—Miss Conduct **Miss C. J. Ive**
10 SHUTTHEGATE (IRE), 6, b g Milan—Miss Conduct **Miss C. J. Ive**
11 STYLISH DANCER, 6, b m Nathaniel (IRE)—Hazy Dancer **John J Reilly & Dan Skelton**
12 SWEEPING ROCK (IRE), 10, b g Rock of Gibraltar (IRE)—Sweeping Story (USA) **Kinnersley Partnership II**

THREE-YEAR-OLDS

13 HY EALES (IRE), b f Passing Glance—Miss Conduct **Miss C. J. Ive**

TWO-YEAR-OLDS

14 B c 09/06 Califet (FR)—Miss Conduct (Overbury (IRE)) **Miss C. J. Ive**

Other Owners: Mr T. P. Morrissey, Miss R. S. Newell, Mr J. J. Reilly, Mr D. N. Skelton.

Assistant Trainer: Miss C. Ive.

499

MR RICHARD SPENCER, Newmarket
Postal: Sefton Lodge, 8 Bury Road, Newmarket, Suffolk, CB8 7BT
Contacts: PHONE 01638 675780

1 BERNARDO O'REILLY, 6, b g Intikhab (USA)—Baldovina **Rebel Racing (2)**
2 CALIFORNIA LOVE, 4, ch f Power—La Pantera **Mr A. Cunningham**
3 CIGARETTESNALCOHOL (IRE), 4, ch g Ocovango—Moylisha Red (IRE) **Rebel Jumping II**
4 HANDSOME SAMSON, 5, b g Nathaniel (IRE)—Factice (USA) **Rebel Racing**
5 ITS'AFREEBEE (IRE), 10, br g Danroad (AUS)—Aphra Benn (IRE) **Rebel Jumping**
6 KEYSER SOZE (IRE), 6, ch g Arcano (IRE)—Causeway Queen (IRE) **Rebel Racing (2)**
7 LOUIS TREIZE (IRE), 4, ch g Slade Power (IRE)—Black Rodded **Rebel Racing Premier**
8 MAGICAL RIDE, 5, ch g Paco Boy (IRE)—Decorative (IRE) **The Magic Horse Syndicate**
9 OUTLANDER (IRE), 12, b g Stowaway—Western Whisper (IRE) **Gowing's Eleven**
10 PHILAMUNDO (IRE), 5, b g Sir Prancealot (IRE)—Rublevka Star (USA) **Rebel Racing**
11 RED ARCHANGEL (IRE), 4, b f Dark Angel (IRE)—Illuminating Dream (IRE) **Mr P. M. Cunningham**
12 REVICH (IRE), 4, b g Requinto (IRE)—Kathleen Rafferty (IRE) **Middleham Park LXVII & Phil Cunningham**
13 ROLL WITH IT (IRE), 4, b g Sholokhov (IRE)—Que Pasa (IRE) **Rebel Jumping II**
14 SIR JACK YEATS (IRE), 9, b g Yeats (IRE)—Quadrennial (IRE) **Gowing's Eleven**
15 STAY CLASSY (IRE), 4, ch f Camacho—Hollow Green (IRE) **Balasuriya, Cook, Cunningham, Gowing, Spencer**
16 THISTIMENEXTYEAR, 6, gr g New Approach (IRE)—Scarlet Empire (IRE) **Rebel Racing (2)**

MR RICHARD SPENCER - continued

17 **THRILLA IN MANILA**, 4, b g Iffraaj—Tesary **Rebel Racing Premier** 18
   TWISTEDFIRESTARTER (IRE), 4, b g Sageburg (IRE)—Mercy Mission **Rebel Jumping II**
19 **WONDERWALL (IRE)**, 4, b g Yeats (IRE)—Rock Me Gently **Rebel Jumping II**

THREE-YEAR-OLDS

20 **ALABAMA WHITMAN**, b f Ivawood (IRE)—Mutoon (IRE) **Rebel Racing III**
21 **ALL OF THE LIGHTS (IRE)**, b c Elzaam (AUS)—Abandon (USA) **Mr A. Cunningham**
22 **BARBELO (IRE)**, gr ro f Dark Angel (IRE)—Skehana (IRE) **Brown & Hathorns**
23 **BILL THE BUTCHER (IRE)**, ch c Starspangledbanner (AUS)—Laurelita (IRE) **Rebel Racing Premier II**
24 **BORN TO DESTROY**, b g Camacho—Sahath (USA) **William & Camilla Haines & Phil Cunningham**
25 **BRIGHT VALENTINE**, b f Showcasing—Melbourne Memories **Mr M P Coleman, Mr R J Coleman**
26 **CHAMPAGNE SUPANOVA (IRE)**, b g Camacho—Flawless Pink **Mr P. M. Cunningham**
27 **DON'TYOUWANTMEBABY (IRE)**, b f Kodiac—Miss Corinne **Mr P. M. Cunningham**
28 **DUTUGAMUNU (IRE)**, ch c Ivawood (IRE)—Bunditten (IRE) **Balasuriya, Cook, Cunningham, Gowing, Spencer**
29 **GERTCHA (IRE)**, b c Slade Power (IRE)—Elouges (IRE) **Team DCL**
30 **GRACE PLUNKETT**, b f Brazen Beau (AUS)—Goodnightsuzy (IRE) **Mr P. M. Cunningham**
31 **JOANIE STUBBS**, b f Garswood—Cherry Malotte **Mr P. M. Cunningham**
32 **JOHNNY UTAH (IRE)**, b g Dandy Man (IRE)—Caramel Sundae **Rebel Racing III**
33 **KATNISS EVERDEEN (IRE)**, b f Camacho—Luanas Pearl (IRE) **Rebel Racing III**
34 **LONDON CALLING (IRE)**, b g Requinto (IRE)—Bellechance **Mr Jonny Allison & Mr Phil Cunningham**
35 **ODYSSEY GIRL (IRE)**, gr f Gutaifan (IRE)—Lady Marita (IRE) **Mrs E. Cunningham**
36 **ONE STEP BEYOND (IRE)**, b c Exceed And Excel (AUS)—Yours Truly (IRE) **Rebel Racing Premier II**
37 **SEFTON WARRIOR**, b g Frankel—Maid To Master (IRE) **Rebel Racing Premier II**
38 **SKONTONOVSKI**, b c Harbour Watch (IRE)—An Ghalanta (IRE) **Rebel Racing Premier II**
39 **THE CITY'S PHANTOM**, b c Free Eagle (IRE)—Meet Marhaba (IRE) **Mr P. M. Cunningham, Mr Ed Babington**
40 **TOO SHY SHY (IRE)**, gr f Kodiac—Satwa Ruby (FR) **Mr P. M. Cunningham**
41 **TYLER DURDEN (IRE)**, b g Bungle Inthejungle—Starfleet **Rebel Racing III**
42 **TYSON FURY**, ch c Iffraaj—Za Za Zoom (IRE) **Balasuriya, Cook, Cunningham, Gowing, Spencer**

TWO-YEAR-OLDS

43 Ch f 18/03 Charming Thought—Cherry Malotte (Pivotal) (14000) **Mr P. M. Cunningham**
44 **CHIM CHIMNEY**, b c 09/03 Cockney Rebel (IRE)—
   Wonderful Life (IRE) (Canford Cliffs (IRE)) (800) **Mr P. M. Cunningham**
45 **DANDY MAESTRO**, ch c 18/02 Dandy Man (IRE)—
   Maids Causeway (IRE) (Giant's Causeway (USA)) (60060) **Mr J. Power**
46 B f 06/01 Cityscape—Elegant Annie (Lawman (FR)) (571) **Mr P. M. Cunningham, Mr Richard Spencer**
47 B br c 04/03 Cable Bay (IRE)—Granadilla (Zafonic (USA)) (44616) **Rebel Racing Premier III**
48 Br c 16/04 Markaz (IRE)—On The Dark Side (Kheleyf (USA)) (6190) **Onthedarkside Racing Club**
49 Ch c 25/02 Footstepsinthesand—Ondeafears (IRE) (Chineur (FR)) (95238) **Rebel Racing Premier III**
50 **PROFESSIONAL WIDOW (IRE)**, gr f 01/02 Markaz (IRE)—
   Petite Cherie (Fasliyev (USA)) (4719) **Mrs E. Cunningham**
51 B f 01/02 Siyouni (FR)—Raylasa (IRE) (Rock of Gibraltar (IRE)) (76190)
52 B f 18/03 Mehmas (IRE)—Rise Up Lotus (IRE) (Zebedee) (32380)
53 B c 13/03 Due Diligence (USA)—River Song (USA) (Siphon (BRZ)) (71428) **Rebel Racing Premier III**
54 Gr f 13/04 The Gurkha (IRE)—Satwa Ruby (FR) (Verglas (IRE)) (24761)
55 B c 06/03 Acclamation—Shy Audience (IRE) (Sir Prancealot (IRE)) (66666) **Rebel Racing Premier III**
56 **SKATERBOI**, b g 20/03 Cockney Rebel (IRE)—Encantar (Equiano (FR)) **Miss Lauren Cunningham**
57 Br c 06/04 Equiano (FR)—Tesary (Danehill (USA)) (43809) **Rebel Racing Premier III**
58 **THEFASTNTHECURIOUS**, ch f 18/04 Fast Company (IRE)—
   Dame Plume (IRE) (Amadeus Wolf) (19000) **Mr P. M. Cunningham**
59 **WINGS OF A DOVE**, gr f 22/01 Dark Angel (IRE)—Silk Bow (Elusive City (USA)) (78095) **Mr P. M. Cunningham**

Other Owners: Father & Sons, Ahmad Al Shaikh, Mr J. Allison, Six Amigos, Cheveley Park Stud Limited, Moorecool & Cool Racing, Mr P. Cunningham, Mr P. M. Cunningham, Mr Chris Giles, Mrs C. Haines, Mr W. R. Haines, Middleham Park Racing LXVII, T. S. Palin, M. Prince, Equinox Racing, Mainline Racing, Rebel Racing Premier, Mr Gerald Spencer.

Assistant Trainer: Mr Mitchell Hunt, **Head Lad:** Mr Joe Akehurst, Mr Robert Stevenson, **Travelling Head:** Miss Tegan Kerr, **Racing Secretary:** Mrs Chris Hills, **Secretary:** Miss Roisin Carey.

Apprentice Jockey: Mr Sean Kiranne.

500   MR SEB SPENCER, Malton
Postal: **79 Harvest Drive, Malton, North Yorkshire, YO17 7BF**
Contacts: **MOBILE 07790 060050**
EMAIL **sebspencerracing@gmail.com**

1 **ADIATOR**, 12, b m Needwood Blade—Retaliator **Jetset Racing Club**
2 **CASTLE QUARTER (IRE)**, 4, b g Zoffany (IRE)—Queen's Pudding (IRE) **Mr R. Postlethwaite**
3 **COOLAGH MAGIC**, 4, b g Sepoy (AUS)—Miliika **N. Bycroft**
4 **DON'T BE SURPRISED**, 5, ch g Monsieur Bond (IRE)—Julie's Gift **Dukes Group**
5 **DONNCHA (IRE)**, 9, br g Captain Marvelous (IRE)—Seasonal Style (IRE) **Mr D. Bannon**
6 **JET SET GO**, 5, ch m Equiano (FR)—Golden Valley **Jetset Racing Club**
7 **PICTURE YOUR DREAM**, 5, ch m Kheleyf (USA)—Another Sunset **B. Dunn**

THREE-YEAR-OLDS
8 **BANDSMAN RICE**, b g Haafhd—Allashka (FR) **E.A. Moorey & E.G. Moorey**
9 **MUST DREAM**, ch g Mustajeeb—Golden Valley **Enjoy Racing**

Other Owners: Mr E. A. Moorey, Mr E. G. Moorey.

Assistant Trainer: Geoff Oldroyd.

---

501   MR HENRY SPILLER, Newmarket
Postal: **Henry Spiller Racing, Sackville House Stables, Sackville Street, Newmarket, Suffolk, CB8 8DX**
Contacts: **PHONE 07786 263997 MOBILE 07786 263997**
EMAIL **office@henryspillerracing.com** WEBSITE **www.henryspillerracing.com**

1 **BAROSSA BAL (IRE)**, 4, b f Delegator—Anamarka **Dethrone Racing**
2 **BOLEYBEG (IRE)**, 4, ch c Makfi—Soho Rocks **Dethrone Racing**
3 **IRISH TIMES**, 5, b g Swiss Spirit—Amouage Royale (IRE) **Mr H. Simcock**
4 **KING OF ROOKS**, 7, b g Acclamation—Slap Shot (IRE) **Dethrone Racing**
5 **LAST TO BID (FR)**, 4, ch c Makfi—Last Song **Mr R. P. A. Spiller**
6 **PARKNACILLA (IRE)**, 4, br f Mukhadram—Patuca **Charles & Fiona Spiller**
7 **PICTURE POET (IRE)**, 4, b g Camacho—Cockney Rhyme **Birdie Racing Club**
8 **POETA BRASILEIRO (IRE)**, 5, b g Poet's Voice—Top Act (FR) **Mr P. Moyles**
9 **RINTY MAGINTY (IRE)**, 4, b g Camacho—Peanut Butter (IRE) **Select-Racing-Club.co.uk & Partner**
10 **RODERICK**, 4, b g Pastoral Pursuits—Reeling N Rocking
11 **SEPAHI**, 4, ch f Sepoy (AUS)—Katevan (IRE) **Birdie Racing Club**
12 **STALLONE (IRE)**, 4, b g Dandy Man—Titian Queen **Mr K. Clarke**

THREE-YEAR-OLDS
13 **ANALYST**, gr g Outstrip—Ariyfa (IRE) **Franconson Partners**
14 **B f** Sepoy (AUS)—Appointee (IRE) **Mr R. P. A. Spiller**
15 **CROQUEMBOUCHE**, b c Kheleyf—Sarcira
16 **FAIR WARNING**, b g Helmet (AUS)—Critical Path (IRE) **The Champagne Poppers**
17 **HENDERSON**, b g Kitten's Joy (USA)—Heated Exchange (USA) **Franconson Partners**
18 **KENN**, b g Mukhadram—Kasakiya (IRE) **Franconson Partners**
19 **PHIL**, b g Showcasing—Pin Cushion **Franconson Partners**
20 **ROCHFORD (IRE)**, b c Ivawood (IRE)—Lady Berta **Mr V. Chitkara**
21 **SEA WILLOW**, ch f Dream Ahead (USA)—Showbird **Select-Racing-Club.co.uk & Partner**
22 **TERBRUGGHEN**, b c Dutch Art—Moon Eyes **Birdie Racing Club**

TWO-YEAR-OLDS
23 B f 05/04 Evasive—Biloka (Sunday Break)
24 B c 22/03 Captain Gerrard (IRE)—Country Madam (IRE) (Medaglia d'Oro (USA))
25 B c 30/01 Twilight Son—Embroidery (IRE) (Mastercraftsman (IRE))
26 B f 14/02 Ivawood (IRE)—Hazel Blue (IRE) (Kodiac) (4290)
27 B c 05/03 Kendargent (FR)—Nova Zarga (IRE) (Dubawi)
28 B f 06/04 Awtaad (IRE)—Patuca (Teofilo (IRE)) (5000) **Charles & Fiona Spiller**

MR HENRY SPILLER - continued

29 B f 10/05 Le Havre (IRE)—Scalambra (Nayef (USA)) (60060) **Mr R. P. A. Spiller**
30 Ch c 22/02 Mukhadram—Shamana (USA) (Woodman (USA)) (2000) **Birdie Racing Club**

Other Owners: Mrs C. Cummings, Mr K. Lines, Mr C. R. G. Spiller, Mrs F. J. D. Spiller, Mr H. C. Spiller, The Select Racing Club Limited.

---

502 **MR MICHAEL SQUANCE, Newmarket**
Postal: Trainer did not wish details of their string to appear

---

503 **MR FOZZY STACK, Cashel**
Postal: **Thomastown Castle Stud, Golden, Cashel, Co. Tipperary, Ireland**
Contacts: **PHONE +353 62 54129**
EMAIL contact@stackracing.ie WEBSITE www.stackracing.ie

1 BAMBARI (IRE), 7, b g Arcano (IRE)—Blue Dahlia (IRE)
2 CARLO BIRAGHI (IRE), 5, ch h Galileo (IRE)—Kirinda (IRE)
3 DRUMQUINA (IRE), 4, b f Holy Roman Emperor (IRE)—Tarascon (IRE)
4 ELEGANCE AND GRACE, 4, b f War Command (USA)—Medican Star (IRE)
5 GATSBY CAP (IRE), 4, b c Gale Force Ten—Blue Dahlia (IRE)
6 LADY WANNABE (IRE), 4, b f Camelot—Wannabe Better (IRE)
7 NEVEREVERSAYNEVER (IRE), 4, b f No Nay Never (USA)—Dowager
8 SHIFTED STRATEGY (IRE), 5, b g Choisir (AUS)—Pure Greed (IRE)
9 SON OF REST, 6, b h Pivotal—Hightime Heroine (IRE)
10 STARLITE DANCER, 4, b c Canford Cliffs—Pivotalia (IRE)
11 WOODY CREEK, 4, b f Zoffany—Belle Isle

THREE-YEAR-OLDS
12 B f Battle of Marengo (IRE)—Annmary Girl
13 BACK TO BRUSSELS, ch f Starspangledbanner (AUS)—Big Boned (USA)
14 CHANELL ECLIPSE, b f Cable Bay (IRE)—Gentle Breeze (IRE)
15 DENDROBIUM, b c Holy Roman Emperor (IRE)—Dark Orchid
16 Ch c Anjaal—Fancy Vivid (IRE)
17 Ch f Starspangledbanner (AUS)—Fataawy (IRE)
18 HIGHPOINT WARRIER, b br c Warrior's Reward (USA)—Fly Again (USA)
19 KOOLA BUALA (IRE), ch f Raven's Pass (USA)—Naizah (USA)
20 LAUREL GROVE, b f Zoffany (IRE)—Private Paradise (IRE)
21 LYNN BRITT CABIN, b f Dark Angel (IRE)—Taraeff (IRE)
22 MEANINGFUL VOTE, ch c Pivotal—Adore
23 B f Lawman (FR)—Miracolia (IRE)
24 ORDEROFRETALIATION, ch c Declaration of War (USA)—Alegendinmyownmind
25 PIECE OF PARADISE, b f Holy Roman Emperor (IRE)—Double Fantasy (GER)
26 SABLE CAMP, b f No Nay Never (USA)—Mala Mala (IRE)
27 B c Gleneagles (IRE)—Snowfields (IRE)
28 STALINGRAD, b c War Front (USA)—I Am Beautiful (IRE)
29 STAR OF CASHEL, b c No Nay Never (USA)—Queen of Lyons (USA)
30 SWEETTASTEOFLOVE, b c Power—Love Rosie (USA)
31 TOO SOON TO PANIC, b f Gleneagles (IRE)—Scream Blue Murder (IRE)
32 YOU'RE SO BEAUTIFUL, ch f No Nay Never (USA)—Hula Angel (USA)

TWO-YEAR-OLDS
33 B f 02/03 Starspangledbanner (AUS)—Acid (Clodovil (IRE)) (50000)
34 B f 10/05 Canford Cliffs (IRE)—Addictedtoprogress (IRE) (Holy Roman Emperor (IRE))
35 Ch f 17/04 The Gurkha (IRE)—Await (IRE) (Peintre Celebre (USA))
36 B f 19/02 Mastercraftsman (IRE)—Blessing (USA) (Pulpit (USA)) (102960)
37 B f 07/04 The Last Lion (IRE)—Blue Dahlia (IRE) (Shamardal (USA))

MR FOZZY STACK - continued

38 Ch f 21/01 Starspangledbanner (AUS)—Brazilian Samba (IRE) (Sadler's Wells (USA)) (60060)
39 B f 12/02 Air Force Blue (USA)—Cry Me A River (IRE) (Danehill Dancer (IRE)) (90089)
40 B g 03/02 Holy Roman Emperor (IRE)—Divisme (USA) (Elusive Quality (USA)) (57142)
41 B c 04/02 Galileo (IRE)—Fix (NZ) (Iffraaj)
42 B f 12/05 The Gurkha (IRE)—Fountain of Peace (USA) (Kris S (USA))
43 B f 14/04 Holy Roman Emperor (IRE)—Holly Blue (Bluebird (USA)) (85800)
44 B f 29/01 Fastnet Rock (AUS)—Khione (Dalakhani (IRE)) (17160)
45 B gr c 20/05 Dark Angel (IRE)—La Collina (IRE) (Strategic Prince) (94380)
46 **LINDA BARRETT (IRE),** b gr f 05/03 Dark Angel (IRE)—Plagiarism (USA) (Lonhro (AUS)) (235949)
47 B f 16/03 Zoffany (IRE)—Loved (IRE) (Galileo (IRE)) (81509)
48 B f 03/05 Starspangledbanner (AUS)—Medicean Star (IRE) (Galileo (IRE))
49 B c 22/04 Gale Force Ten—Muizenberg Nights (IRE) (Shamardal (USA))
50 **PITA PINTA (IRE),** b f 14/03 Sir Percy—Bantam (IRE) (Teofilo (IRE))
51 B f 20/02 Starspangledbanner (AUS)—Precariously Good (Oasis Dream) (66666)
52 Ch c 13/03 Pride of Dubai (AUS)—Pure Greed (IRE) (Galileo (IRE))
53 B f 10/04 Pride of Dubai (AUS)—Rohain (IRE) (Singspiel (IRE)) (55769)
54 B c 26/04 Zoffany (IRE)—Santa Teresa (IRE) (Cape Cross (IRE)) (51480)
55 B f 20/04 Galileo (IRE)—Scream Blue Murder (IRE) (Oratorio (IRE))
56 B c 31/01 Galileo (IRE)—Sea Siren (AUS) (Fastnet Rock (AUS))
57 B c 23/02 Air Force Blue (USA)—Sense of Class (IRE) (Fusaichi Pegasus (USA)) (208333)
58 **SLOANE PETERSON (IRE),** b f 19/02 Kodiac—Capriole (Noverre (USA)) (188760)
59 B f 17/05 No Nay Never (USA)—Subtle Charm (Machiavellian (USA)) (120000)
60 B f 15/03 Starspangledbanner (AUS)—Zain Art (IRE) (Excellent Art) (57485)

Owners: Mr Rick Barnes, Mr Michael Begley, Craig Bernick, Peter Chiu, Iman Hartono, Mr T. Hyde Jnr, Mr D. Keoghan, Mrs J. Magnier, Mr Casey McLiney, Mr B. Parker, Mr P. Piller, Mrs Jane Rowlinson, Mary Slack, Mr Michael Tabor, The New Pension Fund Syndicate, The Pension Fund II Syndicate, Emily Alexander, Peter Barnett, Genevieve Britton, Richard Brodie, Tony Cullinane, Flaxman Stables, Forthepeopleracing, Koola Buala Partnership, R O'Callaghan, D Pearson, Phoenix Thoroughbred Ltd, B Sangster, David Reid Scott, Cayton Park Stud.

Flat Jockey: Chris Hayes, Conor Maxwell, Andrew Slattery.

---

504   ## MR EUGENE STANFORD, Newmarket
Postal: **2 Rous Memorial Cottages, Old Station Road, Newmarket, Suffolk, CB8 8DP**
Contacts: PHONE **01638 665507** MOBILE **07761 223096**
EMAIL e.stanford077@btinternet.com WEBSITE www.eugenestanfordracing.com

1 AMNA, 6, b m Sayif (IRE)—Island Dreams (USA) **Mr E. V. Stanford**
2 BELLA BLUR, 8, ch m Showcasing—Ellablue **Miss C. R. Williams**
3 ISLAND AUTHORITY, 8, b m Authorized (IRE)—Island Odyssey **Mr E. V. Stanford**
4 OCEAN SPRAY, 5, ch m Showcasing—Gibraltar Lass (USA) **Mr M. W. Goodridge**
5 Q CEE, 7, b g Denounce—Gibraltar Lass (USA) **Mr M. W. Goodridge**
6 TINKERBIRD, 4, br c Gregorian (IRE)—Swan Queen **Mr E. V. Stanford**
7 UNTIL MIDNIGHT (IRE), 10, b g Moss Vale (IRE)—Emma's Star (ITY) **Newmarketracingclub.com**

---

505   ## MR DANIEL STEELE, Henfield
Postal: **Blacklands House, Wheatsheaf Road, Wineham, Henfield, West Sussex, BN5 9BE**
Contacts: PHONE **07809 405036**
EMAIL danielsteele14@hotmail.co.uk

1 BLAZING DESTINY (IRE), 6, b m Arcadio (GER)—Sweet Liss (IRE) **Mr D. R. Steele**
2 CASSIVELLAUNUS (IRE), 8, b g Danehill Dancer (IRE)—Celtic Heroine (IRE) **Vectis Racing**
3 CHIVERS (IRE), 9, b g Duke of Marmalade (IRE)—Thara (USA) **Mr D. R. Steele**
4 MADNESS LIGHT (FR), 11, b g Satri (IRE)—Majestic Lady (FR) **Mr C. G. Russell**

MR DANIEL STEELE - continued

TWO-YEAR-OLDS

  5 B c 10/06 Linda's Lad—Dainty Diva (IRE) (Indian Danehill (IRE)) **Vectis Racing**
  6 B f 04/03 Arvico (FR)—Mad Moll (IRE) (Heron Island (IRE))

---

506 | **MRS JACKIE STEPHEN, Inverurie**
Postal: **Conglass Farmhouse, Inverurie, Aberdeenshire, AB51 5DN**
Contacts: **PHONE 01467 621267 MOBILE 07980 785924 FAX 01467 620511**
EMAIL jackiestephen123@hotmail.com WEBSITE www.jackiestephenracing.com

  1 AMILLIONTIMES (IRE), 12, b g Olden Times—Miss Million (IRE) **Mr P. G. Stephen**
  2 BERMONDSEY BELLE (IRE), 6, b m Sir Percy—Bermondsey Girl **Mrs J. S. Stephen**
  3 BRIDANE HIGH (IRE), 7, b g Mountain High (IRE)—Maylee (IRE) **Truscott & Stephen**
  4 DROGON (IRE), 4, b g Zoffany (IRE)—Flames To Dust (GER) **APCC Limited**
  5 KILFINAN BAY (IRE), 5, b g Mahler—Midnight Special (IRE) **Mrs J. S. Stephen**
  6 4, B g Lucarno (USA)—La Grande Villez (FR)
  7 LADYVIE (FR), 13, b m Vic Toto (FR)—Ladykish (FR) **Mrs J. S. Stephen**
  8 LOVELY SCHTUFF (IRE), 8, b g Court Cave (IRE)—The Long Bill (IRE) **High Country Racing**
  9 MIDNIGHT KATE (IRE), 6, gr m Midnight Legend—Primrose Time **Mr C. T. Reid**
10 SCHIEHALLION RIDGE (IRE), 5, b g Mountain High (IRE)—Upton Lodge (IRE) **Mrs J. S. Stephen**
11 SCULLYS FORGE (IRE), 6, ch g Doyen (IRE)—Queen of Questions (IRE) **Mrs J. S. Stephen**
12 4, B g Kalanisi (IRE)—Sister Shannon (IRE)
13 STAROZOV (IRE), 7, b g Morozov (USA)—Star of Arcady (IRE) **Jackie Stephen Racing Club**
14 THE GREAT GEORGIE, 5, b g Multiplex—For More (FR) **Mr P. G. Stephen**
15 WHOA BLACK BETTY (IRE), 5, br m Jeremy (USA)—Strong Lady (IRE) **Jackie Stephen Racing Club**
16 WOLFCATCHER (IRE), 8, b g King's Best (USA)—Miss Particular (IRE) **Mr P. G. Stephen**

Other Owners: Mrs J. S. Stephen, Mr G. Truscott.

Assistant Trainer: Patrick Stephen.

---

507 | **MRS KATIE STEPHENS, Shaldon**
Postal: **Sikymsa Meadow, Short Lane, Shaldon, Devon, TQ14 0HE**
EMAIL sikymsaracing@gmail.com

  1 D'WATERSIDE, 6, b g Sir Percy—Santorini Sunset **Phensdell Racing**
  2 LA MADRINA (IRE), 8, b m Milan—Edermine Blossom (IRE) **Mrs K. J. Stephens**
  3 ROYAL PLAZA, 9, b g King's Theatre—Friendly Craic (IRE) **Friends Have Fun Racing**
  4 SHADARPOUR (IRE), 11, b g Dr Fong (USA)—Shamadara (IRE) **Phensdell Racing**
  5 TEMPLIER (IRE), 7, b g Mastercraftsman (IRE)—Tigertail (IRE) **Catherine Payne & Melvyn Langdell**

Other Owners: Mr M. J. Langdell, Mrs C. Payne, Mrs K. J. Stephens.

---

508 | **MR ROBERT STEPHENS, Caldicot**
Postal: **The Knoll, St. Brides Netherwent, Caldicot, Gwent, NP26 3AT**
Contacts: **MOBILE 07717 477177**
EMAIL robertdavidstephens@btinternet.com WEBSITE www.robertstephensracing.com

  1 BELTOR, 9, b g Authorized (IRE)—Carahill (AUS) **A. J. Mossop**
  2 BROPHIES DOLL (IRE), 8, ch m Gamut (IRE)—Crossbar Lady (IRE) **Mr T. J. Moynihan**
  3 BUMBLE BAY, 10, b g Trade Fair—Amica **A Mossop & H Scale**
  4 CASTLELYONS (IRE), 8, br g Papal Bull—Summercove (IRE) **Lycett Racing 1**
  5 COMEONTHEBULL (IRE), 8, ch g Papal Bull—Maratanas Gift (IRE) **M Duthie & T Moynihan**
  6 ECHO DU LARGE (FR), 6, b g Blue Bresil (FR)—Gardagua (FR) **Castle Farm Racing**

MR ROBERT STEPHENS - continued

  7 **ESPRESSO FREDDO (IRE),** 6, b g Fast Company (IRE)—Spring Bouquet (IRE) **Threes Company**
  8 **FIRST DESTINATION,** 8, b m Rail Link—Hollow Quaill (IRE) **A. J. Mossop**
  9 **G'DAY (FR),** 4, b g Australia—Main Spring **Mr R. D. Stephens**
10 **GOLDEN GLORY (IRE),** 6, b m Fame And Glory—Howyakeepan (IRE) **Mr R. D. Stephens**
11 **GOLDEN GROVE (IRE),** 5, b g Stowaway—Follyfoot (IRE) **Mr R. D. Stephens**
12 4, Ch f Black Sam Bellamy (IRE)—Maria Antonia (IRE) **Threes Company**
13 **MERE ANARCHY (IRE),** 9, b g Yeats (IRE)—Maracana (IRE) **Les Oxley & R Stephens**
14 **MILE HOUSE (IRE),** 12, b g Close Conflict (USA)—Clogheen Lass (IRE) **Castle Farm Racing**
15 **MUSKETEER,** 8, ch g Schiaparelli (GER)—Suave Shot **Mr R. D. Stephens**
16 **PASSIN' THRU,** 4, b f Nathaniel (IRE)—Go Between **M Duthie & T Moynihan**
17 5, Br m Arcadio (GER)—Pippedatthepost
18 **PUSH THE TEMPO (IRE),** 7, b g Gold Well—Fairpark (IRE) **Castle Farm Racing**
19 **QUINNSBOROTEMPTRES (IRE),** 8, ch m Gamut (IRE)—Quinnsboro Native (IRE) **Mr R. D. Stephens**
20 **SECONDO (FR),** 10, b g Sakhee's Secret—Royal Jade **Robert Stephens Racing Club**
21 4, Ch f Power—Street Diva (USA) **Mr R. Miles**
22 4, B g Dick Turpin (IRE)—Tamara **Mr R. D. Stephens**
23 **THE CALLER,** 9, b g Yeats (IRE)—Wyldello **Mrs C. Ford-Ellis**
24 **TUDORS TREASURE,** 9, b g Dr Massini (IRE)—Rude Health **Four Seasons Partnership**

TWO-YEAR-OLDS

25 Br c 03/05 Markaz (IRE)—Melatonina (IRE) (King Charlemagne (USA)) (4290) **Mr T. J. Moynihan**

Other Owners: Mr I. J. K. Croker, Mr M. Duthie, Lycett Racing Ltd, A. J. Mossop, Mr T. J. Moynihan, Mr L. T. Oxley, Mr W. B. H. Scale, D. T. Shorthouse, Mr K. Slade, Mr R. D. Stephens.

Assistant Trainer: Rosie Stephens.

NH Jockey: Micheal Nolan, Tom O'Brien. **Conditional Jockey:** Ciaran Gethings. **Amateur Jockey:** Mr Craig Dowson, Mr Morgan Winstone.

---

509   **MR WILLIAM STONE,** West Wickham
Postal: **The Meadow, Streetly End, West Wickham, Cambridge, Cambridgeshire, CB21 4RP**
Contacts: **MOBILE 07788 971094**
EMAIL williamstone1@hotmail.co.uk

  1 **DIAMOND LADY,** 9, b m Multiplex—Ellen Mooney **Dr C. M. Scott**
  2 **EVENING ATTIRE,** 9, b g Pastoral Pursuits—Markova's Dance **Dr C. M. Scott**
  3 **INVISIBLE STORM,** 5, gr m Multiplex—Dawn Lightning **Mr A Wittering & Dr C Scott**
  4 **JEANETTE MAY,** 4, b f Dick Turpin (IRE)—Clock Opera (IRE) **Mr Shane Fairweather & Dr C Scott**
  5 **LALANIA,** 5, br m Kheleyf (USA)—George's Gift **Dr C. M. Scott**
  6 **MISTRESS NELLIE,** 5, ch m Mount Nelson—Watchoverme **Mrs Denis Haynes & Dr Caroline Scott**
  7 **THE JEAN GENIE,** 6, b br m Lawman (FR)—Miracle Seeker **Dr C. M. Scott**

THREE-YEAR-OLDS

  8 **DASHING ROGER,** b g Fast Company (IRE)—Croeso Cusan **Mrs Stephanie Oliver & Mr Ron Spore**
  9 **JOSEPHINE,** b f Champs Elysees—Puya **Mrs E. A. P. Haynes**
10 **LITTLE BROWN TROUT,** b g Casamento (IRE)—Clock Opera (IRE) **Mr Shane Fairweather & Dr C Scott**
11 **SEA TROUT,** ch g Equiano (FR)—Smile For Me (IRE) **Dr C. M. Scott**

Other Owners: Mr S. A. Fairweather, Mrs E. A. P. Haynes, Mrs S. Oliver, Dr C. M. Scott, R. C. Spore, Mr A. J. Wittering.

---

510 **MR WILF STOREY, Consett**
Postal: **Grange Farm & Stud, Muggleswick, Consett, County Durham, DH8 9DW**
Contacts: **PHONE 01207 255259 MOBILE 07860 510441**
EMAIL wlstorey@metronet.co.uk **WEBSITE** www.wilfstorey.com

1 **BETTY GRABLE (IRE)**, 6, b m Delegator—Danella (IRE) **Mr W. L. Storey**
2 **CARD HIGH (IRE)**, 10, b g Red Clubs (IRE)—Think (FR) **Gremlin Racing**
3 **CIRCUIT**, 6, br m Foxwedge (AUS)—Lady Circe (USA) **Gremlin Racing**
4 **NEARLY THERE**, 7, b g Virtual—Nicoise (IRE) **Mr W. L. Storey, Geegeez.co.uk 1, Mr M. Bisogno**
5 **PERFECT SOLDIER (IRE)**, 6, b g Kodiac—Independent Girl (IRE) **wilfstoreyracingclub**
6 **SOMEWHAT SISYPHEAN**, 4, b g Mount Nelson—Nine Red **Mr W. L. Storey, Geegeez.co.uk 1, Mr M. Bisogno**
7 **TARNHELM**, 5, b m Helmet (AUS)—Anosti **H. S. Hutchinson & W. Storey, Mr W. L. Storey, H. S. Hutchinson**

Assistant Trainer: Miss S. Storey.

Amateur Jockey: Miss S. M. Doolan.

---

511 **SIR MICHAEL STOUTE, Newmarket**
Postal: **Freemason Lodge, Bury Road, Newmarket, Suffolk, CB8 7BY**
Contacts: **PHONE 01638 663801 FAX 01638 667276**

1 **ALIGNAK**, 4, gr c Sea The Moon (GER)—Albanova
2 **ANNA OF LORRAINE**, 4, b f Dutch Art—Ladyship
3 **CALCULATION**, 4, br g Dubawi (IRE)—Estimate (IRE)
4 **DAVYDENKO**, 4, ch c Intello (GER)—Safina
5 **DEREVO**, 4, b c Dansili—Pavlosk (USA)
6 **DREAM OF DREAMS (IRE)**, 6, ch g Dream Ahead (USA)—Vasilia
7 **JOYFUL MISSION (USA)**, 4, b g Noble Mission—Hint of Joy (USA)
8 **JUBILOSO**, 4, b f Shamardal (USA)—Joyeuse
9 **LAAFY (USA)**, 4, b g Noble Mission—Miner's Secret (USA)
10 **LAST WINTER (SAF)**, 7, b h Western Winter (USA)—Field Flower (SAF)
11 **MUBAKKER (USA)**, 4, gr c Speightstown (USA)—Ready to Act (USA)
12 **MUSTASHRY**, 7, b br g Tamayuz—Safwa (IRE)
13 **QUEEN POWER (IRE)**, 4, ch f Shamardal (USA)—Princess Serena (USA)
14 **RABDAN**, 5, ch h Frankel—Shotgun Gulch (USA)
15 **REGAL REALITY**, 5, b g Intello (GER)—Regal Realm
16 **ROMOLA**, 4, b f Pivotal—Dianora
17 **SANGARIUS**, 4, b c Kingman—Trojan Queen (USA)
18 **SEXTANT**, 5, b g Sea The Stars (IRE)—Hypoteneuse (IRE)
19 **SHEPHERD MARKET (IRE)**, 5, b m Reckless Abandon—Shepherdia (IRE)
20 **SOLID STONE (IRE)**, 4, br g Shamardal (USA)—Landmark (USA)
21 **SOVEREIGN GRANT**, 4, b c Kingman—Momentary
22 **VERACIOUS**, 5, b m Frankel—Infallible
23 **VIVIONN**, 4, ch f Dubawi (IRE)—Giants Play (USA)
24 **ZAAKI**, 5, b g Leroidesanimaux (BRZ)—Kesara

THREE-YEAR-OLDS

25 **A LA VOILE**, b f Invincible Spirit (IRE)—All At Sea
26 **ALMAREEKH (USA)**, b br f War Front (USA)—Orate (USA)
27 **AREEHAA (IRE)**, b f Kingman—Ashaaqa (IRE)
28 **ASTRO KING (IRE)**, b c Kingman—Astroglia (USA)
29 **ATHEEB**, b c Muhaarar—Lady Francesca
30 **BAAZIGHAH**, b f Muhaarar—Maakrah
31 **BOSS POWER (IRE)**, b c Frankel—La Vinchina (GER)
32 **BRIDESHEAD**, ch f Sea The Stars (IRE)—Emaratiya Ana (IRE)
33 **CHAI YO POWER (IRE)**, b c Le Havre (IRE)—Stella Bellissima (IRE)
34 **CHAIRMAN POWER**, b c Galileo (IRE)—Best Terms
35 **CHICHESTER**, b c Dansili—Havant

SIR MICHAEL STOUTE - continued

36 **CLINICIAN,** b f Kingman—Clinical
37 **CROSSING THE BAR (IRE),** b c Poet's Voice—Ship's Biscuit
38 **CRYSTAL PEGASUS,** ch c Australia—Crystal Etoile
39 **DESERT WAVE,** b c Kingman—Waila
40 **DOLLAR BID,** b c Frankel—Cape Dollar (IRE)
41 **DUSK (IRE),** b f Galileo (IRE)—Dank
42 **DUSK TO DAWN (IRE),** b f Galileo (IRE)—Dawning (USA)
43 **FIRST RECEIVER,** b c New Approach (IRE)—Touchline
44 **FOX NEVER QUIT,** br c Dark Angel (IRE)—Minwah (IRE)
45 **FRENCH ASSET (IRE),** b c Siyouni (FR)—Blue Chip
46 **FULL AUTHORITY (IRE),** b c Kingman—Ashley Hall (USA)
47 **GALATA BRIDGE,** b c Golden Horn—Infallible
48 **GLITTERING GIFT,** ch g Dubawi (IRE)—Golden Stream (IRE)
49 **GOLDEN PINE (IRE),** b c Golden Horn—Snow Pine
50 **HASTY SAILOR (IRE),** b c Fastnet Rock (AUS)—Galileano (IRE)
51 **HEAVEN FORFEND,** b c Frankel—Heaven Sent
52 **HIGHEST GROUND (IRE),** b c Frankel—Celestial Lagoon (JPN)
53 **HYDROS,** b c Frankel—Trojan Queen (USA)
54 **INHERENT,** b c Dubawi (IRE)—Integral
55 **JEAN BAPTISTE,** b c Invincible Spirit (IRE)—Pioneer Bride (USA)
56 **JOVIAL,** b f Dubawi (IRE)—Joyeuse
57 **KATARA (FR),** b f Deep Impact (JPN)—Asyad (IRE)
58 **KESARINA,** b f Medicean—Kesara
59 **KHADAASH,** b c Kingman—Honorlina (FR)
60 **LAW OF ONE (IRE),** ch c Galileo (IRE)—Strawberry Fledge (USA)
61 **LEHWAIYLA,** b f Toronado (IRE)—Strawberrydaiquiri
62 **LIGHTS ON,** ch f Siyouni (FR)—In The Light
63 **MARS LANDING (IRE),** b g Dark Angel (IRE)—Psychometry (FR)
64 **MEKNAS (FR),** b c Gleneagles (IRE)—Barenia (FR)
65 **MELNIKOVA,** ch f Frankel—Safina
66 **MOHAYYA,** b f Le Havre (IRE)—Queen Margherita
67 **MUZDAJER (FR),** b c Le Havre (IRE)—Puggy (IRE)
68 **MY FRANKEL,** b c Frankel—My Special J's (USA)
69 **MY INTENTION,** b c Siyouni (FR)—Wannabe Posh (IRE)
70 **MY POEM,** ch f Poet's Voice—Watchoverme
71 **NASHY (IRE),** b c Camelot—Venus de Milo (IRE)
72 **OSLO,** b g Gleneagles (IRE)—Intercontinental
73 **PLATH,** b f Poet's Voice—Ebble
74 Ch c Shamardal (USA)—Prime Run
75 **PRINCE IMPERIAL (USA),** b c Frankel—Proportional
76 **PROPRIETY (IRE),** b f Galileo (IRE)—Wannabe Better (IRE)
77 **QUEEN'S FAVOUR,** b f Muhaarar—Queen's Best
78 **QUICK WALTZ,** b f Australia—Momentary
79 **RABAABAH (IRE),** br f Shamardal (USA)—Safwa (IRE)
80 **RAGHAAYIB,** gr f Siyouni (FR)—Raddeh
81 **RANSOM,** b c Kingman—Arizona Jewel
82 **RAOOF,** gr c Dark Angel (IRE)—Swiss Diva
83 **REAL POET (IRE),** b g Poet's Voice—Milady Eileen (IRE)
84 **SAEER (IRE),** ch g Australia—Pivotalia (IRE)
85 **SATONO JAPAN (JPN),** b c Deep Impact (JPN)—Dubawi Heights
86 **SNOW SHOWER,** b f Lope de Vega (IRE)—Solar Pursuit
87 **SOCIETY LION,** b c Invincible Spirit (IRE)—Pavlosk (USA)
88 **SOFFIKA (IRE),** b f Zoffany (IRE)—Rosika
89 **SOLAR CYCLE (FR),** b f Pivotal—Zibeling (IRE)
90 **SOLAR STAR (IRE),** b f Sea The Stars (IRE)—Solar Moon
91 **SORREL (IRE),** b br f Dansili—Anice Stellato (IRE)
92 **TAMAAS (IRE),** b f Iffraaj—Spiritual Air
93 **TANITA,** b f Frankel—Shoal
94 **TAWREED (USA),** ch f Speightstown (USA)—Hearty Laugh (USA)

SIR MICHAEL STOUTE - continued

95 THIBAAN (USA), b c War Front (USA)—Lahudood
96 TOUTATIS (USA), b g Karakontie (JPN)—Afleet Lass (USA)
97 VASARI (USA), b g Muhaarar—Honest Quality (USA)
98 VINDICATE, ch c Lope de Vega (IRE)—Aurore (IRE)
99 WOODHOUSE, b f Kingman—Danvina (IRE)

TWO-YEAR-OLDS

100 Ch c 19/02 Le Havre (IRE)—Al Jassasiyah (IRE) (Galileo (IRE))
101 B c 14/03 American Pharoah (USA)—Ann of The Dance (USA) (English Channel (USA)) (275297)
102 B c 30/04 Kingman—Applauded (IRE) (Royal Applause) (260000)
103 ATACAMA DESERT (IRE), ch c 05/06 Galileo (IRE)—Ikat (IRE) (Pivotal)
104 B c 26/01 Siyouni (FR)—Bal de La Rose (IRE) (Cadeaux Genereux) (450000)
105 B c 25/03 Camelot—Beach Frolic (Nayef (USA)) (300000)
106 CRYSTAL STARLET, b f 21/02 Frankel—Crystal Zvezda (Dubawi (IRE))
107 DEGREE, b f 16/02 Dubawi (IRE)—Echelon (Danehill (USA))
108 DIVINE HERALD, b f 02/04 Frankel—Heaven Sent (Pivotal)
109 Ch c 17/04 Gleneagles (IRE)—Fastnet Mist (IRE) (Fastnet Rock (AUS)) (240000)
110 FINAL WATCH, b g 10/05 Mukhadram—Watchoverme (Haafhd)
111 Ch f 18/02 Exceed And Excel (AUS)—Galileano (IRE) (Galileo (IRE))
112 B f 30/01 Zoffany (IRE)—Geisha Girl (IRE) (Galileo (IRE)) (200000)
113 GEOMETRIST, b f 11/03 Kingman—Hypoteneuse (IRE) (Sadler's Wells (USA))
114 B f 21/01 Camacho—Glamorous Air (IRE) (Air Express (IRE))
115 Ch c 10/02 New Approach (IRE)—Glenmayne (IRE) (Duke of Marmalade (IRE)) (105000)
116 B c 16/02 Shalaa (IRE)—Green Swallow (FR) (Green Tune (USA)) (130000)
117 B br f 09/05 American Pharoah (USA)—Grosse Pointe Anne (USA) (Silver Deputy (CAN))
118 HALIC, b c 21/05 Golden Horn—Pavlosk (USA) (Arch (USA))
119 B c 12/05 Air Force Blue (USA)—High Finance (IRE) (Entrepreneur)
120 B f 01/02 Shalaa (IRE)—Iltemas (USA) (Galileo (IRE))
121 INIGO JONES, b c 20/02 New Approach (IRE)—Spacious (Nayef (USA))
122 IRREPROACHABLE, b c 13/05 Frankel—Infallible (Pivotal)
123 JUST FINE (IRE), b c 10/02 Sea The Stars (IRE)—Bint Almatar (USA) (Kingmambo (USA))
124 Ch c 15/02 Iffraaj—Justice Belle (IRE) (Montjeu (IRE))
125 KING CAPELLA, b c 24/01 Kingman—Crystal Capella (Cape Cross (IRE))
126 B c 12/03 No Nay Never (USA)—Lady Soldier (IRE) (Erewhon (USA)) (325000)
127 B f 23/04 Gleneagles (IRE)—Like A Dame (Danehill (USA)) (400000)
128 B f 17/04 Frankel—Marine Bleue (IRE) (Desert Prince (IRE))
129 MAXIMAL, b c 03/03 Galileo (IRE)—Joyeuse (Oasis Dream)
130 MAYTAL, ch f 10/05 Sea The Stars (IRE)—Midsummer (Kingmambo (USA))
131 B f 07/04 Galileo (IRE)—Midday (Oasis Dream)
132 Ch f 15/02 Dubawi (IRE)—Muthabara (IRE) (Red Ransom (USA))
133 B c 09/05 Awtaad (IRE)—Nisriyna (IRE) (Intikhab (USA))
134 POSSIBLE MAN, b c 04/04 Le Havre (IRE)—Baldovina (Tale of The Cat (USA))
135 POTAPOVA, b f 21/05 Invincible Spirit (IRE)—Safina (Pivotal)
136 QUEEN'S FAIR, b f 16/04 Dansili—Queen's Best (King's Best (USA))
137 RED HOT MAMA, b f 19/03 Kingman—Hi Calypso (IRE) (In The Wings)
138 Ch f 20/04 Dubawi (IRE)—Rifqah (IRE) (Elusive Quality (USA))
139 B f 27/03 Muhaarar—Ripples Maid (Dansili)
140 Ch c 30/04 Speightstown (USA)—Rosalind (USA) (Broken Vow (USA)) (427827)
141 SAILOR (GER), b c 08/02 Sea The Moon (GER)—Sail (IRE) (Sadler's Wells (USA)) (95000)
142 Gr f 13/05 Dark Angel (IRE)—Samaah (IRE) (Cape Cross (IRE))
143 B c 20/03 Golden Horn—Samira Gold (FR) (Gold Away (FR)) (160000)
144 SATONO CHEVALIER (IRE), b c 22/02 Invincible Spirit (IRE)—Albisola (IRE) (Montjeu (IRE)) (386100)
145 SHOWLIANA, ch f 26/02 Showcasing—Russelliana (Medicean)
146 B c 23/01 Street Sense (USA)—Snapdragon (USA) (Super Saver (USA)) (326040)
147 Ch c 09/03 Lope de Vega (IRE)—Spirit of Xian (IRE) (Kodiac) (300000)
148 B c 23/05 Shamardal (USA)—Sundus (USA) (Sadler's Wells (USA))
149 SUNRISE VALLEY (USA), b f 06/03 Karakontie (JPN)—Story (USA) (War Front (USA))
150 B c 19/03 Kingman—Sunsemperchi (Montjeu (IRE)) (280000)
151 Ch f 01/04 Dawn Approach (IRE)—Tabassum (IRE) (Nayef (USA))

SIR MICHAEL STOUTE - continued

152 **THALER**, b c 02/03 Dubawi (IRE)—Timepiece (Zamindar (USA))
153 B c 04/04 Kingman—Toquette (IRE) (Acclamation) (380000)
154 **TRAILA**, ch c 23/02 Australia—Waila (Notnowcato)
155 **TUCSON CLOUD (IRE)**, b f 20/02 Fastnet Rock (AUS)—Transhumance (IRE) (Galileo (IRE))
156 Br gr c 14/03 Shalaa (IRE)—Vayasa (FR) (Zamindar (USA)) (110000)
157 B c 21/05 Awtaad (IRE)—Yanabeeaa (USA) (Street Cry (IRE))
158 **ZIKANY**, b c 11/04 Zoffany (IRE)—Rosika (Sakhee (USA))

Owners: Her Majesty The Queen, K. Abdullah, Hamdan bin Rashid Al Maktoum, Sheikh A. H. F. M. A. Al Sabah, Al Shaqab Racing UK Limited, Mr A. Alotaibi, Mr S. M. Bel Obaida, Cheveley Park Stud Limited, Flaxman Stables Ireland Ltd, Mrs Denis Haynes, Highclere T'bred Racing - Levison Wood, King Power Racing Co Ltd, Lady C. Laidlaw, Mr Philip Newton, Mr R. Ng, Niarchos Family, M. Obaida, Orchard Bloodstock Ltd, Qatar Racing, Miss K. Rausing, Satomi Horse Company Ltd, Miss J. Slack, Mr George Strawbridge, Mr S. Suhail, J. Wigan, Sir Evelyn de Rothschild.

SIR MICHAEL STOUTE - continued

---

512 | MRS ALI STRONGE, Eastbury
Postal: **Castle Piece Racing Stables, Eastbury, Hungerford, Berkshire, RG17 7JR**
Contacts: **PHONE 01488 72818 MOBILE 07779 285205 FAX 01488 670378**
EMAIL office@castlepiecestables.com WEBSITE www.castlepiecestables.com

1 **AMANTO (GER)**, 10, b g Medicean—Amore (GER) **Shaw Racing Partnership 2**
2 4, B g Poet's Voice—Amber Heights **The Jury's Out Partnership**
3 **ANNIE ODDS (IRE)**, 6, ch m Mahler—Taking My Time (IRE) **Pieces Of Eight Racing**
4 **ARDMAYLE (IRE)**, 8, ch g Whitmore's Conn (USA)—Welsh Connection (IRE) **The Wishful Thinkers**
5 **BALGEMMOIS (FR)**, 7, ch g Balko (FR)—Venise Doree (FR) **Marlborough Racing-(Balgemmois)**
6 **BLU CAVALIER**, 10, b g Kayf Tara—Blue Ride (IRE) **Pimlico Racing Partnerships I**
7 **BRICKLAGGER (IRE)**, 5, ch g Frozen Power (IRE)—Annaofcompton (IRE) **Mrs Linda Austin & Mr Dennis Coles**
8 **CAMAKASI (IRE)**, 9, b g Camacho—Innocence **Mrs A. J. Stronge**
9 **CHEZ CASTEL MAIL (FR)**, 8, ch g My Risk (FR)—Queenly Mail (FR) **The One and Only Partnership**
10 **DON'T CRY ABOUT IT (IRE)**, 5, ch g Casamento (IRE)—Back At de Front (IRE) **Mrs A. J. Stronge**
11 **DREWMAIN LEGEND**, 8, b m Midnight Legend—Ryders Hill **Hot To Trot Jumping & Mrs Jane Andrews**
12 **ESTRELA STAR (IRE)**, 4, ch g Casamento (IRE)—Reem Star **Mr James Burley & Mrs Ali Stronge**
13 **GETABUCK (IRE)**, 7, b g Getaway (GER)—Buck's Blue (FR) **Shawracing Partnership 2 & Miss. A. Hyde**
14 **GRANDAD'S LEGACY**, 4, b g Harbour Watch (IRE)—Vodka Shot (USA) **Ms J. Powell**
15 **HE'S OUR STAR (IRE)**, 5, b g Lord Shanakill (USA)—Afilla **Mrs S. R. Keable**
16 **HEPBURN**, 7, b m Sixties Icon—Mighty Splash **ROA Racing Partnership**
17 **HERESMYNUMBER (IRE)**, 10, b g Kalanisi (IRE)—Broken Rein (IRE) **Kings Of The Castle**
18 **I LIKE HIM (FR)**, 4, gr g Gris de Gris (IRE)—Upside Down Cake **P Whitehead, C Spencer Herbert, S Keable**
19 **ILLUSTRIOUS SPIRIT**, 5, b g Swiss Spirit—Darling Daisy **Mrs P. A. Scott-Dunn**
20 5, B g Arcadio (GER)—Inch Rose (IRE)
21 **JALINGO (IRE)**, 9, b g Cape Cross (IRE)—Just Special **Paul Whitehead & Clare Spencer-Herbert**
22 **NAVAJO WAR DANCE**, 7, br g Makfi—Navajo Rainbow **Mrs A. J. Stronge**
23 **RENARDEAU**, 4, b g Foxwedge (AUS)—La Cucina (IRE) **Mr L. A. Bellman**
24 **SCORPION HAZE (IRE)**, 7, b g Scorpion (IRE)—Sea Maiden (IRE) **Shaw Racing Partnership 2**
25 **SHIROCCO SUNFLOWER**, 5, ch m Shirocco (GER)—Fleur de Nikos (FR) **Wellington Thoroughbred Racing 1**
26 **SIR CANFORD (IRE)**, 4, b g Canford Cliffs (IRE)—Alexander Divine **The Select Racing Club Limited**
27 **SIR DENNIS**, 4, b c Dunaden (FR)—Double Green (IRE) **Miss A. B. Hyde**
28 **STAR OF ATHENA**, 5, b m Champs Elysees—Aswaaq (IRE) **Tim Dykes & Hugh Doubtfire**
29 **STORM MELODY**, 7, b g Royal Applause—Plume **Shaw Racing Partnership 2**
30 4, B g Olympic Glory (IRE)—Tunkwa (FR) **Mrs A. J. Stronge**
31 **ZAYRIYAN (IRE)**, 5, ch g Shamardal (USA)—Zariyna (IRE) **Friends Of Castle Piece**
32 **ZOFFANY BAY (IRE)**, 6, b g Zoffany (IRE)—Trois Graces (USA) **Mrs Margaret Kidger & Mr Geoffrey Bishop**

THREE-YEAR-OLDS

33 **AL VERDE**, ch g Al Kazeem—Greenery (IRE) **Larkhills & Shaw Racing 2**

MRS ALI STRONGE - continued

34 **CASTLETROY (IRE)**, b g Famous Name—Gilah (IRE) **The Castletroy Partnership**
35 **HANNALITE**, ch f Nathaniel (IRE)—Bravia **Mr L. A. Bellman**
37 **ROS'S DREAM**, b f Cityscape—Bella's Charm **Mrs V. M. Bayliffe**

TWO-YEAR-OLDS

38 Ch c 08/05 Helmet (AUS)—Catbells (IRE) (Rakti) (15000)
39 Gr c 23/03 Kendargent (FR)—Clara Luna (IRE) (Muhtathir) (16000)
40 Ch c 15/01 Al Kazeem—Go Between (Daggers Drawn) (USA)) (8580)
41 B c 19/03 Due Diligence (USA)—
  Nellie Ellis (IRE) (Compton Place) (11428) **Mr Tim Dykes & Hope Eden Racing Ltd**

Other Owners: Mrs J. Andrews, Mrs L. L. Austin, Mr N. Barnett, Mr G. S. Bishop, G Bishop, I Kidger & A Kirkland, Mr J. Burley, Buscott Racing, Mr D. L. Coles, Mr J. R. Corsan, Mr H. G. Doubtfire, Mr T. J. Dykes, Mrs S. Evans, Hope Eden Racing Limited, Mr R. S. Hoskins, Hot To Trot Jumping, Miss A. B. Hyde, Mrs S. R. Keable, Mr I. Kidger, Mrs M. Kidger, Dr A. I. Kirkland, Larkhills Racing Partnership, Ms J. Powell, G. C. Pratt, Shaw Racing Partnership 2, Ms A. M. Simmons, Ms C. L. Spencer-Herbert, Mrs A. J. Stronge, T. E. Vaughan, Mr P. Whitehead.

Assistant Trainer: Sam Stronge.

---

513 **MRS LINDA STUBBS, Malton**
Postal: **Beverley House Stables, Beverley Road, Malton, North Yorkshire, YO17 9PJ**
Contacts: **HOME 01653 698731**
EMAIL l.stubbs@btconnect.com

1 **BRONZE BEAU**, 13, ch g Compton Place—Bella Cantata **Miss K. Stubbs**
2 **CASIET**, 4, b g Iffraaj—Caskelena (IRE) **Mrs B. J. Sands**
3 **FIRST RESPONSE**, 5, b g First Defence (USA)—Promising Lead **D.M.Smith, P.G.Shorrock & L.Stubbs**
4 **MR BUTTONS (IRE)**, 4, b g Elzaam (AUS)—Clann Force **P.G.Shorrock & Verona Racing**
5 **STARLIGHT ROMANCE (IRE)**, 6, b m Excelebration (IRE)—Takizada (IRE) **Mr D. M. Smith**

Other Owners: Mr P. G. Shorrock, Mr D. M. Smith, Mrs L. Stubbs, Verona Racing.

---

514 **MR ROB SUMMERS, Solihull**
Postal: **Summerhill Cottage, Danzey Green, Tanworth-in-Arden, Solihull**
Contacts: **PHONE 01564 742667 MOBILE 07775 898327**

1 **ATLANTIC STORM (IRE)**, 8, b g September Storm (GER)—Double Dream (IRE) **Mr A. R. Price**
2 **EPSOM DAY (IRE)**, 7, b g Teofilo (IRE)—Dubai Flower **Mrs G. M. Summers**
3 **SECRET BERI**, 6, ch m Schiaparelli (GER)—Secret Whisper **Mrs G. M. Summers**
4 **ST MERRYN (IRE)**, 9, b g Oscar (IRE)—Kigali (IRE) **Mrs G. M. Summers**

Assistant Trainer: Mrs G. M. Summers.

---

515 **MR TOM SYMONDS, Hentland**
Postal: **Dason Court Cottage, Hentland, Ross-On-Wye, Herefordshire, HR9 6LW**
Contacts: **PHONE 01989 730869 MOBILE 07823 324649**
EMAIL dasoncourt@gmail.com WEBSITE www.thomassymonds.co.uk

1 **ASK CATKIN (IRE)**, 8, b m Ask—Simple Reason (IRE) **Mrs C. M. Antcliff**
2 **BOBO MAC (IRE)**, 9, gr g Whitmore's Conn (USA)—Blazing Love (IRE) **C & M Baker, K Ibberson, H Pearman**
3 **BRUSHED UP**, 7, b m Doyen (IRE)—Definite Artist (IRE) **The Mumbo Jumbos**
4 **EATON MILLER (IRE)**, 8, b g Milan—Four Fields (IRE) **Mr K. J. Price**
5 **EST ILLIC (IRE)**, 6, b br g Court Cave (IRE)—Ten Friends (IRE) **Mr F Green & Mr J Chinn**

MR TOM SYMONDS - continued

6 **EVERYTHING NOW (IRE)**, 6, b g Gold Well—Givehertime (IRE) **Mr T. R. Symonds**
7 **FAZAYTE (FR)**, 5, b g Spider Flight (FR)—Vakina (FR) **Mrs C. M. Antcliff**
8 **FIL D'ARIANE (FR)**, 5, b g Gris de Gris (IRE)—Vibraye (FR) **Sir Peter & Lady Gibbings**
9 **FLEURSALS**, 4, b f Poet's Voice—Entitlement **Mr T. R. Symonds, Mr S. Davies**
10 **FRANKLY SPEAKING**, 10, ch g Flemensfirth (USA)—No More Money **David Jenks & Celia & Michael Baker**
11 **HOLLYWOODIEN (FR)**, 9, gr g Martaline—Incorrigible (FR) **Sir Peter & Lady Gibbings**
12 **KAKI DE LA PREE (FR)**, 13, b g Kapgarde (FR)—Kica (FR) **Mr T. R. Symonds**
13 **LEGENDARY RHYTHM**, 4, b f Midnight Legend—Hot Rhythm **Mr D. J. Clark**
14 **LLANDINABO LAD**, 5, ch g Malinas (GER)—Hot Rhythm **Celia & Michael Baker**
15 **LLANTARA**, 9, b m Kayf Tara—Lady Llancillo (IRE) **Bailey-Carvill Equine**
16 **LOUD AS LIONS (IRE)**, 7, b g Flemensfirth (USA)—Misspublican (IRE) **C & M Baker, K Ibberson, H Pearman**
17 **LUGG RIVER**, 6, b m Kayf Tara—Supreme Gem (IRE) **Frank Green & Mike Roberts**
18 **METEORITE**, 6, b g Bollin Eric—Running Hotter **Matthew Engel & David Clark**
19 **PRESENTEDWITHWINGS (IRE)**, 6, br g Presenting—Rosa Rugosa (IRE) **Mr S. Davies**
20 **RHIAN DE SIVOLA**, 4, b f Kayf Tara—R de Rien Sivola (FR) **Mr S. Davies**
21 **RIVER ARROW**, 9, b m Kayf Tara—Supreme Gem (IRE) **Frank Green & Mike Roberts**
22 **ROYAL CLARET**, 8, b m Yeats (IRE)—Kerada (FR) **The Nigel Jones & Roy Ovel Syndicate**
23 **SAINT DE VASSY (FR)**, 7, br g Saint des Saints (FR)—
Mona Vassy (FR) **Jakeman,Booth,Lanchbury,Mason,Hewlett**
24 **SIXTY'S BELLE**, 6, b m Gold Well—Over Sixty **Mr S. Davies**
25 **SONG FOR SOMEONE (GER)**, 5, ch g Medicean—Sweni Hill (IRE) **Sir Peter & Lady Gibbings**
26 **STRIKE HOLLOW**, 7, ch m Beat Hollow—Tazzarine (FR) **Bailey-Carvill Equine**

Other Owners: Mr D. J. Clark, Mr T. R. Symonds.

---

516 **MR JAMES TATE, Newmarket**
Postal: **Jamesfield Place, Hamilton Road, Newmarket, Suffolk, CB8 7JQ**
Contacts: PHONE **01638 669861** MOBILE **07703 601283** FAX **01638 676634**
EMAIL **james@jamestateracing.com** WEBSITE **www.jamestateracing.com**

1 **ALNASHERAT**, 4, b c Kingman—Split Trois (FR) **S. Manana**
2 **FAR ABOVE (IRE)**, 4, b c Farhh—Dorraar (IRE) **Sheikh R. D. Al Maktoum**
3 **HEY GAMAN**, 5, b br h New Approach (IRE)—Arsaadi (IRE) **S. Ali**
4 **NEW GRADUATE (IRE)**, 5, ch h New Approach (IRE)—Srda (USA) **S. Manana**
5 **SAMEEM (IRE)**, 4, b g New Approach (IRE)—Ahla Wasahl **S. Ali**
6 **SHIMMERING DAWN (IRE)**, 4, b f Morpheus—Subtle Shimmer **Sheikh J. D. Al Maktoum**
7 **TOP RANK (IRE)**, 4, gr c Dark Angel (IRE)—Countess Ferrama **S. Manana**
8 **WISE WORDS**, 4, b f Sepoy (AUS)—Akhmatova **Sheikh R. D. Al Maktoum**

THREE-YEAR-OLDS

9 **AIM FOR THE STARS**, b f Muhaarar—Bright Approach (IRE) **S. Manana**
10 **BIG IMPRESSION**, b c Dubawi (IRE)—Nashmiah (IRE) **S. Manana**
11 **BILINGUAL**, b f Le Havre (IRE)—Downhill Dancer (IRE) **S. Manana**
12 **BLAZING HOT**, ch c New Streak (IRE)—A Great Beauty **Sheikh R. D. Al Maktoum**
13 **CLAUDIUS SECUNDUS (IRE)**, br c Holy Roman Emperor (IRE)—Tasha's Dream (USA) **S. Manana**
14 **COURT OF APPEAL (IRE)**, b c Golden Horn—Gwael (USA) **S. Manana**
15 **CROWN COURT (IRE)**, b f Lawman (FR)—Greatest Place (IRE) **S. Manana**
16 **DESERT ECLIPSE**, b c Muhaarar—Rainbow Desert (USA) **Saif Ali & Saeed H. Altayer**
17 **DISTANT THUNDER (IRE)**, b f Night of Thunder (IRE)—Mathanora (IRE) **S. Manana**
18 **DREAM SHOT (IRE)**, b br c Dream Ahead (USA)—Miss Buckshot (IRE) **S. Manana**
19 **DRIVING FORCE**, b c Sir Percy—Hanzada (USA) **S. Manana**
20 **ELEVATED (IRE)**, b c Siyouni (FR)—Kahira (IRE) **S. Manana**
21 **GARDEN PARADISE (IRE)**, b f Night of Thunder (IRE)—Coral Garden **S. Manana**
22 **HIGH ACCOLADE (IRE)**, gr c Outstrip—Honeymead (IRE) **S. Manana**
23 **HOT TO HANDLE (IRE)**, ch c Hot Streak (IRE)—Royal Sister Two (IRE) **S. Ali**
24 **INEXPLICABLE (IRE)**, b gr c Dark Angel (IRE)—Bikini Babe (IRE) **S. Manana**
25 **LINE OF ENQUIRY**, b c New Approach (IRE)—Cadenza (FR) **S. Manana**

MR JAMES TATE - continued

26 **LORD OF THE SKY,** b c Dansili—Cloud Castle **S. Manana**
27 **LYRICAL BEAUTY (IRE),** b f No Nay Never (USA)—Virginia Celeste (IRE) **S. Manana**
28 **MAGICAL JOURNEY (IRE),** ch f Night of Thunder (IRE)—Aljaazya (USA) **S. Manana**
29 **MEDIA STORM,** b c Night of Thunder (IRE)—Raskutani **S. Manana**
30 **MELODIC CHARM (IRE),** ch f Exceed And Excel (AUS)—Folk Melody (IRE) **S. Manana**
31 **MILLICENT,** b f Iffraaj—Marmalade Cat **S. Manana**
32 **NASAIYM (USA),** b f More Than Ready (USA)—Beyond Our Reach (IRE) **Sheikh J. D. Al Maktoum**
33 **NEW ARRIVAL (IRE),** gr f Gutaifan (IRE)—Doula (USA) **S. Manana**
34 **NIGHT APPROACHING (IRE),** b f New Approach (IRE)—Cape of Night (IRE) **S. Ali**
35 **NIGHT VOYAGER (IRE),** b c Dandy Man (IRE)—Journey's End (IRE) **S. Manana**
36 **OPENING NIGHT (IRE),** ch f Night of Thunder (IRE)—Varsity **S. Manana**
37 **PIVOTAL DECISION,** ch f Pivotal—Crinoline (USA) **S. Manana**
38 **RELAUNCH (IRE),** ch c Night of Thunder (IRE)—Doors To Manual (USA) **S. Manana**
39 **SCHOOL OF THOUGHT,** ch c Sir Percy—Lady Sylvia **S. Manana**
40 **SKY COMMANDER (IRE),** b c War Command (USA)—Queen of Skies (IRE) **S. Manana**
41 **SO SHARP,** b f Bated Breath—Theladyinquestion **Sheikh R. D. Al Maktoum**
42 **STATELY HOME (IRE),** gr c Clodovil (IRE)—Lady Spangles (IRE) **S. Manana**
43 **SUPREME RULE (IRE),** b c Shamardal (USA)—Saltanat (IRE) **S. Manana**
44 **TRANSCRIPT,** b f Night of Thunder (IRE)—Storyland (USA) **S. Manana**
45 **TURN OF PHRASE,** ch f Kitten's Joy (USA)—Gotcha Good (USA) **S. Manana**
46 **UNDER THE STARS (IRE),** b f Night of Thunder (IRE)—Jumeirah Palm Star **S. Manana**
47 **WITH VIRTUE,** b f Iffraaj—Lalectra **S. Manana**
48 **ZAWALAH (IRE),** b f Sea The Stars (IRE)—Quixada (GER) **S. Manana**

TWO-YEAR-OLDS

49 B c 07/03 New Approach (IRE)—Al Baidaa (Exceed And Excel (AUS)) (37000) **S. Ali**
50 B c 04/01 Dark Angel (IRE)—Ambiguous (Kheleyf (USA)) **Sheikh R. D. Al Maktoum**
51 Ch c 26/04 Bobby's Kitten (USA)—Amelia May (Dansili) (21000) **S. Manana**
52 B f 21/01 Dawn Approach (IRE)—Beyond Intensity (IRE) (Intense Focus (USA)) (55000) **S. Manana**
53 Ch f 23/03 Gleneagles (IRE)—Blue Geranium (IRE) (Dansili) (32000) **S. Manana**
54 B f 18/03 Camacho—Boucheron (Galileo (IRE)) (32000) **S. Manana**
55 B f 30/04 Dandy Man (IRE)—Bronte Sister (IRE) (Acclamation) (47619) **S. Manana**
56 B c 01/03 Dawn Approach (IRE)—Brown Diamond (IRE) (Fastnet Rock (AUS)) (42000) **S. Manana**
57 **CASTING SHADOWS,** b f 29/03 Twilight Son—Ziggy Zaggy (Diktat) (7500) **S. Manana**
58 B f 06/04 Holy Roman Emperor (IRE)—Chantilly Cream (IRE) (Acclamation) (36000) **S. Manana**
59 B c 05/03 Gleneagles (IRE)—Cherrington (IRE) (Lope de Vega (IRE)) (50000) **Sheikh J. D. Al Maktoum**
60 B c 09/02 Twilight Son—Crinkle (IRE) (Distant Relative) (81509) **S. Manana**
61 **ENCHANTED NIGHT,** ch f 09/02 Night of Thunder (IRE)—Khaseeb (Dutch Art) (37000) **S. Manana**
62 B c 08/02 Acclamation—Excelette (IRE) (Exceed And Excel (AUS)) (150000) **Mr H. Dalmook Al Maktoum**
63 B c 12/03 New Approach (IRE)—Fashionable Spirit (IRE) (Invincible Spirit (IRE)) (50000) **S. Manana**
64 **FINAL VOYAGE,** b c 13/03 Camacho—Shamayel (Pivotal) (64349) **S. Manana**
65 B f 25/02 Awtaad (IRE)—Fluvial (IRE) (Exceed And Excel (AUS)) (41183) **Sheikh R. D. Al Maktoum**
66 B f 19/03 Awtaad (IRE)—Full Moon Fever (IRE) (Azamour (IRE)) (32000) **S. Manana**
67 B br f 13/01 Sea The Stars (IRE)—Galactic Heroine (Galileo (IRE)) (50000) **S. Manana**
68 **GLOBAL VISION (IRE),** gr gr c 22/04 Markaz (IRE)—
  Vision of Peace (IRE) (Invincible Spirit (IRE)) (40000) **S. Manana**
69 Ch f 12/04 Le Havre (IRE)—Gold Sands (IRE) (Cape Cross (IRE)) (50000) **S. Manana**
70 **HEADLINER (IRE),** b f 12/02 The Last Lion (IRE)—Countess Ferrama (Authorized (IRE)) (66923) **S. Manana**
71 Ch c 31/03 Helmet (AUS)—Hometime (Dubai Destination (USA)) (37000) **S. Manana**
72 B c 27/03 Iffraaj—I'm Yours (Invincible Spirit (IRE)) (60000) **S. Manana**
73 Ch f 04/03 Dutch Art—Infatuation (Invincible Spirit (IRE)) (64349) **Sheikh J. D. Al Maktoum**
74 **INFINITE BEAUTY (IRE),** gr ro f 07/02 Dark Angel (IRE)—Natural Beauty (Oasis Dream) (70000) **S. Manana**
75 Ch c 18/04 Night of Thunder (IRE)—Jameela's Dream (Nayef (USA)) (68640) **Mr H. Dalmook Al Maktoum**
76 Ch c 03/04 Helmet (AUS)—Jubilant Queen (Kyllachy) (40000) **S. Manana**
77 Gr f 10/04 Dark Angel (IRE)—Lady Duxyana (Most Welcome) (30476) **Sheikh J. D. Al Maktoum**
78 Ch f 21/03 Night of Thunder (IRE)—Lady Vyrnwy (IRE) (Bertolini (USA)) (33333) **S. Manana**
79 B f 20/01 Zoffany (IRE)—Laureldean Spirit (IRE) (Whipper (USA)) (15000) **S. Manana**
80 B f 01/05 The Gurkha (IRE)—Louve des Reves (IRE) (Sadler's Wells (USA)) (25000) **Mr A. H. M. A. Salman**
81 B c 06/05 Iffraaj—Ninas Rainbow (Rainbow Quest (USA)) (55000) **Mr H. Dalmook Al Maktoum**

MR JAMES TATE - continued

82 B f 26/02 Zoffany (IRE)—Novalina (IRE) (Galileo (IRE)) (27000) **S. Manana**
83 Ch f 08/04 Night of Thunder (IRE)—Orange Pip (Bold Edge) (38609) **S. Manana**
84 **PEARL OF WISDOM (IRE)**, ch f 24/02 New Approach (IRE)—
 Notion of Beauty (USA) (Harlan's Holiday (USA)) (8000) **S. Manana**
85 B f 26/04 Camelot—Penny Post (IRE) (Green Desert (USA)) (55769) **S. Manana**
86 **PIVOTAL MOMENT**, b f 07/05 Pivotal—Chantry (Galileo (IRE)) (35000) **S. Manana**
87 **PUBLICIST**, b f 06/02 Dark Angel (IRE)—Diary (IRE) (Green Desert (USA)) (100000) **S. Manana**
88 Ch f 17/03 Sepoy (AUS)—Queen's Novel (King's Best (USA)) (6500) **S. Manana**
89 B c 14/02 Zoffany (IRE)—Rain Flower (IRE) (Indian Ridge) (30000) **S. Manana**
90 B f 27/01 Iffraaj—Rebecca de Winter (Kyllachy) (25000) **S. Manana**
91 Gr f 10/02 Mastercraftsman (IRE)—Rhiannon (IRE) (High Chaparral (IRE)) (25740) **S. Manana**
92 B f 09/02 Mehmas (IRE)—Scarlet Pimpernel (Sir Percy) (34000) **S. Manana**
93 **SHOW YOURSELF**, b f 01/05 Acclamation—Dare To Dream (Exceed And Excel (AUS)) (100000) **S. Manana**
94 Ch c 07/03 Sepoy (AUS)—Sloane Square (Teofilo (IRE)) (5000) **S. Manana**
95 **SPECIAL EFFECTS (IRE)**, b c 20/04 Dark Angel (IRE)—
 Danseuse de Reve (IRE) (Invincible Spirit (IRE)) (55769) **S. Manana**
96 B f 28/02 Free Eagle (IRE)—Starletina (IRE) (Sea The Stars (IRE)) (20000) **S. Manana**
97 B f 04/04 Oasis Dream—Taaqah (USA) (Arch (USA)) (22000) **Sheikh J. D. Al Maktoum**
98 C b 18/05 Territories (IRE)—Terentia (Diktat) (45000) **Sheikh J. D. Al Maktoum**
99 B f 31/03 Fountain of Youth (IRE)—Wether Girl (Major Cadeaux) (4000) **S. Manana**
100 **WORLDS APART (IRE)**, b f 26/02 New Bay—Oriental Magic (GER) (Doyen (IRE)) (40000) **S. Manana**
101 B c 12/04 Siyouni (FR)—Zibeling (IRE) (Cape Cross (IRE)) (20000) **S. Manana**

Assistant Trainer: Mrs Lucinda Tate.

---

517 MR TOM TATE, Tadcaster
Postal: **Castle Farm, Hazelwood, Tadcaster, North Yorkshire, LS24 9NJ**
Contacts: **PHONE 01937 836036 MOBILE 07970 122818**
EMAIL **tomtate@zen.co.uk** WEBSITE **www.tomtate.co.uk**

1 **AWAKE MY SOUL (IRE)**, 11, ch g Teofilo (IRE)—Field of Hope (IRE) **T T Racing**
2 **BAYRAAT**, 4, b g Heeraat (IRE)—Baymist **T T Racing**
3 **DESTROYER**, 7, b g Royal Applause—Good Girl (IRE) **T T Racing**
4 **EQUIANO SPRINGS**, 6, b g Equiano (FR)—Spring Clean (FR) **T T Racing**
5 **FAIR ALIBI**, 4, b g Paco Boy (IRE)—Alybgood (CAN) **T T Racing**
6 **FIRST DANCE (IRE)**, 6, b m Cape Cross (IRE)—Happy Wedding (IRE) **T T Racing**
7 **GROUPIE**, 6, b m Requinto (IRE)—Amour Fou (IRE) **T T Racing**
8 **LUCY'S LAW (IRE)**, 6, b m Lawman (FR)—Lucy Limelites **Ms Fionnuala Cassidy & Mr T. P. Tate**
9 **RIVER GLADES**, 5, b g Cape Cross (IRE)—Everglades **The Ivy Syndicate**
10 **YOUNG TIGER**, 7, b g Captain Gerrard (IRE)—Blades Princess **T T Racing**

THREE-YEAR-OLDS

11 B g Night of Thunder (IRE)—Regal Hawk **T T Racing**

TWO-YEAR-OLDS

12 B c 17/03 Poet's Voice—Certral (Iffraaj) (761)
13 B c 15/04 Twilight Son—Riccoche (IRE) (Oasis Dream) (21000)

Other Owners: Ms M. F. Cassidy, D. M. W. Hodgkiss, Mrs S. A. Hodgkiss, T. P. Tate.

Assistant Trainer: Hazel Tate.

Flat Jockey: Andrew Mullen, James Sullivan.

518 MR ROGER TEAL, Hungerford
Postal: Windsor House Stables, Crowle Road, Lambourn, Hungerford, Berkshire, RG17 8NR
Contacts: PHONE 01488 491623 MOBILE 07710 325521
EMAIL info@rogertealracing.com WEBSITE www.rogertealracing.co.uk

1 **AGINCOURT REEF (IRE)**, 11, b g Gold Well—Hillside Native (IRE) **Mrs S. M. Teal**
2 **ARANS CHOICE (IRE)**, 7, b m Scorpion (IRE)—Miss Greylands **The Rat Racers**
3 **BEAR FORCE ONE**, 4, b g Swiss Spirit—Shesha Bear **Joe Bear Racing**
4 **CHANTECLER**, 9, b g Authorized (IRE)—Snow Goose **David White & Dean Gibbs**
5 **CINZENTO (IRE)**, 4, gr g Lawman (FR)—Silver Samba **Mr & Mrs G. Bhatti**
6 **EPIC ADVENTURE (FR)**, 5, ch g Shamalgan (FR)—Larafale (FR) **Withyslade**
7 **FITWOOD STAR**, 4, b g Archipenko (USA)—Sasheen **Calne Engineering Ltd**
8 **JONNIGRAIG (IRE)**, 7, b g Masterofthehorse (IRE)—Vanudski (IRE) **Mrs S. M. Teal**
9 **KYLLACHYS TALE (IRE)**, 6, b m Kyllachy—Betray **Barry Kitcherside & Darren Waterer**
10 **LAWYERSGUNSN'MONEY**, 5, gr g Indian Haven—Non Disclosure (IRE) **Starting Gate Racing**
11 **LOOK SURPRISED**, 7, ch m Kier Park (IRE)—Crystal **Starting Gate Racing**
12 **LUCKY LOUIE**, 7, ch g Dutch Art—Ardessie **Great Shefford Racing**
13 **MASTER SAM BELLAMY**, 7, b g Black Sam Bellamy (IRE)—Mistress Nell **Hamilton Hallows Racing**
14 **OCEAN WIND**, 4, b c Teofilo (IRE)—Chan Tong (BRZ) **Rockingham Reins Limited**
15 **OXTED**, 4, b g Mayson—Charlotte Rosina **S. Piper, T. Hirschfeld & D. Fish**
16 **ROCK ICON**, 7, b g Sixties Icon—Monashee Rock (IRE) **Mr M. J. Goggin**
17 **ROSIE ROYALE (IRE)**, 8, gr m Verglas (IRE)—Fearn Royal (IRE) **Idle B's & Sue Teal**
18 **SCOOBY (IRE)**, 9, b g Dubai Destination (USA)—Maggie Howard (IRE) **Mrs S. M. Teal**
19 **SHAKE ME HANDY**, 5, gr g Eastern Anthem (IRE)—Cloridja **Starting Gate Racing**
20 **SPIRIT OF MAY**, 4, ch g Coach House (IRE)—Bengers Lass (USA) **Mrs C. A. Borras**
21 **STONEMADFORSPEED (IRE)**, 12, b g Fruits of Love (USA)—Diamond Forever **Mr R. A. Teal**
22 **SWISS PRIDE (IRE)**, 4, b g Swiss Spirit—Encore Encore (FR) **Mr M. J. Goggin**
23 **TAUREAN DANCER (IRE)**, 5, b g Intello (GER)—Traou Mad (IRE) **C. B. Goodyear**
24 **TIP TWO WIN**, 5, gr h Dark Angel (IRE)—Freddie's Girl (USA) **Mrs A. Cowley**
25 **WHELANS WAY**, 4, b g Requinto (IRE)—Lupine (IRE) **Mr Austin Whelan**

THREE-YEAR-OLDS

26 **BOCKOS AMBER (IRE)**, ch f Kyllachy—Goldcrest **Mr R. A. Teal**
27 **GERT LUSH (IRE)**, b f Bated Breath—Agent Allison **Mrs Muriel Forward & Dr G C Forward**
28 **KENZAI WARRIOR (USA)**, b br c Karakontie (JPN)—Lemon Sakhee (CAN) **Rae & Carol Borras**
29 **KING LEWLEW**, b g Swiss Spirit—Aura **Mr M. J. Goggin**
30 **MARION'S BOY (IRE)**, ch c Mastercraftsman (IRE)—Freddie's Girl (USA) **Mrs A. Cowley**
31 **ROCKING REG (IRE)**, gr c Gutaifan (IRE)—Princess of Troy (IRE) **Mr T. J. Smith**
32 **ROCKINGHAM JILL**, b f Cable Bay (IRE)—Bubbly Ballerina **Rockingham Reins Limited**
33 B f Due Diligence (USA)—Shesha Bear **Joe Bear Racing**

TWO-YEAR-OLDS

34 B c 10/02 Mayson—Charlotte Rosina (Choisir (AUS))
35 **DANCING MASTER (IRE)**, br gr c 09/02 Mastercraftsman (IRE)—Poisson d'Or (Cape Cross (IRE)) **Fishdance Ltd**
36 **FITTLETON FERRY**, br f 30/03 Equiano (FR)—Sasheen (Zafeen (FR)) **Sasheen Partnership**
37 **GURKHA GIRL (IRE)**, b f 30/04 The Gurkha (IRE)—Freddie's Girl (USA) (More Than Ready (USA)) **Mrs A. Cowley**

Other Owners: Mrs C. J. Bhatti, Mr G. Bhatti, A. J. Chambers, Fishdance Ltd, Dr G. C. Forward, Mrs M. E. Forward, Mr D. Gibbs, Homecroft Wealth Racing, Mrs H. I. Jinks, B. Kitcherside, Mr R. B. Kolien, Mr B. Pettis, Mr S. J. Piper, Mr M. A. Ransom, Mr S. M. Ransom, Scuderia Vita Bella, Mr R. A. Teal, Mrs S. M. Teal, The Idle B'S, Mr D. G. Waterer, Mr D. White.

Assistant Trainer: Harry Teal.

519 MR SAM THOMAS, Cardiff
Postal: **Crossways, St Mellons Road, Lisvane, Cardiff, South Glamorgan, CF14 0SH**
Contacts: **PHONE 07929 101751**
EMAIL samthomasracing@outlook.com, emma@samthomasracing.com WEBSITE www.
samthomasracing.com

1 CHERUBIN DE PAIL (FR), 5, b g Blue Bresil (FR)—Peremption (FR) **Walters Plant Hire & Potter Group**
2 COAL STOCK (IRE), 5, ch g Red Jazz (USA)—Scar Tissue **Walters Plant Hire Ltd Egan Waste Ltd**
3 FALBERTO (FR), 5, b g Alberto Giacometti (IRE)—Valrina (FR) **Walters Plant Hire Ltd**
4 GLENTROOL, 7, b g Passing Glance—Killala Bay (IRE) **Mr S. C. Appelbee**
5 GOOD RISK AT ALL (FR), 4, ch g No Risk At All (FR)—Sissi Land (FR)
6 IVY'S SHADOW (IRE), 5, b m Jammaal—Red Chili (IRE) **Mr W. D. Morris**
7 IWILLDOIT, 7, b g Flying Legend (USA)—Lyricist's Dream **Diamond Racing Ltd**
8 JAZZ KING (FR), 4, gr g Kapgarde (FR)—Jaragua (FR)
9 KALA NOIRE (FR), 6, b g Kalanisi (IRE)—Lady Taipan (IRE) **Mr & Mrs Capper, Mr Trolan & Mr Stovin**
10 LA REINE POUTINE (FR), 5, b m Kapgarde (FR)—Miss Poutine (FR) **Walters Plant Hire & Potter Group**
11 MARIO DE PAIL (FR), 5, gr g Blue Bresil (FR)—Sauveterre (FR) **Walters Plant Hire & Potter Group**
12 MARVELLOUS MARVEL (FR), 4, b br g Masked Marvel—Miss Rodeo (FR) **Walters Plant Hire Ltd**
13 MEGA MIND (IRE), 7, ch g Captain Rio—Final Leave (IRE) **Mr S. J. Thomas**
14 MICK MANHATTAN (FR), 6, b g Blue Bresil (FR)—Normanville (IRE) **Walters Plant Hire Ltd**
15 NEW MOON (FR), 6, b g Kapgarde (FR)—Not Lost (FR) **Walters Plant Hire & Potter Group**
16 NOT A ROLE MODEL (IRE), 8, b g Helissio (FR)—Mille Et Une Nuits (FR) **St Mamadasado**
17 POWERSTOWN PARK (IRE), 7, b g Craigsteel—Smiths Lady (IRE) **The Ipsden Invincibles**
18 ROCKINGHAM SOUTH, 4, b g Kayf Tara—Safari Run (IRE)
19 ROYAL MAGIC (IRE), 8, b g Whitmore's Conn (USA)—Room To Room Magic (IRE) **Luke Harvey Racing Club**
20 SLIP ROAD (IRE), 5, gr g Shantou (USA)—Agladora (FR)
21 SPONTHUS (FR), 5, b g Alianthus (GER)—Pavane du Kalon (FR) **Walters Plant Hire Ltd**
22 SWEDISHHORSEMAFIA (IRE), 5, b g Shantou (USA)—Carrigmoorna Style (IRE) **Mr S. J. Thomas**
23 THE CANNISTER MAN (IRE), 8, b g Arakan (USA)—Ladyrosaro (IRE) **Keith Ali & Eamon Murchan**
24 TORHOUSEMUIR, 9, b g Sagamix (FR)—Royal Musical **Honourable Scoundrels**
25 WHISPER (FR), 12, b g Astarabad (USA)—Belle Yepa (FR) **Walters Plant Hire Ltd**
26 WORD TO THE WISE (FR), 4, gr f Montmartre (FR)—Rosewater (GER)

THREE-YEAR-OLDS
27 AMAZING TANGO (GER), b g Tai Chi (GER)—Amazing Model (GER) **Walters Plant Hire Ltd**
28 B g Fame And Glory—Gales Present (IRE) **Walters Plant Hire Ltd**
29 B g Pether's Moon—Henri Bella **Walters Plant Hire Ltd**
30 HURRICANE DEAL (FR), gr g Hurricane Cat (USA)—Diluvienne (FR)
31 JUBILEE EXPRESS (FR), b g No Risk At All (FR)—Bella Lawena (IRE)
32 NEXT ONE PLEASE (FR), gr g Cima de Triomphe (IRE)—Next More (GER)
33 NO RISK NO FUN (FR), b g No Risk At All (FR)—Incorrigible (FR)
34 PRINCE DES FICHAUX (FR), b c No Risk At All (FR)—Princesse Kap (FR) **Walters Plant Hire Ltd**
35 SHOMEN UCHI (FR), b g Great Pretender (IRE)—Vavea (FR)
36 B g Blue Bresil (FR)—Tara Potter **Walters Plant Hire Ltd**

TWO-YEAR-OLDS
37 B f 16/04 Norse Dancer (IRE)—Another Kate (IRE) (Norwich)
38 B f 09/04 Universal (IRE)—Haidees Reflection (Byron)

Other Owners: Mr K. Ali, Mrs P. L. Capper, Egan Waste Services Ltd, Mr C. Haslam, Mr A. P. G. Holmes, Mr T. L. Llewellyn, Mr E. Murchan, Mrs J. C. Noel, Mr W. D. Stovin, Sundorne Products (Llanidloes) Ltd, Mr S. J. Thomas, Mr J. Trolan, Walters Plant Hire Ltd.

NH Jockey: James Davies, Charlie Deutsch. **Conditional Jockey:** Harry Beswick, Richard Patrick.

520 MRS JOANNE THOMASON-MURPHY, Chelmsford
Postal: Oakview, Leighams Road, Bicknacre, Chelmsford, Essex, CM3 4HF

1 **AYALOR (FR)**, 10, b g Khalkevi (IRE)—Physicienne (FR) **Mrs J. Thomason-Murphy**
2 **CANDY LOU**, 6, b m Schiaparelli (GER)—Candello **Mrs J. Thomason-Murphy**
3 **DANDY TIMES (IRE)**, 7, b g Central Park (IRE)—Distinctly Flo Jo (IRE) **Mrs J. Thomason-Murphy**
4 **EASTER DAY (FR)**, 12, b g Malinas (GER)—Sainte Lea (FR) **Mrs J. Thomason-Murphy**

521 MR DAVID THOMPSON, Darlington
Postal: South View Racing, Ashley Cottage, South View, Bolam, Darlington, County Durham, DL2 2UP
Contacts: PHONE 01388 832658, 01388 835806 MOBILE 07795 161657 FAX 01325 835806
EMAIL dwthompson61@hotmail.co.uk WEBSITE www.dwthompson.co.uk

1 **CONHALT**, 8, b g Rainbow High—Girl of Pleasure (IRE) **J. A. Moore**
2 **COUP DE GOLD (IRE)**, 4, br g Maxios—Astroglia (USA) **Mr N. Park**
3 **DIRCHILL (IRE)**, 6, b g Power—Bawaakeer (USA) **Mr S. Murray**
4 **GLAN Y GORS (IRE)**, 8, b br g High Chaparral (IRE)—Trading Places **Mr B. Lapham & J Souster**
5 **HIGHWAYMAN**, 7, b g Dick Turpin (IRE)—Right Rave (IRE) **Mr N. Park**
6 **IRISH MINISTER (USA)**, 5, b g Americain (USA)—Spanked (USA) **Mr J. Souster**
7 **LORD ROB**, 9, b g Rob Roy (USA)—First Grey **A. Suddes**
8 **LOSTNFOUND**, 7, b m Midnight Legend—La Cerisaie **Mr S. Murray**
9 **LUKOUTOLDMAKEZEBAK**, 7, b g Arabian Gleam—Angelofthenorth **NE1 Racing Club**
10 **MAZZA ROCKS (IRE)**, 5, b m Red Rocks (IRE)—Sun City **Mr B. Lapham**
11 **PRIZE WINNER (IRE)**, 5, ch g Teofilo (IRE)—Beta **Mr J. Souster**
12 **RAJAPUR**, 7, gr ro g Dalakhani (IRE)—A Beautiful Mind (GER) **Mr B. Lapham**
13 **RED STAR DANCER (IRE)**, 6, b g Tamayuz—Red Planet **Mrs J. Snailum**
14 **SEABOROUGH (IRE)**, 5, b g Born To Sea (IRE)—Nobilissima (IRE) **Mr J. Souster & Mr A. Livingston**
15 **SHAIYZAR (IRE)**, 11, b g Azamour (IRE)—Shaiyzima (IRE) **J. A. Moore**
16 **SHOULDN'T BE HERE (IRE)**, 6, b g Oscar (IRE)—Inver Leader (IRE) **J. A. Moore**
17 **SOMEONE EXCITING**, 7, b m Notnowcato—Quite Something **Mr J. Souster**
18 **SPLASH OF VERVE (IRE)**, 8, b g Fast Company (IRE)—
Ellistown Lady (IRE) **R Hudson B Walton B Lapham Mrs A Kenny**
19 **VALGOR DU RONCERAY (FR)**, 11, gr g Al Namix (FR)—Malta de Ronceray (FR)
20 **VISITANT**, 7, ch g Pivotal—Invitee **Mr N. Park**

THREE-YEAR-OLDS

21 **POCO CONTANTE**, b f Fast Company (IRE)—Littlemoor Lass **NE1 Racing Club**

Other Owners: Mr R. Hudson, Mrs A. Kenny, Mr B. Lapham, Mr A. J. Livingston, Mr J. Souster, Mr B. Walton.

Assistant Trainer: J. A. Moore.

Flat Jockey: Tony Hamilton.

522 MR RONALD THOMPSON, Doncaster
Postal: No 2 Bungalow, Haggswood Racing Stable, Stainforth, Doncaster, South Yorkshire, DN7 5PS
Contacts: PHONE 01302 845904 MOBILE 07713 251141 FAX 01302 845904
EMAIL ronracing@gmail.com

1 **CHEAP JACK**, 4, b g Coach House (IRE)—Ice Mayden **Ronald Thompson**
2 **CLAUDIA RANIERI (IRE)**, 5, b br m Most Improved (IRE)—Holly Hill (IRE) **Exors of the Late Mr N. D. Rawcliffe**
3 **DEBBI'S DREAM**, 5, b m Foxwedge (AUS)—Let's Dance (IRE) **Ronald Thompson**
4 **DOTHRAKI (IRE)**, 4, b g Bungle Inthejungle—Ellistown Lady (IRE) **Ronald Thompson**
5 **FAZAMOUR (FR)**, 5, b m Legolas (JPN)—Salina d'Airy (FR) **Mr N D Rawcliffe & Mr R Thompson**
6 **FURNI FACTORS**, 5, b g Captain Gerrard (IRE)—Calgary **B. Bruce & R. Thompson**
7 **ISE LODGE BABE**, 5, b m Libranno—Scented Garden **Mr N D Rawcliffe & Mr R Thompson**

MR RONALD THOMPSON - continued

8 **MAJOR CRISPIES**, 9, b g Pastoral Pursuits—Nellie Melba **Mrs A. Harrison**
9 **MR STRUTTER (IRE)**, 6, ch g Sir Prancealot (IRE)—Khajool (IRE) **Mrs A. Harrison**
10 **MY DANNY BOY**, 4, b g Burwaaz—Cara's Delight (AUS) **Ronald Thompson**
11 **STAINFORTH SWAGGER**, 4, b g Havana Gold (IRE)—Ferayha (IRE) **Exors of the Late Mr N. D. Rawcliffe**

THREE-YEAR-OLDS

12 **HANNAH CAVAGIN**, b f Music Master—Dimashq **Mr A Bell & Mr R Thompson**
13 **ONTHERADAR (IRE)**, b g Morpheus—Tap The Dot (IRE) **Ronald Thompson**

Other Owners: A. Bell, Mr B. Bruce, Exors of the Late Mr N. D. Rawcliffe, Ronald Thompson.

---

523 **MR VICTOR THOMPSON, Alnwick**
Postal: **Link House Farm, Newton By The Sea, Embleton, Alnwick, Northumberland, NE66 3ED**
Contacts: **PHONE 01665 576272 MOBILE 07739 626248**

1 **BOW STREET RUNNER**, 5, b g Sixties Icon—Lakaam **V. Thompson**
2 **CHALLOW (IRE)**, 6, b g Acclamation—Starlight Smile (USA) **V. Thompson**
3 **DOLLY'S DOT (IRE)**, 9, b m Vertical Speed (FR)—Our Dot (IRE) **V. Thompson**
4 **DUHALLOWCOUNTRY (IRE)**, 14, b g Beneficial—Milltown Lass (IRE) **V. Thompson**
5 **HERE IN THE DARK**, 5, b g Harbour Watch (IRE)—Behest **V. Thompson**
6 **MUROOR**, 7, ch g Nayef (USA)—Raaya (USA) **V. Thompson**
7 **PC DIXON**, 7, ch g Sixties Icon—Lakaam **V. Thompson**
8 **RAPID FRITZ**, 11, ch g Kutub (IRE)—Another Pet (IRE) **V. Thompson**
9 **SCORPO (IRE)**, 9, b g Scorpion (IRE)—Maltesse (IRE) **V. Thompson**
10 **TRUST ME I'M A DR (IRE)**, 11, b g Dr Massini (IRE)—Friendly Flick (IRE) **V. Thompson**

Assistant Trainer: M Thompson.

---

524 **MR SANDY THOMSON, Greenlaw**
Postal: **Lambden, Greenlaw, Duns, Berwickshire, TD10 6UN**
Contacts: **PHONE 01361 810211 MOBILE 07876 142787**
EMAIL sandy@lambdenfarm.co.uk WEBSITE www.sandythomsonracing.co.uk

1 **ALOOMOMO (FR)**, 10, b g Tirwanako (FR)—Kayola (FR) **The Large G & T Partnership**
2 **ARTHURS SECRET**, 10, ch g Sakhee's Secret—Angry Bark (USA) **Mr J. K. McGarrity**
3 **BLUE KASCADE (IRE)**, 13, ch g Kaieteur (USA)—Lydia Blue (IRE) **Mr J. K. McGarrity**
4 **BUCKLED**, 10, b g Midnight Legend—Mulberry Wine **Mrs M. Coppola**
5 **CAPARD KING (IRE)**, 11, b g Beneficial—Capard Lady (IRE) **E Chapman, J Beaumont, Q Thomson**
6 **CAVENTARA**, 8, b g Kayf Tara—L'Aventure (FR) **Mr C. J. Harriman**
7 **DELUXE RANGE (IRE)**, 5, b g Westerner—Kildea Cailin (IRE) **Watson & Lawrence**
8 **DIAMOND ROCK**, 9, b g Kayf Tara—Crystal Princess (IRE) **Quona Thomson & Ken McGarrity**
9 **DIMPLE (FR)**, 9, gr g Montmartre (FR)—Dynella (FR) **D&D Armstrong Limited**
10 **DONNA'S DELIGHT (IRE)**, 9, b g Portrait Gallery (IRE)—Hot Lips (IRE) **D&D Armstrong Limited**
11 **DUC DE GRISSAY (FR)**, 7, b g Denham Red (FR)—Rhea de Grissay (FR) **Watson & Lawrence**
12 **ELF DE RE (FR)**, 6, ch g Anabaa Blue—Ninon de Re (FR) **Mrs Q. R. Thomson**
13 **EMPIRE STEEL (IRE)**, 6, gr g Aizavoski (IRE)—Talk of Rain (FR) **Mr A. J. Wight**
14 **FAIR MINX**, 6, gr m Fair Mix (FR)—Blazing Diva (IRE) **Mr J. K. McGarrity**
15 **GERONIMO**, 9, ch g Kadastrof (FR)—Triggers Ginger **Mr J. K. McGarrity**
16 **HASTRUBAL (FR)**, 10, br g Discover d'Auteuil (FR)—Miss Montrose **Mr & Mrs S Townshend**
17 **JOHN WILLIAMS (IRE)**, 11, b g Presenting—Duhallow Park (IRE) **Mrs C. S. Stephenson**
18 **KING'S WHARF (IRE)**, 11, gr g Clodovil (IRE)—Global Tour (USA) **Ken McGarrity & the Western Chasers**
19 **LARGY PERK (IRE)**, 6, b g Scorpion (IRE)—Ellens Perk (IRE) **Mrs Q. R. Thomson**
20 **MANORBANK (IRE)**, 5, b g Arcadio (GER)—Kind Word (IRE)
21 **MCGOWAN'S PASS**, 9, b g Central Park (IRE)—Function Dreamer **Mrs A. E. Lee**
22 **MILVALE (IRE)**, 6, b g Ask—House-of-Hearts (IRE) **Trading Products Limited**

MR SANDY THOMSON - continued

23 **MYMILAN (IRE),** 7, b g Milan—Jill's Girl (IRE) **Tweed Valley Racing Club**
24 **OFF THE BEAT,** 6, ch g Black Sam Bellamy (IRE)—Off By Heart **Mrs Q. R. Thomson**
25 **OVERCOURT,** 6, b g Court Cave (IRE)—Overlady **Mr W. F. Jeffrey**
26 **ROMPA STOMPA (IRE),** 5, b g Dylan Thomas (IRE)—Handikova (IRE) **D&D Armstrong Limited**
27 **SAINT LEO (FR),** 7, b g Maresca Sorrento (FR)—Sainte Lea (FR) **Mr & Mrs Raymond Anderson Green**
28 **SARYSHAGANN (FR),** 7, gr g Iffraaj—Serasana **Mr J. K. McGarrity**
29 **SEEMORELIGHTS (IRE),** 8, b g Echo of Light—Star Lodge **Watson & Lawrence**
30 **SHADES OF MIDNIGHT,** 10, b g Midnight Legend—Hannah Park (IRE) **The Potassium Partnership**
31 **SIRWILLIAMWALLACE (IRE),** 7, b g Getaway (GER)—Mrs Milan (IRE) **Mr J. K. McGarrity**
32 **SOPHIE FATALE,** 8, b m Robin des Champs (FR)—Buffy **Midnight Racing Club**
33 **STRADIVARIUS DAVIS (FR),** 7, b g Turgeon (USA)—Trumpet Davis (FR) **D & M Macdonald & M & M McPherson**
34 **THE FERRY MASTER (IRE),** 7, b g Elusive Pimpernel (USA)—Dinghy (IRE) **The Potassium Partnership**

Other Owners: J. J. Beaumont, Mr N. Boyle, Mr E. Chapman, Mrs M. Macdonald, Mr W. D. Macdonald, Mr J. K. McGarrity, Mr D. W. McIntyre, Mr M. H. McPherson, Mrs M. W. McPherson, Michelle And Dan Macdonald, The Western Chasers, Mrs Q. R. Thomson, Mr S. Townshend, Mrs S. Townshend.

Assistant Trainer: Mrs A. M. Thomson.

NH Jockey: Rachael McDonald.

---

525 **MR NIGEL TINKLER, Malton**
Postal: **Trainer did not wish details of their string to appear**

---

526 **MR COLIN TIZZARD, Sherborne**
Postal: **Venn Farm, Milborne Port, Sherborne, Dorset, DT9 5RA**
Contacts: **PHONE 01963 250598 MOBILE 07976 778656 FAX 01963 250598**
EMAIL info@colintizzard.co.uk WEBSITE www.colintizzard.co.uk

1 **AINCHEA (IRE),** 7, b g Flemensfirth (USA)—Lady Petit (IRE) **Ann & Alan Potts Limited**
2 **AMBION HILL (IRE),** 5, b br g Getaway (GER)—Vertality (IRE) **Mr O. C. R. Wynne & Mrs S. J. Wynne**
3 **ASKINVILLAR (IRE),** 5, b g Jeremy (USA)—Cuddle In A Fog (IRE) **Sherborne Utilities Ltd**
4 **BALLY LONGFORD (IRE),** 12, b g Gold Well—Stay On Line (IRE) **Ann & Alan Potts Limited**
5 **BATTLE OF IDEAS (IRE),** 7, ch g Fracas (IRE)—Haven't A Notion **Coral Champions Club**
6 **BEAUFORT WEST (IRE),** 6, b g Getaway (GER)—Blessingindisguise (IRE) **Taylor & O'Dwyer**
7 5, B g Kayf Tara—Bird Without Wings (IRE) **John & Heather Snook**
8 **BOLD CONDUCT (IRE),** 6, b g Stowaway—Vics Miller (IRE) **J P Romans & Terry Warner**
9 **BUCKHORN GEORGE,** 5, gr g Geordieland (FR)—Waimea Bay **The Buckhorn Racing Team**
10 **BUTTERWICK BROOK (IRE),** 5, b g Getaway (GER)—Sheriussa (IRE) **The Butterwick Syndicate**
11 **CAPTURED MY HEART,** 4, br gr g Geordieland (FR)—Woodland Retreat
12 **CARRICK ROADS (IRE),** 6, ch g Robin des Champs (FR)—Jay Lo (IRE) **Brocade Racing**
13 **CATCH THE CUBAN,** 4, b g Havana Gold (IRE)—Reyamour **Castro's Army**
14 4, B g Fame And Glory—Chevalier Jet (IRE)
15 **CHRISTMAS IN APRIL (FR),** 8, b g Crillon (FR)—Similaresisoldofa (FR) **Swallowfield Racing**
16 **COASTAL DRIFT,** 6, b g Black Sam Bellamy (IRE)—Absalom's Girl **Brocade Racing**
17 **COPPERHEAD,** 6, ch g Sulamani (IRE)—How's Business **Mrs G. C. Pritchard**
18 **DARLAC (FR),** 7, b br g Lucarno (USA)—Pail Mel (FR) **Mrs G. C. Pritchard**
19 **DINOS BENEFIT (IRE),** 8, ch m Mr Dinos (IRE)—Beneficial Lady (IRE) **Mr A Maddox & Mr S Langdon**
20 4, B g Norse Dancer (IRE)—Doubly Guest
21 **DRINKS INTERVAL,** 8, b m King's Theatre (IRE)—Dame Fonteyn **The Land Value Partnership**
22 **DUC KAUTO (FR),** 7, b g Ballingarry (IRE)—Kauto Lorette (FR) **Ann & Alan Potts Limited**
23 **EARL OF WISDOM,** 5, ch g Flemensfirth (USA)—Golden Sunbird (IRE) **The Wychwood Partnership**
24 **EARLY DAYS (IRE),** 6, b m Stowaway—Inchiquin Cailin (IRE) **Gale Force Seven**
25 **EARTH BUSINESS (IRE),** 4, b g Westerner—Shellys Creek (IRE) **Mrs C. E. Penny**
26 **ELDORADO ALLEN (FR),** 6, gr g Khalkevi (IRE)—Hesmeralda (FR) **J P Romans & Terry Warner**
27 **ELEGANT ESCAPE (IRE),** 8, b g Dubai Destination (USA)—Graineuaile (IRE) **Mr J. P. Romans**

MR COLIN TIZZARD - continued

28 **ELIXIR DE NUTZ (FR)**, 6, gr g Al Namix (FR)—Nutz (FR) **J. T. Warner**
29 **EXXARO (IRE)**, 10, b g Presenting—Mandys Gold (IRE) **Ann & Alan Potts Limited**
30 **FAUSTINOVICK**, 6, b g Black Sam Bellamy (IRE)—Cormorant Cove **Taylor & O'Dwyer**
31 **FIDDLERONTHEROOF (IRE)**, 6, b g Stowaway—Inquisitive Look **Taylor, Burley & O'Dwyer**
32 **FLEMENCO TEMPO (IRE)**, 6, ch g Flemensfirth (USA)—Tap The Beat (IRE) **Wendy & Malcolm Hezel**
33 **FLOY JOY (IRE)**, 4, b g Arcadio (GER)—The Scorpion Queen (IRE) **Jay Three Racing**
34 **FLY TO MARS**, 6, b g Schiaparelli (GER)—Patsie Magern **Brocade Racing**
35 **FOX NORTON (FR)**, 10, b g Lando (GER)—Natt Musik (FR) **Ann & Alan Potts Limited**
36 **GETAWAY FRED (IRE)**, 6, b g Getaway (GER)—Cloch Anna (IRE) **Victor & Celia Goaman**
37 **GLENCOUM LASS (IRE)**, 6, b m Court Cave (IRE)—Clare Belle (IRE) **Beswick Brothers Bloodstock**
38 **GOLDEN SUNRISE (IRE)**, 7, ch g Stowaway—Fairy Dawn (IRE) **Brocade Racing**
39 **GUY DE GUYE (IRE)**, 4, b g Tiger Groom—Kasibelle de Guye (FR) **Mr J. P. McManus**
40 **HARRY SENIOR (IRE)**, 6, b g Oscar (IRE)—Surf Like A Lady (IRE) **Brocade Racing**
41 **HELFORD RIVER**, 6, b g Presenting—Lovely Origny (FR) **Brocade Racing**
42 **HIGHEST SUN (FR)**, 6, b g Sunday Break (JPN)—Highest Price (FR) **Mr A. J. Head**
43 **HONEST EXCHANGE (IRE)**, 6, b g Gold Well—Final Instalment (IRE)
44 **INVESTMENT MANAGER**, 4, b g Nathaniel (IRE)—Two Days In Paris (FR) **Brocade Racing**
45 **JAYTRACK PARKHOMES**, 6, b g Multiplex—Sudden Beat **DT Hoyland JS Hoyland JP Romans**
46 **KALARIKA (IRE)**, 7, br m Kalanisi (IRE)—Katariya (IRE) **Gale Force Three**
47 **KATAHDIN (IRE)**, 7, b g Kayf Tara—Keyaza (IRE) **Jay Three Racing**
48 **KAUTO THE KING (FR)**, 6, b g Ballingarry (IRE)—Kauto Luisa (FR) **Jenny Perry & Celia Goaman**
49 **KILBRICKEN STORM (IRE)**, 9, b g Oscar (IRE)—Kilbricken Leader (IRE) **A Selway & P Wavish**
50 **KINGS WALK (IRE)**, 9, b g King's Theatre (IRE)—Shuil Sionnach (IRE) **Mrs J. R. Bishop**
51 **L'AIR DU VENT (FR)**, 6, b g Coastal Path—Bleu Perle (FR) **Brocade Racing**
52 **LAMANVER PIPPIN**, 7, b g Apple Tree (FR)—Lamanver Homerun **Dr D. Christensen**
53 **LIEUTENANT ROCCO (IRE)**, 5, ch g Shirocco (GER)—Five Star Present (IRE) **Sherborne Utilities Ltd**
54 **LILLINGTON (IRE)**, 8, br g Westerner—Kind Word (IRE) **The Colin Tizzard Racing Club**
55 **LITTLE VERN (IRE)**, 6, b g Oscar (IRE)—Silver Valley (IRE) **Nightingale Syndicate**
56 **LIZZIE LANGTON**, 9, b m Kayf Tara—Madam Flora **Wendy Pope & Tim Swaffield**
57 4, B g Flemensfirth (USA)—Loadsapromise (IRE) **C. L. Tizzard**
58 **LOSTINTRANSLATION (IRE)**, 8, b g Flemensfirth (USA)—Falika (FR) **Taylor & O'Dwyer**
59 **MASTER DEBONAIR**, 6, br g Yeats (IRE)—Swincombe Flame **The Gosden Mob & Sprayclad Uk**
60 **MISTER MALARKY**, 7, ch g Malinas (GER)—Priscilla **Wendy & Malcolm Hezel**
61 **MOCACREME HAS (FR)**, 5, b g Saint des Saints (FR)—Monika (FR) **Mr J. P. McManus**
62 **MOLINEAUX (IRE)**, 9, b g King's Theatre (IRE)—Steel Grey Lady (IRE) **John & Heather Snook**
63 **MOVING DAY (IRE)**, 5, b g Getaway (GER)—Little Demand (IRE) **The Reserve Tankers**
64 **MUFFINS FOR TEA**, 10, ch g With The Flow (USA)—Countess Point **Mr D. S. Purdie**
65 **MY LADY GREY**, 6, gr m Presenting—Wassailing Queen **M, V & JM Messenger & Buob-Aldorf**
66 **MYTHICAL JEWEL (IRE)**, 5, b h Arcadio (GER)—Carrigtohilljewel (IRE) **Chasing Gold Limited**
67 **NATIVE RIVER (IRE)**, 10, ch g Indian River (FR)—Native Mo (IRE) **Brocade Racing**
68 **NATIVEGETAWAY (IRE)**, 7, b g Getaway (GER)—Clonsingle Native (IRE) **Orchard Racing**
69 **NEVER LEARN (IRE)**, 9, b g King's Theatre (IRE)—Hamari Gold (IRE) **Brocade Racing J P Romans Terry Warner**
70 **NEW TO THIS TOWN (IRE)**, 9, b g Milan—Jade River (FR) **Ann & Alan Potts Limited**
71 **NO HUBS NO HOOBS (IRE)**, 4, b g Flemensfirth (USA)—Miss Brandywell (IRE) **Taylor & O'Dwyer**
72 **NORSE LEGEND**, 9, b g Norse Dancer (IRE)—Methodical **Woodhaven Racing Syndicate**
73 **OFALLTHEGINJOINTS (IRE)**, 6, b g Stowaway—Dinos Luso (IRE) **The Reserve Tankers**
74 **OFTEN OVERLOOKED (IRE)**, 4, b br g Elusive Pimpernel (USA)—Alpinia (IRE) **Coral Champions Club**
75 **PADLEYOUROWNCANOE**, 6, b g Nayef (USA)—
Pooka's Daughter (IRE) **Kevin Corcoran Aaron Pierce Chris Weare**
76 **PINGSHOU (IRE)**, 10, b g Definite Article—Quest of Passion (FR) **Ann & Alan Potts Limited**
77 **PREMIUMACCESS (IRE)**, 5, b g Milan—De Loose Mongoose (IRE) **Taylor & O'Dwyer**
78 **PRINCESS MIDNIGHT**, 6, ch m Midnight Legend—Setter's Princess **The Gardens Entertainments Ltd**
79 **QUEEN OF THE WIND**, 7, b m Shirocco (GER)—Kaydee Queen (IRE) **Chasing Gold Limited**
80 **QUITE BY CHANCE**, 11, b g Midnight Legend—Hop Fair **T Hamlin, J M Dare, J W Snook, J T Warner**
81 **QUIZ MASTER (IRE)**, 8, b g Ask—Good Bye Dolly (IRE) **Brocade Racing**
82 **RAREST DIAMOND (IRE)**, 6, b m Milan—Lace Parasol (IRE) **The Colin Tizzard Racing Club**
83 **RECTORY OAK (IRE)**, 5, b br g Oscar (IRE)—Betty Roe (IRE) **Mrs G. C. Pritchard**
84 **RESERVE TANK (IRE)**, 6, b g Jeremy (USA)—Lady Bellamy (IRE) **The Reserve Tankers**
85 4, B g Black Sam Bellamy (IRE)—Reverse Swing

MR COLIN TIZZARD - continued

86 **ROBINSFIRTH (IRE),** 11, b g Flemensfirth (USA)—Phardester (IRE) **Christine Knowles & Wendy Carter**
87 **ROCKPOINT,** 7, b g Shirocco (GER)—Tinagoodnight (FR) **John & Heather Snook**
88 **ROSE OF ARCADIA (IRE),** 5, b m Arcadio (GER)—Rosie Lea (IRE) **Cheveley Park Stud Limited**
89 **ROYAL CROWN (FR),** 5, ch g Creachadoir (IRE)—Royal Army (GER) **The Wychwood Partnership**
90 **ROYAL VACATION (IRE),** 10, b g King's Theatre (IRE)—Summer Break (IRE) **Mrs J. R. Bishop**
91 **RUFFLING FEATHERS (IRE),** 6, b g Presenting—Oilily (IRE) **Mr & Mrs R. Tizzard**
92 **RUSSIAN EXILE,** 6, b g Pasternak—Psychosis **Reed, Abrahams & Spershott**
93 **SANDY BEACH,** 10, b g Notnowcato—Picacho (IRE) **Brocade Racing**
94 **SHANAHAN'S TURN (IRE),** 12, b g Indian Danehill (IRE)—Chanson Indienne (FR) **Ann & Alan Potts Limited**
95 **SHERBORNE (IRE),** 4, b g Getaway (GER)—Luck of The Deise (IRE) **Sharp, Nicholas & Kennington**
96 **SHOAL BAY (IRE),** 7, b g Gold Well—Ring Hill **Mrs C. Skan**
97 **SHYBAIRNSGETNOWT (IRE),** 4, gr g Cloudings (IRE)—Quarry Endeavour (IRE) **The Wychwood Partnership**
98 **SIZING AT MIDNIGHT (IRE),** 8, br g Midnight Legend—Issaquah (IRE) **Ann & Alan Potts Limited**
99 **SIZING CODELCO (IRE),** 11, b g Flemensfirth (USA)—La Zingarella (IRE) **Ann & Alan Potts Limited**
100 **SIZING CUSIMANO,** 7, b g Midnight Legend—Combe Florey **Ann & Alan Potts Limited**
101 **SIZING GRANITE (IRE),** 12, br g Milan—Hazel's Tisrara (IRE) **Ann & Alan Potts Limited**
102 **SIZING PLATINUM (IRE),** 12, b g Definite Article—Quest of Passion (FR) **Ann & Alan Potts Limited**
103 **SIZING TARA,** 7, b g Kayf Tara—As Was **Ann & Alan Potts Limited**
104 **SIZING TENNESSEE (IRE),** 12, ch g Robin des Champs (FR)—Jolivia (FR) **Ann & Alan Potts Limited**
105 **SKIBET (FR),** 4, b g Buck's Boum (FR)—Sacree City (FR)
106 **SLATE HOUSE (IRE),** 8, b g Presenting—Bay Pearl (FR) **Eric Jones, Geoff Nicholas, John Romans**
107 **STORM HOME (IRE),** 8, br g King's Theatre (IRE)—Miss Mayberry (IRE) **Mr J. P. Romans**
108 **THATSENTERTAINMENT (IRE),** 4, b g Leading Light (IRE)—Dyrick Daybreak (IRE) **The Wychwood Partnership**
109 **THE BIG BREAKAWAY (IRE),** 5, ch g Getaway (GER)—
                                            Princess Mairead (IRE) **Eric Jones, Geoff Nicholas, John Romans**
110 4, B g Sholokhov (IRE)—The Malteasiereyes (IRE) **Mr W. P. Drew**
111 **THE RUSSIAN DOYEN (IRE),** 7, b g Doyen (IRE)—Namloc (IRE) **The Gosden Mob**
112 **THE STRAP MAN,** 6, b g Schiaparelli (GER)—Lady Racquet (IRE) **M, V & JM Messenger & Buob-Aldorf**
113 **THE WIDDOW MAKER,** 6, ch g Arvico (FR)—Countess Point **Mr D. S. Purdie**
114 **THEATRE GUIDE (IRE),** 13, b g King's Theatre (IRE)—Erintante (IRE) **Mrs J. R. Bishop**
115 **THISTLECRACK,** 12, b g Kayf Tara—Ardstown **John & Heather Snook**
116 **ULTRAGOLD (FR),** 12, b br g Kapgarde (FR)—Hot d'Or (FR) **Brocade Racing J P Romans Terry Warner**
117 **VISION DES FLOS (FR),** 7, b g Balko (FR)—Marie Royale (FR) **Ann & Alan Potts Limited**
118 **WAR LORD (GER),** 5, gr g Jukebox Jury (IRE)—Westalin (GER) **The Wychwood Partnership**
119 **WEST APPROACH,** 10, b g Westerner—Ardstown **John & Heather Snook**
120 **WHITE MOON (GER),** 8, gr g Sholokhov (IRE)—Westalin (GER) **Brocade Racing**
121 **WHO SHOT JR (IRE),** 6, b g Scorpion (IRE)—Ariesanne (IRE) **Wednesday Night Syndicate**

Other Owners: Ms J. Abrahams, Mr G. S. Bennet, Mr J. G. Bennet, Mrs A. E. M. Broom, Mr G. R. Broom, Mr J. P. R. Buob-Aldorf, Mrs V. K. Buob-Aldorf, Mr N. Burley, Mrs W. Carter, K. J. Corcoran, Mr J. M. Dare, Mr A. L. Ellison, Mrs C. J. Goaman, Mr V. Goaman, Mr I. F. Gosden, T. Hamlin, Mr M. W. Hezel, Mrs W. M. Hezel, M. M. Hooker, Mr D. T. Hoyland, Mr J. S. Hoyland, Mr E. Jones, Mr R. Jones, Mr G. Kennington, Mrs C. Knowles, Mr S. R. Langdon, Mr G. J. Le Prevost, Mr A. P. Maddox, Mr D. A. Makins, Mr D. A. Mayes, Mr D. R. Mayes, Mrs S. A. Mayes, Mrs M. Messenger, Mr G. Nicholas, Mr R. O'Dwyer, Mrs J. M. Perry, Mr A. T. Pierce, Mrs W. M. Pope, Miss J. E. Reed, Mr J. P. Romans, Mr D. J. Rushbrook, A. G. Selway, Mr M. L. Sharp, Mrs H. A. Snook, J. W. Snook, Mr D. G. Spershott, SprayClad UK, Mr T. J. Swaffield, Mr R. L. Tappin, Mr P. A. Taylor, The Gosden Mob, J. T. Warner, Mr J. A. Waterworth, Mr P. T. J. Wavish, Mr C. E. Weare, O. C. R. Wynne, Mrs S. J. Wynne.

Assistant Trainer: Mrs Kim Gingell, Joe Tizzard.

NH Jockey: Harry Cobden, Jonjo O'Neill jr, Robbie Power. **Conditional Jockey:** Harry Kimber.

527 SIR MARK TODD, Swindon
Postal: **Badgerstown, Foxhill, Swindon, Wiltshire, SN4 0DR**
Contacts: PHONE **01793 791228**
EMAIL **mtoddracing@gmail.com**

1 **I CAN (IRE)**, 5, b g So You Think (NZ)—Walk On Water **Bloomsbury Stud**
2 **KING OF COMEDY (IRE)**, 4, b c Kingman—Stage Presence (IRE) **Lady Bamford**
3 **PETIT BAY**, 4, b f Dick Turpin (IRE)—Sky High Diver (IRE) **Miss Italia Keogh & Bobby Allan**

THREE-YEAR-OLDS
4 **DUTCH HARBOR**, b c Kodiac—Complexion **Dutch Harbor Partnership**
5 **ENCHANTEE (IRE)**, b f Gale Force Ten—Love Valentine (IRE) **Enchantee**
6 **KYLLINGA (IRE)**, ch f Kyllachy—Katevan (IRE) **The Katchy Partnership**
7 **SANDS SOUCI**, b f Footstepsinthesand—Natural Choice **The Sands Souci Partnership**
8 **SOYOUNIQUE (IRE)**, ch g Siyouni (FR)—Adventure Seeker (FR) **MTV Syndicate**
9 **TIPPLER**, gr g Iffraaj—Present Day **Tippler Partnership**

TWO-YEAR-OLDS
10 B f 23/02 Camelot—First of Many (Darshaan) (111540) **Sir P. J. Vela**
11 B c 24/01 Fastnet Rock (AUS)—Gertrude Gray (IRE) (Hurricane Run (IRE))
12 Ch f 12/05 Exceed And Excel (AUS)—Mumtaza (Nayef (USA)) (50000)
13 B c 01/03 The Wow Signal (IRE)—Naive (IRE) (Nayef (USA)) (35000)
14 B c 14/02 Siyouni (FR)—Nessun Dorma (GER) (Lawman (FR))
15 B c 10/03 Le Havre (IRE)—Purely Priceless (IRE) (Galileo (IRE)) (188760) **Sir P. J. Vela**

Other Owners: Mr B. Allan, BJ & JEA Lindsay Partnership, Bloomsbury Stud, Mrs A. Christie, Dame L. P. Goddard, Mr T. Henderson, Miss I. Keogh, Mrs T. L. Miller, Lady C. Todd, Sir M. J. Todd, Sir P. J. Vela.

528 MR MARTIN TODHUNTER, Penrith
Postal: **The Park, Orton, Penrith, Cumbria, CA10 3SD**
Contacts: PHONE **015396 24314** MOBILE **07976 440082** FAX **015396 24314**
WEBSITE **www.martintodhunter.co.uk**

1 **ASKING FOR ANSWERS (IRE)**, 7, ch g Ask—Equation (IRE) **Mrs Mrs Matthews & Mrs G Hazeldean**
2 **BOCASIEN DESBOIS (FR)**, 9, gr g Smadoun (FR)—Quocasienne (FR) **J. D. Gordon**
3 **BULLS HEAD (IRE)**, 8, b g Darsi (FR)—Mrs Jenks **Murphy's Law Partnership**
4 **CHOCOLAT NOIR (IRE)**, 7, b m Yeats (IRE)—Valrhona (IRE) **Javas Charvers**
5 **COOL COUNTRY (IRE)**, 5, b g Dylan Thomas (IRE)—Mae's Choice (IRE) **J. D. Gordon**
6 **DARRY DESBOIS (FR)**, 7, ch g Ballingarry (IRE)—Tiwa (FR) **Mr & Mrs Ian Hall**
7 **JOIE DE VIVRE (IRE)**, 5, gr m Mastercraftsman (IRE)—Fragonard **Leeds Plywood & Doors Ltd**
8 **MONBEG RIVER (IRE)**, 11, br g Indian River (FR)—So Pretty (IRE) **Bill Hazeldean & V Vyner-brookes**
9 **OLDTIMER (IRE)**, 9, br g Olden Times—Supreme Surprise (IRE) **Park Farms Racing Syndicate 1**
10 **PLAN OF ESCAPE (IRE)**, 7, ch g Presenting—Pilgara (IRE) **Mr Bill Hazeldean & Mr & Mrs Ian Hall**
11 **PORTOFINO (IRE)**, 4, ch g Australia—Song of My Heart (IRE) **Sir Robert Ogden**
12 **PRETTY MISS MAHLER (IRE)**, 9, b m Mahler—So Pretty (IRE) **Murphy's Law Partnership**
13 **PUB MURPHY (IRE)**, 5, br g Califet (FR)—Royal Stream (IRE) **Murphy's Law Partnership**
14 **RINGARINGAROSIE (IRE)**, 7, ch m Stowaway—Megan's Magic **Mr G Fell & Mr R V Brass**
15 **SOPHIE OLIVIA (IRE)**, 8, gr m Ask—Gill's Honey (IRE) **Mr A. Bell**
16 **SOUTHEAST ROSE (IRE)**, 7, b m Beat Hollow—Sunny South East (IRE) **The Surf & Turf Partnership**
17 **TALKOFGOLD (IRE)**, 8, gr m Gold Well—Talk of Rain (FR) **Leeds Plywood & Doors Ltd**
18 **ULTERIOR MOTIVES (IRE)**, 6, ch m Stowaway—Ballinapierce Lady (IRE) **Coniston Old Men & Partners**
19 **WESTERN AUSSIE (IRE)**, 7, b g Westerner—Squeekaussie (IRE) **Mr & Mrs Ian Hall**

THREE-YEAR-OLDS
20 **BRITANNIA BAY (IRE)**, b f Charm Spirit (IRE)—Tiger Lilly (IRE) **Sir R. Ogden C.B.E., LLD**

Other Owners: Mr P. G. Airey, Mr R. V. Brass, P. W. Clement, Mr W. Downs, Mr G. Fell, Mr & Mrs Ian Hall, Mrs G. M. Hazeldean, J. W. Hazeldean, Mrs S. Magnier, Mrs S. J. Matthews, Sir R. Ogden C.B.E., LLD, Mr D. M. Todhunter, Mr V. R. Vyner-Brooks.

529 MR MARCUS TREGONING, Whitsbury

Postal: **Whitsbury Manor Racing Stables, Whitsbury, Fordingbridge, Hampshire, SP6 3QQ**
Contacts: **PHONE 01725 518889 MOBILE 07767 888100**
EMAIL info@marcustregoningracing.co.uk WEBSITE www.marcustregoningracing.co.uk

1 **AJAAD (IRE),** 4, b g Tamayuz—Rahlah **Hamdan bin Rashid Al Maktoum**
2 **ATALANTA BREEZE,** 4, b f Champs Elysees—Craighall **Miss S. M. Sharp**
3 **BARON SLICK (IRE),** 4, b g Raven's Pass (USA)—Namely (IRE) **Mr M. P. Tregoning**
4 **CLOVELLY BAY (IRE),** 9, b g Bushranger (IRE)—Crystalline Stream (FR) **Mr M. P. Tregoning**
5 **GHALYOON,** 5, b g Invincible Spirit (IRE)—Swiss Lake (USA) **Hamdan bin Rashid Al Maktoum**
6 **LANDUE,** 5, b g Champs Elysees—Time of Gold (USA) **Mr M. P. Tregoning**
7 **MARGUB,** 5, ch g Bated Breath—Bahamian Babe **Hamdan bin Rashid Al Maktoum**
8 **MISS BLONDELL,** 7, ch m Compton Place—Where's Broughton **Miss S. M. Sharp**
9 **MISS SWIFT,** 4, b f Sir Percy—Lady Hestia (USA) **The FOPS**
10 **MOHAATHER,** 4, b c Showcasing—Roodeye **Hamdan bin Rashid Al Maktoum**
11 **MUBAAELGH,** 6, b g Dark Angel (IRE)—Poppet's Passion **Hamdan bin Rashid Al Maktoum**
12 **POWER OF DARKNESS,** 5, b g Power—Summers Lease **R. C. C. Villers**
13 **SADLERS BEACH (IRE),** 4, b f Pour Moi (IRE)—Dusty Boots (IRE) **Mr R. E. Kingston**
14 **SEAFARER (IRE),** 6, br g Henrythenavigator (USA)—Rose of Petra (IRE) **Green, Hoare, Raw & Tregoning**
15 **SPIRIT OF ANGEL (IRE),** 4, b g Dark Angel (IRE)—Spirit of Cuba (IRE) **Owenstown Stud & Mr M. P. N. Tregoning**
16 **STRATHSPEY STRETTO (IRE),** 5, ch m Kyllachy—
                                              Rhythm And Rhyme (IRE) **Miss S Sharp & Mr M. P. N. Tregoning**
17 **TASHDEED (USA),** 4, b g Kitten's Joy (USA)—Keertana (USA) **Hamdan bin Rashid Al Maktoum**
18 **TELL WILLIAM,** 4, b g Invincible Spirit (IRE)—Swiss Kiss **R. C. C. Villers**
19 **TRELINNEY (IRE),** 4, b f Dandy Man (IRE)—Silvertine (IRE) **Mr M. P. Tregoning**

THREE-YEAR-OLDS
20 **ASIAAF,** b f New Approach (IRE)—Baqqa (IRE) **Hamdan bin Rashid Al Maktoum**
21 **DARTINGTON (IRE),** b c Siyouni (FR)—Secret Pursuit (IRE) **Mr G. C. B. Brook**
22 **IMPRESSOR (IRE),** b c Footstepsinthesand—Little Empress (IRE) **R. C. C. Villers**
23 **LADY ALEXANDRIA,** b f Sir Percy—Desert Run (IRE) **Mr & Mrs A. E. Pakenham**
24 **MODMIN (IRE),** b c Tamayuz—Arsheef (USA) **Hamdan bin Rashid Al Maktoum**
25 **MUTALAHEF (IRE),** b c Kingman—Raasekha **Hamdan bin Rashid Al Maktoum**
26 **RAASEL,** ch c Showcasing—Dubai Affair **Hamdan bin Rashid Al Maktoum**
27 **RAATEA,** b c Invincible Spirit (IRE)—Darajaat (USA) **Hamdan bin Rashid Al Maktoum**
28 **SAMARITAINE,** ch f Mukhadram—Samando (FR) **Miss K. Rausing**
29 **SILENT PARTNER,** b g Fast Company (IRE)—Peace Lily **Park Walk Racing - 2019**
30 **SMUGGLER,** b g Sir Percy—Patronella (IRE) **Park Walk Racing - 2019**
31 **TAJAMHOR (USA),** b f Candy Ride (ARG)—Alshadiyah (USA) **Hamdan bin Rashid Al Maktoum**
32 **TAWTHEEF (IRE),** b g Muhaarar—Miss Beatrix (IRE) **Hamdan bin Rashid Al Maktoum**

TWO-YEAR-OLDS
33 **ALCACHOCA,** gr f 04/04 Bobby's Kitten (USA)—Albacocca (With Approval (CAN)) **Miss K. Rausing**
34 B c 14/02 Oasis Dream—Blinking (Marju (IRE)) (115000) **Hamdan bin Rashid Al Maktoum**
35 B c 15/02 Showcasing—Blue Bayou (Bahamian Bounty) (80000) **Hamdan bin Rashid Al Maktoum**
36 Ch c 05/02 Showcasing—Bright Glow (Exceed And Excel (AUS)) (205920) **Hamdan bin Rashid Al Maktoum**
37 B c 13/05 Sir Percy—Entre Nous (IRE) (Sadler's Wells (USA)) (17000) **Halcyon Thoroughbreds - MT2**
38 B c 09/04 Adaay (IRE)—Flemish School (Dutch Art) (109523) **Hamdan bin Rashid Al Maktoum**
39 Ch c 26/03 New Approach (IRE)—Gimasha (Cadeaux Genereux) (55000) **R. C. C. Villers**
40 B f 01/02 Kingman—Hawaafez (Nayef (USA)) **Hamdan bin Rashid Al Maktoum**
41 B c 25/04 Awtaad (IRE)—Lucky Clio (IRE) (Key of Luck (USA)) (343200) **Hamdan bin Rashid Al Maktoum**
42 B c 16/03 Mukhadram—Mea Parvitas (IRE) (Oasis Dream) **Mrs C. J. Wates**
43 **MOLHIM (USA),** b c 07/04 War Front (USA)—Firdaws (IRE) (Mr Greeley (USA)) **Hamdan bin Rashid Al Maktoum**
44 B f 20/02 Nayef (USA)—Mooakada (IRE) (Montjeu (IRE)) **Hamdan bin Rashid Al Maktoum**
45 **PEROTTO,** ch c 28/03 New Bay—Tschierschen (IRE) (Acclamation) (28000) **Halcyon Thoroughbreds - MT1**
46 B f 13/01 Dark Angel (IRE)—Rathaath (IRE) (Oasis Dream) **Hamdan bin Rashid Al Maktoum**
47 Br c 27/02 Invincible Spirit (IRE)—Rihaam (IRE) (Dansili) **Hamdan bin Rashid Al Maktoum**
48 B c 17/02 Showcasing—Rowan Brae (Haafhd) (160000) **Hamdan bin Rashid Al Maktoum**
49 B c 15/05 Frankel—Rumoush (USA) (Rahy (USA)) **Hamdan bin Rashid Al Maktoum**
50 B c 19/04 Shalaa (IRE)—Seven Magicians (USA) (Silver Hawk (USA)) (45000) **Mr J A Tabet**

MR MARCUS TREGONING - continued

51 Ch f 22/03 Sea The Stars (IRE)—Sortita (GER) (Monsun (GER)) **Hamdan bin Rashid Al Maktoum**
52 B c 23/04 Dark Angel (IRE)—Staceymac (IRE) (Elnadim (USA)) (119047) **Hamdan bin Rashid Al Maktoum**
53 Ch f 02/06 Hunter's Light (IRE)—Starlit Sky (Galileo (IRE)) **Mr & Mrs John Raw**
54 B c 18/02 Showcasing—Suelita (Dutch Art) (220000) **Hamdan bin Rashid Al Maktoum**
55 B c 01/03 Estidhkaar (IRE)—Via Ballycroy (IRE) (Lawman (FR)) (120000) **Hamdan bin Rashid Al Maktoum**

Other Owner: Lady Tennant.

Assistant Trainer: Angie Kennedy.

Flat Jockey: Martin Dwyer. **Amateur Jockey:** Mr George Tregoning.

---

530 **MR GRANT TUER, Northallerton**
Postal: **Home Farm, Great Smeaton, Northallerton, North Yorkshire, DL6 2EP**
Contacts: **PHONE 01609 881094 MOBILE 07879 698869 FAX 01609 881094**
EMAIL grant_tuer@btinternet.com

1 **ARABIC CULTURE (USA)**, 6, b g Lonhro (AUS)—Kydd Gloves (USA) **Grant Tuer & Ng Racing**
2 **CUSTARD**, 4, ch g Monsieur Bond (IRE)—Ailsa Craig (IRE) **Mr G. F. Tuer**
3 **ESCAPE CLAUSE (IRE)**, 6, b g Lawman (FR)—Discophilia **Mr G. F. Tuer**
4 **ETIKAAL**, 6, ch g Sepoy (AUS)—Hezmah **Moment Of Madness**
5 **FYRECRACKER (IRE)**, 9, ch g Kheleyf (USA)—Spirit of Hope (IRE) **Allerton Racing**
6 **GUVENOR'S CHOICE (IRE)**, 5, gr g Intikhab (USA)—Exempt **Royale Racing Syndicate**
7 **KAAFY (IRE)**, 4, b g Alhebayeb (IRE)—Serene Dream **Miss M. Thompson & Moment of Madness**
8 **KERMOUSTER**, 4, b f Garswood—Rise **D. R. Tucker**
9 **MYWAYISTHEONLYWAY (IRE)**, 7, b g Tamayuz—Soul Custody (CAN) **Moment Of Madness**
10 4, B c Epaulette (AUS)—Point Perfect **Hornby Hornets**
11 **SO MACHO (IRE)**, 5, ch g Camacho—Turban Heights (IRE) **Mr G. F. Tuer, Mr J. A. Swinbank**
12 **SWINGING EDDIE**, 4, b g Swiss Spirit—Bling Bling (IRE) **NG Racing**
13 **TERMONATOR**, 4, ch g Monsieur Bond (IRE)—Easy Terms **E. Tuer**

THREE-YEAR-OLDS

14 **ANGELS FACES (IRE)**, b f Gutaifan (IRE)—Worthington (IRE) **Miss M. A. Thompson**
15 B f Fountain of Youth (IRE)—Citron **Mr G. F. Tuer**
16 B f Champs Elysees—Easy Terms **E. Tuer**
17 **FORUS**, b g Mukhadram—Anbella (FR) **NG Racing**
18 Ch f Anjaal—Generous Heart **Mr G. F. Tuer**
19 **ILLUSIONIST (GER)**, b g Hot Streak (IRE)—Irishstone (IRE) **Mr G. F. Tuer**
20 **LAKELAND MAGIC (IRE)**, b g Magician (IRE)—Thewandaofu (IRE) **Miss M. Thompson & Moment of Madness**
21 **LEZARDRIEUX**, b g Due Diligence (USA)—M'Selle (IRE) **D. R. Tucker**
22 **OUT OF BREATH**, b g Bated Breath—Parisi **Moment Of Madness**
23 B g Nathaniel (IRE)—Shenir
24 Gr g Gutaifan (IRE)—Suite (IRE) **Mr G. F. Tuer**

TWO-YEAR-OLDS

25 B c 06/02 Lethal Force (IRE)—Break Free (Oasis Dream) **Mr & Mrs G. Turnbull**
26 B f 09/03 Power—Jen Jos Enigma (IRE) (Kodiac) **Mr & Mrs G. Turnbull**
27 B c 26/02 War Command (USA)—Malayan Mist (IRE) (Dansili) (25714)
28 B c 03/03 Dandy Man (IRE)—Percolator (Kheleyf (USA)) (20952)
29 Ch c 31/01 Hot Streak (IRE)—Pigeon Pie (Bahamian Bounty) (12000)
30 B c 29/03 Lawman (FR)—Sibaya (Exceed And Excel (AUS)) **Mr & Mrs G. Turnbull**

Other Owners: Mr J. Black, Moment Of Madness, NG Racing, Miss M. A. Thompson, Mr G. F. Tuer, Mr T. Wilson.

531 | MR JOSEPH TUITE, Lambourn
Postal: **Felstead Stables, Folly Road, Lambourn, Hungerford, Berkshire, RG17 8QE**
Contacts: **MOBILE 07769 977351**
EMAIL joe.tuite@tuiteracing.com WEBSITE www.tuiteracing.co.uk

1 **BLACK KALANISI (IRE)**, 7, b g Kalanisi (IRE)—Blackthorne Winter (IRE) **The Harefield Racing Club**
2 **BOARDMAN**, 4, b c Kingman—Nimble Thimble (USA) **Bright, Jackson, Hillen**
3 **CLARION**, 4, b f Dubawi (IRE)—Caraboss **Mrs R. G. Hillen**
4 **COCKNEY HILL**, 4, b g Bated Breath—Espagnolette **Mr D. A. Klein**
5 **CONKERING HERO (IRE)**, 6, ch g Arakan (USA)—Brioney (IRE) **Mr J. M. Tuite**
6 **DUNKERRON**, 4, b g Kuroshio (AUS)—Triple Cee (IRE) **Ron Sullivan & Kingston Stud**
7 **FAME N FORTUNE**, 4, b g Thewayyouare (USA)—Acapella Star (IRE) **Fame n Fortune Syndicate**
8 **FAST DANCER (IRE)**, 8, b g Fast Company (IRE)—Tereed Elhawa **Alan & Christine Bright**
9 **FORTUNE AND GLORY (USA)**, 7, b g War Front (USA)—Spain (USA) **Mr R. J. Gurr**
10 **HAPPY FACE (IRE)**, 4, b f Kingman—Intense Pink **Mrs R. G. Hillen**
11 **KIMIFIVE (IRE)**, 5, ch g Born To Sea (IRE)—Appletreemagic (IRE) **Mr R. J. Gurr**
12 **PESTO**, 4, br g New Approach (IRE)—Pickle **Alison Jackson Racing & Partner**
13 **REDGRAVE (IRE)**, 6, b g Lope de Vega (IRE)—Olympic Medal **Crab Apple Racing Limited**
14 **SCARLETT O'HALO**, 4, b f Garswood—Red Halo **High Rollers**
15 **SOPHOSC (IRE)**, 4, ch g Society Rock (IRE)—Ichiuma (USA) **The Harefield Racing Club**
16 **SURREY BLAZE (IRE)**, 5, b g Thewayyouare (USA)—Catadalya (IRE) **Rabble Racing**
17 **TOPOLOGY**, 7, br g Passing Glance—Bold Byzantium **The Singleton Park Partnership 2**
18 **WHO TOLD JO JO (IRE)**, 6, b g Bushranger (IRE)—Shenkara (IRE) **Felstead Court Flyers**

THREE-YEAR-OLDS
19 **ALBERTI BASE**, b g Swiss Spirit—Night Premiere (IRE) **Mrs R. F. Greener**
20 **ALCHEMYSTIQUE (IRE)**, b f Authorized (IRE)—Nice To Know (FR) **Mr P. Hancock**
21 **BYTHEBAY**, br g Cable Bay (IRE)—Kristollini **Red Hot Partnership**
22 **HARES ROCKET (IRE)**, ch g Zebedee—Ichiuma (USA) **The Harefield Racing Club**
23 Ch f Starspangledbanner (AUS)—Know (IRE)
24 **RARE GLAM (IRE)**, b f Australia—Ayshea **Mr A. Mansergh Wallace**
25 **SURREY FLAME (FR)**, ch g Teofilo (IRE)—Ryedale Mist **Surrey Racing (SF)**
26 **SURREY PRIDE (IRE)**, b c Lope de Vega (IRE)—La Conquerante **Surrey Racing (SP)**
27 **TIGERTEN**, b g Born To Sea (IRE)—Morning Bride (IRE) **Mr R. J. Gurr**
28 **YOU DON'T OWN ME (IRE)**, b f Evasive—Hypatia (IRE) **Klein, Forbes & Partner**

TWO-YEAR-OLDS
29 **LULLABY MOON**, b f 04/04 Belardo (IRE)—Bold Bidder (Indesatchel (IRE)) (16000) **Phillip Cove & Gb Horseracing**
30 B f 02/03 Bungle Inthejungle—Shine Likeadiamond (Atlantic Sport (USA)) (4761) **A. F. Walls**

Other Owners: Mr D. Barrett, Mrs D. M. Barrett, Mr A. D. Bright, Mrs C. Bright, Mr N. S. G. Bunter, Mr P. Cove, Mr M. S. Cresswell, M. I. Forbes, GB Horseracing, Mrs R. G. Hillen, Mrs A. J. Jackson, Alan King, Kingston Stud, Mr D. A. Klein, Mr P. T. Mott, G. J. Pascoe, Mr P. J. Scargill, Mr R. T. Sullivan, Mr J. M. Tuite.

532 | MR BILL TURNER, Sherborne
Postal: **Sigwells Farm, Sigwells, Corton Denham, Sherborne, Dorset, DT9 4LN**
Contacts: **PHONE 01963 220523 MOBILE 07932 100173 FAX 01963 220046**
EMAIL billturnerracing@gmail.com

1 **BORN AT MIDNIGHT**, 5, b g Midnight Legend—Wavet **Mr B. J. Goldsmith**
2 **CASSIS DE REINE**, 6, ch m Quatre Saisons—Reine de Violette **R. A. Bracken**
3 **DARK STORM**, 4, b g Geordieland (FR)—Flaviola (IRE) **C.P.S. Syndicate**
4 **DEVIL OR ANGEL**, 5, ch m Assertive—Level Pegging (IRE) **Mrs P. A. Turner**
5 **HOLDENHURST**, 5, gr g Hellvelyn—Michelle Shift **Ansells Of Watford**
6 **IL SICARIO (IRE)**, 6, b g Zebedee—Starring (FR) **Mrs H. A. Heal**
7 **KATHERINE PLACE**, 5, b m Showcasing—Folly Drove **Ansells Of Watford**
8 **LETSBE AVENUE (IRE)**, 5, b g Lawman (FR)—Aguilas Perla (IRE) **Mr C. J. Sprake**

MR BILL TURNER - continued

9 **LITTLE BOY BLUE**, 5, gr g Hellvelyn—Dusty Dazzler (IRE) **Mrs P. A. Turner**
10 **MARETTIMO (IRE)**, 6, b g Harbour Watch (IRE)—Renowned (IRE) **R. A. Bracken**
11 **MIDNIGHT CALAMITY**, 6, ch m Malinas (GER)—Miss Calamity **The Floral Farmers**
12 **MIDNIGHT WAVE**, 4, b g Midnight Legend—Wavet **Mrs C. M. Goldsmith**
13 **MOTHER BROWN**, 4, ch f Coach House (IRE)—Lisa Jane **Mrs P. A. Turner**
14 **WHAT A DAZZLER**, 4, ch f Coach House (IRE)—Dusty Dazzler (IRE) **Mrs P. A. Turner**

THREE-YEAR-OLDS

15 **DEVONGATE**, b c Delegator—Up And Running **Miss J. S. Dorey**
16 **DIAMONDS AND RUST**, b f Casamento (IRE)—Constant Craving **Mascalls Stud**
17 **DRAKEY BOY**, b g Sixties Icon—Majigal **Mr J. E. Drake**
18 **HELL OF A JOKER**, br c Hellvelyn—Oceanico Dot Com (IRE) **Mr J. Pyatt**
19 B f Hellvelyn—Lady Fiona **Mrs P. A. Turner**
20 **QUEENS ROAD (IRE)**, b f Make Believe—Okba (USA) **Mrs B. C. Ansell**

TWO-YEAR-OLDS

21 Ch c 17/03 Garswood—Halfwaytoparadise (Observatory) (USA) **Mascalls Stud**
22 Br c 24/03 Markaz (IRE)—Heartstrings (Invincible Spirit (IRE)) (4290) **Mrs P. A. Turner**
23 **HILLBILLY**, b g 24/03 Coach House (IRE)—Dusty Dazzler (IRE) (Titus Livius (FR)) **Mrs P. A. Turner**
24 B c 31/01 Epaulette (AUS)—Jessie K (Compton Place) (857) **Mrs P. A. Turner**
25 B gr c 19/02 Hellvelyn—Liberty Lady (IRE) (Statue of Liberty (USA))
26 **PACO LOCO**, b c 01/03 Heeraat (IRE)—Pack of Dreams (IRE) (Paco Boy (IRE)) (761) **Mrs S. M. Manning**
27 Ch c 17/03 Dawn Approach (IRE)—Sou Anguillarina (IRE) (Bushranger (IRE)) (8580) **Mrs P. A. Turner**
28 B f 30/01 Dawn Approach (IRE)—Superstitious (USA) (Kingmambo (USA)) (3003) **Mrs P. A. Turner**

Other Owners: Mr B. C. Ansell, Mrs B. C. Ansell, B. M. W. Hearn, Mrs S. J. Hearn.

Assistant Trainer: Kathy While.

533
MRS KAREN TUTTY, Northallerton
Postal: Trenholme House Farm, Osmotherley, Northallerton, North Yorkshire, DL6 3QA
Contacts: PHONE 01609 883624 MOBILE 07967 837406 FAX 01609 883624
EMAIL karentutty@btinternet.com WEBSITE www.karentuttyracing.co.uk

1 **ELIXSOFT (IRE)**, 5, b m Elzaam (AUS)—Grandegrandegrande (IRE) **Thoroughbred Homes Ltd**
2 **GLOBAL EXCEED**, 5, b g Exceed And Excel (AUS)—Blue Maiden **Irvine Lynch & Thoroughbred Homes Ltd**
3 **IDEAL CANDY (IRE)**, 5, b m Canford Cliffs (IRE)—Forever More (IRE) **Mr D. A. Robinson**
4 **IDEAL DESTINY**, 4, b f Dawn Approach (IRE)—Early Morning Rain (IRE) **Mr D. A. Robinson**
5 **LYDIATE LADY**, 8, b m Piccolo—Hireath **Thoroughbred Homes Ltd**
6 **MUQARRED (USA)**, 8, b br g Speightstown (USA)—Bawaara (FR) **Thoroughbred Homes Ltd**
7 **SANDS CHORUS**, 8, b g Footstepsinthesand—Wood Chorus **Thoroughbred Homes Ltd**
8 **SEVEN CLANS (IRE)**, 8, b g Cape Cross (IRE)—Cherokee Rose (IRE) **Thoroughbred Homes Ltd**
9 **TANGLED (IRE)**, 5, b g Society Rock (IRE)—Open Verse (USA) **Grange Park Racing XIX**
10 **TWIN APPEAL (IRE)**, 9, b g Oratorio (IRE)—Velvet Appeal (IRE) **Mrs Mary Winetroube & Thoroughbred Homes**
11 **WITH APPROVAL (IRE)**, 8, b g Approve (IRE)—Kelsey Rose **Thoroughbred Homes Ltd**

THREE-YEAR-OLDS

12 **CANVILLE (IRE)**, b f Canford Cliffs (IRE)—Colleville **Grange Park Racing XVIII**
13 **HELMOONA**, ch g Helmet (AUS)—Maimoona (IRE) **Grange Park Racing XVIII**
14 **IDEAL STORM (IRE)**, gr f Zebedee—Furnival (USA) **Mr D. A. Robinson**

Other Owners: I. M. Lynch, Thoroughbred Homes Ltd, Mrs M. T. Winetroube.

Flat Jockey: Gemma Tutty.

534 **MR NIGEL TWISTON-DAVIES, Cheltenham**
Postal: T/a Grange Hill Farm Limited, Grange Hill Farm, Naunton, Cheltenham, Gloucestershire,
GL54 3AY
Contacts: PHONE 01451 850278 MOBILE 07836 664440
EMAIL nigel@nigeltwistondavies.co.uk WEBSITE www.nigeltwistondavies.co.uk

1 **AL DANCER (FR)**, 7, gr g Al Namix (FR)—Steel Dancer (FR) **Walters Plant Hire Ltd**
2 **ALFSBOY (IRE)**, 5, b g Shirocco (GER)—Full of Spirit (IRE) **Carl Hinchy & Mark Scott**
3 **ALL ABOUT YOU (IRE)**, 6, b g Thewayyouare (USA)—Fake Tan (IRE) **Mr N. A. Twiston-Davies**
4 **ANOTHER FRONTIER (IRE)**, 9, b g Darsi (FR)—Scent With Love (IRE) **Jump For Fun Racing**
5 **ARCTIC GOLD (IRE)**, 9, b g Gold Well—Arctic Warrior (IRE) **Geoffrey & Donna Keeys**
6 **ARTHUR'S GIFT (IRE)**, 9, b g Presenting—Uncertain Affair (IRE) **Arthur's Gift Partnership**
7 **BABY TED**, 7, ch g Pasternak—Dd's Glenalla (IRE) **Mr J. Goodman**
8 **BALLYART (IRE)**, 7, b br g Scorpion (IRE)—Candle Massini (IRE) **Mr N. A. Twiston-Davies**
9 **BALLYMALIN (IRE)**, 10, b g Presenting—Murrurundi (IRE) **Mills & Mason Partnership**
10 **BALLYMILLSY**, 4, b g Lucarno (USA)—Brackenmoss (IRE)
11 **BALLYMOY (IRE)**, 7, b g Flemensfirth (USA)—John's Eliza (IRE) **Mr Simon Munir & Mr Isaac Souede**
12 **BALLYOPTIC (IRE)**, 10, b g Old Vic—Lambourne Lace (IRE) **Mills & Mason Partnership**
13 **BEAUPORT (IRE)**, 4, b g Califet (FR)—Byerley Beauty (IRE) **Bryan & Philippa Burrough**
14 **BLUE FLIGHT (FR)**, 7, b g Blue Bresil (FR)—Lover Flight (FR) **Mr J. Fyffe**
15 **BOMBER'S MOON**, 9, b g Erhaab (USA)—Flaviola (IRE) **J. A. B. Old**
16 **BRISTOL DE MAI (FR)**, 9, gr g Saddler Maker (IRE)—La Bole Night (FR) **Mr Simon Munir & Mr Isaac Souede**
17 **CHANCE A TUNE (IRE)**, 5, b g My Risk (FR)—Lyric Melody (FR) **Mr C. S. Hinchy**
18 **CHINENSIS (IRE)**, 7, b g Well Chosen—Emily Vard (IRE) **Mr T. J. Hemmings**
19 **COGRY**, 11, b g King's Theatre (IRE)—Wyldello **Graham & Alison Jelley**
20 **COUNT MERIBEL**, 8, ch g Three Valleys (USA)—Bakhtawar (IRE) **C. C. Walker**
21 **CRIEVEHILL (IRE)**, 8, b g Arcadio (GER)—Ma Douce (IRE) **Highclere T'Bred Racing- Crievehill**
22 **DARLING ALKO (FR)**, 7, b g Al Namix (FR)—Padalko Tatou (FR) **Walters Plant Hire & Potter Group**
23 **DINO BOY (FR)**, 7, b g Diamond Boy (FR)—Odeline (FR) **Million in Mind Partnership**
24 **DON'T SHOUT (IRE)**, 6, b g Oscar (IRE)—Asta Belle (FR) **Walters Plant Hire & Potter Group**
25 **DONT GO GENTLE (IRE)**, 4, b g Dylan Thomas (IRE)—Caedlih Davis (FR) **Mr P. Trainor**
26 **EARLOFTHECOTSWOLDS (FR)**, 6, bl g Axxos (GER)—Sissi Land (FR) **Twiston-Davies, Mason, Greer & Kiely**
27 **ECHIQUIER (FR)**, 6, b g Network (GER)—Regate (FR) **Mr Simon Munir & Mr Isaac Souede**
28 **ELMDALE (FR)**, 6, gr g Martaline—Victoire Jaguine (FR) **Mr R. J. Rexton**
29 **EMPHATIC QUALM (IRE)**, 5, b g Califet (FR)—Supreme Touch (IRE) **Graham & Alison Jelley**
30 **FANTASTIKAS (FR)**, 5, b g Davidoff (GER)—Negresse de Cuta (FR) **Imperial Racing Partnership 2016**
31 **FIER ECHEZEAUX (FR)**, 5, b g Network (GER)—Montre En Main (FR) **Ged Mason & Jim McGoff**
32 **FLORRIE BOY (IRE)**, 9, b g Milan—Second Best (IRE) **Options O Syndicate**
33 **FLYING ANGEL (IRE)**, 9, gr g Arcadio (GER)—Gypsy Kelly (IRE) **Mr R. J. Rexton**
34 **GALILEO SILVER (IRE)**, 5, gr g Galileo (IRE)—Famous (IRE) **Walters Plant Hire & Potter Group**
35 **GEORGE OF NAUNTON (IRE)**, 5, br g Arakan (USA)—Rosee des Bieffes (FR) **The Preston Family Racing**
36 **GOA LIL (FR)**, 4, br g Samum (GER)—Unekaina (FR) **Mr Simon Munir & Mr Isaac Souede**
37 **GOOD BOY BOBBY (IRE)**, 7, b g Flemensfirth (USA)—Princess Gaia (FR) **Mr & Mrs Paul & Clare Rooney**
38 **GREY DIAMOND (FR)**, 6, b g Gris de Gris (FR)—Diamond of Diana (FR) **Walters Plant Hire Ltd**
39 **GUARD YOUR DREAMS**, 4, b g Fame And Glory—Native Sunrise (FR) **Graham & Alison Jelley**
40 **GUY (IRE)**, 5, ch g Getaway (GER)—Sept Verites (FR) **The Hons W. G. & A. G. Vestey**
41 **HIGHLAND PARC (IRE)**, 4, ch g Leading Light (IRE)—Back To My Place (IRE)
42 **HILLARY C**, 8, b m Kayf Tara—Dd's Glenalla (IRE) **Mr N. A. Twiston-Davies**
43 **IMPERIAL ACOLYTE**, 6, b g Kalanisi (IRE)—Isabello (IRE) **Imperial Racing Partnership**
44 **IMPERIAL NEMESIS (IRE)**, 7, b g Stowaway—Liss Alainn (IRE) **Imperial Racing Partnership 2016**
45 **JELSKI (GER)**, 6, b g Kallisto (GER)—Just Zoud **Mr T. J. Hemmings**
46 **KAPGARRY (FR)**, 7, b g Ballingarry (IRE)—Kaprissima (FR) **Options O Syndicate**
47 **KILPIN (IRE)**, 5, b g Milan—Come And Fight (IRE) **The Hons W. G. & A. G. Vestey**
48 **KINGOFTHECOTSWOLDS (IRE)**, 6, b g Arcadio (GER)—Damoiselle **Alan & Sally Coney**
49 **KINGSPLACE (IRE)**, 8, b g Ask—Winsome Breeze (IRE) **Mr R. J. Rexton**
50 **LEROY BROWN**, 5, b g Pasternak—Grenfell (IRE) **Mr N. A. Twiston-Davies**
51 **LOCKER ROOM TALK (IRE)**, 7, b g Beneficial—Whistling Gypse (IRE) **Mr C. S. Hinchy**
52 **LUCKOFTHEDRAW (FR)**, 7, gr g Martaline—La Perspective (FR) **Mr N. A. Twiston-Davies**
53 **MONARCHOFTHEGRANGE (IRE)**, 5, ch g Imperial Monarch (IRE)—Saipan Storm (IRE) **Mr N. A. Twiston-Davies**
54 **MOSSY FEN (IRE)**, 5, b g Milan—Inch Native (IRE) **Carl Hinchy & Mark Scott**

MR NIGEL TWISTON-DAVIES - continued

55 **MR ANTOLINI (IRE)**, 10, b g Catcher In The Rye (IRE)—Victory Run (IRE) **Alan & Sally Coney**
56 **MR STAN**, 5, b g Scorpion (IRE)—Dametori (FR) **Mr N. A. Twiston-Davies**
57 **MURATELLO (FR)**, 6, b g Blue Bresil (FR)—Nesle de La Roque (FR) **Mr Simon Munir & Mr Isaac Souede**
58 **NOBLE SAVAGE (IRE)**, 5, b g Arcadio (GER)—Callerdiscallerdat (IRE) **C. C. Walker**
59 **NYE BEVAN (IRE)**, 5, b g Arcadio (GER)—Emma Jane (IRE) **Mr J. Neild**
60 **ONCHAN (IRE)**, 5, b g Oscar (IRE)—Satellite Dancer (IRE) **Mr T. J. Hemmings**
61 **ONE FINE MAN (IRE)**, 5, br g Jeremy (USA)—American Jennie (IRE) **Mr & Mrs Paul & Clare Rooney**
62 **ONE FOR ROSIE**, 7, gr g Getaway (GER)—Whisky Rose (IRE) **Mr & Mrs Paul & Clare Rooney**
63 **ONE FORTY SEVEN (IRE)**, 8, b g Beneficial—Still Bubbly (IRE) **Graham & Alison Jelley**
64 **OUR POWER (IRE)**, 5, b g Power—Scripture (IRE) **Walters Plant Hire & Potter Group**
65 **PERFECT PERCY**, 5, b g Presenting—Pollystone (IRE) **Mr N. A. Twiston-Davies**
66 **REDFORD ROAD**, 6, b g Trans Island—Maryscross (IRE) **Options O Syndicate**
67 **RIDERS ONTHE STORM (IRE)**, 7, br g Scorpion (IRE)—Endless Moments (IRE) **Carl Hinchy & Mark Scott**
68 **RIZZARDO**, 8, gr g Tikkanen (USA)—Last Spruce (USA) **Mr N. A. Twiston-Davies**
69 **ROBINSHILL (IRE)**, 9, ch g Robin des Champs (FR)—I Remember It Well (IRE) **Mr R. J. Rexton**
70 **ROCCO (IRE)**, 7, b g Shantou (USA)—Navaro (IRE) **Mr & Mrs P Carter**
71 **ROOTLESS TREE (IRE)**, 5, b g Jeremy (USA)—Miss Compliance (IRE) **Mr C. S. Hinchy**
72 **SCARLETT OF TARA**, 7, b m Kayf Tara—Late For Class (IRE) **Mr N. A. Twiston-Davies**
73 **SCOTCHTOWN (IRE)**, 8, ch g Beneficial—Always Present (IRE) **Valda Burke & Bryan Burrough**
74 **SINISTER MINISTER**, 5, bl gr g Malinas (GER)—Champagne Lil **Mr C. S. Hinchy**
75 **SIR VALENTINE (GER)**, 7, b g Cacique (IRE)—Singuna (GER) **Walters Plant Hire & Potter Group**
76 **STADMALLEN (IRE)**, 4, b g Getaway (GER)—Honey Blond (IRE) **Mr M. L. Berryman**
77 **STOLEN SILVER (FR)**, 5, gr g Lord du Sud (FR)—Change Partner (FR) **Walters Plant Hire & Potter Group**
78 **SUMMIT LIKE HERBIE**, 8, ch g Sulamani (IRE)—Colline de Fleurs **Friends Of Herbie**
79 **SUPAKALANISTIC (IRE)**, 7, b g Kalanisi (IRE)—Keys Hope (IRE) **Jump For Fun Racing**
80 **THE HOLLOW GINGE (IRE)**, 7, b g Oscar (IRE)—Some Gem (IRE) **The Ginge Army**
81 **THE MICK PRESTON (IRE)**, 4, gr g Shirocco (GER)—Izzy du Berlais (IRE) **The Preston Family Racing**
82 **THE NEWEST ONE (IRE)**, 5, b g Oscar (IRE)—Thuringe (FR) **S Such & CG Paletta**
83 **TIP TOP CAT (IRE)**, 5, b g Milan—Pilgara (IRE) **Ms J. E. McGivern**
84 **TOOK THE LOT**, 6, b g Black Sam Bellamy (IRE)—Riverbank Rainbow **The True Acre Partnership**
85 **TOPOFTHECOTSWOLDS (IRE)**, 6, b g Arcadio (GER)—Bambootcha (IRE) **Mr C. J. Haughey**
86 **TORN AND FRAYED (FR)**, 6, b g Califet (FR)—Chic Et Zen (FR) **Mr C. S. Hinchy**
87 **TORPILLO (FR)**, 5, ch g Alanadi (FR)—Astherate (FR) **Mr Simon Munir & Mr Isaac Souede**
88 **TOWNSHEND (GER)**, 9, b g Lord of England (GER)—Trikolore (GER) **Mr J. Neild**
89 **TURNING GOLD**, 6, ch g Pivotal—Illusion **Turning Gold**
90 **VIENNA COURT (IRE)**, 5, b br m Mahler—Gales Present (IRE) **James and Jean Potter Ltd**
91 **VULCAN BOMBER**, 4, b g Native Ruler—Definitley Lovely **Mr N. A. Twiston-Davies**
92 **WAITONIT (IRE)**, 5, b g Presenting—Askanna (IRE) **Carl Hinchy & Mark Scott**
93 **WHISKEY MOON**, 8, b g Erhaab (USA)—Flaviola (IRE) **J. A. B. Old**
94 **WHOLESTONE (IRE)**, 9, br g Craigsteel—Last Theatre (IRE) **Mr Simon Munir & Mr Isaac Souede**
95 **WICKED WILLY (IRE)**, 9, br g Arcadio (GER)—How Provincial (IRE) **Mr C. Roberts**
96 **ZAMBELLA (FR)**, 5, b m Zambezi Sun—Visby (FR) **Mr Simon Munir & Mr Isaac Souede**

THREE-YEAR-OLDS

97 **DORCHESTER DOM (IRE)**, ch g Starspangledbanner (AUS)—Moriches (IRE) **Mr W Twiston Davies & Partner**

Other Owners: Mrs V. F. Burke, B. R. H. Burrough, Mrs P. J. Burrough, Mrs J. Carter, Mr P. A. Carter, Mr A. R. Coney, Mrs S. Coney, P. D. Evans, Mrs J. A. Fowler, Mr C. S. Hinchy, Mrs A. D. Jelley, G. S. Jelley, Mr C. J. Jenkins, Mrs C. M. Keeys, G. F. Keeys, Mr D. M. Mason, G. A. Mason, Mr J. M. McGoff, F. J. Mills, W. R. Mills, S. E. Munir, Mr J. Neild, Mr P. Preston, Mr R. J. Rexton, Mr M. S. Scott, Mr I. Souede, Sundorne Products (Llanidloes) Ltd, Mr W. Twiston-Davies, The Hon A. G. Vestey, The Hon W. G. Vestey, Walters Plant Hire Ltd, J. Wenman, Mrs S. Wenman.

NH Jockey: Jamie Bargary, Tom Bellamy, Sam Twiston-Davies. **Conditional Jockey:** Jordan Nailor.

535 MR JAMES UNETT, Wolverhampton
Postal: **1 Dunstall Mews, Gorsebrook Road, Wolverhampton, West Midlands, WV6 0PE**
Contacts: PHONE **01691 610001** MOBILE **07887 534753** FAX **01691 610001**
EMAIL **jamesunett1327@yahoo.co.uk** WEBSITE **www.jamesunettracing.com**

1 **CITTA D'ORO,** 5, b g Cityscape—Corsa All Oro (USA) **P. S. Burke**
2 **EBQAA (IRE),** 6, b m Cape Cross (IRE)—Estedaama (IRE) **J. W. Unett**
3 **KING OSWALD (USA),** 7, b g Street Cry (IRE)—Northern Melody (IRE) **M. Watkinson & Mr P. Steadman**
4 **LOVEATFIRSTLIGHT (IRE),** 4, b f Es Que Love (IRE)—Spark Up **J. W. Unett**
5 **QUIXOTE (GER),** 10, b h Pivotal—Quebrada (IRE) **J. W. Unett**
6 **SYMPHONY (IRE),** 4, gr f Gregorian (IRE)—Anazah (USA) **Paul Steadman & Partner**

THREE-YEAR-OLDS
7 B c Requinto (IRE)—Coastal Storm

Other Owners: Mr D. P. Steadman, J. W. Unett, Mr M. Watkinson.

Assistant Trainer: Miss C. H. Jones.

536 MR MARK USHER, Lambourn
Postal: **Rowdown House Stables, Upper Lambourn, Hungerford, Berkshire, RG17 8QP**
Contacts: PHONE **01488 73630, 01488 72598** MOBILE **07831 873531**
EMAIL **markusher.racing@btconnect.com** WEBSITE **www.markusherracing.co.uk**

1 **APEX KING (IRE),** 6, b g Kodiac—Rainbowskia (FR) **G. B. Firmager & G. H. Firmager**
2 **ARLECCHINO'S ARC (IRE),** 5, ch g Arcano (IRE)—Sir Cecil's Girl (IRE) **Mr K. Senior**
3 **ARLECCHINO'S LEAP,** 8, br g Kheleyf (USA)—Donna Giovanna **Mr K. Senior**
4 **BAASHIQ (IRE),** 6, b g New Approach (IRE)—Fatanah (IRE) **P. Kelly**
5 **BAYSTON HILL,** 6, br g Big Bad Bob (IRE)—Jessica Ennis (USA) **High Five Racing and Partners**
6 **BIRD FOR LIFE,** 6, b m Delegator—Birdolini **The Mark Usher Racing Club**
7 **BIRD TO LOVE,** 6, b m Delegator—Bird Over **The Mark Usher Racing Club**
8 **BORN TO PLEASE,** 6, b m Stimulation (IRE)—Heart Felt **The Mark Usher Racing Club**
9 **DREAMBOAT ANNIE,** 5, b m Piccolo—Bold Rose **Ushers Court**
10 **DYLAN'S SEA SONG,** 6, b m Dylan Thomas (IRE)—Mary Sea (FR) **Ushers Court**
11 **MARSHALL AID (IRE),** 7, b g Lawman (FR)—Dievotchkina (IRE) **Mr B. C. Rogan**
12 **MIRACLE OF MEDINAH,** 9, ch g Milk It Mick—Smart Ass (IRE) **The Mark Usher Racing Club**
13 **MISU PETE,** 8, b g Misu Bond (IRE)—Smart Ass (IRE) **The Mark Usher Racing Club**
14 **PADURA BRAVE,** 4, b f Havana Gold (IRE)—Audaz **Twenty Four Carrot Racing**
15 **POINT IN TIME (IRE),** 5, b m Champs Elysees—Creme Anglaise **GAF Racing**
16 **SELLINGALLTHETIME (IRE),** 9, ch g Tamayuz—Anthyllis (GER) **Mr Kirk Jefferies & Partner**
17 **TIN FANDANGO,** 5, b g Steele Tango (USA)—Littlemoor Lass **Mr M. A. Humphreys**
18 **WAQAAS,** 6, b g Showcasing—Red Mischief (IRE) **Goodracing Partnership**

THREE-YEAR-OLDS
19 **EVAPORUST (IRE),** b g Gale Force Ten—Bigalo's Laura B (IRE) **Twenty Four Carrot Racing**
20 **ON THE RIGHT TRACK,** gr g Mukhadram—Jessica Ennis (USA) **Mrs T. J. Channing-Williams**
21 **SKYLLACHY,** b c Kyllachy—Sweetest Revenge (IRE) **The Ridgeway Partnership**

TWO-YEAR-OLDS
22 **BLUE GALAXY,** gr c 14/02 Telescope—Indigo (Medicean)
23 B c 02/04 Charm Spirit—Columella (Kyllachy)
24 B c 16/03 Gleneagles—Destalink (Rail Link)
25 B f 25/01 Iffraaj—Light Fantastic (Acclamation)
26 **THE BAY WARRIOR (IRE),** b c 27/04 The Gurkha (IRE)—Fraulein (Acatenango (GER)) (42000) **Andy & Lizzie Cova**

Other Owners: Mr P. Brett, Mrs T. J. Channing-Williams, Mr A. Cova, Mrs E. Cova, Mr D. P. Duffy, Paul Duffy, David Semmens, Viv Williams, Mr G. B. Firmager, Mr G. H. Firmager, High Five Racing, Mr P. Hobbs, Mr K. Jefferies, Mr N. P. McEntyre, Ms D. M. Ray, Mr D. M. Semmens, Mr M. D. I. Usher.

Assistant Trainer: Michael Usher.

537 **MR ROGER VARIAN, Newmarket**
Postal: **Carlburg Stables, 49 Bury Road, Newmarket, Suffolk, CB8 7BY**
Contacts: **PHONE 01638 661702 FAX 01638 667018**
EMAIL office@varianstable.com WEBSITE www.varianstable.com

1 **APPARATE**, 4, b c Dubawi (IRE)—Appearance **Sheikh Mohammed Obaid Al Maktoum**
2 **AUSTRALIS (IRE)**, 4, b g Australia—Quiet Down (USA) **Biddestone Racing XX**
3 **BARSANTI (IRE)**, 8, b g Champs Elysees—Silver Star **Sheikh Mohammed Obaid Al Maktoum**
4 **CAPE BYRON**, 6, ch g Shamardal (USA)—Reem Three **Sheikh Mohammed Obaid Al Maktoum**
5 **DEFOE (IRE)**, 6, gr g Dalakhani (IRE)—Dulkashe (IRE) **Sheikh Mohammed Obaid Al Maktoum**
6 **EMIRATES KNIGHT (IRE)**, 4, b c Dark Angel (IRE)—Interim Payment (USA) **Ziad A. Galadari**
7 **FARNHAM**, 4, b f Farhh—Purple Tiger (IRE) **Clipper Logistics**
8 **FARZEEN**, 4, ch f Farhh—Zee Zee Gee **Helena Springfield Ltd**
9 **FEARLESSLY (IRE)**, 4, gr f Dalakhani (IRE)—Mid Mon Lady (IRE) **Saif Ali**
10 **FIFTH POSITION (IRE)**, 4, b g Dark Angel (IRE)—Ballet Move **Sheikh Mohammed Obaid Al Maktoum**
11 **FUJAIRA PRINCE (IRE)**, 6, gr ro g Pivotal—Zam Zoom (IRE) **Sheikh Mohammed Obaid Al Maktoum**
12 **GAME PLAYER (IRE)**, 5, gr g Dark Angel (IRE)—Lucky Clio (IRE) **Sheikh Mohammed Obaid Al Maktoum**
13 **GOING PLACES**, 4, ch c Frankel—Khor Sheed **Sheikh Mohammed Obaid Al Maktoum**
14 **INVITATIONAL**, 4, ch f Poet's Voice—Platinum Pearl **Ziad A. Galadari**
15 **KHUZAAM (USA)**, 4, ch c Kitten's Joy (USA)—Afraah (USA) **Mr Hamdan Al Maktoum**
16 **LOOK CLOSELY**, 4, b g Sea The Stars (IRE)—Lady Heidi **Sheikh Mohammed Obaid Al Maktoum**
17 **MACKAAR (IRE)**, 4, b g Cape Cross (IRE)—Albemarle **Sheikh Ahmed Al Maktoum**
18 **MOTIVATE ME (FR)**, 4, b f Motivator—Jomana (IRE) **Saif Ali**
19 **MOUNTAIN ANGEL (IRE)**, 6, b g Dark Angel (IRE)—Fanciful Dancer **Ziad A. Galadari**
20 **MUTAMAASIK**, 4, ch g Dubawi (IRE)—Muhawalah (IRE) **Mr Hamdan Al Maktoum**
21 **MUTASAAMY (IRE)**, 4, b g Oasis Dream—Eswarah **Mr Hamdan Al Maktoum**
22 **PRINCE EIJI**, 4, ch c Dubawi (IRE)—Izzi Top **Sheikh Mohammed Obaid Al Maktoum**
23 **ROSEMAN (IRE)**, 4, b c Kingman—Go Lovely Rose (IRE) **Sheikh Mohammed Obaid Al Maktoum**
24 **SALAYEL**, 4, b f Bated Breath—Hurry Home Hillary (USA) **Sheikh Ahmed Al Maktoum**
25 **SAN DONATO (IRE)**, 4, b c Lope de Vega (IRE)—Boston Rocker (IRE) **Sheikh Mohammed Obaid Al Maktoum**
26 **SHARJA BRIDGE**, 6, b g Oasis Dream—Quetena (GER) **Sheikh Mohammed Obaid Al Maktoum**
27 **SPANISH CITY**, 7, ch g Exceed And Excel (AUS)—Annabelle's Charm (IRE) **Merry Fox Stud Limited**
28 **SPECIALISE**, 4, gr f Mastercraftsman (IRE)—My Special J's (USA) **Saif Ali**
29 **TURJOMAAN (USA)**, 4, b br c War Front (USA)—Almoutezah (USA) **Mr Hamdan Al Maktoum**
30 **UAE JEWEL**, 4, b c Dubawi (IRE)—Gemstone (IRE) **Sheikh Mohammed Obaid Al Maktoum**
31 **UAE PRINCE (IRE)**, 7, b g Sea The Stars (IRE)—By Request **Sheikh Mohammed Obaid Al Maktoum**
32 **WILLIE JOHN**, 5, b h Dansili—Izzi Top **Sheikh Mohammed Obaid Al Maktoum**
33 **ZABEEL PRINCE (IRE)**, 7, ch g Lope de Vega (IRE)—
                                                Princess Serena (USA) **Sheikh Mohammed Obaid Al Maktoum**

THREE-YEAR-OLDS
34 **AFFWONN (IRE)**, b c Free Eagle (IRE)—Shauna's Princess (IRE) **Sheikh Ahmed Al Maktoum**
35 **ALASH ORDA**, b f Kodiac—Albanka (USA) **Nurlan Bizakov**
36 **ANGEL POWER**, b f Lope de Vega (IRE)—Burning Rules (IRE) **King Power Racing Co Ltd**
37 **AQUILEO (IRE)**, b c Gleneagles (IRE)—Nobilis **China Horse Club International Limited**
38 **ASCENSION**, gr c Dark Angel (IRE)—Making Eyes (IRE) **Highclere T'Bred Racing - Benedict Allen**
39 **BELIEVE IN LOVE (IRE)**, b f Make Believe—Topka (FR) **Koji Maeda**
40 B f Lope de Vega (IRE)—Beyond Desire **Clipper Logistics**
41 **BLAZING BEAU (IRE)**, b c War Front (USA)—My Dark Rosaleen **Merry Fox Stud Limited**
42 **CABALETTA**, gr f Mastercraftsman (IRE)—Allegretto **Cheveley Park Stud**
43 **CHARMING SPIRIT (IRE)**, b f Invincible Spirit (IRE)—Willow View (USA) **Merry Fox Stud Limited**
44 **DAAHYEH**, ch f Bated Breath—Affluent **H.H. Sheikh Nasser Bin Hamad Al Khalifa**
45 **DEAR POWER (IRE)**, b f Acclamation—Debutante **King Power Racing Co Ltd**
46 **DELTA'S ROYALTY (IRE)**, b f Galileo (IRE)—Royal Delta (USA) **Benjamin Leon Jr**
47 **DESERT EMPEROR**, b c Camelot—Praia (GER) **Sheikh Mohammed Obaid Al Maktoum**
48 **DUBLIN PHARAOH (USA)**, ch c American Pharoah (USA)—Wile Cat (USA) **Damien Brennan**
49 **ESPRIT ROSE (IRE)**, b f Invincible Spirit (IRE)—Intense Pink **Sheikh Mohammed Obaid Al Maktoum**
50 **ESTABLISH**, ch c Australia—Azenzar **Mr A D Spence**
51 **FAHAD**, b c Farhh—Radhaadh (IRE) **Hussain Alabbas Lootah**
52 **FOORAAT (IRE)**, b f Dubawi (IRE)—Nahrain **Sheikh Ahmed Al Maktoum**

MR ROGER VARIAN - continued

53 **GOLD WAND (IRE)**, b f Golden Horn—Los Ojitos (USA) **Khaled A Rahim**
54 **GOOD HUMOR**, b c Distorted Humor (USA)—Time On **Mr R Barnett & Partner**
55 **HAAFITHAH**, ch f Nathaniel (IRE)—Muhawalah (IRE) **Mr Hamdan Al Maktoum**
56 **HASEENAH (IRE)**, ch f Intello (GER)—Murahana (IRE) **Mr Hamdan Al Maktoum**
57 **HIBERNIAN WARRIOR (USA)**, b br c War Front (USA)—Quarter Moon (IRE) **Damien Brennan**
58 **I NEVER SAY NO (IRE)**, b f No Nay Never (USA)—Shelley Beach (IRE)
59 **IKEBANA**, b f Pivotal—Sea The Bloom **Cheveley Park Stud**
60 **JAAIZAH**, b f Dansili—Hadaatha (IRE) **Mr Hamdan Al Maktoum**
61 **JAARIYAH (USA)**, b br f Shamardal (USA)—Jiwen (CAN) **Mr Hamdan Al Maktoum**
62 **JUMAIRA BAY (FR)**, b c Siyouni—Desert Sunrise **Al Kamda Racing**
63 **KANNOOR**, b f New Approach (IRE)—Tantshi (IRE) **Sheikh Ahmed Al Maktoum**
64 **KHALAF**, b g Gutaifan (IRE)—Dominatrix **Mr Hamdan Al Maktoum**
65 **KHALOOSY (IRE)**, gr c Dubawi (IRE)—Elshaadin **Mr Hamdan Al Maktoum**
66 **KING RAGNAR**, b c Hot Streak (IRE)—Park Law (IRE) **Sheikh Mana Bin Mohammed Al Maktoum**
67 **LIGERA**, b f Showcasing—Lashyn (USA) **Nurlan Bizakov**
68 **LORD CAMPARI (IRE)**, b c Kingman—Blanche Dubawi (IRE) **Sheikh Mohammed Obaid Al Maktoum**
69 **MAGNETISED**, b c Shamardal (USA)—Princess Nada **Sheikh Mohammed Obaid Al Maktoum**
70 **MAQTAL (USA)**, b g Distorted Humor (USA)—Almoutezah (USA) **Mr Hamdan Al Maktoum**
71 **MARREYR**, ch c Pivotal—Maid For Winning (USA) **Sheikh Ahmed Al Maktoum**
72 **MILLVINA**, b f Dutch Art—Molly Brown **Cheveley Park Stud**
73 **MOLATHAM**, ch c Night of Thunder (IRE)—Cantal **Mr Hamdan Al Maktoum**
74 **MONDAMMEJ**, b g Lope de Vega (IRE)—Lamps of Heaven (IRE) **Mr Hamdan Al Maktoum**
75 **MONTATHER (IRE)**, ch c Dubawi (IRE)—Lanansaak (IRE) **Mr Hamdan Al Maktoum**
76 **MORROOJ (IRE)**, b f Invincible Spirit (IRE)—Alwarga (USA) **Sheikh Ahmed Al Maktoum**
77 **MOTAMAYIZ**, b g Charm Spirit (IRE)—Chanterelle (FR) **Ahmad Bintooq**
78 **MOTTRIB (IRE)**, b c Invincible Spirit (IRE)—Freezy (IRE) **Sheikh Ahmed Al Maktoum**
79 **MOUNT MAYON (IRE)**, b c Kodiac—Nisriyna (IRE) **Cheveley Park Stud**
80 **MUSICALITY**, b c Kyllachy—Allegro Viva (USA) **Biddestone Racing XIII**
81 **NAIZAGAI**, b c Dark Angel (IRE)—Nazym (IRE) **Nurlan Bizakov**
82 **NEHAALL**, ch f Pivotal—Khatiba (IRE) **Sheikh Ahmed Al Maktoum**
83 **PERFECTED**, ch c Night of Thunder (IRE)—Semayyel (IRE) **H Moorhead, C Fahy & J Collins**
84 **PIERRE LAPIN (IRE)**, b c Cappella Sansevero—Beatrix Potter (IRE) **Sheikh Mohammed Obaid Al Maktoum**
85 **POSTILEO (IRE)**, b c Galileo (IRE)—Posterity (IRE) **Sheikh Mohammed Obaid Al Maktoum**
86 **PREMIER POWER**, ch c Siyouni (FR)—Pelerin (IRE) **King Power Racing Co Ltd**
87 **PROGRESSIVE**, b f Nathaniel (IRE)—Graduation **Cheveley Park Stud**
88 **QAADDIM (IRE)**, ch g Hot Streak (IRE)—Never In (IRE) **Sheikh Ahmed Al Maktoum**
89 **QUEEN DAENERYS (IRE)**, b f Frankel—Song to Remember (USA) **H.H. Sheikh Nasser Bin Hamad Al Khalifa**
90 **RAINFORD**, ch g Sea The Moon (GER)—Cushat Law (IRE) **M & M Franklin**
91 **RASTAMA**, b f Le Havre (IRE)—Raushan (IRE) **Nurlan Bizakov**
92 **RETROSPECT (IRE)**, b c Frankel—Looking Back (IRE) **Sheikh Mohammed Obaid Al Maktoum**
93 **RIDESON**, b f Golden Horn—Rekdhat (IRE) **Sheikh Ahmed Al Maktoum**
94 **ROCK OF FAME**, b f Fastnet Rock (AUS)—Familliarity **Helena Springfield Ltd**
95 **SAMAAWAAT (IRE)**, ch f Dubawi (IRE)—Mubadarat **Mr Hamdan Al Maktoum**
96 **SEMSER**, b c Siyouni (FR)—Serres (IRE) **Nurlan Bizakov**
97 **SEPTEMBER POWER (IRE)**, b f Mastercraftsman (IRE)—Lisanor **King Power Racing Co Ltd**
98 **SHANDOZ**, b c Golden Horn—Shabyt **Nurlan Bizakov**
99 **SOLAR SCREEN (IRE)**, gr c Golden Horn—Screen Star (IRE) **Sheikh Mohammed Obaid Al Maktoum**
100 **STYLISTIQUE**, b f Dansili—Sleek **Miss Yvonne Jacques**
101 **SUBELLA (IRE)**, b f Teofilo (IRE)—Suba (USA) **Sheikh Mohammed Obaid Al Maktoum**
102 **SUNDAY SOVEREIGN**, b c Equiano (FR)—Red Sovereign **King Power Racing Co Ltd**
103 **SURFSEEKER**, b f Golden Horn—Shimmering Surf (IRE) **P Winkworth**
104 **SWAN RIVER (IRE)**, b f Australia—Theann **Cheveley Park Stud**
105 Gr f Mastercraftsman (IRE)—Sweet Sixteen (IRE) **Mr Fahad Abdullah Al Harthi**
106 **SWOOPING EAGLE (IRE)**, b g Free Eagle (IRE)—Weekend Lady (IRE) **Varian Racing I**
107 **TASAAMUH (USA)**, b br f Candy Ride (ARG)—Afraah (USA) **Mr Hamdan Al Maktoum**
108 **TINKER TOY**, b c War Front (USA)—Cursory Glance (USA) **Merry Fox Stud Limited**
109 **TROLL PENINSULA (USA)**, b g Karakontie (JPN)—Perfect Step (USA) **Flaxman Stables Ireland Ltd**
110 **TURKESTAN**, b c New Approach (IRE)—Totally Devoted (USA) **Nurlan Bizakov**
111 **UNION (IRE)**, b c New Approach (IRE)—Shahnila (FR) **Highclere T'Bred Racing - Hannah Stodel**

MR ROGER VARIAN - continued

112 **VALYRIAN STEEL (IRE)**, b c Frankel—Sabratah **H.H. Sheikh Nasser Bin Hamad Al Khalifa**
113 **VILLAIN'S VOICE**, ch c Poet's Voice—Balayage (IRE) **Promenade Bloodstock Limited**
114 B c Frankel—Vodka (JPN)
115 **WALEYDD**, b c Nathaniel (IRE)—Ta Ammol **Sheikh Ahmed Al Maktoum**
116 **WALIYAK (FR)**, br f Le Havre (IRE)—Vadariya **Fawzi Abdulla Nass**
117 **WINTER THORN (IRE)**, gr c Muhaarar—Rose of Summer (USA) **Sheikh Mohammed Obaid Al Maktoum**
118 **WONDROUS WORDS (IRE)**, b f Lope de Vega (IRE)—Wonderfully (IRE) **Ballylinch Stud**
119 **ZEEBAND (IRE)**, b g Sea The Stars (IRE)—Zeeba (IRE) **Sheikh Mohammed Obaid Al Maktoum**
120 **ZEGALO (IRE)**, b c Zoffany (IRE)—Mzyoon (IRE) **Hussain Alabbas Lootah**
121 **ZEZENIA (IRE)**, b f Oasis Dream—Lahaleeb (IRE) **Khaled A Rahim**

TWO-YEAR-OLDS

122 Gr c 15/04 Sea The Stars (IRE)—Aghaany (Dubawi (IRE)) **Mr Hamdan Al Maktoum**
123 **ALBANMAN (IRE)**, b c 20/03 Lawman (FR)—Albanka (USA) (Giant's Causeway (USA)) **Nurlan Bizakov**
124 **AQUAMAN (IRE)**, b c 10/03 Kodiac—
                                 Aqualis (Sea The Stars (IRE)) (300000) **Sheikh Mohammed Obaid Al Maktoum**
125 B f 22/03 Harzand (IRE)—Athenaire (IRE) (Duke of Marmalade (IRE)) (130000) **Hussain Alabbas Lootah**
126 **ATHERS (IRE)**, ch c 12/04 Dubawi (IRE)—
                                 Kelly Nicole (IRE) (Rainbow Quest (USA)) (320000) **Sheikh Mohammed Obaid Al Maktoum**
127 B c 06/03 Cable Bay (IRE)—Ballet Move (Oasis Dream) (160000) **Mr Hamdan Al Maktoum**
128 Ch c 20/05 Gleneagles (IRE)—Blue Butterfly (Kyllachy) (90000)
129 B c 22/01 Cable Bay (IRE)—Bonhomie (Shamardal (USA)) (166666) **Mr Hamdan Al Maktoum**
130 **BOOMSHALAA**, b c 11/03 Shalaa (IRE)—
                                 Summer Collection (IRE) (Teofilo (IRE)) (350000) **Sheikh Mohammed Obaid Al Maktoum**
131 B c 18/02 Kingman—Brevity (USA) (Street Cry (IRE)) (425000) **H.H. Sheikh Nasser Bin Hamad Al Khalifa**
132 **BROAD STRIPES**, ch f 03/02 Starspangledbanner (AUS)—Jantina (Dutch Art) **Cheveley Park Stud**
133 B c 30/03 Siyouni (FR)—
                                 Candinie (USA) (Bernardini (USA)) (171600) **H.H. Sheikh Nasser Bin Hamad Al Khalifa & Partner**
134 B f 03/03 Kodiac—
                                 Compostela (Sea The Stars (IRE)) (64350) **H.H. Sheikh Nasser Bin Hamad Al Khalifa & Partner**
135 B c 11/04 Galileo (IRE)—Crown Queen (USA) (Smart Strike (CAN)) **Benjamin Leon Jr**
136 B c 29/04 Camelot—Danehill's Dream (IRE) (Danehill (USA)) (150149) **Highclere Tbred Racing-Charles Church**
137 Ch c 16/04 Night of Thunder (IRE)—Divisimo (Dansili) (360000) **Mr Hamdan Al Maktoum**
138 **DUBAWI SANDS**, ch c 14/04 Dubawi (IRE)—
                                 Galicuix (Galileo (IRE)) (260000) **Sheikh Mohammed Obaid Al Maktoum**
139 **ECO FRIENDLY (IRE)**, b f 26/03 Sea The Stars (IRE)—
                                 Edisia (Holy Roman Emperor (IRE)) (72000) **W. J. and T. C. O. Gredley**
140 **EL DRAMA (IRE)**, ch c 19/02 Lope de Vega (IRE)—
                                 Victoire Finale (Peintre Celebre (USA)) (425000) **Sheikh Mohammed Obaid Al Maktoum**
141 B f 11/03 Belardo (IRE)—Elite (Invincible Spirit (IRE)) (10476)
142 B c 27/02 Mehmas (IRE)—Entreat (Pivotal) (247619) **H.H. Sheikh Nasser Bin Hamad Al Khalifa & Partner**
143 B f 20/02 Showcasing—Exceptionelle (Exceed And Excel (AUS))
144 B c 10/04 Dark Angel (IRE)—Facade (IRE) (Galileo (IRE)) (95000)
145 Ch c 15/02 Dubawi (IRE)—Ferdoos (Dansili) **Sheikh Ahmed Al Maktoum**
146 **FRANKAI (IRE)**, b f 15/04 Frankel—
                                 Dubai Queen (USA) (Kingmambo (USA)) **Sheikh Mohammed Obaid Al Maktoum**
147 Ch f 26/04 New Approach (IRE)—Gee Kel (IRE) (Danehill Dancer (IRE)) (60000) **Sheikh Juma Dalmook Al Maktoum**
148 B br c 04/03 Muhaarar—Go Lovely Rose (IRE) (Pivotal) (260000) **Amo Racing Limited**
149 B c 20/02 Siyouni (FR)—Goathemala (GER) (Black Sam Bellamy (IRE)) (160000) **King Power Racing Co Ltd**
150 B c 29/04 Dark Angel (IRE)—
                                 Graciously (Shamardal (USA)) (120120) **H.H. Sheikh Nasser Bin Hamad Al Khalifa & Partner**
151 B f 30/03 Iffraaj—Habita (IRE) (Montjeu (IRE)) (49523) **Mr M. Almarzooqi**
152 **HEY MR**, b c 23/02 Territories (IRE)—Filona (IRE) (Motivator) (104761) **Amo Racing Limited**
153 **JARAMILLO**, b c 27/03 Oasis Dream—Guajara (GER) (Montjeu (IRE)) (50000) **Teme Valley 2**
154 **JET ENGINE (IRE)**, b br c 20/04 No Nay Never (USA)—
                                 Double Fantasy (GER) (Indian Ridge) (320000) **Sheikh Mohammed Obaid Al Maktoum**
155 **KINDRED SPIRIT (IRE)**, b f 15/05 Invincible Spirit (IRE)—
                                 Pontenuovo (FR) (Green Tune (USA)) **Merry Fox Stud Limited**

MR ROGER VARIAN - continued

156 KING FRANCIS (IRE), b c 04/05 Le Havre (IRE)— Princess Nada (Barathea (IRE)) **Sheikh Mohammed Obaid Al Maktoum**

157 KING TRITON (IRE), b c 31/01 Invincible Spirit (IRE)—Nada (Teofilo (IRE)) **Sheikh Mohammed Obaid Al Maktoum**

158 B f 11/04 Shamardal (USA)—Lanansaak (USA) (Zamindar (USA)) **Mr Hamdan Al Maktoum**

159 LANKARAN, ch c 15/03 Kendargent (FR)—Lashyn (USA) (Mr Greeley (USA)) **Nurlan Bizakov**

160 LEGEND OF DUBAI, b c 01/03 Dubawi (IRE)— Speedy Boarding (Shamardal (USA)) (500000) **Sheikh Mohammed Obaid Al Maktoum**

161 LEGION OF HONOUR, b c 07/03 Wootton Bassett—Miss Vendome (IRE) (Medicean) (266666) **Teme Valley 2**

162 B f 26/04 Oasis Dream—Longing To Dance (Danehill Dancer (IRE)) (160000) **Sheikh Ahmed Al Maktoum**

163 B c 02/04 Invincible Spirit (IRE)—Los Ojitos (USA) (Mr Greeley (USA)) **Khaled A Rahim**

164 MA QUALITE (IRE), ch c 31/01 Night of Thunder (IRE)—Paris To Peking (ITY) (Intikhab (USA)) (68640)

165 Ch c 25/03 Pride of Dubai (AUS)—Mensoora (SAF) (Jet Master (SAF))

166 MINDPOWER (IRE), ch c 17/05 Gleneagles (IRE)— Common Knowledge (Rainbow Quest (USA)) (120000) **Sheikh Mohammed Obaid Al Maktoum**

167 Ch c 29/03 Equiano (FR)—Miss Rimex (IRE) (Ezzoud (IRE)) (9523) **Varian Racing V**

168 Ch c 08/05 Mayson—Moon Goddess (Rainbow Quest (USA)) (23809) **Varian Racing IV**

169 MOSHAAWER, gr c 27/03 Frankel—Hadaatha (IRE) (Sea The Stars (IRE)) **Mr Hamdan Al Maktoum**

170 MOVIN TIME, b c 29/04 Fastnet Rock (AUS)— Time On (Sadler's Wells (USA)) (170000) **Sheikh Mohammed Obaid Al Maktoum**

171 B f 09/03 New Bay—Musalaha (IRE) (Nayef (USA)) (60000) **Mr M. Almarzooqi**

172 NAGANO, b c 06/04 Fastnet Rock (AUS)—Nazym (IRE) (Galileo (IRE)) **Nurlan Bizakov**

173 Ch f 09/03 Sea The Stars (IRE)—Nahrain (Selkirk (USA)) **Sheikh Ahmed Al Maktoum**

174 PAPACITO (IRE), br c 20/02 Estidhkaar (IRE)— Out of Time (IRE) (Anabaa (USA)) (140000) **Sheikh Mohammed Obaid Al Maktoum**

175 B c 27/03 Giant's Causeway (USA)—Piracicaba (IRE) (Dansili) **H.H. Sheikh Mohammed bin Khalifa Al-Thani**

176 PRAIANO (GER), b c 31/03 Dubawi (IRE)— Praia (GER) (Big Shuffle (USA)) (500000) **Sheikh Mohammed Obaid Al Maktoum**

177 PUY MARY, ch f 30/03 Intello (GER)—Cantal (Pivotal) **Cheveley Park Stud**

178 RAADOBARG (IRE), b c 27/03 Night of Thunder (IRE)— Queen Bodicea (IRE) (Revoque (IRE)) (190476) **Amo Racing Limited**

179 B c 01/02 Iffraaj—Riskit Fora Biskit (IRE) (Kodiac) (142857) **Mr Hamdan Al Maktoum**

180 RIVER DANCE, b f 28/02 Frankel—Cursory Glance (USA) (Distorted Humor (USA)) **Merry Fox Stud Limited**

181 ROYAL CHAMPION (IRE), b c 28/02 Shamardal (USA)— Emirates Queen (Street Cry (IRE)) **Sheikh Mohammed Obaid Al Maktoum**

182 SARDINIA SUNSET (IRE), gr f 30/01 Gutaifan (IRE)—Rush (Compton Place) (90476) **Amo Racing Limited**

183 B f 19/01 Shalaa (IRE)—Sarlisa (FR) (Rainbow Quest (USA)) (45714) **Varian Racing II**

184 SHABANDOZ, b c 12/03 Wootton Bassett—Shabyt (Sadler's Wells (USA)) **Nurlan Bizakov**

185 SHE DO, b f 27/02 Siyouni (FR)—Minnaloushe (IRE) (Lawman (FR)) (100000) **W. J. and T. C. O. Gredley**

186 B c 04/03 New Bay— Sister Dam's (IRE) (Mastercraftsman (IRE)) (57142) **H.H. Sheikh Nasser Bin Hamad Al Khalifa & Partner**

187 SKYLINER, b c 15/03 Dark Angel (IRE)— A Huge Dream (IRE) (Refuse To Bend (IRE)) (220000) **Sheikh Mohammed Obaid Al Maktoum**

188 B f 27/03 Footstepsinthesand—Sommorell (IRE) (Fast Company (IRE)) (160000) **Amo Racing Limited**

189 B c 24/03 New Bay—Soteria (IRE) (Acclamation) (38095) **Varian Racing III**

190 B c 05/05 Kingman—Sotka (Dutch Art) (343200) **King Power Racing Co Ltd**

191 Ch c 19/02 Kitten's Joy (USA)—Street Interest (USA) (Street Cry (IRE)) (241815) **Mr Hamdan Al Maktoum**

192 B f 22/03 Invincible Spirit (IRE)— Swift Campaign (IRE) (Intikhab (USA)) (50000) **Sheikh Juma Dalmook Al Maktoum**

193 B f 02/02 Golden Horn—Ta Ammol (Halling (USA)) **Sheikh Ahmed Al Maktoum**

194 THIRD REALM, b c 02/03 Sea The Stars (IRE)— Reem Three (Mark of Esteem (IRE)) **Sheikh Mohammed Obaid Al Maktoum**

195 TIMELESS SOUL (GER), ch f 19/02 Night of Thunder (IRE)— Tatienne (IRE) (Nayef (USA)) (72930) **Mr M. Almarzooqi**

196 TYRRHENIAN SEA (IRE), gr c 09/05 Dark Angel (IRE)— Nocturne (GER) (Rock of Gibraltar (IRE)) **Flaxman Stables Ireland Ltd**

197 Ch c 22/01 Frankel—Vasilia (Dansili) (260000) **King Power Racing Co Ltd**

Assistant Trainer: John O'Donoghue.

Flat Jockey: Andrea Atzeni, David Egan, Jack Mitchell.

538 MR ED VAUGHAN, Newmarket
Postal: **Machell Place Cottage, Old Station Road, Newmarket, Suffolk, CB8 8DW**
Contacts: **PHONE 01638 667411 MOBILE 07799 144901 FAX 01638 667452**
EMAIL ed@efvaughan.com WEBSITE www.efvaughan.com

1 **DAME MALLIOT**, 4, b f Champs Elysees—Stars In Your Eyes **A. E. Oppenheimer**
2 **LOVE EXPLODES**, 4, b f Champs Elysees—Acquainted **Moroney & Singh**
3 **MAGIC J (USA)**, 4, ch c Scat Daddy (USA)—Miss Lamour (USA) **Phoenix Thoroughbred Limited**

THREE-YEAR-OLDS
4 **ANGELIC TIME (IRE)**, gr c Dark Angel (IRE)—Danetime Out (IRE) **Phoenix Thoroughbred Limited**
5 **COTO DONANA**, b f Kingman—Nyarhini **A. E. Oppenheimer**
6 **FORGE VALLEY LAD**, b c Cityscape—Tamara **A. M. Pickering**
7 **FRENCH BATTLE (USA)**, b f Declaration of War (USA)—Star of Paris (USA) **Phoenix Thoroughbred Limited**
8 **INHALATION**, b g Bated Breath—Al Joudha (FR) **Mr C. J. Murfitt**
9 **JANE DOE (IRE)**, b f Hallowed Crown (AUS)—Snowdrops **Mr E. F. Vaughan**
10 **KIRSCH (IRE)**, b f Swiss Spirit—Maybe I Will (IRE) **Swiss Bliss Syndicate**
11 **LITTLE BECKY**, b f Sir Percy—Amelia May **A. E. Oppenheimer**
12 **NIGHT BEAR**, ch c Dragon Pulse (IRE)—Contenance (IRE) **Mr S. B. M. Al Qassimi**
13 **OH SO CHIC**, b f Farhh—Lady Hen **A. Coombs & J. W. Rowley**
14 **ROCCALUCE**, b f Zoffany (IRE)—Magic Nymph (IRE) **A. E. Oppenheimer**
15 **SCARBOROUGH CASTLE**, b g Fastnet Rock (AUS)—Charlotte O Fraise (IRE) **A. M. Pickering**
16 **VICTORY WON (USA)**, b c Declaration of War (USA)—Magical Victory (USA) **Phoenix Thoroughbred Limited**
17 **WAR CROSS (USA)**, b br c War Front (USA)—Curvy **Phoenix Thoroughbred Limited**
18 **WHITBY HARBOUR**, b c No Nay Never (USA)—Secrets Away (IRE) **A. M. Pickering**

TWO-YEAR-OLDS
19 B c 14/04 Free Eagle (IRE)—Alice Treasure (IRE) (Canford Cliffs (IRE)) (12000) **Lee, Moroney, Singh & Partner**
20 **BRIDLINGTON BOBBY**, b g 20/01 Swiss Spirit—Primrose Valley (Pastoral Pursuits) **A. M. Pickering**
21 B f 20/01 Zoffany (IRE)—Chenchikova (IRE) (Sadler's Wells (USA)) (188760) **Phoenix Thoroughbred Limited**
22 Gr c 11/04 Outstrip—Full Bloom (Camacho) (8000) **Hawkes, Lee & Partner**
23 **HACKNESS HARRY**, b g 22/02 Swiss Spirit—Miss Fridaythorpe (Pastoral Pursuits) **A. M. Pickering**
24 B f 10/02 Mayson—Kaminari (IRE) (Sea The Stars (IRE)) (20000) **Mr E. F. Vaughan**
25 B f 18/02 Kingman—Madam President (Royal Applause) (270000) **Phoenix Thoroughbred Limited**
26 B f 13/03 Estidhkaar (IRE)—Mitchelton (FR) (High Chaparral (IRE)) (1500) **Moroney, Singh & Partner**
27 **VOICE OF GLORY**, b f 04/05 Poet's Voice—Vanity Rules (New Approach (IRE)) **A. E. Oppenheimer**

Other Owners: A. C. Coombs, Mr P. A. Moroney, Mr J. W. F. Rowley, Mr J. Singh.

539 MR TIM VAUGHAN, Cowbridge
Postal: **Pant Wilkin Stables, Aberthin, Cowbridge, CF71 7GX**
Contacts: **PHONE 01446 771626 MOBILE 07841 800081 FAX 01446 774371**
EMAIL tim@timvaughanracing.com WEBSITE www.timvaughanracing.com

1 **ADHERENCE**, 7, b g Sir Percy—Straight Laced **The Bill & Ben Partnership**
2 **AERONISI (IRE)**, 4, b g Kalanisi (IRE)—Carrigeen Lonicera (IRE) **Aircraft Tool Hire Ltd**
3 **AKKAPENKO (FR)**, 6, b g Archipenko (USA)—Akka **The Bill & Ben Partnership**
4 **ALASKAN BOY (FR)**, 5, b g Muhtathir—Laskaline (FR) **T. E. Vaughan**
5 **ALLTIMEGOLD (IRE)**, 7, b g Gold Well—Carryonharriet (IRE) **Mr B Jones & Son**
6 4, B g Sageburg (IRE)—Anna's Melody (IRE) **T. E. Vaughan**
7 **BABOIN (FR)**, 6, b g Creachadoir (IRE)—Brouhaha (FR) **Chepstow & Ffos Las Racing Club**
8 **BARNTOWN (IRE)**, 6, b g Jeremy—Anna's Melody (IRE) **The Pant Wilkin Partnership**
9 **BARRIER REEF (IRE)**, 5, b g Galileo (IRE)—Honour Bright (IRE) **Equinox Racing & Geriant Anstee**
10 **BASSARABAD (FR)**, 9, b g Astarabad (USA)—Grivette (FR) **Pearn's Pharmacies Ltd**
11 **BELLS OF AILSWORTH (IRE)**, 10, b g Kayf Tara—Volverta (FR) **Mr S. Grys & Mr M. O'Boyle**
12 **BELLS OF BARNACK (IRE)**, 5, b g Jeremy (USA)—Gimli's Treasure (IRE) **Mr S. Grys & Mr M. O'Boyle**
13 **BELLS OF PETERBORO (IRE)**, 5, gr g Carlotamix (FR)—Power of Future (GER) **Mr S. Grys & Mr M. O'Boyle**
14 **BLEU ET NOIR**, 9, b g Enrique—Gastina (FR) **The Rydon Pynes Partnership**

MR TIM VAUGHAN - continued

15 **BLUNDER BUSS (IRE)**, 7, b g Court Cave (IRE)—Shantou Rose (IRE) **Kings Head Duffield Racing Partnership**
16 **BOBMAHLEY (IRE)**, 5, b g Mahler—Supreme Von Pres (IRE) **Mrs B. N. Ead**
17 **BOHEMIAN MAESTRO (IRE)**, 5, b g Mahler—Escrea (IRE) **R. M. Kirkland**
18 **BOLTON BOY (IRE)**, 6, br g Arcadio (GER)—Peggy Maddock (IRE) **JRFB Ltd**
19 **BRANDY JAMES (GER)**, 5, b g Motivator—Bold Classic (USA) **T. E. Vaughan**
20 **BRIAC (FR)**, 9, b g Kapgarde (FR)—Jarwin Do (FR) **Mr O. S. Harris**
21 **BRIGADE OF GUARDS (IRE)**, 6, b g Presenting—Lasado (IRE) **Lycett Racing 100 Club**
22 **CAFFE MACCHIATO (IRE)**, 5, b h Fast Company (IRE)—Cappuccino (IRE) **Michael Owen Racing Club**
23 **CANTON PRINCE (IRE)**, 9, b g Shantou (USA)—Hasainm (IRE) **Tertia Racing**
24 **CAP ST VINCENT (FR)**, 7, b g Muhtathir—Criquetot (FR) **Mr B Jones & Son**
25 **CAPE ROBIN (IRE)**, 6, ch g Robin des Champs (FR)—Our Pride **T. E. Vaughan**
26 **CAROLINE'S QUEST (IRE)**, 5, b m Beat Hollow—Tramp Stamp (IRE) **Lycett Racing Ltd**
27 **CHAMPAGNE CHASER**, 10, b g Tobougg (IRE)—Champagne Lil **Mrs M. A. O'Sullivan**
28 **CHIMES OF DYLAN (IRE)**, 7, b g Court Cave (IRE)—What A Princess (IRE) **Oceans Racing**
29 **CHOZEN (IRE)**, 8, b g Well Chosen—Kneeland Lass (IRE) **Pearn's Pharmacies Ltd**
30 **CLONDAW ACE (IRE)**, 7, b g Flemensfirth (USA)—Peace Time Beauty (IRE) **Paul & Louise Bowtell**
31 **COLD SHOULDER**, 6, b g Passing Glance—Averami **Kings Head Duffield Racing Partnership**
32 **COPPER GONE WEST (IRE)**, 7, b m Westerner—Copper Dusht (IRE) **Paul & Louise Bowtell**
33 **DADSINLUCK**, 7, b g Presenting—Gemini Lucy (IRE) **Paul & Louise Bowtell**
34 **DADSINTROUBLE (IRE)**, 10, b g Presenting—Gemini Lucy (IRE) **Mr J. P. M. Bowtell**
35 **DANBORU (IRE)**, 9, b g Brian Boru—Dandouce **Lycett Racing 100 Club**
36 **DE FORGOTTEN ONE**, 6, b g Malinas (GER)—As Was **Mr D. W. Fox**
37 **DEBECE**, 9, b g Kayf Tara—Dalamine (FR) **R. M. Kirkland**
38 **DOTHRAKI PRINCE**, 6, b g Sulamani (IRE)—Crystal Princess (IRE) **Lycett Racing Ltd**
39 **DOVILS DATE**, 11, gr g Clodovil (IRE)—Lucky Date (IRE) **Itsfuninit**
40 **ELECTRON BLEU (FR)**, 6, b g Saddex—Odyssee du Cellier (FR) **Mr B Jones & Son**
41 **ERIC THE THIRD (IRE)**, 11, b g Mountain High (IRE)—Commanche Princess (IRE) **optimumracing.co.uk**
42 **EVA'S OSKAR (IRE)**, 6, gr g Shirocco (GER)—Sardagna (FR) **Mrs Sally & Richard Prince**
43 **FORT DENISON (IRE)**, 6, b g Galileo (IRE)—Honour Bright (IRE) **Mr L. DI Franco**
44 **FREEDELIVERY (IRE)**, 6, b g Sholokhov (IRE)—Gaye Melody (IRE) **Lycett Racing Ltd**
45 **FULL OF ROQUE (FR)**, 5, b g Blue Bresil (FR)—Pearl de La Roque (FR) **Mrs Sally & Richard Prince**
46 **GLIMPSE OF GOLD**, 9, b g Passing Glance—Tizzy Blue (IRE) **Mr G. Anstee**
47 **HAWA BLADI (IRE)**, 4, ch g Sea The Stars (IRE)—Gentle On My Mind (IRE) **Pimlico Racing Partnerships I**
48 **HAZM (IRE)**, 5, br g Shamardal (USA)—Hikari (IRE) **Mr P. A. Syson**
49 **HICKEY'S ROCK (IRE)**, 8, b g Westerner—Golden Odyssey (IRE) **T. E. Vaughan**
50 **IONA LAD (IRE)**, 5, b g Scorpion (IRE)—April Thistle (IRE) **R. M. Kirkland**
51 **ISLE OF ARON**, 4, gr g Kayf Tara—Maggie Aron **Oceans Racing**
52 **JEAN GENIE (FR)**, 4, gr g Turgeon (USA)—Lady Koko **Oceans Racing**
53 **JEFFERSON DAVIS (IRE)**, 7, b g Duke of Marmalade (IRE)—Samorra (IRE) **Syson & Vaughan**
54 **JEMBUG DRUMMER (IRE)**, 6, b g Jeremy (USA)—Drumbug (IRE) **Paul & Louise Bowtell**
55 **JIMMYJAMES**, 8, b g Arvico (FR)—On Their Toes **Lycett Racing Ltd**
56 **JOSEPH HOBSON (IRE)**, 5, b g Dubawi (IRE)—Profound Beauty (IRE) **The Wheatsheafs**
57 **JUDEX LEFOU (IRE)**, 5, b g Le Fou (IRE)—Knockalaghan Maid (IRE) **S. Clarke & and the Late Mr M. S. Clarke**
58 **KONIGSDESS**, 4, b g Dansili—Modesta (IRE) **Mr D. R. Passant**
59 **KOVERA (FR)**, 8, b g Antarctique (IRE)—Kesakao (FR) **Oceans Racing**
60 **LANDSMAN (IRE)**, 7, b g Canford Cliffs (IRE)—Mowaadah (IRE) **Mr D. W. Fox**
61 **LAUBERHORN ROCKET (GER)**, 5, b g Maxios—La Hermana **JRFB Ltd**
62 **LAUGHARNE**, 9, b g Authorized (IRE)—Corsican Sunset (USA) **Oceans Racing**
63 **LE MILOS**, 5, b g Shirocco (GER)—Banjaxed Girl **Bovian Racing**
64 **LEN BRENNAN (IRE)**, 7, b g Westerner—Letthedancebegin (IRE) **The Oxymorons**
65 **LET THE HEIRS WALK (IRE)**, 6, b g Vocalised (USA)—Heir Today (IRE) **Mr O. S. Harris**
66 **LOCO COCO (IRE)**, 5, br g Califet (FR)—Clondalee (IRE) **Mrs Sally & Richard Prince**
67 **LOOKSNOWTLIKEBRIAN (IRE)**, 9, b g Brian Boru—Sheebadiva (IRE) **SC Botham & RG Botham**
68 **LOS ALAMOS (IRE)**, 7, b g Galileo (IRE)—Artistique (IRE) **Michael Owen Racing Club**
69 **MADERA MIST (IRE)**, 6, ch m Stowaway—Odonimee (IRE) **T. E. Vaughan**
70 **MISTER BUDDY (IRE)**, 7, gr g Fairly Ransom (USA)—Hasainm (IRE) **T. E. Vaughan**
71 **NORWEGIAN WOODS (IRE)**, 7, b g Arcadio (GER)—Water Ore (IRE) **David & Susan Luke & the Lucky Strats**
72 **NUMERO UNO**, 4, b g Dubawi (IRE)—Casual Look (USA) **Recommended Freight Ltd & Trade Trux**
73 **ORIENTAL CROSS (IRE)**, 7, b m Cape Cross (IRE)—Orion Girl (GER) **Mr J Durston & Mr N Harris**

MR TIM VAUGHAN - continued

74 **OSCA LOCA (IRE)**, 7, b m Oscar (IRE)—Lohort Castle (IRE) **Paul & Louise Bowtell**
75 **PLENEY**, 6, b g Martaline—Knock Down (IRE) **Pearn's Pharmacies Ltd**
76 **POINT OF PRINCIPLE (IRE)**, 7, b g Rip Van Winkle (IRE)—L'Ancresse (IRE) **Oceans Racing**
77 **PRINCE CHARMIN' (IRE)**, 7, b g High Chaparral (IRE)—Dream Club **select-racing-club.co.uk & Mr C Davies**
78 **ROBINS FIELD (IRE)**, 5, b g Robin des Champs (FR)—Sweet Poli (IRE) **R. M. Kirkland**
79 **ROYALE DJANGO (IRE)**, 11, b g Kayf Tara—Royale Boja (FR) **Mr J Durston & Mr N Harris**
80 4, B g Court Cave (IRE)—Royale Video (FR) **T. E. Vaughan**
81 **SAD EYED DYLAN**, 7, br g Multiplex—Congressional (IRE) **S. Clarke & and the Late Mr M. S. Clarke**
82 **SHAMAN DU BERLAIS (FR)**, 7, b g Saint des Saints (FR)—Shinca (FR) **Mrs C. M. Marles**
83 **SILVER IN DISGUISE**, 6, gr g Sulamani (IRE)—Silver Spinner **Mr D. W. Fox**
84 **SPECTATOR**, 9, br g Passing Glance—Averami **Pearn's Pharmacies Ltd**
85 **STICKY SITUATION (IRE)**, 9, ch g Hurricane Run (IRE)—Lightning Queen (USA) **Mr B Jones & Son**
86 **TAKE EM OUT (IRE)**, 8, b g Amadeus Wolf—Toorah Laura La (USA) **The Bill & Ben Partnership**
87 **THELIGNY (FR)**, 9, gr g Martaline—Romilly (FR) **Pearn's Pharmacies Ltd**
88 **THREE COLOURS RED (IRE)**, 8, b g Camacho—Colour's Red (IRE) **The Red Partnership**
89 **TIGHT CALL (IRE)**, 6, ch g Mahler—Victory Anthem (IRE) **ER Newnham & JD Shinton**
90 **TIMELY GIFT (IRE)**, 7, b g Presenting—Give It Time **Carl, JJ, Chris, Mike, John & Hugh**
91 **TIPPINGITUPTONANCY (IRE)**, 6, ch m Stowaway—Dyrick Daybreak (IRE) **Paul & Louise Bowtell**
92 **TRIANGLE ROCK (IRE)**, 7, b g Stowaway—Lucy Cooper (IRE) **T. E. Vaughan**
93 **TRIXSTER (IRE)**, 7, b g Beneficial—Our Trick (IRE) **The Pant Wilkin Partnership**
94 **TWASN'T THE PLAN (IRE)**, 7, b g Presenting—Gentle Alice (IRE) **Mr B Jones & Son**
95 **WAX AND WANE**, 5, br g Maxios—Moonavvara (IRE) **ER Newnham & JD Shinton**
96 **YORKSHIRE LEGEND (IRE)**, 5, b g Fame And Glory—Ryehill Lady (IRE) **R. M. Kirkland**

THREE-YEAR-OLDS

97 B g Pour Moi (IRE)—Dalamine (FR) **Mrs B. N. Ead**

Other Owners: Mr G. Anstee, Mr N. Barnett, Mr C. Bennett, Mr R. G. Botham, S. C. Botham, Mr A. Bott, Mr J. P. M. Bowtell, Mrs L. Bowtell, Exors of the Late Mr M. S. Clarke, Mr S. A. Clarke, Mr C. Davies, Mr J. Durston, Golden Equinox Racing, Mr S. Grys, Mr G. Handley, Mr N. Harris, Mrs K. E. Hollingworth, Mr B. Jagger, Mr D. M. Jenkins, Mr B. M. Jones, Mr W. Jones, Mr D. A. Luke, David & Susan Luke, Mrs S. Luke, Mr E. R. Newnham, Mr M. O'Boyle, Miss D. E. Pettle, R. J. Prince, Mrs S. Prince, Recommended Freight Ltd, Mr J. D. Shinton, Mr A. Spencer, Mr M. A. Stratford, Mr P. A. Syson, The Lucky Strats, The Select Racing Club Limited, Tradetrux Ltd, T. E. Vaughan, Mr N. D. Whitham, Mrs C. S. Wilson, Mr C. J. Woods.

Assistant Trainer: Robbie Llewelyn.

Flat Jockey: David Probert. **NH Jockey:** Alan Johns, Richard Johnson. **Conditional Jockey:** Charlie Price. **Amateur Jockey:** Mr Mark Gallighan.

---

540 **MR CHRISTIAN VON DER RECKE, Weilerswist**
Postal: **Rennstall Recke GmbH, Hovener Hof 1, D-53919, Weilerswist, Germany**
Contacts: **PHONE +49 2254 845314 MOBILE +49 171 5425050 FAX +49 2254 845315**
EMAIL **recke@t-online.de** WEBSITE **www.rennstall-recke.de**

1 **ALHAMMER (GER)**, 4, ch g Martillo (GER)—All I Want **E.-A. Wahler**
2 **BAHAMA MOON (IRE)**, 8, b g Lope de Vega (IRE)—Bahama Bay (GER) **Stall Wollin**
3 **BOX OFFICE (FR)**, 9, b g Great Pretender (IRE)—Quelle Mome (FR) **Gabriele Gaul**
4 **BRICKLEBRIT**, 4, ch f Sir Percy—Blush's Gift **Rennstall Recke GmbH**
5 **CAPITAN (FR)**, 4, b g Le Havre (IRE)—Time Pressure **Cabkhat s.r.o.**
6 **FAIR HURRICANE (GER)**, 5, b g Hurricane Run (IRE)—Fair Vision (GER) **Stall Margarethe**
7 **FISHERMAN'S BLUES (IRE)**, 7, b g Zebedee—Southern Barfly (USA) **Stall esto87**
8 **GO LADY (GER)**, 4, b f Soldier Hollow—Gondola (FR) **Mr Wilhelm Bischoff**
9 **LATROYA (GER)**, 6, ch m Toylsome—Legata (GER) **Gestut Haus Hahn**
10 **MELODINO (GER)**, 5, b g Dabirsim (FR)—Melody Fair (IRE) **Stall Chevalex**
11 **MONCEAU**, 4, b c Dansili—Palmette **Stall Wollin**
12 **REMARKABLE**, 7, b g Pivotal—Irresistible **Rennstall Recke GmbH**
13 **RICHELIEU (GER)**, 4, b g Lilbourne Lad (IRE)—Right Key (IRE) **Stall Chevalex**

MR CHRISTIAN VON DER RECKE - continued

14 **SCALERO (USA)**, 5, b g Lemon Drop Kid (USA)—Scolara (USA) **E.-A. Wahler**
15 **SHALIN (GER)**, 9, b m Tertullian (USA)—Shahil (GER) **M. Trommershausen**
16 **SHOWDANCE KID**, 6, b g Showcasing—Maid To Dance **M. E. Veeck**
17 **SHRUBLAND**, 7, b g High Chaparral (IRE)—Ratukidul (IRE) **St. Ahrens u.a.**
18 **ST STEPHENS GREEN (IRE)**, 9, b g Diamond Green (FR)—Lily Shing Shang **E.-A. Wahler**
19 **WELAN (GER)**, 6, b g Mamool (IRE)—Weissagung (FR) **M. Trommershausen**
20 **WONDERGIRL (IRE)**, 6, b m Court Cave (IRE)—Young Elodie (FR) **M-B-A Racing**
21 **ZAKYNTHOS (FR)**, 4, b g Evasive—Zuckerpuppe (GER) **M-B-A Racing**

THREE-YEAR-OLDS
22 **ACHAT (GER)**, b c Lawman (FR)—Aslana (IRE) **Stall Nizza**
23 **DYNAMITE STAR (GER)**, b gr f Jukebox Jury (IRE)—Dynamite Cat (GER) **Rennstall Saarbrucken e.V.**
24 **GALWAY GIRL (GER)**, b f Thewayyoure (USA)—Giralda (IRE) **von Hodenberg Marquardt**
25 **LAGUNE (GER)**, b f Amarillo (GER)—Larmina (FR) **Stall Nizza**
26 **ORIHIME (IRE)**, br f Canford Cliffs (IRE)—Rub A Dub Dub **Ulrike Alck und Heiner**
27 **PETUNIE (FR)**, b f Slickly (FR)—Pepples Shuffle (FR) **Stall Konigshorst**
28 **SERGEANT (FR)**, b c Nutan (IRE)—Stella Marina (IRE) **Stall Nizza**
29 **SHADOW STAR (GER)**, ch c Amaron—Shadow Queen (GER) **Stall Pinotage**
30 **SIR CHANCEALOT (IRE)**, b g Sir Prancealot (IRE)—Hypocrisy **Stephanie Sofsky**

TWO-YEAR-OLDS
31 **AIDENSFIELD (GER)**, b c 04/05 Guiliani (IRE)—A Night Like This (Indian Danehill (IRE)) **Dieter Brand**
32 **AIKIDO (GER)**, b c 21/01 Nutan (IRE)—Athenry (GER) (Nicaron (GER)) (8151) **Stall Nizza**
33 **COLLINGHAM (GER)**, b c 19/04 Samum (GER)—Chandos Rose (IRE) (Mull of Kintyre (USA)) **Dieter Brand**
34 **INTERSTELLA (GER)**, b f 12/02 Nutan (IRE)—Invisible Flash (Invincible Spirit (IRE)) **Stall Nizza**
35 **LIONHEART (GER)**, b c 28/02 Nutan (IRE)—Larmina (FR) (Thewayyoure (USA)) **Stall Nizza**
36 **NEWA (IRE)**, ch f 20/04 Australia—Night of Magic (IRE) (Peintre Celebre (USA)) **Stall Nizza**
37 B c 28/03 Canford Cliffs (IRE)—Sacre Fleur (IRE) (Acclamation) (12011) **Stall Sternental**
38 **SERBELLONI (GER)**, ch f 28/04 Amarillo (GER)—Stella Marina (IRE) (Dylan Thomas (IRE)) **Stall Nizza**

---

541   **MRS LUCY WADHAM, Newmarket**
Postal: **The Trainer's House, Moulton Paddocks, Newmarket, Suffolk, CB8 7PJ**
Contacts: **PHONE 01638 662411 MOBILE 07980 545776**
EMAIL lucy@wadhamracing.com WEBSITE www.lucywadhamracing.co.uk

1 **ADMIRAL BARRATRY (FR)**, 7, b g Soldier of Fortune (IRE)—Haskilclara (FR) **Forster, Pepper & Summers**
2 5, b g Jeremy (USA)—Ballynarry (IRE) **Mr J. D. Abell**
3 **CONNIE WILDE (IRE)**, 5, b m Oscar (IRE)—Mandys Native (IRE) **The Sanguiners**
4 **DANCE TO PARIS**, 5, b g In Champs Elysees—Riabouchinska **The Calculated Speculators**
5 **EASTER GOLD (FR)**, 6, b m Kapgarde—Une Dame d'Or (FR) **Mr J. Summers**
6 **ECLAIR DE GUYE (FR)**, 6, gr g Lord du Sud (FR)—
              Jouvence de Guye (FR) **E R Wakelin, R W Hayward & J J W Wadham**
7 4, B f Fame And Glory—Firth of Five (IRE) **Ms E. L. Banks**
8 **GALMARLEY**, 5, b m Sir Percy—Crystal Gal (IRE) **Chasemore Farm LLP**
9 4, B f Shirocco (GER)—Gentle Alice (IRE) **Ms E. L. Banks**
10 **GREGARIOUS (IRE)**, 7, gr g Big Bad Bob (IRE)—Sense of Greeting (IRE) **Mr J. Summers**
11 **HARBOUR BREEZE (IRE)**, 5, b g Le Havre (IRE)—Retiens La Nuit (USA) **Mr B. J. Painter**
12 **ICONIC SKY**, 7, gr m Sixties Icon—Kentucky Sky **Mr T. R. Wood**
13 4, B g Curtain Time (IRE)—Isserkelly Lady (IRE) **J. J. W. Wadham**
14 4, B f Fame And Glory—Jeunopse (IRE) **Mr J. Summers**
15 **LE REVE (IRE)**, 12, br g Milan—Open Cry (IRE) **P. H. Betts**
16 **LITTLE LIGHT (IRE)**, 6, b m Walk In The Park (IRE)—Luna Rossa (IRE) **Suiter Developments Limited**
17 **MARTELLO SKY**, 4, gr f Martaline—Kentucky Sky **Mr T. R. Wood**
18 4, B f Dylan Thomas (IRE)—Megaeuros (IRE) **J. J. W. Wadham**
19 **MISS HERITAGE (IRE)**, 6, b m Pour Moi (IRE)—Haretha (IRE) **The Miss Heritage Partnership**
20 **MISTRAL TOMMY**, 4, b g Dylan Thomas (IRE)—Mistral Reine **Sara Dennis & Dominic Reilly**
21 **MOVIE LEGEND**, 10, b g Midnight Legend—Cyd Charisse **Dale Hing & Nicole Langstaff**

MRS LUCY WADHAM - continued

22 **NORTHERN PRINCESS**, 6, b m Authorized (IRE)—Julatten (IRE) **Mr J. D. Abell**
23 **PEARLY ISLAND**, 4, b g Trans Island—Shinrock Pearl (IRE) **Mr S. C. McIntyre**
24 **POTTERS HEDGER**, 8, b g Midnight Legend—Loose Morals (IRE) **Mrs J. May**
25 **POTTERS LEGEND**, 10, b g Midnight Legend—Loose Morals (IRE) **Mrs J. May**
26 **REGARDING RUTH (IRE)**, 6, b m Flemensfirth (USA)—
            May's June (IRE) **Suiter Developments Ltd & JJW Wadham**
27 **SHAMBRA (IRE)**, 6, b m Clodovil (IRE)—Shambodia (IRE) **Pali Pali Syndicate**
28 **SHANROE SANTOS (IRE)**, 11, b g Definite Article—Jane Hall (IRE) **Mr J. Summers**
29 **SHANTUNG (IRE)**, 7, ch m Shantou (USA)—Sarah's Cottage (IRE) **Mrs G J Redman & Sons of Peter Philipps**
30 **SOMEKINDOFSTAR (IRE)**, 7, ch g Getaway (GER)—Katty Barry (IRE) **G. Pascoe & S. Brewer**
31 **SORBET**, 5, b m Passing Glance—Fireburst **Mrs P. J. Toye**
32 **TENSION TIME (IRE)**, 6, b g Dubai Destination (USA)—Leader's Hall (IRE) **Suiter Developments Limited**
33 **THE QUIET DON (IRE)**, 5, b g Sholokhov (IRE)—Ailincala (IRE) **Mr J. Summers**
34 **THE WHITE MOUSE (IRE)**, 6, br m Stowaway—Maxwells Demon (IRE) **Ms E. L. Banks**
35 **TRINCOMALEE**, 7, b g Malinas (GER)—Royal Tango **Hot to Trot Jumping&Mrs E Gordon Lennox**
36 **WATERFALL**, 4, b f Mukhadram—Jump Ship **J. J. W. Wadham**
37 **WILL STING (IRE)**, 5, br g Scorpion (IRE)—Undecided Hall (IRE) **The Cyclones**

THREE-YEAR-OLDS

38 **ABOUND**, b f Sir Percy—Atwix **The Considered Speculators**
39 **EAST END GIRL**, b f Youmzain (IRE)—Bermondsey Girl **Mr & Mrs A E Pakenham & J J W Wadham**
40 **FANTASY DIVA**, b f Make Believe—Famusa **Mr & Mrs A. E. Pakenham**
41 **GIGABIT**, b g Dunaden (FR)—Fashionable Gal (IRE) **Dr Clive Layton**
42 **SIR DANDY**, b g Sir Percy—Cartoon **The FOPS**
43 **WAND**, b f Camelot—Ape Attack **Chasemore Farm LLP**

TWO-YEAR-OLDS

44 B f 06/03 Sir Percy—Crystal Gal (IRE) (Galileo (IRE)) (100000) **The FOPS**

Other Owners: Mrs S. Dennis, Mr R. Forster, Mrs E. C. Gordon Lennox, D. J. Hing, Mr R. S. Hoskins, Hot To Trot Jumping, Miss N. J. Langstaff, Mr A. E. Pakenham, Mr & Mrs A. E. Pakenham, Mrs V. H. Pakenham, M. L. Pepper, Mr C. E. L. Philipps, Mr G. P. A. Philipps, Mr J. A. H. Philipps, Mrs G. J. Redman, Mr D. G. J. Reilly, Suiter Developments Limited, Mr J. Summers, J. J. W. Wadham.

NH Jockey: Leighton Aspell, Maxime Tissier.

---

542   **MISS TRACY WAGGOTT, Spennymoor**
      Postal: **Awakening Stables, Merrington Road, Spennymoor, County Durham, DL16 7HD**
      Contacts: **PHONE 01388 819012 MOBILE 07979 434498**
      EMAIL **tracywaggott@hotmail.com**

1 **BILLY WEDGE**, 5, b g Arabian Gleam—Misu Billy **Mr D. Tate**
2 **CURFEWED (IRE)**, 4, br g Most Improved (IRE)—Evening Sunset (GER) **Tracy Waggott & Sally Booth**
3 **FLASH POINT (IRE)**, 4, ch g Iffraaj—Permission Slip (IRE) **Elsa Crankshaw Gordon Allan**
4 **GHATHANFAR (IRE)**, 4, br g Invincible Spirit (IRE)—Cuis Ghaire (IRE) **Mr W. J. Laws**
5 **HENLEY**, 8, b g Royal Applause—Making Waves (IRE) **Mr D. Tate**
6 **KIND REVIEW**, 4, b g Kodiac—Melodique (FR) **Elsa Crankshaw Gordon Allan**
7 **PAPARAZZI**, 5, b g Iffraaj—Columella **Gordon Allan Elsa Crankshaw**
8 **PROCEEDING**, 5, b g Acclamation—Map of Heaven **Mr D. Tate**
9 **SALAD DAYS (FR)**, 4, gr g Dalakhani (IRE)—Naive (IRE) **Mr W. J. Laws**
10 **WINDFORPOWER (IRE)**, 10, b g Red Clubs (IRE)—Dubai Princess (IRE) **Mr D. Tate**

THREE-YEAR-OLDS

11 **INTRINSIC BOND**, b g Intrinsic—Misu Billy **Mr D. Tate**
12 **MAJOR BOND**, ch g Monsieur Bond (IRE)—Ex Gracia **Mr D. Tate**
13 B c Casamento (IRE)—Saru **Elsa Crankshaw Gordon Allan**

Other Owners: Mr G. Allan, Miss S. A. Booth, Miss E. Crankshaw, Miss T. Waggott.

543 MR JOHN WAINWRIGHT, Malton
Postal: **Granary House, Beverley Road, Norton, Malton, North Yorkshire, YO17 9PJ**
Contacts: **PHONE 01653 692993 MOBILE 07798 778070**
EMAIL jswainwright@googlemail.com

1 ANGIE B (IRE), 5, b m Acclamation—Musical Peace (IRE) **Mr W Bavill & Mr D. Bavill**
2 CLAYTON HALL (IRE), 7, b g Lilbourne Lad (IRE)—Hawk Dance (IRE) **I. J. Barran**
3 DILLY DILLY (IRE), 4, b f Moohaajim (IRE)—Scarlet Rosefinch **Mr W Bavill & Mr D. Bavill**
4 EZANAK (IRE), 7, b g Sea The Stars (IRE)—Ebaza (IRE) **Gareth Davis & John Wainwright**
5 HOWS JOHNNY, 7, b g Multiplex—Compton Chick (IRE) **Mr A. J. Ross**
6 JUST HEATHER (IRE), 6, gr m Zebedee—Miss Sundance (IRE) **Mr T. G. Davies**
7 MUATADEL, 7, b g Exceed And Excel (AUS)—Rose Blossom **Caballo Racing**
8 PRINCE CONSORT (IRE), 5, b g Most Improved (IRE)—Fame And Fortune (IRE) **Caballo Dos**
9 TICKERTY BOO (IRE), 8, gr m Tikkanen (USA)—La Fille d'Or (IRE) **I. J. Barran**
10 ZARKAVON, 6, b m Avonbridge—Zarkavean **J. S. Wainwright & Peter Clarke**

THREE-YEAR-OLDS
11 DANDY'S ANGEL (IRE), b f Dandy Man (IRE)—Party Pipit (IRE) **Anthony Ross & Amy Abbott**
12 POWER POINT, br g Cable Bay (IRE)—Frabjous **Mr W Bavill & Mr D. Bavill**
13 SWEET EMBRACE (IRE), b f Kodiac—Zarkalia (IRE) **Mr W Bavill & Mr D. Bavill**
14 THE SADDLE ROCK (IRE), b f Bated Breath—Dream Role **D. R. & E. E. Brown**

Other Owners: Mrs A. E. Abbott, D. R. Brown, Mrs E. E. Brown, Mr P. R. Clarke, Mr T. G. Davies, Mr A. J. Ross, J. S. Wainwright.

Assistant Trainer: Mrs Fiona Wainwright.

Flat Jockey: Paddy Aspell, Tom Eaves.

544 MR ROBERT WALEY-COHEN, Banbury
Postal: **Upton Viva, Banbury, Oxfordshire, OX15 6HT**
Contacts: **PHONE 01295 670538**

1 FACILE BIEN (IRE), 9, b g Beneficial—Up A Dee (IRE) **Mr R. B. Waley-Cohen**
2 LUCARNO EXPRESS, 9, b g Lucarno (USA)—Tay Jay Vay (IRE) **Mr R. B. Waley-Cohen**
3 MAITREE EXPRESS, 6, br g Malinas (GER)—Shatabdi (IRE) **Mr R. B. Waley-Cohen**
4 THE JAFFNA QUEEN, 7, b m Black Sam Bellamy (IRE)—Shatabdi (IRE) **Mr R. B. Waley-Cohen**
5 THEATRE TERRITORY (IRE), 10, b m King's Theatre—Specifiedrisk (IRE) **Mr R. B. Waley-Cohen**
6 WYKHAM, 6, b g Shirocco (GER)—Liberthine (FR) **Mr R. B. Waley-Cohen**

545 MR MARK WALFORD, Sheriff Hutton
Postal: **Cornborough Manor, Cornborough Road, Sheriff Hutton, York, North Yorkshire, YO60 6QN**

1 BIT OF A QUIRKE, 7, ch g Monsieur Bond (IRE)—Silk (IRE) **Mr A. Quirke & Mrs G. B. Walford**
2 BRAVANTINA, 5, b m Trans Island—Falbrina (IRE) **Nunstainton Racing Club & Partner**
3 CARLOVIAN, 7, b g Acclamation—Mimisel **Profit Pony Racing**
4 CASH TO ASH (IRE), 7, b g Westerner—Knocklayde Rose (IRE) **Amigos, Morrell, Johnson, Evans & Cowan**
5 CORNBOROUGH, 9, ch g Sir Percy—Emirates First (IRE) **Cornborough Racing Club**
6 ELYSEE STAR, 5, b m Champs Elysees—Alushta **Go Alfresco Racing Partners**
7 EVENT OF SIVOLA (FR), 6, ch g Noroit (GER)—Surprise de Sivola (FR) **Cw Racing Club & Ursa Major Racing**
8 EXTRA BALD (FR), 6, b g Linda's Lad—Palatyne (FR) **Mrs G. B. Walford**
9 GIOVANNI CHANGE (FR), 5, gr g French Fifteen (FR)—Ask For Rain **Readers & Wiggy, the 8 Amigos & J Burns**
10 GLORIOUS DANE, 4, b g Olympic Glory (IRE)—Kaminari (IRE) **L. Bolingbroke, Mersey Racing, P. Molony**
11 HALF BOLLY, 4, ch g Haafhd—Zefooha (FR) **Mr Bolingbroke & Mrs G B Walford**
12 ILLUSTRISSIME (USA), 7, b g Mizzen Mast (USA)—Ghost Friendly (USA) **Ursa Major Racing & Mr D Gibbons**
13 KODIMOOR (IRE), 7, b g Kodiac—Victoria Lodge (IRE) **Ursa Major Racing & Partner**
14 MASTERS APPRENTICE (IRE), 5, ch g Mastercraftsman (IRE)—Maghzaa (IRE) **Vision Bloodstock & Partner**

MR MARK WALFORD - continued

15 **MISS AMELIA,** 7, b m Midnight Legend—Miss Pross **Cambridge People & Mr John Craggs**
16 **ORKAN,** 6, b g Shirocco (GER)—Zefooha (FR) **Mr C J Grindal & Mr J Scarrow**
17 **PARIS PROTOCOL,** 7, b g Champs Elysees—Island Vista **Mrs G. B. Walford**
18 **QUEST FOR LIFE,** 8, b g Dapper—Lewesdon Duchess **Little & Large Racing Partnership**
19 **RICKYROADBOY,** 5, b g Mazameer (IRE)—Black Baccara **The 8 Amigos & Mrs G B Walford**
20 **RISAALAAT (IRE),** 4, b f Mukhadram—Naadrah **Mrs G. B. Walford**
21 **ROCKMANN (FR),** 5, b g Kap Rock (FR)—All Berry (FR) **Mr C. N. Herman**
22 **TOUR DE PUB (IRE),** 6, ch g Aizavoski (IRE)—Gallant Express (IRE) **J Scarrow, J Cowan & S Evans**
23 **UNO VALOROSO (FR),** 12, b g Voix du Nord (FR)—Danse d'Avril (FR) **Mr C. N. Herman**
24 **VINTAGE ROSE,** 4, ch f Cityscape—Jozafeen **Mrs C. Steel**

THREE-YEAR-OLDS

25 B g Westerner—Annimation (IRE)
26 B g Getaway (GER)—Bright Cloud (IRE) **Mrs M. Cooper**
27 **CITY GOLD,** ch f Cityscape—Jozafeen **Mrs C. Steel**
28 **CLIFFTOP HEAVEN,** b g Canford Cliffs (IRE)—Heaven's Sake **Ursa Major Racing, S Morrell & A Parrish**
29 **DORSET BLUE (IRE),** b g Canford Cliffs (IRE)—Spinning Lucy (IRE) **Mrs G. B. Walford**
30 **MAGICAL MAX,** gr g Coach House (IRE)—Vellena **Mrs E Holmes, Mr M Johnson & Mrs Walford**
31 **MAHZARIN,** b f Golden Horn—Handana (IRE) **Mrs E. Holmes**
32 **NEWSICAL,** b g Music Master—Front Page News **Cornborough Racing Club**

TWO-YEAR-OLDS

33 **ALL ABOUT CHARLEY,** b f 22/03 Music Master—Lorimer's Lot (IRE) (Camacho)
34 **AMAZING ANNA,** ch f 29/03 Coach House (IRE)—Talqaa (Exceed And Excel (AUS)) (952) **Mrs G. B. Walford**
35 **CANDESCENCE,** ch f 01/03 Power—Bright Flash (Dutch Art) (7619)
36 B g 02/03 Cannock Chase (USA)—Hawsies Dream (Dubawi (IRE)) (5714)
37 B g 01/03 Due Diligence (USA)—New Road Side (Paco Boy (IRE)) (20000)

Other Owners: Mr N. J. Blencowe, Mr L. A. Bolingbroke, Mr J. R. Burns, Mr D. Burrell, CW Racing Club, Cambridge People, Cambridge Racing Limited, S. Cannon, Mr P. A. P. Clays, Mr James E. Cowan, Mr J. Craggs, Mr C. T. Dawson, D. J. Dickson, Mr A. R. Douglas, Mr S. N. Evans, Mr G. S. Felston, Mr D. I. Firth, Mr D. M. Gibbons, C. J. Grindal, Mr S. R. Henry, Mrs E. Holmes, Mr M. Johnson, Mr M. Lenton, Mersey Racing, Mrs S. V. Milner, Mr P Molony, Mrs S. E. Morrell, Nunstainton Racing Club, A. R. Parrish, Mr D. Percival, Mr A. K. Quirke, Mr J. N. Readman, Mr J. A. Scarrow, Mr C. Talbot, The 8 Amigos, URSA Major Racing, Vision Bloodstock, Mrs G. B. Walford, Mr P. L. Welsby, Mr T. J. Wigglesworth, Mr G. Wilson.

---

546   **MR ROBERT WALFORD, Blandford**
Postal: Heart of Oak Stables, Okeford Fitzpane, Blandford, Dorset, DT11 0LW
Contacts: **MOBILE 07815 116209**
EMAIL robertwalford1@gmail.com

1 **ACARO (FR),** 6, b g Sinndar (IRE)—Accusation (IRE) **Alvin Trowbridge & Christine Hinks**
2 **BLACK CENTAUR (IRE),** 7, b g Oscar (IRE)—Arcanum (IRE) **Davies King Selway Wavish**
3 **CASTCARRIE (IRE),** 5, b m Yeats (IRE)—Turtle Lady (IRE) **Sue & Clive Cole & Ann & Tony Gale**
4 **CHLOE'S COURT (IRE),** 7, br m Court Cave (IRE)—Howaya Pet (IRE) **Cole, Gale, Levy & Mortimer**
5 **CUCKLINGTON,** 9, b g Kayf Tara—Ardrom **Mrs C. M. Hinks**
6 **DUSKY LARK,** 10, b g Nayef (USA)—Snow Goose **Mrs Sara Biggins & Mrs Celia Djivanovic**
7 **EDE'IFFS ELTON,** 6, b g Geordieland (FR)—Ede'iff **Mr A. Lees**
8 **ENRY IGGINS,** 6, b g Schiaparelli (GER)—Eliza Doalott (IRE) **The Pygmalion Syndicate**
9 **ESCRIME D'ART (FR),** 6, b g Spider Flight (FR)—Quiss Mi (FR) **Ksb, Mike Doughty & C Djivanovic**
10 **FIRENZO (FR),** 5, b g Network (GER)—Toscane (FR) **Mrs S. De Wilde**
11 **FLAGRANT DELITIEP (FR),** 5, gr g Fragrant Mix (FR)—Naltiepy (FR) **Mrs C. M. Hinks**
12 **FRESNO EMERY (FR),** 5, b g Vision d'Etat (FR)—Urfie Star (FR) **Mr E Eames, Mr A Ham & Mr R Trevor**
13 **FU FU,** 7, b m Eastern Anthem (IRE)—Kasamba **Starting Gate Racing**
14 **HOT SMOKED,** 7, br m Eastern Anthem (IRE)—Waheeba **Starting Gate Racing**
15 **L'HOMME PRESSE (FR),** 5, b br g Diamond Boy (FR)—Romance Turgot (FR)
16 **LE BOIZELO (FR),** 9, b g Irish Wells (FR)—Bois Tendre (FR) **Dr & Mrs John Millar**

MR ROBERT WALFORD - continued

17 **MANVERS HOUSE,** 7, b g Schiaparelli (GER)—Freydis (IRE) **K S B, Mr M Doughty & Mrs Sarah Tizzard**
18 **MOVING IN STYLE (IRE),** 9, ch g Mountain High (IRE)—Good To Travel (IRE) **B. A. Derrick**
19 **MR MEDIC,** 9, b g Dr Massini (IRE)—Danse Slave (FR) **The White Hart Company**
20 **ONE FOR DUNSTAN (IRE),** 5, b g Sholokhov (IRE)—Park Rose (IRE) **Gale Force Six**
21 **OUR MERLIN,** 8, b g Pasternak—Lorgnette **A. J. M. Trowbridge**
22 **SPRING WOLF,** 12, br g Loup Sauvage (USA)—Spring Grass **B. J. M. Ryall**
23 **THE BROTHERS (IRE),** 7, b g Flemensfirth (USA)—Laboc **DT Hoyland JS Hoyland JP Romans**
24 **TITANEASY,** 5, b g Thewayyouare (USA)—Titian's Pride (USA) **Adams & McNeill**
25 **VAZIANI (FR),** 6, b g Sinndar (IRE)—Visinova (FR) **Chris Pugsley & Acorn Builders Dorset**
26 **WALK IN THE MILL (FR),** 10, b g Walk In The Park (IRE)—Libre Amour (FR) **Baroness D. M. Harding**

Other Owners: Acorn Builders Dorset LTD, Mr M. Adams, Mrs S. J. Biggins, Mr C. Cole, Mrs S. S. Cole, Mrs C. E. Davies, Mrs C. J. Djivanovic, Mr M. Doughty, Mr E. R. D. Eames, Mrs A. G. Gale, Mr A. P. Gale, Mr A. G. Ham, Mrs C. M. Hinks, Mr D. T. Hoyland, Mr J. S. Hoyland, K S B Bloodstock, Mrs L. M. King, Mr A. R. Levy, Mr D. E. T. McNeill, Mrs J. D. Millar, Dr J. W. Millar, Mr B. Mortimer, C. C. Pugsley, Mr J. P. Romans, A. G. Selway, Mrs S. L. Tizzard, Mr R. Trevor, A. J. M. Trowbridge, Mr P. T. J. Wavish, Mr E. W. White.

NH Jockey: James Best.

---

547 | **MR ED WALKER, Upper Lambourn**
Postal: Kingsdown Stables, Upper Lambourn, Hungerford, Berkshire, RG17 8QX
Contacts: **PHONE 01488 674148 MOBILE 07787 534145**
EMAIL ed@edwalkerracing.com WEBSITE www.edwalkerracing.com

1 **AL DAIHA,** 4, ch f Olympic Glory (IRE)—Alpen Glen **Al Shaqab Racing UK Limited**
2 **ASSIMILATION (IRE),** 4, b c Xtension (IRE)—Park Glen (IRE) **Mr C. E. Dale, B. J. R. Greenwood, Mrs J Cestar**
3 **BEGUILING CHARM (IRE),** 4, b f Charm Spirit (IRE)—Bryanstown (IRE) **Mr M. J. Cottis**
4 **BLACKHEATH,** 5, b g Excelebration (IRE)—Da's Wish (IRE) **Mr M. J. Cottis**
5 **BRIGHAM YOUNG,** 5, br g Street Cry (IRE)—Bible Belt (IRE) **Mrs G. Walker**
6 **CAME FROM THE DARK (IRE),** 4, gr c Dark Angel (IRE)—Silver Shoon (IRE) **Mr P. K. Siu**
7 **CAP FRANCAIS,** 4, b g Frankel—Miss Cap Ferrat **John Pearce Racing Limited**
8 **CAPRIOLETTE (IRE),** 5, b m Most Improved (IRE)—Greta d'Argent (IRE) **Mr & Mrs Andrew Blaxland**
9 **CARADOC (IRE),** 5, b g Camelot—Applause (IRE) **Mr P. K. Siu**
10 **DESERT DOCTOR (IRE),** 5, ch g Society Rock (IRE)—Dorn Hill **Mrs F. H. Hay**
11 **DREAMWEAVER (IRE),** 4, b g Mastercraftsman (IRE)—Livia's Dream (IRE) **Mrs O. Hoare**
12 **ICONIC KNIGHT (IRE),** 5, b g Sir Prancealot (IRE)—Teutonic (IRE) **J Nicholls, J Moorhouse & J Kinning**
13 **JACK D'OR,** 4, b g Raven's Pass (USA)—Inchberry **Ebury Racing 2**
14 **MAYGOLD,** 5, b m Mayson—Spanish Gold **Farleigh Racing**
15 **MOLLS MEMORY,** 5, ch m Helmet (AUS)—Bright Moll **Mr A. R. F. Buxton**
16 **MOUNTAIN PEAK,** 5, b g Swiss Spirit—Nolas Lolly (IRE) **Ebury Racing**
17 **NOBLE QUEEN,** 4, ch f Noble Mission—Dinvar Diva **Brightwalton Bloodstock Limited**
18 **ROYAL INTERVENTION (IRE),** 4, ch f Exceed And Excel (AUS)—
Exciting Times (FR) **Lord Lloyd Webber & Mr W S Farish**
19 **SHERPA TRAIL (USA),** 4, gr ro g Gio Ponti (USA)—Vapour Musing **Mrs G. Walker**
20 **SILENT WITNESS (IRE),** 4, b f First Defence (USA)—Stealth Bolt (USA) **Windmill Racing Ii**
21 **SINGING SHERIFF,** 5, b g Lawman (FR)—La Felicita **Mr R. Ng**
22 **STARFIGHTER,** 4, b g Sea The Stars (IRE)—Starlit Sands **Mr L. A. Bellman**
23 **STORMY ANTARCTIC,** 6, ch g Stormy Atlantic (USA)—Bea Remembered **Mr P. K. Siu**
24 **SUNDAY STAR,** 4, b f Kodiac—Northern Star (IRE) **Mr D. Ward**
25 **SWINDLER,** 4, b g Invincible Spirit (IRE)—Priceless Jewel **B. E. Nielsen**
26 **TONYX,** 4, b f Nathaniel (IRE)—Kadoma **NYX Racing Club**
27 **TOP FOX,** 4, b g Frankel—Lady Linda (USA) **King Power Racing Co Ltd**
28 **VERIFY,** 4, b g Dansili—Victoire Finale **B. J. R. Greenwood**

THREE-YEAR-OLDS

29 **ABSOLUTE ALTITUDE,** b g Cacique (IRE)—Nougaboo (USA) **The Derring Do Partnership**
30 **AMNIARIX (USA),** ch f Speightstown (USA)—Bold Lass (IRE) **B. E. Nielsen**

MR ED WALKER - continued

31 **APPLETART (IRE),** b f Nathaniel (IRE)—Gertrude Gray (IRE) **Lady Bamford**
32 **BALZAC,** b g Lope de Vega (IRE)—Miss You Too **Mr Bjorn Nielsen & Eastwind Racing Ltd**
33 **BE EASY (GER),** b f Samum (GER)—Bandeira (GER) **B. E. Nielsen**
34 **BOLD SUITOR,** b c Brazen Beau (AUS)—Samasana (IRE) **Kangyu International Racing (HK) Limited**
35 **BRIGHT EYED EAGLE (IRE),** ch c Gleneagles (IRE)—Euphrasia (IRE) **Mr P. K. Siu**
36 **BUCEPHALUS (GER),** b c Soldier Hollow—Batya (IRE) **Quantum Leap Racing VII**
37 **CLEGANE,** ch f Iffraaj—Cradle of Life (IRE) **Chasemore Farm LLP**
38 **COCONUT,** ch f Australia—Spinning Queen **The Hon N. P. V. J. Rothschild**
39 **COLOURING,** b f Showcasing—Blue Lyric **Mainline Racing**
40 **CONSTANCE (IRE),** b f Camelot—Emirates Joy (USA) **Mr D. Ward**
41 **CRITIQUE (IRE),** b g Cacique (IRE)—Noble Fantasy (GER) **Ebury Racing 4**
42 **DAME JOAN,** b f Invincible Spirit (IRE)—Kelly Nicole (IRE) **Lord A. Lloyd Webber**
43 **DARK SILVER (IRE),** b g Dark Angel (IRE)—Silver Shoon (IRE) **Mr P. K. Siu**
44 **DARK SPECTRE (IRE),** b g Declaration of War (USA)—Easton Arch (USA) **Mr C. U. F. Ma**
45 **DIVINE SUMMER (USA),** gr ro f Summer Front (USA)—Seattle Grey (USA) **Mr C Wright & the Crispily Patnership**
46 **DREAMLOPER (IRE),** b f Lope de Vega (IRE)—Livia's Dream (IRE) **Mrs Olivia Hoare & Mrs Paola Hewins**
47 **EAGLES CRAG (IRE),** b g Fastnet Rock (AUS)—La Salina (GER) **O.T.I Racing & Partner**
48 **ENGLISH KING (FR),** b c Camelot—Platonic **B. E. Nielsen**
49 B c Exceed And Excel (AUS)—Falling Petals (IRE) **Mr P. K. Siu**
50 **FIRST CHARGE (IRE),** b g Dansili—Melodramatic (IRE) **Mr L. A. Bellman**
51 **FIRST STREET,** b g Golden Horn—Ladys First **Lady Bamford**
52 **GLORIOUS CAESAR,** b g Holy Roman Emperor—Electric Feel **Kangyu International Racing (HK) Limited**
53 **GLORIOUS ENCOUNTER,** b g Kyllachy—Belle Josephine **Kangyu Int. Racing (HK) Ltd & Mr F Ma**
54 **ICE EAGLE (IRE),** b f Free Eagle (IRE)—Malaspina (IRE) **Lord Lloyd Webber & Mr A Rosen**
55 **JOYFILLY (IRE),** b f Kodiac—Table Bay (IRE) **Mr L. A. Bellman**
56 **JUAN LES PINS,** b g Invincible Spirit (IRE)—Miss Cap Ferrat **John Pearce Racing Limited**
57 B g Footstepsinthesand—Key Rose (IRE) **Mr R Pegum & Partner**
58 **MARJORAM,** b f Kodiac—Marywell **The Hon N. P. V. J. Rothschild**
59 **MASACCIO (IRE),** gr g Mastercraftsman (IRE)—Ange Bleu (USA) **B. E. Nielsen**
60 **MATTHEW FLINDERS,** b c Siyouni (FR)—Cascata (IRE) **Mr S. A. Stuckey**
61 **MONASH (IRE),** b g Lawman (FR)—True Crystal (IRE) **Mr Pegum, Mr & Mrs Lowe & Mr & Mrs Grant**
62 **MOUNT MOGAN,** b g Helmet (AUS)—Super Midge **Mr P. Chau**
63 **NINA BAILARINA,** b f Lope de Vega (IRE)—Vesnina **Brightwalton Bloodstock Limited**
64 **NOBLE STEED,** ch g Sir Percy—Amanjena **Kangyu International Racing (HK) Limited**
65 **OLD FRIEND (FR),** b g Fast Company (IRE)—Alpen Glen **Mr P. K. Siu**
66 **PAXOS (IRE),** gr c Outstrip—Ella Fitz **Mr R Pegum & Partner**
67 **QUEEN AYA,** ch f Helmet (AUS)—Show Aya (IRE) **S. Al Ansari**
68 **RED NAOMI (IRE),** ch f Tamayuz—Dutch Rose (IRE) **Middleham Park Racing XVI & Colin Dale**
69 **SHAKERMAKER (IRE),** gr c Mastercraftsman (IRE)—Fine Threads **Lady Bamford**
70 **SIBERIAN NIGHT (IRE),** b g Siyouni (FR)—Sweet Dream **Dubai Thoroughbred Racing**
71 **STARMAN,** b c Dutch Art—Northern Star (IRE) **Mr D. Ward**
72 **SUMMIT FEVER,** b c Exceed And Excel (AUS)—Swiss Dream **Kangyu Int. Racing (HK) Ltd & Mr F Ma**
73 **TRUE SCARLET (IRE),** b f Make Believe—Lady Pimpernel **Mr P. K. Siu**

TWO-YEAR-OLDS

74 B c 05/02 Archipenko (USA)—Aksaya (Sea The Stars (IRE)) (80000) **Kangyu International Racing (HK) Limited**
75 **ALABAMA BOY (IRE),** b c 23/03 Awtaad (IRE)—Gabardine (Pivotal) (30029) **Mr L. A. Bellman**
76 **BELOVED (IRE),** b f 07/03 Frankel—Love And Bubbles (USA) (Loup Sauvage (USA)) (350000) **Mr D. Ward**
77 **BEOWULF (IRE),** b c 03/04 Camelot—Hug And A Kiss (USA) (Thewayyouare (USA)) (75000) **Mr M. J. Cottis**
78 Gr c 20/03 Gutaifan (IRE)—Best New Show (IRE) (Clodovil (IRE)) (17142) **Mr L. A. Bellman**
79 B c 18/02 Olympic Glory (IRE)—Borja (IRE) (Lope de Vega (IRE)) (11000)
80 B c 30/04 Frankel—Cascata (IRE) (Montjeu (IRE)) (210000) **Mr S. A. Stuckey**
81 B c 07/04 Zoffany (IRE)—Catch The Moon (IRE) (Peintre Celebre (USA)) (85000) **Mrs F. H. Hay**
82 **CHICA BOOM,** b c 15/02 Tamayuz—Chicane (Motivator) (42000) **Mr A Nicholls & Mr J Moorhouse**
83 **CLOSING BELL,** b f 26/02 Siyouni (FR)—Wiener Valkyrie (Shamardal (USA)) **Car Colston Hall Stud**
84 B c 04/03 Due Diligence—Cloud's Rest
85 **CROCUS (IRE),** b c 23/02 New Bay—Bluebell (IRE) (Mastercraftsman (IRE)) (22000) **Mindy Hammond & Partners**
86 B c 25/02 Kodiac—Etesian Flow (Bated Breath) (30887) **Mr P. Afia, Mr J. Hobson**
87 **FLOTILLA,** b c 15/03 Cable Bay (IRE)—Ancestral Way (Mtoto) (35000) **Highclere Tbred Racing-Nichola Eddery**

MR ED WALKER - continued

88 Ch c 19/02 Sea The Stars (IRE)—Fly (Pastoral Pursuits) (90000) **Mr E. C. D. Walker**
89 B f 26/03 Mehmas (IRE)—Fondled (Selkirk (USA)) (55000) **Mr L. A. Bellman**
90 B c 27/02 Oasis Dream—Got To Dream **Hot To Trot Racing, Fittocks Stud**
91 **LODESTAR,** b f 27/03 Kingman—Northern Star (IRE) (Montjeu (IRE)) **Mr D. Ward**
92 **MISS SCALETTA,** b f 16/04 Sea The Stars (IRE)—Miss Cap Ferrat (Darshaan) **John Pearce Racing Limited**
93 **NASTASIYA,** ch f 21/04 Archipenko (USA)—Nezhenka (With Approval (CAN)) **Miss K. Rausing**
94 **PEINTRE D'ETOILES,** b c 05/02 Sea The Stars (IRE)—Persian Sky (Galileo (IRE)) (130000) **Mr D. Ward**
95 B f 22/04 Zoffany (IRE)—Pink Damsel (IRE) (Galileo (IRE)) **Mrs F. H. Hay**
96 Ch c 09/05 Dutch Art—Pink Flames (IRE) (Redback) (42000) **Kennet Valley Thoroughbreds VI**
97 **PRIMO BACIO (IRE),** b f 10/02 Awtaad (IRE)—Suvenna (IRE) (Arcano (IRE)) (100000) **Mr D. Ward**
98 B f 23/03 Adaay (IRE)—Rahyah (Acclamation) (15238)
99 **REINA DEL MAR (IRE),** b f 12/02 Awtaad (IRE)—Star Approval (IRE) (Hawk Wing (USA)) (120000) **Mr D. Ward**
100 Ch f 03/02 Fast Company (IRE)—Siphon Melody (USA) (Siphon (BRZ)) (56000) **Mr D. Ward**
101 B c 25/03 Kodi Bear (IRE)—Solace (USA) (Langfuhr (CAN)) (58000) **Kangyu International Racing (HK) Limited**
102 **ST GEORGE'S BAY,** b c 03/05 Cable Bay (IRE)—Basque Beauty (Nayef (USA)) **Lady Coventry & Partners**
103 **SUNSET BAY,** b f 04/02 Cable Bay (IRE)—Light of Love (Dylan Thomas (IRE)) **Brightwalton Bloodstock Limited**
104 **TEMPLE BRUER,** b c 22/03 Showcasing—Kendal Mint (Kyllachy) **Mrs J. M. M. Scott**

Other Owners: Mr P. Afia, Miss Emily Charlotte Asprey, Mr A. M. Basing, A. Blaxland, Mrs T. J. Blaxland, Mr C. G. A. Budgett, Mr P. Chau, The Racegoers Club Owners Group, Colin Dale & Partner, Mr M. J. Cottis, Mr L. Cowan, Crispily Partnership, Mr C. E. Dale, Dubai Thoroughbred Racing, East Wind Racing Ltd, Mr W. S. Farish, Mrs J. M. Forman Hardy, N. J. Forman Hardy, Mrs E. Grant, Mr S. P. Grant, Mrs E. A. Harris, T. F. Harris, Mr T. Henderson, Mrs P. Hewins, Mrs O. Hoare, Lady A. Hobhouse, Sir C. J. S. Hobhouse, Mr J. Hobson, Mr D. M. James, John Nicholls (Trading) Ltd, Kangyu International Racing (HK) Limited, Mr J. Kinning, Lord A. Lloyd Webber, Mr K. Lowe, Mrs M. Lowe, MLP Consultancy Limited, Mr C. U. F. Ma, Mrs Fiona Marner, Lady E. Mays-Smith, Middleham Park Racing XVI, Mr J. H. Moorhouse, Mr J. A. M. Nicholls, B. E. Nielsen, Mr S. O'Donnell, O.T.I. Racing, T. S. Palin, Mr R. A. Pegum, M. Prince, Mr R. Pritchard, Mr A. Rosen, Mr S. Straker, Mr I. R. Twigden, Mr E. C. D. Walker, Mr C. N. Wright.

---

548 | **MR CHRIS WALL, Newmarket**
Postal: Induna Stables, Fordham Road, Newmarket, Suffolk, CB8 7AQ
Contacts: HOME 01638 668896 MOBILE 07764 940255 FAX 01638 667279
EMAIL christianwall@btconnect.com WEBSITE www.chriswallracing.co.uk

1 **BLACK LOTUS,** 5, b m Declaration of War (USA)—Ravensburg **Mr Salah Fustok**
2 **CAPLA HUNTRESS,** 4, gr f Sir Percy—Great White Hope (IRE) **Strawberry Fields Stud**
3 **CARLEEN,** 4, ch f Sepoy (AUS)—Generous Lady **Mr Salah Fustok**
4 **DELILAH PARK,** 6, b m Delegator—Sarah Park (IRE) **Mr & Mrs D & J Cash & P Turner**
5 **FOLLOW INTELLO (IRE),** 5, b g Intello (GER)—Sauvage (FR) **Mr Salah Fustok**
6 **HAN SOLO BERGER (IRE),** 5, b g Lord Shanakill (USA)—Dreamaway (IRE) **Mrs B. J. Berresford**
7 **HI HO SILVER,** 6, gr g Camacho—Silver Spell **Mrs C. A. Wall**
8 **ICE LORD (IRE),** 8, gr g Verglas (IRE)—Special Lady (FR) **Hintlesham Racing Ltd**
9 **OH IT'S SAUCEPOT,** 6, b m Sir Percy—Oh So Saucy **The Eight of Diamonds**
10 **PROMISE OF SUCCESS,** 4, b f Dansili—Summer School (IRE) **The Clodhoppers**
11 **PURGATORY,** 4, b g Dark Angel (IRE)—Meet Me Halfway **Mr D. M. Thurlby**
12 **SOLFEGGIO (IRE),** 4, br f Bated Breath—Superfonic (FR) **Hughes & Scott, C. J. A. Hughes, Mr K. D. Scott**
13 **THE CORPORAL (IRE),** 4, b g Dansili—Ideal **Bringloe & Clarke, Mr R. A. Clarke, Mr M. J. Bringloe**
14 **THE FIDDLER,** 5, b g Big Bad Bob (IRE)—Strings **The Equema Partnership**
15 **TURNTABLE,** 4, b g Pivotal—Masarah (USA) **Induna Racing**
16 **WALK IT TALK IT,** 4, b f Nathaniel (IRE)—Windy Britain **Scuderia Giocri Ltd**

THREE-YEAR-OLDS

17 **CHEESE AND WINE,** b f Nathaniel (IRE)—Meet Me Halfway **Mr D. M. Thurlby**
18 **DOUBLE OR BUBBLE (IRE),** b f Exceed And Excel (AUS)—Mango Lady **Mr Salah Fustok**
19 **FLYING STANDARD (IRE),** ch g Starspangledbanner (AUS)—Snow Scene (IRE) **Hintlesham Racing Ltd**
20 **FRONT OF LINE,** b f Cable Bay (IRE)—Pivotal Drive (IRE) **Mr D. M. Thurlby**
21 **GLEN ESK,** b g Kyllachy—Ski Slope **Botham & Partner, Mr M. Tilbrook, P. J. W. Botham**

MR CHRIS WALL - continued

22 **GOLDIE HAWK,** b f Golden Horn—Always Remembered (IRE) **Mr Salah Fustok**
23 **GREEK OASIS,** b f Oasis Dream—Greek Goddess (IRE) **Mr Salah Fustok**
24 **MOLLY SHAW,** b f Helmet (AUS)—Paradise Isle **Mr D. M. Thurlby**
25 **PENKELLA,** b f Archipenko (USA)—Ermyn Express **The Leap Year Partnership**
26 **SMOKE SHADOW (IRE),** b g Mayson—Ravensburg **Mr Salah Fustok**

TWO-YEAR-OLDS

27 **BAGUE D'OR (IRE),** ch c 09/03 Belardo (IRE)—Ravensburg (Raven's Pass (USA)) (18000) **Mr Salah Fustok**
28 **CASTANA DIA (IRE),** ch f 04/03 Dandy Man (IRE)—Day By Day (Kyllachy) (20000) **B. R. Westley**
29 **CLASS IS PERMANENT,** b f 26/03 Swiss Spirit—Taweyla (Teofilo (IRE)) (5500) **Mr D. M. Thurlby**
30 **DRIFTING SANDS,** b f 21/01 Pride of Dubai (AUS)—
                                     Drift And Dream (Exceed And Excel (AUS)) (7000) **Lady Juliet Tadgell**
31 **KINGMANIA (IRE),** b f 10/02 Kingman—Greek Goddess (IRE) (Galileo (IRE)) **Mr Salah Fustok**
32 **MANGO BOY,** gr c 08/05 New Bay—Mango Lady (Dalakhani (IRE)) (30000) **Mr Salah Fustok**
33 **MINI RIVO (IRE),** b f 15/02 Nathaniel—Toujours L'Amour (Authorized (IRE)) **Mr Salah Fustok**
34 **MODERN BEAUTY (IRE),** b br c 24/01 Helmet (AUS)—Ludi Lu (FR) (New Approach (IRE)) **Mr Salah Fustok**
35 **OH ITS OH SO SMART,** b g 03/03 Mukhadram—Oh So Saucy (Imperial Ballet (IRE)) **The Eight of Diamonds**
36 **POSH GIRL,** gr f 02/03 Outstrip—Sauvage (FR) (Sri Pekan (USA)) **Mr Salah Fustok**
37 B c 27/03 Brazen Beau (AUS)—Sarah Park (IRE) **Mr & Mrs D & J Cash & P Turner**
38 B f 06/04 Poet's Voice—Sparkle Park (Kyllachy) **Mr & Mrs D & J Cash & P Turner**
39 **SWEET EXPECTATION,** b f 25/02 Charming Thought—
                                  Hope Island (IRE) (Titus Livius (FR)) (6000) **Sweet Expectation Partners**

Flat Jockey: George Wood.

---

549   **MR TREVOR WALL, Ludlow**
Postal: **Gorsty Farm Flat, Whitcliffe, Ludlow, Shropshire, SY8 2HD**
Contacts: **PHONE 01588 660219 MOBILE 07972 732080**
EMAIL trevorwall56@outlook.com

1 **LONGVILLE LILLY,** 5, b m Mawatheeq (USA)—Curtains **A. H. Bennett**
2 **MAY MIST,** 8, b m Nayef (USA)—Midnight Mist (IRE) **A. H. Bennett**
3 **NOSEYBOY,** 6, ch g Like A Boy—Left Nostril (IRE)

Assistant Trainer: Mrs J. A. Wall.

Conditional Jockey: Josh Wall.

---

550   **MR CHARLIE WALLIS, Ardleigh**
Postal: **Benson Stud, Harts Lane, Ardleigh, Colchester, Essex, CO7 7QE**
Contacts: **PHONE 01206 230779 MOBILE 07725 059355**
EMAIL cwallis86@hotmail.com

1 **AGUEROOO (IRE),** 7, b g Monsieur Bond (IRE)—Vision of Peace (IRE) **P. E. Axon**
2 **ARZAAK (IRE),** 6, br g Casamento (IRE)—Dixieland Kiss (USA) **Mr M. M. Foulger**
3 **AWAKE IN ASIA,** 4, ch g Dragon Pulse (IRE)—Gladiatrix **Miss J. A. Challen, J. E. Titley, J.Titley & Jane Challen**
4 **BADGER BERRY,** 4, b g Epaulette (AUS)—Snow Shoes **Strawberry Fields Stud**
5 **BINT DANDY (IRE),** 9, b m Dandy Man (IRE)—Ceol Loch Aoidh (IRE) **Mr M. M. Foulger**
6 **CAPPANANTY CON,** 6, gr g Zebedee—Fairmont (IRE) **Mr J. Biggane**
7 **DARK SIDE DREAM,** 8, b g Equiano (FR)—Dream Day **Mr M. M. Foulger & Mrs Shelley Dwyer**
8 **FAREEQ,** 6, gr g Dark Angel (IRE)—Spate (IRE) **P. E. Axon**
9 4, B f Sakhee (USA)—Florie **Strawberry Fields Stud**
10 **INDIAN AFFAIR,** 10, br g Sleeping Indian—Rare Fling (USA) **Mrs H. Wallis**
11 **KING ROBERT,** 7, b g Royal Applause—Generously Gifted **Dallas Racing, Jane Challen, H Wallis**

MR CHARLIE WALLIS - continued

12 **KYLLUKEY,** 7, b g Kyllachy—Money Note **Dallas Racing & Hayley Wallis**
13 **POTTERS QUESTION,** 4, b c Cardinal—Scipmylo
14 **PRECIOUS PLUM,** 6, b m Equiano (FR)—Miss Polly Plum **Mrs J. V. Hughes**
15 **SHARP OPERATOR,** 7, ch g Medicean—Helen Sharp **Mr L. Brooks**
16 **SIR HECTOR (IRE),** 5, ch g Sir Prancealot (IRE)—Awwal Malika (USA) **Mrs H. Wallis**
17 **TARSEEKH,** 7, b g Kyllachy—Constitute (USA) **P. E. Axon**
18 **TIME TO REASON (IRE),** 7, b g Kyllachy—Danehurst **J.E.Titley & J.Goddard**
19 **ZAC BROWN (IRE),** 9, b g Kodiac—Mildmay (USA) **Porterhouse Ltd. J Goddard**

THREE-YEAR-OLDS

20 **CONKER,** b g Swiss Spirit—Starlight Walk **P. E. Axon**
21 **HOWIZEEGEEZER,** b g Mukhadram—Tadpole **Mr L. Brooks**
22 **SCORPIO'S DREAM,** b g Due Diligence (USA)—Small Fortune **P. E. Axon**
23 **SMOKEY,** gr f Outstrip—Lady Tabitha (IRE) **Saxtead Livestock Ltd**

Other Owners: Miss J. A. Challen, Dallas Racing, Mrs S. Dwyer, Mr M. M. Foulger, Mr M. A. Glassett, Mr J. W. Goddard, Porterhouse Building Services Ltd, The Uxbridge Road Syndicate, J. E. Titley, Mrs H. Wallis.

Assistant Trainer: Hayley Wallis.

---

551 **MRS JANE WALTON, Otterburn**
Postal: **Dunns houses stables, Otterburn, Newcastle upon Tyne, Northumberland, NE19 1LB**
Contacts: **PHONE 01830 520677 MOBILE 07808 592701 FAX 01830 520677**
EMAIL dunnshouses@hotmail.com WEBSITE www.janewaltonhorseracing.co.uk

1 **EVEQUE (FR),** 6, ch g Kotky Bleu (FR)—Gloria IV (FR) **Mrs J. M. Walton**
2 **REAL ARMANI,** 8, ch g Sulamani (IRE)—Reel Charmer **Jane Walton & George Charlton Partner**
3 **REVERSE THE CHARGE (IRE),** 13, b g Bishop of Cashel—Academy Jane (IRE) **Mrs J. M. Walton**
4 **UPTOWN HARRY (IRE),** 6, b br g Morozov (USA)—Tudor Glyn (IRE) **Fresh Start Partnership**
5 **WESTEND THEATRE (IRE),** 11, b g Darsi (FR)—Ballyvelig Lady (IRE) **Mrs J. M. Walton**

Other Owners: Mr G. A. G. Charlton, Mrs M. R. Ridley, Miss J. Rutherford, Mrs J. M. Walton.

---

552 **MR JASON WALTON, Morpeth**
Postal: **Flotterton Hall, Thropton, Morpeth, Northumberland, NE65 7LF**
Contacts: **PHONE 01669 640253 MOBILE 07808 592701 FAX 01669 640288**

1 **CATCHAMAT,** 11, b m Overbury (IRE)—More Flair **Messrs F. T. Walton**
2 **CENTRAL FLAME,** 12, ch g Central Park (IRE)—More Flair **Messrs F. T. Walton**
3 **CROW STONE,** 6, b g Sulamani (IRE)—Merry Tina **Messrs F. T. Walton**
4 **CUDGEL,** 7, b g Sulamani (IRE)—Posh Stick **Messrs F. T. Walton**
5 **DUN FAW GOOD,** 13, br g Grape Tree Road—Dun Rose **Messrs F. T. Walton**
6 **FRANKIES FIRE,** 7, b m Flying Legend (USA)—Watch The Wind **Messrs F. T. Walton**
7 **MATTHEW MAN,** 9, b g Bollin Eric—Garden Feature **Messrs F. T. Walton**
8 **PLAY PRACTICE,** 10, b m Josr Algarhoud (IRE)—More Flair **Messrs F. T. Walton**
9 **RIPSTICK,** 9, b g Lucarno (USA)—Posh Stick **Messrs F. T. Walton**
10 **ROLL OF THUNDER,** 11, b g Antonius Pius (USA)—Ischia **Messrs F. T. Walton**
11 **STILL A SPARK,** 5, gr m Proclamation (IRE)—Merry Tina **Messrs F. T. Walton**
12 **TEMPLE GUIDE,** 6, b g Bahri (USA)—Posh Stick **Messrs F. T. Walton**

Other Owners: F. A. Walton, J. B. Walton.

553 **MRS SHEENA WALTON, Hexham**
Postal: **Linacres, Wark, Hexham, Northumberland, NE48 3DP**
Contacts: PHONE **01434 230656** MOBILE **07752 755184**
EMAIL **linacres@btconnect.com**

1 SAILING AWAY (IRE), 7, ch m Stowaway—Drama Chick **R. H. & S. C. Walton**
2 THE CONN (IRE), 10, b g Milan—Grandy Invader (IRE) **R. H. & S. C. Walton**

Other Owners: R. H. Walton, Mrs S. Walton.

Assistant Trainer: Mr R. H. Walton.

Amateur Jockey: Miss C. Walton.

554 **MR JASON WARD, Thirsk**
Postal: **Tall Trees, Sessay, Thirsk, North Yorkshire, YO7 3ND**
Contacts: HOME **01845 501578** MOBILE **07967 357595**
EMAIL **info@jasonwardracing.co.uk** WEBSITE **www.jasonwardracing.co.uk**

1 DE LATOUR, 4, b g Epaulette (AUS)—Zerka **Tall Trees Racing**
2 INGLEBY GEORGE, 6, b g Rail Link—Ingleby Princess **Ingleby Bloodstock Limited**
3 INGLEBY MOLLY (IRE), 5, ch m Choisir (AUS)—Mistress Twister **Ingleby Bloodstock Limited**
4 KING'S PAVILION (IRE), 7, b g King's Best (USA)—Embassy **Mr P. Ward**
5 OSMOSIS, 4, gr f Tamayuz—Spectacle **Mr P. Ward**
6 SWEETNESSANDLIGHT, 11, b m Aussie Rules (USA)—Taschlynn (IRE) **Mrs J. Ward**
7 THORNABY GEORGE, 4, b g Requinto (IRE)—Ingleby Princess **Ingleby Bloodstock Limited**
8 THORNABY NASH, 9, br g Kheleyf (USA)—Mistress Twister **Ingleby Bloodstock Limited**
9 THORNABY PRINCESS, 9, b m Camacho—Ingleby Princess **Ingleby Bloodstock Limited**
10 THORNABY SPIRIT (IRE), 5, b g Swiss Spirit—Ingleby Princess **Ingleby Bloodstock Limited**

THREE-YEAR-OLDS

11 BELLA BELIEVE (FR), gr f Rajsaman (FR)—Clutter **Mr David Dacosta & Tall Trees Racing**
12 B f Intrinsic—Dutch Girl **Tall Trees Racing**
13 INGLEBY COMMAND, b c War Command (USA)—Mistress Twister **Ingleby Bloodstock Limited**
14 INGLEBY EXILE, b f Rock of Gibraltar (IRE)—Ingleby Exceed (IRE) **Ingleby Bloodstock Limited**
15 B f Intrinsic—Spring Goddess (IRE) **Tall Trees Racing**
16 B f Casamento (IRE)—Sweetnessandlight **Tall Trees Racing**
17 TAMOSHANTER KID, b f Helmet (AUS)—The City Kid (IRE) **Mr G. Lampard**

TWO-YEAR-OLDS

18 B c 02/04 War Command (USA)—Curtains (Dubawi (IRE)) (3523) **Ingleby Bloodstock Limited**
19 B c 29/03 Slade Power (IRE)—Hot Wired (Rock of Gibraltar (IRE)) (1904) **Tall Trees Racing**
20 Ch c 03/05 Eagle Top—Ingleby Exceed (IRE) (Exceed And Excel (AUS)) **Ingleby Bloodstock Limited**
21 B g 24/03 Pearl Secret—Juncea (Elnadim (USA)) (3809) **Ingleby Bloodstock Ltd & Tall Trees Racing**
22 Br c 14/04 Swiss Spirit—Mistress Twister (Pivotal) **Ingleby Bloodstock Limited**
23 OLIVIA AND GRACE, b gr f 06/04 Lethal Force (IRE)—
Peace March (Invincible Spirit (IRE)) (4285) **Ingleby Bloodstock Ltd, The Ivy League & Tall Trees Racing**
24 B c 11/05 Brazen Beau (AUS)—Sweetnessandlight (Aussie Rules (USA)) (9523)
25 Gr f 29/04 Outstrip—Tattling (Warning) (2857) **Ingleby Bloodstock Limited**

Other Owners: Mr D. W. Dacosta, Ingleby Bloodstock Limited, Tall Trees Racing, Mrs J. Ward, Mrs T. Ward.

555 **MR TOM WARD, Upper Lambourn**
Postal: **Neardown Stables, Neardown, Upper Lambourn, Hungerford, Berkshire, RG17 8QP**
WORK EMAIL tom@tomwardracing.com

1 **BALGEES TIME (FR)**, 4, b f Dabirsim (FR)—Cindy Bould
2 **CHEEKY RASCAL (IRE)**, 5, b g Most Improved (IRE)—Bessie Lou (IRE)
3 **DIRTY RASCAL (IRE)**, 4, b c Acclamation—Refusetolisten (IRE)
4 **FIRE ISLAND**, 4, b f Iffraaj—Pink Flames (IRE)
5 **MOURIYANI (USA)**, 4, b g City Zip (USA)—Mouraniya (IRE)
6 **ROCKET NAAN**, 4, ch f Beat Hollow—Sleeping Shadow
7 **TINTORETTO (IRE)**, 5, b g Lilbourne Lad (IRE)—Fanacanta (IRE)
8 **VENTURE (IRE)**, 4, b g Showcasing—Starfly (IRE)

THREE-YEAR-OLDS

9 **COLADA COVE (IRE)**, b c Harbour Watch (IRE)—Sweet Coconut
10 **STAR OF WELLS (IRE)**, b c Sea The Stars (IRE)—Seas of Wells (IRE)
11 **VALENTINE BLUES (IRE)**, gr f Clodovil (IRE)—Grecian Artisan (IRE)
12 **VINTAGE RASCAL (FR)**, b c Nathaniel (IRE)—Irish Vintage (FR)

TWO-YEAR-OLDS

13 **AMAZALI**, b f 31/03 Elzaam (AUS)—Taffetta (Paco Boy (IRE)) (15000)
14 B c 21/02 Charm Spirit (IRE)—Amira (Efisio)
15 **BILANDY**, b f 01/02 Adaay (IRE)—Showstoppa (Showcasing) (33333)
16 B f 08/02 Fast Company (IRE)—Bright New Day (IRE) (New Approach (IRE)) (17142)
17 B c 12/04 Gleneagles (IRE)—Coolibah (IRE) (Peintre Celebre (USA)) (78000)
18 **DEVIL'S CUB**, b c 15/02 Hellvelyn—Noor Al Haya (IRE) (Tamayuz) (1904)
19 **DIAMOND BAY**, ch c 11/02 New Bay—Amarillo Starlight (IRE) (Dalakhani (IRE)) (17000)
20 **FILLE D'OR**, b c 03/02 Dandy Man (IRE)—Frabrika (IRE) (Intense Focus (USA)) (40000)
21 **FLIRTY RASCAL**, b f 02/02 Acclamation—Enliven (Dansili) (31745)
22 B f 24/04 Dandy Man (IRE)—Happy Land (IRE) (Refuse to Bend (IRE)) (32603)
23 Ch c 10/04 Free Eagle (IRE)—Hip (Pivotal) (7721)
24 B f 11/03 Vadamos (FR)—La Marchesa (IRE) (Duke of Marmalade (IRE)) (30000)
25 **LITTE MISS RASCAL**, b f 21/01 Zoffany (IRE)—Hibiscus (IRE) (Galileo (IRE)) (30476)
26 **MERRY SECRET**, b c 08/02 Elzaam (AUS)—Secret Liaison (IRE) (Dandy Man (IRE)) (35238)
27 B c 21/02 Belardo (IRE)—No Such Zone (Oasis Dream) (14285)
28 Ch f 11/01 Mehmas (IRE)—Obsara (Observatory (USA)) (17000)
29 **RAGING RASCAL (IRE)**, b c 22/03 Coulsty (IRE)—Limousine (Beat Hollow) (30000)
30 Ch c 29/04 Australia—Refusetolisten (IRE) (Clodovil (IRE)) (45000)
31 B f 24/01 Fascinating Rock (IRE)—Serenity Dove (Harbour Watch (IRE)) (21449)
32 B c 15/03 Swiss Spirit—Sleeping Shadow (Sleeping Indian)
33 Ch c 28/03 Twilight Son—Wake Up (GER) (Soldier of Fortune (IRE)) (13727)
34 Br gr c 02/05 Mastercraftsman (IRE)—Wood Fairy (Haafhd) (17000)

Head Lad: Anthony James, **Travelling Head:** Joe Kirby, **Business & Racing Manager:** Alex Lowe, **Yard Sponsor:** The Pheasant Inn, Hungerford.

Apprentice Jockey: Laura Coughlan.

556 **MISS TRACEY WATKINS, Kington**
Postal: **Rose Villa, Holmes Marsh, Lyonshall, Kington, Herefordshire, HR5 3JS**
Contacts: **MOBILE 07812 804758**
EMAIL traceyswatkins@googlemail.com

1 **BIG WATER (IRE)**, 12, ch g Saffron Walden (FR)—Magic Feeling (IRE) **K. M. Parry**
2 **GOAL (IRE)**, 12, b g Mujadil (USA)—Classic Lin (FR) **K. M. Parry**
3 **ONE COOL BOY (IRE)**, 11, b br g One Cool Cat (USA)—Pipewell (IRE) **K. M. Parry**

Assistant Trainer: Kevin Parry.

NH Jockey: Ben Poste. **Amateur Jockey:** Miss Brodie Hampson, Miss Natalie Parker.

557 **MR ARCHIE WATSON, Upper Lambourn**
Postal: **Saxon Gate, Upper Lambourn, Hungerford, Berkshire, RG17 8QH**
Contacts: **PHONE 01488 491247**
EMAIL office@archiewatsonracing.com WEBSITE www.archiewatsonracing.com

1 **ALICIA DARCY (IRE),** 4, b f Sir Prancealot (IRE)—Ballet of Doha (IRE)
2 **ATTAIN,** 11, b g Dansili—Achieve
3 **BAZAROV (IRE),** 7, br g Stowaway—Booley Bay (IRE)
4 **BUDANOVA,** 4, b f Epaulette (AUS)—Generously Gifted
5 **CLOCKERS CORNER (IRE),** 4, ch g No Nay Never (USA)—Starlight Night (USA)
6 **CORINTHIA KNIGHT (IRE),** 5, ch g Society Rock (IRE)—Victoria Lodge (IRE)
7 **GLEN SHIEL,** 6, ch g Pivotal—Gonfilia (GER)
8 **HASSAAD,** 4, b f Kodiac—Samaah (IRE)
9 **HAWAFEZ (IRE),** 4, ch f Shamardal (USA)—Devotee (USA)
10 **HIGHLAND DRESS,** 4, b g Shamardal (USA)—Crinoline (USA)
11 **JUGE ET PARTI (FR),** 7, gr g Martaline—Nakota Rag (FR)
12 **LETMESTOPYOUTHERE (IRE),** 6, ro g Sir Prancealot (IRE)—Romanylei (IRE)
13 **LUNA MAGIC,** 6, b m Mayson—Dayia (IRE)
14 **MEDAL WINNER (FR),** 4, gr g Olympic Glory (IRE)—Pax Mina (FR)
15 **MENIN GATE (IRE),** 4, gr g Farhh—Telegraphy (USA)
16 **ONE TO GO,** 4, gr g Champs Elysees—Tina's Spirit (IRE)
17 **PERCY PROSECCO,** 5, b g Sir Percy—Grapes Hill
18 **PREMIER D'TROICE (FR),** 6, b g Great Pretender (IRE)—Mick Bora (FR)
19 **TIMETOROE (IRE),** 6, b m Vinnie Roe (IRE)—Shokalocka Baby (IRE)
20 **VARIYANN (FR),** 4, b c Shamardal (USA)—Vazira (FR)

THREE-YEAR-OLDS
21 **ABOVE (FR),** b c Anjaal—Broken Applause (IRE)
22 **BAMBOO QUEEN (IRE),** b f Dandy Man (IRE)—Crown Light
23 **BAND PRACTICE (IRE),** ch f Society Rock (IRE)—Grand Zafeen
24 **BEHIND THE WALL (IRE),** b g Society Rock (IRE)—Few Words
25 **BUY ME BACK,** b f Lethal Force (IRE)—Delft
26 **CANAGAT,** ch c Zoffany (IRE)—Caskelena (IRE)
27 **CUBAN TREASURE,** ch f Havana Gold (IRE)—Arbella
28 **DANCING FEET (IRE),** b f Footstepsinthesand—Speronella
29 **DRAMATIC SANDS (IRE),** b g Footstepsinthesand—Melodrama (IRE)
30 **DRAMATISTA (IRE),** ch f Lope de Vega (IRE)—Aoife Alainn (IRE)
31 **ELECTRIC LADYLAND (IRE),** b f Cable Bay (IRE)—Conversational (IRE)
32 **ENDLESS JOY,** b f Showcasing—Funny Enough
33 **GALISPEED (FR),** b g Galiway—Becquaspeed (FR)
34 **GALLASIDE (FR),** b c Lucayan (FR)—Gallaecia (SPA)
35 **HARRISON POINT (IRE),** ch c Speightstown (USA)—Summer Surprice (FR)
36 **HE'S A LADDIE (IRE),** ch g Fast Company (IRE)—Crimson Lass (IRE)
37 **HIDDEN ANGEL (IRE),** b f Dark Angel (IRE)—Hidden Brief
38 **HIGHER KINGDOM,** b c Kingman—Noozhah
39 **HOLY ELEANOR (IRE),** b f Holy Roman Emperor (IRE)—Tennessee Moon
40 **ICE ICE LADY,** b f Due Diligence (USA)—Frozen Princess
41 **IT'SMABIRTHDAY (IRE),** ch g Society Rock (IRE)—Birthday (IRE)
42 **JAM AND MAM (IRE),** b f Invincible Spirit (IRE)—Love Magic
43 **KEANE'S KINGDOM (FR),** b c Joshua Tree (IRE)—Dip Down (FR)
44 **LAMBETH WALK,** b f Charm Spirit (IRE)—Cockney Dancer
45 **MANAP,** b g Sepoy (AUS)—Monshak (IRE)
46 **MAYSTAR (IRE),** b g Mayson—Oakley Star
47 **MRS UPJOHN (FR),** b f Dabirsim (FR)—Zamiria (FR)
48 **OLEKSANDR,** b c Teofilo (IRE)—Ollie Olga (IRE)
49 **PARENT'S PRAYER (IRE),** b f Kingman—Pure Excellence
50 **PORTUGUESEPRINCESS (IRE),** b f Camacho—Royal Visit (IRE)
51 **QUIET WORD (IRE),** b f Dandy Man (IRE)—Angel Spirit (IRE)
52 **RHUBARB BIKINI (IRE),** b c Zoffany (IRE)—Pearlitas Passion (IRE)
53 **RIVER SONG (IRE),** b f Battle of Marengo (IRE)—Yurituni

MR ARCHIE WATSON - continued

54 **ROYAL NATION**, b f Nathaniel (IRE)—Royal Empress (IRE)
55 **SALKEEV (IRE)**, b f Cappella Sansevero—Hadya (IRE)
56 **SANSEVERO (IRE)**, b c Cappella Sansevero—Seraphina (IRE)
57 **SHARED BELIEF (IRE)**, b g Dandy Man (IRE)—Hidden Belief (IRE)
58 **SHARNEY**, b f Mastercraftsman (IRE)—Champagne Ceri
59 **SILVER MACHINE**, gr f Brazen Beau (AUS)—Blue Crest (FR)
60 **STAG HORN**, b c Golden Horn—Starfala
61 **TAGOVAILOA (IRE)**, b g Elzaam (AUS)—Signora Lina (IRE)
62 **THE PERFECT CROWN (IRE)**, b c Hallowed Crown (AUS)—Perfect Fun
63 **WORLD TITLE (IRE)**, b c Dandy Man (IRE)—Piccola Sissi (IRE)
64 **YES MY BOY (IRE)**, b c Footstepsinthesand—Amazing Krisken (USA)
65 **YULONG GOLD TEMPLE (IRE)**, br c No Nay Never (USA)—Cool Cap (IRE)
66 **ZERE**, b f Iffraaj—Zimira (IRE)

Assistant Trainer: Christopher Grassick, Stephanie Joannides.

Flat Jockey: Hollie Doyle, Adam McNamara. **Apprentice Jockey:** Pierre-Louis Jamin, Kate Leahy. **Amateur Jockey:** Miss Brodie Hampson.

558
MR FRED WATSON, Sedgefield
Postal: **Beacon Hill, Sedgefield, Stockton-On-Tees, Cleveland, TS21 3HN**
Contacts: **PHONE 01740 620582 MOBILE 07773 321472**
EMAIL fredwatson@talktalk.net

1 **DESTINATION AIM**, 13, b g Dubai Destination (USA)—Tessa Reef (IRE) **F. Watson**
2 **FALSE ID**, 7, b g Aqlaam—Miss Dutee **Mr M. Marsh**
3 **GLEAMING ARCH**, 6, b g Arabian Gleam—Mrs Quince **F. Watson**
4 **HOP MADDOCKS (IRE)**, 5, b g Roderic O'Connor (IRE)—Yurituni **Mr M. Marsh**
5 **JOYFUL STAR**, 10, b g Teofilo (IRE)—Extreme Beauty (USA) **F. Watson**
6 **LUCYHILUCYLOW**, 8, b m Josr Algarhoud (IRE)—Shardda **Mr M. Marsh**
7 **NEWSPEAK (IRE)**, 8, b g New Approach (IRE)—Horatia (IRE) **F. Watson**
8 **STAR CITIZEN**, 8, b g New Approach (IRE)—Faslen (USA) **F. Watson**

THREE-YEAR-OLDS

9 **WRONGROADTOMAYO**, b f Paco Boy (IRE)—Female Spring **Mr M. Marsh**

559
MRS SHARON WATT, Richmond
Postal: **Rosey Hill Farm, Scorton Road, Brompton on Swale, Richmond, North Yorkshire, DL10 7EQ**
Contacts: **PHONE 01748 812064 MOBILE 07970 826046 FAX 01748 812064**
EMAIL wattfences@aol.com

1 **ARCTIC VODKA**, 8, gr g Black Sam Bellamy (IRE)—Auntie Kathleen **Rosey Hill Partnership**
2 **CHAMPAGNE RULES**, 9, gr g Aussie Rules (USA)—Garabelle (IRE) **Rosey Hill Partnership**
3 **MOON RUA (IRE)**, 7, b g Sandmason—Dusky Palm (IRE) **Rosey Hill Partnership**
4 **POT LUCK**, 4, b f Phoenix Reach (IRE)—Marajuana **Major E. J. Watt**
5 **TOO MANY CHIEFS (IRE)**, 9, br g Indian River (FR)—Wahiba Hall (IRE) **Major E. J. Watt**

560 **MR SIMON WAUGH, Morpeth**
Postal: **A G Waugh & Sons Limited, Molesden House, Molesden, Morpeth, Northumberland, NE61 3QF**
Contacts: **MOBILE 07860 561445**
EMAIL swaugh@dircon.co.uk

1 **BORIC,** 12, b g Grape Tree Road—Petrea **Mrs S. A. York**
2 **DARK AND DANGEROUS (IRE),** 12, b g Cacique (IRE)—Gilah (IRE) **Yacht London Racing Ltd**
3 **IMPERIAL FOCUS (IRE),** 7, b g Intense Focus (USA)—Mrs Cee (IRE) **Yacht London Racing Ltd**
4 **MAYBE MURPHY,** 5, b g Kayf Tara—Mays Delight (IRE) **A. R. G. Waugh**
5 **ROYAL FLUSH,** 9, b g Multiplex—Mystical Feelings (BEL) **S. G. Waugh**
6 **SHANTOU STREET (IRE),** 6, b m Shantou (USA)—Par Street (IRE) **Northumberland Racing Club**
7 **SKYE CHIEF,** 8, b g Sulamani (IRE)—Isle of Skye **Mrs S. A. Sutton**
8 **TOTAL ASSETS,** 12, b m Alflora (IRE)—Maid Equal **Northumberland Racing Club**

561 **MR MARK WEATHERER, Leyburn**
Postal: **The Flat, Bolton Hall Racing Stables, Wensley, Leyburn, North Yorkshire, DL8 4UF**
Contacts: **PHONE 01969 625735**
EMAIL markweatherer@btinternet.com

1 **MUZETTA'S WALTZ (IRE),** 6, ch m Tobougg (IRE)—Brer Rabbit **M. Weatherer**
2 **PARISIAN CHARMER,** 13, gr g Paris House—Tea For Texas **M. Weatherer**
3 **SIR TAAJ,** 4, b c Sintarajan (IRE)—Brer Rabbit **M. Weatherer**

THREE-YEAR-OLDS

4 **DEE DAY LANDING,** b c Intrinsic—Heidenheim (IRE) **M. Weatherer**

TWO-YEAR-OLDS

5 **MAGDALANA,** b f 29/03 Intrinsic—Parisien Tea Dance (Paris House) **M. Weatherer**

562 **MR PAUL WEBBER, Banbury**
Postal: **Cropredy Lawn, Cropredy, Banbury, Oxfordshire, OX17 1DR**
Contacts: **PHONE 01295 750226 MOBILE 07836 232465**
EMAIL paul@paulwebberracing.com WEBSITE www.paulwebberracing.com

1 **AGENT ZIGZAG (IRE),** 6, ch g Shamardal (USA)—Farranjordan **Bowden Bailey North**
2 **BIG DATA (IRE),** 6, br g Oscar (IRE)—Nolagh Supreme (IRE) **Mrs L. M. Shanahan**
3 **BOUGHTBEFORELUNCH (IRE),** 7, b g Dubai Destination (USA)—Anie (IRE) **The Let's Do Lunch Partnership**
4 **COPPERFACEJACK (IRE),** 10, b g Robin des Pres (FR)—Leone Des Pres (FR) **R. W. Barnett**
5 **DOCTOR ZEN (FR),** 4, gr g Doctor Dino (FR)—Zenitude (FR) **Keith Hunter & Francis Ong**
6 **DON'T FENCE ME IN (IRE),** 5, b m Fame And Glory—Great Idea (IRE) **P. R. Webber**
7 **EURKASH (FR),** 6, b g Irish Wells (FR)—Meralda (FR) **Paul Webber & Partner**
8 **FIRST ROMANCE,** 5, b m Shirocco (GER)—Alasi **The Starjac Partnership**
9 **FORGET YOU NOT (FR),** 5, ch g Smadoun (FR)—Baby Sitter (FR) **The Unforgettables**
10 **GO AS YOU PLEASE (IRE),** 7, b g Jeremy (USA)—Aweebounce (IRE) **Mr J. P. McManus**
11 **GUMBO FLYER (FR),** 4, b g Rail Link—Sariette de L'Isle (FR) **The Train Wreck Partnership**
12 **GWAFA (IRE),** 9, gr g Tamayuz—Atalina (FR) **Cropredy Lawn Racing**
13 **HARRY THE NORSEMAN,** 4, ch g Norse Dancer (IRE)—Titled Lady **Mr J. Nettlefold**
14 **HELLO SUNSHINE (FR),** 4, ch f Kapgarde (FR)—Louvisy (FR) **Nigel Jones & Paul Bowden**
15 **HOUSE ISLAND (IRE),** 6, ch g Casamento (IRE)—Fuaigh Mor (IRE) **Economic Security 1**
16 **IN THE DETAIL (IRE),** 5, b g Milan—Customary Chorus (IRE) **Mr M. B. Hughes**
17 **INDEFATIGABLE (IRE),** 7, b m Schiaparelli (GER)—
                                                    Spin The Wheel (IRE) **Mr Philip Rocher & Mr John B. O'Connor**
18 **JAYCEEBEE,** 4, b f Gentlewave (IRE)—Alasi **Swanbridge Bloodstock Limited**
19 **LITIGATE (IRE),** 5, b g Shantaram—Spin The Wheel (IRE) **Mr & Mrs Philip Rocher**

MR PAUL WEBBER - continued

20 **MAXI JAZZ (FR)**, 5, gr g Enrique—Andria (FR) **Mr & Mrs Bill Bailey**
21 **MISS BLAH BLAH**, 4, b f Gentlewave (IRE)—Manaphy (FR) **Triple Crown Partnership**
22 **NEW AGENDA**, 8, b g New Approach (IRE)—Prove **The New Agenda Syndicate**
23 **SPECIAL ACCEPTANCE**, 7, b g Malinas (GER)—Doubly Guest **The Syndicators 2**
24 **STARJAC (FR)**, 6, gr g Linda's Lad—Star's Mixa (FR) **The Starjac Partnership**
25 **THE CITY COBBLER**, 5, b m Mount Nelson—Galante (FR) **Sir John Timpson**
26 **VOLT FACE (FR)**, 11, ch g Kapgarde (FR)—Jourenuit (FR) **Mrs V. Shaw**
27 **WINGED AFFAIR (IRE)**, 5, b g Winged Love (IRE)—Kiss Jolie (FR) **Mr & Mrs Philip Rocher**
28 **YOUR THOUGHTS (FR)**, 4, b f So You Think (NZ)—Moraga (IRE) **The Your Thoughts Partnership**

THREE-YEAR-OLDS

29 **EVENING VERSE (IRE)**, ch f Poet's Voice—Tap Dance Way (IRE) **Mr J. B. O Connor**
30 **GLORIANO (IRE)**, b c Authorized (IRE)—Gloriana (FR) **Mr M. B. Hughes**
31 **IVAHUNCH**, b g Ivawood (IRE)—Galante (FR) **Miss K. J. Keir**
32 **VOICE OF DUBAWI**, b f Poet's Voice—Fame Game (IRE) **Bailey Daluma Racing Club**

Other Owners: Mr Dennis Baker, Mr Peter Bell, Mr Mark Bishop, Mr P. Bowden, Mr Steve Brown, Mr D. Carrington, Mr Rob Chapman, Mr Victor Chapman, Mr R C Dodson, Mr Nigel Godwin, Mrs Rosemary Gunn, K. L. Hunter, Mr Paul Isaacs, Mr Ian Magee, Mr Rory McGrath, Mr & Mrs Bill Bailey, Mr & Mrs David Higgins, Mr & Mrs Kevin Stokes, Mr & Mrs Philip Rocher, Mr & Mrs Simon Scriven, Mr Jason Neville, Mr Nick Newbold, Mr Robert North, Mr J. B. O Connor, Mr John G O'Neill, Miss Sheena Pilkington, Mr Gordon Simpson, Mr Charles Waddington, P. R. Webber, Mr Alastair Wells, Mr Stewart Yates, Mr George Yeandle.

---

563 **MR ADAM WEST, Epsom**
Postal: **Flat 2, Lorretta Lodge, Tilley Lane, Headley, Epsom, Surrey, KT18 6EP**
Contacts: **MOBILE 07939 030046**
EMAIL westtraining@outlook.com

1 **AND YET SHE MOVES (IRE)**, 4, ch f Roderic O'Connor (IRE)—Ms Cromby (IRE) **Mr S. W. Lang**
2 **BAMBINO LOLA**, 5, b m Helmet (AUS)—Lifetime Romance (IRE)
3 **CAPALA (IRE)**, 4, b g Swiss Spirit—Jezebel **Mr R. C. P. Deacon**
4 **COULDN'T COULD SHE**, 5, b m Sixties Icon—Emperatriz **Mr R. C. P. Deacon, Mr D. R. Botterill, Mr E. Boumans**
5 **DANSEPO**, 4, ch g Sepoy (AUS)—Danzanora **Mr F. Hutchinson**
6 4, B f Thewayyouare (USA)—Dubaianswer **All Seasons Racing**
7 **FINAL CHOICE**, 7, b g Makfi—Anasazi (IRE) **Mr A. J. Morton**
8 5, B m Kayf Tara—Gold Reef **West Racing Partnership**
9 **HEERCOMESHARRIE**, 4, b g Heeraat (IRE)—Aunt Minnie
10 **ILLEGITIMATE GAINS**, 4, b f Zebedee—Jillolini **Mr S. W. Lang**
11 **INTREPID (IRE)**, 10, b g Invincible Spirit (IRE)—Imiloa (USA) **Mr D. Phelan**
12 **ONE HANDSOME DUDE (IRE)**, 5, b g Canford Cliffs (IRE)—Allegrina (IRE) **Steve & Jolene de'Lemos**
13 **PEGGIE SUE**, 5, b m Captain Gerrard (IRE)—Aunt Minnie **West Racing Partnership**
14 **PRINCIPIA**, 5, b m High Chaparral (IRE)—Zero Gravity **The Slater Family**
15 4, Bl f Maxios—Purely By Chance
16 **RAINBOW JAZZ (IRE)**, 5, b g Red Jazz (USA)—Let's Pretend **Mr S. W. Lang**
17 **REGULAR INCOME (IRE)**, 5, b g Fast Company (IRE)—Max Almabrouka (USA)
18 **ROCKSETTE**, 6, b m Mount Nelson—Native Nickel (IRE) **Hide & Seekers**
19 **TATTENHAMS**, 4, b f Epaulette (AUS)—Tattling **Mr Peter Hagger & Mrs Roseanne Hagger**
20 **THEDEVILINNEVILLE**, 4, b g Paco Boy (IRE)—Ribbon Royale **Flash Harries**
21 **THESPINNINGWHEEL (IRE)**, 5, b g Arakan (USA)—Dancing Jest (IRE) **Padraic O'Neill & Janice West**
22 **ULYSSES OF TROY**, 8, ch g Rock of Gibraltar (IRE)—Takegawa **Mr Peter Hagger & Mrs Roseanne Hagger**

THREE-YEAR-OLDS

23 **AM I DREAMING (IRE)**, b f Make Believe—Queen Jock (USA) **Mr A. J. Morton**
24 **AUSTIN TAETIOUS**, b g Archipenko (USA)—Akdarena **Mrs J. M. West, Mr R. C. P. Deacon, Mr S. W. Lang**
25 Ch f Hunter's Light (IRE)—Belle Lumiere **All Seasons Racing**
26 **BUGZ BUNNY**, b f Nayef (USA)—Zaaneh (IRE) **Mr S. K. McPhee**
27 **CESIFIRE (IRE)**, b f War Command (USA)—Caterina di Cesi **The Maverick Syndicate**
28 **FRANCISCO PIZARRO (IRE)**, b g Bungle Inthejungle—Gemini Diamond (IRE) **Mrs J. M. West**

MR ADAM WEST - continued

29 **KING RAJ,** b c Footstepsinthesand—Cape Rocker **Mr R. S. Matharu**
30 **KRISHMAYA (IRE),** b f Dandy Man (IRE)—Tomintoul Magic (IRE) **Raj Matharu & Suresh Sivagnanam**
31 **LITTLE TIPSY,** b f Harbour Watch (IRE)—B Berry Brandy (USA) **Mr A. J. Morton**
32 **LIVE IN THE MOMENT (IRE),** ch g Zebedee—Approaching Autumn **Steve & Jolene de'Lemos**
33 **LORETTA LASS,** b f Elzaam (AUS)—Irina Princess **West Racing Partnership**
34 **NOAFENCE (IRE),** gr f Outstrip—Strasbourg Place **Farm Fencing Limited**
35 **UNDERLAY,** b g Harbour Watch (IRE)—Kodiac Island **Mr S. Wingrove**

TWO-YEAR-OLDS

36 Ch c 25/04 Havana Gold (IRE)—Actionplatinum (IRE) (Act One) **Mrs J. M. West**
37 B c 19/04 Heeraat (IRE)—Aunt Minnie (Night Shift (USA))
38 **BLACKTHIRTYONE,** gr c 22/04 Gregorian (IRE)—Morena Park (Pivotal) (2500) **Mrs J. M. West**
39 B c 08/05 Toronado (IRE)—Chetwynd (IRE) (Exit To Nowhere (USA)) (4500) **Mr R. C. P. Deacon**
40 **DAPHNE MAY,** b f 11/05 Mayson—Cambridge Duchess (Singspiel (IRE)) (2380) **Ownaracehorse Ltd**
41 **FALINE,** b f 01/03 Hellvelyn—Lifetime Romance (IRE) (Mozart (IRE)) (9000) **Mr R. C. P. Deacon**
42 Ch c 09/02 Equiano (FR)—La Jwaab (Alhaarth (IRE)) (800)
43 B c 27/02 Fountain of Youth (IRE)—Lady Moscou (IRE) (Sir Percy) **Mr C. D. J. O'Dowd**
44 **LAVISH OVATIONS,** b gr f 14/04 Hellvelyn—Sing Me Sing Me (Motivator) **Mr C. D. J. O'Dowd**
45 B f 09/04 Helmet (AUS)—Malladore (IRE) (Lawman (FR)) **Mr D. Phelan**
46 B c 31/03 Outstrip—Petit A Petit (IRE) (Holy Roman Emperor (IRE)) **Star Pointe Ltd**
47 B f 25/02 Charming Thought—Powder Blue (Daylami (IRE))
48 **SIR TEN T,** b c 29/04 Sir Prancealot (IRE)—Dutch Lady (Dutch Art) (6666) **Ownaracehorse Ltd**
49 B f 31/01 Proconsul—Sopran Cross (ITY) (Cape Cross (IRE)) (9523) **All Seasons Racing**

Other Owners: Mr S. De'Lemos-Pratt, Mr T. Francis, Mr P. Hagger, Mrs R. Hagger, Hever Stud Farm Ltd, Janice West & Partner,
Mr R. S. Matharu, Mr P. O'Neill, Ownaracehorse & Partners II, Ownaracehorse Ltd, Mrs M. Parker, Mr G. Reeves, Ross Deacon &
Partners, Mr S. Sivagnanam, Mrs J. M. West, Mrs J. de'Lemos.

---

564 MISS SHEENA WEST, Lewes

Postal: **5 Balmer Farm Cottages, Brighton Road, Lewes, East Sussex, BN7 3JN**
Contacts: **MOBILE 07748 181804 FAX 01273 622189**
EMAIL sheenawest11@aol.com FACEBOOK @sheenawestracing

1 **AIR HAIR LAIR (IRE),** 4, ch g Zebedee—Blond Beauty (USA) **I Poysden,R Heal,B Beesley,D Harper-Jones**
2 **BARD OF BRITTANY,** 6, b g Sayif (IRE)—Lily Le Braz **Mr M. Moriarty**
3 **CHERRY COLA,** 4, ch f Sixties Icon—Rose Cheval (USA) **Mr A. J. Head**
4 **CRYSTAL TIARA,** 4, gr f Gregorian (IRE)—Petaluma **Mark Albon & Sheena West**
5 **DING DING,** 9, ch m Winker Watson—Five Bells (IRE) **Mr I. E. Poysden**
6 **EVIE MAY,** 4, b f Excelebration (IRE)—Visanilla (FR)
7 **HARMONISE,** 6, b m Sakhee's Secret—Composing (IRE) **Mr I. E. Poysden**
8 **JUSTANOTHER MUDDLE,** 11, gr g Kayf Tara—Spatham Rose **Saloop**
9 **KENNY GEORGE,** 5, b g Mawatheeq (USA)—One For Philip **Mrs Fletcher Price & Partner**
10 **LIMELIGHTER,** 4, b g Harbour Watch (IRE)—Steal The Curtain **Mr Ricki Vaughan & Partner**
11 **LYRICA'S LION (IRE),** 6, b g Dragon Pulse (IRE)—Shishangaan (IRE) **Mr R. Vaughan**
12 **MOOTERAM (IRE),** 4, br f Moohaajim (IRE)—Easee On (IRE) **The Tribesmen**
13 **SIXTIES IDOL,** 7, b m Sixties Icon—Fading Away **Wocket Woy Wacing Club**
14 **SIXTIES SECRET,** 5, b m Sixties Icon—Jollyhockeysticks **Mr M. Moriarty**
15 **THE TOPP NOTES,** 4, b g Sixties Icon—Hi Note **Miss S. West**
16 **ZOLTAN VARGA,** 6, b g Sayif (IRE)—Mar Blue (FR) **Mr Ashley Head & Mr Garry Dreher**

THREE-YEAR-OLDS

17 **NOW I'M A BELIEVER,** b f Gregorian (IRE)—Alpha Spirit **Miss S. West**
18 **SHE'S A DIAMOND,** b f Captain Gerrard (IRE)—Symboline

Other Owners: Mr M. L. Albon, Barry Walters Farms, Mr B. R. D. Beesley, M. R. Channon, Mr G. C. Dreher, Mrs D. Fletcher-Price,
Mr D. T. Harper-Jones, Mr A. J. Head, Mr R. J. Heal, Miss M. M. Poulton, Mr I. E. Poysden, Mr R. Vaughan, Miss S. West.

NH Jockey: Marc Goldstein.

565 **MR SIMON WEST, Middleham**
Postal: **14A St Alkeldas Road, Middleham, Leyburn, North Yorkshire, DL8 4PW**
Contacts: **MOBILE 07855 924529**
EMAIL simonwest21@hotmail.co.uk WEBSITE www.mkmracing.co.uk

1 AMOOD (IRE), 9, ch g Elnadim (USA)—Amanah (USA) **Mr S. G. West**
2 BANDOL (IRE), 12, b g Zagreb (USA)—Formal Affair **Mr P. Hothersall**
3 BEAUTIFUL MIX, 8, b m Fair Mix (IRE)—Just Beautiful (FR) **The Kerr and Mechie Families**
4 CRANK EM UP (IRE), 9, b g Royal Anthem (USA)—Carrawaystick (IRE) **Mr P. Hothersall**
5 DORA DE JANEIRO (FR), 7, b m Ballingarry (IRE)—Katana (GER) **Mr P. Hothersall**
6 ELLA NUTRARGILE (FR), 6, gr m Kapgarde (FR)—Odile de Neulliac (FR) **Mrs B. Hothersall**
7 ERUDIT (FR), 6, b g Maresca Sorrento (FR)—Miss d'Anjou (FR) **Mr P. Hothersall**
8 FABULEUX DU CLOS (FR), 5, b g Blue Bresil (FR)—Osmazome (FR) **Mr P. Hothersall**
9 IT'S JUST TOMMY (IRE), 7, b g Tikkanen (USA)—Dusty Road (IRE) **Mr S. G. West**
10 JESSE JUDE (IRE), 7, ch g Doyen (IRE)—La Belle Bleu (IRE) **J. D. Gordon**
11 JIMINY CRICKET (IRE), 9, ch g Golden Lariat (USA)—Lady Smurfette (IRE) **J. D. Gordon**
12 KODI KOH (IRE), 5, b m Kodiac—Laywaan (USA) **Wild West Racing**
13 MAXIMISER (IRE), 12, gr g Helissio (FR)—Clydeside (IRE) **J. D. Gordon**
14 NELLIE DEEN (IRE), 7, b m Dream Ahead (USA)—Dorothy Dene **Mr S. G. West**
15 NEWS FOR PASCAL (IRE), 12, b g Kutub (IRE)—Direction **Mr P. Hothersall**
16 SHORT HEAD (GER), 5, b m Fastnet Rock (AUS)—Slight Advantage (IRE) **Wild West Racing**
17 SLIPPER SATIN (IRE), 10, b m Excellent Art—In The Ribbons **Mrs J. M. L. Milligan**
18 SO YOU THOUGHT (USA), 6, b g So You Think (NZ)—Lady of Akita (USA) **J. D. Gordon**

Other Owners: Mrs L. E. Mechie, N. Mechie.

566 **MR DAVID WESTON, West Overton**
Postal: **c/o Flintstone Stud, West Overton, Marlborough, Wiltshire, SN8 4ER**
Contacts: **MOBILE 07966 641001**
EMAIL flintstone007@icloud.com

1 ADMIRAL'S SUNSET, 7, b m Mount Nelson—Early Evening **Miss E. Tanner**
2 DALAKINA (IRE), 4, ro f Mastercraftsman (IRE)—White Cay **Miss E. Tanner**
3 EASY TIGER, 8, b g Refuse To Bend (IRE)—Extremely Rare (IRE) **Miss E. Tanner**
4 HEEZARARITY, 12, b g Librettist (USA)—Extremely Rare (IRE) **Miss E. Tanner**
5 SOLSTALLA, 8, b m Halling (USA)—Solstice **Miss E. Tanner**
6 THE LION QUEEN, 5, b m Helmet (AUS)—Bisaat (USA) **Miss E. Tanner**

567 **MR TOM WESTON, Hindlip**
Postal: **Offerton Farm, Offerton Lane, Hindlip, Worcester, Worcestershire, WR3 8SX**
Contacts: **MOBILE 07752 313698**

1 COOPERS SQUARE (IRE), 9, b g Mahler—Jessaway (IRE) **Mr T. H. Weston**
2 COURT INFORMANT (IRE), 4, b g Court Cave (IRE)—Princess Minnie **Mr T. H. Weston**
3 CROCODILE DUNDEE (IRE), 10, b g Westerner—Outback Ivy (IRE) **Mr T. H. Weston**
4 FISCAL FIREPOWER (IRE), 4, b g Ocovango—Miss Your Top (IRE) **Mr T. H. Weston**
5 HANNA HVAR, 6, b m Pour Moi (IRE)—Visanilla (FR) **Mr M. Jones**
6 IRON PORT (IRE), 4, b g Morozov (USA)—Portobello Lady (IRE) **Mr T. H. Weston**
7 LITTLE BATTLER (IRE), 6, b g Arakan (USA)—Masamor (IRE) **Mr E. T. Davies**
8 MEMBERS BOUNCE (IRE), 4, ch g Ask—Super Sandie (IRE) **Mr T. H. Weston**
9 SAQUON (IRE), 4, b g Arcadio (GER)—Seana Ghael (IRE) **Mr T. H. Weston**
10 THE LATE LEGEND, 7, ch g Midnight Legend—Vin Rose **Mr G. J. Fisher**

568 MR ALISTAIR WHILLANS, Hawick

Postal: **Hilltop House, Newmill on Slitrig, Hawick, Roxburghshire, TD9 9UQ**
Contacts: **PHONE 01450 376642 MOBILE 07771 550555 FAX 01450 376082**
EMAIL acwracing@hotmail.com

1 **ABOUTTIMEYOUTOLDME,** 6, ch g Mastercraftsman (IRE)—Mary Boleyn (IRE) **Miss D. Auld**
2 **AMAZING ALBA,** 4, ch f Helmet (AUS)—Silcasue **Mr F. Lowe**
3 **ANNIE BROWN,** 5, b m And Beyond (IRE)—Nevsky Bridge **Mr J. R. L. Wilson**
4 **ATLANTIC DANCER (IRE),** 7, b m Waky Nao—Sarika (IRE) **Mr C. Lynn**
5 **BABY BLUESKY,** 6, gr m Shirocco (GER)—Lady Bluesky **Mrs L. M. Whillans**
6 **BILLY BATHGATE,** 4, ch g New Approach (IRE)—Bustling **Mrs E. B. Ferguson**
7 **CLATTERING FORD (IRE),** 5, br g Shirocco (GER)—Hollygrove Gabbana (IRE) **Mr I. J. Herbert**
8 **CLOVENSTONE,** 4, b g Mazameer (IRE)—Macqueen **Star Racing**
9 **CORKED (IRE),** 7, b m Mastercraftsman (IRE)—Dama'a (IRE) **Shmelt For Gold**
10 **CORRIEBEN REIVER,** 6, ch g Malinas (GER)—Wild Child Lucy **John & Liz Elliot**
11 **COURT BALOO (IRE),** 9, b g Court Cave (IRE)—Tremplin (IRE) **A. C. Whillans**
12 **CRACKING DESTINY (IRE),** 7, b g Dubai Destination (USA)—Cracking Gale (IRE) **Mr A. G. Williams**
13 **DARWINA,** 4, gr f Dark Angel (IRE)—Anadolu (IRE) **K & L Fitzsimons**
14 **DONNACHIES GIRL (IRE),** 7, b m Manduro (GER)—Russian Society **Mrs K. Spark**
15 **EMPTY QUARTER,** 5, b g Pivotal—Desert Skies (IRE) **Mr W. J. Muir**
16 **FIRSTEEN,** 4, b f Requinto (IRE)—Teide Mistress (USA) **Star Racing**
17 **FOLKS LIKE US (IRE),** 5, b g Sans Frontieres (IRE)—Nia (IRE) **Charlie Baxter Bloodstock**
18 **FORRESTERS PARK (IRE),** 6, b g Scorpion (IRE)—Creanna Lady (IRE) **A. C. Whillans**
19 **GRUMPY BOOTS (IRE),** 6, b g Stowaway—Reina Reed (IRE) **Mr A. S. Crawford**
20 **GUN CASE,** 8, b g Showcasing—Bassinet (USA) **A. C. Whillans**
21 **K C BAILEY,** 4, b f Norse Dancer (IRE)—Wild Child Lucy **John & Liz Elliot**
22 **KAIZER,** 5, ch g Nathaniel (IRE)—Perse **Mrs E. B. Ferguson**
23 **KALAHARRY (IRE),** 8, b g Kalanisi (IRE)—Full Imperatrice (FR) **Big Teeree Racing & Partner**
24 **LADY GRIGIO (IRE),** 5, gr m Casamento (IRE)—Park Approach (IRE) **Big Teeree Racing**
25 **LEOSTAR,** 6, ch g Nathaniel (IRE)—Gaditana **Mrs E. B. Ferguson**
26 **LIZZIE LOCH,** 4, br f Maxios—Quenched **Mrs E. B. Ferguson**
27 **LYFORD (IRE),** 5, ch g Intense Focus (USA)—Nurture (IRE) **A. C. Whillans**
28 **MERCER'S TROOP (IRE),** 5, b g Canford Cliffs (IRE)—Meek Appeal (USA) **On the Road Again 2**
29 **NEW RHYTHM,** 5, b m Monsieur Bond (IRE)—Social Rhythm **A. C. Whillans**
30 **PUT THE LAW ON YOU (IRE),** 5, b g Declaration of War (USA)—Spirit of Tara (IRE) **Mr J D Wright & Mrs S Wright**
31 **ROOM AT THE TOP (IRE),** 5, b g New Approach (IRE)—Baila Me (GER) **Mrs E. B. Ferguson**
32 **ROYAL SHAHEEN (FR),** 7, b g Myboycharlie (IRE)—Viola Royale (IRE) **Mr F. Lowe**
33 **SAMSTOWN,** 13, b g Kingsalsa (USA)—Red Peony **Mrs E. B. Ferguson**
34 **SIENNA DREAM,** 5, b m Swiss Spirit—Angry Bark (USA) **A. C. Whillans**
35 **THE BRORA POBBLES,** 5, b m Helmet (AUS)—Snow Blossom **Mrs L. M. Whillans**
36 **WEST END WOODY (IRE),** 5, b g Court Cave (IRE)—Poncho Murray (IRE) **Mrs K. Spark**
37 **WIND OF HOPE (IRE),** 11, b g September Storm (GER)—Ciara's Run (IRE) **A. J. Brown**
38 **WISE COCO,** 7, b m Shirocco (GER)—Sensible **Mclafferty & Pacheco**
39 **ZEALOUS (IRE),** 7, br g Intense Focus (USA)—Velvet Kiss (IRE) **Mr W J E Scott & Mrs M A Scott**

THREE-YEAR-OLDS

40 **RALPHY BOY TWO (IRE),** b g Gutaifan (IRE)—St Athan **Mr F. Lowe**
41 **SEA EWE,** b f Proclamation (IRE)—Dispol Katie **K & L Fitzsimons**

Other Owners: J. D. Baxter, Big Teeree Racing, Mr D. Brooks, Mr F. A. D. Currie, Mrs E. J. Elliot, Mr J. J. Elliot, K. Fitzsimons, Mrs L. Fitzsimons, Mr D. N. French, Mr S. O. S. Haddadin, Mr S. W. Hogg, Mr M. Mclafferty, Mr W. J. Muir, Mr J. Parkes, Mrs A. M. Rhind, Mrs M. A. Scott, W. J. E. Scott, Mr S. A. Taylor, A. C. Whillans, Mr J. J. Wilkinson, J. D. Wright, Mrs S. L. Wright.

569 MR DONALD WHILLANS, Hawick
Postal: **Dodlands Steading, Hawick, Roxburghshire, TD9 8LG**
Contacts: **PHONE 01450 379810 MOBILE 07565 609007**
EMAIL garrywhillans@gmail.com WEBSITE www.donaldwhillansracing.com

1 **BABY TICKER**, 11, ch m Endoli (USA)—Baby Gee **D. W. Whillans**
2 4, B g Frammassone (IRE)—Ball Park (IRE) **Beswick Brothers Bloodstock**
3 **BANKS O' HOUXTY**, 10, b g Generous (IRE)—Border Mist (IRE) **Mr W. M. Aitchison**
4 4, B g Libertarian—Be Donn (IRE) **The Buyers Club**
5 **BIG BAD DREAM (IRE)**, 8, b g Mountain High (IRE)—Stay At Home (IRE) **The Brave Lads Partnership**
6 **BONNY HOUXTY**, 7, b m Native Ruler—Izons Croft **Mr W. M. Aitchison**
7 **DALI MAIL (FR)**, 7, gr g Satri (IRE)—Queenly Mail (FR) **The Zidane Partnership**
8 **DANCED EVERY DANCE (IRE)**, 7, b m Oscar (IRE)—Kinnegads Pride (IRE) **Denholm Park Racing**
9 5, B g Prince Flori (GER)—Dark Daisy (IRE) **The Buyers Club**
10 **ETERNALLY YOURS**, 7, b m Sulamani (IRE)—Well Disguised (IRE) **Mr A. J. M. Duncan**
11 4, B br g Valirann (FR)—Godlylady (IRE)
12 **HONDA FIFTY (IRE)**, 6, b g Arakan (USA)—Shuil Le Vic (IRE) **D. W. Whillans**
13 **KEYBOARD GANGSTER (IRE)**, 9, b g Gamut (IRE)—Vic O'Tully (IRE) **The Buyers Club**
14 **LADY VILLANELLE (IRE)**, 5, b m Shantou (USA)—Definite Deploy (IRE) **Td9 Racing**
15 **OUR ELSIE**, 5, b m Yeats (IRE)—Well Disguised (IRE) **Mr S. B. Chamberlain**
16 **PAPER PROMISE (IRE)**, 8, ch m Gamut (IRE)—Rose Vic (IRE) **Mrs E. Smith**
17 **PAPER ROSES (IRE)**, 9, b m Gamut (IRE)—Rose Vic (IRE) **Mrs E. Smith**
18 4, B f Califet (FR)—Rose Vic (IRE)
19 **SEE MY BABY JIVE**, 4, ch f Coach House (IRE)—Lady Fiona **Mrs H. M. Whillans**
20 **STAINSBY GIRL**, 6, ch m Shirocco (GER)—Charmaine Wood **Mr A. J. M. Duncan**
21 4, Ch g Midnight Legend—Well Disguised (IRE) **Mr A. J. M. Duncan**
22 4, B g Sageburg (IRE)—Your Place Or Mine (IRE) **The Buyers Club**

Other Owners: Mr G. Aitken, Mr C. Murphy, D. W. Whillans, Mrs H. M. Whillans.

Assistant Trainer: Callum Whillans.

NH Jockey: Callum Whillans.

---

570 MR RICHARD WHITAKER, Scarcroft
Postal: **Hellwood Racing Stables, Hellwood Lane, Scarcroft, Leeds, West Yorkshire, LS14 3BP**
Contacts: **PHONE 0113 289 2265 MOBILE 07831 870454**
EMAIL rmwhitaker@btconnect.com WEBSITE www.richardwhitaker.org

1 **DAWN BREAKING**, 5, b g Firebreak—Jubilee Dawn **D Gration, G Sutcliffe, N Farman, Jeaton**
2 **HAWK IN THE SKY**, 4, ch g Coach House (IRE)—Cocabana **Mr M. Hawkins**
3 **JILL ROSE**, 4, ch f Coach House (IRE)—Wotatomboy **J.W.'s Wotafun Club**
4 **MOONLIGHT STAR**, 4, b f Dick Turpin (IRE)—Cosmic Song
5 **NEWHALL GRANGE**, 5, ch g Equiano (FR)—Wotatomboy **Mr R. M. Whitaker**
6 **PENNY POT LANE**, 7, b m Misu Bond (IRE)—Velvet Band **Mr A. Melville**
7 **QUINLANDIO (IRE)**, 10, b g Thousand Words—La Shalak (IRE) **Mr T. M. Clarke**
8 **ROUND THE ISLAND**, 7, b g Royal Applause—Luanshya **Nice Day Out Partnership**
9 **SILK MILL BLUE**, 6, b g Piccolo—Marysienka **Nice Day Out Partnership**
10 **SPEEDY LOST SOCK**, 5, b g Erhaab (USA)—Jilmah (IRE) **Mr N. Zayani**
11 **STONEY LANE**, 5, b g Mayson—Spin A Wish **Country Lane Partnership**

THREE-YEAR-OLDS

12 **CINDY LOOPER**, gr f Coach House (IRE)—Velvet Band **Mr A. Melville**
13 **THRILLER'S MOON**, ch g Mayson—Rio's Rosanna (IRE) **Mr James Marshall & Mr Chris Marshall**

TWO-YEAR-OLDS

14 **LIBERTY BREEZE**, b f 14/03 Equiano (FR)—Avon Breeze (Avonbridge) (9523) **Grange Park RacingXVII**
15 Br g 25/01 Outstrip—Tumblewind (Captain Rio) (7142)

MR RICHARD WHITAKER - continued

Other Owners: Mr N. Farman, Mr D. Gration, Jeaton Ltd, Mr C. R. Marshall, J. R. Marshall, Mr G. Sutcliffe.

Assistant Trainer: Simon R Whitaker.

---

571 **MR ARTHUR WHITEHEAD, Craven Arms**
Postal: **Lawn Farm, Beambridge, Aston on Clun, Craven Arms, Shropshire, SY7 0HA**
Contacts: **PHONE 01588 660424**
EMAIL ajwhitehead@farming.co.uk

1 DELLA SUN (FR), 14, b g Della Francesca (USA)—Algarve Sunrise (IRE) **A. J. Whitehead**
2 MILAN OF CRYSTAL (IRE), 11, b m Milan—Native Crystal (IRE) **A. J. Whitehead**
3 ZALIAPOUR (FR), 14, b g Daliapour (IRE)—Spleen (FR) **A. J. Whitehead**

---

572 **MR HARRY WHITTINGTON, Sparsholt**
Postal: **Harry Whittington Racing Ltd, Hill Barn, Sparsholt, Wantage, Oxfordshire, OX12 9XB**
Contacts: **PHONE 01235 751869 MOBILE 07734 388357**
EMAIL info@harrywhittington.co.uk WEBSITE www.harrywhittington.co.uk

1 ARCADIAN SPRING (IRE), 6, b g Arcadio (GER)—Chloes Choice (IRE) Holt,Macnabb,Robinson,Taylor,Tucker
2 ARIA ROSE, 5, b g Cityscape—Leelu **P. Banfield**
3 BIGMARTRE (FR), 9, b g Montmartre (FR)—Oh La Miss (FR) **Mr P J Dixon & Mr C Nash**
4 BLACK ABBEY (FR), 4, bl g Hannouma (FR)—Alta Stima (IRE) **Black Abbey Partnership**
5 BOOLEY BEACH (IRE), 4, b f Valirann (FR)—Booley Bay (IRE) **Harry Whittington & Partners II**
6 CAPTAIN TOMMY (IRE), 6, b g Court Cave—Freemantle Doctor (IRE) **Mr R. J. Gurr**
7 CARDY (IRE), 6, b m Vinnie Roe (IRE)—Wednesday Girl (IRE) **Lead The Way Syndicate**
8 CATELINE (IRE), 5, b m Martaline—Kitara (GER) **The Atkin Family**
9 COURT LIABILITY (IRE), 7, b g Court Cave—
                                            Whataliability (IRE) **Nashwebbpavervandenberghe&10percenters**
10 DARGIANNINI (IRE), 5, b g Fame And Glory—You Take Care (IRE) **Dominic Burke & Kate & Andrew Brooks**
11 DEER HUNTER (IRE), 4, b g Fame And Glory—Subtle Gem (IRE) **Marley & Whittington.**
12 DESIGNER DESTINY (IRE), 6, b m Jeremy (USA)—Gaye Steel (IRE) **A Graham - Bankruptcy Trustee M Stanley**
13 EMERGING FORCE (IRE), 10, b g Milan—Danette (GER) **Webb Holt Carpenter Tucker**
14 FRANIGANE (FR), 5, ch g Coastal Path—Nobless d'Aron (FR) **Edgedale & Robinson**
15 HENRIETTA BELL (IRE), 7, b m Shantou (USA)—Close To Shore (IRE) **The Racing Demon Partnership**
16 JAMMY GEORGE (IRE), 7, b g Multiplex—Dantes Mile (IRE) **Kate & Andrew Brooks**
17 KHAGE (IRE), 7, b g Stowaway—Made Easy (IRE) **Kate & Andrew Brooks**
18 KLEOS (IRE), 6, b m Fame And Glory—Ginandit (IRE) **Holt,Atkin,Macnabb,O'Connor, Milton**
19 4, B g Califet (FR)—La Feuillarde (FR) **Harry Whittington & Partners II**
20 LANTIERN (IRE), 6, ch g Salutino (GER)—Luas Luso (IRE) **Holt, Robinson, Macnabb, Clark, Weedon**
21 4, B f Getaway (GER)—Lucky Start (IRE) **Holtmacnabbclarkjeffreymiltonrobinson**
22 MEDALLA DE ORO, 6, b g Teofilo (IRE)—Nyarhini **Mr A. R. Elliott**
23 MR KATANGA (IRE), 6, b g Flemensfirth (USA)—Pomme Tiepy (FR) **Graeme Moore, Kate & Andrew Brooks**
24 NEVERBEEN TO PARIS (IRE), 5, b g Champs Elysees—Island Paradise (IRE) **Mr P. M. Claydon**
25 OVERTRUMPED, 5, b m Champs Elysees—Perfect Hand **Harry Whittington Racing Syndicate**
26 PAT KELLY, 5, ch g Makfi—Speech **Mrs J. A. Fowler**
27 REBEL LEADER (IRE), 6, b g Milan—Chicharito's Gem (IRE) **The Rebel Leaders**
28 ROUGE VIF (FR), 6, b g Sageburg (IRE)—Rouge Amour (FR) **Kate & Andrew Brooks**
29 SAINT CALVADOS (FR), 7, b g Saint des Saints (FR)—Lamorrese (FR) **Kate & Andrew Brooks**
30 SALTO CHISCO (IRE), 12, b g Presenting—Dato Fairy (IRE) **British Racing Club**
31 SCARDINO (FR), 4, ch g Doctor Dino (FR)—Scarlock (FR) **Harry Whittington & Partners II**
32 SERGEANT O'LEARY (IRE), 4, b g Milan—Fuel Queen (IRE) **Incitatus**
33 SHAFFIRE, 4, b f Clodovil (IRE)—Wigan Lane **Mr R. J. Gurr**
34 SHANTOU VOW (IRE), 5, b g Shantou (USA)—Holy Vow (IRE) **Holt, Carpenter, Peters, Macnabb, Webb**
35 SHE'SONEOFOUROWN (IRE), 4, br f Sageburg (IRE)—Seavelvet (IRE) **Graeme Moore, Kate & Andrew Brooks**
36 SHEILA NASH (IRE), 5, b m Flemensfirth (USA)—Hollygrove Rumba (IRE) **Harry Whittington & Partners**

MR HARRY WHITTINGTON - continued

37 **SHORE SHANTY (IRE)**, 5, b m Shantou (USA)—Close To Shore (IRE) **A Holt J Robinson I Macnabb & C Clark**
38 **SIMPLY THE BETTS (IRE)**, 7, b g Arcadio (GER)—Crimson Flower (IRE) **Kate & Andrew Brooks**
39 **SIROBBIE (IRE)**, 6, br g Arakan (USA)—Presentbreeze (IRE) **Mr R. J. Gurr**
40 **STICK WITH BILL (IRE)**, 6, b g Oscar (IRE)—Made In Kk (IRE) **Kate & Andrew Brooks**
41 **THE KINGS BABY (IRE)**, 9, b br m King's Theatre (IRE)—Assidua (IRE) **Harry Whittington Racing Syndicate**
42 **VINNIE LEWIS (IRE)**, 9, b g Vinnie Roe (IRE)—Ballyann Lewis (IRE) **The Racing Demon Partnership**
43 **YOUNG BULL (IRE)**, 6, b g Dubai Destination (USA)—Jane Hall (IRE) **Nash & Webb**

Other Owners: 10 Percenters, Mrs C. J. Atkin, Mr A. L. Brooks, Mrs K. L. Brooks, Mr D. J. Burke, Mr B. D. Carpenter, Mr C. N. Clark, Mr G. Clemett, Mr P. D. Dennis, Mr P. J. Dixon, Mr J. W. Edgedale, Mrs A. M. Fitzgerald O'Connor, Mr A. Holt, Miss A. Jeffrey, Mr I. Macnabb, Mrs L. N. Major, Mr R. J. Marley, Mr C. J. Milton, Mr G. Moore, Mr C. T. Nash, Mr G. J. Paver, Mr A. Penfold, Mr D. G. Peters, Mr J. D. Robinson, Mr P. J. Robinson, Mr A. Taylor, Mr A. J. Tucker, M. J. Vandenberghe, Exors of the late Mr H. J. M. Webb, Mrs I. M. Webb, Mr J. Weedon, C. H. O. Whittington.

Assistant Trainer: Joe Quintin.

NH Jockey: Harry Bannister.

---

573 **MR MICHAEL WIGHAM, Newmarket**
Postal: **Hamilton Stables, Hamilton Road, Newmarket, Suffolk, CB8 7JQ**
Contacts: **PHONE 01638 668806 MOBILE 07831 456426**
EMAIL michaelwigham@hotmail.co.uk WEBSITE www.michaelwighamracing.co.uk

1 **ACCESSOR (IRE)**, 5, b g Exceed And Excel (AUS)—Amarette (GER)
2 **ALVARO**, 4, b g Archipenko (USA)—Aloha
3 **AWSAAF**, 5, b g Swiss Spirit—Atheera (IRE)
4 **DEPUTISE**, 4, b g Kodiac—Dolly Colman (IRE)
5 **FOXY FOREVER (IRE)**, 10, b g Kodiac—Northern Tara (IRE)
6 **GLENAMOY LAD**, 6, b g Royal Applause—Suzy Alexander
7 **GLOVES LYNCH**, 4, b g Mukhadram—Suelita
8 **MUJID (IRE)**, 5, b g Frankel—Bethrah (IRE)
9 **MY TARGET (IRE)**, 9, b g Cape Cross (IRE)—Chercheuse (USA)
10 **OMRAN**, 6, ch g Choisir (AUS)—Ruff Shod (USA)
11 **SANAADH**, 7, ch g Exceed and Excel (AUS)—Queen's Logic (IRE)
12 **VERNE CASTLE**, 7, ch g Sakhee's Secret—Lochangel

THREE-YEAR-OLDS

13 **MURAT ASSET**, b c Mount Nelson—Elis Eliz (IRE)

Assistant Trainer: Sharon Kenyon.

---

574 **MR CHRISTIAN WILLIAMS, Bridgend**
Postal: **The Hollies, Heol Yr Ysgol, Coity, Bridgend, Mid Glamorgan, CF35 6BL**
Contacts: **MOBILE 07702 896759**

1 **BACKINTHEOLDTIMES (IRE)**, 7, b m Olden Times—Tinas Friend **Ms S. A. Howell**
2 **BIG CHIP AND PIN**, 8, b g Generous (IRE)—Supreme Cove **Smerdon Tree Services Ltd**
3 **BLAZING TOM**, 9, b g Dr Massini (IRE)—Blazing Ember **Mr W. P. Thomas**
4 **CAP DU NORD (FR)**, 7, br g Voix du Nord (FR)—Qualite Controlee (FR) **The Unnamed Favourites**
5 **CONAS TAOI (IRE)**, 11, b g Exit To Nowhere (USA)—Zudika (IRE) **Burr & Dudwell Racing**
6 **COTTONVALE (IRE)**, 9, b g Touch of Land (FR)—Shuil Le Vic (IRE) **Christian Williams Racing Club**
7 **DEFUTURE IS BRIGHT (IRE)**, 6, b g Westerner—Dustys Delight (IRE) **The Can't Say No Partnership**
8 **FIVE STAR GETAWAY (IRE)**, 6, b g Getaway (GER)—Hapeney (IRE) **Carl Hinchy & Mark Scott**
9 **GAME LINE (IRE)**, 6, ch g Sandmason—Superline (IRE) **Roggie Crew**
10 **INDIETIR (FR)**, 8, b br g Muhtathir—Indietra (USA) **Mr A. L. Brooks**
11 **ISHYABOI (IRE)**, 8, b g Wareed (IRE)—She's Our Luck (IRE) **Christian Williams Racing Club**

MR CHRISTIAN WILLIAMS - continued

12 **JOEY STEEL (IRE)**, 7, b g Craigsteel—Tower Project (IRE) **Christian Williams Racing Club**
13 **JOSIE ABBING (IRE)**, 6, b m Fame And Glory—Bella Venezia (IRE) **Burr & Dudwell Racing**
14 **JUST FOR TARA**, 7, b m Malinas (GER)—Just For Jean (IRE) **Mr C. R. P. Williams**
15 **KILCHREEST MOON (IRE)**, 9, ch g Moon Ballad (IRE)—Kilchreest Queen (IRE) **Thrills and Spills**
16 **KITTY'S LIGHT**, 4, b g Nathaniel (IRE)—Daraiyna (FR) **Mr C. R. P. Williams**
17 **KUIPER BELT (USA)**, 6, b g Elusive Quality (USA)—Youre So Sweet (USA) **Christian Williams Racing Club**
18 **LIMITED RESERVE (IRE)**, 8, b g Court Cave (IRE)—Lady Blackie (IRE) **All Stars Sports Racing**
19 **LORD IN RED (GER)**, 8, ch g Noroit (GER)—Lady In Red (GER) **Christian Williams Racing Club**
20 **MASSINI'S DREAM**, 9, b m Dr Massini (IRE)—Cathy's Dream (IRE) **Mr T. J. Rees**
21 **PADDYS RUNNER**, 8, gr g Sir Percy—Frosty Welcome (USA) **Paddys Runner Partnership**
22 **PERPIGNAN (IRE)**, 8, b g Robin des Champs (FR)—Reevolesa (IRE) **All Stars Sports Racing**
23 **POTTERS CORNER (IRE)**, 10, b g Indian Danehill (IRE)—
Woodford Beauty (IRE) **All Stars Sports Racing & J Davies**
24 **PRIMAL FOCUS (IRE)**, 6, b g Intense Focus (USA)—
Churn Dat Butter (USA) **John & Paul Stanaway & Nicola Reed**

Other Owners: All Stars Sports Racing, Mr J. J. V. Davies, Mr C. S. Hinchy, Mr A. James, Mr G. C. Maule, Mr M. S. Scott.

Assistant Trainer: Nicky Williams.

---

575 | MR DAI WILLIAMS, Compton
Postal: **Flat Ashley House, Hodson, Swindon, Wiltshire, SN4 0QG**
Contacts: HOME **01488 638636** MOBILE **07879 403595, 07879 403160** FAX **01488 638121**

1 **BABYTAGGLE (IRE)**, 9, b g Brian Boru—Ardnataggle (IRE) **Mr F. Michael**
2 **BEAN LIATH (IRE)**, 9, gr m Portrait Gallery (IRE)—Coolnasmear (IRE) **Hewitt & Williams Partnership**
3 **BENNYS GIRL (IRE)**, 12, b m Beneficial—Be My Flower (IRE) **We Must Be Barmy**
4 **HAVE A GO HERO (IRE)**, 12, b g Flemensfirth (USA)—Blue Bank (IRE) **Mr S. R. Williams**
5 **LINGUINE (FR)**, 10, ch g Linngari (IRE)—Amerissage (USA) **Mr A. M. Rennison**
6 **MIDNIGHT REQUEST**, 11, b g Midnight Legend—Friendly Request **Mr S. R. Williams**
7 **MIGHTY ALTOGETHER**, 6, ch g Shirocco (GER)—Ryde To Arms
8 **NORUKI (IRE)**, 10, b g Flemensfirth (USA)—Classic Material **Mr F. Michael**
9 **PONIEL**, 8, b g Bahri (USA)—Rafta (IRE) **Mr S. R. Williams**
10 **POSITIVE TOUCH (IRE)**, 9, b g Misternando—Independant Flora **Mr S. R. Williams**
11 **SHE'S A NOVELTY (IRE)**, 5, b m Approve (IRE)—Novel Fun (IRE) **Mr N. Sander**

Other Owners: Mr G. Bell, R. J. Hewitt, Mr A. M. Rennison, Mr S. R. Williams.

Assistant Trainer: Miss Lucy Horner.

Amateur Jockey: Miss L. Horner.

---

576 | MR EVAN WILLIAMS, Llancarfan
Postal: **Fingerpost Farm, Llancarfan, Nr Barry, Vale of Glamorgan, CF62 3AE**
Contacts: PHONE **01446 754069** MOBILE **07950 381227** FAX **01446 754069**
EMAIL **cath@evanwilliams.co.uk** WEBSITE **www.evanwilliamsracing.co.uk**

1 **AGENT WESTY (IRE)**, 6, b g Fame And Glory—Isis Du Berlais (FR) **R. E. R. Williams**
2 **ANNSAM**, 5, b g Black Sam Bellamy (IRE)—Bathwick Annie **H. M. W. Clifford**
3 **ARCADE ATTRACTION (IRE)**, 6, b g Arcadio (GER)—Tobetall **Border Pointers & Feilim O Muiri**
4 **ARCTIC SNOW**, 4, b g Frankel—Winter Solstice **R. E. R. Williams**
5 **ARIZONA GLORY**, 4, gr g Universal (IRE)—Phoenix City (USA) **H. M. W. Clifford**
6 **ASTRA VIA**, 5, b m Multiplex—Wou Oodd **Mrs J. Davies**
7 **BALLINSKER (IRE)**, 5, b g Court Cave (IRE)—Brownie Points (IRE) **Gg Thoroughbreds Xii & Partner**
8 **BALLYBREEN (IRE)**, 7, b g Gold Well—Miss Colclough (IRE) **R. E. R. Williams**
9 **BILLY BRONCO**, 9, ch g Central Park (IRE)—Nan **Mr & Mrs William Rucker**
10 **BOLD PLAN (IRE)**, 6, b g Jeremy (USA)—Kings Orchid (IRE) **Mr & Mrs William Rucker**

MR EVAN WILLIAMS - continued

11 CARDIFF BAY, 5, br g Arcadio (GER)—Spangle Island **Mr & Mrs William Rucker**
12 CARPOOL (IRE), 6, b m Mahler—Buslane (IRE) **Hush Hush Partnership**
13 CASWELL BAY, 5, b g Fame And Glory—Lauderdale (GER) **Mr David M. Williams**
14 CESAR COLLONGES (FR), 8, ch g Fragrant Mix (IRE)—Prouesse Collonges (FR) **Mr & Mrs William Rucker**
15 CHOOSEYOURWEAPON (IRE), 7, br g Flemensfirth (USA)—Definite Love (IRE) **Mr & Mrs William Rucker**
16 CLYNE, 10, b g Hernando (FR)—Lauderdale (GER) **Mr D. M. Williams**
17 COCONUT SPLASH (IRE), 5, ch g Stowaway—Presenting Chaos (IRE) **Mr & Mrs William Rucker**
18 COURT DANCER (IRE), 5, b g Court Cave (IRE)—Windsor Dancer (IRE) **Mrs J. Davies**
19 COURT ROYALE (IRE), 7, b g Court Cave (IRE)—Windsor Dancer (IRE) **Mrs Janet Davies**
20 CRACKLE LYN ROSIE, 6, b m Kayf Tara—Native Sunrise (IRE) **R. E. R. Williams**
21 DANS LE VENT (FR), 7, b g Skins Game—Boreade (FR) **R J Gambarini Racing**
22 DESTINYS CHOICE (IRE), 7, b m Dubai Destination (USA)—Leader's Hall (IRE) **Wayne Clifford & Ian Gosden**
23 DIAMON DES FLOS (FR), 4, b g Balko (FR)—Marie Royale (FR)
24 4, B g Shirocco (GER)—Dreams And Songs
25 ESPRIT DU LARGE (FR), 6, b g No Risk At All (FR)—Tuffslolyloly (FR) **Mr & Mrs William Rucker**
26 FADO DES BROSSES (FR), 5, b g Balko (FR)—Nanou des Brosses (FR) **Mr & Mrs William Rucker**
27 FALETHAO D'ANA (FR), 5, b g Khalkevi (IRE)—Histoire des Ifs (FR) **T Harris & O Chandler**
28 FINVARRA (IRE), 5, b g Finsceal Fior (IRE)—Titania **Mr W. J. Eddy-Williams**
29 FLIGHT TO MILAN (IRE), 7, b g Milan—Kigali (IRE) **R. E. R. Williams**
30 GIGA WHITE (IRE), 4, gr g Dark Angel (IRE)—Lightwood Lady (IRE) **R. E. R. Williams**
31 GILWEN GRAYSON, 5, b g Multiplex—Gilwen Glory (IRE) **Keith & Sue Lowry**
32 GO LONG (IRE), 10, b g Hurricane Run (IRE)—Monumental Gesture **Mr & Mrs William Rucker**
33 GOLDEN WHISKY (IRE), 7, ch g Flemensfirth (USA)—Derry Vale (IRE) **Mr & Mrs William Rucker**
34 GRANIA O'MALLEY (IRE), 7, ch m Beat Hollow—Oh Susannah (FR) **Ms Sue Howell I**
35 HOLDBACKTHERIVER (IRE), 8, b g Presenting—Fairy Lane (IRE) **W J Evans Racing**
36 HOLLY JAMES, 6, b g Black Sam Bellamy (IRE)—Miss Chinchilla **Walters Plant, Spiers & Hartwell, Pt Eng**
37 4, B g Leading Light (IRE)—Holy Vow (IRE)
38 IMPERIAL FLEM (IRE), 5, b g Flemensfirth (USA)—Glamorous Leader (IRE) **Mr & Mrs William Rucker**
39 INCH LALA (IRE), 8, ch m Mahler—Aboo Lala (IRE) **Clifford, Gosden & House**
40 JOHN CONSTABLE (IRE), 9, b g Montjeu (IRE)—Dance Parade (USA) **W J Evans Racing**
41 JOUR A LA PLAGE (FR), 5, gr g Coastal Path—Juntina (FR) **Mr & Mrs William Rucker**
42 KEEPING FAITH (IRE), 6, br m Sholokhov (IRE)—Elphis (IRE) **Mr & Mrs William Rucker**
43 KHANISARI (IRE), 6, gr g Dark Angel (IRE)—Kadayna (IRE) **Pos Partnership 2**
44 KING'S ODYSSEY (IRE), 11, b g King's Theatre (IRE)—Ma Furie (FR) **Mr & Mrs William Rucker**
45 LUSITANIEN (FR), 4, b g Muhtathir—Easter Rose (FR)
46 MAC AMARA, 6, b m Dick Turpin (IRE)—Macnance (IRE) **Keith & Sue Lowry**
47 MAC BELLA, 8, ch m Black Sam Bellamy (IRE)—Macnance (IRE) **Keith & Sue Lowry**
48 MAC KAYLA, 5, b m Kayf Tara—Macnance (IRE) **Keith & Sue Lowry**
49 MACK THE MAN (IRE), 6, b g Flemensfirth (USA)—Nifty Nuala (IRE) **Mr & Mrs William Rucker**
50 MARBLE MOON (IRE), 8, b g Millenary—Royal Marble (IRE) **Mr Emrys Jones & Partner**
51 4, B g Califet (FR)—Market Niche (IRE)
52 MEMPHIS BELL (IRE), 6, b m Yeats (IRE)—Andrea Gale (IRE) **Mr W. P. Bates**
53 MISS ZIP (IRE), 7, b m Getaway (GER)—Lady Lace (IRE) **Tony Cromwell & Partner**
54 MOTASHAKEL (IRE), 4, b g Olympic Glory (IRE)—River Test **Irving Struel Racing**
55 MOUSEINTHEHOUSE (IRE), 6, b g Milan—Mandysue (IRE) **R J Gambarini Racing**
56 NO REMATCH (IRE), 6, b g Westerner—Loadsofability (IRE) **Mr & Mrs William Rucker**
57 OLYMPIC HONOUR (IRE), 4, b g Olympic Glory (IRE)—Shamah **Mr R Abbott & Mr M Stavrou**
58 ON THE QUIET (IRE), 5, b m Ballingarry (IRE)—Royale Sulawesie (FR) **Hush Hush Partnership**
59 ON THE ROAD (IRE), 10, b g Stowaway—B Greenhill **Mrs C. A. Williams**
60 ON TOUR (IRE), 12, b g Croco Rouge (IRE)—Galant Tour (IRE) **Mr T. Hywel Jones**
61 ONETWOTREE (IRE), 5, b g Sholokhov (IRE)—Elphis (IRE) **R. E. R. Williams**
62 OXWICH BAY (IRE), 8, b g Westerner—Rose de Beaufai (FR) **Mr David M. Williams**
63 PETERBOROUGH (FR), 7, b g Fuisse (FR)—Peony Girl (FR) **Norwester Racing Club & Partner**
64 POBBLES BAY (IRE), 10, b g Oscar (IRE)—Rose de Beaufai (FR) **Mr D. M. Williams**
65 PRESENT VALUE (IRE), 6, b g Gold Well—Presenting Shares (IRE) **Mr & Mrs William Rucker**
66 PRIME VENTURE (IRE), 9, br g Primary (USA)—Next Venture (USA) **Mrs Janet Davies**
67 QUOI DE NEUF (FR), 6, b g Anzillero (GER)—Qualite Controlee (FR) **Mr & Mrs William Rucker**
68 RAILROAD JUNKIE (IRE), 7, b g Thousand Words—Eckbeag (USA) **Mrs J. Davies**
69 RING THE MOON, 7, b g Spanish Moon (USA)—Get The Ring (FR) **W. J. Evans**

MR EVAN WILLIAMS - continued

70 **SABBATHICAL (FR)**, 5, b g Sunday Break (JPN)—Ulcy Pressive (FR) **R. E. R. Williams**
71 **SECRET REPRIEVE (IRE)**, 6, b g Flemensfirth (USA)—Oscar's Reprieve (IRE) **Mr & Mrs William Rucker**
72 **SIGN OF WAR (IRE)**, 6, b g Oscar (IRE)—Irish Wedding (IRE) **R. E. R. Williams**
73 **SILVER STREAK (IRE)**, 7, gr g Dark Angel (IRE)—Happy Talk (IRE) **Mr T. L. Fell**
74 **SKEWIFF**, 8, b m Doyen (IRE)—Skew **Mrs Janet Davies**
75 **STILL BELIEVING (IRE)**, 12, ch m Blueprint (IRE)—Im A Believer (IRE) **R. E. R. Williams**
76 **SUPREME ESCAPE (IRE)**, 6, b g Milan—Silent Whisper (IRE) **Walters Plant, Spiers & Hartwell, Pt Eng**
77 **SUTTER'S MILL (IRE)**, 9, b g Gold Well—Shamriyna (IRE) **R. E. R. Williams**
78 4, Br g Sageburg (IRE)—Swell Sister (IRE)
79 **THE GIPPER (IRE)**, 10, b g King's Theatre (IRE)—Merrill Gaye (IRE) **POS Partnership**
80 **THE LAST DAY (IRE)**, 8, b g Oscar (IRE)—The Last Bank (IRE) **Mr & Mrs William Rucker**
81 **TIMASSINI (IRE)**, 5, b m Dr Massini (IRE)—Timoca (IRE) **Mrs J. Davies**
82 **TREASURE DILLON (IRE)**, 6, b g Sans Frontieres (IRE)—Treasure Trix (IRE) **Mr R Abbott & Mr M Stavrou**
83 **VIRGINIA CHICK (FR)**, 8, b g Nickname (FR)—Sweet Jaune (FR) **Mrs C. A. Williams**
84 **VOODOO DOLL (IRE)**, 7, b g Getaway (GER)—Voodoo Magic (GER) **R. E. R. Williams**
85 4, B g Dylan Thomas (IRE)—Whenever Wherever (IRE)
86 **WINDS OF FIRE (USA)**, 5, b g Kitten's Joy (USA)—Laureldean Gale (USA) **Mr T. L. Fell**

Other Owners: R. J. Abbott, Mr O. T. W. Chandler, H. M. W. Clifford, Mr C. T. Cromwell, Mrs J. Davies, M. V. Dawson, Mr W. J. Eddy-Williams, W. J. Evans, GG Thoroughbreds XII, Mr R. J. Gambarini, Mr G. Gill, Mr I. F. Gosden, Mr T. R. Harris, Mr R. House, Ms S. A. Howell, Mr E. C. Jones, Mr T. H. Jones, Mr D. G. Long, K. R. Lowry, Mrs S. B. Lowry, W. J. G. Morse, Norwester Racing Club, Mr F. T. O'Muiri, P T Civil Engineering Ltd, POS Partnership, Spiers & Hartwell Ltd, M. Stavrou, Mr I. Struel, Mr C. Trigg, Walters Plant Hire Ltd, Mrs C. A. Williams, Mr D. M. Williams, R. E. R. Williams, Mr S. Williams.

Assistant Trainer: Cath Williams.

NH Jockey: Adam Wedge. **Conditional Jockey:** Conor Ring. **Amateur Jockey:** Miss Isabel Williams.

---

577 | **MR IAN WILLIAMS, Alvechurch**
Postal: **Dominion Racing Stables, Seafield Lane, Alvechurch, Birmingham, B48 7HL**
Contacts: **PHONE 01564 822392 MOBILE 07976 645384 FAX 01564 829475**
EMAIL info@ianwilliamsracing.com WEBSITE www.ianwilliamsracing.com

1 **ABEL TASMAN**, 6, b g Mount Nelson—Helena Molony (IRE) **Mr I. Furlong**
2 **ACES (IRE)**, 8, b g Dark Angel (IRE)—Cute Ass (IRE) **Mr P. E. Wildes**
3 **AKARITA LIGHTS (IRE)**, 6, b g Arctic Cosmos (USA)—Akarita (IRE) **Mr Allan Stennett & Mickley Stud**
4 5, B g Winged Love (IRE)—Ally Rose (IRE)
5 **ALMOST GOLD (IRE)**, 7, b g Gold Well—Shining Lights (IRE) **Mr S. Cox**
6 **ALWAYS RESOLUTE**, 9, b g Refuse To Bend (IRE)—Mad Annie (USA) **Ne-Chance**
7 **AMBER GAMBLER (GER)**, 10, b g Doyen (IRE)—Auenglocke (GER) **P. Kelly**
8 **ARMED (IRE)**, 5, b g Invincible Spirit (IRE)—Ange Bleu (USA) **Turton & O'Shea**
9 **AUTUMN WAR (IRE)**, 5, ch g Declaration of War (USA)—Autumn Leaves (FR) **The JAM Partnership**
10 **BANDITRY (IRE)**, 8, b g Iffraaj—Badalona **Buxted Partnership**
11 **BLUE LAUREATE**, 5, b g Poet's Voice—Powder Blue **Mr A. Dale**
12 **BOL D'AIR (FR)**, 9, b g Blue Bresil (FR)—Holding (FR) **Mr P. Hernon**
13 **BONSAI BAY**, 5, b g Multiplex—Bonsai (IRE) **A. Stennett**
14 **BOY IN THE BAR**, 9, ch g Dutch Art—Lipsia (IRE) **Allwins Stables**
15 **BYRON FLYER**, 9, b g Byron—Nursling (IRE) **Anchor Men**
16 **CENTRAL CITY (IRE)**, 5, b g Kodiac—She Basic (IRE) **Mr S. Coomes**
17 5, Ch g Sholokhov (IRE)—Chiltern Hills (IRE)
18 **CHOSEN SHANT (IRE)**, 4, b br f Shantou (USA)—Ratheniska (IRE) **Golden Equinox Racing**
19 **DADS LEGACY**, 5, ch g Schiaparelli (GER)—Our Jess (IRE) **Mrs S. J. Vasey**
20 **DEADLY ACCURATE**, 5, br g Lethal Force (IRE)—Riccoche (IRE) **Mr S. Bell**
21 **DIABOLEO (FR)**, 4, ch g Galileo (IRE)—Beautifix (GER) **Mr P. E. Wildes**
22 **DIRTY DIANA (FR)**, 5, b br m Siyouni (FR)—Gipson Dessert (USA) **M. C. Denmark**
23 **DOUBLE UP**, 9, b g Exceed And Excel (AUS)—My Love Thomas (IRE) **Mr & Mrs H. Parmar**
24 **DRAGON BONES**, 5, br m Passing Glance—Sainte Kadette (FR) **The Ferandlin Peaches**
25 **DYNALI**, 4, b g Dansili—Lunar Phase (IRE) **Golden Equinox Racing**

MR IAN WILLIAMS - continued

26 **EJTILAAB (IRE)**, 4, b g Slade Power (IRE)—Miranda Frost (IRE) **Mr P. E. Wildes**
27 **EMBRACE THE MOMENT (IRE)**, 4, b f Le Havre (IRE)—Kithonia (FR) **Middleham Park Racing XCIII**
28 **EMRAAN (IRE)**, 4, b g Invincible Spirit (IRE)—Wissal (USA) **Mr T. H. J. Green**
29 **ERNESTO (GER)**, 5, b h Reliable Man—Enrica **Buxted Partnership**
30 **EVERYTHING FOR YOU (IRE)**, 6, b g Pivotal—Miss Delila (USA) **Mr D. A. Thorpe**
31 **FIFRELET (FR)**, 5, br g Diamond Boy (FR)—Unique Star (FR) **Asd Contracts Ltd**
32 **FOILLAN (IRE)**, 5, b g Le Fou (IRE)—Castlevennon (IRE) **Mr T. J. Hemmings**
33 **FURQAAN (IRE)**, 4, b f Dark Angel (IRE)—Surrey Storm **Mr A. Dale**
34 **GETAWAY MISSION (IRE)**, 6, b g Getaway (GER)—Emeranna **Andrew Dick & Steve Roberts**
35 4, B g Sholokhov (IRE)—Ginger Bazouka (FR)
36 **GOLDEN GRENADE (FR)**, 4, b g Zanzibari (USA)—King's Parody (IRE) **Ian Williams Racing Club**
37 **GRACIOUS JOHN (IRE)**, 7, b g Baltic King—Dorn Hill **T. Reffell**
38 **HARLOW**, 6, b g Harlan's Holiday (USA)—Glowing (IRE) **I. P. Williams**
39 **HASANABAD (IRE)**, 5, b g Nathaniel (IRE)—Hasanka (IRE) **Teme Valley 2**
40 **HEAD ON (IRE)**, 4, br g Robin des Champs (FR)—Miss Baloo (IRE) **Mr S. Cox**
41 **HOLLOW GOLD (IRE)**, 4, br g Sea The Stars (IRE)—Martine's Spirit (IRE) **The Alyasan Partnership**
42 **HYDROPLANE (IRE)**, 4, b g Pour Moi (IRE)—Walk On Water **John Nicholls (Trading) Ltd, Mrs Jane Nicholls**
43 **IDILICO (FR)**, 5, b g Lawman (FR)—Ydillique (IRE) **Mr A. D. Dick**
44 **JAM SESSION (IRE)**, 8, ch g Duke of Marmalade (IRE)—Night Dhu **Mr A. L. R. Morton**
45 **JAWSHAN (USA)**, 5, b g Denman (AUS)—Diamond Baby (USA) **Ever Hopefuls**
46 **JAYTEE**, 5, ch g Schiaparelli (GER)—Archway Copse **J. Tredwell**
47 **KICK ON KICK ON**, 5, b g Swiss Spirit—Catmint **I. P. Williams**
48 **KING OF REALMS (IRE)**, 8, b g King's Theatre (IRE)—Sunny South East (IRE) **Chandler Ferguson Hanafin Kelly**
49 **KLUTE (IRE)**, 4, br g Kodiac—Fonda (USA) **Buxted Partners**
50 **LADY SHIROCCO (IRE)**, 5, b m Shirocco (GER)—Estarana (GER) **The DTTW Partnership**
51 **LONG MARCH (IRE)**, 5, b g Bellamy Road (USA)—Magnifica (USA) **Dr C. K. C. Tan**
52 **LUCKY'S DREAM**, 5, ch g Yorgunnabelucky (USA)—Dream Esteem **R. S. Brookhouse**
53 4, B g Shantou (USA)—Marias Dream (IRE) **Eventmasters Racing**
54 **MATEWAN (IRE)**, 5, b g Epaulette (AUS)—Cochin (USA) **Roy David, The Tuesday Syndicate**
55 5, B g Great Pretender (IRE)—Mewstone **The Ferandlin Peaches**
56 **MEXICAN DAVE**, 5, b g Sakhee (USA)—Artic Bliss **First Chance Racing**
57 **MICHAEL'S MOUNT**, 7, ch g Mount Nelson—Dumnoni **Andrew Dick & Mark Dennis**
58 **MOKAATIL**, 5, br g Lethal Force (IRE)—Moonlit Garden (IRE) **Midtech**
59 **MONJENI**, 7, b g Montjeu (IRE)—Polly's Mark (IRE) **Corinthian Racing Club**
60 6, B m Jeremy (IRE)—Monsignorita (IRE) **M. C. Denmark**
61 **MR PERFECT (IRE)**, 5, b g Mustameet—Crescendor (FR) **Mr S. Coomes**
62 **MUSTARRID (IRE)**, 6, b g Elzaam (AUS)—Symbol of Peace (IRE) **Mr A. Dale**
63 **NIGH OR NEVER (IRE)**, 6, b g Excelebration (IRE)—Nigh (IRE) **P. Kelly**
64 **NOBLE BEHEST**, 6, b g Sir Percy—Lady Hestia (USA) **Mr A. C. Elliott**
65 **OI THE CLUBB OI'S**, 5, gr g Champs Elysees—Red Boots (IRE) **The Albatross Club**
66 **ONE MORE FLEURIE (IRE)**, 6, b g Mustameet—Auburn Cherry (IRE) **Mr K. McKenna**
67 **OUR IDIC BOY (IRE)**, 6, b g Royal Anthem (USA)—Next Best Thing (IRE) **Mr K. McKenna**
68 **PADDY THE CHEF (IRE)**, 5, b g Dandy Man (IRE)—The Reek **Mr & Mrs H. Parmar**
69 **POKER SCHOOL (IRE)**, 10, b g Gold Well—Broken Pockets (IRE) **Mr A Aniol, Mr S Turner, Mr A Chandler**
70 **PORTWAY FLYER (IRE)**, 12, br g King's Theatre (IRE)—Next Best Thing (IRE) **P. Kelly**
71 **POUR JOIE**, 5, b g Pour Moi (IRE)—Lupa Montana (USA) **Helen Jameson Racing Partnership**
72 **PUERTO BANUS**, 4, b g Bated Breath—Three Ducks **Teme Valley 2**
73 **REGABY (IRE)**, 5, b g Stowaway—Anjum (USA) **Mr T. J. Hemmings**
74 **ROBELLI (IRE)**, 5, b g Getaway (GER)—Marhab Dancer (IRE) **John Nicholls (Trading) Ltd**
75 **ROYAL VILLAGE (IRE)**, 8, b g Scorpion (IRE)—Etoile Margot (FR) **R Triple H**
76 6, B m Arvico (FR)—Sainte Kadette (FR) **The Ferandlin Peaches**
77 **SATURDAYNIGHTFEVER**, 8, b g King's Theatre (IRE)—Get Me Home (IRE) **M. C. Denmark**
78 **SEA SOVEREIGN (IRE)**, 7, b g Sea The Stars (IRE)—Lidakiya (IRE) **G. C. Stevens**
79 **SEVEN DE BAUNE (FR)**, 7, ch g Tiger Groom—Venus de Baune (FR) **R. S. Brookhouse**
80 **SHADY MCCOY (USA)**, 10, b g English Channel (USA)—Raw Gold (USA) **I. P. Williams**
81 **SHAMRAD (FR)**, 4, b g Casamento (IRE)—Shamsa (FR) **Midtech 2**
82 4, B g Sageburg (IRE)—Shining Lights (IRE)
83 **SHIP OF THE FEN**, 5, b g Champs Elysees—Ruffled **Midtech, McKenna, Macable**
84 **SIR MAXIMILIAN (IRE)**, 11, b g Royal Applause—Nebraska Lady (IRE) **Mr P. E. Wildes**

MR IAN WILLIAMS - continued

85 **SOMETIMES ALWAYS (IRE)**, 5, b g Presenting—Noras Fancy (IRE) **Mr S. Cox**
86 **SPEED COMPANY (IRE)**, 7, b g Fast Company (IRE)—Trentini (IRE) **A. Stennett**
87 **STELLARISTA (IRE)**, 6, b m Mastercraftsman (IRE)—Stellarina (IRE) **Ian Williams Racing Club**
88 **TANQEEB**, 4, b g Garswood—Oasis Mirage **Asd Contracts Ltd**
89 **THE GRAND VISIR**, 6, b g Frankel—Piping (IRE) **Andy Bell**
90 **TIDE TIMES (IRE)**, 6, gr g Vinnie Roe (IRE)—Lady Wagtail (IRE) **The DTTW Partnership**
91 **WALHAAN (IRE)**, 4, gr g Dark Angel (IRE)—Back In The Frame **Allwins Stables**
92 **WAR BRIGADE (FR)**, 6, b g Manduro (GER)—Adjudicate **The DTTW Partnership**
93 **WESTERN DUKE (IRE)**, 6, b g High Chaparral (IRE)—Witch of Fife (USA) **Mr K. A. Cosby**
94 **ZERACHIEL (IRE)**, 10, b g Winged Love (IRE)—At Dawn (IRE) **John Nicholls (Trading) Ltd**
95 **ZUBAYR (IRE)**, 8, b g Authorized (IRE)—Zaziyra (IRE) **Mr P. J. Vogt**

THREE-YEAR-OLDS

96 **COOL TO BE A CAT (FR)**, b g Style Vendome (FR)—Forward Feline (IRE) **Mr P. R. Williams**
97 **KANGAROO POINT (IRE)**, b g Australia—Magic Peak (IRE)
98 **THUNDER FLASH**, b g Night of Thunder (IRE)—Sultanah Heyam **John Nicholls (Trading) Ltd**

Other Owners: Mr G. Anderson, Mr M. Aniol, Mr M. R. Askew, Buxted Partnership, CLXX, Mr D. E. Carolan, Mr G. Castle, Mr A. Chandler, Mr M. J. S. Cockburn, Mr A. Cocum, Mr R. Deeley, Mr M. N. Dennis, Mr A. I. Derry, Mr J. I. Derry, Mr A. D. Dick, Dr P. A. I. Doro, Mr A. C. Elliott, Mr R. M. Faccenda, Sir A. Ferguson, Mr N. D. Ford, Mrs M. Forsyth, Mr D. Hanafin, J. P Hanifin, Ms R. J. Harris, Ian Williams Racing Club, Mrs H. Jameson, P. Kelly, Mr R. Kent, Mr S. Mackintosh, P. J. Makin, Mr C. R. Mander, Mr K. McKenna, Michael Watt & Billy Slater (aus), Mr F. Mooney, Mr A. J. R. Moseley, Mr Allan Stennett & Mickley Stud, Mr J. O'Shea, Mr H. Parmar, Mrs K. Parmar, Mr M. Rapley, Mr P Ratcliffe, Mr S. Roberts, J. L. Rowsell, Mr S. Rudolf, Mrs J. Ruthven, Mr W. N. Slater, Mr P. Southall, A. Stennett, Teme Valley 2, J. Tredwell, Mr S. W. Turner, R. J. Turton, M. H. Watt, I. P. Williams.

Assistant Trainer: Ben Brookhouse.

NH Jockey: Will Kennedy, Tom O'Brien. **Apprentice Jockey:** Joshua Thorman.

---

578 | MRS JANE WILLIAMS, South Molton
Postal: Culverhill Farm, George Nympton, South Molton, Devon, EX36 4JE
Contacts: **HOME 01769 574174 MOBILE 07977 457350**

1 **AFTER THE FOX**, 5, b g Universal (IRE)—Foxglove **Mrs J. R. Williams**
2 **AUBUSSON (FR)**, 11, b g Ballingarry (IRE)—Katioucha (FR) **Mrs J. R. Williams**
3 **DAIM PIERJI (FR)**, 7, b g Coastal Path—Keensland (FR) **Mrs J. R. Williams**
4 **ERICK LE ROUGE (FR)**, 6, ch g Gentlewave (IRE)—Imperia II (FR) **The Culverhill Racing Club**
5 **FOLLY GATE (FR)**, 5, b g Montmartre (FR)—Cate Bleue (FR) **Mrs J Williams & Mr R Stark**
6 **FOX PRO (FR)**, 5, b g Coastal Path—Devise II (FR) **Mrs J. R. Williams**
7 **GALICE MACALO (FR)**, 4, b f Saddler Maker (IRE)—Victoire de Forme (FR) **Culverhill Racing Club II**
8 **GLADIATEUR ALLEN (FR)**, 4, b g Saint des Saints (FR)—Une Epoque (FR) **Mrs J. R. Williams**
9 **LE CRUNCH (FR)**, 4, b g Cokoriko (FR)—Line Divine (FR) **Mr O. Matthews**
10 **MONSIEUR LECOQ (FR)**, 6, b g Diamond Boy (FR)—Draga (FR) **Mrs J. R. Williams**
11 **MONTESTREL (FR)**, 5, b g Montmartre (FR)—La Estrella (GER) **Mrs J. R. Williams**
12 **ROCOCO RIVER**, 6, b g Shirocco (GER)—Noun de La Thinte (FR) **Mrs J Williams & Mr R Stark**
13 **TEA FOR TWO**, 11, b g Kayf Tara—One For Me **Mrs Jane Williams & Mr Len Jakeman**

THREE-YEAR-OLDS

14 **BALKO SAINT (FR)**, b g Balko (FR)—Sainte Cupid (FR) **Mrs J. R. Williams**
15 **HAMILTON DICI (FR)**, b g Coastal Path—Umbria Dici (FR) **Mrs J. R. Williams**
16 **HIPSTER MACALO (FR)**, b g Cokoriko (FR)—Victoire de Forme (FR) **Mrs J. R. Williams**
17 **HONNEUR D'AJONC (FR)**, b g Diamond Boy (FR)—Fleur d'Ajonc (FR) **Mrs J. R. Williams**
18 B c Balko (FR)—Singaminnie (FR) **Culverhill RacingClub III**

TWO-YEAR-OLDS

19 B c 19/04 Telescope (IRE)—Fragrant Rose (Alflora (IRE)) (14285) **Mrs J. R. Williams**
20 B c 13/06 Saint des Saints (FR)—Jolie Menthe (FR) (Bateau Rouge) **Mrs J. R. Williams**

Other Owners: Culverhill Racing Club II, Mr L. J. Jakeman, Mr R. Stark, Mrs J. R. Williams.

579 **MR NICK WILLIAMS, South Molton**
Postal: **Culverhill Farm, George Nympton, South Molton, Devon, EX36 4JE**
Contacts: **PHONE 01769 574174 MOBILE 07855 450379**
EMAIL nandjwilliams@live.co.uk

1 **AGRAPART (FR),** 9, b br g Martaline—Afragha (IRE) **Gascoigne, Brookes & Barker**
2 **AIMEE DE SIVOLA (FR),** 6, ch m Network (GER)—Neva de Sivola (FR) **Larkhills Racing Partnership IV**
3 **BORO BABE (FR),** 4, ch f Sea The Stars (IRE)—Lockup (IRE) **Mrs E. K. M. J. Morgan Joseph**
4 **CHOCKS AWAY (FR),** 4, b g Le Havre (IRE)—Salvation **The Macaroni Beach Society**
5 **COLONEL MANDERSON (FR),** 4, b g Kapgarde (FR)—Playact (IRE) **Babbit Racing**
6 **CULTURE DE SIVOLA (FR),** 8, b m Assessor (IRE)—Neva de Sivola (FR) **Larkhills Racing Partnership II**
7 **DENTLEY DE MEE (FR),** 7, b g Lauro (GER)—Natty Twigy (FR) **Babbit Racing**
8 **FAIRE PART SIVOLA (FR),** 5, b g Noroit (GER)—Lettre d'Estruval (FR) **K Alexander/ R Watts**
9 **FAVORI DE SIVOLA (FR),** 5, b g Noroit (GER)—Suave de Sivola (FR) **John White & Anne Underhill**
10 **FELICIDAD (FR),** 5, b m Racinger (FR)—Sacade (FR) **Mr K. Alexander**
11 **GALAHAD QUEST (FR),** 4, b g American Post—Atacames (IRE) **Holt, Macnabb, Robinson & Jeffrey**
12 **GINGEMBRE MENTHE (FR),** 4, ch g Barastraight—Jolie Menthe (FR) **French Gold**
13 **HORATIO HORNBLOWER (IRE),** 12, b br g Presenting—Countess Camilla **Chasing Gold Limited**
14 **LE CAMELEON,** 5, b br g Great Pretender (IRE)—Countess Camilla **The Pretenders**
15 **LE ROCHER (FR),** 10, b g Saint des Saints (FR)—Belle du Roi (FR) **John White & Anne Underhill**
16 **NIGHT OF SIN (FR),** 7, gr g Sinndar (IRE)—Natt Musik (FR) **Simon Brown & Ron Watts**
17 **ONE FOR THE TEAM,** 6, b g Shirocco (GER)—One Gulp **Forty Winks Syndicate 2**
18 **ONE OF US,** 8, b g Presenting—One Gulp **Forty Winks Syndicate**
19 **PRUDHOMME (FR),** 5, ch g Martaline—Panzella (FR) **Gascoigne, Brookes & Barker**
20 **SIRUH DU LAC (FR),** 7, b g Turgeon (USA)—Margerie (FR) **John White & Anne Underhill**

THREE-YEAR-OLDS

21 **ALBERIC (FR),** b g Poliglote—Khayance (FR)
22 **FIGHTING TIGER (FR),** b g Elvstroem (AUS)—Ma Preference (FR)
23 **HECTOR DE SIVOLA (FR),** b g Noroit (GER)—Little Memories (IRE) **Larkhills Racing Partnership III**
24 **HELIOS ALLEN (FR),** b g Coastal Path—Silane (FR) **French Gold**
25 **HURRICANE SIVOLA (FR),** b g Noroit (GER)—Surprise de Sivola (FR) **Mr N. S. L. Williams**
26 **YGGDRASIL (FR),** b g Kapgarde (FR)—Margerie (FR) **John White & Anne Underhill**

TWO-YEAR-OLDS

27 **I'M THE DIVA (FR),** b f 14/03 Network (GER)—Sunny Vic (FR) (Robin des Champs (FR)) **Mr N. S. L. Williams**
28 **INTERNE DE SIVOLA (FR),** b g 01/04 Noroit (GER)—Kerrana (FR) (Cadoudal (FR)) **Mr N. S. L. Williams**
29 Ch g 02/05 Martaline—Panzella (FR) (Kahyasi) **Gascoigne, Brookes & Barker**

Other Owners: Mr K. Alexander, K. Barker, J. N. W. Brookes, Mr S. J. Brown, Mr K. Conlan, Mr G. Devlin, Mr R. Forster, Mr M. J. Freer, Mr C. J. Garner, Mr S. D. Garner, D. A. Gascoigne, Mr A. Holt, Miss A. Jeffrey, Mr J. E. Lawrence, Mr I. Macnabb, Mr I. Paye, M. L. Pepper, Mr J. D. Robinson, Mrs K. Salters, Mr J. Summers, Mrs A. Underhill, Mr R. C. Watts, Mr A. J. White, Mr N. S. L. Williams.

NH Jockey: Lizzie Kelly. **Conditional Jockey:** Chester Williams.

---

580 **MR NOEL WILLIAMS, Blewbury**
Postal: **Churn Stables, Churn Estate, Blewbury, Didcot, Oxfordshire, OX11 9HG**
Contacts: **PHONE 01235 850806 MOBILE 07887 718678**
EMAIL info@noelwilliamsracing.co.uk WEBSITE www.noelwilliamsracing.co.uk

1 **ANOTHER CRICK,** 7, b g Arcadio (GER)—Suetsu (IRE) **Mr D. J. S. Sewell**
2 **ANOTHER DRAMA (IRE),** 8, b g Gamut (IRE)—Rachrush (IRE) **Mr N. Williams**
3 **ATOMIX (GER),** 9, b g Doyen (IRE)—Aloe (GER) **Mr G. Wragg**
4 **AUTHORIZED TOO,** 9, b g Authorized (IRE)—Audaz **Stonepoint Racing Club**
5 **BALLI MARTINE (FR),** 7, b g Ballingarry (IRE)—Miss Martine (FR) **Alma Vale Racing**
6 **BREAKING WAVES (IRE),** 6, b g Yeats (IRE)—Acoola (IRE) **Colin Peake & Julie Slater**
7 **BRIERY EXPRESS,** 7, b m Rail Link—Blackbriery Thyne (IRE) **Helen Plumbly & Kathryn Leadbeater**

MR NOEL WILLIAMS - continued

8 **CUILLIN (USA)**, 5, b m Arch (USA)—Zahrah (USA) **Mr N. Williams**
9 **DELIGHT OF DUBAI (IRE)**, 6, b br m Dubai Destination (USA)—Bonny Hall (IRE) **Daniel MacAuliffe & Anoj Don**
10 **DRUNKEN PIRATE**, 7, b g Black Sam Bellamy (IRE)—Peel Me A Grape **Mrs E. A. Prowting**
11 **EDWARD BLUE (IRE)**, 5, b br g Vinnie Roe (IRE)—Gold Shot **Mr R. Skillen**
12 **ELLOFAGETAWAY (IRE)**, 4, b g Getaway (GER)—Ellaway Rose (IRE) **Didntt Partnership**
13 **FANTASTIC MS FOX**, 4, b f Foxwedge (AUS)—Cracking Lass (IRE) **Mr T. A. Lee**
14 **GINO WOTIMEAN (USA)**, 4, b br g Gio Ponti (USA)—Promulgation (USA) **Mr D. J. S. Sewell**
15 **KALINIHTA (IRE)**, 6, b g Kalanisi (IRE)—Valamareha (IRE) **Mr J Allison & Mr A Allison**
16 4, B f Universal (IRE)—Mays Dream **Stonepoint Racing Club**
17 **OSPREY CALL (IRE)**, 5, br g Winged Love (IRE)—Courting Whitney (IRE) **Allison, Allison, Williams**
18 **PURE COUNTRY**, 5, b g Frankel—Plante Rare (IRE) **Mr N. Williams**
19 **REDMOND (IRE)**, 10, b g Tikkanen (USA)—Medal Quest (FR) **Mr P E. Walters**
20 **SENSULANO (IRE)**, 7, b m Milan—Espresso Lady (IRE) **Allison, Allison, Williams**
21 **SOL PLUM CREEK (FR)**, 4, b g Canyon Creek (IRE)—Solenrana (FR) **Stonepoint Racing Club**
22 **SOUND OF MUSIC**, 5, ch m Universal (IRE)—Sounds Familiar (IRE) **Mrs M. L. Luck**
23 **SPEECH BUBBLE (IRE)**, 5, b m Well Chosen—Teamplin (IRE)
24 **STEP TO THE TOP (IRE)**, 5, b m Doyen (IRE)—Step On My Soul (IRE) **Mr G. Wragg**
25 **THEATRE GOER**, 11, b m King's Theatre (IRE)—Clover Green (IRE) **Mr N. Williams**
26 **TWIN STAR (IRE)**, 6, ch g Tagula (IRE)—Chronicle **Happy Star Partnership**
27 **VINNIE DEV (IRE)**, 6, b g Vinnie Roe (IRE)—Nifty Milan (IRE) **David J S Sewell & Tim Leadbeater**
28 **ZIGGY ROSE (IRE)**, 6, b m Fame And Glory—Koko Rose (IRE) **Elaine Chivers Racing**

THREE-YEAR-OLDS

29 **MICKEY DRIPPIN (IRE)**, b g Mustajeeb—Ghaidaa (IRE) **Mr T. A. Lee**

Other Owners: Mr J. Allison, S. A. Allison, Miss C. I. Chivers, Ms E. C. Chivers, Ms L. D. Chivers, Mr E. T. D. Leadbeater, Mrs K. B. Leadbeater, Mr C. Peake, Mrs H. Plumbly, Mr D. J. S. Sewell, Mrs J. E. Slater, Mr N. Williams.

NH Jockey: Leighton Aspell, Paddy Brennan.

581

MR OLLY WILLIAMS, Market Rasen
Postal: **Stone Cottage, Nettleton Top, Market Rasen, Lincolnshire, LN7 6SY**
Contacts: **MOBILE 07793 111600**
EMAIL williams.olly@yahoo.co.uk **WEBSITE** www.ollywilliamsracing.co.uk

1 **BATTLE COMMANDER**, 4, b g Avonbridge—Antica Medusa **Mr O. R. Williams**
2 **COOL SPIRIT**, 5, b g Swiss Spirit—Marmot Bay (IRE) **Mr D. Milthorp**
3 **ESSENTIAL**, 6, b g Pivotal—Something Blue **Mr D. Milthorp**
4 **GOING NATIVE**, 5, ch m Speightstown (USA)—Latin Love (IRE) **D. L. Bayliss**
5 **INEXORABLE**, 7, b g Sulamani (IRE)—Princess Amelia (IRE) **Mr D. J. Ablott**
6 **LINCOLN RED**, 4, ch g Monsieur Bond (IRE)—Roxy Hart **Top of the Wolds Racing**
7 **RASPBERRY**, 4, b f Avonbridge—Spennymoor (IRE) **Olly Williams Rhys Williams James Hanna**
8 **VIKING WAY (IRE)**, 5, ch g Society Rock (IRE)—Patrimony **Folk From The Shire**

TWO-YEAR-OLDS

9 B g 10/05 Al Kazeem—Melodica (Dansili) **Olly Williams Rhys Williams James Hanna**
10 **NORTHERN GENERAL (IRE)**, ch c 28/03 Ivawood (IRE)—
Cealtra Star (IRE) (Mujadil (USA)) (5238) **Mrs H. R. Townsend**

Other Owners: Mr D. J. Ablott, Mr N. B. Baker, Mr J. Hanna, Mr T. A. Pocklington, Mr T. Smithson, Mr E. Williams, Mr O. R. Williams, Mr R. T. Williams.

Assistant Trainer: Lynsey Williams.

582 MR STUART WILLIAMS, Newmarket

Postal: **Diomed Stables, Hamilton Road, Newmarket, Suffolk, CB8 0PD**
Contacts: HOME **01638 560143** PHONE **01638 663984** MOBILE **07730 314102**
EMAIL **stuart@stuartwilliamsracing.co.uk** WEBSITE **www.stuartwilliamsracing.co.uk**
TWITTER **@Williamsstuart**

1 ALAADEL, 7, ch g Dubawi (IRE)—Infallible **Mr T. W. Morley**
2 ALEMARATALYOUM (IRE), 6, ch g Lope de Vega (IRE)—Heart of Ice (IRE) **Mrs M. J. Morley**
3 ALLEGIANT (USA), 5, b g City Zip (USA)—Preferential **Mr T W Morley & Partner**
4 BREATHLESS TIMES, 5, b g Bated Breath—Bea Menace (USA) **Morley, Reynolds & Watkins**
5 BREATHTAKING LOOK, 5, b m Bated Breath—Love Your Looks **J. W. Parry**
6 BROUGHTON EXCELS, 5, b g Kyllachy—Excello **Broughton Thermal Insulations**
7 COMMANDER HAN (FR), 5, ch g Siyouni (FR)—Acentela (IRE) **Tw Morley & Notting Hill Racing**
8 DASCHAS, 6, b g Oasis Dream—Canada Water **Mr T. W. Morley**
9 ENTHAAR, 5, ch g Sepoy (AUS)—Caledonia Princess **Mr B Piper & Mr D Cobill**
10 EQUITATION, 6, b g Equiano (FR)—Sakhee's Song (IRE) **Mr A Lyons & Mr T W Morley**
11 EXCELLENT GEORGE, 8, b g Exceed And Excel (AUS)—Princess Georgina **Mr Stuart Williams & Mr J W Parry**
12 GIVE IT SOME TEDDY, 6, b g Bahamian Bounty—Croeso Cariad **TW Morley, Terry Long & Partners**
13 GLENN COCO, 6, gr g Aussie Rules (USA)—Las Hilanderas (USA) **Miss Emily Stevens Partnership**
14 HART STOPPER, 6, b g Compton Place—Angel Song **Mr T. W. Morley**
15 HERCULEAN, 5, ch g Frankel—African Rose **Morley, Reynolds,Watkins & Partner**
16 HUMAN NATURE (IRE), 7, b g Kodiac—Sundown **Mr W Enticknap & Mr B Ralph**
17 INDIAN RAJ, 6, b g Iffraaj—Princess Georgina **Mr J W Parry & Partner**
18 KEYSTROKE, 8, b h Pivotal—Fondled **GG Thoroughbreds XI**
19 LETHAL ANGEL, 5, gr m Lethal Force (IRE)—Heliograph **The Secretly Hopeful Partnership**
20 LUNAR DEITY, 11, b g Medicean—Luminda (USA) **Mr W E Enticknap & Partner**
21 MARRONNIER (IRE), 4, ch g Lope de Vega (IRE)—Beach Bunny (IRE) **GG Thoroughbreds III**
22 MOUNT WELLINGTON, 5, b g Invincible Spirit (IRE)—Marvada (IRE) **GG Thoroughbreds IX**
23 MY BOY SEPOY, 5, ch g Sepoy (AUS)—Emily Carr (IRE) **Mr & Mrs G. Bhatti**
24 PACTOLUS (IRE), 9, b g Footstepsinthesand—Gold Marie (IRE) **T W Morley & Mrs J Morley**
25 PAPA STOUR (USA), 5, b g Scat Daddy (USA)—Illaunglass (IRE) **Mr T. W. Morley**
26 PENNYWHISTLE (IRE), 4, b f Iffraaj—Folk Melody (IRE) **Mr R. C. Watts**
27 PERSIAN SUN, 5, b g Dansili—Khor Sheed **Mrs T. Lyons**
28 PHOENIX STAR (IRE), 4, b g Alhebayeb (IRE)—Volcanic Lady (IRE) **Flying High Syndicate**
29 PINNATA (IRE), 6, b g Shamardal (USA)—Lavande Violet (GER) **Mr David N Reynolds & Mr C D Watkins**
30 PRINCE OF HARTS, 4, br g Dalakhani (IRE)—Real **Mr T. W. Morley**
31 RESTLESS ROSE, 5, ch m Power—Albany Rose (IRE) **Happy Valley Racing & Breeding Limited**
32 REVOLUTIONISE (IRE), 4, gr g Lope de Vega (IRE)—Modeeroch (IRE) **T W Morley & Regents Racing**
33 RHYTHMIC INTENT (IRE), 4, ch c Lope de Vega (IRE)—Kerry Gal (IRE) **Happy Valley Racing & Breeding Limited**
34 ROYAL BIRTH, 9, b g Exceed And Excel (AUS)—Princess Georgina **The Morley Family**
35 SANDY STEVE, 4, b g Aussie Rules (USA)—Lady Guinevere **J. W. Parry**
36 SHAMSHON (IRE), 9, b g Invincible Spirit (IRE)—Greenisland (IRE) **T W Morley & Regents Racing**
37 STREET PARADE, 4, b g Swiss Spirit—Jollification (IRE) **Mr T. W. Morley**
38 SWIFT APPROVAL (IRE), 8, ch g Approve (IRE)—Tiltili (IRE) **JLM Racing**
39 TAWNY PORT, 6, ch g Arcano (IRE)—Tawaasul **Mrs M. J. Morley**
40 THE GILL BROTHERS, 4, gr g Mukhadram—Si Belle (IRE) **The Gill Brothers**
41 TONE THE BARONE, 4, ch g Lope de Vega (IRE)—A Huge Dream (IRE) **Mr B Piper & Partner**
42 VIA SERENDIPITY, 6, b g Invincible Spirit (IRE)—Mambo Light (USA) **Happy Valley Racing & Breeding Limited**

THREE-YEAR-OLDS

43 AGENT SHIFTWELL, b c Equiano (FR)—Holley Shiftwell **J. W. Parry**
44 BAJAN BREEZE, gr g Lethal Force (IRE)—Semaphore **Patrick B Doyle (Construction) Ltd**
45 BIG BROWN (IRE), b g Canford Cliffs (IRE)—Caravan of Dreams (IRE) **Mr S. C. Williams**
46 BOOM BOOM BOOM, ch g Raven's Pass (USA)—Futureland **Mr S. C. Williams**
47 DAWN VIEW (IRE), b f Dawn Approach (IRE)—Villetta (GER) **Essex Racing Club et al**
48 DRAMATICA (IRE), ch f Lope de Vega (IRE)—Miss Georgie **J. W. Parry**
49 GOLDEN DRAGON (IRE), b c Starspangledbanner (AUS)—
                                    Emerald Cutter (USA) **Happy Valley Racing & Breeding Limited**
50 MADAME WINNER, ch f Sir Percy—Lady Guinevere **J. W. Parry**
51 Ch f Sepoy (AUS)—Pivotting **J. W. Parry**

MR STUART WILLIAMS - continued

52 **PRINCE CASPER,** b g Casamento (IRE)—Princess Georgina **Mr J W Parry & Partner**
53 **SHANDRANI SUNRISE,** b f Sir Percy—Acclamatory **Mrs C. I. Shekells**
54 **SPEARMINX,** gr f Lethal Force (IRE)—Midnight Fantasy **Mr A. H. Slone**
55 **VITELLIUS,** b g Lope de Vega (IRE)—Lunar Spirit **GG Thoroughbreds X**
56 **WINNING STREAK,** ch c Hot Streak (IRE)—Positivity **Mr T. W. Morley**

TWO-YEAR-OLDS

57 Ch f 24/02 Equiano (FR)—Holley Shiftwell (Bahamian Bounty) **J. W. Parry**
58 B f 26/03 Super Saver (USA)—Powerful Elegance (USA) (Smart Strike (CAN)) **Mr T. W. Morley**
59 B c 12/04 Mshawish (USA)—Ringmistress (USA) (Bandini (USA)) **Mr T. W. Morley**
60 B c 14/03 Muhaarar—Squash (Pastoral Pursuits) (55000) **Opulence Thoroughbreds**
61 B f 20/04 Toronado (IRE)—Tipping Over (IRE) (Aussie Rules (USA)) (5500) **Essex Racing Club**

Other Owners: Mrs C. J. Bhatti, Mr G. Bhatti, Mr D. L. Cobill, W. E. Enticknap, Essex Racing Club, Mr A. A. Lyons, Mrs M. J. Morley, Mr T. W. Morley, Notting Hill Racing, J. W. Parry, Mr B. V. Piper, Mr B. Ralph, Regents Racing, Mr D. N. Reynolds, Mrs J. P. Root, Mr R. B. Root, Mrs C. I. Shekells, Miss E. V. Stevens, P. W. Stevens, Mr C. D. Watkins, Mr S. C. Williams.

Assistant Trainer: J W Parry.

Apprentice Jockey: Marco Ghiani, Matteo Pinna. **Amateur Jockey:** Miss Julia Engstrom.

---

583 **MISS VENETIA WILLIAMS, Hereford**
Postal: **Aramstone, Kings Caple, Hereford, Herefordshire, HR1 4TU**
Contacts: **PHONE 01432 840646 MOBILE 07770 627108**
EMAIL office@venetiawilliams.com WEBSITE www.venetiawilliams.com

1 **ARQALINA (IRE),** 8, b m Arcano (IRE)—Pride Celebre (IRE) **The Hon Lady Heber-Percy & V Williams**
2 **ASO (FR),** 10, b br g Goldneyev (USA)—Odyssee du Cellier (FR) **The Bellamy Partnership**
3 **BELAMI DES PICTONS (FR),** 9, b g Khalkevi (IRE)—Nina des Pictons (FR) **Hills of Ledbury Ltd**
4 **BONNE QUESTION (FR),** 11, gr g Tagula (IRE)—Amonita (GER) **Falcon's Line Ltd**
5 **BRIANSTORM (IRE),** 8, b g Brian Boru—Coco Moon (IRE) **David & Carol Shaw**
6 **BURROWS PARK (FR),** 8, b g Astarabad (USA)—La Vie de Boitron (FR) **Venetia Williams Racehorse Syndicate III**
7 **BURTONS WELL (IRE),** 11, b g Well Chosen—Despute (IRE) **Mr T. J. Hemmings**
8 **CEPAGE (FR),** 8, b g Saddler Maker (IRE)—Sience Fiction (FR) **The Bellamy Partnership**
9 **CHAMBARD (FR),** 8, b g Gris de Gris (IRE)—Regina Park (FR) **David & Carol Shaw**
10 **CLOUDY GLEN (IRE),** 7, b g Cloudings (IRE)—Ribble (IRE) **Mr T. J. Hemmings**
11 **COCK A DOODLE DOO (FR),** 8, b m Della Francesca (USA)—Jiletta (FR) **Wake Up Call**
12 **COMMIS D'OFFICE (FR),** 8, b g Califet (FR)—Pas de Bal (FR) **Julian Blackwell & Mrs Angus Maclay**
13 **COMMODORE (FR),** 8, gr g Fragrant Mix (IRE)—Morvandelle (FR) **Mrs C Watson & Mrs S Graham**
14 **CRYPTO (IRE),** 6, b g Gold Well—Top Lot (IRE) **Mr P. Davies**
15 **CUBAN PETE (IRE),** 8, b g Flemensfirth (USA)—Gee Whizz (FR) **Mrs J. Jones**
16 **DESQUE DE L'ISLE (FR),** 7, b g Special Kaldoun (FR)—Naiade de L'Isle (FR) **The Hon Lady M. J. Heber-Percy**
17 **DESTINEE ROYALE (FR),** 7, b m Balko (FR)—Viana (FR) **C. Boultbee-Brooks**
18 **EASY AS THAT (IRE),** 5, b g Sans Frontieres (IRE)—Bell Storm (IRE) **Kate & Andrew Brooks**
19 **ECEPARTI (FR),** 6, b g Enrique—La Pommeraie (FR) **Mrs S. M. Champ**
20 **ELEANOR BOB,** 5, b m Midnight Legend—Red And White (IRE) **F. M. P. Mahon**
21 **ELIXIR DU GOUET (FR),** 6, ch g Vision d'Etat (FR)—My Asadore (FR) **Charles & Mary Rose Barlow**
22 **EMINENT POET,** 9, b g Montjeu (IRE)—Contare **B. C. Dice**
23 **ENZO D'AIRY (FR),** 6, b g Anzillero (GER)—Panzara d'Airy (FR) **Dr M. A. Hamlin**
24 **ESPOIR DE GUYE (FR),** 6, b g Khalkevi (IRE)—Penelope de Guye (FR) **Mrs J. Hitchings**
25 **FALLY JEM (FR),** 5, b m Authorized (IRE)—Ballymena Lassie **Bendall & Anderson**
26 **FANION D'ESTRUVAL (FR),** 5, b g Enrique—Urfe d'Estruval (FR) **Mr D. C. A. Wilson**
27 **FARRANTS WAY (IRE),** 6, b g Shantou (USA)—Shuil A Hocht (IRE) **Mr T. J. Hemmings**
28 **FIONN MAC CUL (IRE),** 9, b g Oscar (IRE)—No Moore Bills **David & Carol Shaw**
29 **FONTAINE COLLONGES (FR),** 5, b m Saddler Maker (IRE)—Saturne Collonges (FR) **Mr P. Davies**
30 **FRENCHY DU LARGE (FR),** 5, gr g Al Namix (FR)—Quadence de Sivola (FR) **Mr A. O. Wiles**
31 **FRERO BANBOU (FR),** 5, b g Apsis—Lady Banbou (FR) **Mr P. Davies**
32 **FUNAMBULE SIVOLA (FR),** 5, b g Noroit (GER)—Little Memories (IRE) **My Racing Manager Friends**

MISS VENETIA WILLIAMS - continued

33 **GEORDIE B,** 7, gr g Geordieland (FR)—Sari Rose (FR) **C. Boultbee-Brooks**
34 **GLEN WYLLIN (IRE),** 5, b g Yeats (IRE)—Deep Leader (IRE) **Mr T. J. Hemmings**
35 **GRAND TURINA,** 9, b m Kayf Tara—Cesana (IRE) **Mr A. J. Taylor**
36 **HAZZAAR (IRE),** 6, b g Flemensfirth (USA)—Una Sorpresa (GER) **C. Boultbee-Brooks**
37 **HOLD THAT TAUGHT,** 5, b g Kayf Tara—Belle Magello (FR) **Mr P. Davies**
38 **IBLEO (FR),** 7, b g Dick Turpin (IRE)—Mahendra (GER) **The Bellamy Partnership**
39 **JACK VALENTINE (IRE),** 7, b g Scorpion (IRE)—Mangan Rose (IRE) **Venetia Williams Racehorse Syndicate IV**
40 **JURYS OUT (IRE),** 7, b g Witness Box (USA)—No Complaints But (IRE) **Venetia Williams Racehorse Syndicate III**
41 **KAPGA DE LILY (FR),** 7, ch m Kapgarde (FR)—Louvisy (FR) **Lady Judith Price & Mrs Carol Shaw**
42 **KRACQUER,** 6, ch g Schiaparelli (GER)—Norma Hill **Mr G. Lloyd**
43 **LADY CHARTREUSE (IRE),** 7, ch m Flemensfirth (USA)—Verde Goodwood **Old Carthusian Racing Society (I)**
44 4, B f Kayf Tara—Lily Grey (FR) **Lily Filly Partnership**
45 **LITTLE GINGE (FR),** 7, ch g Kapgarde (FR)—Aconit (FR) **C. Boultbee-Brooks**
46 **LONGHOUSESIGNORA (IRE),** 8, b m Milan—Moscow Madame (IRE) **Nora's Playmates**
47 **MIDNIGHT SONATA (IRE),** 6, b g Big Bad Bob (IRE)—Symphonique (FR) **Mrs P. Pink**
48 **MOUNTAIN LEOPARD (IRE),** 5, b g Shantou (USA)—Laurel Gift (IRE) **The Shantou Partnership**
49 **NESTERENKO (GER),** 11, b g Doyen (IRE)—Nordwahl (GER) **Mrs V. A. Bingham**
50 **ONE STYLE (FR),** 10, b g Desert Style (FR)—Arieta (FR) **Miss V. M. Williams**
51 **PENNY MALLOW (FR),** 6, b m Kapgarde (FR)—Louvisy (FR) **Kate & Andrew Brooks**
52 **PINK LEGEND,** 6, b m Midnight Legend—Red And White (IRE) **F. M. P. Mahon**
53 **PONIENTE,** 6, br m Shirocco (GER)—Tazzarine (FR) **Bailey-Carvill Equine**
54 **QUICK WAVE (FR),** 7, b m Gentlewave (IRE)—Magicaldoun (FR) **Mrs S. A. J. Kinsella**
55 **QUIETLYFLOWSTHEDON,** 5, ch m Sholokhov (IRE)—Tazzarine (FR) **Bailey-Carvill Equine**
56 **REALM KEEPER (USA),** 7, b g Arch (USA)—La Lodola (USA) **Venetia Williams Racehorse Syndicate V**
57 **REALM OF GLORY (IRE),** 5, b g Fame And Glory—Ebony Queen **Venetia Williams Racehorse Syndicate V**
58 4, Ch g Dunaden (FR)—Red And White (IRE) **F. M. P. Mahon**
59 **ROLL AGAIN (FR),** 6, b g Walk In The Park (IRE)—Olina (FR) **David & Carol Shaw**
60 **ROYALE PAGAILLE (FR),** 6, b g Blue Bresil (FR)—Royale Cazoumaille (FR) **Mrs S. Ricci**
61 5, B g Yeats (IRE)—Seasonselite **Mrs S. A. J. Kinsella**
62 **SENDHERVICTORIA'S (IRE),** 5, b g Shirocco (GER)—Midnight Flirt (IRE) **Tim & Sarah Stevens**
63 **SHALAKAR (FR),** 7, b g Cape Cross (IRE)—Shalanaya (IRE) **Sheila Schwartz & Lady Eliza Mays-Smith**
64 **SNUFF BOX (IRE),** 9, b g Witness Box (USA)—Dara Supreme (IRE) **Mrs J. R. L. Young**
65 **STAR ACADEMY (IRE),** 6, b g Stowaway—Academy Miss (IRE) **John Nicholls (Trading) Ltd**
66 **STORM WIZARD (IRE),** 8, b g Milan—Tempest Belle (IRE) **Miss V. M. Williams**
67 **SUBCONTINENT (IRE),** 8, b g Dubawi (IRE)—Saree **Shire Birds**
68 **TARA CHIEFTAIN,** 5, b g Kayf Tara—Molly Flight (FR) **The Winter Partnership**
69 **TENOR NIVERNAIS (FR),** 13, b g Shaanmer (IRE)—Hosanna II (FR) **C. Boultbee-Brooks**
70 **THE CROONER (FR),** 5, gr g Martaline—Viva Maria (FR) **The Crooner Partnership**
71 **TOP AND DROP,** 9, b m Kayf Tara—Ismene (FR) **Lady Judith Price & Mrs Carol Shaw**
72 **UHLAN BUTE (FR),** 12, ch g Brier Creek (USA)—Jonquiere (FR) **The Autumn Partnership**
73 **WHERE'S BOB (IRE),** 5, b g Stowaway—Bobbina (IRE) **My Racing Manager Friends**
74 **YALLTARI,** 9, gr g Kayf Tara—Lily Grey (FR) **Venetia Williams Racehorse Syndicates II**

Other Owners: Mr S. Batcheler, Mr D. Cliff, Mr G. P. Ford, Mr R. Gaskins, Mrs H. A. E. Herdman, Mr N. D. Peace, Mr P. R. Turner, Ms C. F. Wilson.

NH Jockey: Charlie Deutsch. **Conditional Jockey:** Hugh Nugent. **Amateur Jockey:** Miss Lucy Turner.

---

584 **MRS LISA WILLIAMSON, Tarporley**
Postal: **Kelsall Hill Equestrian Centre, Middlewich Road, Tarporley, Cheshire, CW6 0SR**
Contacts: **PHONE 07970 437679**
EMAIL info@lisawilliamson.co.uk WEBSITE www.lisawilliamson.co.uk

1 **ANDIES ARMIES,** 4, b g Piccolo—Shaymee's Girl **Mr I. Furlong**
2 **BRANDY STATION (IRE),** 5, b g Fast Company (IRE)—Kardyls Hope (IRE) **A V Wilding (Chester) Ltd**
3 **CALEDONIAN GOLD,** 7, b m Acclamation—Moonlight Rhapsody (IRE) **Heath House Racing**
4 **CELERITY (IRE),** 6, ch m Casamento (IRE)—Shinko Dancer (IRE) **Heath House Racing**
5 **GEMINI GLORY (USA),** 6, b m Tale of Ekati (USA)—Misconduct (USA) **E. H. Jones (Paints) Ltd**

MRS LISA WILLIAMSON - continued

6 **HILBRE LAKE (USA)**, 4, b br g Revolutionary (USA)—Countess Clare (USA) **E. H. Jones (Paints) Ltd**
7 **ISABELLA RUBY**, 5, b m Power—Scarlet Rocks (IRE) **WB Fat Boar Racing**
8 **KINGS WAY**, 4, ch g Leroidesanimaux (BRZ)—Apparatchika **E. H. Jones (Paints) Ltd**
9 **MARIAH'S MELODY (IRE)**, 5, gr m Graydar (USA)—In Seconds (USA) **E. H. Jones (Paints) Ltd**
10 **PETERS PUDDING (IRE)**, 4, ch g Fast Company (IRE)—Whats For Pudding (IRE) **Mrs L. V. Williamson**
11 **PICCOLO RAMOSCELLO**, 7, b m Malinas (GER)—Dusky Dancer **Mr P. R. D'Amato**
12 **RED DEREK**, 4, b g Steele Tango (USA)—Maydream **Mr G. L. Shepherd**
13 **RED STRIPES (USA)**, 8, b g Leroidesanimaux (BRZ)—Kaleidoscopic (USA) **E. H. Jones (Paints) Ltd**
14 **TAN**, 6, b g Aqlaam—Sunburnt **E. H. Jones (Paints) Ltd**
15 **YOUR GIFTED (IRE)**, 13, b m Trans Island—Dame Laura (IRE) **Mr A. T Sykes**

THREE-YEAR-OLDS

16 **EILEEN'S MAGIC**, gr f Zebedee—Art Critic (USA) **Mr A. T Sykes**
17 **LA CHICA LOBO**, b f Captain Gerrard (IRE)—Senora Lobo (IRE) **Miss H. J. Roberts**
18 **MRS TIFFEN**, b f Finjaan—Fancy Rose (USA) **A V Wilding (Chester) Ltd**

Other Owners: Mrs J. T. Pierpoint, Mr S. W. Pierpoint.

---

585 **MR ANDREW WILSON, Greystoke**
Postal: **Silver Howe, Orton, Penrith, Cumbria, CA10 3RQ**
Contacts: PHONE **015396 24071** MOBILE **07813 846768**
EMAIL **andywilsonorton@gmail.com**

1 **CULLY MAC (IRE)**, 9, b g Coroner (IRE)—Catch Those Kisses **Mr A. C. Wilson**
2 **FRIENDS IN HEAVEN (IRE)**, 8, br g Asian Heights—Native Bev (IRE) **Mr A. C. Wilson**
3 **KINGS ECLIPSE (IRE)**, 10, b g Double Eclipse (IRE)—Good Times Ahead (IRE) **Mr A. C. Wilson**
4 **SAINT JUDE (IRE)**, 7, ch g Presenting—Native Monk (IRE) **Mr A. C. Wilson**

---

587 **MR KEN WINGROVE, Bridgnorth**
Postal: **6 Netherton Farm Barns, Netherton Lane, Highley, Bridgnorth, Shropshire, WV16 6NJ**
Contacts: HOME **01746 861534** MOBILE **07974 411267**
EMAIL **kenwingrove@btinternet.com**

1 **BIG AMIGO (IRE)**, 7, b g Bahamian Bounty—Goldamour (IRE) **Mr D. G. Wingrove**
2 **FALLING LEAF (IRE)**, 10, ch m Sandmason—Turbine Hill (IRE) **Mr D. G. Wingrove**
3 **LORD MURPHY (IRE)**, 7, b g Holy Roman Emperor (IRE)—Tralanza (IRE) **Mr D. G. Wingrove**
4 **LYME PARK**, 9, gr m Multiplex—So Cloudy **Mr D. G. Wingrove**
5 **MIDTECH VALENTINE**, 9, b m Act One—Eveon (IRE) **Mr D. G. Wingrove**
6 **PLAY WITH ME**, 6, ch m Captain Gerrard (IRE)—Plead (FR) **Mr D. G. Wingrove**
7 **RAKASTAVA (IRE)**, 4, bl gr g Clodovil (IRE)—Shemissa (IRE) **Mr D. G. Wingrove**

THREE-YEAR-OLDS

8 B f Yorgunnabelucky (USA)—Seedless **Mr D. G. Wingrove**

Assistant Trainer: Isobel Willer.

---

588 **MR PETER WINKS, Barnsley**
Postal: **Homefield, Rotherham Road, Little Houghton, Barnsley, South Yorkshire, S72 0HA**
Contacts: MOBILE **07846 899993**
EMAIL **pwracing@outlook.com**

1 **AGENTLEMAN (IRE)**, 10, b g Trans Island—Silvine (IRE) **Mr R. H. Lee**
2 **BALL D'ARC (FR)**, 9, b g Network (GER)—Pretty Moon (FR) **Mr E. Cumberland**
3 **BALLYFARSOON (IRE)**, 9, ch g Medicean—Amzara (IRE) **Barnsley Burglars**

MR PETER WINKS - continued

4 **CAVALRY**, 5, b h Exceed And Excel (AUS)—Queen's Best **Mr P Rowbottom & Mr R Taberner**
5 **GROW NASA GROW (IRE)**, 9, ch g Mahler—Dereenavurrig (IRE) **Nature and Science Agriculture Limited**
6 **HARTSIDE (GER)**, 11, b g Montjeu (IRE)—Helvellyn (USA) **Peter Winks Racing Club**
7 **HEDIDDODINTHE (IRE)**, 6, gr g Kendargent (FR)—Damoiselle (USA) **Severnwinks**
8 **SCOTTSDALE**, 7, b g Cape Cross (IRE)—High Praise (USA) **Mr P. Winks, Mr P. W. O'Mara**
9 **TAKE THE CROWN**, 11, gr g Fair Mix (IRE)—Miss Wizadora **Mr P. Winks**
10 **WEST CLASS (IRE)**, 9, b g Westerner—Catch The Class (IRE) **Peter Winks Racing Club**

Other Owners: A. R. Barnes, Mr A Barnes, Mr P W O'Mara & Mr P Winks, Mr P. Connor, Mr P. W. O'Mara, Mr P. Rowbottom, Mr R. Taberner, Mr P. Winks.

Assistant Trainer: Ryan Winks.

589
MR ADRIAN WINTLE, Westbury-On-Severn
Postal: **Yew Tree Stables, Rodley, Westbury-On-Severn, Gloucestershire, GL14 1QZ**
Contacts: **MOBILE 07767 351144**

1 **ALEX THE LION (IRE)**, 7, b g Let The Lion Roar—Belle Dame (IRE) **Mr A. J. Rhead**
2 **AMLOVI (IRE)**, 7, b m Court Cave (IRE)—Portanob (IRE) **Mr S. R. Whistance**
3 **BARATINEUR (FR)**, 9, ch g Vendangeur (IRE)—Olmantina (FR) **Inspire Racing Club Ltd**
4 **BOYCIE**, 7, b g Paco Boy (IRE)—Eve **A. A. Wintle**
5 **BOYFROMNOWHERE (IRE)**, 13, br g Old Vic—Eist Do Gale (IRE) **Mr R. G. Owens**
6 **COOPERESS**, 7, b m Sixties Icon—Vilnius **Exors of the Late J. Parfitt**
7 **DE BENE ESSE (IRE)**, 10, br g Scorpion (IRE)—Benedicta Rose (IRE) **A. A. Wintle**
8 **DUBAI MISSION (IRE)**, 7, b g New Approach (IRE)—Al Joza **G. Byard**
9 **IS LOVE ALIVE**, 11, ch g Presenting—Lovely Origny (FR) **Mr S. R. Whistance**
10 **KENSTONE (FR)**, 7, gr g Kendargent (FR)—Little Stone (FR) **G. Byard**
11 **MARJU'S QUEST (IRE)**, 10, b g Marju (IRE)—Queen's Quest **Mrs Lisa Boddington & Adrian Wintle**
12 **PLEASUREAPLENTY**, 5, b g Multiplex—Playful Girl (IRE) **J. N. Dalton**
13 **ROCKET RONNIE (IRE)**, 10, b g Antonius Pius (USA)—Ctesiphon (USA) **Inspire Racing Club Ltd**
14 **SEA TEA DEA**, 6, b m Archipenko (USA)—Half Sister (IRE) **Wintle Racing Club**
15 **SEAFORTH (IRE)**, 8, b g Acclamation—Hendrina (IRE) **Wintle Racing Club**
16 **SECRET GLANCE**, 8, b g Sakhee's Secret—Look Here's Dee **A. A. Wintle**
17 **SUNNY GIRL (IRE)**, 6, b m Arcadio (GER)—Vincenta (IRE) **Mr S. R. Whistance**
18 5, B m Multiplex—Tashkiyla (FR) **A. A. Wintle**
19 **TAWAAFOQ**, 6, b g Showcasing—Gilt Linked **Mr S. R. Whistance**

THREE-YEAR-OLDS

20 Ch f Casamento (IRE)—Arctic Royal (IRE)

Other Owners: Mrs L. J. E. Boddington, A. A. Wintle.

590
MISS REBECCA WOODMAN, Chichester
Postal: **Souters Cottage, 21 East Lavant, Chichester, West Sussex, PO18 0AG**
Contacts: **PHONE 01243 527260 MOBILE 07821 603063**
EMAIL rebeccawoodman@msn.com

1 **ECHO BRAVA**, 10, gr g Proclamation (IRE)—Snake Skin **Miss R. Woodman**
2 **MILLDEAN FELIX (IRE)**, 4, br g Red Jazz (USA)—Plausabelle **Milldean Racing Syndicate**
3 **RED ORATOR**, 11, ch g Osorio (GER)—Red Roses Story (FR) **Miss R. Woodman**

591 | MR STEVE WOODMAN, Chichester
Postal: **Parkers Barn Stables, East Lavant, Chichester, West Sussex, PO18 0AU**
Contacts: **PHONE 01243 527136 MOBILE 07889 188519 FAX 01243 527136**
EMAIL stevewoodman83@msn.com

1 **BLACK LACE**, 5, b m Showcasing—Ivory Lace **The Lacemakers**
2 **LORD ALDERVALE (IRE)**, 13, br g Alderbrook—Monavale (IRE) **Mr D. N. Boxall**
3 **SOLVEIG'S SONG**, 8, b m Norse Dancer (IRE)—Ivory Lace **Sally Woodman & D. Mortimer**

THREE-YEAR-OLDS
4 **VICE ROYAL**, b g Swiss Spirit—Ivory Lace **Vice Royal Partnership**

Other Owners: Dr J. A. H. Miles, Mr D. Mortimer, Mrs P. M. Tyler, Mrs S. B. Woodman.

592 | MRS KAYLEY WOOLLACOTT, South Molton
Postal: **Big Brook Park, Rose Ash, South Molton, Devon, EX36 4RQ**
Contacts: **PHONE 01769 550483**
EMAIL info@richardwoollacottracing.co.uk WEBSITE www.richardwoollacottracing.co.uk

1 **CASPERS COURT (IRE)**, 6, gr g Court Cave (IRE)—Kindle Ball (FR) **Mr D Stevens & Mrs S Stevens**
2 **CLONDAW'S ANSWER (IRE)**, 7, b g Ask—Monabricka Lady (IRE) **D. G. Staddon**
3 **DORRANA (IRE)**, 6, br m Darsi (FR)—Arts Theater (IRE) **Gale Force Five**
4 **ENORMOUSE**, 7, b g Crosspeace (IRE)—Mousiemay **M. H. Dare**
5 **EQUUS GOLD (IRE)**, 5, b g Court Cave (IRE)—Dahoar **D. G. Staddon**
6 **ESPECIALLY SO**, 5, br m So You Think (NZ)—Behra (IRE) **BumpersToJumpers3**
7 **EXIT PLAN**, 7, b g Exit To Nowhere (USA)—Baily Morning **Mr D Stevens & Mrs S Stevens**
8 **GOODGIRLTERESA (IRE)**, 10, b m Stowaway—Decheekymonkey (IRE) **Kayley Woollacott Racing Club**
9 **JACK THE FARMER**, 4, br g Kalanisi (IRE)—Deploys Dream (IRE) **Mrs K. Woollacott**
10 **LALOR (GER)**, 8, b g It's Gino (GER)—Laviola (GER) **D. G. Staddon**
11 **LESTER KRIS (IRE)**, 6, b g Fame And Glory—Wood Sprite **Kayley Woollacott Racing Club**
12 **MIDNIGHT JEWEL**, 4, b g Midnight Legend—Follow The Dream **Ms G. E. Morgan**
13 **THE KINGS WRIT (IRE)**, 9, b g Brian Boru—Letterwoman (IRE) **Mr D Stevens & Mrs S Stevens**
14 **THE MAJOR**, 7, b g Major Cadeaux—Ballerina Suprema (IRE) **Mr D Stevens & Mrs S Stevens**
15 **TIPALONG TYLER**, 6, br m Winged Love (IRE)—Supreme Cove **Kayley Woollacott Racing Club**

Other Owners: Mr D. J. Stevens, Mrs S. E. Stevens.

593 | MR PHILLIP YORK, Effingham Common
Postal: **Mornshill Farm, Banks Lane, Effingham, Leatherhead, Surrey, KT24 5JB**
Contacts: **PHONE 01372 457102**

1 **AMBANADORA**, 11, b g Amber Life—La Ganadora **Mrs K. H. York**
2 **CARRIED AWAY**, 8, b m Trans Island—Carry Me (IRE) **Mrs K. H. York**
3 **GERSJOEYCASEY (IRE)**, 11, b m Milan—Derrigra Sublime (IRE) **Mrs K. H. York**
4 **INTERCOOLER TURBO (IRE)**, 11, gr g Dr Massini (IRE)—Moigh Endeavour (IRE) **Mrs K. H. York**
5 **LEGAL OK (IRE)**, 8, b g Echo of Light—Desert Trail (IRE) **P. York**
6 **MAGEN'S MOON (IRE)**, 6, b m Henrythenavigator (USA)—Magen's Star (IRE) **P. York**
7 **REBEL COLLINS (IRE)**, 9, gr g Jeremy (USA)—Million All Day (IRE) **P. York**
8 **RENDEZVOUS PEAK**, 11, b g High-Rise (IRE)—Jurado Park (IRE) **Mrs K. H. York**
9 **ROBIN DES MANA (IRE)**, 9, br g Robin des Pres (FR)—Kokopelli Mana (IRE) **P. York**
10 **SPENDABLE**, 8, ch m Spendent—Eastern Point **Mrs K. H. York**
11 **SPIRITOFCHARTWELL**, 12, ch g Clerkenwell (USA)—Rollin Rock **Mrs K. H. York**

594 MRS LAURA YOUNG, Bridgwater
Postal: **Rooks Castle Stables, Broomfield, Bridgwater, Somerset, TA5 2EW**
Contacts: **PHONE 01278 664595 MOBILE 07766 514414 FAX 01278 661555**
EMAIL ljyracing@hotmail.com WEBSITE www.laurayoungracing.com

1 **AUENWIRBEL (GER),** 9, b g Sholokhov (IRE)—Auentime (GER) **Mr T. J. Moynihan**
2 **AUMIT HILL,** 7, b g Authorized (IRE)—Eurolinka (IRE) **Mr G. C. Vining**
3 **BUCKBORU (IRE),** 12, b m Brian Boru—Buckland Filleigh (IRE) **Mrs L. J. Young**
4 **EGGESFORD,** 6, b g Foxwedge (AUS)—Elegant Pride **Mrs L. J. Young**
5 **JIGSAW FINANCIAL (IRE),** 14, b g Brian Boru—Ardcolm Cailin (IRE) **Mrs L. J. Young**
6 **MEGAUDAIS SPEED (FR),** 8, b g Puit d'Or (IRE)—La Rouadiere (FR) **The Isle Of Frogs Partnership**
7 **MOYNIHANS GIRL (IRE),** 6, ch m Frammassone (IRE)—Catch Ball **Mr T. J. Moynihan**
8 **SUFFICE (IRE),** 11, b g Iffraaj—Shallat (IRE) **Mrs L. J. Young**
9 **THEDANCINGMAN,** 7, b g Jeremy (USA)—Broadway Dancer **Mrs L. J. Young**
10 **TRUE THOUGHTS (IRE),** 5, b g So You Think (NZ)—True Joy (IRE) **Soul Galore**
11 **VALSHAN TIME (IRE),** 8, b br g Atraf—Valshan (IRE) **Mrs L. J. Young**
12 **WHITE NILE (IRE),** 11, b h Galileo (IRE)—Super Gift (IRE) **Mrs L. J. Young**

Other Owners: Mr M. J. Rees, Mr C. V. Vining, Mr G. C. Vining, Mrs L. J. Young.

Assistant Trainer: James Young.

NH Jockey: Robert Dunne.

595 MR WILLIAM YOUNG, Carluke
Postal: **Watchknowe Lodge, Crossford, Carluke, Lanarkshire, ML8 5QT**
Contacts: **PHONE 01555 860226, 01555 860856 MOBILE 07900 408210 FAX 01555 860137**
EMAIL watchknowe@talktalk.net

1 **AERTON BRAE,** 7, b m Bahri (USA)—Roadworthy (IRE) **W. G. Young**
2 **APOLLO CREED (IRE),** 8, b g Vinnie Roe (IRE)—Just Cassandra (IRE) **W. G. Young**
3 **ARDERA CROSS (IRE),** 9, ch g Shantou (USA)—Fair Maid Marion (IRE) **W. G. Young**
4 **COOL VALLEY (IRE),** 11, b g Zerpour (IRE)—Jilly Jaffa Cake (IRE) **W. G. Young**
5 **FORMIDABLEOPPONENT (IRE),** 13, b g Arakan (USA)—Sliding **W. G. Young**
6 **GALAHILL,** 7, gr m Ferrule (IRE)—Gala Queen **W. G. Young**
7 **HERE COMES LOVE (IRE),** 10, b g Winged Love (IRE)—Heres McGoogan (IRE) **W. G. Young**
8 **KICKS BEFORE SIX (IRE),** 8, b g Scorpion (IRE)—Square Up (IRE) **W. G. Young**
9 **SOME AMBITION (IRE),** 7, b g Westerner—Heath Heaven **W. G. Young**
10 **SPECIALIST (IRE),** 6, b g Mastercraftsman (IRE)—My Lass **W. G. Young**

Assistant Trainer: William G Young Snr.

INDEX TO HORSES

The Figure before the name of the horse refers to the number of the team in which it appears and
The Figure after the horse supplies a ready reference to each animal. Horses are indexed strictly alphabetically, e.g.
THE CATTLEJOBBER appears in the T's, MR NICE GUY In the MR's, ST BASIL in the ST's etc.

185 **ALISIA R** (IRE) 1
426 **ALIVE WIRE** 17
295 **ALIX JAMES** 47
163 **ALIZES** (FR) 8
116 **ALJADY** (FR) 1
251 **ALJALELA** (FR) 41
49 **ALJARI** 1
483 **ALJUMAR** (IRE) C 65
408 **ALJUNOOD** (IRE) 1
222 **ALKA STEP** (IRE) 2
43 **ALKADEMON** (IRE) 2
381 **ALKANADA** (FR) 2
227 **ALKETIOS** (GR) 2
228 **ALKHAT** 37
251 **ALKHAWARAH** (USA) C 135
430 **ALKOPOP** (GER) 1
545 **ALL ABOUT CHARLEY** 33
534 **ALL ABOUT YOU** (IRE) 3
220 **ALL FUR COAT** F 17
479 **ALL GOOD THINGS** (IRE) 1
368 **ALL HAIL CAESAR** (IRE) 1
144 **ALL IS GOOD** (IRE) 1
71 **ALL KINGS** (IRE) 1
485 **ALL MY LOVE** (IRE) 2
499 **ALL OF THE LIGHTS** (IRE) 21
102 **ALL RILED UP** 1
211 **ALL SET TO GO** (IRE) 1
17 **ALL YOU WISH** 54
123 **ALL YOURS** (FR) 1
392 **ALLAHO** (FR) 4
436 **ALLAMOOR BOY** 1
268 **ALLART** (IRE) 2
395 **ALLAVINA** (IRE) 4
30 **ALLEGATION** (FR) C 58
582 **ALLEGIANT** (USA) 3
251 **ALLEGRANZA** 140
347 **ALLEGRO JETE** (FR) 14
186 **ALLEN A DALE** (IRE) 2
274 **ALLENBY** (IRE) 1
84 **ALLERBY** 37
460 **ALLERTHORPE** 8
47 **ALLERTON** (USA) C 59
254 **ALLEZ ALLEZ ALLEZ** (IRE) 78
393 **ALLEZ LOUISE** (IRE) 36
304 **ALLEZ SOPHIA** (IRE) 24
305 **ALLGOLD** (FR) 38
484 **ALLMANKIND** 6
481 **ALLSFINEANDANDY** (IRE) 1
51 **ALLTHATGLISTENS** (IRE) 1
17 **ALLTHERIGHTMOVES** (IRE) C 124
539 **ALLTIMEGOLD** (IRE) 5
323 **ALLUCINATION** 17
368 **ALLURING STAR** C 70
577 **ALLY ROSE** (IRE) G 4
276 **ALLYSSON MONTERG** (FR) 1
483 **ALMANIA** (IRE) 2
511 **ALMAREEKH** (USA) 26
338 **ALMAZHAR GARDE** (FR) 1
228 **ALMIGHWAR** 38
251 **ALMINAR** (IRE) 2
183 **ALMONTASER** (FR) 3
577 **ALMOST GOLD** (IRE) 5
483 **ALMOST MIDNIGHT** 3
305 **ALMQVIST** 39
27 **ALMUERZO LOCO** (IRE) 30
76 **ALMUFEED** (IRE) 17
422 **ALMUFTI** 1
346 **ALMURR** (IRE) 1

484 **ALNADAM** (FR) 7
516 **ALNASHERAT** 1
408 **ALNEEL** (IRE) 2
29 **ALOE VERA** 3
251 **ALOISI** F 136
122 **ALONG CAME THEO** (IRE) 1
251 **ALONG THE SHORE** (IRE) F 137
309 **ALONSO CANO** (IRE) 1
524 **ALOOMOMO** (FR) 1
17 **ALOUNAK** (FR) 2
49 **ALPACA FINA** (CAN) C 60
6 **ALPEN ROSE** (IRE) 33
368 **ALPH** (IRE) 2
395 **ALPHA CARINAE** (IRE) 5
486 **ALPHA DELPHINI** 1
94 **ALPHA SPIRIT** C 77
487 **ALPHA TAURI** (USA) 1
439 **ALPHABETICAL** 9
272 **ALPIN KING** (IRE) 21
309 **ALPINE MISTRAL** (IRE) 18
483 **ALPINE SPIRIT** (IRE) C 66
254 **ALPINE STAR** (IRE) 79
439 **ALPINISTA** 10
87 **ALQAAB** (IRE) 1
76 **ALQIFAAR** (USA) 18
228 **ALRAJAA** 1
91 **ALRAMZ** 1
272 **ALREHB** (USA) 22
128 **ALRIGHT SUNSHINE** (IRE) 1
496 **ALRIGHTJACK** (IRE) 2
315 **ALSA MIX** (FR) 1
239 **ALSAADEN** F 22
33 **ALSAMARA** 1
291 **ALSUKAR** 40
317 **ALSVINDER** 4
409 **ALTA ANNA** (FR) C 115
272 **ALTAAYSHSH** (IRE) 72
251 **ALTERNANTHERA** (IRE) C 138
162 **ALTERNATIVE FACT** 1
6 **ALTHIQA** 34
268 **ALTIOR** (IRE) 3
94 **ALTONA** (IRE) F 78
374 **ALTRUISM** (IRE) 1
419 **ALVARINO** 40
573 **ALVARO** 2
349 **ALVEDA** 7
97 **ALWAAB** (FR) 3
465 **ALWAATN SOUND** (IRE) 34
307 **ALWAYS ABLE** (IRE) 1
62 **ALWAYS AMAZING** 1
251 **ALWAYS FEARLESS** (IRE) 42
577 **ALWAYS RESOLUTE** 6
321 **ALWAYS THE LADY** F 18
381 **ALYS ROCK** (IRE) 3
97 **ALYSHKA** (FR) 23
318 **ALZANTI** (USA) F 26
563 **AM I DREAMING** (IRE) 23
121 **AMAAN** 26
170 **AMADEUS GREY** (IRE) 5
94 **AMAHORO** F 79
101 **AMALFI BAY** 64
128 **AMALFI DOUG** (FR) 2
61 **AMANGIRI** (IRE) 1
384 **AMANJENA** C 49
446 **AMANOFHISWORD** (IRE) 1
512 **AMANTO** (GER) 1
54 **AMARETTO** 1
192 **AMARILLO STAR** (IRE) 26

117 **AMARSANAA** 23
73 **AMASOVA** 78
198 **AMATEUR** (IRE) 1
318 **AMATHUS** (IRE) 13
186 **AMAYSMONT** 61
555 **AMAZALI** 13
568 **AMAZING ALBA** 2
476 **AMAZING AMAYA** 1
545 **AMAZING ANNA** 34
27 **AMAZING GRAZING** (IRE) 2
472 **AMAZING NEWS** 10
162 **AMAZING RED** (IRE) 2
519 **AMAZING TANGO** (GER) 27
401 **AMAZON PRINCESS** 1
593 **AMBANADORA** 1
98 **AMBASSADORIAL** (USA) 1
158 **AMBELLA** (IRE) F 17
577 **AMBER GAMBLER** (GER) 7
512 **AMBER HEIGHTS** G 2
6 **AMBER ISLAND** (IRE) 35
185 **AMBER ROCK** (USA) 2
128 **AMBER STORM** (IRE) 71
468 **AMBERINE** 1
150 **AMBERLEY HEIGHTS** (IRE) C 51
452 **AMBEROSE** 1
516 **AMBIGUOUS** C 50
526 **AMBION HILL** (IRE) 2
240 **AMBITIOUS ICARUS** 1
409 **AMBITIOUS LADY** C 116
103 **AMBRE** (FR) 11
97 **AMBRE SOLEIL** (FR) 79
411 **AMELIA MAY** C 51
119 **AMELIA R** (IRE) 1
356 **AMELIA'S DANCE** (IRE) 3
405 **AMENON** (FR) 4
150 **AMERICA FIRST** (IRE) 22
242 **AMERICA NOVA** (FR) C 116
167 **AMERICAN CRAFTSMAN** (IRE) 1
419 **AMERICAN DREAMER** 12
256 **AMERICAN GRAFFITI** (FR) 1
256 **AMERICAN LIFE** (FR) 3
45 **AMERICAN PIE** (IRE) 7
393 **AMERICAN SPIRIT** (IRE) F 37
57 **AMERICAN TOM** (FR) 2
213 **AMETHEA** (IRE) 1
242 **AMETIST** 40
409 **AMHRAN NA BHFIANN** (IRE) 17
363 **AMI DESBOIS** (FR) 3
7 **AMI LI BERT** (FR) 96
188 **AMICABLE** 28
256 **AMICABLE TERMS** F 32
49 **AMICIA** 22
506 **AMILLIONTIMES** (IRE) 1
101 **AMIR KABIR** 20
555 **AMIRA** C 14
483 **AMIRA'S CROWN** (USA) 29
16 **AMISI** 2
413 **AMJAADY** (USA) 2
413 **AMLIBA** 3
589 **AMLOVI** (IRE) 2
272 **AMLWCH** (IRE) 73
504 **AMNA** 1
60 **AMNAA** 11
547 **AMNIARIX** (USA) 30
565 **AMOOD** (IRE) 1
484 **AMOOLA GOLD** (GER) 8
180 **AMOR FATI** (IRE) 1
393 **AMOR KETHLEY** 1

265 **AMOUR D'OR** 1
405 **AMOUR DE NUIT** (IRE) 5
119 **AMOURI CHIEF** 2
119 **AMOURI GLEAM** 3
119 **AMOURIE** 4
150 **AMPLIFICATION** (USA) 1
269 **AMRON KALI** (IRE) 2
179 **AMSBY** 15
228 **AMTIYAZ** 39
49 **AMURMAR** (IRE) C 61
94 **AMY BEACH** (IRE) 80
20 **AMZAC MAGIC** 1
491 **AN FEAR CIUIN** (IRE) 5
29 **AN GHALANTA** F 91
501 **ANALYST** 13
99 **ANANYA** 9
228 **ANASTARSIA** (IRE) 40
124 **ANAX** (IRE) 2
297 **ANCORA** (IRE) F 29
73 **ANCYRE** (FR) 22
189 **AND THE NEW** (IRE) 2
563 **AND YET SHE MOVES** (IRE) 1
363 **ANDALEEP** (IRE) 4
392 **ANDALUSA** (FR) 5
456 **ANDAPA** (FR) 1
584 **ANDIES ARMIES** 1
367 **ANDITSNONAYNEVER** 14
62 **ANDRE AMAR** 1
387 **ANEEDH** 2
445 **ANFIELD** G 10
132 **ANFIELD GIRL** (IRE) 19
132 **ANGEL ALEXANDER** (IRE) 1
192 **ANGEL AMADEA** 56
453 **ANGEL EYES** 1
236 **ANGEL FORCE** (IRE) 1
17 **ANGEL GREY** 55
422 **ANGEL OF DELIGHT** (IRE) 17
73 **ANGEL OF THE GLEN** (FR) 23
163 **ANGEL ON HIGH** (IRE) 9
73 **ANGEL PALANAS** 1
537 **ANGEL POWER** 36
465 **ANGEL VISION** (IRE) C 81
73 **ANGEL VOICES** (IRE) G 24
10 **ANGEL'S ACCLAIM** (IRE) 1
393 **ANGEL'S WHISPER** (IRE) 2
388 **ANGELA'S HOPE** 1
309 **ANGELIC FLAME** (IRE) 19
134 **ANGELIC KITTEN** (IRE) C 9
538 **ANGELIC TIME** (IRE) 4
323 **ANGELISSIMA** (FR) 18
156 **ANGELS ANTICS** 1
268 **ANGELS BREATH** (IRE) 4
530 **ANGELS FACES** (IRE) 14
54 **ANGELS ROC** 14
272 **ANGELS WINGS** (IRE) F 74
543 **ANGIE B** (IRE) 1
192 **ANGLO SAXSON** (IRE) 27
270 **ANIF** (IRE) 1
424 **ANIGHTINLAMBOURN** (IRE) 1
317 **ANIKNAM** (FR) 5
494 **ANIMAL** (IRE) 1
439 **ANIMAL INSTINCT** 11
295 **ANIMORE** 1
301 **ANISOPTERA** (IRE) 12
286 **ANJAALETTA** (IRE) 40
121 **ANJAH** (IRE) 27
29 **ANJAZ** (USA) F 130
511 **ANN OF THE DANCE** (USA) C 101

409 **ANNA KARENINA** (IRE) C 117
186 **ANNA MARIA** 62
6 **ANNA MIA** (GER) F 117
251 **ANNA NERIUM** 1
511 **ANNA OF LORRAINE** 2
6 **ANNA SALAI** (USA) C 118
539 **ANNA'S MELODY** (IRE) G 6
623 **ANNA'S VISION** (IRE) F 29
35 **ANNAJEMIMA** 1
99 **ANNAKONDA** (IRE) 1
97 **ANNALYSE** (FR) 24
392 **ANNAMIX** (FR) 6
305 **ANNANDALE** (IRE) 141
35 **ANNAS THEATRE** C 3
272 **ANNE OF KIEV** (IRE) F 75
83 **ANNEBELLE** (IRE) 2
568 **ANNIE BROWN** 3
29 **ANNIE DE VEGA** 37
132 **ANNIE JONES** (IRE) 20
254 **ANNIE KATE** 2
24 **ANNIE KENNEY** C 20
416 **ANNIE MC** (IRE) 3
512 **ANNIE ODDS** (IRE) 3
437 **ANNIE QUICKSTEP** (IRE) 13
99 **ANNIE THE DOC** C 18
230 **ANNIE'S GIFT** (IRE) G 2
65 **ANNIEAREYOUOK** 1
21 **ANNIEMATION** (IRE) 18
545 **ANNIVERSARY** (IRE) G 25
503 **ANNMARY GIRL** F 12
439 **ANNO LUCIS** (IRE) 12
30 **ANNO MAXIMO** (GER) 10
576 **ANNSAM** 2
227 **ANNUAL INVICTUS** (IRE) 3
228 **ANOINTED** 41
63 **ANOTHER ANGEL** (IRE) 1
339 **ANOTHER APPROACH** (FR) 1
26 **ANOTHER BATT** (IRE) 2
580 **ANOTHER CRICK** 1
580 **ANOTHER DRAMA** (IRE) 2
233 **ANOTHER EMOTION** (IRE) 1
534 **ANOTHER FRONTIER** (IRE) 4
40 **ANOTHER GLANCE** 1
519 **ANOTHER KATE** (IRE) F 37
220 **ANOTHER NAME** (USA) F 18
221 **ANOTHER STOWAWAY** (IRE) 3
418 **ANOTHER THEATRE** (IRE) 3
317 **ANOTHER THEATRE** (IRE) 6
186 **ANOTHER TOUCH** 3
233 **ANOTHER TUCO** (IRE) 2
14 **ANOTHER VENTURE** (IRE) 3
220 **ANSE VICTORIN** (USA) C 19
323 **ANSILIA** (IRE) 3
486 **ANTAGONIZE** 2
331 **ANTEROS** (IRE) 1
392 **ANTEY** (GER) 7
465 **ANTHEM ALEXANDER** (IRE) C 82
409 **ANTHONY VAN DYCK** (IRE) 1
144 **ANTI COOL** (IRE) 3
6 **ANTIANNA** (USA) 36
158 **ANTICIPATE** (IRE) 1
175 **ANTICO LADY** (IRE) 2
210 **ANTIDOTE** (IRE) 1
390 **ANTON DOLIN** (IRE) 1
29 **ANTONIA DE VEGA** (IRE) 4
378 **ANTONY** (FR) 6
484 **ANTUNES** 9
212 **ANY DRAMA** (IRE) 3

305 **ANYONECANHAVEITALL** 1
94 **ANYONEWHOHADAHEART** 26
496 **ANYTHINGFORLOVE** 3
413 **ANYTHINGTODAY** (IRE) 4
484 **ANYTIME WILL DO** (IRE) 10
416 **ANYWAYYOULOOKATIT** (IRE) 4
62 **APACHE BLAZE** 3
202 **APACHE CHIEF** 1
416 **APACHE CREEK** (IRE) 5
23 **APACHE PILOT** 1
211 **APACHITO** 29
536 **APEX KING** (IRE) 1
381 **APHRODISIAS** (FR) G 4
242 **APLOMB** (IRE) 3
29 **APOLLINAIRE** 38
595 **APOLLO CREED** (IRE) 2
537 **APPARATE** 1
17 **APPLAUDABLE** (IRE) 56
511 **APPLAUDED** (IRE) C 102
249 **APPLAUS** (GER) 2
52 **APPLE BANK** 2
373 **APPLE MACK** 1
424 **APPLE ROCK** (IRE) 1
260 **APPLES ACRE** (IRE) 36
331 **APPLESANDPIERRES** (IRE) 2
547 **APPLETART** (IRE) 31
170 **APPOINTED** 6
501 **APPOINTEE** (IRE) F 14
392 **APPRECIATE IT** (IRE) 8
190 **APPROVE THE DREAM** (IRE) 1
30 **APPROXIMATE** 11
141 **APRICOT STAR** (IRE) 11
97 **APRIL FOOLS** (IRE) 25
327 **APRIL GREEN** (FR) C 74
258 **APRIL RISING** 2
41 **APRILS ROSE** 1
10 **APRON STRINGS** 2
374 **APTLY PUT** (IRE) 2
121 **AQAAREB** (IRE) 28
89 **AQUA LIBRE** 2
352 **AQUADABRA** (IRE) 1
537 **AQUAMAN** (IRE) 124
98 **AQUARIUM** 2
7 **AQUARIUS** (IRE) 3
163 **AQUASCAPE** (IRE) 10
97 **AQUASTAR** (IRE) 4
326 **AQUATINTA** (GER) C 18
537 **AQUILEO** (IRE) 37
184 **AQUITAINE BOY** (FR) 1
378 **AR MEST** (FR) 7
334 **ARABESCATO** 14
323 **ARABIAN BELLE** (IRE) 19
6 **ARABIAN GIRL** (IRE) 37
193 **ARABIAN KING** 1
465 **ARABIAN MAIDEN** 35
29 **ARABIAN MOON** 39
73 **ARABIAN MUSIC** (IRE) F 79
425 **ARABIAN OASIS** 1
39 **ARABIAN ROMANCE** (IRE) 45
39 **ARABIAN WARRIOR** 46
39 **ARABIC CHARM** (IRE) 47
530 **ARABIC CULTURE** (USA) 1
39 **ARABIC WELCOME** (IRE) 48
188 **ARADENA** (IRE) 57
186 **ARAIFJAN** 63
170 **ARAKA LI** (IRE) 97
242 **ARAMAIC** (IRE) 117
239 **ARAMIS GREY** (IRE) 9

73 **ASTRO JAKK** (IRE) 2
511 **ASTRO KING** (IRE) 28
214 **ASTRODONNA** C 64
179 **ASTROGEM** 16
428 **ASTROMACHIA** 2
179 **ASTROMAN** 17
132 **ASTRONOMIC CHOICE** 52
481 **ASTROPHYSICS** 2
196 **ASTROSPEED** (IRE) 1
486 **ASTROZONE** 21
491 **ASTUTE BOY** (IRE) 4
228 **ASWAAT** 43
272 **AT EASE** 23
416 **AT FIRST GLANCE** (IRE) 8
274 **AT ITS OWN EXPENSE** (IRE) 2
268 **AT POETS CROSS** (IRE) 7
377 **AT YOUR EASE** (IRE) 1
19 **AT YOUR SERVICE** 1
272 **ATAB** (IRE) C 77
511 **ATACAMA DESERT** (IRE) 103
121 **ATACAMENA** (IRE) 74
192 **ATAILOF TWO CITIES** (IRE) 28
529 **ATALANTA BREEZE** 2
62 **ATALANTA QUEEN** 4
367 **ATALANTA'S BOY** 2
49 **ATALIS BAY** 62
26 **ATEESCOMPONENT** (IRE) 3
511 **ATHEEB** 29
537 **ATHENAIRE** (IRE) F 125
537 **ATHERS** (IRE) 126
61 **ATHINEA** (FR) G 29
87 **ATHMAD** (IRE) 3
405 **ATHOLL STREET** (IRE) 10
228 **ATIAAF** 44
26 **ATIYAH** 39
131 **ATJIMA** (IRE) 2
129 **ATLANTA ABLAZE** 2
107 **ATLANTIC CROSSING** (IRE) 13
568 **ATLANTIC DANCER** (IRE) 1
422 **ATLANTIC ISLE** (GER) C 58
514 **ATLANTIC STORM** (IRE) 1
183 **ATLANTIC SUNSHINE** 4
99 **ATLAS FLAME** (IRE) 10
162 **ATLAS SILK** C 49
180 **ATLETICO** (IRE) 2
43 **ATOMIC ARTICLE** (IRE) 3
16 **ATOMIC JACK** 3
52 **ATOMIC RUMBLE** (IRE) 3
580 **ATOMIX** (GER) 3
67 **ATRAFAN** (IRE) 1
557 **ATTAIN** 2
148 **ATTENTION PLEASE** (IRE) 2
97 **ATTIRANCE** (FR) 5
346 **ATTRACTED TO YOU** (IRE) G 14
419 **ATTRACTED TO YOU** (IRE) C 41
97 **ATTRACTIVE LADY** F 80
352 **ATTY'S EDGE** 2
487 **ATWAAR** 2
106 **ATWIX** C 16
476 **ATYAAF** 2
142 **AUBIS PARK** (FR) 2
578 **AUBUSSON** (FR) 2
305 **AUCHTERARDER** (IRE) 41
260 **AUCKLAND LODGE** (IRE) 37
233 **AUDACITY** 1
188 **AUDARYA** (FR) 2
428 **AUDITORIA** 23
467 **AUDLEY** F 6

89 **AUDREY BROWN** G 79
594 **AUENWIRBEL** (GER) 1
298 **AUGHNACURRA KING** (IRE) 1
413 **AUGUSTUS CAESAR** (USA) 59
212 **AUJIANG** (GER) G 7
409 **AULD ALLIANCE** (IRE) C 118
379 **AULD BOY** (USA) 1
341 **AUMERLE** 1
594 **AUMIT HILL** 2
254 **AUNT BEE** (IRE) 80
340 **AUNT HELEN** (USA) 1
563 **AUNT MINNIE** C 37
66 **AUNTIE JUNE** 1
327 **AURELIA OR** (IRE) 1
233 **AURELLO** 5
228 **AUREUM** (USA) 45
17 **AURIFEROUS** (IRE) 125
419 **AURORA SPRING** (IRE) C 42
384 **AURORA STAR** (FR) 50
463 **AURORA THUNDER** 4
221 **AUSSIE BREEZE** 4
286 **AUSSIE STORMER** (IRE) 41
420 **AUSTIN FRIARS** 1
563 **AUSTIN TAETIOUS** 24
537 **AUSTRALIS** (IRE) 2
320 **AUTHOR'S DREAM** 1
428 **AUTHORA** (IRE) F 40
392 **AUTHORIZED ART** (FR) 12
580 **AUTHORIZED TOO** 4
234 **AUTHORIZO** (FR) 6
317 **AUTONOMY** 8
212 **AUTORISATION** (FR) 8
493 **AUTUMM SPIRIT** G 3
128 **AUTUMN COLOURS** (USA) 73
491 **AUTUMN FLAME** 31
170 **AUTUMN FLIGHT** (IRE) 8
189 **AUTUMN GOLD** 3
39 **AUTUMN LEAF** 3
305 **AUTUMN LILY** (USA) F 42
57 **AUTUMN SPLENDOUR** (IRE) 3
239 **AUTUMN TRAIL** 11
577 **AUTUMN WAR** (IRE) 9
15 **AUXILIARY** 1
418 **AVANTGARDIST** (GER) 5
84 **AVANZATA** 15
365 **AVASELLE** C 17
242 **AVEBURY** (IRE) 41
47 **AVEC LAURA** 2
17 **AVENANTE** C 126
305 **AVENTURIERE** 43
54 **AVENTURINA** 22
362 **AVENUE OF STARS** 1
29 **AVETA** (FR) 92
39 **AVIACION** (BRZ) F 131
363 **AVIATEWOSEA** (IRE) 8
431 **AVION** 1
223 **AVITHOS** 1
142 **AVOID DE MASTER** (IRE) 3
283 **AVOIR DE SOINS** (IRE) 2
342 **AVONROSE** G 1
342 **AVONROSE** G 17
378 **AVORISK ET PERILS** (FR) 8
97 **AVYON** (FR) 26
503 **AWAIT** (IRE) F 35
274 **AWAKE AT MIDNIGHT** 3
550 **AWAKE IN ASIA** 3
517 **AWAKE MY SOUL** (IRE) 1
242 **AWARD SCHEME** 42

356 **AWAY AT DAWN** (IRE) 7
256 **AWAY FOR SLATES** (IRE) 4
375 **AWAY HE GOES** (IRE) 1
315 **AWEEDRAM** (IRE) 1
94 **AWEEMAWEH** (IRE) 27
409 **AWESOME MARIA** (USA) F 119
217 **AWESOMEDUDE** 1
573 **AWSAAF** 3
19 **AXEL JACKLIN** 2
364 **AXXELERATION** 2
520 **AYALOR** (FR) 1
486 **AYASHA** C 33
411 **AYE AYE CHARLIE** 5
229 **AYE RIGHT** (IRE) 1
17 **AYO GORKHALI** 127
7 **AYR HARBOUR** 97
225 **AYR POET** 1
162 **AYSAR** (FR) 22
47 **AYUN** (USA) F 26
164 **AZARI** 3
98 **AZETS** 3
227 **AZOR AHAI** 4
461 **AZTEC DREAMS** 1
107 **AZTEC QUEEN** F 26
384 **AZTEC QUEEN** F 51
486 **AZTECA** 22
179 **AZURE MIST** C 25
394 **AZZECCAGARBUGLI** (IRE) 2
315 **AZZERTI** (FR) 4
484 **AZZURRI** 14
367 **B BERRY BRANDY** (USA) F 28
196 **B FIFTY TWO** (IRE) 2
242 **BAAEED** 118
228 **BAAQY** (IRE) 46
242 **BAARRIJ** (IRE) 43
76 **BAASEM** (USA) 2
536 **BAASHIQ** (IRE) 4
272 **BAASHIR** (IRE) 24
511 **BAAZIGHAH** 30
251 **BABAJAN** (IRE) 139
29 **BABBO'S BOY** (IRE) 5
539 **BABOIN** (FR) 7
568 **BABY BLUESKY** 5
46 **BABY JANE** (IRE) 2
221 **BABY KING** (IRE) 5
339 **BABY STEPS** 2
534 **BABY TED** 7
569 **BABY TICKER** 1
575 **BABYTAGGLE** (IRE) 1
392 **BACARDYS** (FR) 13
392 **BACHASSON** (FR) 14
39 **BACK FROM DUBAI** (IRE) 49
308 **BACK ON THE LASH** 1
503 **BACK TO BRUSSELS** 13
574 **BACKINTHEOLDTIMES** (IRE) 1
484 **BACKOFTHEENVELOPE** (IRE) 15
368 **BACKPACKER** (IRE) 4
140 **BACON'S REBELLION** 1
361 **BAD ATTITUDE** 11
378 **BAD BOY DU POULDU** (FR) 9
54 **BAD COMPANY** 15
368 **BAD RABBIT** (IRE) 57
49 **BADALONA** C 63
214 **BADAYEL** (IRE) 1
227 **BADDELEY** (IRE) 5
227 **BADDESLEY KNIGHT** (IRE) 6
227 **BADDESLEY PRINCE** (IRE) 7
291 **BADENSCOTH** 2

17 **BADESSA** 3
550 **BADGER BERRY** 4
364 **BADR AL BADOOR** (IRE) C 26
188 **BADR AL BADOOR** (IRE) C 58
272 **BADRAH** (USA) 25
49 **BADREPUTATION** 23
272 **BADRI** 26
217 **BADWEIA** (USA) F 13
23 **BAFANA BLUE** 3
405 **BAGAD BIHOUE** (FR) 11
235 **BAGAN** 1
212 **BAGS GROOVE** (IRE) 9
548 **BAGUE D'OR** (IRE) 27
122 **BAH LAMB** 2
540 **BAHAMA MOON** (IRE) 2
420 **BAHAMIAN HEIGHTS** 2
76 **BAHEEJA** C 52
239 **BAHIA STAR** 23
62 **BAHIE** C 30
317 **BAHKIT** (IRE) 9
339 **BAHUTA ACHA** 3
233 **BAILARICO** (IRE) 6
7 **BAILE GHILIBERT** (IRE) 4
469 **BAILEYS ARTIST** 1
60 **BAILEYS FREEDOM** 13
305 **BAILEYS JUBILEE** F 142
305 **BAILEYS PRINCESS** 44
382 **BAILY GORSE** (IRE) 1
382 **BAILY THUNDER** 2
6 **BAISSE** F 120
393 **BAJA MOON** (IRE) 38
582 **BAJAN BREEZE** 44
40 **BAJARDO** (IRE) 3
132 **BAKERSBOY** 53
148 **BAKO DE LA SAULAIE** (IRE) 3
347 **BAL AMIE** (FR) 1
511 **BAL DE LA ROSE** (IRE) C 104
444 **BAL MAL** (FR) 24
342 **BALADIO** (IRE) 2
316 **BALAGAN** 1
419 **BALAMIYDA** (IRE) C 43
412 **BALANCING ACT** (IRE) 35
356 **BALATA BAY** 8
104 **BALGAIR** 1
555 **BALGEES TIME** (FR) 1
512 **BALGEMMOIS** (FR) 5
467 **BALINKA** F 7
578 **BALKO SAINT** (FR) 14
588 **BALL D'ARC** (FR) 2
569 **BALL PARK** (IRE) G 2
221 **BALLADAME** (FR) 6
364 **BALLADE'S GIRL** (USA) C 43
458 **BALLADEER** 1
480 **BALLAQUANE** (IRE) 3
164 **BALLARD DOWN** (IRE) 4
145 **BALLELA'S DREAM** 1
420 **BALLESTEROS** 3
537 **BALLET MOVE** C 127
94 **BALLET OF DOHA** (IRE) C 81
6 **BALLET QUEEN** 38
34 **BALLETLOU** (IRE) F 23
580 **BALLI MARTINE** (FR) 5
576 **BALLINSKER** (IRE) 7
378 **BALLINSLEA BRIDGE** (IRE) 10
420 **BALLON ONABUDGET** (IRE) 7
274 **BALLOTIN** (FR) 4
297 **BALLY CONOR** (IRE) 1
144 **BALLY LAGAN** (IRE) 4

526 **BALLY LONGFORD** (IRE) 4
465 **BALLYALLA** F 37
419 **BALLYALLA** F 44
463 **BALLYARE** 95
534 **BALLYART** (IRE) 8
107 **BALLYBACKA LADY** (IRE) C 27
233 **BALLYBEGG** (IRE) 7
473 **BALLYBOUGH NORA** (IRE) 2
576 **BALLYBREEN** (IRE) 8
484 **BALLYCALLAN FAME** (IRE) 16
220 **BALLYCROSS** 1
249 **BALLYCRYSTAL** (IRE) 3
368 **BALLYCRYSTAL COURT** (IRE) 5
338 **BALLYDINE** (IRE) 2
458 **BALLYDONAGH BOY** (IRE) 2
378 **BALLYDOYLE** (GER) 11
409 **BALLYDOYLE** (FR) F 120
351 **BALLYDUN OSCAR** (IRE) 2
588 **BALLYFARSOON** (IRE) 3
411 **BALLYHOME** (IRE) 6
365 **BALLYHOT BOY** (IRE) 5
20 **BALLYJIM** (IRE) 3
286 **BALLYLEMON** (IRE) 1
261 **BALLYMAGROARTY BOY** (IRE) 3
534 **BALLYMALIN** (IRE) 9
388 **BALLYMILAN** 3
534 **BALLYMILLSY** 10
534 **BALLYMOY** (IRE) 11
1 **BALLYNANTY** (IRE) 3
541 **BALLYNARRY** (IRE) 2
534 **BALLYOPTIC** (IRE) 12
175 **BALLYVIC BORU** (IRE) 3
315 **BALLYWOOD** (FR) 5
437 **BALMORAL CASTLE** 2
268 **BALMUICK** (IRE) 8
463 **BALRANALD** (FR) 5
6 **BALSAMINE** (USA) C 121
413 **BALTIC BARON** (IRE) 7
12 **BALTIC EAGLE** (GER) 1
89 **BALTIC PRINCE** (IRE) 3
214 **BALTIC STATE** (IRE) 39
50 **BALTIC WOLVE** 8
547 **BALZAC** 32
392 **BAMAKO MORIVIERE** (FR) 15
434 **BAMBAJEE** (FR) 1
503 **BAMBARI** (IRE) 1
111 **BAMBI DU NOYER** (FR) 1
563 **BAMBINO LOLA** 2
557 **BAMBOO QUEEN** (IRE) 22
394 **BAMO MC** 3
378 **BAN SHOOF** 12
424 **BANANA JOE** (IRE) 4
1 **BANCNUANAHEIREANN** (IRE) 5
557 **BAND PRACTICE** (IRE) 23
577 **BANDITRY** (IRE) 10
565 **BANDOL** (IRE) 2
484 **BANDSMAN** 17
500 **BANDSMAN RICE** 8
473 **BANG ON** (IRE) 3
424 **BANGERS AND CASH** (IRE) 5
17 **BANGKOK** (IRE) 4
221 **BANISH** (USA) 8
186 **BANK HOLIDAY** (IRE) 66
169 **BANKAWI** 54
569 **BANKS O' HOUXTY** 3
196 **BANKSEA** 5
385 **BANMI** (IRE) 5
121 **BANNA** 30

221 **BANNISTER** (FR) 82
461 **BANNIXTOWN BOY** (IRE) 2
356 **BANNIXTOWN GLORY** (IRE) 9
229 **BANNOCKBURN** (IRE) 2
377 **BANNTOWN GIRL** (IRE) 2
356 **BANRION SCAIRP** (IRE) 10
34 **BANTA BAY** 2
242 **BANTU** F 119
392 **BAPAUME** (FR) 16
76 **BARAAJEEL** 3
133 **BARACALU** (FR) 2
165 **BARATHEA DANCER** (IRE) C 18
589 **BARATINEUR** (FR) 3
175 **BARAWEEZ** (IRE) 4
268 **BARBADOS BLUE** (IRE) 9
405 **BARBADOS BUCK'S** (IRE) 12
465 **BARBARELLA** (FR) 38
71 **BARBARIAN** (IRE) 3
270 **BARBAROSA** (IRE) 3
365 **BARBARY MASTER** 6
499 **BARBELO** (IRE) 22
94 **BARBILL** (IRE) 2
127 **BARBOUKHA** 3
274 **BARBROOK STAR** (IRE) 5
201 **BARCA** (USA) 1
564 **BARD OF BRITTANY** 2
414 **BARDD** (IRE) 1
230 **BARFLY** 5
204 **BARISTA** (IRE) 1
180 **BARKING MAD** 27
101 **BARN OWL** 65
83 **BARNAY** 4
186 **BARNES WALLIS** (IRE) 67
586 **BARNEY BULLET** (IRE) 1
368 **BARNEY BULLET** (IRE) 6
16 **BARNEY FREDERICK** (FR) 4
6 **BARNEY ROY** 2
382 **BARNEY STINSON** (IRE) 3
251 **BARNEZET** (GR) C 140
539 **BARNTOWN** (IRE) 8
378 **BARON ALCO** (FR) 13
175 **BARON DE MIDLETON** (IRE) 5
73 **BARON RUN** 3
529 **BARON SLICK** (IRE) 3
186 **BARONIAL PRIDE** 4
501 **BAROSSA BAL** (IRE) 1
17 **BAROSSA RED** (IRE) 5
242 **BARQEYYA** (IRE) F 120
272 **BARRAAQAH** (IRE) 27
363 **BARRACK BUSTER** G 9
539 **BARRIER REEF** (IRE) 9
7 **BARRINGTON** (IRE) 6
254 **BARRINGTON COURT** 4
16 **BARRITUS** 5
496 **BARROWLANDS** (IRE) 6
391 **BARROWMOUNT** (IRE) 8
175 **BARRYS JACK** (IRE) 6
537 **BARSANTI** (IRE) 3
94 **BARTAT** 28
425 **BARTHOLOMEW J** (IRE) 4
106 **BARTIMAEUS** (IRE) 1
342 **BARTON KNOLL** 3
347 **BARWICK** 2
26 **BARYSHNIKOV** 4
35 **BASHFUL BOY** (IRE) 4
242 **BASHKIROVA** 121
365 **BASS REEVES** 123
539 **BASSARABAD** (FR) 10

73 **BIRTHSTONE** F 82
163 **BISCAY** 26
414 **BISHOPSLOUGH** (IRE) 2
545 **BIT OF A QUIRKE** 1
4 **BITASWEETSYMPHONY** (IRE) 2
375 **BITHIAH** (IRE) 2
305 **BITOOH** F 144
222 **BIZZI LIZZI** 48
572 **BLACK ABBEY** (FR) 4
89 **BLACK BUBLE** (FR) 7
465 **BLACK CASPIAN** (IRE) 39
546 **BLACK CENTAUR** (IRE) 2
405 **BLACK CORTON** (FR) 15
297 **BLACK EBONY** 2
362 **BLACK FRIDAY** 3
378 **BLACK GERRY** (IRE) 19
236 **BLACK ISLE BOY** (IRE) 5
531 **BLACK KALANISI** (IRE) 1
144 **BLACK KALAROSA** 5
249 **BLACK KETTLE** (IRE) 6
260 **BLACK KRAKEN** 2
79 **BLACK LABEL** 2
591 **BLACK LACE** 1
284 **BLACK LIGHTNING** (IRE) 2
548 **BLACK LOTUS** 1
408 **BLACK MARKET** (IRE) 3
376 **BLACK MEDICK** 2
212 **BLACK MISCHIEF** 10
189 **BLACK NOAH** 7
221 **BLACK OP** (IRE) 11
292 **BLACK OPIUM** 1
308 **BLACK PANTHER** (IRE) 6
184 **BLACK PIRATE** 7
308 **BLACK PRINCE** (FR) 7
364 **BLACK RODDED** C 44
484 **BLACK SAM BELLA** 20
128 **BLACK STAR DANCING** (USA) 74
129 **BLACK TULIP** 5
393 **BLACKBERRY JACK** (IRE) 39
392 **BLACKBOW** (IRE) 22
286 **BLACKCASTLE STORM** 12
67 **BLACKCURRENT** 2
173 **BLACKFINCH** 3
547 **BLACKHEATH** 4
67 **BLACKJACK** 3
405 **BLACKJACK KENTUCKY** (IRE) 16
315 **BLACKO** (FR) 9
563 **BLACKTHIRTYONE** 38
169 **BLACKWEST** (FR) 6
268 **BLAIRGOWRIE** (IRE) 14
94 **BLAIRLOGIE** 30
305 **BLAKE'S VISION** (IRE) 47
356 **BLAKENEY POINT** 13
94 **BLAKESHALL ROSE** F 82
349 **BLAME CULTURE** (USA) 1
315 **BLAME IT ON SALLY** (IRE) 10
76 **BLANC DE CHINE** (IRE) C 53
137 **BLARNEY BATELEUR** (IRE) 1
493 **BLASTER YEATS** 5
386 **BLAUGRANA** (IRE) C 33
355 **BLAUSEE** (IRE) 10
463 **BLAYDON** (IRE) 9
392 **BLAZER** (FR) 23
395 **BLAZER'S MILL** (IRE) 7
537 **BLAZING BEAU** (IRE) 41
505 **BLAZING DESTINY** (IRE) 1
260 **BLAZING DREAMS** (IRE) 3
392 **BLAZING EMILY** (IRE) 24

144 **BLAZING GOLD** 6
516 **BLAZING HOT** 12
133 **BLAZING PORT** (IRE) 3
473 **BLAZING SADDLES** 5
574 **BLAZING TOM** 3
14 **BLAZON** 5
483 **BLESS HIM** (IRE) 4
84 **BLESSED** (IRE) 7
393 **BLESSED TO EMPRESS** (IRE) 4
503 **BLESSING** (USA) F 36
392 **BLEU BERRY** (FR) 25
539 **BLEU ET NOIR** 14
73 **BLEU NIL** (IRE) F 83
283 **BLEUE AWAY** (IRE) 4
59 **BLIMEY CHARLIE** 1
260 **BLINDINGLY** (GER) 4
529 **BLINKING** C 34
97 **BLISS FOR EVER** (FR) 6
214 **BLISSAMORE** F 65
310 **BLISSFUL** (IRE) 22
310 **BLISTERING BARNEY** (IRE) 3
315 **BLISTERING BOB** 11
426 **BLITZLE** 11
413 **BLONDE WARRIOR** (IRE) 10
30 **BLONDIKOVA** F 60
463 **BLOORIEDOTCOM** (IRE) 10
50 **BLOSSOM MILLS** G 9
50 **BLOSSOM MILLS** C 12
297 **BLOSSOMING FORTH** (IRE) 3
274 **BLOW A GASKET** (IRE) C 8
312 **BLOW BY BLOW** (IRE) 1
192 **BLOW YOUR HORN** (FR) 30
98 **BLOWING DIXIE** 4
150 **BLOWING WIND** (IRE) 52
305 **BLOWN BY WIND** 4
18 **BLU CAVALIER** 6
233 **BLUBERRY HIGH** (IRE) 9
6 **BLUE ANGEL** (IRE) F 125
188 **BLUE ARTEMIS** 59
131 **BLUE ARTICLE** (IRE) G 4
150 **BLUE BAHIA** (IRE) F 53
234 **BLUE BALLERINA** (IRE) 7
215 **BLUE BATTALION** 1
529 **BLUE BAYOU** C 35
386 **BLUE BEIRUT** (IRE) 1
152 **BLUE BERET** 23
173 **BLUE BIKINI** 4
537 **BLUE BUTTERFLY** C 128
179 **BLUE CABLE** (IRE) 1
503 **BLUE DAHLIA** (IRE) F 37
242 **BLUE DAWN** 44
116 **BLUE DE VEGA** (GER) 4
326 **BLUE EAGLE** (IRE) 3
39 **BLUE FLAME** (IRE) 54
534 **BLUE FLIGHT** (IRE) 14
536 **BLUE GALAXY** 22
516 **BLUE GERANIUM** (IRE) F 53
108 **BLUE HAWAII** (IRE) 1
30 **BLUE HERO** (CAN) 61
249 **BLUE HUSSAR** (IRE) 3
524 **BLUE KASCADE** (IRE) 3
577 **BLUE LAUREATE** 11
392 **BLUE LORD** (FR) 26
340 **BLUE MEDICI** 3
101 **BLUE MIST** 2
411 **BLUE MONDAY** (IRE) 11
455 **BLUE RAMBLER** 2
392 **BLUE SARI** (FR) 27

176 **BLUE SKYLINE** (IRE) 12
379 **BLUE SLATE** (IRE) 9
146 **BLUE STREAK** 29
244 **BLUE WOOD** (IRE) 2
468 **BLUEBELL TIME** (IRE) 2
184 **BLUEFORTYTWO** 8
7 **BLUELION** 11
62 **BLUELLA** 6
128 **BLUESKYANDSUNSHINE** (IRE) 4
62 **BLUETTA** 7
539 **BLUNDER BUSS** (IRE) 15
404 **BLUSHES** (FR) F 10
327 **BLUSHING RED** (FR) 4
286 **BO TAIFAN** (IRE) 13
452 **BOA ISLAND** (IRE) 5
221 **BOAGRIUS** (IRE) 12
315 **BOARD OF TRADE** 12
531 **BOARDMAN** 2
192 **BOASTY** (IRE) 31
405 **BOB AND CO** (FR) 17
283 **BOB BACKUS** (IRE) 5
26 **BOB BEACH** 5
446 **BOB FORD** (IRE) 4
233 **BOB MAHLER** (IRE) 10
144 **BOB MAXWELL** (IRE) 7
405 **BOB PEBBLE** (IRE) 18
8 **BOB'S CALL** (IRE) 2
390 **BOB'S GIRL** 2
36 **BOB'S GIRLFRIEND** 1
32 **BOB'S OSS** (IRE) 16
389 **BOBBA TEE** 2
308 **BOBBLE EMERALD** (IRE) 8
23 **BOBBY BOUCHER** (IRE) 4
465 **BOBBY JANE** F 84
87 **BOBBY JOE LEG** 5
106 **BOBBY KENNEDY** 17
117 **BOBBY WHEELER** (IRE) 1
14 **BOBHOPEORNOHOPE** (IRE) 6
539 **BOBMAHLEY** (IRE) 16
493 **BOBNDAVE** (IRE) 6
493 **BOBNVAL** (IRE) G 7
515 **BOBO MAC** (IRE) 1
34 **BOBS LAD** 24
528 **BOCASIEN DESBOIS** (FR) 2
6 **BOCCACCIO** (IRE) 40
518 **BOCKOS AMBER** (IRE) 26
444 **BODACIOUS NAME** (IRE) 6
439 **BODYLINE** (IRE) 13
15 **BOGARDUS** 7
210 **BOGOSS DU PERRET** (FR) 2
539 **BOHEMIAN MAESTRO** (IRE) 17
430 **BOHER LAD** (IRE) 1
251 **BOITRON** (FR) 3
577 **BOL D'AIR** (FR) 12
216 **BOLAND'S MILL** (IRE) 3
526 **BOLD CONDUCT** (IRE) 8
89 **BOLD DECISION** 8
576 **BOLD PLAN** (IRE) 10
327 **BOLD REASON** (GER) 5
268 **BOLD RECORD** (IRE) 15
411 **BOLD RED** 12
233 **BOLD SOLDIER** 11
32 **BOLD STATEMENT** (IRE) 1
547 **BOLD SUITOR** 34
13 **BOLDMERE** 1
501 **BOLEYBEG** (IRE) 2
44 **BOLISTER** (FR) 1
170 **BOLLIN ACE** 9

583 **BRIANSTORM** (IRE) 5
36 **BRIARDALE** (IRE) 2
249 **BRICKADANK** (IRE) 8
512 **BRICKLAGGER** (IRE) 7
540 **BRICKLEBRIT** 4
409 **BRIDAL DANCE** (IRE) C 123
404 **BRIDAL PATH** F 11
506 **BRIDANE HIGH** (IRE) 3
511 **BRIDESHEAD** 32
436 **BRIDEY'S LETTUCE** (IRE) 2
269 **BRIDGETS CROSS** 4
98 **BRIDGEWATER BAY** (IRE) 5
94 **BRIDIE FFRENCH** F 83
175 **BRIDLE BELLE** G 58
378 **BRIDLE LOANAN** (IRE) 22
538 **BRIDLINGTON BOBBY** 20
411 **BRIEF AMBITION** 13
368 **BRIENNA** (IRE) M 8
13 **BRIERY BUNNY** 2
580 **BRIERY EXPRESS** 7
539 **BRIGADE OF GUARDS** (IRE) 21
330 **BRIGADIER BOB** (IRE) 1
77 **BRIGAND** 4
547 **BRIGHAM YOUNG** 5
73 **BRIGHT APPARITION** 85
6 **BRIGHT BEACON** C 127
545 **BRIGHT CLOUD** (IRE) G 26
547 **BRIGHT EYED EAGLE** (IRE) 35
424 **BRIGHT FORECAST** (IRE) 9
529 **BRIGHT GLOW** C 36
6 **BRIGHT MELODY** (IRE) 41
555 **BRIGHT NEW DAY** (IRE) F 16
275 **BRIGHT SAFFRON** 2
251 **BRIGHT SAPPHIRE** (IRE) C 148
356 **BRIGHT SIDE OFLIFE** (IRE) 14
39 **BRIGHT START** (USA) 55
39 **BRIGHT SUNSET** (IRE) 56
499 **BRIGHT VALENTINE** 25
121 **BRIGHT VIEW** (IRE) 32
163 **BRIGHTON PIER** (GER) 1
308 **BRILLARE MOMENTO** (IRE) 9
39 **BRILLIANT LIGHT** 57
272 **BRING HIM HOME** (FR) 28
235 **BRING THE BACON** 2
94 **BRING THE MONEY** (IRE) 31
7 **BRINGING GLORY** (IRE) 98
128 **BRINGITONBORIS** (USA) 77
480 **BRINGTHEHOUSEDOWN** (IRE) 7
297 **BRINKHILL** (IRE) 4
435 **BRINKLEY** (FR) 2
220 **BRINKLEYS KATIE** 2
534 **BRISTOL DE MAI** (FR) 16
378 **BRITANIO BELLO** (FR) 23
528 **BRITANNIA BAY** (IRE) 20
323 **BRIVIESCA** F 56
29 **BRIYOUNI** (FR) 8
437 **BROAD APPEAL** 3
537 **BROAD STRIPES** 132
153 **BROADCLYST** (IRE) 3
257 **BROADHAVEN DREAM** (IRE) 2
257 **BROADHAVEN HONEY** (IRE) 3
384 **BROADLANDS** F 53
148 **BROADSTRUTHER** (IRE) 5
230 **BROADWAY BELLE** 7
251 **BROADWAY DUCHESS** (IRE) F 149
1 **BROADWAY JOE** (IRE) 6
379 **BROCKAGH CAILIN** 2
180 **BROCKEY RISE** (IRE) 4

46 **BROCTUNE RED** 4
73 **BRODICK** 27
376 **BROGANS BAY** (IRE) 3
164 **BROKE AWAY** (IRE) 7
405 **BROKEN HALO** 23
142 **BROKEN QUEST** (IRE) 5
214 **BROKEN RIFLE** 41
118 **BROKEN SPEAR** 1
406 **BROMANCE** 2
392 **BRONAGH'S BELLE** (IRE) 30
516 **BRONTE SISTER** (IRE) F 55
513 **BRONZE BEAU** 1
423 **BRONZE FLORIN** 9
17 **BRONZE RIVER** 64
214 **BROOKLYN BOY** 3
132 **BROOKSIDE BANNER** (IRE) 24
213 **BROOM TIP** (IRE) 2
409 **BROOME** (IRE) 2
508 **BROPHIES DOLL** (IRE) 2
377 **BROSNA GEORGE** (IRE) 3
137 **BROTHER BENNETT** (FR) 3
257 **BROTHER BENTLEY** 4
89 **BROTHER IN ARMS** (IRE) 10
170 **BROTHER MCGONAGALL** 14
356 **BROTHER PAT** 15
79 **BROTHER SCOTT** 3
274 **BROTHER TEDD** 9
206 **BROTHERLY COMPANY** (IRE) 1
334 **BROUAINS** (FR) 2
582 **BROUGHTON EXCELS** 6
104 **BROUGHTON SUNPEARL** 13
402 **BROUGHTONS ADMIRAL** 9
480 **BROUGHTONS BEAR** (IRE) 8
273 **BROUGHTONS COMPASS** 5
355 **BROUGHTONS FLARE** (IRE) 2
104 **BROUGHTONS GOLD** 14
242 **BROUGHTONS REVIVAL** C 126
480 **BROUGHTONS RHYTHM** 9
516 **BROWN DIAMOND** (IRE) C 56
94 **BROWN EYED GIRL** 32
465 **BROWN EYED HONEY** C 85
379 **BROWN EYES BLUE** (IRE) 10
375 **BROWN HONEY** 3
251 **BRUISA** 45
480 **BRUMMIE BOYS** (IRE) 10
150 **BRUNCH** 27
286 **BRUNEL CHARM** 16
94 **BRUNEL'S BOY** 33
422 **BRUNNERA** 60
515 **BRUSHED UP** 3
179 **BRUSHING** C 26
272 **BRUSHWORK** 6
170 **BRUTALAB** 13
321 **BRUTE FORCE** 2
413 **BRUXCALINA** (FR) C 95
291 **BRUYERE** (FR) 3
83 **BRYDEN BOY** (IRE) 6
153 **BRYHER** 20
439 **BRYNELLO** (FR) 38
318 **BUBBLE AND SQUEAK** 2
168 **BUBBLES ARCADE** 2
395 **BUBBLES OF GOLD** (IRE) 5
228 **BUBBLING UP** (IRE) 50
370 **BUCCANEERS VAULT** (IRE) 2
547 **BUCEPHALUS** (GER) 36
365 **BUCK ASPEN** F 139
448 **BUCK BRAVO** (IRE) 2
356 **BUCK CASSIDY** (IRE) 16

18 **BUCK'S BEAUTIFUL** (FR) 1
392 **BUCK'S BILLIONAIRE** (FR) 31
221 **BUCK'S BIN'S** (IRE) 16
594 **BUCKBORU** (IRE) 3
526 **BUCKHORN GEORGE** 9
304 **BUCKINGHAM** (IRE) 4
524 **BUCKLED** 4
496 **BUCKO'S BOY** 10
557 **BUDANOVA** 4
463 **BUDDHA SCHEME** (IRE) 13
363 **BUDDING ROBIN** (IRE) 11
1 **BUFFALO BALLET** 7
401 **BUG BOY** (IRE) 1
444 **BUGLER BOB** (IRE) 7
563 **BUGZ BUNNY** 26
272 **BUKHTURI** (IRE) 29
173 **BUILDING BRIDGES** 6
392 **BUILDMEUPBUTTERCUP** 32
29 **BULLACE** 94
7 **BULLDOZER** (IRE) 99
101 **BULLFINCH** 22
378 **BULLFROG** (IRE) 24
98 **BULLINGTON BOY** (FR) 6
184 **BULLION** (FR) 9
212 **BULLIONAIRE** (IRE) 12
528 **BULLS HEAD** (IRE) 3
275 **BULLSEMPIRE** (IRE) 3
508 **BUMBLE BAY** 3
150 **BUMBLEDOM** 4
281 **BUMBLEKITE** 1
221 **BUN DORAN** (IRE) 17
76 **BUNDITTEN** (IRE) C 54
255 **BUNGEE JUMP** (IRE) 4
94 **BUNGLE BEE** (IRE) 34
185 **BUNGLE BILLY** (IRE) 3
370 **BUNIANN** (IRE) 3
331 **BUONAROTTI BOY** (IRE) 4
162 **BURANO BOY** (IRE) 24
57 **BURAUQ** 4
268 **BURBANK** (IRE) 20
249 **BURDIGALA** (IRE) 3
339 **BURFORD BROWN** 4
403 **BURGESS DREAM** (IRE) 2
77 **BURGUILLOS** 5
81 **BURGUNDY** (IRE) 2
251 **BURADAN** (FR) 6
29 **BURIRAM** (FR) 9
360 **BURLINGTON BERT** (FR) 1
175 **BURN SOME DUST** (IRE) 9
249 **BURNAGE BOY** (IRE) 10
192 **BURNING** (IRE) 33
419 **BURNING DAWN** (USA) F 46
493 **BURNING ISSUES** (IRE) 9
121 **BURNING SUN** (IRE) 33
392 **BURNING VICTORY** (FR) 33
315 **BURREN WALK** 13
493 **BURROWS DIAMOND** (FR) 10
268 **BURROWS EDGE** (FR) 21
583 **BURROWS PARK** (FR) 6
392 **BURROWS SAINT** (FR) 34
317 **BURROWS SEESIDE** (FR) 82
212 **BURROWS TREAT** (FR) 13
73 **BURSEA LADY** 28
315 **BURTON ASH** F 14
583 **BURTONS WELL** (IRE) 7
81 **BURTONWOOD** 3
30 **BUSHTUCKER TRIAL** (IRE) 14
444 **BUSINESS** (FR) 25

550 **CAPPANANTY CON** 6
415 **CAPPARATTIN** 1
280 **CAPPELLA FELLA** (IRE) 15
103 **CAPRICE DES DIEUX** (FR) 46
308 **CAPRICIA** (IRE) 11
19 **CAPRICIOUS** 14
378 **CAPRICORN PRINCE** 26
547 **CAPRIOLETTE** (IRE) 8
335 **CAPTAIN AULMES** (FR) 3
395 **CAPTAIN BIGGLES** (IRE) 12
221 **CAPTAIN BLACKPEARL** 18
439 **CAPTAIN BONNY** 39
405 **CAPTAIN CATTISTOCK** 27
484 **CAPTAIN CHAOS** (IRE) 25
304 **CAPTAIN CLARET** 29
5 **CAPTAIN CORCORAN** (IRE) 13
81 **CAPTAIN CORELLI** (IRE) 21
363 **CAPTAIN DINOSAUR** (IRE) 13
214 **CAPTAIN DION** 4
212 **CAPTAIN DRAKE** (IRE) 14
163 **CAPTAIN HADDOCK** (IRE) 11
49 **CAPTAIN HELMET** 64
189 **CAPTAIN IVAN** (IRE) 9
444 **CAPTAIN JAMESON** (IRE) 8
392 **CAPTAIN KANGAROO** (IRE) 38
207 **CAPTAIN MARMALADE** (IRE) 3
365 **CAPTAIN MC** (IRE) 7
493 **CAPTAIN MOIRETTE** (FR) 11
69 **CAPTAIN MOORHOUSE** (IRE) 5
368 **CAPTAIN MOWBRAY** 9
15 **CAPTAIN PEAKY** 5
110 **CAPTAIN REDBEARD** (IRE) 5
234 **CAPTAIN REVELATION** 9
141 **CAPTAIN RYAN** 1
498 **CAPTAIN SEDGWICK** (IRE) 3
334 **CAPTAIN SPEAKING** (FR) 5
214 **CAPTAIN ST LUCIFER** 43
402 **CAPTAIN TOM CAT** (IRE) 12
572 **CAPTAIN TOMMY** (IRE) 6
268 **CAPTAIN WOODIE** (IRE) 26
145 **CAPTAIN ZEBO** (IRE) 2
189 **CAPTAINS RUN** (IRE) 10
169 **CAPTON** 10
526 **CAPTURED MY HEART** 11
244 **CARA KATHERINE** (IRE) 26
547 **CARADOC** (IRE) 9
251 **CARAMELISED** 152
63 **CARANBOLA** C 2
422 **CARAVAN OF HOPE** (IRE) 2
510 **CARD HIGH** (IRE) 2
576 **CARDIFF BAY** 11
338 **CARDIGAN BAY** (FR) 4
386 **CARDRONA** C 34
309 **CARDS** C 20
305 **CARDSHARP** 7
572 **CARDY** (IRE) 7
392 **CAREFULLY SELECTED** (IRE) 39
349 **CARIBBEAN SPRING** (IRE) 2
268 **CARIBEAN BOY** (FR) 27
439 **CARIBENO** 15
346 **CARLA ERANGEY** (IRE) 16
401 **CARLA KOALA** 2
548 **CARLEEN** 3
447 **CARLINGFORD PRINCE** (IRE) 2
75 **CARLITOS BAY** (IRE) 1
503 **CARLO BIRAGHI** (IRE) 2
75 **CARLO ROCKS** (IRE) 3
483 **CARLOS FELIX** (IRE) 32

545 **CARLOVIAN** 3
310 **CARLOW BOY** (IRE) 4
338 **CARLOW FARMER** (IRE) 5
299 **CARMELA SOPRANO** 31
106 **CARMENERE** 12
183 **CARNAGE** 5
188 **CARNIVAL ROSE** 4
496 **CARNTOP** 11
192 **CARNWENNAN** (IRE) 4
488 **CARO DES FLOS** (FR) 1
388 **CAROLE'S DESTRIER** 5
393 **CAROLE'S TEMPLER** 5
539 **CAROLINE'S QUEST** (IRE) 26
388 **CAROLINES CHARM** (IRE) 6
198 **CARP KID** (IRE) 4
576 **CARPOOL** (IRE) 12
12 **CARRAUNTOOHIL** (IRE) F 12
281 **CARRIAGE CLOCK** 11
526 **CARRICK ROADS** (IRE) 12
593 **CARRIED AWAY** 2
26 **CARRIESMATIC** 20
496 **CARRIG COPPER** (IRE) 12
365 **CARRIGEEN ROSE** (IRE) 15
490 **CARRIGMOORNA MATT** (IRE) 1
411 **CARROLLS MILAN** (IRE) 17
356 **CARRY ON** 17
323 **CARTES** 1
216 **CARTRON** (IRE) 5
299 **CARVELAS** (IRE) 3
329 **CARVELLE'S CUTTER** 1
416 **CARYS' COMMODITY** 11
34 **CASA COMIGO** (IRE) 5
378 **CASA LOUPI** 131
221 **CASA TALL** (FR) 19
443 **CASABLANCA KID** (IRE) 6
268 **CASABLANCA MIX** (FR) 28
7 **CASARUAN** 100
193 **CASCADING** C 8
547 **CASCATA** (IRE) C 80
268 **CASCOVA** (IRE) 29
7 **CASE KEY** 17
7 **CASEMENT** (IRE) 18
260 **CASH AGAIN** (FR) 2
392 **CASH BACK** (FR) 40
7 **CASH N CARRIE** (IRE) 19
545 **CASH TO ASH** (IRE) 4
7 **CASHEL** (IRE) 20
513 **CASIET** 2
169 **CASILLI** 55
110 **CASIMIR DU CLOS** (FR) 6
49 **CASINA DI NOTTE** (IRE) 3
365 **CASK MATE** (IRE) 16
405 **CASKO D'AIRY** (FR) 28
62 **CASO DO LAGO** (IRE) 8
592 **CASPERS COURT** (IRE) 1
7 **CASPIAN PRINCE** (IRE) 21
286 **CASPIAN QUEEN** (IRE) 17
163 **CASSIDY JO** (IRE) 12
170 **CASSIQUE LADY** (IRE) G 102
532 **CASSIS DE REINE** 2
505 **CASSIVELLAUNUS** (IRE) 2
49 **CASSOWARY** (IRE) 65
170 **CASSY O** (IRE) 103
363 **CAST IN GREY** (IRE) 14
548 **CASTANA DIA** (IRE) 28
257 **CASTANEA** 5
67 **CASTASHADOW** 4
546 **CASTCARRIE** (IRE) 3

321 **CASTELO** (IRE) 3
516 **CASTING SHADOWS** 57
132 **CASTING SPELLS** 4
121 **CASTING VOTE** (IRE) 34
21 **CASTLE NORTH** (IRE) 2
230 **CASTLE ON A CLOUD** (IRE) 8
500 **CASTLE QUARTER** (IRE) 2
338 **CASTLE ROBIN** (IRE) 6
452 **CASTLE RUSHEN** (IRE) 7
392 **CASTLEBAWN WEST** (IRE) 41
222 **CASTLEDHEM** (IRE) 5
480 **CASTLEGRACE ROSE** (IRE) 11
169 **CASTLEHILL LAD** 56
260 **CASTLEHILL RETREAT** 38
17 **CASTLEINTHESAND** (IRE) 66
508 **CASTLELYONS** (IRE) 4
280 **CASTLERA TESS** 1
458 **CASTLETOWN** (FR) 3
512 **CASTLETROY** (IRE) 34
133 **CASUAL CAVALIER** (IRE) 4
101 **CASUAL REPLY** 3
128 **CASUAL SMILE** F 79
29 **CASUARINA** 95
576 **CASWELL BAY** 13
305 **CAT O' NINE TAILS** F 49
77 **CAT ROYALE** (IRE) 6
455 **CAT SIX** (USA) F 4
455 **CAT SIX** (USA) C 13
405 **CAT TIGER** (FR) 29
402 **CATAMARAN DU SEUIL** (FR) 13
309 **CATAPULT** 7
512 **CATBELLS** (IRE) C 38
14 **CATCH ME NOT** 7
464 **CATCH MY BREATH** 3
526 **CATCH THE CUBAN** 13
547 **CATCH THE MOON** (IRE) C 81
552 **CATCHAMAT** 1
289 **CATCHIN TIME** (IRE) 2
422 **CATCHLINE** (USA) C 61
83 **CATCHMEIFYOUCAN** (IRE) 8
572 **CATELINE** (IRE) 8
309 **CATFISH** (IRE) F 21
378 **CATH THE GREAT** (IRE) 132
452 **CATHAL'S STAR** 8
48 **CATHEADANS FIYAH** 2
48 **CATHEADANS FURY** 3
84 **CATHERINE BAY** 21
337 **CATIVO RAGAZZO** 2
313 **CATLIN** 3
418 **CATLOW** (IRE) 6
242 **CAUSA PROXIMA** (FR) C 127
128 **CAUSTIC LOVE** (IRE) 7
588 **CAVALRY** 4
381 **CAVALRY SCOUT** (IRE) 8
234 **CAVE TOP** (IRE) 10
448 **CAVEAT EMPTOR** (IRE) 1
524 **CAVENTARA** 6
424 **CAVOK** (IRE) 10
234 **CAWTHORNE** 11
170 **CAWTHORNE LAD** 16
254 **CAYENNE PEPPER** 85
166 **CAYIRLI** (FR) 2
301 **CAYUGA** 2
243 **CEARA BE** (IRE) 3
172 **CECCO BRAVO** 12
370 **CECE CEYLON** 34
225 **CECI WELLS** 36
439 **CEDAR CAGE** 16

295 **CEDAR HILL** (IRE) 3
188 **CEDAR'S STARS** 61
242 **CEDRIC MORRIS** (IRE) 128
584 **CELERITY** (IRE) 4
465 **CELESTIAL BLISS** 41
242 **CELESTIAL BOW** (IRE) F 129
405 **CELESTIAL FORCE** (IRE) 30
431 **CELESTIAL MAGIC** 4
254 **CELESTIAL OBJECT** 86
128 **CELESTIAL WOOD** (IRE) 80
323 **CELESTIAL WOODS** (USA) F 21
97 **CELESTIN** (FR) 31
97 **CELESTISSIME** (FR) 7
228 **CELESTRAN** 53
184 **CELLAR VIE** 11
461 **CELMA DES BOIS** (FR) 4
104 **CELSIUS** (IRE) 2
107 **CELTIC ART** (FR) 14
368 **CELTIC ARTISAN** (IRE) 10
107 **CELTIC CLASSIC** (IRE) 2
305 **CELTIC FILLY** (IRE) C 147
463 **CELTIC FLAMES** (IRE) 16
409 **CELTIC HIGH KING** (IRE) 23
327 **CELTIC JOY** (IRE) 10
309 **CELTIC MIST** (IRE) 22
221 **CELTIC RISING** (IRE) 20
313 **CELTIC SIXPENCE** (IRE) G 12
395 **CELTIC TARA** 13
323 **CELTRA** (IRE) 22
228 **CEMHAAN** 54
1 **CENTENIER** (FR) 9
577 **CENTRAL CITY** (IRE) 16
552 **CENTRAL FLAME** 2
200 **CENTREOFEXCELLENCE** (IRE) 1
121 **CENTURY DREAM** (IRE) 4
583 **CEPAGE** (FR) 8
251 **CEPHALONIE** (USA) C 153
94 **CERTAIN LAD** 4
451 **CERTAINLY RED** 1
39 **CERTIFY** (USA) C 137
517 **CERTRAL** C 12
480 **CERVARO MIX** (FR) 12
576 **CESAR COLLONGES** (FR) 14
395 **CESAR DU GOUET** (FR) 13
388 **CESAR ET ROSALIE** (FR) 7
563 **CESIFIRE** (FR) 27
484 **CH'TI DIAMOND** (FR) 26
484 **CH'TIBELLO** (FR) 27
6 **CHACHAMAIDEE** (IRE) C 128
392 **CHACUN POUR SOI** (FR) 42
511 **CHAI YO POWER** 33
474 **CHAIN OF BEACONS** 1
378 **CHAIN SMOKER** 20
511 **CHAIRMAN POWER** 34
94 **CHAIRMANOFTHEBOARD** (IRE) 5
224 **CHALIS** 5
242 **CHALK STREAM** 130
150 **CHALLET** (IRE) 28
523 **CHALLOW** (IRE) 2
251 **CHALLOW HILLS** (USA) C 154
140 **CHALOSSE** F 25
29 **CHAMADE** 44
97 **CHAMAILLE IRE** 32
583 **CHAMBARD** (FR) 9
321 **CHAMOMILE** 4
268 **CHAMP** (IRE) 30
367 **CHAMP AYR** 3
170 **CHAMPAGNE ANGEL** (IRE) 104

200 **CHAMPAGNE CASTLE** (IRE) 2
371 **CHAMPAGNE CHAMP** 3
539 **CHAMPAGNE CHASER** 27
221 **CHAMPAGNE CITY** 21
473 **CHAMPAGNE COURT** (IRE) 8
365 **CHAMPAGNE DIVA** 17
170 **CHAMPAGNE FOUNTAIN** 105
153 **CHAMPAGNE IDEAS** (IRE) 4
254 **CHAMPAGNE IZZY** 9
446 **CHAMPAGNE MIST** (IRE) 7
146 **CHAMPAGNE MONDAYS** 7
268 **CHAMPAGNE MYSTERY** (IRE) 31
338 **CHAMPAGNE NOIR** (IRE) 7
268 **CHAMPAGNE PLATINUM** (IRE) 32
559 **CHAMPAGNE RULES** 2
499 **CHAMPAGNE SUPANOVA** (IRE) 26
299 **CHAMPAGNE VINTAGE** (IRE) 4
411 **CHAMPAGNE WELL** (IRE) 18
416 **CHAMPAGNE WILDE** (IRE) 12
395 **CHAMPAGNESUPEROVER** (IRE) 15
435 **CHAMPERS ON ICE** (IRE) 4
379 **CHAMPION BROGIE** (IRE) 3
48 **CHAMPION CHASE** (FR) 4
44 **CHAMPS DE REVES** 3
534 **CHANCE A TUNE** (IRE) 17
405 **CHANCE FINALE** (FR) 31
189 **CHANCE IT** (IRE) 11
370 **CHANCE OF BUBBLES** (IRE) G 38
110 **CHANCEANOTHERFIVE** (IRE) 7
463 **CHANCEITON** (IRE) 17
446 **CHANCEUX** (IRE) 8
503 **CHANELL ECLIPSE** 14
97 **CHANGING SKIES** (IRE) F 83
422 **CHANKAYA** 19
7 **CHANNEL PACKET** 22
518 **CHANTECLER** 4
516 **CHANTILLY CREAM** (IRE) F 58
1 **CHANTING HILL** (IRE) 10
268 **CHANTRY HOUSE** (IRE) 33
114 **CHAPATI** (FR) 1
452 **CHAPEL STILE** (IRE) 9
87 **CHAPLIN BAY** (IRE) 6
496 **CHAPMANSHYPE** (IRE) 13
305 **CHAQUIRAS** (USA) C 148
14 **CHARBEL** (IRE) 8
254 **CHARCON** (IRE) 10
465 **CHARDONEIGH** 42
98 **CHARES** (GER) 24
240 **CHARLEMAGNE DIVA** C 17
107 **CHARLEMAINE** (IRE) 15
93 **CHARLES MOLSON** 1
290 **CHARLIE ALPHA** (IRE) 3
286 **CHARLIE ARTHUR** (IRE) 3
365 **CHARLIE BASSETT** (IRE) 125
132 **CHARLIE D** (USA) 5
472 **CHARLIE FELLOWES** (IRE) 26
496 **CHARLIE GEORGE** (IRE) 14
167 **CHARLIE MON** (IRE) 3
365 **CHARLIE SIRIONG** 18
205 **CHARLIE SNOW ANGEL** 2
16 **CHARLIE'S QUEEN** (IRE) C 40
518 **CHARLOTTE ROSINA** C 34
1 **CHARM OFFENSIVE** (FR) 11
184 **CHARMANT** (FR) 12
368 **CHARMING DREAM** (FR) 11
291 **CHARMING KID** 4
228 **CHARMING ROSE** 55
537 **CHARMING SPIRIT** (IRE) 43

463 **CHARMIX** (FR) 18
29 **CHARTERED** 10
409 **CHARTREUSE** (FR) F 125
346 **CHASAMAX** (IRE) 34
251 **CHASE THE LADY** (USA) F 155
206 **CHASE THE WIND** (IRE) 3
409 **CHASING ICE** (IRE) C 126
254 **CHASING THE DAWN** 87
472 **CHASTUSHKA** (IRE) F 27
367 **CHATEAU D'IF** 30
175 **CHATEAU MARMONT** (IRE) 10
99 **CHATEAU PEAPOD** 13
452 **CHATEAU ROBIN** (IRE) 10
156 **CHATELIER** (FR) 5
94 **CHATTRI** 84
14 **CHAZZA** (IRE) 9
522 **CHEAP JACK** 1
241 **CHEAP N CHIC** F 11
126 **CHEAT** (IRE) 1
444 **CHEBSEY BEAU** 9
338 **CHECKITOUT** (IRE) 8
83 **CHEDDLETON** 9
230 **CHEEKY CHES** 9
555 **CHEEKY RASCAL** (IRE) 2
450 **CHEEKY RICCO** 1
144 **CHEER'S DELBOY** (IRE) 8
325 **CHEERS JD** (IRE) 1
548 **CHEESE AND WINE** 17
274 **CHEF D'EQUIPE** (FR) 12
402 **CHEF DE TROUPE** (FR) 14
392 **CHEF DES OBEAUX** (FR) 43
73 **CHELLALLA** F 86
356 **CHELSEA FLYER** (IRE) 18
409 **CHELSEA ROSE** (IRE) C 127
356 **CHELSEA SHOWCASE** 23
356 **CHELSEA'S BOY** (IRE) 19
339 **CHELSEY JAYNE** (IRE) C 52
538 **CHENCHIKOVA** (IRE) F 21
104 **CHENG GONG** 3
389 **CHENILLE** (IRE) 8
378 **CHEQUE EN BLANC** (FR) 28
29 **CHEQUERED VIEW** 12
29 **CHERCHEZ** 96
89 **CHERISH** (FR) 81
365 **CHEROKEE BILL** 19
6 **CHEROKEE MIST** (CAN) 42
228 **CHEROKEE TRAIL** (USA) 56
516 **CHERRINGTON** (IRE) C 59
564 **CHERRY COLA** 3
409 **CHERRY HINTON** F 128
499 **CHERRY MALOTTE** F 43
79 **CHERRY PRINCESS** 4
169 **CHERRYCOMBE-ROW** C 57
519 **CHERUBIN DE PAIL** (FR) 1
36 **CHESHIRE** 16
7 **CHESS MOVE** (IRE) 23
424 **CHESS PLAYER** (IRE) 11
391 **CHESTERFIELD** (IRE) 5
493 **CHESTERMAN** (IRE) 12
331 **CHESTNUT PETE** 5
89 **CHETAN** 12
526 **CHETWYND** (IRE) C 39
512 **CHEVALIER JET** (IRE) G 14
512 **CHEZ CASTEL MAIL** (FR) 9
405 **CHEZ HANS** (GER) 32
395 **CHEZ HANS** (IRE) 16
164 **CHIAVARI** (IRE) 8
367 **CHIAVE DI VOLTA** 4

117 **CHIBOLA** (ARG) C 68
276 **CHIC NAME** (FR) 2
305 **CHICA BONITA** 149
547 **CHICA BOOM** 82
152 **CHICA DEL DIA** 17
265 **CHICA RAPIDA** 2
315 **CHICAGO DOLL** 17
315 **CHICAGO GUY** 18
170 **CHICAGO MAY** (IRE) 17
511 **CHICHESTER** 35
452 **CHIDSWELL** (IRE) 11
386 **CHIEF BRODY** 2
192 **CHIEFOFCHIEFS** 1
211 **CHIEFTAIN'S CHOICE** (IRE) 4
140 **CHIFA** (IRE) 22
422 **CHIGUN** F 62
17 **CHIL CHIL** 10
17 **CHILD STAR** 67
254 **CHILDERS** 88
194 **CHILL IN THE WOOD** 1
439 **CHILL OUT** (IRE) 40
129 **CHILLI FILLI** 7
577 **CHILTERN HILLS** (IRE) G 17
499 **CHIM CHIMNEY** 44
539 **CHIMES OF DYLAN** (IRE) 28
87 **CHINA CHERUB** F 41
87 **CHINA CHERUB** F 48
462 **CHINA EXCELS** 2
328 **CHINA FLOWER** (IRE) 2
21 **CHINA LILY** (USA) F 27
486 **CHINACONNECTION** (IRE) F 35
538 **CHINDIT** (IRE) 22
251 **CHINDIT** (IRE) 156
534 **CHINENSIS** (IRE) 18
7 **CHINESE ALPHABET** 24
427 **CHINESE SPIRIT** (IRE) 1
315 **CHINESE WHISPERER** (FR) 141
29 **CHINESE WHITE** (IRE) C 97
409 **CHINTZ** (IRE) F 129
388 **CHINWAG** 8
388 **CHIRICO VALLIS** (FR) 9
321 **CHITRA** 5
384 **CHIVALRY** 23
505 **CHIVERS** (IRE) 3
268 **CHIVES** 35
546 **CHLOE'S COURT** (IRE) 4
299 **CHLOELLIE** 5
16 **CHLOHOLTEEN** 41
19 **CHOCCO STAR** (IRE) 4
579 **CHOCKS AWAY** (FR) 4
486 **CHOCOHOLIC** 23
444 **CHOCOLAAT HEER** 26
528 **CHOCOLAT NOIR** (IRE) 4
340 **CHOCOLATE BOX** (IRE) 5
251 **CHOCOLATE HILLS** (FR) F 47
409 **CHOCTAW RIDGE** (IRE) 24
246 **CHOIX DES ARMES** (FR) 2
128 **CHOOKIE DUNEDIN** 8
6 **CHOOSE ME** (C 129
169 **CHOOSEY** (IRE) 11
576 **CHOOSEYOURWEAPON** (IRE) 15
24 **CHOP CHOP** (IRE) 3
337 **CHORAL MUSIC** 3
256 **CHORAL SINGER** C 33
242 **CHORAL WORK** 48
148 **CHOSEN FLAME** (IRE) 2
444 **CHOSEN MARK** (IRE) 54
315 **CHOSEN PATH** (IRE) 19

577 **CHOSEN SHANT** (IRE) 18
30 **CHOSEN STAR** 17
17 **CHOSEN TARGET** 133
81 **CHOSEN WORLD** 1
539 **CHOZEN** (IRE) 29
526 **CHRISTMAS IN APRIL** (FR) 15
1 **CHRISTMAS IN USA** (FR) 12
426 **CHRISTMAS MORNING** (IRE) 18
426 **CHRISTMAS NIGHT** 2
322 **CHRISTOPHER ROBIN** (IRE) 3
405 **CHRISTOPHER WOOD** (IRE) 33
10 **CHROMIUM** 35
356 **CHTI BALKO** (FR) 20
117 **CHURCHILL BAY** 69
70 **CHURCHTOWN GLEN** (IRE) 1
273 **CHUTZPAH** (IRE) 1
356 **CHUVELO** (IRE) 21
384 **CIDER APPLE** 54
261 **CIDER KILT** (IRE) 7
392 **CIEL DE NEIGE** (FR) 44
499 **CIGARETTESNALCOHOL** (IRE) 3
6 **CIGOLI** (IRE) 43
392 **CILAOS EMERY** (FR) 45
480 **CILAOS GLACE** (FR) 13
405 **CILL ANNA** (IRE) 34
198 **CILLIAN'S WELL** (IRE) 5
170 **CILLUIRID** (IRE) 18
270 **CIMETTA** 5
570 **CINDY LOOPER** 12
432 **CINEVATOR** (IRE) 1
101 **CINNABAR** 24
518 **CINZENTO** (IRE) 5
49 **CIPANGO** 26
510 **CIRCUIT** 3
98 **CIRCUS COUTURE** (IRE) 7
409 **CIRCUS MAXIMUS** (IRE) 3
6 **CIRQUE ROYAL** 4
251 **CIRRUS** 157
530 **CITRON** F 15
535 **CITTA D'ORO** 1
305 **CITY CHIC** (USA) C 150
29 **CITY CODE** 98
411 **CITY DERBY** (IRE) 19
90 **CITY DIVA** 2
239 **CITY ESCAPE** (IRE) 12
218 **CITY FLAME** 2
39 **CITY GLAM** (ARG) F 138
545 **CITY GOLD** 27
308 **CITY NEVER SLEEPS** (IRE) 13
326 **CITY OF LOVE** 1
472 **CITY ON SEA** F 28
451 **CITY TOUR** 2
244 **CITY VAULTS GIRL** (IRE) C 65
39 **CITY WALK** (IRE) 58
94 **CITY WANDERER** (IRE) 6
251 **CITYZEN SERG** (IRE) 48
82 **CIVIL ENSIGN** (FR) 1
419 **CIVILITY CAT** (USA) F 47
49 **CLABA DI SAN JORE** (IRE) C 66
75 **CLABARE** 2
405 **CLAN DES OBEAUX** (FR) 35
1 **CLAN LEGEND** 3
437 **CLAN SPIRIT** 15
483 **CLAP YOUR HANDS** 5
512 **CLARA LUNA** (IRE) C 39
61 **CLARENDON** 3
394 **CLARENTINE** F 25
364 **CLAREYBLUE** (IRE) 28

305 **CLARIETTA** F 151
531 **CLARION** 3
89 **CLASHANISKA** (IRE) 13
409 **CLASS ACT** 25
26 **CLASS CLOWN** (IRE) 21
548 **CLASS IS PERMANENT** 29
173 **CLASSIC BEN** (IRE) 7
291 **CLASSIC CHARM** 5
402 **CLASSIC ESCAPE** (IRE) 15
17 **CLASSIC LORD** (GER) 134
196 **CLASSIC PURSUIT** 4
291 **CLASSIC STAR** 6
167 **CLASSIC TUNE** 4
38 **CLASSICAL MILANO** (IRE) 4
148 **CLASSICAL SOUND** (IRE) 7
171 **CLASSY CREWELLA** G 2
172 **CLASSY DAME** (IRE) 13
73 **CLASSY MOON** (IRE) 29
568 **CLATTERING FORD** (IRE) 7
205 **CLAUD AND GOLDIE** (IRE) 3
522 **CLAUDIA RANIERI** (IRE) 2
516 **CLAUDIUS SECUNDUS** (IRE) 13
491 **CLAVIERE** 7
128 **CLAY REGAZZONI** 81
543 **CLAYTON HALL** (IRE) 2
221 **CLEAR ON TOP** (IRE) 22
364 **CLEAR VOICE** (USA) G 29
295 **CLEARANCE** 7
89 **CLEARLY CAPABLE** (IRE) 14
547 **CLEGANE** 37
381 **CLEM** (IRE) 9
12 **CLEM A** 2
159 **CLEMENCIA** (IRE) 1
444 **CLEMENTO** (IRE) 10
94 **CLENAGHCASTLE LADY** (IRE) C 85
518 **CLEONTE** (IRE) 11
257 **CLEVEDON** (IRE) 6
402 **CLEVER AS A FOX** (IRE) 16
30 **CLEVER CANDY** 18
92 **CLEVER GIRL** (IRE) 29
465 **CLEVER TRICK** 43
83 **CLICK AND COLLECT** 10
128 **CLIFF BAY** (IRE) 9
91 **CLIFF FACE** (IRE) 2
439 **CLIFF WIND** 17
419 **CLIFFS OF CAPRI** 3
29 **CLIFFS OF DOONEEN** (IRE) 11
405 **CLIFFS OF DOVER** 36
545 **CLIFFTOP HEAVEN** 28
150 **CLIFTON DANCER** F 54
114 **CLIFTON ENCORE** (USA) G 2
511 **CLINICIAN** 36
17 **CLIP** 135
467 **CLIPPER LINE** (USA) C 1
7 **CLIPSHAM TIGER** (IRE) 25
251 **CLOAK OF SPIRITS** (IRE) 49
557 **CLOCKERS CORNER** (IRE) 5
305 **CLOG MAKER** (IRE) 50
26 **CLON COULIS** (IRE) 6
308 **CLONDALEE** (IRE) G 38
539 **CLONDAW ACE** (IRE) 30
484 **CLONDAW ANCHOR** (IRE) 28
397 **CLONDAW BANKER** (IRE) 3
382 **CLONDAW BERTIE** (IRE) 5
494 **CLONDAW BISTO** (IRE) 2
297 **CLONDAW CAITLIN** (IRE) 6
221 **CLONDAW CASTLE** (IRE) 23
331 **CLONDAW CIAN** (IRE) 6

411 **DAN GUN** (IRE) 24
405 **DAN McGRUE** (IRE) 42
132 **DANA FOREVER** (IRE) 26
94 **DANAMIGHT** (IRE) C 87
539 **DANBORU** (IRE) 35
17 **DANCE AT NIGHT** 138
117 **DANCE FEVER** (IRE) 27
170 **DANCE KING** 23
1 **DANCE OF FIRE** 16
321 **DANCE OF LIGHT** (USA) F 19
272 **DANCE ON THE HILL** (IRE) C 80
541 **DANCE TO PARIS** 4
569 **DANCED EVERY DANCE** (IRE) 8
229 **DANCEWITHTHEWIND** (IRE) 3
150 **DANCIN BOY** 8
242 **DANCIN INTHESTREAM** 55
101 **DANCING APPROACH** 27
316 **DANCING DORIS** 7
439 **DANCING DUCHESS** (IRE) F 41
446 **DANCING EMILY** (IRE) G 12
306 **DANCING EMILY** (IRE) G 17
557 **DANCING FEET** (IRE) 28
197 **DANCING GIRL** (IRE) F 7
265 **DANCING GREY** 3
101 **DANCING HARRY** (IRE) 28
402 **DANCING IN THE SKY** (IRE) 20
364 **DANCING JEST** (IRE) C 47
94 **DANCING JO** 7
285 **DANCING LILLY** 4
518 **DANCING MASTER** (IRE) 35
295 **DANCING MOON** (IRE) F 48
211 **DANCING PRIMO** C 38
413 **DANCING RAVE** 16
131 **DANCING SHADOW** (IRE) 6
15 **DANCING SPEED** (IRE) 7
422 **DANCING TO WIN** 65
486 **DANCINGINTHESAND** (IRE) 24
291 **DANCINGINTHEWOODS** 42
233 **DANCINGWITH STORMS** (IRE) 14
346 **DANDE** (IRE) 17
404 **DANDIZETTE** (IRE) 7
254 **DANDJIRA** 13
388 **DANDOLO DU GITE** (FR) 13
338 **DANDRIDGE** 10
14 **DANDY DAN** (IRE) 13
431 **DANDY LASS** (IRE) 5
499 **DANDY MAESTRO** 45
392 **DANDY MAG** (FR) 52
170 **DANDY STORY** (IRE) 108
520 **DANDY TIMES** (IRE) 3
543 **DANDY'S ANGEL** (IRE) 11
465 **DANDY'S BEANO** (IRE) 7
191 **DANDYS GOLD** (IRE) 6
142 **DANECASE** 7
465 **DANEGA** C 87
215 **DANEHILL DESTINY** F 21
537 **DANEHILL'S DREAM** (IRE) C 136
170 **DANGEROFFIZZ** (IRE) 109
180 **DANGEROUS DUO** (IRE) C 43
301 **DANGEROUS ENDS** 3
312 **DANGEROUS GROUND** (IRE) 2
73 **DANGEROUS MOONLITE** (IRE) F 87
394 **DANGLYDONTASK** 4
73 **DANIEL DERONDA** 30
73 **DANIEL DRAVOT** 5
150 **DANIELSFLYER** (IRE) 9
315 **DANKING** 142
405 **DANNY KIRWAN** (IRE) 43

73 **DANNY OCEAN** (IRE) 31
405 **DANNY WHIZZBANG** (IRE) 44
103 **DANS LA LUNE** (FR) 1
576 **DANS LE VENT** (FR) 21
379 **DANSE DE LA LUNE** (IRE) 11
405 **DANSE IDOL** (IRE) 45
563 **DANSEPO** 5
16 **DANTE'S VIEW** (IRE) 11
422 **DANTORA** 66
304 **DANVILLE** 58
76 **DANYAH** (IRE) 22
170 **DANZAN** (IRE) 24
7 **DANZENA** 28
7 **DANZENO** 29
83 **DAPA LAD** (IRE) 15
268 **DAPHNE DU CLOS** (FR) 41
563 **DAPHNE MAY** 40
191 **DAPPER MAN** (IRE) 7
228 **DARAIN** 60
214 **DARALIMI** (FR) 6
339 **DARANOVA** (IRE) 8
59 **DARAZ LEGACY** 2
20 **DARCY WARD** (FR) 4
47 **DARE** 13
378 **DAREBIN** (GER) 30
317 **DARES TO DREAM** (IRE) 12
117 **DARGEL** (IRE) 2
572 **DARGIANNINI** (IRE) 10
104 **DARING GUEST** (IRE) 5
230 **DARIUS DES SOURCES** (FR) 10
338 **DARIYA** (USA) 11
560 **DARK AND DANGEROUS** (IRE) 9
76 **DARK CRUSADER** (IRE) C 56
427 **DARK CRYSTAL** 2
569 **DARK DAISY** (IRE) G 9
27 **DARK DEFENDER** 4
383 **DARK DEVIL** (IRE) 3
274 **DARK EPISODE** (IRE) 15
461 **DARK FLAME** (IRE) 6
305 **DARK HEART** 55
304 **DARK ILLUSION** 59
367 **DARK IMAGE** 32
170 **DARK JEDI** (IRE) 25
286 **DARK KRIS** (IRE) 19
251 **DARK LADY** 52
128 **DARK LOCHNAGAR** (USA) 12
347 **DARK MOONLIGHT** (IRE) 15
29 **DARK MOTIVE** 100
180 **DARK OPTIMIST** (IRE) 29
107 **DARK PHOENIX** (IRE) 16
87 **DARK POET** 7
162 **DARK RED** (IRE) 3
305 **DARK REGARD** 56
49 **DARK SCIMITAR** (USA) 27
304 **DARK SHIFT** 60
146 **DARK SHOT** 6
464 **DARK SIDE DIVISION** 13
550 **DARK SIDE DREAM** 7
547 **DARK SILVER** (IRE) 43
485 **DARK SPEC** 3
547 **DARK SPECTRE** (IRE) 44
532 **DARK STORM** 3
305 **DARK VISION** (IRE) 11
429 **DARK WHITE** 21
409 **DARKEST** (IRE) 28
378 **DARKEST DAY** (IRE) 31
526 **DARLAC** (FR) 18
534 **DARLING ALKO** (IRE) 22

221 **DARLING DU LARGE** (FR) 30
405 **DARLING MALTAIX** (FR) 46
418 **DARLYN** 9
76 **DARRAAJ** (IRE) 23
528 **DARRY DESBOIS** (FR) 6
364 **DARSAN** (IRE) C 48
416 **DARSI IN THE PARK** (IRE) 19
289 **DARSI ROSE** (IRE) 3
529 **DARTINGTON** (IRE) 21
416 **DARTMOOR** (IRE) 20
117 **DARTRIX** C 71
186 **DARTUM TEMPUS** (IRE) 8
568 **DARWINA** 13
33 **DAS KAPITAL** 2
582 **DASCHAS** 8
92 **DASH OF BLUE** 5
176 **DASH OF SPICE** (IRE) 2
76 **DASH TO THE FRONT** C 57
473 **DASHEL DRASHER** 10
402 **DASHING PERK** 21
509 **DASHING ROGER** 8
320 **DASHING SPIRIT** (IRE) 14
17 **DASHING WILLOUGHBY** 13
17 **DAT IL DO** C 139
386 **DATA PROTECTION** 4
320 **DATA ROOM** 15
496 **DATSALRIGHTGINO** (GER) 17
228 **DAUNTLESS** 61
6 **DAVANTAGE** (FR) C 132
29 **DAVE DEXTER** 12
288 **DAVID JOHN** 1
28 **DAVID'S BEAUTY** (IRE) 1
365 **DAVY'S DILEMMA** 24
511 **DAVYDENKO** 4
185 **DAWAALEEB** (USA) 6
76 **DAWAAM** (USA) 5
36 **DAWAAWEEN** (IRE) 4
73 **DAWN BLAZE** 5
570 **DAWN BREAKING** 1
175 **DAWN LANDING** (IRE) 59
409 **DAWN PATROL** (IRE) 29
409 **DAWN RISING** (IRE) 30
331 **DAWN TREADER** (IRE) 7
261 **DAWN TROUPER** (IRE) 10
582 **DAWN VIEW** (IRE) 47
72 **DAWN'S LITTLE LADY** 1
364 **DAWNING** (IRE) 31
345 **DAWRY** (IRE) 2
241 **DAWSON CITY** 2
206 **DAY OF ROSES** (IRE) 5
363 **DAYDREAM AULMES** (FR) 15
121 **DAYMOOMA** F 76
305 **DAYROSE** F 155
73 **DAYS OF SUMMER** (IRE) C 88
135 **DAYS TO REMEMBER** 4
76 **DAYSAN** (USA) 24
371 **DAYTADAY** 35
278 **DAYTIME AHEAD** (IRE) 2
117 **DAYVILLE** (USA) F 72
21 **DAZACAM** 3
16 **DAZIBAO** (FR) 12
419 **DAZZLE DANCER** (IRE) C 15
485 **DAZZLING DAN** (IRE) 4
413 **DAZZLING DES** (IRE) 60
424 **DE BARLEY BASKET** (IRE) 14
589 **DE BENE ESSE** (IRE) 7
236 **DE BRUYNE HORSE** 6
539 **DE FORGOTTEN ONE** 36

7 **DI'S DILEMMA** C 32
378 **DIABLE DE SIVOLA** (FR) 34
268 **DIABLO DE ROUHET** (FR) 42
577 **DIABOLEO** (FR) 21
378 **DIAKALI** (FR) 35
409 **DIALAFARA** (FR) C 132
244 **DIAMIL** (IRE) 66
296 **DIAMINDA** (IRE) F 22
576 **DIAMON DES FLOS** (FR) 23
555 **DIAMOND BAY** 19
1 **DIAMOND BRIG** 17
468 **DIAMOND COTTAGE** 9
116 **DIAMOND DOUGAL** (IRE) 6
272 **DIAMOND FIFE** 81
411 **DIAMOND FORT** (IRE) 26
14 **DIAMOND GAIT** 14
405 **DIAMOND GUY** (FR) 48
150 **DIAMOND HAZE** (IRE) 56
392 **DIAMOND HILL** (IRE) 56
280 **DIAMOND JILL** (IRE) 13
509 **DIAMOND LADY** 1
422 **DIAMOND OASIS** 5
409 **DIAMOND RING** (IRE) 33
268 **DIAMOND RIVER** (IRE) 43
360 **DIAMOND ROAD** (IRE) 2
524 **DIAMOND ROCK** 8
488 **DIAMOND ROSE** 2
428 **DIAMOND RUBY** 26
30 **DIAMOND RUN** F 67
198 **DIAMOND SHOWER** (IRE) 7
16 **DIAMOND STAR** (IRE) F 42
463 **DIAMOND STATE** (IRE) 7
257 **DIAMOND VINE** (IRE) 8
532 **DIAMONDS AND RUST** 16
41 **DIAMONDS DREAM** 9
24 **DIAMONIQUE** 14
6 **DIBAJJ** (FR) C 135
244 **DICEBOX** (IRE) 28
413 **DICK DATCHERY** (IRE) 61
496 **DIDDLY DO** 18
315 **DIDONATO** (IRE) 25
222 **DIDTHEYLEAVEUOUTTO** (IRE) 8
405 **DIEGO DU CHARMIL** (FR) 49
317 **DIEU BENISSE** (FR) 15
121 **DIFFERENT** F 77
338 **DIGER DAUDAIE** (FR) 12
97 **DIGRESSION** (IRE) 33
103 **DIJLAH** F 47
97 **DILAG** (IRE) C 86
323 **DILAR** 23
319 **DILGURA** G 20
117 **DILIGENT HARRY** 73
10 **DILIGENT LADY** 36
45 **DILIGENT LASS** 8
465 **DILITHIUM** (FR) 45
244 **DILIYMI** (IRE) 29
543 **DILLY DILLY** (IRE) 3
461 **DILLY THE PINK** (IRE) 8
49 **DIMA** 28
524 **DIMPLE** (FR) 9
365 **DINARD ROSE** (IRE) 28
564 **DING DING** 5
315 **DINGO DOLLAR** (IRE) 26
534 **DINO BOY** (FR) 23
315 **DINO VELVET** (FR) 27
526 **DINOS BENEFIT** (IRE) 19
475 **DINSDALE** 9
29 **DIOCLES OF ROME** (IRE) 13

17 **DIOCLETIAN** (IRE) 14
362 **DIODORUS** (IRE) 4
365 **DIOL KER** (FR) 29
484 **DIOMEDE DES MOTTES** (FR) 32
274 **DIPLOMATE SIVOLA** (FR) 19
521 **DIRCHILL** (IRE) 3
179 **DIRECTORY** 2
29 **DIRTY DANCER** (FR) 47
577 **DIRTY DIANA** (FR) 22
555 **DIRTY RASCAL** (IRE) 3
365 **DIS DONC** (FR) 30
470 **DISARMING** (IRE) 6
276 **DISCKO DES PLAGES** (FR) 4
228 **DISCO FEVER** 63
254 **DISCORDANTLY** (IRE) 14
272 **DISCOTEQUE** (IRE) 82
6 **DISCOURSE** (USA) F 136
48 **DISCOVERY ISLAND** 48
256 **DISCREET HERO** 6
409 **DISCREET MARQ** (USA) C 133
352 **DISEY'S EDGE** 7
76 **DISPEL** F 58
180 **DISRUPTOR** (FR) 6
194 **DISTANT APPLAUSE** (IRE) 2
6 **DISTANT GODDESS** 49
516 **DISTANT THUNDER** (IRE) 17
90 **DISTANT UNIVERSE** 4
309 **DISTANT WATERS** F 24
73 **DISTINCTION** (IRE) 89
321 **DISTINCTIVE** C 20
378 **DISTINGO** (IRE) 36
318 **DISTURBING BEAUTY** 3
411 **DIV INE TARA** 27
16 **DIVA KAREEM** (IRE) 32
16 **DIVA ROCK** 33
16 **DIVA SPIRIT** (IRE) 13
413 **DIVERT** (IRE) F 100
465 **DIVINA GLORIA** (FR) 46
6 **DIVINE BLESSING** 50
212 **DIVINE CAYRAS** (IRE) G 17
437 **DIVINE CONNECTION** 16
242 **DIVINE CONSENT** 57
295 **DIVINE GIFT** (IRE) 7
511 **DIVINE HERALD** 108
420 **DIVINE MESSENGER** 5
458 **DIVINE PORT** (USA) 4
375 **DIVINE POWER** C 27
190 **DIVINE QUEEN** 17
268 **DIVINE SPEAR** (IRE) 44
547 **DIVINE SUMMER** (USA) 45
17 **DIVINE TOUCH** (FR) C 140
537 **DIVISIMO** C 137
503 **DIVISME** (USA) G 40
15 **DIXIELAND** (IRE) 8
416 **DJANGO DJANGO** (FR) 24
381 **DJARKEVI** (FR) 11
367 **DJUMAMA** (IRE) C 33
155 **DLTRIPLESEVEN** (IRE) 2
330 **DO IT FOR THY SEN** (IRE) 4
148 **DO NOT DISTURB** (IRE) 10
338 **DO WANNA KNOW** (IRE) 13
73 **DO YOU LOVE ME** (IRE) 32
327 **DO YOU THINK** 14
475 **DO YOUR JOB** (IRE) 10
327 **DOC PENFRO** 15
89 **DOC SPORTELLO** (IRE) 18
268 **DOCTE DINA** (FR) 45
159 **DOCTOR BROWN BEAR** (IRE) 14

221 **DOCTOR DEX** (IRE) 31
7 **DOCTOR JAZZ** (IRE) 33
340 **DOCTOR NUNO** 34
336 **DOCTOR PARKES** 2
562 **DOCTOR ZEN** (FR) 5
211 **DOCUMENTING** 1
390 **DODGY BOB** 3
14 **DOES HE KNOW** 15
484 **DOG OF WAR** (FR) 33
176 **DOGGED** 13
405 **DOGON** 50
405 **DOIN'WHATSHELIKES** (IRE) 51
388 **DOING FINE** (IRE) 16
269 **DOITFORTHEVILLAGE** (IRE) 7
148 **DOKTOR GLAZ** (FR) 11
6 **DOLCE STREGA** (IRE) C 137
392 **DOLCITA** (FR) 57
251 **DOLLA DOLLA BILL** (IRE) 54
221 **DOLLAR AND A DREAM** (IRE) 32
511 **DOLLAR BID** 40
327 **DOLLNAMIX** (FR) 16
76 **DOLLY COLMAN** (IRE) C 59
23 **DOLLY DANCER** (IRE) 7
111 **DOLLY DUPREE** 4
90 **DOLLY MCQUEEN** 5
523 **DOLLY'S DOT** (IRE) 3
299 **DOLLYWAGGON PIKE** 8
405 **DOLOS** (FR) 52
101 **DOLPHIN** 70
274 **DOLPHIN SQUARE** (IRE) 20
258 **DOLPHIN VILLAGE** (IRE) 3
29 **DOLPHIN VISTA** (IRE) 14
216 **DOM GARO CATELINE** (FR) 6
123 **DOMAINE DE L'ISLE** (FR) 3
25 **DOMINANNIE** (IRE) 1
480 **DOMINATEUR** (FR) 3
260 **DOMINIC'S GREY** 41
242 **DOMINO DARLING** 58
272 **DOMITIA** C 33
129 **DON JUAN DU GOUET** (FR) 8
283 **DON LAMI** (FR) 8
233 **DON'T ASK** 15
500 **DON'T BE SURPRISED** 4
365 **DON'T CROSS ME** (FR) 31
512 **DON'T CRY ABOUT IT** (IRE) 10
188 **DON'T CRY FOR ME** (USA) C 64
32 **DON'T DO IT** (IRE) 2
562 **DON'T FENCE ME IN** (IRE) 6
401 **DON'T GIVE UP** 3
87 **DON'T JOKE** 42
341 **DON'T JUMP GEORGE** (IRE) 2
56 **DON'T LAUGH AT ME** 4
534 **DON'T SHOUT** (IRE) 24
257 **DON'T STOP DANCING** (IRE) 30
392 **DON'T TELL ALLEN** (IRE) 58
321 **DON'T TELL CLAIRE** 11
227 **DON'T TELL KATE** (IRE) 11
499 **DON'TYOUWANTMEBABY** (IRE) 27
122 **DONALD DUX** (IRE) 5
378 **DONALD LLEWELLYN** 133
142 **DONATELLO MAIL** (FR) 9
101 **DONATIA** C 71
480 **DONLADD** (IRE) 16
94 **DONNA RAY** 39
524 **DONNA'S DELIGHT** (IRE) 10
230 **DONNA'S DIAMOND** (IRE) 11
568 **DONNACHIES GIRL** (IRE) 14
500 **DONNCHA** (IRE) 5

27 **DONNELLY'S RAINBOW** (IRE) 5	539 **DOVILS DATE** 39	239 **DREAMBOAT GIRL** (IRE) 14
14 **DONNIE BRASCO** (FR) 16	365 **DOWN ACE** F 32	305 **DREAMING BEAUTY** C 159
228 **DONNYBROOK** (IRE) 64	327 **DOWN BY THE SEA** (IRE) G 17	186 **DREAMING BLUE** 77
378 **DONNYTWOBUCKETS** (IRE) 37	327 **DOWN THE HIGHWAY** (IRE) 54	411 **DREAMING OF GLORY** (IRE) 28
49 **DONO** 29	58 **DOWN TO THE SEA** (FR) 3	169 **DREAMING OF STELLA** (IRE) C 60
344 **DONO DI DIO** 4	237 **DOWNE MILKING LANE** 1	547 **DREAMLOPER** (IRE) 46
203 **DONT BE ROBIN** (IRE) 1	466 **DOWNLOADTHEAPP** (IRE) 1	576 **DREAMS AND SONGS** G 24
457 **DONT CALL ME DORIS** 2	399 **DOWNTON FOX** 1	169 **DREAMS AND VISIONS** (IRE) 17
534 **DONT GO GENTLE** (IRE) 25	268 **DOWNTOWN GETAWAY** (IRE) 46	278 **DREAMS OF GLORY** 3
158 **DONT TELL NAN** C 20	20 **DOYANNIE** (IRE) 5	170 **DREAMSELLER** (IRE) 28
13 **DONT TELL THE WIFE** 6	407 **DOYEN BREED** (IRE) 2	308 **DREAMSUNDERMYFEET** (IRE) 16
305 **DONTASKMEAGAIN** (USA) 58	96 **DOYEN EXPRESS** (IRE) 1	419 **DREAMT** C 51
142 **DONTCOUNTURCHIKENS** (IRE) 10	94 **DOZEN** (FR) F 88	547 **DREAMWEAVER** (IRE) 11
249 **DONTDELAY** (IRE) 20	418 **DR DES** (IRE) 11	446 **DRENAGH** (IRE) 13
144 **DONTMINDDBOYS** (IRE) 9	463 **DR HOOVES** (IRE) 22	184 **DRENEK** (FR) 14
241 **DOODLE DANDY** (IRE) 3	284 **DR KEENAN** (IRE) 3	21 **DREW BREEZE** (IRE) 20
77 **DOOGAN'S WARREN** (IRE) 10	418 **DR OAKLEY** (IRE) 12	512 **DREWMAIN LEGEND** 11
225 **DOON STAR** 6	196 **DR RICHARD KIMBLE** (IRE) 5	414 **DREYFUS** (IRE) 4
291 **DOR'S DIAMOND** 8	52 **DR ROBIN** (IRE) 9	52 **DRIFT ROCK** 10
291 **DOR'S LAW** 9	405 **DR SANDERSON** (IRE) 54	548 **DRIFTING SANDS** 30
565 **DORA DE JANEIRO** (FR) 5	392 **DRACONIEN** (FR) 61	130 **DRIFTWOOD HAZE** 4
319 **DORA'S FIELD** (IRE) 2	577 **DRAGON BONES** 24	746 **DRINKS INTERVAL** 21
30 **DORADISTA** 21	268 **DRAGON D'ESTRUVAL** (FR) 47	516 **DRIVING FORCE** 19
92 **DORADO DOLLAR** (IRE) 6	219 **DRAGON KHAN** (IRE) 3	506 **DROGON** (IRE) 4
405 **DORAH** 53	368 **DRAGON MALL** (IRE) 13	286 **DROMARA KING** 20
242 **DORCAS LANE** C 134	128 **DRAGON MOUNTAIN** 15	435 **DROMINEER** (IRE) 10
236 **DORCHA KNIGHT** (IRE) 17	251 **DRAGON SUN** 7	291 **DROMISKIN** 10
534 **DORCHESTER DOM** (IRE) 97	367 **DRAGONS VOICE** 7	165 **DROP KICK MURPHI** (IRE) 1
310 **DORETTE** (FR) 7	249 **DRAGONS WILL RISE** (IRE) 21	204 **DROPZONE** (USA) 3
322 **DORKING BOY** 5	63 **DRAKEFELL** (IRE) 5	212 **DRUMCLIFF** (IRE) 18
322 **DORKING COCK** (IRE) 6	532 **DRAKEY BOY** 17	64 **DRUMLEE CITY** (IRE) 1
378 **DORKING LAD** 38	388 **DRAMATIC APPROACH** (IRE) 17	233 **DRUMLEE WATAR** (IRE) 16
236 **DORMIO** 7	557 **DRAMATIC SANDS** (IRE) 29	485 **DRUMMOND WARRIOR** (IRE) 5
121 **DOROTHY B** (IRE) C 78	582 **DRAMATICA** (IRE) 48	503 **DRUMQUINA** (IRE) 3
264 **DOROTHY'S FLAME** 2	557 **DRAMATISTA** (IRE) 30	14 **DRUMREAGH** (IRE) 17
592 **DORRANA** (IRE) 3	7 **DREADNOUGHTUS** 35	230 **DRUMS OF WAR** (IRE) 12
392 **DORRELLS PIERJI** (FR) 59	465 **DREAM ACADEMY** (IRE) 47	257 **DRUMSHANBO DESTINY** (FR) 9
291 **DORS TOYBOY** (IRE) 43	456 **DREAM BAIE** (FR) 3	580 **DRUNKEN PIRATE** 10
545 **DORSET BLUE** (IRE) 29	416 **DREAM BERRY** (FR) 25	392 **DRURY** (IRE) 62
101 **DORTE** (IRE) 72	448 **DREAM BOLT** (IRE) 4	268 **DU DESTIN** (FR) 49
454 **DORTON GIRL** 1	39 **DREAM CASTLE** 9	48 **DUALAGI** G 14
274 **DOSTAL PHIL** (FR) 21	163 **DREAM CHASER** (IRE) 27	269 **DUARIGLE** (IRE) 8
26 **DOT THE EYES** 23	365 **DREAM CONTI** (FR) 33	186 **DUBAI ACCLAIM** (IRE) 11
522 **DOTHRAKI** (IRE) 4	251 **DREAM DAY** C 164	297 **DUBAI ANGEL** (IRE) 9
539 **DOTHRAKI PRINCE** 38	482 **DREAM DE DREAM** (IRE) 2	39 **DUBAI BLUE** (USA) 11
331 **DOTHRAKI RAIDER** 8	213 **DREAM DOC** (IRE) 3	1 **DUBAI DAYS** (IRE) 18
429 **DOTTIES DELIGHT** 3	268 **DREAM DU GRAND VAL** (FR) 48	476 **DUBAI ELEGANCE** 3
150 **DOUBLE COFFEE** 2	260 **DREAM GAME** 42	483 **DUBAI EMPEROR** (FR) 70
215 **DOUBLE D'S** 31	170 **DREAM HOUSE** 27	212 **DUBAI GLORY** G 19
121 **DOUBLE KODIAC** (IRE) 5	281 **DREAM ISLE** (IRE) 13	395 **DUBAI GUEST** (IRE) 21
428 **DOUBLE LEGEND** 4	305 **DREAM KART** (IRE) 59	39 **DUBAI HORIZON** (IRE) 12
191 **DOUBLE MARTINI** (IRE) 3	39 **DREAM LOCATION** 10	388 **DUBAI KEY** (IRE) 19
548 **DOUBLE OR BUBBLE** (IRE) 18	388 **DREAM MACHINE** (IRE) 18	39 **DUBAI LEGACY** (USA) 13
7 **DOUBLE REFLECTION** 34	340 **DREAM MAGIC** (IRE) 7	39 **DUBAI LIFE** (USA) 63
221 **DOUBLE SHUFFLE** (IRE) 33	81 **DREAM MOUNT** (IRE) 5	39 **DUBAI LUXURY** 14
496 **DOUBLE TREASURE** 19	511 **DREAM OF DREAMS** (IRE) 6	39 **DUBAI MIRAGE** (IRE) 64
577 **DOUBLE UP** 23	419 **DREAM ROLE** F 50	589 **DUBAI MISSION** (IRE) 8
297 **DOUBLE W'S** (IRE) 8	17 **DREAM ROUND** (IRE) 70	298 **DUBAI OUTLAW** (IRE) 3
422 **DOUBLING DICE** 26	150 **DREAM SCENARIO** F 57	39 **DUBAI QUALITY** (IRE) 65
140 **DOUBLY BEAUTIFUL** (IRE) 5	516 **DREAM SHOT** 18	97 **DUBAI ROSE** C 87
189 **DOUBLY CLEVER** (IRE) 14	409 **DREAM THE BLUES** (IRE) C 134	368 **DUBAI SEA** (USA) F 71
526 **DOUBLY GUEST** G 20	419 **DREAM TODAY** (IRE) 4	39 **DUBAI SOUQ** (USA) 66
459 **DOUGLAS FIR** (IRE) 2	412 **DREAM TOGETHER** (FR) 38	73 **DUBAI STATION** 33
402 **DOUNYAPOUR** (FR) 22	305 **DREAM WITH ME** (IRE) 60	305 **DUBAI SUNSHINE** (IRE) F 160
93 **DOURADO** (IRE) 2	97 **DREAM WORKS** 34	228 **DUBAI WARRIOR** 5
392 **DOURSAN** (FR) 60	7 **DREAM WORLD** (IRE) 36	39 **DUBAI WELCOME** 67
436 **DOUX PRETENDER** (FR) 4	536 **DREAMBOAT ANNIE** 9	563 **DUBAIANSWER** F 6
291 **DOVER LIGHT** 44	287 **DREAMBOAT DAVE** (IRE) 5	362 **DUBAWI FIFTY** 5

537 **DUBAWI SANDS** 138
49 **DUBAWI'S SPIRIT** (IRE) C 67
150 **DUBAYA** F 58
317 **DUB DES CHAMPS** (IRE) 16
192 **DUBIAN TO** (IRE) F 36
363 **DUBLIN FOUR** (IRE) 21
537 **DUBLIN PHARAOH** (USA) 48
465 **DUBLIN ROCKER** (IRE) 48
435 **DUC DE BEAUCHENE** (FR) 11
405 **DUC DE BOURBON** (FR) 55
524 **DUC DE GRISSAY** (FR) 11
392 **DUC DES GENIEVRES** (FR) 63
526 **DUC KAUTO** (FR) 22
132 **DUCHESS ANDORRA** (IRE) C 56
305 **DUCHESS DORA** (IRE) C 161
378 **DUCHESS OF AVON** 39
321 **DUCISSA** C 21
242 **DUCK AND VANISH** 59
15 **DUCK EGG BLUE** (IRE) 9
476 **DUE A DIAMOND** 22
486 **DUE A WIN** 25
101 **DUE CARE** 29
192 **DUEL IN THE SUN** (IRE) 37
186 **DUESENBERG** (IRE) 78
39 **DUFAY** (FR) F 140
313 **DUFFY ALLEN** (FR) 3
283 **DUHALLOW GESTURE** (IRE) 9
306 **DUHALLOW LAD** (IRE) 2
523 **DUHALLOWCOUNTRY** (IRE) 4
492 **DUHR** (IRE) 1
482 **DUISBURG** (FR) 3
30 **DUJAC** 68
419 **DUKE DEBONAIR** (IRE) 5
342 **DUKE OF ALBA** (IRE) 7
268 **DUKE OF CHALFONT** (FR) 50
315 **DUKE OF CONDICOTE** 143
14 **DUKE OF EARL** (FR) 18
236 **DUKE OF FIRENZE** 8
107 **DUKE OF HAZZARD** (FR) 3
308 **DUKE OF LUCKLEY** (IRE) 37
452 **DUKE OF NAVAN** (IRE) 14
296 **DUKE OF VERONA** (IRE) 23
170 **DUKE OF YORKSHIRE** 29
402 **DUKE STREET** (IRE) 23
290 **DUKES MEADOW** 5
272 **DULAS** (IRE) 34
73 **DULCIMA** (IRE) 34
66 **DUN BAY CREEK** 4
552 **DUN FAW GOOD** 5
17 **DUNADINA** 141
89 **DUNBRODY** (FR) C 90
395 **DUNDRUM WOOD** (IRE) 22
173 **DUNEFINCH** 9
531 **DUNKERRON** 6
184 **DUNLY** (FR) 15
299 **DURATION** (IRE) 9
323 **DURBANVILLE** 3
484 **DURL ROCK** (IRE) 34
177 **DURLINGTON** (FR) 1
418 **DUROUYN** 13
188 **DURRELL** 5
483 **DURSTON** 9
511 **DUSK** (IRE) 41
511 **DUSK TO DAWN** (IRE) 42
435 **DUSKY HERCULES** (IRE) 12
546 **DUSKY LARK** 6
251 **DUST FLICKER** C 165
402 **DUSTIN DES MOTTES** (FR) 24

24 **DUSTING** (IRE) F 16
394 **DUSTY DAMSEL** 6
242 **DUSTY DREAM** 60
444 **DUSTY'S CHOICE** (IRE) 12
251 **DUTCH COURAGE** F 166
305 **DUTCH DECOY** 61
554 **DUTCH GIRL** F 12
527 **DUTCH HARBOR** 4
188 **DUTCH LIGHT** 65
30 **DUTCH PAINTING** 22
171 **DUTCH PURSUIT** (IRE) 14
29 **DUTCH SCHULTZ** 48
368 **DUTCH SPIRIT** 59
428 **DUTCH STORY** 5
420 **DUTIFUL SON** (IRE) 6
39 **DUTOTA DESEJADA** (BRZ) C 141
499 **DUTUGAMUNU** (IRE) 28
64 **DUTY GIRL** (IRE) 2
339 **DWYFRAN** 35
425 **DYAGILEV** 4
16 **DYAMI** (FR) 34
186 **DYLAN DE VEGA** 79
536 **DYLAN'S SEA SONG** 10
137 **DYLANSEOGHAN** (IRE) 7
13 **DYLIEV** (FR) 7
577 **DYNALI** 25
388 **DYNAMIC KATE** (IRE) 20
405 **DYNAMITE DOLLARS** (FR) 56
540 **DYNAMITE STAR** (GER) 23
476 **DYNAMO WALT** (IRE) 4
392 **DYSART DIAMOND** (IRE) 64
76 **EADLIBB** 75
413 **EAGLE COURT** (IRE) 62
428 **EAGLE ONE** 42
1 **EAGLE RIDGE** (IRE) 19
36 **EAGLE'S FOOT** 17
439 **EAGLE'S REALM** 42
395 **EAGLEHILL** (FR) 23
30 **EAGLES BY DAY** (IRE) 2
547 **EAGLES CRAG** (IRE) 47
104 **EAGLESGLEN** 16
435 **EAMON AN CNOIC** (IRE) 13
442 **EARCOMESALI** 1
442 **EARCOMESTHEDREAM** (IRE) 2
424 **EARL BIFFY BIFFEN** (FR) 18
211 **EARL OF BANNACURRY** (IRE) 6
254 **EARL OF DESMOND** 15
233 **EARL OF HARROW** 17
526 **EARL OF WISDOM** 23
534 **EARLOFTHECOTSWOLDS** (FR) 26
122 **EARLY BOY** 7
526 **EARLY DAYS** (IRE) 24
378 **EARLY DU LEMO** (FR) 40
97 **EARLY LIGHT** (FR) 88
393 **EARLY MORNING MIST** (IRE) 41
496 **EARLY MORNING RAIN** (FR) 20
94 **EARLY START** C 89
159 **EARLY VOICE** (FR) 1
472 **EARTH AND SKY** (USA) 3
526 **EARTH BUSINESS** (IRE) 25
20 **EARTH KING** (IRE) 6
274 **EARTH LORD** (IRE) 22
274 **EARTH MOOR** (IRE) 23
20 **EARTH STAR** (IRE) 7
335 **EARTHLY** (USA) 4
72 **EASKEY LAD** (IRE) 2
541 **EAST END GIRL** 39
422 **EAST OF EDEN** (IRE) 27

170 **EAST STREET REVUE** 30
520 **EASTER DAY** (FR) 4
393 **EASTER ERIC** 7
541 **EASTER GOLD** (FR) 5
393 **EASTER ROCKET** 8
327 **EASTERLY** 19
483 **EASTERN GENERAL** (IRE) 35
6 **EASTERN JOY** F 138
441 **EASTERN LADY** (IND) 3
422 **EASTERN SHERIFF** 28
6 **EASTERN WORLD** (IRE) 51
186 **EASTWELL PARK** 80
583 **EASY AS THAT** (IRE) 18
186 **EASY DESIRE** 81
392 **EASY GAME** (FR) 65
530 **EASY TERMS** F 16
566 **EASY TIGER** 3
124 **EASY WOOD** (FR) 5
405 **EASYRUN DE VASSY** (FR) 57
330 **EATON COLLINA** (IRE) 5
330 **EATON HILL** (IRE) 6
515 **EATON MILLER** (IRE) 4
424 **EAU TOP** (FR) 19
318 **EAUX DE VIE** 27
244 **EBASARI** (FR) 67
121 **EBBRAAM** 6
146 **EBITDA** 7
169 **EBONY ADAMS** 61
300 **EBONY BELLE** (IRE) 6
274 **EBONY GALE** 24
1 **EBONY JEWEL** (IRE) 20
444 **EBONY LEGEND** 29
419 **EBONY STREET** (USA) F 52
535 **EBQAA** (IRE) 2
437 **EBRAH** F 41
364 **EBURY** 6
405 **ECCO** 58
583 **ECEPARTI** (FR) 19
534 **ECHIQUIER** (FR) 27
412 **ECHO** (IRE) 7
590 **ECHO BRAVA** 1
508 **ECHO DU LARGE** (FR) 6
276 **ECHO WATT** (FR) 5
541 **ECHOES IN RAIN** (FR) 66
541 **ECLAIR DE GUYE** (FR) 6
440 **ECLAIR DES SABLONS** (FR) 3
338 **ECLAIR ON LINE** (FR) 14
327 **ECLAIR SURF** (FR) 20
295 **ECLAIRCIE** (IRE) C 56
308 **ECLAT DES MOTTES** (FR) 17
392 **ECO FRIENDLY** (IRE) 139
323 **ECOLO** (FR) 4
32 **ECONOMIC CRISIS** (IRE) 3
422 **ECOSSE** 67
323 **ECRIVAIN** (FR) 24
417 **ECTOR** (FR) 18
274 **ECU DE LA NOVERIE** (FR) 25
165 **ED CUVEE** 2
378 **EDAM DU MESTIVEL** (FR) 41
198 **EDDIEMAURICE** (IRE) 8
204 **EDDIES PEARL** (IRE) 4
34 **EDDYSTONE ROCK** (IRE) 7
546 **EDE'IFFS ELTON** 7
429 **EDE'S** 4
391 **EDEBEZ** (IRE) 46
514 **EDEN DU HOUX** (FR) 14
392 **EDEN FLIGHT** (FR) 67
409 **EDEN QUAY** (IRE) 34

338 **FANFARONADE** (USA) 15
583 **FANION D'ESTRUVAL** (FR) 26
94 **FANNIE BY GASLIGHT** 9
365 **FANNIE PORTER** 129
54 **FANNY CHENAL** 6
228 **FANNY LOGAN** (IRE) 9
191 **FANSURPER** (FR) 36
121 **FANTAIL** 37
365 **FANTASIA ROQUE** (FR) 36
473 **FANTASIA STORM** (IRE) 14
375 **FANTASTIC BLUE** 4
291 **FANTASTIC FLYER** 13
268 **FANTASTIC LADY** (FR) 55
580 **FANTASTIC MS FOX** 13
534 **FANTASTIKAS** (FR) 30
272 **FANTASY BELIEVER** (IRE) 36
541 **FANTASY DIVA** 40
257 **FANTASY JUSTIFIER** (IRE) 13
7 **FANTASY KEEPER** 41
7 **FANTASY LOVER** (IRE) 102
475 **FANTASY SHIFT** (IRE) 13
340 **FANTOM FORCE** 35
276 **FANZIO** (FR) 7
516 **FAR ABOVE** (IRE) 2
386 **FAR FROM A RUBY** 24
363 **FARADAY LADY** (IRE) G 26
228 **FARAMMAN** 69
189 **FARCEUR DE MAULNE** (FR) 15
365 **FARCEUR DU LARGE** (FR) 37
385 **FARD** 9
550 **FAREEQ** 8
49 **FARES POET** (IRE) 6
30 **FAREWELL KISS** (IRE) 23
384 **FARHH SIGHTED** 56
170 **FARHH TO GO** 111
10 **FARHHMORECREDIT** 37
392 **FARID** (FR) 82
23 **FARLAM KING** 9
440 **FARM THE ROCK** (IRE) 4
151 **FARMER BOY** (IRE) 4
316 **FARNE** (IRE) 9
537 **FARNHAM** 7
221 **FARO DE KERSER** (FR) 37
23 **FAROCCO** (GER) 12
268 **FAROUK DE CHENEAU** (FR) 56
491 **FARRAN DANCER** (IRE) 9
583 **FARRANTS WAY** (IRE) 27
537 **FARZEEN** 8
196 **FASCINATING SPIRIT** (IRE) 6
251 **FASHION** 172
128 **FASHION ADVICE** 82
7 **FASHION FREE** 103
254 **FASHION STATEMENT** F 156
516 **FASHIONABLE SPIRIT** (IRE) C 63
239 **FASHIONESQUE** (FR) 3
397 **FAST AND FRIENDLY** (IRE) 6
166 **FAST ART** (IRE) 4
392 **FAST BUCK** (FR) 83
531 **FAST DANCER** (IRE) 8
170 **FAST DEAL** 112
416 **FAST GETAWAY** (IRE) 28
413 **FAST PICK** (IRE) C 102
458 **FAST SCENIC** (FR) 5
121 **FAST SPIN** (USA) 38
175 **FAST TRACK FLYER** (IRE) 61
106 **FASTEN UP** C 18
317 **FASTERKHANI** 21
413 **FASTMAN** (IRE) 19

511 **FASTNET MIST** (IRE) C 109
503 **FATAAWY** (IRE) F 17
117 **FATAAWY** (FR) C 76
76 **FATANAH** (IRE) F 60
268 **FATHER JOHN** (FR) 57
30 **FATHER OF JAZZ** 24
392 **FAUGHEEN** (IRE) 84
365 **FAUGUERNON** (FR) 38
526 **FAUSTINOVICK** 30
116 **FAUSTUS** 46
579 **FAVORI DE SIVOLA** (FR) 9
242 **FAVORITE MOON** (GER) 61
405 **FAVORITO BUCK'S** (FR) 64
272 **FAVOURED DESTINY** (USA) 37
330 **FAY CE QUE VOUDRAS** (IRE) 7
339 **FAYETTA** 9
242 **FAYLAQ** 8
522 **FAZAMOUR** (FR) 5
515 **FAZAYTE** (FR) 7
16 **FEAR NAUGHT** 35
395 **FEARLESS** (IRE) 29
221 **FEARLESS FRACAS** (IRE) 38
34 **FEARLESS LAD** (IRE) 9
304 **FEARLESS WARRIOR** (FR) 6
537 **FEARLESSLY** (IRE) 9
398 **FEARSOME FRED** 2
327 **FEDELTA** (IRE) 22
356 **FEDERICI** 30
340 **FEDORA FITS** 36
187 **FEEBI** 2
7 **FEEL GOOD FACTOR** 104
411 **FEEL THE PINCH** 29
146 **FEEL THE THUNDER** 8
184 **FEETRONIE DE KERVI** (FR) 18
212 **FEHILY** (IRE) 21
162 **FEISTY GAL** (IRE) 28
419 **FELCINE** (FR) F 56
428 **FELDSPAR** 27
186 **FELICIA BLUE** 85
29 **FELICIANA DE VEGA** 15
579 **FELICIDAD** (FR) 10
49 **FELIX** 7
480 **FELIX D'AUTRY** (FR) 17
110 **FELIX MENDELSSOHN** (IRE) 9
268 **FELONY** (IRE) 58
92 **FELTON BELLEVUE** (FR) 8
323 **FEMINA** (IRE) 25
121 **FEMININE FELICITY** 39
244 **FEMINISM** (IRE) 30
239 **FEN BREEZE** 4
190 **FEN TIGER** (IRE) 21
486 **FENDALE** 5
45 **FENELLA ROSE** C 45
391 **FENLONS COURT** (IRE) 7
346 **FENNAAN** (IRE) 3
41 **FENNANN** 3
495 **FENRIR BINDING** 2
392 **FENTA DES OBEAUX** (FR) 85
221 **FENTARA** G 39
328 **FEODORA** 5
496 **FERALKAT** 23
434 **FERAYHA** (IRE) F 9
220 **FERAYHA** (IRE) C 20
537 **FERDOOS** C 145
101 **FEREVIA** (IRE) F 76
92 **FERN HILL** (IRE) 9
388 **FERN OWL** 23
1 **FERNHILL LAD** (IRE) 23

392 **FERNY HOLLOW** (IRE) 86
484 **FERROBIN** (IRE) 40
175 **FERRY ALL** (FR) 18
305 **FESTIVAL DAY** 64
39 **FESTIVAL OF COLOUR** (IRE) 72
30 **FESTIVE LOVE** 25
121 **FESTIVE STAR** 40
269 **FETHARD FLYER** (IRE) 9
257 **FETHIYE BOY** 14
274 **FEUILLE DE CHENE** (FR) 30
351 **FEVERTRE** (IRE) 9
316 **FFORBIDDEN LOVE** 10
340 **FIACH STONEY** (IRE) 37
315 **FIBONACCI** 35
526 **FIDDLERONTHEROOF** (IRE) 31
64 **FIDDLERS BOW** (IRE) 4
405 **FIDELIO VALLIS** (FR) 65
315 **FIDUX** (FR) 36
255 **FIELD EXHIBITION** (IRE) 7
263 **FIELD MASTER** (IRE) 1
198 **FIELD OF VISION** 6
101 **FIELDS OF DREAMS** 6
89 **FIELDSMAN** (USA) 22
534 **FIER ECHEZEAUX** (FR) 31
103 **FIERCE RIVAL** 20
172 **FIERY BREATH** 4
230 **FIERY MISSION** (USA) 14
395 **FIESOLE** 30
29 **FIESTY** 105
577 **FIFRELET** (FR) 31
472 **FIFTH COMMANDMENT** (IRE) F 29
537 **FIFTH POSITION** (IRE) 10
378 **FIFTY BALL** (FR) 50
173 **FIGARELLA BORGET** (FR) 10
334 **FIGEAC** (FR) 6
163 **FIGHTING DON** (FR) 14
163 **FIGHTING IRISH** (IRE) 3
291 **FIGHTING TEMERAIRE** (IRE) 14
579 **FIGHTING TIGER** (FR) 22
121 **FIGURES** 79
483 **FIJI** 39
515 **FIL D'ARIANE** (FR) 8
66 **FILAMENT OF GOLD** (USA) 5
66 **FILBERT STREET** 6
422 **FILIA REGINA** C 69
317 **FILLE D'AVIGNON** (IRE) 22
555 **FILLE D'OR** 20
378 **FILLES DE FLEUR** 51
142 **FILLYBUSTA** (IRE) 12
15 **FILLYDELPHIA** (IRE) 10
132 **FILO'S FLYER** (IRE) 58
274 **FILOU DES ISSARDS** (FR) 31
392 **FILS SPIRITUEL** (FR) 87
356 **FIN AND GAME** (IRE) 31
160 **FINAGHY AYR** (IRE) 3
267 **FINAIR** 7
280 **FINAL ATTACK** (IRE) 2
563 **FINAL CHOICE** 7
384 **FINAL ENCORE** 29
117 **FINAL FANTASY** 7
148 **FINAL FLING** (IRE) 15
87 **FINAL FRONTIER** (IRE) 9
476 **FINAL LEGACY** 5
142 **FINAL NUDGE** (IRE) 13
386 **FINAL OPTION** 25
1 **FINAL REMINDER** (IRE) 24
39 **FINAL SONG** (IRE) 73
6 **FINAL STAGE** F 145

39 **FINAL STORY** (USA) 74
370 **FINAL VENTURE** 5
516 **FINAL VOYAGE** 64
511 **FINAL WATCH** 110
128 **FINALLY MINE** (USA) 83
92 **FINALLYFREE** (IRE) G 10
348 **FINANCIAL CONDUCT** (IRE) 3
124 **FINANCIAL OUTCOME** (IRE) 6
330 **FINANCIER** 2
244 **FINANS BAY** (IRE) 31
395 **FINAWN BAWN** (IRE) 31
426 **FIND A PENNY** 21
210 **FINDUSATGORCOMBE** 4
128 **FINE BLEND** (IRE) F 102
488 **FINE BY HER** 3
424 **FINE CASTING** (IRE) 23
375 **FINE SILK** (USA) C 29
121 **FINELY TUNED** (IRE) 41
73 **FINERY** 38
121 **FINEST SOUND** (IRE) 42
356 **FINGAL D'ARTHEL** (FR) 32
388 **FINGERONTHESWITCH** (IRE) 24
223 **FINISHER** (IRE) 3
272 **FINISHINGTHEHAT** F 84
356 **FINIX RIVER** 33
137 **FINNEGAN'S GARDEN** (IRE) 8
331 **FINNISTON FARM** 9
132 **FINOAH** (IRE) 8
6 **FINTRY** (IRE) C 146
415 **FINULA** (IRE) 2
576 **FINVARRA** (IRE) 28
583 **FIONN MAC CUL** (IRE) 28
484 **FIRAK** (FR) 41
20 **FIRE AND ICE** (IRE) G 8
305 **FIRE FIGHTING** (IRE) 14
555 **FIRE ISLAND** 4
342 **FIRE JET** (IRE) 8
251 **FIREBELLY** C 173
420 **FIREGUARD** 7
188 **FIRENZE** F 67
60 **FIRENZE ROSA** (IRE) 5
546 **FIRENZO** (FR) 10
117 **FIREPOWER** (FR) 29
268 **FIRESTEP** (IRE) 59
186 **FIREWATER** 15
106 **FIREY RED** (IRE) G 13
225 **FIRLINFEU** 8
413 **FIRMAMENT** 20
365 **FIRST APPROACH** (IRE) 39
18 **FIRST ASSEMBLY** (IRE) 6
305 **FIRST BLUSH** (IRE) C 163
547 **FIRST CHARGE** (IRE) 50
517 **FIRST DANCE** (IRE) 6
508 **FIRST DESTINATION** 8
53 **FIRST EXCEL** 3
401 **FIRST FLIGHT** (IRE) 4
14 **FIRST FLOW** (IRE) 21
150 **FIRST GREYED** (FR) 60
112 **FIRST HARMONY** F 27
444 **FIRST IMPRESSION** (FR) 30
228 **FIRST IN LINE** 10
242 **FIRST KINGDOM** (IRE) 62
11 **FIRST LINK** (USA) 2
435 **FIRST LORD DE CUET** (FR) 18
39 **FIRST MAGIC** (USA) 75
234 **FIRST MAN** (IRE) 17
6 **FIRST NATION** 8
527 **FIRST OF MANY** F 10

481 **FIRST OF NEVER** (IRE) 5
163 **FIRST PIROUETTE** (IRE) 28
388 **FIRST QUEST** (USA) 25
511 **FIRST RECEIVER** 43
513 **FIRST RESPONSE** 3
378 **FIRST REVOLUTION** (IRE) 52
562 **FIRST ROMANCE** 8
39 **FIRST SNOWFALL** 76
547 **FIRST STREET** 51
39 **FIRST TARGET** 77
6 **FIRST VICTORY** (IRE) C 147
7 **FIRST VOYAGE** (IRE) 42
6 **FIRST WINTER** (IRE) 58
330 **FIRSTCOAT** (FR) 9
568 **FIRSTEEN** 10
541 **FIRTH OF FIVE** (IRE) F 7
6 **FIRTH OF LORNE** (IRE) C 148
567 **FISCAL FIREPOWER** (IRE) 4
170 **FISHABLE** 113
23 **FISHER GREEN** (IRE) 11
540 **FISHERMAN'S BLUES** (IRE) 7
131 **FISHERMANS COVE** (IRE) 7
212 **FISHKHOV** (FR) 22
351 **FISTON DE BAUNE** (FR) 10
6 **FITFUL SKIES** (IRE) F 149
37 **FITSAOHA** (FR) 1
518 **FITTLETON FERRY** 36
518 **FITWOOD STAR** 7
103 **FITZCARRALDO** 21
140 **FITZROVIA** 6
395 **FITZROY** (IRE) 32
78 **FITZY** 2
392 **FIVE BAR BRIAN** (IRE) 88
295 **FIVE HELMETS** (IRE) 10
392 **FIVE O'CLOCK** (IRE) 89
318 **FIVE RINGS** 28
574 **FIVE STAR GETAWAY** (IRE) 8
180 **FIVEHUNDREDMILES** (IRE) 9
395 **FIVETOTWELVE** 33
503 **FIX** (NZ) C 41
378 **FIX BAYONETS** (IRE) 53
268 **FIX SUN** (FR) 60
348 **FIXED RATE** 4
227 **FIZZLESTIX** (FR) 12
339 **FIZZY FEET** (IRE) 10
546 **FLAGRANT DELITIEP** (FR) 11
230 **FLAKARNA** 15
323 **FLAMBEUR** (USA) 5
493 **FLAMBOYANT JOYAUX** (FR) 15
304 **FLAME OF FREEDOM** (IRE) 62
305 **FLAME OF GIBRALTAR** (IRE) C 164
73 **FLAMES OF YORK** 39
6 **FLAMEWOOD** (USA) 59
200 **FLAMING CHARMER** (IRE) 3
474 **FLAMING GLORY** (IRE) 3
323 **FLAMING ROUGE** (USA) 26
291 **FLAMING SPEAR** (IRE) 15
378 **FLAMINGER** (FR) 54
413 **FLAMMARION** (GER) 21
335 **FLANAGANS FIELD** (IRE) 5
365 **FLANKING MANEUVER** (FR) 40
363 **FLANN** 27
405 **FLASH COLLONGES** (FR) 66
402 **FLASH DE CLERVAL** (FR) 29
405 **FLASH DE TOUZAINE** (FR) 67
254 **FLASH GORDON** (IRE) 23
542 **FLASH POINT** (IRE) 3
484 **FLASH THE STEEL** (IRE) 42

214 **FLASH TO BANG** 45
461 **FLASHDANZA** 9
305 **FLASHING APPROACH** (IRE) 65
322 **FLASHING GLANCE** 9
129 **FLASHJACK** (IRE) 11
291 **FLASHY FLYER** 45
163 **FLAT STONE** 4
197 **FLAT TO THE MAX** (FR) 1
228 **FLATLEY** 70
98 **FLAUNT IT** (IRE) 11
412 **FLAVIUS TITUS** 9
6 **FLECHE D'OR** C 150
409 **FLEETING** (IRE) 5
297 **FLEETING ARROW** (IRE) G 10
272 **FLEETING PRINCE** (IRE) 38
363 **FLEETING VISIT** 28
46 **FLEETWOOD BLACK** 7
484 **FLEGMATIK** (FR) 43
327 **FLEMCARA** (IRE) 23
526 **FLEMENCO TEMPO** (IRE) 32
297 **FLEMENS FLEUR** (IRE) 11
405 **FLEMENSTIDE** (IRE) 68
327 **FLEMINGS** (IRE) 24
416 **FLEMINPORT** (IRE) 29
529 **FLEMISH SCHOOL** C 38
395 **FLETCH** (IRE) 34
101 **FLEUR DE CACTUS** (IRE) C 77
242 **FLEUR DE GUY** 138
29 **FLEUR DE NUIT** (IRE) C 106
402 **FLEUR DU SEUIL** (FR) 30
334 **FLEUR IRLANDAISE** (FR) 7
515 **FLEURSALS** 9
245 **FLEURY** 3
222 **FLIBINIGHT** (IRE) 11
405 **FLIC OU VOYOU** (FR) 69
416 **FLIGHT DECK** (IRE) 30
62 **FLIGHT OF THUNDER** (IRE) 33
98 **FLIGHT PATH** 26
576 **FLIGHT TO MILAN** (IRE) 29
441 **FLIGHT TO NOWHERE** 4
30 **FLIGHTY CLARETS** (IRE) C 71
274 **FLINCK** (IRE) 32
297 **FLINT HILL** 12
486 **FLINT SAID NO** 6
18 **FLINTARA** 7
268 **FLINTEUR SACRE** (FR) 61
58 **FLINTHAM** 5
316 **FLINTROCK** (GER) 11
261 **FLINTS LEGACY** 13
272 **FLIPPA THE STRIPPA** (IRE) 39
43 **FLIRTATIOUS** G 8
14 **FLIRTATIOUS GIRL** (IRE) 22
555 **FLIRTY RASCAL** 21
464 **FLIRTY THIRTY** (IRE) F 20
426 **FLISS FLOSS** 22
483 **FLOAT** (FR) 40
251 **FLOATING ARTIST** 9
322 **FLOATING ROCK** (IRE) 10
295 **FLOOD DEFENCE** (IRE) 11
39 **FLOODWATER** (FR) 78
254 **FLOR DE LA LUNA** 91
496 **FLORAL BOUQUET** 24
187 **FLORENZA** 3
268 **FLORESSA** (FR) 62
550 **FLORIE** F 9
39 **FLORISTRY** C 145
534 **FLORRIE BOY** (IRE) 32
243 **FLORRIE KNOX** (IRE) 6

228 **FRANCONIA** 71
572 **FRANIGANE** (FR) 14
164 **FRANK BRIDGE** 16
87 **FRANK ROGERS** 12
496 **FRANKADORE** (IRE) 27
537 **FRANKAI** (IRE) 146
97 **FRANKEL'S MAGIC** (FR) 36
249 **FRANKELIO** (FR) 27
444 **FRANKENSTELLA** (IRE) 31
484 **FRANKEUR** (FR) 44
207 **FRANKIE** 4
233 **FRANKIE BABY** (IRE) 24
206 **FRANKIE BALLOU** (IRE) 6
425 **FRANKIE JAZZ** 8
552 **FRANKIES FIRE** 6
228 **FRANKLY DARLING** 72
30 **FRANKLY MR SHANKLY** (GER) 27
515 **FRANKLY SPEAKING** 10
249 **FRANKSTER** (FR) 28
413 **FRANKUS** (IRE) 22
485 **FRANSHAM** 7
442 **FRANZ KLAMMER** 3
416 **FRASCATO BELLO** (FR) 32
268 **FRASER ISLAND** (IRE) 66
315 **FRATERNEL** (FR) 39
388 **FRAU GEORGIA** (IRE) 27
434 **FREA** 2
268 **FRED** (FR) 67
305 **FRED** 67
123 **FREDDIE CORBITT** (IRE) 4
212 **FREDDIE DARLING** (IRE) 23
319 **FREDDY FANATAPAN** 4
33 **FREE BIRD** 6
318 **FREE DANCER** 29
44 **FREE GIFT** 6
7 **FREE LOVE** 44
365 **FREE RANGER** (IRE) 41
4 **FREE SKI** (IRE) 3
254 **FREE SOLO** (IRE) 93
10 **FREE TALKIN** 9
29 **FREE WILL** 108
539 **FREEDELIVERY** (IRE) 44
44 **FREEDOM AND WHEAT** (IRE) 7
219 **FREEDOM CHIMES** 4
434 **FREEDOM FIGHTER** (IRE) 3
121 **FREEDOM FLYER** (IRE) 44
220 **FREEDOM REIGNS** (IRE) F 21
192 **FREEROLLING** 8
338 **FREETHINKER** (IRE) 17
285 **FREEZING** (IRE) 17
34 **FRENCH ACCENT** C 32
511 **FRENCH ASSET** (IRE) 45
538 **FRENCH BATTLE** (USA) 4
181 **FRENCH DE GUYE** (FR) 4
242 **FRENCH DRESSING** C 140
382 **FRENCH DYNAMITE** (FR) 9
27 **FRENCH FLYER** (IRE) 8
89 **FRENCH KISS** (IRE) 25
326 **FRENCH MINSTREL** (IRE) 4
482 **FRENCH PARADOXE** (FR) 6
242 **FRENCH POLISH** 63
98 **FRENCH RIVIERA** (FR) 12
339 **FRENCH TWIST** 11
583 **FRENCHY DU LARGE** (FR) 30
64 **FREQUENCY CODE** (FR) 6
409 **FREQUENTIAL** C 139
254 **FREQUENTLY** F 157
583 **FRERO BANBOU** (FR) 31

97 **FRESH AIR** (IRE) F 91
395 **FRESH NEW DAWN** (IRE) 36
39 **FRESH SNOW** (IRE) 79
460 **FRESHFIELD FERRIS** 1
546 **FRESNO EMERY** (FR) 12
382 **FRIARY ROCK** (IRE) 10
90 **FRICKA** 6
340 **FRIDAY FIZZ** (IRE) 10
405 **FRIEND OR FOE** (FR) 71
128 **FRIENDLY ADVICE** (IRE) 22
489 **FRIENDS DON'T ASK** 5
585 **FRIENDS IN HEAVEN** (IRE) 2
157 **FRIENDSHIP BAY** 5
385 **FRIENDSHIP IS LOVE** C 12
469 **FRIGHTENED RABBIT** (USA) 5
364 **FRILLY** 9
353 **FRILLY FROCK** (IRE) 3
493 **FRIMEUR DE LANCRAY** (FR) 16
416 **FRISCO BAY** (FR) 33
484 **FRISSON COLLONGES** (FR) 45
405 **FRODON** (FR) 72
274 **FROM THE HEART** (FR) 36
251 **FROMNOWON** (IRE) 60
321 **FRONSAC** 6
48 **FRONT FIVE** (IRE) 6
548 **FRONT OF LINE** 20
323 **FRONTGATE** (USA) 58
428 **FRONTISPIECE** 6
405 **FROSTY LADY** (FR) 182
141 **FROSTY TERN** 2
251 **FROZEN WATERS** (IRE) 61
242 **FRUITION** 64
546 **FU FU** 13
260 **FUAIGH MOR** (IRE) C 153
14 **FUBAR** (IRE) 23
188 **FUCHSIA** 36
128 **FUENTE** 23
268 **FUGITIVES DRIFT** (IRE) 68
537 **FUJAIRA PRINCE** (IRE) 11
61 **FUKUTO** (FR) 10
437 **FULL APPROVAL** (IRE) 43
511 **FULL AUTHORITY** (IRE) 46
378 **FULL BACK** (FR) 56
538 **FULL BLOOM** C 23
118 **FULL CIRCLE** 7
134 **FULL HOUSE** 11
425 **FULL INTENTION** 5
439 **FULL MARKS** (IRE) 43
516 **FULL MOON FEVER** (IRE) F 66
2 **FULL MOON RISING** 6
539 **FULL OF ROQUE** (FR) 45
388 **FULL OF SURPRISES** (FR) 28
186 **FULL SECRET** (FR) 87
220 **FULL SPECTRUM** (IRE) 13
439 **FULL SPEIGHT** (USA) 19
233 **FULL SPES** (FR) 25
214 **FULL STRENGTH** 46
492 **FULL SUIT** 2
6 **FULL VERSE** (IRE) 60
367 **FULLAAH** (IRE) C 34
62 **FUMBLEINTHEFOREST** 34
27 **FUMBO JUMBO** (IRE) 9
378 **FUME** (FR) 57
135 **FUN DE NUIT** (FR) 6
384 **FUN MAC** (GER) 9
583 **FUNAMBULE SIVOLA** (FR) 32
260 **FUNKADELIC** 5
117 **FUNKY BEAR** 79

128 **FUNKY DUNKY** (IRE) 84
142 **FUNKY SENSATION** 15
413 **FUNNY MAN** 23
316 **FUNWAY MONARCH** (IRE) 12
378 **FURIA D'OUDAIRIES** (FR) 58
483 **FURIOUS** 10
72 **FURIOUSLY FAST** (IRE) 4
234 **FURIUS DE CIERGUES** (FR) 19
522 **FURNI FACTORS** 6
577 **FURQAAN** (IRE) 33
186 **FURZIG** 18
315 **FUSEAU** (FR) 40
268 **FUSIL RAFFLES** (FR) 69
250 **FUSIONFORCE** (IRE) 3
395 **FUSIONICE** (FR) 37
483 **FUTURE FORTUNE** (FR) 73
29 **FUTURE INVESTMENT** 16
39 **FUTURE KING** (IRE) 80
365 **FUTURE PROOF** (FR) 42
49 **FUTURISTIC** (IRE) 8
91 **FUWAIRT** (IRE) 8
463 **FYFIN PATSY** (IRE) 33
530 **FYRECRACKER** (FR) 5
186 **G FOR GABRIAL** (IRE) 88
508 **G'DAY** (FR) 9
455 **G'DAY AUSSIE** 5
496 **GA LAW** (FR) 28
383 **GABRIAL THE DEVIL** (IRE) 4
383 **GABRIAL THE ONE** (IRE) 5
186 **GABRIAL THE SAINT** (IRE) 19
383 **GABRIAL THE TIGER** (IRE) 6
186 **GABRIAL THE WIRE** 20
186 **GABRIALS BOY** 21
356 **GABRIEL OAK** 31
435 **GABRIELLE DU SEUIL** (FR) 21
323 **GADEA** (IRE) 28
251 **GADWA** C 176
153 **GAELIC FLOW** 9
272 **GAELIC KINGDOM** (IRE) 40
356 **GAELIK COAST** (FR) 35
97 **GAGARINA** (FR) C 92
61 **GAIA VALLIS** (FR) 11
17 **GAINFUL** (USA) C 73
158 **GAINSBORO GREY** 13
365 **GAIUS DE MARCIGNY** (FR) 43
274 **GALA BALL** (FR) 37
405 **GALA DE CORTON** (FR) 73
100 **GALA ROSE** G 2
516 **GALACTIC HEROINE** F 67
144 **GALACTIC POWER** (IRE) 10
181 **GALACTIC SPIRIT** 6
97 **GALACTICA** (FR) 93
465 **GALADRIEL** 50
29 **GALAH** 109
579 **GALAHAD QUEST** (FR) 11
94 **GALAHAD THREEPWOOD** 40
595 **GALAHILL** 6
268 **GALAN DES PLANCHES** (FR) 70
511 **GALATA BRIDGE** 47
323 **GALAWI** (IRE) 29
6 **GALE FORCE** C 151
150 **GALE FORCE MAYA** 10
128 **GALE GREEN** F 103
363 **GALEA DU LIVET** (FR) 30
519 **GALES PRESENT** (IRE) G 28
578 **GALICE MACALO** (FR) 7
511 **GALILEANO** (IRE) F 111
198 **GALILEO JADE** (IRE) 10

534 **GALILEO SILVER** (IRE) 34
557 **GALISPEED** (FR) 33
228 **GALLAGHER** 73
51 **GALLAHERS CROSS** (IRE) 3
557 **GALLASIDE** (FR) 34
353 **GALLERY EXHIBITION** (IRE) 4
119 **GALLEY CAT** 6
136 **GALLIC DESTINY** (IRE) 3
156 **GALLIC GEORDIE** 7
186 **GALLIPOLI** (IRE) 22
6 **GALLIPOT** C 152
346 **GALLOWAY HILLS** 4
541 **GALMARLEY** 8
228 **GALSWORTHY** 74
396 **GALTEE MOUNTAIN** (IRE) 1
540 **GALWAY GIRL** (GER) 24
434 **GAMBATTE** C 10
74 **GAMBLING GAMUT** (IRE) 2
254 **GAMBLING MISTRESS** 24
304 **GAMBON** (GER) 7
17 **GAME AND SET** 84
574 **GAME LINE** (IRE) 9
439 **GAME PLAN** 44
537 **GAME PLAYER** (IRE) 12
260 **GAMEFACE** (IRE) 5
370 **GAMESOME** (FR) 6
234 **GAMESTERS ICON** 20
382 **GANDY MAN** (IRE) 11
164 **GANG WARFARE** 17
233 **GANGSTER** (FR) 26
169 **GAOLBREAKER** (IRE) 22
212 **GAOT** (FR) 24
402 **GARBANZO** (IRE) 31
368 **GARDE FORESTIER** (FR) 20
274 **GARDE LA VICTOIRE** (FR) 38
170 **GARDEN OASIS** 37
516 **GARDEN PARADISE** (IRE) 21
225 **GARGOYLE GIRL** G 9
491 **GARNOCK VALLEY** 29
331 **GARO DE JUILLEY** (FR) 10
272 **GARRA MOLLY** (IRE) C 85
473 **GARRANE** (IRE) 15
395 **GARRETTSTOWN** (IRE) 38
356 **GARRIX DE LA SEE** (FR) 36
160 **GARRON CRESCENT** (IRE) 4
272 **GARRUS** (IRE) 9
416 **GARRY CLERMONT** (FR) 34
400 **GARRYDUFF CROSS** (IRE) 2
7 **GARSMAN** (IRE) 105
394 **GARTH ROCKETT** 7
190 **GAS MONKEY** 3
1 **GASPAISIELLE** F 26
189 **GASTARA** 17
178 **GATACRE STREET** 5
379 **GATAMALATA** (IRE) C 23
24 **GATES PASS** 4
316 **GATEWAY TO EUROPE** 13
56 **GATS AND CO** 5
503 **GATSBY CAP** (IRE) 5
409 **GAUNTLET** (FR) 42
315 **GAVI DI GAVI** (FR) 41
320 **GAVLAR** 2
274 **GAVROCHEKA** (FR) 39
318 **GAWDAWPALIN** (IRE) 4
485 **GAYTON** 8
101 **GAZELLE** 31
92 **GAZETTE BOURGEOISE** (FR) 12
305 **GEAR UP** (IRE) 165

537 **GEE KEL** (IRE) F 147
30 **GEETANJALI** (IRE) 3
118 **GEHT FASTEUR** (IRE) F 8
511 **GEISHA GIRL** (IRE) F 112
49 **GEIZY TEIZY** (IRE) 9
274 **GELBOE DE CHANAY** (FR) 40
405 **GELINO BELLO** (FR) 74
188 **GEMINGA** 68
584 **GEMINI GLORY** (USA) 5
463 **GEMOLOGIST** (IRE) 34
409 **GEMS** C 140
309 **GENERAL ALLENBY** 7
417 **GENERAL BROOK** (IRE) 5
331 **GENERAL BUX** 11
156 **GENERAL CONSENSUS** 8
392 **GENERAL COUNSEL** (IRE) 95
395 **GENERAL CUSTARD** (IRE) 2
232 **GENERAL GIRLING** 2
26 **GENERAL JOE** (IRE) 24
107 **GENERAL LEE** 29
52 **GENERAL MALARKEY** (IRE) 14
473 **GENERAL PROBUS** 16
386 **GENERAL ZOFF** 5
46 **GENERALISATION** (IRE) 8
416 **GENERATION GAP** (IRE) 35
329 **GENERATOR CITY** (IRE) 3
418 **GENEROUS DAY** (IRE) 15
233 **GENEROUS GIRL** 2
530 **GENEROUS HEART** F 18
472 **GENEROUS HEART** F 30
486 **GENEROUSLY GIFTED** F 38
17 **GENETICS** (FR) 23
135 **GENEVA BARRACKS** (IRE) 7
30 **GENEVA DIVA** 72
132 **GENEVER DRAGON** (IRE) 29
411 **GENIAL HAWKSTONE** (FR) 31
128 **GENNADY** (IRE) 24
541 **GENTLE ALICE** (IRE) F 9
39 **GENTLE LOOK** 15
244 **GENTLE M'AM** (IRE) 5
446 **GENTLE RIVER** 16
485 **GENTLE ROSE** 9
163 **GENTLEMAN AT ARMS** (IRE) 15
263 **GENTLEMAN FARMER** 2
212 **GENTLEMAN KAP** (FR) 25
336 **GENTLEMAN MOORE** (IRE) 3
424 **GENTLEMAN VALLEY** (FR) 25
378 **GENTLEMAN'S DREAM** (FR) 59
364 **GENTLY SPOKEN** (FR) 33
77 **GENUINE APPROVAL** (IRE) 15
29 **GENUINE QUALITY** (USA) C 110
491 **GEOGRAPHY TEACHER** (IRE) 13
511 **GEOMETRIST** 113
444 **GEONICE** (FR) 14
583 **GEORDIE** B 33
124 **GEORDIE DES CHAMPS** (IRE) 7
261 **GEORDIE WASHINGTON** (IRE) 14
148 **GEORDIELANDGANGSTA** 16
458 **GEORDIES DREAM** 6
16 **GEORGE BAKER** (IRE) 14
30 **GEORGE BANCROFT** 73
186 **GEORGE BOWEN** (IRE) 23
443 **GEORGE DRYDEN** (IRE) 1
325 **GEORGE GENTLY** (FR) 2
206 **GEORGE HASTINGS** 7
465 **GEORGE MALLORY** 10
84 **GEORGE MORLAND** 38
16 **GEORGE OF HEARTS** (FR) 15

534 **GEORGE OF NAUNTON** (IRE) 35
472 **GEORGE PEABODY** (IRE) 31
169 **GEORGE RIDSDALE** 23
192 **GEORGE SCOTT** (IRE) 60
172 **GEORGE THOMAS** 5
212 **GEORGE VALENTINE** (FR) 26
254 **GEORGETTE FUN** (IRE) 25
329 **GEORGIAN FIREBIRD** 4
193 **GEORGIE HYDE** C 9
424 **GERBOISE BORGET** (FR) 26
49 **GERIKA** (FR) C 68
298 **GEROLAMO CARDANO** 5
524 **GERONIMO** 15
91 **GERRY THE GLOVER** (IRE) 9
593 **GERSJOEYCASEY** (IRE) 3
518 **GERT LUSH** (IRE) 27
499 **GERTCHA** (IRE) 29
527 **GERTRUDE GRAY** (IRE) C 11
52 **GET AN OSCAR** (IRE) 15
212 **GET BACK GET BACK** (IRE) 27
128 **GET BOOSTING** 85
110 **GET HELP** (IRE) 10
356 **GET IN ROBIN** (IRE) 37
117 **GET IT** 80
150 **GET KNOTTED** (IRE) 11
405 **GET ME HOME** (IRE) F 75
484 **GET ON THE YAGER** 46
225 **GET OUT THE GATE** (IRE) 10
424 **GET PREPARED** 27
418 **GET REAL** (IRE) 16
317 **GET REAL** (IRE) 23
405 **GET THE APPEAL** (IRE) 76
64 **GET THE FACTS** (IRE) 7
379 **GET THE LOOK** (IRE) 14
417 **GET UP THEM STEPS** 6
131 **GET WISHING** (IRE) 8
148 **GET WITH IT** (IRE) 17
392 **GETABIRD** (IRE) 96
512 **GETABUCK** (IRE) 13
432 **GETALEAD** (IRE) 4
298 **GETAMAN** (IRE) 6
392 **GETAREASON** (IRE) 97
484 **GETARIVER** (IRE) 47
432 **GETAROUND** (IRE) 5
493 **GETAWAY BAY** (IRE) 17
526 **GETAWAY FRED** (IRE) 36
392 **GETAWAY GERRY** 4
392 **GETAWAY GORGEOUS** (IRE) 98
246 **GETAWAY KID** (IRE) 4
395 **GETAWAY LUV** (IRE) 40
484 **GETAWAY MAG** (IRE) 48
577 **GETAWAY MISSION** (IRE) 34
436 **GETAWAY NORTH** 5
494 **GETAWAY SUZY** (IRE) 6
446 **GETAWAY TOTHEROCK** (IRE) 17
405 **GETAWAY TRUMP** (IRE) 77
124 **GETAWAY WITHIT** (IRE) 8
479 **GETAWAYTONEWBAY** (IRE) 2
117 **GETCHAGETCHAGETCHA** 3
138 **GETTYSBURGH** (IRE) 1
397 **GEYSER** 7
175 **GHADBBAAN** 20
339 **GHAITH** 12
6 **GHAIYYATH** (IRE) 9
27 **GHALIB** (IRE) 10
39 **GHALY** 16
529 **GHALYOON** 5
272 **GHANAATI** (USA) C 86

540 **GO LADY** (GER) 8
576 **GO LONG** (IRE) 32
537 **GO LOVELY ROSE** (IRE) C 148
173 **GO MILLIE GO** (IRE) 9
221 **GO ON BRYCEY LAD** (FR) 44
476 **GO ON MY COCKER** 6
233 **GO PHARISEE FLYER** (FR) 28
484 **GO STEADY** 51
197 **GO WELL SPICY** (IRE) 8
227 **GO WHATEVER** (IRE) 14
534 **GOA LIL** (FR) 36
365 **GOAHEADWITHTHEPLAN** 47
556 **GOAL** (IRE) 2
537 **GOATHEMALA** (GER) C 149
305 **GOBI SUNSET** 69
254 **GOD KNOWS WHY** (IRE) 27
221 **GOD'S OWN** (IRE) 45
464 **GODDESS OF FIRE** 15
132 **GODFATHER** (IRE) 32
228 **GODHEAD** 13
569 **GODLYLADY** (IRE) G 11
173 **GOELETTE** (FR) 12
356 **GOFFSBRIDGE GIRL** (IRE) 39
178 **GOING MOBILE** (IRE) 6
581 **GOING NATIVE** 4
537 **GOING PLACES** 13
83 **GOLAN CLOUD** (IRE) 19
369 **GOLAN FORTUNE** (IRE) 2
392 **GOLAZO** (IRE) 99
423 **GOLCONDA PRINCE** (IRE) 2
326 **GOLD ARCH** 2
386 **GOLD AT MIDNIGHT** 6
7 **GOLD BROCADE** (IRE) 106
305 **GOLD BUBBLES** (USA) C 167
91 **GOLD CLUB** 11
451 **GOLD DECREE** (IRE) 3
254 **GOLD DES BOIS** 28
251 **GOLD DESERT** 62
381 **GOLD FIELDS** 12
200 **GOLD HUNTER** (IRE) 4
212 **GOLD IN DOHA** (FR) 28
327 **GOLD LINK** (FR) 28
189 **GOLD MAN** (IRE) 19
254 **GOLD MAZE** (IRE) 95
410 **GOLD MERLION** (IRE) 4
308 **GOLD MOUNTAIN** (IRE) 20
128 **GOLD OPERA** (IRE) 27
114 **GOLD PATROL** (IRE) 4
268 **GOLD PRESENT** (IRE) 75
563 **GOLD REEF** F 8
305 **GOLD RIBBON** (70)
516 **GOLD SANDS** (IRE) F 69
305 **GOLD SOUK** (IRE) 71
89 **GOLD STANDARD** (IRE) 27
39 **GOLD STAR** 20
97 **GOLD TRIP** (FR) 37
294 **GOLD VENTURE** (IRE) 5
537 **GOLD WAND** (IRE) 53
305 **GOLD ZABEEL** (IRE) 72
305 **GOLDCREST** F 168
170 **GOLDEN APOLLO** 39
132 **GOLDEN ARMOUR** 61
192 **GOLDEN BEAR** (IRE) 61
378 **GOLDEN BOY GREY** (FR) 61
51 **GOLDEN CHANCER** 4
17 **GOLDEN CRUSADER** 147
29 **GOLDEN CYGNET** 50
188 **GOLDEN DAWN** (IRE) 37

214 **GOLDEN DIRHAM** C 68
582 **GOLDEN DRAGON** (IRE) 49
388 **GOLDEN EMBLEM** (IRE) 30
61 **GOLDEN FIREBIRD** (IRE) G 12
192 **GOLDEN FORCE** 9
305 **GOLDEN FOUNTAIN** (IRE) 73
405 **GOLDEN GIFT** (IRE) 81
132 **GOLDEN GLIMMER** (IRE) F 62
508 **GOLDEN GLORY** (IRE) 10
577 **GOLDEN GRENADE** (FR) 36
508 **GOLDEN GROVE** (IRE) 11
117 **GOLDEN HORDE** (IRE) 30
168 **GOLDEN HOUR** (USA) 4
435 **GOLDEN JEFFREY** (SWI) 23
163 **GOLDEN LIPS** (IRE) 16
242 **GOLDEN MELODY** (IRE) 141
376 **GOLDEN NECTAR** 5
422 **GOLDEN PASS** 32
511 **GOLDEN PINE** (IRE) 49
74 **GOLDEN POET** (IRE) 3
493 **GOLDEN ROBIN** (IRE) 18
228 **GOLDEN RULES** 76
295 **GOLDEN SANDBANKS** 49
251 **GOLDEN SHADOW** (IRE) C 179
117 **GOLDEN SHINE** C 81
274 **GOLDEN SOVEREIGN** (IRE) 42
392 **GOLDEN SPREAD** 100
526 **GOLDEN SUNRISE** (IRE) 38
411 **GOLDEN TAIPAN** (IRE) 35
305 **GOLDEN TIMES** (SWI) 74
374 **GOLDEN TOWN** (IRE) 5
2 **GOLDEN WATTLE** (IRE) 7
576 **GOLDEN WHISKY** (IRE) 33
89 **GOLDEN WOLF** (IRE) 28
128 **GOLDENCARD** (IRE) 28
388 **GOLDENEYE VEE** 31
62 **GOLDFOX GREY** 13
548 **GOLDIE HAWK** 22
323 **GOLDISTYLE** (IRE) 59
279 **GOLDRAPPER** (IRE) 2
247 **GOLDSLINGER** (FR) 2
18 **GOLEADOR NAO** (FR) 9
128 **GOMETRA GINTY** (IRE) 29
6 **GOMBARDA** (GER) C 154
243 **GONE IN SIXTY** 34
448 **GONE PLATINUM** (IRE) 6
317 **GONN AWAY** (IRE) 24
473 **GONNABEGOOD** (IRE) 17
31 **GONZAGA** 1
356 **GOOBINATOR** (USA) 40
324 **GOOCHYPOOCHYPRADER** G 2
411 **GOOD AND HARDY** (IRE) 36
242 **GOOD AND PROPER** 142
116 **GOOD ANSWER** 9
17 **GOOD BIRTHDAY** (IRE) 24
534 **GOOD BOY BOBBY** (IRE) 37
179 **GOOD COP** 27
419 **GOOD EARTH** (IRE) 19
375 **GOOD EFFORT** (IRE) 6
193 **GOOD FOR HER** C 11
6 **GOOD FORTUNE** 12
537 **GOOD HUMOR** 54
72 **GOOD IMPRESSION** 5
251 **GOOD JOB POWER** (IRE) 63
370 **GOOD LUCK FOX** (IRE) 7
362 **GOOD MAN** (IRE) 7
221 **GOOD MAN JIM** (FR) 44
315 **GOOD MAN PAT** (IRE) 45

94 **GOOD MORNING LADY** C 95
451 **GOOD NEWS** 4
7 **GOOD OLE WINNIE** 46
519 **GOOD RISK AT ALL** (FR) 5
392 **GOOD THYNE TARA** 101
228 **GOOD TIDINGS** (FR) 14
35 **GOOD TIME AHEAD** (IRE) 10
117 **GOOD TIME CHARLIE** 31
150 **GOOD VIBES** 34
411 **GOODBYE DANCER** (FR) 37
592 **GOODGIRLTERESA** (IRE) 8
210 **GOODGOLLYMISSJOLLY** (IRE) 6
213 **GOODNIGHT CHARLIE** 4
330 **GOODTOKNOW** 10
320 **GOODWOOD GLEN** 33
320 **GOODWOOD REBEL** (IRE) 16
73 **GOOSE LIGHTNING** 41
85 **GOOSEN MAVERICK** (IRE) 3
210 **GORCOMBE'S RASCAL** 7
317 **GORDALAN** 25
107 **GORDONSTOUN** 30
389 **GORGEOUS GENERAL** 3
112 **GORGEOUS GOBOLINA** 3
378 **GORHAM'S CAVE** 62
304 **GORING** (GER) 10
403 **GORING ONE** (IRE) 3
484 **GORTROE JOE** (IRE) 52
17 **GOSBECK** C 148
378 **GOSHEN** (FR) 63
274 **GOSHEVEN** (IRE) 43
402 **GOSPELUS** (FR) 32
364 **GOSSIP** 34
378 **GOSSIPING** 64
480 **GOT AWAY** (FR) 18
128 **GOT THE T SHIRT** 87
547 **GOT TO DREAM** C 90
254 **GOT TRUMPED** 29
162 **GOTTARDO** (IRE) 8
234 **GOUET DES BRUYERES** (FR) 21
244 **GOUGANE BARRA** (USA) 6
457 **GOULANES** (IRE) 3
47 **GOUREL** (FR) 4
376 **GOUTEZ MOI** (FR) 6
112 **GOWANBUSTER** 4
317 **GOWANLAD** 83
112 **GOWANLASSIE** 25
424 **GOWITHTHEFLOW** (IRE) 29
186 **GRACE AND DANGER** (IRE) 25
6 **GRACE AND FAVOUR** C 155
186 **GRACE AND VIRTUE** (IRE) 89
29 **GRACE NOTE** 51
499 **GRACE PLUNKETT** 30
25 **GRACEFUL ACT** 4
207 **GRACEFUL JAMES** (IRE) 5
172 **GRACEFUL LADY** 6
92 **GRACEFUL LEGEND** 13
304 **GRACEFUL MAGIC** 36
132 **GRACEFUL MOMENT** (IRE) 63
395 **GRACES ORDER** (IRE) 42
7 **GRACIE'S GIRL** 107
207 **GRACIOUS GEORGE** (IRE) 6
577 **GRACIOUS JOHN** (IRE) 37
537 **GRACIOUSLY** C 150
15 **GRAFFITI** C 24
411 **GRAGEELAGH GIRL** (IRE) 38
16 **GRAIGNES** (FR) 16
29 **GRAIN OF SENSE** (IRE) 52
287 **GRAINEYHILL** (IRE) 6

255 **GRAMS AND OUNCES** 8
268 **GRAN LUNA** (FR) 76
499 **GRANADILLA** C 47
228 **GRAND BAZAAR** 71
104 **GRAND CANAL** (IRE) 18
234 **GRAND COUREUR** (FR) 22
249 **GRAND DU NORD** (FR) 29
279 **GRAND ENTERPRISE** 3
382 **GRAND GOSIER** (FR) 35
151 **GRAND INQUISITOR** 6
173 **GRAND LORD** (FR) 13
268 **GRAND MOGUL** (IRE) 77
463 **GRAND MORNING** 35
170 **GRAND PIANOLA** 114
242 **GRAND ROCK** (IRE) 65
268 **GRAND ROI** (FR) 78
405 **GRAND SANCY** (FR) 82
405 **GRAND SLAM** (FR) 83
583 **GRAND TURINA** 35
512 **GRANDAD'S LEGACY** 14
427 **GRANDADS BEST GIRL** 12
395 **GRANDADS COTTAGE** (IRE) 43
291 **GRANDBOB** 46
251 **GRANDE RUMORE** 64
191 **GRANDEE** (IRE) 12
7 **GRANDEE DAISY** 47
116 **GRANDFATHER TOM** 10
175 **GRANDMA** 62
162 **GRANDSCAPE** 9
441 **GRANDSTAND** (IRE) 5
249 **GRANGE RANGER** (IRE) 30
435 **GRANGECLARE GLORY** (IRE) 24
227 **GRANGECLARE RHYTHM** (IRE) F 15
576 **GRANIA O'MALLEY** (IRE) 34
407 **GRANITE CITY DOC** 3
391 **GRANITIC** (IRE) 8
299 **GRANNY FRANKHAM** 10
254 **GRANNY FRANNY** F 96
26 **GRANNY GREY** (IRE) 25
188 **GRANNY MELBA** 69
119 **GRANNY ROZ** 8
424 **GRANNY'S SECRET** (IRE) 30
36 **GRANTLEY** (IRE) 25
215 **GRAPE SODA** 1
331 **GRAPEVINE** (IRE) 12
12 **GRASMERE** (FR) 3
345 **GRATOT** (FR) 3
73 **GRAVITY FORCE** 42
198 **GRAVITY WAVE** (IRE) 11
356 **GRAY DAY** (IRE) 41
69 **GRAYBOY** 1
237 **GRAYHAWK** (IRE) 2
364 **GRAYLING** 10
110 **GRAYSTOWN** (IRE) 11
405 **GREANETEEN** (FR) 84
29 **GREAT AMBASSADOR** 53
46 **GREAT COLACI** 9
39 **GREAT EXAMPLE** 21
392 **GREAT FIELD** (FR) 102
405 **GREAT GABLE** (FR) 85
445 **GREAT HALL** 2
39 **GREAT HONOUR** (IRE) 81
305 **GREAT HOPE** (IRE) C 169
39 **GREAT IMAGE** (IRE) 82
435 **GREAT TEMPO** (FR) 25
392 **GREAT WHITE SHARK** (FR) 103
437 **GREATER LOVE** 19
7 **GREATEST JOURNEY** 48

188 **GREEK FLAME** (FR) 70
409 **GREEK GLADIATOR** (IRE) 43
445 **GREEK KODIAC** (IRE) 3
548 **GREEK OASIS** 2
88 **GREEK SPIRIT** (IRE) C 26
175 **GREEN BOOK** (FR) 63
212 **GREEN DOLPHIN** (IRE) 29
116 **GREEN DOOR** (IRE) 11
446 **GREEN ETOILE** 19
47 **GREEN GLORY** (FR) 28
388 **GREEN OR BLACK** (IRE) 32
215 **GREEN POWER** 4
409 **GREEN ROOM** (USA) F 141
47 **GREEN SIREN** (FR) 5
47 **GREEN SPIRIT** (FR) 14
511 **GREEN SWALLOW** (FR) C 116
259 **GREEN ZONE** (IRE) 1
470 **GREENERY** (IRE) F 8
133 **GREENGAGE** (IRE) 6
254 **GREENISLAND** C 159
84 **GREENSIDE** 1
473 **GREENVIEW PARADISE** (IRE) 18
62 **GREG** 14
541 **GREGARIOUS** (IRE) 10
291 **GREGORIAN GIRL** (IRE) 16
483 **GREGORY K** (USA) 42
281 **GREGORY THE GREAT** 2
305 **GRENADIER GUARD** (IRE) 15
409 **GRENADINE** (IRE) 44
365 **GREY ANGEL** (FR) 142
334 **GREY D'ARS** (FR) 9
534 **GREY DIAMOND** (FR) 38
224 **GREY EMINENCE** 7
112 **GREY EXPECTATIONS** 5
14 **GREY FELIX** 24
14 **GREY FLINT** 25
327 **GREY FOX** (FR) 73
405 **GREY GETAWAY** (IRE) 86
362 **GREY MIST** 8
463 **GREY WAR** (IRE) 96
261 **GREYBOUGG** 16
371 **GREYCICAL GIRL** (IRE) 39
188 **GREYCOAT** 38
26 **GREYFIRE** 26
123 **GRIGGY** (IRE) 5
292 **GRIMTHORPE** 3
251 **GRINLING** (IRE) 65
463 **GRIPPER** 36
279 **GRIS DE PRON** (FR) 4
315 **GRISBI DE BERCE** (FR) 46
116 **GRISONS** (FR) 12
254 **GRIZZLY** (IRE) 97
446 **GROOVEUR** (FR) 20
405 **GROOVY KIND** (FR) 87
511 **GROSSE POINTE ANNE** (USA) F 117
315 **GROSVENOR COURT** 47
370 **GROUNDWORKER** (FR) 8
17 **GROUP ONE POWER** 75
315 **GROUP STAGE** (GER) 48
517 **GROUPIE** 7
485 **GROUSEMAN** 23
17 **GROVE FERRY** 76
412 **GROVEMAN** 11
588 **GROW NASA GROW** (IRE) 19
568 **GRUMPY BOOTS** (IRE) 19
128 **GRUMPY MCGRUMPFACE** (IRE) 30
63 **GUADALOUP** F 23
392 **GUARD OF HONOUR** (IRE) 104

534 **GUARD YOUR DREAMS** 39
191 **GUARDIA SVIZZERA** (IRE) 13
261 **GUARDIA TOP** (FR) 17
335 **GUARDIOLA** (USA) 7
424 **GUENA DES MOTTES** (FR) 31
274 **GUERNSEY** (FR) 44
378 **GUGUSS COLLONGES** (FR) 65
365 **GUIDED BY YOU** (IRE) 48
356 **GUILDHALL** 42
93 **GUILTY PARTY** (IRE) 18
73 **GUIPURE** 43
452 **GUITAR PETE** (IRE) 20
169 **GULF OF POETS** 24
90 **GULLAND ROCK** 7
170 **GULLANE ONE** (IRE) 40
413 **GULLIVER** 24
20 **GULSHANIGANS** 10
274 **GUMBALL** (FR) 45
562 **GUMBO FLYER** (FR) 11
568 **GUN CASE** 20
327 **GUNFLEET** (IRE) 29
87 **GUNMAKER** (IRE) 13
26 **GUNMETAL** (IRE) 8
420 **GUNNER MOYNE** 8
268 **GUNNERY** (FR) 79
395 **GUNSIGHT RIDGE** 44
69 **GUPTA** 2
362 **GURKHA FRIEND** 9
518 **GURKHA GIRL** (IRE) 37
386 **GURMIL** 7
49 **GUROOR** 10
137 **GUSTAV** (IRE) 10
251 **GUSTAV HOLST** (IRE) 180
1 **GUSTAV'S DREAM** (IRE) 57
331 **GUSTAVE AITCH** (IRE) 13
446 **GUSTAVE MAHLER** (IRE) 21
283 **GUSTAVIAN** (IRE) 12
530 **GUVENOR'S CHOICE** (IRE) 6
534 **GUY** (IRE) 40
526 **GUY DE GUYE** (FR) 39
562 **GWAFA** (IRE) 12
474 **GWEEDORE** 16
323 **GWENDOLA** 6
384 **GWENHWYVAR** (IRE) 57
261 **GWENNOLINE** (FR) 18
170 **GWYRE** (IRE) G 41
211 **GYPSY TRAVELLER** 30
367 **GYPSY WHISPER** 16
305 **HA'PENNY BRIDGE** (IRE) 75
93 **HAABIS** (USA) 5
485 **HAAFAPIECE** 10
537 **HAAFITHAH** 55
76 **HAAJOOS** (USA) 62
381 **HAASAB** (IRE) 13
251 **HAAYEM** (FR) 12
300 **HAB SAB** (IRE) 7
49 **HABIT ROUGE** 38
537 **HABITA** (IRE) F 151
76 **HABUB** (USA) 8
211 **HACHERT** 31
429 **HACKBRIDGE** 7
538 **HACKNESS HARRY** 24
315 **HACKSAW RIDGE** (IRE) 49
365 **HAD TO BE DONE** G 49
251 **HADDAD** (IRE) 66
305 **HADEED** 76
76 **HAFEETH** (USA) 26
251 **HAFEZ** (IRE) 181

103 **HAGWAAT** (FR) 25
142 **HAHADI** (IRE) 16
272 **HAIDA GWAII** (IRE) 46
76 **HAIDARAH** 27
519 **HAIDEES REFLECTION** F 38
76 **HAIKAL** 28
483 **HAILEY D'ORO** (USA) C 74
15 **HAJJAM** 12
486 **HAKURAA** (IRE) F 39
465 **HALA HALA** (IRE) F 90
484 **HALA PRINCESS** (IRE) 53
6 **HALAY** C 156
368 **HALCYON DAYS** 21
131 **HALDON HILL** (IRE) 9
349 **HALEY BOP** (IRE) C 13
545 **HALF BOLLY** 11
255 **HALF NELSON** 9
416 **HALF OF SEVEN** 102
365 **HALF THE ODDS** (IRE) 50
419 **HALFACROWN** (IRE) 20
532 **HALFWAYTOPARADISE** C 21
228 **HALFWAYTOTHEMOON** (IRE) 78
511 **HALIC** 118
220 **HALLE'S HARBOUR** 3
341 **HALLINGS COMET** 4
154 **HALLO SEXY** C 3
371 **HALLOWED CASTLE** (IRE) 21
211 **HALLOWED DREAM** (IRE) 32
274 **HALLOWEEN HARRY** (IRE) 46
76 **HAMAAYIM** (FR) 29
244 **HAMARIYNA** (IRE) 7
578 **HAMILTON DICI** (FR) 15
268 **HAMILTON'S FANTASY** 80
242 **HAMISH** 10
422 **HAMISH MACBETH** 33
413 **HAMLOOLA** C 103
76 **HAMMAD** (USA) 30
476 **HAMMER GUN** (USA) 7
386 **HAMMY END** (IRE) 8
548 **HAN SOLO BERGER** (IRE) 6
76 **HANAFY** (USA) 31
175 **HANATI** (IRE) 21
117 **HAND ON MY HEART** 32
251 **HANDBELL** (IRE) C 182
42 **HANDFUL OF GOLD** (IRE) 15
226 **HANDIWORK** 4
128 **HANDLEBARS** (IRE) 88
499 **HANDSOME SAMSON** 4
214 **HANDSOME YANK** (USA) 47
356 **HANDY HOLLOW** (IRE) 43
371 **HANDYTALK** (IRE) 6
327 **HANG IN THERE** (IRE) 30
416 **HANG TOUGH** 37
319 **HANGARD** 26
6 **HANKY PANKY** (IRE) C 157
567 **HANNA HVAR** 5
522 **HANNAH CAVAGIN** 12
512 **HANNALITE** 35
47 **HANZI BELINE** (FR) 15
30 **HAPPINESS NEEDSART** 74
489 **HAPPY CRAF** (ARG) 10
330 **HAPPY DIVA** (IRE) 11
531 **HAPPY FACE** (IRE) 10
83 **HAPPY HOLLOW** 20
101 **HAPPY HOLLY** (IRE) F 32
555 **HAPPY LAND** (IRE) F 22
238 **HAPPY NEWS** 8
17 **HAPPY POWER** (IRE) 26

251 **HAPPY ROMANCE** (IRE) 183
14 **HAPPYGOLUCKY** (IRE) 26
228 **HAQEEQY** (IRE) 79
244 **HARAKANN** (IRE) 32
315 **HARAMBE** 50
78 **HARAZ** (FR) 4
541 **HARBOUR BREEZE** (IRE) 11
388 **HARBOUR FORCE** (FR) 33
62 **HARBOUR FRONT** 15
170 **HARBOUR MIST** (IRE) 115
49 **HARBOUR OF GRACE** (FR) 39
7 **HARBOUR POINT** 108
89 **HARBOUR PROJECT** 3
93 **HARBOUR QUAY** 6
62 **HARBOUR STORM** 16
258 **HARBOUR SUNRISE** 4
93 **HARBOUR TIMES** (IRE) 7
476 **HARBOUR VISION** 8
317 **HARCANA LE DUN** (FR) 84
405 **HARD FROST** (FR) 183
302 **HARD KNOCKS** (IRE) 5
427 **HARD NUT** (IRE) 13
413 **HARD SOLUTION** 25
418 **HARD TO FORGET** (IRE) 17
347 **HARD TO HANDEL** 5
2 **HARD TOFFEE** (IRE) 2
142 **HARDY ARTICOS** (IRE) 17
73 **HAREEM QUEEN** (IRE) 7
227 **HAREFIELD** (IRE) 16
531 **HARES ROCKET** (IRE) 22
305 **HARLEM SOUL** 170
320 **HARLEQUIN** 17
93 **HARLEQUIN ROSE** (IRE) 8
112 **HARLEYS MAX** 6
577 **HARLOW** 38
393 **HARMATTAN** 10
564 **HARMONISE** 7
26 **HARMONY BAY** (IRE) C 42
132 **HARMONY LIL** (IRE) 64
191 **HAROME** (IRE) 14
29 **HARPIST** (IRE) C 111
392 **HARRIE** (IRE) F 105
557 **HARRISON POINT** (FR) 35
54 **HARROGATE** (IRE) 8
228 **HARROVIAN** 15
315 **HARROWBY** 51
365 **HARRY ALONZO** (IRE) 51
175 **HARRY GEORGE** (IRE) 22
137 **HARRY HAZARD** 11
130 **HARRY HAZE** 3
16 **HARRY HURRICANE** 17
426 **HARRY LOVE** (IRE) 12
526 **HARRY SENIOR** (IRE) 40
562 **HARRY THE NORSEMAN** 13
188 **HARRY'S BAR** 7
5 **HARRY'S RIDGE** (IRE) 4
186 **HARRYJOEJOE** 25
179 **HARSTON** 28
211 **HART FELL** 10
356 **HART OF STEEL** (IRE) 44
582 **HART STOPPER** 14
465 **HART'S DREAM** 52
261 **HARTLAND QUAY** (IRE) 19
131 **HARTNOLL HERO** (IRE) 10
588 **HARTSIDE** (GER) 6
186 **HARTSWOOD** 90
365 **HARVEST BOW** (IRE) 52
169 **HARVEST DAY** 25

577 **HASANABAD** (IRE) 39
381 **HASANKEY** 15
244 **HASANZA** (USA) F 70
537 **HASEENAH** (IRE) 56
405 **HASHTAG BOUM** (IRE) 184
419 **HASHTAGMETOO** (USA) 21
389 **HASILI FILLY** 4
557 **HASSAAD** 3
524 **HASTRUBAL** (FR) 16
511 **HASTY SAILOR** (IRE) 50
484 **HATCHER** (IRE) 54
269 **HATCHET JACK** (IRE) 11
54 **HATEYA** (IRE) 9
305 **HATHEEM** (IRE) 77
76 **HATHRAH** (IRE) C 63
94 **HATS OFF TO LARRY** 10
429 **HATSAWAY** (IRE) 7
39 **HATTA MOUNTAINS** (IRE) 83
363 **HATTAAB** 31
279 **HATTONS HILL** (IRE) 5
39 **HAUGHTILY** (IRE) C 147
268 **HAUL AWAY** (IRE) 81
463 **HAUL US IN** (IRE) 37
463 **HAUTE ESTIME** (IRE) 97
218 **HAVACUPPA** 4
292 **HAVANA BAY** 4
103 **HAVANA BOUND** 26
346 **HAVANA DAWN** 18
173 **HAVANA HERMANO** (IRE) 14
314 **HAVANA JACK** (IRE) 2
34 **HAVANA KNIGHT** 25
295 **HAVANA PARTY** 58
189 **HAVANA RIVER** (IRE) 20
17 **HAVANA ROCKET** (IRE) 27
394 **HAVANA SUNSET** 8
575 **HAVE A GO HERO** (IRE) 4
437 **HAVE TO HAVE** 44
77 **HAVEONEYERSELF** (IRE) 16
339 **HAVERGATE** F 54
192 **HAVERLAND** (IRE) 10
316 **HAVEYOUBEEN** (IRE) F 14
295 **HAVEYOUMISSEDME** 59
117 **HAVIN' A GOOD TIME** (IRE) C 82
539 **HAWA BLADI** (IRE) 47
529 **HAWAAFEZ** F 40
76 **HAWAAJIS** (IRE) 32
557 **HAWAFEZ** (IRE) 9
54 **HAWK DANCE** (IRE) C 23
170 **HAWK HIGH** (IRE) 42
570 **HAWK IN THE SKY** 2
424 **HAWK WIND** (IRE) 32
327 **HAWK'S WELL** (IRE) 31
222 **HAWKERLAND** (IRE) 14
228 **HAWKISH** 80
371 **HAWRIDGE FLYER** 7
371 **HAWRIDGE STORM** (IRE) 8
545 **HAWSIES DREAM** G 36
393 **HAWTHORN COTTAGE** (IRE) 11
27 **HAYADH** 11
491 **HAYMARKET** 16
170 **HAYUPLASS** 116
55 **HAYYEL** (IRE) 1
295 **HAZALOU** 60
331 **HAZAMAR** (IRE) 14
244 **HAZARABA** (IRE) F 71
388 **HAZEL BANK LASS** (IRE) F 107
501 **HAZEL BLUE** (IRE) F 26
539 **HAZM** (IRE) 48

412 **HAZY DANCER** F 54
153 **HAZY DREAM** 10
583 **HAZZAAR** (IRE) 36
422 **HE DO** 72
329 **HE'S A GOER** (IRE) 5
132 **HE'S A KEEPER** (IRE) 33
557 **HE'S A LADDIE** (IRE) 36
208 **HE'S GUILTY** (USA) 4
197 **HE'S MAGIC** 3
512 **HE'S OUR STAR** (IRE) 15
327 **HEAD FOR THE HILLS** 32
280 **HEAD HIGH** (IRE) 5
475 **HEAD HUNTER** (IRE) 14
484 **HEAD LAD** (FR) 55
121 **HEAD OF THE HOUSE** (IRE) 45
577 **HEAD ON** (IRE) 40
129 **HEAD TO THE STARS** 13
305 **HEADING NORTH** C 171
364 **HEADLAND** 11
152 **HEADLEY GEORGE** (IRE) 18
516 **HEADLINER** (IRE) 70
101 **HEADMAN** 8
452 **HEADSCARF LIL** (IRE) 21
101 **HEALING MUSIC** (FR) F 78
214 **HEALING POWER** 14
150 **HEAR ME ROAR** (IRE) 61
258 **HEAR THE CHIMES** 5
315 **HEART OF A LION** (IRE) 52
261 **HEART OF KERNOW** (IRE) 20
383 **HEART OF SOUL** (IRE) 7
29 **HEART REEF** F 54
112 **HEARTASIA** (IRE) 7
356 **HEARTBREAK KID** (IRE) 45
483 **HEARTLESS** F 75
342 **HEARTSTAR** 18
532 **HEARTSTRINGS** C 22
439 **HEAT AND DUST** 45
150 **HEATH CHARNOCK** 12
238 **HEATHER FEATHER** (IRE) F 9
30 **HEATHERDOWN MATRON** 75
112 **HEATHERLEA** (IRE) 8
511 **HEAVEN FORFEND** 51
409 **HEAVEN OF HEAVENS** (IRE) 45
33 **HEAVEN UP HERE** (IRE) 7
422 **HEAVEN'S ANGEL** (IRE) F 73
411 **HEAVENLY PROMISE** (IRE) 39
270 **HEAVENLY RAINBOW** (IRE) 8
49 **HEAVENLY SCENT** F 69
133 **HEAVENLY TALE** (IRE) 7
186 **HEAVENS OPEN** 91
94 **HEAVENTREE** (IRE) 42
388 **HEAVEY** 34
579 **HECTOR DE SIVOLA** (FR) 23
152 **HECTOR LOZA** 19
463 **HECTOR MASTER** (FR) 98
214 **HECTOR'S HERE** 15
76 **HEDAAYA** (FR) F 64
304 **HEDGING** (IRE) 11
588 **HEDIDDODINTHE** (IRE) 7
300 **HEER ME** 21
180 **HEER WE GO AGAIN** 30
563 **HEERCOMESHARRIE** 9
566 **HEEZARARITY** 4
272 **HEHO** C 87
192 **HEIGHT OF VANITY** (IRE) G 38
9 **HEIR** (FR) 38
365 **HEISENBERG** (IRE) 53
267 **HELETA** 8

526 **HELFORD RIVER** 41
192 **HELIAEBEL** 39
162 **HELIAN** (IRE) 10
254 **HELIERS BAY** (IRE) 30
579 **HELIOS ALLEN** (FR) 24
532 **HELL OF A JOKER** 18
212 **HELL'S KITCHEN** 30
437 **HELLAVAPACE** 45
156 **HELLO BOB** 9
363 **HELLO BUDDY** (IRE) 32
562 **HELLO SUNSHINE** (FR) 14
465 **HELLO YOUMZAIN** (FR) 12
441 **HELLOFAGAME** 6
7 **HELMET HOUSE** 109
533 **HELMOONA** 13
486 **HELOVAPLAN** (IRE) 7
211 **HELVETIAN** 11
29 **HELVEZIA** (IRE) 55
365 **HELVIC DREAM** 130
438 **HEMINGWAY** (IRE) 2
233 **HEN** (IRE) 29
372 **HENCHARD** 2
501 **HENDERSON** 17
389 **HENET** (IRE) 9
542 **HENLEY** 5
320 **HENLEY PARK** 18
519 **HENRI BELLA** G 29
330 **HENRI LE BON** (IRE) 12
572 **HENRIETTA BELL** (IRE) 15
62 **HENRIETTA'S DREAM** 17
365 **HENRY BROWN** (IRE) 54
89 **HENRY CROFT** 29
416 **HENRY GONDOFF** 38
495 **HENRY OLIVER** (IRE) 3
146 **HENRY THE SIXTH** 10
356 **HENRY'S JOY** (IRE) 46
233 **HENSCHKE** (IRE) 30
512 **HEPBURN** 16
173 **HEPIJEU** (FR) 15
395 **HER DREAM** (IRE) 45
192 **HER HONOUR** (IRE) F 62
315 **HER INDOORS** (IRE) 145
101 **HER WAY** 79
170 **HERBERT POCKET** 117
582 **HERCULEAN** 15
29 **HERE AGAIN** 112
29 **HERE AND NOW** 17
595 **HERE COMES LOVE** (IRE) 7
395 **HERE COMES MCCOY** (IRE) 46
22 **HERE COMES MOLLY** (IRE) 2
395 **HERE COMES TRUBLE** (IRE) 47
523 **HERE IN THE DARK** 5
218 **HERE'S BINGO** 5
218 **HERE'S HERBIE** 6
278 **HERE'S TWO** 4
29 **HEREBY** (IRE) 18
388 **HEREIA** (IRE) 35
512 **HERESMYNUMBER** (IRE) 17
180 **HERM** (IRE) 10
312 **HERMANUS** (IRE) 4
342 **HERMOCRATES** (FR) 9
242 **HERO OF THE HOUR** 66
17 **HERODOTUS** (IRE) 77
365 **HEROESANDVILLAINS** 55
301 **HERON** (USA) 5
429 **HERRE DITTERY** 23
88 **HERRIDGE** (IRE) C 27
282 **HERRING BAY** 8

489 **HERRINGSWELL** (FR) 6
365 **HES A HARDY BLOKE** (IRE) 56
14 **HES NO TROUBLE** (IRE) 27
390 **HES OUR ROBIN** (IRE) 6
36 **HESSLEWOOD** (IRE) 5
73 **HESSSA** 44
437 **HESTERCOMBE** 46
391 **HEWN FROM GRANITE** 9
101 **HEXAGON** (IRE) 33
230 **HEY BOB** (IRE) 18
473 **HEY BUD** 19
516 **HEY GAMAN** 3
29 **HEY GRACIE** 19
273 **HEY HO LET'S GO** 2
122 **HEY JAZZY LADY** (IRE) 8
416 **HEY JOE** (IRE) 39
465 **HEY JONESY** (IRE) 13
537 **HEY MR** 152
88 **HI HARRY** (IRE) 18
173 **HI HO SILVA LINING** (IRE) 16
548 **HI HO SILVER** 7
94 **HI NOTE** F 96
344 **HI THERE SILVER** (IRE) 7
188 **HI WAY** 39
6 **HIBAAYEB** F 158
537 **HIBERNIAN WARRIOR** (USA) 57
339 **HIC BIBI** 14
539 **HICKEY'S ROCK** (IRE) 49
243 **HICONIC** 35
557 **HIDDEN ANGEL** (IRE) 37
245 **HIDDEN CARGO** (IRE) 4
16 **HIDDEN COVE** (IRE) F 44
388 **HIDDEN DEPTHS** (IRE) 36
77 **HIDDEN DREAM** (FR) 17
39 **HIDDEN EMOTION** (USA) 84
424 **HIDDEN GLEN** (IRE) 33
6 **HIDDEN GOLD** (IRE) F 159
33 **HIDDEN PEARL** 8
17 **HIDDEN VALLEY** C 149
339 **HIDE YOUR HEART** (IRE) 15
361 **HIDEAWAY** 2
283 **HIDEAWAY VIC** (IRE) 13
161 **HIER ENCORE** (FR) 1
244 **HIEROGLYPHIC** 33
16 **HIERONYMUS** 18
402 **HIGGS** (IRE) 33
156 **HIGGY HIGGINS** (IRE) 10
516 **HIGH ACCOLADE** (IRE) 22
228 **HIGH AMBITION** 81
122 **HIGH ANXIETY** 9
272 **HIGH CHANGE** (IRE) 10
304 **HIGH CLASS AFFAIR** (IRE) 37
107 **HIGH COMMISSIONER** (IRE) 4
250 **HIGH COUNSEL** (IRE) 4
260 **HIGH DRAMA** (IRE) C 52
39 **HIGH END** 22
511 **HIGH FINANCE** (IRE) C 119
132 **HIGH FLYING BIRD** (IRE) 34
362 **HIGH FORT** (IRE) 10
16 **HIGH HEELED HOPE** (USA) F 45
97 **HIGH LIMITS** (IRE) C 96
340 **HIGH MAINTENANCE** 38
2 **HIGH MEADOW ROSE** F 5
170 **HIGH MOON** 43
412 **HIGH MOOR FLYER** 39
249 **HIGH NOON** (IRE) 31
305 **HIGH PEAK** (IRE) 172
385 **HIGH REGARDS** (IRE) F 8

409 **HIGH SAVANNAH** (IRE) C 142
30 **HIGH SHINE** 29
94 **HIGH SOCIETY GIRL** (IRE) G 43
244 **HIGH SOCIETY GIRL** (IRE) F 42
378 **HIGH UP IN THE AIR** (IRE) 66
363 **HIGH WELLS** 33
395 **HIGHATE HILL** (IRE) 48
477 **HIGHDAWN** (IRE) 1
420 **HIGHER COURT** (USA) 9
557 **HIGHER KINGDOM** 38
511 **HIGHEST GROUND** (IRE) 52
526 **HIGHEST SUN** (FR) 42
179 **HIGHFALUTING** (IRE) 5
134 **HIGHJACKED** 3
413 **HIGHLAND ACCLAIM** (IRE) 26
395 **HIGHLAND BOBBY** 49
365 **HIGHLAND CHARGE** (IRE) 57
107 **HIGHLAND CHIEF** (IRE) 18
6 **HIGHLAND DANCER** (IRE) 62
413 **HIGHLAND DANDY** (IRE) 104
192 **HIGHLAND DREAMER** (IRE) 40
557 **HIGHLAND DRESS** 10
452 **HIGHLAND GOLD** 22
405 **HIGHLAND HUNTER** (IRE) 88
534 **HIGHLAND PARC** (IRE) 41
175 **HIGHLAND SKY** (IRE) 23
431 **HIGHLAND SUN** (IRE) 6
181 **HIGHLIGHT GIRL** M 7
27 **HIGHLIGHT REEL** (IRE) 12
327 **HIGHLY PRIZED** 33
185 **HIGHLY SPRUNG** (IRE) 7
323 **HIGHPHAR** F 60
420 **HIGHPLAINS DRIFTER** (IRE) 10
503 **HIGHPOINT WARRIER** 18
128 **HIGHWAY COMPANION** (IRE) 31
338 **HIGHWAY GIRL** 20
16 **HIGHWAY ONE** (USA) 19
227 **HIGHWAY ONE O ONE** (IRE) 17
227 **HIGHWAY ONE O TWO** (IRE) 18
190 **HIGHWAY ROBBERY** 4
52 **HIGHWAY STAR** (FR) 14
35 **HIGHWAY TO SUCCESS** (IRE) 11
170 **HIGHWAYGREY** 44
521 **HIGHWAYMAN** 5
265 **HIJA** 4
268 **HIJACK** (IRE) 82
418 **HIJRAN** (IRE) 18
584 **HILBRE LAKE** (USA) 6
493 **HILL SIXTEEN** 19
17 **HILL WELCOME** C 150
534 **HILLARY** C 42
123 **HILLARY JOHN** (IRE) 6
532 **HILLBILLY** 23
173 **HILLFINCH** 38
112 **HILLS OF CONNEMARA** (IRE) 9
170 **HILLWALKER** 45
44 **HIMEMIYA** 8
368 **HIMITAS** (FR) G 22
296 **HINDAAM** (USA) 4
254 **HINT OF STARS** (IRE) 98
34 **HIORNE TOWER** (FR) 11
555 **HIP** C 23
423 **HIPPOLYTE BOUCHARD** 3
578 **HIPSTER MACALO** (FR) 16
91 **HIROMICHI** (FR) 97
464 **HIROSHIMA** 4
416 **HIS DREAM** (IRE) 40
39 **HISTORIC** (IRE) 85

465 **HISTORICAL** 53
367 **HISTORY WRITER** (IRE) 8
411 **HIT THE BOTTLE** 40
227 **HIT THE HIGHWAY** (IRE) 7
378 **HIT THE ROCKS** (IRE) 67
148 **HITMAN FRED** (IRE) 18
422 **HLAITAN** 34
304 **HMS PRESIDENT** (IRE) 38
296 **HO LENG LUI** 11
169 **HO WHOLE DREAM** (IRE) 26
163 **HOBBY** C 29
305 **HOCHFELD** (IRE) 16
395 **HOGAN** (IRE) 50
496 **HOGAN'S HEIGHT** (IRE) 29
327 **HOI POLLOI** (IRE) 34
104 **HOLBROOK PARK** 6
182 **HOLD COURT** (IRE) 2
241 **HOLD ME TIGHT** (IRE) 4
386 **HOLD STILL** (IRE) 9
583 **HOLD THAT TAUGHT** 37
94 **HOLD THE NOTE** (IRE) 11
215 **HOLD YOUR BREATH** 5
212 **HOLDBACKTHENIGHT** (IRE) 31
576 **HOLDBACKTHERIVER** (IRE) 35
532 **HOLDENHURST** 5
22 **HOLEINTHEWALL BAR** (IRE) 3
91 **HOLIDAY MAGIC** (IRE) 12
164 **HOLLANDER** 18
582 **HOLLEY SHIFTWELL** F 57
577 **HOLLOW GOLD** (IRE) 41
440 **HOLLOW PARK** (IRE) 5
94 **HOLLY BALOO** (IRE) G 12
503 **HOLLY BLUE** F 43
128 **HOLLY FLIGHT** (FR) 32
576 **HOLLY JAMES** 36
304 **HOLLYANNA** 63
14 **HOLLYMOUNT HOLLY** (IRE) 28
103 **HOLLYWOOD** (IRE) 27
477 **HOLLYWOOD KEN** (IRE) 2
29 **HOLLYWOOD LADY** 113
515 **HOLLYWOODIEN** (FR) 11
452 **HOLME ABBEY** 23
30 **HOLY BEE** (IRE) 76
557 **HOLY ELEANOR** (IRE) 39
260 **HOLY GRAIL** (IRE) F 53
211 **HOLY HYMN** (IRE) 12
104 **HOLY KINGDOM** (IRE) 7
409 **HOLY ROMAN EMPRESS** (IRE) 46
164 **HOLY SMOKE** G 19
19 **HOLY TIBER** (IRE) 6
576 **HOLY VOW** (IRE) G 37
305 **HOME AND DRY** (IRE) 173
128 **HOME BEFORE DUSK** 33
413 **HOME FOR HALF PAST** (IRE) 64
464 **HOMEGROWNALLIGATOR** 16
472 **HOMEMADE JACK** (IRE) 32
268 **HOMER** (IRE) 83
305 **HOMESPIN** (USA) 78
516 **HOMETIME** C 71
173 **HOMETOWN BOY** (IRE) 17
484 **HOMETOWN HERO** (IRE) 56
363 **HOMING STAR** 34
347 **HONCHO** (IRE) 6
569 **HONDA FIFTY** (IRE) 12
526 **HONEST EXCHANGE** (IRE) 43
129 **HONEST VIC** (IRE) 14
141 **HONEY BOO** 3
88 **HONEY GG** 1

472 **HONEY HUNTER** (IRE) C 33
318 **HONEYDEW** (IRE) 30
409 **HONG KONG** (USA) 47
472 **HONG KONG DRAGON** 12
97 **HONGBAO** (FR) 9
578 **HONNEUR D'AJONC** (FR) 17
424 **HONOR GREY** (IRE) 34
378 **HONORABLE** (FR) 68
274 **HONORARY COLONEL** (IRE) 47
84 **HONORE DAUMIER** (IRE) 24
148 **HONOURABLE GENT** 19
184 **HONOURARY GIFT** (IRE) 22
178 **HONOURMISSION** (FR) 7
163 **HONOURS** 30
169 **HOOF'S SO LUCKY** F 84
175 **HOOFLEPUFF** (IRE) 24
392 **HOOK UP** (FR) 106
221 **HOOLIGAN** (IRE) 47
268 **HOOPER** 84
265 **HOOPER'S LEGEND** 5
465 **HOORAY** C 91
84 **HOORAY HENRY** 25
62 **HOORAYFORTHEGREY** 36
73 **HOOROO** (IRE) 45
76 **HOORREYA** 37
338 **HOOT AT MIDNIGHT** 21
558 **HOP MADDOCKS** (IRE) 4
60 **HOPE BAY** (IRE) 14
33 **HOPE IS HIGH** 9
59 **HOPE'S WISHES** 3
323 **HOPEFUL** (FR) 30
491 **HOPEFULL** 17
392 **HOPEFULLY** (FR) 107
103 **HOPISSIME** (FR) 50
579 **HORATIO HORNBLOWER** (IRE) 13
227 **HORATIO STAR** 20
475 **HORIZON BLEU** (FR) 46
17 **HORN OF PLENTY** 78
10 **HORNBY** 10
274 **HORSE FORCE ONE** (IRE) 48
162 **HORSE SENSE** (IRE) F 54
30 **HORSEFLY** (IRE) 77
413 **HORTZADAR** 27
251 **HOST** (IRE) 184
315 **HOSTILE** 53
132 **HOT AFFAIR** 35
296 **HOT AS** (IRE) 12
291 **HOT CHESNUT** 52
349 **HOT DATE** 8
469 **HOT GOSSIP** (IRE) 6
89 **HOT HOT HOT** 84
215 **HOT POPPY** 16
165 **HOT PROPERTY** (USA) G 20
422 **HOT SAUCE** (IRE) C 74
546 **HOT SMOKED** 14
516 **HOT TO HANDLE** (IRE) 23
271 **HOT TO TROT** 2
422 **HOT TOUCH** 35
554 **HOT WIRED** C 19
254 **HOTEL DU NORD** (FR) 31
315 **HOTTER THAN HELL** (FR) 54
88 **HOUSE DEPOSIT** 2
30 **HOUSE EDGE** 4
562 **HOUSE ISLAND** (IRE) 15
164 **HOW ABOUT IT** (IRE) 20
15 **HOW BIZARRE** 13
368 **HOW FORTUNATE** C 72
85 **HOW'S MY FRIEND** 4

189 **HOW'S THE CRICKET** (IRE) 21
319 **HOWABOUTRIGHTNOW** (IRE) 6
131 **HOWARDIAN HILLS** (IRE) 11
496 **HOWDILYOUDO** (IRE) 30
550 **HOWIZEEGEEZER** 21
156 **HOWLING MILAN** (IRE) 11
227 **HOWLONGISAFOOT** (IRE) 21
543 **HOWS JOHNNY** 5
386 **HOWTONSTREET HARRY** (IRE) 26
13 **HOWYA HUN** (IRE) 9
128 **HOWZER BLACK** (IRE) 34
413 **HOYAMY** F 105
73 **HOYLAKE** 46
318 **HTILOMINLO** 5
128 **HUA MULAN** (IRE) 89
305 **HUBOOR** (IRE) 79
435 **HUCCABY** 26
320 **HUDDLE** 3
323 **HUETOR** (FR) 31
413 **HUGO 'N TAZ** 21
92 **HUGO'S REFLECTION** (IRE) 14
225 **HUGOIGO** 13
405 **HUGOS OTHER HORSE** 89
76 **HUKUM** (IRE) 34
2 **HULA BALLEW** G 27
107 **HULCOTE ROSE** (IRE) C 31
39 **HUMA BIRD** C 148
296 **HUMAN ACTION** 24
582 **HUMAN NATURE** (IRE) 16
228 **HUMANITARIAN** (USA) 16
413 **HUMBERT** (IRE) 28
484 **HUMBLE HERO** (IRE) 57
300 **HUMBLE MARY** 8
135 **HUME LOUGH** 8
94 **HUNDRED ISLES** (IRE) 44
104 **HUNNI** 8
411 **HUNNY MOON** 41
395 **HUNTERS CALL** (IRE) 51
322 **HUNTING PERCIVAL** 13
243 **HUNTSMAN SON** (IRE) 9
121 **HUNTSMAN'S CALL** (IRE) 46
86 **HUNTSMANS JOG** (IRE) 1
486 **HURAA** 26
305 **HURAIZ** (IRE) 80
186 **HURCLE** (IRE) 92
273 **HURRICANE ALERT** 3
342 **HURRICANE ALI** (IRE) 10
44 **HURRICANE ARCADIO** (IRE) 9
519 **HURRICANE DEAL** (FR) 30
211 **HURRICANE DYLAN** (IRE) 13
411 **HURRICANE HARVEY** 42
476 **HURRICANE HEIDI** 9
395 **HURRICANE HERO** (IRE) 52
97 **HURRICANE IVOR** (IRE) 39
212 **HURRICANE MITCH** (IRE) 32
151 **HURRICANE RITA** (IRE) 7
579 **HURRICANE SIVOLA** (FR) 25
8 **HURRICANE VIC** 3
203 **HURRY HENRY** (IRE) 2
39 **HUSH MONEY** (CHI) C 149
351 **HUSHED UP** (IRE) G 11
76 **HUWAITEB** 35
498 **HY EALES** (IRE) 13
304 **HYANNA** 12
392 **HYBERY** (FR) 108
321 **HYDRAULIC** 12
577 **HYDROPLANE** (IRE) 42
511 **HYDROS** 53

388 **HYGROVE PERCY** 37
477 **HYMN AND A PRAYER** 3
170 **HYPERFOCUS** (IRE) 46
395 **HYPNOS** (IRE) 53
365 **HYPNOTICE FORCE** 58
323 **HYPOCONDRIAC** (FR) 61
228 **HYPOTHETICAL** (IRE) 82
6 **HYSTERICAL** (IRE) 63
132 **I AM** (IRE) C 65
370 **I AM A DREAMER** 9
184 **I AM DANDY** (IRE) 23
198 **I AM PLASTERED** 12
527 **I CAN** (IRE) 1
220 **I CAN SKIP TOO** 4
128 **I CAN'T REMEMBER** (IRE) 90
104 **I HAD A DREAM** 19
316 **I HOPE STAR** (IRE) 15
493 **I JUST KNOW** (IRE) 20
395 **I K BRUNEL** 54
81 **I KNOW HOW** (IRE) 6
512 **I LIKE HIM** (FR) 18
7 **I LOVE YOU BABY** 49
537 **I NEVER SAY NO** (IRE) 58
391 **I SEE YOU WELL** (FR) 10
305 **I SPIED** 81
339 **I THINK SO** (IRE) 16
416 **I'DLIKETHEOPTION** (IRE) 41
81 **I'LL BE BRIEF** 7
32 **I'LL BE GOOD** 5
147 **I'LL BE YOUR CLOWN** (IRE) 1
435 **I'LLETYOUGONOW** 28
454 **I'M A STARMAN** 3
135 **I'M BRIAN** 9
493 **I'M DELILAH** G 21
286 **I'M DIGBY** (IRE) 21
169 **I'M EASY** 63
58 **I'M HERE** (IRE) 6
85 **I'M IN CHARGE** 5
306 **I'M NOTAPARTYGIRL** 4
159 **I'M SHEIKRA** (IRE) C 3
254 **I'M SO BUSY** (IRE) 32
424 **I'M SPELLBOUND** (IRE) 35
579 **I'M THE DIVA** (FR) 27
128 **I'M TO BLAME** (IRE) 35
257 **I'M WATCHING YOU** 32
411 **I'M WISER NOW** (IRE) 43
516 **I'M YOURS** C 72
365 **IAMASTARTOO** (IRE) 59
378 **IBALLISTICVIN** 69
17 **IBECKE** C 151
409 **IBERIA** (IRE) 48
276 **IBIS DU RHEU** (FR) 8
101 **IBIZA** 34
385 **IBIZA DREAM** F 13
272 **IBIZA ROCKS** 88
583 **IBLEO** (FR) 38
79 **IBN AL EMARAT** (IRE) 5
312 **ICARIO** (FR) 2
304 **ICE AGE** (IRE) 13
211 **ICE CANYON** 14
365 **ICE COLD SOUL** (IRE) 60
330 **ICE COOL CHAMPS** (IRE) 13
547 **ICE EAGLE** (IRE) 54
317 **ICE GALLEY** (IRE) 27
557 **ICE ICE LADY** 40
548 **ICE LORD** (IRE) 8
477 **ICE NELLY** (IRE) F 4
217 **ICE PALACE** C 6

317 **ICE PYRAMID** (IRE) 28
443 **ICE ROCK** (IRE) C 2
347 **ICE ROYAL** (IRE) 7
242 **ICE SPRITE** 67
29 **ICE STATION ZEBRA** 56
445 **ICKY WOO** F 16
317 **ICONIC BELLE** 29
132 **ICONIC CHOICE** 9
128 **ICONIC CODE** 36
294 **ICONIC FIGURE** (IRE) 2
300 **ICONIC FLIGHT** 9
547 **ICONIC KNIGHT** (IRE) 12
378 **ICONIC MUDDLE** 70
29 **ICONIC QUEEN** 114
541 **ICONIC SKY** 12
365 **IDAS BOY** (IRE) 61
533 **IDEAL CANDY** (IRE) 3
533 **IDEAL DESTINY** 4
24 **IDEAL GRACE** 5
533 **IDEAL STORM** (IRE) 14
367 **IDEALIST** C 35
103 **IDEECHIC** (FR) C 51
461 **IDIDITFORYOOOO** (IRE) 10
577 **IDILICO** (FR) 43
103 **IDLE TEARS** F 52
36 **IDOAPOLOGISE** 2
242 **IDOL** 143
58 **IDOLS'S EYE** (FR) 7
256 **IF KARL'S BERG DID** 8
242 **IF SO** C 144
212 **IF THE CAP FITS** (IRE) 33
405 **IF YOU SAY RUN** (IRE) 90
130 **IFANDABUT** (IRE) 4
417 **IFFORCEDTOTELL** 18
305 **IFFRAAZ** (IRE) 82
94 **IFICANIWILL** (IRE) F 98
365 **IFICUDIWUD** (IRE) 62
87 **IFTON** 14
186 **IFYOUCARESHARE** 26
392 **IFYOUCATCHMENOW** (IRE) 109
2 **IGNATIUS** (IRE) 12
285 **IGNIGHT** 6
17 **IGNIS AWAY** (FR) C 152
268 **IGOR** 85
537 **IKEBANA** 59
217 **IKIGAI** 7
272 **IL BANDITO** (IRE) 89
378 **IL RE DI NESSUNO** (FR) 71
532 **IL SICARIO** (IRE) 6
483 **ILALLIQA** (IRE) 43
242 **ILARAAB** (IRE) 68
249 **ILAYA** (FR) 32
215 **ILEY BOY** 6
89 **ILHABELA FACT** 30
323 **ILLA ALQMAR** 7
440 **ILLDOITTOMORROW** 6
338 **ILLEGAL MODEL** (IRE) 22
563 **ILLEGITIMATE GAINS** 5
14 **ILLUMINATED BEAUTY** (IRE) 29
530 **ILLUSIONIST** (GER) 19
512 **ILLUSTRIOUS SPIRIT** 19
545 **ILLUSTRISSIME** (USA) 12
146 **ILSERENO** 30
511 **ILTEMAS** (USA) F 120
134 **IM DAPPER TOO** 4
368 **IM TOO GENEROUS** 23
452 **IMADA** (IRE) 24
309 **IMAGE OF THE MOON** 6

409 **IMAGINE** (IRE) C 143
317 **IMAJORBLUSH** 30
57 **IMHOTEP** 7
305 **IMMACULATE** 174
192 **IMMORTAL BELOVED** 41
376 **IMPART** 7
29 **IMPATIENT** 57
365 **IMPATIENT PARTNER** (IRE) 63
534 **IMPERIAL ACOLYTE** 43
411 **IMPERIAL ALCAZAR** (IRE) 44
14 **IMPERIAL AURA** (IRE) 30
416 **IMPERIAL COMMAND** (IRE) 103
107 **IMPERIAL DAWN** 32
413 **IMPERIAL EIGHT** (IRE) 106
411 **IMPERIAL ELYSIAN** (IRE) 45
6 **IMPERIAL EMPIRE** 64
212 **IMPERIAL ESPRIT** (IRE) 34
576 **IMPERIAL FLEM** (IRE) 38
560 **IMPERIAL FOCUS** (IRE) 3
14 **IMPERIAL ICON** (IRE) 31
424 **IMPERIAL KNIGHT** (IRE) 36
534 **IMPERIAL NEMESIS** (IRE) 44
274 **IMPERIAL PRESENCE** (IRE) 49
160 **IMPERIAL PRINCE** (IRE) 5
334 **IMPERIL** (FR) 10
10 **IMPERIUM** (IRE) 9
105 **IMPERTINENT** F 2
105 **IMPERTINENT** G 4
365 **IMPETIOUS** C 143
378 **IMPHAL** 72
6 **IMPORTANT TIME** (IRE) C 160
386 **IMPRESSIONABLE** 10
17 **IMPRESSIONIST ART** (USA) C 153
529 **IMPRESSOR** (IRE) 22
137 **IMPULSIVE LEADER** (IRE) 12
388 **IMPULSIVE STAR** (IRE) 38
422 **IMRAHOR** 95
61 **IN A TIZZ** (FR) 13
174 **IN ARREARS** (IRE) 1
101 **IN DEMAND** (IRE) 10
17 **IN DUBAI** (USA) C 154
378 **IN REM** (FR) 73
101 **IN THE BREEZE** 80
251 **IN THE COVE** (IRE) 13
562 **IN THE DETAIL** (IRE) 16
254 **IN THE PRESENT** (USA) 99
489 **IN THE RED** (IRE) 7
295 **IN THE SOUP** (USA) C 61
481 **IN VINO VERITAS** (IRE) 6
365 **IN YOUR SHADOW** (IRE) 64
94 **IN YOUR TIME** C 99
77 **INAAM** (IRE) 18
489 **INAGH RIVER** C 13
97 **INATTENDU** (FR) 10
338 **INAWHILECROCODILE** (IRE) 23
260 **INCA GOLD** (IRE) 16
409 **INCA PRINCESS** (IRE) C 144
14 **INCA ROSE** 32
319 **INCENTIVE** 7
235 **INCERTAINE** 4
576 **INCH LALA** (IRE) 39
512 **INCH ROSE** (IRE) G 20
315 **INCHICORE** (IRE) 146
496 **INCLUDED** 31
17 **INCLYNE** 28
140 **INCUS** 8
194 **INDEED** 3
562 **INDEFATIGABLE** (IRE) 17

24 **INDEPENDENCE** (USA) 6
19 **INDEPENDENCE DAY** (IRE) 7
550 **INDIAN AFFAIR** 10
388 **INDIAN BRAVE** (IRE) 39
94 **INDIAN CREAK** (IRE) 45
268 **INDIAN GLORY** (IRE) 86
243 **INDIAN NATIVE** (IRE) 10
6 **INDIAN PETAL** C 161
444 **INDIAN PURSUIT** (IRE) 15
582 **INDIAN RAJ** 17
370 **INDIAN SOUNDS** (IRE) 10
60 **INDIAN STAR** 15
447 **INDIAN TEMPLE** (IRE) 3
116 **INDIAN TINKER** 13
249 **INDIAN VISION** (IRE) 33
23 **INDIAN VOYAGE** (IRE) 13
87 **INDIAN WARRIOR** 15
382 **INDIANA JONES** (IRE) 13
224 **INDIANAPOLIS** (IRE) 2
94 **INDIANNIE MOON** F 46
427 **INDIARO** 3
228 **INDIE ANGEL** (IRE) 83
574 **INDIETIR** (FR) 10
228 **INDIGO LAKE** 84
7 **INDIGO PRINCESS** 10
483 **INDIGO TIMES** (IRE) 44
150 **INDUCTIVE** 35
435 **INDUNO** (IRE) 29
142 **INDY FIVE** (IRE) 18
391 **INDYZEB** (IRE) 47
214 **INEXES** 16
581 **INEXORABLE** 5
516 **INEXPLICABLE** (IRE) 24
251 **INEZ** F 185
465 **INFANT HERCULES** 92
16 **INFANTA ISABELLA** 20
463 **INFATUATE** C 102
516 **INFATUATION** F 73
94 **INFFIRAAJ** (IRE) C 100
516 **INFINITE BEAUTY** (IRE) 74
413 **INFINITE GRACE** 65
329 **INFINITI** (IRE) 7
425 **INFLAMED** 9
29 **INFLAMMABLE** F 115
413 **INFLUENCE** (FR) F 107
493 **INFORMATEUR** (FR) 22
364 **INFRASTRUCTURE** 12
554 **INGLEBY COMMAND** 13
554 **INGLEBY EXCEED** (IRE) C 20
554 **INGLEBY EXILE** 14
554 **INGLEBY GEORGE** 2
413 **INGLEBY HOLLOW** 29
554 **INGLEBY MOLLY** (IRE) 3
538 **INHALATION** 8
30 **INHALE** 5
73 **INHALER** 92
511 **INHERENT** 54
17 **INHIBITION** C 155
44 **INIESTA** (IRE) 10
511 **INIGO JONES** 121
251 **INIS BOFFIN** C 186
441 **INITIATIVE** (IRE) 7
419 **INKLING** (USA) C 57
29 **INKY BLINDER** 58
315 **INN THE BULL** (GER) 55
146 **INN WITH THE GIN** 11
340 **INNER CIRCLE** (IRE) 11
315 **INNER DRIVE** (IRE) 56

281 **INNER SEA** (USA) G 13
483 **INNER SEA** (USA) C 76
39 **INNER SECRET** (USA) C 150
49 **INNER TREASURES** 40
261 **INNERPICKLE** 21
186 **INNINGS** 93
38 **INNIS SHANNON** (IRE) 6
409 **INNISFREE** (IRE) 49
142 **INNISFREE LAD** (IRE) 19
368 **INNISHMORE** (IRE) F 60
228 **INNOVATION** 85
295 **INNSE GALL** 62
165 **INSPECTOR BLAKE** 21
285 **INSPIRE** 7
391 **INSPIREUS** (IRE) 11
140 **INSPIRING LOVE** 26
158 **INSPIRING NORA** 14
39 **INSPIRITER** 151
412 **INSTANT ATTRACTION** (IRE) 12
175 **INSTANT REPLAY** (IRE) 25
254 **INSTANT RETURN** 33
259 **INSTINGTIVE** (IRE) 2
97 **INSTRUIT** 40
225 **INSURPLUS** (IRE) 14
121 **INTAGLIA** F 81
49 **INTELDREAM** 11
97 **INTELLOGENT** (IRE) 11
443 **INTENSE STYLE** (IRE) 3
393 **INTENT** (IRE) F 43
215 **INTERCESSOR** 17
593 **INTERCOOLER TURBO** (IRE) 4
63 **INTERNATIONAL LAW** 2
186 **INTERNATIONAL LION** 94
186 **INTERNATIONALANGEL** (IRE) 95
186 **INTERNATIONALTIGER** 96
579 **INTERNE DE SIVOLA** (FR) 28
540 **INTERSTELLA** (GER) 34
355 **INTIMATE MOMENT** 11
413 **INTISAAB** 30
438 **INTO DEBT** 9
367 **INTO FAITH** (FR) 17
184 **INTO THE BREACH** (FR) 24
136 **INTO THE MIST** 4
435 **INTO THE WOODS** (IRE) 30
169 **INTO THE ZONE** 27
563 **INTREPID** (IRE) 11
251 **INTREPID ITALIAN** 67
321 **INTRIGUE** F 23
542 **INTRINSIC BOND** 11
101 **INTROSPECTIVE** F 35
73 **INTRUSIVE** 93
30 **INVEIGLE** 78
296 **INVENTUS** 13
445 **INVER PARK** 17
526 **INVESTMENT MANAGER** 44
494 **INVICTA LAKE** (IRE) 7
227 **INVINCIBLE CAVE** (IRE) 22
445 **INVINCIBLE LARNE** (IRE) 4
300 **INVINCIBLE SEA** (IRE) 10
117 **INVINCIBLE SOLDIER** (IRE) 83
509 **INVISIBLE STORM** 3
128 **INVISIONANDQMARTYN** (IRE) 37
537 **INVITATIONAL** 14
50 **INVOLVED** 3
94 **INYAMAZANE** (IRE) 47
272 **INYORDREAMS** F 90
469 **IOLANI** (GER) 7
488 **IONA DAYS** (IRE) 4

393 **JAMESSAINTPATRICK** (IRE) 12
292 **JAMIH** 6
292 **JAMIL** (IRE) 7
97 **JAMILYA** (FR) 41
233 **JAMMIN MASTERS** (IRE) 31
572 **JAMMY GEORGE** (IRE) 16
297 **JAMPOT EDDIE** 13
292 **JAN DE HEEM** 8
270 **JAN VAN HOOF** (IRE) 9
538 **JANE DOE** (IRE) 9
76 **JANE EYRE** C 65
228 **JANE MARPLE** 88
361 **JANE VICTORIA** 3
263 **JANESLITTLEVOICE** 3
392 **JANIDIL** (FR) 110
94 **JANIE JONES** 101
268 **JANIKA** (FR) 91
254 **JANUARY JETS** 34
103 **JANULIS** (FR) 53
256 **JANUS** (IRE) 11
409 **JAPAN** 6
237 **JAPPELOUP** (IRE) 4
537 **JARAMILLO** 153
391 **JARLATH** 12
97 **JARNAC** (FR) 42
411 **JARVEYS PLATE** (IRE) 46
121 **JASH** (IRE) 8
435 **JASMIN DES BORDES** (FR) 33
188 **JASMINE JOY** (IRE) 72
478 **JASPER JAY** 1
184 **JASSAS** (FR) 25
274 **JATILUWIH** (FR) 50
171 **JAUNTY FREYJA** 3
171 **JAUNTY SPIRIT** G 4
171 **JAUNTY VIKING** 5
14 **JAVA POINT** (IRE) 33
6 **JAVANA** 163
386 **JAVELIN** 14
577 **JAWSHAN** (USA) 45
150 **JAWWAAL** 13
329 **JAXLIGHT** 7
315 **JAY BEE WHY** (IRE) 59
389 **JAY ME LO** (IRE) 7
493 **JAYAAAH** (IRE) 24
562 **JAYCEEBEE** 18
577 **JAYTEE** 46
526 **JAYTRACK PARKHOMES** 45
186 **JAZZ HANDS** (IRE) 28
519 **JAZZ KING** (FR) 8
462 **JAZZ LEGEND** (USA) 4
481 **JAZZ MAGIC** (IRE) 7
107 **JAZZ PARTY** 20
69 **JAZZ STYLE** (IRE) 7
285 **JAZZAMEER** 8
392 **JAZZAWAY** (IRE) 111
459 **JAZZY CARD** (IRE) 1
93 **JE M'EN FICHE** 9
444 **JE SUIS CHARLIE** 16
39 **JEALOUS AGAIN** (USA) F 152
511 **JEAN BAPTISTE** (FR) 55
539 **JEAN GENIE** (FR) 52
312 **JEAN MARY** 15
390 **JEANE DE BELLVILLE** 8
509 **JEANETTE MAY** 4
29 **JEANNE GREY** (IRE) 60
156 **JEANS GENIE** 12
53 **JEANS MAITE** 5
76 **JEDDEYD** (IRE) 37

412 **JEDHI** 14
365 **JEFF KIDDER** (IRE) 131
539 **JEFFERSON DAVIS** (IRE) 53
225 **JEFFREY HARRIS** 15
29 **JELLYSTONE** (IRE) 61
254 **JELONA** (IRE) 35
534 **JELSKI** (GER) 45
88 **JEM SCUTTLE** (USA) 4
539 **JEMBUG DRUMMER** (IRE) 54
327 **JEMIMA P** (IRE) 36
67 **JEMS BOND** 5
530 **JEN JOS ENIGMA** (IRE) F 26
268 **JEN'S BOY** 92
251 **JEN'S FELLA** (FR) 69
251 **JEN'S LAD** (IRE) 70
338 **JENKINS** (IRE) 26
280 **JENNY REN** 6
440 **JENNYS DAY** (IRE) 8
283 **JEPECK** (IRE) 14
365 **JERANDME** (IRE) 66
170 **JERBOURG** 120
77 **JEREJAK** 46
416 **JEREMEE** (IRE) 42
192 **JEREMIAH** 11
212 **JEREMIAH JAMES** (IRE) 36
405 **JEREMY PASS** (IRE) 92
142 **JEREMY THE JINN** (IRE) 20
315 **JERMINNIE GREEN** (IRE) 60
274 **JERRYSBACK** (IRE) 51
480 **JERSEY BEAN** (IRE) 19
365 **JERSEY CREAM** F 144
419 **JERSEY GREY** (FR) 22
480 **JERSEY LADY** (IRE) 20
419 **JERSEY MASTER** (IRE) 23
419 **JERSEY WONDER** (IRE) 6
36 **JERVAULX** 19
365 **JESSE EVANS** (IRE) 67
565 **JESSE JUDE** (IRE) 10
335 **JESSE'S LADY** 8
363 **JESSICA RABBIT** 36
365 **JESSICA'S BOY** (IRE) 68
225 **JESSIE ALLAN** (IRE) 16
532 **JESSIE K** C 24
238 **JESSIE LIGHTFOOT** (IRE) 10
437 **JESSIE'S SPIRIT** (IRE) F 47
160 **JESSIEMAC** (IRE) 6
537 **JET ENGINE** (IRE) 154
338 **JET SET** (IRE) 27
500 **JET SET GO** 6
395 **JETAWAY JOEY** (IRE) 57
298 **JETSTREAM** (IRE) 9
254 **JETT** (IRE) 36
338 **JETTISON** 28
254 **JETZ** (IRE) 37
469 **JEU DE MOTS** (FR) 9
541 **JEUNOPSE** (IRE) F 14
239 **JEWEL IN MY CROWN** 26
170 **JEWEL MAKER** (IRE) 48
175 **JIGS PRINCESS** 78
594 **JIGSAW FINANCIAL** (IRE) 5
570 **JILL ROSE** 3
194 **JIM 'N' TOMIC** (IRE) 12
565 **JIMINY CRICKET** (IRE) 11
243 **JIMMI CHEW** (IRE) 11
227 **JIMMY** 7
417 **JIMMY BELL** 7
275 **JIMMY MAC** 6
402 **JIMMY RABBITTE** (IRE) 34

129 **JIMMY THE DIGGER** 16
358 **JIMMY'S GIRL** (IRE) C 14
539 **JIMMYJAMES** 55
230 **JINKABELL** 20
230 **JINKAMAN** 21
305 **JM JACKSON** (IRE) 83
305 **JO BO BO** (IRE) C 175
230 **JO CASHFLOW** 22
159 **JOAN OF PIMLICO** (IRE) 10
499 **JOANIE STUBBS** 31
221 **JOBESGREEN LAD** 48
4 **JOBSONFIRE** 4
124 **JOE FARRELL** (IRE) 9
299 **JOE PROUD** 33
388 **JOE WARBRICK** 41
170 **JOE'S WAY** 121
574 **JOEY STEEL** (IRE) 12
10 **JOEY'S GIFT** 38
351 **JOG ON** (IRE) 12
242 **JOHAN** 70
261 **JOHANOS** (FR) 22
223 **JOHN BETJEMAN** 4
136 **JOHN BISCUIT** (IRE) 6
485 **JOHN CLARE** (IRE) 11
576 **JOHN CONSTABLE** (IRE) 40
85 **JOHN DANIELL** 6
413 **JOHN JASPER** (USA) 66
309 **JOHN JOINER** 7
150 **JOHN KIRKUP** 14
162 **JOHN LEEPER** (IRE) 55
29 **JOHN LOCKE** 62
16 **JOHN THE DIVA** (FR) 36
524 **JOHN WILLIAMS** (IRE) 17
322 **JOHNBB** (IRE) 14
24 **JOHNI BOXIT** 8
370 **JOHNNY CAVAGIN** 12
17 **JOHNNY DRAMA** (IRE) 29
17 **JOHNNY KIDD** 30
193 **JOHNNY REB** 2
499 **JOHNNY UTAH** (IRE) 32
210 **JOHNOFGORCOMBE** 4
528 **JOIE DE VIVRE** (IRE) 7
209 **JOINT ACCOUNT** (IRE) 2
493 **JOKE DANCER** 25
1 **JOLIE CRICKETTE** (FR) 29
578 **JOLIE MENTHE** (FR) C 20
212 **JOLLY'S CRACKED IT** (FR) 37
416 **JOLY MAKER** (IRE) 43
475 **JOLYON** 16
150 **JOMONT** (FR) 36
339 **JOMROK** 17
392 **JON SNOW** (FR) 112
132 **JONAH JONES** (IRE) 11
69 **JONBOY** 3
395 **JONES WELL** (IRE) 58
243 **JONJOELA** (IRE) 12
148 **JONNIESOFA** (IRE) 21
518 **JONIGRAIG** (IRE) 8
91 **JONNYSIMPSON** (IRE) 14
132 **JONQUERETS** (FR) 66
295 **JORGIE** (FR) 50
7 **JORVIK PRINCE** 53
539 **JOSEPH HOBSON** (IRE) 56
509 **JOSEPHINE** 9
420 **JOSHLEE** (IRE) 11
26 **JOSHUA R** (IRE) 28
365 **JOSHUA WEBB** 69
574 **JOSIE ABBING** (IRE) 13

27 **JOSIEBOND** 14
124 **JOUEUR BRESILIEN** (FR) 10
576 **JOUR A LA PLAGE** (FR) 41
84 **JOUSKA** 26
511 **JOVIAL** 56
424 **JOVIAL SPIRIT** (IRE) 37
419 **JOYCE COMPTON** (IRE) F 60
547 **JOYFILLY** 62
77 **JOYFUL DREAM** (IRE) 19
305 **JOYFUL HOPE** C 176
511 **JOYFUL MISSION** (USA) 7
6 **JOYFUL SONG** (IRE) 65
558 **JOYFUL STAR** 5
327 **JOYRIDER** (IRE) 37
175 **JUALS SPIRIT** (IRE) 26
17 **JUAN DE MONTALBAN** (IRE) 157
309 **JUAN DE VALDES** 8
465 **JUAN ELCANO** 55
443 **JUAN HORSEPOWER** 4
547 **JUAN LES PINS** 26
10 **JUANITO CHICO** (IRE) 11
321 **JUBILANT LADY** (USA) F 24
516 **JUBILANT QUEEN** F 76
519 **JUBILEE EXPRESS** (FR) 31
511 **JUBILOSO** 8
327 **JUBILYMPICS** 38
539 **JUDEX LEFOU** (IRE) 57
30 **JUDGMENT OF PARIS** 31
811 **JUDICIAL** (IRE) 8
557 **JUGE ET PARTI** (IRE) 11
103 **JUKEBOX DANCER** (FR) 28
183 **JUKEBOX JUNIOR** 9
281 **JULES** (IRE) F 18
50 **JULIA DREAM** F 13
305 **JULIE JOHNSTON** 177
472 **JULIUS MAXIMUS** (IRE) 13
74 **JULLY LES BUXY** 4
537 **JUMAIRA BAY** (FR) 62
304 **JUMBY** (IRE) 64
101 **JUMBY BREEZE** 81
116 **JUMIRA BRIDGE** 14
242 **JUMOOH** F 145
295 **JUMP THE GUN** (IRE) 51
378 **JUMPING CATS** 76
78 **JUMPING JACK** (IRE) 5
554 **JUNCEA** G 21
315 **JUNDERSTAND** 61
68 **JUNGLE BOOGALOO** (IRE) 3
15 **JUNGLE BOOK** (GER) 23
94 **JUNGLE CAPERS** (IRE) 48
254 **JUNGLE COVE** 101
346 **JUNGLE INTHEBUNGLE** (IRE) 5
254 **JUNGLE JUNCTION** (IRE) 38
222 **JUNGLE PROSE** (IRE) 16
295 **JUNGLE ROCK** (IRE) 52
186 **JUNGLE SECRET** (IRE) 29
214 **JUNGLE SPEED** (IRE) 18
73 **JUNINHO** (IRE) 48
219 **JUNIORS DREAM** (IRE) 19
29 **JUNIUS BRUTUS** (FR) 20
378 **JUNKANOO** 135
212 **JUNO MINT** M 38
215 **JUNOESQUE** 7
251 **JUNVIEVE** (FR) 71
164 **JUPITER** 21
313 **JURISTE** (IRE) 31
583 **JURYS OUT** (IRE) 40
88 **JUS PIRES** (USA) 5

13 **JUST A DEAL** 10
194 **JUST A JEROBOAM** 13
281 **JUST A MINUTE** 3
233 **JUST A SIP** 32
212 **JUST A STING** (IRE) 39
124 **JUST A THOUGHT** (IRE) 11
141 **JUST ALBERT** 13
290 **JUST AN IDEA** (IRE) 9
46 **JUST CALL ME AL** (IRE) 10
368 **JUST CALL ME ELLA** 61
198 **JUST CHAMPION** 3
80 **JUST DEEGEETEEBEE** 1
198 **JUST DYMOKE** 14
511 **JUST FINE** (IRE) 123
574 **JUST FOR TARA** 14
185 **JUST FRANK** 18
493 **JUST GEORGIE** 26
42 **JUST GO FOR IT** 2
234 **JUST GOT TO GET ON** 23
543 **JUST HEATHER** (IRE) 6
388 **JUST HENNY** 42
20 **JUST HERE** (IRE) F 11
170 **JUST HISS** 49
386 **JUST HUBERT** (IRE) 15
378 **JUST IN A MUDDLE** (IRE) 77
315 **JUST IN TIME** 62
249 **JUST JEAN** (IRE) 70
97 **JUST LADY** 43
491 **JUST LIKE A WOMAN** G 30
195 **JUST LIKE BETH** 4
170 **JUST MAGIC** 50
243 **JUST MARVIN** (IRE) 13
117 **JUST MAY** 35
44 **JUST MAYBE** 11
126 **JUST NORMAN** 6
217 **JUST ONCE** 2
198 **JUST RIGHT** 15
253 **JUST SKITTLES** 1
313 **JUST SMOKIE** F 4
142 **JUST SO COOL** (IRE) 21
42 **JUST SPOT** 3
80 **JUST TARA** 2
29 **JUST TELLEM** (IRE) 117
10 **JUST THAT LORD** 12
6 **JUST THE JUDGE** (IRE) F 164
117 **JUST THE MAN** (FR) 5
94 **JUST VIOLET** F 102
483 **JUST WOOD** (FR) C 78
338 **JUST YOUR TYPE** (IRE) 29
564 **JUSTANOTHER MUDDLE** 8
465 **JUSTANOTHERBOTTLE** (IRE) 11
133 **JUSTATENNER** 8
249 **JUSTFORJAMES** (IRE) 36
167 **JUSTGIVEMEAREASON** (IRE) 5
511 **JUSTICE BELLE** (IRE) C 124
475 **JUSTICE KNIGHT** (IRE) 17
32 **JUSTICE SHALLOW** (FR) 6
305 **JUSTIFIED** 84
254 **JUSTINA** 102
219 **JUSTTHEGREY** (IRE) 6
568 **K C BAILEY** 21
122 **K O KENNY** 12
116 **K REX** (USA) 48
530 **KAAFY** (IRE) 7
392 **KAATSKILL NAP** (FR) 113
446 **KABRIT** (IRE) 22
132 **KACHY** 12
244 **KADIYAMA** (IRE) 34

291 **KADRIZZI** (FR) 18
242 **KADUPUL** (FR) 146
17 **KAFEE** (IRE) 82
483 **KAHALAH FANTASY** C 79
24 **KAHDIAN** (IRE) 9
60 **KAHPEHLO** 16
335 **KAISAN** 9
422 **KAITEN** 37
568 **KAIZER** 22
452 **KAJAKI** (IRE) 25
221 **KAKAMORA** 49
515 **KAKI DE LA PREE** (FR) 12
519 **KALA NOIRE** (FR) 9
74 **KALABEE** (IRE) 5
496 **KALAHARI QUEEN** 33
568 **KALAHARRY** (IRE) 23
378 **KALAKAWA ENKI** (FR) 78
103 **KALANI** 29
392 **KALANISI OG** (IRE) 114
323 **KALAOS** (IRE) 62
244 **KALAPOUR** (IRE) 35
526 **KALARIKA** (IRE) 46
393 **KALASHNIKOV** (IRE) 13
189 **KALASKADEEMILLEY** 22
59 **KALAYA** (IRE) 4
244 **KALAYENA** (IRE) 36
94 **KALEIDOSCOPIC** 49
117 **KALFU** 36
320 **KALIMOTXO** 19
580 **KALINIHTA** (IRE) 15
312 **KALL TO ALMS** 6
412 **KALL TO ALMS** 15
400 **KALMBEFORETHESTORM** 4
388 **KALONDRA** (IRE) 43
274 **KALOOKI** (GER) 52
367 **KALOOR** 9
17 **KALSARA** 83
6 **KAMAKURA** (USA) C 165
244 **KAMARAZI** (IRE) 73
17 **KAMEKO** (USA) 84
279 **KAMIL** (FR) 7
538 **KAMINARI** (IRE) F 25
405 **KANDOO KID** (FR) 93
577 **KANGAROO POINT** (IRE) 97
418 **KANGAROO VALLEY** (USA) 19
317 **KANGAROO VALLEY** (USA) 32
243 **KANKIN** 14
328 **KANNAPOLIS** (IRE) 7
537 **KANNOOR** 63
411 **KANSAS CITY** (FR) G 91
388 **KANSAS CITY CHIEF** (IRE) 44
328 **KAP AUTEUIL** (FR) 8
97 **KAPANI** (FR) 97
378 **KAPDAD** (FR) 79
244 **KAPERA** (FR) C 74
583 **KAPGA DE LILY** (FR) 41
534 **KAPGARRY** (FR) 46
164 **KAPITALISTE** (FR) 22
261 **KAPITALL** 23
191 **KAPONO** 15
210 **KAPOUPAKAP** (FR) 9
431 **KAPRICIA SPEED** (FR) F 10
395 **KAPROYALE** 59
97 **KAPSALIANA** (FR) 44
338 **KAPSIZE** (FR) 30
7 **KARABUNGA DUDE** 54
255 **KARAKORAM** 11
244 **KARALARA** (IRE) C 75

48 **KARALIUS** (NZ) 7
448 **KARANNELLE** (IRE) 7
295 **KARASHENI** (IRE) 17
315 **KARASTANI** 63
6 **KARENINE** C 166
286 **KARIBANA** (IRE) 23
407 **KARINGO** 4
184 **KARISMATIK** (FR) 26
244 **KARIYNA** (IRE) 76
323 **KARKHOV** (IRE) 63
392 **KARL DER GROSSE** (GER) 115
223 **KARL MARX** (IRE) 5
411 **KARL PHILIPPE** (FR) 47
180 **KARLINHA** (IRE) C 46
60 **KARLUK RIVER** 20
32 **KASALLA** (IRE) M 7
483 **KASAMAN** FR 11
7 **KASBAAN** 55
339 **KASER** (IRE) 18
76 **KASHAAF** 38
17 **KASHI** (FR) 85
180 **KASHID** (USA) 12
304 **KASHMIRELLA** (IRE) 39
26 **KASHOOF** F 43
244 **KASMIYRA** (IRE) 37
356 **KATACHENKO** (IRE) 47
323 **KATAFONIC** (FR) 32
526 **KATAHDIN** (IRE) 47
77 **KATALAN** (GER) 20
463 **KATALYSTIC** (IRE) 40
511 **KATARA** (FR) 57
198 **KATCHAR KISS** 19
76 **KATE THE GREAT** C 66
186 **KATELLI** (IRE) 98
165 **KATES STAR** 5
322 **KATESON** 15
286 **KATH'S LUSTRE** 4
286 **KATH'S TOYBOY** 48
87 **KATHEEFA** (USA) 16
532 **KATHERINE PLACE** 7
254 **KATIE BO KAT** 103
274 **KATIES ESCAPE** (IRE) 53
244 **KATIYMANN** (IRE) 8
318 **KATIYRA** (IRE) F 32
305 **KATLA** (IRE) C 178
499 **KATNISS EVERDEEN** (IRE) 33
402 **KATPOLI** (FR) 35
175 **KATSONIS** (IRE) 64
7 **KATTANI** (IRE) 56
224 **KATY NOWAITEE** F 8
117 **KATY NOWAITEE** F 85
187 **KATY ROYAL** 4
251 **KAUTO D'AMOUR** (FR) 27
493 **KAUTO D'AMOUR** (FR) 27
235 **KAUTO RIKO** (FR) 5
526 **KAUTO THE KING** (IRE) 48
384 **KAVADI** 30
378 **KAVEMAN** 80
401 **KAY SERA** 5
274 **KAYF ADVENTURE** 54
238 **KAYF ANEDA** 11
363 **KAYF BLANCO** 37
283 **KAYF SERA SERA** 15
275 **KAYFS FANCY** (IRE) G 7
298 **KAYLEN'S MISCHIEF** 10
187 **KAYLYN** 13
268 **KAYMAR** 93
101 **KAZEEM** F 38

308 **KAZONTHERAZZ** 21
6 **KAZZIANA** C 167
295 **KEALSHORE LASS** G 18
557 **KEANE'S KINGDOM** (FR) 43
175 **KEARNEY HILL** (IRE) 27
409 **KEATS** (IRE) 50
117 **KEBEK KHAN** (FR) 37
61 **KEEL OVER** 14
268 **KEEN ON** 94
444 **KEEP BUSY** (IRE) 32
251 **KEEP IT BRIEF** 73
429 **KEEP IT COUNTRY TV** 8
274 **KEEP MOVING** (FR) 55
77 **KEEP ON LAUGHING** (IRE) 21
251 **KEEP RIGHT ON** (IRE) 187
274 **KEEP ROLLING** (IRE) 56
295 **KEEP THE RIVER** 19
320 **KEEP THE SECRET** G 20
274 **KEEP WONDERING** (IRE) 57
101 **KEEPER** 82
233 **KEEPER HILL** (IRE) 33
251 **KEEPER'S RING** (USA) C 188
576 **KEEPING FAITH** (IRE) 42
485 **KEEPUP KEVIN** 12
400 **KEEPYOURHEADUP** 5
365 **KEILOGUE** C 145
317 **KEITH'S GIRL** (IRE) 33
320 **KEKOVA** G 34
437 **KELADORA** (USA) C 48
445 **KELINDA DICE** 12
345 **KELIS** (IRE) 5
291 **KELLY** B 47
73 **KELLY'S DINO** (FR) 8
367 **KELMSCOTT** (IRE) 36
463 **KELPIES MYTH** 41
473 **KELTUS** (FR) 20
233 **KEMBLE'S CASCADE** (IRE) 34
392 **KEMBOY** (FR) 116
97 **KEN COLT** (IRE) 12
319 **KEN'S BOY** 21
136 **KEN'S WELL** (IRE) 7
188 **KENDAL MINT** (IRE) 5
261 **KENDELU** (IRE) 24
199 **KENDERGARTEN KOP** (IRE) 3
412 **KENDRED SOUL** (IRE) 41
501 **KENN** 18
424 **KENNACK BAY** (FR) 38
38 **KENNEDYS FIELD** 7
393 **KENNOCHA** (IRE) 14
564 **KENNY GEORGE** 9
186 **KENSINGTON ART** 30
287 **KENSINGTON GARDENS** F 20
589 **KENSTONE** (FR) 10
391 **KENTFORD HEIRESS** 13
391 **KENTFORD MALLARD** 14
385 **KENTUCKY HARDBOOT** (IRE) 9
181 **KENTUCKY KINGDOM** (IRE) 8
486 **KENTUCKYCONNECTION** (USA) 8
254 **KENZADARGENT** C 161
518 **KENZAI WARRIOR** (USA) 28
483 **KEOWEE CLAI** (USA) F 80
435 **KEPAGGE** (IRE) 34
304 **KEPALA** 40
244 **KERANDI** (IRE) 38
473 **KERR LINE** (IRE) 21
530 **KERMOUSTER** 8
291 **KERRERA** 19
395 **KERRKENNY GOLD** (IRE) 60

204 **KERRY'S BOY** (IRE) 5
251 **KESARA** C 189
511 **KESARINA** 58
228 **KESIA** (IRE) 17
392 **KESSELRING** 117
479 **KESTREL VALLEY** 3
345 **KESWICK** 6
409 **KEW GARDENS** (IRE) 7
242 **KEW PALACE** 71
5 **KEY CHOICE** 6
121 **KEY LOOK** (IRE) 47
547 **KEY ROSE** (IRE) G 57
186 **KEY SPIRIT** 99
498 **KEY TO THE WEST** (IRE) 6
6 **KEY VICTORY** (IRE) 15
569 **KEYBOARD GANGSTER** (IRE) 13
316 **KEYBOARD JOAN** (IRE) 17
8 **KEYNOTE** (IRE) 4
499 **KEYSER SOZE** (IRE) 6
582 **KEYSTROKE** 18
272 **KHAADEM** (IRE) 11
76 **KHAALIS** (IRE) 39
7 **KHAAN** 57
39 **KHABAAB** (IRE) 86
511 **KHADAASH** 59
572 **KHAGE** (IRE) 17
141 **KHAJOOL** (IRE) F 5
50 **KHAKI** (FR) F 14
537 **KHALAF** 64
413 **KHALEESI WIND** (IRE) C 108
17 **KHALIFA SAT** (IRE) 86
537 **KHALOOSY** (IRE) 15
356 **KHAMSIN MOOR** 48
576 **KHANISARI** (IRE) 43
39 **KHATM** 87
6 **KHAWLAH** (IRE) F 168
76 **KHAYYAAL** (USA) 40
87 **KHAZAF** 17
315 **KHIBRAAT** G 147
503 **KHIONE** F 44
292 **KHITAAMY** (IRE) 9
26 **KHOBARAA** F 44
2 **KHUFU** 8
39 **KHULOOD** (USA) F 153
537 **KHUZAAM** (USA) 15
87 **KIBAAR** 18
169 **KIBENGA** C 85
577 **KICK ON KICK ON** 47
156 **KICKONMYSON** 13
595 **KICKS BEFORE SIX** (IRE) 8
283 **KID COMMANDO** 14
244 **KID GLOVES** C 77
186 **KIDDA** 100
412 **KIEFER** 16
448 **KIERA ROYALE** (IRE) 8
92 **KILBREW BOY** (IRE) 15
526 **KILBRICKEN STORM** (IRE) 49
416 **KILBROOK** (IRE) 44
473 **KILCARA** (IRE) 22
8 **KILCARAGH BOY** (IRE) 5
574 **KILCHREEST MOON** (IRE) 15
283 **KILCONNY BRIDGE** (IRE) 17
413 **KILCONQUHAR** 57
263 **KILCREA BRIDGE** 4
279 **KILCULLEN LADY** (IRE) 8
64 **KILDAVEN SPIDER** (IRE) 9
298 **KILDIMO** (IRE) 11
424 **KILDISART** (IRE) 39

418 **KILFILUM CROSS** (IRE) 20
506 **KILFINAN BAY** (IRE) 5
97 **KILFRUSH MEMORIES** (FR) 13
170 **KILIG** 122
137 **KILINAKIN** (IRE) 13
168 **KILKEASKIN MOLLY** (IRE) 6
70 **KILLABRAHER CROSS** (IRE) 2
356 **KILLANE** (IRE) 49
418 **KILLARO BOY** (IRE) 21
327 **KILLER CLOWN** (IRE) 39
365 **KILLER MILLER** (IRE) 70
365 **KILLER MODE** (IRE) 71
407 **KILLOUGHEY BABE** (IRE) G 39
392 **KILLULTAGH BELLA** (IRE) 118
392 **KILLULTAGH VIC** (IRE) 119
405 **KILMINGTON ROSE** (IRE) 94
534 **KILPIN** (IRE) 47
496 **KILTEALY BRIGGS** (IRE) 34
339 **KIM WEXLER** (IRE) 55
188 **KIMBERLEY** 42
322 **KIMBERLITE CANDY** (IRE) 16
531 **KIMIFIVE** (IRE) 11
135 **KIMS DIAMOND** (IRE) 10
542 **KIND REVIEW** 6
371 **KINDIA** (IRE) F 40
169 **KINDLY** 28
537 **KINDRED SPIRIT** (IRE) 155
413 **KINDU** C 109
378 **KING ATHELSTAN** (IRE) 81
511 **KING CAPELLA** 125
192 **KING CARNEY** 42
49 **KING CHARLES** (USA) 41
275 **KING CNUT** (FR) 8
377 **KING CON** (FR) 7
378 **KING COOL** 82
123 **KING CRIMSON** 8
484 **KING D'ARGENT** (FR) 59
424 **KING ERIK** 40
242 **KING FAIRY** (IRE) 72
305 **KING FAN** 85
537 **KING FRANCIS** (IRE) 156
202 **KING FRANK** 2
302 **KING GOLAN** (IRE) 6
234 **KING GYPSY** (IRE) 24
228 **KING LEONIDAS** 89
518 **KING LEWLEW** 29
456 **KING MURO** 4
228 **KING OF ARMS** 90
409 **KING OF ATHENS** (USA) 51
251 **KING OF CHANGE** 14
384 **KING OF CLUBS** 59
527 **KING OF COMEDY** (IRE) 2
228 **KING OF COMEDY** (IRE) 18
160 **KING OF FASHION** (IRE) 7
577 **KING OF REALMS** (IRE) 48
501 **KING OF ROOKS** 4
483 **KING OF SPIES** (USA) 46
437 **KING OF THE NORTH** (IRE) 20
405 **KING OF THE RING** 95
137 **KING OF THE SHARKS** (IRE) 14
326 **KING OF THE SOUTH** (IRE) 6
413 **KING OF TONGA** (IRE) 31
356 **KING ORRY** (IRE) 50
535 **KING OSWALD** (IRE) 3
192 **KING OTTOKAR** (FR) 12
97 **KING PACHA** (IRE) 45
537 **KING RAGNAR** 66
563 **KING RAJ** 29

550 **KING ROBERT** 11
212 **KING ROLAND** (IRE) 40
537 **KING TRITON** (IRE) 157
305 **KING ZAIN** (IRE) 179
305 **KING'S ADVICE** 17
305 **KING'S CAPER** 86
242 **KING'S CASTLE** (IRE) 73
413 **KING'S CHARISMA** (IRE) 68
178 **KING'S COINAGE** (IRE) 8
6 **KING'S COMMAND** 66
321 **KING'S COUNSEL** 7
272 **KING'S KNIGHT** (IRE) 47
17 **KING'S LYNN** 87
435 **KING'S MILLER** (IRE) 35
576 **KING'S ODYSSEY** (IRE) 44
554 **KING'S PAVILION** (IRE) 4
256 **KING'S PROCTOR** (IRE) 12
117 **KING'S SLIPPER** 6
435 **KING'S SOCKS** (IRE) 36
524 **KING'S WHARF** (IRE) 18
305 **KINGBROOK** 87
97 **KINGDOME COME** C 98
375 **KINGDOMFORAHORSE** 14
142 **KINGFAST** (IRE) 22
417 **KINGLAMI** 8
548 **KINGMANIA** (IRE) 31
339 **KINGMANS SPIRIT** (IRE) 38
337 **KINGMON'S BOY** 4
534 **KINGOFTHECOTSWOLDS** (IRE) 48
458 **KINGRULLAH** (IRE) 7
365 **KINGS ARTIST** F 72
315 **KINGS CREEK** (IRE) 148
585 **KINGS ECLIPSE** (IRE) 3
214 **KINGS HIGHWAY** (IRE) 20
330 **KINGS MONARCH** 14
343 **KINGS OWN** 1
305 **KINGS PRINCE** 180
315 **KINGS ROYAL HUSSAR** (FR) 64
268 **KINGS RYDE** 95
92 **KINGS TEMPTATION** 16
526 **KINGS WALK** (IRE) 50
584 **KINGS WAY** 8
77 **KINGSLEY KLARION** (IRE) 22
157 **KINGSMILL GIN** 4
186 **KINGSON** (IRE) 31
534 **KINGSPLACE** (IRE) 49
320 **KINGSTON KURRAJONG** 4
223 **KINGSTON MIMOSA** 6
84 **KINGSTON STAR** (IRE) 39
6 **KINGSWEAR** 67
475 **KINGSWELL THEATRE** 18
29 **KINROSS** 63
242 **KINSMAN** 74
270 **KIPLIN** 10
409 **KIPLING** (IRE) 52
384 **KIPPS** (IRE) 31
203 **KIRA'S STAR** 3
214 **KIRALEAH** 21
169 **KIRBY UNDERDALE** 66
304 **KIRKLAND FOREVER** 14
538 **KIRSCH** (IRE) 10
188 **KIRSTENBOSCH** 8
68 **KIRTLING** 1
365 **KIRWANS LANE** (IRE) 73
486 **KISKADEE** 27
315 **KISMAT** 65
392 **KISMET HARDY** 120
473 **KISSESFORKATIE** (IRE) 23

249 **KISUMU** 37
483 **KITAABAAT** 12
242 **KITCARA** F 147
117 **KITCARINA** (FR) 7
4 **KITEINAHURRICANE** (IRE) 5
186 **KITTEN'S DREAM** 101
205 **KITTY FISHER** (IRE) 4
452 **KITTY HALL** (IRE) 26
170 **KITTY'S COVE** 51
574 **KITTY'S LIGHT** 16
497 **KIWAYU** 4
477 **KIWI MYTH** 5
103 **KIWIANA** 4
422 **KIZOMBA** 76
221 **KK LEXION** (IRE) 50
392 **KLASSICAL DREAM** (FR) 121
572 **KLEOS** (IRE) 18
63 **KLIPPERTY KLOPP** 7
63 **KLOPP** 8
117 **KLOPP OF THE KOP** (IRE) 38
378 **KLOUD GATE** (FR) 83
577 **KLUTE** (IRE) 49
405 **KNAPPERS HILL** (IRE) 96
117 **KNAPSACK** (IRE) 39
446 **KNICKERBOCKERGLORY** (IRE) 23
333 **KNIGHT COMMANDER** 2
200 **KNIGHT COMMANDER** 5
417 **KNIGHT CRUSADER** 9
416 **KNIGHT DESTROYER** (IRE) 45
82 **KNIGHT IN ARMOUR** (IRE) 2
484 **KNIGHT IN DUBAI** (USA) 60
409 **KNIGHT OF MALTA** (IRE) 53
371 **KNIGHT'S GATE** (IRE) 22
170 **KNIGHTCAP** 123
465 **KNIGHTED** (IRE) 15
356 **KNOCK HOUSE** (IRE) 51
318 **KNOCK KNOCK** (IRE) 15
89 **KNOCKABOUT QUEEN** 32
340 **KNOCKACURRA** (IRE) 39
395 **KNOCKGRAFFON** (IRE) 61
11 **KNOCKMAOLE BOY** (IRE) 3
250 **KNOCKNAGOSHEL** (IRE) 6
6 **KNOCKNAGREE** (IRE) C 169
249 **KNOCKNAMONA** (IRE) 38
23 **KNOCKOURA** (IRE) 15
337 **KNOCKOUT BLOW** 5
184 **KNOCKREA** (IRE) 27
356 **KNOCKROBIN** (IRE) 52
531 **KNOW** F 23
132 **KNOW NO LIMITS** (IRE) 36
435 **KNOW THE SCORE** (IRE) 37
188 **KNOWING** 9
186 **KNOWING GLANCE** (IRE) 32
268 **KNOWN** (IRE) 96
1 **KOALA KEEL** (IRE) 30
565 **KODI KOH** (IRE) 12
132 **KODIAC BROWN BEAR** (IRE) 67
81 **KODIAC DANCER** (IRE) 9
474 **KODIAC LASS** (IRE) 5
439 **KODIAC PRIDE** 3
318 **KODIAK ATTACK** (IRE) 7
180 **KODILINE** (IRE) 13
545 **KODIMOOR** (IRE) 13
94 **KOEMAN** 13
242 **KOLISI** (IRE) 148
323 **KOLKA** 64
150 **KOLOSSUS** 15
270 **KOMMANDER KIRKUP** 11

437 **KOMMODITY KID** (IRE) 21
287 **KOMPETE** F 8
287 **KOMPETE** C 21
327 **KON TIKY** (FR) G 40
117 **KONCHEK** 3
89 **KONDRATIEV WAVE** (IRE) 85
539 **KONIGSBERG** 58
503 **KOOLA BUALA** (IRE) 19
6 **KOORA** C 170
254 **KOREA** (IRE) 162
392 **KOSHARI** 122
378 **KOST A COAT** (FR) 84
444 **KOTSI** (IRE) C 57
539 **KOVERA** (FR) 59
315 **KOZIER** (GER) 66
170 **KRABI** 124
583 **KRACQUER** 42
116 **KRAFLA** (USA) 30
165 **KRAKA** (IRE) 4
97 **KRAQUANTE** 46
395 **KRAZY PAVING** 62
330 **KRIS SPIN** (FR) 15
563 **KRISHMASA** (FR) 30
426 **KROY** 3
379 **KRYNICA** (USA) C 24
33 **KRYPTOS** 10
146 **KRYSTALLITE** 12
574 **KUIPER BELT** (USA) 17
405 **KUMARA PLOUGH** (IRE) 97
413 **KUMASI** 69
191 **KUPA RIVER** (IRE) 16
228 **KURAMATA** (IRE) 91
81 **KUREDU** 10
84 **KURIOUS** 5
251 **KUWAIT CURRENCY** (USA) 15
251 **KUWAIT DIRECTION** (IRE) 74
186 **KUWAIT SHIELD** 102
251 **KUZNETSOVA** 190
304 **KWELA** 15
7 **KYBOSH** (IRE) 58
269 **KYLENOE FAIRY** (IRE) G 12
87 **KYLIE RULES** 19
394 **KYLLA LOOKS** 19
481 **KYLLACHY CASTLE** 8
454 **KYLLACHY DRAGON** (IRE) 4
49 **KYLLACHY GALA** 12
389 **KYLLACHY WARRIOR** (IRE) 5
518 **KYLLACHYS TALE** (IRE) 9
146 **KYLLARNEY** F 32
527 **KYLLINGA** (IRE) 6
512 **KYLLISHI** 36
16 **KYLLISHI** 37
550 **KYLLUKEY** 12
111 **KYMATA** 6
323 **KYNISKA** (IRE) 65
26 **KYNREN** (IRE) 9
526 **L'AIR DU VENT** (FR) 51
268 **L'AMI SERGE** (IRE) 97
315 **L'AVENTURE** (FR) G 67
95 **L'ES FREMANTLE** (FR) 2
546 **L'HOMME PRESSE** (FR) 15
295 **L'INGANNO FELICE** (FR) 20
382 **L'INTEMPOREL** (FR) 14
6 **LA ARENOSA** (IRE) F 171
233 **LA BAGUE AU ROI** (FR) 35
46 **LA CALINDA** G 11
584 **LA CHICA LOBO** 17
483 **LA CHICANA** (IRE) F 81

503 **LA COLLINA** (IRE) C 45
106 **LA CONCORDE** (FR) F 19
42 **LA CYBORG** (FR) F 4
321 **LA DONACELLA** F 25
30 **LA DRAGONTEA** 32
128 **LA ESTATUA** F 104
572 **LA FEUILLARDE** (FR) G 19
156 **LA FILLE FRANCAISE** (FR) 14
29 **LA FOGLIETTA** 64
506 **LA GRANDE VILLEZ** (FR) G 6
134 **LA HOOFON** F 14
17 **LA HULOTTE** (IRE) 88
563 **LA JWAAB** C 42
84 **LA LUNE** 6
507 **LA MADRINA** (IRE) 2
16 **LA MAQUINA** 21
555 **LA MARCHESA** (IRE) F 24
153 **LA MARETTE** F 11
6 **LA MORTOLA** C 172
465 **LA NAPOULE** F 93
254 **LA NEGRA** C 163
128 **LA NOE** F 105
256 **LA PALMA** C 30
217 **LA PIETA** (AUS) C 15
465 **LA POMME D'AMOUR** F 94
45 **LA POSEUR** (IRE) 9
188 **LA PUNTALINA** (IRE) 43
386 **LA PYLE** (FR) F 35
169 **LA RAV** (IRE) 29
519 **LA REINE POUTINE** (FR) F 10
141 **LA ROCA DEL FUEGO** (IRE) 6
132 **LA ROSIERE** (USA) G 37
409 **LA TRAVIATA** (USA) C 146
191 **LA TRINIDAD** 37
225 **LA VECCHIA SCUOLA** (IRE) F 17
281 **LA VOIX MAGIQUE** 4
26 **LA ZAMORA** G 45
323 **LA ZUBIA** F 66
511 **LAAFY** (USA) 9
121 **LABEEB** (IRE) 48
315 **LABEL DES OBEAUX** (FR) 68
409 **LABURNUM** (IRE) 54
417 **LAC MARMOT** (FR) G 10
198 **LAC SACRE** (FR) 17
30 **LACAN** (IRE) 6
1 **LACEY'S LANE** F 173
305 **LACILY** (USA) C 181
117 **LACING** C 86
409 **LADDIES POKER TWO** (IRE) C 147
108 **LADRONNE** (FR) 2
270 **LADY ALAVESA** 12
529 **LADY ALEXANDRIA** 23
228 **LADY ANDAZ** (IRE) 92
49 **LADY ARGENTO** (IRE) 70
305 **LADY ARIELLA** 182
306 **LADY AVERY** (IRE) 6
460 **LADY AZAMOUR** (IRE) F 3
318 **LADY BABOOSHKA** F 33
122 **LADY BABS** 13
429 **LADY BEAT** 25
188 **LADY BERGAMOT** (FR) 10
244 **LADY BLAKENEY** 39
282 **LADY BLING** F 9
19 **LADY BLING** F 15
254 **LADY BONES** F 104
374 **LADY BOWES** F 1
296 **LADY BOWTHORPE** 5
17 **LADY BRORA** F 158

317 **LADY BUTTONS** 34
170 **LADY CALCARIA** 52
317 **LADY CAMELOT** (IRE) 35
7 **LADY CARDUROS** (IRE) 59
186 **LADY CELIA** 103
583 **LADY CHARTREUSE** (IRE) 43
424 **LADY CHUFFNELL** (IRE) 41
10 **LADY CODEE** 39
244 **LADY CONWAY** (USA) C 78
89 **LADY CYLLA** 33
176 **LADY DANCEALOT** (IRE) 5
214 **LADY DANDY** (IRE) 48
192 **LADY DAUPHIN** (IRE) 13
49 **LADY DE VEGA** 42
244 **LADY DE VESCI** (IRE) 9
7 **LADY DIVA** 60
516 **LADY DUXYANA** F 77
227 **LADY EILE** (IRE) C 25
188 **LADY ELEANOR** 44
304 **LADY ELYSIA** 16
394 **LADY ESTA** 20
251 **LADY ESTELLA** (IRE) C 191
306 **LADY EXCALIBUR** (IRE) 15
117 **LADY FANDITHA** (IRE) 40
532 **LADY FIONA** F 19
468 **LADY FLORENCE** (IRE) 10
321 **LADY FRANCESCA** F 26
391 **LADY FRIEND** G 48
242 **LADY G** (IRE) 75
220 **LADY GABRIELLE** (IRE) F 22
323 **LADY GOLDFRAPP** (IRE) 33
568 **LADY GRIGIO** (IRE) 24
498 **LADY GWHINNYVERE** (IRE) 7
483 **LADY HEIDI** F 82
215 **LADY ILEY** 18
480 **LADY IN HIDING** (IRE) 21
12 **LADY ISABEL** (IRE) 13
240 **LADY JOANNA VASSA** (IRE) 6
157 **LADY KINGSMILL** 5
404 **LADY KYLLAR** C 12
317 **LADY KYRIA** (FR) 36
94 **LADY LAHAR** C 103
73 **LADY LATTE** (IRE) 49
30 **LADY LIGHT** 33
162 **LADY LINDA** (USA) C 29
50 **LADY LIZABETH** (IRE) C 15
286 **LADY LYNETTA** (IRE) 24
437 **LADY MAGDA** 22
189 **LADY MAKFI** (IRE) 23
257 **LADY MANGO** (IRE) 16
475 **LADY MARWAH** (IRE) 19
13 **LADY MASTER** 11
472 **LADY MEGA** (IRE) C 34
413 **LADY MELODY** (IRE) 70
282 **LADY MONICA** 2
378 **LADY MORPHEUS** 85
563 **LADY MOSCOU** (IRE) C 43
281 **LADY MUK** 5
231 **LADY NATASHA** (IRE) 2
158 **LADY NECTAR** (IRE) 15
192 **LADY OF ARAN** (IRE) 14
431 **LADY OF AUTHORITY** 11
483 **LADY OF SHALOTT** 13
465 **LADY OF THE DESERT** (USA) C 95
14 **LADY OF THE NIGHT** 34
19 **LADY OF YORK** 8
489 **LADY PENDRAGON** 11
163 **LADY PENKO** (FR) C 31

13 **LORD SPARKY** 12
30 **LORD WARBURTON** (IRE) 35
228 **LORDOFTHEHORIZON** (FR) 99
81 **LORETTA** (IRE) 11
563 **LORETTA LASS** 33
17 **LORIENT** C 162
386 **LORNA COLE** (IRE) 17
81 **LORTON** 12
539 **LOS ALAMOS** (IRE) 68
254 **LOS ANDES** 165
215 **LOS CAMACHOS** (IRE) 8
256 **LOS CERRITOS** (SWI) 13
537 **LOS OJITOS** (USA) C 163
322 **LOSSIEMOUTH** 20
251 **LOST EDEN** (IRE) 79
163 **LOST EMPIRE** (IRE) 18
498 **LOST HISTORY** (IRE) 8
275 **LOST ON YOU** 9
526 **LOSTINTRANSLATION** (IRE) 58
521 **LOSTNFOUND** 8
51 **LOSTOCK HALL** (IRE) 5
291 **LOTHARIO** 8
14 **LOTS OF LUCK** (IRE) 36
298 **LOTTIE DENO** 13
116 **LOTTIE MARIE** 32
515 **LOUD AS LIONS** (IRE) 16
101 **LOUGANINI** 39
493 **LOUGH DERG FARMER** (IRE) 29
356 **LOUGH DERG JEWEL** (IRE) 58
405 **LOUGH DERG SPIRIT** (IRE) 100
411 **LOUGH HAR** (IRE) 51
374 **LOUGH KENT** 7
493 **LOUGH LEGEND** (IRE) 30
240 **LOUGH SALT** (IRE) 8
221 **LOUGHADERRA PRINCE** (IRE) 52
484 **LOUGHAN** (IRE) 65
117 **LOUIE DE PALMA** 13
499 **LOUIS TREIZE** (IRE) 7
418 **LOUIS' VAC POUCH** (IRE) 23
317 **LOUIS' VAC POUCH** (IRE) 40
409 **LOUISIANA** (IRE) 56
394 **LOUISIANA BEAT** (IRE) 9
87 **LOULIN** 20
23 **LOULOUMILLS** 17
332 **LOUPGAROU** (FR) 1
338 **LOUSE TALK** (IRE) 37
365 **LOUTKA** C 146
516 **LOUVE DES REVES** (IRE) F 80
254 **LOUVE NATIONALE** C 106
132 **LOVABLE CHOICE** 38
402 **LOVATO** (GER) 38
409 **LOVE** (IRE) 57
198 **LOVE AND BE LOVED** 18
422 **LOVE AND LAUGHTER** (IRE) F 79
409 **LOVE BRACELET** (USA) 58
44 **LOVE DREAMS** (IRE) 12
244 **LOVE EXCELLING** (IRE) C 42
538 **LOVE EXPLODES** 2
419 **LOVE IN THE DESERT** C 63
305 **LOVE IS GOLDEN** (IRE) 188
101 **LOVE IS YOU** (IRE) 84
409 **LOVE LOCKET** (IRE) 59
251 **LOVE LOVE** 80
48 **LOVE MY LIFE** (IRE) 15
60 **LOVE NOT MONEY** 17
244 **LOVE NOTE** (USA) C 79
305 **LOVE OF ZOFFANY** (IRE) 189
470 **LOVE POEMS** (IRE) 7

251 **LOVE POWERFUL** (IRE) 81
146 **LOVE RAT** 14
416 **LOVE THE DREAM** (IRE) 48
189 **LOVE THE LEADER** (IRE) 25
243 **LOVE THE WELL** (IRE) 15
413 **LOVE THIRTY** C 112
535 **LOVEATFIRSTLIGHT** (IRE) 4
503 **LOVED** (IRE) F 47
30 **LOVEHEART** 7
268 **LOVEHERANDLEAVEHER** (IRE) 101
409 **LOVELIER** (IRE) 60
285 **LOVELY ACCLAMATION** (IRE) 10
422 **LOVELY BREEZE** (IRE) 80
379 **LOVELY DANCER** (IRE) G 15
464 **LOVELY LOU** LOU 5
422 **LOVELY PASS** (IRE) C 81
506 **LOVELY SCHTUFF** (IRE) 8
422 **LOVELY SURPRISE** (IRE) C 82
422 **LOVER'S MOON** (IRE) 38
315 **LOVERBOY** (FR) 72
186 **LOVERS CRY** 108
364 **LOVING GLANCE** 13
101 **LOVING KISS** (IRE) 85
33 **LOVING PEARL** 11
81 **LOW FELL** 24
27 **LOW PROFILE** 17
392 **LOW SUN** 131
205 **LOWANBEHOLD** (IRE) 7
483 **LOWER STREET** 83
212 **LOXHILL LADY** F 45
6 **LOXLEY** (IRE) 16
50 **LUA DE MEL** (IRE) 10
208 **LUATH** 5
29 **LUCANDER** (IRE) 66
23 **LUCARMNOLADY** 9
544 **LUCARNO EXPRESS** 2
486 **LUCAS** 28
165 **LUCAYAN** 22
440 **LUCCA LADY** (IRE) 9
242 **LUCELLE** (IRE) C 154
101 **LUCID DREAMER** 86
482 **LUCINDA** 7
17 **LUCK OF CLOVER** 32
444 **LUCK ON SUNDAY** (IRE) 34
534 **LUCKOFTHEDRAW** (FR) 52
84 **LUCKY BAY** 41
393 **LUCKY BEAU** (IRE) 47
236 **LUCKY BEGGAR** (IRE) 11
140 **LUCKY BREEZE** (IRE) F 27
308 **LUCKY CIRCLE** 23
529 **LUCKY CLIO** (IRE) C 41
214 **LUCKY DATE** (IRE) F 51
140 **LUCKY DRAW** 23
463 **LUCKY FLIGHT** (FR) 45
317 **LUCKY ICON** (IRE) 41
419 **LUCKY LEIGH** F 64
472 **LUCKY LESLIE** (IRE) 14
63 **LUCKY LODGE** 9
93 **LUCKY LOU** (IRE) 50
518 **LUCKY LOUIE** 12
234 **LUCKY LOVER BOY** (IRE) 27
186 **LUCKY LUCKY MAN** (IRE) 33
392 **LUCKY ONE** (FR) 132
175 **LUCKY ROBIN** (IRE) 32
572 **LUCKY START** (IRE) F 21
371 **LUCKY TOKEN** (IRE) F 41
427 **LUCKY VIOLET** (IRE) 6
577 **LUCKY'S DREAM** 52

432 **LUCKYJOHNHOBBS** (IRE) 7
249 **LUCOU** (FR) 40
233 **LUCY IN THE SKY** (IRE) 37
26 **LUCY PARSONS** (IRE) G 46
426 **LUCY RULES** (IRE) 23
517 **LUCY'S LAW** (IRE) 8
558 **LUCYHILUCYLOW** 6
101 **LUDISIA** 87
95 **LUDUAMF** (IRE) 3
515 **LUGG RIVER** 17
367 **LUIGI VAMPA** (IRE) 19
186 **LUIS VAZ DE TORRES** (IRE) 34
365 **LUKE SHORT** 133
365 **LUKES WELL** C 147
521 **LUKOUTOLDMAKEZEBAK** 9
531 **LULLABY MOON** 29
170 **LULU BALOO** 55
6 **LUMIERE** C 177
244 **LUMINANCE** (IRE) C 80
364 **LUMINATION** 14
557 **LUNA MAGIC** 13
349 **LUNA WISH** 9
416 **LUNAR BABY** (IRE) 49
582 **LUNAR DEITY** 20
342 **LUNAR JET** 12
446 **LUNAR LANDER** (IRE) 25
121 **LUNCIES** 51
411 **LUNGARNO PALACE** (USA) 52
192 **LUS NA GREINE** (IRE) C 63
89 **LUSCIFER** 86
576 **LUSITANIEN** (FR) 45
268 **LUST FOR GLORY** (IRE) 102
121 **LUSTROUS** F 86
274 **LUTTRELL LAD** (IRE) 62
49 **LUVMEDO** (IRE) C 72
378 **LUXFORD** 88
242 **LUXOR** 11
30 **LYDFORD** 36
405 **LYDFORD LAD** (IRE) 101
221 **LYDIA VIOLET** (IRE) 53
162 **LYDIATE** (IRE) F 56
533 **LYDIATE LADY** 5
568 **LYFORD** (IRE) 27
129 **LYGON ROCK** (IRE) 20
587 **LYME PARK** 4
391 **LYN'S SECRET** (IRE) 15
99 **LYNCHPIN** (IRE) 3
230 **LYNDALE** 23
503 **LYNN BRITT CABIN** 21
254 **LYNWOOD GOLD** (IRE) 41
405 **LYONS** (IRE) 102
251 **LYRIC GOLD** 82
564 **LYRICA'S LION** (IRE) 11
162 **LYRICAL** 30
6 **LYRICAL APPROACH** 72
388 **LYRICAL BALLAD** (IRE) 50
516 **LYRICAL BEAUTY** (IRE) 27
117 **LYRICIST** F 87
49 **LYRICIST VOICE** 45
331 **LYSANDER BELLE** (IRE) 17
364 **LYZBETH** (FR) 15
440 **M' LADY MAY** 10
391 **MA BAKER** (IRE) G 16
379 **MA BELLA PAOLA** (IRE) F 26
97 **MA DECLARATION** (IRE) 48
294 **MA PETIT LUMIER** 4
537 **MA QUALITE** (IRE) 164
269 **MAASAI WARRIOR** (IRE) 15

91 **MAAZEL** (IRE) 15
300 **MAB DAB** (IRE) 11
462 **MABAADY** 6
121 **MABDAA** 87
319 **MABEL JANE** 14
180 **MABRE** (IRE) 34
170 **MAC AILEY** 56
576 **MAC AMARA** 46
576 **MAC BELLA** 47
249 **MAC CENNETIG** (IRE) 41
339 **MAC JETES** 19
576 **MAC KAYLA** 48
87 **MAC MCCARTHY** (IRE) 43
52 **MAC TOTTIE** 22
112 **MACARDLE** (IRE) 11
6 **MACAROON** (USA) F 178
104 **MACHINE GUN** (IRE) 20
17 **MACHIOS** 91
260 **MACHO PRIDE** (IRE) 54
73 **MACHO TIME** (IRE) 53
73 **MACHO TOUCH** (IRE) 54
88 **MACHREE** (IRE) 8
193 **MACK THE KNIFE** (IRE) 6
576 **MACK THE MAN** (IRE) 49
537 **MACKAAR** (IRE) 11
286 **MACKELLY** (IRE) 26
356 **MACKENBERG** (GER) 59
40 **MACKSVILLE** (IRE) 5
312 **MACS BLESSINGS** (IRE) 9
493 **MACS GIFT** (IRE) 31
441 **MAD BARRY** 8
319 **MAD ENDEAVOUR** 8
505 **MAD MOLL** (IRE) F 6
190 **MADAL BEE** 18
24 **MADALLI** (IRE) 11
152 **MADAM HASHTAG** 20
233 **MADAM MALINA** 38
538 **MADAM PRESIDENT** F 26
292 **MADAM SCULLY** 10
168 **MADAME MOZAIK** (USA) G 7
192 **MADAME PELTIER** (IRE) 44
431 **MADAME RITZ** (IRE) 12
304 **MADAME TANTZY** 17
494 **MADAME VOGUE** 9
582 **MADAME WINNER** 50
291 **MADAMES GIRL** (IRE) 48
395 **MADE FOR YOU** 64
49 **MADE IN ITALY** (IRE) 46
92 **MADE IN KK** (IRE) G 18
159 **MADE IN PIMLICO** (IRE) 11
317 **MADEEH** 42
84 **MADELEINE BOND** 8
539 **MADERA MIST** (IRE) 69
76 **MADEYNA** (USA) 41
315 **MADIBA PASSION** (FR) 73
239 **MADISON AVENUE** 15
505 **MADNESS LIGHT** (FR) 4
483 **MADONNA DELL'ORTO** C 84
89 **MADRINHO** (FR) 38
391 **MAEBH** (IRE) 17
140 **MAERCHENGARTEN** 9
121 **MAESTRO STICK** 52
260 **MAEVE'S MEMORY** (IRE) 55
251 **MAFIA POWER** 83
561 **MAGDALANA** 5
484 **MAGELLAN** 66
593 **MAGEN'S MOON** (IRE) 6
97 **MAGEVA** 49

5 **MAGHFOOR** 7
254 **MAGI NOIRE** F 166
330 **MAGIC DANCER** 17
150 **MAGIC ECHO** 37
538 **MAGIC J** (USA) 3
365 **MAGIC LADY** (IRE) 80
6 **MAGIC LILY** 17
371 **MAGIC LUTE** (FR) 24
454 **MAGIC MIRROR** 5
483 **MAGIC MISSION** C 85
170 **MAGIC MUSIC** (IRE) G 128
254 **MAGIC OF LIGHT** (IRE) 42
256 **MAGIC RIVER** (IRE) 14
405 **MAGIC SAINT** (FR) 103
408 **MAGIC SHIP** (IRE) 4
197 **MAGIC TIMING** 10
409 **MAGIC WAND** (IRE) 9
409 **MAGICAL** (IRE) 5
117 **MAGICAL DRAGON** (IRE) 41
87 **MAGICAL EFFECT** (IRE) 21
16 **MAGICAL FLOWER** F 46
371 **MAGICAL FORCE** 25
516 **MAGICAL JOURNEY** (IRE) 28
245 **MAGICAL MAN** 8
545 **MAGICAL MAX** 30
272 **MAGICAL MEMORY** (IRE) 12
465 **MAGICAL MOMENT** (FR) 57
228 **MAGICAL MORNING** 100
499 **MAGICAL RIDE** 8
465 **MAGICAL SPIRIT** (IRE) 18
388 **MAGICAL THOMAS** 51
251 **MAGICAL WISH** (IRE) 16
337 **MAGICINTHEMAKING** (USA) 7
444 **MAGNA MORALIA** (IRE) 35
165 **MAGNA OF ILLUSION** 23
241 **MAGNETIC** (IRE) 5
537 **MAGNETISED** 69
315 **MAGNIFICAT** (IRE) 150
162 **MAGNIFICIA** (IRE) 31
463 **MAGNUM** (DEN) 46
263 **MAGNUM** (IRE) 5
15 **MAGREVIO** (IRE) 16
475 **MAGS MELODY** (IRE) 6
340 **MAGWADIRI** (IRE) 16
38 **MAH MATE BOB** (IRE) 10
117 **MAHALA BAY** 42
17 **MAHANAKHON POWER** 92
270 **MAHARASHTRA** 13
413 **MAHARG'S PRINCESS** (IRE) 71
38 **MAHLER SUPREME** (IRE) 14
131 **MAHLER'S FIRST** (IRE) 12
391 **MAHLER'S PROMISE** (IRE) 18
315 **MAHLERMADE** (IRE) 74
233 **MAHLERVOUS** (IRE) 39
155 **MAHNA MAHNA** (IRE) 3
97 **MAHTHOUF** (IRE) 99
215 **MAHUIKA** 9
545 **MAHZARIN** 31
5 **MAID IN INDIA** (IRE) 8
368 **MAID IN MANHATTAN** (IRE) 28
98 **MAID MILLIE** 13
110 **MAID O'MALLEY** 13
403 **MAID OF CAMELOT** (IRE) 4
305 **MAID TO DREAM** (IRE) 190
84 **MAIDEN CASTLE** 9
162 **MAIDEN'S TOWER** (IRE) 1
49 **MAIL EXPRESS** (IRE) F 73
435 **MAIN FACT** (USA) 41

484 **MAIRE BANRIGH** 67
309 **MAISIE MOO** 9
238 **MAISIEBELLA** 12
154 **MAISON BRILLET** (IRE) 1
249 **MAISON D'OR** (IRE) 42
544 **MAITREE EXPRESS** 3
242 **MAJAALIS** (FR) 12
175 **MAJALAAT** (IRE) 33
27 **MAJESTE** 18
94 **MAJESTIC** (IRE) 104
244 **MAJESTIC DANCER** (IRE) C 81
107 **MAJESTIC DAWN** (IRE) 5
257 **MAJESTIC HERO** (IRE) 17
121 **MAJESTIC JEWEL** 53
278 **MAJESTIC MERLIN** 5
228 **MAJESTIC NOOR** 101
6 **MAJESTIC QUEEN** (IRE) F 179
186 **MAJESTIC SANDS** (IRE) 109
81 **MAJESTIC STONE** (IRE) 13
274 **MAJESTIC TOUCH** (IRE) 63
199 **MAJESTYK FIRE** (IRE) 8
242 **MAJEYDA** (USA) F 155
285 **MAJOR ASSAULT** 11
542 **MAJOR BOND** 12
522 **MAJOR CRISPIES** 8
247 **MAJOR DAVIS** (FR) 4
365 **MAJOR DESTINATION** (IRE) 81
315 **MAJOR DUNDEE** (IRE) 75
437 **MAJOR FORCE** 50
465 **MAJOR JUMBO** 19
39 **MAJOR PARTNERSHIP** (IRE) 26
368 **MAJOR SNUGFIT** 29
268 **MAJOR STING** (IRE) 103
417 **MAJOR VALENTINE** 11
24 **MAJORETTE** 12
166 **MAKAARIM** 5
19 **MAKAMBE** (IRE) 9
81 **MAKANAH** 14
176 **MAKE HASTE SLOWLY** 6
121 **MAKE IT RAIN** (IRE) 54
244 **MAKE IT TURBO** (IRE) 82
435 **MAKE ME A BELIEVER** (IRE) 42
251 **MAKEEN** 84
480 **MAKETY** 24
401 **MAKINDI** C 14
39 **MAKING HISTORY** (IRE) 90
392 **MAKITORIX** (FR) 133
402 **MAKKA PAKKA** (IRE) 39
101 **MAKRAM** (IRE) 40
61 **MAKTAY** 16
73 **MAKTHECAT** (IRE) 11
305 **MAKYON** (IRE) 89
101 **MAKZEEM** 11
424 **MALACHYS GIRL** (IRE) 50
435 **MALANGEN** (IRE) 42
13 **MALAPIE** (IRE) 13
405 **MALAYA** (FR) 104
530 **MALAYAN MIST** (IRE) C 27
254 **MALAYSIAN** (IRE) 167
70 **MALDONADO** (FR) 30
388 **MALIBOO** (IRE) 52
7 **MALIKA I JAHAN** (FR) 64
117 **MALILLA** (FR) F 88
261 **MALINA OCARINA** 29
181 **MALINDI BAY** (FR) 10
424 **MALINELLO** 51
563 **MALLADORE** (IRE) F 45
305 **MALMOOSA** (IRE) C 191

49 **MALOTRU** 47
356 **MALPAS** (IRE) 60
406 **MALYSTIC** 3
198 **MAMA AFRICA** (IRE) 19
29 **MAMBO GOLD** (USA) C 119
305 **MAMBO HALO** (USA) C 192
97 **MAMBO LIGHT** (USA) C 100
251 **MAMBO NIGHTS** (IRE) 85
305 **MAMBO PARADISE** F 193
312 **MAMDOOD** (IRE) 10
16 **MAMILLIUS** 2
242 **MAMMA MORTON** (IRE) C 156
178 **MAMOO** 9
188 **MAN OF LIGHT** (FR) 46
331 **MAN OF PLENTY** 18
6 **MAN OF PROMISE** (USA) 73
251 **MAN OF THE NIGHT** (FR) 86
89 **MAN OF THE NORTH** 9
388 **MAN OF THE SEA** (IRE) 53
317 **MAN OF VERVE** (FR) 43
242 **MANAAJIM** (IRE) 79
121 **MANAATIG** 55
260 **MANAMITE** (FR) 20
557 **MANAP** 45
279 **MANCE RAYDER** (IRE) 9
493 **MANCINELLIE** 32
233 **MANDALAYAN** (IRE) 40
214 **MANDARIN** (GER) 26
98 **MANDARIN DUCK** 34
132 **MANDIBLE** (FR) 39
39 **MANDINGA** (BRZ) C 156
1 **MANETTI** (IRE) 35
211 **MANFADH** (IRE) 15
548 **MANGO BOY** 32
134 **MANGO CHUTNEY** 5
245 **MANHATTAN MEAD** 9
224 **MANIA** (IRE) C 13
251 **MANIGORDO** (USA) 87
416 **MANINTHESHADOWS** (IRE) 50
339 **MANJAAM** (IRE) 20
192 **MANKAYAN** (IRE) 16
480 **MANNING ESTATE** (IRE) 25
463 **MANNOCHMORE** 47
221 **MANOFTHEMOMENT** (IRE) 54
327 **MANOFTHEMOUNTAIN** (IRE) 44
413 **MANOLITH** 72
315 **MANOR PARK** 76
524 **MANORBANK** (IRE) 20
24 **MANS NOT TROT** (IRE) 13
21 **MANSFIELD** 8
370 **MANSHOOD** (IRE) 15
16 **MANTON GRANGE** 8
212 **MANTOVANI** (FR) 46
428 **MANUCCI** (IRE) 8
29 **MANUELA DE VEGA** (IRE) 21
546 **MANVERS HOUSE** 17
178 **MANWELL** (IRE) 10
224 **MANY A STAR** (IRE) 9
409 **MANY COLOURS** F 151
342 **MANY TALES** 13
169 **MANZIL** (IRE) 31
413 **MANZO DURO** (IRE) 73
286 **MAORI KNIGHT** (IRE) 27
537 **MAQTAL** (USA) 70
344 **MAQUISARD** (FR) 8
225 **MARAAKIZ** (IRE) 157
339 **MARACUJA** F 57
484 **MARADA** 68

392 **MARAJMAN** (FR) 134
162 **MARBELLA** (IRE) 11
180 **MARBLE BAY** (IRE) 35
576 **MARBLE MOON** (IRE) 50
363 **MARBLE SANDS** (FR) 40
29 **MARCELA DE VEGA** 67
87 **MARCELLA** 22
416 **MARCH IS ON** (IRE) 51
242 **MARDIE GRAS** F 158
94 **MARE IMBRIUM** (USA) F 51
335 **MARENGO** 10
260 **MARENGO SALLY** (IRE) 45
244 **MARENKO** C 83
532 **MARETTIMO** (IRE) 10
358 **MARGARET** J 5
242 **MARGARET'S MISSION** (IRE) C 159
393 **MARGARETHA** (IRE) 48
12 **MARGIE** (IRE) F 14
344 **MARGIE'S CHOICE** (GER) 9
529 **MARGUB** 7
508 **MARIA ANTONIA** (IRE) F 12
243 **MARIA MAGDALENA** (IRE) 16
228 **MARIA ROSA** (USA) 102
584 **MARIAH'S MELODY** (IRE) 9
577 **MARIAS DREAM** (IRE) G 53
384 **MARIDADI** 12
97 **MARIE** (FR) 101
6 **MARIE BAA** (FR) C 180
6 **MARIE DE MEDICI** (USA) C 181
305 **MARIE'S DIAMOND** (IRE) 18
268 **MARIE'S ROCK** (IRE) 104
316 **MARIENSTAR** (IRE) 19
21 **MARIETTA ROBUSTI** (IRE) 9
84 **MARIETTY** 29
165 **MARIGAY'S MAGIC** C 24
439 **MARIKA** C 48
283 **MARILYN MONROE** (IRE) 20
170 **MARINA GROVE** (IRE) 129
511 **MARINE BLEUE** (IRE) F 128
402 **MARINE ONE** 40
519 **MARIO DE PAIL** (FR) 11
518 **MARION'S BOY** (IRE) 30
547 **MARJORAM** (IRE) 58
589 **MARJU'S QUEST** (IRE) 11
251 **MARK OF GOLD** 88
87 **MARK'S CHOICE** (IRE) 23
413 **MARKAZI** (FR) 37
576 **MARKET NICHE** (IRE) G 51
395 **MARKOV** (IRE) 65
393 **MARLBOROUGH SOUNDS** 19
1 **MARLEE MASSIE** (IRE) 36
157 **MARLEY FIRTH** (IRE) 7
371 **MARLINGFORD** G 42
364 **MARLYN** (IRE) 16
378 **MARMALADE DAY** 89
242 **MARMALADY** (AUS) F 160
136 **MARMONT** 8
57 **MARNI GREY** 8
183 **MAROC** 11
452 **MAROWN** (IRE) 29
142 **MARQUIS OF CARABAS** (IRE) 23
484 **MARRACUDJA** (FR) 69
537 **MARREYR** 71
582 **MARRONNIER** (IRE) 21
511 **MARS LANDING** (IRE) 63
384 **MARSABIT** (IRE) 61
304 **MARSELAN** (IRE) 65
121 **MARSH DAISY** F 88

173 **MARSH WREN** 19
345 **MARSHAL DAN** (IRE) 8
536 **MARSHALL AID** (IRE) 11
254 **MARTAGON LILY** G 107
541 **MARTELLO SKY** 17
233 **MARTHA BRAE** 41
465 **MARTHA WATSON** (IRE) C 97
83 **MARTHA YEATS** (IRE) 23
457 **MARTHA'S DREAM** 4
256 **MARTHA'S WAY** G 15
458 **MARTILA** (IRE) 8
77 **MARTIN KING** 23
295 **MARTIN'S BRIG** (IRE) 54
88 **MARTINA FRANCA** 7
99 **MARTINENGO** (IRE) 4
77 **MARTINEO** 24
435 **MARTINHAL** (IRE) 44
322 **MARTY TIME** (FR) 21
81 **MARVEL** 15
249 **MARVELLOUS JOE** (IRE) 43
519 **MARVELLOUS MARVEL** (FR) 12
169 **MARWARI** (FR) 32
242 **MARY CASSATT** 161
220 **MARY LE BOW** 6
254 **MARY MCPHEE** 168
6 **MARY RITA** (USA) C 182
338 **MARY THE MERMAID** 38
26 **MARY THOMAS** (IRE) C 47
12 **MARYELLEN** 8
409 **MARYLEBONE** (USA) C 152
1 **MARYLINE TRITT** (FR) 37
547 **MASACCIO** (IRE) 59
29 **MASCAT** 68
187 **MASHAM MOOR** 10
305 **MASHAM STAR** (IRE) 19
173 **MASKADA** 17
309 **MASKED IDENTITY** 10
402 **MASON JAR** (FR) 41
88 **MASONBROOK LADY** (IRE) C 28
164 **MASQUE** 23
388 **MASQUERADE BLING** (IRE) 54
409 **MASSARRA** F 153
244 **MASSIF CENTRAL** (IRE) 10
221 **MASSINI MAN** 55
574 **MASSINI'S DREAM** 20
297 **MASTER ALAN** 15
489 **MASTER BAMBU** (ARG) 12
388 **MASTER BURBIDGE** 55
233 **MASTER CARD** 42
526 **MASTER DEBONAIR** 59
371 **MASTER GREY** (IRE) 9
356 **MASTER MALACHY** (IRE) 61
384 **MASTER MALCOLM** 32
164 **MASTER MEAD** 24
327 **MASTER MILLINER** (IRE) 45
317 **MASTER NEWTON** (IRE) 44
121 **MASTER OF COMBAT** (IRE) 89
375 **MASTER OF THE MOON** 7
98 **MASTER ROCCO** (IRE) 29
518 **MASTER SAM BELLAMY** 13
107 **MASTER SPY** (IRE) 22
446 **MASTER SUNRISE** (IRE) 26
162 **MASTER THE STARS** (GER) 32
176 **MASTER THE WORLD** (IRE) 7
405 **MASTER TOMMYTUCKER** 105
373 **MASTER TRADESMAN** (IRE) 3
431 **MASTER VINTAGE** 13
274 **MASTER WORK** (FR) 64

30 **MASTERMAN** (FR) 82	429 **MAYTHEORSEBEWITHU** (IRE) 10	439 **MEISTERZINGER** (IRE) 49
545 **MASTERS APPRENTICE** (IRE) 14	429 **MAZALTO** (IRE) 11	511 **MEKNAS** (FR) 64
274 **MASTERS LEGACY** (IRE) 65	392 **MAZE RUNNER** (IRE) 136	419 **MEKONG** 7
13 **MATCHMAKING** (GER) 14	290 **MAZEKINE** 10	21 **MELABI** (IRE) 11
323 **MATELLO** (FR) 36	286 **MAZIKEEN** 28	63 **MELANDRE** F 24
494 **MATERIAL WORLD** G 15	165 **MAZMERIZE** 5	508 **MELATONINA** (IRE) C 25
577 **MATEWAN** (IRE) 54	121 **MAZUNA** (IRE) F 90	242 **MELBOURNE MEMORIES** C 162
192 **MATHANORA** (IRE) C 64	244 **MAZYAD** (FR) 84	98 **MELBURNIAN** 14
422 **MATHOOL** (IRE) C 83	521 **MAZZA ROCKS** (IRE) 10	325 **MELDRUM LAD** (IRE) 4
60 **MATIRA BAY** (IRE) 21	428 **MAZZURI** (IRE) 9	82 **MELDRUM WAY** (IRE) 3
413 **MATRON** C 113	325 **MCCRACKENS GATE** (IRE) 3	274 **MELEKHOV** (IRE) 67
547 **MATTHEW FLINDERS** 60	405 **MCFABULOUS** (IRE) 106	169 **MELGATE MAGIC** 33
552 **MATTHEW MAN** 7	418 **MCGARRY** (IRE) 24	169 **MELGATE MAJEURE** 34
315 **MATTIE ROSS** 77	317 **MCGARRY** 45	214 **MELISSA** (FR) 27
254 **MAUD GONNE SPIRIT** (IRE) 108	1 **MCGINTY'S DREAM** (IRE) 38	101 **MELITO** (AUS) C 88
128 **MAULESDEN MAY** (IRE) 41	524 **MCGOWAN'S PASS** 21	227 **MELLOW BEN** 7
241 **MAUNA KEA** (IRE) 6	402 **MCGROARTY** (IRE) 43	365 **MELLY AND ME** (IRE) 82
81 **MAURICE DANCER** 25	274 **MCNAMARAS BAND** (IRE) 66	511 **MELNIKOVA** 65
21 **MAURICIO** (IRE) 10	99 **MDINA** 16	516 **MELODIC CHARM** (IRE) 30
101 **MAURIMO** 41	377 **ME TOO PLEASE** (IRE) 8	217 **MELODIC THUNDER** (FR) 9
76 **MAWKEB** (USA) 67	81 **MEA CULPA** (IRE) 16	581 **MELODICA** G 9
369 **MAWLOOD** (IRE) 3	529 **MEA PARVITAS** (IRE) C 42	540 **MELODINO** (GER) 10
463 **MAX APPEAL** (IRE) 48	261 **MEAD VALE** 30	384 **MELODIQUE** (FR) C 62
435 **MAX DO BRAZIL** (FR) 45	268 **MEADOWSWEET** (IRE) 105	444 **MELODY KING** (IRE) 36
392 **MAX DYNAMITE** (FR) 135	331 **MEAGHER'S FLAG** (IRE) 19	260 **MELODY OF SCOTLAND** (FR) 21
40 **MAX DYNAMO** 6	503 **MEANINGFUL VOTE** 22	392 **MELON** 137
153 **MAX FORTE** (IRE) 13	340 **MEANT TWO B** (IRE) 48	64 **MELONY** 11
32 **MAX GUEVARA** (IRE) 10	295 **MEARING** 23	348 **MELSONBY** 10
8 **MAX O** (IRE) 6	39 **MEASURED TEMPO** F 157	170 **MELTING** (IRE) 57
29 **MAX VEGA** 69	61 **MEBA FISTA** (IRE) F 17	567 **MEMBERS BOUNCE** (IRE) 8
339 **MAX'S VOICE** (IRE) 4	409 **MECCA'S ANGEL** (IRE) C 11	620 **MEMORABILIS** (IRE) 62
493 **MAXED OUT KING** (IRE) 33	150 **MECCA'S HOT STEPS** 38	305 **MEMORIA** F 195
402 **MAXENCHOP** (FR) 42	29 **MECHANISM** F 120	180 **MEMORY HILL** (IRE) 15
30 **MAXI BOY** 37	169 **MEDAILLE D'OR** C 67	576 **MEMPHIS BELL** (IRE) 52
562 **MAXI JAZZ** (FR) 20	175 **MEDAKI ROC** (IRE) 34	446 **MEMPHIS BLEEK** 27
511 **MAXIMAL** 129	557 **MEDAL WINNER** (FR) 14	272 **MENAI BRIDGE** 93
29 **MAXIMILIUS** (GER) 70	572 **MEDALLA DE ORO** 22	400 **MENAPIAN** (FR) 7
565 **MAXIMISER** (IRE) 13	67 **MEDAM** F 10	347 **MENDACIOUS HARPY** (IRE) 9
99 **MAXIMIZE** 15	267 **MEDBURN STAR** 9	179 **MENDOZA** (IRE) 6
170 **MAXIMUM RISK** (IRE) 160	126 **MEDDLE** C 9	557 **MENIN GATE** (IRE) 15
163 **MAXINE** (IRE) 32	516 **MEDIA STORM** 29	537 **MENSOORA** (SAF) C 165
549 **MAY MIST** 2	434 **MEDICEAN BLISS** (IRE) C 11	254 **MENTE HERMOSA** 109
17 **MAY NIGHT** 163	503 **MEDICEAN STAR** (IRE) F 48	103 **MENTHE PASTILLE** (FR) 5
117 **MAY ROSE** (IRE) F 89	441 **MEDICI MOON** 9	29 **MEPHISTO** (IRE) 71
272 **MAY SONIC** 13	107 **MEDIEVAL** (IRE) 6	103 **MER BLANCHE** 30
409 **MAYBE** (IRE) F 154	17 **MEDIKA** (IRE) 93	305 **MERAAS** 90
560 **MAYBE MURPHY** 9	299 **MEDITERRANEAN SEA** (IRE) F 25	434 **MERAKI** 4
413 **MAYBE NOW BABY** (IRE) C 114	169 **MEDIUM OF EXCHANGE** (USA) C 86	147 **MERCENARY ROSE** (IRE) 7
121 **MAYBE TODAY** 9	345 **MEDORAS CHILDE** 9	568 **MERCER'S TROOP** (IRE) 28
170 **MAYBEAGREY** G 130	435 **MEEP MEEP MAG** (IRE) 46	78 **MERCERS** 6
32 **MAYBELLENE** (IRE) 17	251 **MEET ME HALFWAY** C 195	213 **MERCERS COURT** (IRE) 5
192 **MAYFAIR POMPETTE** (FR) 17	34 **MEET THE PARENTS** 26	400 **MERCHANT IN MILAN** (IRE) 8
192 **MAYFAIR SPIRIT** (IRE) 18	409 **MEETING** (IRE) 61	188 **MERCHANT OF VENICE** 11
257 **MAYFLOWER LADY** (IRE) 33	193 **MEETING WATERS** F 11	309 **MERCHANTS BREATH** 27
547 **MAYGOLD** 14	326 **MEEZNAH** (USA) F 20	393 **MERCIAN KNIGHT** (IRE) 20
6 **MAYHEM** (IRE) F 183	374 **MEGA DOUBLE** (IRE) 8	393 **MERCIAN PRINCE** (IRE) 21
299 **MAYKIR** 11	519 **MEGA MIND** (IRE) 5	371 **MERCURIST** 26
17 **MAYNE** (IRE) 33	297 **MEGA YEATS** (IRE) 16	162 **MERCURY DIME** (IRE) 12
452 **MAYO STAR** (IRE) 30	92 **MEGABOOST** (IRE) 19	416 **MERCUTIO ROCK** (FR) 53
315 **MAYOLYNN** (USA) F 151	336 **MEGABUCKS** (IRE) 4	405 **MERCY MERCY ME** 107
73 **MAYORSTONE** (IRE) C 94	541 **MEGAEUROS** (IRE) F 18	44 **MERDON CASTLE** (IRE) 13
416 **MAYPOLE CLASS** (IRE) 52	269 **MEGALODON** (IRE) 16	508 **MERE ANARCHY** (IRE) 13
580 **MAYS DREAM** F 16	101 **MEGANS APPROACH** 42	26 **MERESIDE BLUE** 29
309 **MAYSON MOUNT** 26	594 **MEGAUDAIS SPEED** (FR) 6	464 **MERHOOB** (IRE) 6
465 **MAYSON QUEEN** 48	163 **MEGEC BLIS** (FR) C 33	295 **MERRICOURT** (IRE) 24
162 **MAYSONG** 33	117 **MEGHAN SPARKLE** (IRE) 14	439 **MERRITT ISLAND** C 50
557 **MAYSTAR** (IRE) 46	228 **MEHDAAYIH** 21	370 **MERRY BANTER** 16
511 **MAYTAL** 130	305 **MEHRONISSA** C 194	411 **MERRY BERRY** 53

351 **MERRY MILAN** (IRE) 13
413 **MERRY MILLER** (IRE) 74
142 **MERRY MISSED** (IRE) F 24
555 **MERRY SECRET** 26
315 **MERRY YARN** (IRE) 78
7 **MERRYWEATHER** 111
101 **MERSIN** 43
345 **MERWEB** 10
300 **MERYEMS WAY** (IRE) 12
29 **MESEIKA** (USA) F 121
87 **MESHARDAL** (GER) 24
305 **MESMERIC** (GER) 91
251 **MESOPOTAMIA** 196
315 **MESSIRE DES OBEAUX** (FR) 79
278 **MET BY MOONLIGHT** 6
196 **METAL EXCHANGE** 7
186 **METALLIC BLACK** 35
323 **METAPHORE** (FR) 37
135 **METATRONS CUBE** (IRE) 12
515 **METEORITE** 18
243 **METHAG** (FR) 17
463 **METHODTOTHEMADNESS** (IRE) 49
431 **METHODTOTHEMAGIC** (IRE) 14
315 **METHUSALAR** (IRE) 80
212 **METIER** (IRE) 47
51 **METRO BOULOT DODO** (IRE) 6
434 **MEVAGISSEY COVE** 12
69 **MEWS HOUSE** 8
577 **MEWSTONE** G 55
577 **MEXICAN DAVE** 56
173 **MEXICO** (GER) 21
416 **MEYER LANSKY** (IRE) 54
128 **MI CAPRICHO** (IRE) 42
234 **MI LADDO** (IRE) 5
50 **MI RUBINA** (IRE) F 16
76 **MIA DILETTA** C 68
17 **MIA DOLAN** (USA) 94
99 **MIA MENTO** (IRE) 5
437 **MIA MIA** 51
19 **MIAELLA** 10
412 **MIAM GRACE** 17
37 **MIAMI PRESENT** (IRE) 2
409 **MIARIXA** (FR) C 156
184 **MIATURK** 29
577 **MICHAEL'S MOUNT** 57
251 **MICHAEL'S SONG** (IRE) C 197
296 **MICHAELS CHOICE** 6
7 **MICHELE STROGOFF** 65
249 **MICK** (IRE) 71
313 **MICK MAESTRO** (FR) 5
519 **MICK MANHATTAN** (IRE) 14
446 **MICK MONA** (FR) 28
405 **MICK PASTOR** (IRE) 108
132 **MICKEY** (IRE) 13
378 **MICKEY BUCKMAN** 90
580 **MICKEY DRIPPIN** (IRE) 29
392 **MICRO MANAGE** (IRE) 138
230 **MICRO MISSION** (IRE) F 24
180 **MICROSCOPIC** (IRE) 36
511 **MIDDAY** F 131
356 **MIDDLEBROW** (IRE) 62
377 **MIDLAND MILLIE** (IRE) 9
153 **MIDNIGHT ANNIE** 14
108 **MIDNIGHT ANTICS** (IRE) 3
532 **MIDNIGHT CALAMITY** 11
283 **MIDNIGHT CALLISTO** 21
496 **MIDNIGHT CHILL** 38
117 **MIDNIGHT DRIFT** 43

170 **MIDNIGHT FANTASY** C 161
7 **MIDNIGHT FUN** G 66
315 **MIDNIGHT GINGER** 81
315 **MIDNIGHT GLANCE** 82
274 **MIDNIGHT GLORY** 68
486 **MIDNIGHT IN HAVANA** 9
592 **MIDNIGHT JEWEL** 12
48 **MIDNIGHT JITTERBUG** 8
506 **MIDNIGHT KATE** (IRE) 9
317 **MIDNIGHT LEGACY** (IRE) 46
315 **MIDNIGHT MAESTRO** 83
435 **MIDNIGHT MAGIC** 47
65 **MIDNIGHT MAKEOVER** 2
170 **MIDNIGHT MALIBU** (IRE) 58
20 **MIDNIGHT MALIN** 13
117 **MIDNIGHT MARTINI** F 90
173 **MIDNIGHT MARY** 22
39 **MIDNIGHT MEETING** (IRE) 27
234 **MIDNIGHT MOSS** 29
350 **MIDNIGHT MUSTANG** 5
254 **MIDNIGHT MYSTIC** F 169
251 **MIDNIGHT OASIS** C 198
167 **MIDNIGHT OWLE** 7
350 **MIDNIGHT POPSTAR** 3
575 **MIDNIGHT REQUEST** 6
484 **MIDNIGHT RIVER** 70
265 **MIDNIGHT SAPPHIRE** 5
488 **MIDNIGHT SENSATION** 5
493 **MIDNIGHT SHADOW** 34
583 **MIDNIGHT SONATA** (IRE) 47
107 **MIDNIGHT TRAVELLER** (IRE) 23
283 **MIDNIGHT TUNE** 22
25 **MIDNIGHT WARRIOR** 5
532 **MIDNIGHT WAVE** 12
93 **MIDNIGHT WELCOME** 19
315 **MIDNIGHTREFERENDUM** 84
92 **MIDNIGHTREFLECTION** 20
315 **MIDNIGHTS LEGACY** 152
315 **MIDNIGHTS' GIFT** 85
465 **MIDNITE BRIDE** 59
376 **MIDOURA** 8
242 **MIDRARR** (IRE) 80
587 **MIDTECH VALENTINE** 5
268 **MIGHT BITE** (IRE) 106
212 **MIGHT I** (IRE) 48
25 **MIGHTASWELLSMILE** 7
575 **MIGHTY ALTOGETHER** 7
431 **MIGHTY ELSA** 15
299 **MIGHTY ENDEAVOUR** 26
26 **MIGHTY MARIACHI** 30
234 **MIGHTY MARVEL** 30
395 **MIGHTY MEG** 66
254 **MIGHTY MEGGSIE** (IRE) 43
186 **MIGHTY SPIRIT** (IRE) 110
463 **MIGHTY THUNDER** 50
367 **MIGRATION** (IRE) 10
170 **MIKMAK** 59
491 **MILABELLA** 20
317 **MILADYGRACE** 47
73 **MILAGRE DA VIDA** (IRE) 12
283 **MILAN IN MAY** (IRE) 23
571 **MILAN OF CRYSTAL** (IRE) 2
339 **MILAN REEF** (IRE) 21
411 **MILANESE ROSE** (IRE) 54
316 **MILANSBAR** (IRE) 20
317 **MILANVERA** (IRE) 48
372 **MILBERRY** (IRE) 3
305 **MILDENBERGER** 20

508 **MILE HOUSE** (IRE) 14
129 **MILESHA** (IRE) 21
259 **MILEVA ROLLER** 3
350 **MILITARIAN** 4
39 **MILITARY MARCH** 91
370 **MILITIA** 17
438 **MILITRY DECORATION** (IRE) 4
388 **MILKWOOD** (IRE) 56
268 **MILL GREEN** 107
110 **MILL ISLAND** (IRE) 14
170 **MILL RACE KING** (IRE) 60
229 **MILLARVILLE** (IRE) 4
212 **MILLBANK FLYER** (IRE) 49
420 **MILLDEAN BILLY** (IRE) 13
590 **MILLDEAN FELIX** (IRE) 2
420 **MILLDEAN PANTHER** 14
35 **MILLDEAN SILVA** (IRE) 13
212 **MILLE SUSSURRI** (IRE) 50
393 **MILLEFIORI** (IRE) C 58
243 **MILLERS BANK** 18
516 **MILLICENT** 31
228 **MILLICENT FAWCETT** 22
207 **MILLIE MAY** 7
469 **MILLIE THE MINX** (IRE) 11
457 **MILLIE'S FLYING** 5
413 **MILLIONAIA** (IRE) C 115
107 **MILLIONAIRE WALTZ** 2
376 **MILLIONS MEMORIES** 9
254 **MILLISLE** 110
315 **MILLSTONE** 86
94 **MILLTOWN STAR** 52
537 **MILLVINA** 72
110 **MILLY ON AIR** 15
227 **MILNTHORPE** (IRE) 28
388 **MILREU HAS** (FR) 57
331 **MILROW** (IRE) 20
237 **MILTON** 5
27 **MILTON ROAD** 19
52 **MILUTONA HAS** (FR) G 23
524 **MILVALE** (IRE) 22
77 **MIME DANCE** 25
392 **MIN** (FR) 139
486 **MINA VELOUR** 10
385 **MIND THAT JET** (IRE) 14
212 **MIND THE CRACK** (IRE) 51
388 **MIND YOUR BACK** (IRE) 58
537 **MINDPOWER** (IRE) 166
365 **MINDY** C 148
74 **MINE'S A PINT** 6
73 **MINEANDYOURS** 95
496 **MINELLA BEAT** (IRE) 39
416 **MINELLA BEAUTY** (IRE) 55
124 **MINELLA BOBO** (IRE) 15
374 **MINELLA CHARMER** (IRE) 9
52 **MINELLA DADDY** (IRE) 24
392 **MINELLA ENCORE** (IRE) 140
233 **MINELLA EXAMINER** 43
365 **MINELLA FAIR** (IRE) 83
493 **MINELLA FIVEO** (IRE) 35
221 **MINELLA FOR ME** (IRE) 56
153 **MINELLA MOJO** (IRE) 15
438 **MINELLA RISING** (IRE) 5
416 **MINELLA ROCCO** (IRE) 56
167 **MINELLA STYLE** (IRE) 8
411 **MINELLA TARA** (IRE) 55
356 **MINELLA TRUMP** (IRE) 63
269 **MINELLA TWEET** (IRE) 17
164 **MINELLA VOUCHER** 25

14 **MINELLA WARRIOR** (IRE) 37	
431 **MINELLA WHISPER** 16	
440 **MINELLACELEBRATION** (IRE) 11	
175 **MINI CHEDDA** (IRE) 65	
548 **MINI RIVO** (IRE) 33	
136 **MINIATURE DAFFODIL** (IRE) 9	
6 **MINIDRESS** C 184	
229 **MINIMUM** F 5	
324 **MINMORE GREY** (IRE) 4	
131 **MINNIE ESCAPE** 13	
473 **MINNIE TURBO** (IRE) G 24	
38 **MINNIMO** 12	
393 **MINOGUE** 22	
188 **MINORI** (USA) 47	
31 **MINSTER** (IRE) 31	
490 **MINSTREL SONG** 3	
83 **MINT CONDITION** 24	
463 **MINT GOLD** (IRE) 51	
390 **MINTY JONES** 9	
2 **MINUTE LIMIT** (IRE) C 47	
323 **MINX AT MIDNIGHT** (IRE) 38	
972 **MINZA** (FR) F 102	
98 **MIRABAI** 15	
62 **MIRABELLE PLUM** (IRE) 18	
175 **MIRABILE DICTU** (IRE) F 79	
66 **MIRACLE GARDEN** 7	
536 **MIRACLE OF MEDINAH** 12	
503 **MIRACOLIA** (IRE) F 23	
107 **MIRAGE** (IRE) F 33	
50 **MIRAGE MAC** 17	
291 **MIRAKUHL** 49	
132 **MIRAMICHI** (IRE) 69	
132 **MIRAMONT** C 70	
405 **MIRANDA** (IRE) 109	
251 **MIRAZ** (IRE) 89	
88 **MIRDHAK** C 29	
173 **MISAPS** 23	
170 **MISCHIEF MANAGED** (IRE) 61	
413 **MISCHIEF STAR** 75	
212 **MISCHIEVOUS POPPY** 52	
272 **MISDAQEYA** C 94	
206 **MISDFLIGHT** (IRE) 10	
463 **MISFITS** (IRE) 7	
29 **MISHHAR** (IRE) G 122	
228 **MISHRIFF** (IRE) 103	
141 **MISREAD** 7	
545 **MISS AMELIA** 15	
225 **MISS ANNELIESE** (IRE) G 37	
308 **MISS ANTIPOVA** 24	
36 **MISS APRICOT** G 26	
384 **MISS AUSTEN** (IRE) 13	
463 **MISS BATTEN** (IRE) 53	
562 **MISS BLAH BLAH** 21	
529 **MISS BLONDELL** 8	
413 **MISS CAPE** (IRE) F 116	
439 **MISS CELESTIAL** (IRE) 5	
169 **MISS CHILLI** 68	
356 **MISS CILLA** (IRE) F 64	
365 **MISS COGNAC** 84	
498 **MISS CONDUCT** C 14	
188 **MISS DASHWOOD** F 76	
234 **MISS DELIGHTED** (IRE) 31	
395 **MISS DENMAN** (IRE) F 67	
286 **MISS DIAMOND** (IRE) 50	
10 **MISS DITSY** (IRE) 16	
155 **MISS DUSKY DIVA** (IRE) 3	
304 **MISS ELSA** 18	
152 **MISS ENIGMA** (IRE) 4	

268 **MISS FARAGE** (IRE) 108	
470 **MISS FIRECRACKER** (IRE) 3	
268 **MISS FISHER** (IRE) 109	
424 **MISS FLYING FOX** 52	
439 **MISS FRANGIPANI** 25	
14 **MISS GEMSTONE** 38	
116 **MISS GRADENKO** 15	
160 **MISS HAMDA** (IRE) 43	
241 **MISS HARRIETT** 7	
541 **MISS HERITAGE** 19	
233 **MISS HONEY RYDER** (IRE) 44	
93 **MISS ICON** 11	
388 **MISS JEANNE MOON** (IRE) 59	
363 **MISS KATNISS** 41	
412 **MISS LAMB** 18	
483 **MISS LATIN** (IRE) 14	
291 **MISS LESLEY** C 53	
6 **MISS LUCIFER** (FR) F 185	
435 **MISS M** (IRE) 48	
88 **MISS MACCHIATO** (IRE) C 30	
496 **MISS MAHMITE** (IRE) 40	
461 **MISS MARAUDER** G 11	
461 **MISS MARAUDER** G 12	
6 **MISS MARJURIE** (IRE) C 186	
129 **MISS MASH** 22	
304 **MISS MATTERHORN** 41	
251 **MISS MELTEMI** (IRE) C 199	
452 **MISS MILANO** (IRE) 31	
73 **MISS MILBY** (IRE) 96	
338 **MISS MOLINARI** 39	
84 **MISS MORRIS** 30	
472 **MISS MULLIGAN** (IRE) 15	
444 **MISS NAY NEVER** (IRE) 58	
242 **MISS O CONNOR** (IRE) 13	
439 **MISS PALOMA** 51	
391 **MISS PLATINUM** (IRE) G 19	
242 **MISS PLIMSOLL** (USA) C 163	
290 **MISS POLLYANNA** (IRE) 7	
392 **MISS PUNCH** (IRE) 141	
344 **MISS RECYCLED** 10	
537 **MISS RIMEX** (IRE) C 167	
547 **MISS SCALETTA** 92	
419 **MISS SLIGO** (IRE) 25	
244 **MISS SNOSSYBOOTS** (IRE) 11	
529 **MISS SWIFT** 9	
419 **MISS THOUGHTFUL** 26	
286 **MISS TIKI** 51	
435 **MISS TYNTE** (IRE) 49	
272 **MISS VILLANELLE** 48	
437 **MISS WORK OF ART** G 24	
376 **MISS YEATS** (IRE) 10	
228 **MISS YODA** (GER) 104	
576 **MISS ZIP** (IRE) 53	
317 **MISSCARLETT** (IRE) 49	
233 **MISSED APPROACH** (IRE) 45	
21 **MISSESGEEJAY** 12	
287 **MISSHIROCCO** (IRE) 11	
305 **MISSISIPI STAR** (IRE) F 196	
470 **MISSISSIPPI MISS** 4	
382 **MISSISSIPPI WINE** (IRE) 17	
306 **MISSMEBUTLETMEGO** 7	
363 **MISSTHECUDDLES** (IRE) 42	
484 **MISSTREE SONG** 71	
463 **MISSY MAY** 54	
30 **MISTER BLUE** 38	
392 **MISTER BLUE SKY** (IRE) 142	
539 **MISTER BUDDY** (IRE) 70	
402 **MISTER CHIANG** 44	

268 **MISTER COFFEY** (FR) 110	
89 **MISTER DEPENDABLE** (IRE) 40	
148 **MISTER DON** (IRE) 25	
268 **MISTER FISHER** (IRE) 111	
433 **MISTER FIZZ** 1	
51 **MISTER FLEMINGTON** (IRE) 7	
93 **MISTER FREEZE** (IRE) 12	
526 **MISTER MALARKY** 60	
248 **MISTER MANDURO** (FR) 2	
140 **MISTER MERLIN** 10	
461 **MISTER MURCHAN** (IRE) 13	
89 **MISTER MUSIC** 41	
278 **MISTER MUSICMASTER** 7	
286 **MISTER SNOWDON** 29	
251 **MISTER SPEEDY** (FR) 200	
489 **MISTER TICKLE** (IRE) 8	
80 **MISTER TIMMYTUCKS** 3	
424 **MISTER WATSON** 53	
94 **MISTER WHITAKER** (IRE) 15	
395 **MISTERCOBAR** (FR) 68	
314 **MISTERMOONBOY** (IRE) 3	
214 **MISTIC MAGIC** (IRE) G 28	
541 **MISTRAL TOMMY** 20	
509 **MISTRESS NELLIE** 6	
404 **MISTRESS OF ROME** F 13	
365 **MISTRESS POPE** G 85	
554 **MISTRESS TWISTER** C 22	
6 **MISTRUSTING** (IRE) C 187	
282 **MISTRY GIRL** 10	
29 **MISTY** 22	
327 **MISTY BLOOM** (IRE) 46	
409 **MISTY FOR ME** (IRE) F 157	
305 **MISTY GREY** (IRE) 92	
448 **MISTY MAI** (IRE) 9	
212 **MISTY WHISKY** 53	
536 **MISU PETE** 13	
538 **MITCHELTON** (FR) F 27	
29 **MITCHUM** 7	
77 **MITCHUM SWAGGER** 23	
99 **MITIGATOR** 6	
29 **MITZI WINKS** (USA) F 123	
446 **MIX OF CLOVER** 29	
409 **MIXFEELING** (IRE) C 158	
76 **MIZAAH** (IRE) 9	
395 **MIZEN MASTER** (IRE) 69	
239 **MJOLNIR** 16	
52 **MO TOTTIE** 25	
405 **MOABIT** (GER) 110	
272 **MOBARHIN** (IRE) 95	
299 **MOBHAM** (IRE) 12	
526 **MOCACREME HAS** (IRE) 61	
349 **MOCEAD CAPPALL** 3	
98 **MOCHALOV** 16	
73 **MODAKHAR** (IRE) 13	
349 **MODEL GUEST** 3	
29 **MODERAH** F 124	
548 **MODERN BEAUTY** (IRE) 34	
6 **MODERN IDEALS** C 188	
240 **MODERN LADY** F 18	
29 **MODERN MILLIE** 24	
364 **MODERNSTONE** C 51	
29 **MODESTA** C 125	
529 **MODMIN** (IRE) 24	
26 **MODULAR MAGIC** 31	
298 **MODULUS** 14	
391 **MOGESTIC** (IRE) 20	
412 **MOGSY** (FR) 19	
409 **MOGUL** 63	

529 **MOHAATHER** 10
484 **MOHAAYED** 72
7 **MOHAREB** 67
511 **MOHAYYA** 66
483 **MOHICAN HEIGHTS** (IRE) 47
17 **MOI MEME** C 164
436 **MOIDORE** 2
251 **MOJO STAR** (IRE) 201
577 **MOKAATIL** 58
164 **MOLAAHETH** 26
537 **MOLATHAM** 73
351 **MOLE TRAP** 14
529 **MOLHIM** (USA) 43
386 **MOLINARI** (IRE) 27
526 **MOLINEAUX** (IRE) 62
472 **MOLL DAVIS** (IRE) 5
388 **MOLLIANA** 60
547 **MOLLS MEMORY** 15
388 **MOLLY CAREW** 61
173 **MOLLY CHILDERS** (IRE) 24
355 **MOLLY MAI** 5
484 **MOLLY OLLYS WISHES** 73
548 **MOLLY SHAW** 24
490 **MOLLY WHUPPIE** 4
139 **MOLLY'S ANGEL** 5
332 **MOLPEG** 2
226 **MOLTEN LAVA** (IRE) 5
212 **MOMELLA** (IRE) 54
483 **MOMENT IN TIME** (IRE) C 86
483 **MOMENT OF HOPE** (IRE) 15
165 **MOMENT OF PEACE** 17
393 **MOMENT OF TIME** F 59
73 **MOMENTSAFTAMIDNITE** (USA) 55
63 **MOMENTUM** 18
116 **MOMENTUM SWING** 33
242 **MOMKIN** (IRE) 14
476 **MOMTALIK** (USA) 12
120 **MOMTATHIL** 1
365 **MOMUS** (IRE) 86
97 **MON AMOUR** (IRE) 103
242 **MON BIJOU** (IRE) C 164
17 **MON CHOIX** 95
52 **MON ELDORADO** (FR) 26
14 **MON PALOIS** (FR) 39
137 **MON PETIT CHERI** 15
395 **MON PORT** (IRE) 70
87 **MONAADHIL** (IRE) 25
465 **MONACO SHOW** (FR) C 98
409 **MONARCH OF EGYPT** (USA) 64
534 **MONARCHOFTHEGRANGE** (IRE) 53
547 **MONASH** (IRE) 61
475 **MONBEG AQUADUDE** (IRE) 23
268 **MONBEG LEGEND** 112
528 **MONBEG RIVER** (IRE) 8
496 **MONBEG THEATRE** (IRE) 41
395 **MONBEG ZENA** (IRE) 71
540 **MONCEAU** 11
537 **MONDAMMEJ** 74
409 **MONDAY MONDAY** (IRE) 65
242 **MONDELICE** C 165
374 **MONDLICHT** (USA) 10
436 **MONDO CANE** (IRE) 7
210 **MONET MOOR** 11
257 **MONETA** 18
339 **MONEY NOTE** C 58
148 **MONFASS** (IRE) 26
242 **MONICA SHERIFF** 15
577 **MONJENI** 59

203 **MONKEY HARRIS** (IRE) 5
480 **MONKEY PUZZLE** 26
364 **MONOGAMY** 17
305 **MONOSKI** (USA) 93
224 **MONSARAZ** 10
128 **MONSIEUR CO** (FR) 43
484 **MONSIEUR D'ARQUE** (IRE) 74
451 **MONSIEUR FOX** 5
104 **MONSIEUR LAMBRAYS** 9
578 **MONSIEUR LECOQ** (FR) 10
154 **MONSIEUR ROYALE** 2
577 **MONSIGNORITA** (IRE) M 60
405 **MONT DES AVALOIRS** (FR) 111
152 **MONT KIARA** (FR) 5
283 **MONT SEGUR** (FR) 24
254 **MONTALCINO** (FR) 170
191 **MONTALVAN** (IRE) 17
17 **MONTANARI** 96
52 **MONTANNA** 27
422 **MONTAQEM** (FR) 39
242 **MONTATHAM** 19
537 **MONTATHER** (IRE) 75
325 **MONTE ALBAN** (FR) 5
268 **MONTE CRISTO** (FR) 113
42 **MONTEGO BREEZE** C 6
122 **MONTELIMAR** 14
342 **MONTENAY** 14
338 **MONTESTREL** (FR) 11
338 **MONTY'S AWARD** (IRE) 40
60 **MONTYS ANGEL** (IRE) 6
251 **MONTYS INN** 17
405 **MONTYS MEDOC** (IRE) 112
409 **MONUMENT VALLEY** (IRE) 66
272 **MONYA** (IRE) 14
95 **MONZINO** (IRE) 4
529 **MOOAKADA** (IRE) F 44
31 **MOOD FOR MISCHIEF** 2
305 **MOOD INDIGO** (IRE) F 197
228 **MOOHAREEBA** 105
121 **MOOLHIM** (FR) 56
428 **MOOMBA** (IRE) 29
45 **MOON ARTIST** (FR) 3
97 **MOON DREAM** (IRE) 50
537 **MOON GODDESS** C 168
29 **MOON KING** (IRE) 25
384 **MOON OF BARODA** 14
186 **MOON OF LOVE** (IRE) 111
49 **MOON OVER WATER** (IRE) C 74
73 **MOON POWER** 56
559 **MOON RUA** (IRE) 3
97 **MOON SPIRIT** 51
192 **MOON SWIFT** 19
7 **MOON TROUBLE** (IRE) 68
73 **MOONBOOTZ** (IRE) 57
378 **MOONDANCE** 137
162 **MOONEE VALLEY** (IRE) C 58
57 **MOONGAZER** 9
186 **MOONLIGHT ECHO** 112
228 **MOONLIGHT IN PARIS** (IRE) 106
124 **MOONLIGHT MUSIC** (IRE) F 16
472 **MOONLIGHT MYSTERY** F 35
6 **MOONLIGHT SPIRIT** (IRE) 18
570 **MOONLIGHT STAR** 4
465 **MOONLIGHTING** 60
429 **MOONLIT SEA** 12
7 **MOONRAKER** 69
254 **MOONSHINE BAY** (IRE) 44
211 **MOONSHINE MO** 33

409 **MOONSTONE** F 159
413 **MOONWOOD** F 76
395 **MOORE MARGAUX** (IRE) 72
444 **MOORE'S MELODY** (IRE) F 59
177 **MOORLANDS MIST** 3
213 **MOORSHOLME** 6
564 **MOOTERAM** (IRE) 12
272 **MOQADAMA** (IRE) 96
251 **MOOLA** F 202
17 **MORANDO** (FR) 34
489 **MORANI KALI** 14
272 **MORAWETH** (USA) 97
121 **MORDIN** (IRE) 10
251 **MORDRED** (IRE) 18
52 **MORE BUCK'S** (IRE) 28
97 **MORE JOY** (FR) 104
1 **MORE MADNESS** (IRE) 39
129 **MORE OVERDRAUGHT** 23
251 **MORE THAN A PRINCE** 90
183 **MORE THAN LIKELY** 5
170 **MORE THAN LOVE** 131
198 **MOREECE** (IRE) 20
409 **MORELLO** (AUS) C 160
29 **MORETTA BLANCHE** F 126
185 **MORETTI** (IRE) 8
132 **MORISCO** (IRE) 40
483 **MORLAIX** 48
348 **MORNEY WING** (IRE) 11
17 **MORNING FURY** 97
374 **MORNING ROYALTY** (IRE) 11
305 **MORNING SHADOW** 94
416 **MORNING SPIRIT** (IRE) 57
268 **MORNING VICAR** (IRE) 114
391 **MORODER** (IRE) 21
227 **MOROMAC** (IRE) 29
254 **MOROSINI** (FR) 45
332 **MOROVAL** (IRE) 3
356 **MORRAMAN** (IRE) 65
537 **MORROOJ** (IRE) 76
262 **MORTENS LEAM** 3
242 **MORTGAGE THE HOUSE** (USA) F 166
405 **MORTLAH** 113
426 **MOSAKHAR** 5
221 **MOSAMBO** (IRE) 57
101 **MOSEY** (IRE) 44
537 **MOSHAAWER** 169
36 **MOSS GILL** (IRE) 6
486 **MOSS TOP** (FR) C 41
26 **MOSSBAWN** 32
181 **MOSSING** 11
534 **MOSSY FEN** (USA) 54
391 **MOSSY GLEN** (IRE) 22
116 **MOST TEMPTING** C 50
370 **MOSTAHEL** 18
345 **MOSTAWAA** 11
228 **MOSTLY** 107
268 **MOT A MOT** (FR) 115
272 **MOTAGALLY** 15
88 **MOTAHASSEN** (IRE) 8
537 **MOTAMAYIZ** 77
381 **MOTARAABET** 15
576 **MOTASHAKEL** (IRE) 54
7 **MOTAWAAFEQ** (FR) 70
191 **MOTAWAAZY** 18
378 **MOTDEPAS** (FR) 91
532 **MOTHER BROWN** 13
305 **MOTION** 95
537 **MOTIVATE ME** (FR) 18

537 **MOTTRIB** (IRE) 78
293 **MOTUEKA** (IRE) 2
318 **MOULMEIN** 17
73 **MOUNT ARARAT** (IRE) 14
134 **MOUNT BARINA** 6
411 **MOUNT BATUR** (IRE) 56
409 **MOUNT EVEREST** (IRE) 11
537 **MOUNT MAYON** (IRE) 79
356 **MOUNT MEWS** (IRE) 66
547 **MOUNT MOGAN** 62
388 **MOUNT OLIVER** (IRE) 62
304 **MOUNT OLYMPUS** 66
582 **MOUNT WELLINGTON** (IRE) 22
227 **MOUNT WINDSOR** (IRE) 30
537 **MOUNTAIN ANGEL** (IRE) 19
371 **MOUNTAIN ASH** 43
305 **MOUNTAIN BRAVE** 96
305 **MOUNTAIN DREAMS** (USA) 97
170 **MOUNTAIN HAWK** (IRE) 62
39 **MOUNTAIN HUNTER** (USA) 28
39 **MOUNTAIN LAKE** 92
583 **MOUNTAIN LEOPARD** (IRE) 48
43 **MOUNTAIN OF MOURNE** (IRE) 5
208 **MOUNTAIN OF STARS** 6
547 **MOUNTAIN PEAK** 16
82 **MOUNTAIN RAPID** (IRE) 4
196 **MOUNTAIN RESCUE** (IRE) 8
305 **MOUNTAIN RULER** 21
216 **MOUNTAIN SO HIGH** (IRE) 7
555 **MOURIYANI** (USA) 5
384 **MOUSEBIRD** (IRE) 15
576 **MOUSEINTHEHOUSE** (IRE) 55
243 **MOVE CLOSER** (FR) 19
18 **MOVE OVER DARLIN** 13
272 **MOVEMENTNEVERLIES** G 49
541 **MOVE LEGEND** 21
537 **MOVIN TIME** 170
128 **MOVIN'ON UP** (IRE) 44
526 **MOVING DAY** (IRE) 63
47 **MOVING FLAME** 29
546 **MOVING IN STYLE** (IRE) 18
39 **MOVING LIGHT** (IRE) 93
426 **MOVING WAVES** (IRE) G 24
340 **MOXY MARES** 17
594 **MOYNIHANS GIRL** (IRE) 7
62 **MOYNSHA LADY** (IRE) F 37
365 **MOYROSS** 87
302 **MOZZARO** (IRE) 25
392 **MR ADJUDICATOR** 143
419 **MR ALCHEMY** 27
534 **MR ANTOLINI** (IRE) 55
419 **MR BEAU BLUE** 28
513 **MR BUTTONS** (IRE) 4
402 **MR CAFFREY** 45
317 **MR CARBONATOR** 50
170 **MR CARPENTER** (IRE) 63
475 **MR CHUA** (IRE) 24
435 **MR CLARKSON** (IRE) 50
26 **MR COCO BEAN** (USA) 11
481 **MR CONUNDRUM** 9
134 **MR COOL CASH** 7
149 **MR DEALER** (IRE) 1
340 **MR DIB DAB** (FR) 40
480 **MR DORRELL SAGE** (FR) 27
62 **MR DUEPEARL** 38
136 **MR FITZROY** (IRE) 10
10 **MR FOX** 17
430 **MR FRANKIE** 4

186 **MR FUDGE** 113
242 **MR** G 81
453 **MR GAMBINO** 4
405 **MR GLASS** (IRE) 114
186 **MR GUS** (IRE) 114
216 **MR HARP** (IRE) 8
254 **MR HENDRICKS** 46
300 **MR JACK** (IRE) 13
132 **MR JONES AND ME** 41
572 **MR KATANGA** (IRE) 23
30 **MR KIKI** (IRE) 39
180 **MR KODI** (IRE) 37
189 **MR LANDO** 26
382 **MR LOMBARDI** (IRE) 18
484 **MR LOVE** (IRE) 75
30 **MR LUIGI** 83
186 **MR LUPTON** (IRE) 36
267 **MR MAC** 3
74 **MR MAGILL** (FR) 7
356 **MR MCGO** (IRE) 67
219 **MR MCGUINESS** (IRE) 7
546 **MR MEDIC** 19
164 **MR MINERALS** 27
402 **MR MULDOON** (IRE) 24
275 **MR NICE GUY** (IRE) 10
320 **MR NUTHERPUTT** (IRE) 21
212 **MR ONE MORE** (IRE) 55
370 **MR ORANGE** (IRE) 19
144 **MR PALMTREE** (IRE) 12
200 **MR PEANUT** 1
577 **MR PERFECT** (IRE) 61
57 **MR POTTER** 10
384 **MR POY** 33
315 **MR PUMBLECHOOK** 87
30 **MR RYDER** 84
85 **MR SATCO** (IRE) 7
269 **MR SCAFF** (IRE) 18
152 **MR SCARAMANGA** 6
412 **MR SCRUMPY** 20
379 **MR SHADY** (IRE) 16
153 **MR SOCIABLE** 55
534 **MR STAN** 56
430 **MR STANDFAST** 5
522 **MR STRUTTER** (IRE) 9
269 **MR STUBBS** (IRE) 10
409 **MR TAMBOURINE MAN** (IRE) 67
419 **MR TERRY** (IRE) 29
463 **MR TOASTIE** 55
180 **MR TOP HAT** 16
444 **MR WAGYU** (IRE) 19
142 **MR WASHINGTON** (IRE) 25
175 **MR WHIPPED** (IRE) 35
292 **MR WIGGINS** 11
272 **MR WILTON** (IRE) 50
316 **MR WOOLLEY** 7
44 **MR ZEE** (IRE) 18
431 **MRS BARNES** (IRE) 17
29 **MRS BEETON** (IRE) F 72
45 **MRS BENSON** (IRE) 4
305 **MRS BOUQUET** 98
445 **MRS DISCOMBE** 5
384 **MRS FITZHERBERT** (IRE) 63
169 **MRS GREELEY** C 87
186 **MRS HOO** (IRE) 37
411 **MRS HYDE** (IRE) 57
29 **MRS IVY** 26
300 **MRS JACK** (IRE) 14
391 **MRS MEADER** 23

435 **MRS MIGGINS** (IRE) 51
251 **MRS MOGG** C 203
443 **MRS MUNNELLY** (IRE) 7
424 **MRS ROBERTS** G 54
584 **MRS TIFFEN** 18
42 **MRS TROUT** 7
557 **MRS UPJOHN** (FR) 47
110 **MRS VONN** (IRE) 16
418 **MRSGREY** (IRE) 25
417 **MS INTRIGUE** 12
392 **MT LEINSTER** (IRE) 144
1 **MTPOCKETS** (IRE) F 40
17 **MU'AJIZA** C 165
543 **MUATADEL** 1
529 **MUBAALEGH** 11
511 **MUBAKKER** (USA) 11
6 **MUBTASIM** (IRE) 19
242 **MUBTASIMAH** 17
446 **MUCHO TALENTO** 30
36 **MUDAWWAN** (IRE) 7
375 **MUFAWITH** (IRE) 31
526 **MUFFINS FOR TEA** 64
408 **MUFTAKKER** 5
76 **MUHAARAR'S NEPHEW** 10
483 **MUHADATHAT** F 87
346 **MUHAJJAL** 7
184 **MUHTAMAR** (FR) 30
484 **MUILEAN NA MADOG** (IRE) 76
503 **MUIZENBERG NIGHTS** (IRE) C 49
6 **MUJARAH** (IRE) F 189
331 **MUJASSAM** 21
76 **MUJASSID** (USA) 69
272 **MUJBAR** 98
573 **MUJID** (IRE) 8
242 **MUJTABA** 167
346 **MUKHADRAM WAY** 19
170 **MUKHAYYAM** 64
170 **MUKHTOON** (IRE) 132
233 **MULCAHYS HILL** (IRE) 46
34 **MULLARKEY** 13
191 **MULLIGATAWNY** (IRE) 19
83 **MULLINAVAT** (IRE) 25
170 **MULTELLIE** 65
304 **MULTI GRAIN** F 67
484 **MULTICOLOUR WAVE** (IRE) C 88
184 **MULTIPEDE** 31
62 **MULTITALENTED** 19
394 **MULZIM** 10
251 **MUMMY BEAR** (IRE) 204
98 **MUMS THE LAW** 30
251 **MUMS TIPPLE** (IRE) 91
340 **MUMSBIRTHDAYGIRL** (IRE) 41
527 **MUMTAZA** F 12
152 **MUNGO'S QUEST** (IRE) 21
191 **MUNTADAB** (IRE) 20
533 **MUQARRED** (USA) 6
76 **MURAAD** (IRE) 11
419 **MURAAHIN** 8
57 **MURAAQEB** 11
573 **MURAT ASSET** 13
534 **MURATELLO** (FR) 57
188 **MURAU** 77
177 **MURCHISON RIVER** 4
451 **MURHIB** (IRE) 6
444 **MURITZ** 37
523 **MUROOR** 6
135 **MURRAY MOUNT** (IRE) 13
452 **MURVAGH BEACH** (IRE) 32

244 **MUSAADAQA** (IRE) C 85
537 **MUSALAHA** (IRE) F 171
413 **MUSCIKA** 38
238 **MUSE OF FIRE** (IRE) 13
89 **MUSEE D'ORSAY** (IRE) 42
88 **MUSHARRIF** 9
39 **MUSIC CHART** (USA) C 158
10 **MUSIC MAJOR** 18
437 **MUSIC PEARL** (IRE) C 52
88 **MUSIC SEEKER** (IRE) 10
170 **MUSIC SOCIETY** (IRE) 66
472 **MUSIC THERAPIST** (IRE) 16
420 **MUSICAL BEAT** (IRE) C 162
483 **MUSICAL SANDS** F 89
274 **MUSICAL SLAVE** (IRE) 69
243 **MUSICAL STARDUST** 20
537 **MUSICALITY** 80
486 **MUSICORA** F 42
508 **MUSKETEER** 15
318 **MUST BE AN ANGEL** (IRE) 18
500 **MUST DREAM** 9
496 **MUSTANG ALPHA** (IRE) 42
150 **MUSTAQBAL** (IRE) 16
577 **MUSTARRID** (IRE) 62
511 **MUSTASHRY** 12
321 **MUSTAVIM** 27
416 **MUSTMEETALADY** (IRE) 58
63 **MUTABAAHY** (IRE) 10
370 **MUTAFARRID** (IRE) 20
39 **MUTAFAWWIG** 29
529 **MUTALAHEF** (IRE) 25
537 **MUTAMAASIK** 20
87 **MUTAMADED** (IRE) 26
323 **MUTAMAKINA** 8
87 **MUTANAASEQ** (IRE) 27
537 **MUTASAAMY** (IRE) 21
493 **MUTAWAASEL** 36
346 **MUTAWAFFER** (IRE) 8
76 **MUTEBAH** (IRE) C 70
305 **MUTEELA** C 198
511 **MUTHABARA** (IRE) F 132
431 **MUTHABIR** (IRE) 18
121 **MUTHEERA** F 91
254 **MUTINY** (IRE) 111
259 **MUWALLA** 4
212 **MUY BIEN** (IRE) 56
492 **MUZAAWEL** 3
511 **MUZDAJER** (FR) 67
561 **MUZETTA'S WALTZ** (IRE) 1
336 **MY AMAZING ONE** (IRE) 5
138 **MY ANCHOR** 3
413 **MY BEST FRIEND** (IRE) 117
376 **MY BOY JAMES** (IRE) 11
191 **MY BOY LEWIS** (IRE) 21
467 **MY BOY MONTY** 3
582 **MY BOY SEPOY** 23
388 **MY BROTHER** (IRE) 63
211 **MY BROTHER MIKE** (IRE) 16
112 **MY BROWN EYED GIRL** 12
363 **MY CHARITY** (IRE) 43
444 **MY DANDY DOC** (IRE) 38
522 **MY DANNY BOY** 10
98 **MY DORRIS** (IRE) 31
242 **MY FAIRY** (IRE) F 168
399 **MY FOXY LADY** 2
511 **MY FRANKEL** 68
368 **MY GALWAY GIRL** (IRE) 30

173 **MY GIRL LOLLIPOP** (IRE) 25
305 **MY GIRL MAGGIE** 99
240 **MY GIRL MAISIE** (IRE) 9
365 **MY HENRIETTA** C 149
393 **MY INSPIRATION** (IRE) C 60
511 **MY INTENTION** 69
186 **MY KINDA DAY** (IRE) 115
526 **MY LADY GREY** 65
419 **MY LASS** F 65
351 **MY LAST OSCAR** (IRE) 15
242 **MY OBERON** (IRE) 82
452 **MY OLD GOLD** (IRE) 33
37 **MY PAINTER** (IRE) 3
470 **MY PERFECT COUSIN** 5
511 **MY POEM** 70
118 **MY PRETTY GIRL** F 11
170 **MY REWARD** 67
121 **MY SENORITA** (FR) 57
106 **MY SHEILA** (IRE) 14
367 **MY SILVER BEAR** 20
186 **MY SISTER JO** 116
392 **MY SISTER SARAH** (IRE) 145
1 **MY SON JOHN** 41
6 **MY SPIRIT** (IRE) C 190
317 **MY STRONG MAN** (IRE) 51
304 **MY STYLE** (IRE) 19
573 **MY TARGET** (IRE) 9
228 **MY THOUGHT** (IRE) 108
242 **MY TITANIA** (IRE) F 169
211 **MY TOWN CHICAGO** (USA) 17
469 **MY VALENTINO** (IRE) 12
39 **MY VISION** 94
405 **MY WAY** 115
268 **MY WHIRLWIND** (IRE) 116
423 **MYKINDOFSUNSHINE** (IRE) 4
254 **MYKONOS** (IRE) 112
419 **MYKONOS ST JOHN** 30
180 **MYLAPORYOURS** (IRE) F 50
309 **MYLINGTON LIGHT** F 28
75 **MYLITTLEOULBUDDY** (IRE) 4
524 **MYMILAN** (IRE) 23
316 **MYPLACEATMIDNIGHT** 22
419 **MYRICA** C 66
150 **MYRMIDONS** (IRE) 17
305 **MYRTLE MACLAGAN** (IRE) 199
121 **MYSEVEN** (IRE) 58
271 **MYSPACENOTYOURS** 3
73 **MYSTERIOUS GIRL** (IRE) C 97
384 **MYSTIC MAC** (IRE) 34
251 **MYSTERY POWER** (IRE) 92
424 **MYSTIC COURT** (IRE) 55
217 **MYSTIC DRAGON** 3
222 **MYSTIC DREAMER** (IRE) 17
406 **MYSTIC GLEN** F 4
385 **MYSTIC MELODY** (IRE) C 15
193 **MYSTIC RIVER** (IRE) 7
315 **MYSTICAL CLOUDS** (IRE) 88
283 **MYSTICAL KNIGHT** 25
101 **MYSTIQUESTAR** (IRE) 12
409 **MYTHIC** (IRE) 68
409 **MYTHICAL** (FR) 69
409 **MYTHICAL BRIDE** (USA) C 161
526 **MYTHICAL JEWEL** (IRE) 66
152 **MYTHICAL MADNESS** 7
6 **MYTHICAL MAGIC** (IRE) 20
81 **MYTHICAL SPIRIT** (IRE) 17
486 **MYTHMAKER** 11
530 **MYWAYISTHEONLYWAY** (IRE) 9

305 **MZYOON** (IRE) C 200
7 **N OVER J** 71
408 **NAASIK** 6
121 **NABARAAT** (USA) C 92
335 **NABHAN** 11
375 **NABLAWYH** (IRE) 15
475 **NADA TO PRADA** 25
424 **NADAITAK** 56
39 **NADIA** C 159
299 **NADIA'S SPIRIT** (IRE) 27
368 **NADINE** 31
185 **NAFA** (IRE) C 19
11 **NAFAAYES** (IRE) 4
305 **NAFURA** F 201
537 **NAGANO** 172
242 **NAHAARR** (IRE) 18
164 **NAHHAM** (IRE) 28
39 **NAHOODH** (IRE) C 160
537 **NAHRAIN** F 173
244 **NAILA'S BABY** 43
323 **NAISSANCE ROYALE** F 67
527 **NAIVE** (IRE) C 13
537 **NAIZAGAI** 81
326 **NAJAM** C 21
191 **NAJASHEE** (IRE) 22
101 **NAJEEBA** 89
191 **NAJIB** (IRE) 23
465 **NAJIM AL THRAYA** (FR) F 99
242 **NAJIMA** (IRE) 83
295 **NAKEETA** 25
286 **NAMASTE** (IRE) 52
305 **NAMHROODAH** (IRE) F 202
327 **NAMIB DANCER** (IRE) 47
126 **NAMPARA** 2
340 **NANANITA** (IRE) 18
107 **NANCY STAR** (IRE) F 34
483 **NANS NED** (IRE) C 90
101 **NANTES** (GER) C 90
321 **NANTOSUELTA** (IRE) 28
375 **NANTYGLO** C 32
305 **NAOMH GEILEIS** (USA) F 203
409 **NAPA VALLEY** (IRE) 70
474 **NAPLES BAY** 6
17 **NAPPER TANDY** 166
393 **NAPPING** 23
419 **NAQRAH** (IRE) F 67
472 **NARAK** 6
365 **NARCISSISTIC** (IRE) 8
111 **NARIMA** (GER) G 8
376 **NARJES** 12
422 **NARRATE** 40
516 **NASAIYM** (USA) 32
328 **NASHVILLE NIPPER** (IRE) 9
511 **NASHY** (IRE) 71
76 **NASMATT** F 71
228 **NASRAAWY** (USA) 109
101 **NASSIMA** 91
29 **NASSUVIAN PEARL** F 127
547 **NASTASIYA** 93
409 **NASTY STORM** (USA) C 162
323 **NAT KING** 39
226 **NAT LOVE** (IRE) 10
251 **NATAGORA** (FR) F 205
365 **NATAHOOLABABY** (IRE) 134
260 **NATALEENA** (IRE) 22
94 **NATALIE JAY** G 53
422 **NATALISA** (IRE) C 84
10 **NATCH** 19

170 **OBEE JO** (IRE) 70
62 **OBLATE** 23
391 **OBORNE LADY** (IRE) 26
555 **OBSARA** F 28
251 **OCASIO CORTEZ** (IRE) 97
371 **OCEAN BLUFF** (IRE) C 45
411 **OCEAN COVE** (IRE) 58
480 **OCEAN DRIFTER** (IRE) 31
6 **OCEAN HEIGHTS** 77
254 **OCEAN MONARCH** (IRE) 113
228 **OCEAN PEARL** (IRE) 111
441 **OCEAN REACH** 10
504 **OCEAN SPRAY** 4
97 **OCEAN TALENT** F 105
99 **OCEAN TEMPTRESS** 7
388 **OCEAN TRANSIT** (IRE) H 68
518 **OCEAN WIND** 14
121 **OCEANS MEET** 60
469 **OCEANUS** (IRE) 13
304 **OCHO GRANDE** (IRE) 43
214 **OCHRE RIU** (IRE) 53
356 **OCTOBER STORM** 73
186 **ODDS ON OLI** 38
6 **ODE TO DUTY** (USA) 78
463 **ODEEKA** (IRE) G 56
222 **ODEN** 20
159 **ODISHA** (USA) C 16
412 **ODYSSEE** (FR) F 56
499 **ODYSSEY GIRL** (IRE) 35
89 **OEIL DE TIGRE** (FR) 44
321 **OF COURSE DARLING** C 30
526 **OFALLTHEGINJOINTS** (IRE) 73
356 **OFCOURSEIWILL** (IRE) 74
524 **OFF THE BEAT** 24
1 **OFF THE HOOK** (IRE) 45
274 **OFF THE PLANET** (IRE) 73
35 **OFFICER DRIVEL** (IRE) 16
463 **OFFTHESHOULDER** (IRE) 57
526 **OFTEN OVERLOOKED** (IRE) 74
112 **OGARITMO** F 28
254 **OH GOODNESS ME** F 172
548 **OH IT'S SAUCEPOT** 9
548 **OH ITS OH SO SMART** 35
316 **OH LAND ABLOOM** (IRE) 26
169 **OH MARY OH MARY** 70
23 **OH NO** 20
251 **OH PURPLE REIGN** 98
117 **OH SIMPLE THING** (IRE) C 92
463 **OH SO BEAUTIFUL** (IRE) G 58
538 **OH SO CHIC** 13
89 **OH SO NICE** 45
251 **OH THIS IS US** (IRE) 19
409 **OHIO STATE** (USA) 74
577 **OI THE CLUBB OI'S** 65
23 **OISHIN** 21
424 **OISTRAKH LE NOIR** (FR) 61
97 **OK BOOMER** (IRE) 106
268 **OK CORRAL** (IRE) 119
148 **OKAVANGO DELTA** (IRE) 27
178 **OKSANA** 11
94 **OKSANA ASTANKOVA** 54
413 **OLCAN** 78
547 **OLD FRIEND** (FR) 65
305 **OLD HARBOUR** 101
331 **OLD HARRY ROCKS** (IRE) 22
338 **OLD JEROBOAM** (IRE) 44
51 **OLD JEWRY** (IRE) 8
286 **OLD NEWS** 30

6 **OLD PERSIAN** 21
446 **OLD PRIDE** (IRE) 31
327 **OLD RASCALS** (IRE) 48
312 **OLD SALT** (IRE) 11
328 **OLD TIMES** (IRE) 10
275 **OLDABBEY BRIDGE** (IRE) 11
484 **OLDGRANGEWOOD** 82
528 **OLDTIMER** (IRE) 7
405 **OLEG** (GER) 119
557 **OLEKSANDER** 48
26 **OLIVE MARY** C 48
46 **OLIVER'S BETTY** 16
111 **OLIVER'S ISLAND** (IRE) 10
554 **OLIVIA AND GRACE** 23
185 **OLIVIA R** (IRE) 9
413 **OLLIVANDER** (IRE) 40
274 **OLLY GOLLY** 74
484 **OLLY THE BRAVE** 83
17 **OLOROSO** (IRE) 36
188 **OLYMPIC CONQUEROR** (IRE) 13
576 **OLYMPIC HONOUR** (FR) 57
48 **OLYMPIC LEGEND** (IRE) 11
30 **OLYMPIC THEATRE** 85
29 **OMAN** (IRE) 128
73 **OMANY AMBER** 100
29 **OMBRE** C 129
97 **OMNIA MUNDA MUNDIS** 107
573 **OMRAN** 10
452 **ON A PROMISE** (IRE) 37
228 **ON GUARD** 112
312 **ON HIGH** F 17
424 **ON SPRINGS** (IRE) 62
416 **ON THE BANDWAGON** (IRE) 61
268 **ON THE BLIND SIDE** (IRE) 120
304 **ON THE BRIGHTSIDE** (IRE) 44
499 **ON THE DARK SIDE** (IRE) C 48
306 **ON THE METER** (IRE) 8
492 **ON THE NOD** 4
254 **ON THE PRAIRIE** F 50
576 **ON THE QUIET** (FR) 58
536 **ON THE RIGHT TRACK** 20
576 **ON THE ROAD** (IRE) 59
227 **ON THE SLOPES** 32
6 **ON THE WARPATH** 22
402 **ON THE WILD SIDE** (IRE) 49
315 **ON TO VICTORY** 95
576 **ON TOUR** (IRE) 60
302 **ON WE GO** (IRE) 7
371 **ONARAGGATIP** 46
192 **ONASSIS** (IRE) 41
534 **ONCHAN** (IRE) 60
21 **ONDA DISTRICT** (IRE) 13
499 **ONDEAFEARS** (IRE) C 49
437 **ONE ABOVE** (IRE) 26
291 **ONE ALC** (FR) 50
44 **ONE BIG DREAM** 14
556 **ONE COOL BOY** (IRE) 3
291 **ONE COOL DADDY** (USA) 26
101 **ONE DAY** 92
534 **ONE FINE MAN** (IRE) 61
463 **ONE FOR ARTHUR** (IRE) 59
484 **ONE FOR BILLY** 84
32 **ONE FOR BRAD** (IRE) 12
546 **ONE FOR DUNSTAN** (IRE) 33
534 **ONE FOR ROSIE** 62
579 **ONE FOR THE TEAM** 17
274 **ONE FOR YOU** (IRE) 75
534 **ONE FORTY SEVEN** (IRE) 63

563 **ONE HANDSOME DUDE** (IRE) 12
121 **ONE IDEA** 61
409 **ONE LAST DANCE** (AUS) C 164
225 **ONE LAST HUG** 20
242 **ONE MASTER** 21
577 **ONE MORE FLEURIE** (IRE) 66
296 **ONE NIGHT STAND** 14
579 **ONE OF US** 18
63 **ONE ONE SEVEN** (IRE) 11
499 **ONE STEP BEYOND** (IRE) 36
583 **ONE STYLE** (IRE) 50
557 **ONE TO GO** 16
424 **ONE TOUCH** (IRE) 63
254 **ONE VOICE** 114
20 **ONE WILD NIGHT** G 15
89 **ONEBABA** (IRE) 46
437 **ONEDOWNUNDER** 5
212 **ONEFORTHEROADTOM** 57
144 **ONEIDA TRIBE** (IRE) 14
316 **ONEMOREFORTHEROAD** 27
163 **ONENIGHTINMIAMI** (FR) 34
496 **ONEOFTHESENIGHTS** (IRE) 44
434 **ONEOVDEM** 5
405 **ONETHREEFIVENOTOUT** (FR) 120
576 **ONETWOTREE** (IRE) 61
20 **ONEUPMANSHIP** (IRE) 16
405 **ONEWAYORTHEOTHER** (IRE) G 121
242 **ONLINE ALEXANDER** (IRE) C 171
412 **ONLY ALONE** (IRE) 42
254 **ONLY HUMAN** (IRE) 115
227 **ONLY MONEY** (IRE) 33
412 **ONLY SPOOFING** (IRE) 21
249 **ONLYFOOLSOWNHORSES** (IRE) 45
23 **ONOMATOMANIA** (USA) C 101
356 **ONTHEFRONTFOOT** (IRE) 75
522 **ONTHERADAR** (IRE) 13
392 **ONTHEROPES** (IRE) 148
52 **ONTOPOFTHEWORLD** (IRE) 30
415 **ONURBIKE** 3
297 **ONWARD ROUTE** (IRE) 18
134 **OOH LA LAH** 12
242 **OOJOOBA** C 172
428 **OPEN HANDED** 10
39 **OPEN STORY** 98
251 **OPEN VERSE** (USA) F 207
428 **OPEN WIDE** (USA) 11
516 **OPENING NIGHT** (IRE) 36
289 **OPERA BUFFA** (IRE) 4
305 **OPERA FAN** (FR) C 206
17 **OPERA GIFT** 100
121 **OPERATIC** (IRE) 94
402 **OPERATIC EXPORT** (IRE) 50
463 **OPERATION OVERLORD** (IRE) 60
30 **OPINE** (FR) 41
364 **OPPORTUNIST** 18
15 **OPTIMA PETAMUS** 17
181 **OPTIMISTIC BIAS** (IRE) 13
339 **ORANGE JUSTICE** 41
516 **ORANGE PIP** F 83
140 **ORANGE SUIT** (IRE) 15
413 **ORBAAN** 41
258 **ORBIT OF IOLITE** 6
412 **ORBURSTOCK** (IRE) 22
435 **ORCHARD THIEVES** (IRE) 55
473 **ORCHARDSTOWN CROSS** (IRE) 28
65 **ORCHESTRATED** (IRE) 3
244 **ORCHID GARDENS** (IRE) 44
251 **ORCZY** (IRE) 99

409 **ORDER OF AUSTRALIA** (IRE) 75
463 **ORDER OF THISTLE** (IRE) 61
503 **ORDEROFRETALIATION** 24
313 **OREGON GOLD** (FR) 6
431 **ORGANDI** (FR) 19
160 **ORIENT SUNSET** 10
483 **ORIENTAL ART** 91
539 **ORIENTAL CROSS** (IRE) 73
225 **ORIENTAL LILLY** 21
483 **ORIENTAL MYSTIQUE** 49
39 **ORIENTAL NIGHT** (IRE) 99
87 **ORIENTAL SPLENDOUR** (IRE) 28
334 **ORIGINAL CHOICE** (IRE) 12
540 **ORIHIME** (IRE) 26
437 **ORIN SWIFT** (IRE) 27
392 **ORION D'AUBRELLE** (FR) 149
170 **ORION'S BOW** 71
419 **ORION'S SHORE** (IRE) 9
463 **ORIONINVERNESS** (IRE) 62
545 **ORKAN** 16
117 **ORLAITH** (IRE) 45
112 **ORLAS ABBEY** 13
356 **ORMESHER** 76
189 **ORMSKIRK** 28
236 **ORNATE** 12
422 **ORNELIA RUEE** (FR) F 86
163 **ORPHA** F 35
416 **ORRISDALE** (IRE) 62
52 **ORSINO** (IRE) 31
370 **ORVAR** (IRE) 22
539 **OSCA LOCA** (IRE) 74
395 **OSCAR ACADEMY** (IRE) 75
124 **OSCAR ASCHE** (IRE) 17
360 **OSCAR BLUE** (IRE) 6
312 **OSCAR CEREMONY** (IRE) 12
128 **OSCAR CLOUDS** (IRE) 48
395 **OSCAR MAGUIRE** (IRE) 76
250 **OSCAR NOMINATION** (IRE) 10
221 **OSCAR ROBERTSON** (IRE) 59
411 **OSCAR ROSE** (IRE) 59
493 **OSCAR WILDE** (IRE) 39
101 **OSCAR'S RIDGE** (IRE) 13
83 **OSCARS LEADER** (IRE) 26
405 **OSCARS MOONSHINE** (IRE) 122
494 **OSCARSMAN** (IRE) 10
411 **OSKI** (IRE) 60
511 **OSLO** 72
554 **OSMOSIS** 5
413 **OSO RAPIDO** (IRE) 79
580 **OSPREY CALL** (IRE) 17
121 **OSTILIO** 12
405 **OSTUNI** (FR) 123
30 **OTAGO** 42
463 **OTELLO MOOR** (IRE) 63
242 **OTI MA BOATI** 86
210 **OTTER LYNN** 13
6 **OTTOMAN COURT** 79
356 **OTTONIAN** 77
305 **OUD METHA** G 102
190 **OUD METHA BRIDGE** (IRE) 8
321 **OUI SAY OUI** (IRE) C 31
173 **OUR BUBBA** (IRE) 27
122 **OUR CILLA** 15
4 **OUR DELBOY** 6
137 **OUR DOT'S BABY** (IRE) 17
569 **OUR ELSIE** 15
430 **OUR ETHEL** F 6
402 **OUR GIRL KATIE** 51

577 **OUR IDIC BOY** (IRE) 67
384 **OUR JESTER** 17
296 **OUR JOY** (IRE) F 25
94 **OUR LAD** 55
389 **OUR LITTLE PONY** 7
10 **OUR LORD** 21
51 **OUR LUCAS** (IRE) 9
89 **OUR MAN IN HAVANA** 47
546 **OUR MERLIN** 21
38 **OUR MORRIS** (IRE) 13
269 **OUR NEST EGG** (IRE) 20
423 **OUR OYSTERCATCHER** 5
338 **OUR PERCY** (IRE) 45
534 **OUR POWER** (IRE) 64
112 **OUR PROMISE** 14
446 **OUR ROCKSTAR** (IRE) 32
356 **OUR RODNEY** (IRE) 78
59 **OURMULLION** 6
261 **OURO BRANCO** (FR) 33
422 **OURS PUISSANT** (IRE) 10
480 **OURVILLE'S MILLION** (FR) 32
7 **OUT FOR A DUCK** 113
440 **OUT FOR JUSTICE** (IRE) 12
530 **OUT OF BREATH** 22
175 **OUT OF FITRAH** (IRE) 80
251 **OUT OF THE DARK** (IRE) F 208
4 **OUT ON THE TEAR** (IRE) 7
245 **OUT THE GLEN** (IRE) 10
305 **OUTBACK BOY** 207
121 **OUTBOX** 13
83 **OUTCROP** (IRE) 27
198 **OUTER SPACE** 22
499 **OUTLANDER** (IRE) 9
304 **OUTLANE** 20
189 **OUTLAW JACK** (IRE) 29
322 **OUTLAW JESSE JAMES** 24
240 **OUTLAW TORN** (IRE) 12
460 **OUTOFTHEGLOOM** 9
212 **OUTOFTHISWORLD** (IRE) 58
315 **OUTONPATROL** (IRE) 96
321 **OUTRAGE** 8
35 **OUTRATH** (IRE) 17
87 **OUTTAKE** 45
251 **OUZO** 20
431 **OVER STATED** (IRE) 20
228 **OVER THE OCEAN** 113
212 **OVER TO SAM** 59
221 **OVERALL MAJORITY** (IRE) 60
238 **OVERAWED** 15
291 **OVERBECK** (FR) 27
524 **OVERCOURT** 25
140 **OVERHAUGH STREET** 12
221 **OVERNIGHT FAME** (IRE) F 83
436 **OVERTHETOP** (IRE) 77
436 **OVERTOUGEORGE** 8
436 **OVERTOUJAY** 9
572 **OVERTRUMPED** 25
338 **OVERWORKEDUNDERPAID** (IRE) 46
305 **OVERWRITE** (IRE) 103
14 **OWBEG** (IRE) 41
162 **OWHATANIGHT** 35
364 **OWNEY MADDEN** 35
395 **OXFORD BLU** 78
518 **OXTED** 15
576 **OXWICH BAY** (IRE) 62
83 **OZARK** 28
176 **OZGOOD** (IRE) 18

351 **OZZIE THE OSCAR** (IRE) 16
418 **OZZY THOMAS** (IRE) 27
152 **PABLO DEL PUEBLO** (IRE) 24
242 **PABLO ESCOBARR** (IRE) 22
413 **PABLO HERNANDEZ** 80
6 **PABOUCHE** (FR) F 192
63 **PACIFIC COAST** 19
483 **PACIFICA HIGHWAY** (USA) C 92
496 **PACIFY** 45
383 **PACINO** 8
250 **PACKETTOTHERAFTERS** (IRE) 11
532 **PACO LOCO** 26
214 **PACT OF STEEL** 30
582 **PACTOLUS** (IRE) 24
249 **PADDLING** (FR) 46
413 **PADDY AGAIN** (IRE) F 119
175 **PADDY ELLIOTT** (IRE) 68
51 **PADDY MELIA** (IRE) 10
186 **PADDY POWER** (IRE) 39
577 **PADDY THE CHEF** (IRE) 68
51 **PADDY THE PANDA** (IRE) 11
222 **PADDY'S POEM** 21
481 **PADDY'S ROCK** (IRE) 10
133 **PADDYPLEX** 10
574 **PADDYS RUNNER** 21
526 **PADLEYOUROWNCANOE** 75
254 **PADMINI** F 173
51 **PADS** (IRE) 12
212 **PADSTOW HARBOUR** 60
536 **PADURA BRAVE** 14
444 **PAELLA** (IRE) F 60
29 **PAGAILLE** (GER) 75
7 **PAGEANT MASTER** (IRE) 73
416 **PAGERO** (FR) 63
153 **PAHASKA** (GER) 17
368 **PAIN AU CHOCOLAT** (FR) 34
318 **PAINT IT BLACK** 19
411 **PAINT THE DREAM** 61
190 **PAINTBALL WIZARD** (IRE) 9
235 **PAINTED CLIFFS** (IRE) 8
349 **PAINTED DREAM** 4
246 **PAINTERS LAD** (IRE) F 5
409 **PAINTING** (IRE) C 165
327 **PAISLEY PARK** (IRE) 16
83 **PAKIE'S DREAM** (IRE) 29
409 **PALACE** (IRE) C 166
228 **PALACE PIER** 114
483 **PALAMOS** 10
427 **PALAVICINI RUN** (IRE) 7
486 **PALAZZO** 13
101 **PALIMONY** (IRE) F 93
268 **PALLADIUM** 10
175 **PALLAS DANCER** 69
409 **PALM BEACH** (IRE) 76
416 **PALMERS HILL** (IRE) 64
150 **PALO SANTO** 39
323 **PALOMBA** (IRE) 9
225 **PAMMI** 22
164 **PANATOS** (FR) 30
6 **PANEGYRIC** F 193
377 **PANI PROBLEM** (FR) 10
388 **PANIA** 69
392 **PANIC ATTACK** (IRE) 150
243 **PANKO** (IRE) 21
579 **PANZELLA** (IRE) G 29
17 **PAPA POWER** 101
582 **PAPA STOUR** (USA) 25
416 **PAPA TANGO CHARLY** (FR) 65

537 **PAPACITO** (IRE) 174
480 **PAPAGANA** 33
397 **PAPAGAYO** (IRE) 8
254 **PAPAL PEARL** (IRE) 52
542 **PAPARAZZI** 7
254 **PAPER BEAR** 115
569 **PAPER PROMISE** (IRE) 16
269 **PAPER ROSES** (IRE) 17
323 **PAPUA** (FR) 40
166 **PARA MIO** (IRE) 6
345 **PARA QUEEN** (IRE) 13
228 **PARADISE ON EARTH** 115
409 **PARADISE PLAYGIRL** (USA) F 167
356 **PARADISE RUN** (IRE) 79
409 **PARADISO** (IRE) 77
73 **PARALLEL WORLD** (IRE) 15
29 **PARAMARIBO** (IRE) 130
76 **PARDOVEN** (IRE) C 72
557 **PARENT'S PRAYER** (IRE) 49
435 **PARICOLOR** (FR) 56
162 **PARIKARMA** (IRE) 36
103 **PARIS BEAUTY** 33
268 **PARIS DIXIE** 122
545 **PARIS PROTOCOL** 19
434 **PARIS SUNRISE** (IRE) C 13
316 **PARISIAN AFFAIR** 28
268 **PARISIAN BLUE** 123
561 **PARISIAN CHARMER** 2
119 **PARK HOUSE** 9
444 **PARK LANE DANCER** (IRE) 39
341 **PARK PADDOCKS** (IRE) 5
24 **PARKER'S BOY** 17
501 **PARKNACILLA** (IRE) 6
263 **PARLOUR MAID** 6
29 **PARNELL'S DREAM** C 131
132 **PARSNIP** (IRE) F 71
287 **PARSONAL** (IRE) 12
212 **PARSONS PLEASURE** (FR) 61
365 **PART TIME FARMER** (IRE) 90
251 **PARTRIDGE** (IRE) 100
17 **PARTY** (IRE) C 102
14 **PARTY FUZZ** 42
106 **PARTY ISLAND** (IRE) 15
315 **PARTY POTENTIAL** (USA) 153
305 **PARTY SPIRIT** 208
409 **PARTY STARTER** (USA) C 168
305 **PARVENUE** (FR) F 209
170 **PARYS MOUNTAIN** (IRE) 72
480 **PASEO** 34
376 **PASS CARD** (IRE) 13
38 **PASS RUSHER** (IRE) 14
126 **PASS THE VINO** (IRE) 3
167 **PASSAM** 9
47 **PASSEFONTAINE** (FR) 16
508 **PASSIN' THRU** 16
97 **PASSING BY** F 108
10 **PASSING CLOUDS** 22
413 **PASSING NOD** 81
388 **PASSING OCEANS** 70
363 **PASSING SHADOW** 46
409 **PASSION** (IRE) 78
26 **PASSION FRUIT** F 49
224 **PASSION OVERFLOW** (USA) C 11
121 **PASSIONAL** 62
84 **PAST MASTER** 11
468 **PASTFACT** 4
211 **PASTIME** 18
108 **PAT CARROT** (IRE) 4

572 **PAT KELLY** 26
365 **PAT'S PICK** (IRE) 91
76 **PATH OF PEACE** C 73
6 **PATH OF THUNDER** (IRE) 80
165 **PATIENCE** G 26
165 **PATIENCEISAVIRTUE** 6
335 **PATRICIADPLASTERER** (IRE) 14
370 **PATRICK** (IRE) 23
39 **PATRONESS** C 162
405 **PATSIE MAGERN** G 124
56 **PATSIO** (IRE) 14
170 **PATTAYA** 73
254 **PATTLE REEF** (IRE) 116
501 **PATUCA** F 28
370 **PAVERS PRIDE** 24
84 **PAVONINE** F 43
117 **PAWPAW** 46
132 **PAWS FOR THOUGHT** (IRE) 72
483 **PAX BRITANNICA** (IRE) 51
547 **PAXOS** (IRE) 66
483 **PAYCHECK** 52
523 **PC DIXON** 7
178 **PEACE APPROVED** (IRE) 12
6 **PEACE CAMP** (USA) C 194
318 **PEACE CONCLUDED** C 36
54 **PEACE PREVAILS** 12
257 **PEACE SEEKER** 19
586 **PEACE TALKS** G 3
412 **PEACE TALKS** G 43
305 **PEACE TREATY** (IRE) 104
409 **PEACEFUL** (IRE) 79
116 **PEACEFUL DREAM** 34
24 **PEACEFUL SOUL** (USA) C 18
395 **PEACHEY** (IRE) 79
390 **PEACHEY CARNEHAN** 11
305 **PEACOAT** C 210
397 **PEAK HILL** 9
419 **PEAKED TOO SOON** 32
227 **PEAKY** 34
236 **PEARL ACCLAIM** (IRE) 13
320 **PEARL BEACH** 22
296 **PEARL EARING** (IRE) G 26
409 **PEARL GREY** F 169
146 **PEARL NOIR** 15
62 **PEARL OF INDIA** 41
364 **PEARL OF MANAMA** (USA) 19
133 **PEARL OF QATAR** 11
516 **PEARL OF WISDOM** (IRE) 84
261 **PEARL ROYALE** (IRE) 34
326 **PEARL SEA** (IRE) C 23
358 **PEARL SPECTRE** (USA) 6
150 **PEARL STREAM** 40
25 **PEARL'S CALLING** (IRE) 8
541 **PEARLY ISLAND** 23
179 **PEARLY REDD** 21
30 **PEARLY STEPH** (FR) C 86
77 **PECHEURS DE PERLES** (IRE) 27
315 **PECKINPAH** (IRE) 97
420 **PEDDERY** 16
58 **PEDDLER** (IRE) 10
199 **PEDESTAL** (IRE) 4
409 **PEEPING FAWN** (USA) F 170
150 **PEERLESS PERCY** (IRE) 41
563 **PEGGIE SUE** 13
89 **PEGGOTTY** 48
312 **PEGGY'S ANGEL** 13
547 **PEINTRE D'ETOILES** 94
411 **PEKING ROSE** 62

384 **PELAGIA** (IRE) F 64
305 **PELERIN** (IRE) F 211
381 **PELICAN PIE** 16
13 **PELLADY** 15
473 **PELORIC** 29
541 **PELTWELL** (IRE) 71
327 **PEMBERLEY** (IRE) 50
135 **PEMBROKE HOUSE** 14
165 **PENARTH PIER** (IRE) 7
305 **PENCARROW** C 105
305 **PENCARROW** C 212
424 **PENCREEK** (FR) 64
409 **PENDANT** (IRE) 80
392 **PENHILL** 151
548 **PENKELLA** 25
101 **PENMAEN SPIRIT** (IRE) 47
346 **PENMELLYN** (IRE) 20
220 **PENNARD** (IRE) C 23
45 **PENNEYS HUN** (IRE) 5
488 **PENNIES AND POUNDS** 6
317 **PENNINE CROSS** 55
128 **PENNY BLAK** 49
428 **PENNY DIAMOND** 30
272 **PENNY DROPS** C 99
497 **PENNY HILL** (IRE) 6
583 **PENNY MALLOW** (FR) 51
388 **PENNY POET** (IRE) 72
516 **PENNY POST** (IRE) F 85
570 **PENNY POT LANE** 6
1 **PENNY RIVER** 46
321 **PENNY ROSE** F 32
321 **PENNY'S GIFT** C 33
582 **PENNYWHISTLE** (IRE) 26
486 **PENOMBRE** 43
188 **PENPAL** (IRE) 48
416 **PENS MAN** (IRE) 66
112 **PENTELITUBBY** 15
346 **PENTEWAN** 21
34 **PENTIMENTO** 14
268 **PENTLAND HILLS** (IRE) 124
437 **PENTREATH** 54
186 **PENWORTHAM** (IRE) 40
30 **PEPPER BAY** 43
437 **PEPPERCORN** 55
254 **PEPPERONI PETE** 53
14 **PEPYS** 14
530 **PERCOLATOR** C 28
196 **PERCY** (IRE) 9
348 **PERCY ALEXANDER** 12
249 **PERCY B SHELLEY** 47
388 **PERCY POPS** 73
557 **PERCY PROSECCO** 17
435 **PERCY STREET** 57
135 **PERCY THROWER** (IRE) 15
165 **PERCY TOPLIS** 8
304 **PERCY WILLIS** 68
304 **PERCY'S LAD** 69
428 **PERCY'S PRINCE** 12
484 **PERCY'S WORD** 85
254 **PERES ET FILS** (IRE) 54
49 **PERFECIMPERFECTION** (IRE) 14
39 **PERFECT ARCH** (IRE) 100
411 **PERFECT CANDIDATE** (IRE) 63
416 **PERFECT CITY** (IRE) C 67
17 **PERFECT COVER** (IRE) 170
121 **PERFECT FOCUS** (IRE) 63
175 **PERFECT FUN** C 81
315 **PERFECT HARMONY** (IRE) 98

26 **PERFECT HAVEN** F 50
192 **PERFECT INCH** 46
6 **PERFECT LIGHT** (IRE) F 195
395 **PERFECT MAN** (IRE) 80
456 **PERFECT MOMENT** (IRE) 5
316 **PERFECT MYTH** 29
39 **PERFECT NUMBER** 31
117 **PERFECT OUTING** 47
534 **PERFECT PERCY** 65
315 **PERFECT PREDATOR** 99
413 **PERFECT PULSE** (IRE) 82
117 **PERFECT REFUGE** 16
305 **PERFECT ROSE** 106
117 **PERFECT SHOWDANCE** 17
510 **PERFECT SOLDIER** (IRE) 5
17 **PERFECT SUNSET** 103
170 **PERFECT SWISS** 74
423 **PERFECT SYMPHONY** (IRE) 6
39 **PERFECT WINTER** (IRE) 32
537 **PERFECTED** 83
239 **PERFORMANCE POET** 17
117 **PERHAPS TONIGHT** (IRE) 93
179 **PERIPHERIQUE** 8
24 **PERLE ROSE** (IRE) 14
214 **PERMAISURI** (IRE) F 69
148 **PERMISSION GRANTED** (IRE) 28
192 **PERONISM** (USA) C 65
228 **PERONISTA** (IRE) 116
529 **PEROTTO** 45
124 **PEROVSKIA** (USA) G 18
574 **PERPIGNAN** (IRE) 22
365 **PERRY OWENS** (IRE) 135
188 **PERSARIO** F 78
79 **PERSEID** (IRE) 6
409 **PERSIA** (IRE) 81
121 **PERSIAN BEAUTY** (IRE) 14
167 **PERSIAN DELIGHT** 10
582 **PERSIAN SUN** 27
6 **PERSUADING** (IRE) 23
272 **PERSUASION** (IRE) 52
146 **PERTEMPS SIA** (IRE) 31
7 **PERUVIAN LILY** (FR) 74
211 **PERUVIAN SUMMER** (IRE) 19
96 **PERUVIEN BLEU** (FR) 2
531 **PESTO** 12
64 **PETE SO HIGH** (GER) 12
137 **PETE'S CHOICE** (IRE) 18
484 **PETER THE MAYO MAN** (IRE) 86
338 **PETER'S PORTRAIT** (IRE) 47
576 **PETERBOROUGH** (FR) 63
584 **PETERS PUDDING** (IRE) 10
563 **PETIT A PETIT** (IRE) C 46
527 **PETIT BAY** 3
221 **PETIT PALAIS** 61
452 **PETITE GANACHE** (IRE) 38
316 **PETITE JACK** 30
411 **PETITE POWER** (IRE) 64
463 **PETITE RHAPSODY** (IRE) 64
134 **PETITIONER** (IRE) 8
276 **PETIVILLE** (FR) 10
298 **PETRASTAR** 15
129 **PETRONELLA MANNERS** 24
298 **PETRUCCI** (IRE) 16
60 **PETTOCHSIDE** 7
540 **PETUNIE** (FR) 27
480 **PEUR DE RIEN** (FR) 35
362 **PHANTASMAL** 11
368 **PHANTOM ISLE** 35

419 **PHARADELLE** (IRE) C 69
228 **PHAROAH KING** (USA) 117
60 **PHAROH JAKE** 8
47 **PHEDRE** (FR) 30
501 **PHIL** 19
499 **PHILAMUNDO** (IRE) 10
128 **PHILIP'S WISH** 50
393 **PHILIPA VICTORIA** 50
412 **PHILOSOPHICAL** 44
409 **PHIZ** (GER) F 171
144 **PHOEBUS LESCRIBAA** (FR) 15
411 **PHOENICIAN STAR** (IRE) 65
170 **PHOENIX APPROACH** (IRE) 138
166 **PHOENIX AQUILUS** (IRE) 11
2 **PHOENIX DAWN** 3
416 **PHOENIX ROCK** (IRE) 68
415 **PHOENIX SONG** 4
582 **PHOENIX STAR** (IRE) 28
260 **PHOENIX STRIKE** 46
212 **PHOENIX WAY** (IRE) 62
428 **PHOLAS** 31
472 **PHOSPHORESCENCE** (IRE) 7
251 **PHOTOGRAPH** (IRE) 101
254 **PHOTOPHORE** F 174
132 **PHUKET POWER** (IRE) 42
90 **PIANISSIMO** 8
244 **PIANO SOLO** (FR) 12
60 **PIAZOLA** (IRE) 22 •
64 **PIAZON** 13
405 **PIC D'ORHY** (FR) 125
431 **PICANHA** 21
233 **PICARA'S PROMISE** 48
285 **PICC AN ANGEL** 13
285 **PICC AND GO** 14
242 **PICCOLA SISSI** (IRE) C 173
584 **PICCOLO RAMOSCELLO** 11
356 **PICHELOT** (FR) 80
348 **PICKAMIX** 13
491 **PICKING PEACHES** (IRE) 21
251 **PICKLE** F 209
313 **PICKNICK PARK** 7
453 **PICKS PINTA** 2
97 **PICOSA CITY** (IRE) 55
39 **PICTURE FRAME** 101
501 **PICTURE POET** (IRE) 7
500 **PICTURE YOUR DREAM** 7
211 **PIDDIES PRIDE** (IRE) C 39
169 **PIECE OF MAGIC** F 88
503 **PIECE OF PARADISE** 25
412 **PIEDITA** (IRE) 23
365 **PIENTA** (USA) 92
284 **PIERLOW** (IRE) 5
537 **PIERRE LAPIN** (IRE) 84
305 **PIETRAFIORE** (IRE) F 213
530 **PIGEON PIE** C 29
416 **PIGGY WINKLE** (IRE) 69
180 **PIKE CORNER CROSS** (IRE) 17
223 **PILANSBERG** 9
364 **PILATES** (IRE) F 52
274 **PILEON** (IRE) 76
498 **PILLAR OF STEEL** 9
179 **PILLARS OF EARTH** 22
89 **PILOT WINGS** (IRE) 49
159 **PIMLICO PUBLICAN** (IRE) 12
260 **PINARELLA** (IRE) 23
6 **PINATUBO** (IRE) 81
117 **PINBALL WIZARD** (IRE) 94
356 **PINCH OF GINGER** (IRE) 81

77 **PINCHPOINT** (IRE) 28
419 **PINDROP** C 70
173 **PINE WARBLER** 28
351 **PINEAPPLE RUSH** 17
526 **PINGSHOU** (IRE) 76
547 **PINK DAMSEL** (IRE) F 95
56 **PINK EYED PEDRO** 7
547 **PINK FLAMES** (IRE) C 96
10 **PINK FLAMINGO** 23
120 **PINK ICEBURG** (IRE) 2
583 **PINK LEGEND** 52
242 **PINK SANDS** (IRE) 87
445 **PINK SHEETS** (IRE) 6
122 **PINKIE PIE** (IRE) 16
308 **PINNACLE PEAK** 26
582 **PINNATA** (IRE) 29
463 **PINSPOT** 65
323 **PIONEER OF THE SKY** (USA) 41
191 **PIONEERING** (IRE) 24
378 **PIONEERING** (IRE) 95
280 **PIPA COIN** 9
17 **PIPER ARROW** 37
87 **PIPERS NOTE** 29
166 **PIPES OF PEACE** (IRE) 7
268 **PIPESMOKER** (FR) 125
508 **PIPPEDATTHEPOST** F 17
537 **PIRACICABA** (IRE) C 175
242 **PIRANESI** (IRE) 88
192 **PIRATE KING** 20
55 **PIRATE LASS** (IRE) 4
61 **PIRATE SAM** 20
97 **PISANELLO** (IRE) 56
496 **PISGAH PIKE** (IRE) 46
145 **PISTOL** (IRE) 3
175 **PISTOL PARK** (IRE) 39
268 **PISTOL WHIPPED** (IRE) 126
409 **PISTOLETTO** (USA) 82
503 **PITA PINTA** (IRE) 50
117 **PITCHCOMBE** 48
228 **PITCHER'S POINT** (USA) 118
480 **PITON PETE** (IRE) 36
254 **PIVKA** F 175
17 **PIVOINE** (IRE) 38
426 **PIVOTAL ART** (IRE) 14
516 **PIVOTAL DECISION** 37
516 **PIVOTAL MOMENT** 86
483 **PIVOTAL'S PRINCESS** (IRE) F 93
17 **PIVOTALIA** (IRE) F 171
251 **PIVOTIQUE** F 210
582 **PIVOTTING** F 51
305 **PIVOTTING** F 214
254 **PIXEL POWER** 117
139 **PIXELATIT** 3
244 **PIXIE BELLE** (IRE) C 86
220 **PIXIE LOC** 7
406 **PIXIEPOT** 5
188 **PLACATED** 79
76 **PLACE IN MY HEART** C 74
214 **PLACE PASDELOUP** (FR) 31
426 **PLACEBO EFFECT** (IRE) 6
23 **PLACEDELA CONCORDE** 22
39 **PLACIDIA** (IRE) F 163
528 **PLAN OF ESCAPE** (IRE) 10
148 **PLANET NINE** (IRE) 29
34 **PLANTADREAM** 15
391 **PLANTAGENET** 27
30 **PLATFORM NINETEEN** (IRE) 8
511 **PLATH** 73

180 **PLATINUM DARLING** (IRE) C 51
378 **PLATINUM PRINCE** 140
39 **PLATINUM STAR** (IRE) 102
128 **PLATINUMCARD** (IRE) 51
428 **PLATITUDE** 13
552 **PLAY PRACTICE** 8
587 **PLAY WITH ME** 6
391 **PLAYA BLANCA** (IRE) 28
244 **PLAYA DEL DUQUE** (IRE) 46
392 **PLEASANT COMPANY** (IRE) 152
6 **PLEASCACH** (IRE) C 196
439 **PLEASURE GARDEN** (USA) 26
589 **PLEASUREAPLENTY** 12
251 **PLEBEYA** (IRE) C 211
291 **PLEDGE OF HONOUR** 28
6 **PLEDGE OF PEACE** (IRE) 82
539 **PLENEY** 75
475 **PLENTY OF BUTTY** (IRE) 27
320 **PLOVER** G 23
464 **PLUCKY** F 21
254 **PLUM SUGAR** C 176
339 **PLUMETTE** 22
77 **PLUNGER** 29
162 **PLUNKETT** 23
444 **PLYMOUTH ROCK** (IRE) 40
576 **POBBLES BAY** (IRE) 64
101 **POCKET SQUARE** 48
228 **POCKET VETO** (IRE) 119
192 **POCKETEER** (IRE) 66
521 **POCO CONTANTE** 21
170 **POET'S DAWN** 75
192 **POET'S EYE** 47
26 **POET'S LADY** 33
437 **POET'S MAGIC** 7
6 **POET'S MIND** (USA) 83
43 **POET'S REFLECTION** (IRE) 6
501 **POETA BRASILEIRO** (IRE) 8
89 **POETIC FORCE** (IRE) 50
367 **POETIC LILLY** 21
284 **POETIC PRESENCE** (IRE) 6
411 **POETIC RHYTHM** (IRE) 66
169 **POETIC VERSE** F 89
378 **POETRY AND ART** 141
239 **POETS DANCE** 18
272 **POGO** (IRE) 16
212 **POGO I AM** 63
356 **POGUE** (IRE) 82
248 **POINT BREAK** (IRE) 4
536 **POINT IN TIME** (IRE) 15
539 **POINT OF PRINCIPLE** (IRE) 76
292 **POINT OF WOODS** 2
530 **POINT PERFECT** C 10
274 **POINTED AND SHARP** (IRE) 77
216 **POINTED SPEAR** (IRE) 9
306 **POKARI** (FR) 9
355 **POKER MASTER** (IRE) 12
435 **POKER PLAY** (FR) 58
577 **POKER SCHOOL** (IRE) 69
261 **POL CROCAN** (IRE) 78
261 **POLA CHANCE** (FR) 35
242 **POLAR APPEAL** (IRE) 89
384 **POLAR CIRCLE** (USA) F 65
345 **POLAR CLOUD** 14
439 **POLAR ICE** 52
269 **POLAR LIGHT** 21
476 **POLARBROOK** (IRE) 14
305 **POLICORO** (IRE) F 215
411 **POLISH** 67

409 **POLISHED GEM** (IRE) C 172
189 **POLISHED ROCK** (IRE) 30
254 **POLISHED STEEL** (IRE) 55
148 **POLITENESS** (FR) 30
405 **POLITOLOGUE** (FR) 126
322 **POLLYGON** (IRE) 25
49 **POLYGON** (USA) F 76
342 **POLYPHONY** (IRE) 15
6 **POMOLOGY** (USA) C 197
361 **POMPEIA** F 14
14 **POND ROAD** (FR) 43
575 **PONIEL** 9
583 **PONIENTE** 53
392 **PONT AVAL** (FR) 153
392 **PONT AVEN** (FR) 154
340 **PONTBLYDDYN** 19
272 **PONTIUS** (IRE) 100
480 **PONTRESINA** (IRE) 37
110 **POOKIE PEKAN** (IRE) 17
390 **POOR DUKE** (IRE) 12
89 **POP DANCER** (IRE) 87
431 **POP MISTRESS** (IRE) 22
416 **POP ROCKSTAR** (IRE) 70
378 **POP THE CONFETTI** (IRE) 142
416 **POP THE CORK** 71
94 **POPE GREGORY** 56
427 **POPPING CORKS** (IRE) 8
211 **POPPOP** (FR) 20
211 **POPPY JAG** (IRE) 21
224 **POPPY MAY** (IRE) 3
428 **POPULAIRE** (FR) 32
97 **PORCELAINE** (FR) 57
296 **PORFIN** (IRE) 27
95 **PORT LAIRGE** 6
255 **PORT NOIR** 22
395 **PORT OF MARS** (IRE) 81
146 **PORT SOIF** 16
254 **PORT STANLEY** 56
57 **PORT WINSTON** (IRE) 22
36 **PORTLEDGE** (IRE) 8
60 **PORTO FERRO** (IRE) 9
528 **PORTOFINO** (IRE) 11
242 **PORTRAY** 90
233 **PORTRUSH TED** (IRE) 49
160 **PORTSTORM** 11
557 **PORTUGUESEPRINCESS** (IRE) 50
577 **PORTWAY FLYER** (IRE) 70
548 **POSH GIRL** 36
117 **POSITIVE** 49
244 **POSITIVE SPIN** C 87
575 **POSITIVE TOUCH** (IRE) 10
511 **POSSIBLE MAN** 134
268 **POST WAR** 127
251 **POSTED** 21
305 **POSTERITAS** (USA) C 216
179 **POSTIE** 9
537 **POSTILEO** (IRE) 85
391 **POSTMAN** (FR) 29
292 **POSTULANT** F 20
559 **POT LUCK** 4
132 **POT OF PAINT** 43
511 **POTAPOVA** 135
162 **POTATO PARK** 59
88 **POTENCIA** (IRE) 19
179 **POTENZA** (IRE) 10
409 **POTION** F 173
315 **POTTERMAN** 100
574 **POTTERS CORNER** (IRE) 23

541 **POTTERS HEDGER** 24
541 **POTTERS LEGEND** 25
550 **POTTERS QUESTION** 13
274 **POTTERS VENTURE** (IRE) 79
327 **POTTERS VISION** (IRE) 51
328 **POTTLEREAGHEXPRESS** (IRE) 11
94 **POUCOR** 16
107 **POULAINE BLEUE** C 35
46 **POUND OFF YOU** 17
192 **POUND STERLING** F 67
577 **POUR JOIE** 71
89 **POUR LA VICTOIRE** (IRE) 51
128 **POUR ME A DRINK** 52
372 **POUR UNE RAISON** (FR) 4
563 **POWDER BLUE** F 47
402 **POWDER PATH** (FR) 52
106 **POWER HOME** (IRE) 3
529 **POWER OF DARKNESS** 12
392 **POWER OF PAUSE** (IRE) 155
422 **POWER OF STATES** (IRE) 11
6 **POWER OF TIME** (IRE) 84
126 **POWER ON** (IRE) 10
87 **POWER PLAYER** 30
543 **POWER POINT** 12
383 **POWERALLIED** (IRE) 9
422 **POWERFUL BREEZE** 42
257 **POWERFUL DREAM** (IRE) 20
582 **POWERFUL ELEGANCE** (USA) F 58
223 **POWERFUL SOCIETY** (IRE) 10
365 **POWERFUL TED** (IRE) 93
519 **POWERSTOWN PARK** (IRE) 17
422 **POWERTRAIN** (IRE) 43
90 **POY** 15
277 **POYLE GEORGE TWO** 1
220 **POYLE SOPHIE** F 24
87 **POYLE VINNIE** 31
348 **PRABENI** 14
39 **PRALL** F 164
537 **PRAIANO** (GER) 176
493 **PRAIRIE CALL** (IRE) G 40
318 **PRAIRIE MOPPINS** (USA) 20
89 **PRAIRIE TOWN** (IRE) 52
305 **PRAISE DANCING** (IRE) C 217
242 **PRAISED** 91
422 **PRALINE** (IRE) C 174
422 **PRANCE** (IRE) F 87
260 **PRANCING OSCAR** (IRE) 24
305 **PRAXEOLOGY** (IRE) 107
323 **PRAXIAS** (IRE) 10
156 **PRAY FOR A RAINBOW** 15
503 **PRECARIOUSLY GOOD** F 51
283 **PRECIOUS** 27
268 **PRECIOUS CARGO** (IRE) 128
163 **PRECIOUS DREAM** (USA) F 36
129 **PRECIOUS ELEANOR** (FR) 25
42 **PRECIOUS GROUND** 8
340 **PRECIOUS MOMENTO** (IRE) 20
409 **PRECIOUS MOMENTS** (IRE) 83
550 **PRECIOUS PLUM** 14
176 **PRECISELY** 19
340 **PRECISION PRINCE** (IRE) 21
340 **PRECISION STORM** 42
439 **PREDOMINANT** 53
188 **PREENING** 14
416 **PREFONTAINE** (IRE) 72
483 **PREJUDICE** 18
363 **PRELUDE** F 47
557 **PREMIER D'TROICE** (FR) 18

537 **PREMIER POWER** 86
526 **PREMIUMACCESS** (IRE) 77
117 **PREQUEL** (IRE) C 95
227 **PRES** (IRE) 35
145 **PRESENCE FELT** (IRE) 4
395 **PRESENCE OF MIND** (IRE) 82
429 **PRESENCE PROCESS** 13
416 **PRESENT CHIEF** 73
338 **PRESENT ENDEAVOUR** (IRE) 48
431 **PRESENT FROM DUBAI** (IRE) 23
576 **PRESENT VALUE** 65
356 **PRESENTANDCOUNTING** (IRE) 83
515 **PRESENTEDWITHWINGS** (IRE) 19
  8 **PRESENTING LAZARUS** (IRE) G 7
388 **PRESENTING LUCINA** (IRE) 74
380 **PRESENTING MIRANDA** 2
256 **PRESENTING YEATS** (IRE) 17
191 **PRESIDENTIAL** (IRE) 25
 49 **PRESIDENTIAL SWEET** (ITY) 49
254 **PRESS CONFERENCE** (IRE) 57
227 **PRESS YOUR LUCK** (IRE) 36
286 **PRESTO LEVANTER** F 56
274 **PRESUMING ED** (IRE) 80
300 **PRET A PORTER** (UAE) F 15
 97 **PRETTY BOY** (IRE) 16
104 **PRETTY DARLING** (IRE) C 31
305 **PRETTY DIAMOND** (IRE) C 218
 49 **PRETTY IN GREY** 50
305 **PRETTY LADY** (IRE) 108
528 **PRETTY MISS MAHLER** (IRE) 12
437 **PRETTY PACKET** (FR) 27
242 **PRETTY PICKLE** (IRE) 92
388 **PRETTYLITTLETHING** (IRE) 75
 17 **PREVEZA** (FR) G 172
305 **PRIANCA** (GER) F 109
305 **PRICELESS JEWEL** C 219
163 **PRIDE OF AMERICA** (FR) 19
378 **PRIDE OF ANGELS** 96
117 **PRIDE OF ENGLAND** 96
371 **PRIDE OF HAWRIDGE** (IRE) 47
411 **PRIDE OF LECALE** 68
161 **PRIDE OF PEMBERLEY** (IRE) 2
159 **PRIDE OF PIMLICO** F 5
242 **PRIDE OF PRIORY** 175
214 **PRIDE OF PUNJAB** 54
467 **PRIDE OF THE OAKS** G 4
467 **PRIDE OF THE OAKS** F 9
162 **PRIMA LUCE** (IRE) F 60
574 **PRIMAL FOCUS** (IRE) 24
301 **PRIME APPROACH** (IRE) 7
511 **PRIME RUN** C 74
305 **PRIME RUN** F 220
576 **PRIME VENTURE** (IRE) 66
547 **PRIMO BACIO** (IRE) 97
439 **PRIMO LADY** C 54
225 **PRIMO'S COMET** 23
407 **PRIMROSE TIME** G 6
 29 **PRINCE ALEX** 76
582 **PRINCE CASPER** 52
251 **PRINCE CASPIAN** 102
539 **PRINCE CHARMIN'** (IRE) 77
543 **PRINCE CONSORT** (IRE) 8
519 **PRINCE DES FICHAUX** (FR) 34
463 **PRINCE DUNDEE** (IRE) 66
537 **PRINCE EIJI** 22
416 **PRINCE ESCALUS** (IRE) 18
511 **PRINCE IMPERIAL** (USA) 75
128 **PRINCE KAYF** 53

 47 **PRINCE KERALI** (FR) 7
356 **PRINCE KHURRAM** 84
 97 **PRINCE LANCELOT** 109
345 **PRINCE LLYR** (IRE) 15
 14 **PRINCE LLYWELYN** 44
192 **PRINCE OF ARRAN** 21
326 **PRINCE OF EAGLES** (IRE) 8
582 **PRINCE OF HARTS** 30
286 **PRINCE OF ROME** (IRE) 6
181 **PRINCE OF STEAL** (IRE) 14
192 **PRINCE OF TIDES** (IRE) 48
378 **PRINCE PERCY** 143
152 **PRINCE ROCK** (IRE) 8
401 **PRINCELY** 9
465 **PRINCES DES SABLES** 20
340 **PRINCESS ALOOF** (IRE) C 49
112 **PRINCESS AVERY** (IRE) 16
162 **PRINCESS CAMMIE** (IRE) C 61
174 **PRINCESS CAVE** (IRE) 2
464 **PRINCESS FLORENCE** (IRE) 8
445 **PRINCESS HARLEY** (IRE) 7
103 **PRINCESS KAGUYA** (IRE) 34
445 **PRINCESS KEIRA** (IRE) 8
 94 **PRINCESS LAHAR** 57
526 **PRINCESS MIDNIGHT** 78
356 **PRINCESS MONONOKE** (IRE) 85
 15 **PRINCESS NEARCO** (IRE) 18
 21 **PRINCESS OF ROCK** F 29
 26 **PRINCESS PATSKY** (IRE) G 51
 92 **PRINCESS ROXY** 22
445 **PRINCESS SIYOUNI** (IRE) 13
 34 **PRINCESS SPIRIT** F 33
388 **PRINCESS** T 76
220 **PRINCESS WAY** (IRE) 5
429 **PRINCESSE ANIMALE** 26
  6 **PRINCESSE DANSANTE** (IRE) F 198
316 **PRINCETON ROYALE** (IRE) 31
563 **PRINCIPIA** 14
233 **PRINTING DOLLARS** (IRE) 50
 34 **PRIONSA** (IRE) 16
355 **PRISCILLA'S DREAM** 6
355 **PRISCILLA'S STAR** 13
228 **PRISMATIC** (IRE) 120
339 **PRISSY MISSY** (IRE) 42
368 **PRISSY MISSY** (IRE) 63
254 **PRIVATE ALEXANDER** F 177
272 **PRIVATE DANCER** (FR) F 101
327 **PRIVATE MALONE** (IRE) 8
393 **PRIVATE MATTER** (IRE) 59
121 **PRIVATE PARADISE** (IRE) C 95
103 **PRIVATE ROMANCE** (IRE) 35
439 **PRIVATE TREATY** 27
117 **PRIZE FIGHTING** 50
521 **PRIZE WINNER** (IRE) 11
542 **PROCEEDING** 8
228 **PROCEEDING** (USA) 121
 81 **PROCLAIMER** 26
315 **PRODUCTION** 101
 73 **PRODUCTIVE** (IRE) 59
499 **PROFESSIONAL WIDOW** (IRE) 50
255 **PROFILE PICTURE** (IRE) 14
537 **PROGRESSIVE** 87
320 **PROGRESSIVE EZ** (IRE) 35
320 **PROGRESSIVE RATING** 24
444 **PROJECT BLUEBOOK** (FR) 20
411 **PROJECT MARS** (IRE) 69
548 **PROMISE OF SUCCESS** 10
 17 **PROMISED MONEY** (IRE) C 173

 49 **PROMISES** (IRE) 51
228 **PROMISSORY** (IRE) 24
395 **PROMPTING** 83
456 **PRONOUNCED** (IRE) 6
117 **PROP FORWARD** 97
486 **PROPER BEAU** 29
411 **PROPER TICKET** (IRE) 70
327 **PROPHETS PRAYER** (IRE) 53
511 **PROPRIETY** (IRE) 76
409 **PROSE** (IRE) 84
450 **PROSECUTE** (FR) 2
 49 **PROSILI** (IRE) 52
254 **PROTAGONIST** (IRE) 118
349 **PROTECTED GUEST** 5
260 **PROTEK DES FLOS** (FR) 25
484 **PROTEKTORAT** (FR) 87
 89 **PROTON** (IRE) 53
150 **PROUD ARCHI** (IRE) 18
228 **PROVEN** (IRE) 122
254 **PROVOCATEUSE** (IRE) 178
  7 **PROXY** 75
579 **PRUDHOMME** (FR) 19
305 **PRUFROCK** (IRE) F 221
484 **PRUSSIA WITH LOVE** 88
368 **PRYERS PRINCESS** F 73
254 **PSYCHE** 119
 73 **PSYCHIC POWER** (IRE) 60
286 **PTARMIGAN RIDGE** 7
528 **PUB MURPHY** (IRE) 13
 84 **PUBLICISE** 32
516 **PUBLICIST** 87
470 **PUBLILIA** F 9
 63 **PUCHITA** (IRE) 12
472 **PUDDING** (IRE) G 36
491 **PUDDING CHARE** (IRE) 22
286 **PUDS** 8
577 **PUERTO BANUS** 72
282 **PUERTO ORO** (IRE) F 11
175 **PUERTO SOL** (IRE) 70
 39 **PULCINELLA** (IRE) C 165
356 **PULL GREEN** (IRE) 86
 62 **PULL HARDER CON** 42
173 **PULL TOGETHER** (IRE) 29
317 **PULLMAN BROWN** (USA) 56
 92 **PULP FICTION** (IRE) 23
339 **PULSE FICTION** (IRE) 43
370 **PUMAFLOR** (IRE) 25
295 **PUMBLECHOOK** 31
251 **PUMMEL** (IRE) 103
159 **PUNCH BAG** (IRE) 6
304 **PUNCHBOWL FLYER** (IRE) 45
  6 **PUNCTILIOUS** C 199
 17 **PUNCTUATION** 104
254 **PUNITA AURORA** 120
197 **PUNJAB MAIL** 5
472 **PUNTA ARENAS** (USA) 37
103 **PUNTARELLE** (FR) 36
286 **PUNTING** (IRE) 31
175 **PUNXSUTAWNEY PHIL** (IRE) 71
284 **PUPPET WARRIOR** 7
170 **PUPPETONASTRING** 76
215 **PURBECK HILLS** (IRE) 10
148 **PURCELL'S BRIDGE** (FR) 31
 17 **PURDEY'S GIFT** 39
 39 **PURE BEAUTY** 33
212 **PURE BLISS** 64
580 **PURE COUNTRY** 18
  6 **PURE DIAMOND** F 200

483 **PURE EXCELLENCE** C 94
503 **PURE GREED** (IRE) C 52
251 **PURE LINE** C 212
54 **PURE PURFECTION** (IRE) 18
283 **PURE VISION** (IRE) 28
351 **PURE VODKA** 17
563 **PURELY BY CHANCE** F 15
527 **PURELY PRICELESS** (IRE) C 15
476 **PURELY PROSECCO** 15
10 **PURFORD GREEN** 24
548 **PURGATORY** 11
214 **PURPLE EMPRESS** 55
292 **PURPLE HARRY** 13
473 **PURPLE JAZZ** (IRE) 30
402 **PURPLE KING** (IRE) 53
73 **PURPLE KNIGHT** (FR) 61
392 **PURPLE MOUNTAIN** (IRE) 156
207 **PURPLE PADDY** 8
445 **PURPLE POWER** 14
62 **PURPLE SANDPIPER** 43
207 **PURPLE TOMMY** 9
439 **PURRZEALOT** 15
41 **PURSUIT OF PURPOSE** F 7
215 **PUSEY STREET LADY** F 22
215 **PUSEY STREET VALE** F 23
280 **PUSH AHEAD** (IRE) 10
295 **PUSH FOR SIXTY** 63
508 **PUSH THE TEMPO** (IRE) 18
77 **PUSHKIN MUSEUM** (IRE) 30
86 **PUSHMI PULLYU** (IRE) 3
281 **PUSHOVER** 14
391 **PUT ON HOLD** (IRE) F 30
568 **PUT THE LAW ON YOU** (IRE) 30
74 **PUTDECASHONTHEDASH** (IRE) 8
388 **PUTTING GREEN** 77
261 **PUXTON PARK** 36
537 **PUY MARY** 177
371 **PUZZLE CACHE** 10
268 **PYM** (IRE) 129
254 **PYRAMID ROCK** (IRE) 121
504 **Q CEE** 5
537 **QAADDIM** (IRE) 88
63 **QAARAAT** 13
192 **QANATEER** (IRE) C 68
101 **QARASU** (IRE) 14
340 **QASBAZ** (IRE) 43
188 **QATAR QUEEN** (IRE) 15
272 **QAWAASEM** (IRE) F 102
169 **QAWAMEES** (IRE) 37
251 **QAYSAR** (FR) 22
413 **QUADRI** F 120
101 **QUADRILATERAL** 49
62 **QUAIL LANDING** C 44
384 **QUAINT** (IRE) 36
470 **QUALIFICATION** (USA) F 10
15 **QUANAH** (IRE) 19
295 **QUANTUM** (IRE) G 55
305 **QUANTUM DAWN** (IRE) 110
411 **QUANTUM OF SOLACE** 71
416 **QUARENTA** (FR) 75
320 **QUARRY BAY** (IRE) 25
84 **QUARRY BEACH** 12
256 **QUARRY WIZARD** (IRE) 18
356 **QUART DE GARDE** (FR) 87
392 **QUART DU RHEU** (FR) 157
436 **QUASHA** 10
119 **QUAY QUEST** 10

7 **QUDURAAT** 76
150 **QUE AMORO** (IRE) 19
152 **QUE QUIERES** (USA) 9
295 **QUE SERA SERA** C 64
435 **QUEEN ADELAIDE** 59
137 **QUEEN AMONG KINGS** (IRE) 19
547 **QUEEN AYA** 67
296 **QUEEN CONSTANTINE** (GER) 7
537 **QUEEN DAENERYS** (IRE) 89
305 **QUEEN GAMRAH** 111
419 **QUEEN HERMIONE** (IRE) F 71
465 **QUEEN JO JO** 21
94 **QUEEN LAHAR** 58
88 **QUEEN MIA** (IRE) 11
286 **QUEEN OF ALL** 32
251 **QUEEN OF ASIA** (IRE) 213
165 **QUEEN OF BURGUNDY** 9
412 **QUEEN OF CAMELOT** (IRE) 45
254 **QUEEN OF CARTHAGE** C 179
6 **QUEEN OF JAZZ** (IRE) 85
185 **QUEEN OF KALAHARI** 10
17 **QUEEN OF POWER** (IRE) C 174
317 **QUEEN OF ROCK** (IRE) 85
94 **QUEEN OF SILCA** 99
85 **QUEEN OF THE COURT** (IRE) 8
39 **QUEEN OF THE SEA** (IRE) 53
483 **QUEEN OF THE WAVES** 103
526 **QUEEN OF THE WIND** 79
511 **QUEEN POWER** (IRE) 13
34 **QUEEN RANAVOLA** (USA) F 27
242 **QUEEN'S COURSE** (IRE) 93
17 **QUEEN'S DREAM** (GER) F 175
511 **QUEEN'S FAIR** 136
511 **QUEEN'S FAVOUR** 77
465 **QUEEN'S LOGIC** (IRE) F 101
388 **QUEEN'S MAGIC** (IRE) 78
516 **QUEEN'S NOVEL** F 88
465 **QUEEN'S ORDER** 62
465 **QUEEN'S SARGENT** (FR) 22
446 **QUEEN'S SOLDIER** (GER) 33
173 **QUEENOHEARTS** (IRE) 30
435 **QUEENS CAVE** (IRE) 60
50 **QUEENS PARK** F 18
328 **QUEENS PRESENT** (IRE) 12
532 **QUEENS ROAD** (IRE) 20
254 **QUEENSCLIFF** C 180
405 **QUEL DESTIN** (FR) 127
163 **QUELLE VITESSE** (GER) 37
107 **QUEMONDA** 8
215 **QUENCH DOLLY** 11
422 **QUENELLE D'OR** 88
158 **QUERCUS** (IRE) 16
545 **QUEST FOR LIFE** 18
378 **QUIANA** 9
437 **QUICK BREATH** 8
23 **QUICK BREW** 23
379 **QUICK CHAT** (USA) F 27
322 **QUICK DRAW** 26
411 **QUICK GRABIM** (IRE) 72
169 **QUICK LOOK** 38
258 **QUICK MONET** (IRE) 7
56 **QUICK N' EASY** (IRE) 8
83 **QUICK PICK** (IRE) 30
365 **QUICK QUICK** (IRE) 136
132 **QUICK RECAP** (IRE) 44
511 **QUICK WALTZ** 78
583 **QUICK WAVE** (FR) 54
175 **QUICKLY DOES IT** 40

17 **QUICKSTEP LADY** 105
384 **QUICKTHORN** 37
356 **QUIDS IN** (IRE) 88
39 **QUIET EVENING** (IRE) 104
484 **QUIET FLOW** 89
272 **QUIET NIGHT** (IRE) 53
475 **QUIET SHY** (FR) 28
116 **QUIET SUNSHINE** (USA) F 51
557 **QUIET WORD** (FR) 51
583 **QUIETLYFLOWSTHEDON** 55
356 **QUIK SHIFT** 89
101 **QUILTED** 94
570 **QUINLANDIO** (IRE) 7
508 **QUINNSBOROTEMPTRES** (IRE) 19
210 **QUINTO** 14
94 **QUIRKY GERTIE** (IRE) 17
526 **QUITE BY CHANCE** 80
365 **QUITE INCREDIBLE** (IRE) 94
395 **QUIVVY LOUGH** (IRE) 84
535 **QUIXOTE** (GER) 5
526 **QUIZ MASTER** (IRE) 81
378 **QULOOB** 98
576 **QUOI DE NEUF** (FR) 67
6 **QUORTO** (IRE) 24
249 **QUOTELINE DIRECT** 48
17 **QUSHCHI** C 176
7 **R BERNARD** 22
114 **RAADEA** 114
537 **RAADOBARG** (IRE) 178
39 **RAAEB** (IRE) 106
272 **RAAJIN** 50
214 **RAAJIS** (IRE) F 56
483 **RAAKIB ALHAWA** (IRE) 19
76 **RAAQY** (FR) C 75
39 **RAASED** (IRE) 107
121 **RAASEKHA** F 96
529 **RAASEL** 26
178 **RAASHDY** (IRE) 13
529 **RAATEA** 27
511 **RABAABAH** (IRE) 79
511 **RABDAN** 14
416 **RABSKI** (FR) 76
422 **RACE IN FOCUS** (IRE) F 89
122 **RACEMAKER** 17
84 **RACHEL WALL** (IRE) 33
422 **RACHEL ZANE** (IRE) 12
422 **RACHMANINOV** (USA) 44
97 **RACING GLORY** (IRE) 58
1 **RACING PULSE** (IRE) 47
455 **RACING SPIRIT** 7
281 **RACY STACEY** 15
249 **RADDLE AND HUM** (IRE) 49
88 **RADJASH** 12
297 **RAECIUS FELIX** (IRE) 19
491 **RAEMOIR** (FR) 23
368 **RAFFERTY'S RETURN** 36
305 **RAFFLE PRIZE** (IRE) 112
6 **RAFFLE TICKET** (USA) F 201
378 **RAFIOT** (USA) 99
511 **RAGHAAYIB** 80
365 **RAGIN CAJUN** (IRE) 95
555 **RAGING RASCAL** (IRE) 29
274 **RAGNAR** 81
359 **RAGSTONE ROAD** (IRE) 1
371 **RAGSTONE VIEW** (IRE) 11
163 **RAGTIME SALLY** 20

528 **RINGARINGAROSIE** (IRE) 14
582 **RINGMISTRESS** (USA) C 59
332 **RINGMOYLAN** (IRE) 4
424 **RINTULLA** (IRE) 67
501 **RINTY MAGINTY** (IRE) 9
395 **RIO QUINTO** (FR) 86
394 **RIO RONALDO** (IRE) 11
392 **RIO VIVAS** (FR) 162
118 **RIO'S GIRL** F 9
225 **RIOJA DAY** (IRE) 25
228 **RIOT** (IRE) 125
412 **RIOT OF COLOUR** C 58
497 **RIP VAN GO** 9
251 **RIPALONG** (IRE) C 215
413 **RIPLEY ROSE** 121
158 **RIPON SPA** 6
176 **RIPP ORF** (IRE) 9
511 **RIPPLES MAID** F 139
552 **RIPSTICK** 9
545 **RISAALAAT** (IRE) 20
364 **RISE HALL** 20
499 **RISE UP LOTUS** (IRE) F 52
305 **RISEN SUN** C 227
463 **RISING MARIENBARD** (IRE) 69
217 **RISING SEAS** 4
57 **RISING SUNSHINE** (IRE) 12
286 **RISK A LOOK** C 57
446 **RISK D'ARGENT** (FR) 34
117 **RISK TAKER** (IRE) 51
537 **RISKIT FORA BISKIT** (IRE) C 179
260 **RITCHIE STAR** (IRE) 27
104 **RITCHIE VALENS** (IRE) 11
463 **RIVABODIVA** (IRE) 70
17 **RIVAL** 178
215 **RIVAS ROB ROY** 12
392 **RIVEN LIGHT** (IRE) 163
251 **RIVER ALWEN** (IRE) 216
515 **RIVER ARROW** 21
131 **RIVER BRAY** (IRE) 14
537 **RIVER DANCE** 180
89 **RIVER DART** (FR) 56
107 **RIVER DAWN** 9
260 **RIVER FROST** 28
517 **RIVER GLADES** 9
295 **RIVER ICON** 32
117 **RIVER NYMPH** 52
417 **RIVER OF INTRIGUE** (IRE) 14
128 **RIVER OF KINGS** (IRE) 91
65 **RIVER PURPLE** 4
557 **RIVER SONG** (IRE) 53
499 **RIVER SONG** (USA) C 53
321 **RIVER SPRITE** 13
484 **RIVER TYNE** 95
17 **RIVERFRONT** (FR) 41
244 **RIVERS OF BABYLON** (IRE) F 91
192 **RIVIERA BELLE** 49
121 **RIZEENA** (IRE) C 99
534 **RIZZARDO** 68
150 **ROAD RAGE** (IRE) 43
439 **ROAD TO PARIS** (IRE) 6
365 **ROAD TO RESPECT** (IRE) 98
356 **ROAD TO REWARD** (FR) 90
368 **ROAD WARRIOR** 37
69 **ROADRUNNER** (IRE) 10
140 **ROAR** (IRE) 13
150 **ROARING DRAGON** (IRE) 44
27 **ROARING FORTIES** (IRE) 20
393 **ROARING FURY** (IRE) 27

426 **ROARING RORY** 7
114 **ROB ROYAL** (FR) 5
348 **ROBADDAN** (IRE) 15
474 **ROBBEN RAINBOW** 4
487 **ROBBIAN** 4
175 **ROBEAM** (IRE) 41
577 **ROBELLI** (IRE) 74
305 **ROBERT GUISCARD** (IRE) 114
242 **ROBERTO ESCOBARR** (IRE) 99
392 **ROBIN DE CARLOW** 164
317 **ROBIN DES CHAPP** (IRE) 61
392 **ROBIN DES FORET** (IRE) 165
593 **ROBIN DES MANA** (IRE) 9
254 **ROBIN DES SIVOLA** (IRE) 59
475 **ROBIN DES THEATRE** (IRE) 29
484 **ROBIN DEL** (IRE) 96
448 **ROBIN OF SHERWOOD** (IRE) 10
14 **ROBIN THE RAVEN** (IRE) 46
378 **ROBIN'S DREAM** 103
317 **ROBINCOLLETTE** (IRE) 62
539 **ROBINS FIELD** (IRE) 78
526 **ROBINSFIRTH** (IRE) 86
534 **ROBINSHILL** (IRE) 69
251 **ROBINSON CRUSOE** (IRE) 24
242 **ROBIOLA** (IRE) 177
323 **ROBLE** 44
196 **ROBOT BOY** (IRE) 10
308 **ROBSAM** (IRE) 29
297 **ROBYN PUD** (IRE) 22
411 **ROBYNDZONE** (IRE) 75
97 **ROC ANGEL** (FR) 18
493 **ROC MIRAGE** G 43
162 **ROCA MAGICA** 15
538 **ROCCALUCE** 14
534 **ROCCO** (IRE) 70
378 **ROCCO DU BERLAIS** (IRE) 104
233 **ROCCOWITHLOVE** 51
305 **ROCHESTER HOUSE** (IRE) 23
501 **ROCHFORD** (IRE) 20
340 **ROCK BOY GREY** (IRE) 24
364 **ROCK CAKE** (IRE) C 53
406 **ROCK CANDY** (IRE) F 11
29 **ROCK EAGLE** 28
305 **ROCK FOLLIES** C 228
518 **ROCK ICON** 16
77 **ROCK IN SOCIETY** (IRE) 32
169 **ROCK MAGIC** (IRE) G 91
537 **ROCK OF FAME** 94
340 **ROCK OF PENSAX** (IRE) 44
291 **ROCK OF REDMOND** (IRE) 51
393 **ROCK ON BAILEYS** 28
260 **ROCK ON FRUITY** (IRE) 29
221 **ROCK ON ROCCO** (IRE) 62
479 **ROCK ON ROCKY** 4
129 **ROCK ON TIGER** (FR) 27
395 **ROCK ON TOMMY** 87
88 **ROCK SOUND** (IRE) 14
405 **ROCK THE BABY** (IRE) C 131
274 **ROCK THE KASBAH** (IRE) 84
254 **ROCK THE WORLD** (IRE) 60
390 **ROCK WARBLER** (IRE) 15
180 **ROCKAHOOLABABY** (IRE) F 53
339 **ROCKESBURY** 24
116 **ROCKET ACTION** 18
169 **ROCKET DANCER** 73
555 **ROCKET NAAN** 6
422 **ROCKET ROD** (IRE) 45
589 **ROCKET RONNIE** (IRE) 13

254 **ROCKET SCIENCE** (IRE) 122
394 **ROCKETEER** 21
132 **ROCKETS RED GLARE** (IRE) 74
318 **ROCKIN' N RAVEN** 23
518 **ROCKING REG** (IRE) 31
518 **ROCKINGHAM JILL** 32
519 **ROCKINGHAM SOUTH** 18
317 **ROCKINOVERTHEWORLD** 28
474 **ROCKLEY POINT** 8
249 **ROCKLIFFE** 50
545 **ROCKMANN** (FR) 21
437 **ROCKMORE** 29
295 **ROCKNROLLBABY** (IRE) C 65
526 **ROCKPOINT** 87
563 **ROCKSETTE** 18
419 **ROCKSTAR BLONDE** 72
106 **ROCKSTAR MAX** (GER) 4
251 **ROCKY DREAMS** 105
14 **ROCKY'S TREASURE** (IRE) 47
578 **ROCOCO RIVER** 12
226 **ROCOCO STYLE** 7
260 **RODDY RANSOM** 47
501 **RODERICK** 10
17 **RODIN** 108
34 **RODNEY LE ROC** 28
483 **RODRIGO DIAZ** 55
367 **ROGER SEZ** (IRE) F 38
104 **ROGUE ASSASSIN** (IRE) 22
104 **ROGUE POWER** 33
503 **ROHAIN** (IRE) F 53
484 **ROKSANA** (IRE) 97
583 **ROLL AGAIN** (FR) 59
552 **ROLL OF THUNDER** 10
499 **ROLL WITH IT** (IRE) 13
169 **ROLLADICE** 40
340 **ROLLER** 25
436 **ROLLERBALL ROCCO** (IRE) 11
475 **ROLLERCOSTER** (IRE) 30
23 **ROLLERRULER** 25
97 **ROLLEVILLE** (FR) 59
274 **ROLLING DYLAN** (IRE) 85
23 **ROMA BANGKOK** 26
405 **ROMAIN DE SENAM** (FR) 132
176 **ROMAN MELODY** 21
382 **ROMAN ROCK** (IRE) 20
239 **ROMAN SPINNER** 6
128 **ROMAN STONE** (USA) 56
244 **ROMAN TURBO** (IRE) 48
339 **ROMAN'S EMPRESS** (IRE) 45
368 **ROMAN'S EMPRESS** (IRE) 65
391 **ROMANOR** 31
413 **ROMANTIC SETTINGS** F 122
29 **ROME IMPERIAL** (IRE) 77
317 **ROMEO BROWN** 63
465 **ROMERO** (IRE) 66
305 **ROMIE'S KASTETT** (GER) C 229
511 **ROMOLA** 16
524 **ROMPA STOMPA** (IRE) 26
384 **ROMSEY** 39
148 **ROMULUS DU DONJON** (IRE) 33
286 **RONALDSAY** C 58
272 **RONDO** (USA) 55
304 **ROODICA** 47
304 **ROODLE** F 70
394 **ROOF GARDEN** 12
388 **ROOKIE TRAINER** (IRE) 80
568 **ROOM AT THE TOP** (IRE) 31
159 **ROOM FOR GLORY** (IRE) 18

384 **ROOSTER** 66
52 **ROOSTER COGBURN** (IRE) 32
534 **ROOTLESS TREE** (IRE) 71
349 **ROPEY GUEST** 10
249 **RORY AND ME** (FR) 51
512 **ROS'S DREAM** 37
84 **ROSA BONHEUR** 44
239 **ROSA GOLD** 19
190 **ROSA LUXEMBURG** F 22
29 **ROSADORA** (IRE) 78
511 **ROSALIND** (USA) C 140
239 **ROSARDO SENORITA** 20
19 **ROSARNO** (IRE) 11
315 **ROSCOE TARA** 105
312 **ROSE BANDIT** (IRE) 16
305 **ROSE BONHEUR** F 230
192 **ROSE CHEVAL** (USA) F 69
251 **ROSE DIAMOND** (IRE) C 217
89 **ROSE HIP** 57
224 **ROSE KAZAN** (IRE) F 15
460 **ROSE MARMARA** 4
222 **ROSE OF AGHABOE** (IRE) 22
526 **ROSE OF ARCADIA** (IRE) 88
233 **ROSE OF CIMARRON** (IRE) 52
142 **ROSE OF CLARE** G 28
305 **ROSE OF KILDARE** (IRE) 115
402 **ROSE SEA HAS** (FR) 56
1 **ROSE TANNER** (IRE) G 48
14 **ROSE TO FAME** 48
569 **ROSE VIC** (IRE) F 18
73 **ROSEBRIDE** C 104
339 **ROSEINA'S VOICE** 46
440 **ROSEISAROSEISAROSE** (IRE) 14
537 **ROSEMAN** (IRE) 23
212 **ROSEMARY RUSSET** 65
491 **ROSEMAY** (FR) 25
62 **ROSENCRANTZ** (IRE) 99
308 **ROSERAIE** (IRE) C 231
254 **ROSES BLUE** (IRE) 184
386 **ROSES'S BOY** (IRE) 30
80 **ROSEYROO** (IRE) 3
365 **ROSGALME** (IRE) 100
356 **ROSIE ALL OVER** F 91
475 **ROSIE AND MILLIE** (IRE) 31
17 **ROSIE COTTON** (IRE) C 179
101 **ROSIE PROBERT** F 95
518 **ROSIE ROYALE** (IRE) 17
309 **ROSINA ROSE** 29
384 **ROSINKA** (IRE) F 67
244 **ROSKEEN** (IRE) C 92
251 **ROSLEA LADY** (IRE) C 218
14 **ROSMUC RELAY** (IRE) 49
42 **ROSSERK ABBEY** (IRE) 9
402 **ROSTELLO** (FR) 57
292 **ROSY RYAN** (IRE) 14
494 **ROSY WORLD** 11
107 **ROTHERWICK** (IRE) 10
89 **ROUDRAPOUR** (FR) 58
572 **ROUGE VIF** (FR) 28
94 **ROUGH COURTE** (IRE) C 105
243 **ROUGH NIGHT** (IRE) 22
121 **ROULSTON SCAR** (IRE) 17
570 **ROUND THE ISLAND** 8
12 **ROUNDABOUT MAGIC** (IRE) 11
431 **ROUNDHEAD** 24
133 **ROUSSIMOFF** (IRE) 12
483 **ROVANIEMI** (IRE) 56
428 **ROVERA** (IRE) 33

529 **ROWAN BRAE** C 48
173 **ROWLAND WARD** 32
43 **ROWLEY PARK** (IRE) 7
249 **ROXYFET** (FR) 52
255 **ROXZANE** 15
33 **ROY ROCKET** (FR) 12
135 **ROYAL ACT** 16
116 **ROYAL APPOINTMENT** 35
388 **ROYAL ARCADE** (IRE) 81
39 **ROYAL ARRIVAL** (IRE) 109
384 **ROYAL ASTRONOMER** 40
144 **ROYAL BASSETT** (FR) 25
305 **ROYAL BIG NIGHT** (USA) 24
582 **ROYAL BIRTH** 34
87 **ROYAL BLOSSOM** (IRE) G 49
441 **ROYAL BORN** (IRE) 11
27 **ROYAL BRAVE** (IRE) 21
244 **ROYAL CASAMENTO** (IRE) 49
6 **ROYAL CASTLE** (IRE) 91
537 **ROYAL CHAMPION** (IRE) 181
199 **ROYAL CHARMER** 9
43 **ROYAL CHIEFTAIN** (IRE) 8
170 **ROYAL CIRCLES** G 140
515 **ROYAL CLARET** 22
272 **ROYAL COMMANDO** (IRE) 56
300 **ROYAL CONCORDE** (IRE) 16
272 **ROYAL CONFIDENCE** G 105
186 **ROYAL COSMIC** 43
7 **ROYAL COUNCIL** (IRE) 117
407 **ROYAL COUNTESS** 8
526 **ROYAL CROWN** (FR) 89
6 **ROYAL CRUSADE** 92
422 **ROYAL DALAKHANI** (IRE) F 90
318 **ROYAL DANCER** 9
409 **ROYAL DORNOCH** (IRE) 86
385 **ROYAL DYNASTY** 3
36 **ROYAL ELOQUENCE** (IRE) C 28
272 **ROYAL EMPRESS** (IRE) F 106
94 **ROYAL FFANCI** C 106
560 **ROYAL FLUSH** 5
254 **ROYAL FREE HOTEL** 123
451 **ROYAL GOLDIE** (IRE) 8
121 **ROYAL HARMONY** (IRE) 100
242 **ROYAL HIDEAWAY** (IRE) 100
392 **ROYAL ILLUSION** (IRE) 166
547 **ROYAL INTERVENTION** (IRE) 49
371 **ROYAL IVY** F 49
228 **ROYAL LINE** 25
409 **ROYAL LYTHAM** (FR) 87
519 **ROYAL MAGIC** (IRE) 19
39 **ROYAL MARINE** (IRE) 36
218 **ROYAL MARTIAN** 8
228 **ROYAL MEWS** (FR) 126
272 **ROYAL MUSKETEER** 107
557 **ROYAL NATION** 54
39 **ROYAL PARTNERSHIP** 110
507 **ROYAL PLAZA** 1
439 **ROYAL PLEASURE** (IRE) 57
315 **ROYAL PRETENDER** (IRE) 106
407 **ROYAL PRINCESS** 15
268 **ROYAL REEL** 131
407 **ROYAL REGENT** 9
392 **ROYAL RENDEZVOUS** (IRE) 167
463 **ROYAL RESERVE** 71
158 **ROYAL RESIDENCE** 7
268 **ROYAL RUBY** 132
101 **ROYAL SECRETS** (IRE) F 96
568 **ROYAL SHAHEEN** (FR) 32

526 **ROYAL VACATION** (IRE) 90
577 **ROYAL VILLAGE** (IRE) 75
39 **ROYAL VOTE** (USA) 111
162 **ROYAL WARRANTY** C 63
251 **ROYAL WHISPER** F 219
483 **ROYALE DANEHILL** (IRE) C 96
539 **ROYALE DJANGO** (IRE) 79
47 **ROYALE OFFENSE** (IRE) 19
583 **ROYALE PAGAILLE** (FR) 60
539 **ROYALE VIDEO** (FR) G 80
348 **ROYALS AND REBELS** (IRE) 16
97 **ROYAUMONT** (FR) 60
471 **ROYBUOY** 2
169 **ROYCANO** 41
188 **ROZALIA** 50
26 **ROZENE** (IRE) F 52
244 **ROZIYNA** (IRE) 93
137 **RUACANA** 20
133 **RUBENESQUE** (IRE) 13
88 **RUBY DREAM** 20
77 **RUBY GATES** (IRE) 33
251 **RUBY POWER** (IRE) 106
428 **RUBY RED EMPRESS** (IRE) 34
139 **RUBY RUBLES** 6
186 **RUBY SHIELD** (USA) 118
324 **RUBY TAYLOR** 5
473 **RUBY WINE** 31
413 **RUBY WONDER** 84
378 **RUBY YEATS** 105
452 **RUBYTWO** 41
393 **RUDAINA** 51
192 **RUDY LEWIS** (IRE) 22
49 **RUFFLED** C 77
526 **RUFFLING FEATHERS** (IRE) 91
212 **RUFIO** 66
272 **RUFOOF** C 108
178 **RUKWA** (FR) 14
62 **RULER OF NATIVES** 24
210 **RULER RYDE** 15
192 **RUM BABA** 23
287 **RUMBLE B** (IRE) 13
6 **RUMH** (GER) C 202
529 **RUMOUSH** (USA) C 49
150 **RUMSHAK** (IRE) 20
308 **RUN A RIG** 30
301 **RUN AFTER GENESIS** (IRE) 9
192 **RUN OF THE DAY** G 50
192 **RUN OF THE DAY** F 70
431 **RUN ROSIE RUN** 25
84 **RUN TO FREEDOM** 45
131 **RUN TO MILAN** (IRE) 15
228 **RUN WILD** (GER) 127
204 **RUNAIOCHT** (IRE) 6
388 **RUNASIMI RIVER** 82
340 **RUNNING CLOUD** (IRE) 26
55 **RUNNING WAVE** (IRE) 2
243 **RUNNING WOLF** (IRE) 23
392 **RUNRIZED** (FR) 168
327 **RUNSWICK BAY** 55
248 **RUNSWICK ROYAL** (IRE) 5
465 **RUNWAY DANCER** F 102
257 **RUPERTCAMBELLBLACK** (IRE) 22
413 **RURAL CELEBRATION** F 123
170 **RUSALKA** (IRE) 141
482 **RUSPER'S GIFT** (IRE) 8
104 **RUSPER'S LAD** 23
365 **RUSSIAN BILL** 101
409 **RUSSIAN EMPEROR** (IRE) 88

526 **RUSSIAN EXILE** 92
416 **RUSSIAN INVASION** (IRE) 79
455 **RUSSIAN MEMORIES** (FR) C 14
214 **RUSSIAN PUNCH** C 70
367 **RUSSIAN RHAPSODY** C 22
249 **RUSSIAN ROYALE** 53
437 **RUSSIAN RUMOUR** (IRE) 30
156 **RUSSIAN SERVICE** 16
97 **RUSSIAN SYMBOL** (IRE) C 110
265 **RUSSIAN'S LEGACY** 8
153 **RUSSIE WITH LOVE** C 18
124 **RUTHLESS ARTICLE** (IRE) 20
170 **RUX RUXX** (IRE) 83
256 **RWANDA** 19
463 **RYALEX** (IRE) 72
378 **RYDAN** (IRE) 106
1 **RYEDALE RACER** 49
313 **SAABOOG** F 11
39 **SAAFY** 112
428 **SAAHEQ** 14
121 **SAARYAA** (IRE) 64
326 **SABAWEEYA** C 14
576 **SABBATHICAL** (FR) 70
503 **SABLE CAMP** 26
254 **SABLEROSE** F 185
304 **SABLET** 48
405 **SABRINA** (IRE) 133
334 **SACHAMAK** (FR) 16
316 **SACKETT** 34
455 **SACKFULLOFDREAMS** (IRE) 8
121 **SACRE BLEU** 65
117 **SACRE COEUR** F 98
540 **SACRE FLEUR** (IRE) C 37
242 **SACRED** 178
169 **SACRED ASPECT** (IRE) C 92
6 **SACRED DANCE** 93
257 **SACRED LEGACY** (IRE) 34
33 **SACRED SPRITE** 13
539 **SAD EYED DYLAN** 81
245 **SADDLERS QUEST** 11
190 **SADIIGAH** F 23
94 **SADLER'S SOUL** (USA) 18
14 **SADLERMOR** (IRE) 50
529 **SADLERS BEACH** (IRE) 13
324 **SADMA** 6
511 **SAEER** (IRE) 84
76 **SAFARJAL** (IRE) F 76
305 **SAFE HOUSE** (IRE) C 232
251 **SAFE PASSAGE** 220
444 **SAFE VOYAGE** (IRE) 21
340 **SAFFA GARDEN** (IRE) C 50
121 **SAFFRAN** (FR) 18
163 **SAFFRON LANE** 22
347 **SAFIRA MENINA** 11
29 **SAFIYNA** (FR) F 79
39 **SAFIYNA** (FR) F 167
299 **SAGA SPRINT** (IRE) 13
136 **SAGGAZZA** 12
392 **SAGLAWY** (FR) 169
364 **SAHARA SKY** (IRE) F 54
367 **SAHARAN SHIMMER** 23
141 **SAHHAB** (USA) 14
6 **SAHRAAH** (USA) F 203
321 **SAIGON SUZI** 14
553 **SAILING AWAY** (IRE) 1
511 **SAILOR** (GER) 141
23 **SAINT ARVANS** (FR) 27
572 **SAINT CALVADOS** (FR) 29

338 **SAINT DALINA** (FR) 50
405 **SAINT DE REVE** (FR) 134
515 **SAINT DE VASSY** (FR) 23
463 **SAINT FREULE** (FR) 73
585 **SAINT JUDE** (IRE) 4
524 **SAINT LEO** (FR) 27
7 **SAINT MAC** 78
374 **SAINT PATRIC** 55
392 **SAINT ROI** (FR) 170
405 **SAINT SONNET** (FR) 135
405 **SAINT XAVIER** (FR) 136
411 **SAINTBURY LADY** 76
388 **SAINTE DOCTOR** (FR) 83
577 **SAINTE KADETTE** (FR) M 76
405 **SAINTEMILION** (FR) 137
412 **SAISONS D'OR** (IRE) 27
121 **SAJJHAA** F 101
71 **SAKANDI** 8
317 **SAKHEE'S CITY** (FR) 64
391 **SAKHEE'S CONQUEST** 32
6 **SAKURA PETAL** 94
251 **SALACIA** (IRE) F 221
542 **SALAD DAYS** (FR) 9
465 **SALAM YA FAISAL** (IRE) 67
383 **SALAM ZAYED** 12
305 **SALAMANCA SCHOOL** (FR) 116
465 **SALATEEN** 24
537 **SALAYEL** 24
135 **SALAZAR** (IRE) 17
392 **SALDIER** (FR) 171
91 **SALEH** (IRE) 17
101 **SALIGO BAY** (IRE) 97
47 **SALINAS GRANDE** (FR) 20
557 **SALKEEV** (IRE) 55
418 **SALLY CAN'T WAIT** 28
215 **SALLY HOPE** 13
323 **SALLY IS THE BOSS** F 68
97 **SALMON PLEASE** (FR) 19
103 **SALOCIN** (FR) 37
239 **SALONNIERE** 27
318 **SALOUEN** (IRE) 10
409 **SALSA** (IRE) 89
321 **SALSA DIP** (IRE) 15
305 **SALSA STEPS** (USA) C 233
140 **SALSA VERDE** (IRE) 14
412 **SALSADA** (IRE) 47
392 **SALSARETTA** (FR) 172
26 **SALTIE GIRL** 15
51 **SALTMARKET** 13
572 **SALTO CHISCO** (IRE) 30
370 **SALUTI** (IRE) 26
34 **SALVE DEL RIO** (IRE) 17
327 **SAM BARTON** 56
283 **SAM BROWN** 31
135 **SAM CHISOLM** (IRE) 18
29 **SAM COOKE** (IRE) 29
266 **SAM MIGUEL** 1
412 **SAM SPINNER** 28
175 **SAM'S ADVENTURE** 42
169 **SAM'S CALL** 74
169 **SAM'S GUNNER** 42
511 **SAMAAH** (IRE) F 142
537 **SAMAAWAAT** (IRE) 95
529 **SAMARITAINE** 28
212 **SAMARQUAND** 67
101 **SAMBA BRAZIL** (GER) C 98
21 **SAMBARINA** (IRE) F 23
388 **SAMBELLA** 84

162 **SAMBORA GIRL** 64
370 **SAMBUCCA SPIRIT** 27
274 **SAMBURU SHUJAA** (FR) 86
356 **SAME CIRCUS** (IRE) 92
516 **SAMEEM** (IRE) 5
405 **SAMETEGAL** (FR) 138
227 **SAMI BEAR** 40
393 **SAMILLE** (IRE) 52
511 **SAMIRA GOLD** (FR) C 143
480 **SAMMY BILL** 40
29 **SAMMY SUNSHINE** (GER) 135
363 **SAMMYLOU** (IRE) 49
146 **SAMOVAR** 18
244 **SAMPERS SEVEN** (IRE) 50
476 **SAMPHIRE COAST** 17
382 **SAMS PROFILE** 21
568 **SAMSTOWN** 33
308 **SAMTARA** 31
397 **SAMTU** (IRE) 10
373 **SAMUEL JACKSON** 5
405 **SAN BENEDETO** (FR) 139
309 **SAN CARLOS** 12
537 **SAN DONATO** (IRE) 25
97 **SAN FABRIZIO** (FR) 14
97 **SAN HUBERTO** (IRE) 20
409 **SAN PEDRO** (IRE) 90
378 **SAN PEDRO DE SENAM** (FR) 107
170 **SAN ROCH** (FR) 142
315 **SAN RUMOLDO** 107
162 **SAN SEBASTIAN** (IRE) 16
573 **SANAADH** 11
392 **SANCTA SIMONA** (FR) 173
84 **SANCTIFIED** 46
434 **SAND AND DELIVER** F 14
120 **SAND DIEGO** (IRE) 3
101 **SAND IN MY SHOES** (FR) 99
120 **SAND JUNE** 4
189 **SANDFORD CASTLE** (IRE) 31
246 **SANDHURST LAD** 6
260 **SANDRET** (IRE) 30
464 **SANDRIDGE LAD** (IRE) 9
533 **SANDS CHORUS** 7
181 **SANDS COVE** (IRE) 15
186 **SANDS OF GIZA** (FR) 119
305 **SANDS OF TIME** 234
527 **SANDS SOUCI** 2
526 **SANDY BEACH** 93
274 **SANDY BOY** (IRE) 87
291 **SANDY HEARTBEAT** 30
97 **SANDY LIGHT** (FR) F 111
212 **SANDY MARASCHINO** (IRE) 68
582 **SANDY STEVE** 35
356 **SANDY STREET** 93
94 **SANDY TIMES** (IRE) F 107
107 **SANDYMAN** 11
388 **SANDYMOUNT ROSE** (IRE) 85
511 **SANGARIUS** 17
395 **SANGHA RIVER** (IRE) 88
304 **SANKALPA** 71
146 **SANS SOUCI BAY** 19
557 **SANSEVERO** (IRE) 56
503 **SANTA TERESA** (IRE) C 54
409 **SANTIAGO** (IRE) 91
34 **SANTIBURI SPIRIT** 34
268 **SANTINI** 133
315 **SANTON** (IRE) 108
60 **SANTORINI SAL** 18
405 **SAO** (FR) 140

184 **SAO MAXENCE** (FR) 33
94 **SAONA ISLAND** C 108
426 **SAPPHIRE JUBILEE** 8
392 **SAPPHIRE LADY** (IRE) 174
180 **SAPPHIRE LAKE** (IRE) C 54
159 **SAPPHIRE PEARL** (IRE) 13
361 **SAPPHIRE STAR** 7
193 **SAPPHIRE WATERS** (IRE) C 12
6 **SAQQARA KING** (USA) 95
97 **SAQR** (FR) 112
61 **SAQUEBOUTE** (FR) 28
567 **SAQUON** (IRE) 9
379 **SARACEN STAR** 17
334 **SARAH BERRY** G 17
169 **SARAH BERRY** F 93
548 **SARAH PARK** (IRE) C 37
257 **SARAH'S VERSE** 35
242 **SARAHA** C 179
29 **SARAMENHA** 136
215 **SARAS HOPE** 19
220 **SARASOTA** (IRE) 9
308 **SARASOTA STAR** (IRE) 32
272 **SARATOGA GOLD** 109
254 **SARAWATI** C 186
121 **SARAY PRINCE** (IRE) 102
188 **SARAYAAT** (IRE) 51
537 **SARDINIA SUNSET** (IRE) 182
106 **SARI MAREIS** 5
233 **SARIM** (IRE) 53
537 **SARLISA** (IRE) F 183
385 **SARRDAR** (IRE) 17
444 **SARSANET** (IRE) 43
214 **SARTAJ** (USA) 32
542 **SARU** C 13
472 **SARVAN** 18
225 **SARVI** 25
524 **SARYSHAGANN** (FR) 28
87 **SAS** (IRE) G 50
438 **SASHCORD** 8
318 **SASHENKA** (GER) 11
169 **SASSIE** (IRE) 43
418 **SASTRUGA** (IRE) 29
57 **SATCHVILLE FLYER** 13
409 **SATIN AND SILK** (IRE) 92
62 **SATIN PRINCESS** (IRE) F 25
244 **SATIN SLIPPER** (IRE) 51
112 **SATIS HOUSE** 19
511 **SATONO CHEVALIER** (IRE) 144
511 **SATONO JAPAN** (JPN) 85
189 **SATOSHI** (IRE) 32
117 **SATSUMA** F 99
472 **SATULAGI** (USA) F 19
577 **SATURDAYNIGHTFEVER** 77
475 **SATURN 'N SILK** 32
121 **SATURN GIRL** (IRE) F 66
392 **SATURNAS** (FR) 175
499 **SATWA RUBY** (FR) F 54
64 **SAUCHIEHALL STREET** (IRE) 14
428 **SAUCY ENCORE** 35
274 **SAUCY POEM** (IRE) 88
249 **SAUCY SALLY** (IRE) 54
94 **SAULIRE STAR** (IRE) 109
251 **SAUNTON** (IRE) 222
214 **SAURON'S EYE** 33
16 **SAUVIGNON** 24
186 **SAVAGE BEAUTY** (IRE) 120
116 **SAVALAS** (IRE) 19
422 **SAVANNA GOLD** (IRE) 46

146 **SAVANNAH BEAU** 20
30 **SAVEASEA** 89
91 **SAVITAR** (IRE) 18
258 **SAVLAD** 8
10 **SAVOY BROWN** 26
38 **SAVOY COURT** (IRE) 17
18 **SAWPIT SIENNA** 10
76 **SAWWAAH** 12
133 **SAXA VORD** 14
331 **SAXO JACK** (FR) 23
158 **SAY A PRAYER** F 22
165 **SAY IF I CAN** 10
186 **SAY IT SIMPLE** 121
321 **SAY IT'S ME** 10
326 **SAY NO NOW** (IRE) C 25
162 **SAY NOTHING** 17
221 **SAY THE WORD** 63
428 **SAYIFYOUWILL** 44
392 **SAYO** 176
496 **SAZERAK** (IRE) 49
392 **SCAGLIETTI** (IRE) 177
501 **SCALAMBRA** F 29
540 **SCALERO** (USA) 14
378 **SCALLYWAGTAIL** (IRE) 144
384 **SCANNING** 9
405 **SCARAMANGA** (IRE) 141
189 **SCARAMUCCI** (IRE) 33
538 **SCARBOROUGH CASTLE** 15
384 **SCARBOROUGH FAIR** F 68
572 **SCARDINO** (FR) 31
388 **SCARDURA** (IRE) 86
132 **SCARLET BEAR** (IRE) 75
378 **SCARLET COUTURE** 108
315 **SCARLET DRAGON** 109
516 **SCARLET PIMPERNEL** F 92
468 **SCARLET RED** 5
101 **SCARLET RUBY** 51
531 **SCARLETT O'HALO** 14
534 **SCARLETT OF TARA** 72
461 **SCARLETTE D'OR** G 23
392 **SCARPETA** (IRE) 178
268 **SCARPIA** (IRE) 134
219 **SCARTARE** (IRE) 8
315 **SCEAU ROYAL** (IRE) 110
338 **SCENE NOT HERD** (IRE) 51
10 **SCENIC LADY** 27
10 **SCENT OF AMBER** 59
228 **SCENTASIA** 26
169 **SCENTED GARDEN** C 94
84 **SCEPTRED ISLE** 35
368 **SCHALKE** 38
213 **SCHAP** 3
186 **SCHERZO** 122
325 **SCHIAPARANNIE** 6
249 **SCHIEHALLION MUNRO** 55
506 **SCHIEHALLION RIDGE** (IRE) 10
304 **SCHILTHORN** 72
437 **SCHMOOZIE** (IRE) 31
142 **SCHNABEL** (IRE) 29
365 **SCHOOL BOY HOURS** (IRE) 102
516 **SCHOOL OF THOUGHT** 39
413 **SCHUMLI** 85
286 **SCHWARTZ** (IRE) 60
116 **SCIACCA** (IRE) F 52
117 **SCIARRA** C 100
180 **SCOFFLAW** 18
518 **SCOOBY** (IRE) 18
17 **SCOOP** (IRE) 180

260 **SCOOP THE POT** (IRE) 31
29 **SCOPE** (IRE) 137
368 **SCORCHED BREATH** 39
484 **SCORCHED EARTH** (IRE) 98
493 **SCORCHIN** 44
550 **SCORPIO'S DREAM** 22
512 **SCORPION HAZE** (IRE) 24
523 **SCORPO** (IRE) 9
534 **SCOTCHTOWN** (IRE) 73
17 **SCOTS FERN** F 181
225 **SCOTS SONNET** 27
341 **SCOTSBROOK NIGHT** 7
341 **SCOTSBROOK RHULA** 8
368 **SCOTTISH ACCENT** (IRE) 40
383 **SCOTTISH BLADE** (IRE) 13
252 **SCOTTISH SUMMIT** (IRE) 4
588 **SCOTTSDALE** 8
89 **SCRAFTON** 59
503 **SCREAM BLUE MURDER** (IRE) F 55
211 **SCREECHING DRAGON** (IRE) 35
188 **SCRIBONIA** F 80
137 **SCRUTINISE** 21
214 **SCUDAMORE** (FR) 58
506 **SCULLYS FORGE** (IRE) 11
82 **SE YOU** 5
444 **SEA ART** 22
39 **SEA BAY** 113
10 **SEA BRIGHT** 41
39 **SEA CAVE** 114
63 **SEA CREST** C 25
157 **SEA DESTINATION** (IRE) 9
377 **SEA DUCOR** 11
568 **SEA EWE** 41
180 **SEA FOX** (IRE) 19
175 **SEA ME WIN** (IRE) 43
242 **SEA MOOD** (FR) 101
163 **SEA OF CHARM** (FR) 38
464 **SEA OF COOL** (IRE) 18
242 **SEA OF FAITH** (IRE) 23
239 **SEA OF MARIA** 21
305 **SEA OF MARMOON** 117
7 **SEA OF MYSTERY** (IRE) 79
169 **SEA OF SHADOWS** 75
242 **SEA OF STYLE** (IRE) 102
243 **SEA PRINCE** 24
17 **SEA SCULPTURE** 42
190 **SEA SHACK** 11
503 **SEA SIREN** (AUS) C 56
395 **SEA SISTER** (IRE) 89
577 **SEA SOVEREIGN** (IRE) 78
158 **SEA STORM** 9
14 **SEA STORY** 51
589 **SEA TEA DEA** 14
272 **SEA THE GLORY** 57
305 **SEA THE SHELLS** 235
29 **SEA THE SIX** 80
394 **SEA THE SPIRIT** 22
54 **SEA THE SUN** (GER) C 24
420 **SEA THE WAVES** 19
376 **SEA TIDE** 16
509 **SEA TROUT** 11
242 **SEA TROUT REACH** (IRE) 103
62 **SEA WHISPER** G 26
501 **SEA WILLOW** 21
273 **SEA'S ARIA** (IRE) 4
93 **SEABORN** (IRE) 13
521 **SEABOROUGH** (IRE) 14
323 **SEACHANGE** (FR) 45

465 **SEACLUSION** 103
251 **SEADANCE** 107
529 **SEAFARER** (IRE) 14
589 **SEAFORTH** (IRE) 15
323 **SEAMIA** 46
175 **SEAMOUR** (IRE) 44
308 **SEANA GHAEL** (IRE) G 40
206 **SEAPOINT** (IRE) 11
166 **SEAPORT** 8
34 **SEAQUINN** 18
368 **SEARANGER** (USA) 41
39 **SEARCH FOR LIGHT** (IRE) 37
255 **SEARCHING** (IRE) 16
413 **SEAS OF ELZAAM** (IRE) 86
254 **SEAS OF WELLS** C 187
232 **SEASEARCH** 3
424 **SEASIDE GIRL** (IRE) 68
583 **SEASONSELITE** G 61
305 **SEASONY** (IRE) 118
480 **SEASTON SPIRIT** 41
416 **SEATON CAREW** (IRE) 80
419 **SEATONE** (USA) F 73
318 **SEATTLE ROCK** 37
440 **SEB'S SISTER** (IRE) 15
424 **SEBASTIAN BEACH** (IRE) 69
322 **SEBASTOPOL** (IRE) 28
373 **SECOND CAPTAIN** (IRE) 6
89 **SECOND COLLECTION** 60
188 **SECOND SLIP** (IRE) 52
97 **SECOND TO NONE** (IRE) 113
508 **SECONDO** (IRE) 20
309 **SECRATARIO** (FR) 13
321 **SECRET ACQUISITION** 16
6 **SECRET ADVISOR** (FR) 25
378 **SECRET ART** (IRE) 109
514 **SECRET BERI** 37
439 **SECRET BOX** 58
409 **SECRET CHARM** (IRE) C 177
144 **SECRET COURT** (IRE) 16
88 **SECRET DIARY** 21
169 **SECRET DREAM** (IRE) C 95
220 **SECRET EQUITY** 15
386 **SECRET ERA** C 37
6 **SECRET GESTURE** F 204
589 **SECRET GLANCE** 16
242 **SECRET HAUNT** 180
39 **SECRET HINT** F 168
390 **SECRET IDENTITY** 22
405 **SECRET INVESTOR** 142
135 **SECRET MELODY** 19
39 **SECRET MOMENT** (IRE) 115
265 **SECRET PALACE** 9
257 **SECRET POTION** 23
405 **SECRET POTION** (GER) 143
17 **SECRET PURSUIT** (IRE) F 182
576 **SECRET REPRIEVE** (IRE) 71
97 **SECRET TIME** (GER) 62
165 **SECRET TREATIES** 11
465 **SECRET VENTURE** 25
6 **SECRET VICTORY** 96
323 **SECRETE** (FR) F 69
297 **SECRETE STREAM** (IRE) 23
468 **SECRETFACT** 6
390 **SECRETINTHEPARK** 16
221 **SEDDON** (IRE) 64
173 **SEDGE WREN** 39
17 **SEE EMILY PLAY** (IRE) C 183
411 **SEE FOREVER** (IRE) 77

569 **SEE MY BABY JIVE** 19
179 **SEE THE CITY** (IRE) 12
356 **SEE THE SEA** (IRE) 94
162 **SEE YOU LATER** C 65
473 **SEEANYTHINGYOULIKE** (IRE) 32
587 **SEEDLESS** F 8
405 **SEELOTMOREBUSINESS** (IRE) 144
395 **SEEMINGLY SO** (IRE) 90
524 **SEEMORELIGHTS** (IRE) 29
398 **SEERAJ** 3
243 **SEEUBACKINCOPPERS** (IRE) 25
484 **SEEUSOON** (IRE) 99
365 **SEEYOUINVINNYS** (IRE) 103
251 **SEFAAT** F 223
499 **SEFTON WARRIOR** 37
413 **SEGARELLI** (IRE) 43
189 **SEHAYLI** (IRE) 34
359 **SEI BELLA** 2
320 **SEINESATIONAL** 6
73 **SEIZE THE TIME** (IRE) 64
101 **SELECTO** 52
73 **SELF ASSESSMENT** (IRE) 17
385 **SELF CENTRED** C 18
367 **SELFARA** C 39
188 **SELINO** 17
169 **SELKA** (FR) C 96
472 **SELL OUT** C 39
365 **SELLARBRIDGE** (IRE) 104
536 **SELLINGALLTHETIME** (IRE) 16
320 **SELSEY SIZZLER** 26
242 **SELYL** F 181
364 **SEMARAL** (IRE) F 55
251 **SEMAYYEL** (IRE) C 224
537 **SEMSER** 96
251 **SENADORA** (GER) C 225
186 **SENDACARD** 123
583 **SENDHERVICTORIA'S** (IRE) 62
405 **SENDING LOVE** (IRE) 145
244 **SENDMYLOVETOYOU** (IRE) 14
321 **SENECA CHIEF** 9
315 **SENIOR CITIZEN** 111
48 **SENNEN** 16
128 **SENOR LOMBARDY** (IRE) 57
384 **SENSATIONALLY** C 69
503 **SENSE OF CLASS** (IRE) 17
6 **SENSE OF FUN** (USA) F 205
580 **SENSULANO** (IRE) 20
305 **SENT FROM HEAVEN** (IRE) C 236
409 **SENTA'S DREAM** F 178
242 **SENTARIL** C 182
97 **SENTILLY** (IRE) F 114
192 **SEOLAN** (IRE) F 71
501 **SEPAHI** 11
128 **SEPAL** (USA) 58
251 **SEPARATE** 108
315 **SEPHTON** 112
393 **SEPRANI** 29
221 **SEPTEMBER DAISY** 65
537 **SEPTEMBER POWER** (IRE) 97
49 **SERAPHIM** 15
296 **SERAPHINITE** (IRE) 15
540 **SERBELLONI** (IRE) 38
132 **SEREN DEVIOUS** C 76
214 **SERENA'S PRIDE** F 71
29 **SERENA'S QUEEN** (IRE) 138
29 **SERENA'S SYMPHONY** (IRE) 139
188 **SERENADING** 18
6 **SERENE BEAUTY** (USA) C 206

254 **SERENE SPIRIT** (IRE) 124
305 **SERENGETI STAR** 119
107 **SERENHILL** 37
254 **SERENISA** 61
555 **SERENITY DOVE** F 31
540 **SERGEANT** (FR) 28
156 **SERGEANT BRODY** 17
572 **SERGEANT O'LEARY** (IRE) 32
452 **SERIOUS EGO** (GER) 42
325 **SERIOUS MOOD** (IRE) 7
449 **SERJEANT PAINTER** 2
416 **SERMANDO** (FR) 81
132 **SERMON** (IRE) 45
234 **SEROSEVSKY** (IRE) 93
409 **SERPENTINE** (IRE) 93
400 **SERVEONTIME** (IRE) 10
481 **SERVO** (IRE) 11
251 **SESAME BIRAH** (IRE) 109
17 **SET FIRE** (IRE) C 184
368 **SET IN STONE** (IRE) 42
268 **SETTIE HILL** (USA) 135
49 **SETTIMA LUNA** 53
26 **SETTING FORTH** (IRE) F 53
405 **SETTLE DOWN** (FR) 146
429 **SETTLE PETAL** 5
323 **SEULOMONDE** 70
480 **SEVARANO** (GER) 42
493 **SEVEN ARCHES** 45
533 **SEVEN CLANS** (IRE) 8
577 **SEVEN DE BAUNE** (FR) 79
480 **SEVEN EVEN** (FR) G 43
412 **SEVEN FOR A POUND** (USA) 29
529 **SEVEN MAGICIANS** (USA) C 50
73 **SEVEN VEILS** (IRE) C 105
464 **SEVENNA STAR** (IRE) 10
30 **SEVENTEEN O FOUR** (IRE) 45
172 **SEVENTII** 8
94 **SEVERANCE** 19
511 **SEXTANT** 18
140 **SEXY BEAST** 15
435 **SEXY LOT** (GER) 64
425 **SEXY SECRET** 7
446 **SEYMOUR SOX** 35
404 **SFUMATO** 3
132 **SHA LA LA LEE** 16
76 **SHABAABY** 13
29 **SHABABIYA** 140
537 **SHABANDOZ** 184
356 **SHABBA DADA DO** (IRE) 95
383 **SHABEEB** (USA) 14
507 **SHADARPOUR** (IRE) 4
42 **SHADDEYA** (IRE) C 16
465 **SHADEN** (IRE) C 104
117 **SHADES OF BLUE** (IRE) 18
524 **SHADES OF MIDNIGHT** 30
318 **SHADES OF RED** 38
17 **SHADN** (IRE) 109
17 **SHADOW DANCING** C 185
304 **SHADOW GLEN** 49
150 **SHADOW LEADER** 45
540 **SHADOW STAR** (GER) 29
431 **SHADOW WALKER** (IRE) 26
335 **SHADOW'S GIRL** 15
234 **SHADY CHARACTER** 36
251 **SHADY COVE** 226
363 **SHADY GLEN** (IRE) 50
577 **SHADY MCCOY** (USA) 80

89 **SHOWU** 61
182 **SHREWD TACTICS** (IRE) 3
540 **SHRUBLAND** 17
272 **SHURAFFA** (IRE) 59
227 **SHUT THE BOX** (IRE) 41
498 **SHUTTHEGATE** (IRE) 11
412 **SHUTTLECOCK** F 59
419 **SHY APPEAL** (IRE) C 33
437 **SHY APPEAL** (IRE) F 56
499 **SHY AUDIENCE** (IRE) C 55
165 **SHYARCH** 12
526 **SHYBAIRNSGETNOWT** (IRE) 97
165 **SHYJACK** 13
349 **SHYMAY** 11
91 **SHYRON** 19
6 **SIAMSAIOCHT** (IRE) F 207
175 **SIANNES STAR** (IRE) 46
530 **SIBAYA** C 30
547 **SIBERIAN NIGHT** (IRE) 70
179 **SIBLE HEDINGHAM** 13
348 **SID HOODIE** (IRE) 17
128 **SIDI ISMAEL** (FR) 59
238 **SIDSTEEL** 17
123 **SIEGE OF BOSTON** (IRE) 9
319 **SIEMPRE RAPIDO** 16
317 **SIENA MIA** 67
568 **SIENNA DREAM** 34
244 **SIENNA LADY** (IRE) 52
473 **SIENNA ROYALE** (IRE) 33
73 **SIESTA TIME** C 107
422 **SIGLO SIX** 14
576 **SIGN OF WAR** (IRE) 72
320 **SIGNAL TWENTY NINE** 27
463 **SIGNIFIANT** (FR) 75
465 **SIGNORA QUEEN** (FR) F 105
192 **SIGNS AND SIGNALS** (IRE) C 73
105 **SIGNSEALDELIVERED** 3
206 **SIGURD** (GER) 12
244 **SILAIYLI** (IRE) 95
323 **SILASTAR** 47
97 **SILENCE** 115
254 **SILENCE PLEASE** (IRE) 126
327 **SILENT ASSISTANT** (IRE) 59
89 **SILENT ATTACK** 62
267 **SILENT ECHO** 4
92 **SILENT ENCORE** (IRE) 26
39 **SILENT ESCAPE** (IRE) 118
371 **SILENT FLAME** 50
39 **SILENT HUNTER** 38
305 **SILENT MOMENT** (USA) C 240
529 **SILENT PARTNER** 29
422 **SILENT PERFORMANCE** (IRE) 48
316 **SILENT STEPS** (IRE) 35
547 **SILENT WITNESS** (IRE) 20
192 **SILIRISA** (FR) C 74
570 **SILK MILL BLUE** 9
1 **SILK OR SCARLET** (IRE) 50
39 **SILK WORDS** C 170
485 **SILKSTONE** (IRE) 15
305 **SILKWOOD** F 241
493 **SILVA ECLIPSE** 48
378 **SILVER CLIFFS** (IRE) 145
326 **SILVER DESERT** (IRE) 12
215 **SILVER DIVA** 24
186 **SILVER DUST** (IRE) 45
405 **SILVER FOREVER** (IRE) 147
409 **SILVER FOX** (IRE) 95
422 **SILVER GAMES** (IRE) F 91

394 **SILVER GRACE** (IRE) 23
411 **SILVER HALLMARK** 78
67 **SILVER HALO** G 6
84 **SILVER HALO** C 47
539 **SILVER IN DISGUISE** 83
14 **SILVER KAYF** 55
39 **SILVER LINE** (IRE) 39
557 **SILVER MACHINE** 59
290 **SILVER MARIZAH** F 12
186 **SILVER MISSION** (IRE) 125
391 **SILVER NICKEL** (IRE) 35
210 **SILVER QUAY** (IRE) 16
60 **SILVER REFLECTION** 23
39 **SILVER RIVER** 40
49 **SILVER SAMURAI** 54
254 **SILVER SHEEN** (IRE) 62
170 **SILVER SNIPER** 144
576 **SILVER STREAK** (IRE) 73
249 **SILVER TASSIE** (IRE) 56
117 **SILVER TIDE** (USA) F 102
89 **SILVERTURNSTOGOLD** 63
355 **SIMBA SAMBA** 7
417 **SIMBIRSK** 16
255 **SIMON THE GREAT** 17
132 **SIMONETTA** (IRE) F 47
73 **SIMONS KING** (IRE) 108
367 **SIMPLETWISTOF FATE** (USA) 12
409 **SIMPLY A STAR** (IRE) C 180
305 **SIMPLY AMAZING** 242
16 **SIMPLY LOVELY** (IRE) 49
497 **SIMPLY LUCKY** (IRE) 10
406 **SIMPLY MANI** 6
406 **SIMPLY MYSTIC** F 7
452 **SIMPLY NED** (IRE) 44
388 **SIMPLY SIN** (IRE) 88
572 **SIMPLY THE BETTS** (IRE) 38
244 **SIMSIR** (IRE) 16
469 **SIMUL AMICIS** 15
472 **SIMULATION THEORY** (IRE) 40
282 **SINA** (GER) G 12
244 **SINAWANN** (IRE) 53
317 **SINCERELY RESDEV** 68
188 **SINCERITY** 19
244 **SINDHIA** (IRE) 54
465 **SINDIRANA** (IRE) C 106
331 **SINFONIETTA** (FR) 24
476 **SING BERTIE** (IRE) 18
344 **SING OUT LOUD** (IRE) 11
578 **SINGAMINNIE** (FR) C 18
274 **SINGAPORE SAGA** 90
429 **SINGER IN THE SAND** (IRE) 16
547 **SINGING SHERIFF** 21
371 **SINGING THE BLUES** (IRE) 12
169 **SINGITTA** C 98
94 **SINGLE** (IRE) 64
221 **SINGLEFARMPAYMENT** 66
27 **SINGMAN** (IRE) 22
47 **SINGSTREET** (FR) 8
534 **SINISTER MINISTER** 74
375 **SINISTRY** 10
242 **SINJAARI** (IRE) 24
280 **SINNDARELLA** (IRE) 11
207 **SIONNACH RUA** 10
295 **SIOUX FRONTIER** (IRE) 34
547 **SIPHON MELODY** (USA) F 100
320 **SIR BUSKER** (IRE) 8
512 **SIR CANFORD** (IRE) 26
540 **SIR CHANCEALOT** (IRE) 30

170 **SIR CHARLES PUNCH** 145
225 **SIR CHAUVELIN** 28
176 **SIR DANCEALOT** (IRE) 10
541 **SIR DANDY** 42
512 **SIR DENNIS** 27
409 **SIR DRAGONET** (IRE) 13
241 **SIR DYLAN** 8
322 **SIR EGBERT** 29
146 **SIR GEOFFREY** (IRE) 21
492 **SIR GORDON** 5
12 **SIR HAMILTON** (IRE) 9
186 **SIR HAVELOCK** (IRE) 126
550 **SIR HECTOR** (IRE) 5
89 **SIR I'LL CHANCE IT** (IRE) 88
212 **SIR IVAN** 70
499 **SIR JACK YEATS** (IRE) 14
297 **SIR JIM** (IRE) 3
305 **SIR JOHN BOWDLER** (IRE) 243
16 **SIR JOSEPH SWAN** 50
89 **SIR MAGNUM** 64
577 **SIR MAXIMILIAN** (IRE) 84
97 **SIR OLAF** (IRE) 116
286 **SIR OLIVER** (IRE) 34
371 **SIR PLATO** (IRE) 13
291 **SIR PRIZE** 31
405 **SIR PSYCHO** (IRE) 148
371 **SIR RODERIC** (IRE) 14
299 **SIR RODNEYREDBLOOD** 28
305 **SIR RON PRIESTLEY** 25
251 **SIR RUMI** (IRE) 230
249 **SIR RUNS A LOT** 57
268 **SIR SHOLOKHOV** (IRE) 137
561 **SIR TAAJ** 3
563 **SIR TEN** T 48
434 **SIR THOMAS GRESHAM** (IRE) 6
534 **SIR VALENTINE** (GER) 75
24 **SIRBOWTIEMAN** (GER) 19
94 **SIRI** C 110
12 **SIRIUS SLEW** 10
460 **SIRIUS STAR** 5
572 **SIROBBIE** (IRE) 39
218 **SIROP DE MENTHE** (FR) 9
579 **SIRUH DU LAC** (FR) 20
524 **SIRWILLIAMWALLACE** (IRE) 31
537 **SISTER DAM'S** (IRE) C 186
319 **SISTER GURU** G 17
225 **SISTER MIDNIGHT** (IRE) 29
506 **SISTER SHANNON** (IRE) G 12
439 **SISU** 59
305 **SITARA** C 244
323 **SITOUTVABIEN** (FR) 48
243 **SITRON** 27
35 **SIX GUN SERENADE** (IRE) 20
230 **SIX ONE NINE** (IRE) 29
7 **SIX STRINGS** 81
62 **SIX TIL TWELVE** (IRE) 27
384 **SIXPENNY SWEETS** (IRE) C 70
365 **SIXSHOOTER** (IRE) 106
168 **SIXTH OF JUNE** 8
469 **SIXTIES GLENARK** 16
564 **SIXTIES IDOL** 11
564 **SIXTIES SECRET** 14
187 **SIXTIES STAR** 6
515 **SIXTY'S BELLE** 24
486 **SIYAHAMBA** (IRE) 16
97 **SIYOUNOW** (IRE) 117
473 **SIZABLE SAM** 34
497 **SIZE MATTERS** 11

526 **SIZING AT MIDNIGHT** (IRE) 98
526 **SIZING CODELCO** (IRE) 99
526 **SIZING CUSIMANO** 100
526 **SIZING GRANITE** (IRE) 101
382 **SIZING JOSHUA** (IRE) 22
526 **SIZING PLATINUM** (IRE) 102
254 **SIZING POTTSIE** 63
254 **SIZING POTTSIE** (FR) 64
526 **SIZING TARA** 103
526 **SIZING TENNESSEE** (IRE) 104
368 **SKA RIDGE** 45
395 **SKANDIBURG** (FR) 91
242 **SKARDU** 25
499 **SKATERBOI** 56
405 **SKATMAN** (IRE) 149
369 **SKEAPING** 4
444 **SKEETAH** 23
188 **SKERRYVORE** 20
576 **SKEWIFF** 74
526 **SKIBET** (FR) 105
317 **SKID** (IRE) F 69
452 **SKIDDAW TARA** 45
452 **SKIDDAW VALLEYS** 46
381 **SKIPPING ON** (IRE) 17
363 **SKIPTHECUDDLES** (IRE) 51
112 **SKIPTHESCALES** (IRE) 20
499 **SKONTONOVICH** 38
516 **SKY COMMANDER** (IRE) 40
49 **SKY CRYSTAL** (GER) F 79
305 **SKY DEFENDER** 26
227 **SKY FULL OF STARS** (IRE) 42
463 **SKY KHAN** 76
49 **SKY LAKE** (GER) 55
416 **SKY PIRATE** 83
251 **SKY POWER** (IRE) 111
244 **SKY SEVEN** (IRE) 17
384 **SKY STORM** 41
560 **SKYE CHIEF** 7
169 **SKYE DREAMING** (FR) 76
246 **SKYHILL** (IRE) 7
416 **SKYLANA BREEZE** (IRE) 84
183 **SKYLARK LADY** (IRE) 13
212 **SKYLARK NINETEEN** (IRE) 71
537 **SKYLINER** 187
444 **SKYLLA** G 45
536 **SKYLLACHY** 21
29 **SKYMAX** (GER) 30
242 **SKYRUNNER** (IRE) 184
242 **SKYTREE** 185
97 **SKYWARD** (FR) 21
460 **SKYWARDS MILES** (IRE) G 10
460 **SKYWARDS MILES** (IRE) F 14
378 **SLADE KING** (IRE) 110
474 **SLADE STORM** (IRE) 9
463 **SLAINTE MHOR** (IRE) 77
148 **SLANELOUGH** (IRE) 34
230 **SLANEMORE HILL** (IRE) 30
221 **SLAP DASH HARRY** (IRE) 67
526 **SLATE HOUSE** (IRE) 106
54 **SLAVONIC DANCE** (IRE) 20
97 **SLEEK GOLD** F 118
331 **SLEEP EASY** 25
464 **SLEEPDANCER** (IRE) 11
188 **SLEEPING LION** (USA) 21
555 **SLEEPING SHADOW** C 32
83 **SLEEPY HAVEN** (IRE) 33
384 **SLEIGHT** 71
268 **SLEIGHT OF HAND** (IRE) 138

415 **SLEPTWITHMEBOOTSON** 5
251 **SLIABH LUACHRA** (IRE) C 231
244 **SLIEVE BEARNAGH** (IRE) 55
486 **SLINGSHOT** 31
519 **SLIP ROAD** (IRE) 20
565 **SLIPPER SATIN** (IRE) 17
424 **SLIPWAY** (IRE) 72
503 **SLOANE PETERSON** (IRE) 58
516 **SLOANE SQUARE** C 94
63 **SLOWMO** (IRE) 14
94 **SLY MINX** 65
395 **SMACKWATER JACK** (IRE) 92
392 **SMALL FARM** (IRE) 181
97 **SMALL FIRES** (FR) 119
192 **SMALL PIANIST** 51
493 **SMALL PRESENT** (IRE) 49
483 **SMART CHAMPION** 22
272 **SMART CONNECTION** (IRE) 60
395 **SMART GETAWAY** (IRE) 93
295 **SMART LASS** (IRE) 35
23 **SMART PACO** 28
327 **SMARTER** (IRE) 60
274 **SMARTY WILD** 91
497 **SMASHING LASS** (IRE) 12
191 **SMEATON** (IRE) 26
305 **SMILE A MILE** (IRE) 27
340 **SMILEY BAGEL** (IRE) 27
451 **SMITH** (IRE) 9
315 **SMITH'S BAY** 114
475 **SMITHS CROSS** (IRE) 34
192 **SMOKE ON THE WATER** 24
548 **SMOKE SHADOW** (IRE) 26
292 **SMOKEN ROSA** (USA) F 21
550 **SMOKEY** 23
101 **SMOKEY BEAR** (IRE) 53
180 **SMOKEY LANE** (IRE) 21
243 **SMOOTH STEPPER** 28
529 **SMUGGLER** 30
221 **SMUGGLER'S BLUES** (IRE) 68
148 **SMUGGLER'S STASH** (IRE) 35
361 **SMUGGLERS CREEK** (IRE) 8
227 **SMURPHY ENKI** (FR) 43
211 **SNAFEE TIGER** 24
511 **SNAPDRAGON** (USA) C 146
322 **SNAPDRAGON FIRE** (IRE) 30
117 **SNAZZY JAZZY** (IRE) 19
167 **SNEAKY FEELING** (IRE) 11
17 **SNEAKY PEEK** 45
292 **SNITCH** (IRE) 15
281 **SNOOKER JIM** 6
175 **SNOOKERED** (IRE) 47
356 **SNOUGAR** (IRE) 99
409 **SNOW** (IRE) 96
365 **SNOW FALCON** (IRE) 107
89 **SNOW LEOPARD** (IRE) 65
338 **SNOW LEOPARDESS** 54
180 **SNOW OCEAN** (IRE) 22
39 **SNOW POWDER** (IRE) C 171
511 **SNOW SHOWER** 86
305 **SNOW SPACE** (IRE) 28
251 **SNOWBALL JACKSON** 112
194 **SNOWBIRD** (IRE) 5
79 **SNOWED IN** (IRE) 7
503 **SNOWFIELDS** (IRE) C 27
65 **SNOWPIERCER** (FR) 5
251 **SNOWY AMOUR** (IRE) F 232
583 **SNUFF BOX** (IRE) 64
413 **SO BELOVED** 45

256 **SO CANNIE** F 20
386 **SO CLAIRE** 19
254 **SO DANDY** F 188
443 **SO DISCREET** C 10
286 **SO I TOLD YOU** (IRE) 35
121 **SO IMPRESSED** (IRE) 104
33 **SO LOVED** 15
530 **SO MACHO** (IRE) 11
295 **SO SATISFIED** 36
516 **SO SHARP** 41
386 **SO SPECIAL** 31
409 **SO WONDERFUL** (USA) 97
565 **SO YOU THOUGHT** (USA) 18
465 **SOAR** C 107
77 **SOAR ABOVE** 34
416 **SOARING GLORY** (IRE) 85
291 **SOARING SPIRITS** (IRE) 32
465 **SOARING STAR** (IRE) 69
461 **SOARLIKEANEAGLE** (IRE) 15
140 **SOBRIQUET** (IRE) 24
16 **SOCIAL** F 51
89 **SOCIAL CITY** 66
162 **SOCIAL MEDIA** F 66
381 **SOCIALIST AGENDA** 18
146 **SOCIALITES RED** 22
472 **SOCIALIZE** 21
73 **SOCIALLY SHADY** 65
94 **SOCIETY GUEST** (IRE) 20
511 **SOCIETY LION** 87
186 **SOCIETY QUEEN** (IRE) 46
186 **SOCIETY RED** 47
116 **SOCIETY STAR** 20
146 **SOCIOLOGIST** (FR) 23
169 **SOCRU** (IRE) 44
511 **SOFFIKA** (IRE) 88
484 **SOFIA'S ROCK** (FR) 102
318 **SOFT ICE** (IRE) C 39
169 **SOFT SUMMER RAIN** 45
286 **SOGHAN** (IRE) 9
393 **SOIS REBELLE** (FR) 53
283 **SOJOURN** (IRE) 33
133 **SOL DE MAYO** 16
580 **SOL PLUM CREEK** (IRE) 21
547 **SOLACE** (USA) C 101
323 **SOLANIA** (IRE) 71
511 **SOLAR CYCLE** (FR) 89
39 **SOLAR FLAME** (IRE) 119
10 **SOLAR PARK** (IRE) 29
537 **SOLAR SCREEN** (IRE) 99
511 **SOLAR STAR** (IRE) 90
405 **SOLDIER OF LOVE** 150
393 **SOLDIER ON PARADE** 54
328 **SOLDIER TO FOLLOW** 13
128 **SOLDIER'S MINUTE** 60
84 **SOLDIER'S SON** 13
416 **SOLDIEROFTHESTORM** (IRE) 105
73 **SOLEMN PLEDGE** 66
132 **SOLENT GATEWAY** (IRE) 77
548 **SOLFEGGIO** (IRE) 12
511 **SOLID STONE** (IRE) 20
109 **SOLID STRIKE** 2
388 **SOLIGHOSTER** (FR) 89
405 **SOLO** (FR) 151
146 **SOLO HUNTER** 24
260 **SOLO SAXOPHONE** (IRE) 32
164 **SOLOIST** (IRE) 35
484 **SOLOMON GREY** (FR) 103
566 **SOLSTALLA** 5

412 **SPINAMISS** (IRE) F 60
413 **SPINATRIX** F 124
1 **SPINNING AWAY** F 58
305 **SPINNING CLOUD** (USA) F 245
23 **SPINNING SCOOTER** 29
186 **SPIRIT DANCER** 127
17 **SPIRIT MIXER** 189
529 **SPIRIT OF ANGEL** (IRE) 15
75 **SPIRIT OF DREAMS** (IRE) 5
83 **SPIRIT OF HALE** (IRE) 35
319 **SPIRIT OF ISHY** 9
1 **SPIRIT OF KAYF** 51
295 **SPIRIT OF LUND** (IRE) 38
518 **SPIRIT OF MAY** 20
74 **SPIRIT OF ROME** (IRE) 9
312 **SPIRIT OF SARWAN** (IRE) 14
132 **SPIRIT OF SISRA** (IRE) 78
412 **SPIRIT OF SOUND** C 61
170 **SPIRIT OF SUCCESS** G 146
117 **SPIRIT OF THE BAY** 103
225 **SPIRIT OF THE SEA** (IRE) C 38
186 **SPIRIT OF THE SKY** 128
395 **SPIRIT OF WATERLOO** 95
81 **SPIRIT OF WEDZA** (IRE) 18
272 **SPIRIT OF WINNING** F 113
511 **SPIRIT OF XIAN** (IRE) C 147
5 **SPIRIT POWER** 10
17 **SPIRIT WARNING** 46
349 **SPIRITED GUEST** 6
593 **SPIRITOFCHARTWELL** 11
484 **SPIRITOFTHEGAMES** (IRE) 106
465 **SPIRITOFTHENORTH** (FR) 70
251 **SPIRITS HIGH** (FR) 113
521 **SPLASH OF VERVE** (IRE) 15
83 **SPLASH THE CASH** (IRE) 36
73 **SPLENDIDLY** 67
358 **SPLIT DOWN SOUTH** 9
188 **SPLIT TROIS** (FR) F 81
65 **SPOCK** (FR) 6
486 **SPONTANEITY** (IRE) C 46
519 **SPONTHUS** (FR) 21
272 **SPOOF** 18
189 **SPORTING BOY** 36
274 **SPORTING JOHN** (IRE) 92
128 **SPORTING PRESS** (IRE) 61
384 **SPOSABELLA** (IRE) 42
6 **SPOTIFY** (FR) 27
286 **SPOTLIGHT** C 62
27 **SPOTTON** (IRE) 23
262 **SPOTTY DOG** 7
54 **SPREADSHEET** (IRE) 21
286 **SPRING BLOOM** 68
30 **SPRING CAMPAIGN** (IRE) 48
54 **SPRING CLEAN** (FR) C 25
365 **SPRING CROCUS** C 152
84 **SPRING FLING** F 49
17 **SPRING GLOW** 112
554 **SPRING GODDESS** (IRE) F 15
57 **SPRING HOLLY** (IRE) 14
6 **SPRING OF LOVE** 98
291 **SPRING ROMANCE** (IRE) 33
437 **SPRING RUN** 9
164 **SPRING STEEL** (IRE) 36
546 **SPRING WOLF** 22
221 **SPRINGFIELD FOX** 69
39 **SPRINGLIKE** (IRE) C 173
274 **SPRINGTOWN LAKE** (IRE) 93
395 **SPRINGVALE** 96

340 **SPRINGVALE LAD** 45
169 **SPRITZERIA** F 99
272 **SPUROFTHEMOMENT** 61
408 **SPY FI** 7
249 **SQUARE VIVIANI** (FR) 58
582 **SQUASH** C 60
239 **SQUELCH** 7
251 **SRI SENE POWER** (IRE) 114
274 **ST BARTS** (IRE) 94
110 **ST BASIL** 19
254 **ST CLERANS** (IRE) 128
157 **ST ERNEY** 10
305 **ST FRANCIS WOOD** (USA) F 246
395 **ST GALLEN** (IRE) 97
547 **ST GEORGE'S BAY** 102
409 **ST JAMES'S SQUARE** (USA) 99
395 **ST LAWRENCE GAP** (IRE) 98
514 **ST MERRYN** (IRE) 4
540 **ST STEPHENS GREEN** (IRE) 18
40 **STAAR** (IRE) 8
243 **STACEY SUE** 29
529 **STACEYMAC** (IRE) C 52
534 **STADMALLEN** (IRE) 76
557 **STAG HORN** 60
17 **STAG PARTY** (IRE) 190
475 **STAGE STAR** (IRE) 155
29 **STAGIAIRE** 81
522 **STAINFORTH SWAGGER** 11
569 **STAINSBY GIRL** 20
268 **STAITHES** (IRE) 141
291 **STAKE ACCLAIM** (IRE) 34
103 **STAKING** (FR) 8
503 **STALINGRAD** 28
501 **STALLONE** (IRE) 12
98 **STAMFORD RAFFLES** 18
402 **STAMINA CHOPE** (FR) 59
221 **STAMP YOUR FEET** (IRE) 70
306 **STAND BY ME** (FR) 10
208 **STAND FREE** 7
39 **STAND STRONG** (IRE) 121
17 **STANFORD** (IRE) 113
30 **STANLEY BALDWIN** 90
101 **STANLEY STANLEY** 54
323 **STANZO** 49
583 **STAR ACADEMY** (IRE) 65
365 **STAR ADVENTURE** (IRE) 108
375 **STAR APPROACH** (IRE) 19
169 **STAR ARCHER** 46
83 **STAR ASCENDING** (IRE) 37
228 **STAR CATCHER** 2
558 **STAR CITIZEN** 8
106 **STAR COMMAND** (IRE) 9
225 **STAR CRACKER** (IRE) 31
192 **STAR DREAMER** 54
117 **STAR IN THE MAKING** 55
512 **STAR OF ATHENA** 28
228 **STAR OF BENGAL** 35
503 **STAR OF CASHEL** 29
233 **STAR OF LANKA** 55
238 **STAR OF RORY** (IRE) 18
323 **STAR OF SAINTS** (FR) 73
7 **STAR OF SOUTHWOOD** (FR) 82
186 **STAR OF ST JAMES** (GER) 129
443 **STAR OF ST LOUIS** (FR) 9
305 **STAR OF THE EAST** (IRE) 29
481 **STAR OF VALOUR** (IRE) 12
555 **STAR OF WELLS** (IRE) 10
413 **STAR SHIELD** 46

251 **STAR TERMS** 25
26 **STAR TREK** F 54
11 **STAR WAVES** (IRE) F 7
397 **STARABA** (FR) G 11
384 **STARCAT** 43
60 **STARCHANT** 10
65 **STARCROSSED** 4
547 **STARFIGHTER** 22
17 **STARFISH** (IRE) C 191
220 **STARFLY** (IRE) F 26
37 **STARGAZER** (IRE) 70
323 **STARIFIGURE** (IRE) 13
562 **STARJAC** (FR) 24
516 **STARLETINA** (IRE) F 96
513 **STARLIGHT PRINCESS** (IRE) C 76
513 **STARLIGHT ROMANCE** (IRE) 5
153 **STARLIT NIGHT** 19
529 **STARLIT SKY** F 53
503 **STARLITE DANCER** 10
349 **STARLINE JEWEL** C 14
547 **STARMAN** 71
323 **STARMANIAC** 14
506 **STAROZOV** (IRE) 13
128 **STARPLEX** 62
465 **STARS IN THE NIGHT** (IRE) 71
176 **STARSHIBA** 22
405 **STARSKY** (IRE) 156
439 **STARTER** 7
21 **STARTER FOR TEN** 24
6 **STATE CROWN** (IRE) 99
305 **STATE OF BLISS** 247
338 **STATE VISION** (FR) 55
516 **STATELY HOME** (IRE) 42
437 **STATION HOUSE** (IRE) F 57
14 **STATION MASTER** (IRE) 56
117 **STATION TO STATION** 56
392 **STATTLER** (IRE) 183
52 **STATUARIO** 34
170 **STAXTON** 85
186 **STAXTON HILL** 130
214 **STAY CALM** (IRE) 59
499 **STAY CLASSY** (IRE) 15
458 **STAY HUMBLE** (IRE) 11
290 **STAY IN THE LIGHT** 8
27 **STAYCATION** (IRE) 24
371 **STAYCEE** 29
351 **STEADY AWAY** (IRE) 20
416 **STEADY THE SHIP** (IRE) 86
97 **STEADYMAN** (FR) 120
268 **STEAL A MARCH** 142
211 **STEAL THE SCENE** (IRE) 25
359 **STEALTH COMMAND** 6
365 **STEEL CABLE** 109
43 **STEEL EXPRESS** (IRE) 9
37 **STEEL HELMET** (IRE) 5
448 **STEEL NATIVE** (IRE) 11
250 **STEEL WAVE** (IRE) 12
234 **STEEL YARD** (IRE) 37
334 **STEELCRAFT** 13
270 **STEELRIVER** (IRE) 14
274 **STEELY ADDITION** (IRE) 95
92 **STEIN CASTLE** (IRE) F 27
356 **STEINKRAUS** (IRE) 102
577 **STELLARISTA** (IRE) 87
371 **STELLAVERA** (FR) F 15
58 **STEP BACK** (IRE) 9
101 **STEP SEQUENCE** C 101
580 **STEP TO THE TOP** (IRE) 24

305 **SUMMER MOON** 30
124 **SUMMER NAME** (IRE) 22
6 **SUMMER ROMANCE** (IRE) 103
439 **SUMMER'S KNIGHT** 60
36 **SUMMERBRIDGE** (IRE) 22
413 **SUMMERGHAND** (IRE) 49
286 **SUMMERONSEVENHILLS** (USA) 36
221 **SUMMERVILLE BOY** (IRE) 74
547 **SUMMIT FEVER** 72
534 **SUMMIT LIKE HERBIE** 78
29 **SUMMIT REACH** 82
409 **SUMORA** (IRE) F 182
391 **SUMTIME** 36
228 **SUN BEAR** 130
186 **SUN CRYSTAL** (IRE) 133
30 **SUN FESTIVAL** 92
251 **SUN POWER** (FR) 115
29 **SUN TIDE** 83
260 **SUNBULA** (USA) F 57
195 **SUNDANCE BOY** F
461 **SUNDAY AT AUGUSTA** (IRE) 16
475 **SUNDAY SESSION** (IRE) 38
537 **SUNDAY SOVEREIGN** 102
547 **SUNDAY STAR** 24
391 **SUNDIAL STORM** 37
39 **SUNDROP** (JPN) C 174
511 **SUNDUS** (IRE) C 148
17 **SUNFLOWER SEED** 192
98 **SUNG CHOI BAO** 19
233 **SUNNY EXPRESS** (IRE) 56
589 **SUNNY GIRL** (IRE) 17
350 **SUNNY LEDGEND** 5
390 **SUNNY PARKES** M 18
325 **SUNNYHILL LAD** (IRE) 8
228 **SUNRAY MAJOR** 131
268 **SUNRISE RUBY** (IRE) 145
511 **SUNRISE VALLEY** (USA) 149
428 **SUNS UP GUNS UP** 36
511 **SUNSEMPERCHI** C 150
547 **SUNSET BAY** 103
439 **SUNSET BREEZE** 29
426 **SUNSET KATIE** 28
30 **SUNSET KISS** 51
246 **SUNSET MARQUIS** (IRE) 8
251 **SUNSET SEEKER** (IRE) 116
124 **SUNSET SHOWDOWN** (IRE) 23
268 **SUNSHADE** 146
419 **SUNSHINE FUN** (USA) 34
233 **SUNSHINE RAYS** F 57
180 **SUNSHINEANDBUBBLES** 23
177 **SUNSTORM** 7
255 **SUNVISOR** (IRE) 18
534 **SUPAKALANISTIC** (IRE) 79
254 **SUPASUNDAE** 67
404 **SUPER FLORENCE** (IRE) 4
365 **SUPER FOLLO** (FR) 110
409 **SUPER MAJESTY** (USA) C 183
88 **SUPER SATURDAY** (FR) F 31
272 **SUPER SLEUTH** (IRE) F 115
263 **SUPER SNIPE** 7
47 **SUPERIOR BADOLAT** (IRE) 22
104 **SUPERIOR MOMENT** (IRE) 24
73 **SUPERIORITY** (IRE) 69
77 **SUPERSEDED** (IRE) 35
242 **SUPERSTAR LEO** (IRE) C 188
77 **SUPERSTITIOUS** (FR) 66
532 **SUPERSTITIOUS** (USA) F 28
413 **SUPERYACHT** (IRE) 50

258 **SUPREME DREAM** 10
576 **SUPREME ESCAPE** (IRE) 76
516 **SUPREME RULE** (IRE) 43
96 **SUPREME SOVIET** (IRE) 3
484 **SUPREMELY LUCKY** (IRE) 107
116 **SUR MER** 36
94 **SURAVA** C 113
101 **SURE I'M YOUR MAN** (IRE) 56
242 **SURF DANCER** (IRE) 105
268 **SURF WALK** (IRE) 147
537 **SURFSEEKER** 103
483 **SURPRISE ENCOUNTER** 59
6 **SURPRISE MOMENT** (IRE) F 211
104 **SURRAJAH** (IRE) 25
531 **SURREY BLAZE** (IRE) 16
531 **SURREY FLAME** (IRE) 25
384 **SURREY GOLD** (IRE) 72
531 **SURREY PRIDE** (IRE) 26
274 **SURROUND** (IRE) 106
244 **SURROUNDING** (IRE) 19
274 **SURTITLE** (IRE) 99
170 **SUSHI POWER** (IRE) 148
426 **SUSIE JAVEA** 15
378 **SUSSEX RANGER** (USA) 113
466 **SUSSEX ROAD** (IRE) 3
203 **SUSTAINABLE STAR** (IRE) 7
576 **SUTTER'S MILL** (IRE) 77
463 **SUTTON MANOR** (IRE) 81
112 **SUTTON WAY** 21
87 **SUWAAN** (IRE) 34
98 **SUZI'S CONNOISSEUR** 20
319 **SUZY WONG** G 22
395 **SWAFFHAM BULBECK** (IRE) 100
437 **SWALLOWDALE** 59
537 **SWAN RIVER** (IRE) 104
140 **SWANTON BLUE** (IRE) 16
356 **SWASHBUCKLE** 104
519 **SWEDISHHORSEMAFIA** (IRE) 22
384 **SWEEP THE STARS** 73
498 **SWEEPING ROCK** (IRE) 12
251 **SWEEPSTAKE** (IRE) F 235
251 **SWEET ACCLAIM** (IRE) C 236
131 **SWEET ADARE** (IRE) 16
361 **SWEET AND DANDY** (IRE) 9
19 **SWEET APPLAUSE** (IRE) C 17
148 **SWEET AS CANDY** (IRE) 38
49 **SWEET CELEBRATION** (IRE) 16
106 **SWEET CHARITY** 10
33 **SWEET CHILD O'MINE** G 16
412 **SWEET DIME** 11
97 **SWEET DREAMS BABY** (IRE) F 67
543 **SWEET EMBRACE** (IRE) 13
548 **SWEET EXPECTATION** 39
302 **SWEET FLORA** (IRE) 8
386 **SWEET JEMIMA** (USA) 20
186 **SWEET JOANNA** (IRE) 134
17 **SWEET MANDOLIN** F 193
175 **SWEET MARMALADE** (IRE) 48
376 **SWEET NATURE** (IRE) 17
188 **SWEET PROMISE** 23
371 **SWEET PURSUIT** 17
437 **SWEET REWARD** (IRE) 32
76 **SWEET SECRET** F 78
193 **SWEET SHIRLEY MAE** (USA) C 13
128 **SWEET SIOUX** F 109
537 **SWEET SIXTEEN** (IRE) F 105
116 **SWEET TALKED** 17
46 **SWEET VINETTA** 19

73 **SWEET'N SASSY** (IRE) G 70
497 **SWEETEST SMILE** (IRE) 14
16 **SWEETHEART ABBEY** F 52
554 **SWEETNESSANDLIGHT** 5
554 **SWEETNESSANDLIGHT** F 16
554 **SWEETNESSANDLIGHT** C 24
503 **SWEETTASTEOFLOVE** 30
402 **SWEETTOWATCH** (IRE) 62
576 **SWELL SISTER** (IRE) 62
116 **SWELL SONG** 21
272 **SWELL SWILLY** (IRE) 62
103 **SWIFT ACTION** (IRE) F 57
582 **SWIFT APPROVAL** (IRE) 38
537 **SWIFT CAMPAIGN** (IRE) F 192
1 **SWIFT GETAWAY** (IRE) F 60
463 **SWIFT GETAWAY** (IRE) G 100
228 **SWIFT VERDICT** 132
322 **SWIFT WING** 31
243 **SWILLY SUNSET** 31
241 **SWINCOMBE SCORCHIO** 9
547 **SWINDLER** 25
413 **SWING LOW** 126
530 **SWINGING EDDIE** 12
249 **SWINTON DIAMOND** (IRE) 61
417 **SWIPER** (IRE) 17
409 **SWISS ACE** 184
437 **SWISS CHEER** (FR) 10
486 **SWISS CONNECTION** 17
169 **SWISS KNIGHT** 47
518 **SWISS PRIDE** (IRE) 22
358 **SWISS VINNARE** 10
142 **SWISSAL** (IRE) 30
405 **SWITCH HITTER** (IRE) 159
465 **SWITCHMAN** (IRE) 72
537 **SWOOPING EAGLE** (IRE) 106
304 **SWORD BEACH** (IRE) 52
214 **SWORD EXCEED** (GER) 36
314 **SWORD OF FATE** (IRE) 4
364 **SYCAMORE** (IRE) 38
318 **SYDNEY SIREN** 24
351 **SYKES** (IRE) 21
244 **SYLVIA PLATH IRE** 58
6 **SYMBOL OF LOVE** 104
84 **SYMBOL OF PEACE** (IRE) F 50
397 **SYMBOLIC STAR** (IRE) 12
94 **SYMBOLINE** F 114
17 **SYMBOLIZE** (IRE) 114
375 **SYMPHONIC DANCER** (USA) F 34
535 **SYMPHONY** (IRE) 6
233 **SYMPHONY HALL** (IRE) 58
460 **SYMPHONY STAR** (IRE) C 15
162 **SYNERGY** (FR) F 68
16 **SYRNA** (FR) F 53
422 **SYSTEMIC** 50
537 **TA AMMOL** F 193
440 **TA DAAH** 16
272 **TAAMEEN** 63
516 **TAAQAH** (USA) F 97
76 **TAAWFAN** (IRE) 42
413 **TABAAHY** 51
405 **TABACHINES** (FR) C 185
251 **TABARRAK** (IRE) 26
511 **TABASSUM** (IRE) F 151
76 **TABDEED** 14
155 **TABLE BLUFF** (IRE) 5
307 **TABLE MOUNTAIN** (FR) 2
368 **TABOU BEACH BOY** 48
101 **TACITLY** 57

188 **THE PINTO KID** (FR) 24
315 **THE PIRATE'S QUEEN** (IRE) F 123
429 **THE PREMIER CELTIC** 17
377 **THE PRIESTS LEAP** (IRE) 12
304 **THE PRINCES POET** 77
36 **THE QUEENS LADIES** 29
541 **THE QUIET DON** (IRE) 33
391 **THE RAVEN'S RETURN** 40
365 **THE RED MENACE** (IRE) 112
281 **THE RED WITCH** 16
317 **THE RESDEV WAY** 73
249 **THE RETRIEVER** (IRE) 63
116 **THE RIGHT BIRD** (USA) C 53
193 **THE RIGHT CHOICE** (IRE) 4
463 **THE ROAD HOME** (IRE) 84
33 **THE ROCKET PARK** (IRE) 14
488 **THE RORY STORY** (IRE) 7
484 **THE ROSARY FLYER** 111
526 **THE RUSSIAN DOYEN** (IRE) 111
249 **THE RUTLAND REBEL** (IRE) 64
543 **THE SADDLE ROCK** (IRE) 14
343 **THE SASKATOON** 2
251 **THE SEVENTH DAY** (IRE) 120
33 **THE SIMPLE TRUTH** (FR) 17
95 **THE SOCIETY MAN** (IRE) 7
356 **THE SOME DANCE KID** (IRE) 109
329 **THE SPOKEN PHRASE** 8
404 **THE STALKING MOON** (IRE) 6
374 **THE STEWARD** (USA) 17
526 **THE STRAP MAN** 112
166 **THE SWAGMAN** (USA) 9
327 **THE SWEENEY** (IRE) 63
211 **THE THROSTLES** 28
439 **THE TIDE TURNS** 61
188 **THE TIN MAN** 25
227 **THE TIN MINER** (IRE) 46
463 **THE TOFT** F 101
238 **THE TOOJUMBLE** 19
564 **THE TOPP NOTES** 15
315 **THE TOURARD MAN** (IRE) 124
305 **THE TRADER** (IRE) 32
413 **THE TRENDY MAN** (IRE) 87
254 **THE TRUANT** 129
275 **THE TURFACCOUNTANT** (IRE) 12
176 **THE TURPINATOR** (IRE) 24
388 **THE TWISLER** 95
351 **THE TWO AMIGOS** 7
315 **THE UNIT** (IRE) 125
30 **THE VEGAS RAIDER** 94
249 **THE VERY THING** (IRE) 65
20 **THE VOCALIST** 18
338 **THE VOLLAN** (IRE) 6
91 **THE WARRIOR** (IRE) 21
388 **THE WEASEL** (IRE) 96
305 **THE WEED MACHINE** (IRE) 123
330 **THE WELSH PADDIES** (IRE) 20
392 **THE WEST AWAITS** (IRE) 189
541 **THE WHITE MOUSE** (IRE) 34
388 **THE WICKET CHICKEN** (IRE) 97
526 **THE WIDOW MAKER** 113
128 **THE WINE CELLAR** (IRE) 92
198 **THE WIRE FLYER** 24
395 **THE WOLF** (FR) 103
221 **THE WORLDS END** (IRE) 77
388 **THE YOUNG MASTER** 98
580 **THEATRE GOER** 25
526 **THEATRE GUIDE** (IRE) 114
230 **THEATRE LEGEND** 33

157 **THEATRE MIX** 11
544 **THEATRE TERRITORY** (IRE) 5
412 **THEATRO** (IRE) 33
496 **THEBANNERKINGREBEL** (IRE) 54
382 **THEBELLSOFSHANDON** (IRE) 24
228 **THEBIAN** 136
218 **THEBUDINPUNDIT** 12
378 **THECHILDREN'STRUST** (IRE) 118
173 **THECLOCKISTICKING** (IRE) 33
466 **THECORNISHBARRON** (IRE) 4
594 **THEDANCINGMAN** 9
563 **THEDEVILINNEVILLE** 20
365 **THEDEVILSCOACHMAN** (IRE) 113
499 **THEFASTNTHECURIOUS** 58
317 **THEFLICKERINGLIGHT** (IRE) 74
83 **THEFLYINGPORTRAIT** (IRE) 41
411 **THEGALLANTWAY** (IRE) 82
225 **THEGLASGOWWARRIOR** 33
254 **THEGOAHEADMAN** (IRE) 70
393 **THEGREATESTSHOWMAN** 33
257 **THEGREYVTRAIN** 27
439 **THEHEARTNEVERLIES** 32
268 **THEINVAL** (FR) 150
539 **THELIGNY** (FR) 87
30 **THELMA TODD** (IRE) 53
493 **THELONGWAYAROUND** (IRE) 52
316 **THEMANFROM MINELLA** (IRE) 39
194 **THEMATIC** (USA) 6
305 **THEMAXWECAN** (IRE) 33
416 **THEME TUNE** (IRE) 95
235 **THENIGHTISYOUNG** (IRE) 10
402 **THEO** (FR) 14
222 **THEO'S CHARM** (IRE) 24
251 **THEOTHERSIDE** (IRE) 121
364 **THEOULE** (FR) 22
135 **THEQUEENBEE** (IRE) 21
2 **THEREDBALLOON** 4
413 **THESETHINGSHAPPEN** 127
563 **THESPINNINGWHEEL** (IRE) 21
42 **THESTOPPERDUNNE** (IRE) 13
100 **THEYDON BOXER** 4
100 **THEYDON SPIRIT** 5
511 **THIBAAN** (USA) 95
14 **THIBAULT** 61
45 **THIEL** F 12
374 **THINK AHEAD** 18
435 **THINKING** (IRE) 70
338 **THINQUE TANK** 60
437 **THIQA** G 60
537 **THIRD REALM** 194
484 **THIRD TIME LUCKI** (IRE) 112
384 **THIRD WIND** 21
210 **THIS BREAC** (IRE) 17
339 **THIS GIRL** 28
464 **THIS IS THE DAY** F 19
305 **THIS IS THE DAY** F 250
499 **THISTIMENEXTYEAR** 16
496 **THISTLE DO NICELY** (IRE) 55
526 **THISTLECRACK** 115
253 **THOMAS BLOSSOM** (IRE) 2
292 **THOMAS CRANMER** (USA) 17
395 **THOMAS DARBY** (IRE) 104
356 **THOMAS DO** (IRE) 110
67 **THOMAS HAWK** 7
496 **THOMAS MACDONAGH** 56
322 **THOMAS PATRICK** (IRE) 34
345 **THOMAS PERCY** 24
13 **THOMAS SHELBY** (IRE) 17

381 **THOMAS TODD** 21
327 **THOOR CASTLE** (IRE) 64
475 **THOR DE CERISY** (FR) 41
554 **THORNABY GEORGE** 7
554 **THORNABY NASH** 8
554 **THORNABY PRINCESS** 9
554 **THORNABY SPIRIT** (IRE) 10
348 **THORNDALE** 24
169 **THORNTON LE CLAY** 48
463 **THORPE** (IRE) 85
14 **THOSE TIGER FEET** (IRE) 62
170 **THOUGH** (IRE) F 163
99 **THOUGHT IS FREE** F 20
296 **THOUGHTFULLY** (IRE) 8
378 **THOUNDER** (FR) 119
242 **THOWQ** (IRE) 108
405 **THRAVE** 163
251 **THREAT** (IRE) 122
144 **THREE BULLET GATE** (IRE) 21
50 **THREE C'S** (IRE) 6
346 **THREE CARD TRICK** 11
128 **THREE CASTLES** 65
539 **THREE COLOURS RED** (IRE) 88
395 **THREE COUNTY'S** (IRE) 105
260 **THREE DRAGONS** 48
20 **THREE IN ONE** (IRE) 19
318 **THREE LITTLE BIRDS** 12
413 **THREE SAINTS BAY** (IRE) 52
50 **THREE TIMES** C 21
496 **THREE WAYS** 57
489 **THREEFEETFROMGOLD** (IRE) 9
405 **THREEUNDERTHRUFIVE** (IRE) 164
169 **THRILL** C 100
242 **THRILL SEEKER** (IRE) 109
499 **THRILLA IN MANILA** 17
570 **THRILLER'S MOON** 13
440 **THROCKLEY** 17
295 **THRONE** C 67
465 **THRONE HALL** 73
76 **THUMUR** (USA) 45
163 **THUNDER AHEAD** 39
6 **THUNDER BAY** (USA) F 216
577 **THUNDER FLASH** 98
463 **THUNDER IN MILAN** (IRE) 86
393 **THUNDER KING** (FR) 55
146 **THUNDERBELL** 3
384 **THUNDERCLAP** (IRE) 74
146 **THUNDERCLOUD** 26
367 **THUNDERING BLUE** (USA) 13
89 **THUNDEROAD** 70
305 **THUNDEROUS** (IRE) 124
363 **THUNDERSOCKSSUNDAE** (IRE) 55
327 **THUNDERSTRUCK** (IRE) 65
274 **THYME HILL** 101
405 **THYME WHITE** (FR) 165
323 **TIA KIA** (IRE) G 75
7 **TIANA** F 116
106 **TIAR NA NOG** (IRE) 11
319 **TIBBIE DUNBAR** 10
175 **TIBERIUS AUGUSTUS** 84
543 **TICKERTY BOO** (IRE) 9
243 **TICKET TO L A** (IRE) 32
469 **TICO TIMES** (IRE) 19
274 **TIDAL FLOW** 102
281 **TIDAL POINT** (IRE) 8
117 **TIDAL RACER** 59
315 **TIDAL RUN** F 126
416 **TIDAL WATCH** (IRE) 96

577 **TIDE TIMES** (IRE) 90
228 **TIEMPO VUELA** 137
27 **TIERCEL** 25
327 **TIERRA VERDE** 66
309 **TIFARITI** (USA) F 31
238 **TIFFANY'S CAT** (IRE) 20
172 **TIFFINDELL** (IRE) 9
483 **TIGER CRUSADE** (FR) 62
77 **TIGER LYON** (USA) 37
409 **TIGER MOTH** (IRE) 101
139 **TIGER PRINT** 4
392 **TIGER TAP TAP** (GER) 190
103 **TIGER TOUCH** (AUS) 40
117 **TIGER ZONE** (IRE) 60
395 **TIGERBYTHETAIL** (IRE) 106
282 **TIGERINMYTANK** 6
29 **TIGERSKIN** 33
531 **TIGERTEN** 27
539 **TIGHT CALL** (IRE) 89
7 **TIGRAY** (USA) 65
140 **TIJUCA** (IRE) C 28
341 **TIKANITE** (IRE) 10
493 **TIKERTY TOK** 53
473 **TIKERBYTHEBOX** (IRE) 38
146 **TILLY DEVINE** 2
188 **TILLY FRANKL** 54
272 **TILSIT** (USA) 65
299 **TILSWORTH EMERALD** 15
299 **TILSWORTH LUKEY** 16
299 **TILSWORTH PRISCA** 17
299 **TILSWORTH ROSE** 18
299 **TILSWORTH SAMMY** 19
122 **TILTILYS ROCK** (IRE) 21
234 **TIM ROCCO** (GER) 39
576 **TIMASSINI** (IRE) 81
192 **TIMBA** C 78
22 **TIMBER HOUSE** (IRE) 4
268 **TIMBERMAN** (IRE) 151
496 **TIMCODA** (IRE) 58
239 **TIME BEING** F 28
285 **TIME CLASH** G 16
285 **TIME CLASH** G 19
268 **TIME FLIES BY** (IRE) 152
83 **TIME FOR ANOTHER** (IRE) 42
183 **TIME FOR CHAMPERS** (IRE) 16
101 **TIME INTERVAL** 104
411 **TIME TO MOVE ON** (IRE) 83
550 **TIME TO REASON** (IRE) 18
77 **TIME TO SEA** (IRE) 38
483 **TIME TO STRIKE** (IRE) 63
405 **TIME TO TINKER** (IRE) 166
444 **TIME VOYAGE** (IRE) 46
171 **TIMEFORADANCE** 7
171 **TIMEFORAGIN** G 8
364 **TIMELESS CALL** (IRE) F 40
537 **TIMELESS SOUL** (GER) 195
539 **TIMELY GIFT** (IRE) 90
463 **TIMESAWAITING** (IRE) 87
431 **TIMETOBENEFIT** (IRE) 27
380 **TIMETOCHILL** (IRE) 4
347 **TIMETODOCK** 12
557 **TIMETOROE** (IRE) 19
496 **TIMOSHENKO** 59
310 **TIMOTEO** (FR) 127
68 **TIMSSAAH** 2
536 **TIN FANDANGO** 1
304 **TIN HAT** (IRE) 22
476 **TINA TEASPOON** 19

413 **TINANDALI** (IRE) 53
65 **TINCTORIA** 8
345 **TINDRUM** 25
98 **TINGLEO** C 36
201 **TINGO IN THE TALE** (IRE) 3
537 **TINKER TOY** 108
504 **TINKERBIRD** 6
419 **TINNAHALLA** (IRE) 35
496 **TINSMITH** 60
57 **TINTERN SPIRIT** (IRE) 17
428 **TINTO** 15
555 **TINTORETTO** (IRE) 7
465 **TINY DANSER** 108
128 **TIP IT ON THE TOP** (IRE) F 111
386 **TIP TOP** 32
534 **TIP TOP CAT** (IRE) 83
518 **TIP TWO WIN** 24
592 **TIPALONG TYLER** 15
117 **TIPOFTHETONGUE** 106
73 **TIPPERARY BOUTIQUE** (IRE) C 115
34 **TIPPERARY JACK** (USA) 20
582 **TIPPING OVER** (FR) F 61
539 **TIPPINGITUPTONANCY** (IRE) 91
527 **TIPPLER** 9
304 **TIPSY LAIRD** 78
306 **TIQUER** (FR) 11
422 **TIRITOMBA** (IRE) 51
244 **TIRMIZI** (FR) 20
44 **TIS FANTASTIC** (FR) 15
117 **TIS MARVELLOUS** 20
546 **TITANEASY** 24
170 **TITIAN SAGA** (IRE) F 164
422 **TITIVATION** G 52
295 **TITUS BOLT** (IRE) 42
468 **TITUS SECRET** 7
281 **TIZWOTITIZ** 9
42 **TIZZY FRIZZY** F 14
98 **TO BE WILD** (IRE) 21
228 **TO NATHANIEL** 138
284 **TOAD** 8
413 **TOAST OF THE TOWN** (IRE) C 128
245 **TOBEFAIR** 12
424 **TOBY MAGUIRE** (IRE) 80
167 **TODAY PLEASE** (IRE) 14
251 **TODAY POWER** (IRE) 123
395 **TODD** 107
88 **TOFFEE HAMMER** 24
97 **TOGETHER APART** 68
409 **TOGETHER FOREVER** (IRE) C 185
368 **TOI STOREY** (IRE) 52
295 **TOKARAMORE** 43
6 **TOKEN OF LOVE** C 217
6 **TOLMOUNT** 105
176 **TOM COLLINS** 25
88 **TOM TULLIVER** 25
450 **TOM'S ANNA** (IRE) 4
215 **TOMAHAWK RIDGE** (IRE) 14
268 **TOMBEE DU CIEL** (FR) 153
150 **TOMBOLO** (FR) 46
335 **TOMBSTONE** (IRE) 16
29 **TOMFIRE** 84
401 **TOMILY** (IRE) 11
391 **TOMMIE BEAU** (IRE) 41
272 **TOMMY DE VITO** 66
225 **TOMMY** G 34
484 **TOMMY RAPPER** (IRE) 113
117 **TOMMY ROCK** (IRE) 61
397 **TOMMY SHELBY** (FR) 13

405 **TOMMY SILVER** (FR) 167
83 **TOMMY THE RASCAL** 43
175 **TOMMY TITTLEMOUSE** (IRE) 85
497 **TOMMYCOLE** 16
344 **TOMMYS GEAL** 13
202 **TOMOROZ MAN** (IRE) 3
295 **TOMORROW'S ANGEL** 44
242 **TOMORROW'S DREAM** (FR) 110
39 **TOMOUH DUBAI** 124
116 **TOMSHALFBROTHER** 22
582 **TONE THE BARONE** 4
89 **TONI'S A STAR** 71
469 **TONTO'S SPIRIT** 20
30 **TONY MONTANA** 95
547 **TONYX** 26
305 **TOO HARD TO HOLD** (IRE) 125
559 **TOO MANY CHIEFS** (IRE) 5
83 **TOO MUCH TO ASK** (IRE) 44
499 **TOO SHY SHY** (IRE) 40
503 **TOO SOON TO PANIC** 31
23 **TOO WISE MAN** (IRE) 30
77 **TOOFI** (FR) 39
534 **TOOK THE LOT** 84
12 **TOOLATETODELEGATE** 15
404 **TOOLENTIDHAAR** (USA) F 15
199 **TOOLMAKER** 10
300 **TOOR GENERAL** (IRE) 18
254 **TOORA LOORA** 130
234 **TOORSINAA** (IRE) 40
112 **TOOYOU** 23
583 **TOP AND DROP** 71
187 **TOP ATTRACTION** 11
223 **TOP BEAK** (IRE) 11
89 **TOP BOY** 72
286 **TOP BREEZE** (IRE) 10
170 **TOP BUCK** (IRE) 150
23 **TOP CAT DJ** (IRE) 31
251 **TOP CLASS ANGEL** (IRE) 124
156 **TOP DECISION** (IRE) 19
17 **TOP DROP** (IRE) 117
527 **TOP FOX** 27
330 **TOP GAMBLE** (IRE) 21
463 **TOP HER UP** (IRE) F 88
227 **TOP MAN** (IRE) 47
251 **TOP MODEL** (IRE) F 239
268 **TOP NOTCH** (FR) 154
52 **TOP NURSE** (IRE) F 35
328 **TOP OF THE MORNING** (IRE) 14
234 **TOP OF THE ROCKS** (FR) 41
17 **TOP POWER** (FR) 50
516 **TOP RANK** (IRE) 7
117 **TOP SECRET** 62
348 **TOP UP THE FASHION** (IRE) 25
317 **TOP VILLE BEN** (IRE) 75
380 **TOP WOOD** (FR) 5
179 **TOPANTICIPATION** 23
73 **TOPARALI** G 71
17 **TOPIC** (USA) C 197
103 **TOPKAPI** (FR) 41
393 **TOPKAPI STAR** 56
19 **TOPLIGHT** 18
534 **TOPOFTHECOTSWOLDS** (IRE) 85
405 **TOPOFTHEGAME** (IRE) 168
531 **TOPOLOGY** 17
371 **TOPTIME** 51
511 **TOQUETTE** (IRE) C 153
196 **TOR** 11
34 **TORBELLINO** 21

73 **VITRALITE** (IRE) 20
272 **VITRUVIUS** 20
39 **VITUISA** C 176
98 **VIVA GLORIA** (GER) 23
108 **VIVA JEZ VEGAS** (IRE) 6
235 **VIVA LA VEGA** 13
327 **VIVA VITTORIA** (IRE) 69
26 **VIVA VOCE** (IRE) 35
346 **VIVACIOUS SPIRIT** 12
338 **VIVAS** (FR) 62
87 **VIVAX** (IRE) 39
214 **VIVE AUDACTER** 60
170 **VIVE LA DIFFERENCE** (IRE) 94
89 **VIVE LE ROI** (IRE) 76
472 **VIVE LES ROUGES** C 44
305 **VIVID DIAMOND** (IRE) 35
272 **VIVIDLY** 19
511 **VIVIONN** 23
327 **VIXEN** (IRE) 70
384 **VIZA** 46
212 **VIZEAN** (IRE) G 81
344 **VLANNON** 14
159 **VOCAL DUKE** (IRE) 7
159 **VOCAL QUEEN** (IRE) 8
144 **VOCALISER** (IRE) 23
537 **VODKA** (JPN) C 114
351 **VODKA ALL THE WAY** (IRE) 23
19 **VOICE OF A LEADER** (IRE) 12
562 **VOICE OF DUBAWI** 32
538 **VOICE OF GLORY** 28
475 **VOILA ERIC** 43
463 **VOIX D'EAU** (FR) 92
392 **VOIX DES TIEP** (FR) 201
392 **VOIX DU REVE** (FR) 202
128 **VOLATILE ANALYST** (USA) 96
159 **VOLATILE LADY** (IRE) 9
95 **VOLCANIC JACK** (IRE) 8
39 **VOLCANIC SKY** 41
333 **VOLCANO** (FR) 5
375 **VOLCANO BAY** 21
483 **VOLEUSE DE COEURS** (IRE) C 101
6 **VOLKAN STAR** (IRE) 108
562 **VOLT FACE** (FR) 26
335 **VOLTAIC** 18
309 **VOLUNTEER** 16
576 **VOODOO DOLL** (IRE) 84
378 **VORASHANN** (FR) 125
101 **VORDA** (FR) F 106
402 **VOSNE ROMANEE** 66
6 **VOTTORIA LIGHT** 109
268 **VOYAGE DE RETOUR** (IRE) 160
24 **VOYBURG** (IRE) 66
494 **VUE CAVALIERE** (FR) 13
163 **VULCAN** (IRE) 24
534 **VULCAN BOMBER** 91
357 **W G GRACE** (IRE) 2
415 **W S GILBERT** 6
413 **WAARIF** (IRE) 56
6 **WADAA** (USA) F 223
305 **WADACRE GIGOLO** 132
286 **WADDAT** (FR) 39
170 **WADE'S MAGIC** 154
170 **WADI AL SALAAM** (IRE) 155
76 **WADILSAFA** 19
409 **WADING** (IRE) C 188
476 **WAFFLETON** 21
283 **WAGNER** (IRE) 37

150 **WAHOO** 21
427 **WAHWEI SPIRIT** (IRE) 10
61 **WAHWONAISA** 23
483 **WAHYLAH** (IRE) C 102
418 **WAIHEKE** 31
378 **WAIKIKI WAVES** (FR) 126
49 **WAILEA NIGHTS** (IRE) 57
176 **WAIT FOR THE LORD** 11
49 **WAIT FOREVER** (IRE) 18
224 **WAITAKI** (IRE) 4
81 **WAITANGI** 28
368 **WAITING FOR RICHIE** 55
493 **WAITING FOREVER** (IRE) 60
297 **WAITING PATIENTLY** (IRE) 28
44 **WAITINONASUNNYDAY** (IRE) 17
534 **WAITONIT** (IRE) 92
493 **WAKANDA** (IRE) 61
555 **WAKE UP** (GER) C 33
305 **WAKE UP CALL** C 253
49 **WAKEUP LITTLE SUZY** (IRE) C 81
1 **WAKOOL** (FR) 56
228 **WALDKONIG** 145
537 **WALEYDD** 115
577 **WALHAAN** (IRE) 91
537 **WALIYAK** (FR) 116
546 **WALK IN THE MILL** (FR) 26
548 **WALK IT TALK IT** 16
437 **WALK ON WALTER** (FR) 12
225 **WALKIN IN THE RAIN** (IRE) 5
251 **WALKINTHESAND** (IRE) 29
434 **WALKMAN** (IRE) 7
94 **WALKONBY** 71
292 **WALLACE** 18
323 **WALLAROO** (IRE) 79
150 **WALLGATE** 49
214 **WALLS HAVE EARS** (IRE) 15
299 **WALLY'S WISDOM** 20
388 **WALT** (IRE) 103
472 **WALTER MITTY** 45
6 **WALTON STREET** 28
339 **WANAASAH** 29
541 **WAND** 43
422 **WANDERING SPIRIT** (GER) G 55
14 **WANDRIN STAR** (IRE) 67
77 **WANEEN** (IRE) 41
296 **WANNABE BETSY** (IRE) 19
192 **WANNABE SAFE** (IRE) 80
94 **WANSDYKE LASS** F 72
107 **WANTAGE** (IRE) 39
59 **WAPPING** (USA) 7
536 **WAQAAS** 18
38 **WAR AT SEA** (IRE) 18
577 **WAR BRIGADE** (FR) 92
254 **WAR CABINET** (IRE) 133
315 **WAR CHIEF** 133
538 **WAR CROSS** (USA) 17
170 **WAR DEFENDER** 156
244 **WAR DIARY** 21
251 **WAR EFFORT** (USA) F 244
190 **WAR EMPRESS** (IRE) 13
251 **WAR GLORY** (IRE) 30
409 **WAR LEADER** (USA) 107
526 **WAR LORD** (GER) 118
73 **WAR OF CLANS** (IRE) 73
401 **WAR OF SUCCESSION** 12
57 **WAR PLAN** 19
315 **WAR PRINCESS** (IRE) 134
274 **WAR SOUND** 107

370 **WAR WHISPER** (IRE) 33
242 **WARDA** F 194
272 **WARDAT DUBAI** C 119
110 **WARENDORF** (FR) 20
16 **WARGRAVE** (IRE) 28
39 **WARM SUNSET** (IRE) 126
305 **WARNE'S ARMY** 133
39 **WARNING SHOT** (IRE) 127
10 **WARRANTED** 34
305 **WARRANTY** (FR) 134
422 **WARREN ROSE** 56
335 **WARRIOR DISPLAY** (IRE) 19
77 **WARRIOR GODDESS** 42
406 **WARRIOR'S SPIRIT** (IRE) 9
236 **WARRIOR'S VALLEY** 16
128 **WARRIORS STORY** 67
405 **WARRIORS TALE** 172
116 **WARSAW ROAD** (IRE) 23
228 **WASAAYEF** (IRE) 146
234 **WASASTYLEQUEEN** 45
416 **WASDELL DUNDALK** (FR) 99
256 **WASEEM FARIS** (IRE) 26
186 **WASNTEXPECTINGTHAT** 52
251 **WATAN** 31
137 **WATAR ALLSTAR** (IRE) 23
356 **WATCH AND LEARN** 116
97 **WATCH HIM** (IRE) 124
413 **WATCHABLE** 57
183 **WATCHMAN** (IRE) 18
404 **WATCHTHISNOW** (IRE) 16
357 **WATER THIEF** (USA) 3
327 **WATER WAGTAIL** 71
16 **WATER'S EDGE** (IRE) 29
541 **WATERFALL** 36
309 **WATERPROOF** 17
254 **WATERVILLE LADY** (IRE) 134
191 **WATHEER** 29
405 **WATSON RIVER** (IRE) G 173
340 **WATTREY** F 31
249 **WAVERBECK** (IRE) M 67
9 **WAVERING** (IRE) C 177
473 **WAVERING DOWN** (IRE) 43
539 **WAX AND WANE** 95
333 **WAY OF THE WORLD** (IRE) 6
124 **WAYFINDER** (IRE) 24
246 **WAYUPINTHESKY** (IRE) 11
231 **WAYWARD SUN** (IRE) 5
356 **WAZOWSKI** 117
250 **WBEE** (IRE) 13
429 **WE ARE ALL DOTTIE** 18
305 **WE ARE NINETY** (IRE) F 254
424 **WE RUN THE NIGHT** (FR) 84
413 **WE'LL GO WALKING** (IRE) C 129
461 **WE'LLCWHATHAPPENS** (IRE) 22
257 **WE'RE REUNITED** (FR) 38
331 **WE'VE GOT PAYET** 30
390 **WE'VE GOT THE LOVE** (IRE) 21
175 **WEAKFIELD** (FR) 55
362 **WEATHER FRONT** (USA) 14
447 **WEAVE SOME MAGIC** 5
419 **WEBUYANYHORSE** 36
21 **WEDDING BREAKFAST** (IRE) 16
251 **WEDDING DATE** 32
134 **WEDGEWOOD STAR** F 17
424 **WEE DINNS** (FR) G 85
229 **WEE GOLDIE** 9
228 **WEEKENDER** 32
341 **WEEKLY GOSSIP** (IRE) 13

116 **WEISSE SOCKEN** (IRE) C 54
242 **WEJDAN** (FR) 112
540 **WELAN** (GER) 19
463 **WELL ABOVE PAR** (IRE) 93
569 **WELL DISGUISED** (IRE) G 21
244 **WELL DONE ME** (IRE) C 98
36 **WELL FUNDED** (IRE) 12
119 **WELL I NEVER** 12
59 **WELL IN COMMAND** (IRE) 9
6 **WELL OF WISDOM** 110
444 **WELL PLANTED** (FR) 50
251 **WELL PREPARED** 127
178 **WELL SMITTEN** (IRE) 16
485 **WELLAND** 17
52 **WELLS DE LUNE** (FR) 36
170 **WELLS FARHH GO** (IRE) 95
177 **WELLS GOLD** (IRE) 8
77 **WELOOF** (FR) 43
268 **WELSH SAINT** (IRE) 161
132 **WELSH WAYNE** (IRE) 49
317 **WEMYSS POINT** 77
61 **WENCESLAUS** (GER) 24
217 **WENDREDA** 10
27 **WENSLEY** 27
419 **WENTWORTH AMIGO** (IRE) 37
252 **WENTWORTH FALLS** 5
268 **WENYERREADYFREDDIE** (IRE) 162
214 **WEOOD** (FR) F 62
9 **WESAM** (FR) 42
324 **WESSINGTON PARK** 7
526 **WEST APPROACH** 119
588 **WEST CLASS** (IRE) 10
480 **WEST COAST FLYER** 53
330 **WEST COAST GLORY** (IRE) 23
484 **WEST CORK** 117
491 **WEST DRIVE** (IRE) 28
305 **WEST END CHARMER** (IRE) 36
305 **WEST END GIRL** 135
568 **WEST END WOODY** (IRE) 36
411 **WEST RIVER** (USA) F 89
472 **WEST SUFFOLK** 46
436 **WEST TO CROSSGALES** (IRE) 13
484 **WEST TO THE BRIDGE** (IRE) 5
73 **WEST WAY NEVER** (IRE) 120
331 **WEST WIZARD** (FR) 31
94 **WESTBROOK BERTIE** 23
274 **WESTEND STORY** (IRE) 108
551 **WESTEND THEATRE** (IRE) 5
391 **WESTERBERRY** (IRE) 43
528 **WESTERN AUSSIE** (IRE) 19
409 **WESTERN AUSTRALIA** (IRE) 15
418 **WESTERN CLIMATE** (IRE) 32
346 **WESTERN DAWN** (IRE) 13
577 **WESTERN DUKE** (IRE) 93
365 **WESTERN FANCY** (IRE) 120
465 **WESTERN HERO** (IRE) 77
474 **WESTERN LASS** (IRE) 14
338 **WESTERN MILLER** (IRE) 63
429 **WESTERN RANGER** (IRE) 19
233 **WESTERN RYDER** (IRE) 61
169 **WESTERN SKY** F 102
233 **WESTERN STARLET** (IRE) 62
189 **WESTERN SUNRISE** (IRE) 39
474 **WESTERN SUPERNOVA** 15
26 **WESTERN TUNE** (IRE) F 56
164 **WESTERNER OCEAN** (IRE) 42
405 **WESTHILL** (IRE) 174
480 **WESTSTREET** (IRE) 54

256 **WETANWINDY** 27
516 **WETHER GIRL** F 99
452 **WETLANDS** (IRE) 51
299 **WHALEWEIGH STATION** 21
14 **WHAT A BALOO** (IRE) 68
191 **WHAT A BUSINESS** (IRE) 39
532 **WHAT A DAZZLER** 14
250 **WHAT A LAUGH** 14
435 **WHAT A MOMENT** (IRE) 74
242 **WHAT A PICTURE** (FR) C 195
17 **WHAT A TREASURE** (IRE) C 200
338 **WHAT ABOUT TIME** (IRE) 64
167 **WHAT ABOUT US** (IRE) 15
186 **WHAT IS LIFE** (IRE) 143
254 **WHAT NEXT** (IRE) 71
395 **WHAT WILL BE** (IRE) 111
20 **WHAT'LLBEWILLBE** (IRE) 20
493 **WHAT'S THE SCOOP** (IRE) 62
128 **WHAT'S THE STORY** 68
432 **WHATABOUTWALT** (IRE) 8
186 **WHATAGUY** 53
212 **WHATAKNIGHT** 77
74 **WHATCOLOURISHE** (IRE) 11
38 **WHATEVA NEXT** (IRE) 19
129 **WHATMORE** 33
86 **WHATS NOT TO LIKE** (GER) 4
402 **WHATSDASTORY** (IRE) 67
418 **WHATSMEANTTOBE** 33
382 **WHATSNOTOKNOW** (IRE) 25
274 **WHATSTHECRAICJACK** 109
424 **WHATSUPWITHYOU** (IRE) 86
268 **WHATSWRONGWITHYOU** (IRE) 163
194 **WHATTHEBUTLERSAW** (IRE) 7
240 **WHATWOULDYOUKNOW** (IRE) 16
395 **WHATYA ON ABOUT** 112
110 **WHEELBAHRI** 21
480 **WHEESHT** (IRE) 55
518 **WHELANS WAY** (IRE) 25
339 **WHEN COMES HERE** (IRE) 51
416 **WHEN YOU'RE READY** (IRE) 100
576 **WHENEVER WHEREVER** (IRE) G 85
180 **WHERE NEXT JO** 40
583 **WHERE'S BOB** (IRE) 73
169 **WHERE'S JEFF** 53
344 **WHERE'S TOM** 15
254 **WHERETHEWINDSBLOW** 72
244 **WHEREWITHAL** 22
177 **WHEREWOULDUGETIT** (IRE) 9
467 **WHIGWHAM** 3
30 **WHIM** F 98
117 **WHISKEY 'N' CHIPS** 109
175 **WHISKEY AND WATER** 56
395 **WHISKEY IN THE JAR** (IRE) 113
103 **WHISKEY LULLABY** 44
405 **WHISKEY LULLABY** 175
534 **WHISKEY MOON** 93
392 **WHISKEY SOUR** (IRE) 203
216 **WHISKY** (IRE) G 10
45 **WHISP** (FR) F 13
519 **WHISPER** (FR) 25
251 **WHISPER NOT** 128
295 **WHISPERING WATERS** (IRE) 46
254 **WHISPERINTHEBREEZE** 73
356 **WHISPERS IN MOSCOW** (IRE) F 118
378 **WHISTLER BOWL** 127
142 **WHISTLING GYPSE** (IRE) G 32
169 **WHISTLING STRAITS** (IRE) G 103
538 **WHITBY HARBOUR** 18

391 **WHITE CHOCOLATE** (IRE) 44
150 **WHITE COPPER** 50
242 **WHITE DRESS** (IRE) F 196
282 **WHITE FACE** (IRE) 13
212 **WHITE HART LADY** (IRE) 78
272 **WHITE LADY** (IRE) 120
62 **WHITE LION** 46
422 **WHITE MOCHA** (USA) 15
526 **WHITE MOON** (GER) 120
39 **WHITE MOUNTAIN** 43
594 **WHITE NILE** (IRE) 12
357 **WHITE TOWER** (IRE) 4
446 **WHITE TURF** (IRE) 39
484 **WHITE WALKER** 119
356 **WHITECHURCH** (IRE) 119
252 **WHITEHALL** 6
384 **WHITEHAVEN** (FR) 47
212 **WHITEHOTCHILLIFILI** (IRE) 79
356 **WHITEOAK FLEUR** (IRE) 120
268 **WHITLOCK** 164
315 **WHO DARES WINS** (IRE) 135
526 **WHO SHOT JR** (IRE) 121
19 **WHO SPLASHED ME** C 19
531 **WHO TOLD JO JO** (IRE) 18
359 **WHO WHAT WHEN** 3
313 **WHO'S IN THE BOX** (IRE) 9
276 **WHO'S MY JOCKEY** (IRE) 13
173 **WHO'S THE BOSS** (IRE) 35
249 **WHO'S THE GUV'NOR** (IRE) 68
506 **WHOA BLACK BETTY** (IRE) 15
305 **WHOLESOME** (USA) F 255
524 **WHOLESTONE** (IRE) 94
129 **WHOOPSEY** 34
377 **WHOSHOTTHESHERIFF** (IRE) 78
402 **WHOSHOTWHO** (IRE) 68
377 **WHOWONTHETOSS** (IRE) 13
430 **WHY LIE** (IRE) 10
465 **WHY NOT QUEEN** (IRE) C 111
413 **WHY NOW** C 130
210 **WHY SO KEEN BOB** (IRE) 21
472 **WHYZZAT** 47
20 **WIBBLE WOBBLE** F 21
409 **WICHITA** (IRE) 108
534 **WICKED WILLY** (IRE) 95
406 **WICKLOW WARRIOR** 10
76 **WIDAAD** 46
94 **WIGHTMAN** (IRE) 73
472 **WIKI TIKI** C 48
338 **WILBERDRAGON** 65
128 **WILD ACADEMY** (IRE) F 112
359 **WILD ANIMAL** 4
254 **WILD CHILD** C 194
93 **WILD DANCER** 16
132 **WILD EDRIC** 18
361 **WILD FLOWER** (IRE) 10
17 **WILD HERO** (IRE) 120
465 **WILD HOPE** 30
6 **WILD HUNT** 111
405 **WILD MAX** (GER) 176
148 **WILD POLLY** (IRE) 42
484 **WILD ROMANCE** (IRE) 120
23 **WILD SAM** (IRE) 33
422 **WILD STORM** F 95
251 **WILD THUNDER** (IRE) 129
170 **WILDBEAUTIFULTHING** 157
484 **WILDE ABOUT OSCAR** (IRE) 121
315 **WILDE BLUE YONDER** (IRE) 136
129 **WILDE SPIRIT** (IRE) 35

TO ADVERTISE IN THE 2021 EDITION

OF HORSES IN TRAINING

OR TO REQUEST A RATE CARD,

PLEASE CALL

GARY MILLONE ON 01603 772463

RACING POST SHOP

Classic *reads*

£20

STARTING FROM SCRATCH INSPIRED TO BE A JUMP JOCKEY
HENRIETTA KNIGHT
Foreword by Sir Anthony McCoy

TIGER ROLL THE LITTLE LEGEND
RACING POST LEGENDS
EDITED BY ANDREW PENNINGTON

£20

Order now

 racingpost.com/shop   01933 304858

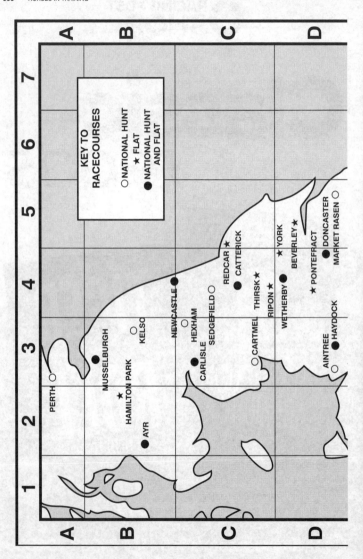

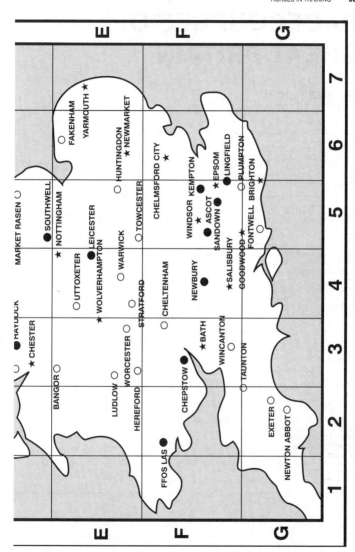

RACECOURSES OF GREAT BRITAIN

AINTREE (L.H)
Grand National Course: Triangular, 2m2f (16 fences) 494y run-in with elbow. Perfectly flat. A severe test for both horse and rider, putting a premium on jumping ability, fitness and courage.
Mildmay Course: Rectangular, 1m4f (8) 260y run-in. A very fast, flat course with sharp bends.
Address: Aintree Racecourse, Ormskirk Road, Aintree, Liverpool, L9 5AS Tel: 0151 523 2600
Website: www.aintree.co.uk
Managing Director: John Baker
Clerk of the Course: Sulekha Varma
By Road: North of the City, near the junction of the M57 and M58 with the A59 (Preston).
By Rail: Aintree Station is adjacent to the Stands, from Liverpool Central.
By Air: Liverpool (John Lennon) Airport is 10 miles. Helicopter landing facility by prior arrangement.

ASCOT (R.H)
Flat: Right-handed triangular track just under 1m6f in length. The Round course descends from the 1m4f start into Swinley Bottom, the lowest part of the track. It then turns right-handed and joins the Old Mile Course, which starts on a separate chute. The course then rises to the right-handed home turn over an underpass to join the straight mile course. The run-in is about 3f, rising slightly to the winning post. The whole course is of a galloping nature with easy turns.
N.H. Triangular, 1m6f (10), 240y run-in mostly uphill. A galloping course with an uphill finish, Ascot provides a real test of stamina. The fences are stiff and sound jumping is essential, especially for novices.
Address: Ascot Racecourse, Ascot, Berkshire SL5 7JX Tel: 08707 271234
Website: www.ascot.co.uk
Clerk of the Course: Chris Stickels 01344 878502 / 07970 621440
Chief Executive: Guy Henderson
By Road: West of the town on the A329. Easy access from the M3 (Junction 3) and the M4 (Junction 6). Car parking adjoining the course and Ascot Heath.
By Rail: Regular service from Waterloo to Ascot (500y from the racecourse).
By Air: Helicopter landing facility at the course. London (Heathrow) Airport 15 miles, White Waltham Airfield 12 miles (01427) 718800.

AYR (L.H)
Flat: A left-handed, galloping, flat oval track of 1m4f with a 4f run-in. The straight 6f is essentially flat.
N.H. Oval, 1m4f (9), 210y run-in. Relatively flat and one of the fastest tracks in Great Britain. It is a well-drained course and the ground rarely becomes testing. The track suits the long-striding galloper.
Address: Ayr Racecourse, Whitletts Road, Ayr, KA8 0JE Tel: 01292 264179
Website: www.ayr-racecourse.co.uk
Clerk of the Course: Graeme Anderson
Managing Director: David Brown
By Road: East of the town on the A758. Free parking for buses and cars.
By Rail: Ayr Station (trains on the half hour from Glasgow Central). Journey time 55 minutes. Buses and taxis also to the course.
By Air: Prestwick International Airport (10 minutes), Glasgow Airport (1 hour).

BANGOR-ON-DEE (L.H)

N.H. Circular, 1m4f (9), 325y run-in. Apart from some 'ridge and furrow', this is a flat course notable for three sharp bends, especially the paddock turn. Suits handy, speedy sorts.

Address: Bangor-On-Dee Racecourse, Overton Road, Bangor-On-Dee, Wrexham, LL13 0DA Tel: 01978 782081

Website: www.bangorondeeraces.co.uk

Clerk of the Course and Racing Manager: Andrew Morris

Chief Executive: Richard Thomas

General Manager: Jeannie Chantler

By Road: 5 miles south-east of Wrexham, off the B5069.

By Rail: Wrexham Station (bus or taxi to the course).

By Air: Helicopters may land by prior arrangement with Clerk of the Course.

BATH (L.H)

Flat: Galloping, left-handed, level oval of 1m4f, with long, stiff run-in of about 4f which bends to the left. An extended chute provides for sprint races.

Address: The Racecourse, Lansdown, Bath, BA1 9BU Tel: 01225 424609

Website: www.bath-racecourse.co.uk

Clerk of the Course: Tim Long

Executive Director: Liam Johnson

By Road: 2 miles northwest of the City (M4 Junction 18) at Lansdown. Unlimited free car and coach parking immediately behind the stands. Special bus services operate from Bath to the racecourse.

By Rail: Bath Station (from Paddington).

By Air: Bristol or Colerne Airports. Helicopter landing facilities available by prior arrangement.

BEVERLEY (R.H)

Flat: A right-handed oval of 1m3f, generally galloping, with an uphill run-in of two and a half furlongs. The 5f course is very stiff.

Address: Beverley Race Co. Ltd., York Road, Beverley, Yorkshire HU17 9QZ Tel: 01482 867488 / 882645

Website: www.beverley-racecourse.co.uk

Chief Executive and Clerk of the Course: Sally Iggulden 07850 458605

By Road: 7 miles from the M62 (Junction 38) off the A1035. Free car parking opposite the course. Owners and trainers use a separate enclosure.

By Rail: Beverley Station (Hull-Scarborough line). Occasional bus service to the course (1 mile).

BRIGHTON (L.H)

Flat: Left-handed, 1m4f horseshoe with easy turns and a run-in of three and a half furlongs. Undulating and sharp, the track suits handy types.

Address: Brighton Racecourse, Brighton, East Sussex BN2 2XZ Tel: 01273 603580

Website: www.brighton-racecourse.co.uk

Clerk of the Course: Philip Hide

Executive Director: Paul Ellison

By Road: East of the city on the A27 (Lewes Road). Car park adjoins the course.

By Rail: Brighton Station (from Victoria on the hour, London Bridge or Portsmouth). Special bus service to the course from the station (approx 2 miles).

By Air: Helicopters may land by prior arrangement.

CARLISLE (R.H)

Flat: Right-handed, 1m4f pear-shaped track. Galloping and undulating with easy turns and a stiff uphill run-in of three and a half furlongs. The 6f course begins on an extended chute.

N.H. Pear-shaped, 1m5f (9), 300y run-in uphill. Undulating and a stiff test of stamina, ideally suited to the long-striding thorough stayer.

Address: Carlisle Racecourse, Durdar Road, Carlisle CA2 4TS Tel: 01228 554700

Website: www.carlisle-races.co.uk

Regional Director: Dickon White

Joint Clerks of the Course: Sulekha Varma and Kirkland Tellwright

General Manager: Molly Dingwall

By Road: 2 miles south of the city (Durdar Road). Easy access from the M6 (Junction 42). The car park is free (adjacent to the course).

By Rail: Carlisle Station (2 miles from the course).

By Air: Helicopter landing facility by prior arrangement.

CARTMEL (L.H)

N.H. Oval, 1m1f (6), 800y run-in. Almost perfectly flat but very sharp, with the longest run-in in the country, approximately half a mile. The fences are stiff but fair.

Address: Cartmel Racecourse, Cartmel, nr Grange-Over-Sands, Cumbria LA11 6QF Tel: 01539 536340

Out of season: 01539 533335

Website: www.cartmel-racecourse.co.uk

General Manager: Geraldine McKay

Clerk of the Course: Anthea Morshead 07837 559861

By Road: 1 mile west of the town, 2 miles off the B5277 (Grange-Haverthwaite road). M6 (Junction 36).

By Rail: Cark-in-Cartmel Station (2 miles) (Carnforth-Barrow line). Raceday bus service.

By Air: Light aircraft facilities available at Cark Airport (4 miles from the course). Helicopter landing facility at the course, by prior arrangement only.

CATTERICK (L.H)

Flat: A sharp, left-handed, undulating oval of 1m180y with a downhill run-in of 3f.

N.H. Oval, 1m1f (9), 240y run-in. Undulating, sharp track that favours the handy, front-running sort, rather than the long-striding galloper.

Address: The Racecourse, Catterick Bridge, Richmond, North Yorkshire DL10 7PE Tel: 01748 811478

Website: www.catterickbridge.co.uk

General Manager and Clerk of the Course: Fiona Needham 07831 688625

By Road: The course is adjacent to the A1, 1 mile northwest of the town on the A6136. There is a free car park.

By Rail: Darlington Station (special buses to course - 14-mile journey).

By Air: Helicopters can land by prior arrangement. Fixed wing planes contact RAF Leeming Tel: 01677 423041

CHELMSFORD CITY (L.H)

Flat: A left-handed, floodlit Polytrack oval of 1m with sweeping bends and a 2f home straight. Races over 7f and 1m start from separate chutes.

Address: Chelmsford City Racecourse, Great Leighs, Essex, CM3 1QP Tel: 01245 362412

Website: www.chelmsfordcityracecourse.com

Manager: Fraser Garrity

Clerk of the Course: Andy Waitt

By Road: At Great Leighs, five miles north of Chelmsford on the A31

By Rail: Chelmsford station (from Liverpool Street)

By Air: Stansted Airport (17 miles)

CHELTENHAM (L.H)

Old Course: Oval, 1m4f, (9) 350y run-in. A testing, undulating track with stiff fences. The ability to stay is essential.

New Course: Oval, 1m5f (10), 220y run-in. Undulating, stiff fences, testing course, uphill for the final half-mile.

Address: Cheltenham Racecourse, Prestbury Park, Cheltenham, Gloucestershire GL50 4SH Tel: 01242 513014

Website: www.cheltenham.co.uk

Regional Director: Ian Renton

Regional Head of Racing and Clerk of the Course: Simon Claisse 07785 293966

By Road: 1.5 miles north of the town on the A435. M5 (Junction 10 or 11).

By Rail: Cheltenham Spa Station. Buses and taxis to course.

By Air: Helicopter landing site to the northeast of the stands.

CHEPSTOW (L.H)

Flat: A left-handed, undulating oval of about 2m, with easy turns, and a straight run-in of 5f. There is a straight track of 1m14y.

N.H. Oval, 2m (11), 240y run-in. Many changing gradients, five fences in the home straight. Favours the long-striding front-runner, but stamina is important.

Address: Chepstow Racecourse, Chepstow, Monmouthshire NP16 6BE Tel: 01291 622260

Website: www.chepstow-racecourse.co.uk

General Manager: Caroline Williams

Clerk of the Course: Libby O'Flaherty 07970 831987

Executive Director: Phil Bell

By Road: 1 mile north-west of the town on the A466. (1 mile from Junction 22 of the M4 (Severn Bridge) or M48 Junction 2. There is a free public car park opposite the entrance.

By Rail: Chepstow Station (from Paddington, change at Gloucester or Newport). The course is a mile from the station.

By Air: Helicopter landing facility in the centre of the course.

CHESTER (L.H)

Flat: A level, sharp, left-handed, circular course of 1m73y, with a short run-in of 230y.

Chester is a specialists' track which generally suits the sharp-actioned horse.

Address: The Racecourse, Chester CH1 2LY Tel: 01244 304600

Website: www.chester-races.co.uk

Racing Manager and Clerk of the Course: Andrew Morris

Chief Executive: Richard Thomas

By Road: The course is near the centre of the city on the A548 (Queensferry Road). The Owners' and Trainers' car park is adjacent to the Leverhulme Stand. There is a public car park in the centre of the course.

By Rail: Chester Station (3/4 mile from the course). Services from Euston, Paddington and Northgate.

By Air: Hawarden Airport (2 miles). Helicopters are allowed to land on the racecourse by prior arrangement only.

DONCASTER (L.H)

Flat: A left-handed, flat, galloping course of 1m7f 110y, with a long run-in which extends to a straight mile.

N.H. Conical, 2m (11), 247y run-in. A very fair, flat track ideally suited to the long-striding galloper.

Address: Doncaster Racecourse, Leger Way, Doncaster, DN2 6BB Tel: 01302 304200

Website: www.doncaster-racecourse.co.uk

Clerk of the Course: Roderick Duncan 07772 958685

Exective Director: Rachel Harwood

General Manager: Nikki Griffiths

By Road: East of the town, off the A638 (M18 Junctions 3 and 4). Club members' car park reserved. Large public car park free and adjacent to the course.

By Rail: Doncaster Central Station (from King's Cross). Special bus service from the station (1 mile).

By Air: Helicopter landing facility by prior arrangement only. Doncaster Robin Hood Airport is 15 minutes from the racecourse.

EPSOM (L.H)

Flat: Left-handed and undulating with easy turns, and a run-in of just under 4f. The straight 5f course is also undulating and downhill all the way, making it the fastest 5f in the world.
Address: The Racecourse, Epsom Downs, Surrey KT18 5LQ Tel: 01372 726311
Website: www.epsomderby.co.uk
Regional Director: Phil White
Clerk of the Course: Andrew Cooper Tel: 01372 726311 Mobile: 07774 230850
General Manager: Simon Durrant
  By Road: Two miles south of the town on the B290 (M25 Junctions 8 and 9). For full car park particulars apply to: The Club Secretary, Epsom Grandstand, Epsom Downs, Surrey KT18 5LQ. Tel: 01372 726311.
By Rail: Epsom, Epsom Downs or Tattenham Corner Stations (trains from London Bridge, Waterloo, Victoria). Regular bus services run to the course from Epsom and Morden Underground Station.
By Air: London (Heathrow) and London (Gatwick) are both within 30 miles of the course. Heliport (Derby Meeting only) - apply to Hascombe Aviation. Tel: 01279 680291.

EXETER (R.H)

N.H. Oval, 2m (11), 300y run-in uphill. Undulating with a home straight of half a mile. A good test of stamina, suiting the handy, well-balanced sort.
Address: Exeter Racecourse, Kennford, Exeter, Devon EX6 7XS Tel: 01392 832599
Website: www.exeter-racecourse.co.uk
Regional Director: Ian Renton
Clerk of the Course: Daniel Cooper 07976 413045
General Manager: Jack Parkinson
By Road: The course is at Haldon, 5 miles south-west of Exeter on the A38 (Plymouth) road, 2 miles east of Chudleigh.
By Rail: Exeter (St Davids) Station. Free bus service to course.
By Air: Helicopters can land by prior arrangement.

FAKENHAM (L.H)

N.H. Square, 1m (6), 200y run-in. On the turn almost throughout and undulating, suiting the handy front-runner. The going rarely becomes heavy.
Address: The Racecourse, Fakenham, Norfolk NR21 7NY Tel: 01328 862388
Website: www.fakenhamracecourse.co.uk
Clerk of the Course and Chief Executive: David Hunter Tel: 01328 862388 Mobile: 07767 802206
By Road: A mile south of the town on the B1146 (East Dereham) road.
By Rail: Norwich Station (26 miles) (Liverpool Street line), King's Lynn (22 miles) (Liverpool Street/Kings Cross).
By Air: Helicopter landing facility in the centre of the course by prior arrangement only.

FFOS LAS (L.H)

Flat The track is a 60m wide, basically flat, 1m4f oval with sweeping bends. Races over 5f and 6f start on a chute.
N.H. A flat, 1m4f oval (9). The going is often testing which places the emphasis on stamina.
Address: Ffos Las Racecourse, Trimsaran, Carmarthenshire SA17 4DE Tel: 01554 811092
Website: www.ffoslasracecourse.com
Executive Director: Phil Bell
Clerk of the Course and General Manager: Dai Jones
By Road: From the east take J48 from the M4 and join the A4138 to Llanelli, then follow the brown tourist signs to the racecourse. From the west take the A48 to Carmarthen then the A484 to Kidwelly before following the brown signs.
By Air: The course has the facilities to land helicopters on race days.

FONTWELL PARK (Fig. 8)
N.H. 2m (7), 230y run-in with left-hand bend close home. The figure-of-eight chase course suits handy types and is something of a specialists' track. The left-handed hurdle course is oval and one mile round. The bottom bend, which is shared, has been converted to Fibresand.
Address: Fontwell Park Racecourse, nr Arundel, West Sussex BN18 0SX Tel: 01243 543335
Website: www.fontwellpark.co.uk
Clerk of the Course: Philip Hide
Executive Director and General Manager: Jonathan Acott
By Road: South of village at the junction of the A29 (Bognor) and A27 (Brighton-Chichester) roads.
By Rail: Barnham Station (2 miles). Brighton-Portsmouth line (access via London Victoria).
By Air: Helicopter landing facility by prior arrangement with the Clerk of the Course.

GOODWOOD (R.H)
Flat: A sharp, undulating, essentially right-handed track with a long run-in. There is also a straight 6f course.
Address: Goodwood Racecourse Ltd., Goodwood, Chichester, West Sussex PO18 0PX Tel: 01243 755022
Website: www.goodwood.co.uk
Managing Director: Adam Waterworth
General Manager: Alex Eade
Clerk of the Course: Ed Arkell
By Road: 6 miles north of Chichester between the A286 and A285. There is a car park adjacent to the course. Ample free car and coach parking.
By Rail: Chichester Station (from Victoria or London Bridge). Regular bus service to the course (6 miles).
By Air: Helicopter landing facility by prior arrangement 01243 755030. Goodwood Airport 2 miles (taxi to the course).

HAMILTON PARK (R.H)
Flat: A sharp, undulating, right-handed course of 1m5f with a five and a half-furlong, uphill run-in. There is a straight track of 6f.
Address: Hamilton Park Racecourse, Bothwell Road, Hamilton, Lanarkshire ML3 0DW Tel: 01698 283806
Website: www.hamilton-park.co.uk
Clerk of the Course: to be announced
Chief Executive: Vivien Currie 01698 283806
By Road: Off the A72 on the B7071 (Hamilton-Bothwell road). (M74 Junction 5). Free parking for cars and buses.
By Rail: Hamilton West Station (1 mile).
By Air: Glasgow Airport (20 miles).

HAYDOCK PARK (L.H)
Flat: A galloping, almost flat, oval track, 1m5f round, with a run-in of four and a half furlongs and a straight six-furlong course.
N.H. Oval, 1m5f (10), 440y run-in. A flat, galloping chase course using portable fences. The hurdles track, which is sharp, is inside the chase course and has some tight bends.
Address: Haydock Park Racecourse, Newton-le-Willows, Merseyside WA12 0HQ Tel: 01942 402609
Website: www.haydock-park.co.uk
Regional Director: Dickon White
Regional Head of Racing and Clerk of the Course: Kirkland Tellwright 01942 725963 or 07748 181595
By Road: The course is on the A49 near Junction 23 of the M6.
By Rail: Newton-le-Willows Station (Manchester-Liverpool line) is 2.5 miles from the course. Earlstown 3 miles from the course. Warrington Bank Quay and Wigan are on the London to Carlisle/Glasgow line.
By Air: Landing facilities in the centre of the course for helicopters and planes not exceeding 10,000lbs laden weight.

HEREFORD (R.H)

N.H. Square, 1m4f (9), 300y run-in. The turns, apart from the final one that is on falling ground, are easily negotiated, placing the emphasis on speed rather than stamina. A handy position round the home turn is vital, as winners rarely come from behind. The hurdle track is on the outside of the chase course.

Address: Hereford Racecourse, Roman Road, Holmer, Hereford, HR4 9QU Tel: (01432) 273560
Website: www.hereford-racecourse.co.uk
Regional Executive Director: Rebecca Davies
Clerk of the Course: Tim Long
By Road: 1 mile north-west of the city centre off the A49 (Leominster) road.
By Rail: Hereford Station (1 mile from the course).

HEXHAM (L.H)

N.H. Oval, 1m4f (10), 220y run-in. An undulating course that becomes very testing when the ground is soft, it has easy fences and a stiff climb to the finishing straight, which is on a separate spur.

Address: Hexham Racecourse, The Riding, Hexham, Northumberland NE46 2JP Tel: 01434 606881
Racedays: 01434 603738
Website: www.hexham-racecourse.co.uk
Chief Executive: Robert Whitelock
Clerk of the Course: James Armstrong 01434 606881 or 07801 166820
By Road: 1.5 miles south-west of the town off the B6305.
By Rail: Hexham Station (Newcastle-Carlisle line). Free bus to the course.
By Air: Helicopter landing facility in centre of course (by special arrangement only).

HUNTINGDON (R.H)

N.H. Oval, 1m4f (9), 200y run-in. A perfectly flat, galloping track with a tricky open ditch in front of the stands. The two fences in the home straight can cause problems for novice chasers. Suits front-runners.

Address: The Racecourse, Brampton, Huntingdon, Cambridgeshire PE28 4NL Tel: 01480 453373
Website: www.huntingdon-racecourse.co.uk
Regional Director: Amy Starkey
Clerk of the Course: Jack Pryor
General Manager: to be announced
By Road: The course is situated at Brampton, 2 miles west of Huntingdon on the A14. Easy access from the A1 (1/2 mile from the course).
By Rail: Huntingdon Station. Buses and taxis to course.
By Air: Helicopter landing facility by prior arrangement.

KELSO (L.H)

N.H. Oval, 1m1f (8), uphill run-in of just over a furlong. Rather undulating with two downhill fences opposite the stands, it suits the nippy, front-running sort, though the uphill finish helps the true stayer. The hurdle course is smaller and very sharp with a tight turn away from the stands.

Address: Kelso Racecourse, Kelso, Roxburghshire TD5 7SX Tel: 01668 280800
Website: www.kelso-races.co.uk
Clerk of the Course: Anthea Morshead
Managing Director: Jonathan Garratt
By Road: 1 mile north of the town, off the B6461.
By Rail: Berwick-upon-Tweed Station. 23-mile bus journey to Kelso.
By Air: Helicopters can land at course by arrangement, fixed wing aircraft at Winfield, regular aircraft at Edinburgh.

KEMPTON PARK (R.H)

Flat: A floodlit Polytrack circuit. A 1m2f outer track accommodates races over 6f, 7f, 1m, 1m3f, 1m4f and 2m. The 1m inner track caters for races over 5f and 1m2f.

N.H. Triangular, 1m5f (10), 175y run-in. A practically flat, sharp course where the long run between the last obstacle on the far side and the first in the home straight switches the emphasis from jumping to speed. The hurdles track is on the outside of the chase track. The course crosses the Polytrack at two points on each circuit.

Address: Kempton Park Racecourse, Sunbury-on-Thames, Middlesex TW16 5AQ Tel: 01932 782292

Website: www.kempton.co.uk

Regional Director: Phil White

Clerk of the Course and Director of Racing: Brian Clifford 07880 784484

Assistant Clerk of the Course: Sarah Dunster

General Manager: Steve Parlett

By Road: On the A308 near Junction 1 of the M3.

By Rail: Kempton Park Station (from Waterloo).

By Air: London (Heathrow) Airport 6 miles.

LEICESTER (R.H)

Flat: A stiff, galloping, right-handed oval of 1m5f, with a 5f run-in. There is a straight course of seven furlongs.

N.H. Rectangular, 1m6f (10), 250y run-in uphill. An undulating course with an elbow 150y from the finish,it can demand a high degree of stamina, as the going can become extremely testing and the last three furlongs are uphill.

Address: Leicester Racecourse, Oadby, Leicester, LE2 4AL Tel: 01162 716515

Website: www.leicester-racecourse.co.uk

Clerk of the Course: Jimmy Stevenson 01162 712115 or 07774 497281

General Manager: Rob Bracken

By Road: The course is 2.5 miles south-east of the city on the A6 (M1, Junction 21). The car park is free.

By Rail: Leicester Station (from St Pancras) is 2.5 miles.

By Air: Helicopter landing facility in the centre of the course.

LINGFIELD PARK (L.H)

Flat, Turf: A sharp, undulating left-handed circuit, with a 7f 140y straight course.

Flat, Polytrack: The left-handed Polytrack is 1m2f round, with an extended chute to provide a 1m5f start. It is a sharp, level track with a short run-in.

N.H. Conical, 1m5f (10), 200y run-in. Severely undulating with a tight downhill turn into the straight, the chase course suits front-runners.

Address: Lingfield Park Racecourse, Lingfield, Surrey RH7 6PQ Tel: 01342 834800

Website: www.lingfield-racecourse.co.uk

Clerk of the Course: George Hill

Executive Director: Amy Smith

General Manager: Russell Bowes

By Road: South-east of the town off the A22; M25 (Junction 6). Ample free parking.

By Rail: Lingfield Station (regular services from London Bridge and Victoria). Half-mile walk to the course.

By Air: London (Gatwick) Airport 10 miles. Helicopter landing facility south of wind-sock.

LUDLOW (R.H)

N.H. Oval, 1m4f (9), 185y run-in. The chase course is flat and has quite sharp bends into and out of the home straight, although long-striding horses never seem to have any difficulties. The hurdle course is on the outside of the chase track and is not so sharp.

Address: Ludlow Race Club Ltd, The Racecourse, Bromfield, Ludlow, Shropshire SY8 2BT Tel: 01584 856221 (Racedays) or see below.

Website: www.ludlowracecourse.co.uk

General Manager and Clerk of the Course: Simon Sherwood

By Road: The course is situated at Bromfield, 2 miles north of Ludlow on the A49.

By Rail: Ludlow Station (Hereford-Shrewsbury line) 2 miles.

By Air: Helicopter landing facility in the centre of the course by arrangement with the Clerk of the Course

MARKET RASEN (R.H)

N.H. Oval, 1m2f (8), 250y run-in. A sharp, undulating course with a long run to the straight, it favours the handy, front-running type.

Address: Market Rasen Racecourse, Legsby Road, Market Rasen, Lincolnshire LN8 3EA Tel: 01673 843434

Website: www.marketrasenraces.co.uk

Regional Director: Amy Starkey

Clerk of the Course: Jack Pryor

General Manager: Nadia Powell

By Road: The town is just off the A46, and the racecourse is one mile east of the town on the A631. Free car parks.

By Rail: Market Rasen Station 1 mile (King's Cross - Cleethorpes line).

By Air: Helicopter landing facility by prior arrangement only.

MUSSELBURGH (R.H)

Flat: A sharp, level, right-handed oval of 1m2f, with a run-in of 4f. There is an additional 5f straight course.

N.H. Rectangular, 1m3f (8), 150y run-in (variable). A virtually flat track with sharp turns, suiting the handy, front-running sort. It drains well. There is a section of Polytrack going away from the stands.

Address: Musselburgh Racecourse, Linkfield Road, Musselburgh, East Lothian EH21 7RG

Tel: 01316 652859

Website: www.musselburgh-racecourse.co.uk

Clerk of the Course: Harriet Graham 07843 380401

General Manager: Bill Farnsworth 07710 536134

By Road: The course is situated at Musselburgh, 5 miles east of Edinburgh on the A1. Car park, adjoining course, free for buses and cars.

By Rail: Waverley Station (Edinburgh). Local Rail service to Musselburgh.

By Air: Edinburgh (Turnhouse) Airport 30 minutes.

NEWBURY (L.H)

Flat: Left-handed, oval track of about 1m7f, with a slightly undulating straight mile. The round course is level and galloping with a four and a half-furlong straight. Races over the round mile start on the adjoining chute.

N.H. Oval, 1m6f (11), 255y run-in. Slightly undulating, wide and galloping in nature. The fences are stiff and sound jumping is essential. One of the fairest tracks in the country.

Address: Newbury Racecourse, Newbury, Berkshire RG14 7NZ Tel: 01635 40015

Website: www.newbury-racecourse.co.uk

Chief Executive: Julian Thick

Clerk of the Course: Keith Ottesen 07813 043453

By Road: East of the town off the A34 (M4, Junction 12 or 13). Car park, adjoining enclosures, free.

By Rail: Newbury Racecourse Station adjoins the course.

By Air: Light Aircraft landing strip East/West. 830 metres by 30 metres wide. Helicopter landing facilities.

NEWCASTLE (L.H)

Flat: A 1m6f Tapeta track outside the jumps course. The straight mile is floodlit.

N.H. Oval, 1m6f (11), 220y run-in. A gradually rising home straight of four furlongs makes this galloping track a true test of stamina, especially as the ground can become very heavy.

Address: High Gosforth Park, Newcastle-Upon-Tyne, NE3 5HP Tel: 01912 362020

Website: www.newcastle-racecourse.co.uk

Clerk of the Course: James Armstrong 07801 166820

Executive Director: David Williamson

By Road: 4 miles north of the city on the A6125 (near the A1). Car and coach park free.

By Rail: Newcastle Central Station (from King's Cross). A free bus service operates from South Gosforth and Regent Centre Metro Station.

By Air: Helicopter landing facility by prior arrangement. The Airport is 4 miles from the course.

NEWMARKET (R.H)

Rowley Mile Course: There is a straight ten-furlong course, which is wide and galloping. Races over 1m4f or more are right-handed. The Rowley Mile course has a long run-in and a stiff finish.

July Course: Races up to a mile are run on the Bunbury course, which is straight. Races over 1m2f or more are right-handed, with a 7f run-in. Like the Rowley Mile course, the July Course track is stiff.

Address: Newmarket Racecourse, Westfield House, The Links, Newmarket, Suffolk CB8 0TG Tel: 01638 663482 (Main Office) 01638 663762 (Rowley Mile) 01638 675416 (July) .

Website: www.newmarketracecourses.co.uk

Clerk of the Course and Racing Director: Michael Prosser 01638 675504 or 07802 844578

Regional Director: Amy Starkey

General Manager: Sophie Able

By Road: South-west of the town on the A1304 London Road (M11 Junction 9). Free car parking at the rear of the enclosure. Annual Badge Holders' car park free all days. Courtesy bus service from Newmarket Station, Bus Station and High Street. , commencing 90 minutes prior to the first race.

By Rail: Infrequent rail service to Newmarket Station from Cambridge (Liverpool Street) or direct bus service from Cambridge (13-mile journey).

By Air: Landing facilities for light aircraft and helicopters on racedays at both racecourses. See Flight Guide. Cambridge Airport 11 miles.

NEWTON ABBOT (L.H)

N.H. Oval, 1m2f (7), 300y run-in. Flat with two tight bends. The nippy, agile sort is favoured. The run-in can be very short on the hurdle course.

Address: Newton Abbot Races Ltd., Kingsteignton Road, Newton Abbot, Devon TQ12 3AF Tel: 01626 353235

Website: www.newtonabbotracing.com

Clerk of the Course: Jason Loosemore 07766 228109

Managing Director: Pat Masterson Tel: 01626 353235 Mobile: 07917 830144

By Road: North of the town on the A380. Torquay 6 miles, Exeter 17 miles.

By Rail: Newton Abbot Station (from Paddington) 3/4 mile. Buses and taxis operate to and from the course.

By Air: Helicopter landing pad in the centre of the course.

NOTTINGHAM (L.H)

Flat: Left-handed, galloping, oval of about 1m4f, and a straight of four and a half furlongs. Flat with easy turns.

Address: Nottingham Racecourse, Colwick Park, Nottingham, NG2 4BE Tel: 0870 8507634

Website: www.nottinghamracecourse.co.uk

Regional Director: Amy Starkey

Clerk of the Course: Jane Hedley

Managing Director: James Knox

By Road: 2 miles east of the city centre on the B686.

By Rail: Nottingham (Midland) Station. Regular bus service to course (2 miles).

By Air: Helicopter landing facility in the centre of the course.

PERTH (R.H)

N.H. Rectangular, 1m2f (8), 283y run-in. A flat, easy track with sweeping turns. Not a course for the long-striding galloper.
Address: Perth Racecourse, Scone Palace Park, Perth, PH2 6BB Tel: 01738 551597
Website: www.perth-races.co.uk
Clerk of the Course: Matthew Taylor
General Manager: Hazel Peplinski
By Road: 4 miles north of the town off the A93.
By Rail: Perth Station (from Dundee) 4 miles. There are buses to the course.
By Air: Scone Airport (3.75 miles). Edinburgh Airport 45 minutes.

PLUMPTON (L.H)

N.H. Oval, 1m1f (7), 200y run-in uphill. A tight, undulating circuit with an uphill finish, Plumpton favours the handy, fast jumper. The ground often gets heavy, as the course is based on clay soil.
Address: Plumpton Racecourse, Plumpton, East Sussex BN7 3AL Tel: 01273 890383
Website: www.plumptonracecourse.co.uk
Clerk of the Course: Mark Cornford 07759 151617
Chief Executive: Daniel Thompson
By Road: 2 miles north of the village off the B2116.
By Rail: Plumpton Station (from Victoria) adjoins course.
By Air: Helicopter landing facility by prior arrangement with the Clerk of the Course.

PONTEFRACT (L.H)

Flat: Left-handed oval, undulating course of 2m133y, with a short run-in of 2f. It is a particularly stiff track with the last 3f uphill.
Address: Pontefract Park Race Co. Ltd., The Park, Pontefract, West Yorkshire Tel: 01977 781307
Website: www.pontefract-races.co.uk
Managing Director: Norman Gundill 01977 781307
Assistant Manager and Clerk of the Course: Richard Hamill
By Road: 1 mile north of the town on the A639. Junction 32 of M62. Free car park adjacent to the course.
By Rail: Pontefract Station (Tanshelf, every hour to Wakefield), 1 1/2 miles from the course. Regular bus service from Leeds.
By Air: Helicopters by arrangement only. (Nearest Airfields: Robin Hood (Doncaster), Sherburn-in-Elmet, Yeadon (Leeds Bradford).

REDCAR (L.H)

Flat: Left-handed, level, galloping, oval course of 1m6f with a straight run-in of 5f. There is also a straight mile.
Address: Redcar Racecourse, Redcar, Cleveland TS10 2BY Tel: 01642 484068
Website: www.redcarracing.org
Clerk of the Course: Jonjo Sanderson Tel: 01642 484068 Mobile: 07766 022893
General Manager: Amy Fair
By Road: In the town off the A1085. Free parking adjoining the course for buses and cars.
By Rail: Redcar Station (1/4 mile from the course).
By Air: Landing facilities at Turners Arms Farm (600yds runway) Yearby, Cleveland. Two miles south of the racecourse - transport available. Durham Tees Valley airport (18 miles west of Redcar).

RIPON (R.H)

Flat: A sharp, undulating, right-handed oval of 1m5f, with a 5f run-in. There is also a 6f straight course.
Address: Ripon Racecourse, Boroughbridge Road, Ripon, North Yorkshire HG4 1UG Tel: 01765 530530
Website: www.ripon-races.co.uk
Clerk of the Course and Managing Director: James Hutchinson 07860 679904
By Road: The course is situated 2 miles south-east of the city, on the B6265. There is ample free parking for cars and coaches.
By Rail: Harrogate Station (11 miles) or Thirsk (15 miles). Bus services to Ripon.
By Air: Helicopters only on the course. Otherwise Leeds/Bradford airport.

SALISBURY (R.H)

Flat: Right-handed and level, with a run-in of 4f. There is a straight mile track. The last half-mile is uphill, providing a stiff test of stamina.
Address: Salisbury Racecourse, Netherhampton, Salisbury, Wiltshire SP2 8PN Tel: 01722 326461
Website: www.salisburyracecourse.co.uk
Clerk of the Course and General Manager: Jeremy Martin 07880 744999
By Road: 3 miles south-west of the city on the A3094 at Netherhampton. Free car park adjoins the course.
By Rail: Salisbury Station is 3.5 miles (from London Waterloo). Bus service to the course.
By Air: Helicopter landing facility near the 1m2f start.

SANDOWN PARK (R.H)

Flat: An easy right-handed oval course of 1m5f with a stiff, straight uphill run-in of 4f. Separate straight 5f track is also uphill. Galloping.
N.H. Oval, 1m5f (11), 220y run-in uphill. Features seven fences on the back straight; the last three (the Railway Fences) are very close together and can often decide the outcome of races. The stiff climb to the finish puts the emphasis very much on stamina, but accurate-jumping, free-running sorts are also favoured. Hurdle races are run on the Flat course.
Address: Sandown Park Racecourse, Esher, Surrey KT10 9AJ Tel: 01372 464348
Website: www.sandown.co.uk
Regional Director: Phil White
Clerk of the Course: Andrew Cooper: 01372 461213 Mobile: 07774 230850
By Road: Four miles south-west of Kingston-on-Thames, on the A307 (M25 Junction 10).
By Rail: Esher Station (from Waterloo) adjoins the course.
By Air: London (Heathrow) Airport 12 miles.

SEDGEFIELD (L.H)

N.H. Oval, 1m2f (8), 200y run-in. Undulating with fairly tight turns, it doesn't suit big, long-striding horses.
Address: Sedgefield Racecourse, Sedgefield, Stockton-on-Tees, Cleveland TS21 2HW Tel: 01740 621925
Website: www.sedgefield-racecourse.co.uk
Clerk of the Course: Michael Naughton
General Manager: Emma White
By Road: 3/4 mile south-west of the town, near the junction of the A689 (Bishop Auckland) and the A177 (Durham) roads. The car park is free.
By Rail: Darlington Station (9 miles). Durham Station (12 miles).
By Air: Helicopter landing facility in car park area by prior arrangement only.

SOUTHWELL (L.H)
Flat, Fibresand: Left-handed oval, Fibresand course of 1m2f with a 3f run-in. There is a straight 5f. Track floodlit from 2019. Sharp and level, Southwell suits front-runners.
N.H. Oval, 1m 1f (7), 220y run-in. A tight, flat track with a short run-in, it suits front-runners.
Address: Southwell Racecourse, Rolleston, Newark, Nottinghamshire NG25 0TS Tel: 01636 814481
Website: www.southwell-racecourse.co.uk
Executive Director: Mark Clayton
Clerk of the Course: Paul Barker
By Road: The course is situated at Rolleston, 3 miles south of Southwell, 5 miles from Newark.
By Rail: Rolleston Station (Nottingham-Newark line) adjoins the course.
By Air: Helicopters can land by prior arrangement.

STRATFORD-ON-AVON (L.H)
N.H. Triangular, 1m2f (8), 200y run-in. Virtually flat with two tight bends, and quite a short home straight. A sharp and turning course, it suits the well-balanced, handy sort.
Address: Stratford Racecourse, Luddington Road, Stratford-upon-Avon, Warwickshire CV37 9SE
Tel: 01789 267949
Website: www.stratfordracecourse.net
Managing Director: Ilona Barnett
Clerk of the Course: Nessie Chanter
By Road: A mile from the town centre, off the A429 (Evesham road).
By Rail: Stratford-on-Avon Station (from Birmingham New Street or Leamington Spa) 1 mile.
By Air: Helicopter landing facility by prior arrangement.

TAUNTON (R.H)
N.H. Elongated oval, 1m2f (8), 150y run-in uphill. Sharp turns, especially after the winning post, with a steady climb from the home bend. Suits the handy sort.
Address: Taunton Racecourse, Orchard Portman, Taunton, Somerset TA3 7BL Tel: 01823 337172
Website: www.tauntonracecourse.co.uk
Clerk of the Course: Jason Loosemore
Chief Executive: Bob Young
By Road: Two miles south of the town on the B3170 (Honiton) road (M5 Junction 25).
By Rail: Taunton Station 2 miles. There are buses and taxis to course.
By Air: Helicopter landing facility by prior arrangement.

THIRSK (L.H)
Flat: Left-handed oval of 1m2f with sharp turns and an undulating run-in of 4f. There is a straight 6f track.
Address: The Racecourse, Station Road, Thirsk, North Yorkshire YO7 1QL Tel: 01845 522276
Website: www.thirskracecourse.net
Clerk of the Course and Managing Director: James Sanderson
By Road: West of the town on the A61. Free car park adjacent to the course for buses and cars.
By Rail: Thirsk Station (from King's Cross), 1/2 mile from the course.
By Air: Helicopters can land by prior arrangement. Tel: Racecourse 01845 522276. Fixed wing aircraft can land at RAF Leeming. Tel: 01677 423041. Light aircraft at Bagby. Tel: 01845 597385 or 01845 537555

TOWCESTER (R.H)
No fixtures scheduled for 2020

UTTOXETER (L.H)

N.H. Oval, 1m2f (8), 170y run-in. A few undulations, easy bends and fences and a flat home straight of over half a mile. Suits front-runners, especially on the 2m hurdle course.
Address: The Racecourse, Wood Lane, Uttoxeter, Staffordshire ST14 8BD Tel: 01889 562561
Website: www.uttoxeter-racecourse.co.uk
Clerk of the Course: Eloise Quayle
General Manager: Brian Barrass
By Road: South-east of the town off the B5017 (Marchington Road).
By Rail: Uttoxeter Station (Crewe-Derby line) adjoins the course.
By Air: Helicopters can land by prior arrangement with the raceday office.

WARWICK (L.H)

N.H. Circular, 1m6f (10), 240y run-in. Undulating with tight bends, five quick fences in the back straight and a short home straight, Warwick favours handiness and speed rather than stamina.
Address: Warwick Racecourse, Hampton Street, Warwick, CV34 6HN Tel: 01926 491553
Website: www.warwickracecourse.co.uk
Regional Director: Ian Renton
Clerk of the Course: Jane Hedley
General Manager: Andre Klein
By Road: West of the town on the B4095 adjacent to Junction 15 of the M40.
By Rail: Warwick or Warwick Parkway Stations.
By Air: Helicopters can land by prior arrangement with the Clerk of the Course.

WETHERBY (L.H)

Flat: First used in 2015, the Flat course is left-handed with a 1m4f circuit.
N.H. Oval, 1m4f (9), 200y run-in slightly uphill. A flat, very fair course which suits the long-striding galloper.
Address: The Racecourse, York Road, Wetherby, LS22 5EJ Tel: 01937 582035
Website: www.wetherbyracing.co.uk
Clerk of the Course and Chief Executive: Jonjo Sanderson 07831 437453
By Road: East of the town off the B1224 (York Road). Adjacent to the A1. Excellent bus and coach facilities. Car park free.
By Rail: Leeds Station 12 miles. Buses to Wetherby.
By Air: Helicopters can land by prior arrangement

WINCANTON (R.H)

N.H. Rectangular, 1m3f (9), 200y run-in. Good galloping course where the going rarely becomes heavy. The home straight is mainly downhill.
Address: Wincanton Racecourse, Wincanton, Somerset BA9 8BJ Tel: 01963 435840
Website: www.wincantonracecourse.co.uk
Regional Director: Ian Renton
Clerk of the Course: Daniel Cooper 07976 413045
General Manager: Huw Williams
By Road: 1 mile north of the town on the B3081.
By Rail: Gillingham Station (from Waterloo) or Castle Cary Station (from Paddington). Buses and taxis to the course.
By Air: Helicopter landing area is situated in the centre of the course.

WINDSOR (Fig. 8)

Flat: Figure of eight track of 1m4f 110y. The course is level and sharp with a long run-in. The 6f course is essentially straight.
Address: Royal Windsor Racecourse, Maidenhead Road, Windsor, Berkshire SL4 5JJ Tel: 01753 498400
Website: www.windsor-racecourse.co.uk
Clerk of the Course: Sophie Candy
Executive Director: Simon Williams
By Road: North of the town on the A308 (M4 Junction 6).
By Rail: Windsor Central Station (from Paddington) or Windsor and Eton Riverside Station (from Waterloo).
By Air: London (Heathrow) Airport 15 minutes. Also White Waltham Airport (West London Aero Club) 15 minutes.
River Bus: Seven minutes from Barry Avenue promenade at Windsor.

WOLVERHAMPTON (L.H)

Flat: Left-handed, floodlit, oval Tapeta track of 1m, with a run-in of 380y. A level track with sharp bends.
Address: Wolverhampton Racecourse, Dunstall Park, Gorsebrook Road, Wolverhampton, WV6 0PE Tel: 01902 390000
Website: www.wolverhampton-racecourse.co.uk
Clerk of the Course: Fergus Cameron 07971 531162
General Manager: Dave Roberts
By Road: 1 mile north of the city centre on the A449 (M54 Junction 2 or M6 Junction 12).
Car parking free.
By Rail: Wolverhampton Station (from Euston) 1 mile.
By Air: Halfpenny Green Airport 8 miles.

WORCESTER (L.H)

N.H. Elongated oval, 1m5f (9), 220y run-in. Flat with easy turns, it is a very fair, galloping track.
Address: Worcester Racecourse, Pitchcroft, Worcester, WR1 3EJ Tel: 01905 25364
Website: www.worcester-racecourse.co.uk
Clerk of the Course: Tim Long
Regional Executive Director: Rebecca Davies
General Manager: Michael Thomas
By Road: West of the city centre off the A449 (Kidderminster road) (M5 Junction 8).
By Rail: Foregate Street Station, Worcester (from Paddington) ³/₄ mile.
By Air: Helicopter landing facility in the centre of the course, by prior arrangement only.

YARMOUTH (L.H)

Flat: Left-handed, level circuit of 1m4f, with a run-in of 5f. The straight course is 1m long.
Address: The Racecourse, Jellicoe Road, Great Yarmouth, Norfolk NR30 4AU Tel: 01493 842527
Website: www.greatyarmouth-racecourse.co.uk
Clerk of the Course: Richard Aldous 07738 507643
Executive Director: Glenn Tubby
By Road: 1 mile east of town centre (well signposted from A47 and A12).
By Rail: Great Yarmouth Station (1 mile). Bus service to the course.
By Air: Helicopter landing available by prior arrangement with Racecourse Office

YORK (L.H)

Flat: Left-handed, level, galloping track, with a straight 6f. There is also an adjoining chute for races over 7f.
Address: The Racecourse, York, YO23 1EX Tel: 01904 683932
Website: www.yorkracecourse.co.uk
Clerk of the Course and Chief Executive: William Derby 07812 961176
Assistant Clerk of the Course: Anthea Morshead
By Road: 1 mile south-east of the city on the A1036.
By Rail: 1 1/2 miles York Station (from King's Cross). Special bus service from station to the course.
By Air: Light aircraft and helicopter landing facilities available at Rufforth aerodrome (5,000ft tarmac runway). Leeds Bradford airport (25 miles).

THE INVESTEC DERBY STAKES (GROUP 1)
EPSOM DOWNS ON SATURDAY 6TH JUNE 2020

SECOND ENTRIES BY NOON APRIL 7TH; SUPPLEMENTARY ENTRIES BY NOON JUNE 1ST.

HORSE	TRAINER	HORSE	TRAINER
AJMAN SEA	HENRI FRANCOIS DEVIN	DAWN PATROL (IRE)	AIDAN O'BRIEN
AL AASY (IRE)	WILLIAM HAGGAS	DAWN RISING (IRE)	AIDAN O'BRIEN
AL FAYYAAFY	OWEN BURROWS	DAYLIGHT COME (IRE)	J. S. BOLGER
AL SALT (IRE)	WILLIAM HAGGAS	DELPHI (IRE)	AIDAN O'BRIEN
AL ZARAQAAN	WILLIAM HAGGAS	DELTA DAWN (IRE)	AIDAN O'BRIEN
ALLGOLD (IRE)	MARK JOHNSTON	DESERT EMPEROR	ROGER VARIAN
ALMIGHWAR	JOHN GOSDEN	DESERT HIGHWAY (IRE)	D. K. WELD
ALPHABETICAL	SIR MARK PRESCOTT BT	DESERT WAVE	SIR MICHAEL STOUTE
AMHRAN NA BHFIANN (IRE)	AIDAN O'BRIEN	DIYARI (IRE)	JOHN GOSDEN
ANCESTRY	J. S. BOLGER	DO YOU LOVE ME (IRE)	K. R. BURKE
ARMORY (IRE)	AIDAN O'BRIEN	DOLLAR BID	SIR MICHAEL STOUTE
ARROW OF GOLD (IRE)	KEVIN RYAN	DREAM WITH ME (IRE)	MARK JOHNSTON
ARTHUR'S KINGDOM (IRE)	AIDAN O'BRIEN	DUKE OF ORLEANS (IRE)	AIDAN O'BRIEN
ASHTARAK (IRE)	D. K. WELD	DUNE OF PILAT (FR)	JOSEPH PATRICK O'BRIEN
ASTRO KING (IRE)	SIR MICHAEL STOUTE	EAGLESGLEN	TOM CLOVER
ATLANTIC CROSSING (IRE)	PAUL COLE	EDREMI (FR)	JEAN CLAUDE ROUGET
BARON SAMEDI	JOSEPH PATRICK O'BRIEN	EMARATY HERO	K. R. BURKE
BERKSHIRE ROCCO (FR)	ANDREW BALDING	EMPEROR OF THE SUN (IRE)	DONNACHA AIDAN O'BRIEN
BEYOND HAPPY (IRE)	J. S. BOLGER	ENEMY	JOHN GOSDEN
BLIGH (IRE)	JOSEPH PATRICK O'BRIEN	ENGLISH KING (FR)	ED WALKER
BLOW YOUR HORN (IRE)	CHARLIE FELLOWES	EZEKIEL (IRE)	J. S. BOLGER
BODYLINE (IRE)	SIR MARK PRESCOTT BT	FATHER OF JAZZ	MICHAEL BELL
BOSS POWER (IRE)	SIR MICHAEL STOUTE	FIRST RECEIVER	SIR MICHAEL STOUTE
BRACKISH	JOHN GOSDEN	FISCAL RULES (IRE)	J. S. BOLGER
BRIGHT EYED EAGLE (IRE)	ED WALKER	FLASHING APPROACH (IRE)	MARK JOHNSTON
BUSINESS (FR)	JOHN QUINN	FLYING SCOTSMAN (IRE)	AIDAN O'BRIEN
BYZANTINE EMPIRE	JOHN GOSDEN	FOX DUTY FREE (IRE)	ANDREW BALDING
CABOT CLIFFS (IRE)	CHARLES HILLS	FRATERCULUS (IRE)	J. S. BOLGER
CABOT HILLS (IRE)	DONNACHA AIDAN O'BRIEN	FRENCH ASSET (IRE)	SIR MICHAEL STOUTE
CALCULATING	P. BARY	FRONT PAGING (IRE)	J. S. BOLGER
CALDWELL	D. K. WELD	GAUNTLET (IRE)	AIDAN O'BRIEN
CANBERRA (IRE)	PETER CHAPPLE-HYAM	GIBSON DESERT	MRS J. HARRINGTON
CAPE PALACE	JOHN GOSDEN	GOLD COAST (IRE)	AIDAN O'BRIEN
CARIBENO	SIR MARK PRESCOTT BT	GOLD SOUK (IRE)	MARK JOHNSTON
CASPIAN SEA (IRE)	AIDAN O'BRIEN	GOLDEN PINE (IRE)	SIR MICHAEL STOUTE
CELTIC HIGH KING (IRE)	AIDAN O'BRIEN	GOLDEN RULES	JOHN GOSDEN
CHACHNAK (FR)	FABRICE VERMEULEN	GRAND BAZAAR	JOHN GOSDEN
CHAIRMAN POWER	SIR MICHAEL STOUTE	GRAND ROCK (IRE)	WILLIAM HAGGAS
CHEROKEE TRAIL (USA)	JOHN GOSDEN	GREEK GLADIATOR (IRE)	AIDAN O'BRIEN
CHOCTAW RIDGE (IRE)	AIDAN O'BRIEN	HAFEETH (USA)	OWEN BURROWS
CHRONOS	P. BARY	HARAKANN (IRE)	M. HALFORD
CIEL D'AFRIQUE (IRE)	D. K. WELD	HARPOCRATES (IRE)	AIDAN O'BRIEN
CIVILIAN	F. HEAD	HEATH	
CLASSICAL WAVE	HENRI FRANCOIS DEVIN	HERMAN HESSE	S. BROGI
COINCIDENCE	WILLIAM HAGGAS	HERO OF THE HOUR	WILLIAM HAGGAS
COLONIZE	JOHN GOSDEN	HIGHEST GROUND (IRE)	SIR MICHAEL STOUTE
CONAN DOYLE (IRE)	AIDAN O'BRIEN	HMS PRESIDENT (IRE)	EVE JOHNSON HOUGHTON
CONSCIOUS	ROGER CHARLTON	HONORE DAUMIER (IRE)	HENRY CANDY
CONVICT	WILLIAM HAGGAS	HOOK HEAD (IRE)	J. S. BOLGER
COPPER POINT (IRE)	JOHN GOSDEN	HOOTTON (FR)	FABRICE VERMEULEN
CORMORANT (IRE)	AIDAN O'BRIEN	HORSE	TRAINER
COUNT OF AMAZONIA (IRE)	RICHARD HANNON	HOSIER (IRE)	JOSEPH PATRICK O'BRIEN
COUNTER ATTACK (IRE)	AIDAN O'BRIEN	HOVER (IRE)	MARTYN MEADE
COVENTRY (IRE)	AIDAN O'BRIEN	HUKUM (IRE)	OWEN BURROWS
COZONE	AMANDA PERRETT	HYDROS	SIR MICHAEL STOUTE
CROSSING THE BAR (IRE)	SIR MICHAEL STOUTE	IBERIA (IRE)	AIDAN O'BRIEN
CRYSTAL PEGASUS	SIR MICHAEL STOUTE	INCENDIERE (IRE)	FABRICE VERMEULEN
DARAIN	JOHN GOSDEN	INDIGO LAKE	JOHN GOSDEN
DARKOT (FR)	M. DELZANGLES	INDURO DE FONTAINE (FR)	GAY KELLEWAY

HORSE	TRAINER	HORSE	TRAINER
INNISFREE (IRE)	AIDAN O'BRIEN	PAPA POWER	ANDREW BALDING
IRISH MASTER (IRE)	MRS J. HARRINGTON	PARADISO (IRE)	AIDAN O'BRIEN
JACKSONIAN	RALPH BECKETT	PASO DOBLE (IRE)	J. S. BOLGER
JULIUSJULIUSSON (USA)	P. BARY	PERSIA (IRE)	AIDAN O'BRIEN
KAMEKO (USA)	ANDREW BALDING	PHAROAH KING (USA)	JOHN GOSDEN
KATZOFF (IRE)	RICHARD HANNON	PLATEAU (IRE)	AIDAN O'BRIEN
KEATS (IRE)	AIDAN O'BRIEN	PORT LOCKROY (FR)	AIDAN O'BRIEN
KELLS (IRE)	AIDAN O'BRIEN	POSTILEO (IRE)	ROGER VARIAN
KHABAAB (IRE)	SAEED BIN SUROOR	POTALA PALACE	JOSEPH PATRICK O'BRIEN
KHALIFA SAT (IRE)	ANDREW BALDING	PRINCE IMPERIAL (USA)	SIR MICHAEL STOUTE
KHALOOSY (IRE)	ROGER VARIAN	PRINCE OF EAGLES (IRE)	DAVID LANIGAN
KHATM	SAEED BIN SUROOR	RAAMEZ (IRE)	J. HAMMOND
KING FAIRY (IRE)	WILLIAM HAGGAS	RAANY	J. HAMMOND
KINGBROOK	MARK JOHNSTON	RAMESSES THE GREAT (USA)	AIDAN O'BRIEN
KINGDOMFORAHORSE	ISMAIL MOHAMMED	RED CELEBRE (IRE)	ED DUNLOP
KIPLING (IRE)	AIDAN O'BRIEN	REPUBLIC (IRE)	J. S. BOLGER
KIPPS (IRE)	HUGHIE MORRISON	RETROSPECT (IRE)	ROGER VARIAN
LANDMARK (IRE)	AIDAN O'BRIEN	RIDWAAN (FR)	M. DELZANGLES
LAW OF ONE (IRE)	SIR MICHAEL STOUTE	ROBERT WALPOLE	
LE SOLAIRE	P. BARY	ROCKET ROD (IRE)	HUGO PALMER
LOKHAR (FR)	M. DELZANGLES	ROYAL ARRIVAL (IRE)	SAEED BIN SUROOR
LONGSIDER (IRE)	DAVID LANIGAN	ROYAL COUNTY DOWN (IRE)	AIDAN O'BRIEN
LOPE Y FERNANDEZ (IRE)	AIDAN O'BRIEN	ROYAL DORNOCH (IRE)	AIDAN O'BRIEN
LORDOFTHEHORIZON (FR)	JOHN GOSDEN	ROYAL LYTHAM (FR)	AIDAN O'BRIEN
LOST EDEN (IRE)	RICHARD HANNON	ROYAUME UNI (IRE)	AIDAN O'BRIEN
LOUISIANA (IRE)	AIDAN O'BRIEN	RUSKIN (IRE)	P. BARY FRANCE
LOUVE	FABRICE VERMEULEN	RUSSIAN EMPEROR (IRE)	AIDAN O'BRIEN
LUCK ON SUNDAY (IRE)	JOHN QUINN	SAN PEDRO (IRE)	AIDAN O'BRIEN
LUNCIES	SIMON CRISFORD	SANTIAGO (IRE)	AIDAN O'BRIEN
LYDFORD	MICHAEL BELL	SATONO JAPAN (JPN)	SIR MICHAEL STOUTE
MAMBO NIGHTS (IRE)	RICHARD HANNON	SERPENTINE (IRE)	AIDAN O'BRIEN
MAORI KNIGHT (IRE)	RICHARD HUGHES	SHEER BRAVADO (IRE)	J. S. BOLGER
MARK OF GOLD	RICHARD HANNON	SHEKHEM (IRE)	D. K. WELD
MASTERDREAM (FR)	JOHN M. OXX	SHERAZ (FR)	A. DE ROYER DUPRE
MATTHEW FLINDERS	ED WALKER	SHERPA (IRE)	DONNACHA AIDAN O'BRIEN
MEMORABILIS (IRE)	AIDAN O'BRIEN	SHOSHONE WARRIOR (IRE)	AIDAN O'BRIEN
MET OFFICE (IRE)	HENRI FRANCOIS DEVIN	SILVER FOX (IRE)	AIDAN O'BRIEN
MOGUL	AIDAN O'BRIEN	SINJAR (USA)	
MOLINARI (IRE)	WILLIAM MUIR	SKY COMMANDER (IRE)	JAMES TATE
MONARCH OF EGYPT (USA)	AIDAN O'BRIEN	SOLAR SCREEN (IRE)	ROGER VARIAN
MONOPOLY (IRE)	JOSEPH PATRICK O'BRIEN	SOLAR SYSTEM (IRE)	J. S. BOLGER
MONUMENT VALLEY (IRE)	AIDAN O'BRIEN	SON OF RED (IRE)	ALAN KING
MOOMBA (IRE)	AMANDA PERRETT	SOUTHERN HILLS (IRE)	AIDAN O'BRIEN
MOSHADID (IRE)	F. HEAD	SPANISH CHESTNUT (USA)	AIDAN O'BRIEN
MR CURIOSITY		SPANISH KISS	WILLIAM KNIGHT
MR G	WILLIAM HAGGAS	ST JUST	WILLIAM HAGGAS
MR POY	HUGHIE MORRISON	STAR OF JUNIPER (JPN)	DONNACHA AIDAN O'BRIEN
MR TAMBOURINE MAN (IRE)	SIR MICHAEL STOUTE	STAR OF WELLS (IRE)	TOM WARD
MY FRANKEL	SIR MICHAEL STOUTE	STARCAT	HUGHIE MORRISON
MY INTENTION	SIR MICHAEL STOUTE	STEPNEY CAUSEWAY	MICHAEL BELL
MY OBERON (IRE)	WILLIAM HAGGAS	SUMMIT REACH	RALPH BECKETT
MYKONOS (IRE)	AIDAN O'BRIEN	SUNCHART	A. SLATTERY
MYTHICAL (FR)	AIDAN O'BRIEN	SWITCHMAN (IRE)	KEVIN RYAN
NAPA VALLEY (IRE)	AIDAN O'BRIEN	TAMMANI	WILLIAM HAGGAS
NASHY (IRE)	SIR MICHAEL STOUTE	TAQAREER (IRE)	JOHN GOSDEN
NASRAAWY (USA)	JOHN GOSDEN	TARAMANSOUR (IRE)	D. K. WELD
NEVENDON	MICHAEL BELL	TEXTUS RECEPTUS (IRE)	J. S. BOLGER
NIBRAS WISH (IRE)	ISMAIL MOHAMMED	THAI POWER (IRE)	ANDREW BALDING
NOBEL PRIZE (IRE)	AIDAN O'BRIEN	THAMES RIVER	JOSEPH PATRICK O'BRIEN
NOONDAY GUN	RICHARD HANNON	THANK YOU POWER (IRE)	DAVID ELSWORTH
NOVA ROMA	JOHN GOSDEN	THE BOATMAN (IRE)	AIDAN O'BRIEN
NUGGET	RICHARD HANNON	THE CITY'S PHANTOM	RICHARD SPENCER
NUMBERONESON (IRE)	JOSEPH PATRICK O'BRIEN	THE SEVENTH DAY (IRE)	RICHARD HANNON
NUMEN (IRE)	AIDAN O'BRIEN	THEOCRAT (IRE)	J. S. BOLGER
ORDER OF AUSTRALIA (IRE)	AIDAN O'BRIEN	THRILL SEEKER (IRE)	WILLIAM HAGGAS
PALM BEACH (IRE)	AIDAN O'BRIEN	THUMUR (USA)	OWEN BURROWS

HORSE	TRAINER
THUNDEROUS (IRE)	MARK JOHNSTON
TIGER MOTH (IRE)	AIDAN O'BRIEN
TIMOURID (IRE)	D. K. WELD
TO NATHANIEL	JOHN GOSDEN
TORONTO (IRE)	AIDAN O'BRIEN
TRADING UP (IRE)	J. S. BOLGER
TRUMPET MAN	MARK JOHNSTON
TUSCAN GAZE (IRE)	JOHN GOSDEN
TYSON FURY	RICHARD SPENCER
UNDARK (USA)	A. FABRE
URSA MINOR (IRE)	JOHN GOSDEN
VADABAD (FR)	A. DE ROYER DUPRE
VAKILABAD (FR)	A. DE ROYER DUPRE
VALYRIAN STEEL (IRE)	ROGER VARIAN
VATICAN CITY (IRE)	AIDAN O'BRIEN
VELAMAR (FR)	JEAN CLAUDE ROUGET

HORSE	TRAINER
VERDON GORGE (IRE)	JOSEPH PATRICK O'BRIEN
VERINI (FR)	A. DE ROYER DUPRE
VERMILION CLIFFS (IRE)	AIDAN O'BRIEN
VICTORY ROAD (IRE)	AIDAN O'BRIEN
VICTORY WON (USA)	ED VAUGHAN
VINDICATE	SIR MICHAEL STOUTE
VINTAGE RASCAL (FR)	TOM WARD
WALDKONIG	JOHN GOSDEN
WAR CABINET (IRE)	AIDAN O'BRIEN
WAR CROSS (USA)	ED VAUGHAN
WOODSTOCK PARK	A. FABRE
YANKEE STADIUM (IRE)	AIDAN O'BRIEN
YEAR OF THE TIGER (IRE)	AIDAN O'BRIEN
ZEYREK (FR)	A. DE ROYER DUPRE
EX LAHINCH CLASSICS (IRE)	AIDAN O'BRIEN
EX MAGICAL DREAM (IRE)	AIDAN O'BRIEN

HENRIETTA KNIGHT

STARTING FROM SCRATCH INSPIRED TO BE A JUMP JOCKEY

Foreword by Sir Anthony McCoy

£20

RACING POST SHOP

Order now

racingpost.com/shop

01933 304858

THE BET365
EUROPEAN FREE HANDICAP STAKES
NEWMARKET CRAVEN MEETING 2020
(ON THE ROWLEY MILE COURSE)
WEDNESDAY APRIL 15TH

The bet365 European Free Handicap Stakes (Class 1) (Listed race) with total prize fund of £50,000 for **three-year-olds only** (Two-year-olds of 2019 which are included in the European 2-y-o Thoroughbred Rankings or which, in 2019, either ran in Great Britain or ran for a trainer who at the time was licensed by the British Horseracing Authority, and are Rated 100 or above); lowest weight 8st; highest weight 9st 7lb.

Penalty for a winner after December 31st 2019 to be at the discretion of the BHA Handicapper. Seven furlongs.

Rating		st	lb	Rating		st	lb
128	**Pinatubo** (IRE)	9	7	108	**So Wonderful** (USA)	8	1
118	**Earthlight** (IRE)	8	11	107	**Al Dabaran** (GB)	8	0
118	**Kameko** (USA)	8	11	107	**Boomer** (GB)	8	0
116	**Arizona** (IRE)	8	9	107	**Fort Myers** (USA)	8	0
115	**Millisle** (IRE)	8	8	107	**Lope Y Fernandez** (IRE)	8	0
115	**Mums Tipple** (IRE)	8	8	107	**Mythical** (FR)	8	0
114	**Albigna** (IRE)	8	7	107	**Tammani** (GB)	8	0
114	**Golden Horde** (IRE)	8	7	107	**Ventura Rebel** (GB)	8	0
114	**Quadrilateral** (GB)	8	7	106	**Cloak of Spirits** (IRE)	7	13
114	**Raffle Prize** (IRE)	8	7	106	**Dark Lady** (GB)	7	13
114	**Siskin** (USA)	8	7	106	**Iberia** (IRE)	7	13
114	**Threat** (IRE)	8	7	106	**Kimari** (USA)	7	13
114	**Victor Ludorum** (GB)	8	7	106	**Living In The Past** (IRE)	7	13
114	**Wichita** (IRE)	8	7	106	**Platinum Star** (IRE)	7	13
113	**Military March** (GB)	8	6	106	**Shadn** (IRE)	7	13
113	**Positive** (GB)	8	6	106	**Sir Boris** (IRE)	7	13
113	**Powerful Breeze** (GB)	8	6	106	**Stylistique** (GB)	7	13
112	**A'Ali** (IRE)	8	5	106	**Sunday Sovereign** (GB)	7	13
112	**Al Suhail** (GB)	8	5	106	**Under The Stars** (IRE)	7	13
112	**King's Command** (GB)	8	5	106	**Valdermoro** (USA)	7	13
112	**Mkfancy** (FR)	8	5	106	**Vitalogy** (GB)	7	13
112	**Rubaiyat** (FR)	8	5	105	**Air Force Jet** (GB)	7	12
112	**Wonderful Moon** (GER)	8	5	105	**Alpen Rose** (IRE)	7	12
111	**Alson** (GER)	8	4	105	**Harpocrates** (IRE)	7	12
111	**Innisfree** (IRE)	8	4	105	**Kinross** (GB)	7	12
111	**Love** (IRE)	8	4	105	**Liberty Beach** (GB)	7	12
111	**Monarch of Egypt** (USA)	8	4	105	**Maven** (USA)	7	12
111	**Royal Lytham** (FR)	8	4	105	**Run Wild** (GER)	7	12
111	**Tropbeau** (GB)	8	4	105	**Strive For Glory** (USA)	7	12
110	**Armory** (IRE)	8	3	105	**Visinari** (FR)	7	12
110	**Cayenne Pepper** (IRE)	8	3	104	**Al Raya** (GB)	7	11
110	**Daahyeh** (GB)	8	3	104	**Alligator Alley** (GB)	7	11
110	**Ecrivain** (FR)	8	3	104	**Band Practice** (IRE)	7	11
110	**Max Vega** (IRE)	8	3	104	**Berkshire Rocco** (FR)	7	11
110	**Mogul** (GB)	8	3	104	**Dr Simpson** (FR)	7	11
110	**Mystery Power** (IRE)	8	3	104	**Dream Shot** (IRE)	7	11
110	**Pierre Lapin** (IRE)	8	3	104	**Guildsman** (GB)	7	11
110	**Royal Crusade** (GB)	8	3	104	**Summer Romance** (IRE)	7	11
110	**Royal Dornoch** (IRE)	8	3	104	**Tango** (IRE)	7	11
110	**Year of The Tiger** (IRE)	8	3	104	**Temple of Heaven** (GB)	7	11
109	**Lord of The Lodge** (IRE)	8	2	104	**Well of Wisdom** (GB)	7	11
109	**Summer Sands** (GB)	8	2	104	**Wheels On Fire** (FR)	7	11
108	**Juan Elcano** (GB)	8	1	103	**Final Song** (IRE)	7	10
108	**King Neptune** (USA)	8	1	103	**Pistoletto** (USA)	7	10
108	**Pocket Square** (GB)	8	1	103	**Pyledriver** (GB)	7	10

Rating		st	lb	Rating		st	lb
103	**Queen Daenerys** (IRE)	7	10	101	**Lady Penelope** (IRE)	7	8
103	**Rose of Kildare** (IRE)	7	10	101	**Night Colours** (IRE)	7	8
103	**Sound of Cannons** (GB)	7	10	101	**Nurse Barbara** (IRE)	7	8
103	**Streamline** (GB)	7	10	101	**Repartee** (IRE)	7	8
103	**Thunderous** (IRE)	7	10	101	**Ropey Guest** (GB)	7	8
102	**Blissful** (IRE)	7	9	101	**Show Me Show Me** (GB)	7	8
102	**Kenzai Warrior** (USA)	7	9	101	**Southern Hills** (IRE)	7	8
102	**King Carney** (GB)	7	9	101	**Sun Power** (FR)	7	8
102	**Miss Yoda** (GER)	7	9	101	**Troubador** (IRE)	7	8
102	**Mohican Heights** (IRE)	7	9	101	**Walk In Marrakesh** (IRE)	7	8
102	**Molatham** (GB)	7	9	100	**Above** (NZ)	7	7
102	**Nina Bailarina** (GB)	7	9	100	**Born With Pride** (IRE)	7	7
102	**Persia** (IRE)	7	9	100	**Celtic Beauty** (IRE)	7	7
102	**Royal Commando** (IRE)	7	9	100	**Etoile** (USA)	7	7
102	**Symbolize** (IRE)	7	9	100	**Geometrical** (IRE)	7	7
102	**Volatile Analyst** (USA)	7	9	100	**Lazuli** (IRE)	7	7
101	**Aberama Gold** (GB)	7	8	100	**Malotru** (GB)	7	7
101	**Ananya** (GB)	7	8	100	**Maxi Boy** (GB)	7	7
101	**Celtic Art** (FR)	7	8	100	**Milltown Star** (GB)	7	7
101	**Divine Spirit** (GB)	7	8	100	**Monoski** (USA)	7	7
101	**Fan Club Rules** (IRE)	7	8	100	**Oh Purple Reign** (IRE)	7	7
101	**Good Vibes** (GB)	7	8	100	**Peaceful** (IRE)	7	7
101	**Highland Chief** (IRE)	7	8	100	**Premier Power** (GB)	7	7
101	**Isabeau** (IRE)	7	8	100	**Ventura Lightning** (FR)	7	7
101	**Istanbul** (IRE)	7	8	100	**Wyclif** (GB)	7	7

LONGINES WORLD'S BEST RACEHORSE RANKINGS AND EUROPEAN THOROUGHBRED RANKINGS 2019

for **three-year-olds** rated 115 or greater by the IFHA World's Best Racehorse Rankings Conference. Horses rated 114-110 by the European Thoroughbred Rankings Conference do not constitute a part of the World's Best Racehorse Rankings. Those ratings were compiled on behalf of the European Pattern Committee.

Rating		Trained
123	Sottsass (FR)	FR
122	Code of Honor (USA)	USA
122	Japan (GB)	IRE
122	Maximum Security (USA)	USA
122	Ten Sovereigns (IRE)	IRE
121	Too Darn Hot (GB)	GB
120	Aethero (AUS)	HK
120	Castelvecchio (AUS)	AUS
120	King of Change (GB)	GB
120	Magna Grecia (IRE)	IRE
120	Omaha Beach (USA)	USA
120	Saturnalia (JPN)	JPN
120	Shancelot (USA)	USA
120	Yes Yes Yes (AUS)	AUS
119	Advertise (GB)	GB
119	Phoenix of Spain (IRE)	GB
119	Roger Barows (JPN)	JPN
119	Spun To Run (USA)	USA
119	World Premiere (JPN)	JPN
118	Admire Mars (JPN)	JPN
118	Anthony Van Dyck (IRE)	IRE
118	Bivouac (AUS)	AUS
118	Chrysoberyl (JPN)	JPN
118	Circus Maximus (IRE)	IRE
118	Country House (USA)	USA
118	Danon Kingly (JPN)	JPN
118	Exceedance (AUS)	AUS
118	Hello Youmzain (FR)	GB
118	King of Comedy (IRE)	GB
118	Logician (GB)	GB
118	Sovereign (IRE)	IRE
118	Velox (JPN)	JPN
117	Broome (IRE)	IRE
117	Covfefe (USA)	USA
117	Gran Alegria (JPN)	JPN
117	Madhmoon (IRE)	IRE
117	Nao Da Mais (BRZ)	BRZ
117	Persian King (IRE)	FR
117	Sir Dragonet (IRE)	IRE
116	Cape Of Good Hope (IRE)	AUS
116	Game Winner (USA)	USA
116	Glass Slippers (GB)	GB
116	Il Paradiso (USA)	IRE
116	Improbable (USA)	USA
116	Iridessa (IRE)	IRE
116	Mirinaque (ARG)	ARG
116	Mucho Gusto (USA)	USA
116	Search For A Song (IRE)	IRE
116	Serengeti Empress (USA)	USA
116	Sir Winston (USA)	USA
116	Tacitus (USA)	USA
116	Technician (IRE)	GB
116	War Of Will (USA)	USA
116	Watch Me (FR)	FR
115	Bellafina (USA)	USA
115	Catalyst (NZ)	NZ
115	Concrete Rose (USA)	USA
115	Curren Bouquetd'or (JPN)	JPN
115	Duke of Hazzard (FR)	GB
115	Dunbar Road (USA)	USA
115	Fox Tal (GB)	GB
115	Guarana (USA)	USA
115	Headman (GB)	GB
115	Hermosa (IRE)	IRE
115	Laccario (GER)	GER
115	Line of Duty (IRE)	GB
115	Look Pen (CHI)	CHI
115	Master Fencer (JPN)	JPN
115	Mestre Do Iguassu (BRZ)	BRZ
115	Mo Forza (USA)	USA
115	Mr Money (USA)	USA
115	Roadster (USA)	USA
115	Roman Joy (ARG)	ARG
115	Satono Lux (JPN)	JPN
115	Shaman (IRE)	FR
115	Shango (SAF)	SAF
115	Springdom (ARG)	ARG
115	Star Catcher (GB)	GB
115	Tax (USA)	USA
115	Warning (AUS)	AUS
114	Anapurna (GB)	GB
114	Constantinople (IRE)	IRE/AUS
114	Fleeting (IRE)	IRE
114	Happy Power (IRE)	GB
114	Khaadem (IRE)	GB
114	Mount Everest (IRE)	IRE
114	Roseman (IRE)	GB
114	San Donato (IRE)	GB
114	Shine So Bright (GB)	GB
114	Skardu (GB)	GB
114	Soldier's Call (GB)	GB
114	Space Blues (IRE)	GB
114	Villa Marina (GB)	FR
113	Delphinia (IRE)	IRE
113	Just Wonderful (USA)	IRE
113	Mehdaayih (GB)	GB
113	Mohaather (GB)	GB
113	Motamarris (IRE)	FR
113	Sangarius (GB)	GB
113	Singstreet (FR)	FR
113	Space Traveller (GB)	GB
113	Telecaster (GB)	GB

Rating		Trained	Rating		Trained
112	Accon (GER)	GER	111	UAE Jewel (GB)	GB
112	Bangkok (IRE)	GB	110	Ashrun (FR)	GER
112	Calyx (GB)	GB	110	Axana (GER)	GER
112	Channel (IRE)	FR	110	Beat Le Bon (FR)	GB
112	Decrypt (GB)	IRE	110	Dame Malliot (GB)	GB
112	Delaware (GB)	FR	110	Dashing Willoughby (GB)	GB
112	Django Freeman (GER)	GER	110	Edisa (USA)	FR
112	Donjah (GER)	GER	110	Fox Chairman (IRE)	GB
112	Fairyland (IRE)	IRE	110	Graignes (FR)	FR
112	Flop Shot (IRE)	FR	110	Grand Glory (FR)	FR
112	Forever In Dreams (IRE)	IRE	110	Jalmoud (GB)	GB
112	Great Scot (GB)	GB	110	Jubiloso (GB)	GB
112	Lord North (IRE)	GB	110	Keep On Fly (IRE)	ITY
112	Mohawk (IRE)	IRE	110	Lady Kaya (IRE)	IRE
112	Nayef Road (IRE)	GB	110	Lavender's Blue (IRE)	GB
112	Out of Time (ITY)	ITY	110	Moonlight Spirit (IRE)	GB
112	Sir Ron Priestley (GB)	GB	110	Munitions (USA)	FR
112	Slalom (FR)	FR	110	Norway (IRE)	IRE
112	Turgenev (GB)	GB	110	Obligate (GB)	FR
111	Buckhurst (IRE)	IRE	110	Pink Dogwood (IRE)	IRE
111	Castle Lady (IRE)	FR	110	Set Piece (GB)	GB
111	Commes (FR)	FR	110	Soft Light (FR)	FR
111	Diamanta (GER)	GER	110	Spanish Mission (USA)	GB
111	Dubai Warrior (GB)	GB	110	Terebellum (IRE)	GB
111	Roman Candle (GB)	FR	110	Veronesi (FR)	FR
111	So Perfect (USA)	IRE			

OLDER HORSES 2019

for **four-year-olds and up** rated 115 or greater by the IFHA World's Best Racehorse Rankings Conference. Horses rated 114-110 by the European Thoroughbred Rankings Conference do not constitute a part of the World's Best Racehorse Rankings. Those ratings were compiled on behalf of the European Pattern Committee.

Rating		Age	Trained	Rating		Age	Trained
128	Crystal Ocean (GB)	5	GB	118	Al Ain (JPN)	5	JPN
128	Enable (GB)	5	GB	118	Barahin (SAF)	4	SAF
128	Waldgeist (GB)	5	FR	118	Blue Prize (ARG)	6	USA
127	Beauty Generation (NZ)	7	HK	118	Brave Smash (JPN)	6	AUS
126	Battaash (IRE)	5	GB	118	Cross Counter (GB)	4	UAE
126	Ghaiyyath (IRE)	4	GB	118	Defoe (IRE)	5	GB
126	Lys Gracieux (JPN)	5	JPN	118	Donjuan Triumphant (IRE)	6	GB
126	Vino Rosso (USA)	4	USA	118	French King (GB)	4	FR
125	Benbatl (GB)	5	GB	118	Le Romain (AUS)	7	AUS
125	Glory Vase (JPN)	4	JPN	118	Master of Reality (IRE)	4	IRE
125	Winx (AUS)	8	AUS	118	Mystic Journey (AUS)	4	AUS
124	Almond Eye (JPN)	4	JPN	118	North America (GB)	7	UAE
124	Blue Point (IRE)	5	GB	118	Osborne Bulls (AUS)	6	AUS
124	City Of Light (USA)	5	USA	118	Redzel (AUS)	7	AUS
124	Santa Ana Lane (AUS)	7	AUS	118	Romanised (IRE)	4	IRE
123	McKinzie (USA)	4	USA	118	Sistercharlie (IRE)	5	USA
123	Mitole (USA)	4	USA	118	Stelvio (JPN)	4	JPN
122	Bricks And Mortar (USA)	5	USA	118	Te Akau Shark (NZ)	5	NZ
122	Happy Clapper (AUS)	9	AUS	118	Uni (GB)	5	USA
122	Magical (IRE)	4	IRE	118	United (USA)	4	USA
122	Nature Strip (AUS)	5	AUS	118	You Can Smile (JPN)	4	JPN
122	Old Persian (GB)	4	UAE	117	Alizee (AUS)	5	AUS
122	Stradivarius (IRE)	5	GB	117	Angel Of Truth (AUS)	4	AUS
121	Beat The Clock (AUS)	6	HK	117	Capezzano (USA)	5	UAE
121	Do It Again (SAF)	5	SAF	117	Cirillo (SAF)	4	SAF
121	Mustashry (GB)	5	GB	117	City Light (FR)	5	FR
121	Suave Richard (JPN)	5	JPN	117	Dream of Dreams (IRE)	5	GB
121	Thunder Snow (IRE)	5	UAE	117	Elate (USA)	5	USA
120	Blast Onepiece (JPN)	4	JPN	117	Full Of Beauty (AUS)	5	HK
120	Elarqam (GB)	4	GB	117	Gold Dream (JPN)	6	JPN
120	Exultant (IRE)	5	HK	117	Hey Doc (AUS)	6	AUS
120	Gift Box (USA)	6	USA	117	Inti (JPN)	5	JPN
120	Gronkowski (USA)	4	UAE	117	Kluger (JPN)	7	JPN
120	Hartnell (GB)	8	AUS	117	Kolding (NZ)	4	AUS
120	Hawwaam (SAF)	4	SAF	117	Lord Glitters (FR)	6	GB
120	Hot King Prawn (AUS)	5	HK	117	Mer De Glace (JPN)	4	JPN
120	Imperial Hint (USA)	6	USA	117	National Park (SAF)	4	SAF
120	Indy Champ (JPN)	4	JPN	117	One World (SAF)	4	SAF
120	Kiseki (JPN)	5	JPN	117	Preservationist (USA)	6	USA
120	Roy H (USA)	7	USA	117	Rattan (NZ)	6	HK
120	Trapeze Artist (AUS)	5	AUS	117	Rise High (FR)	5	HK
120	Win Bright (JPN)	5	JPN	117	Rushing Fall (USA)	4	USA
119	Addeybb (IRE)	6	GB	117	The Autumn Sun (AUS)	4	AUS
119	Avilius (GB)	5	AUS	117	The Tin Man (GB)	7	GB
119	Cheval Grand (JPN)	7	JPN	117	Time Warp (GB)	6	HK
119	Danon Premium (JPN)	4	JPN	117	Tower Of London (JPN)	4	JPN
119	Dee Ex Bee (GB)	4	GB	117	Undercover Agent (SAF)	5	SAF
119	Fierement (JPN)	4	JPN	117	Vardy (SAF)	4	SAF
119	Kew Gardens (IRE)	4	IRE	117	Wagnerian (JPN)	4	JPN
119	Midnight Bisou (USA)	4	USA	117	Waikuku (IRE)	4	HK
119	Mr Stunning (AUS)	7	HK	117	Zabeel Prince (IRE)	6	GB
119	Pierata (AUS)	5	AUS	116	Arklow (USA)	5	USA
119	Rainbow Bridge (SAF)	5	SAF	116	Aspetar (FR)	4	GB
119	Regal Reality (GB)	4	GB	116	Beat The Bank (GB)	5	GB
119	Soqrat (AUS)	4	SAF	116	Billesdon Brook (GB)	4	GB
119	Sungrazer (JPN)	5	JPN	116	Black Heart Bart (AUS)	9	AUS
119	The Revenant (GB)	4	FR	116	Brando (GB)	7	GB
119	Yoshida (JPN)	5	USA	116	Catalina Cruiser (USA)	5	USA

Rating		Age	Trained
116	Channel Maker (CAN)	5	USA
116	Conte (AUS)	6	HK
116	Dream Castle (GB)	5	UAE
116	Glorious Forever (GB)	5	HK
116	Grunt (NZ)	5	AUS
116	Gunnevera (USA)	5	USA
116	Harlem (GB)	7	AUS
116	Head Honcho (SAF)	6	SAF
116	Higher Power (USA)	4	USA
116	Holdthasigreen (FR)	7	FR
116	Homesman (USA)	5	AUS
116	Little Giant (NZ)	7	HK
116	Melody Belle (NZ)	5	NZ
116	Mirage Dancer (GB)	5	AUS
116	Mongolian Groom (USA)	4	USA
116	Morando (FR)	6	GB
116	Muntazah (GB)	5	UAE
116	Nagano Gold (GB)	5	CZE
116	Pakistan Star (GER)	6	HK
116	Persian Knight (JPN)	5	JPN
116	Promises Fulfilled (USA)	4	USA
116	Robert Bruce (CHI)	5	USA
116	Sadler's Joy (USA)	6	USA
116	Samadoubt (AUS)	5	AUS
116	Southern Legend (AUS)	7	HK
116	Trekking (AUS)	5	AUS
116	Wishful Thinker (AUS)	6	HK
116	World Of Trouble (USA)	4	USA
116	Ya Primo (CHI)	4	CHI
116	Ziyad (GB)	4	FR
115	Air Windsor (JPN)	5	JPN
115	Annals Of Time (USA)	6	USA
115	Arcadia Queen (AUS)	5	AUS
115	Audible (USA)	4	USA
115	Battle Of Midway (USA)	5	USA
115	Bostonian (NZ)	5	NZ
115	Brutal (NZ)	4	AUS
115	Call The Wind (GB)	5	FR
115	Catholic Boy (USA)	4	USA
115	Channel Cat (USA)	5	USA
115	Chuwa Wizard (JPN)	4	JPN
115	Coal Front (USA)	5	USA
115	Communique (IRE)	5	GB
115	Coronet (GB)	5	GB
115	Danceteria (FR)	4	GB
115	Danzdanzdance (AUS)	5	NZ
115	Dark Dream (AUS)	5	HK
115	D B Pin (NZ)	7	HK
115	Deirdre (JPN)	5	JPN
115	Delta Prince (USA)	6	USA
115	Desert Encounter (IRE)	7	GB
115	Dixie Wave (ARG)	7	PER
115	Dreamforce (AUS)	5	AUS
115	Epoca D'Oro (JPN)	4	JPN
115	Firenze Fire (USA)	4	USA
115	Furore (NZ)	4	HK
115	Gatting (AUS)	6	AUS
115	George Washington (BRZ)	4	BRZ
115	Got Stormy (USA)	4	USA
115	Graff (AUS)	4	AUS
115	Hunting Horn (IRE)	4	IRE
115	Inns of Court (IRE)	5	FR
115	In Her Time (AUS)	7	AUS
115	Ispolini (GB)	4	UAE/GB
115	Kasimir (SAF)	5	SAF
115	Laurens (FR)	4	GB
115	Lucky Lilac (JPN)	4	JPN
115	Magic Wand (IRE)	4	IRE
115	Makahiki (JPN)	6	JPN
115	Malaguerra (AUS)	8	AUS
115	Manuel (AUS)	6	AUS
115	Meisho Tekkon (JPN)	4	JPN
115	Mr Quickie (AUS)	4	AUS
115	My Style (JPN)	5	JPN
115	Omega Perfume (JPN)	4	JPN
115	One Master (GB)	5	GB
115	Paradise Woods (USA)	5	USA
115	Pavel (USA)	5	USA
115	Plumatic (GB)	5	FR
115	Quip (USA)	4	USA
115	Rey De Oro (JPN)	5	JPN
115	Salouen (IRE)	5	GB
115	Sandino Ruler (ARG)	4	ARG
115	Scales Of Justice (AUS)	7	AUS
115	Seas Alabada (ARG)	4	ARG
115	Seeking The Soul (USA)	6	USA
115	Soffia (GB)	4	IRE
115	Square de Luynes (FR)	4	SWE
115	Stiffelio (JPN)	5	JPN
115	Storm Rodrigo (CHI)	5	PER
115	Stormy Liberal (USA)	7	USA
115	Study of Man (IRE)	4	FR
115	Tom's D'Etat (USA)	6	USA
115	Twist Of Fate (SAF)	4	SAF
115	Vasilika (USA)	5	USA
115	Verry Elleegant (NZ)	4	AUS
115	Whitmore (USA)	6	USA
115	Without Parole (GB)	4	USA
115	X Y Jet (USA)	7	USA
115	Zulu Alpha (USA)	6	USA
114	Limato (IRE)	7	GB
114	Kachy (GB)	6	GB
114	Marmelo (GB)	6	GB
114	Safe Voyage (IRE)	6	GB
114	Stormy Antarctic (GB)	6	GB
114	Way To Paris (GB)	6	FR
114	Accidental Agent (GB)	5	GB
114	Called To The Bar (IRE)	5	FR
114	Sir Dancealot (IRE)	5	GB
114	Alounak (FR)	4	GER
114	Impulsif (GB)	4	FR
114	Matterhorn (IRE)	4	GB
114	Olmedo (FR)	4	FR
114	Wissahickon (USA)	4	GB
113	Alpha Delphini (GB)	8	GB
113	Mustajeer (GB)	6	IRE/AUS
113	Prince of Arran (GB)	6	GB
113	Twilight Payment (IRE)	6	IRE
113	Cape Byron (GB)	5	GB
113	Mabs Cross (GB)	5	GB
113	Royal Line (GB)	5	GB
113	Sharja Bridge (GB)	5	GB
113	Trais Fluors (GB)	5	FR
113	Waldpfad (GER)	5	GER
113	Enbihaar (GB)	4	GB
113	Glorious Journey (GB)	4	GB
113	Invincible Army (IRE)	4	GB
113	Lah Ti Dar (GB)	4	GB
113	Skalleti (FR)	4	FR
113	Southern France (IRE)	4	IRE/AUS
113	Veracious (GB)	4	GB
113	With You (GB)	4	FR

Rating		Age	Trained	Rating		Age	Trained
113	Zaaki (GB)	4	GB	111	Musis Amica (IRE)	4	FR
112	Itobo (GER)	7	GER	111	Rawdaa (GB)	4	GB
112	Librisa Breeze (GB)	7	GB	111	Spinning Memories (IRE)	4	FR
112	Subway Dancer (IRE)	7	CHR	111	Sun Maiden (GB)	4	GB
112	Gold Mount (GB) (ex Primitivo)	6	GB	111	Young Rascal (FR)	4	GB
112	Wai Key Star (GER)	6	GER	110	Thomas Hobson (GB)	9	IRE
112	Finesse (TUR)	5	TUR	110	Flight Risk (IRE)	8	IRE
112	Forest Ranger (IRE)	5	GB	110	Suedois (FR)	8	GB
112	Laraaib (IRE)	5	GB	110	El Astronaute (IRE)	6	GB
112	Le Brivido (FR)	5	IRE	110	Mr Lupton (IRE)	6	GB
112	Weekender (GB)	5	GB	110	Oh This Is Us (IRE)	6	GB
112	Downdraft (IRE)	4	IRE	110	Red Tea (GB)	6	IRE
112	Flag of Honour (IRE)	4	IRE	110	Red Verdon (USA)	6	GB
112	Hey Gaman (GB)	4	GB	110	Tabarrak (IRE)	6	GB
112	Intellogent (GB)	4	FR	110	True Self (IRE)	6	IRE
112	Knight To Behold (IRE)	4	GB	110	Be My Sheriff (GER)	5	GER
112	Latrobe (IRE)	4	IRE	110	Dakota Gold (GB)	5	GB
112	Make A Challenge (IRE)	4	IRE	110	Desert Skyline (IRE)	5	GB
112	Marianafoot (FR)	4	FR	110	Graphite (FR)	5	FR
112	Mer Et Nuages (FR)	4	FR	110	Hit The Bid (GB)	5	IRE
112	Mootasadir (GB)	4	GB	110	I Kirk (SWE)	5	SWE
112	Move Swiftly (GB)	4	GB	110	Mankib (GB)	5	GB
112	Nancho (GER)	4	HUN	110	Morgan Le Faye (GB)	5	FR
112	Polydream (FR)	4	FR	110	Soleil Marin (IRE)	5	FR
112	Raymond Tusk (IRE)	4	GB	110	Windstoss (GER)	5	GER
112	Rhythm Divine (TUR)	4	TUR	110	Assiro (GB)	4	ITY
112	Royal Youmzain (FR)	4	GER	110	Chief Ironside (GB)	4	GB
112	Vintager (GB)	4	GB	110	Diamond Vendome (FR)	4	FR
111	Silverwave (FR)	7	FR	110	Duca di Como (IRE)	4	NOR
111	King Malpic (FR)	6	FR	110	Hazapour (IRE)	4	IRE
111	Withhold (GB)	6	GB	110	Kronprinz (GER)	4	GER
111	Anda Muchacho (IRE)	5	ITY	110	Ligne d'Or (GB)	4	FR
111	Barney Roy (GB)	5	GB	110	Monsieur Croco (FR)	4	GER
111	Capri (IRE)	5	IRE	110	On The Warpath (GB)	4	GB
111	Escobar (IRE)	5	GB	110	Petit Fils (FR)	4	FR
111	King's Advice (GB)	5	GB	110	Raa Atoll (GB)	4	IRE
111	Mountain Angel (IRE)	5	GB	110	Speak In Colours (GB)	4	IRE
111	I Can Fly (GB)	4	IRE	110	Wells Farhh Go (IRE)	4	GB
111	Mekong (GB)	4	GB				

RACEFORM CHAMPIONS 2019

ONLY HORSES WHICH HAVE RUN IN EUROPE ARE INCLUDED

FOUR-YEAR-OLDS AND UP

BATTAASH	129	GHAIYYATH	128
CRYSTAL OCEAN	129	WALDGEIST	128
ENABLE	128	BLUE POINT	127

THREE-YEAR-OLD COLT

JAPAN	125	ADVERTISE	121
TEN SOVEREIGNS	125	HELLO YOUMZAIN	121
TOO DARN HOT	125	KING OF COMEDY	121
SOTTSASS	123	MAGNA GRECIA	121
KING OF CHANGE	122		

THREE-YEAR-OLD FILLY

SEARCH FOR A SONG	118	HERMOSA	115
GLASS SLIPPERS	117	MEHDAAYIH	115
WATCH ME	117	STAR CATCHER	115
FLEETING	115	VILLA MARINA	115

SPRINTER

BATTAASH	129	ADVERTISE	121
BLUE POINT	127	HELLO YOUMZAIN	121
TEN SOVEREIGNS	125	DREAM OF DREAMS	121

STAYER

STRADIVARIUS	123	CROSS COUNTER	119
KEW GARDENS	122	LOGICIAN	119
DEE EX BEE	121	MASTER OF REALITY	119

TWO-YEAR-OLD COLT

PINATUBO	128	KAMEKO	117
EARTHLIGHT	119	GOLDEN HORDE	116
MUMS TIPPLE	118	WICHITA	116
ARIZONA	117		

TWO-YEAR-OLD FILLY

MILLISLE	116	RAFFLE PRIZE	114
QUADRILATERAL	115	ALBIGNA	112
POWERFUL BREEZE	114		

MEDIAN TIMES 2020

The following Raceform median times are used in the calculation of the Split Second speed figures. They represent a true average time for the distance, which has been arrived at after looking at the winning times for all races over each distance within the past five years, except for those restricted to two or three-year-olds.

Some current race distances have been omitted as they have not yet had a sufficient number of races run over them to produce a reliable average time.

ASCOT

5f..............................1m 0.70	1m Straight................1m 41.40	1m 7f 209y................3m 33.30
6f............................1m 13.70	1m 1f 212y.................2m 7.70	2m 3f 210y................4m 22.00
7f............................1m 27.50	1m 3f 211y................2m 32.60	2m 5f 143y................4m 43.60
7f 213y Round 1m 40.60	1m 6f 34y..................3m 4.30	

AYR

5f............................4m 43.60	1m...........................1m 42.80	1m 7f......................3m 27.00
5f 110y.....................1m 6.50	1m 1f 20y..................2m 0.20	2m 1f 105y...............4m 1.50
6f............................1m 13.10	1m 2f......................2m 12.40	
7f 50y......................1m 32.50	1m 5f 26y.................2m 54.40	

BATH

5f 10y.......................1m 2.00	1m 2f 37y.................2m 11.10	1m 6f......................3m 6.10
5f 160y....................1m 11.10	1m 3f 137y................2m 30.80	2m 1f 24y................3m 51.40
1m...........................1m 41.70	1m 5f 11y.................2m 52.80	

BEVERLEY

5f............................1m 2.90	1m 100y...................1m 46.40	1m 4f 23y................2m 38.80
7f 96y......................1m 32.60	1m 1f 207y................2m 5.70	2m 32y....................3m 37.90

BRIGHTON

5f 60y.......................1m 3.00	6f 210y....................1m 23.80	1m 1f 207y...............2m 5.00
5f 215y....................1m 11.10	7f 211y....................1m 36.90	1m 3f 198y...............2m 36.00

CARLISLE

5f............................1m 2.10	7f 173y....................1m 40.00	1m 6f 32y................3m 11.60
5f 193y....................1m 14.60	1m 1f......................1m 59.00	2m 1f 47y................3m 54.30
6f 195y....................1m 28.00	1m 3f 39y.................2m 29.70	

CATTERICK

5f............................1m 0.50	7f 6y.......................1m 27.40	1m 5f 192y...............3m 7.60
5f 212y....................1m 13.60	1m 4f 13y.................2m 40.60	1m 7f 189y...............3m 36.00

CHELMSFORD (A.W)

5f............................1m 0.20	1m...........................1m 39.90	1m 6f......................3m 3.20
6f............................1m 13.70	1m 2f......................2m 8.60	2m...........................3m 30.00
7f............................1m 27.20	1m 5f 66y.................2m 53.60	

CHEPSTOW

5f 16y.........................59.40	1m 14y....................1m 36.00	2m...........................3m 42.10
6f 16y......................1m 11.50	1m 2f......................2m 12.80	2m 2f......................4m 9.90
7f 16y......................1m 23.90	1m 4f......................2m 40.30	

CHESTER

5f 15y.......................1m 2.10	7f 127y....................1m 35.70	1m 5f 84y................2m 56.60
5f 110y.....................1m 9.00	1m 2f 70y.................1m 14.30	1m 6f 87y................3m 9.80
6f 17y......................1m 15.50	1m 3f 75y.................2m 27.40	1m 7f 196y...............3m 31.90
7f 1y........................1m 27.50	1m 4f 63y.................2m 42.20	2m 2f 140y...............4m 4.60

DONCASTER

5f 3y.. 59.60	7f 6y.................................... 1m 26.40	1m 3f 197y........................... 2m 36.60
5f 143y..................................... 1m 8.10	7f 213y Round.................... 1m 40.80	1m 6f 115y........................... 3m 11.60
6f 2y....................................... 1m 12.70	1m Straight......................... 1m 40.20	2m 109y............................... 3m 40.40
6f 111y................................... 1m 19.60	1m 2f 43y........................... 2m 12.30	2m 1f 197y........................... 3m 55.00

EPSOM

5f.. 55.30	7f 3y.................................... 1m 23.40	1m 2f 17y............................. 2m 10.00
6f 3y.. 1m 9.90	1m 113y.............................. 1m 46.40	1m 4f 6y............................... 2m 40.80

FFOS LAS

5f.. 59.00	1m.. 1m 42.90	1m 6f..................................... 3m 8.60
6f.. 1m 10.90	1m 2f.................................... 2m 12.70	2m.. 3m 36.70
7f 80y..................................... 1m 33.10	1m 3f 209y........................... 2m 40.20	

GOODWOOD

5f.. 58.10	1m 1f 11y............................ 1m 57.40	1m 6f..................................... 3m 3.70
6f.. 1m 12.10	1m 1f 197y........................... 2m 8.90	2m.. 3m 30.90
7f.. 1m 26.70	1m 3f 44y............................ 2m 28.30	2m 4f 134y........................... 4m 31.80
1m... 1m 39.20	1m 3f 218y........................... 2m 39.60	

HAMILTON

5f 7y....................................... 1m 0.40	1m 1f 35y............................ 1m 59.00	1m 5f 16y............................. 2m 54.70
6f 6y....................................... 1m 12.70	1m 3f 15y............................ 2m 25.50	
1m 68y.................................... 1m 48.40	1m 4f 15y............................ 2m 38.60	

HAYDOCK

5f.. 1m 0.40	7f 37y.................................. 1m 31.40	1m 3f 140y Inner 2m 33.30
5f Inner.................................. 1m 0.40	7f 212y Inner 1m 42.70	1m 3f 175y........................... 2m 33.30
6f.. 1m 13.90	1m.. 1m 42.70	1m 6f Inner........................... 3m 4.60
6f Inner.................................. 1m 13.90	1m 37y.................................. 1m 44.90	1m 6f..................................... 3m 4.60
6f 212y Inner 1m 29.30	1m 2f 42y Inner 2m 10.80	2m 45y Inner 3m 36.70
7f.. 1m 29.30	1m 2f 100y........................... 2m 16.60	2m 45y.................................. 3m 36.70

KEMPTON (A.W)

5f.. 1m 0.50	1m.. 1m 39.80	1m 3f 219y........................... 2m 34.50
6f.. 1m 13.10	1m 1f 219y........................... 2m 8.00	1m 7f 218y........................... 3m 30.10
7f.. 1m 26.00	1m 2f 219y........................... 2m 21.00	

LEICESTER

5f.. 1m 1.80	7f.. 1m 25.70	1m 2f..................................... 2m 9.20
6f.. 1m 12.10	1m 53y.................................. 1m 46.30	1m 3f 179y........................... 2m 35.00

LINGFIELD

4f 217y..................................... 58.70	7f 135y................................ 1m 31.70	1m 3f 133y........................... 2m 34.00
6f.. 1m 11.50	1m 1f.................................... 1m 56.90	1m 6f..................................... 3m 11.20
7f.. 1m 24.30	1m 2f.................................... 2m 12.20	2m 68y.................................. 3m 36.00

LINGFIELD (A.W)

5f 6y... 58.80	1m 1y.................................... 1m 38.20	1m 5f..................................... 2m 46.00
6f 1y....................................... 1m 11.90	1m 2f.................................... 2m 6.60	1m 7f 169y........................... 3m 25.70
7f 1y....................................... 1m 24.80	1m 4f.................................... 2m 33.00	

MUSSELBURGH

5f 1y....................................... 59.70	1m 208y............................... 1m 53.10	1m 5f 216y........................... 3m 3.90
7f 33y..................................... 1m 29.00	1m 4f 104y........................... 2m 44.50	1m 7f 217y........................... 3m 31.50
1m 2y..................................... 1m 40.00	1m 5f.................................... 2m 51.70	

NEWBURY

5f 34y 1m 1.50	1m Round 1m 40.50	1m 5f 61y 2m 54.40
6f 1m 13.20	1m 1f 1m 55.70	2m 3m 39.40
6f 110y 1m 20.10	1m 2f 2m 9.70	2m 110y 3m 46.30
7f Straight 1m 27.00	1m 3f 2m 23.20	2m 2f 4m 6.80
1m Straight 1m 39.90	1m 4f 2m 38.00	

NEWCASTLE (A.W)

5f 59.50	1m 5y 1m 38.60	2m 56y 3m 35.00
6f 1m 12.50	1m 2f 42y 2m 10.40	
7f 14y 1m 26.20	1m 4f 98y 2m 41.10	

NEWMARKET (ROWLEY MILE)

5f Rowly 59.10	1m 1f Rowly 1m 51.10	2m Rowly 3m 29.30
6f Rowly 1m 11.90	1m 2f Rowly 2m 5.40	2m 2f Rowly 3m 55.50
7f Rowly 1m 25.40	1m 4f Rowly 2m 32.50	
1m Rowly 1m 38.40	1m 6f Rowly 2m 57.10	

NEWMARKET (JULY COURSE)

5f July 58.70	1m July 1m 40.00	1m 5f July 2m 45.90
6f July 1m 12.10	1m 2f July 2m 7.10	1m 6f July 2m 59.90
7f July 1m 25.70	1m 4f July 2m 33.90	2m July 3m 28.40

NOTTINGHAM

5f 8y Inner 1m 0.20	1m 75y Inner 1m 46.70	1m 6f 3m 6.40
5f 8y 1m 0.20	1m 2f 50y 2m 13.40	2m 3m 34.50
6f 18y 1m 13.80	1m 2f 50y Inner 2m 13.40	
1m 75y 1m 46.70	1m 6f Inner 3m 6.40	

PONTEFRACT

5f 3y 1m 3.90	1m 2f 5y 2m 15.00	2m 2f 2y 4m 7.70
6f 1m 17.10	1m 4f 5y 2m 41.10	2m 5f 139y 4m 58.00
1m 6y 1m 45.90	2m 1f 27y 3m 49.20	

REDCAR

5f 58.50	7f 219y 1m 36.60	1m 5f 218y 3m 7.00
5f 217y 1m 11.80	1m 1f 1m 54.50	1m 7f 217y 3m 33.70
7f 1m 25.40	1m 2f 1y 2m 6.90	

RIPON

5f 59.40	1m 1f 1m 54.70	1m 4f 10y 2m 36.30
6f 1m 12.50	1m 1f 170y 2m 4.60	1m 6f 3m 2.40
1m 1m 41.00	1m 2f 190y 2m 19.00	2m 3m 32.40

SALISBURY

5f 1m 0.50	1m 1m 43.50	1m 6f 44y 3m 6.60
6f 1m 14.50	1m 1f 201y 2m 10.50	
6f 213y 1m 28.70	1m 4f 5y 2m 37.60	

SANDOWN

5f 10y 1m 1.30	1m 1f 1m 56.30	2m 50y 3m 37.90
7f 1m 29.30	1m 1f 209y 2m 10.20	
1m 1m 43.30	1m 6f 3m 6.00	

SOUTHWELL (A.W)

4f 214y 59.70	1m 13y 1m 43.70	1m 6f 21y 3m 8.30
6f 16y 1m 16.50	1m 3f 23y 2m 28.00	2m 102y 3m 45.50
7f 14y 1m 30.30	1m 4f 14y 2m 41.00	2m 2f 98y 4m 11.50

THIRSK

5f.................................... 59.40	7f.................................... 1m 27.60	1m 4f 8y........................ 2m 40.00
6f.............................. 1m 12.80	7f 218y...................... 1m 41.70	2m 13y.......................... 3m 33.60

WETHERBY

5f 110y...................... 1m 5.80	1m................................ 1m 41.60	1m 6f............................ 3m 7.00
7f.............................. 1m 27.20	1m 2f.......................... 2m 9.30	2m.............................. 3m 33.700

WINDSOR

5f 21y........................ 1m 0.10	1m 31y........................ 1m 44.50	1m 3f 99y...................... 2m 29.70
6f 12y...................... 1m 12.10	1m 2f.......................... 2m 9.00	

WOLVERHAMPTON (A.W)

5f 21y........................ 1m 1.90	1m 142y...................... 1m 50.10	1m 5f 219y.................... 3m 1.00
6f 20y...................... 1m 14.50	1m 1f 104y.................. 2m 0.80	2m 120y........................ 3m 39.30
7f 36y...................... 1m 28.80	1m 4f 51y.................... 2m 40.80	

YARMOUTH

5f 42y........................ 1m 1.90	1m 3y.......................... 1m 38.20	1m 3f 104y.................... 2m 27.80
6f 3y........................ 1m 12.60	1m 1f 21y.................... 1m 54.50	1m 6f 17y...................... 3m 4.70
7f 3y........................ 1m 25.10	1m 2f 23y.................... 2m 8.80	

YORK

5f.................................... 58.20	7f 192y...................... 1m 37.50	1m 5f 188y.................... 3m 0.20
5f 89y........................ 1m 3.60	1m 177y...................... 1m 50.40	2m 56y.......................... 3m 33.90
6f.............................. 1m 11.60	1m 2f 56y.................... 2m 10.30	
7f.............................. 1m 24.60	1m 3f 188y.................. 2m 33.20	

RACEFORM RECORD TIMES (FLAT)

ASCOT

DISTANCE	TIME	AGE	WEIGHT	GOING	HORSE	DATE
5f	58.80	2	9-1	Good To Firm	NO NAY NEVER	Jun 20 2013
5f	57.44	6	9-1	Good To Firm	MISS ANDRETTI	Jun 19 2007
6f	1m 12.39	2	9-1	Good To Firm	RAJASINGHE	Jun 20 2017
6f	1m 11.05	3	9-1	Good To Firm	BLUE POINT	May 3 2017
7f	1m 25.73	2	9-3	Good	PINATUBO	Jun 22 2019
7f	1m 24.28	4	8-11	Good To Firm	GALICIAN	Jul 27 2013
7f 213y (Rnd)	1m 39.55	2	8-12	Good	JOSHUA TREE	Sep 26 2009
7f 213y (Rnd)	1m 35.89	3	9-0	Good To Firm	ALPHA CENTAURI	Jun 22 2018
1m (Str)	1m 36.60	4	9-0	Good To Firm	RIBCHESTER	Jun 20 2017
1m 1f 212y	2m 1.90	5	8-11	Good To Firm	THE FUGUE	Jun 18 2014
1m 3f 211y	2m 24.60	4	9-7	Good To Firm	NOVELLIST	Jul 27 2013
1m 7f 209y	3m 24.12	4	8-12	Good To Firm	MIZZOU	Apr 29 2015
2m 3f 210y	4m 16.92	6	9-2	Good To Firm	RITE OF PASSAGE	Jun 17 2010
2m 5f 143y	4m 45.67	7	9-2	Good To Firm	ORIENTAL FOX	Jun 20 2015

AYR

DISTANCE	TIME	AGE	WEIGHT	GOING	HORSE	DATE
5f	56.98	2	8-11	Good	BOOGIE STREET	Sep 18 2003
5f	55.68	3	8-11	Good To Firm	LOOK BUSY	Jun 21 2008
6f	1m 9.73	2	7-10	Good	SIR BERT	Sep 17 1969
6f	1m 8.37	5	8-6	Good To Firm	MAISON DIEU	Jun 21 2008
7f 50y	1m 28.99	2	9-0	Good	TAFAAHUM	Sep 19 2003
7f 50y	1m 26.43	4	9-4	Good To Firm	HAJJAM	May 22 2018
1m	1m 39.18	2	9-7	Good	MOONLIGHTNAVIGATOR	Sep 18 2014
1m	1m 36.00	4	7-13	Firm	SUFI	Sep 16 1959
1m 1f 20y	1m 50.30	4	9-3	Good	RETIREMENT	Sep 19 2003
1m 2f	2m 4.02	4	9-9	Good To Firm	ENDLESS HALL	Jul 17 2000
1m 5f 26y	2m 45.81	4	9-7	Good To Firm	EDEN'S CLOSE	Sep 18 1993
1m 7f	3m 13.16	3	9-4	Good	ROMANY RYE	Sep 19 1991
2m 1f 105y	3m 45.20	4	6-13	Firm	CURRY	Sep 16 1955

BATH

DISTANCE	TIME	AGE	WEIGHT	GOING	HORSE	DATE
5f 10y	59.50	2	9-2	Firm	AMOUR PROPRE	Jul 24 2008
5f 10y	58.75	3	8-12	Firm	ENTICING	May 1 2007
5f 160y	1m 8.70	2	8-12	Firm	QALAHARI	Jul 24 2008
5f 160y	1m 8.10	6	9-0	Firm	MADRACO	May 22 1989
1m 5y	1m 39.51	2	9-2	Firm	NATURAL CHARM	Sep 14 2014
1m 5y	1m 37.20	5	8-12	Good To Firm	ADOBE	Jun 17 2000
1m 5y	1m 37.20	3	8-7	Firm	ALASHA	Aug 18 2002
1m 2f 37y	2m 5.80	3	9-0	Good To Firm	CONNOISSEUR BAY	May 29 1998
1m 3f 137y	2m 25.74	3	9-0	Hard	TOP THE CHARTS	Sep 8 2005
1m 5f 11y	2m 47.20	4	10-0	Firm	FLOWN	Aug 13 1991
1m 6f	2m 58.97	4	9-10	Firm	CHARLIE D	Sep 15 2019
2m 1f 24y	3m 43.41	6	7-9	Firm	YAHESKA	Jun 14 2003

BEVERLEY

DISTANCE	TIME	AGE	WEIGHT	GOING	HORSE	DATE
5f	1m 0.89	2	8-12	Good To Firm	LANGAVAT	Jun 8 2013
5f	59.77	5	9-3	Good To Firm	JUDICIAL	Jun 20 2017
7f 96y	1m 31.10	2	9-7	Good To Firm	CHAMPAGNE PRINCE	Aug 10 1995
7f 96y	1m 31.10	2	9-0	Firm	MAJAL	Jul 30 1991
7f 96y	1m 29.50	3	7-8	Firm	WHO'S TEF	Jul 30 1991
1m 100y	1m 43.30	2	9-0	Firm	ARDEN	Sep 24 1986
1m 100y	1m 42.20	3	8-4	Firm	LEGAL CASE	Jun 14 1989
1m 1f 207y	2m 1.00	3	9-7	Good To Firm	EASTERN ARIA	Aug 29 2009
1m 4f 23y	2m 33.35	5	9-2	Good To Firm	TWO JABS	Apr 23 2015
2m 32y	3m 28.62	4	9-11	Good To Firm	CORPUS CHORISTER	Jul 18 2017

BRIGHTON

DISTANCE	TIME	AGE	WEIGHT	GOING	HORSE	DATE
5f 60y	1m 0.10	2	9-0	Firm	BID FOR BLUE	May 6 1993
5f 60y	59.30	3	8-9	Firm	PLAY HEVER GOLF	May 26 1993
5f 215y	1m 8.10	2	8-9	Firm	SONG MIST	Jul 16 1996
5f 215y	1m 7.12	8	9-6	Good To Firm	DIAMOND LADY	Apr 20 2019
5f 215y	1m 7.30	3	8-9	Firm	THIRD PARTY	Jun 3 1997
6f 201y	1m 19.90	2	8-11	Hard	RAIN BURST	Sep 15 1988
6f 201y	1m 19.40	4	9-3	Good To Firm	SAWAKI	Sep 3 1991
7f 211y	1m 32.80	2	9-7	Firm	ASIAN PETE	Oct 3 1989
7f 211y	1m 30.50	5	8-11	Firm	MYSTIC RIDGE	May 27 1999
1m 1f 207y	2m 4.70	2	9-0	Good To Soft	ESTEEMED MASTER	Nov 2 2001
1m 1f 207y	1m 57.20	3	9-0	Firm	GET THE MESSAGE	Apr 30 1984
1m 3f 198y	2m 25.80	4	8-2	Firm	NEW ZEALAND	Jul 4 1985

CARLISLE

DISTANCE	TIME	AGE	WEIGHT	GOING	HORSE	DATE
5f	1m 0.10	2	8-5	Firm	LA TORTUGA	Aug 2 1999
5f	58.80	3	9-8	Good To Firm	ESATTO	Aug 21 2002
5f 193y	1m 12.30	2	9-2	Good To Firm	BURRISHOOLE ABBEY	Jun 22 2016
5f 193y	1m 10.83	4	9-0	Good To Firm	BO MCGINTY	Sep 11 2005
6f 195y	1m 24.30	3	8-9	Good To Firm	MARJURITA	Aug 21 2002
7f 173y	1m 35.84	5	8-12	Good To Firm	WAARIF	Jun 27 2018
1m 1f	1m 53.84	3	9-0	Firm	LITTLE JIMBOB	Jun 14 2004
1m 3f 39y	2m 20.46	5	10-0	Firm	AASHEQ	Jun 27 2018
1m 3f 206y	2m 29.13	5	9-8	Good To Firm	TEMPSFORD	Sep 19 2005
1m 6f 32y	3m 2.20	6	8-10	Firm	EXPLOSIVE SPEED	May 26 1994

CATTERICK

DISTANCE	TIME	AGE	WEIGHT	GOING	HORSE	DATE
5f	57.60	2	9-0	Firm	H HARRISON	Oct 8 2002
5f	57.10	4	8-7	Firm	KABCAST	Jul 6 1989
5f 212y	1m 11.40	2	9-4	Firm	CAPTAIN NICK	Jul 11 1978
5f 212y	1m 9.86	9	8-13	Good To Firm	SHARP HAT	May 30 2003
7f 6y	1m 24.10	2	8-11	Firm	LINDA'S FANTASY	Sep 18 1982
7f 6y	1m 22.56	6	8-7	Firm	DIFFERENTIAL	May 31 2003
1m 4f 13y	2m 30.50	3	8-8	Good To Firm	RAHAF	May 30 2003
1m 5f 192y	2m 54.80	3	8-5	Firm	GERYON	May 31 1984
1m 7f 189y	3m 20.80	4	7-11	Firm	BEAN BOY	Jul 8 1982

CHELMSFORD (AW)

DISTANCE	TIME	AGE	WEIGHT	GOING	HORSE	DATE
5f	58.52	2	9-6	Standard	PRINCE OF ROME	Sep 20 2018
5f	57.30	7	8-13	Standard	BROTHER TIGER	Feb 7 2016
6f	1m 11.14	2	8-10	Standard	SECOND LOVE	Sep 5 2019
6f	1m 10.00	4	9-2	Standard	RAUCOUS	Apr 27 2017
7f	1m 22.59	7	8-0	Standard	BOY IN THE BAR	Sep 22 2018
1m	1m 37.15	2	9-3	Standard	DRAGON MALL	Sep 26 2015
1m	1m 35.46	4	9-7	Standard	MINDUROWNBUSINESS	Nov 23 2015
1m 2f	2m 1.81	5	9-7	Standard	BIN BATTUTA	Sep 28 2019
1m 5f 66y	2m 47.00	4	8-7	Standard	COORG	Jan 6 2016
1m 6f	2m 55.61	3	9-0	Standard	BRASCA	Sep 5 2019
2m	3m 55.65	3	9-8	Standard	DUCHESS OF MARMITE	Nov 23 2015
2m	3m 22.37	5	9-3	Standard	NOTARISED	Mar 3 2016

CHEPSTOW

DISTANCE	TIME	AGE	WEIGHT	GOING	HORSE	DATE
5f 16y	57.60	2	8-11	Firm	MICRO LOVE	Jul 8 1986
5f 16y	56.80	3	8-4	Firm	TORBAY EXPRESS	Sep 15 1979
6f 16y	1m 8.50	2	9-2	Firm	NINJAGO	Jul 27 2012
6f 16y	1m 8.10	3	9-7	Firm	AMERICA CALLING	Sep 18 2001
7f 16y	1m 20.48	2	9-0	Good	FESTIVAL DAY	Sep 17 2019
7f 16y	1m 19.30	3	9-0	Firm	TARANAKI	Sep 18 2001
1m 14y	1m 33.10	2	8-11	Good To Firm	SKI ACADEMY	Aug 28 1995
1m 14y	1m 31.60	3	8-13	Firm	STOLI	Sep 18 2001
1m 2f 36y	2m 4.10	3	8-5	Good To Firm	ELA ATHENA	Jul 23 1999
1m 2f 36y	2m 4.10	5	8-9	Hard	LEONIDAS	Jul 5 1983
1m 2f 36y	2m 4.10	5	7-8	Good To Firm	IT'S VARADAN	Sep 9 1989
1m 4f 23y	2m 31.00	5	8-11	Hard	THE FRIEND	Aug 29 1983
1m 4f 23y	2m 31.00	3	8-9	Good To Firm	SPRITSAIL	Jul 13 1989
2m 49y	3m 27.70	4	9-0	Good To Firm	WIZZARD ARTIST	Jul 1 1989
2m 2f	3m 56.40	5	8-7	Good To Firm	LAFFAH	Jul 8 2000

CHESTER

DISTANCE	TIME	AGE	WEIGHT	GOING	HORSE	DATE
5f 15y	59.94	2	9-2	Good To Firm	LEIBA LEIBA	Jun 26 2010
5f 15y	58.88	3	8-7	Good To Firm	PETERKIN	Jul 11 2014
5f 110y	1m 6.39	2	8-7	Good To Soft	KINEMATIC	Sep 27 2014
5f 110y	1m 4.54	5	8-5	Good	BOSSIPOP	Sep 1 2018
6f 17y	1m 12.54	2	8-12	Good	GLASS SLIPPERS	Sep 1 2018
6f 17y	1m 12.02	5	9-5	Good To Firm	DEAUVILLE PRINCE	Jun 13 2015
7f 1y	1m 25.29	2	9-0	Good To Firm	DUE RESPECT	Sep 25 2002
7f 1y	1m 23.75	5	8-13	Good To Firm	THREE GRACES	Jul 9 2005
7f 127y	1m 32.29	2	9-0	Good To Firm	BIG BAD BOB	Sep 25 2002
7f 127y	1m 30.62	5	9-10	Good	OH THIS IS US	Sep 1 2018
1m 2f 70y	2m 7.15	3	8-8	Good To Firm	STOTSFOLD	Sep 23 2006
1m 3f 75y	2m 22.17	3	8-12	Good To Firm	PERFECT TRUTH	May 6 2009
1m 4f 63y	2m 33.70	3	8-10	Good To Firm	FIGHT YOUR CORNER	May 7 2002
1m 5f 84y	2m 45.43	5	8-11	Firm	RAKAPOSHI KING	May 7 1987
1m 7f 196y	3m 20.33	4	9-0	Good To Firm	GRAND FROMAGE	Jul 13 2002
2m 2f 140y	3m 58.89	7	9-2	Good To Firm	GREENWICH MEANTIME	May 9 2007

DONCASTER

DISTANCE	TIME	AGE	WEIGHT	GOING	HORSE	DATE
5f 3y	58.04	2	9-1	Good	GUTAIFAN	Sep 11 2015
5f 3y	57.31	7	9-10	Good	TABARET	Aug 14 2010
5f 143y	1m 5.38	4	9-7	Good	MUTHMIR	Sep 13 2014
6f 2y	1m 10.33	2	9-4	Good To Firm	COMEDY	Jun 29 2018
6f 2y	1m 9.56	3	8-10	Good To Firm	PROCLAIM	May 30 2009
6f 111y	1m 17.19	2	8-9	Good	MR LUPTON	Sep 10 2015
7f 6y	1m 22.78	2	9-5	Good	BASATEEN	Jul 24 2014
7f 6y	1m 21.81	6	8-7	Good To Firm	SIGNOR PELTRO	May 30 2009
7f 213y (Rnd)	1m 38.37	2	8-6	Good To Soft	ANTONIOLA	Oct 23 2009
7f 213y (Rnd)	1m 34.46	4	8-12	Good To Firm	STAYING ON	Apr 18 2009
1m (Str)	1m 36.72	2	8-12	Good	DANCE OF FIRE	Sep 13 2014
1m (Str)	1m 34.95	6	8-9	Firm	QUICK WIT	Jul 18 2013
1m 2f 43y	2m 4.81	4	8-13	Good To Firm	RED GALA	Sep 12 2007
1m 3f 197y	2m 27.48	3	8-4	Good To Firm	SWIFT ALHAARTH	Sep 10 2011
1m 6f 115y	3m 0.27	3	9-1	Good To Firm	LOGICIAN	Sep 14 2019
2m 109y	3m 34.52	7	9-0	Good To Firm	INCHNADAMPH	Nov 10 2007
2m 1f 197y	3m 48.41	4	9-4	Good To Firm	SEPTIMUS	Sep 14 2007

EPSOM

DISTANCE	TIME	AGE	WEIGHT	GOING	HORSE	DATE
5f	55.02	2	8-9	Good To Firm	PRINCE ASLIA	Jun 9 1995
5f	54.00	6	8-13	Good To Firm	ORNATE	Jun 1 2019
6f 3y	1m 7.85	2	8-11	Good To Firm	SHOWBROOK	Jun 5 1991
6f 3y	1m 6.20	9	8-11	Good To Firm	WATCHABLE	Jun 1 2019
7f 3y	1m 21.30	2	8-9	Good To Firm	RED PEONY	Jul 29 2004
7f 3y	1m 20.15	4	8-7	Firm	CAPISTRANO	Jun 7 1972
1m 113y	1m 42.80	2	8-5	Good To Firm	NIGHTSTALKER	Aug 30 1988
1m 113y	1m 40.46	4	9-6	Good To Firm	ZAAKI	Jun 1 2019
1m 2f 17y	2m 3.50	5	7-11	Firm	CROSSBOW	Jun 7 1967
1m 4f 6y	2m 31.33	3	9-0	Good To Firm	WORKFORCE	Jun 5 2010

FFOS LAS

DISTANCE	TIME	AGE	WEIGHT	GOING	HORSE	DATE
5f	57.06	2	9-3	Good To Firm	MR MAJEIKA	May 5 2011
5f	56.35	5	8-8	Good	HAAJES	Sep 12 2009
6f	1m 9.00	2	9-5	Good To Firm	WONDER OF QATAR	Sep 14 2014
6f	1m 7.46	6	10-2	Good To Firm	HANDYTALK	Jul 29 2019
1m	1m 39.36	2	9-2	Good To Firm	HALA HALA	Sep 2 2013
1m	1m 37.12	5	9-0	Good To Firm	ZEBRANO	May 5 2011
1m 2f	2m 4.85	8	8-12	Good To Firm	PELHAM CRESCENT	May 5 2011
1m 3f 209y	2m 31.18	3	9-9	Good	TRUESHAN	Aug 29 2019
1m 6f	2m 58.61	4	9-7	Good To Firm	LADY ECLAIR	Jul 12 2010
2m	3m 25.42	4	9-3	Good To Firm	LONG JOHN SILVER	Jul 24 2018

GOODWOOD

DISTANCE	TIME	AGE	WEIGHT	GOING	HORSE	DATE
5f	57.14	2	9-1	Good	YALTA	Jul 27 2016
5f	56.20	5	9-5	Good To Firm	BATTAASH	Aug 2 2019
6f	1m 9.81	2	8-11	Good To Firm	BACHIR	Jul 28 1999
6f	1m 9.10	6	9-0	Good To Firm	TAMAGIN	Sep 12 2009
7f	1m 24.99	2	8-11	Good To Firm	EKRAAR	Jul 29 1999
7f	1m 23.75	4	9-3	Good	BILLESDON BROOK	Aug 2 2019
1m	1m 37.21	2	9-0	Good	CALDRA	Sep 9 2006
1m	1m 35.28	3	8-13	Good To Firm	BEAT LE BON	Aug 2 2019
1m 1f 11y	1m 56.27	2	9-3	Good To Firm	DORDOGNE	Sep 22 2010
1m 1f 11y	1m 52.81	3	9-6	Good	VENA	Jul 27 1995
1m 1f 197y	2m 2.81	3	9-3	Good To Firm	ROAD TO LOVE	Aug 3 2006
1m 3f 44y	2m 22.77	3	9-3	Good	KHALIDI	May 26 2017
1m 3f 218y	2m 31.39	3	9-1	Firm	CROSS COUNTER	Aug 4 2018
1m 6f	2m 57.61	4	9-6	Good To Firm	MEEZNAH	Jul 28 2011
2m	3m 21.55	5	9-10	Good To Firm	YEATS	Aug 3 2006
2m 4f	4m 11.75	3	7-10	Firm	LUCKY MOON	Aug 2 1990

HAMILTON

DISTANCE	TIME	AGE	WEIGHT	GOING	HORSE	DATE
5f 7y	57.95	2	8-8	Good To Firm	ROSE BLOSSOM	May 29 2009
5f 7y	57.20	5	9-4	Good To Firm	DAPPER MAN	Jun 27 2019
6f 6y	1m 10.00	2	8-12	Good To Firm	BREAK THE CODE	Aug 24 1999
6f 6y	1m 9.30	4	8-7	Firm	MARCUS GAME	Jul 11 1974
1m 68y	1m 45.46	2	9-5	Good To Firm	LAAFIRAAQ	Sep 20 2015
1m 68y	1m 42.70	6	7-7	Firm	CRANLEY	Sep 25 1972
1m 1f 35y	1m 53.60	5	9-6	Good To Firm	REGENT'S SECRET	Aug 10 2005
1m 3f 15y	2m 18.66	3	9-3	Good To Firm	POSTPONED	Jul 18 2014
1m 4f 15y	2m 30.52	5	9-10	Good To Firm	RECORD BREAKER	Jun 10 2009
1m 5f 16y	2m 45.10	6	9-6	Firm	MENTALASANYTHIN	Jun 14 1995

HAYDOCK

DISTANCE	TIME	AGE	WEIGHT	GOING	HORSE	DATE
5f	58.56	2	8-2	Good To Firm	BARRACUDA BOY	Aug 11 2012
5f	56.39	5	9-4	Firm	BATED BREATH	May 26 2012
5f (Inner)	58.51	2	9-1	Good	FOUR DRAGONS	Oct 14 2016
5f (Inner)	57.38	7	9-12	Good To Firm	FOXY FOREVER	Jul 21 2017
6f	1m 8.56	3	9-0	Firm	HARRY ANGEL	May 27 2017
6f	1m 10.98	4	9-9	Good To Firm	WOLFHOUND	Sep 4 1993
6f (Inner)	1m 9.04	3	8-11	Good To Firm	PRINCES DES SABLES	Aug 8 2019
6f (Inner)	1m 10.58	2	9-2	Good To Firm	PRESTBURY PARK	Jul 21 2017
6f 212y	1m 27.29	2	9-2	Good To Firm	NAYEF ROAD	Aug 10 2018
6f 212y (Inner)	1m 27.29	2	9-2	Good To Firm	DROGON	Jul 5 2018
6f 212y (Inner)	1m 25.28	3	9-8	Good To Firm	MYSTIC FLIGHT	Jun 7 2018
7f 37y	1m 27.57	2	9-2	Good To Firm	CONTRAST	Aug 5 2016
7f 37y	1m 25.50	3	8-11	Good	FORGE	Sep 1 2016
7f 212y (Inner)	1m 37.80	3	9-4	Good To Firm	SIDEWINDER	May 26 2017
1m 37y	1m 38.50	4	8-11	Good To Firm	EXPRESS HIMSELF	Jun 10 2015
1m 2f 42y (Inner)	2m 7.25	3	8-9	Good To Firm	LARAAIB	May 26 2017
1m 2f 100y	2m 7.71	3	8-8	Good To Firm	ROYAL ARTILLERY	Aug 6 2016
1m 3f 140y (Inner)	2m 25.52	5	9-9	Good To Firm	DECEMBER SECOND	Aug 8 2019
1m 3f 175y	2m 25.53	4	8-12	Good To Firm	NUMBER THEORY	May 24 2012
1m 6f	2m 55.20	5	9-9	Good To Firm	HUFF AND PUFF	Sep 7 2012
2m 45y	3m 26.98	5	8-13	Good To Firm	DE RIGUEUR	Jun 8 2013

KEMPTON (AW)

DISTANCE	TIME	AGE	WEIGHT	GOING	HORSE	DATE
5f	58.96	2	8-6	Standard	GLAMOROUS SPIRIT	Nov 28 2008
5f	58.07	5	8-12	Standard To Slow	A MOMENTOFMADNESS	Apr 7 2018
6f	1m 11.02	2	9-1	Standard To Slow	INVINCIBLE ARMY	Sep 9 2017
6f	1m 9.79	4	8-11	Standard	TRINITYELITEDOTCOM	Mar 29 2014
7f	1m 23.79	2	8-0	Standard	ELSAAKB	Nov 8 2017
7f	1m 23.10	6	9-9	Standard	SIRIUS PROSPECT	Nov 20 2014
1m	1m 37.26	2	9-0	Standard	CECCHINI	Nov 8 2017
1m	1m 35.73	3	8-9	Standard	WESTERN ARISTOCRAT	Sep 15 2011
1m 1f 219y	2m 2.93	3	8-11	Standard To Slow	PLY	Sep 25 2017
1m 2f 219y	2m 15.65	4	8-8	Standard To Slow	FORBIDDEN PLANET	Mar 30 2019
1m 3f 219y	2m 28.99	6	9-3	Standard	SPRING OF FAME	Nov 7 2012
1m 7f 218y	3m 21.50	4	8-12	Standard	COLOUR VISION	May 2 2012

LEICESTER

DISTANCE	TIME	AGE	WEIGHT	GOING	HORSE	DATE
5f 2y	58.40	2	9-0	Firm	CUTTING BLADE	Jun 9 1986
5f 2y	57.85	5	9-5	Good To Firm	THE JOBBER	Sep 18 2006
5f 218y	1m 9.99	2	9-0	Good	EL MANATI	Aug 1 2012
5f 218y	1m 9.12	6	8-12	Good To Firm	PETER ISLAND	Apr 25 2009
7f 9y	1m 23.33	2	9-5	Good To Firm	HIGHEST GROUND	Sep 23 2019
7f 9y	1m 20.80	3	8-7	Firm	FLOWER BOWL	Jun 9 1986
1m 53y	1m 44.05	2	8-11	Good To Firm	CONGRESSIONAL	Sep 6 2005
1m 53y	1m 41.89	5	9-7	Good To Firm	VAINGLORY	Jun 18 2009
1m 1f 216y	2m 5.30	2	9-1	Good To Firm	WINDSOR CASTLE	Oct 14 1996
1m 1f 216y	2m 2.40	3	8-11	Firm	EFFIGY	Nov 4 1985
1m 1f 216y	2m 2.40	4	9-6	Good To Firm	LADY ANGHARAD	Jun 18 2000
1m 3f 179y	2m 27.10	5	8-12	Good To Firm	MURGHEM	Jun 18 2000

LINGFIELD (TURF)

DISTANCE	TIME	AGE	WEIGHT	GOING	HORSE	DATE
4f 217y	56.76	2	9-2	Good	GLORY FIGHTER	May 11 2018
4f 217y	56.09	3	9-4	Good To Firm	WHITECREST	Sep 16 2011
6f	1m 9.41	2	9-0	Good To Firm	COMPANY MINX	Jul 10 2019
6f	1m 8.48	4	9-6	Good To Firm	REWAAYAT	Jul 17 20193
7f	1m 21.22	2	9-9	Good To Firm	SIR ARTHUR DAYNE	Jly 24 2019
7f	1m 20.46	4	9-4	Good To Firm	MAGICAL RIDE	Aug 3 2019
7f 135y	1m 29.32	2	9-3	Good To Firm	DUNDONNELL	Aug 4 2012
7f 135y	1m 26.73	3	8-6	Good To Firm	HIAAM	Jul 11 1987
1m 1f	1m 50.45	4	9-3	Good To Firm	ENZEMBLE	May 30 2019
1m 2f	2m 0.54		9-0	Standard	BANGKOK	Feb 1 2020
1m 3f 133y	2m 23.95	3	8-5	Firm	NIGHT-SHIRT	Jul 14 1990
1m 6f	2m 59.10	5	9-5	Firm	IBN BEY	Jul 1 1989
2m 68y	3m 23.71	3	9-5	Good To Firm	LAURIES CRUSADOR	Aug 13 1988

LINGFIELD (AW)

DISTANCE	TIME	AGE	WEIGHT	GOING	HORSE	DATE
5f 6y	57.59	2	9-7	Standard	AUGUSTUS CAESAR	Sep 24 2019
5f 6y	56.67	5	8-12	Standard	LADIES ARE FOREVER	Mar 16 2013
6f 1y	1m 9.76	2	9-4	Standard	RED IMPRESSION	Nov 24 2018
6f 1y	1m 8.32	6	9-0	Standard	KACHY	Feb 2 2019
7f 1y	1m 22.67	3	9-3	Standard	COMPLICIT	Nov 23 2013
7f 1y	1m 21.90	4	9-9	Standard	CARDSHARP	Mar 13 2019
1m 1y	1m 35.70	2	8-13	Standard	QAADDIM	Oct 3 2019
1m 1y	1m 34.34	5	8-13	Standard	MY TARGET	Dec 31 2016
1m 2f	2m 0.54	4	9-0	Standard	BANGKOK	Feb 1 2020
1m 4f	2m 26.99	6	9-11	Standard	PINZOLO	Jan 21 2017
1m 5f	2m 39.70	3	8-10	Standard	HIDDEN GOLD	Oct 30 2014
1m 7f 169y	3m 15.18	4	9-1	Standard	WINNING STORY	Apr 14 2017

MUSSELBURGH

DISTANCE	TIME	AGE	WEIGHT	GOING	HORSE	DATE
5f 1y	57.66	2	9-2	Good To Firm	IT DONT COME EASY	Jun 3 2017
5f 1y	56.77	9	9-10	Good To Firm	CASPIAN PRINCE	Jun 3 2018
7f 33y	1m 27.46	2	8-8	Good	DURHAM REFLECTION	Sep 14 2009
7f 33y	1m 25.00	9	8-8	Good To Firm	KALK BAY	Jun 4 2016
1m 2y	1m 40.34	2	8-12	Good To Firm	SUCCESSION	Sep 26 2004
1m 2y	1m 36.83	3	9-5	Good To Firm	GINGER JACK	Jul 13 2010
1m 208y	1m 50.42	8	8-11	Good To Firm	DHAULAR DHAR	Sep 3 2010
1m 4f 104y	2m 36.80	3	8-3	Good To Firm	HARRIS TWEED	Jun 5 2010
1m 5f	2m 46.41	3	9-5	Good To Firm	ALCAEUS	Sep 29 2013
1m 5f 216y	2m 57.98	7	8-5	Good To Firm	JONNY DELTA	Apr 18 2014
1m 7f 217y	3m 25.62	4	8-3	Good To Firm	ALDRETH	Jun 13 2015

NEWBURY

DISTANCE	TIME	AGE	WEIGHT	GOING	HORSE	DATE
5f 34y	59.19	2	8-6	Good To Firm	SUPERSTAR LEO	Jul 22 2000
5f 34y	58.44	5	9-1	Good To Firm	ROBOT BOY	Apr 17 2015
6f 8y	1m 11.07	2	8-4	Good To Firm	BAHATI	May 30 2009
6f 8y	1m 9.42	3	8-11	Good To Firm	NOTA BENE	May 13 2005
6f 110y	1m 18.06	2	9-5	Good To Firm	TWIN SAILS	Jun 11 2015
7f (Str)	1m 23.04	2	8-11	Good To Firm	HAAFHD	Aug 15 2003
7f (Str)	1m 20.80	3	9-0	Good To Firm	MUHAARAR	Apr 18 2015
1m (Str)	1m 38.45	2	8-12	Good	TRITONIC	Sep 20 2019
1m	1m 33.59	6	9-0	Firm	RAKTI	May 14 2005
1m 1f	1m 49.65	3	8-0	Good To Firm	HOLTYE	May 21 1995
1m 2f	2m 1.29	3	8-7	Good To Firm	WALL STREET	Jul 20 1996
1m 3f 5y	2m 16.54	3	8-9	Good To Firm	GRANDERA	Sep 22 2001
1m 4f 5y	2m 28.26	4	9-7	Good To Firm	AZAMOUR	Jul 23 2005
1m 5f 61y	2m 44.90	5	10-0	Good To Firm	MYSTIC HILL	Jul 20 1996

NEWCASTLE (AW)

Distance	Time	Age	Weight	Going	HORSE	Date
5f	57.78	3	8-9	Standard	ASTRAEA	Dec 15 2018
6f	1m 9.86	3	9-2	Standard	UNABATED	Mar 22 2017
7f 14y	1m 24.10	3	9-0	Standard	NORTHERNPOWERHOUSE	Dec 18 2019
1m 5y	1m 36.26	2	9-1	Standard	KAMEKO	Nov 1 2019
1m 2f 42y	2m 4.88	3	8-6	Standard	PALISADE	Oct 16 2016
1m 4f 98y	2m 36.76	3	8-7	Standard	AJMAN PRINCE	Oct 14 2016
2m 56y	3m 29.87	4	9-8	Standard	DANNYDAY	Jun 25 2016

NEWMARKET (ROWLEY MILE)

DISTANCE	TIME	AGE	WEIGHT	GOING	HORSE	DATE
5f	58.69	2	8-12	Good To Firm	MRS DANVERS	Oct 7 2016
5f	56.81	6	9-2	Good To Firm	LOCHSONG	Apr 30 1994
6f	1m 9.31	2	9-0	Good	EARTHLIGHT	Sep 28 2019
6f	1m 9.55	3	9-1	Good To Firm	CAPTAIN COLBY	May 16 2015
7f	1m 22.37	2	9-1	Good	U S NAVY FLAG	Oct 14 2017
7f	1m 21.98	3	9-0	Good To Firm	TUPI	May 16 2015
1m	1m 35.13	2	9-0	Good	ROYAL DORNOCH	Sep 28 2019
1m	1m 34.07	4	9-0	Good To Firm	EAGLE MOUNTAIN	Oct 3 2008
1m 1f	1m 46.99	3	8-10	Good	LORD NORTH	Sep 28 2019
1m 2f	2m 2.76	2	9-2	Good	KEW GARDENS	Oct 14 2017
1m 2f	2m 0.13	3	8-12	Good	NEW APPROACH	Oct 18 2008
1m 4f	2m 26.07	3	8-9	Good To Firm	MOHEDIAN LADY	Sep 22 2011
1m 6f	2m 51.59	3	8-7	Good	ART EYES	Sep 29 2005
2m	3m 18.64	5	9-6	Good To Firm	TIMES UP	Sep 22 2011
2m 2f	3m 45.59	4	8-8	Good	WITHHOLD	Oct 14 2017

NEWMARKET (JULY COURSE)

Following remeasurement of the track by the BHA and RCA in 2017, some starts were moved to retain traditional race distances.

DISTANCE	TIME	AGE	WEIGHT	GOING	HORSE	DATE
5f	57.31	4	9-2	Good To Firm	MOUNTAIN PEAK	Jly 12 2019
6f	1m 9.09	2	9-3	Good To Firm	RAFFLE PRIZE	Jly 12 2019
6f	1m 9.31	3	9-0	Good To Firm	TEN SOVEREIGNS	Jly 13 2019
7f	1m 23.33	2	9-1	Good To Firm	BIRCHWOOD	Jul 11 2015
7f	1m 21.78	3	8-13	Good To Firm	LIGHT AND DARK	Jly 12 2019
1m	1m 37.47	2	8-13	Good	WHIPPERS LOVE	Aug 28 2009
1m	1m 35.89	4	9-7	Good To Firm	VERACIOUS	Jly 12 2019
1m 2f	2m 2.21	7	8-10	Good	KAPSTADT	Jun 10 2017
1m 4f	2m 30.01	3	8-11	Good	REVEREND JACOBS	Aug 22 2008
1m 5f	2m 44.06	4	9-12	Good To Firm	PUMBLECHOOK	Jun 24 2017
1m 2f	2m 0.61	3	9-7	Good To Firm	WALKINTHESAND	Jly 12 2019
1m 4f	2m 27.52	3	8-5	Good	DAME MALLIOT	Jly 20 2019
1m 5f	2m 39.96	3	9-1	Good To Firm	SPANISH MISSION	Jly 11 2019
1m 6f	2m 53.53	5	9-4	Good To Firm	KING'S ADVICE	Jly 12 2019

NOTTINGHAM

DISTANCE	TIME	AGE	WEIGHT	GOING	HORSE	DATE
5f 8y (Inner)	59.05	2	9-0	Good To Firm	MAIN DESIRE	May 2 2017
5f 8y (Inner)	57.01	3	8-12	Good To Firm	GARRUS	Apr 10 2019
5f 8y	57.90	2	8-9	Firm	HOH MAGIC	May 13 1994
5f 8y	57.58	5	7-11	Good To Firm	PENNY DREADFUL	Jun 19 2017
6f 18y	1m 11.40	2	8-11	Firm	JAMEELAPI	Aug 8 1983
6f 18y	1m 10.00	4	9-2	Firm	AJANAC	Aug 8 1988
1m 72y (Inner)	1m 45.14	2	9-6	Good	RASHFORD'S DOUBLE	Nov 2 2016
1m 75y (Inner)	1m 41.60	4	8-13	Good To Firm	RISE HALL	Apr 10 2019
1m 75y	1m 44.75	2	9-0	Good	VIVID DIAMOND	Oct 3 2018
1m 75y	1m 42.02	3	9-0	Good To Firm	GANAYEM	May 11 2018
1m 2f 50y	2m 7.13	5	9-8	Good To Firm	VASILY	Jul 19 2013
1m 2f 52y (Inner)	2m 16.66	2	9-3	Soft	LETHAL GLAZE	Oct 1 2008
1m 2f 52y (Inner)	2m 9.40	3	9-5	Good	CENTURIUS	Apr 20 2013
1m 6f	2m 57.80	3	8-10	Firm	BUSTER JO	Oct 1 1985
1m 7f 219y (Inner)	3m 34.39	3	8-0	Good	BENOZZO GOZZOLI	Oct 28 2009
2m	3m 25.25	3	9-5	Good	BULWARK	Sep 27 2005

PONTEFRACT

DISTANCE	TIME	AGE	WEIGHT	GOING	HORSE	DATE
5f 3y	1m 1.10	2	9-0	Firm	GOLDEN BOUNTY	Sep 20 2001
5f 3y	1m 0.49	5	9-5	Good To Firm	JUDICIAL	Apr 24 2017
6f	1m 14.00	2	9-3	Firm	FAWZI	Sep 6 1983
6f	1m 12.60	3	7-13	Firm	MERRY ONE	Aug 29 1970
1m 6y	1m 42.80	2	9-13	Firm	STAR SPRAY	Sep 6 1983
1m 6y	1m 42.80	2	9-0	Firm	ALASIL	Sep 26 2002
1m 6y	1m 40.60	4	9-10	Good To Firm	ISLAND LIGHT	Apr 13 2002
1m 2f 5y	2m 10.10	2	9-0	Firm	SHANTY STAR	Oct 7 2002
1m 2f 5y	2m 8.20	4	7-8	Hard	HAPPY HECTOR	Jul 9 1979
1m 2f 5y	2m 8.20	3	7-13	Hard	TOM NODDY	Aug 21 1972
1m 4f 5y	2m 33.72	3	8-7	Firm	AJAAN	Aug 8 2007
2m 1f 27y	3m 40.67	4	8-7	Good To Firm	PARADISE FLIGHT	Jun 6 2005
2m 2f 2y	3m 51.10	3	8-8	Good To Firm	KUDZ	Sep 9 1986
2m 5f 139y	4m 47.80	4	8-4	Firm	PHYSICAL	May 14 1984

REDCAR

DISTANCE	TIME	AGE	WEIGHT	GOING	HORSE	DATE
5f	56.88	2	9-7	Good To Soft	WOLFOFWALLSTREET	Oct 27 2014
5f	56.01	10	9-3	Firm	HENRY HALL	Sep 20 2006
5f 217y	1m 8.84	2	8-3	Good To Firm	OBE GOLD	Oct 2 2004
5f 217y	1m 8.60	3	9-2	Good To Firm	SIZZLING SAGA	Jun 21 1991
7f	1m 21.28	2	9-3	Firm	KAROO BLUE	Sep 20 2006
7f	1m 21.00	3	9-1	Firm	EMPTY QUARTER	Oct 3 1995
7f 219y	1m 34.37	2	9-0	Firm	MASTERSHIP	Sep 20 2006
7f 219y	1m 32.42	4	10-0	Firm	NANTON	Sep 20 2006
1m 1f	1m 52.44	3	9-0	Firm	SPEAR	Sep 13 2004
1m 1f	1m 48.50	5	8-12	Firm	MELLOTTIE	Jul 25 1990
1m 2f 1y	2m 10.10	2	8-11	Good	ADDING	Nov 10 1989
1m 2f 1y	2m 1.40	5	9-2	Firm	ERADICATE	May 28 1990
1m 5f 218y	2m 59.54	6	8-5	Good To Firm	LEODIS	Jun 23 2018
1m 7f 217y	3m 24.90	3	9-3	Good To Firm	SUBSONIC	Oct 8 1991

RIPON

DISTANCE	TIME	AGE	WEIGHT	GOING	HORSE	DATE
5f	57.80	2	8-8	Firm	SUPER ROCKY	Aug 5 1991
5f	57.28	5	8-12	Good	DESERT ACE	Sep 24 2016
6f	1m 10.40	2	9-2	Good	CUMBRIAN VENTURE	Aug 17 2002
6f	1m 9.09	5	8-13	Good To Firm	SANDRA'S SECRET	May 20 2018
1m	1m 38.77	2	9-4	Good	GREED IS GOOD	Sep 28 2013
1m	1m 36.62	4	8-11	Good	GRANSTON	Aug 29 2005
1m 1f	1m 49.97	6	9-3	Firm	GINGER JACK	Jun 20 2013
1m 2f	2m 2.60	3	9-4	Firm	SWIFT SWORD	Jul 20 1991
1m 4f 10y	2m 31.40	4	8-8	Good To Firm	DANDINO	Apr 16 2011
2m	3m 27.07	5	9-12	Good To Firm	GREENWICH MEANTIME	Aug 30 2005

SALISBURY

DISTANCE	TIME	AGE	WEIGHT	GOING	HORSE	DATE
5f	59.30	2	9-0	Good To Firm	AJIGOLO	May 12 2005
5f	59.18	7	8-10	Good To Firm	EDGED OUT	Jun 18 2017
6f	1m 12.10	2	8-0	Good To Firm	PARISIAN LADY	Jun 10 1997
6f	1m 11.09	3	9-0	Firm	L'AMI LOUIS	May 1 2011
6f 213y	1m 25.97	2	9-0	Firm	MORE ROYAL	Jun 29 1995
6f 213y	1m 24.91	3	9-4	Firm	CHILWORTH LAD	May 1 2011
1m	1m 40.48	2	8-13	Firm	CHOIR MASTER	Sep 17 2002
1m	1m 38.29	3	8-7	Good To Firm	LAYMAN	Aug 11 2005
1m 1f 198y	2m 4.00	4	9-2	Good To Firm	CHAIN OF DAISIES	Aug 10 2016
1m 4f 5y	2m 31.69	3	9-5	Good To Firm	ARRIVE	Jun 27 2001
1m 6f 44y	3m 0.48	7	9-2	Good To Firm	HIGHLAND CASTLE	May 23 2015

SANDOWN

DISTANCE	TIME	AGE	WEIGHT	GOING	HORSE	DATE
5f 10y	59.48	2	9-3	Firm	TIMES TIME	Jul 22 1982
5f 10y	58.57	3	8-12	Good To Firm	BATTAASH	Jul 8 2017
7f	1m 26.56	2	9-0	Good To Firm	RAVEN'S PASS	Sep 1 2007
7f	1m 26.36	3	9-0	Firm	MAWSUFF	Jun 14 1986
1m 14y	1m 43.90	2	9-5	Good	VIA DE VEGA	Sep 18 2019
1m 14y	1m 38.87	7	9-10	Good To Firm	PRINCE OF JOHANNE	Jul 6 2013
1m 1f	1m 54.63	2	8-8	Good To Firm	FRENCH PRETENDER	Sep 20 1988
1m 1f	1m 52.40	7	9-3	Good To Firm	BOURGAINVILLE	Aug 11 2005
1m 1f 209y	2m 2.14	4	8-11	Good	KALAGLOW	May 31 1982
1m 6f	3m 1.08	3	8-9	Good	JUST HUBERT	Jly 25 2019
2m 50y	3m 29.38	6	9-0	Good To Firm	CAUCUS	Jul 6 2013

SOUTHWELL (AW)

DISTANCE	TIME	AGE	WEIGHT	GOING	HORSE	DATE
4f 214y	57.61	2	9-2	Standard	THE BELL CONDUCTOR	Nov 7 2019
4f 214y	56.80	5	9-7	Standard	GHOSTWING	Jan 3 2012
6f 16y	1m 14.00	2	8-5	Standard	PANALO	Nov 8 1989
6f 16y	1m 13.49	4	9-7	Standard	ROCK SOUND	Nov 5 2019
7f 14y	1m 26.82	2	8-12	Standard	WINGED ICARUS	Aug 28 2012
7f 14y	1m 26.29	7	8-9	Standard To Slow	WELD AL AMARAT	Feb 27 2019
1m 13y	1m 38.00	2	8-9	Standard	ALPHA RASCAL	Nov 13 1990
1m 13y	1m 38.00	2	8-10	Standard	ANDREW'S FIRST	Dec 30 1989
1m 13y	1m 37.25	3	8-6	Standard	VALIRA	Nov 3 1990
1m 3f 23y	2m 21.50	4	9-7	Standard	TEMPERING	Dec 5 1990
1m 4f 14y	2m 33.90	4	9-12	Standard	FAST CHICK	Nov 8 1989
1m 6f 21y	3m 1.60	3	7-8	Standard	EREVNON	Dec 29 1990
2m 102y	3m 37.60	9	8-12	Standard	OLD HUBERT	Dec 5 1990

THIRSK

DISTANCE	TIME	AGE	WEIGHT	GOING	HORSE	DATE
5f	57.20	2	9-7	Good To Firm	PROUD BOAST	Aug 5 2000
5f	56.92	5	9-6	Firm	CHARLIE PARKES	Apr 11 2003
6f	1m 9.20	2	9-6	Good To Firm	WESTCOURT MAGIC	Aug 25 1995
6f	1m 8.80	6	9-4	Firm	JOHAYRO	Jul 23 1999
7f	1m 23.70	2	8-9	Firm	COURTING	Jul 23 1999
7f	1m 22.80	4	8-5	Firm	SILVER HAZE	May 21 1988
7f 218y	1m 37.97	2	9-0	Firm	SUNDAY SYMPHONY	Sep 4 2004
7f 218y	1m 34.80	4	8-13	Firm	YEARSLEY	May 5 1990
1m 4f 8y	2m 29.90	5	9-12	Firm	GALLERY GOD	Jun 4 2001
2m 13y	3m 22.30	3	9-0	Firm	TOMASCHEK	Jul 17 1981

WETHERBY

DISTANCE	TIME	AGE	WEIGHT	GOING	HORSE	DATE
5f 110y	1m 6.14	2	9-5	Good To Firm	COASTAL MIST	May 30 2019
7f	1m 24.72	4	9-2	Good	SLEMY	Jul 21 2015
1m	1m 38.79	4	9-4	Good To Firm	THOMAS CRANMER	Jun 6 2018
1m 2f	2m 5.13	5	9-5	Good	FIRST SARGEANT	Jul 21 2015
1m 6f	3m 0.41	3	9-7	Good To Firm	DAVY'S DILEMMA	Jun 19 2017

WINDSOR

DISTANCE	TIME	AGE	WEIGHT	GOING	HORSE	DATE
5f 21y	58.69	2	9-0	Good To Firm	CHARLES THE GREAT	May 23 2011
5f 21y	58.08	5	8-13	Good To Firm	TAURUS TWINS	Apr 4 2011
6f 12y	1m 10.50	2	9-5	Good To Firm	CUBISM	Aug 17 1998
6f 12y	1m 9.58	7	9-0	Good To Firm	TROPICS	Jun 1 2015
1m 31y	1m 41.73	2	9-5	Good To Firm	SALOUEN	Aug 7 2016
1m 31y	1m 39.81	5	9-7	Good	FRENCH NAVY	Jun 29 2013
1m 1f 194y	2m 1.62	6	9-1	Good	AL KAZEEM	Aug 23 2014
1m 3f 99y	2m 21.50	3	9-2	Firm	DOUBLE FLORIN	May 19 1980

WOLVERHAMPTON (AW)

DISTANCE	TIME	AGE	WEIGHT	GOING	HORSE	DATE
5f 21y	59.75	2	9-6	Standard	QUATRIEME AMI	Nov 13 2015
5f 21y	59.33	5	9-6	Standard	LOMU	Dec 3 2019
6f 20y	1m 12.16	2	9-2	Standard	MUBAKKER	Nov 14 2015
6f 20y	1m 11.44	5	9-6	Standard	KACHY	Dec 26 2018
7f 36y	1m 26.77	2	8-11	Standard	RICHARD R H B	Nov 23 2019
7f 36y	1m 25.35	4	9-3	Standard	MISTER UNIVERSE	Mar 12 2016
1m 142y	1m 47.38	2	9-5	Standard	JACK HOBBS	Dec 27 2014
1m 142y	1m 45.43	4	9-4	Standard	KEYSTROKE	Nov 26 2016
1m 1f 104y	1m 57.99	2	9-2	Standard	EMISSARY	Oct 12 2019
1m 1f 104y	1m 55.91	6	8-8	Standard	STORM AHEAD	Nov 18 2019
1m 4f 51y	2m 33.44	4	9-5	Standard	PATHS OF GLORY	Oct 19 2019
1m 5f 219y	2m 57.83	4	9-8	Standard	GIVEN CHOICE	Jan 7 2019
2m 120y	3m 31.92	7	9-3	Standard	WATERSMEET	Jan 15 2018
2m 120y	3m 31.80	4	9-0	Standard	AIRCRAFT CARRIER	Jan 14 2019

YARMOUTH

DISTANCE	TIME	AGE	WEIGHT	GOING	HORSE	DATE
5f 42y	1m 0.37	2	8-11	Good To Firm	PINK ICEBURG	Jul 11 2018
5f 42y	59.16	5	8-8	Good To Firm	DASCHAS	Sep 18 2019
6f 3y	1m 10.40	2	9-0	Firm	LANCHESTER	Sep 15 1988
6f 3y	1m 9.14	3	9-0	Good To Firm	CARTOGRAPHER	May 24 2017
7f 3y	1m 22.20	2	9-0	Good To Firm	WARRSHAN	Sep 14 1988
7f 3y	1m 22.12	4	9-4	Good To Firm	GLENBUCK	Apr 26 2007
1m 3y	1m 36.30	2	8-2	Firm	OUT RUN	Sep 15 1988
1m 3y	1m 33.49	7	9-0	Firm	BINT DANDY	May 16 2018
1m 1f 21y	1m 52.00	3	9-5	Good To Firm	TOUCH GOLD	Jul 5 2012
1m 2f 23y	2m 2.83	3	8-8	Firm	REUNITE	Jul 18 2006
1m 3f 104y	2m 23.10	3	8-9	Firm	RAHIL	Jul 1 1993
1m 6f 17y	2m 57.80	3	8-2	Good To Firm	BARAKAT	Jul 24 1990
2m	3m 26.70	4	8-2	Good To Firm	ALHESN	Jul 26 1999

YORK

DISTANCE	TIME	AGE	WEIGHT	GOING	HORSE	DATE
5f	57.11	2	9-0	Good To Firm	BIG TIME BABY	Aug 20 2016
5f	55.90	5	9-11	Good To Firm	BATTAASH	Aug 23 2019
5f 89y	1m 3.20	2	9-3	Good To Firm	THE ART OF RACING	Sep 9 2012
5f 89y	1m 1.72	4	9-7	Good To Firm	BOGART	Aug 21 2013
6f	1m 8.90	2	9-0	Good	TIGGY WIGGY	Aug 21 2014
6f	1m 8.23	3	8-11	Good To Firm	MINCE	Sep 9 2012
7f	1m 22.32	2	9-1	Good To Firm	DUTCH CONNECTION	Aug 20 2014
7f	1m 21.00	3	9-1	Good To Firm	SHINE SO BRIGHT	Aug 24 2019
7f 192y	1m 36.92	2	9-5	Good	AWESOMETANK	Oct 14 2017
7f 192y	1m 34.95	3	9-3	Good To Firm	POGO	Aug 23 2019
1m 177y	1m 46.76	5	9-8	Good To Firm	ECHO OF LIGHT	Sep 5 2007
1m 2f 56y	2m 5.29	3	8-11	Good To Firm	SEA THE STARS	Aug 18 2009
1m 3f 188y	2m 25.40	4	8-8	Good To Firm	TAMREER	Aug 23 2019
1m 5f 188y	2m 53.48	5	9-9	Good To Firm	MUNTAHAA	Aug 25 2018
2m 56y	3m 27.06	5	9-6	Good To Firm	STRADIVARIUS	Aug 23 2019

TOP FLAT JOCKEYS IN BRITAIN 2019

(JANUARY 1st - DECEMBER 31st)

WINS-RUNS	%	JOCKEY	2ND	3RD	TOTAL PRIZE	WIN PRIZE
220-1106	20%	OISIN MURPHY	197	150	4,377,361	2,801,466
159-792	20%	DANIEL TUDHOPE	121	100	2,891,446	1,802,923
137-916	15%	BEN CURTIS	105	112	1,559,342	1,011,096
136-1054	13%	TOM MARQUAND	127	132	1,764,905	1,063,097
135-810	17%	JOE FANNING	109	92	1,983,622	1,454,306
132-901	15%	P J McDONALD	106	106	1,917,924	1,094,210
126-575	22%	JIM CROWLEY	57	69	3,251,864	2,312,090
126-795	16%	ADAM KIRBY	118	115	2,051,017	1,211,609
116-819	14%	HOLLIE DOYLE	113	87	1,201,634	693,462
112-1209	9%	DAVID PROBERT	133	138	1,194,353	631,187
106-738	14%	RICHARD KINGSCOTE	101	106	1,662,424	987,074
105-561	19%	JAMES DOYLE	82	74	4,223,501	2,300,898
105-1265	8%	LUKE MORRIS	125	140	1,111,972	549,753
103-620	17%	SILVESTRE DE SOUSA	67	60	3,144,444	1,927,733
97-744	13%	JASON WATSON	99	72	1,781,477	1,237,908
91-640	14%	ROBERT HAVLIN	86	82	1,274,131	733,556
91-700	13%	FRANNY NORTON	101	95	1,612,722	882,000
89-521	17%	JACK MITCHELL	83	56	724,055	540,303
88-701	13%	JASON HART	72	78	951,436	577,583
81-612	13%	HARRY BENTLEY	71	70	1,484,957	865,404
77-688	11%	DAVID EGAN	100	81	1,206,252	634,808
76-480	16%	ANDREA ATZENI	64	63	2,388,730	1,490,329
76-618	12%	DAVID ALLAN	84	71	927,787	585,388
71-443	16%	RYAN MOORE	81	56	5,179,345	2,698,904
71-567	13%	PAUL HANAGAN	72	70	1,009,028	576,460
75-559	9%	KIERAN O'NEILL	67	72	656,896	388,748
66-255	26%	FRANKIE DETTORI	45	33	7,365,868	5,951,232
66-485	14%	SEAN LEVEY	83	53	1,860,693	1,369,950
65-620	10%	GRAHAM LEE	65	72	620,700	359,758
65-621	10%	ROSSA RYAN	64	68	665,935	396,155
63-509	12%	HECTOR CROUCH	44	60	537,120	338,587
62-479	13%	CIEREN FALLON	60	61	892,795	430,510
58-704	8%	SHANE KELLY	73	75	577,460	308,922
57-668	9%	PAUL MULRENNAN	72	79	765,590	357,170
56-640	9%	SEAN DAVIS	65	58	556,321	301,069
55-619	9%	ROB HORNBY	53	76	752,519	456,292
53-387	14%	CLIFFORD LEE	35	53	453,264	297,911
52-287	18%	DANE O'NEILL	48	31	648,442	439,300
52-577	9%	CALLUM SHEPHERD	61	59	530,529	298,508
48-348	14%	JAMIE SPENCER	40	43	1,387,430	651,428
48-359	13%	BARRY McHUGH	31	36	546,003	354,261
48-578	8%	NICOLA CURRIE	47	48	550,638	325,891
48-601	8%	LIAM KENIRY	58	49	508,419	301,206
47-575	8%	PHIL DENNIS	56	45	575,663	350,913
45-309	15	PAT COSGROVE	39	34	407,765	246,323
45-542	8%	CHARLES BISHOP	52	55	613,822	275,607
45-655	7%	ANDREW MULLEN	60	67	411,367	190,419
44-406	11%	ALISTAIR RAWLINSON	42	44	536,566	320,470
44-438	10%	MARTIN DWYER	36	42	515,611	312,392
44-483	9%	STEVIE DONOHOE	46	46	480,784	274,100

TOP FLAT TRAINERS IN BRITAIN 2019

TRAINER	LEADING HORSE	W-R	2ND	3RD	4TH	WIN PRIZE	TOTAL PRIZE
JOHN GOSDEN	Enable	192-714	141	100	66	6,282,133	8,000,228
A P O'BRIEN	Magical	24-220	31	20	28	4,391,269	7,680,547
MARK JOHNSTON	Dee Ex Bee	249-1459	204	193	183	3,174,442	5,399,661
RICHARD HANNON	King Of Change	153-1286	158	150	138	2,732,962	4,012,258
ANDREW BALDING	Donjuan Triumphant	126-852	117	102	115	2,343,511	3,601,158
SIR MICHAEL STOUTE	Crystal Ocean	83-395	63	56	58	1,815,792	3,480,587
WILLIAM HAGGAS	Addeybb	142-646	106	78	72	1,635,918	3,125,480
ROGER VARIAN	Defoe	116-602	104	89	84	1,796,113	2,662,806
RICHARD FAHEY	Summer Sands	178-1514	173	188	178	1,391,189	2,545,525
DAVID O'MEARA	Lord Glitters	130-952	123	117	112	1,555,135	2,421,588
CHARLIE APPLEBY	Blue Point	71-275	55	36	28	1,688,272	2,191,331
CHARLES HILLS	Battaash	68-480	53	59	54	1,223,116	1,623,003
TIM EASTERBY	Copper Knight	126-1244	117	124	139	856,773	1,392,889
CLIVE COX	Golden Horde	71-567	74	81	66	733,573	1,271,685
ARCHIE WATSON	Soldier's Call	133-776	117	100	91	668,302	1,270,046
RALPH BECKETT	Manuela De Vega	82-517	58	53	51	763,306	1,242,800
SAEED BIN SUROOR	Red Galileo	81-346	58	52	36	725,045	1,193,629
KEVIN RYAN	Hello Youmzain	65-531	56	56	56	654,227	1,166,191
TOM DASCOMBE	Kachy	67-457	66	50	54	712,085	1,145,874
K R BURKE	Living In The Past	68-583	71	82	65	565,303	1,105,043
MICHAEL APPLEBY	Danzeno	99-922	90	94	96	652,841	1,102,798
ROGER CHARLTON	Quadrilateral	54-324	40	40	42	734,555	1,017,588
STUART WILLIAMS	Royal Birth	74-577	83	67	53	577,462	979,365
DAVID SIMCOCK	Desert Encounter	52-423	48	64	62	615,986	931,730
JAMES TATE	Invincible Army	72-306	44	36	41	659,928	926,097
KEITH DALGLEISH	What's The Story	80-691	74	82	79	523,042	889,456
MICHAEL DODS	Dakota Gold	44-462	46	53	43	455,710	807,314
IAN WILLIAMS	Time To Study	53-528	52	42	65	452,979	791,108
HUGO PALMER	Powerful Breeze	53-383	49	53	47	445,490	785,091
ED WALKER	Caradoc	56-416	61	36	34	497,678	728,508
MARTYN MEADE	Advertise	17-126	19	18	14	448,407	718,622
MICK CHANNON	Kinks	65-636	77	77	79	351,644	705,711
JOHN QUINN	Safe Voyage	36-370	33	42	44	333,596	663,650
SIMON CRISFORD	A'Ali	52-263	45	47	31	450,825	653,582
ALAN KING	Trueshan	33-274	29	36	30	408,913	647,299
JAMES FANSHAWE	The Tin Man	53-327	46	51	33	324,348	621,966
ROGER FELL	Tamreer	58-558	53	56	66	354,863	621,131
G M LYONS	Mustajeer	2-10	0	1	1	602,781	611,414
EVE JOHNSON HOUGHTON	Accidental Agent	44-382	40	43	42	331,194	609,004
TONY CARROLL	Recon Mission	74-669	72	68	58	385,656	607,720
DAVID ELSWORTH	Sir Dancealot	14-156	12	18	14	363,020	593,857
DAVID EVANS	Good Vibes	67-599	54	64	63	326,037	547,016
F-H GRAFFARD	Watch Me	1-3	1	0	0	283,550	520,050
RICHARD HUGHES	Gold Filigree	55-450	55	58	51	284,256	519,020
HUGHIE MORRISON	Telecaster	29-304	34	35	33	299,754	518,379
MITSURU HASHIDA	Deirdre	1-3	0	1	0	340,260	496,586
MICHAEL BELL	Bighearted	47-355	30	33	41	273,551	493,468
CHARLIE FELLOWES	Carnwennan	34-259	35	30	30	324,362	490,650
ROBERT COWELL	Raucous	34-354	43	42	41	248,706	488,222
DAVID BARRON	Kynren	24-257	31	29	27	251,641	461,542
AMANDA PERRETT	Open Wide	26-247	32	28	25	179,421	447,819
NIGEL TINKLER	Kaeso	38-372	30	53	43	220,544	430,260
ROD MILLMAN	Bettys Hope	34-294	39	33	22	299,537	418,638
JEDD O'KEEFFE	Jazeel	31-213	30	28	17	244,904	414,105
RUTH CARR	Poyle Vinnie	37-523	40	50	54	230,488	413,896
A FABRE	Waldgeist	1-8	0	5	0	155,952	413,017
HENRY CANDY	Limato	24-217	31	21	34	213,406	410,275
SIR MARK PRESCOTT BT	Land Of Oz	41-287	40	43	26	250,411	398,745
PAUL COLE	Duke Of Hazzard	23-191	25	27	28	261,950	383,125
KEVIN PRENDERGAST	Madhmoon	0-2	1	0	1	0	377,448

TOP FLAT OWNERS IN BRITAIN IN 2019

OWNER	LEADING HORSE	W-R	2ND	3RD	4TH	WIN PRIZE	TOTAL PRIZE
HAMDAN AL MAKTOUM	BATTAASH	151-638	87	79	73	2,551,692	3,764,789
DERRICK SMITH & MRS JOHN MAGNIER & MICHAEL TABOR	MAGICAL	8-79	15	13	9	2,127,565	3,692,320
K ABDULLAH	ENABLE	71-291	41	39	35	2,924,229	3,407,943
GODOLPHIN	BLUE POINT	157-655	117	94	67	2,385,395	3,372,498
KING POWER RACING CO LTD	DONJUAN TRIUMPHANT	59-375	39	40	44	1,536,542	2,362,351
MRS JOHN MAGNIER & MICHAEL TABOR & DERRICK SMITH	ANTHONY VAN DYCK	7-46	4	2	5	1,199,416	1,794,833
SHEIKH HAMDAN BIN MOHAMMED AL MAKTOUM	DEE EX BEE	58-359	57	47	42	852,904	1,610,654
SHEIKH MOHAMMED OBAID AL MAKTOUM	DEFOE	40-208	31	40	26	1,009,087	1,465,676
CHEVELEY PARK STUD	THREAT	50-328	51	45	50	663,631	1,358,525
SIR EVELYN DE ROTHSCHILD	CRYSTAL OCEAN	5-21	4	2	0	533,506	1,049,627
B E NIELSEN	STRADIVARIUS	10-33	3	3	1	911,168	1,022,877
MICHAEL TABOR & DERRICK SMITH & MRS JOHN MAGNIER	HERMOSA	4-60	8	4	9	408,862	1,006,353
CLIPPER LOGISTICS	LIVING IN THE PAST	50-247	30	40	25	509,669	883,724
LORD LLOYD-WEBBER	TOO DARN HOT	5-15	1	3	0	673,594	819,353
ALI ABDULLA SAEED	KING OF CHANGE	3-7	2	1	0	650,375	764,579
SHEIKH AHMED AL MAKTOUM	ADDEYBB	36-162	37	32	22	280,154	753,370
A E OPPENHEIMER	STAR CATCHER	13-49	12	7	3	526,810	633,144
SAEED MANANA	INVINCIBLE ARMY	51-229	37	26	29	464,772	629,928
DAVID SPRATT	MUSTAJEER	2-3	0	0	0	603,428	603,428
FLAXMAN STABLES, MRS MAGNIER, M TABOR, D SMITH	CIRCUS MAXIMUS	2-6	1	0	1	348,057	598,077
GEOFF & SANDRA TURNBULL	LORD GLITTERS	16-136	19	17	12	418,314	559,347
SHEIKH JUMA DALMOOK AL MAKTOUM	DRAMATIC QUEEN	37-147	22	22	14	399,666	548,377
THE QUEEN	KING'S LYNN	29-147	24	19	24	393,260	542,542
TOJI MORITA	DEIRDRE	1-3	0	1	0	340,260	496,586
QATAR RACING LIMITED	KAMEKO	27-117	24	13	9	356,891	486,687
HRH PRINCESS HAYA OF JORDAN	FOREST OF DEAN	12-68	17	9	5	225,899	452,938
DR MARWAN KOUKASH	GROWL	31-309	35	31	28	218,209	449,938
PAUL & CLARE ROONEY	GOOD VIBES	24-163	19	24	22	240,277	433,379
MRS FITRI HAY	DUKE OF HAZZARD	21-161	20	16	23	292,780	407,111
C BENHAM/ D WHITFORD/ L QUINN/ K QUINN	SIR DANCEALOT	2-39	2	3	5	238,267	396,592
JOHN DANCE	LAURENS	17-135	29	12	14	114,570	395,711
PHOENIX THOROUGHBRED LIMITED 1	ADVERTISE	1-6	2	0	0	283,550	394,778
HELENA SPRINGFIELD LTD	ANAPURNA	7-38	5	2	4	340,918	388,164
GEORGE STRAWBRIDGE	WISSAHICKON	17-94	20	16	11	203,481	378,041
WELDSPEC GLASGOW LIMITED	WHAT'S THE STORY	20-135	17	21	10	238,616	370,107
JABER ABDULLAH	HELLO YOUMZAIN	15-64	7	8	7	281,774	363,289
TONY BLOOM	STRATUM	6-23	2	2	0	315,455	359,849
HH SHEIKHA AL JALILA RACING	FANNY LOGAN	16-45	7	8	3	263,835	358,641
WITHERNSEA THOROUGHBRED LIMITED	ESCOBAR	5-49	3	9	6	267,991	357,679
SMITH/MRS MAGNIER/TABOR/ FLAXMAN STABLES	MAGNA GRECIA	2-9	0	1	1	300,447	350,576
SAEED SUHAIL	DREAM OF DREAMS	9-65	12	8	8	129,381	342,594
PAUL DEAN	SIR RON PRIESTLEY	5-7	1	0	0	180,111	330,045
LADY BAMFORD	KING OF COMEDY	8-57	11	10	6	61,206	318,645
DAVID W ARMSTRONG	MABS CROSS	22-131	22	17	18	174,573	308,615
T W MORLEY	RAUCOUS	18-141	22	13	10	168,462	305,845
ABDULLA AL MANSOORI	DESERT ENCOUNTER	16-116	13	13	19	231,687	292,292
ALEXANDER TAMAGNI	WATCH ME	1-1	0	0	0	283,550	283,550
MOHAMED OBAIDA	NAYEF ROAD	5-24	5	4	3	124,892	277,993
THE COOL SILK PARTNERSHIP	SUMMER SANDS	16-101	10	14	12	186,104	270,214
SHEIKH RASHID DALMOOK AL MAKTOUM	MOVE SWIFTLY	19-66	8	4	8	235,562	269,689
LAEL STABLE	ONE MASTER	2-14	3	1	1	29,888	264,486
PALL MALL PARTNERS & MRS R J MCCREERY	BILLESDON BROOK	3-7	1	1	0	239,245	260,670

TOP FLAT HORSES
IN BRITAIN 2019

HORSE (AGE)	WIN & PLACE £	W-R	TRAINER	OWNER	BREEDER
ENABLE (5)	1,375,217	3-3	John Gosden	K Abdullah	Juddmonte Farms Ltd
MAGICAL (4)	1,184,422	1-4	A P O'Brien	Derrick Smith & John Magnier & Michael Tabor	Orpendale, Chelston & Mrs Wynatt
CRYSTAL OCEAN (5)	1,018,919	3-5	Sir Michael Stoute	Sir Evelyn De Rothschild	Southcourt Stud
ANTHONY VAN DYCK (3)	955,563	2-3	A P O'Brien	Mrs John Magnier & Michael Tabor & Derrick Smith	Orpendale, Chelston & Wynatt
STRADIVARIUS (5)	941,729	5-6	John Gosden	B E Nielsen	Bjorn Nielsen
JAPAN (3)	913,835	2-4	A P O'Brien	Derrick Smith & Mrs John Magnier & Michael Tabor	Newsells Park Stud
KING OF CHANGE (3)	762,981	3-4	Richard Hannon	Ali Abdulla Saeed	Rabbah Bloodstock Limited
TOO DARN HOT (3)	686,836	1-3	John Gosden	Lord Lloyd-Webber	Watership Down Stud
BLUE POINT (5)	623,810	2-2	Charlie Appleby	Godolphin	Oak Lodge Bloodstock
MUSTAJEER (6)	600,000	1-1	Kris Lees	Australian Bloodstock, C Pickford Et Al	Shadwell Estate Company Limited
CIRCUS MAXIMUS (3)	595,933	2-5	A P O'Brien	Flaxman Stables, Mrs Magnier, M Tabor, D Smith	Flaxman Stables Ireland Ltd
BATTAASH (5)	567,985	3-4	Charles Hills	Hamdan Al Maktoum	Ballyphilip Stud
LOGICIAN (3)	514,013	5-5	John Gosden	K Abdullah	Juddmonte Farms Ltd
PINATUBO (2)	509,285	5-5	Charlie Appleby	Godolphin	Godolphin
DEIRDRE (5)	496,586	1-3	Mitsuru Hashida	Toji Morita	Northern Farm
STAR CATCHER (3)	446,894	3-4	John Gosden	A E Oppenheimer	Hascombe And Valiant Studs
ADDEYBB (5)	417,068	2-5	William Haggas	Sheikh Ahmed Al Maktoum	Rabbah Bloodstock Limited
DEFOE (5)	404,673	2-5	Roger Varian	Sheikh Mohammed Obaid Al Maktoum	Darley
ADVERTISE (3)	391,050	1-4	Martyn Meade	Phoenix Thoroughbred Limited 1	Cheveley Park Stud Ltd
HERMOSA (3)	391,050	1-4	A P O'Brien	Michael Tabor & Derrick Smith & Mrs John Magnier	Beauty Is Truth Syndicate
LORD GLITTERS (6)	382,885	1-5	David O'Meara	Geoff & Sandra Turnbull	S C A Elevage De Tourgeville Et Al
MADHMOON (3)	377,448	0-2	Kevin Prendergast	Hamdan Al Maktoum	Shadwell Estate Company Limited
KEW GARDENS (4)	372,370	1-3	A P O'Brien	Derrick Smith & Mrs John Magnier & Michael Tabor	Barronstown Stud
DONJUAN TRIUMPHANT (6)	356,151	1-7	Andrew Balding	King Power Racing Co Ltd	Patrick Cosgrove & Dream Ahead Syndicate
DEE EX BEE (4)	337,098	2-5	S bin Ghadayer	Sheikh Hamdan bin Mohammed Al Maktoum	Godolphin
QUADRILATERAL (2)	336,564	3-3	Roger Charlton	K Abdullah	Juddmonte Farms Ltd
ENBIHAAR (4)	334,090	4-5	John Gosden	Hamdan Al Maktoum	Haras Du Mezeray
SIR RON PRIESTLEY (3)	330,611	5-7	Mark Johnston	Paul Dean	Mascalls Stud
TEN SOVEREIGNS (3)	329,838	1-4	A P O'Brien	Derrick Smith & Mrs John Magnier & Michael Tabor	Camas Park, Lynch Bages & Summerhill
ANAPURNA (3)	324,163	3-4	John Gosden	Helena Springfield Ltd	Meon Valley Stud
MAGNA GRECIA (3)	297,018	1-2	A P O'Brien	Smith/Mrs Magnier/Tabor/ Flaxman Stables	Woodnook Farm Pty Ltd
MUSTASHRY (6)	293,168	2-5	Sir Michael Stoute	Hamdan Al Maktoum	Shadwell Estate Company Limited
WATCH ME (3)	283,550	1-1	F-H Graffard	Alexander Tamagni & Mme R Vannod	Mme A Tamagni & Cocheese Bloodstock Anstalt
HELLO YOUMZAIN (3)	278,721	2-5	Kevin Ryan	Haras d'Etreham and Cambridge Stud	Rabbah Bloodstock Limited
BEAT THE BANK (5)	265,104	2-4	Andrew Balding	King Power Racing Co Ltd	A S Denniff
BILLESDON BROOK (4)	260,670	3-6	Richard Hannon	Pall Mall Partners & Mrs R J McCreery	Stowell Hill Partners
THREAT (2)	260,340	3-6	Richard Hannon	Cheveley Park Stud	La Lumiere Partnership
NAYEF ROAD (3)	257,301	2-8	Mark Johnston	Mohamed Obaida	B V Sangster
MATTERHORN (4)	255,753	5-13	Mark Johnston	Sheikh Hamdan bin Mohammed Al Maktoum	Barronstown Stud
VERACIOUS (5)	254,182	1-6	Sir Michael Stoute	Cheveley Park Stud	Cheveley Park Stud Ltd
SIR DANCEALOT (5)	252,359	2-6	David Elsworth	C Benham/ D Whitford/ L Quinn/ K Quinn	Vincent Duignan
ELARQAM (4)	247,392	3-6	Mark Johnston	Hamdan Al Maktoum	Floors Farming
CAPE BYRON (5)	238,207	3-6	Roger Varian	Sheikh Mohammed Obaid Al Maktoum	Darley
THE REVENANT (4)	236,500	0-1	F-H Graffard	Al Asayl France	Al Asayl Bloodstock Ltd
ONE MASTER (5)	232,932	0-3	William Haggas	Lael Stables	Lael Stables
ESCOBAR (5)	222,266	2-10	David O'Meara	Withernsea Thoroughbred Limited	Peter Evans
KING OF COMEDY (3)	220,717	2-6	John Gosden	Lady Bamford	Lady Bamford
STRATUM (6)	217,875	1-2	W P Mullins	Tony Bloom	Al Asayl Bloodstock Ltd
WALDGEIST (5)	215,200	0-2	A Fabre	Gestut Ammerland & Newsells Park	The Waldlerche Partnership
SAFE VOYAGE (6)	213,842	3-5	John Quinn	Ross Harmon	Schneider Adolf

TOP NH JOCKEYS
IN BRITAIN 2018/19

WINS-RUNS	%	JOCKEY	2ND	3RD	TOTAL PRIZE	WIN PRIZE
200-979	20%	RICHARD JOHNSON	152	134	2,262,552	1,383,134
178-745	24%	HARRY SKELTON	122	102	2,083,624	1,402,679
146-888	16%	BRIAN HUGHES	143	128	1,459,714	862,021
109-518	21%	HARRY COBDEN	93	55	2,306,516	1,440,912
105-681	15%	SAM TWISTON-DAVIES	86	78	1,460,165	957,700
95-582	16%	AIDAN COLEMAN	68	90	1,247,414	891,420
91-593	15%	SEAN BOWEN	79	64	1,375,012	1,007,573
88-413	21%	WAYNE HUTCHINSON	64	48	1,033,048	670,556
86-381	23%	NICO DE BOINVILLE	56	32	1,751,175	1,393,217
82-685	12%	TOM SCUDAMORE	83	75	1,214,417	760,424
78-548	14%	TOM O'BRIEN	65	75	1,114,802	698,385
72-481	15%	JAMES BOWEN	58	56	823,156	538,360
69-411	17%	GAVIN SHEEHAN	74	37	739,705	402,449
68-553	12%	PADDY BRENNAN	95	70	1,050,132	533,536
61-472	13%	SEAN QUINLAN	52	50	750,377	513,639
59-504	12%	ADAM WEDGE	57	68	863,916	478,681
58-370	16%	DARYL JACOB	50	36	1,197,920	626,791
55-334	16%	DAVID BASS	50	36	687,511	436,184
50-307	16%	BRYONY FROST	43	30	988,839	704,953
45-377	12%	JONATHAN BURKE	39	45	578,657	302,658
44-308	14%	LEIGHTON ASPELL	40	38	500,682	308,703
43-257	17%	NOEL FEHILY	38	35	682,159	441,987
41-368	11%	TOM CANNON	46	33	415,650	228,465
41-416	10%	ROBERT DUNNE	51	54	456,473	219,394
39-377	10%	HENRY BROOKE	37	43	462,152	292,573
37-269	14%	ALAN JOHNS	29	30	272,149	165,625
37-318	12%	DANNY COOK	42	58	664,718	437,787
36-343	10%	ROSS CHAPMAN	41	33	354,032	215,837
35-150	23%	BARRY GERAGHTY	29	13	1,071,117	582,819
34-376	9%	JAMIE MOORE	32	47	544,043	368,397
32-187	17%	REX DINGLE	20	28	285,970	185,873
31-390	8%	NICK SCHOLFIELD	44	41	359,663	179,774
30-194	15%	JONJO O'NEILL JR	23	27	408,000	283,956
30-310	10%	KIELAN WOODS	38	45	363,506	215,557
28-275	10%	BEN POSTE	25	28	286,618	189,768
27-194	14%	CHARLIE DEUTSCH	21	23	571,108	345,388
27-256	11%	CIARAN GETHINGS	28	29	348,408	208,960
26-295	9%	HARRY BANNISTER	42	44	320,212	175,983
26-314	8%	RICHIE MCLERNON	27	36	296,728	148,540
25-191	13%	BRIDGET ANDREWS	20	19	288,872	150,597
25-243	10%	CHARLIE HAMMOND	30	20	254,915	163,408
25-256	10%	ALAIN CAWLEY	18	28	236,418	148,613
24-1214	11%	JEREMIAH MCGRATH	26	31	405,000	247,582
24-246	10%	RICHARD PATRICK	27	31	309,975	152,957
22-156	14%	LORCAN WILLIAMS	27	15	270,715	115,036
22-168	13%	JOSHUA MOORE	23	25	268,355	179,352
21-184	11%	CONNOR BRACE	24	20	227,870	158,199
21-200	11%	HARRY REED	22	22	161,304	85,431
21-221	10%	CONOR O'FARRELL	25	28	185,775	100,134
21-282	7%	JACK QUINLAN	38	31	332,069	197,043

TOP NH TRAINERS IN BRITAIN 2018/19

TRAINER	LEADING HORSE	W-R	2ND	3RD	4TH	WIN PRIZE	TOTAL PRIZE
PAUL NICHOLLS	Frodon	135-589	111	67	55	2,211,224	3,307,171
NICKY HENDERSON	Altior	141-544	89	56	48	2,147,578	2,908,080
DAN SKELTON	Roksana	204-986	146	115	92	1,514,536	2,298,848
COLIN TIZZARD	Elegant Escape	77-600	73	62	55	1,021,264	1,888,756
W P MULLINS	Al Boum Photo	8-74	7	6	4	919,795	1,409,434
GORDON ELLIOTT	Tiger Roll	55-206	26	19	18	1,041,795	1,358,678
PHILIP HOBBS	Defi Du Seuil	106-560	75	70	68	905,087	1,305,373
ALAN KING	Sceau Royal	91-499	84	61	65	724,517	1,259,790
NIGEL TWISTON-DAVIES	Bristol De Mai	63-530	67	50	53	738,487	1,257,830
TOM GEORGE	God's Own	52-376	53	59	36	456,505	902,459
HARRY FRY	If The Cap Fits	47-242	31	24	26	604,767	823,437
EVAN WILLIAMS	Silver Streak	53-507	59	67	62	420,389	822,908
GARY MOORE	Baron Alco	59-421	58	61	39	498,910	747,096
VENETIA WILLIAMS	Aso	42-277	39	29	23	455,895	735,000
PETER BOWEN	Lord Napier	64-368	35	45	39	523,688	717,638
EMMA LAVELLE	Paisley Park	35-262	35	41	25	537,542	710,468
NICKY RICHARDS	Takingrisks	42-221	37	36	23	479,451	680,689
OLLY MURPHY	Thomas Darby	82-429	62	52	56	399,059	661,547
DR RICHARD NEWLAND	Caid du Lin	53-217	41	21	23	464,963	645,005
JONJO O'NEILL	Champagne At Tara	56-472	46	64	49	390,041	639,239
NEIL MULHOLLAND	The Young Master	49-521	59	64	59	364,746	636,703
DONALD MCCAIN	Lofgren	63-558	81	79	71	337,729	627,919
BEN PAULING	Kildisart	44-313	33	33	25	439,780	614,858
KIM BAILEY	Charbel	51-263	44	30	24	401,041	601,872
DAVID PIPE	Ramses De Teillee	44-364	50	40	52	313,813	583,292
WARREN GREATREX	La Bague Au Roi	38-307	48	39	37	282,165	563,034
FERGAL O'BRIEN	Mighty Leader	49-408	59	57	53	311,732	550,653
CHARLIE LONGSDON	Hammersly Lake	36-364	36	51	49	320,019	545,004
IAN WILLIAMS	First Assignment	36-313	44	51	35	296,722	506,081
SUE SMITH	Vintage Clouds	29-247	31	39	37	301,811	475,939
PHILIP KIRBY	Lady Buttons	43-272	29	27	29	342,159	475,893
NEIL KING	Cubswin	40-249	50	29	36	284,651	470,743
MRS JOHN HARRINGTON	Magic Of Light	4-15	2	1	0	198,291	428,469
LUCINDA RUSSELL	One For Arthur	36-392	46	54	48	194,984	413,128
TIM VAUGHAN	Eric The Third	45-387	45	44	30	215,867	388,256
HENRY DE BROMHEAD	Ornua	6-33	3	2	3	253,469	379,505
TOM LACEY	Jester Jet	38-178	34	26	14	219,400	377,918
BRIAN ELLISON	Definitly Red	20-159	25	22	20	246,612	369,902
JAMIE SNOWDEN	Monbeg Theatre	31-242	51	22	29	202,954	357,274
SEAMUS MULLINS	Kentford Heiress	37-302	22	31	35	185,762	339,084
OLIVER SHERWOOD	Papagana	34-237	35	33	36	189,644	338,718
JEREMY SCOTT	Dashel Drasher	39-211	21	30	32	211,145	322,272
GAVIN CROMWELL	Espoir D'Allen	6-52	6	7	1	281,162	308,525
CHRISTIAN WILLIAMS	Potters Corner	27-201	22	19	17	238,803	308,170
N W ALEXANDER	Lake View Lad	25-202	19	28	28	204,202	307,037
MICKY HAMMOND	Cornerstone Lad	34-355	34	48	34	162,417	302,924
HENRY DALY	Atlanta Ablaze	23-189	32	18	16	158,813	290,482
NICK WILLIAMS	Siruh Du Lac	13-98	16	13	14	189,104	275,998
ROBERT WALFORD	Walk In The Mill	9-96	7	11	5	150,402	269,454
STUART EDMUNDS	Classic Ben	19-121	22	14	16	164,012	257,608
HARRY WHITTINGTON	Rouge Vif	24-168	25	24	23	138,681	248,929
JOSEPH PATRICK O'BRIEN	Us And Them	4-24	5	1	1	109,861	245,727
CHARLIE MANN	Morney Wing	19-148	25	17	22	153,971	241,353
IAIN JARDINE	L'Inganno Felice	26-172	30	18	18	151,559	236,388
HENRY OLIVER	Kilfilum Cross	26-192	16	20	33	133,788	228,229
CAROLINE BAILEY	Crosspark	13-103	20	10	19	122,500	227,614
JENNIE CANDLISH	Big Time Dancer	20-176	19	21	21	133,268	223,336
KEITH DALGLEISH	Chica Buena	28-150	20	23	26	141,340	222,374
CHRIS GORDON	Highway One O One	20-184	33	23	21	116,734	220,599
RUTH JEFFERSON	Waiting Patiently	19-99	16	11	7	102,664	210,381

TOP NH OWNERS IN BRITAIN IN 2018/19

OWNER	LEADING HORSE	W-R	2ND	3RD	4TH	WIN PRIZE	TOTAL PRIZE
JOHN P MCMANUS	ESPOIR D'ALLEN	94-489	62	56	31	1,368,739	2,147,993
SIMON MUNIR & ISAAC SOUEDE	BRISTOL DE MAI	32-170	30	16	21	587,869	1,076,155
GIGGINSTOWN HOUSE STUD	TIGER ROLL	3-57	5	8	3	596,365	892,430
ANN & ALAN POTTS LIMITED	MAGIC OF LIGHT	11-103	19	9	7	419,283	806,373
PAUL & CLARE ROONEY	IF THE CAP FITS	47-211	33	35	21	451,332	646,583
MRS PATRICIA PUGH	ALTIOR	7-14	3	0	0	546,187	556,672
P J VOGT	FRODON	5-21	1	4	3	401,007	462,148
MRS J DONNELLY	AL BOUM PHOTO	2-4	1	0	0	354,806	450,425
TREVOR HEMMINGS	LAKE VIEW LAD	27-205	29	25	27	264,349	448,944
MRS JOHNNY DE LA HEY	CYRNAME	7-68	14	9	8	247,858	401,296
ANDREW GEMMELL	PAISLEY PARK	5-5	0	0	0	347,743	347,743
J HALES	POLITOLOGUE	5-20	3	1	3	122,432	289,846
SULLIVAN BLOODSTOCK LIMITED	DUC DES GENIEVRES	7-37	7	2	3	194,014	266,857
KATE & ANDREW BROOKS	ROUGE VIF	29-104	19	10	13	155,173	259,316
GALLOPING ON THE SOUTH DOWNS PARTNERSHIP	TRAFFIC FLUIDE	18-90	14	12	10	186,881	250,865
MR & MRS P K BARBER, G MASON & SIR A FERGUSON	CLAN DES OBEAUX	2-7	3	0	1	170,850	241,630
JOHN WHITE & ANNE UNDERHILL	SIRUH DU LAC	8-29	4	2	7	151,003	218,359
CRIMBOURNE STUD	VERDANA BLUE	5-9	2	0	1	194,031	214,229
MRS S RICCI	MIN	1-17	0	1	4	140,985	208,382
L FELL	SILVER STREAK	2-7	3	1	0	85,102	207,666
CROSSED FINGERS PARTNERSHIP	GOD'S OWN	6-37	9	3	2	83,167	206,805
BROCADE RACING	NATIVE RIVER	14-87	14	10	10	66,669	205,871
J P ROMANS	ELEGANT ESCAPE	3-14	2	0	1	111,607	200,180
BRADLEY PARTNERSHIP	OZZIE THE OSCAR	12-72	13	5	8	121,280	186,437
PHIL & JULIE MARTIN	DEFINITLY RED	7-50	13	5	5	118,371	183,128
THE BELLAMY PARTNERSHIP	ASO	3-10	2	0	1	77,774	182,835
R S BROOKHOUSE	ACTIVIAL	9-60	8	11	9	102,515	182,721
HOOLS & FORCES PARTNERSHIP	PEPPAY LE PUGH	19-66	10	12	6	113,192	174,830
WALTERS PLANT HIRE LTD	AL DANCER	9-59	7	7	6	140,943	172,392
JOHN AND HEATHER SNOOK	THISTLECRACK	3-43	6	3	3	29,702	172,205
GRECH & PARKIN	KUPATANA	17-68	6	8	8	130,659	171,313
FRANK BIRD	TAKINGRISKS	3-9	1	2	1	154,536	170,914
MRS JUNE WATTS	MOHAAYED	11-45	3	0	5	148,125	166,364
RODDY OWEN & PAUL FULLAGAR	BEGGAR'S WISHES	15-68	10	7	6	122,362	164,284
CHEVELEY PARK STUD	ENVOI ALLEN	5-19	3	2	2	120,988	153,793
BARONESS HARDING	WALK IN THE MILL	1-5	0	3	1	84,195	152,833
MRS SARAH FAULKS	ROKSANA	3-23	5	4	0	80,836	147,510
MRS JAYNE SIVILLS	LADY BUTTONS	5-23	2	1	2	115,418	147,418
CHRIS GILES & MR&MRS P K BARBER	TOPOFTHEGAME	1-4	3	0	0	98,472	145,986
TERRY WARNER	ELIXIR DE NUTZ	12-41	7	4	2	115,851	145,180
MRS DIANA L WHATELEY	THOMAS DARBY	13-67	6	10	11	88,468	144,879
THE MEGSONS	GLOBAL CITIZEN	8-31	3	2	3	112,769	142,439
D W FOX	SUMKINDOFKING	10-71	9	12	9	72,822	141,634
R E R WILLIAMS	STILL BELIEVING	9-101	11	21	11	83,387	137,974
MICHAEL BUCKLEY	BRAIN POWER	5-13	2	1	2	120,652	136,699
C W BOOTH	CROSSPARK	4-16	3	1	2	71,036	134,144
PAUL MURPHY	KALASHNIKOV	5-18	4	0	1	112,959	133,329
TAYLOR & O'DWYER	LOSTINTRANSLATION	2-12	5	1	1	76,088	130,986
OWNERS GROUP 031	PENTLAND HILLS	3-3	0	0	0	130,586	130,586
MR & MRS WILLIAM RUCKER	BOLD PLAN	12-75	9	11	10	73,129	125,960

TOP NH HORSES
IN BRITAIN 2018/19

HORSE (AGE IN 2019)	WIN & PLACE £	W-R	TRAINER	OWNER	BREEDER
TIGER ROLL (9)	541,380	2-3	Gordon Elliott	Gigginstown House Stud	G O'Brien
ALTIOR (9)	537,285	5-5	Nicky Henderson	Mrs Patricia Pugh	Paddy Behan
FRODON (7)	406,718	4-5	Paul Nicholls	P J Vogt	Philippe Gasdoue
AL BOUM PHOTO (7)	351,687	1-1	W P Mullins	Mrs J Donnelly	Emmanuel Clayeux & Jacky Rauch
PAISLEY PARK (7)	347,743	5-5	Emma Lavelle	Andrew Gemmell	M Conaghan
MAGIC OF LIGHT (8)	261,409	2-5	Mrs John Harrington	Ann & Alan Potts Limited	Baronrath & Colbinstown Studs
ESPOIR D'ALLEN (5)	253,433	1-1	Gavin Cromwell	John P McManus	Bruno Vagne
CLAN DES OBEAUX (7)	240,295	2-5	Paul Nicholls	Mr & Mrs P K Barber, G Mason & Sir A Ferguson	Mme Marie Devilder
VERDANA BLUE (7)	208,271	4-6	Nicky Henderson	Crimbourne Stud	Edmond Kent
SILVER STREAK (6)	207,666	2-7	Evan Williams	L Fell	Yeomanstown Stud
IF THE CAP FITS (7)	201,812	2-5	Harry Fry	Paul & Clare Rooney	Liam Gilsenan
POLITOLOGUE (8)	199,420	1-5	Paul Nicholls	J Hales	Mme Henri Devin
BRISTOL DE MAI (8)	189,392	1-4	Nigel Twiston-Davies	Simon Munir & Isaac Souede	Jean-Yves Touzaint
ELEGANT ESCAPE (7)	188,353	2-6	Colin Tizzard	J P Romans	Jay Leahy
ANIBALE FLY (9)	172,500	0-2	A J Martin	John P McManus	Earl Baty, Mr V Baty, Mr F Lemercier
TAKINGRISKS (10)	170,298	3-7	Nicky Richards	Frank Bird	James Murray
BUVEUR D'AIR (8)	161,470	2-5	Nicky Henderson	John P McManus	Gerard Ferte
SIZING TENNESSEE (11)	154,396	2-2	Colin Tizzard	Ann & Alan Potts Limited	Philip Hore
WALK IN THE MILL (9)	152,833	1-5	Robert Walford	Baroness Harding	Alain Jollivet & Mme Celine Lefevre
MIN (8)	151,625	1-2	W P Mullins	Mrs S Ricci	Madame Marie-Therese Mimouni
ASO (9)	149,891	2-4	Venetia Williams	The Bellamy Partnership	I Pacault, A Pacault & M Pacault
TOPOFTHEGAME (7)	145,986	1-4	Paul Nicholls	Chris Giles & Mr&mrs P K Barber	Patrick Kavanagh
DEFI DU SEUIL (6)	144,495	3-5	Philip Hobbs	John P McManus	Mme Catherine Boudot
SUPASUNDAE (9)	143,470	1-2	Mrs John Harrington	Ann & Alan Potts Limited	Newsells Park Stud
CHAMP (7)	143,021	5-6	Nicky Henderson	John P McManus	Philip And Mrs Jane Myerscough
SCEAU ROYAL (7)	137,469	1-5	Alan King	Simon Munir & Isaac Souede	Guy Vimont
LADY BUTTONS (9)	135,865	4-6	Philip Kirby	Mrs Jayne Sivills	Keith Sivills
CYRNAME (7)	135,555	2-4	Paul Nicholls	Mrs Johnny de la Hey	S Follain, E Lecoiffier Et Al
PENTLAND HILLS (4)	130,586	3-3	Nicky Henderson	Owners Group 031	Al Asayl Bloodstock Ltd
SIRUH DU LAC (6)	128,402	4-4	Nick Williams	John White & Anne Underhill	Louis Fagalde
LOSTINTRANSLATION (7)	127,879	2-6	Colin Tizzard	Taylor & O'Dwyer	A R M M Kavanagh
CROSSPARK (9)	120,440	3-8	Caroline Bailey	C W Booth	W W & Mrs J E Dennis
KEMBOY (7)	112,260	1-2	W P Mullins	Supreme Horse Racing Club & Brett T Graham & K Sharp	Joelle Morruzzi & Philippe Morruzzi
ROKSANA (7)	111,971	1-3	Dan Skelton	Mrs Sarah Faulks	John O'Leary
LA BAGUE AU ROI (8)	108,446	3-4	Warren Greatrex	Mrs Julien Turner & Andrew Merriam	Comtesse Bertrand De Tarragon
QUEL DESTIN (4)	107,962	5-7	Paul Nicholls	Martin Broughton & Friends	S C E A Haras Des Sablonnets Et Al
BARON ALCO (8)	104,619	1-3	Gary Moore	John Stone	Yves D'Armaille
DUC DES GENIEVRES (6)	102,771	1-1	W P Mullins	Sullivan Bloodstock Limited	Mme Colette Serre
TALKISCHEAP (7)	102,679	2-6	Alan King	Charles Dingwall	Michael Veale
NATIVE RIVER (9)	102,275	0-3	Colin Tizzard	Brocade Racing	Fred Mackey
KILDISART (7)	101,762	3-5	Ben Pauling	Simon Munir & Isaac Souede	William Mangan
LE BREUIL (7)	100,500	2-6	Ben Pauling	Mrs Emma Palmer	Claude-Yves Pelsy
RATHVINDEN (11)	100,000	0-1	W P Mullins	R A Bartlett	Killian Traynor
DEFINITLY RED (10)	98,168	2-4	Brian Ellison	Phil & Julie Martin	James Keegan
GETAWAY TRUMP (6)	97,896	4-8	Paul Nicholls	Owners Group 023	E M O'Sullivan
POTTERS CORNER (9)	97,651	2-6	Christian Williams	All Stars Sports Racing & J Davies	Mrs P J O'Connor
MELON (7)	95,618	0-2	W P Mullins	Mrs J Donnelly	Newsells Park Stud
CAID DU LIN (7)	95,178	2-8	Dr Richard Newland	Foxtrot Racing	Mme Nathalie & M Jean-Pierre Trinquier
GLOBAL CITIZEN (7)	94,127	2-5	Ben Pauling	The Megsons	Martin Byrne
MOHAAYED (7)	92,821	1-6	Dan Skelton	Mrs June Watts	Shadwell Estate Company Limited

LEADING SIRES OF 2019 IN GREAT BRITAIN AND IRELAND

STALLION	BY BREEDING	RNRS	BY WNRS	WINS	WIN MONEY	BY PLACES	PLACE MONEY	TOTAL
GALILEO (IRE)	by Sadler's Wells	191	82	122	7525015	400	4183419	11708434
SEA THE STARS (IRE)	by Cape Cross	143	68	99	2841133	301	1290626	4131759
SHAMARDAL (USA)	by Giant's Causeway	148	67	102	2768515	360	715227	3483742
DUBAWI (IRE)	by Dubai Millennium	177	80	127	2007785	331	1475901	3483686
FRANKEL (GB)	by Galileo	110	52	86	2295786	225	1174019	3469805
DARK ANGEL (IRE)	by Acclamation	270	109	167	1892110	833	1240813	3132923
KODIAC (GB)	by Danehill	334	135	188	1636518	1029	1067083	2703601
INVINCIBLE SPIRIT (IRE)	by Green Desert	173	82	137	1463261	502	881616	2344876
NATHANIEL (IRE)	by Galileo	128	49	73	1901063	342	393834	2294897
LOPE DE VEGA (IRE)	by Shamardal	186	69	105	1209591	445	758874	1968464
CAMELOT (GB)	by Montjeu	132	59	81	898114	315	903362	1801476
ZOFFANY (IRE)	by Dansili	194	73	110	918464	486	854525	1772988
DANDY MAN (IRE)	by Mozart	220	90	155	1076144	690	678710	1754854
BATED BREATH (GB)	by Dansili	164	65	90	1130068	422	549153	1679222
PIVOTAL (GB)	by Polar Falcon	87	42	70	853196	250	722626	1575823
AUSTRALIA (GB)	by Galileo	107	36	65	882641	226	676311	1558952
NO NAY NEVER (USA)	by Scat Daddy	101	43	56	888986	210	649040	1538026
OASIS DREAM (GB)	by Green Desert	148	56	82	937834	370	565475	1503309
KINGMAN (GB)	by Invincible Spirit	122	64	80	805543	214	688010	1493553
SHOWCASING (GB)	by Oasis Dream	163	48	65	746074	410	728887	1474961
FARHH (GB)	by Pivotal	36	21	32	1019316	74	452382	1471698
ACCLAMATION (GB)	by Royal Applause	160	61	93	760239	612	710106	1470345
DANSILI (GB)	by Danehill	115	42	69	959563	275	470296	1429860
TEOFILO (IRE)	by Galileo	137	35	55	656646	332	726719	1383365
DREAM AHEAD (USA)	by Diktat	99	35	58	686140	269	656591	1342731
FOOTSTEPSINTHESAND (GB)	by Giant's Causeway	123	49	74	846551	332	453736	1300286
IFFRAAJ (GB)	by Zafonic	169	51	80	782600	456	506289	1288890

LEADING SIRES OF 2019
(GREAT BRITAIN, IRELAND AND OVERSEAS)

STALLION	BY BREEDING	DOMESTIC WNRS	WIN WINS	OVERSEAS MONEY	WIN WNRS	WINS	MONEY	TOTAL
GALILEO (IRE)	by Sadler's Wells	82	122	7525015	40	60	5201095	12726110
DUBAWI (IRE)	by Dubai Millennium	80	127	200785	70	95	7173107	9180892
SHAMARDAL (USA)	by Giant's Causeway	67	102	2768515	64	102	3805412	6573927
HELMET (AUS)	by Exceed And Excel	40	63	317081	28	46	6121144	6438225
SEA THE STARS (IRE)	by Cape Cross	68	99	2841133	44	72	2115680	4956812
FRANKEL (GB)	by Galileo	52	86	2295786	41	57	2177396	4473181
TEOFILO (IRE)	by Galileo	35	55	656646	36	62	3603201	4259847
DARK ANGEL (IRE)	by Acclamation	109	167	1892110	68	97	1297347	3189457
NATHANIEL (IRE)	by Galileo	49	73	1901063	23	40	1145204	3046267
RAVEN'S PASS (USA)	by Elusive Quality	26	44	483154	27	38	2280115	2763269
DANSILI (GB)	by Danehill	42	69	959563	32	61	1785843	2745406
KODIAC (GB)	by Danehill	135	188	1636518	55	78	1078934	2715452
INVINCIBLE SPIRIT (IRE)	by Green Desert	82	137	1463261	57	71	1227031	2690292
SIYOUNI (FR)	by Pivotal	25	31	218963	91	130	2442122	2661085
PIVOTAL (GB)	by Polar Falcon	42	70	853196	31	61	1728874	2582071
LOPE DE VEGA (IRE)	by Shamardal	69	105	1209591	58	88	1296211	2505802
EXCEED AND EXCEL (AUS)	by Danehill	64	97	655566	42	82	1657039	2312604
OASIS DREAM (GB)	by Green Desert	56	82	937834	53	82	1305608	2243442
ZOFFANY (IRE)	by Dansili	73	110	918464	50	77	1256651	2175115
KINGMAN (GB)	by Invincible Spirit	64	80	805543	23	30	1369410	2174953
HOLY ROMAN EMPEROR (IRE)	by Danehill	31	48	402397	68	107	1663554	2065951
BATED BREATH (GB)	by Dansili	65	90	1130068	35	56	934357	2064426
CAMELOT (GB)	by Montjeu	59	81	898114	47	69	1147177	2045291
CHAMPS ELYSEES (GB)	by Danehill	49	74	837082	38	59	1187286	2024368
NO NAY NEVER (USA)	by Scat Daddy	43	56	888986	22	39	1096475	1985461
MASTERCRAFTSMAN (IRE)	by Danehill Dancer	49	80	671220	55	86	1151122	1822342

LEADING TWO-YEAR-OLD SIRES OF 2019 IN GREAT BRITAIN AND IRELAND

STALLION	BY BREEDING	RNRS	BY WNRS	WINS	WIN MONEY	BY PLACES	PLACE MONEY	TOTAL
GALILEO (IRE)	by Sadler's Wells	64	21	29	721315	75	396188	1117504
SHAMARDAL (USA)	by Giant's Causeway	22	9	15	933679	27	44074	977753
NO NAY NEVER (USA)	by Scat Daddy	60	25	33	388262	105	426161	814423
FOOTSTEPSINTHESAND (GB)	by Giant's Causeway	40	15	25	476113	60	136333	612446
CABLE BAY (IRE)	by Invincible Spirit	55	20	30	367704	106	232206	599909
NIGHT OF THUNDER (IRE)	by Dubawi	41	23	31	343442	63	143579	487020
KODIAC (GB)	by Danehill	103	36	43	244181	208	216382	460563
FRANKEL (GB)	by Galileo	32	10	13	396402	31	61414	457816
GLENEAGLES (IRE)	by Galileo	44	16	22	309933	51	140012	449945
DARK ANGEL (IRE)	by Acclamation	79	27	35	230277	131	212439	442716
DANDY MAN (IRE)	by Mozart	76	27	40	260598	153	178971	439569
STARSPANGLEDBANNER (AUS)	by Choisir	40	16	23	323922	80	114327	438249
ZOFFANY (IRE)	by Dansili	66	22	25	223980	92	201813	425793
WAR FRONT (USA)	by Danzig	27	12	15	180311	50	216405	396716
KINGMAN (GB)	by Invincible Spirit	54	23	27	228790	65	142795	371585
GUTAIFAN (IRE)	by Dark Angel	77	25	34	199846	146	154846	354692
DUE DILIGENCE (USA)	by War Front	43	16	28	242143	66	100301	342444
LOPE DE VEGA (IRE)	by Shamardal	50	16	21	208620	43	118635	327255
IFFRAAJ (GB)	by Zafonic	44	10	16	165781	42	155545	321326
INVINCIBLE SPIRIT (IRE)	by Green Desert	47	15	17	93030	74	211330	304360
BATED BREATH (GB)	by Dansili	36	12	17	185706	40	117477	303183
LETHAL FORCE (IRE)	by Dark Angel	38	13	17	190120	54	105042	295162
SLADE POWER (IRE)	by Dutch Art	30	5	8	148950	36	123356	272306
BUNGLE INTHEJUNGLE (GB)	by Exceed And Excel	25	8	13	219945	49	50187	270132
ANJAAL (GB)	by Bahamian Bounty	45	10	17	204845	80	65271	270116
FIRST DEFENCE (USA)	by Unbridled's Song	1	1	4	263486	0	0	263486

LEADING FIRST CROP SIRES OF 2019 IN GREAT BRITAIN AND IRELAND

STALLION	BY BREEDING	RNRS	BY WNRS	WINS	WIN MONEY	BY PLACES	PLACE MONEY	TOTAL
CABLE BAY (IRE)	by Invincible Spirit	55	20	30	367704	106	232206	599909
NIGHT OF THUNDER (IRE)	by Dubawi	41	23	31	343442	63	143579	487020
GLENEAGLES (IRE)	by Galileo	44	16	22	309933	51	140012	449945
GUTAIFAN (IRE)	by Dark Angel	77	25	34	199846	146	154846	354692
DUE DILIGENCE (USA)	by War Front	43	16	28	242143	66	100301	342444
ANJAAL (GB)	by Bahamian Bounty	45	10	17	204845	80	65271	270116
MAKE BELIEVE (GB)	by Makfi	38	11	16	149386	62	78662	228049
IVAWOOD (IRE)	by Zebedee	47	10	12	80072	86	79515	159587
FREE EAGLE (IRE)	by High Chaparral	33	9	12	94959	32	44604	139562
BRAZEN BEAU (AUS)	by I Am Invincible	44	12	13	66722	56	70130	136852
AMERICAN PHAROAH (USA)	by Pioneerof the Nile	9	3	3	27812	13	98583	126395
MUHAARAR (GB)	by Oasis Dream	40	12	12	66601	47	53605	120205
GOLDEN HORN (GB)	by Cape Cross	39	8	9	67557	41	50975	118532
OUTSTRIP (GB)	by Exceed And Excel	36	10	14	65160	43	39088	104248
HOT STREAK (IRE)	by Iffraaj	36	8	8	42970	69	60348	103318
CAPPELLA SANSEVERO (GB)	by Showcasing	19	5	7	81134	20	15522	96656
FOUNTAIN OF YOUTH (IRE)	by Oasis Dream	34	5	6	26918	45	33635	60553
KARAKONTIE (JPN)	by Bernstein	7	3	5	43623	10	14934	58558
FRENCH NAVY (GB)	by Shamardal	7	2	2	15538	10	27500	43039
HALLOWED CROWN (AUS)	by Street Sense	17	3	3	11578	31	17120	28699
MUSTAJEEB (GB)	by Nayef	5	2	3	19437	4	6020	25456
SUPPLICANT (GB)	by Kyllachy	4	1	1	4033	16	10939	14971
AMARON (GB)	by Shamardal	1	1	1	3881	4	8365	12247
SIDESTEP (AUS)	by Exceed And Excel	5	0	0	0	4	12144	12144
FULBRIGHT (GB)	by Exceed And Excel	9	1	1	3429	18	7412	10840
INTRINSIC (GB)	by Oasis Dream	6	1	1	3429	10	7357	10785
SUMMER FRONT (USA)	by War Front	2	1	2	9412	1	510	9922

LEADING MATERNAL GRANDSIRES OF 2019 IN GREAT BRITAIN AND IRELAND

STALLION	BY BREEDING	RNRS	WINS	BY WNRS	WINS	WIN MONEY	BY PLACES	PLACE MONEY	TOTAL
PIVOTAL (GB)	by Polar Falcon	312	117	175		5002677	794	2384911	7387588
DANEHILL DANCER (IRE)	by Danehill	275	109	175		3011666	710	1660424	4672090
GALILEO (IRE)	by Sadler's Wells	358	129	189		2886976	816	1488385	4375362
SADLER'S WELLS (USA)	by Northern Dancer	264	93	146		2725362	596	909439	3634801
DANEHILL (USA)	by Danzig	158	57	98		2177758	433	994672	3172430
OASIS DREAM (GB)	by Green Desert	262	98	158		1606979	738	1134122	2741100
EXCEED AND EXCEL (AUS)	by Danehill	147	48	75		1662164	419	760682	2422846
SINGSPIEL (IRE)	by In the Wings	141	64	96		1422627	399	883940	2306567
DANSILI (GB)	by Danehill	221	79	110		824335	548	1164616	1988951
MARK OF ESTEEM (IRE)	by Darshaan	71	30	52		1154800	213	741200	1896000
MONTJEU (IRE)	by Sadler's Wells	165	56	83		1170652	423	685796	1856448
SHAMARDAL (USA)	by Giant's Causeway	157	64	106		912317	435	939607	1851924
INVINCIBLE SPIRIT (IRE)	by Green Desert	222	73	121		1213575	607	586322	1799896
CAPE CROSS (IRE)	by Green Desert	200	79	114		1002016	542	740909	1742925
ROYAL APPLAUSE (GB)	by Waajib	175	53	88		1237858	492	442633	1680491
KINGMAMBO (USA)	by Mr. Prospector	85	41	65		625941	260	1038248	1664189
GREEN DESERT (USA)	by Danzig	160	57	91		980788	481	659701	1640490
DALAKHANI (IRE)	by Darshaan	127	38	64		1118993	311	377354	1496347
SELKIRK (USA)	by Sharpen Up	163	58	92		838965	412	628545	1467510
INDIAN RIDGE	by Ahonoora	111	45	66		767423	327	553956	1321379
DAYLAMI (IRE)	by Doyoun	58	27	44		893292	161	347610	1240901
DARSHAAN	by Shirley Heights	73	28	49		599434	230	577829	1177263
BERING	by Arctic Tern	24	8	21		1001961	68	149668	1151629
ACCLAMATION (GB)	by Royal Applause	125	44	70		543914	350	535348	1079263
STREET CRY (IRE)	by Machiavellian	87	37	62		624842	223	383687	1008529
ECHO OF LIGHT (GB)	by Dubai Millennium	14	5	8		709447	36	266735	976182
DYNAFORMER (USA)	by Roberto	51	22	29		761397	133	166886	928283

FLAT STALLIONS' EARNINGS FOR 2019
(includes every stallion who sired a winner on the Flat in Great Britain and Ireland in 2019)

STALLIONS	RNRS	STARTS	WNRS	WINS	PLACES	TOTAL (£)
ACCLAMATION (GB)	160	1055	61	93	612	1470345.14
AD VALOREM (USA)	6	41	2	4	26	33320.45
ALDEBARAN (USA)	1	8	1	2	4	8357.14
ALHEBAYEB (IRE)	55	328	16	21	159	294452.15
AL KAZEEM (GB)	16	51	2	2	32	43439.71
AMADEUS WOLF (GB)	6	49	2	2	32	26814.46
AMARON (GB)	1	5	1	1	4	12246.68
AMERICAN PHAROAH (USA)	9	25	3	3	13	126394.93
AMERICAN POST (GB)	7	38	3	4	15	31208.81
ANIMAL KINGDOM (USA)	13	57	5	8	32	72992.29
ANJAAL (GB)	45	194	10	17	80	270116.40
ANTONIUS PIUS (USA)	5	34	1	1	17	13077.55
APPROVE (IRE)	34	240	14	20	130	319567.42
AQLAAM (GB)	29	224	12	21	139	204458.74
ARAAFA (IRE)	2	15	1	2	7	8561.05
ARABIAN GLEAM (GB)	9	66	6	10	39	50856.12
ARAKAN (USA)	23	113	4	8	59	63424.48
ARCANO (IRE)	77	560	36	59	285	738248.39
ARCH (USA)	9	37	4	7	20	89094.32
ARCHIPENKO (USA)	64	290	19	30	155	258041.16
AREION (GER)	3	24	2	2	14	50186.42
ART CONNOISSEUR (IRE)	9	83	4	6	41	72511.65
ARTIE SCHILLER (USA)	1	8	1	1	4	6565.59
ASHKALANI (IRE)	1	6	1	1	1	5926.13
ASK (GB)	7	35	2	3	13	30312.13
ASSERTIVE (GB)	14	112	6	11	62	86853.73
AUSSIE RULES (USA)	32	231	16	32	126	290853.23
AUSTRALIA (GB)	107	439	36	65	226	1558951.98
AUTHORIZED (IRE)	33	101	7	17	49	143657.95
AVONBRIDGE (GB)	17	112	6	8	69	72808.59
AZAMOUR (IRE)	14	69	3	7	39	59193.84
BAHAMIAN BOUNTY (GB)	31	246	12	22	128	373429.37
BAHRI (USA)	7	36	4	8	20	56672.57
BALTIC KING (GB)	12	66	2	4	28	40259.31
BATED BREATH (GB)	164	805	65	90	422	1679221.89
BATTLE OF MARENGO (IRE)	24	99	7	14	38	92105.76
BEAT HOLLOW (GB)	7	28	2	3	14	79336.44
BERNARDINI (USA)	7	33	4	4	17	38302.99
BERTOLINI (USA)	9	54	2	2	37	21789.09
BIG BAD BOB (IRE)	69	362	22	30	156	270895.15
BIRDSTONE (USA)	1	3	1	1	2	11594.07
BLAME (USA)	8	43	3	5	20	68678.90
BOLLIN ERIC (GB)	2	18	1	1	11	9635.04
BORN TO SEA (IRE)	99	488	22	37	209	459650.86
BRAZEN BEAU (AUS)	44	143	12	13	56	136852.12
BUNGLE INTHEJUNGLE (GB)	68	378	17	30	179	420847.47
BURWAAZ (GB)	5	35	1	1	16	16658.70
BUSHRANGER (IRE)	26	201	8	15	97	114592.07
BYRON (GB)	12	64	2	2	33	66152.45
CABLE BAY (IRE)	55	231	20	30	106	599909.07
CACIQUE (IRE)	24	118	9	14	61	190441.00
CAMACHO (GB)	165	939	44	64	460	785250.96
CAMELOT (GB)	132	608	59	81	315	1801476.29
CAMPANOLOGIST (USA)	4	21	3	9	10	57347.15
CANDY RIDE (ARG)	3	14	1	1	6	12118.99
CANFORD CLIFFS (IRE)	104	599	36	59	289	805437.37
CAN THE MAN (USA)	1	10	1	1	9	7996.29

STALLIONS	RNRS	STARTS	WNRS	WINS	PLACES	TOTAL (£)
CAPE BLANCO (IRE)	7	35	1	1	17	12473.15
CAPE CROSS (IRE)	94	536	42	65	321	813804.41
CAPPELLA SANSEVERO (GB)	19	63	5	7	20	96656.33
CAPTAIN AL (SAF)	1	8	1	1	6	7462.01
CAPTAIN GERRARD (IRE)	47	305	13	23	161	196157.53
CAPTAIN MARVELOUS (IRE)	4	18	1	1	9	11671.20
CAPTAIN RIO (GB)	13	78	3	4	32	42181.43
THE CARBON UNIT (USA)	9	39	1	1	15	17613.22
CASAMENTO (IRE)	108	534	31	45	249	658551.50
CHAMPS ELYSEES (GB)	110	623	49	74	380	1287579.78
CHARM SPIRIT (IRE)	68	372	32	53	200	561456.61
CHOISIR (AUS)	30	225	15	25	119	316812.97
CITYSCAPE (GB)	47	258	15	25	143	251945.97
CITY ZIP (USA)	7	35	2	2	21	27784.21
CLODOVIL (IRE)	62	412	18	20	252	453978.06
COACH HOUSE (IRE)	70	397	20	33	218	421231.43
COMPETITIVE EDGE (USA)	1	8	1	1	5	7662.61
COMPTON PLACE (GB)	43	303	13	17	186	235588.57
CURLIN (USA)	2	6	1	1	4	8698.49
DAAHER (CAN)	1	4	1	1	1	3621.62
DABIRSIM (FR)	27	86	8	9	38	215510.21
DALAKHANI (IRE)	29	150	10	15	101	547809.45
DANDY MAN (IRE)	220	1402	90	155	690	1754853.72
DANEHILL DANCER (IRE)	12	85	3	3	60	65853.10
DANSILI (GB)	115	523	42	69	275	1429859.76
DAPPER (GB)	2	15	1	1	10	16297.12
DAREDEVIL (USA)	2	11	1	1	6	6980.03
DARK ANGEL (IRE)	270	1493	109	167	833	3132922.65
DATA LINK (USA)	3	22	2	4	15	32586.55
DAWN APPROACH (IRE)	112	466	33	47	196	1043321.65
DAY FLIGHT (GB)	1	6	1	2	3	14167.58
DECLARATION OF WAR (USA)	57	329	29	50	195	701904.27
DEEP IMPACT (JPN)	7	22	3	6	12	90018.02
DELEGATOR (GB)	59	365	27	48	186	417798.80
DENON (USA)	1	12	1	1	11	7856.44
DENOUNCE (GB)	7	40	2	4	25	88139.55
DESIDERATUM (GB)	3	25	1	3	13	14477.65
DIALED IN (USA)	2	8	1	2	5	48963.77
DICK TURPIN (IRE)	33	179	8	14	103	110197.62
DISCREET CAT (USA)	3	12	1	2	6	39461.80
DISTORTED HUMOR (USA)	16	60	6	9	35	106411.45
DOCTOR DINO (FR)	1	9	1	2	4	92582.60
DONCASTER ROVER (USA)	5	23	1	4	6	32383.33
DOYEN (IRE)	6	27	3	4	19	19097.04
DRAGON PULSE (IRE)	88	432	22	28	192	361390.34
DREAM AHEAD (USA)	99	512	35	58	269	1342731.02
DUBAWI (IRE)	177	650	80	127	331	3483686.49
DUE DILIGENCE (USA)	43	179	16	28	66	342443.52
DUKE OF MARMALADE (IRE)	17	72	4	7	37	93464.63
DUNADEN (FR)	19	81	4	10	38	192006.83
DUNKERQUE (FR)	3	11	1	1	8	10551.16
DUTCH ART (GB)	107	667	59	88	382	1020437.59
DYLAN THOMAS (IRE)	24	120	4	4	66	88992.05
ECHO OF LIGHT (GB)	6	26	1	1	15	11547.44
ELNADIM (USA)	20	157	4	5	77	153472.26
ELUSIVE CITY (USA)	13	117	7	12	67	106376.05
ELUSIVE PIMPERNEL (USA)	29	106	3	4	27	36357.10
ELUSIVE QUALITY (USA)	19	105	7	9	46	73431.69
ELVSTROEM (AUS)	2	7	1	1	3	6490.44
ELZAAM (AUS)	71	393	26	39	187	506734.96
EMPIRE MAKER (USA)	1	2	1	1	0	5045.82

STALLIONS	RNRS	STARTS	WNRS	WINS	PLACES	TOTAL (£)
ENGLISH CHANNEL (USA)	5	31	1	1	19	18901.83
EPAULETTE (AUS)	94	520	31	42	266	534755.24
EQUIANO (FR)	122	730	37	64	384	894383.98
ES QUE LOVE (IRE)	23	105	8	10	45	120456.34
EVASIVE (GB)	4	13	1	1	6	6040.70
EXCEED AND EXCEL (AUS)	161	973	64	97	547	1204968.15
EXCELEBRATION (IRE)	73	393	17	24	199	673289.71
EXCELLENT ART (GB)	18	126	8	14	69	162168.86
EXCHANGE RATE (USA)	10	50	2	3	30	30520.96
THE FACTOR (USA)	8	30	3	3	14	28324.02
FAME AND GLORY (GB)	2	11	1	6	3	46272.11
FAMOUS NAME (GB)	25	140	9	12	60	305803.28
FARHH (GB)	36	154	21	32	74	1471698.43
FAST COMPANY (IRE)	98	562	37	51	290	734085.55
FASTNET ROCK (AUS)	46	200	12	19	94	641549.43
FINJAAN (GB)	10	80	3	5	44	44940.01
FINSCEAL FIOR (IRE)	13	64	2	4	28	67231.20
FIREBREAK (GB)	24	162	10	16	96	107040.73
FIRST DEFENCE (USA)	12	72	7	13	35	328599.09
FLATTER (USA)	1	3	1	1	2	5168.52
FLEMENSFIRTH (USA)	3	9	1	1	5	15379.73
FOOTSTEPSINTHESAND (GB)	123	681	49	74	332	1300286.45
FOUNTAIN OF YOUTH (IRE)	34	119	5	6	45	60552.82
FOXWEDGE (AUS)	62	401	28	47	221	399304.54
FRAGRANT MIX (IRE)	2	5	1	1	1	10045.50
FRANKEL (GB)	110	440	52	86	225	3469804.85
FREE EAGLE (IRE)	33	97	9	12	32	139562.39
FRENCH NAVY (GB)	7	28	2	2	10	43038.88
FROZEN POWER (IRE)	26	169	9	16	77	128868.16
FUISSE (FR)	1	7	1	1	2	11176.40
FULBRIGHT (GB)	9	36	1	1	18	10840.22
GALE FORCE TEN (GB)	41	207	8	17	82	197507.70
GALILEO (IRE)	191	755	82	122	400	11708434.33
GARSWOOD (GB)	56	260	15	26	139	243937.66
GEORDIELAND (FR)	2	9	1	1	7	6311.38
GEORGE VANCOUVER (USA)	6	25	1	2	17	15353.46
GETAWAY (GER)	10	27	4	8	12	66418.77
GIANT'S CAUSEWAY (USA)	4	29	2	3	18	33107.88
GIO PONTI (USA)	6	21	2	6	8	26854.55
GLENEAGLES (IRE)	44	118	16	22	51	449945.13
GOLDEN HORN (GB)	39	82	8	9	41	118532.19
GREAT JOURNEY (JPN)	1	5	1	1	2	26335.84
GREGORIAN (IRE)	51	293	19	29	152	245829.08
GUTAIFAN (IRE)	77	325	25	34	146	354691.67
HAAFHD (GB)	17	92	5	8	45	79960.53
HAATEF (USA)	13	65	3	6	25	58651.87
HALLING (USA)	14	66	3	9	27	224728.59
HALLOWED CROWN (AUS)	17	63	3	3	31	28698.58
HARBINGER (GB)	2	7	1	1	3	687833.05
HARBOUR WATCH (IRE)	96	461	28	48	232	594228.11
HARD SPUN (USA)	11	54	3	4	34	46446.04
HARLAN'S HOLIDAY (USA)	2	12	1	1	7	14522.52
HAT TRICK (JPN)	4	26	1	1	13	9064.20
HAVANA GOLD (IRE)	87	468	28	46	254	388601.06
HEERAAT (IRE)	62	346	18	30	165	287235.16
HELLVELYN (GB)	34	195	10	13	105	134230.78
HELMET (AUS)	120	672	40	63	352	561972.26
HENRYTHENAVIGATOR (USA)	31	154	6	8	88	94504.93
HIGH CHAPARRAL (USA)	46	234	14	22	124	332967.95
HOLY ROMAN EMPEROR (IRE)	94	554	31	48	295	727620.24
HOT STREAK (IRE)	36	155	8	8	69	103317.79

STALLIONS	RNRS	STARTS	WNRS	WINS	PLACES	TOTAL (£)
HURRICANE CAT (USA)	4	12	1	1	8	8587.87
HURRICANE RUN (IRE)	6	31	2	3	14	23585.76
IFFRAAJ (GB)	169	851	51	80	456	1288889.59
INCLUDE (USA)	1	11	1	2	8	9433.69
INDESATCHEL (IRE)	3	19	1	2	7	14222.35
INDIAN HAVEN (GB)	6	33	1	1	20	11288.42
INTELLO (GER)	63	290	25	36	145	501756.60
INTENSE FOCUS (USA)	45	278	16	21	149	352353.07
INTIKHAB (USA)	28	159	8	11	84	156647.77
INTRINSIC (GB)	6	21	1	1	10	10785.09
INVINCIBLE SPIRIT (IRE)	173	962	82	137	502	2344876.49
ISTAN (USA)	1	5	1	1	4	4684.06
IVAWOOD (IRE)	47	187	10	12	86	159587.15
JEREMY (USA)	24	105	4	5	44	201485.93
JOSHUA TREE (IRE)	3	22	2	2	9	12804.06
JUKEBOX JURY (IRE)	7	31	2	3	18	103955.05
KALANISI (IRE)	6	33	3	4	13	41504.85
KARAKONTIE (JPN)	7	19	3	5	10	58557.50
KENDARGENT (FR)	24	143	11	16	79	254104.35
KHELEYF (USA)	49	373	19	29	206	276320.50
KIER PARK (IRE)	1	11	1	1	7	7600.70
KINGMAN (GB)	122	414	64	80	214	1493553.16
KINGSALSA (USA)	1	10	1	1	9	6034.68
KINGSBARNS (IRE)	2	5	1	1	1	6625.68
KING'S BEST (USA)	5	18	1	2	8	19442.34
KING'S THEATRE (IRE)	2	10	1	3	3	74284.13
KITTEN'S JOY (USA)	40	162	12	14	82	408689.72
KODIAC (GB)	334	1918	135	188	1029	2703600.59
KUROSHIO (AUS)	12	59	4	5	28	96257.28
KYLLACHY (GB)	120	798	43	68	439	972271.17
LAWMAN (FR)	107	575	30	48	292	690251.97
LE CADRE NOIR (IRE)	6	54	4	6	17	60927.75
LE HAVRE (IRE)	40	167	14	25	86	467073.85
LEMON DROP KID (USA)	13	55	4	5	23	79091.96
LEROIDESANIMAUX (BRZ)	27	191	12	23	103	416208.30
LETHAL FORCE (IRE)	100	553	36	58	294	750831.28
LILBOURNE LAD (IRE)	44	293	16	29	154	365117.89
LINNGARI (IRE)	3	10	1	1	5	7331.83
LONHRO (AUS)	13	81	7	13	37	144434.72
LOPE DE VEGA (IRE)	186	852	69	105	445	1968464.44
LORD KANALOA (JPN)	1	4	1	1	2	22157.66
LORD SHANAKILL (USA)	21	158	14	22	91	156773.35
LOVELACE (GB)	3	18	1	1	2	8577.75
LUCAYAN (FR)	1	6	1	3	2	23034.57
LUCKY STORY (USA)	4	30	1	1	25	18025.07
MAGICIAN (IRE)	8	52	4	6	28	69669.96
MAJESTIC MISSILE (IRE)	11	76	5	8	42	69139.88
MAJESTIC WARRIOR (USA)	1	8	1	1	3	6075.20
MAJOR CADEAUX (GB)	13	92	5	17	42	100842.64
MAKE BELIEVE (GB)	38	128	11	16	62	228048.65
MAKFI (GB)	39	231	16	18	139	279003.55
MALIBU MOON (USA)	1	2	1	1	1	5284.85
MAMOOL (IRE)	3	12	1	1	10	11490.17
MANDURO (GER)	18	69	2	3	43	67767.86
MARJU (IRE)	3	4	1	1	0	8324.32
MARTALINE (GB)	3	9	1	1	5	11373.10
MASTERCRAFTSMAN (IRE)	140	691	49	80	351	1188849.23
MAWATHEEQ (USA)	14	54	1	1	30	22660.52
MAXIOS (GB)	29	151	9	13	83	170344.66
MAYSON (GB)	110	657	43	71	343	798427.70
MAZAMEER (IRE)	12	78	2	2	40	28936.51

STALLIONS	RNRS	STARTS	WNRS	WINS	PLACES	TOTAL (£)
MEDAGLIA D'ORO (USA)	17	59	4	7	30	84971.21
MEDICEAN (GB)	46	276	16	27	171	874333.21
MIDNIGHT LEGEND (GB)	4	17	4	6	7	25372.31
MILAN (GB)	5	11	2	2	6	41537.73
MILK IT MICK (GB)	7	59	3	3	41	39024.55
MILLENARY (GB)	3	14	1	1	9	9330.17
MISU BOND (IRE)	4	46	3	5	28	39600.84
MIZZEN MAST (USA)	12	73	4	5	38	54508.51
MONSIEUR BOND (IRE)	47	347	19	33	211	330987.02
MONSUN (GER)	2	6	1	1	4	7143.43
MOOHAAJIM (IRE)	15	56	5	11	28	92946.18
MORE THAN READY (USA)	23	90	9	11	43	131323.81
MORPHEUS (GB)	53	260	11	20	113	164805.63
MOST IMPROVED (IRE)	23	162	6	9	83	92500.87
MOTIVATOR (GB)	25	136	8	11	77	350227.27
MOUNT NELSON (GB)	47	273	20	26	150	382326.98
MUHAARAR (GB)	40	111	12	12	47	120205.36
MUJADIL (USA)	1	9	1	1	3	7422.53
MUKHADRAM (GB)	80	314	30	40	158	418796.24
MULLIONMILEANHOUR (IRE)	6	31	1	2	18	14935.11
MULTIPLEX (GB)	22	132	8	10	72	101352.38
MUSIC MASTER (GB)	4	17	1	2	6	8448.28
MUSTAJEEB (GB)	5	17	2	3	4	25456.22
MUSTAMEET (USA)	6	23	1	1	9	29419.37
MYBOYCHARLIE (IRE)	6	40	2	2	21	16962.31
NAAQOOS (GB)	2	23	1	1	15	9513.31
NATHANIEL (IRE)	128	608	49	73	342	2294896.83
NAYEF (USA)	19	93	5	7	41	51257.29
NEW APPROACH (IRE)	120	493	42	68	251	1068293.42
NIGHT OF THUNDER (IRE)	41	130	23	31	63	487020.29
NOBLE MISSION (GB)	18	92	9	12	44	268311.07
NO NAY NEVER (USA)	101	437	43	56	210	1538026.47
NO RISK AT ALL (FR)	2	11	2	4	4	27337.75
NORSE DANCER (IRE)	8	48	1	1	32	23462.49
NORTH LIGHT (IRE)	1	18	1	4	12	19163.60
NOTNOWCATO (GB)	6	44	3	4	26	22401.61
OASIS DREAM (GB)	148	757	56	82	370	1503309.25
OLDEN TIMES (GB)	4	15	1	1	9	39364.94
OLYMPIC GLORY (IRE)	29	124	8	10	62	381892.97
ORATORIO (IRE)	11	56	3	6	26	44613.67
ORB (USA)	3	18	2	2	9	14971.09
ORIENTOR (GB)	17	138	5	8	86	89216.42
ORPEN (USA)	8	34	1	1	19	41951.31
OSCAR (IRE)	1	4	1	1	2	57779.23
OUTSTRIP (GB)	36	138	10	14	43	104247.83
OXBOW (USA)	1	6	1	2	4	8026.16
PACO BOY (IRE)	56	329	17	27	179	514837.99
PAPAL BULL (GB)	9	42	3	5	18	42668.81
PASSING GLANCE (GB)	16	80	4	5	48	69254.05
PASTORAL PURSUITS (GB)	50	395	17	27	229	296208.08
PASTORIUS (GER)	2	9	1	1	7	17325.82
PEDRO THE GREAT (USA)	3	15	1	2	5	29318.22
PEINTRE CELEBRE (USA)	6	21	2	3	9	16872.49
PERFECT SOUL (IRE)	1	10	1	2	6	50479.29
PHOENIX REACH (IRE)	20	87	2	2	43	27632.87
PICCOLO (GB)	45	324	14	19	179	282707.23
PIONEEROF THE NILE (USA)	2	7	1	2	2	12043.52
PIVOTAL (GB)	87	487	42	70	250	1575822.87
PLANTEUR (IRE)	7	21	1	4	13	141922.44
POET'S VOICE (GB)	132	725	35	52	381	635044.47
POINT OF ENTRY (USA)	4	18	2	3	10	52280.87

STALLIONS	RNRS	STARTS	WNRS	WINS	PLACES	TOTAL (£)
POUR MOI (IRE)	45	234	17	26	116	278950.77
POWER (GB)	60	274	16	26	139	348547.09
PRIME DEFENDER (GB)	1	16	1	2	9	27676.41
PROCLAMATION (IRE)	6	22	2	2	15	14729.26
QUALITY ROAD (USA)	5	37	2	4	24	31689.13
RAIL LINK (GB)	19	114	5	10	66	116884.56
RAJJ (IRE)	5	21	3	3	8	30295.49
RAJSAMAN (FR)	10	43	2	4	21	44282.94
RAVEN'S PASS (USA)	79	399	26	44	188	830704.93
RED CLUBS (IRE)	10	66	3	4	42	30038.15
RED JAZZ (USA)	42	219	10	21	87	201168.81
REDOUTE'S CHOICE (AUS)	14	63	5	9	30	561565.42
REFUSE TO BEND (IRE)	7	53	3	3	33	37000.06
RELIABLE MAN (GB)	6	25	4	4	14	31490.63
REQUINTO (IRE)	62	362	24	35	187	423496.04
RIO DE LA PLATA (USA)	11	42	2	2	25	46382.95
RIP VAN WINKLE (IRE)	65	412	26	39	240	409009.62
ROCK OF GIBRALTAR (IRE)	68	355	17	31	178	555696.96
RODERIC O'CONNOR (IRE)	55	302	23	32	143	446743.91
ROYAL APPLAUSE (GB)	41	286	15	21	152	215786.45
RULER OF THE WORLD (IRE)	21	85	3	5	35	424684.79
RULERSHIP (JPN)	1	4	1	1	0	6659.46
SADDEX (GB)	1	4	1	2	2	26155.31
SAKHEE (USA)	9	32	3	4	15	107460.62
SAKHEE'S SECRET (GB)	35	263	11	19	156	168976.09
SAMUM (GER)	3	22	2	4	12	97200.65
SAYIF (IRE)	16	84	5	7	32	169763.67
SCAT DADDY (USA)	40	167	18	19	81	527381.91
SEA THE MOON (GER)	56	244	21	38	130	579706.30
SEA THE STARS (IRE)	143	587	68	99	301	4131758.93
SEPOY (AUS)	94	565	32	57	316	660467.76
SHAMARDAL (USA)	148	706	67	102	360	3483742.12
SHIROCCO (GER)	14	57	3	3	33	56412.84
SHOWCASING (GB)	163	779	48	65	410	1474961.41
SINGSPIEL (IRE)	3	22	1	2	14	14297.59
SINNDAR (IRE)	6	21	1	1	8	14952.35
SIR PERCY (GB)	84	495	36	61	267	623739.97
SIR PRANCEALOT (IRE)	74	504	23	40	273	772543.88
SIXTIES ICON (GB)	65	411	23	37	238	486875.64
SIYOUNI (FR)	78	257	25	31	125	587892.35
SLADE POWER (IRE)	87	493	30	48	262	700532.35
SLEEPING INDIAN (GB)	18	104	4	6	51	50495.27
SMART STRIKE (CAN)	10	46	1	5	15	33279.39
SOAVE (GER)	1	12	1	2	8	10283.47
SOCIETY ROCK (IRE)	98	594	34	50	310	644644.34
SOLDIER HOLLOW (GB)	11	37	2	2	23	31944.56
SOLDIER OF FORTUNE (IRE)	5	29	1	1	16	32955.54
SOMMERABEND (GB)	1	3	1	2	1	8185.39
SO YOU THINK (NZ)	26	124	4	6	53	71394.74
SPEIGHTSTOWN (USA)	22	127	12	16	75	168896.28
STARSPANGLEDBANNER (AUS)	45	226	19	28	117	495254.10
STEELE TANGO (USA)	3	16	1	1	7	7561.36
STIMULATION (IRE)	17	127	8	13	74	87595.37
STORMY ATLANTIC (USA)	2	11	1	1	6	8577.39
STORMY RIVER (FR)	3	24	1	2	13	49981.34
STOWAWAY (GB)	2	8	1	1	4	5129.89
STRATEGIC PRINCE (GB)	10	65	4	5	36	46809.50
STREET BOSS (USA)	4	14	1	1	8	43895.09
STREET CRY (IRE)	22	145	7	11	95	113519.07
STREET SENSE (USA)	8	45	3	4	24	82588.80
STRIKING AMBITION (GB)	2	21	1	1	17	11330.37

STALLIONS	RNRS	STARTS	WNRS	WINS	PLACES	TOTAL (£)
STYLE VENDOME (FR)	8	47	2	3	21	27145.74
SULAMANI (IRE)	6	37	2	4	23	27464.45
SUMMER FRONT (USA)	2	6	1	2	1	9921.61
SUPERIOR PREMIUM (GB)	1	11	1	2	7	11745.80
SUPER SAVER (USA)	4	21	1	1	11	7086.36
SUPPLICANT (GB)	4	24	1	1	16	14971.42
SWISS SPIRIT (GB)	106	564	36	54	292	425192.82
TAGULA (IRE)	34	146	6	9	65	138975.43
TALE OF THE CAT (USA)	3	8	1	1	6	45544.78
TAMAYUZ (GB)	71	334	22	30	174	748521.03
TAPIT (USA)	3	23	3	4	15	151153.09
TEOFILO (IRE)	137	613	35	55	332	1383365.02
TERTULLIAN (USA)	2	14	1	1	8	22505.40
THEWAYYOUARE (USA)	30	150	9	16	83	128670.90
THOUSAND WORDS (GB)	5	45	1	2	28	19329.95
TOBOUGG (IRE)	6	21	1	2	7	8430.51
TORONADO (IRE)	65	335	29	43	170	462669.71
TOUGH AS NAILS (IRE)	15	110	7	13	54	124496.13
TRADE FAIR (GB)	2	4	1	1	2	8139.35
TRANS ISLAND (GB)	4	22	2	2	6	11644.73
TWIRLING CANDY (USA)	2	8	1	1	4	11552.40
UNION RAGS (USA)	6	18	1	1	4	5281.45
UNIVERSAL (IRE)	8	42	4	7	20	55240.57
URBAN POET (USA)	3	12	1	3	5	30904.50
VALE OF YORK (IRE)	26	168	6	9	78	118010.75
VERGLAS (IRE)	11	48	4	5	31	63758.92
VINNIE ROE (IRE)	2	4	1	1	3	12970.27
VIOLENCE (USA)	2	8	1	2	4	14092.93
VIRTUAL (GB)	5	24	2	5	12	24502.99
VOCALISED (USA)	46	207	11	15	65	214369.53
WAR COMMAND (USA)	77	367	19	26	176	315780.39
WAR FRONT (USA)	65	295	27	40	170	780446.17
WATAR (IRE)	2	9	1	1	1	3893.26
WESTERNER (GB)	7	31	1	1	18	22865.05
WESTLAKE (GB)	1	14	1	1	12	15533.12
WHERE OR WHEN (IRE)	1	13	1	2	6	25400.90
WHIPPER (USA)	5	17	1	1	9	386621.19
WILDCAT HEIR (USA)	1	9	1	4	4	16510.18
WINDSOR KNOT (IRE)	6	29	1	1	13	20536.12
WINGED LOVE (IRE)	2	4	1	1	1	26964.86
WOOTTON BASSETT (GB)	20	93	7	13	45	280029.95
WORTHADD (IRE)	9	31	2	2	10	20766.72
THE WOW SIGNAL (IRE)	3	14	1	1	8	8383.17
XTENSION (IRE)	7	30	2	4	15	39874.33
YORGUNNABELUCKY (USA)	9	50	4	7	16	30041.19
YOUMZAIN (IRE)	12	56	6	6	32	52282.92
ZAMBEZI SUN (GB)	2	8	1	1	6	40162.79
ZAMINDAR (USA)	8	37	3	4	26	91803.60
ZEBEDEE (GB)	152	986	50	73	502	882288.09
ZOFFANY (IRE)	194	966	73	110	486	1772988.34

BY KIND PERMISSION OF WEATHERBYS

NH STALLIONS' EARNINGS FOR 2018/19
(includes every stallion who sired a winner over jumps in Great Britain and Ireland in 2018/19)

STALLIONS	RNRS	STARTS	WNRS	WINS	PLACES	TOTAL (£)
ACAMBARO (GER)	9	35	3	5	10	29467.84
ACCLAMATION (GB)	9	34	1	5	10	92564.00
ACT ONE (GB)	10	35	1	1	18	16116.57
ADLERFLUG (GER)	2	9	1	1	5	10832.74
AIR CHIEF MARSHAL (IRE)	5	25	2	3	14	23239.84
AIZAVOSKI (IRE)	10	29	5	5	10	32859.48
ALANADI (FR)	1	4	1	2	1	19964.00
ALBERTO GIACOMETTI (IRE)	6	13	1	1	6	6775.73
ALDERBROOK (GB)	10	30	2	2	20	24680.87
ALEXANDROS (GB)	2	13	1	5	3	21453.72
ALFLORA (IRE)	39	130	13	19	68	168973.13
ALFRED NOBEL (IRE)	8	31	3	4	11	25773.63
ALHAARTH (IRE)	5	26	2	5	10	47318.49
ALKAADHEM (GB)	16	59	3	4	24	136416.72
AL KAZEEM (GB)	2	8	2	2	5	10250.62
AL NAMIX (FR)	47	157	11	20	70	340391.40
AMADEUS WOLF (GB)	6	20	1	1	9	16116.56
AMERICAN POST (GB)	7	29	1	1	16	38021.91
ANABAA BLUE (GB)	8	23	1	1	12	15410.29
AND BEYOND (IRE)	14	60	4	4	26	30415.19
ANGE GABRIEL (FR)	1	1	1	1	0	4613.58
ANSHAN	6	23	3	3	13	22305.40
ANTARCTIQUE (IRE)	3	21	2	3	13	22107.03
ANTONIUS PIUS (USA)	9	60	5	8	35	109122.37
ANZILLERO (GER)	9	34	4	6	16	145687.94
APPLE TREE (FR)	19	84	4	5	36	42409.57
APPROVE (IRE)	8	30	1	1	7	8962.70
APSIS (GB)	7	24	1	1	16	12820.46
AQLAAM (GB)	18	76	4	4	41	43864.66
ARAAFA (IRE)	3	18	1	1	13	10571.40
ARAKAN (USA)	69	281	16	29	97	327383.08
ARCADIO (GER)	107	435	28	42	158	665361.96
ARCANO (IRE)	24	81	6	7	33	60958.08
ARCH (USA)	5	16	2	3	5	23763.93
ARCHIPENKO (USA)	8	30	1	2	10	15768.87
ARCTIC COSMOS (USA)	10	24	1	1	8	8946.59
AREION (GER)	1	2	1	1	1	11812.28
ASK (GB)	83	308	20	29	107	273518.85
ASSESSOR (IRE)	8	36	2	2	24	217332.91
ASTARABAD (USA)	9	40	4	6	23	145535.49
ASTRONOMER ROYAL (USA)	2	5	1	2	1	9505.26
AUSSIE RULES (USA)	9	37	3	4	21	31219.77
AUTHORIZED (IRE)	62	258	27	45	130	960993.23
AVONBRIDGE (GB)	4	23	1	1	17	10361.62
AXXOS (GER)	3	17	2	5	9	69026.60
AZAMOUR (IRE)	31	120	10	16	58	181154.50
BACH (IRE)	18	78	7	9	18	82802.53
BACHIR (IRE)	1	2	1	1	0	10651.20
BAHRI (USA)	15	49	3	3	17	23374.38
BALAKHERI (IRE)	5	18	1	1	5	28292.88
BALKO (FR)	29	124	9	16	71	297871.35
BALLINGARRY (IRE)	24	92	7	11	43	173700.09
BALTIC KING (GB)	6	21	1	1	10	15305.62
BANDARI (IRE)	1	4	1	1	2	6545.18
BANDMASTER (USA)	2	9	1	2	4	19265.02
BARASTRAIGHT (GB)	4	17	1	4	7	79350.72
BATED BREATH (GB)	4	9	1	1	4	7820.51

STALLIONS	RNRS	STARTS	WNRS	WINS	PLACES	TOTAL (£)
BEAT ALL (USA)	15	76	4	5	27	45796.03
BEAT HOLLOW (GB)	64	247	20	27	109	418856.99
BENEFICIAL (GB)	276	1265	86	144	595	2018219.86
BERING	1	6	1	1	2	5068.46
BERNARDINI (USA)	3	14	1	1	9	46425.56
BERNEBEAU (FR)	4	19	4	5	13	46348.52
BERNSTEIN (USA)	3	10	2	2	4	13514.29
BERTOLINI (USA)	8	26	1	2	7	12399.67
BIENAMADO (USA)	7	29	1	2	22	32895.13
BIG BAD BOB (IRE)	30	128	8	13	57	145300.98
BIG SHUFFLE (USA)	2	11	2	2	9	18018.78
BISHOP OF CASHEL (GB)	2	17	1	4	11	26818.63
BLACK SAM BELLAMY (IRE)	122	428	23	30	216	472788.75
BLUE BRESIL (FR)	18	70	6	11	34	168379.69
BLUEPRINT (IRE)	19	91	5	10	47	117995.32
BOB'S RETURN (IRE)	2	7	1	1	1	3448.00
BOLLIN ERIC (GB)	13	55	2	3	20	31628.61
BONBON ROSE (FR)	11	36	4	4	10	55431.02
BORN KING (JPN)	4	15	1	1	2	8294.00
BORN TO SEA (IRE)	17	65	4	6	42	62350.88
BRIAN BORU (GB)	79	420	28	43	212	632001.50
BRIER CREEK (USA)	2	11	1	1	7	18228.86
BROADWAY FLYER (USA)	10	42	3	5	22	49003.77
BROKEN VOW (USA)	1	11	1	2	8	24432.09
BUCK'S BOUM (FR)	12	47	6	13	30	709482.25
BUSHRANGER (IRE)	18	86	3	5	42	61579.26
BUSY FLIGHT (GB)	3	11	1	1	5	46656.13
CACIQUE (IRE)	12	42	4	7	25	52217.57
CADOUDAL (FR)	1	8	1	1	5	13310.14
CALCUTTA (GB)	1	7	1	1	5	9614.70
CALIFET (FR)	26	98	7	8	48	305495.43
CAMACHO (GB)	8	30	4	5	14	82374.00
CAMELOT (GB)	9	34	5	8	15	176407.32
CAMPANOLOGIST (USA)	3	13	2	2	4	11800.60
CANFORD CLIFFS (IRE)	26	112	13	19	62	198975.95
CAPE BLANCO (IRE)	4	9	1	2	0	8122.50
CAPE CROSS (IRE)	28	113	7	10	65	160646.95
CAPTAIN GERRARD (IRE)	7	20	3	3	8	21484.30
CAPTAIN MARVELOUS (IRE)	2	8	1	1	6	11527.09
CAPTAIN RIO (GB)	16	67	5	9	24	85964.92
CARLO BANK (IRE)	3	8	1	1	6	9098.87
CARLOTAMIX (FR)	9	34	1	2	9	17926.86
CASAMENTO (IRE)	22	74	6	8	21	79848.96
CATCHER IN THE RYE (IRE)	8	32	1	2	15	39201.07
CELTIC SWING (GB)	2	9	2	2	5	9324.87
CENTRAL PARK (IRE)	17	65	3	3	27	77273.57
CHAMPS ELYSEES (GB)	65	215	21	29	107	308934.21
CHEVALIER (IRE)	5	14	1	1	5	6586.87
CHOISIR (AUS)	4	11	2	5	4	31100.16
CIMA DE TRIOMPHE (IRE)	1	6	1	3	3	43399.44
CITY HONOURS (USA)	7	23	2	3	7	12807.68
CITYSCAPE (GB)	4	8	1	1	4	6389.28
CLASSIC CLICHE (IRE)	9	45	3	6	23	72972.76
CLOUDINGS (IRE)	44	156	11	14	71	209141.47
COASTAL PATH (GB)	19	81	6	9	35	148791.52
CONFUCHIAS (IRE)	1	7	1	2	4	10575.16
CORONER (IRE)	5	21	1	1	13	15337.28
COUNTRY REEL (USA)	3	18	1	3	11	29720.31
COURT CAVE (IRE)	165	770	53	85	313	963665.23
CRAIGSTEEL (GB)	72	370	28	42	181	441541.29
CRILLON (FR)	7	33	4	8	20	411121.22

STALLIONS	RNRS	STARTS	WNRS	WINS	PLACES	TOTAL (£)
CROCO ROUGE (IRE)	8	26	1	1	9	82617.38
CROSSHARBOUR (GB)	4	8	1	1	4	12694.52
CROSSPEACE (IRE)	5	18	1	1	4	5474.76
CURTAIN TIME (IRE)	14	58	4	4	28	39538.25
DALAKHANI (IRE)	15	32	1	1	15	11389.03
DANCING FOREVER (USA)	1	8	1	2	4	9792.54
DANEHILL DANCER (IRE)	18	91	4	5	53	73094.34
DANSANT (GB)	13	45	4	7	22	83142.56
DANSILI (GB)	26	94	5	8	56	75455.78
DAPPER (GB)	1	10	1	1	7	10114.36
DARK ANGEL (IRE)	21	98	4	9	46	302715.36
DARSI (FR)	40	122	6	6	52	87704.93
DAVIDOFF (GER)	3	16	2	4	10	90330.44
DAY FLIGHT (GB)	5	29	2	2	19	29905.18
DAYLAMI (IRE)	29	107	6	9	55	115494.36
DECLARATION OF WAR (USA)	8	21	2	2	7	9842.85
DEFINITE ARTICLE (GB)	69	271	18	28	123	407205.53
DELEGATOR (GB)	8	17	1	2	4	19691.64
DELLA FRANCESCA (USA)	13	83	7	11	50	288324.84
DENHAM RED (FR)	9	39	5	6	15	298594.70
DENOUNCE (GB)	3	12	1	1	6	9581.54
DESERT KING (IRE)	11	63	3	10	35	109208.50
DESIDERATUM (GB)	6	22	2	2	13	18220.52
DESIR D'UN SOIR (FR)	1	5	1	2	3	9940.92
DIABLENEYEV (USA)	1	10	1	1	5	16959.92
DIAMOND BOY (FR)	13	52	6	13	25	200650.83
DIAMOND GREEN (FR)	7	31	4	7	14	71777.34
DICK TURPIN (IRE)	8	30	1	1	9	10630.42
DISCOVER D'AUTEUIL (FR)	4	15	1	1	10	13780.66
DISTANT MUSIC (USA)	1	8	1	2	6	10764.04
DISTANT PEAK (IRE)	4	23	1	1	10	8281.04
DOCTOR DINO (FR)	7	23	5	10	9	620375.25
DOM ALCO (FR)	17	79	6	9	49	224039.16
DOUBLE ECLIPSE (IRE)	12	44	2	2	20	34221.16
DOYEN (IRE)	82	331	26	43	139	459891.26
DRAGON PULSE (IRE)	8	30	1	1	8	9920.59
DREAM WELL (FR)	10	42	3	7	22	272766.78
DR FONG (USA)	5	17	1	1	8	13028.52
DR MASSINI (IRE)	56	227	14	19	112	213546.09
DUBAI DESTINATION (USA)	89	347	24	33	153	714091.49
DUBAWI (IRE)	9	25	3	4	12	36632.69
DUKE OF MARMALADE (IRE)	31	122	9	12	43	113906.81
DUSHYANTOR (USA)	7	55	3	4	23	52993.99
DUTCH ART (GB)	9	27	2	2	12	24655.45
DYLAN THOMAS (IRE)	39	171	13	24	82	211119.84
EARLY MARCH (GB)	11	48	4	8	25	187926.96
ECHO OF LIGHT (GB)	16	61	5	7	25	147004.74
ELECTRIC BEAT (GB)	1	6	1	1	4	10825.51
ELUSIVE CITY (USA)	2	6	1	1	3	6373.49
ELUSIVE PIMPERNEL (USA)	32	116	8	12	45	180170.63
ELUSIVE QUALITY (USA)	6	30	2	4	8	39787.39
ENRIQUE (GB)	23	73	9	11	38	83063.92
EPALO (GER)	5	21	2	3	12	32079.84
ERHAAB (USA)	6	28	1	1	15	17124.59
ESKENDEREYA (USA)	1	6	1	1	4	10851.86
EXCEED AND EXCEL (AUS)	5	24	1	2	8	13936.61
EXCELEBRATION (IRE)	12	51	1	1	24	23102.99
EXCELLENT ART (GB)	14	38	1	1	13	20869.85
EXIT TO NOWHERE (USA)	20	100	6	7	59	157043.89
FAIRLY RANSOM (USA)	7	22	1	1	7	6242.02
FAIR MIX (IRE)	76	274	13	21	118	231019.28

STALLIONS	RNRS	STARTS	WNRS	WINS	PLACES	TOTAL (£)
FALCO (USA)	7	21	1	2	12	20665.94
FAME AND GLORY (GB)	75	207	19	24	78	359170.40
FAMOUS NAME (GB)	10	39	1	1	11	18001.50
FAST COMPANY (IRE)	20	67	6	10	33	144417.38
FASTNET ROCK (AUS)	18	51	1	2	15	77849.05
FINE GRAIN (JPN)	1	7	1	2	3	44843.68
FINSCEAL FIOR (IRE)	6	15	2	2	9	25410.63
FIREBREAK (GB)	8	29	1	2	11	17033.66
FIRST DEFENCE (USA)	2	6	1	2	2	9417.50
FLEETWOOD (IRE)	2	10	2	3	3	45154.90
FLEMENSFIRTH (USA)	293	1023	85	118	477	2430211.07
FLYING LEGEND (USA)	17	79	4	7	34	59939.83
FOOTSTEPSINTHESAND (GB)	16	45	3	4	12	27278.12
FRACAS (IRE)	13	79	3	3	33	54303.78
FRAGRANT MIX (IRE)	13	46	4	6	20	67881.82
FRANKEL (GB)	4	12	1	2	5	12675.12
FROZEN FIRE (GER)	10	32	1	1	3	5507.59
FROZEN POWER (IRE)	12	58	2	3	33	45816.76
FRUITS OF LOVE (USA)	40	167	12	16	72	228881.14
FUISSE (FR)	15	53	6	8	26	77745.98
FULL OF GOLD (FR)	9	31	2	2	12	27751.41
GALILEO (IRE)	86	305	28	37	144	811753.52
GAMUT (IRE)	42	198	12	20	95	361792.33
GENEROUS (IRE)	26	123	8	12	64	111219.53
GENTLEMAN'S DEAL (IRE)	2	5	1	1	3	11049.42
GENTLEWAVE (IRE)	10	36	5	11	15	130470.52
GEORDIELAND (FR)	10	22	1	2	3	10684.34
GERMANY (USA)	15	43	4	7	18	248621.60
GETAWAY (GER)	217	849	70	107	336	1382441.22
GOLAN (IRE)	45	176	6	9	66	128425.33
GOLD AWAY (IRE)	3	15	2	2	8	23833.24
GOLDEN LARIAT (USA)	12	37	1	1	16	48495.91
GOLDEN TORNADO (IRE)	11	75	4	10	48	269739.20
GOLDNEYEV (USA)	2	5	1	2	2	149891.00
GOLD WELL (GB)	185	795	70	104	359	1170003.93
GOTHLAND (FR)	1	6	1	1	3	6466.22
GRAPE TREE ROAD (GB)	15	39	2	2	22	30926.77
GREAT EXHIBITION (USA)	5	55	2	5	29	40742.50
GREAT JOURNEY (JPN)	4	24	1	2	11	19380.47
GREAT PALM (USA)	10	46	3	3	16	20816.34
GREAT PRETENDER (IRE)	40	152	15	21	78	276796.41
GREY RISK (FR)	1	3	1	2	1	9320.22
GRIS DE GRIS (IRE)	8	41	3	4	16	31245.42
HAAFHD (GB)	17	51	3	3	22	39626.54
HALLING (USA)	20	78	7	16	42	241197.66
HAMAIRI (IRE)	2	11	1	1	5	7174.32
HARBOUR WATCH (IRE)	14	45	1	4	24	31983.64
HARD SPUN (USA)	4	20	2	4	8	60185.21
HAT TRICK (JPN)	1	5	1	1	1	6588.08
HAWK WING (USA)	4	9	1	1	5	11233.52
HELIOSTATIC (IRE)	5	26	2	2	15	28071.07
HELISSIO (FR)	19	63	3	5	27	52482.50
HELMET (AUS)	18	55	4	5	25	36449.70
HENRYTHENAVIGATOR (USA)	11	41	4	6	14	57712.94
HERON ISLAND (IRE)	31	120	9	10	64	261786.10
HIGH CHAPARRAL (IRE)	61	256	18	26	141	833663.03
HIGH ROCK (IRE)	2	14	2	2	8	27753.62
HOLD THAT TIGER (USA)	2	17	1	2	10	11566.04
HOLY ROMAN EMPEROR (IRE)	22	99	5	7	42	71738.30
HONOLULU (IRE)	3	13	2	2	6	32706.67
HUMBEL (USA)	2	7	1	1	0	8046.85

STALLIONS	RNRS	STARTS	WNRS	WINS	PLACES	TOTAL (£)
HURRICANE RUN (IRE)	15	58	2	2	29	36968.23
ICEMAN (GB)	3	12	1	1	9	6849.44
IFFRAAJ (GB)	22	89	4	5	49	146579.52
INDIAN DANEHILL (IRE)	24	119	9	13	64	206744.29
INDIAN RIVER (FR)	32	158	11	14	95	331204.83
INTELLO (GER)	4	19	1	1	15	18647.98
INTENSE FOCUS (USA)	21	82	3	6	42	67861.03
INTIKHAB (USA)	17	68	3	5	22	139277.33
INVINCIBLE SPIRIT (IRE)	13	49	2	2	19	22393.81
IRISH WELLS (FR)	15	55	3	6	25	75224.25
IT'S GINO (GER)	5	30	4	6	15	79576.52
IVAN DENISOVICH (IRE)	4	22	3	3	9	28708.94
JEREMY (USA)	120	417	35	57	153	764025.74
JIMBLE (FR)	7	54	1	1	28	20468.07
JOSR ALGARHOUD (IRE)	11	24	1	2	8	13142.78
JUKEBOX JURY (IRE)	7	17	2	2	8	26895.28
KADASTROF (FR)	4	12	2	3	5	23860.97
KADEED (IRE)	3	24	1	1	13	18247.71
KAHYASI	4	12	1	1	7	14242.14
KAIETEUR (USA)	4	22	2	3	12	33337.79
KALANISI (IRE)	146	541	34	47	237	689393.91
KALLISTO (GER)	3	15	1	1	6	13584.78
KAMSIN (GER)	6	26	2	2	14	41029.86
KAPGARDE (FR)	65	267	26	42	140	913085.82
KAP ROCK (FR)	9	28	1	2	11	17746.26
KARINGA BAY	9	27	2	3	11	18737.57
KAYF TARA (GB)	226	895	59	84	516	1466523.04
KENDARGENT (FR)	6	16	2	2	11	23407.75
KENTUCKY DYNAMITE (USA)	5	24	4	7	9	35371.97
KHALKEVI (IRE)	17	58	7	10	28	80830.06
KHELEYF (USA)	14	40	1	1	21	15280.95
KINGSALSA (USA)	9	28	4	7	7	47665.61
KING'S BEST (USA)	14	52	3	4	19	35631.15
KING'S THEATRE (IRE)	160	737	70	118	363	1968996.31
KIRKWALL (GB)	6	20	2	2	7	11974.91
KODIAC (GB)	13	50	3	5	25	40942.10
KONIGSTIGER (GER)	1	16	1	3	12	19714.01
KONIG TURF (GER)	8	26	4	5	10	89659.55
KOTKY BLEU (FR)	3	6	1	1	3	31857.12
KUTUB (IRE)	20	100	4	6	39	64116.17
KYLLACHY (GB)	12	37	3	3	13	39945.95
LAKESHORE ROAD (USA)	1	6	1	1	5	8976.94
LAURO (GER)	6	28	4	4	22	63448.97
LAVEROCK (IRE)	5	16	2	2	10	98049.88
LAVERON (GB)	13	56	6	12	31	174339.33
LAWMAN (FR)	34	140	10	12	64	157163.98
LAYMAN (USA)	1	9	1	1	7	52714.00
LE FOU (IRE)	13	47	2	2	20	21886.70
LE HAVRE (IRE)	9	40	7	8	16	79246.97
LETHAL FORCE (IRE)	6	29	1	1	17	23448.51
LET THE LION ROAR (GB)	11	53	4	5	23	68197.47
LIBRETTIST (FR)	11	32	3	6	10	52590.42
LINDA'S LAD (GB)	20	76	7	13	37	176403.31
LOPE DE VEGA (IRE)	13	42	3	3	20	79201.38
LORD DU SUD (FR)	11	38	3	3	21	63898.66
LORD OF ENGLAND (GER)	4	24	2	3	12	90332.99
LORD SHANAKILL (USA)	12	40	5	5	18	32959.52
LOUP BRETON (IRE)	2	10	2	4	4	102977.99
LOUP SAUVAGE (USA)	1	4	1	2	0	12671.10
LUCARNO (USA)	37	128	9	15	61	122063.92
LUCKY STORY (USA)	5	19	1	2	11	15222.21

STALLIONS	RNRS	STARTS	WNRS	WINS	PLACES	TOTAL (£)
LUSO (GB)	9	36	2	2	20	65490.09
MAGADAN (IRE)	1	4	1	1	3	27616.66
MAHLER (GB)	164	739	54	93	342	1143253.64
MAKFI (GB)	17	69	6	9	26	89327.08
MALINAS (GER)	68	216	20	27	104	276504.97
MAMOOL (IRE)	3	13	2	2	7	15253.03
MANDURO (GER)	21	87	9	12	43	195421.08
MARESCA SORRENTO (FR)	22	77	5	7	48	184310.10
MARIENBARD (IRE)	23	84	5	9	40	93737.76
MARIGNAN (USA)	1	13	1	1	3	7620.64
MARJU (IRE)	3	17	1	2	8	23718.72
MARTALINE (GB)	94	391	34	47	214	835102.65
MASTERCRAFTSMAN (IRE)	69	230	18	24	111	262620.40
MASTEROFTHEHORSE (IRE)	11	35	2	4	9	26684.27
MAWATHEEQ (USA)	15	49	2	3	23	26675.19
MAXIOS (GB)	8	26	3	4	8	34198.96
MEDAALY (GB)	6	33	3	5	14	39440.76
MEDICEAN (GB)	30	147	9	13	77	230036.74
MICHEL GEORGES (GB)	2	11	1	5	3	31845.06
MIDNIGHT LEGEND (GB)	167	757	74	124	411	1493432.29
MILAN (GB)	314	1238	86	131	598	2076012.23
MILLENARY (GB)	35	127	7	13	40	102611.69
MILLKOM (GB)	6	17	1	1	9	17426.86
MISTER FOTIS (USA)	3	17	1	2	9	15040.68
MODIGLIANI (USA)	1	7	1	2	2	7947.80
MOHAAJIR (USA)	3	33	2	2	12	21720.76
MONITOR CLOSELY (IRE)	2	10	1	2	6	27519.89
MONSIEUR BOND (IRE)	4	17	2	2	11	21813.71
MONSUN (GER)	7	31	3	5	18	170960.17
MONTJEU (IRE)	20	90	5	6	40	198402.26
MONTMARTRE (FR)	20	95	10	13	47	145007.91
MOROZOV (USA)	56	218	13	23	102	225084.41
MOST IMPROVED (IRE)	11	32	5	5	10	34555.09
MOTIVATOR (GB)	23	107	7	11	58	322058.07
MOUNTAIN HIGH (IRE)	54	253	15	31	106	266139.46
MOUNT NELSON (GB)	42	123	8	12	54	169553.49
MR DINOS (IRE)	14	50	2	3	14	29913.82
MR SIDNEY (USA)	3	11	1	2	5	13394.34
MUHAYMIN (USA)	5	19	1	1	8	8837.45
MUHTATHIR (GB)	18	54	5	13	23	257542.05
MUJAHID (USA)	1	15	1	3	1	34028.31
MULTIPLEX (GB)	59	211	16	22	87	226451.51
MUSTAMEET (USA)	24	81	2	4	30	48867.93
MUTAZAYID (IRE)	1	7	1	1	3	6309.44
NAAQOOS (GB)	4	12	1	2	7	44858.46
NATHANIEL (IRE)	25	84	6	9	43	115225.81
NATIVE RULER (GB)	12	39	1	1	19	16509.09
NAYEF (USA)	20	81	5	6	40	73416.78
NEEDLE GUN (IRE)	5	16	1	3	2	11843.13
NETWORK (GER)	61	255	21	33	124	745375.07
NEW APPROACH (IRE)	25	94	9	10	30	91468.93
NICARON (GER)	1	10	1	2	7	13797.87
NICKNAME (FR)	11	42	8	14	18	680061.03
NIDOR (FR)	1	3	1	1	0	56950.00
NOMADIC WAY (USA)	8	37	5	6	17	37599.47
NO RISK AT ALL (FR)	26	76	6	8	42	120320.97
NOROIT (GER)	13	53	4	5	27	68538.53
NORSE DANCER (IRE)	22	108	5	12	54	127018.78
NORTHERN LEGEND (GB)	1	11	1	3	7	21687.39
NOTNOWCATO (GB)	17	72	5	9	29	116339.33
OASIS DREAM (GB)	15	39	3	5	16	36684.69

STALLIONS	RNRS	STARTS	WNRS	WINS	PLACES	TOTAL (£)
OBSERVATORY (USA)	3	13	1	2	8	20171.07
OLDEN TIMES (GB)	18	54	3	3	22	33934.29
OLD VIC	24	83	5	5	48	88412.81
ORPEN (USA)	2	18	1	1	11	11212.30
OSCAR (IRE)	300	1152	86	128	525	2124412.74
OSCAR SCHINDLER (IRE)	3	9	1	1	5	5772.40
OVERBURY (IRE)	37	179	9	13	119	187291.48
PADDY O'PRADO (USA)	4	24	1	2	11	25839.00
PALACE EPISODE (USA)	1	9	1	3	5	19978.64
PANORAMIC	3	11	1	1	7	71596.34
PAPAL BULL (GB)	33	123	4	7	42	67051.07
PASSING GLANCE (GB)	46	203	19	31	94	238516.30
PASTERNAK (GB)	14	65	3	4	29	63808.86
PEINTRE CELEBRE (USA)	4	14	1	1	9	23529.37
PHOENIX REACH (IRE)	19	79	5	5	45	69012.78
PIERRE (GB)	11	45	3	4	24	38002.22
PIVOTAL (GB)	13	47	5	6	18	67778.56
POET'S VOICE (GB)	18	75	4	7	35	186619.42
POLICY MAKER (IRE)	9	27	1	2	10	99688.27
POLIGLOTE (GB)	29	135	18	28	63	593384.41
PORTRAIT GALLERY (IRE)	20	82	6	8	42	124412.93
POUR MOI (IRE)	19	58	6	6	28	43074.43
POWER (GB)	6	41	3	6	24	71439.35
PRESENTING (GB)	317	1245	93	138	587	1986617.96
PRIMARY (USA)	15	33	2	3	11	37572.92
PRINCE ARCH (USA)	2	9	2	3	4	23340.11
PROCLAMATION (IRE)	8	23	2	4	13	25495.76
PROTEKTOR (GER)	3	11	1	1	7	20127.96
PUBLISHER (USA)	9	33	2	2	11	14640.80
PUIT D'OR (IRE)	5	16	1	2	6	14524.84
PURSUIT OF LOVE (GB)	2	7	1	1	5	10658.42
PUTRA PEKAN (GB)	2	9	1	2	6	23128.90
RACINGER (FR)	4	20	2	3	13	33954.18
RAIL LINK (GB)	13	48	4	5	22	37102.13
RAINBOW HIGH (GB)	8	40	1	2	18	19187.41
RAISE A GRAND (IRE)	1	7	1	1	6	13952.50
RAJJ (IRE)	6	20	1	1	7	11025.81
RAVEN'S PASS (USA)	16	40	4	6	12	41690.74
RECHARGE (IRE)	8	36	1	2	18	15836.99
RED CLUBS (IRE)	5	22	1	1	6	5984.96
REFUSE TO BEND (IRE)	10	44	4	5	19	34862.55
REQUINTO (IRE)	3	7	1	1	2	8976.11
REVOQUE (IRE)	13	46	1	1	16	19615.77
RIP VAN WINKLE (IRE)	33	132	10	15	63	178440.28
ROBIN DES CHAMPS (FR)	101	394	30	50	174	809630.50
ROBIN DES PRES (FR)	75	364	24	35	165	462551.66
ROCK OF GIBRALTAR (IRE)	34	140	14	19	69	129018.29
ROLI ABI (FR)	1	3	1	1	1	9199.56
ROYAL ANTHEM (USA)	21	90	9	13	49	133273.61
ROYAL APPLAUSE (GB)	13	47	6	7	25	75653.84
RUDIMENTARY (USA)	8	37	2	3	13	28949.08
SABREHILL (USA)	1	1	1	1	0	7086.24
SADDEX (GB)	9	40	3	5	20	85444.81
SADDLER MAKER (IRE)	28	108	11	15	62	874190.39
SADDLERS' HALL (IRE)	4	19	1	1	10	12099.35
SAFFRON WALDEN (FR)	9	32	3	5	18	30839.46
SAGACITY (FR)	1	2	1	1	0	13606.19
SAGAMIX (FR)	12	54	2	2	29	38548.87
SAGEBURG (IRE)	18	64	7	13	27	199719.99
SAINT DES SAINTS (FR)	45	183	17	29	93	758362.74
SAKHEE (USA)	21	63	4	4	27	46030.05

STALLIONS	RNRS	STARTS	WNRS	WINS	PLACES	TOTAL (£)
SAKHEE'S SECRET (GB)	9	25	1	1	14	16613.12
SALUTINO (GER)	14	37	2	2	9	17479.45
SAMUM (GER)	6	22	2	3	11	39778.58
SANDMASON (GB)	13	49	1	3	25	72430.88
SANS FRONTIERES (IRE)	21	56	4	4	15	44831.83
SATRI (IRE)	4	21	1	1	13	17308.34
SCHIAPARELLI (GER)	42	138	10	16	62	193782.42
SCORPION (IRE)	219	870	52	71	380	862561.61
SEA THE STARS (IRE)	24	74	2	3	36	42266.64
SECRET SINGER (FR)	8	20	2	4	10	15962.71
SELKIRK (USA)	6	19	2	2	11	21467.67
SEPTEMBER STORM (GER)	40	164	9	19	68	164766.68
SHAANMER (IRE)	6	32	3	4	15	42158.60
SHAMARDAL (USA)	14	44	2	3	12	39731.59
SHAMI (GB)	2	11	1	1	9	11445.94
SHANTOU (USA)	140	555	45	62	248	852285.29
SHIROCCO (GER)	106	371	24	32	165	405742.37
SHOLOKHOV (IRE)	40	178	17	21	82	172931.17
SHOWCASING (GB)	7	26	2	2	17	23182.14
SILVANO (GER)	1	5	1	1	2	5163.84
SILVER CROSS (FR)	1	8	1	2	3	27204.10
SILVER FROST (IRE)	3	15	1	2	4	19133.18
SIMPLEX (FR)	1	1	1	1	0	3248.36
SINNDAR (IRE)	17	58	4	8	26	103119.18
SIR HARRY LEWIS (USA)	13	59	6	7	38	295536.44
SIR PERCY (GB)	39	146	15	23	80	231417.05
SIR PRANCEALOT (IRE)	8	25	2	3	9	26828.14
SIXTIES ICON (GB)	39	169	10	13	81	122883.54
SLEEPING CAR (FR)	2	8	1	1	6	10329.23
SMADOUN (FR)	10	34	1	1	14	82998.97
SNOW CAP (FR)	1	4	1	1	3	10283.19
SOAPY DANGER (GB)	2	7	1	1	4	10314.52
SOCIETY ROCK (IRE)	3	5	1	1	2	30297.02
SOLDIER HOLLOW (GB)	13	55	4	5	30	67098.51
SOLDIER OF FORTUNE (IRE)	21	89	9	12	41	218982.71
SOLON (GER)	3	8	1	1	2	8814.85
SOVIET STAR (USA)	4	24	2	2	8	14754.06
SO YOU THINK (NZ)	18	69	2	3	26	51372.40
SPADOUN (FR)	19	81	3	4	35	73020.83
SPANISH MOON (USA)	13	34	4	7	19	184028.59
SPARTACUS (IRE)	4	22	2	2	12	18827.99
SPECIAL KALDOUN (IRE)	5	16	1	1	5	4524.09
SPEEDMASTER (GER)	2	8	1	1	2	5750.64
SPIRIT ONE (FR)	6	30	3	7	9	35115.73
STIMULATION (IRE)	7	16	1	1	4	6380.69
ST JOVITE (USA)	5	35	2	3	18	56287.46
STORMY ATLANTIC (USA)	1	3	1	2	1	10237.86
STOWAWAY (GB)	245	1042	75	124	472	1540857.03
STRATEGIC PRINCE (GB)	12	41	2	3	20	41941.95
STREET CRY (IRE)	9	42	1	2	27	53137.18
SUBTLE POWER (IRE)	11	48	4	8	21	50945.69
SULAMANI (IRE)	84	325	25	36	132	363875.37
SULEIMAN (IRE)	2	18	1	1	8	9936.52
SUNDAY BREAK (JPN)	4	20	3	4	13	32336.00
SUNSHINE STREET (USA)	1	6	1	1	1	7855.75
SUPERIOR PREMIUM (GB)	1	12	1	1	8	12001.00
SUPREME SOUND (GB)	3	19	1	2	12	20831.17
SYSTEMATIC (GB)	2	10	1	2	6	11819.32
TAGULA (IRE)	9	28	2	2	7	14883.37
TAJRAASI (USA)	11	56	2	6	21	50920.90
TALKIN MAN (CAN)	2	8	1	1	1	3299.22

STALLIONS	RNRS	STARTS	WNRS	WINS	PLACES	TOTAL (£)
TAMAYUZ (GB)	11	42	2	4	21	51257.67
TAMURE (IRE)	7	22	3	3	9	44258.85
TEOFILIO (IRE)	1	2	1	1	1	2881.90
TEOFILO (IRE)	37	156	15	23	73	253545.78
TERIMON	2	9	1	1	7	11147.62
THEWAYYOUARE (USA)	29	102	4	8	44	107269.62
THOUSAND WORDS (GB)	7	24	1	2	11	24740.69
THREE VALLEYS (USA)	4	14	1	2	11	36656.46
TIGER GROOM (GB)	7	22	4	6	5	39116.62
TIGER HILL (IRE)	10	26	2	4	19	35201.58
TIKKANEN (USA)	46	215	12	19	111	205030.18
TITUS LIVIUS (FR)	1	2	1	1	1	5638.72
TOBOUGG (IRE)	45	172	10	14	70	144073.05
TOUCH OF LAND (FR)	21	100	4	4	56	63697.28
TRANS ISLAND (GB)	47	217	13	17	99	205515.18
TREMPOLINO (USA)	6	23	1	2	11	25102.90
TURGEON (USA)	19	73	6	11	38	202945.36
TURTLE BOWL (IRE)	7	29	1	2	17	79557.13
TURTLE ISLAND (IRE)	17	84	3	3	48	98333.19
UNGARO (GER)	2	10	1	1	7	37956.76
URBAN OCEAN (FR)	6	36	2	2	17	41290.39
URBAN POET (USA)	10	45	2	3	23	41900.28
VALANOUR (IRE)	1	12	1	3	9	21634.51
VALE OF YORK (IRE)	8	25	2	2	7	18553.99
VAL ROYAL (FR)	1	1	1	1	0	5451.33
VENDANGEUR (IRE)	6	31	1	1	13	24220.63
VERGLAS (IRE)	9	46	4	7	24	74193.86
VERTICAL SPEED (FR)	17	58	2	2	27	23109.00
VINNIE ROE (IRE)	70	276	18	28	120	462422.15
VIRTUAL (GB)	7	28	1	1	11	15038.96
VISION D'ETAT (FR)	13	46	4	4	21	61647.41
VOIX DU NORD (FR)	34	184	18	39	96	1411121.68
VOLOCHINE (IRE)	4	11	1	1	6	8824.83
WALK IN THE PARK (IRE)	23	121	12	17	61	609104.59
WAREED (IRE)	12	61	3	3	25	34774.97
WELL CHOSEN (GB)	42	167	16	21	69	290564.85
WESTERNER (GB)	208	932	77	120	479	1681757.97
WHITMORE'S CONN (USA)	25	103	7	11	46	112019.34
WINDSOR KNOT (IRE)	15	75	4	7	31	79484.10
WINGED LOVE (IRE)	71	303	17	31	133	404854.57
WINKER WATSON (GB)	3	23	3	4	12	25290.74
WITH THE FLOW (USA)	9	31	1	2	10	10952.70
WITNESS BOX (USA)	20	65	3	3	29	35272.04
YEATS (IRE)	180	809	65	101	405	1125662.04
YOUMZAIN (IRE)	14	56	2	3	33	56328.46
ZAGREB (USA)	14	54	5	7	27	68858.02
ZAMBEZI SUN (GB)	11	36	2	3	12	26842.67
ZAMINDAR (USA)	11	26	2	4	9	58658.41
ZANZIBARI (USA)	3	17	2	2	13	22146.06
ZEBEDEE (GB)	15	43	2	2	21	24431.91
ZERPOUR (IRE)	4	31	1	4	24	41357.20
ZOFFANY (IRE)	27	103	8	11	48	106240.79

BY KIND PERMISSION OF WEATHERBYS

HIGH-PRICED YEARLINGS OF 2019 AT TATTERSALLS SALES

The following yearlings realised 110,000 Guineas and over at Tattersalls Sales in 2019.

Name and Breeding	Purchaser	Guineas
B C DUBAWI (IRE) - ALINA (IRE)	GODOLPHIN	3600000
B C FRANKEL (GB) - FLECHE D'OR (USA)	GODOLPHIN	3100000
B C KINGMAN (GB) - GRACE AND FAVOUR (GB)	GODOLPHIN	2300000
CH F GALILEO (IRE) - QUIET OASIS (IRE)	MV MAGNIER/WESTERBERG	2100000
B C KINGMAN (GB) - ONE LAST DANCE (AUS)	MV MAGNIER	1800000
B C SIYOUNI (FR) - CABARET (IRE)	MV MAGNIER	1300000
CH C GALILEO (IRE) - JACQUELINE QUEST (IRE)	GODOLPHIN	1100000
B C DUBAWI (IRE) - MISS MARJURIE (IRE)	GODOLPHIN	1100000
TARHIB (IRE) B F DARK ANGEL (IRE) - ALLEZ ALAIA (IRE)	SHADWELL ESTATE COMPANY	1050000
B C DUBAWI (IRE) - WITHOUT YOU BABE (USA)	KEVIN RYAN	1000000
B C DUBAWI (IRE) - THE FUGUE (GB)	DAVID REDVERS BS	1000000
CH C NO NAY NEVER (USA) - WINNING SEQUENCE (FR)	MV MAGNIER	900000
CH F GALILEO (IRE) - PENCHANT (GB)	AMANDA SKIFFINGTON	900000
B/BR C SEA THE STARS (IRE) - LOPERA (GER)	GODOLPHIN	875000
B F FRANKEL (GB) - WADYHATTA (GB)	BROADHURST AGENCY	850000
B F GALILEO (IRE) - KEENES ROYALE (GB)	WESTERBERG	850000
B F WAR FRONT (USA) - PERIHELION (GB)	KERRI RADCLIFFE BS	850000
B F LE HAVRE (IRE) - PHIZ (GB)	MV MAGNIER	825000
ALTAAYSHAH (IRE) B F DARK ANGEL (IRE) - ANNA LAW (IRE)	SHADWELL ESTATE COMPANY	800000
B F GALILEO (IRE) - QUESTION TIMES (GB)	DAVID REDVERS BS	800000
B C SIYOUNI (FR) - AMERICA NOVA (FR)	SHADWELL ESTATE COMPANY	800000
B C LOPE DE VEGA (IRE) - BIKINI BABE (IRE)	GODOLPHIN	750000
ZAGATO (GB) B C FRANKEL (GB) - IZZI TOP (GB)	VENDOR	725000
B C FASTNET ROCK (AUS) - PRIDE (FR)	AQUIS FARM	725000
B C SEA THE STARS (IRE) - EMRELIYA (IRE)	GODOLPHIN	725000
MISSILE (GB) B F DUBAWI (IRE) - RIBBONS (GB)	WESTERBERG	725000
B C FRANKEL (GB) - AULD ALLIANCE (IRE)	MV MAGNIER	700000
B F DUBAWI (IRE) - GHURRA (USA)	GODOLPHIN	700000
B F DARK ANGEL (IRE) - FUTURE GENERATION (IRE)	C GORDON-WATSON BS	700000
B F SEA THE STARS (IRE) - JUMOOH (GB)	MANDORE INTERNATIONAL	650000
B C SEA THE STARS (IRE) - POLLYANA (IRE)	STROUD COLEMAN BS	625000
B C KINGMAN (GB) - KAMAKURA (USA)	GODOLPHIN	625000
CH F GALILEO (IRE) - LADY LARA (IRE)	FORM BS	600000
B C SIYOUNI (FR) - MOONLIT GARDEN (IRE)	SHADWELL ESTATE COMPANY	600000
B/BR F INVINCIBLE SPIRIT (IRE) - WADAA (USA)	GODOLPHIN	600000
B F LE HAVRE (IRE) - LADY DARSHAAN (IRE)	JOHN & JAKE WARREN	575000
B C KODIAC (GB) - RAJMAHAL (UAE)	STROUD COLEMAN BS	550000
B C KINGMAN (GB) - NANNINA (GB)	BIG RED FARM	550000
B C KINGMAN (GB) - MARTHA WATSON (IRE)	KEVIN RYAN	550000
B F GALILEO (IRE) - TERROR (IRE)	DAVID REDVERS BS	550000
B C FRANKEL (GB) - ATTRACTION (GB)	PHOENIX THOROUGHBREDS	525000
B F LAWMAN (FR) - LADY GORGEOUS (GB)	JOSEPH O'BRIEN	525000
B C KODIAC (GB) - LANDMARK (USA)	KEVIN RYAN	525000
B C FRANKEL (GB) - VIA MANZONI (IRE)	CHAUVIGNY GLOBAL EQUINE	525000
PRAIANO (GER) B C DUBAWI (IRE) - PRAIA (GER)	ROGER VARIAN	500000
B C SEA THE STARS (IRE) - SARBACANE (GB)	BEN MCELROY AGENT	500000
B C LOPE DE VEGA (IRE) - QUSHCHI (GB)	DAVID REDVERS BS	500000
B F SEA THE STARS (IRE) - KITCARA (GB)	MANDORE INTERNATIONAL	500000
CH C SHAMARDAL (USA) - MEHRONISSA (GB)	DAVID REDVERS BS	500000
TONY MONTANA (GB) GR C FRANKEL (GB) - TROPICAL PARADISE (IRE)	A C ELLIOTT, AGENT	500000
CH C LOPE DE VEGA (IRE) - DASH TO THE FRONT (GB)	SHADWELL ESTATE COMPANY	500000
CH C SEA THE STARS (IRE) - PRETTY DIAMOND (IRE)	SHADWELL ESTATE COMPANY	500000
B C INVINCIBLE SPIRIT (IRE) - SAGAMI (USA)	STROUD COLEMAN BS	500000
SIFTING SANDS (GB) B C DUBAWI (IRE) - YUMMY MUMMY (GB)	MIKE RYAN AGENT	500000
B C GALILEO (IRE) - MODERNSTONE (GB)	AQUIS FARM	500000
B F GALILEO (IRE) - WANNABE BETTER (IRE)	MIKE RYAN AGENT	500000
GR/RO C SHAMARDAL (USA) - LADY ROSAMUNDE (GB)	SHADWELL ESTATE COMPANY	500000
LEGEND OF DUBAI (GB) B C DUBAWI (IRE) - SPEEDY BOARDING (GB)	ROGER VARIAN	500000
B C FRANKEL (GB) - PROMISED MONEY (IRE)	SACKVILLEDONALD	475000
IN ITALIAN (GB) CH F DUBAWI (IRE) - FLORENTINA (AUS)	MIKE RYAN AGENT	475000
B F DUBAWI (IRE) - GLORIOUS SIGHT (IRE)	MIKE RYAN AGENT	450000
B C SIYOUNI (FR) - BAL DE LA ROSE (IRE)	BLANDFORD BS	450000
B C INVINCIBLE SPIRIT (IRE) - PRINCESS LOULOU (IRE)	MIKE RYAN AGENT	450000
EL DRAMA (IRE) CH C LOPE DE VEGA (IRE) - VICTOIRE FINALE (GB)	ROGER VARIAN	425000
B C DARK ANGEL (IRE) - TAMARISK (GER)	SACKVILLEDONALD	425000
B G ARCHIPENKO (USA) - DESERT BERRY (GB)	THE HONG KONG JOCKEY CLUB	425000
CH F NIGHT OF THUNDER (IRE) - BLANCHE NEIGE (GB)	C GORDON-WATSON BS	425000
B/GR C DARK ANGEL (IRE) - BEST TERMS (GB)	SHADWELL ESTATE COMPANY	425000
B C KINGMAN (GB) - BREVITY (USA)	OLIVER ST LAWRENCE BS	425000

Name and Breeding	Purchaser	Guineas
ROYAL RIGHT (IRE) B C FRANKEL (GB) - ROYAL SOLITAIRE (IRE)	VENDOR	420000
KING TRITON (IRE) B C SEA THE STARS (IRE) - LADY KARR (GB)	ROGER VARIAN	400000
B C ZOFFANY (IRE) - STARFISH (IRE)	SACKVILLEDONALD	400000
B C FRANKEL (GB) - OAKLEY GIRL (GB)	VENDOR	400000
GR F LOPE DE VEGA (IRE) - BOASTFUL (IRE)	MIKE RYAN AGENT	400000
B C GALILEO (IRE) - LOOK AT ME (IRE)	A C ELLIOTT, AGENT	400000
SWISS ACE (GB) B C KINGMAN (GB) - SWISS LAKE (USA)	M V MAGNIER	400000
HAFEZ (IRE) BR C DARK ANGEL (IRE) - STELLAR PATH (FR)	PETER & ROSS DOYLE BS	400000
CH F SEA THE STARS (IRE) - FLOWER MARKET (GB)	MANDORE INTERNATIONAL	400000
BALTHUS (IRE) CH C GALILEO (IRE) - FORCES OF DARKNESS (IRE)	MIKE RYAN AGENT	400000
B F GLENEAGLES (IRE) - LIKE A DAME (GB)	BLANDFORD BS	400000
B C DUBAWI (IRE) - KOORA (GB)	GODOLPHIN	400000
B C SIYOUNI (FR) - APHELIE (GB)	SHADWELL ESTATE COMPANY	400000
MOQADAMA (IRE) B F DARK ANGEL (IRE) - WHITE DAFFODIL (IRE)	SHADWELL ESTATE COMPANY	390000
B C DARK ANGEL (IRE) - ANTHEM ALEXANDER (IRE)	KEVIN RYAN	380000
B C KINGMAN (GB) - TOQUETTE (IRE)	BLANDFORD BS	380000
BR F DANSILI (GB) - EL MANATI (IRE)	HIGHFLYER BS	380000
B F NO NAY NEVER (USA) - VERONICA FALLS (GB)	JOSEPH O'BRIEN	375000
RED SQUARE (IRE) B F FRANKEL (GB) - STELLAR GLOW (IRE)	WESTERBERG	375000
GR C DARK ANGEL (IRE) - BEAR CHEEK (IRE)	BLANDFORD BS	375000
B C MUHAARAR (GB) - SEAGULL (IRE)	SHADWELL ESTATE COMPANY	360000
CH C NIGHT OF THUNDER (IRE) - DIVISIMO (GB)	SHADWELL ESTATE COMPANY	360000
CH C FRANKEL (GB) - FRENCH DRESSING (GB)	SHADWELL ESTATE COMPANY	350000
BOOMSHALAA (GB) B C SHALAA (IRE) - SUMMER COLLECTION (IRE)	ROGER VARIAN	350000
B F FRANKEL (GB) - LOVE AND BUBBLES (USA)	SACKVILLEDONALD	350000
B F KINGMAN (GB) - ROSE BLOSSOM (GB)	BLANDFORD BS	350000
B C AWTAAD (IRE) - DAME HESTER (IRE)	SACKVILLEDONALD	350000
B C AMERICAN PHAROAH (USA) - SACRE COEUR (USA)	VENDOR	350000
B C SIYOUNI (FR) - JANE EYRE (GB)	SHADWELL ESTATE COMPANY	350000
B F LOPE DE VEGA (IRE) - AS GOOD AS GOLD (IRE)	PHILIPPA MAINS	350000
B F INVINCIBLE SPIRIT (IRE) - ASHLEY HALL (USA)	VENDOR	350000
CH C LOPE DE VEGA (IRE) - MOI MEME (GB)	ANDREW BALDING	350000
WESTMINSTER ABBEY (GB) B C OASIS DREAM (GB) - SECRET SENSE (USA)	CHINA HORSE CLUB	350000
B F GALILEO (IRE) - ALIVE ALIVE OH (IRE)	BLANDFORD BS	325000
B C NO NAY NEVER (USA) - LADY SOLDIER (IRE)	RABBAH BS	325000
CH C GALILEO (IRE) - WILDWOOD FLOWER (USA)	AQUIS FARM / GUNTHER	325000
B F NO NAY NEVER (USA) - ASPASI (GB)	C GORDON-WATSON BS	325000
B C DANSILI (GB) - KNOCKNAGREE (IRE)	GODOLPHIN	320000
JET ENGINE (IRE) B/BR C NO NAY NEVER (USA) - DOUBLE FANTASY (GER)	ROGER VARIAN	320000
B F NO NAY NEVER (USA) - SEEKING SOLACE (GB)	MAGNOLIA BS	320000
FROSTED ANGEL (IRE) GR F DARK ANGEL (IRE) - CUT NO ICE (IRE)	SACKVILLEDONALD	320000
B C NEW APPROACH (IRE) - TOKEN OF LOVE (GB)	GODOLPHIN	320000
ATHERS (IRE) CH C DUBAWI (IRE) - KELLY NICOLE (IRE)	ROGER VARIAN	320000
LADY PETROL (GB) B F CABLE BAY (IRE) - TEBEE (GB)	MIKE RYAN AGENT	320000
B C KODIAC (GB) - HONEYMEAD (IRE)	GROVE STUD	310000
B F DUBAWI (IRE) - NASHMIAH (IRE)	MIKE RYAN AGENT	300000
B C NO NAY NEVER (USA) - INCA WOOD (UAE)	C GORDON-WATSON BS	300000
CH C AUSTRALIA (GB) - SOPHIE GERMAIN (GB)	PHILIPPA MAINS	300000
B C CAMELOT (GB) - BEACH FROLIC (GB)	SACKVILLEDONALD	300000
B F KINGMAN (GB) - RIVE GAUCHE (GB)	SACKVILLEDONALD	300000
B C AWTAAD (IRE) - VENETIAN BEAUTY (USA)	SHADWELL ESTATE COMPANY	300000
SALIGO BAY (IRE) B C NEW BAY (GB) - GLORIFICATION (GB)	AMANDA SKIFFINGTON BS	300000
B C GOLDEN HORN (GB) - ALWAYS REMEMBERED (IRE)	STROUD COLEMAN BS	300000
B G ACCLAMATION (GB) - FOLK MELODY (GB)	THE HONG KONG JOCKEY CLUB	300000
CH C LOPE DE VEGA (IRE) - SPIRIT OF XIAN (IRE)	SHADWELL ESTATE COMPANY	300000
AQUAMAN (IRE) B C KODIAC (GB) - AQUALIS (GB)	ROGER VARIAN	300000
B C FRANKEL (GB) - LA MORTOLA (GB)	GODOLPHIN	300000
B F FASTNET ROCK (AUS) - BEYOND COMPARE (IRE)	HUGO MERRY BS	290000
B F SEA THE STARS (IRE) - AMBIVALENT (IRE)	HUGO MERRY BS	280000
BR F KODIAC (GB) - ANDRY BRUSSELLES (GB)	KERRI RADCLIFFE BS	280000
B C FRANKEL (GB) - YOU'LL BE MINE (USA)	JOHNSTON RACING	280000
B F LOPE DE VEGA (IRE) - MATARI PEARL (IRE)	BSW EURO VENTURE	280000
B C KINGMAN (GB) - SUNSEMPERCHI (GB)	SHADWELL ESTATE COMPANY	280000
CH C AUSTRALIA (GB) - WHAT A TREASURE (IRE)	SACKVILLEDONALD	280000
CH C FRANKEL (GB) - POSSET (GB)	CHRIS DWYER AGENT	280000
B C INVINCIBLE SPIRIT (IRE) - ANGEL VISION (GB)	KEVIN RYAN	280000
B/BR C GOLDEN HORN (GB) - VALIANT GIRL (GB)	BLANDFORD BS	270000
CH F FRANKEL (GB) - LADYS FIRST (GB)	JUDDMONTE FARMS	270000
B F ZOFFANY (GB) - PANDORA'S BOX (IRE)	BSW EURO VENTURE	270000
CRITICAL (FR) B F NO NAY NEVER (USA) - MAID TO BELIEVE (GB)	PETER & ROSS DOYLE BS	270000
B F KINGMAN (GB) - MADAM PRESIDENT (GB)	PHOENIX THOROUGHBREDS	270000
B F DUBAWI (IRE) - THE MINIVER ROSE (IRE)	MIKE RYAN AGENT	260000
B C PRINCE OF LIR (IRE) - FOLEGANDROS ISLAND (FR)	SACKVILLEDONALD	260000

Name and Breeding	Purchaser	Guineas
B F LOPE DE VEGA (IRE) - ELAS DIAMOND (GB)	BROADHURST AGENCY	260000
B C SEA THE STARS (IRE) - SHARNBERRY (GB)	BLANDFORD BS	260000
B/BR C MUHAARAR (GB) - GO LOVELY ROSE (IRE)	A C ELLIOTT, AGENT	260000
DUBAWI SANDS (GB) CH C DUBAWI (IRE) - GALICUIX (GB)	ROGER VARIAN	260000
B F KODIAC (GB) - AIRFIELD (GB)	SHADWELL ESTATE COMPANY	260000
BR F SHALAA (IRE) - INEZ (GB)	BLANDFORD BS	260000
B F ACCLAMATION (GB) - MARSH DAISY (GB)	STROUD COLEMAN BS	260000
B C FRANKEL (GB) - FANN (USA)	BBA IRELAND	260000
B/BR C NO NAY NEVER (USA) - MIXFEELING (IRE)	MV MAGNIER	260000
B C KINGMAN (GB) - APPLAUDED (IRE)	SACKVILLEDONALD	260000
EDITOR AT LARGE (IRE) CH F LOPE DE VEGA (IRE) - WHAT SAY YOU (IRE)	WHITE BIRCH FARM	260000
MELODY BLUE (IRE) B F INVINCIBLE SPIRIT (IRE) - SCARLETT ROSE (GB)	VENDOR	260000
CH C FRANKEL (GB) - VASILIA (GB)	SACKVILLEDONALD	250000
B F FRANKEL (GB) - GUARANDA (GB)	VENDOR	250000
NATURE (IRE) B F IFFRAAJ (GB) - THE FAIRY (IRE)	JOHN CLARKE	250000
NORTH COUNTRY FAIR (GB) CH F GLENEAGLES (IRE) - SANDSTONE (GB)	WHITE BIRCH FARM	250000
B F SEA THE STARS (IRE) - KNYAZHNA (IRE)	ANDRIY MILOVANOV	240000
CH C GLENEAGLES (IRE) - FASTNET MIST (IRE)	BLANDFORD BS	240000
B/BR F KINGMAN (GB) - ELLBEEDEE (IRE)	BLUE DIAMOND STUD	240000
DEFINED (GB) B C GOLDEN HORN (GB) - CRITERIA (IRE)	VENDOR	240000
B C SEA THE STARS (IRE) - GOWER SONG (GB)	SHADWELL ESTATE COMPANY	230000
B C SHOWCASING (GB) - SUELITA (GB)	SHADWELL ESTATE COMPANY	220000
B F KINGMAN (GB) - GEMSTONE (IRE)	VENDOR	220000
B C KODIAC (GB) - HAIRSPRAY (IRE)	STROUD COLEMAN BS	220000
B C SEA THE STARS (IRE) - HOT SAUCE (IRE)	VENDOR	220000
SKYLINER (GB) B C DARK ANGEL (IRE) - A HUGE DREAM (IRE)	ROGER VARIAN	220000
B C KINGMAN (GB) - QUILITA (GER)	JUDDMONTE FARMS	220000
MOJO STAR (IRE) B C SEA THE STARS (IRE) - GALLEY (GB)	PETER & ROSS DOYLE BS	220000
B C SIYOUNI (FR) - MARSH HAWK (GB)	BYRON ROGERS	220000
B C AWTAAD (IRE) - MAJESTIC JASMINE (IRE)	SHADWELL ESTATE COMPANY	220000
B C KINGMAN (GB) - JUST WOOD (IRE)	SUN BS / ERIC CHAN	220000
CH C DUBAWI (IRE) - FIRST CITY (GB)	GODOLPHIN	210000
B C DUBAWI (IRE) - ROYAL DECREE (USA)	HUGO MERRY BS	210000
B C FRANKEL (GB) - CASCATA (GB)	VENDOR	210000
B C KINGMAN (GB) - GO WHITE LIGHTNING (IRE)	LONGWAYS STABLES	210000
B C DARK ANGEL (IRE) - PASTORAL GIRL (GB)	CREIGHTON SCHWARTZ BS	210000
B C GOLDEN HORN (GB) - WHAT STYLE (GB)	STROUD COLEMAN BS	210000
B C CAMELOT (GB) - ROSENREIHE (IRE)	DAVID REDVERS BS	210000
B F KINGMAN (GB) - ALAMARIE (FR)	SACKVILLEDONALD	210000
CH C NIGHT OF THUNDER (IRE) - ALICE ROSE (IRE)	FEDERICO BARBERINI	210000
B C DARK ANGEL (IRE) - SHADEN (IRE)	KEVIN RYAN	210000
B F SHAMARDAL (USA) - CAPE MAGIC (IRE)	MIKE RYAN BS	205000
B F INVINCIBLE SPIRIT (IRE) - ALSINDI (IRE)	MIKE RYAN BS AGENT	200000
B F KINGMAN (GB) - COMIC (IRE)	RICHARD KNIGHT BS AGENT	200000
B C GLENEAGLES (IRE) - HOORAY (GB)	KEVIN RYAN	200000
CH C AUSTRALIA (GB) - SQUEEZE (IRE)	JS COMPANY	200000
B F KINGMAN (GB) - SEALIFE (IRE)	KLARAVICH STABLES	200000
KODIAK MAMBO (IRE) B C KODIAC (GB) - AL ANDALYYA (USA)	FEATHERBED LANE	200000
B C FRANKEL (GB) - RESTIANA (FR)	OLIVER ST LAWRENCE BS	200000
B F AWTAAD (IRE) - HI KATRIONA (IRE)	PHOENIX THOROUGHBREDS	200000
B F ZOFFANY (IRE) - GEISHA GIRL (IRE)	FORM BS	200000
B F KINGMAN (GB) - DRESS REHEARSAL (IRE)	RICHARD KNIGHT BS AGENT	200000
B C INVINCIBLE SPIRIT (IRE) - DAINTILY DONE (GB)	MIKE RYAN AGENT	200000
GR/RO F KINGMAN (GB) - CHILDA (IRE)	LONGWAYS STABLES	200000
B F KINGMAN (GB) - PRIVACY ORDER (GB)	MIKE RYAN AGENT	200000
B/BR C GOLDEN HORN (GB) - LOMBATINA (FR)	SACKVILLEDONALD	200000
SEE FOR ME (GB) B F SIYOUNI (FR) - BESS OF HARDWICK (GB)	WHITE BIRCH FARM	200000
CH C PIVOTAL (GB) - JAZZI TOP (GB)	SHEIKH A AL-SABAH	200000
B C KODIAC (GB) - HEROINE CHIC (IRE)	BLANDFORD BS	200000
CH C FRANKEL (GB) - GALE FORCE (GB)	GODOLPHIN	200000
B/BR C SHAMARDAL (USA) - AL MAHMEYAH (USA)	PETER & ROSS DOYLE BS	200000
B C FRANKEL (GB) - TROPHEE (FR)	AMANDA SKIFFINGTON	200000
CH C GALILEO (IRE) - WITHORWITHOUTYOU (IRE)	SUN BS	200000
B C CANDY RIDE (ARG) - MYTHOLOGICAL (USA)	SARA'S PLACE	200000
B C DUBAWI (IRE) - VOLEUSE DE COEURS (IRE)	SUN BS RACING	200000
FIGURES (GB) B F FASTNET ROCK (AUS) - GADFLY (GB)	RABBAH BS	200000
B F CAMELOT (GB) - MORA BAI (IRE)	BLANDFORD BS	200000
STAR DEVINE (IRE) B F FASTNET ROCK (AUS) - STARS AT NIGHT (IRE)	MIKE RYAN AGENT	200000
CH C SHAMARDAL (USA) - DOORS TO MANUAL (USA)	SHADWELL ESTATE COMPANY	200000
B C BELARDO (IRE) - LA PATRIA (GB)	EBONOS	200000
B F NIGHT OF THUNDER (IRE) - NAMROODAH (IRE)	SHADWELL ESTATE COMPANY	200000
DESERT ROSE (GB) B F SHOWCASING (GB) - PARK LAW (IRE)	SACKVILLEDONALD	200000
B F DARK ANGEL (IRE) - AGNES STEWART (IRE)	WILLIAM HAGGAS	200000

Name and Breeding	Purchaser	Guineas
ETHNIC TYPE (IRE) B C FAST COMPANY (IRE) - CHIQUITA PICOSA (USA)	NORTHSHORE BLOODSTOCK	200000
B/BR C LE HAVRE (IRE) - MIDDLE PERSIA (GB)	JOHN & JAKE WARREN	200000
WIZARD D'AMOUR (GB) GR/RO C DUTCH ART (GB) - HOLISTIC (GB)	KARL BURKE / CARL WATERS	200000
B C DUBAWI (IRE) - CHACHAMAIDEE (IRE)	GODOLPHIN	200000
B C KODIAC (GB) - CHIBOLA (ARG)	VENDOR	200000
B F KODIAC (GB) - JANINA (GB)	BEN MCELROY AGENT	190000
CH C NEW APPROACH (IRE) - DIBAJJ (FR)	STROUD COLEMAN BS	190000
B F FASTNET ROCK (AUS) - MAP OF HEAVEN (GB)	BLANDFORD BS	190000
B C IFFRAAJ (GB) - MAMMA MORTON (IRE)	SHADWELL ESTATE COMPANY	190000
SKYRUNNER (IRE) B C INVINCIBLE SPIRIT (IRE) - MAIDSERVANT (USA)	JILL LAMB BS	190000
B F ACCLAMATION (GB) - PARTY FOR EVER (IRE)	CREIGHTON SCHWARTZ BS	185000
B C KODIAC (GB) - ONLINE ALEXANDER (IRE)	SHADWELL ESTATE COMPANY	185000
B F LE HAVRE (IRE) - INDIGO RIVER (IRE)	BBA IRELAND	185000
CH F FRANKEL (GB) - ROSE BONHEUR (GB)	JOHNSTON RACING	185000
B C SIYOUNI (FR) - TOI ET MOI (IRE)	SACKVILLEDONALD	180000
B C EXCEED AND EXCEL (AUS) - ALCHEMILLA (GB)	OLIVER ST LAWRENCE	180000
B F NO NAY NEVER (USA) - ALONG THE SHORE (IRE)	PETER & ROSS DOYLE BS	180000
BR C PIVOTAL (GB) - MADONNA DELL'ORTO (GB)	DAVID REDVERS BS	180000
B F HOLY ROMAN EMPEROR (IRE) - DAY AWAY (IRE)	BLUE DIAMOND STUD FARM UK	180000
B C THE GURKHA (IRE) - KASTANIA (GB)	SACKVILLEDONALD	180000
B C CAMELOT (GB) - AMBITIOUS LADY (GB)	SAM SANGSTER BS	180000
B F DUBAWI (IRE) - MEEZNAH (USA)	VENDOR	180000
LOVE IS GOLDEN (IRE) B C GOLDEN HORN (GB) - HOLY MOON (IRE)	JOHNSTON RACING	175000
B C KINGMAN (GB) - KAZEEM (GB)	JAMIE B BS	170000
B F FRANKEL (GB) - ANIPA (GB)	VENDOR	170000
B F MUHAARAR (GB) - GORBAND (USA)	BLANDFORD BS	170000
B F LOPE DE VEGA (IRE) - ALTHEA ROSE (IRE)	BSW EURO VENTURE	170000
B F SHALAA (GB) - ENCORE L'AMOUR (GB)	MIKE RYAN AGENT	170000
B C KINGMAN (GB) - CRUCK REALTA (GB)	JOE FOLEY	170000
MOVIN TIME (GB) B C FASTNET ROCK (AUS) - TIME ON (GB)	ROGER VARIAN	170000
FRENETIC (IRE) B F KODIAC (GB) - MOOJHA (USA)	SACKVILLEDONALD	170000
B F IFFRAAJ (GB) - AFFABILITY (IRE)	JOHN & JAKE WARREN	170000
B C KINGMAN (GB) - PARLE MOI (IRE)	MIKE RYAN AGENT	170000
B C NO NAY NEVER (USA) - PIETRA DURA (GB)	C GORDON-WATSON BS	170000
CH C THE LAST LION (IRE) - DIJARVO (IRE)	STROUD COLEMAN BS	170000
B C NO NAY NEVER (USA) - PRINCESS DESIRE (IRE)	DAVID REDVERS BS	170000
B C IFFRAAJ (GB) - FLORIADE (IRE)	CHINA HORSE CLUB	165000
B C SIYOUNI (FR) - GOATHEMALA (GER)	SACKVILLEDONALD	160000
B F KINGMAN (GB) - BLUE CHIP (GB)	DERMOT FARRINGTON	160000
CH C NEW APPROACH (IRE) - PRINCESS CAMMIE (IRE)	SHADWELL ESTATE COMPANY	160000
B C GALILEO (IRE) - LA VINCHINA (GER)	VENDOR	160000
B C KINGMAN (GB) - BIBLE BELT (IRE)	BIG RED FARM	160000
CH C SHOWCASING (GB) - ROWAN BRAE (GB)	SHADWELL ESTATE COMPANY	160000
B C NO NAY NEVER (USA) - EL DIAMANTE (FR)	C GORDON-WATSON	160000
SCHIELE (IRE) B F SHAMARDAL (USA) - TUTU NGURU (USA)	WHITE BIRCH FARM	160000
B C TEOFILO (IRE) - CELESTE DE LA MER (IRE)	BLANDFORD BS	160000
WHYZZAT (GB) B C DARK ANGEL (IRE) - WHAZZIS (GB)	STETCHWORTH & MIDDLE PARK	160000
B C KODIAC (GB) - NAYFAH (FR)	SHADWELL ESTATE COMPANY	160000
B F FOOTSTEPSINTHESAND (GB) - SOMMORELL (IRE)	A C ELLIOTT, AGENT	160000
B C CABLE BAY (IRE) - BALLET MOVE (GB)	SHADWELL ESTATE COMPANY	160000
B F OASIS DREAM (GB) - LONGING TO DANCE (GB)	SHADWELL ESTATE COMPANY	160000
CH F SLADE POWER (IRE) - FLARE OF FIRELIGHT (USA)	SHADWELL ESTATE COMPANY	160000
B C INVINCIBLE SPIRIT (IRE) - EDARAAT (USA)	RABBAH BS	160000
B C GOLDEN HORN (GB) - SAMIRA GOLD (FR)	BLANDFORD BS	160000
MICROPHONE (IRE) B C SIYOUNI (FR) - FALLEN IN LOVE (FR)	WHITE BIRCH FARM	160000
B C SIYOUNI (FR) - INDIANA WELLS (FR)	VENDOR	160000
B C NO NAY NEVER (USA) - ALJUMAR (IRE)	STEPHEN HILLEN BS	155000
B C SHOWCASING (GB) - LADY ESTELLA (IRE)	SHADWELL ESTATE COMPANY	155000
B C IFFRAAJ (GB) - BALAYAGE (IRE)	PETER & ROSS DOYLE BS	150000
B C ACCLAMATION (GB) - EXCELETTE (IRE)	STROUD COLEMAN BS	150000
CH C NEW APPROACH (IRE) - MAJESTIC MANNER (GB)	SHADWELL ESTATE COMPANY	150000
CH F SHOWCASING (GB) - RAINBOW SPRINGS (IRE)	GER LYONS	150000
CH F IFFRAAJ (GB) - HANA LINA (GB)	MIKE RYAN AGENT	150000
CH C SEA THE STARS (IRE) - GOLDENDALE (IRE)	JEREMY BRUMMITT	150000
B F DUBAWI (IRE) - ROSINKA (IRE)	LOFTS HALL STUD (P.S.)	150000
B F AUSTRALIA (GB) - LOVE AND LAUGHTER (IRE)	DAVID REDVERS BS	150000
FLYIN' HIGH (GB) B C SIYOUNI (FR) - ZEE ZEE TOP (GB)	VENDOR	150000
B C TERRITORIES (IRE) - QUIRITIS (GB)	BLANDFORD BS	150000
B F SHOWCASING (GB) - HELLO GLORY (GB)	J B BS	150000
GR C SEA THE STARS (IRE) - CAUSA PROXIMA (FR)	SHADWELL ESTATE COMPANY	150000
B C SIYOUNI (FR) - REINETTE (GB)	JAMIE B BS	150000
SNIGGER (IRE) B F DUBAWI (IRE) - LAUGH OUT LOUD (GB)	JS BS / G SCOTT RACING	150000
B F EQUIANO (FR) - PERSARIO (GB)	VENDOR	150000

Name and Breeding	Purchaser	Guineas
GR/RO C EXCEED AND EXCEL (AUS) - SOUVIENS TOI (GB)	STROUD COLEMAN BS	150000
B C AWTAAD (IRE) - SOVIET TERMS (GB)	SHADWELL ESTATE COMPANY	150000
CH F EXCEED AND EXCEL (AUS) - SKY CRYSTAL (GER)	VENDOR	150000
CH F EXCEED AND EXCEL (AUS) - KERRY'S DREAM (GB)	SHADWELL ESTATE COMPANY	150000
B F KODIAC (GB) - INTAGLIA (GB)	RABBAH BS	150000
B C KINGMAN (GB) - ISLINGTON (IRE)	KHALIFA DASMAL	150000
B F SEA THE STARS (IRE) - CRYSDAL (GB)	RABBAH BS	150000
B F SHOWCASING (GB) - EYESHINE (GB)	VENDOR	150000
B C WOOTTON BASSETT (GB) - MISTY NIGHT (IRE)	SHADWELL ESTATE COMPANY	150000
B C KITTEN'S JOY (USA) - JEANERETTE (USA)	JOSEPH O'BRIEN	150000
B C SHALAA (GB) - WONDEROUS LIGHT (IRE)	SHADWELL ESTATE COMPANY	150000
B C NO NAY NEVER (USA) - CELESTIAL DREAM (IRE)	POWERSTOWN STUD	150000
B F FRANKEL (GB) - ROCKERY (IRE)	VENDOR	150000
B C SIYOUNI (FR) - EAVESDROP (IRE)	JOSEPH O'BRIEN	150000
B F DARK ANGEL (IRE) - GOLDEN LAUGHTER (USA)	GODOLPHIN	150000
CH C LE HAVRE (IRE) - DEMURELY (IRE)	SHADWELL ESTATE COMPANY	150000
CH C TERRITORIES (IRE) - BROUGHTONS REVIVAL (GB)	SHADWELL ESTATE COMPANY	150000
B F GALILEO (IRE) - SAHARA SKY (IRE)	DERMOT FARRINGTON	150000
B/BR C CABLE BAY (IRE) - COIN A PHRASE (GB)	SHADWELL ESTATE COMPANY	150000
B C SHALAA (GB) - BESOTTED (IRE)	BBA IRELAND	150000
B C BELARDO (IRE) - VANDERGIRL (IRE)	KLARAVICH STABLES	150000
B C FRANKEL (GB) - BLHADAWA (IRE)	GROVE STUD	145000
B F TERRITORIES (IRE) - LOVE YOUR LOOKS (GB)	STROUD COLEMAN BS	145000
B F LE HAVRE (IRE) - PRADEN (USA)	HUGO MERRY BS	145000
B F KODIAC (GB) - WARDA (GB)	RABBAH BS	145000
B F VADAMOS (FR) - LA CHICANA (IRE)	RABBAH BS	145000
B C DARK ANGEL (IRE) - LAND ARMY (IRE)	VENDOR	145000
B C CAMELOT (GB) - LAST TANGO INPARIS (GB)	SPICER THOROUGHBREDS	140000
B C STARSPANGLEDBANNER (AUS) - SHIRLEY BLADE (IRE)	M MOUBARAK	140000
B C ACCLAMATION (GB) - INITIALLY (GB)	MIKE RYAN AGENT	140000
B C LE HAVRE (IRE) - REGATTA (FR)	C GORDON-WATSON BS	140000
B C CAMELOT (GB) - TEMPTRESS (IRE)	BLANDFORD BS	140000
B C MEHMAS (IRE) - PARDOVEN (IRE)	SHADWELL ESTATE COMPANY	140000
B C CABLE BAY (IRE) - CONSERVATORY (GB)	SHADWELL ESTATE COMPANY	140000
B C EXCEED AND EXCEL (AUS) - LANDELA (GB)	SHADWELL ESTATE COMPANY	140000
CH F NEW APPROACH (IRE) - SCRIBONIA (IRE)	DAVID REDVERS BS	140000
B C OASIS DREAM (GB) - SANT ELENA (GB)	RABBAH BS	140000
OMAN (IRE) CH C AUSTRALIA (GB) - AWOHAAM (IRE)	RICHARD FRISBY BS	140000
B C GALILEO (IRE) - MELITO (AUS)	VENDOR	140000
B F AWTAAD (IRE) - DEBUETANTIN (GB)	CREIGHTON SCHWARTZ BS	140000
B F FASCINATING ROCK (IRE) - LADY LIVIUS (IRE)	NEWTOWN ANNER STUD	140000
PAPACITO (IRE) BR C ESTIDHKAAR (IRE) - OUT OF TIME (IRE)	ROGER VARIAN	140000
B C CAMELOT (GB) - SHE'S MINE (IRE)	SPICER THOROUGHBREDS PTY	135000
B C CAMELOT (GB) - DOROTHY B (IRE)	CRISFORD RACING	135000
EMPEROR SPIRIT (IRE) B C HOLY ROMAN EMPEROR (IRE) - ASPASIAS TIZZY (USA)	HUGO MERRY BS	135000
GR F SEA THE STARS (IRE) - FIVE FIFTEEN (FR)	MC BS	135000
B C DARK ANGEL (IRE) - CHEETAH (GB)	SHADWELL ESTATE COMPANY	135000
CH C BELARDO (IRE) - YOU'RE BACK (USA)	SHADWELL ESTATE COMPANY	135000
B C SHOWCASING (GB) - SPRINGLIKE (IRE)	STROUD COLEMAN BS	135000
MIND THAT JET (IRE) B C KODIAC (GB) - RATE (GB)	M MOUBARAK	135000
CHESHIRE PLAIN (FR) B F INVINCIBLE SPIRIT (IRE) - WILLOW VIEW (USA)	VENDOR	130000
B C SEA THE MOON (GER) - HOMEPAGE (GB)	JEREMY GLOVER	130000
B F SEA THE STARS (IRE) - ROSE RIZED (GER)	STROUD COLEMAN BS	130000
CH C NIGHT OF THUNDER (IRE) - MON BIJOU (IRE)	STROUD COLEMAN BS	130000
B F NATHANIEL (GB) - RHAGORI (GB)	SHADWELL ESTATE COMPANY	130000
CH C GLENEAGLES (IRE) - EXPENSIVE DATE (GB)	BIG RED FARM	130000
CH C TWILIGHT SON (GB) - SOAR (GB)	KEVIN RYAN	130000
B F KINGMAN (GB) - SCORN (USA)	KLARAVICH STABLES	130000
B C ACCLAMATION (GB) - ON LOCATION (USA)	VENDOR	130000
B C SHALAA (IRE) - GREEN SWALLOW (FR)	RABBAH BS	130000
HARLEM SOUL (GB) CH C FRANKEL (GB) - GIANTS PLAY (USA)	JOHNSTON RACING	130000
B F HARZAND (IRE) - ATHENAIRE (IRE)	RICHARD KNIGHT BS AGENT	130000
B/BR F MEDAGLIA D'ORO (USA) - SIGURWANA (USA)	MIKE RYAN AGENT	130000
CH F SHOWCASING (GB) - SAMASANA (IRE)	STROUD COLEMAN BS	130000
B F SEA THE STARS (IRE) - PERSIAN SKY (GB)	SACKVILLEDONALD	130000
B C NEW APPROACH (IRE) - ROYALE DANEHILL (IRE)	BLANDFORD BS	130000
UNCLE BRYN (GB) B C SEA THE STARS (IRE) - WALL OF SOUND (GB)	BLANDFORD BS	130000
BR F AWTAAD (IRE) - OASIS SUNSET (IRE)	AMANDA SKIFFINGTON	125000
GR/RO C DARK ANGEL (IRE) - LA PETITE REINE (GB)	BBA IRELAND	125000
CH C NEW APPROACH (IRE) - PRALINE (IRE)	RABBAH BS	125000
B C THE GURKHA (IRE) - DON'T CRY FOR ME (USA)	SUZANNE ROBERTS	125000
B C INVINCIBLE SPIRIT (IRE) - CASCADING (IRE)	AVENUE BS	125000
B C DARK ANGEL (IRE) - CAPULET MONTEGUE (IRE)	AIDAN O'RYAN	125000

Name and Breeding	Purchaser	Guineas
B C FREE EAGLE (IRE) - BADR AL BADOOR (IRE)	STROUD COLEMAN BS	125000
B F MUHAARAAR (GB) - FRONT HOUSE (IRE)	OLIVER ST LAWRENCE BS	125000
NORTH OF AMAZING (GB) B C HAVANA GOLD (GB) - PRINCESS GUEST (IRE)	KARL BURKE	125000
CHLOE (GER) B F KINGMAN (GB) - CALYXA (GB)	YEOMANSTOWN STUD	125000
B F MUHAARAAR (GB) - FORT DEL ORO (IRE)	AL RABBAH RACING / JS BS	125000
SHANGHAI ROCK (GB) B C DARK ANGEL (IRE) - RED LADY (IRE)	PETER & ROSS DOYLE BS	125000
B F KODIAC (GB) - PRANCE (IRE)	RABBAH BS	120000
CH C SHOWCASING (GB) - WAHYLAH (IRE)	SUN BS / QATAR RACING	120000
B F KINGMAN (GB) - LONELY AHEAD (USA)	VENDOR	120000
B C TERRITORIES (IRE) - FAVULUSA (GB)	JOHN & JAKE WARREN	120000
JANIE JONES (GB) CH F LE HAVRE (FR) - COQUET (GB)	KILBRIDE EQUINE	120000
CH C SEA THE MOON (GER) - QUESTABELLA (GER)	VENDOR	120000
B F LOPE DE VEGA (IRE) - MODERAH (GB)	DAVID REDVERS BS	120000
GR C LOPE DE VEGA (IRE) - ALPINE SNOW (IRE)	VENDOR	120000
FOR PEAT'S SAKE (GB) B C SHOWCASING (GB) - PEACEHAVEN (GB)	BLANDFORD BS	120000
B C ESTIDHKAAR (IRE) - VIA BALLYCROY (IRE)	SHADWELL ESTATE COMPANY	120000
B F ZOFFANY (IRE) - WOOING (IRE)	MERIDIAN INTERNATIONAL	120000
B F SHALAA (IRE) - FEDERATION (GB)	TOJI MORITA	120000
B C IFFRAAJ (GB) - SPARRING QUEEN (USA)	SHADWELL ESTATE COMPANY	120000
MINDPOWER (IRE) CH C GLENEAGLES (IRE) - COMMON KNOWLEDGE (GB)	ROGER VARIAN	120000
CH C ZOFFANY (IRE) - SINGLE (FR)	JOSEPH O'BRIEN	120000
B C KODIAC (GB) - DANCING JEST (IRE)	PHOENIX THOROUGHBREDS	120000
CH C LOPE DE VEGA (IRE) - TRIBUTARY (GB)	SHADWELL ESTATE COMPANY	120000
B C MUHAARAAR (GB) - STARFLOWER (GB)	SHADWELL ESTATE COMPANY	120000
BR C INVINCIBLE SPIRIT (IRE) - MAGIC MISSION (GB)	VENDOR	120000
B F AWTAAD (IRE) - STAR APPROVAL (IRE)	SACKVILLEDONALD	120000
B C VADAMOS (FR) - STRAWBERRY MARTINI (GB)	ARMANDO DUARTE	120000
B F NO NAY NEVER (USA) - SUBTLE CHARM (GB)	DE BURGH EQUINE	120000
BALLANTRUAN (GB) B C HARZAND (IRE) - CHINCOTEAGUE (IRE)	HURWORTH BS	120000
B C KODIAC (GB) - MARGARET'S MISSION (IRE)	JILL LAMB BS	120000
B C CAMELOT (GB) - TRAIL OF TEARS (IRE)	RICHARD HUGHES RACING	120000
ZENITH (IRE) GR C INVINCIBLE SPIRIT (IRE) - FREEZY (IRE)	JOHN & JAKE WARREN (P.S.)	120000
EMPRESS MAKEDA (IRE) B F SEA THE STARS (IRE) - SHEBA FIVE (USA)	VENDOR	120000
CH C NEW APPROACH (IRE) - COOLNAGREE (IRE)	MOHAMED MOUBARAK	120000
B C ADAAY (IRE) - DOLLY COLMAN (IRE)	SHADWELL ESTATE COMPANY	120000
CH C ZOFFANY (IRE) - SHELLEY BEACH (IRE)	JOSEPH O'BRIEN	120000
POLAR ICE (GB) B C DANSILI (GB) - QUEEN OF ICE (GB)	BARRY LYNCH	120000
B F KINGMAN (GB) - ADONESQUE (IRE)	SUN BS	120000
B F ZOFFANY (IRE) - ALJAAZYA (USA)	BRIAN GRASSICK BS	115000
B C SHOWCASING (GB) - OVERTURNED (GB)	PHOENIX THOROUGHBREDS	115000
B C KODIAC (GB) - FAIR SAILING (IRE)	H MORRISON	115000
B F TWILIGHT SON (GB) - BEST SIDE (IRE)	DAVID REDVERS BS	115000
B F LE HAVRE (IRE) - AMEYRAH (IRE)	MAGNOLIA BS	115000
B C IFFRAAJ (GB) - CHILI DIP (GB)	STROUD COLEMAN BS	115000
B C OASIS DREAM (GB) - BLINKING (GB)	SHADWELL ESTATE COMPANY	115000
B C FARHH (GB) - FINGERTIPS (GB)	SHADWELL ESTATE COMPANY	115000
B C LOPE DE VEGA (IRE) - STARS SO BRIGHT (IRE)	SHADWELL ESTATE COMPANY	115000
B C DARK ANGEL (IRE) - MAID TO DREAM (GB)	SHADWELL ESTATE COMPANY	115000
B F CAMELOT (GB) - SNOW GRETEL (IRE)	PETER & ROSS DOYLE BS	115000
B F ACCLAMATION (GB) - COLOUR BLUE (IRE)	STROUD COLEMAN BS	115000
B F PRIDE OF DUBAI (AUS) - UNNATURAL (USA)	JOE FOLEY	115000
LAJOSCHA (GB) B C GLENEAGLES (IRE) - LADY LINDA (USA)	VENDOR	115000
B F GOLDEN HORN (GB) - NANCY O (IRE)	REPOLE STABLE	110000
B F SEA THE MOON (GER) - MARISA (GER)	BSW EURO VENTURE	110000
BR/GR C SHALAA (IRE) - VAYASA (FR)	SHADWELL ESTATE COMPANY	110000
B C PRIDE OF DUBAI (AUS) - MONDELICE (GB)	RABBAH BS	110000
B C NIGHT OF THUNDER (IRE) - REDINHA (IRE)	SHADWELL ESTATE COMPANY	110000
B F BELARDO (IRE) - GALLICE (IRE)	MIKE RYAN AGENT	110000
B F FRANKEL (GB) - PALIMONY (IRE)	NICK BRADLEY RACING	110000
BR C SHOWCASING (GB) - ZORA SEAS (IRE)	RICHARD HUGHES RACING	110000
B C EXCEED AND EXCEL (AUS) - ILLUSTRIOUS MISS (USA)	JOHN FOOTE BS	110000
CH F NIGHT OF THUNDER (IRE) - EXEMPT (IRE)	BLANDFORD BS	110000
B C NO NAY NEVER (USA) - MACKENZIE'S FRIEND (GB)	STROUD COLEMAN BS	110000
CH C LOPE DE VEGA (IRE) - HINT OF PINK (GB)	STROUD COLEMAN BS	110000
ROYAL PLEASURE (IRE) B C KINGMAN (GB) - MERRY JAUNT (IRE)	BARRY LYNCH	110000
CH C SEA THE STARS (IRE) - BRAZILIAN BRIDE (IRE)	SUZANNE ROBERTS	110000
B F NEW APPROACH (IRE) - WHITE DRESS (IRE)	BLANDFORD BS	110000
B F LOPE DE VEGA (IRE) - BRYNICA (FR)	VENDOR	110000
B C FAST COMPANY (IRE) - ALTERNANTHERA (GB)	SHADWELL ESTATE COMPANY	110000
B F SHALAA (IRE) - SOCIAL MEDIA (GB)	SHADWELL ESTATE COMPANY	110000
B C TERRITORIES (IRE) - CEPHALONIE (USA)	SACKVILLEDONALD	110000
B F MEHMAS (IRE) - ELKMAIT (IRE)	KARL BURKE / CARL WATERS	110000
B F FASTNET ROCK (AUS) - WANNABE SPECIAL (GB)	TODD PLETCHER / AQUIS FARM	110000

HIGH-PRICED YEARLINGS OF 2019 AT GOFFS

The following yearlings realised 65,000 euros and over at Goffs Sales in 2019:-

Name and Breeding	Purchaser	Euros
B F GALILEO (IRE) - GREEN ROOM (USA)	M V MAGNIER	3000000
MAGIC HOUR (IRE) B F GALILEO (IRE) - ALEAGUEOFTHEIROWN (IRE)	WESTERBERG	2200000
B F GALILEO (IRE) - DEVOTED TO YOU (IRE)	PHOENIX TB	1100000
B F DARK ANGEL (IRE) - BEATRIX POTTER (IRE)	GODOLPHIN	1000000
B C SEA THE STARS (IRE) - OWNWAN (USA)	AQUIS FARM	550000
CH C AUSTRALIA (GB) - GEMS (GB)	M V MAGNIER	525000
CH F FRANKEL (GB) - SWEEPSTAKE (IRE)	SHADWELL ESTATE COMPANY	500000
B C SEA THE STARS (IRE) - MY SPIRIT (IRE)	GODOLPHIN	500000
B C INVINCIBLE SPIRIT (IRE) - AIMHIRGIN LASS (IRE)	GODOLPHIN	460000
B F DARK ANGEL (IRE) - THE HERMITAGE (IRE)	SACKVILLEDONALD	440000
B C EXCEED AND EXCEL (AUS) - SYMPOSIA (GB)	AQUIS BS	430000
B C LOPE DE VEGA (IRE) - DARK CRUSADER (IRE)	SHADWELL ESTATE COMPANY	425000
B/BR G SHOWCASING (GB) - CASILA (IRE)	HKJC	420000
CH C DUBAWI (IRE) - CHOOSE ME (IRE)	GODOLPHIN	400000
B C SEA THE STARS (IRE) - SIODUIL (IRE)	SHADWELL ESTATE COMPANY	400000
B C AWTAAD (IRE) - LUCKY CLIO (IRE)	SHADWELL ESTATE COMPANY	400000
B C STREET SENSE (USA) - SNAPDRAGON (USA)	SACKVILLEDONALD	380000
B C GALILEO (IRE) - CONVOCATE (GB)	PHOENIX TB	380000
B G KODIAC (GB) - VEE GITA (IRE)	HKJC	375000
B C OASIS DREAM (GB) - UIMHIR A HAON (IRE)	HKJC	350000
B F KINGMAN (GB) - GOLDEN REIGN (IRE)	FORM BS	340000
B C THE GURKHA (IRE) - RED BLOSSOM (GB)	CHINA HORSE CLUB	300000
B C LE HAVRE (IRE) - JET SETTING (IRE)	M RICHARDS	300000
B F FRANKEL (GB) - MANDERLEY (IRE)	ROUNDABOUT STABLES	280000
B C FOOTSTEPSINTHESAND (GB) - INIS BOFFIN (GB)	BLANDFORD BS	280000
B F AUSTRALIA (GB) - POTION (GB)	M V MAGNIER	280000
B F IFFRAAJ (IRE) - ABEND (IRE)	P MAINS	280000
LINDA BARRETT (IRE) B/GR F DARK ANGEL (IRE) - PLAGIARISM (USA)	DE BURGH EQUINE	275000
B C KINGMAN (GB) - KITTY LOVE (USA)	PETER & ROSS DOYLE BS	260000
CH C THE GURKHA (IRE) - EUPHRASIA (IRE)	M V MAGNIER	260000
B F NO NAY NEVER (USA) - LESSON IN LIFE (GB)	M V MAGNIER	250000
B C AIR FORCE BLUE (USA) - SECRET CHARM (IRE)	M V MAGNIER	250000
B C SIYOUNI (FR) - EBALISTA (IRE)	M RICHARDS	250000
B F GALILEO (IRE) - REPLETE (GB)	VENDOR	250000
B C DARK ANGEL (IRE) - TAWAYNA (IRE)	SHADWELL ESTATE COMPANY	240000
CH C SHOWCASING (GB) - BRIGHT GLOW (GB)	SHADWELL ESTATE COMPANY	240000
CH F SEA THE STARS (IRE) - SHARED HUMOR (USA)	S DUGAN	225000
B C SEA THE STARS (IRE) - MARTINE'S SPIRIT (IRE)	BBA (IRELAND)	225000
B C PRIDE OF DUBAI (AUS) - FREEFOURRACING (USA)	VENDOR	220000
SLOANE PETERSON (IRE) B F KODIAC (GB) - CAPRIOLE (GB)	DE BURGH EQUINE	220000
B C DANDY MAN (IRE) - LILY'S RAINBOW (IRE)	SACKVILLEDONALD	220000
B C NO NAY NEVER (USA) - HIGH SAVANNAH (IRE)	M V MAGNIER	220000
B F DANDY MAN (IRE) - KAZATZKA (GB)	PATTERN BS	210000
B F CAMELOT (GB) - MISS MACNAMARA (IRE)	PETER & ROSS DOYLE BS	200000
B F FASTNET ROCK (AUS) - LAP OF LUXURY (GB)	FORM BS	200000
B C EXCEED AND EXCEL (AUS) - BUFFALO BERRY (IRE)	FORM BS	200000
CH G MASTERCRAFTSMAN (IRE) - BRIDGE NOTE (USA)	HKJC	200000
B F FOOTSTEPSINTHESAND (GB) - AMAZING KRISKEN (USA)	S DUGAN	200000
B F ACCLAMATION (GB) - SPEEDY SONATA (USA)	J CASSE	185000
B F CAMACHO (GB) - GLAMOROUS AIR (IRE)	BLANDFORD BS	180000
B C ACCLAMATION (GB) - MOLLY DOLLY (IRE)	A C ELLIOTT	180000
B F SHALAA (IRE) - HOLY FREUD (USA)	M O'CALLAGHAN	180000
B C CAMELOT (GB) - DANEHILL'S DREAM (IRE)	J & J WARREN	175000
B C LOPE DE VEGA (IRE) - QUEEN OF CARTHAGE (USA)	BBA (IRELAND)	175000
B F NATHANIEL (IRE) - CHANTREA (IRE)	R M BECKETT	170000
B F SEA THE STARS (IRE) - HEROIC HEART (FR)	S DUGAN	170000
B C GLENEAGLES (IRE) - OBAMA RULE (IRE)	M V MAGNIER	170000
B C KENDARGENT (FR) - RAJARATNA (IRE)	D FARRINGTON	170000
B F KINGMAN (GB) - SPLIT DECISION (IRE)	J & J WARREN (P.S.)	165000
B C ZOFFANY (IRE) - SARAWATI (IRE)	BBA (IRELAND)	165000
B G FAST COMPANY (IRE) - BETT'S GIFT (GB)	HKJC	160000
B C KODIAC (GB) - SOUL SEARCHER (IRE)	PHOENIX TB	160000
B F GLENEAGLES (IRE) - ELBASANA (IRE)	PHOENIX LADIES SYNDICATE	160000
B C PIVOTAL (GB) - FIELD OF MIRACLES (IRE)	G DAVIES	160000
B F FASCINATING ROCK (IRE) - BEBHINN (USA)	NEWTOWN ANNER STUD	160000
CH F AUSTRALIA (GB) - ROCK OF RIDD (IRE)	M AKERS	160000
B F AWTAAD (IRE) - INTIMACY (IRE)	SHADWELL ESTATE COMPANY	160000
CH F GLENEAGLES (IRE) - CASERTA (GB)	B MCELROY	160000
B C STARSPANGLEDBANNER (AUS) - PEARLITAS PASSION (IRE)	MC BS	150000
B F ZOFFANY (IRE) - MANY COLOURS (GB)	M V MAGNIER	150000

Name and Breeding	Purchaser	Guineas
B C NIGHT OF THUNDER (IRE) - WIZARA (IRE)	J MURTAGH	150000
RIVER ALWEN (IRE) GR C DARK ANGEL (IRE) - INTENSE PINK (GB)	SUN BS	145000
B F LOPE DE VEGA (IRE) - PIRATE COVE (IRE)	GATEWOOD BELL	145000
B F SHALAA (IRE) - TARA'S FORCE (IRE)	HURWORTH BS	145000
B F SHALAA (IRE) - RAKIZA (IRE)	GATEWOOD BELL	140000
BR C NO NAY NEVER (USA) - DANE STREET (USA)	FORM BS	140000
MRS FITZHERBERT (IRE) B F KINGMAN (GB) - STUPENDOUS MISS (USA)	VENDOR	140000
B C KINGMAN (GB) - CZABO (GB)	M WACHMAN	140000
CH F LOPE DE VEGA (IRE) - SINGING FIELD (IRE)	BALLYLINCH STUD	140000
B F HOLY ROMAN EMPEROR (IRE) - MY RENEE (USA)	BBA (IRELAND)	140000
B F AUSTRALIA (GB) - D'ORO PRINCESS (USA)	TEN PERCENT BS	140000
BR G MASTERCRAFTSMAN (IRE) - EXCELLENT MARINER (IRE)	HKJC	140000
B C ZOFFANY (IRE) - TIGER LILLY (IRE)	VENDOR	140000
BR F HARZAND (IRE) - BLACK MASCARA (IRE)	SACKVILLEDONALD	135000
B C EXCEED AND EXCEL (AUS) - ORIENTAL STEP (IRE)	J FOLEY	135000
B F KODIAC (GB) - SOVANA (IRE)	TYLICKI/KINIRONS	135000
B F CABLE BAY (IRE) - APPLETON DROVE (USA)	FORM BS	130000
B F AWTAAD (IRE) - LOLWAH (GB)	SHADWELL ESTATE COMPANY	130000
B C NO NAY NEVER (USA) - MARTYENNE (GER)	JAMIE B BS	130000
B F HOLY ROMAN EMPEROR (IRE) - AMARETTE (GER)	SUNDERLAND HOLDING	130000
B F NEW BAY (GB) - NEWSLETTER (IRE)	C DE MOUBRAY	130000
B C CAMELOT (GB) - EMIRATES JOY (USA)	J O'BRIEN	130000
B C KODIAC (GB) - MULTICOLOUR WAVE (IRE)	D REDVERS	125000
GR/RO F FLINTSHIRE (GB) - MORTGAGE THE HOUSE (USA)	D REDVERS	125000
B C AUSTRALIA (GB) - QUEENSCLIFF (IRE)	BBA (IRELAND)	125000
B F SIYOUNI (FR) - STACEY SUTTON (FR)	VENDOR	120000
B C SEA THE STARS (IRE) - EXCEED MY BUDGET (GB)	VENDOR	120000
B F OASIS DREAM (GB) - NEWSROOM (IRE)	R RYAN	120000
GLESGA GAL (IRE) CH F LOPE DE VEGA (IRE) - CRYSTANY (IRE)	AVENUE BS	120000
B C AUSTRALIA (GB) - KIRKINOLA (GB)	J O'BRIEN	120000
B C WOOTTON BASSETT (GB) - BLUE BLUE SEA (GB)	J FOLEY	120000
B C INVINCIBLE SPIRIT (IRE) - AARAAMM (USA)	MC BS	120000
B F MASTERCRAFTSMAN (IRE) - BLESSING (USA)	DE BURGH EQUINE	120000
B F LOPE DE VEGA (IRE) - CONTIDA (GB)	A SKIFFINGTON	120000
B C LOPE DE VEGA (IRE) - ROSIE COTTON (IRE)	FUJIMOTO RACING	120000
B F FOOTSTEPSINTHESAND (GB) - MISS CORINNE (IRE)	B O'RYAN	120000
B C GLENEAGLES (IRE) - ONE SPIRIT (IRE)	BBA (IRELAND)	120000
B F SHOWCASING (GB) - PURE INNOCENCE (IRE)	S DUGAN	120000
CH C SHOWCASING (GB) - PORTHILLY (FR)	STAUFFENBERG BS	120000
QUEEN OF ASIA (IRE) B F EXCEED AND EXCEL (AUS) - ALUMNI (GB)	SACKVILLEDONALD	115000
B F MEHMAS (IRE) - LAUREN'S GIRL (IRE)	M REILLY	115000
B C GALILEO (IRE) - BANIMPIRE (IRE)	VOLTEO HORSE SERVICE	115000
B/GR C DARK ANGEL (IRE) - LA COLLINA (IRE)	C MCCORMACK	110000
B C THE GURKHA (IRE) - RAVISH (GB)	VENDOR	110000
B C INVINCIBLE SPIRIT (IRE) - RECITE (JPN)	OAK TREE FARM	110000
CH F ZOFFANY (IRE) - NIGHT SONG (GB)	K PRENDERGAST	110000
B F ZOFFANY (IRE) - ATTIRE (GB)	J O'BRIEN	110000
B F AIR FORCE BLUE (USA) - CRY ME A RIVER (IRE)	ROCKFIELD STUD	105000
GLANDORE HARBOUR (IRE) B F CAMELOT (GB) - CMONBABYLITEMYFIRE (IRE)	STROUD COLEMAN BS	100000
CH F LOPE DE VEGA (IRE) - MARAMBA (USA)	BRIAN GRASSICK BS	100000
B C FASCINATING ROCK (IRE) - GOLDEN SHADOW (IRE)	PETER & ROSS DOYLE BS	100000
CH C AUSTRALIA (GB) - SEVEN VEILS (IRE)	PHOENIX TB	100000
B C GALILEO (IRE) - VIZ (GB)	J LAVERY	100000
CH C NIGHT OF THUNDER (IRE) - DUST FLICKER (GB)	PETER & ROSS DOYLE BS	100000
B F HOLY ROMAN EMPEROR (IRE) - HOLLY BLUE (GB)	VENDOR	100000
B F LAWMAN (FR) - FACT OR FOLKLORE (IRE)	D FARRINGTON	100000
BR C KODI BEAR (IRE) - ARBEEL (GB)	CHINA HORSE CLUB	100000
B F GLENEAGLES (IRE) - RAINFALL RADAR (USA)	HOWSON & HOULDSWORTH BS	100000
B C SHALAA (IRE) - HAT (USA)	LONGWAYS STABLES	100000
B F DARK ANGEL (IRE) - ENJOYABLE (IRE)	VENDOR	100000
B C SEA THE STARS (IRE) - FLY ON THE NIGHT (GB)	AVAZ ISMOILOV	100000
KOLISI (IRE) B C HARZAND (IRE) - WILD STEP (GER)	JILL LAMB BS	95000
CH F PRIDE OF DUBAI (AUS) - LAMYAA (GB)	HUGO MERRY BS	95000
B F ZOFFANY (IRE) - LOVED (IRE)	M C GRASSICK	95000
B C OASIS DREAM (GB) - WHAT A PICTURE (FR)	CHINA HORSE CLUB	95000
B F IFFRAAJ (GB) - PHOTOPHORE (IRE)	BBA (IRELAND)	95000
KING ZAIN (IRE) B C KINGMAN (GB) - SHREYAS (IRE)	JOHNSTON RACING	95000
B C TWILIGHT SON (GB) - CRINKLE (IRE)	RABBAH BS	95000
CH F THE LAST LION (IRE) - DUTCH COURAGE (GB)	PETER & ROSS DOYLE BS	92000
B C DARK ANGEL (IRE) - HAVIN' A GOOD TIME (IRE)	CLIVE COX RACING	90000
GUSTAV HOLST (IRE) B C SEA THE STARS (IRE) - SCARLET AND GOLD (IRE)	PETER & ROSS DOYLE BS	90000
CH C FREE EAGLE (IRE) - SET FIRE (IRE)	HUGO MERRY BS	90000
B F BUNGLE INTHEJUNGLE (GB) - TITIAN SAGA (IRE)	SACKVILLEDONALD	90000

Name and Breeding	Purchaser	Guineas
B C ZOFFANY (IRE) - ZEE ZEE GEE (GB)	J O'BRIEN	90000
CEDRIC MORRIS (IRE) B C FAST COMPANY (IRE) - BIG BONED (USA)	RICHARD FRISBY BS	90000
B C NOBLE MISSION (GB) - DREAMT (GB)	J OSBORNE	90000
B C TWILIGHT SON (GB) - MODERN ART (GB)	B O'RYAN	90000
B F MEHMAS (IRE) - ESTERLINA (IRE)	HAMISH MACAULEY BS	87000
B F KODIAC (GB) - ACCLIMATISATION (IRE)	M D INVESTMENTS	87000
B C GLENEAGLES (IRE) - BRATISLAVA (GB)	AVENUE BS	85000
DUCHESS ROSE (IRE) B F DREAM AHEAD (USA) - ALAVA (IRE)	R O'RYAN	85000
B C FRANKEL (GB) - APSARA (FR)	J FOLEY	85000
B F ZOFFANY (IRE) - JUST IMAGINING (USA)	B FLAY	85000
B C MUHAARAR (GB) - ABSOLUTELY COOL (IRE)	D REDVERS	82000
B F ZOFFANY (IRE) - WEEK END (GB)	EBONOS	80000
REAMS OF LOVE (GB) B C FRANKEL (GB) - NIGHT OF LIGHT (IRE)	CRONE STUD FARMS	80000
CH C PIVOTAL (GB) - ADJUDICATE (GB)	CRAMPSCASTLE BS	80000
CH C NO NAY NEVER (USA) - COURT CIRCULAR (GB)	SAM SANGSTER BS	80000
CH C CAMACHO (GB) - KAYAK (GB)	SAM SANGSTER BS	80000
B C STARSPANGLEDBANNER (AUS) - SORRY WOMAN (FR)	SACKVILLEDONALD	80000
WHITE LADY (IRE) B F DARK ANGEL (IRE) - WILTSHIRE LIFE (IRE)	BBA (IRELAND)	80000
BOLIVAR ROADS (IRE) B C TAMAYUZ (GB) - BOUNCE (FR)	F ZWICKY	80000
B F TERRITORIES (IRE) - VINTAGE MOLLY (GB)	PETER & ROSS DOYLE BS	80000
B C MUHAARAR (GB) - VENTURA MIST (GB)	DEUCE GREATHOUSE	80000
B F DUBAWI (IRE) - PURR ALONG (GB)	D REDVERS	80000
B F MUHAARAR (GB) - SILENT THOUGHTS (IRE)	ROCKFIELD FARM	80000
B C GLENEAGLES (IRE) - RHYTHM QUEEN (IRE)	GAELIC BS	80000
CH C NIGHT OF THUNDER (IRE) - JAMEELA'S DREAM (GB)	STROUD COLEMAN	80000
CH F NO NAY NEVER (USA) - ART OF DANCE (IRE)	LEX INC	80000
STATE OF BLISS (IRE) B C GLENEAGLES (IRE) - CRYSTAL VALKYRIE (IRE)	JOHNSTON RACING	80000
CH F SEA THE STARS (IRE) - ALAMODE (GB)	BBA (IRELAND)	80000
CH F GLENEAGLES (IRE) - TIMELESS CALL (IRE)	R O'RYAN	80000
B C DARK ANGEL (IRE) - STACEYNAS (IRE)	YEOMANSTOWN STUD	80000
HEADLINER (IRE) B F THE LAST LION (IRE) - COUNTESS FERRAMA (GB)	RABBAH BS	78000
CH F SHOWCASING (GB) - DREAM DANA (IRE)	J & J WARREN	78000
B C MUHAARAR (GB) - WRONG ANSWER (GB)	CHURCH FARM	78000
CH F DUTCH ART (GB) - INFATUATION (GB)	RABBAH BS	75000
FLY MISS HELEN (FR) B F LE HAVRE (IRE) - GROWING GLORY (FR)	PETER & ROSS DOYLE BS	75000
B C OASIS DREAM (GB) - PICCOLA SISSI (IRE)	A O'RYAN	75000
B F TEOFILO (IRE) - WEDDING WISH (GB)	GROVE STUD	75000
B C CAMACHO (GB) - SHAMAYEL (GB)	RABBAH BS	75000
B C ACCLAMATION (GB) - THAKERAH (IRE)	BBA (IRELAND)	75000
ALLIGATE (GB) GR C ARCHIPENKO (USA) - ALBANOVA (GB)	F ZWICKY	75000
B C GLENEAGLES (IRE) - DEFROST MY HEART (IRE)	JOHNSTON RACING	75000
B C CHARM SPIRIT (IRE) - BIJOU A MOI (GB)	MCKEEVER BS	72000
B F INVINCIBLE SPIRIT (IRE) - FAVONIAN (GB)	FORM BS	72000
B C AUSTRALIA (GB) - DANEHILL MUSIC (IRE)	J O'BRIEN	72000
MISS DIAMOND (IRE) CH F NO NAY NEVER (USA) - TWINKLING ICE (USA)	R HUGHES	72000
B F NO NAY NEVER (USA) - DANCING ON AIR (IRE)	CHURCH FARM STABLES	70000
GR C KENDARGENT (FR) - MATORIO (FR)	A C ELLIOTT	70000
B C SHOWCASING (GB) - CANADA WATER (GB)	R HUGHES	70000
CH C SEA THE STARS (IRE) - CLEVER ANNIE (IRE)	HUGO MERRY BS	70000
B C FASTNET ROCK (AUS) - DESIRE MOI (IRE)	GERRY HOGAN BS	70000
B C CHARM SPIRIT (IRE) - STERLING SOUND (IRE)	P ANTONACCI	70000
BLUE HERO (CAN) B C AIR FORCE BLUE (USA) - POMARINE (USA)	A C ELLIOTT	70000
DANDY MAESTRO (GB) CH C DANDY MAN (IRE) - MAIDS CAUSEWAY (GB)	B O'RYAN	70000
B C HOLY ROMAN EMPEROR (IRE) - STAR OF STARS (IRE)	VENDOR	68000
B F SHOWCASING (GB) - LADY OF THE HOUSE (IRE)	A O'RYAN	68000
B F KODIAC (GB) - ACCLIMATISATION (IRE)	VENDOR	65000
B C DARK ANGEL (IRE) - SEAFRONT (GB)	VENDOR	65000
B F AWTAAD (IRE) - ANNEE LUMIERE (IRE)	T RAU	65000
B F ZOFFANY (IRE) - KIRINDA (IRE)	BBA (IRELAND)	65000
B C SEA THE STARS (IRE) - LILTING (IRE)	K WALL	65000
B C DARK ANGEL (IRE) - DANSEUSE DE REVE (IRE)	RABBAH BS	65000
B F DECLARATION OF WAR (USA) - MONTJESS (IRE)	MIDDLEHAM PARK RACING	65000
B C KODIAC (GB) - VICTORIA MONTOYA (GB)	D REDVERS	65000
B F EXCELEBRATION (IRE) - HEIGHT OF ELEGANCE (IRE)	P ANTONACCI	65000
GR F DARK ANGEL (IRE) - SANNA BAY (IRE)	PATTERN BS	65000
STROXX CARLRAS (IRE) B/BR C FOOTSTEPSINTHESAND (GB) - SPECIFIC (IRE)	F ZWICKY	65000
B C KINGMAN (GB) - I AM BEAUTIFUL (IRE)	AVENUE BS	65000
B F PRIDE OF DUBAI (AUS) - ROHAIN (IRE)	F STACK	65000
B F CAMELOT (GB) - PENNY POST (IRE)	RABBAH BS	65000
FANCY ANGEL (IRE) GR F DARK ANGEL (IRE) - VOW (GB)	SACKVILLEDONALD	65000
B F CHARMING THOUGHT (GB) - BADMINTON (IRE)	J FOLEY	65000
KODIAC BROWN BEAR (IRE) B C KODIAC (GB) - OLIVE BRANCH (IRE)	SACKVILLEDONALD	65000
SOLENT GATEWAY (IRE) B C AWTAAD (IRE) - AOIFE ALAINN (IRE)	B O'RYAN	65000

HIGH-PRICED YEARLINGS OF 2019 AT GOFFS UK (DONCASTER)

The following yearlings realised £52,000 and over at Goffs UK Sales in 2019:-

Name and Breeding	Purchaser	Pounds
B C KINGMAN (GB) - SHAMANDAR (FR)	M V MAGNIER	440000
LEGION OF HONOUR (GB) B C WOOTTON BASSETT (GB) - MISS VENDOME (IRE)	R RYAN	280000
B C MEHMAS (IRE) - ENTREAT (GB)	O ST LAWRENCE	260000
B F SIYOUNI (FR) - ANNELI (IRE)	C GORDON-WATSON BS	250000
B C ADAAY (IRE) - PLACE IN MY HEART (GB)	SHADWELL STUD (P.S.)	210000
RAADOBARG (IRE) B C NIGHT OF THUNDER (IRE) - QUEEN BODICEA (IRE)	A C ELLIOTT	200000
B F SIYOUNI (FR) - ARISTOTELICIENNE (IRE)	SHADWELL STUD	200000
B C CABLE BAY (IRE) - BONHOMIE (GB)	SHADWELL STUD	175000
B G DANDY MAN (IRE) - DREAM DATE (IRE)	HONG KONG JOCKEY CLUB	170000
B C MAXIOS (GB) - TASSINA (GER)	SHADWELL STUD	170000
B F MUHAARAR (GB) - FIG ROLL (GB)	LONGWAYS STABLES	170000
B F MEHMAS (IRE) - THREE DECADES (IRE)	ANOJ DON	150000
B C SHOWCASING (GB) - BLUE AEGEAN (GB)	J FOLEY	150000
B C IFFRAAJ (GB) - RISKIT FORA BISKIT (IRE)	SHADWELL STUD	150000
BR C DARK ANGEL (IRE) - RELATION ALEXANDER (IRE)	SHADWELL STUD	145000
B F NO NAY NEVER (USA) - DESERT SKY (IRE)	S QUINN	140000
B G FASTNET ROCK (AUS) - PRETTY PAPER (IRE)	HONG KONG JOCKEY CLUB	140000
B F SIYOUNI (FR) - LADY VIOLA (GB)	CHURCH FARM	140000
B C MUHAARAR (GB) - MELBOURNE MEMORIES (GB)	SHADWELL STUD	130000
B C SHALAA (IRE) - PRESENT DANGER (IRE)	AL SHAQAB RACING	130000
B C DARK ANGEL (IRE) - STACEYMAC (IRE)	SHADWELL STUD	125000
B C KINGMAN (GB) - ASAAWIR (GB)	MC BS	120000
B C ADAAY (IRE) - FLEMISH SCHOOL (GB)	SHADWELL STUD	115000
B C ACCLAMATION (GB) - MEDICEAN QUEEN (IRE)	SHADWELL STUD	110000
B C ESTIDHKAAR (IRE) - SKELETON (IRE)	SHADWELL STUD	110000
HEY MR (GB) B C TERRITORIES (IRE) - FILONA (IRE)	A C ELLIOTT	110000
B C TORONADO (IRE) - GREGORIA (IRE)	GAELIC BS	105000
B F CABLE BAY (IRE) - ANGELS WINGS (IRE)	SHADWELL STUD	105000
KUZNETSOVA (GB) B F SHALAA (IRE) - VESNINA (GB)	CHEVELEY PARK STUD	105000
B F EXCEED AND EXCEL (AUS) - DISPEL (IRE)	SHADWELL STUD	100000
CH C FOOTSTEPSINTHESAND (GB) - ONDEAFEARS (IRE)	B O'RYAN	100000
B C TWILIGHT SON (GB) - ROYAL FFANCI (GB)	VENDOR	100000
B F LE HAVRE (IRE) - DESERT RED (IRE)	SHADWELL	100000
B C FOOTSTEPSINTHESAND (GB) - BEAL BAN (IRE)	PETER & ROSS DOYLE BS	100000
B C ACCLAMATION (GB) - SLIABH LUACHRA (IRE)	SHADWELL STUD	100000
B F ADAAY (IRE) - SATSUMA (GB)	CLIVE COX RACING	100000
B C ACCLAMATION (GB) - MIDNIGHT OASIS (GB)	PETER & ROSS DOYLE BS	95000
SARDINIA SUNSET (IRE) GR F GUTAIFAN (IRE) - RUSH (GB)	A C ELLIOTT	95000
CH C EQUIANO (FR) - BEDOUIN DANCER (IRE)	PETER & ROSS DOYLE BS	92000
B C TERRITORIES (IRE) - BALANCE (GB)	J B BS	90000
B F KODI BEAR (IRE) - MIDNIGHT MARTINI (GB)	CLIVE COX RACING	90000
CH F CHARMING THOUGHT (GB) - MARY READ (GB)	J FOLEY	90000
INNSE GALL (GB) B C TORONADO (IRE) - REAF (GB)	I JARDINE	90000
B F CABLE BAY (IRE) - SHINE (GB)	PETER & ROSS DOYLE BS	85000
VEDUTE (IRE) B C HOLY ROMAN EMPEROR (IRE) - QUADS (IRE)	RICHARD FRISBY BS	85000
CH C PIVOTAL (GB) - SUGAR MILL (GB)	K BURKE	85000
B C ZOFFANY (IRE) - NIDHAAL (IRE)	A O'RYAN	85000
TRIBUTE TO JADE (GB) B F ACCLAMATION (GB) - MAGIC FLORENCE (IRE)	PETER & ROSS DOYLE BS	82000
B C MEHMAS (IRE) - RIPALONG (IRE)	PETER & ROSS DOYLE BS	82000
GR F DARK ANGEL (IRE) - SILK BOW (GB)	B O'RYAN	82000
B C SHALAA (IRE) - WANTING (IRE)	STROUD COLEMAN BS	82000
B F SIYOUNI (FR) - RAYLASA (IRE)	B O'RYAN	80000
CH C DUTCH ART (GB) - IMPASSIONED (GB)	A O'RYAN	80000
BABAJAN (IRE) B C ACCLAMATION (GB) - ALERTED (USA)	PETER & ROSS DOYLE BS	80000
B C TERRITORIES (IRE) - FOLLY BRIDGE (GB)	GAELIC BS	80000
B C KODIAC (GB) - SOUND ASLEEP (USA)	WEST PARK FARM	80000
CH C TERRITORIES (IRE) - DANCING YEARS (IRE)	GAELIC BS	80000
B F KODIAC (GB) - BOBBY JANE (GB)	SHEIKH A AL-SABAH	80000
B C ZOFFANY (IRE) - AURORA SPRING (IRE)	OLIVIA JOHNSTON BS	80000
B/GR C GLENEAGLES (IRE) - SILVER CLOUDS (IRE)	SAM SANGSTER BS	78000
B C DUE DILIGENCE (USA) - RIVER SONG (USA)	B O'RYAN	75000
B F TWILIGHT SON (GB) - MIDNIGHT HUSH (FR)	R FAHEY	75000
B C KODI BEAR (IRE) - FANCY VIVID (IRE)	HILLEN/RYAN	75000
B C NO NAY NEVER (USA) - SAPPHIRE DIVA (IRE)	VENDOR	75000
CH C NIGHT OF THUNDER (IRE) - THURAYAAT (GB)	BROWN ISLAND	72000
B C ACCLAMATION (GB) - XEMA (IRE)	PETER & ROSS DOYLE BS	72000
B F FASTNET ROCK (AUS) - SHALEELA (IRE)	J O'BRIEN	70000
B C ADAAY (IRE) - LEONICA (GB)	VENDOR	70000

Name and Breeding	Purchaser	Guineas
B C DARK ANGEL (IRE) - AINTISARI (IRE)	VENDOR	70000
B C ACCLAMATION (GB) - SHY AUDIENCE (IRE)	B O'RYAN	70000
B/BR C TERRITORIES (IRE) - VIRGINIA HALL (GB)	TOWN MOOR RACING	70000
B F KINGMAN (GB) - KAMBURA (FR)	LONGWAYS STABLES	70000
B C DARK ANGEL (IRE) - ATLANTIC DRIFT (GB)	MAYFIELD	70000
B F STARSPANGLEDBANNER (AUS) - PRECARIOUSLY GOOD (GB)	C MCCORMACK	70000
THE FIRST HURRAH (FR) B F MUHAARAR (GB) - SWEET CECILY (IRE)	JILL LAMB BS	70000
B F OASIS DREAM (GB) - ZAMOURA (IRE)	ALLIANCE BS	70000
REBEL AT DAWN (IRE) B C DANDY MAN (IRE) - RAGTIME DANCER (GB)	K BURKE	68000
RHODA'S CHOICE (FR) B F SHALAA (IRE) - AL MAS (FR)	BADGERS BS	68000
B C PRIDE OF DUBAI (AUS) - GOLDEN SHINE (GB)	CLIVE COX RACING	68000
B C SHALAA (IRE) - GAAZAAL (IRE)	POWERSTOWN STUD	67000
B F FRANKEL (GB) - AINIPPE (IRE)	LONGWAYS STABLES	65000
B F NO NAY NEVER (USA) - PURE VANITY (GB)	GROVE STUD	65000
BOOGIE TIME (IRE) B C KODIAC (GB) - GET UP AND DANCE (GB)	K BURKE	65000
ANDALASKA BEAR (IRE) B F KODIAC (GB) - WELL FOCUSED (IRE)	R O'RYAN	65000
B C MEHMAS (IRE) - TRIGGERS BROOM (IRE)	CLIVE COX RACING	65000
B C SHALAA (IRE) - BLACK RODDED (GB)	D FARRINGTON	65000
B F WOOTTON BASSETT (GB) - BAHAMA SPIRIT (IRE)	GAELIC BS	65000
B C DUE DILIGENCE (USA) - FLIGHTY CLARETS (IRE)	A C ELLIOTT	65000
B C BOBBY'S KITTEN (USA) - MULLEIN (GB)	SHADWELL STUD	65000
B C ELZAAM (AUS) - INSTANT MEMORIES (GB)	B O'RYAN	62000
B C KODIAC (GB) - ELEKTRA MARINO (GB)	R HUGHES	62000
SOLENT GATEWAY (IRE) B C AWTAAD (IRE) - AOIFE ALAINN (IRE)	SACKVILLEDONALD	62000
B C TWILIGHT SON (GB) - ROSLEA LADY (IRE)	PETER & ROSS DOYLE BS	62000
B F FLINTSHIRE (GB) - SPINAMISS (IRE)	J O'KEEFFE	60000
B C BATED BREATH (GB) - HELIOGRAPH (GB)	CLIVE COX RACING	60000
B F SHOWCASING (GB) - STARBOTTON (GB)	A O'RYAN	60000
B C BURATINO (IRE) - OPPORTUNA (GB)	A DUARTE	60000
B C NEW BAY (GB) - SISTER DAM'S (IRE)	O ST LAWRENCE	60000
B F BRAZEN BEAU (AUS) - MOONLIGHT MYSTERY (GB)	O ST LAWRENCE	60000
BR C MEHMAS (IRE) - FADDWA (IRE)	SACKVILLEDONALD	60000
B F KODIAC (GB) - SUTTON VENY (IRE)	GAELIC BS	60000
CH F NO NAY NEVER (USA) - SHARAARAH (IRE)	F ZWICKY	60000
B F KODIAC (GB) - PILATES (IRE)	D FARRINGTON	60000
B C ZOFFANY (IRE) - GALE SONG (GB)	SAM SANGSTER BS	60000
B C NO NAY NEVER (USA) - STARLIGHT PRINCESS (IRE)	J OSBOURNE (P.S.)	60000
B C FOOTSTEPSINTHESAND (IRE) - JUNO MONETA (IRE)	J B BS	60000
B C HOLY ROMAN EMPEROR (IRE) - DIVISME (USA)	C MCCORMACK	60000
B C DANDY MAN (IRE) - AZHAR (GB)	CHURCH FARM	58000
B C BATED BREATH (GB) - CRITICAL PATH (IRE)	SACKVILLEDONALD	58000
ASTRONOMIC CHOICE (GB) B C HAVANA GOLD (IRE) - ADORABLE CHOICE (IRE)	HILLEN/RYAN	58000
B C KAYF TARA (GB) - SUPREME PRESENT (IRE)	BRENDAN BASHFORD BS	58000
ANGEL AMADEA (GB) GR F DARK ANGEL (IRE) - KEENE DANCER (GB)	JILL LAMB BS	55000
ARTORIOUS (IRE) CH C NEW BAY (GB) - SUDU QUEEN (GER)	SACKVILLEDONALD	55000
B C TWILIGHT SON (GB) - GUANA (IRE)	B ROGERS	55000
B C FAST COMPANY (IRE) - SHAMA'S SONG (IRE)	B O'RYAN	55000
B C DARK ANGEL (IRE) - PRICELESS JEWEL (GB)	M JOHNSTON	55000
B C CLODOVIL (IRE) - FANTASTIC ACCOUNT (GB)	CRAMPSCASTLE BS	55000
CH F PEARL SECRET (GB) - SPEED PRINCESS (IRE)	H CANDY	55000
B F KODIAC (GB) - ZALLERINA (GB)	BADGERS BS	52000
CH C BATED BREATH (GB) - BOUVARDIA (GB)	A O'RYAN	52000
B C FASCINATING ROCK (IRE) - WHY NOW (GB)	JASON KELLY BS	52000
B F NO NAY NEVER (USA) - TWO PASS (GB)	LONGWAYS STABLES	52000
B F IFFRAAJ (GB) - HABITA (IRE)	EBONOS	52000
B C KODI BEAR (IRE) - NOTTE ILLUMINATA (IRE)	HILLEN/RYAN	52000
ARTHUR CONAN DOYLE (GB) B C OASIS DREAM (GB) - SECRET KEEPER (GB)	HOWSON & HOULDSWORTH BS	52000
B F ACCLAMATION (GB) - CAELICA (IRE)	B ROGERS	52000
CH C NO NAY NEVER (USA) - ECHO CHARLIE (GER)	SAM SANGSTER BS	52000
B C DARK ANGEL (IRE) - MASAYA (GB)	R RYAN	52000
HOST (IRE) B C MEHMAS (IRE) - MISTRESS MAKFI (IRE)	J & J WARREN	52000
B C CHARM SPIRIT (IRE) - STYBBA (GB)	M O'TOOLE	52000
B C GARSWOOD (GB) - ROSEBRIDE (GB)	K BURKE	52000

HIGH-PRICED YEARLINGS OF 2019 AT TATTERSALLS IRELAND SALES

The following yearlings realised 30,000 euros and over at Tattersalls Ireland Sales in 2019:-

Name and Breeding	Purchaser	Euros
B G NO NAY NEVER (USA) - RIO'S PEARL (GB)	HONG KONG JOCKEY CLUB	165000
B G HOLY ROMAN EMPEROR (IRE) - APE ATTACK (GB)	HONG KONG JOCKEY CLUB	100000
B F HARZAND (IRE) - MEAN LAE (IRE)	VENDOR	100000
ECRIN VERT (FR) B G DOCTOR DINO (FR) - LADIES WISH (FR)	OAK TREE FARM	100000
DRINKING STORM (IRE) B C EXCEED AND EXCEL (AUS) - FALCON'S SONG (USA)	BBA IRELAND	95000
GR C DARK ANGEL (IRE) - DUCHESS ANDORRA (IRE)	SACKVILLEDONALD	90000
B/GR F EXCEED AND EXCEL (AUS) - FIRST PARTY (IRE)	MC BS	90000
BR C FOOTSTEPSINTHESAND (GB) - MAJRAA (FR)	PETER & ROSS DOYLE BS	90000
B C ACCLAMATION (GB) - CLICK AND ROLL (USA)	BBA IRELAND	80000
B F SEA THE STARS (IRE) - HOLY SPRING (IRE)	EOGHAN T O'NEILL	70000
CH F STARSPANGLEDBANNER (AUS) - BRAZILIAN SAMBA (IRE)	DE BURGH EQUINE	70000
SILKY WARRIOR (IRE) CH F DECLARATION OF WAR (USA) - SILKY (IRE)	JUSTIN CASSE	70000
B F STARSPANGLEDBANNER (AUS) - ZAIN ART (IRE)	DE BURGH EQUINE	67000
B F KODIAC (GB) - KATHOE (IRE)	JOHN MCCONNELL	65000
B C NIGHT OF THUNDER (IRE) - AKUNA MAGIC (IRE)	SAUBOUAS BS	65000
B C SHOWCASING (GB) - DAM BEAUTIFUL (GB)	AVENUE BS / HUGO PALMER	65000
CH C AUSTRALIA (GB) - BECAME (IRE)	AMANDA SKIFFINGTON	65000
MACHO PRIDE (IRE) B C CAMACHO (GB) - PROUD MARIA (IRE)	BOBBY O'RYAN	65000
B C EQUIANO (FR) - LOVE ACTION (IRE)	MIDDLEHAM PARK RACING	62000
B F TERRITORIES (IRE) - DEUX SAISONS (GB)	BLANDFORD BS	62000
B C KAYF TARA (GB) - MOLO (GB)	BUSHERSTOWN	62000
B G SHANTOU (USA) - EVA LA DIVA (IRE)	T HILLMAN	62000
B C ACCLAMATION (GB) - KOMEDY (IRE)	A O'RYAN/R FAHEY	60000
B C LOPE DE VEGA (IRE) - ABBAGNATO (GB)	VENDOR	60000
B G VADAMOS (FR) - DUCHESS OF FOXLAND (IRE)	KEVIN ROSS BS	60000
B C FOOTSTEPSINTHESAND (GB) - BAYAN KASIRGA (IRE)	BBA IRELAND	60000
B C SHANTOU (USA) - NED'S JOY (IRE)	JOEY LOGAN BS	60000
BR C FOOTSTEPSINTHESAND (GB) - DARA'S GIRL (IRE)	VENDOR	58000
B C KODIAC (GB) - ETERNAL VIEW (IRE)	M M STABLES	56000
B F DARK ANGEL (IRE) - AMERICAN SPIRIT (IRE)	SHAMROCK THOROUGHBREDS	55000
B C PRIDE OF DUBAI (AUS) - IN MY LIFE (IRE)	BBA IRELAND	55000
B F KODIAC (GB) - SILCA BOO (GB)	JASON KELLY/CLIFF STUD	55000
B C NO NAY NEVER (USA) - STRANDED (GB)	MIDDLEHAM PARK	55000
B C AWTAAD (IRE) - SHAMTARI (IRE)	BYRON ROGERS/STAR BS	52000
CH C MASTERCRAFTSMAN (IRE) - BAYBERRY (UAE)	AVENUE BS	52000
LADY LEONIE (IRE) B F THE LAST LION (IRE) - HALLOWED PARK (IRE)	BLANDFORD BS	52000
B C DANDY MAN (IRE) - COINCIDENTLY (GB)	OAK TREE FARM	52000
B C KODIAC (GB) - YOUNG DAISY MILLER (IRE)	BBA IRELAND	50000
CH G DANDY MAN (IRE) - CRISTAL FASHION (IRE)	HONG KONG JOCKEY CLUB	50000
B C FAST COMPANY (IRE) - ANAYID (IRE)	JOHN OXX	50000
B F FASCINATING ROCK (IRE) - SO SECRET (IRE)	JOHN BUTLER	50000
GR C DARK ANGEL (IRE) - LADY MARITA (IRE)	BELIAR BS	50000
B C NEW BAY (GB) - LUS NA GREINE (IRE)	C GORDON-WATSON	50000
B F DANDY MAN (IRE) - WARM WELCOME (GB)	PETER & ROSS DOYLE BS	50000
CONTACT (IRE) GR C GUTAIFAN (IRE) - LA TULIPE (FR)	HARROWGATE BS	50000
B C FAMOUS NAME (GB) - SAYING GRACE (IRE)	BOBBY O'RYAN/D K WELD	50000
B F KODI BEAR (IRE) - SEMBLANCE (IRE)	JOHN LAVERY	50000
B C CAMELOT (GB) - MYRICA (GB)	JAMIE OSBORNE	50000
B C FOOTSTEPSINTHESAND (GB) - SWEET SURPRISE (IRE)	PETER & ROSS DOYLE BS	50000
B F THE LAST LION (IRE) - BIARAAFA (IRE)	BBA IRELAND	50000
GR C MASTERCRAFTSMAN (IRE) - FLEUR DE NUIT (IRE)	A C ELLIOTT, AGENT	50000
CH C NEW BAY (GB) - LEVANTO (IRE)	GAELIC BS	50000
CH F NIGHT OF THUNDER (IRE) - DEMESNE (IRE)	CHURCH FARM / HORSE PARK	48000
B C EXCEED AND EXCEL (AUS) - ENFIJAAR (IRE)	HYDE PARK STUD	48000
B C WALK IN THE PARK - STEPHANIE FRANCES (IRE)	JOEY LOGAN BS	48000
B C ACCLAMATION (GB) - THATSALLIMSAYING (IRE)	SACKVILLEDONALD	46000
B C CABLE BAY (IRE) - MADAME BOULANGERE (GB)	JJ QUINN RACING	46000
B F FASTNET ROCK (AUS) - INCITATUS GIRL (IRE)	BBA IRELAND	46000
CH F ZOFFANY (IRE) - BROADWAY DUCHESS (IRE)	PETER & ROSS DOYLE BS	45000
CH F PRIDE OF DUBAI (AUS) - ANNAMANAMOUX (USA)	BRENDAN MURPHY	45000
ROCKETS RED GLARE (IRE) CH C STARSPANGLEDBANNER (AUS) - SPIRIT OF PARIS (IRE)	SACKVILLEDONALD	45000
B C ELZAAM (AUS) - ADAPTATION (GB)	KARL BURKE	45000
B C SHALAA (IRE) - MIRACLE SEEKER (GB)	HOWSON & HOULDSWORTH BS	45000
GORYTUS (IRE) B C FOOTSTEPSINTHESAND (GB) - JULIETA (IRE)	R O'RYAN/R FAHEY	45000
CH C THE GURKHA (IRE) - RAMRUMA (USA)	BMS GROUP	45000
B G KITKOU (FR) - ESTRELA ROSE (FR)	J MERNAGH	45000
B G HARZAND (IRE) - AMOYA (GER)	VENDOR	44000
B C SHANTOU (USA) - ERINS STAGE (IRE)	PARK FARM	44000
CH C EXCEED AND EXCEL (AUS) - DUQUESA (IRE)	BROWN ISLAND STABLES	43000
B F FAST COMPANY (IRE) - FIUISE (IRE)	SHAMROCK THOROUGHBREDS	43000

Name and Breeding	Purchaser	Guineas
BR F DRAGON PULSE (IRE) - NEW MAGIC (IRE)	EDWARD LYNAM	42000
CH C AL KAZEEM (GB) - KID GLOVES (GB)	NASIR ASKAR	42000
B F TWILIGHT SON (GB) - MISS GILER (GB)	JANDA BS	42000
B F MAKE BELIEVE (GB) - PADDY AGAIN (IRE)	JASON KELLY BS	42000
B C NIGHT OF THUNDER (IRE) - DARA'S IMAGE (IRE)	JOE FOLEY	42000
B F KODIAC (GB) - ROYAL SISTER TWO (IRE)	VENDOR	42000
B F FLEMENSFIRTH (USA) - MORNING RUN (IRE)	JT BS	42000
B F NIGHT OF THUNDER (IRE) - QUIANIA (IRE)	HOWSON & HOULDSWORTH BS	42000
B F ADAAY (IRE) - GALAKTEA (IRE)	AMANDA SKIFFINGTON	40000
B C ADAAY (IRE) - TOUCHING (IRE)	LONGWAYS STABLES	40000
B C MAKE BELIEVE (GB) - DELTA DREAMER (GB)	AVENUE BS	40000
BR C NO NAY NEVER (USA) - MOMENT IN THE SUN (GB)	VENDOR	40000
NANTOSUELTA (IRE) B F KODIAC (GB) - DEAREST DAISY (GB)	KUBLER RACING	40000
B C POET'S VOICE (GB) - VANITY'S GIRL (GB)	KARL BURKE	40000
B C ADAAY (IRE) - OLYMPIC MEDAL (GB)	MEADOWVIEW STABLES	40000
B C DOYEN (IRE) - POMME TIEPY (FR)	KNOCKBALLY STABLES	40000
B F CABLE BAY (IRE) - DECORATIVE (IRE)	CLIVE COX RACING	38000
CH F CAMACHO (IRE) - COVER GIRL (IRE)	MAGS O'TOOLE	38000
B C FOOTSTEPSINTHESAND (GB) - HARPIST (IRE)	A C ELLIOTT, AGENT	38000
B C HOLY ROMAN EMPEROR (IRE) - IZOLA (GB)	KERN/LILLINGSTON	38000
B C LAWMAN (FR) - LUMIERE ASTRALE (FR)	FRANCISCA CARTON	38000
B F DARK ANGEL (IRE) - CENTRED (IRE)	NICK BRADLEY RACING	38000
B C DANDY MAN (IRE) - UNION CITY BLUES (IRE)	KINGSFIELD STUD	37000
B F SHALAA (IRE) - SKY COLOURS (IRE)	VENDOR	37000
CH C EXCEED AND EXCEL (AUS) - ROSE O'NEAL (IRE)	POWERSTOWN STUD	37000
B C ESTIDHKAAR (IRE) - FUAIGH MOR (IRE)	BOBBY O'RYAN	37000
FLIRTY RASCAL (GB) B F ACCLAMATION (GB) - ENLIVEN (GB)	STROUD COLEMAN BS	37000
BR C STARSPANGLEDBANNER (AUS) - LUMINANCE (IRE)	BBA IRELAND	36000
CH C MEHMAS (IRE) - TOP DOLLAR (GB)	AIDAN O'RYAN/PHIL MAKIN	36000
B C KODIAC (GB) - ETESIAN FLOW (GB)	SACKVILLEDONALD	36000
B F IVAWOOD (IRE) - SUPERCHARGED (IRE)	JOHN LAVERY	35000
B C FOOTSTEPSINTHESAND (GB) - HADRIENNE (GB)	BLANDFORD BS	35000
CH C NIGHT OF THUNDER (IRE) - PIXIE BELLE (IRE)	FATHI EGZIAMA	35000
CH C CAMACHO (IRE) - BEACH CANDY (IRE)	SEAN QUINN	35000
RAINBOW'S PONY (IRE) B F ACCLAMATION (GB) - MIRROR EFFECT (IRE)	PETER & ROSS DOYLE BS	35000
B C HAVANA GOLD (IRE) - LARA AMELIA (IRE)	SACKVILLEDONALD	35000
B F NIGHT OF THUNDER (IRE) - THINK (FR)	MARK GRANT	35000
B C OL' MAN RIVER (IRE) - CARTHANOORA (IRE)	AIDEN MURPHY	35000
ALABAMA BOY (IRE) B C AWTAAD (IRE) - GABARDINE (GB)	SACKVILLEDONALD	35000
B/BR C MEHMAS (IRE) - LADY MEGA (IRE)	JS BS	35000
B C MOUNT NELSON (GB) - GALANT FERNS (GB)	KEVIN ROSS BS	34000
B C WALK IN THE PARK (IRE) - MYZTIQUE (IRE)	MOANMORE STABLES	34000
B C FREE EAGLE (IRE) - KAIULANI (IRE)	GAELIC BS	34000
CH C SHANTOU (USA) - SHEDAN (IRE)	RICHARD ROHAN	34000
B C EQUIANO (FR) - MIRDHAK (GB)	FREDDY TYLICKI	33000
B C WALK IN THE PARK (IRE) - PIPE LADY (IRE)	BALLYGRIFFIN	32000
B F CABLE BAY (IRE) - AMBER QUEEN (IRE)	JOHNNY MURTAGH	32000
CH F ZOFFANY (IRE) - AJA (IRE)	JAMIE OSBORNE	32000
B C MAYSON (GB) - DESCRIPTIVE (IRE)	BLANDFORD BS	32000
B C TAMAYUZ (GB) - BODY BEAUTIFUL (IRE)	KEVIN ROSS BS	32000
B C CABLE BAY (IRE) - POSITIVE SPIN (GB)	BBA IRELAND	32000
B C MILAN (GB) - BLUEBERRY BRAMBLE (IRE)	MATT O'CONNOR BS	32000
B F OLYMPIC GLORY (IRE) - ORNELIA RUEE (FR)	AVENUE BS / HUGO PALMER	31000
B C ACCLAMATION (GB) - MYTURN (IRE)	CHURCH FARM	30000
B C MAYSON (GB) - MADAME VESTRIS (IRE)	A C ELLIOTT, AGENT	30000
BR C MAYSON (GB) - MARIGOT BAY (GB)	JAMIE B BS	30000
B F FREE EAGLE (IRE) - RISING WIND (IRE)	BOBBY O'RYAN/D K WELD	30000
SAVASTANO (FR) B C MARTALINE (GB) - FRIVOLITE (FR)	JASON HIGGINS	30000
CH C BURATINO (IRE) - ZELIE MARTIN (IRE)	NIGEL TINKLER BS	30000
B C PRIDE OF DUBAI (AUS) - TEMPURA (GER)	BROWN ISLAND STABLES	30000
B F ACCLAMATION (GB) - FAVOURABLE TERMS (GB)	GREENHILLS FARM	30000
B C FAST COMPANY (IRE) - DANCE BID (GB)	KEVIN ROSS BS	30000
B F MARKAZ (IRE) - GOLDTHROAT (IRE)	BALINAROONE STUD	30000
B C SHOWCASING (GB) - ALPINE STORM (IRE)	CON MARNANE	30000
B C MASKED MARVEL (GB) - SOURCE LIMPIDE (FR)	VENDOR	30000
B C MUHAARAR (GB) - DEMERGER (USA)	CON MARNANE	30000
B C FREE EAGLE (IRE) - SILIRISA (IRE)	GORDON-WATSON/FELLOWES	30000
B F MASTERCRAFTSMAN (IRE) - BLACKWITCH WOMAN (IRE)	VENDOR	30000
GR/RO C KENDARGENT (FR) - DIVINE TOUCH (GB)	ANDREW BALDING	30000
B C STRATH BURN (GB) - RED FANFARE (GB)	VENDOR	30000
B C DANDY MAN (IRE) - NUTSHELL (GB)	POSSUM BS	30000
B C CHAMPS ELYSEES (GB) - KATIE T (IRE)	VENDOR	30000

2000 GUINEAS STAKES (3y) Newmarket–1 mile

Year	Owner	Winner and Price	Jockey	Trainer	Second	Third	Ran	Time
1982	G Oldham's	**ZINO** (8/1)	F Head	F Boutin	Wind and Wuthering	Tender King	26	1 37.13
1983	R Sangster's	**LOMOND** (9/1)	Pat Eddery	V O'Brien	Tolomeo	Muscatite	16	1 43.87
1984	R Sangster's	**EL GRAN SENOR** (15/8)	Pat Eddery	V O'Brien	Chief Singer	Lear Fan	14	1 37.41
1985	Maktoum Al Maktoum's	**SHADEED** (4/5)	L Piggott	M Stoute	Bairn	Supreme Leader	14	1 37.41
1986	K Abdullah's	**DANCING BRAVE** (15/8)	G Starkey	G Harwood	Green Desert	Huntingdale	15	1 40.00
1987	J Horgan's	**DON'T FORGET ME** (9/1)	W Carson	R Hannon	Bellotto	Midyan	13	1 36.74
1988	H H Aga Khan's	**DOYOUN** (4/5)	W R Swinburn	M Stoute	Charmer	Bellefella	14	1 41.73
1989	Hamdan Al-Maktoum's	**NASHWAN** (3/1)	W Carson	R Hern	Exbourne	Danehill	14	1 36.44
1990	John Horgan's	**TIROL** (9/1)	M Kinane	R Hannon	Machiavellian	Anshan	14	1 35.84
1991	Lady Beaverbrook's	**MYSTIKO** (13/2)	M Roberts	C Brittain	Lycius	Ganges	16	1 37.83
1992	R Sangster's	**RODRIGO DE TRIANO** (6/1)	L Piggott	P Chapple-Hyam	Lucky Lindy	Pursuit of Love	14	1 38.37
1993	K Abdullah's	**ZAFONIC** (5/6)	Pat Eddery	A Fabre	Barathea	Bin Alwaad	23	1 35.32
1994	G R Bailey Ltd's	**MISTER BAILEYS** (16/1)	J Weaver	M Johnston	Grand Lodge	Colonel Collins	11	1 35.08
1995	Sheikh Mohammed's	**PENNEKAMP** (9/2)	T Jarnet	A Fabre	Celtic Swing	Bahri	13	1 35.16
1996	Godolphin's	**MARK OF ESTEEM** (8/1)	L Dettori	S bin Suroor	Even Top	Bijou D'Inde	16	1 37.59
1997	M Tabor & Mrs J Magnier's	**ENTREPRENEUR** (7/2)	M Kinane	M Stoute	Revoque	Poteen	17	1 35.64
1998	M Tabor & Mrs J Magnier's	**KING OF KINGS** (7/2)	M Kinane	A O'Brien	Lend A Hand	Border Arrow	18	1 35.25
1999	M Tabor & Mrs J Magnier's	**ISLAND SANDS** (10/1)	L Dettori	S bin Suroor	Enrique	Mujahid	16	1 37.14
		(Run on July Course)						
2000	Saeed Suhail's	**KING'S BEST** (13/2)	K Fallon	Sir M Stoute	Giant's Causeway	Barathea Guest	27	1 37.77
2001	Lord Weinstock's	**GOLAN** (11/1)	K Fallon	Sir M Stoute	Tamburlaine	Frenchmans Bay	18	1 37.48
2002	Sir A Ferguson & Mrs J Magnier's	**ROCK OF GIBRALTAR** (9/1)	J Murtagh	A O'Brien	Hawk Wing	Redback	22	1 36.50
2003	Moyglare Stud Farm's	**REFUSE TO BEND** (9/2)	P J Smullen	D Weld	Zafeen	Norse Dancer	20	1 36.40
2004	Hamdan Al Maktoum's	**HAAFHD** (11/2)	R Hills	B Hills	Snow Ridge	Azamour	14	1 37.98
2005	M M Tabor & Mrs John Magnier's	**FOOTSTEPSINTHESAND** (13/2)	K Fallon	A O'Brien	Rebel Rebel	Kandidate	19	1 36.60
2006	Mrs J Magnier, Mr M Tabor & Mr D Smith's	**GEORGE WASHINGTON** (6/4)	K Fallon	A O'Brien	Sir Percy	Olympian Odyssey	14	1 36.10
2007	P Cunningham's	**COCKNEY REBEL** (25/1)	O Peslier	G Huffer	Vital Equine	Dutch Art	24	1 36.80
2008	Mrs J. Magnier's	**HENRYTHENAVIGATOR** (11/1)	J Murtagh	A O'Brien	New Approach	Stubbs Art	15	1 35.28
2009	C Tsui's	**SEA THE STARS** (8/1)	M Kinane	J Oxx	Delegator	Gan Amhras	15	1 39.14
2010	M Offenstadt's	**MAKFI** (33/1)	C Lemaire	M Delzangles	Dick Turpin	Canford Cliffs	19	1 35.88
2011	K Abdullah's	**FRANKEL** (1/2)	T Queally	H Cecil	Dubawi Gold	Native Khan	13	1 36.35
2012	D Smith, Mrs J Magnier & M Tabor's	**CAMELOT** (15/8)	J O'Brien	A O'Brien	French Fifteen	Hermival	18	1 42.46
2013	Godolphin's	**DAWN APPROACH** (11/8)	K Manning	J Bolger	Glory Awaits	Van Der Neer	13	1 35.84
2014	Saeed Manara's	**NIGHT OF THUNDER** (40/1)	K Fallon	R Hannon Jnr	Kingman	Australia	14	1 36.61
2015	M Tabor, D Smith & Mrs J Magnier's	**GLENEAGLES** (4/1)	R Moore	A O'Brien	Territories	Ivawood	18	1 37.55
2016	Al Shaqab Racing's	**GALILEO GOLD** (14/1)	L Dettori	H Palmer	Massaat	Ribchester	13	1 35.91
2017	M Tabor, D Smith & Mrs J Magnier's	**CHURCHILL** (6/4)	R Moore	A O'Brien	Barney Roy	Al Wukair	10	1 36.61
2018	D Smith, Mrs J Magnier & M Tabor's	**SAXON WARRIOR** (3/1)	D O'Brien	A O'Brien	Tip Two Win	Masar	14	1 36.55
2019	D Smith/Mrs J Magnier/M Tabor/ Flaxman Stables's	**MAGNA GRECIA** (11/2)	D O'Brien	A O'Brien	King of Change	Skardu	19	1 36.84
						(Run on July Course)		

1000 GUINEAS STAKES (3y fillies) Newmarket-1 mile

Year	Owner	Winner and Price	Jockey	Trainer	Second	Third	Ran	Time
1982	Sir P Oppenheimer's	ON THE HOUSE (33/1)	J Reid	H Wragg	Time Charter	Dione	15	1 40.45
1983	Maktoum Al-Maktoum's	MA BICHE (5/2)	F Head	Mme F Head	Favoridge	Habibti	18	1 41.71
1984	M Lemos's	PEBBLES (8/1)	P Robinson	C Brittain	Meis El-Reem	Desirable	15	1 38.18
1985	Sheikh Mohammed's	OH SO SHARP (2/1)	S Cauthen	H Cecil	Al Bahathri	Bella Colora	15	1 36.85
1986	H Ranier's	MIDWAY LADY (10/1)	R Cochrane	B Hanbury	Maysoon	Sonic Lady	14	1 41.54
1987	S Niarchos's	MIESQUE (15/8)	F Head	F Boutin	Milligram	Interval	14	1 38.48
1988	Ecurie Aland's	RAVINELLA (4/5)	G W Moore	Mme C Head	Dabaweyaa	Diminuendo	12	1 42.09
1989	Sheikh Mohammed's	MUSICAL BLISS (7/2)	W R Swinburn	M Stoute	Kerrera	Aldbourne	67	1 38.06
1990	Hamdan Al-Maktoum's	SALSABIL (6/4)	W Carson	J Dunlop	Heart of Joy	Negligent	10	1 38.06
1991	Hamdan Al-Maktoum's	SHADAYID (4/6)	W Carson	J Dunlop	Kooyonga	Crystal Gazing	16	1 39.45
1992	Maktoum Al-Maktoum's	HATOOF (7/1)	W R Swinburn	C Brittain	Marling	Kenbu	18	1 38.17
1993	Mohamed Obaida's	SAYYEDATI (4/1)	W R Swinburn	C Brittain	Niche	Aljan	15	1 39.34
1994	R Sangster's	LAS MENINAS (12/1)	J Reid	T Stack	Balanchine	Coup de Genie	15	1 36.71
1995	Hamdan Al-Maktoum's	HARAYIR (5/1)	R Hills	Major W R Hern	Aqaarid	Moonshell	14	1 38.72
1996	Wafic Said's	BOSRA SHAM (10/11)	Pat Eddery	H Cecil	Matiya	Dazzle	15	1 37.75
1997	Greenlay Stables Ltd's	SLEEPYTIME (5/1)	K Fallon	H Cecil	Oh Nellie	Dazzle	15	1 37.66
1998	Godolphin's	CAPE VERDI (100/30)	L Dettori	S Bin Suroor	Shahtoush	Exclusive	16	1 37.86
1999	K Abdullah's	WINCE (4/1)	K Fallon	H Cecil	Wannabe Grand	Valentine Waltz	22	1 37.91
		(Run on July Course)						
2000	Hamdan Al-Maktoum's	LAHAN (14/1)	R Hills	J Gosden	Princess Ellen	Petrushka	18	1 36.38
2001	Sheikh Ahmed Al Maktoum's	AMERAT (11/1)	R Robinson	S Jarvis	Muwakleh	Toroca	15	1 38.36
2002	Godolphin's	KAZZIA (11/1)	L Dettori	S Bin Suroor	Snowfire	Alasha	17	1 37.85
2003	Cheveley Park Stud's	RUSSIAN RHYTHM (12/1)	K Fallon	Sir M Stoute	Six Perfections	Intercontinental	19	1 38.43
2004	Duke of Roxburghe's	ATTRACTION (11/2)	K Darley	M Johnston	Sundrop	Hatha	16	1 36.70
2005	Mrs John Magnier & M M Tabor's	VIRGINIA WATERS (12/1)	K Fallon	A O'Brien	Maids Causeway	Vista Bella	20	1 36.50
2006	M Sly, Dr Davies & Mrs P Sly's	SPECIOSA (10/1)	M Fenton	Mrs P Sly	Confidential Lady	Nasheej	13	1 40.50
2007	M Ryan's	FINSCEAL BEO (5/4)	K Manning	P Bolger	Arch Swing	Simply Perfect	21	1 34.94
2008	S Fitborg's	NATAGORA (20/4)	K Lemaire	P Bary	Spacious	Sense Abu	15	1 38.99
2009	Hamdan Al-Maktoum's	GHANAATI (20/1)	R Hills	B Hills	Cuis Ghaire	Super Sleuth	14	1 34.22
	K Abdullah's	SPECIAL DUTY (9/2)	S Pasquier	Mme C Head-Maarek	Jacqueline Quest	Gile Na Greine	17	1 39.66
		(The first two placings were reversed by the Stewards)						
2011	Godolphin's	BLUE BUNTING (16/1)	L Dettori	M Al Zarooni	Together	Maqaasid	18	1 39.27
2012	Mrs John Magnier, M Tabor &	HOMECOMING QUEEN (25/1)	R Moore	A O'Brien	Starscope	Maybe	17	1 40.45
2013	B Keswick's	SKY LANTERN (9/1)	R Hughes	R Hannon	Just The Judge	Moth	15	1 36.38
2014	Ballymore Thoroughbred Ltd's	MISS FRANCE (7/1)	M Guyon	A Fabre	Lightning Thunder	Ihtimal	17	1 37.40
2015	M Tabor, D Smith & Mrs J Magnier's	LEGATISSIMO (13/2)	R Moore	D Wachman	Lucida	Tiggy Wiggy	13	1 34.60
2016	D Smith, Mrs J Magnier & M Tabor's	MINDING (11/10)	R Moore	A O'Brien	Ballydoyle	Alice Springs	16	1 36.53
2017	Mrs John Magnier, M Tabor & D Smith's	WINTER (9/1)	W Lordan	A O'Brien	Rhododendron	Daban	14	1 35.66
2018	Pall Mall Partners & D Smith's	BILLESDON BROOK (66/1)	S Levey	R Hannon	Laurens	Happily	15	1 36.62
2019	M Tabor, D Smith & Mrs John Magnier's Partners	HERMOSA (14/1)	W Lordan	A O'Brien	Lady Kaya	Qabala	15	1 36.89

OAKS STAKES (3y fillies) Epsom-1 mile 4 furlongs 6 yards

Year	Owner	Winner and Price	Jockey	Trainer	Second	Third	Ran	Time
1981	Mrs B Firestone's	BLUE WIND (3/1)	L Piggott	D Weld	Madam Gay	Leap Lively	12	2 40.93
1982	R Barnett's	TIME CHARTER (12/1)	W Newnes	H Candy	Slightly Dangerous	Last Feather	13	2 34.21
1983	Sir M Sobell's	SUN PRINCESS (6/1)	W Carson	R Hern	Acclimatise	New Coins	15	2 40.98
1984	Sir R McAlpine's	CIRCUS PLUME (4/1)	L Piggott	J Dunlop	Media Luna	Poquito Queen	15	2 38.97
1985	Sheikh Mohammed's	OH SO SHARP (6/4)	S Cauthen	H Cecil	Triptych	Dubian	12	2 41.37
1986	H Ranier's	MIDWAY LADY (15/8)	R Cochrane	M Stoute	Untold	Maysoon	15	2 35.60
1987	Sheikh Mohammed's	UNITE (11/1)	W R Swinburn	M Stoute	Bourbon Girl	Three Tails	11	2 38.17
1988	Sheikh Mohammed's	DIMINUENDO (7/4)	S Cauthen	H Cecil	Sudden Love	Animatrice	11	2 35.02
1989	Saeed Maktoum Al Maktoum's	SNOW BRIDE (13/2)	S Cauthen	H Cecil	Roseate Tern	Mamaluna	9	2 34.22

(Alyssa finished first but was subsequently disqualified)

Year	Owner	Winner and Price	Jockey	Trainer	Second	Third	Ran	Time
1990	Hamdan Al-Maktoum's	SALSABIL (2/1)	W Carson	J Dunlop	Game Plan	Knight's Baroness	8	2 38.70
1991	Maktoum Al-Maktoum's	JET SKI LADY (50/1)	C Roche	J Bolger	Shamshir	Shadayid	9	2 37.30
1992	W J Gredley's	USER FRIENDLY (5/1)	G Duffield	C Brittain	All At Sea	Pearl Angel	7	2 39.77
1993	Sheikh Mohammed's	INTREPIDITY (5/1)	M Roberts	A Fabre	Royal Ballerina	Oakmead	14	2 34.19
1994	Godolphin's	BALANCHINE (6/1)	L Dettori	H Ibrahim	Wind In Her Hair	Hawajiss	10	2 40.37
1995	Maktoum Al Maktoum/Godolphin's	MOONSHELL (3/1)	L Dettori	S Bin Suroor	Dance A Dream	Pure Grain	10	2 35.44
1996	Wafic Said's	LADY CARLA (100/30)	Pat Eddery	H Cecil	Pricket	Mezzogiorno	11	2 35.55
1997	K Abdullah's	REAMS OF VERSE (5/6)	K Fallon	H Cecil	Gazelle Royale	Crown of Light	12	2 35.59
1998	Mrs D Nagle & Mrs J Magnier's	SHAHTOUSH (12/1)	M Kinane	A O'Brien	Noushkey	Midnight Line	8	2 38.23
1999	F Salman's	RAMRUMA (9/4)	K Fallon	H Cecil	Kalypso Katie	Zahrat Dubai	10	2 38.72
2000	Lordship Stud's	LOVE DIVINE (9/4)	T Quinn	H Cecil	Flight Of Fancy	Melikah	16	2 43.11
2001	Mrs D Nagle & Mrs J Magnier's	IMAGINE (100/30)	M Kinane	A O'Brien	Quarter Moon	Relish The Thought	14	2 36.70
2002	Godolphin's	KAZZIA (100/30)	L Dettori	S Bin Suroor	Yesterday	Shadow Dancing	14	2 44.52
2003	W S Farish III's	CASUAL LOOK (10/1)	M Dwyer	H Cecil	All Too Beautiful	Summitville	15	2 38.02
2004	Lord Derby's	OUIJA BOARD (7/2)	K Fallon	E Dunlop	Something Exciting	Punctilious	7	2 35.40
2005	Mrs J Magnier, Mr M M Tabor & Mr D Smith's	ESWARAH (11/4)	R Hills	M Jarvis	Rising Cross	Pictavia	12	2 35.90
2006	Mr D Smith's	ALEXANDROVA (9/4)	K Fallon	A O'Brien		Short Skirt	10	2 37.70
2007	Narndos Family's	LIGHT SHIFT (13/2)	T Durcan	H Cecil	Peeping Fawn	All My Loving	14	2 40.38
2008	J H Richmond-Watson's	LOOK HERE (33/1)	S Sanders	R Beckett	Moonstone	Katiyra	16	2 36.89
2009	Lady Bamford's	SARISKA (9/4)	J Spencer	M Bell	Midday	High Heeled	10	2 35.28
2010	Anamoine Ltd's	SNOW FAIRY (9/1)	R Moore	E Dunlop	Remember When	Rumoush	15	2 35.77

(Meeznah finished second but was subsequently disqualified)

Year	Owner	Winner and Price	Jockey	Trainer	Second	Third	Ran	Time
2011	M J & L A Taylor's	DANCING RAIN (20/1)	J Murtagh	W Haggas	Wonder of Wonders	Izzi Top	13	2 41.73
2012	D Smith, Mrs J Magnier & M Tabor's	WAS (20/1)	S Heffernan	A O'Brien	Shirocco Star	The Fugue	12	2 38.68
2013	J L Rowsell & M H Dixon's	TALENT (20/1)	R Hughes	R Beckett	Secret Gesture	The Lark	11	2 42.00
2014	Hamdan Al Maktoum's	TAGHROODA (5/1)	P Hanagan	J Gosden	Tarfasha	Volume	17	2 34.89
2015	Mrs C C Regalado-Gonzalez's	QUALIFY (50/1)	C O'Donoghue	A O'Brien	Legatissimo	Lady of Dubai	11	2 37.41
2016	D Smith, Mrs J Magnier & M Tabor's	MINDING (10/1)	R Moore	A O'Brien	Architecture	Harlequeen	9	2 42.66
2017	K Abdullah's	ENABLE (6/1)	L Dettori	J Gosden	Rhododendron	Alluringly	9	2 34.13
2018	M Tabor, D Smith & Mrs J Magnier's	FOREVER TOGETHER (7/1)	D O'Brien	A O'Brien	Wild Illusion	Bye Bye Baby	9	2 40.39
2019	Helena Springfield Ltd's	ANAPURNA (8/1)	L Dettori	J Gosden	Pink Dogwood	Fleeting	14	2 36.09

DERBY STAKES (3y) Epsom-1 mile 4 furlongs 6 yards

Year	Owner	Winner and Price	Jockey	Trainer	Second	Third	Ran	Time
1982	R Sangster's	GOLDEN FLEECE (3/1)	Pat Eddery	V O'Brien	Touching Wood	Silver Hawk	18	2 34.27
1983	E Moller's	TEENOSO (9/2)	L Piggott	G Wragg	Carlingford Castle	Shearwalk	21	2 49.07
1984	L Miglitti's	SECRETO (14/1)	C Roche	D O'Brien	El Gran Senor	Mighty Flutter	27	2 39.12
1985	Lord H de Walden's	SLIP ANCHOR (9/4)	S Cauthen	H Cecil	Law Society	Damister	14	2 36.23
1986	H H Aga Khan's	SHAHRASTANI (11/2)	W Swinburn	M Stoute	Dancing Brave	Mashkour	17	2 37.13
1987	L Freedman's	REFERENCE POINT (6/4)	S Cauthen	H Cecil	Most Welcome	Bellotto	19	2 33.84
1988	H H Aga Khan's	KAHYASI (11/2)	R Cochrane	L Cumani	Glacial Storm	Doyoun	14	2 34.90
1989	Hamdan Al-Maktoum's	NASHWAN (5/4)	W Carson	H Hern	Terimon	Cacoethes	12	2 37.26
1990	K Abdullah's	QUEST FOR FAME (7/1)	Pat Eddery	R Charlton	Blue Stag	Elmaamul	18	2 34.00
1991	F Salman's	GENEROUS (9/1)	A Munro	P Cole	Marju	Star of Gdansk	13	2 34.51
1992	Sidney H Craig's	DR DEVIOUS (8/1)	J Reid	P Chapple-Hyam	St Jovite	Silver Wisp	18	2 36.19
1993	K Abdullah's	COMMANDER IN CHIEF (15/2)	W Kinane	H Cecil	Blue Judge	Blues Traveller	16	2 34.51
1994	Hamdan Al-Maktoum's	ERHAAB (7/2)	W Carson	J Dunlop	King's Theatre	Colonel Collins	25	2 34.16
1995	Saeed Maktoum Al Maktoum's	LAMMTARRA (14/1)	W Swinburn	Bin Suroor	Tamure	Presenting	15	2 32.31
1996	K Dasmal's	SHAAMIT (12/1)	M Hills	W Haggas	Dushyantor	Shantou	20	2 33.05
1997	K Knight's	BENNY THE DIP (11/1)	W Ryan	J Gosden	Silver Patriarch	Romanov	13	2 35.77
1998	Sheikh Mohammed, Obaid Al Maktoum's	HIGH-RISE (20/1)	O Peslier	L Cumani	City Honours	Border Arrow	15	2 33.88
1999	The Thoroughbred Corporation's	OATH (13/2)	K Fallon	H Cecil	Dalapour	Beat All	16	2 37.43
2000	H H Aga Khan's	SINNDAR (7/1)	J Murtagh	A O'Brien	Sakhee	Beat Hollow	15	2 36.75
2001	M Tabor & Mrs J Magnier's	GALILEO (11/4)	M Kinane	A O'Brien	Golan	Tobougg	12	2 33.27
2002	M Tabor & Mrs J Magnier's	HIGH CHAPARRAL (7/2)	J Murtagh	A O'Brien	Hawk Wing	Moon Ballad	12	2 39.45
2003	Saeed Suhail's	KRIS KIN (6/1)	K Fallon	Sir M Stoute	The Great Gatsby	Alamshar	20	2 33.35
2004	Ballymacoll Stud's	NORTH LIGHT (7/2)	K Fallon	Sir M Stoute	Rule Of Law	Let The Lion Roar	14	2 33.70
2005	The Royal Ascot Racing Club's	MOTIVATOR (3/1)	J Murtagh	M Bell	Walk In The Park	Dubawi	13	2 33.60
2006	A E Pakenham's	SIR PERCY (6/1)	M Dwyer	M Tregoning	Dragon Dancer	Dylan Thomas	18	2 35.20
2007	Salem Al Homaizi & Imad Al Sagar's	AUTHORIZED (5/4)	L Dettori	P Chapple-Hyam	Eagle Mountain	Aqaleem	17	2 34.77
2008	HRH Princess Haya of Jordan's	NEW APPROACH (5/1)	K Manning	J Bolger	Tartan Bearer	Casual Conquest	16	2 36.50
2009	C Tsui's	SEA THE STARS (11/4)	M Kinane	J Oxx	Fame And Glory	Mastertheforce	12	2 36.74
2010	K Abdullah's	WORKFORCE (6/1)	R Moore	Sir M Stoute	At First Sight	Rewilding	12	2 31.33
2011	Mrs John Magnier, M Tabor & D Smith's	POUR MOI (4/1)	M Barzalona	A Fabre	Treasure Beach	Carlton House	13	2 34.54
2012	D Smith, Mrs J Magnier & M Tabor's	CAMELOT (8/13)	J O'Brien	A O'Brien	Main Sequence	Astrology	9	2 33.90
2013	Mrs John Magnier, Michael Tabor & Derrick Smith's	RULER OF THE WORLD (7/1)	R Moore	A O'Brien	Libertarian	Galileo Rock	12	2 39.06
2014	D Smith, Mrs J Magnier, M Tabor's	AUSTRALIA (11/8)	J O'Brien	A O'Brien	Kingston Hill	Romsdal	16	2 33.63
2015	A Oppenheimer's	GOLDEN HORN (13/8)	L Dettori	J Gosden	Jack Hobbs	Storm The Stars	12	2 32.32
2016	H H Aga Khan's	HARZAND (13/2)	P Smullen	D Weld	US Army Ranger	Idaho	16	2 40.09
2017	D Smith, Mrs J Magnier, M Tabor's	WINGS OF EAGLES (40/1)	P Beggy	A O'Brien	Cliffs of Moher	Cracksman	18	2 33.02
2018	Godolphin's	MASAR (16/1)	W Buick	C Appleby	Dee Ex Bee	Roaring Lion	12	2 34.93
2019	Mrs J Magnier, M tabor & D Smith's	ANTHONY VAN DYCK (13/2)	S Heffernan	A O'Brien	Madhmoon	Japan	13	2 33.38

ST LEGER STAKES (3y) Doncaster-1 mile 6 furlongs 115 yards

Year	Owner	Winner and Price	Jockey	Trainer	Second	Third	Ran	Time
1981	Sir J Astor's	CUT ABOVE (28/1)	J Mercer	R Hern	Glint of Gold	Bustomi	7	3 11.60
1982	Maktoum Al Maktoum's	TOUCHING WOOD (7/1)	P Cook	H T Jones	Zilos	Diamond Shoal	15	3 3.53
1983	Sir M Sobell's	SUN PRINCESS (11/8)	W Carson	R Hern	Esprit du Nord	Carlingford Castle	10	3 16.65
1984	I Allan's	COMMANCHE RUN (7/4)	L Piggott	L Cumani	Baynoun	Alphabatim	11	3 9.93
1985	Sheikh Mohammed's	OH SO SHARP (8/11)	S Cauthen	H Cecil	Phardante	Lanfranco	6	3 7.13
1986	Duchess of Norfolk's	MOON MADNESS (9/2)	Pat Eddery	J Dunlop	Celestial Storm	Untold	8	3 5.03
1987	L Freedman's	REFERENCE POINT (4/11)	S Cauthen	H Cecil	Mountain Kingdom	Dry Dock	7	3 5.91
1988	Lady Beaverbrook's	MINSTER SON (15/2)	W Carson	N A Graham	Diminuendo	Sheriff's Star	6	3 6.80
1989	C St George's	MICHELOZZO (6/4)	S Cauthen	H Cecil	Sapience	Roseate Tern	8	3 20.72
	(Run at Ayr)							
1990	M Arbib's	SNURGE (7/2)	T Quinn	P Cole	Hellenic	River God	8	3 8.78
1991	K Abdullah's	TOULON (5/2)	Pat Eddery	A Fabre	Saddlers' Hall	Micheletti	10	3 3.12
1992	W J Gredley's	USER FRIENDLY (7/4)	G Duffield	C Brittain	Sonus	Bonny Scot	10	3 5.48
1993	Mrs G A E Smith's	BOB'S RETURN (3/1)	P Robinson	M Tompkins	Armiger	Edbaysaan	9	3 7.85
1994	Sheikh Mohammed's	MOONAX (40/1)	Pat Eddery	B Hills	Broadway Flyer	Double Trigger	9	3 4.19
1995	Godolphin's	CLASSIC CLICHE (100/30)	L Dettori	S Bin Suroor	Minds Music	Istidaad	10	3 9.74
1996	Sheikh Mohammed's	SHANTOU (8/1)	L Dettori	J Dunlop	Dushyantor	Samraan	11	3 5.10
1997	P Winfield's	SILVER PATRIARCH (5/4)	Pat Eddery	J Dunlop	Vertical Speed	The Fly	10	3 6.92
1998	Godolphin's	NEDAWI (5/2)	J Reid	S Bin Suroor	High and Low	Sunshine Street	9	3 5.61
1999	Godolphin's	MUTAFAWEQ (11/2)	R Hills	S Bin Suroor	Ramruma	Adair	9	3 2.75
2000	N Jones	MILLENARY (11/4)	T Quinn	J Dunlop	Air Marshall	Chimes At Midnight	11	3 2.58
2001	M Tabor & Mrs J Magnier's	MILAN (13/8)	M Kinane	A O'Brien	Demophilos	Mr Combustible	10	3 5.16
2002	Sir Neil Westbrook's	BOLLIN ERIC (7/1)	K Darley	T Easterby	Highest	Phoenix Reach	8	3 2.92
2003	Mrs J Magnier's	BRIAN BORU (5/4)	J P Spencer	A O'Brien	High Accolade	Tycoon	12	3 4.64
2004	Godolphin's	RULE OF LAW (3/1)	K McEvoy	S Bin Suroor	Quiff	Tawqeet	8	3 6.20
2005	Mrs J Magnier & M Tabor's	SCORPION (10/11)	L Dettori	A O'Brien	The Geezer	Red Rocks	6	19.00
2006	Mrs S Roy's	SIXTIES ICON (11/8)	L Dettori	J Noseda	The Last Drop		11	57.20
	(Run at York)							
2007	G Strawbridge's	LUCARNO (7/2)	J Fortune	J Gosden	Mahler	Honolulu	10	3 1.90
2008	Ballymacoll Stud's	CONDUIT (8/1)	L Dettori	Sir M Stoute	Unsung Heroine	Look Here	14	3 7.92
2009	Godolphin's	MASTERY (4/1)	T Durcan	S Bin Suroor	Kite Wood	Monitor Closely	8	3 4.81
2010	B S Flood & R Geffen's	ARCTIC COSMOS (12/1)	W Buick	J Gosden	Midas Touch	Corsica	10	3 3.12
2011	Godolphin's	MASKED MARVEL (15/2)	W Buick	J Gosden	Brown Panther	Sea Moon	9	3 0.44
2012	Godolphin's	ENCKE (25/1)	M Barzalona	M Al Zarooni	Camelot	Michelangelo	9	3 3.81
2013	Derrick Smith & Mrs John Magnier & Michael Tabor's	LEADING LIGHT (7/2)	J O'Brien	A O'Brien	Talent	Galileo Rock	11	3 9.20
2014	Paul Smith's	KINGSTON HILL (9/4)	A Atzeni	R Varian	Romsdal	Snow Sky	12	3 5.42
2015	ORL Sheikh Suhaim Al Thani & M Al Kubaisi's	SIMPLE VERSE (8/1)	A Atzeni	R Beckett	Bondi Beach	Fields of Athenry	7	3 7.12
2016	Mrs Jackie Cornwell's	HARBOUR LAW (22/1)	G Baker	Mrs L Mongan	Ventura Storm	Housesofparliament	9	3 5.48
2017	Derrick Smith & Mrs John Magnier & Michael Tabor's	CAPRI (3/1)	R Moore	A O'Brien	Crystal Ocean	Stradivarius	11	3 4.04
2018	Derrick Smith & Mrs John Magnier & Michael Tabor's	KEW GARDENS (3/1)	R Moore	A O'Brien	Lah Ti Dar	Southern France	12	3 3.34
2019	K Abdullah's	LOGICIAN (5/6)	L Dettori	J Gosden	Sir Ron Priestley	Nayef Road	8	3 0.27

KING GEORGE VI AND QUEEN ELIZABETH STAKES Ascot·1 mile 3 furlongs 211 yards

Year	Owner	Winner and Price	Jockey	Trainer	Second	Third	Ran	Time
1981	H H Aga Khan's	SHERGAR 3-8-8 (2/5)	W Swinburn	M Stoute	Madam Gay	Fingals Cave	9	2 35.40
1982	A Ward's	KALAGLOW 4-9-7 (13-2)	G Starkey	G Harwood	Assert	Glint of Gold	9	2 31.58
1983	R Barnett's	TIME CHARTER 4-9-4 (5/1)	J Mercer	H Candy	Diamond Shoal	Sun Princess	8	2 30.78
1984	E Moller's	TEENOSO 4-9-7 (13/2)	L Piggott	G Wragg	Sadler's Wells	Tolomeo	13	2 27.95
1985	Lady Beaverbrook's	PETOSKI 3-8-8 (2/1)	W Carson	W Hern	Oh So Sharp	Rainbow Quest	12	2 29.49
1986	K Abdullah's	DANCING BRAVE 3-8-8 (6/4)	Pat Eddery	G Harwood	Shardari	Triptych	9	2 34.63
1987	L Freedman's	REFERENCE POINT 3-8-8 (11/10)	S Cauthen	H Cecil	Celestial Storm	Triptych	9	2 37.33
1988	Sheikh Ahmed Al Maktoum's	MTOTO 5-9-7 (4/1)	M Roberts	A C Stewart	Unfuwain	Tony Bin	10	2 32.27
1989	Hamdan Al-Maktoum's	NASHWAN 3-8-8 (2/1)	W Carson	R Hern	Cacoethes	Top Class.	7	2 30.76
1990	Sheikh Mohammed's	BELMEZ 3-8-9 (15/2)	M Kinane	H Cecil	Old Vic	Assatis	11	2 30.85
1991	F Salman's	GENEROUS 3-8-9 (4/6)	A Munro	P Cole	Sanglamore	Rock Hopper	7	2 33.94
1992	Mrs V K Payson's	ST JOVITE 3-8-9 (4/5)	S Craine	J Bolger	Saddlers' Hall	Opera House	8	2 28.92
1993	Sheikh Mohammed's	OPERA HOUSE 5-9-7 (8/1)	M Roberts	M Stoute	White Muzzle	Commander in Chief	10	2 31.01
1994	Sheikh Mohammed's	KING'S THEATRE 3-8-9 (12/1)	M Kinane	H Cecil	White Muzzle	Wagon Master	12	
1995	Saeed Maktoum Al Maktoum's	LAMMTARRA 3-8-9 (9/4)	L Dettori	S bin Suroor	Pentire	Strategic Choice	7	
1996	Mollers Racing's	PENTIRE 4-9-7 (100/30)	M Hills	G Wragg	Classic Cliche	Shaamit.	8	2 28.11
1997	Godolphin's	SWAIN 5-9-7 (16/1)	J Reid	S bin Suroor	Pilsudski	Helissio.	8	2 36.45
1998	Godolphin's	SWAIN 6-9-7 (3/1)	L Dettori	S bin Suroor	High-Rise.	Royal Anthem.	8	2 29.06
1999	Godolphin's	DAYLAMI 5-9-7 (3/1)	L Dettori	S bin Suroor	Nedawi.	Fruits Of Love.	7	2 29.35
2000	M Tabor's	MONTJEU 4-9-7 (1/3)	M Kinane	J Hammond	Fantastic Light.	Daliapour.	12	2 29.98
2001	Mrs J Magnier & M Tabor's	GALILEO 3-8-9 (1/2)	M Kinane	A O'Brien	Fantastic Light.	Hightori.	12	2 27.61
2002	Exors of the late Lord Weinstock's	GOLAN 4-9-7 (11/2)	K Fallon	Sir M Stoute	Nayef.	Zindabad.	11	2 29.70
2003	H H Aga Khan	ALAMSHAR 3-8-9 (3/2)	J Murtagh	J Oxx	Sulamani.	Kris Kin.	11	2 33.26
2004	Godolphin's	DOYEN 4-9-7 (11/10)	L Dettori	S bin Suroor	Hard Buck.	Sulamani.	12	2 33.10
2005	H H Aga Khan's (Run at Newbury)	AZAMOUR 4-9-7 (5/2)	M Kinane	J Oxx	Norse Dancer.	Bago.	12	2 28.20
2006	M Tabor's	HURRICANE RUN 4-9-7 (5/6)	C Soumillon	A Fabre	Electrocutionist.	Heart's Cry.	6	2 30.20
2007	Mrs J Magnier & M Tabor's	DYLAN THOMAS 4-9-7 (5/4)	J Murtagh	A O'Brien	Youmzain.	Maraahel.	7	2 31.10
2008	Mrs J Magnier & M Tabor's	DUKE OF MARMALADE 4-9-7 (4/6)	J Murtagh	A O'Brien	Papal Bull.	Youmzain.	8	2 27.61
2009	Ballymacoll Stud's	CONDUIT 4-9-7 (13/8)	R Moore	Sir M Stoute	Tartan Bearer.	Ask.	9	2 28.73
2010	Highclere Thoroughbred Racing (Adm. Rous)'s	HARBINGER 4-9-7 (4/1)	O Peslier	Sir M Stoute	Cape Blanco.	Youmzain.	8	2 26.78
2011	Lady Rothschild's	NATHANIEL 3-8-9 (11/2)	W Buick	J Gosden	Workforce.	St Nicholas Abbey.	5	2 35.07
2012	Gestüt Burg Eberstein & Teruya Yoshida's	DANEDREAM 4-9-4 (9/1)	A Starke	P Schiergen	Nathaniel.	St Nicholas Abbey.	10	2 31.62
2013	Dr Christophe Berglar's	NOVELLIST 4-9-7 (13/2)	J Murtagh	A Wohler	Trading Leather.	Hillstar.	8	2 24.60
2014	Hamdan Al Maktoum's	TAGHROODA 3-8-6 (7/2)	P Hanagan	J Gosden	Telescope.	Mukhadram.	8	2 28.13
2015	Sheikh Mohammed Obaid Al Maktoum's	POSTPONED 4-9-7 (6/1)	A Atzeni	L Cumani	Eagle Top.	Romsdal.	7	2 31.25
2016	D Smith, Mrs J Magnier &	HIGHLAND REEL 4-9-7 (13/8)	R Moore	A O'Brien	Wings of Desire.	Dartmouth.	7	2 28.97
2017	K Abdullah's	ENABLE 3-8-7 (5/4)	L Dettori	J Gosden	Ulysses.	Idaho.	10	2 36.22
2018	S Suhail's	POET'S WORD 5-9-7 (7/4)	J Doyle	Sir M Stoute	Crystal Ocean.	Coronet.		2 25.84
2019	K Abdullah's	ENABLE 5-9-4 (8/15)	L Dettori	J Gosden	Crystal Ocean.	Waldgeist.	11	2 32.42

PRIX DE L'ARC DE TRIOMPHE ParisLongChamp-1 mile 4 furlongs

Year	Owner	Winner and Price	Jockey	Trainer	Second	Third	Ran	Time
1982	H H Aga Khan's	AKIYDA 3-8-8 (43/4)	Y Saint Martin	F. Mathet	Ardross	Awaasil	17	2 37.00
1983	D Wildenstein's	ALL ALONG 4-9-1 (173/10)	W Swinburn	P. Biancone	Sun Princess	Luth Enchantee	26	2 28.10
1984	D Wildenstein's	SAGACE 4-9-4 (29/10)	Y Saint Martin	P. Biancone	Northern Trick	All Along	22	2 39.10
1985	K Abdullah's	RAINBOW QUEST 4-9-4 (71/10)	Pat Eddery	J. Tree	Sagace	Kozana	15	2 29.50
	(The first two placings were reversed by the Stewards)							
1986	K Abdulla's	DANCING BRAVE 3-8-11 (11/10)	Pat Eddery	G Harwood	Bering	Triptych	15	2 27.70
1987	P de Moussac's	TREMPOLINO 3-8-11 (20/1)	Pat Eddery	A. Fabre	Tony Bin	Triptych	11	2 26.30
1988	Mrs V Gaucci del Bono's	TONY BIN 5-9-4 (14/1)	J Reid	L Camici	Mtoto	Boyatino	24	2 27.30
1989	A Balzarini's	CARROLL HOUSE 4-9-4 (19/1)	M Kinane	M Jarvis	Behera	Saint Andrews	19	2 30.80
1990	B McNall's	SAUMAREZ 3-8-11 (15/1)	G Mosse	N Clement	Epervier Bleu	Snurge	21	2 29.80
1991	H Chalhoub's	SUAVE DANCER 3-8-11 (37/10)	C Asmussen	J Hammond	Magic Night	Pistolet Bleu	14	2 31.40
1992	O Lecerf's	SUBOTICA 4-9-4 (88/10)	T Jarnet	A Fabre	User Friendly	Vert Amande	18	2 39.00
1993	D Tsui's	URBAN SEA 4-9-1 (37/1)	E Saint Martin	J Lesbordes	White Muzzle	Opera House	23	2 37.90
1994	Sheikh Mohammed's	CARNEGIE 3-8-11 (3/1)	T Jarnet	A Fabre	Hernando	Apple Tree	20	2 31.10
1995	Saeed Maktoum Al Maktoum's	LAMMTARRA 3-8-11 (2/1)	L Dettori	S Bin Suroor	Freedom Cry	Swain	16	2 31.80
1996	E Sarasola's	HELISSIO 3-8-11 (18/10)	O Peslier	E Lellouche	Pilsudski	Oscar Schindler	16	2 29.90
1997	J-L Lagardère's	PEINTRE CELEBRE 3-8-11 (22/10)	O Peslier	A Fabre	Pilsudski	Borgia	18	2 24.60
1998	D Wildenstein's	SAGAMIX 3-8-11 (5/2)	O Peslier	J Hammond	Leggera	Tiger Hill	14	2 34.50
1999	M Tabor's	MONTJEU 3-8-11 (6/4)	M Kinane	J Hammond	El Condor Pasa	Croco Rouge	14	2 38.50
2000	H H Aga Khan's	SINNDAR 3-8-11 (6/4)	J Murtagh	J Oxx	Egyptband	Volvoreta	14	2 25.80
2001	Godolphin's	SAKHEE 4-9-5 (22/10)	L Dettori	Sir M Stoute	Aquarelliste	Sagacity	17	2 36.10
2002	Godolphin's	MARIENBARD 5-9-5 (58/10)	L Dettori	S Bin Suroor	Sulamani	High Chaparral	16	2 26.70
2003	H H Aga Khan's	DALAKHANI 3-8-11 (9/4)	C Soumillon	A de Royer-Dupre	Mubtaker	High Chaparral	13	2 32.30
2004	Niarchos Family's	BAGO 3-8-11 (10/1)	T Gillet	J E Pease	Cherry Mix	Ouija Board	13	2 25.00
2005	M Tabor's	HURRICANE RUN 3-8-11 (11/4)	K Fallon	A de Royer-Dupre	Westerner	Bago	8	2 27.40
2006	K Abdullah's	RAIL LINK 3-8-11 (8/1)	S Pasquier	A Fabre	Pride	Hurricane Run	8	2 26.30
	Deep Impact disqualified from third place							
2007	Mrs J Magnier & M Tabor's	DYLAN THOMAS 4-9-5 (11/2)	K Fallon	A O'Brien	Youmzain	Sagara	12	2 28.50
2008	H H Aga Khan's	ZARKAVA 3-8-8 (13/8)	C Soumillon	A de Royer-Dupre	Youmzain	Soldier of Fortune/It's Gino	16	2 28.80
2009	C Tsui's	SEA THE STARS 3-8-11 (4/6)	M Kinane	J Oxx	Youmzain	Cavalryman	19	2 26.30
2010	K Abdullah's	WORKFORCE 3-8-11 (6/1)	R Moore	Sir M Stoute	Nakayama Festa	Sarafina	18	2 35.30
2011	Gestüt Burg Eberstein & T Yoshida's	DANEDREAM 3-8-8 (20/1)	A Starke	P Schiergen	Shareta	Snow Fairy	16	2 24.49
2012	Wertheimer & Frère's	SOLEMIA 4-9-2 (33/1)	O Peslier	C Laffon-Parias	Orfevre	Masterstroke	18	2 37.68
2013	H E Sheikh Joaan Bin Hamad Al Thani's	TREVE 3-8-9 (9/2)	T Jarnet	Mme C Head-Maarek	Orfevre	Intello	17	2 32.04
2014	Al Shaqab Racing's	TREVE 4-9-2 (11/1)	T Jarnet	Mme C Head-Maarek	Flintshire	Taghrooda	20	2 26.05
2015	A E Oppenheimer's	GOLDEN HORN 3-8-11 (9/2)	L Dettori	J Gosden	Flintshire	New Bay	17	2 27.23
2016	M Tabor's D Smith & Mrs V Magnier's *(Run at Chantilly)*	FOUND 4-9-2 (6/1)	R Moore	A O'Brien	Highland Reel	Order of St George	16	2 23.61
2017	K Abdulla's *(Run at Chantilly)*	ENABLE 3-8-9 (10/11)	L Dettori	J Gosden	Cloth of Stars	Ulysses	18	2 28.69
2018	K Abdullah's	ENABLE 4-9-2 (Evs)	L Dettori	J Gosden	Sea Of Class	Cloth Of Stars	19	2 29.24
2019	Gestüt Ammerland & Newsells Park's	WALDGEIST 5-9-5 (131/10)	P-C Boudot	A Fabre	Enable	Sottsass	12	2 31.97

GRAND NATIONAL STEEPLECHASE Aintree 4m 2f 74y (4m 4f before 2013)

Year	Winner and Price	Age & Weight	Jockey	Second	Third	Ran	Time
1974	RED RUM (11/1)	9 12 0	B Fletcher	L'Escargot	Charles Dickens	42	9.20.30
1975	L'ESCARGOT (13/2)	12 11 3	T Carberry	Red Rum	Spanish Steps	31	9.31.10
1976	RAG TRADE (14/1)	10 10 12	J Burke	Red Rum	Eyecatcher	32	9.20.90
1977	RED RUM (9/1)	12 11 8	T Stack	Churchtown Boy	Eyecatcher	42	9.30.30
1978	LUCIUS (14/1)	9 10 9	B R Davies	Sebastian V	Drumroan	37	9.33.90
1979	RUBSTIC (25/1)	10 10 0	M Barnes	Rough and Tumble	Rough and Tumble	34	9.52.90
1980	BEN NEVIS (40/1)	12 10 12	Mr C Fenwick	Rough and Tumble	The Pilgarlic	30	10.17.40
1981	ALDANITI (10/1)	11 10 13	R Champion	Spartan Missile	Royal Mail	39	9.47.20
1982	GRITTAR (7/1)	9 11 5	Mr M Armytage	Hard Outlook	Loving Words	39	9.12.60
1983	CORBIERE (13/1)	8 11 4	B de Haan	Greasepaint	Yer Man	41	9.47.04
1984	HALLO DANDY (13/1)	10 10 2	N Doughty	Greasepaint	Corbiere	40	9.21.04
1985	LAST SUSPECT (50/1)	11 10 5	H Davies	Mr Snugfit	Corbiere	40	9.42.70
1986	WEST TIP (15/2)	9 10 11	R Dunwoody	Young Driver	Classified	40	9.33.00
1987	MAORI VENTURE (28/1)	11 10 3	S C Knight	The Tsarevich	Lean Ar Aghaidh	40	9.19.30
1988	RHYME 'N' REASON (10/1)	10 11 0	B Powell	Durham Edition	Monanore	40	9.53.50
1989	LITTLE POLVEIR (28/1)	12 10 3	J Frost	West Tip	The Thinker	40	10.06.80
1990	MR FRISK (16/1)	11 10 6	Mr M Armytage	Durham Edition	Rinus	38	8.47.80
1991	SEAGRAM (12/1)	11 10 6	M Hawke	Garrison Savannah	Auntie Dot	40	9.29.90
1992	PARTY POLITICS (14/1)	8 10 7	C Llewellyn	Romany King	Laura's Beau	40	9.06.30
1993	RACE VOID - FALSE START						
1994	MIINNEHOMA (16/1)	11 10 8	R Dunwoody	Just So	Moorcroft Boy	36	10.18.80
1995	ROYAL ATHLETE (40/1)	12 10 6	J Titley	Party Politics	Over The Deel	35	9.04.00
1996	ROUGH QUEST (7/1)	9 10 7	M Fitzgerald	Encore Un Peu	Superior Finish	27	10.00.80
1997	LORD GYLLENE (14/1)	9 10 0	A Dobbin	Suny Bay	Camelot Knight	36	9.05.80
1998	EARTH SUMMIT (7/1)	10 10 5	C Llewellyn	Suny Bay	Samlee	37	10.51.40
1999	BOBBYJO (10/1)	10 10 0	P Carberry	Blue Charm	Call It A Day	32	9.14.00
2000	PAPILLON (10/1)	10 10 12	R Walsh	Mely Moss	Niki Dee	40	9.09.70
2001	RED MARAUDER (33/1)	11 10 11	R Guest	Smarty	Blowing Wind	40	11.00.10
2002	BINDAREE (20/1)	8 10 4	J Culloty	What's Up Boys	Blowing Wind	40	9.09.00
2003	MONTY'S PASS (16/1)	10 10 7	B J Geraghty	Supreme Glory	Amberleigh House	40	9.21.70
2004	AMBERLEIGH HOUSE (16/1)	12 10 10	G Lee	Clan Royal	Lord Atterbury	39	10.20.30
2005	HEDGEHUNTER (7/1)	9 11 1	R Walsh	Royal Auclair	Simply Gifted	40	9.20.80
2006	NUMBERSIXVALVERDE (11/1)	10 10 8	N Madden	Hedgehunter	Clan Royal	40	9.41.00
2007	SILVER BIRCH (33/1)	9 10 0	R M Power	McKelvey	Slim Pickings	40	9.13.60
2008	COMPLY OR DIE (7/1)	9 10 9	T Murphy	King Johns Castle	Snowy Morning	40	9.16.60
2009	MON MOME (100/1)	10 11 0	L Treadwell	Comply Or Die	My Will	40	9.32.90
2010	DON'T PUSH IT (10/1)	11 10 12	A P McCoy	Black Apalachi	State Of Play	40	9.04.60
2011	BALLABRIGGS (14/1)	11 11 0	J Maguire	Oscar Time	Don't Push It	40	9.01.20
2012	NEPTUNE COLLONGES (33/1)	11 10 3	D Jacob	Sunnyhillboy	Seabass	40	9.05.10
2013	AURORAS ENCORE (66/1)	8 11 0	R Mania	Cappa Bleu	Teaforthree	40	9.09.90
2014	PINEAU DE RE (25/1)	11 11 6	L Aspell	Balthazar King	Double Seven	40	9.09.80
2015	MANY CLOUDS (25/1)	8 11 1	L Aspell	Saint Are	Monbeg Dude	39	8.56.80
2016	RULE THE WORLD (33/1)	9 10 7	D Mullins	The Last Samuri	Vics Canvas	39	9.29.00
2017	ONE FOR ARTHUR (14/1)	8 10 1	D Russell	Cause of Causes	Saint Are	40	9.03.50
2018	TIGER ROLL (10/1)	8 10 13	D Russell	Pleasant Company	Bless The Wings	38	9.40.10
2019	TIGER ROLL (4/1)	9 11 5	D Russell	Magic of Light	Rathvinden	40	9.01.00

WINNERS OF GREAT RACES

LINCOLN HANDICAP
Doncaster-1m
2010	PENITENT 4-9-2	21
2011	SWEET LIGHTNING 6-9-4	21
2012	BRAE HILL 6-9-1	22
2013	LEVITATE 5-8-4	22
2014	OCEAN TEMPEST 5-9-3	17
2015	GABRIAL 6-9-0	22
2016	SECRET BRIEF 4-9-4	22
2017	BRAVERY 4-9-1	22
2018	ADDEYBB 4-9-2	20
2019	AUXERRE 4-9-3	19

GREENHAM STAKES (3y)
Newbury-7f
2010	DICK TURPIN 9-0	5
2011	FRANKEL 9-0	6
2012	CASPAR NETSCHER 9-0	5
2013	OLYMPIC GLORY 9-0	5
2014	KINGMAN 9-0	10
2015	MUHAARAR 9-0	6
* 2016	TASLEET 9-0	3
2017	BARNEY ROY 9-0	10
2018	JAMES GARFIELD 9-0	7
2019	MOHAATHER 9-0	8

* Run at Chelmsford City on Polytrack

EUROPEAN FREE HANDICAP (3y)
Newmarket-7f
2010	RED JAZZ 9-6	7
2011	PAUSANIAS 8-12	6
2012	TELWAAR 8-11	7
2013	GARSWOOD 9-0	10
2014	SHIFTING POWER 9-1	6
2015	HOME OF THE BRAVE 8-13	5
2016	IBN MALIK 9-6	9
2017	WHITECLIFFSOFDOVER 9-7	7
2018	ANNA NERIUM 8-11	10
2019	SHINE SO BRIGHT 9-3	7

CRAVEN STAKES (3y)
Newmarket-1m
2010	ELUSIVE PIMPERNEL 8-12	9
2011	NATIVE KHAN 8-12	6
2012	TRUMPET MAJOR 9-1	12
2013	TORONADO 9-1	4
2014	TOORMORE 9-3	7
2015	KOOL KOMPANY 9-3	6
2016	STORMY ANTARCTIC 9-0	6
2017	EMINENT 9-0	7
2018	MASAR 9-0	6
2019	SKARDU 9-0	8

JOCKEY CLUB STAKES
Newmarket-1m 4f
2010	JUKEBOX JURY 4-9-3	5
2011	DANDINO 4-8-11	4
2012	AL KAZEEM 4-8-12	8
2013	UNIVERSAL 4-8-12	4
2014	GOSPEL CHOIR 5-9-0	8
2015	SECOND STEP 4-9-0	4

2016	EXOSPHERE 4-9-0	6
2017	SEVENTH HEAVEN 4-9-1	5
2018	DEFOE 4-9-1	5
2019	COMMUNIQUE 4-9-1	7

SANDOWN MILE
Sandown-1m
2010	PACO BOY 5-9-0	9
2011	DICK TURPIN 4-9-0	5
2012	PENITENT 6-9-0	6
2013	TRUMPET MAJOR 4-9-0	7
2014	TULLIUS 6-9-1	6
2015	CUSTOM CUT 6-9-5	6
2016	TOORMORE 5-9-4	7
2017	SOVEREIGN DEBT 8-9-1	9
2018	ADDEYBB 4-9-1	8
2019	BEAT THE BANK 5-9-1	7

CHESTER VASE (3y)
Chester-1m 4f 63yds
2010	TED SPREAD 8-12	7
2011	TREASURE BEACH 8-12	5
2012	MICKDAAM 8-12	5
2013	RULER OF THE WORLD 8-12	4
2014	ORCHESTRA 9-0	8
2015	HANS HOLBEIN 9-0	6
2016	US ARMY RANGER 9-0	6
2017	VENICE BEACH 9-0	8
2018	YOUNG RASCAL 9-0	10
2019	SIR DRAGONET 9-0	6

CHESTER CUP
Chester-2m 2f 140yds
2010	MAMLOOK 6-8-12	17
2011	OVERTURN 7-8-13	17
2012	ILE DE RE 6-8-11	16
2013	ADDRESS UNKNOWN 6-9-0	17
2014	SUEGIOO 5-9-4	17
2015	TRIP TO PARIS 4-8-9	17
2016	NO HERETIC 8-8-13	17
2017	MONTALY 6-9-3	17
2018	MAGIC CIRCLE 6-9-3	16
2019	MAKING MIRACLES 4-9-0	15

OAKS TRIAL (3y fillies)
Lingfield-1m 3f 133yds
2010	DYNA WALTZ 8-12	5
2011	ZAIN AL BOLDAN 8-12	9
* 2012	VOW 8-12	8
2013	SECRET GESTURE 8-12	7
2014	HONOR BOUND 9-0	10
2015	TOUJOURS L'AMOUR 9-0	10
2016	SEVENTH HEAVEN 9-0	5
2017	HERTFORD DANCER 9-0	6
2018	PERFECT CLARITY 9-0	4
2019	ANAPURNA 9-0	7

* Run over 1m4f on Polytrack

DERBY TRIAL (3y)
Lingfield-1m 3f 133yds

2010	**BULLET TRAIN** 8-12	......	7
2011	**DORDOGNE** 8-12	......	6
* 2012	**MAIN SEQUENCE** 8-12	......	4
2013	**NEVIS** 8-12	......	9
2014	**SNOW SKY** 9-0	......	9
2015	**KILIMANJARO** 9-0	......	5
2016	**HUMPHREY BOGART** 9-0	......	5
2017	**BEST SOLUTION** 9-5	......	8
2018	**KNIGHT TO BEHOLD** 9-0	......	9
2019	**ANTHONY VAN DYCK** 9-0	......	10

* Run over 1m4f on Polytrack

MUSIDORA STAKES (3y fillies)
York-1m 2f 56yds

2010	**AVIATE** 8-12	......	8
2011	**JOVIALITY** 8-12	......	5
2012	**THE FUGUE** 8-12	......	6
2013	**LIBER NAUTICUS** 8-12	......	6
2014	**MADAME CHIANG** 9-0	......	9
2015	**STAR OF SEVILLE** 9-0	......	5
2016	**SO MI DAR** 9-0	......	7
2017	**SHUTTER SPEED** 9-0	......	5
2018	**GIVE AND TAKE** 9-0	......	5
2019	**NAUSHA** 9-0	......	10

DANTE STAKES (3y)
York-1m 2f 56yds

2010	**CAPE BLANCO** 9-0	......	5
2011	**CARLTON HOUSE** 9-0	......	6
2012	**BONFIRE** 9-0	......	7
2013	**LIBERTARIAN** 9-0	......	8
2014	**THE GREY GATSBY** 9-0	......	9
2015	**GOLDEN HORN** 9-0	......	6
2016	**WINGS OF DESIRE** 9-0	......	12
2017	**PERMIAN** 9-0	......	10
2018	**ROARING LION** 9-0	......	9
2019	**TELECASTER** 9-0	......	8

MIDDLETON STAKES
(fillies and mares)
York-1m 2f 56yds

2010	**SARISKA** 4-8-12	......	4
2011	**MIDDAY** 5-9-3	......	8
2012	**IZZI TOP** 4-8-12	......	8
2013	**DALKALA** 4-9-0	......	8
2014	**AMBIVALENT** 5-9-0	......	8
2015	**SECRET GESTURE** 5-9-0	......	8
2016	**BEAUTIFUL ROMANCE** 4-9-0	......	7
2017	**BLOND ME** 5-9-0	......	4
2018	**CORONET** 4-9-0	......	7
2019	**LAH TI DAR** 4-9-0	......	6

YORKSHIRE CUP
York-1m 5f 188yds

2010	**MANIFEST** 4-8-12	......	5
2011	**DUNCAN** 6-9-2	......	8
2012	**RED CADEAUX** 6-9-0	......	8
2013	**GLEN'S DIAMOND** 5-9-0	......	8
2014	**GOSPEL CHOIR** 5-9-0	......	12
2015	**SNOW SKY** 4-9-0	......	6
2016	**CLEVER COOKIE** 8-9-1	......	8
2017	**DARTMOUTH** 5-9-1	......	8
2018	**STRADIVARIUS** 4-9-1	......	8
2019	**STRADIVARIUS** 5-9-4	......	8

DUKE OF YORK STAKES
York-6f

2010	**PRIME DEFENDER** 6-9-7	......	12
2011	**DELEGATOR** 5-9-7	......	14
2012	**TIDDLIWINKS** 6-9-7	......	13
2013	**SOCIETY ROCK** 6-9-13	......	17
2014	**MAAREK** 7-9-13.	......	13
2015	**GLASS OFFICE** 5-9-8.	......	15
2016	**MAGICAL MEMORY** 4-9-8.	......	12
2017	**TASLEET** 4-9-8.	......	12
2018	**HARRY ANGEL** 4-9-13	......	5
2019	**INVINCIBLE ARMY** 4-9-3	......	10

LOCKINGE STAKES
Newbury-1m

2010	**PACO BOY** 5-9-0	......	9
2011	**CANFORD CLIFFS** 4-9-0	......	7
2012	**FRANKEL** 4-9-0	......	6
2013	**FARHH** 5-9-0	......	12
2014	**OLYMPIC GLORY** 4-9-0	......	9
2015	**NIGHT OF THUNDER** 4-9-0	......	16
2016	**BELARDO** 4-9-0	......	12
2017	**RIBCHESTER** 4-9-0.	......	8
2018	**RHODODENDRON** 4-8-11	......	14
2019	**MUSTASHRY** 6-9-0.	......	14

HENRY II STAKES
Sandown-2m 50yds

2010	**AKMAL** 4-9-0	......	9
2011	**BLUE BAJAN** 9-9-2	......	8
2012	**OPINION POLL** 6-9-4	......	10
2013	**GLOOMY SUNDAY** 4-8-11	......	10
2014	**BROWN PANTHER** 6-9-4	......	11
2015	**VENT DE FORCE** 4-9-0	......	7
2016	**PALLASATOR** 7-9-6	......	4
2017	**BIG ORANGE** 6-9-2	......	7
2018	**MAGIC CIRCLE** 6-9-2	......	8
2019	**DEE EX BEE** 4-9-4	......	5

TEMPLE STAKES
Haydock-5f

2010	**KINGSGATE NATIVE** 5-9-4	......	9
2011	**SOLE POWER** 4-9-4	......	12
2012	**BATED BREATH** 5-9-4	......	12
2013	**KINGSGATE NATIVE** 8-9-4	......	10
2014	**HOT STREAK** 3-8-10.	......	9
2015	**PEARL SECRET** 6-9-4	......	11
2016	**PROFITABLE** 4-9-4	......	11
2017	**PRICELESS** 4-9-1	......	12
2018	**BATTAASH** 4-9-9	......	11
2019	**BATTAASH** 5-9-4.	......	8

BRIGADIER GERARD STAKES
Sandown-1m 1f 209yds

2010	**STOTSFOLD** 7-9-0	......	8
2011	**WORKFORCE** 4-9-7	......	8
2012	**CARLTON HOUSE** 4-9-0	......	6
2013	**MUKHADRAM** 4-9-0	......	8
2014	**SHARESTAN** 6-9-0.	......	3
2015	**WESTERN HYMN** 4-9-3.	......	5
2016	**TIME TEST** 4-9-5	......	5
2017	**AUTOCRATIC** 4-9-0.	......	7
2018	**POET'S WORD** 5-9-0	......	5
2019	**REGAL REALITY** 4-9-0	......	6

CORONATION CUP
Epsom-1m 4f 6yds
2010	**FAME AND GLORY** 4-9-0	9
2011	**ST NICHOLAS ABBEY** 4-9-0	5
2012	**ST NICHOLAS ABBEY** 5-9-0	5
2013	**ST NICHOLAS ABBEY** 6-9-0	5
2014	**CIRRUS DES AIGLES** 8-9-0	7
2015	**PETHER'S MOON** 5-9-0	4
2016	**POSTPONED** 5-9-0	9
2017	**HIGHLAND REEL** 5-9-0	10
2018	**CRACKSMAN** 4-9-0	6
2019	**DEFOE** 5-9-0	9

CHARITY SPRINT HANDICAP
York-6f
2010	**VICTOIRE DE LYPHAR** 8-7	20
2011	**LEXI'S HERO** 8-11	20
2012	**SHOLAAN** 8-9	17
2013	**BODY AND SOUL** 8-11	19
2014	**SEE THE SUN** 8-7	20
2015	**TWILIGHT SON** 8-10	16
2016	**MR LUPTON** 9-7	17
2017	**GOLDEN APOLLO** 8-3	18
2018	**ENCRYPTED** 8-8	20
2019	**RECON MISSION** 9-2	22

QUEEN ANNE STAKES
Ascot-1m (st)
2010	**GOLDIKOVA** 5-8-11	10
2011	**CANFORD CLIFFS** 4-9-0	7
2012	**FRANKEL** 4-9-0	11
2013	**DECLARATION OF WAR** 4-9-0	13
2014	**TORONADO** 4-9-0	10
2015	**SOLOW** 5-9-0	8
2016	**TEPIN** 5-8-11	13
2017	**RIBCHESTER** 4-9-0	16
2018	**ACCIDENTAL AGENT** 4-9-0	15
2019	**LORD GLITTERS** 6-9-0	16

PRINCE OF WALES'S STAKES
Ascot-1m 2f
2010	**BYWORD** 4-9-0	12
2011	**REWILDING** 4-9-0	9
2012	**SO YOU THINK** 6-9-0	11
2013	**AL KAZEEM** 5-9-0	11
2014	**THE FUGUE** 5-8-11	8
2015	**FREE EAGLE** 4-9-0	9
2016	**MY DREAM BOAT** 4-9-0	6
2017	**HIGHLAND REEL** 5-9-0	8
2018	**POET'S WORD** 5-9-0	7
2019	**CRYSTAL OCEAN** 5-9-0	8

ST JAMES'S PALACE STAKES (3y)
Ascot-7f 213yds (rnd)
2010	**CANFORD CLIFFS** 9-0	9
2011	**FRANKEL** 9-0	9
2012	**MOST IMPROVED** 9-0	16
2013	**DAWN APPROACH** 9-0	9
2014	**KINGMAN** 9-0	7
2015	**GLENEAGLES** 9-0	5
2016	**GALILEO GOLD** 9-0	9
2017	**BARNEY ROY** 9-0	8
2018	**WITHOUT PAROLE** 9-0	10
2019	**CIRCUS MAXIMUS** 9-0	11

COVENTRY STAKES (2y)
Ascot-6f
2010	**STRONG SUIT** 9-1	13
2011	**POWER** 9-1	23
2012	**DAWN APPROACH** 9-1	22
2013	**WAR COMMAND** 9-1	15
2014	**THE WOW SIGNAL** 9-1	15
2015	**BURATINO** 9-1	17
2016	**CARAVAGGIO** 9-1	18
2017	**RAJASINGHE** 9-1	18
2018	**CALYX** 9-1	23
2019	**ARIZONA** 9-1	17

KING EDWARD VII STAKES (3y)
Ascot-1m 4f
2010	**MONTEROSSO** 8-12	8
2011	**NATHANIEL** 8-12	10
2012	**THOMAS CHIPPENDALE** 8-12	5
2013	**HILLSTAR** 8-12	8
2014	**EAGLE TOP** 9-0	9
2015	**BALIOS** 9-0	7
2016	**ACROSS THE STARS** 9-0	9
2017	**PERMIAN** 9-0	12
2018	**OLD PERSIAN** 9-0	9
2019	**JAPAN** 9-0	8

JERSEY STAKES (3y)
Ascot-7f
2010	**RAINFALL** 8-12	13
2011	**STRONG SUIT** 9-6	9
2012	**ISHVANA** 8-12	22
2013	**GALE FORCE TEN** 9-1	21
2014	**MUSTAJEEB** 9-4	23
2015	**DUTCH CONNECTION** 9-4	16
2016	**RIBCHESTER** 9-6	19
2017	**LE BRIVIDO** 9-1	20
2018	**EXPERT EYE** 9-1	21
2019	**SPACE TRAVELLER** 9-1	18

DUKE OF CAMBRIDGE STAKES
(fillies & mares)
Ascot-1m (st)(Windsor Forest Stakes before 2013)
2010	**STRAWBERRYDAIQUIRI** 4-8-12	10
2011	**LOLLY FOR DOLLY** 4-8-12	13
2012	**JOVIALITY** 4-8-12	13
2013	**DUNTLE** 4-8-12	9
2014	**INTEGRAL** 4-9-0	14
2015	**AMAZING MARIA** 4-9-0	6
2016	**USHERETTE** 4-9-3	14
2017	**QEMAH** 4-9-0	14
2018	**ALJAZZI** 5-9-0	11
2019	**MOVE SWIFTLY** 4-9-0	17

QUEEN MARY STAKES (2y fillies)
Ascot-5f
2010	**MAQAASID** 8-12	18
2011	**BEST TERMS** 8-12	14
2012	**CEILING KITTY** 8-12	27
2013	**RIZEENA** 8-12	23
2014	**ANTHEM ALEXANDER** 9-0	21
2015	**ACAPULCO** 9-0	20
2016	**LADY AURELIA** 9-0	17
2017	**HEARTACHE** 9-0	23
2018	**SIGNORA CABELLO** 9-0	22
2019	**RAFFLE PRIZE** 9-0	25

CORONATION STAKES (3y fillies)
Ascot-7f 213yds (rnd)
2010	LILLIE LANGTRY 9-0	13
2011	IMMORTAL VERSE 9-0	11
2012	FALLEN FOR YOU 9-0	10
2013	SKY LANTERN 9-0	17
2014	RIZEENA 9-0	12
2015	ERVEDYA 9-0	9
2016	QEMAH 9-0	13
2017	WINTER 9-0	7
2018	ALPHA CENTAURI 9-0	12
2019	WATCH ME 9-0	9

COMMONWEALTH CUP (3y)
Ascot-6f
2015	MUHAARAR 9-3	18
2016	QUIET REFLECTION 9-0	10
2017	CARAVAGGIO 9-3	12
2018	EQTIDAAR 9-3	22
2019	ADVERTISE 9-3	9

ROYAL HUNT CUP
Ascot-1m (st)
2010	INVISIBLE MAN 4-8-9	29
2011	JULIENAS 4-8-8	28
2012	PRINCE OF JOHANNE 6-9-3	30
2013	BELGIAN BILL 5-8-11	28
2014	FIELD OF DREAM 7-9-1	30
2015	GM HOPKINS 4-9-3	30
2016	PORTAGE 4-9-5	28
2017	ZHUI FENG 4-9-0	29
2018	SETTLE FOR BAY 4-9-1	30
2019	AFAAK 5-9-3	28

QUEEN'S VASE (3y)
Ascot-1m 5f 211yds (2m before 2017)
2010	MIKHAIL GLINKA 9-1	12
2011	NAMIBIAN 9-1	11
2012	ESTIMATE 8-12	10
2013	LEADING LIGHT 9-4	15
2014	HARTNELL 9-3	10
2015	ALOFT 9-3	13
2016	SWORD FIGHTER 9-3	18
2017	STRADIVARIUS 9-0	13
2018	KEW GARDENS 9-0	12
2019	DASHING WILLOUGHBY 9-0	13

DIAMOND JUBILEE STAKES
Ascot-6f
(Golden Jubilee Stakes before 2012)
2010	STARSPANGLEDBANNER 4-9-4	24
2011	SOCIETY ROCK 4-9-4	16
2012	BLACK CAVIAR 6-9-1	14
2013	LETHAL FORCE 4-9-4	18
2014	SLADE POWER 5-9-4	15
2015	UNDRAFTED 5-9-3	14
2016	TWILIGHT SON 4-9-3	9
2017	THE TIN MAN 5-9-3	9
2018	MERCHANT NAVY 3-9-3	12
2019	BLUE POINT 5-9-3	17

NORFOLK STAKES (2y)
Ascot-5f
2010	APPROVE 9-1	12
2011	BAPAK CHINTA 9-1	15
2012	RECKLESS ABANDON 9-1	11
2013	NO NAY NEVER 9-1	14
2014	BAITHA ALGA 9-1	9
2015	WATERLOO BRIDGE 9-1	10
2016	PRINCE OF LIR 9-1	10
2017	SIOUX NATION 9-1	17
2018	SHANG SHANG SHANG 8-12	10
2019	A'ALI 9-1	14

GOLD CUP
Ascot-2m 4f
2010	RITE OF PASSAGE 6-9-2	12
2011	FAME AND GLORY 5-9-2	15
2012	COLOUR VISION 4-9-0	9
2013	ESTIMATE 4-8-11	14
2014	LEADING LIGHT 4-9-0	12
2015	TRIP TO PARIS 4-9-0	12
2016	ORDER OF ST GEORGE 4-9-0	17
2017	BIG ORANGE 6-9-2	14
2018	STRADIVARIUS 4-9-1	9
2019	STRADIVARIUS 5-9-2	11

RIBBLESDALE STAKES (3y fillies)
Ascot-1m 4f
2010	HIBAAYEB 8-12	11
2011	BANIMPIRE 8-12	12
2012	PRINCESS HIGHWAY 8-12	14
2013	RIPOSTE 8-12	9
2014	BRACELET 9-0	12
2015	CURVY 9-0	10
2016	EVEN SONG 9-0	14
2017	CORONET 9-0	12
2018	MAGIC WAND 9-0	10
2019	STAR CATCHER 9-0	11

HARDWICKE STAKES
Ascot-1m 4f
2010	HARBINGER 4-9-0	11
2011	AWAIT THE DAWN 4-9-0	9
2012	SEA MOON 4-9-0	12
2013	THOMAS CHIPPENDALE 4-9-0	6
2014	TELESCOPE 4-9-1	10
2015	SNOW SKY 4-9-1	7
2016	DARTMOUTH 4-9-1	9
2017	IDAHO 4-9-1	12
2018	CRYSTAL OCEAN 4-9-1	5
2019	DEFOE 5-9-1	8

WOKINGHAM STAKES
Ascot-6f
2010	LADDIES POKER TWO 5-8-11	27
2011	DEACON BLUES 4-8-13	25
2012	DANDY BOY 6-9-8	28
2013	YORK GLORY 5-9-2	26
2014	BACCARAT 5-9-2	28
2015	INTERCEPTION 5-9-3	25
2016	OUTBACK TRAVELLER 5-9-1	28
2017	OUT DO 8-8-13	27
2018	BACCHUS 4-9-6	28
2019	CAPE BYRON 5-9-5	26

KING'S STAND STAKES
Ascot-5f

2010	**EQUIANO** 5-9-4	12
2011	**PROHIBIT** 6-9-4	19
2012	**LITTLE BRIDGE** 6-9-4	22
2013	**SOLE POWER** 6-9-4	19
2014	**SOLE POWER** 7-9-4	16
2015	**GOLDREAM** 6-9-4	18
2016	**PROFITABLE** 4-9-4	17
2017	**LADY AURELIA** 3-8-9	17
2018	**BLUE POINT** 4-9-4	14
2019	**BLUE POINT** 5-9-4	12

NORTHUMBERLAND PLATE
Newcastle-2m 56y Tapeta (2m 19y turf before 2016)

2010	**OVERTURN** 6-8-7	19
2011	**TOMINATOR** 4-8-5	19
2012	**ILE DE RE** 6-9-3	16
2013	**TOMINATOR** 6-9-10	18
2014	**ANGEL GABRIAL** 5-8-12	19
2015	**QUEST FOR MORE** 5-9-4	19
2016	**ANTIQUARIUM** 4-9-5	20
2017	**HIGHER POWER** 5-9-9	20
2018	**WITHHOLD** 5-9-1	20
2019	**WHO DARES WINS** 7-9-1	19

ECLIPSE STAKES
Sandown-1m 1f 209yds

2010	**TWICE OVER** 5-9-7	5
2011	**SO YOU THINK** 5-9-7	5
2012	**NATHANIEL** 4-9-7	9
2013	**AL KAZEEM** 5-9-7	7
2014	**MUKHADRAM** 5-9-7	9
2015	**GOLDEN HORN** 3-8-10	5
2016	**HAWKBILL** 3-8-10	7
2017	**ULYSSES** 4-9-7	9
2018	**ROARING LION** 3-8-11	7
2019	**ENABLE** 5-9-4	8

LANCASHIRE OAKS
(fillies and mares)
Haydock-1m 3f 175yds

2010	**BARSHIBA** 6-9-5	10
2011	**GERTRUDE BELL** 4-9-5	7
2012	**GREAT HEAVENS** 3-8-6	9
2013	**EMIRATES QUEEN** 4-9-5	8
2014	**POMOLOGY** 4-9-5	9
2015	**LADY TIANA** 4-9-5	10
2016	**ENDLESS TIME** 4-9-5	6
2017	**THE BLACK PRINCESS** 4-9-5	7
2018	**HORSEPLAY** 4-9-5	10
2019	**ENBIHAAR** 4-9-5	6

DUCHESS OF CAMBRIDGE STAKES
(2y fillies)
Newmarket-6f
(Cherry Hinton Stakes before 2013)

2010	**MEMORY** 8-12	7
2011	**GAMILATI** 8-12	11
2012	**SENDMYLOVETOROSE** 8-12	10
2013	**LUCKY KRISTALE** 8-12	8
2014	**ARABIAN QUEEN** 9-0	5
2015	**ILLUMINATE** 9-0	9
2016	**ROLY POLY** 9-0	10
2017	**CLEMMIE** 9-0	8

2018	**PRETTY POLLYANNA** 9-0	9
2019	**RAFFLE PRIZE** 9-3	7

BUNBURY CUP
Newmarket-7f (Run as 32Red Trophy in 2010)

2010	**ST MORITZ** 4-9-1	19
2011	**BRAE HILL** 5-9-1	20
2012	**BONNIE BRAE** 5-9-9	15
2013	**FIELD OF DREAM** 6-9-7	19
2014	**HEAVEN'S GUEST** 4-9-3	13
2015	**RENE MATHIS** 5-9-1	17
2016	**GOLDEN STEPS** 5-9-0	16
2017	**ABOVE THE REST** 6-8-10	18
2018	**BURNT SUGAR** 4-9-2	18
2019	**VALE OF KENT** 4-9-4	17

PRINCESS OF WALES'S STAKES
Newmarket-1m 4f

2010	**SANS FRONTIERES** 4-9-2	8
2011	**CRYSTAL CAPELLA** 6-8-13	8
2012	**FIORENTE** 4-9-2	7
2013	**AL KAZEEM** 4-9-5	6
2014	**CAVALRYMAN** 8-9-2	6
2015	**BIG ORANGE** 4-9-2	8
2016	**BIG ORANGE** 5-9-2	7
2017	**HAWKBILL** 4-9-2	7
2018	**BEST SOLUTION** 4-9-6	7
2019	**COMMUNIQUE** 4-9-9	6

JULY STAKES (2y)
Newmarket-6f

2010	**LIBRANNO** 8-12	5
2011	**FREDERICK ENGELS** 8-12	7
2012	**ALHEBAYEB** 8-12	7
2013	**ANJAAL** 8-12	11
2014	**IVAWOOD** 9-0	12
2015	**SHALAA** 9-0	9
2016	**MEHMAS** 9-0	9
2017	**CARDSHARP** 9-0	12
2018	**ADVERTISE** 9-0	8
2019	**ROYAL LYTHAM** 9-0	9

FALMOUTH STAKES
(fillies & mares)
Newmarket-1m

2010	**MUSIC SHOW** 3-8-10	8
2011	**TIMEPIECE** 4-9-5	11
2012	**GIOFRA** 4-9-5	10
2013	**ELUSIVE KATE** 4-9-5	4
2014	**INTEGRAL** 4-9-7	7
2015	**AMAZING MARIA** 4-9-7	7
2016	**ALICE SPRINGS** 3-8-12	7
2017	**ROLY POLY** 3-8-12	7
2018	**ALPHA CENTAURI** 3-8-12	7
2019	**VERACIOUS** 4-9-7	6

SUPERLATIVE STAKES (2y)
Newmarket-7f

2010	**KING TORUS** 9-0	6
2011	**RED DUKE** 9-0	7
2012	**OLYMPIC GLORY** 9-0	9
2013	**GOOD OLD BOY LUKEY** 9-0	8
2014	**ESTIDHKAAR** 9-1	8
2015	**BIRCHWOOD** 9-1	8
2016	**BOYNTON** 9-1	9

2017	**GUSTAV KLIMT** 9-1	10
2018	**QUORTO** 9-1	7
2019	**MYSTERY POWER** 9-1	8

JULY CUP
Newmarket-6f

2010	**STARSPANGLEDBANNER** 4-9-5	14
2011	**DREAM AHEAD** 3-8-13	16
2012	**MAYSON** 4-9-5	12
2013	**LETHAL FORCE** 4-9-5	11
2014	**SLADE POWER** 5-9-6	13
2015	**MUHAARAR** 3-9-0	14
2016	**LIMATO** 4-9-6	18
2017	**HARRY ANGEL** 3-9-0	10
2018	**U S NAVY FLAG** 3-9-0	13
2019	**TEN SOVEREIGNS** 9-0	12

WEATHERBYS SUPER SPRINT (2y)
Newbury-5f 34 yds

2010	**TEMPLE MEADS** 8-6	24
2011	**CHARLES THE GREAT** 8-11	25
2012	**BODY AND SOUL** 7-12	22
2013	**PENIAPHOBIA** 8-8	24
2014	**TIGGY WIGGY** 9-1	24
2015	**LATHOM** 9-0	22
2016	**MRS DANVERS** 8-0	23
2017	**BENGALI BOYS** 8-7	23
2018	**GINGER NUT** 8-5	25
2019	**BETTYS HOPE** 8-4	24

SUMMER MILE
Ascot-7f 213yds (rnd)

2010	**PREMIO LOCO** 6-9-1	8
2011	**DICK TURPIN** 4-9-4	5
2012	**FANUNALTER** 6-9-1	8
2013	**ALJAMAAHEER** 4-9-1	11
2014	**GUEST OF HONOUR** 5-9-1	9
2015	**AROD** 4-9-1	6
2016	**MUTAKAYYEF** 5-9-1	10
2017	**MUTAKAYYEF** 6-9-1	9
2018	**BEAT THE BANK** 4-9-1	8
2019	**BEAT THE BANK** 5-9-4	8

PRINCESS MARGARET STAKES
(2y fillies)
Ascot-6f

2010	**SORAAYA** 8-12	11
2011	**ANGELS WILL FALL** 8-12	7
2012	**MAUREEN** 8-12	6
2013	**PRINCESS NOOR** 8-12	10
2014	**OSAILA** 9-0	8
2015	**BESHARAH** 9-0	6
2016	**FAIR EVA** 9-0	7
2017	**NYALETI** 9-0	7
2018	**ANGEL'S HIDEAWAY** 9-0	7
2019	**UNDER THE STARS** 9-0	9

LENNOX STAKES
Goodwood-7f

2010	**LORD SHANAKILL** 4-9-2	12
2011	**STRONG SUIT** 3-8-9	9
2012	**CHACHAMAIDEE** 5-8-13	7
2013	**GARSWOOD** 3-8-9	10
2014	**ES QUE LOVE** 5-9-3	7
2015	**TOORMORE** 4-9-3	7

2016	**DUTCH CONNECTION** 4-9-3	8
2017	**BRETON ROCK** 7-9-3	13
2018	**SIR DANCEALOT** 4-9-3	12
2019	**SIR DANCEALOT** 5-9-3	9

STEWARDS' CUP
Goodwood-6f

2010	**EVENS AND ODDS** 6-8-10	28
2011	**HOOF IT** 4-10-0	27
2012	**HAWKEYETHENOO** 6-9-9	27
2013	**REX IMPERATOR** 4-9-4	27
* 2014	**INTRINSIC** 4-8-11	24
2015	**MAGICAL MEMORY** 3-8-12	27
2016	**DANCING STAR** 3-8-12	27
2017	**LANCELOT DU LAC** 7-9-5	26
2018	**GIFTED MASTER** 5-9-6	26
2019	**KHAADEM** 3-9-6	27

* Run as 32Red Cup in 2014

GORDON STAKES (3y)
Goodwood-1m 4f

2010	**REBEL SOLDIER** 9-0	10
2011	**NAMIBIAN** 9-3	10
2012	**NOBLE MISSION** 9-0	7
2013	**CAP O'RUSHES** 9-0	7
2014	**SNOW SKY** 9-0	7
2015	**HIGHLAND REEL** 9-1	9
2016	**ULYSSES** 9-1	9
2017	**CRYSTAL OCEAN** 9-1	5
2018	**CROSS COUNTER** 9-1	4
2019	**NAYEF ROAD** 9-1	9

VINTAGE STAKES (2y)
Goodwood-7f

2010	**KING TORUS** 9-3	7
2011	**CHANDLERY** 9-0	7
2012	**OLYMPIC GLORY** 9-3	10
2013	**TOORMORE** 9-0	12
2014	**HIGHLAND REEL** 9-1	8
2015	**GALILEO GOLD** 9-1	8
2016	**WAR DECREE** 9-1	9
2017	**EXPERT EYE** 9-1	10
2018	**DARK VISION** 9-1	12
2019	**PINATUBO** 9-1	7

SUSSEX STAKES
Goodwood-1m

2010	**CANFORD CLIFFS** 3-8-13	7
2011	**FRANKEL** 3-8-13	4
2012	**FRANKEL** 4-9-7	4
2013	**TORONADO** 3-8-13	7
2014	**KINGMAN** 3-9-0	4
2015	**SOLOW** 5-9-8	8
2016	**THE GURKHA** 3-9-0	10
2017	**HERE COMES WHEN** 7-9-8	7
2018	**LIGHTNING SPEAR** 7-9-8	8
2019	**TOO DARN HOT** 3-9-0	7

RICHMOND STAKES (2y)
Goodwood-6f

2010	**LIBRANNO** 9-3	6
2011	**HARBOUR WATCH** 9-0	10
2012	**HEAVY METAL** 9-0	8
2013	**SAAYERR** 9-0	10
2014	**IVAWOOD** 9-3	8
2015	**SHALAA** 9-3	8

2016	**MEHMAS** 9-3	4
2017	**BARRAQUERO** 9-0	7
2018	**LAND FORCE** 9-0	9
2019	**GOLDEN HORDE** 9-0	8

KING GEORGE STAKES
Goodwood-5f

2010	**BORDERLESCOTT** 8-9-0	15
2011	**MASAMAH** 5-9-0	11
2012	**ORTENSIA** 7-9-5	17
2013	**MOVIESTA** 3-8-12	17
2014	**TAKE COVER** 7-9-1	15
2015	**MUTHMIR** 5-9-6	15
2016	**TAKE COVER** 9-9-2	17
2017	**BATTAASH** 3-8-13	11
2018	**BATTAASH** 4-9-5	11
2019	**BATTAASH** 5-9-5	8

GOODWOOD CUP
Goodwood-2m

2010	**ILLUSTRIOUS BLUE** 7-9-7	10
2011	**OPINION POLL** 5-9-7	15
2012	**SADDLER'S ROCK** 4-9-7	10
2013	**BROWN PANTHER** 5-9-7	14
2014	**CAVALRYMAN** 8-9-8	8
2015	**BIG ORANGE** 4-9-8	11
2016	**BIG ORANGE** 5-9-8	14
2017	**STRADIVARIUS** 3-8-8	14
2018	**STRADIVARIUS** 4-9-9	7
2019	**STRADIVARIUS** 5-9-9	9

MOLECOMB STAKES (2y)
Goodwood-5f

2010	**ZEBEDEE** 9-0	12
2011	**REQUINTO** 9-0	13
2012	**BUNGLE INTHEJUNGLE** 9-0	10
2013	**BROWN SUGAR** 9-0	8
2014	**COTAI GLORY** 9-1	8
2015	**KACHY** 9-1	10
2016	**YALTA** 9-1	9
2017	**HAVANA GREY** 9-1	10
2018	**RUMBLE INTHEJUNGLE** 9-1	11
2019	**LIBERTY BEACH** 8-12	13

NASSAU STAKES
(fillies and mares)
Goodwood-1m 1f 197yds

2010	**MIDDAY** 4-9-6	7
2011	**MIDDAY** 5-9-6	6
2012	**THE FUGUE** 3-8-11	8
2013	**WINSILI** 3-8-11	14
2014	**SULTANINA** 4-9-7	6
2015	**LEGATISSIMO** 3-8-12	9
2016	**MINDING** 3-8-11	5
2017	**WINTER** 3-8-13	6
2018	**WILD ILLUSION** 3-8-13	6
2019	**DEIRDRE** 5-9-7	9

HUNGERFORD STAKES
Newbury-7f

2010	**SHAKESPEAREAN** 3-8-11	7
2011	**EXCELEBRATION** 3-8-13	9
2012	**LETHAL FORCE** 3-8-12	9
2013	**GREGORIAN** 4-9-3	5
2014	**BRETON ROCK** 4-9-5	6

2015	**ADAAY** 3-9-2	11
2016	**RICHARD PANKHURST** 4-9-6	8
2017	**MASSAAT** 4-9-6	8
2018	**SIR DANCEALOT** 4-9-6	8
2019	**GLORIOUS JOURNEY** 4-9-6	7

GEOFFREY FREER STAKES
Newbury-1m 5f 61yds

2010	**SANS FRONTIERES** 4-9-8	8
2011	**CENSUS** 3-8-6	10
2012	**MOUNT ATHOS** 5-9-4	6
2013	**ROYAL EMPIRE** 4-9-4	10
2014	**SEISMOS** 6-9-4	11
2015	**AGENT MURPHY** 4-9-5	6
2016	**KINGS FETE** 5-9-7	5
2017	**DEFOE** 3-8-10	8
2018	**HAMADA** 4-9-5	6
2019	**TECHNICIAN** 3-8-10	5

INTERNATIONAL STAKES
York-1m 2f 56yds

2010	**RIP VAN WINKLE** 4-9-5	9
2011	**TWICE OVER** 6-9-5	5
2012	**FRANKEL** 4-9-5	9
2013	**DECLARATION OF WAR** 4-9-5	6
2014	**AUSTRALIA** 3-8-12	6
2015	**ARABIAN QUEEN** 3-8-9	7
2016	**POSTPONED** 5-9-6	12
2017	**ULYSSES** 4-9-6	7
2018	**ROARING LION** 3-8-13	8
2019	**JAPAN** 3-8-13	9

GREAT VOLTIGEUR STAKES (3y)
York-1m 3f 188yds

2010	**REWILDING** 8-12	10
2011	**SEA MOON** 8-12	8
2012	**THOUGHT WORTHY** 8-12	6
2013	**TELESCOPE** 8-12	7
2014	**POSTPONED** 9-0	9
2015	**STORM THE STARS** 9-0	7
2016	**IDAHO** 9-0	6
2017	**CRACKSMAN** 9-0	6
2018	**OLD PERSIAN** 9-3	9
2019	**LOGICIAN** 9-0	5

LOWTHER STAKES
(2y fillies)
York-6f

2010	**HOORAY** 8-12	8
2011	**BEST TERMS** 9-1	11
2012	**ROSDHU QUEEN** 8-12	10
2013	**LUCKY KRISTALE** 9-1	9
2014	**TIGGY WIGGY** 9-0	9
2015	**BESHARAH** 9-0	9
2016	**QUEEN KINDLY** 9-0	8
2017	**THREADING** 9-0	9
2018	**FAIRYLAND** 9-0	9
2019	**LIVING IN THE PAST** 9-0	10

YORKSHIRE OAKS
(fillies and mares)
York-1m 3f 188yds

2010	**MIDDAY** 4-9-7	8
2011	**BLUE BUNTING** 3-8-11	8
2012	**SHARETA** 4-9-7	6

2013	THE FUGUE 4-9--7	7
2014	TAPESTRY 3-8-11	7
2015	PLEASCACH 3-8-11	11
2016	SEVENTH HEAVEN 3-8-11	12
2017	ENABLE 3-8-12	6
2018	SEA OF CLASS 3-8-12	8
2019	ENABLE 5-9-7	4

EBOR HANDICAP
York-1m 5f 188yds

2010	DIRAR 5-9-1	20
2011	MOYENNE CORNICHE 6-8-10	20
2012	WILLING FOE 5-9-9	19
2013	TIGER CLIFF 5-9-1	14
2014	MUTUAL REGARD 5-9-4	19
2015	LITIGANT 7-9-1	19
2016	HEARTBREAK CITY 6-9-1	20
2017	NAKEETA 6-9-0	19
2018	MUNTAHAA 5-9-9	20
2019	MUSTAJEER 6-9-5	22

GIMCRACK STAKES (2y)
York-6f

2010	APPROVE 9-1	11
2011	CASPAR NETSCHER 8-12	9
2012	BLAINE 8-12	8
2013	ASTAIRE 8-12	7
2014	MUHAARAR 9-0	9
2015	AJAYA 9-0	8
2016	BLUE POINT 9-0	10
2017	SANDS OF MALI 9-0	10
2018	EMARAATY ANA 9-0	9
2019	THREAT 9-0	12

NUNTHORPE STAKES
York-5f

2010	SOLE POWER 3-9-9	12
2011	MARGOT DID 3-9-6	15
2012	ORTENSIA 7-9-8	19
2013	JWALA 4-9--8	17
2014	SOLE POWER 7-9-11	13
2015	MECCA'S ANGEL 4-9-10	19
2016	MECCA'S ANGEL 5-9-8	19
2017	MARSHA 4-9-8	11
2018	ALPHA DELPHINI 7-9-11	15
2019	BATTAASH 5-9-11	11

LONSDALE CUP
York-2m 56yds

2010	OPINION POLL 4 9-1	8
2011	OPINION POLL 5 9-4	10
2012	TIMES UP 6 9-1	9
2013	AHZEEMAH 4 9-3	7
2014	PALE MIMOSA 5-9-0	7
2015	MAX DYNAMITE 5-9-3	8
2016	QUEST FOR MORE 6-9-3	7
2017	MONTALY 6-9-3	9
2018	STRADIVARIUS 4-9-6	9
2019	STRADIVARIUS 5-9-6	4

PRESTIGE STAKES (2y fillies)
Goodwood-7f

2010	THEYSKENS' THEORY 9-0	7
2011	REGAL REALM 9-0	6
2012	OLLIE OLGA 9-0	8
2013	AMAZING MARIA 9-0	7
2014	MALABAR 9-0	8
2015	HAWKSMOOR 9-0	9
2016	KILMAH 9-0	7
2017	BILLESDON BROOK 9-0	10
2018	ANTONIA DE VEGA 9-0	8
2019	BOOMER 9-0	6

CELEBRATION MILE
Goodwood-1m

2010	POET'S VOICE 3-8-9	4
2011	DUBAWI GOLD 3-8-9	7
2012	PREMIO LOCO 8-9-1	5
2013	AFSARE 6-9-1	8
2014	BOW CREEK 3-8-12	8
2015	KODI BEAR 3-8-12	6
2016	LIGHTNING SPEAR 5-9-4	5
2017	LIGHTNING SPEAR 6-9-4	6
2018	BEAT THE BANK 4-9-7	8
2019	DUKE OF HAZZARD 3-8-12	6

SOLARIO STAKES (2y)
Sandown-7f 16yds

2010	NATIVE KHAN 9-0	6
2011	TALWAR 9-0	4
2012	FANTASTIC MOON 9-0	7
2013	KINGMAN 9-0	4
2014	AKTABANTAY 9-1	5
2015	FIRST SELECTION 9-1	10
2016	SOUTH SEAS 9-1	10
2017	MASAR 9-1	7
2018	TOO DARN HOT 9-1	6
2019	POSITIVE 9-1	6

SPRINT CUP
Haydock-6f

2010	MARKAB 7-9-3	13
2011	DREAM AHEAD 3-9-1	16
2012	SOCIETY ROCK 5-9-3	13
2013	GORDON LORD BYRON 5-9-3	13
2014	G FORCE 3-9-1	17
2015	TWILIGHT SON 3-9-1	15
2016	QUIET REFLECTION 3-8-12	14
2017	HARRY ANGEL 3-9-1	11
2018	THE TIN MAN 5-9-3	12
2019	HELLO YOUMZAIN 3-9-1	11

SEPTEMBER STAKES
Kempton-1m 3f 219yds Polytrack

2010	LAAHEB 4-9-4	9
2011	MODUN 4-9-4	7
2012	DANDINO 5-9-4	9
2013	PRINCE BISHOP 6-9-4	10
2014	PRINCE BISHOP 7-9-12	7
2015	JACK HOBBS 3-9-3	7
2016	ARAB SPRING 6-9-5	6
2017	CHEMICAL CHARGE 5-9-5	6
2018	ENABLE 4-9-2	4
2019	ROYAL LINE 5-9-5	12

MAY HILL STAKES
(2y fillies)
Doncaster-1m

2010	**WHITE MOONSTONE** 8-12		7
2011	**LYRIC OF LIGHT** 8-12		8
2012	**CERTIFY** 8-12		7
2013	**IHTIMAL** 8-12		6
2014	**AGNES STEWART** 9-0		8
2015	**TURRET ROCKS** 9-0		8
2016	**RICH LEGACY** 9-0		9
2017	**LAURENS** 9-0		8
2018	**FLEETING** 9-0		11
2019	**POWERFUL BREEZE** 9-0		9

PORTLAND HANDICAP
Doncaster-5f 143yds

2010	**POET'S PLACE** 5-9-4	22
2011	**NOCTURNAL AFFAIR** 5-9-5	21
2012	**DOC HAY** 5-8-11	20
2013	**ANGELS WILL FALL** 4-9-2	21
2014	**MUTHMIR** 4-9-7	20
2015	**STEPS** 7-9-7	20
2016	**CAPTAIN COLBY** 4-9-0	20
2017	**SPRING LOADED** 5-8-9	22
2018	**A MOMENTOFMADNESS** 5-9-4	21
2019	**OXTED** 3-9-4	22

PARK HILL STAKES
(fillies and mares)
Doncaster-1m 6f 115yds

2010	**EASTERN ARIA** 4-9-4	12
2011	**MEEZNAH** 4-9-4	7
2012	**WILD COCO** 4-9-4	9
2013	**THE LARK** 3-8--6	9
2014	**SILK SARI** 4-9-5	13
2015	**GRETCHEN** 4-9-5	11
2016	**SIMPLE VERSE** 4-9-5	12
2017	**ALYSSA** 4-9-5	10
2018	**GOD GIVEN** 4-9-5	7
2019	**ENBIHAAR** 4-9-5	8

DONCASTER CUP
Doncaster-2m 1f 197yds

2010	**SAMUEL** 6-9-1	10
2011	**SADDLER'S ROCK** 3-8-1	7
2012	**TIMES UP** 6-9-1	10
2013	**TIMES UP** 7-9-3	7
2014	**ESTIMATE** 5-9-0	12
2015	**PALLASATOR** 6-9-3	11
2016	**SHEIKHZAYEDROAD** 7-9-3	8
2017	**DESERT SKYLINE** 3-8-5	9
2018	**THOMAS HOBSON** 8-9-5	8
2019	**STRADIVARIUS** 5-9-10	5

CHAMPAGNE STAKES (2y)
Doncaster-7f 6yds

2010	**SAAMIDD** 8-12	6
2011	**TRUMPET MAJOR** 8-12	5
2012	**TORONADO** 8-12	5
2013	**OUTSTRIP** 8-12	4
2014	**ESTIDHKAAR** 9-3	6
2015	**EMOTIONLESS** 9-0	6
2016	**RIVET** 9-0	6
2017	**SEAHENGE** 9-0	7
2018	**TOO DARN HOT** 9-0	6
2019	**THREAT** 9-3	5

PARK STAKES
Doncaster-7f 6yds

2010	**BALTHAZAR'S GIFT** 7-9-4	12
2011	**PREMIO LOCO** 7-9-4	5
2012	**LIBRANNO** 4-9-4	8
2013	**VIZTORIA** 3-8-11	9
2014	**ANSGAR** 6-9-4	7
2015	**LIMATO** 3-9-0	15
2016	**BRETON ROCK** 6-9-4	8
2017	**ACLAIM** 4-9-4	8
2018	**MUSTASHRY** 5-9-4	9
2019	**SIR DANCEALOT** 5-9-7	5

FLYING CHILDERS STAKES (2y)
Doncaster-5f

2010	**ZEBEDEE** 9-0	12
2011	**REQUINTO** 9-0	10
2012	**SIR PRANCEALOT** 9-0	9
2013	**GREEN DOOR** 9-0	7
2014	**BEACON** 9-1	14
2015	**GUTAIFAN** 9-1	9
2016	**ARDAD** 9-1	11
2017	**HEARTACHE** 8-12	9
2018	**SOLDIER'S CALL** 9-1	8
2019	**A'ALI** 9-1	7

AYR GOLD CUP
Ayr-6f

2010	**REDFORD** 5-9-2	26
2011	**OUR JONATHAN** 4-9-6	26
2012	**CAPTAIN RAMIUS** 6-9-0	26
2013	**HIGHLAND COLORI** 5-8-13	26
2014	**LOUIS THE PIOUS** 6-9-4	27
2015	**DON'T TOUCH** 3-9-1	25
2016	**BRANDO** 4-9-10	23
* 2017	**DONJUAN TRIUMPHANT** 4-9-10	17
2018	**SON OF REST** 4-9-3 dead heated with	
	BARON BOLT 5-8-12	25
2019	**ANGEL ALEXANDER** 3-8-13	24

* Run at Haydock Park as 32Red Gold Cup

MILL REEF STAKES (2y)
Newbury-6f 8yds

2010	**TEMPLE MEADS** 9-1	7
2011	**CASPAR NETSCHER** 9-4	9
2012	**MOOHAAJIM** 9-1	8
2013	**SUPPLICANT** 9-1	7
2014	**TOOCOOLFORSCHOOL** 9-1	6
2015	**RIBCHESTER** 9-1	6
2016	**HARRY ANGEL** 9-1	7
2017	**JAMES GARFIELD** 9-1	9
2018	**KESSAAR** 9-1	7
2019	**PIERRE LAPIN** 9-1	8

ROYAL LODGE STAKES (2y)
Newmarket-1m (run at Ascot before 2011)

2010	**FRANKEL** 8-12	5
2011	**DADDY LONG LEGS** 8-12	6
2012	**STEELER** 8-12	8
2013	**BERKSHIRE** 8-12	6
2014	**ELM PARK** 9-0	6
2015	**FOUNDATION** 9-0	6
2016	**BEST OF DAYS** 9-0	8
2017	**ROARING LION** 9-0	5
2018	**MOHAWK** 9-0	4
2019	**ROYAL DORNOCH** 9-0	7

CHEVELEY PARK STAKES (2y fillies)
Newmarket-6f

2010	HOORAY 8-12	11
2011	LIGHTENING PEARL 8-12	9
2012	ROSDHU QUEEN 8-12	11
2013	VORDA 8-12	7
2014	TIGGY WIGGY 9-0	9
2015	LUMIERE 9-0	8
2016	BRAVE ANNA 9-0	6
2017	CLEMMIE 9-0	11
2018	FAIRYLAND 9-0	11
2019	MILLISLE 9-0	11

SUN CHARIOT STAKES
(fillies and mares)
Newmarket-1m

2010	SAHPRESA 5-9-2	11
2011	SAHPRESA 6-9-3	8
2012	SIYOUMA 4-9-3	8
2013	SKY LANTERN 3-8-13	7
2014	INTEGRAL 4-9-3	7
2015	ESOTERIQUE 5-9-3	9
2016	ALICE SPRINGS 3-9-0	8
2017	ROLY POLY 3-9-0	13
2018	LAURENS 3-9-0	9
2019	BILLESDON BROOK 4-9-3	9

CAMBRIDGESHIRE
Newmarket-1m 1f

2010	CREDIT SWAP 5-8-7	35
2011	PRINCE OF JOHANNE 5-8-9	32
2012	BRONZE ANGEL 3-8-8	33
2013	EDUCATE 4-9-9	31
2014	BRONZE ANGEL 5-8-8	31
2015	THIRD TIME LUCKY 3-8-4	34
2016	SPARK PLUG 5-9-4	31
2017	DOLPHIN VISTA 4-8-7	34
2018	WISSAHICKON 3-9-5	33
2019	LORD NORTH 3-8-10	30

CUMBERLAND LODGE STAKES
Ascot-1m 4f

2010	LAAHEB 4-9-3	6
2011	QUEST FOR PEACE 3-8-7	7
2012	HAWAAFEZ 4-8-11	6
2013	SECRET NUMBER 3-8-7	7
2014	PETHER'S MOON 4-9-6	5
2015	STAR STORM 3-8-8	8
2016	MOVE UP 3-8-13	9
2017	DANEHILL KODIAC 4-9-2	9
2018	LARAAIB 4-9-2	5
2019	MORANDO 6-9-5	7

FILLIES' MILE (2y fillies)
Newmarket-1m
(run at Ascot before 2011)

2010	WHITE MOONSTONE 8-12	9
2011	LYRIC OF LIGHT 8-12	8
2012	CERTIFY 8-12	6
2013	CHRISELLIAM 8-12	8
2014	TOGETHER FOREVER 9-0	7
2015	MINDING 9-0	10
2016	RHODODENDRON 9-0	8
2017	LAURENS 9-0	11
2018	IRIDESSA 9-0	8
2019	QUADRILATERAL 9-0	9

MIDDLE PARK STAKES (2y)
Newmarket-6f

2010	DREAM AHEAD 8-12	8
2011	CRUSADE 8-12	16
2012	RECKLESS ABANDON 8-12	10
2013	ASTAIRE 9-0	10
2014	CHARMING THOUGHT 9-0	6
2015	SHALAA 9-0	7
2016	THE LAST LION 9-0	10
2017	U S NAVY FLAG 9-0	12
2018	TEN SOVEREIGNS 9-0	8
2019	EARTHLIGHT 9-0	8

CHALLENGE STAKES
Newmarket-7f

2010	RED JAZZ 3-9-1	14
2011	STRONG SUIT 3-9-5	8
2012	FULBRIGHT 3-9-1	11
2013	FIESOLANA 4-9-0	9
2014	HERE COMES WHEN 4-9-7	13
2015	CABLE BAY 4-9-3	10
2016	ACLAIM 3-9-1	12
2017	LIMATO 5-9-3	11
2018	LIMATO 6-9-3	8
2019	MUSTASHRY 6-9-8	5

DEWHURST STAKES (2y)
Newmarket-7f

2010	FRANKEL 9-1	6
2011	PARISH HALL 9-1	9
2012	DAWN APPROACH 9-1	6
2013	WAR COMMAND 9-1	6
2014	BELARDO 9-1	6
2015	AIR FORCE BLUE 9-1	7
2016	CHURCHILL 9-1	7
2017	U S NAVY FLAG 9-1	9
2018	TOO DARN HOT 9-1	7
2019	PINATUBO 9-1	9

CESAREWITCH
Newmarket-2m 2f

2010	AIM TO PROSPER 6-7-13	32
2011	NEVER CAN TELL 4-8-11	33
2012	AIM TO PROSPER 8-9-10	34
2013	SCATTER DICE 4-8-8	33
2014	BIG EASY 7-8-7	33
2015	GRUMETI 7-8-2	34
2016	SWEET SELECTION 4-8-8	33
2017	WITHHOLD 4-8-8	34
2018	LOW SUN 5-9-2	33
2019	STRATUM 6-9-7	30

ROCKFEL STAKES (2y fillies)
Newmarket-7f

2010	CAPE DOLLAR 8-12	10
2011	WADING 8-12	9
2012	JUST THE JUDGE 8-12	11
2013	AL THAKHIRA 8-12	8
2014	LUCIDA 9-0	9
2015	PROMISING RUN 9-0	7
2016	SPAIN BURG 9-0	8
2017	JULIET CAPULET 9-0	10
2018	JUST WONDERFUL 9-0	9
2019	DAAHYEH 9-0	8

QIPCO BRITISH CHAMPIONS SPRINT STAKES
Ascot-6f (run as Diadem Stakes before 2011)

2011	**DEACON BLUES** 4-9-0	16
2012	**MAAREK** 5-9-0	15
2013	**SLADE POWER** 4-9-0	14
2014	**GORDON LORD BYRON** 6-9-2	15
2015	**MUHAARAR** 3-9-1	20
2016	**THE TIN MAN** 4-9-2	13
2017	**LIBRISA BREEZE** 5-9-2	12
2018	**SANDS OF MALI** 3-9-1	14
2019	**DONJUAN TRIUMPHANT** 6-9-2	17

QUEEN ELIZABETH II STAKES (BRITISH CHAMPIONS MILE)
Ascot-1m (st - rnd before 2011)

2010	**POET'S VOICE** 3-8-13	8
2011	**FRANKEL** 3-9-0	8
2012	**EXCELEBRATION** 4-9-3	8
2013	**OLYMPIC GLORY** 3-9-0	12
2014	**CHARM SPIRIT** 3-9-1	11
2015	**SOLOW** 5-9-4	9
2016	**MINDING** 3-8-12	13
2017	**PERSUASIVE** 4-9-1	15
2018	**ROARING LION** 3-9-1	13
2019	**KING OF CHANGE** 3-9-1	16

QIPCO BRITISH CHAMPIONS LONG DISTANCE CUP
(formerly Jockey Club Cup, run at Newmarket before 2011)
Ascot-2m

2011	**FAME AND GLORY** 5 9-10	10
2012	**RITE OF PASSAGE** 8-9-7	9
2013	**ROYAL DIAMOND** 7-9-7	12
2014	**FORGOTTEN RULES** 4-9-7	9
2015	**FLYING OFFICER** 5-9-7	13
2016	**SHEIKHZAYEDROAD** 7-9-7	10
2017	**ORDER OF ST GEORGE** 5-9-7	13
2018	**STRADIVARIUS** 4-9-7	6
2019	**KEW GARDENS** 4-9-7	6

QIPCO BRITISH CHAMPIONS FILLIES' AND MARES' STAKES
(formerly Pride Stakes, run at Newmarket before 2011)
Ascot-1m 4f

2011	**DANCING RAIN** 3-8-10	10
2012	**SAPPHIRE** 4-9-3	10
2013	**SEAL OF APPROVAL** 4-9-3	8
2014	**MADAME CHIANG** 3-8-12	10
2015	**SIMPLE VERSE** 3-8-12	12
2016	**JOURNEY** 4-9-5	13
2017	**HYDRANGEA** 3-8-13	10
2018	**MAGICAL** 3-8-13	11
2019	**STAR CATCHER** 3-8-13	12

QIPCO CHAMPION STAKES (BRITISH CHAMPIONS MIDDLE DISTANCE)
Ascot-1m 2f (run at Newmarket before 2011)

2010	**TWICE OVER** 5-9-3	10
2011	**CIRRUS DES AIGLES** 5-9-3	12
2012	**FRANKEL** 4-9-3	6
2013	**FARHH** 5-9-3	10
2014	**NOBLE MISSION** 5-9-5	9
2015	**FASCINATING ROCK** 4-9-5	13
2016	**ALMANZOR** 3-9-0	10
2017	**CRACKSMAN** 3-9-1	10
2018	**CRACKSMAN** 4-9-5	8
2019	**MAGICAL** 4-9-2	12

BALMORAL HANDICAP
Ascot-1m

2014	**BRONZE ANGEL** 5-9-2	27
2015	**MUSADDAS** 5-8-2	20
2016	**YUFTEN** 5-9-1	19
2017	**LORD GLITTERS** 6-9-3	20
2018	**SHARJA BRIDGE** 4-9-5	20
2019	**ESCOBAR** 5-9-6	20

CORNWALLIS STAKES (2y)
Newmarket-5f (run at Ascot before 2014)

2010	**ELECTRIC WAVES** 8-11	14
2011	**PONTY ACCLAIM** 8-11	16
2012	**BUNGLE INTHEJUNGLE** 9-3	6
2013	**HOT STREAK** 9-0	12
2014	**ROYAL RAZALMA** 8-12	12
2015	**QUIET REFLECTION** 8-12	11
2016	**MRS DANVERS** 8-12	9
2017	**ABEL HANDY** 9-1	12
2018	**SERGEI PROKOFIEV** 9-1	14
2019	**GOOD VIBES** 8-12	12

TWO-YEAR-OLD TROPHY (2y)
Redcar-6f

2010	**LADIES ARE FOREVER** 7-12	22
2011	**BOGART** 8-12	22
2012	**BODY AND SOUL** 8-1	21
2013	**VENTURA MIST** 8-7	23
2014	**LIMATO** 8-12	23
2015	**LOG OUT ISLAND** 9-2	20
2016	**WICK POWELL** 8-3	20
2017	**DARKANNA** 8-1	23
2018	**SUMMER DAYDREAM** 8-9	21
2019	**SUMMER SANDS** 8-3	17

HORRIS HILL STAKES (2y)
Newbury-7f

2010	**KLAMMER** 8-12	10
2011	**TELL DAD** 8-12	14
2012	**TAWHID** 8-12	8
2013	**PIPING ROCK** 8-12	11
2014	**SMAIH** 9-0	9
2015	**CRAZY HORSE** 9-0	9
2016	**PLEASELETMEWIN** 9-0	13
2017	**NEBO** 9-0	6
2018	**MOHAATHER** 9-0	8
* 2019	ABANDONED	

VERTEM FUTURITY TROPHY (2y)
(Racing Post Trophy before 2018)
Doncaster-1m (St)

2010	**CASAMENTO** 9-0	10
2011	**CAMELOT** 9-0	5
2012	**KINGSBARNS** 9-0	7
2013	**KINGSTON HILL** 9-0	11
2014	**ELM PARK** 9-1	7
2015	**MARCEL** 9-1	7
2016	**RIVET** 9-1	10
2017	**SAXON WARRIOR** 9-1	12
2018	**MAGNA GRECIA** 9-1	11
* 2019	**KAMEKO** 9-1	11

* Run at Newcastle 1m 5yds (Tapeta)

NOVEMBER HANDICAP
Doncaster-1m 3f 197yds
2010	**TIMES UP** 4-8-13	22
2011	**ZUIDER ZEE** 4-8-13	23
2012	**ART SCHOLAR** 5-8-7	23
2013	**CONDUCT** 6-9-2	23
2014	**OPEN EAGLE** 5-8-12	23
2015	**LITIGANT** 7-9-10	22
2016	**PRIZE MONEY** 3-8-10	15
2017	**SAUNTER** 4-8-13	23
2018	**ROYAL LINE** 4-9-8	23
* 2019	ABANDONED	

Want the **BIGGEST** offers?

Daily PROMOS?

Biggest **BOOKIES?** racingpost.com/freebets

For The Must-Have Racing Offers
RACING POST

Racing Post backs responsible gambling. 18+ begambleaware.org 0808 8020 133

WINNERS OF PRINCIPAL RACES IN IRELAND

IRISH 2000 GUINEAS (3y)
The Curragh-1m

2010	**CANFORD CLIFFS** 9-0	13
2011	**RODERIC O'CONNOR** 9-0	8
2012	**POWER** 9-0	10
2013	**MAGICIAN** 9-0	10
2014	**KINGMAN** 9-0	11
2015	**GLENEAGLES** 9-0	11
2016	**AWTAAD** 9-0	8
2017	**CHURCHILL** 9-0	6
2018	**ROMANISED** 9-0	11
2019	**PHOENIX OF SPAIN** 9-0	14

TATTERSALLS GOLD CUP
The Curragh-1m 2f 110yds

2010	**FAME AND GLORY** 4-9-0	6
2011	**SO YOU THINK** 5-9-1	5
2012	**SO YOU THINK** 6-9-1	5
2013	**AL KAZEEM** 5-9-3	4
2014	**NOBLE MISSION** 5-9-3	5
2015	**AL KAZEEM** 7-9-3	6
2016	**FASCINATING ROCK** 5-9-3	5
2017	**DECORATED KNIGHT** 5-9-3	8
2018	**LANCASTER BOMBER** 4-9-3	5
2019	**MAGICAL** 4-9-0	5

IRISH 1000 GUINEAS (3y fillies)
The Curragh-1m

2010	**BETHRAH** 9-0	19
2011	**MISTY FOR ME** 9-0	15
2012	**SAMITAR** 9-0	8
2013	**JUST THE JUDGE** 9-0	15
2014	**MARVELLOUS** 9-0	11
2015	**PLEASCACH** 9-0	18
2016	**JET SETTING** 9-0	10
2017	**WINTER** 9-0	8
2018	**ALPHA CENTAURI** 9-0	13
2019	**HERMOSA** 9-0	10

IRISH DERBY (3y)
The Curragh-1m 4f

2010	**CAPE BLANCO** 9-0	10
2011	**TREASURE BEACH** 9-0	8
2012	**CAMELOT** 9-0	5
2013	**TRADING LEATHER** 9-0	9
2014	**AUSTRALIA** 9-0	5
2015	**JACK HOBBS** 9-0	8
2016	**HARZAND** 9-0	9
2017	**CAPRI** 9-0	9
2018	**LATROBE** 9-0	12
2019	**SOVEREIGN** 9-0	8

PRETTY POLLY STAKES
(fillies and mares)
Curragh-1m 2f

2010	**CHINESE WHITE** 5-9-9	9
2011	**MISTY FOR ME** 3-8-12	7
2012	**IZZI TOP** 4-9-9	4

2013	**AMBIVALENT** 4-9-10	9
2014	**THISTLE BIRD** 6-9-10	8
2015	**DIAMONDSANDRUBIES** 3-8-12	9
2016	**MINDING** 3-8-12	5
2017	**NEZWAAH** 4-9-8	11
2018	**URBAN FOX** 4-9-8	6
2019	**IRIDESSA** 3-8-12	5

IRISH OAKS (3y fillies)
The Curragh-1m 4f

2010	**SNOW FAIRY** 9-0	15
2011	**BLUE BUNTING** 9-0	9
2012	**GREAT HEAVENS** 9-0	7
2013	**CHICQUITA** 9-0	7
2014	**BRACELET** 9--0	9
2015	**COVERT LOVE** 9-0	10
2016	**SEVENTH HEAVEN** 9-0	11
2017	**ENABLE** 9-0	10
2018	**SEA OF CLASS** 9-0	7
2019	**STAR CATCHER** 9-0	8

PHOENIX STAKES (2y)
The Curragh-6f

2010	**ZOFFANY** 9-1	7
2011	**LA COLLINA** 8-12	9
2012	**PEDRO THE GREAT** 9-3	6
2013	**SUDIRMAN** 9-3	6
2014	**DICK WHITTINGTON** 9-3	5
2015	**AIR FORCE BLUE** 9-3	7
2016	**CARAVAGGIO** 9-3	5
2017	**SIOUX NATION** 9-3	8
2018	**ADVERTISE** 9-3	5
2019	**SISKIN** 9-3	5

MATRON STAKES (fillies and mares)
Leopardstown-1m

2010	**LILLIE LANGTRY** 3-8-12	6
2011	**EMULOUS** 4-9-5	8
*2012	**CHACHAMAIDEE** 5-9-5	11
2013	**LA COLLINA** 4-9-5	12
2014	**FIESOLANA** 5-9-5	10
2015	**LEGATISSIMO** 3-9-0	9
2016	**ALICE SPRINGS** 3-9-0	8
2017	**HYDRANGEA** 3-9-0	10
2018	**LAURENS** 3-9-0	7
2019	**IRIDESSA** 3-9-0	7

* Duntle disqualified from first place

IRISH CHAMPION STAKES
Leopardstown-1m 2f

2010	**CAPE BLANCO** 3-9-0	6
2011	**SO YOU THINK** 5-9-7	6
2012	**SNOW FAIRY** 5-9-4	6
2013	**THE FUGUE** 4-9-4	6
2014	**THE GREY GATSBY** 3-9-0	7
2015	**GOLDEN HORN** 3-9-0	7
2016	**ALMANZOR** 3-9-0	12
2017	**DECORATED KNIGHT** 5-9-7	10

2018	**ROARING LION** 3-9-1	7
2019	**MAGICAL** 4-9-4	8

IRISH CAMBRIDGESHIRE
The Curragh-1m

2010	**HUJAYLEA** 7-8-3	25
2011	**CASTLE BAR SLING** 6-8-11	21
2012	**PUNCH YOUR WEIGHT** 3-8-6	18
2013	**MORAN GRA** 6-8-13	20
2014	**SRETAW** 5-8-8	21
2015	**HINT OF A TINT** 5-9-3	22
2016	**SEA WOLF** 4-9-5	24
2017	**ELUSIVE TIME** 9-8-9	27
2018	**KENYA** 3-9-2	21
2019	**JASSAAR** 4-8-8	25

MOYGLARE STUD STAKES
(2y fillies)
The Curragh-7f

2010	**MISTY FOR ME** 8-12	12
2011	**MAYBE** 9-1	8
2012	**SKY LANTERN** 9-0	13
2013	**RIZEENA** 9-0	7
2014	**CURSORY GLANCE** 9-0	10
2015	**MINDING** 9-0	9
2016	**INTRICATELY** 9-0	7
2017	**HAPPILY** 9-0	8
2018	**SKITTER SKATTER** 9-0	10
2019	**LOVE** 9-0	9

VINCENT O'BRIEN (NATIONAL)
STAKES (2y)
The Curragh-7f

2010	**PATHFORK** 9-1	9
2011	**POWER** 9-1	9
2012	**DAWN APPROACH** 9-3	7
2013	**TOORMORE** 9-3	5
2014	**GLENEAGLES** 9-3	5
2015	**AIR FORCE BLUE** 9-3	5
2016	**CHURCHILL** 9-3	7
2017	**VERBAL DEXTERITY** 9-3	7
2018	**QUORTO** 9-3	7
2019	**PINATUBO** 9-3	8

IRISH ST LEGER
The Curragh-1m 6f

2010	**SANS FRONTIERES** 4-9-11	8
2011	**DUNCAN** 6-9-11 dead heated with	6
	JUKEBOX JURY 5-9-11	6
2012	**ROYAL DIAMOND** 6-9-11	9
2013	**VOLEUSE DE COEURS** 4-9-8	10
2014	**BROWN PANTHER** 6-9-11	11
2015	**ORDER OF ST GEORGE** 3-9-0	11
2016	**WICKLOW BRAVE** 7-9-11	4
2017	**ORDER OF ST GEORGE** 5-9-10	10
2018	**FLAG OF HONOUR** 3-9-1	6
2019	**SEARCH FOR A SONG** 3-8-11	10

IRISH CESAREWITCH
The Curragh-2m

2010	**BRIGHT HORIZON** 3-8-7	23
2011	**MINSK** 3-8-9	19
2012	**VOLEUSE DE COEURS** 3-9-1	27
2013	**MONTEFELTRO** 5-9-4	30
2014	**EL SALVADOR** 5-9-5	21

2015	**DIGENTA** 8-9-10	20
2016	**LAWS OF SPIN** 3-8-6	20
* 2017	**LORD ERSKINE** 4-8-5	24
2018	**BRAZOS** 4-8-12	24
2019	**ROYAL ILLUSION** 7-8-5	18

* Run at Navan

LADBROKES HURDLE (Handicap)
Leopardstown-2m
(Various sponsors)

2011	**FINAL APPROACH** 5-10-9	26
2012	**CITIZENSHIP** 6-10-3	30
2013	**ABBEY LANE** 8-10-8	28
2014	**GILGAMBOA** 6-10-9	24
2015	**KATIE T** 6-10-9	24
2016	**HENRY HIGGINS** 6-10-10	23
2017	**ICE COLD SOUL** 7-10-2	20
2018	**OFF YOU GO** 5-9-10	28
2019	**OFF YOU GO** 6-11-5	19
2020	**THOSEDAYSAREGONE** 7-9-12	22

IRISH CHAMPION HURDLE
Leopardstown-2m

2011	**HURRICANE FLY** 7-11-10	5
2012	**HURRICANE FLY** 8-11-10	5
2013	**HURRICANE FLY** 9-11-10	5
2014	**HURRICANE FLY** 10-11-10	4
2015	**HURRICANE FLY** 11-11-10	6
2016	**FAUGHEEN** 8-11-10	5
2017	**PETIT MOUCHOIR** 6 11-10	4
2018	**SUPASUNDAE** 8-11-10	8
2019	**APPLE'S JADE** 7-11-3	6
2020	**HONEYSUCKLE** 6 11-3	9

IRISH GOLD CUP
Leopardstown-3m(Hennessy Gold Cup before 2016)

2010	**JONCOL** 7-11-10	7
2011	**KEMPES** 8-11-10	9
2012	**QUEL ESPRIT** 8-11-10	7
2013	**SIR DES CHAMPS** 7-11-10	4
2014	**LAST INSTALMENT** 9-11-10	7
2015	**CARLINGFORD LOUGH** 9-11-10	8
2016	**CARLINGFORD LOUGH** 10-11-10	10
2017	**SIZING JOHN** 7-11-10	7
2018	**EDWULF** 9-11-10	10
2019	**BELLSHILL** 9-11-10	4

IRISH GRAND NATIONAL
Fairyhouse-3m 5f

2010	**BLUESEA CRACKER** 8-10-4	26
2011	**ORGANISEDCONFUSION** 6-9-13	25
2012	**LION NA BEARNAI** 10-10-5	29
2013	**LIBERTY COUNSEL** 10-9-5	28
2014	**SHUTTHEFRONTDOOR** 7-10-13	26
2015	**THUNDER AND ROSES** 7-10-6	28
2016	**ROGUE ANGEL** 8-10-6	27
2017	**OUR DUKE** 7-11-4	28
2018	**GENERAL PRINCIPLE** 9-10-0	30
2019	**BURROWS SAINT** 6-10-8	30

WINNERS OF PRINCIPAL RACES IN FRANCE

PRIX GANAY
ParisLongchamp-1m 2f 110yds

2010	**CUTLASS BAY** 4-9-2	9
2011	**PLANTEUR** 4-9-2	7
2012	**CIRRUS DES AIGLES** 6-9-2	6
2013	**PASTORIUS** 4-9-2	9
2014	**CIRRUS DES AIGLES** 8-9-2	8
2015	**CIRRUS DES AIGLES** 9-9-2	7
* 2016	**DARIYAN** 4-9-2	10
* 2017	**CLOTH OF STARS** 4-9-2	7
2018	**CRACKSMAN** 4-9-2	7
2019	**WALDGEIST** 5-9-2	5

* Run at Saint-Cloud

POULE D'ESSAI DES POULAINS (3y)
ParisLongchamp-1m

2010	**LOPE DE VEGA** 9-2	15
2011	**TIN HORSE** 9-2	14
2012	**LUCAYAN** 9-2	12
2013	**STYLE VENDOME** 9-2	18
2014	**KARAKONTIE** 9-2	12
2015	**MAKE BELIEVE** 9-2	18
* 2016	**THE GURKHA** 9-2	13
* 2017	**BRAMETOT** 9-2	13
2018	**OLMEDO** 9-2	11
2019	**PERSIAN KING** 9-2	10

* Run at Deauville

POULE D'ESSAI DES POULICHES (3y filllies)
ParisLongchamp-1m

* 2010	**SPECIAL DUTY** 9-0	10
2011	**GOLDEN LILAC** 9-0	16
2012	**BEAUTY PARLOUR** 9-0	13
2013	**FLOTILLA** 9-0	20
2014	**AVENIR CERTAIN** 9-0	16
2015	**ERVEDYA** 9-0	14
** 2016	**LA CRESSONNIERE** 9-0	14
** 2017	**PRECIEUSE** 9-0	18
2018	**TEPPAL** 9-0	14
2019	**CASTLE LADY** 9-0	10

* Liliside disqualified from first place
** Run at Deauville

PRIX SAINT-ALARY (3y fillies)
ParisLongchamp-1m 2f

2010	**SARAFINA** 9-0	9
2011	**WAVERING** 9-0	12
2012	**SAGAWARA** 9-0	8
2013	**SILASOL** 9-0	8
* 2014	**VAZIRA** 9-0	8
2015	**QUEEN'S JEWEL** 9-0	9
** 2016	**JEMAYEL** 9-0	9
** 2017	**SOBETSU** 9-0	11
2018	**LAURENS** 9-0	5
2019	**SIYARAFINA** 9-0	11

* We Are disqualified from first place
** Run at Deauville

PRIX D'ISPAHAN
ParisLongchamp-1m 1f 55yds

2010	**GOLDIKOVA** 5-8-13	8
2011	**GOLDIKOVA** 6-8-13	9
2012	**GOLDEN LILAC** 4-8-13	8
2013	**MAXIOS** 5-9-2	7
2014	**CIRRUS DES AIGLES** 8-9-2	6
2015	**SOLOW** 5-9-2	4
* 2016	**A SHIN HIKARI** 5-9-2	9
* 2017	**MEKHTAAL** 4-9-2	5
2018	**RECOLETOS** 4-9-2	6
2019	**ZABEEL PRINCE** 6-9-2	9

* Run at Chantilly

PRIX DU JOCKEY CLUB (3y)
Chantilly-1m 2f 110yds

2010	**LOPE DE VEGA** 9-2	22
2011	**RELIABLE MAN** 9-2	16
2012	**SAONOIS** 9-2	20
2013	**INTELLO** 9-2	19
2014	**THE GREY GATSBY** 9-2	16
2015	**NEW BAY** 9-2	14
2016	**ALMANZOR** 9-2	16
2017	**BRAMETOT** 9-2	12
2018	**STUDY OF MAN** 9-2	16
2019	**SOTTSASS** 9-3	15

PRIX DE DIANE (3y fillies)
Chantilly-1m 2f 110yds

2010	**SARAFINA** 9-0	9
2011	**GOLDEN LILAC** 9-0	9
2012	**VALYRA** 9-0	12
2013	**TREVE** 9-0	11
2014	**AVENIR CERTAIN** 9-0	12
2015	**STAR OF SEVILLE** 9-0	17
2016	**LA CRESSONNIERE** 9-0	16
2017	**SENGA** 9-1	16
2018	**LAURENS** 9-0	13
2019	**CHANNEL** 9-0	16

GRAND PRIX DE SAINT-CLOUD
Saint-Cloud-1m 4f

2010	**PLUMANIA** 4-8-13	7
2011	**SARAFINA** 4-8-13	5
2012	**MEANDRE** 4-9-2	4
2013	**NOVELLIST** 4-9-2	11
* 2014	**NOBLE MISSION** 5-9-2	7
2015	**TREVE** 5-8-13	9
2016	**SILVERWAVE** 4-9-2	11
2017	**ZARAK** 4-9-2	10
2018	**WALDGEIST** 4-9-3	6
2019	**CORONET** 5-9-0	7

* Spiritjim disqualified from first place

PRIX JEAN PRAT (3y)
Chantilly-1m

2010	**DICK TURPIN** 9-2	8
2011	**MUTUAL TRUST** 9-2	7
2012	**AESOP'S FABLES** 9-2	8

2013	**HAVANA GOLD** 9-2	12
2014	**CHARM SPIRIT** 9-2	7
2015	**TERRITORIES** 9-2	8
2016	**ZELZAL** 9-2	9
2017	**THUNDER SNOW** 9-3	5
2018	**INTELLOGENT** 9-2	7
2019	**TOO DARN HOT** 9-2	12

GRAND PRIX DE PARIS (3y)
ParisLongchamp-1m 4f

2010	**BÉHKABAD** 9-2	9
2011	**MEANDRE** 9-2	7
2012	**IMPERIAL MONARCH** 9-2	9
2013	**FLINTSHIRE** 9-2	8
2014	**GALLANTE** 9-2	11
2015	**ERUPT** 9-2	6
* 2016	**MONT ORMEL** 9-2	8
* 2017	**SHAKEEL** 9-2	9
2018	**KEW GARDENS** 9-3	6
2019	**JAPAN** 9-2	8

* Run at Saint-Cloud

PRIX ROTHSCHILD
(fillies and mares)
Deauville-1m
(run as Prix d'Astarte before 2008)

2010	**GOLDIKOVA** 5-9-0	7
2011	**GOLDIKOVA** 6-9-2	8
2012	**ELUSIVE KATE** 3-8-9	5
2013	**ELUSIVE KATE** 4-9-2	12
2014	**ESOTERIQUE** 4-9-0	4
2015	**AMAZING MARIA** 4-9-2	8
2016	**QEMAH** 3-8-9	10
2017	**ROLY POLY** 3-8-9	10
2018	**WITH YOU** 3-8-9	10
2019	**LAURENS** 4-9-3	9

PRIX MAURICE DE GHEEST
Deauville-6f 110yds

2010	**REGAL PARADE** 6-9-2	15
2011	**MOONLIGHT CLOUD** 3-8-8	13
2012	**MOONLIGHT CLOUD** 4-8-13	9
2013	**MOONLIGHT CLOUD** 5-8-13	14
2014	**GARSWOOD** 4-9-2	14
2015	**MUHAARAR** 3-8-11	12
2016	**SIGNS OF BLESSING** 5-9-2	15
2017	**BRANDO** 5-9-3	13
2018	**POLYDREAM** 3-8-10	20
2019	**ADVERTISE** 3-8-13	15

PRIX JACQUES LE MAROIS
Deauville-1m

2010	**MAKFI** 3-8-11	8
2011	**IMMORTAL VERSE** 3-8-8	12
2012	**EXCELEBRATION** 4-9-4	11
2013	**MOONLIGHT CLOUD** 5-9-1	13
2014	**KINGMAN** 3-8-13	5
2015	**ESOTERIQUE** 5-9-1	9
2016	**RIBCHESTER** 3-8-13	11
2017	**AL WUKAIR** 3-8-13	6
2018	**ALPHA CENTAURI** 3-8-9	11
2019	**ROMANISED** 4-9-5	8

PRIX MORNY (2y)
Deauville-6f

2010	**DREAM AHEAD** 9-0	11
2011	**DABIRSIM** 9-0	7
2012	**RECKLESS ABANDON** 9-0	11
2013	**NO NAY NEVER** 9-0	10
2014	**THE WOW SIGNAL** 9-0	9
2015	**SHALAA** 9-0	5
2016	**LADY AURELIA** 8-10	5
2017	**UNFORTUNATELY** 9-0	8
2018	**PRETTY POLLYANNA** 8-10	9
2019	**EARTHLIGHT** 9-0	8

PRIX JEAN ROMANET
(fillies and mares)
Deauville-1m 2f

2010	**STACELITA** 4-9-0	8
2011	**ANNOUNCE** 4-9-0	5
* 2012	**IZZI TOP** 4-9-0	8
2013	**ROMANTICA** 4-9-0	6
2014	**RIBBONS** 4-9-0	11
2015	**ODELIZ** 5-9-0	11
2016	**SPEEDY BOARDING** 4-9-0	10
2017	**AJMAN PRINCESS** 4-9-0	10
2018	**NONZA** 4-9-0	9
2019	**CORONET** 4-9-0	8

* Snow Fairy disqualified from first place

PRIX DU MOULIN DE LONGCHAMP
ParisLongchamp-1m

2010	**FUISSE** 4-9-2	6
2011	**EXCELEBRATION** 3-8-11	8
2012	**MOONLIGHT CLOUD** 4-8-13	4
2013	**MAXIOS** 5-9-2	7
2014	**CHARM SPIRIT** 3-8-11	10
2015	**ERVEDYA** 3-8-9	6
* 2016	**VADAMOS** 5-9-3	6
*2017	**RIBCHESTER** 4-9-3	7
2018	**RECOLETOS** 4-9-4	11
2019	**CIRCUS MAXIMUS** 3-8-13	10

* Run at Chantilly

PRIX VERMEILLE (fillies and mares)
ParisLongchamp-1m 4f

* 2010	**MIDDAY** 4-9-3	12
2011	**GALIKOVA** 3-8-8	6
2012	**SHARETA** 4-9-2	13
2013	**TREVE** 3-8-8	10
2014	**BALTIC BARONESS** 4-9-3	9
2015	**TREVE** 5-9-3	9
** 2016	**LEFT HAND** 3-8-8	6
** 2017	**BATEEL** 5-9-3	11
2018	**KITESURF** 4-9-3	8
2019	**STAR CATCHER** 3-8-9	9

* Dar Re Mi disqualified from first place
** Run at Chantilly

PRIX DE LA FORET
ParisLongchamp-7f

2010	**GOLDIKOVA** 5-8-13	10
2011	**DREAM AHEAD** 3-9-0	8
2012	**GORDON LORD BYRON** 4-9-2	11
2013	**MOONLIGHT CLOUD** 5-8-13	11
2014	**OLYMPIC GLORY** 4-9-2	14
2015	**MAKE BELIEVE** 3-9-0	13
* 2016	**LIMATO** 4-9-2	11

* 2017 **ACLAIM** 4-9-2................................10
2018 **ONE MASTER** 4-8-13........................15
2019 **ONE MASTER** 5-8-13........................12
* Run at Chantilly

PRIX DU CADRAN
ParisLongchamp-2m 4f
2010 **GENTOO** 6-9-2................................8
2011 **KASBAH BLISS** 9-9-2........................10
2012 **MOLLY MALONE** 4-8-13......................10
2013 **ALTANO** 7-9-2................................10
2014 **HIGH JINX** 6-9-2............................8
2015 **MILLE ET MILLE** 5-9-2......................10
* 2016 **QUEST FOR MORE** 6-9-2....................12
* 2017 **VAZIRABAD** 5-9-2..........................6
2018 **CALL THE WIND** 4-9-2.......................8
2019 **HOLDTHASIGREEN** 7-9-2.....................10
* Run at Chantilly

PRIX DE L'ABBAYE DE LONGCHAMP
ParisLongchamp-5f
2010 **GILT EDGE GIRL** 4-9-7.......................21
2011 **TANGERINE TREES** 6-9-11....................15
2012 **WIZZ KID** 4-9-7..............................18
2013 **MAAREK** 6-9-11..............................20
2014 **MOVE IN TIME** 6-9-11.......................18
2015 **GOLDREAM** 6-9-11...........................18
** 2016 **MARSHA** 3--9--7...........................17
* 2017 **BATTAASH** 3-9-11..........................13
2018 **MABS CROSS** 4-9-7..........................16
2019 **GLASS SLIPPERS** 3-9-7......................16
** Run at Chantilly

PRIX JEAN-LUC LAGARDERE (2y)
ParisLongchamp-1m (7f before 2015)
2010 **WOOTTON BASSETT** 9-0........................9
2011 **DABIRSIM** 9-0................................7
2012 **OLYMPIC GLORY** 9-0..........................8
2013 **KARAKONTIE** 9-0.............................8
* 2014 **FULL MAST** 9-0.............................9
2015 **ULTRA** 9-0..................................11
** 2016 **NATIONAL DEFENSE** 9-0....................7
** 2017 **HAPPILY** 8-10.............................6
2018 **ROYAL MARINE** 9-0...........................6
2019 **VICTOR LUDORUM** 9-0.........................7
* Gleneagles disqualified from first place
** Run at Chantilly

PRIX MARCEL BOUSSAC (2y fillies)
ParisLongchamp-1m
2010 **MISTY FOR ME** 8-11..........................8
2011 **ELUSIVE KATE** 8-11..........................5
2012 **SILASOL** 8-11...............................9
2013 **INDONESIENNE** 8-11.........................12
2014 **FOUND** 8-11.................................12
2015 **BALLYDOYLE** 8-11............................8
* 2016 **WUHEIDA** 8-11.............................11
* 2017 **WILD ILLUSION** 8-11.......................7
2018 **LILY'S CANDLE** 8-11.........................8
2019 **ALBIGNA** 8-11...............................9
* Run at Chantilly

PRIX DE L'OPERA (fillies and mares)
ParisLongchamp-1m 2f
2010 **LILY OF THE VALLEY** 3-8-11..................11
2011 **NAHRAIN** 3-8-11.............................10
2012 **RIDASIYNA** 3-8-11...........................13
2013 **DALKALA** 4-9-2..............................9
2014 **WE ARE** 3-8-11.............................11
2015 **COVERT LOVE** 3-8-11........................13
* 2016 **SPEEDY BOARDING** 4-9-2....................7
* 2017 **RHODODENDRON** 3-8-11......................13
2018 **WILD ILLUSION** 3-8-11......................15
2019 **VILLA MARINA** 3-8-11.......................12
* Run at Chantilly

PRIX ROYAL-OAK
ParisLongchamp-1m 7f 110yds
2010 **GENTOO** 6-9-4...............................10
2011 **BE FABULOUS** 4-9-1..........................14
2012 **LES BEAUFS** 3-8-9...........................9
2013 **TAC DE BOISTRON** 6-9-4.....................15
2014 **TAC DE BOISTRON** 7-9-4.....................13
2015 **VAZIRABAD** 3-8-10...........................13
* 2016 **VAZIRABAD** 4-9-4...........................9
** 2017 **ICE BREEZE** 3-8-10........................9
2018 **HOLDTHASIGREEN** 6-9-4.......................8
2019 **TECHNICIAN** 3-8-10..........................6
* Run at Chantilly
** Run at Saint-Cloud

CRITERIUM INTERNATIONAL (2y)
Saint-Cloud-7f (1m before 2015)
2010 **RODERIC O'CONNOR** 9-0......................10
2011 **FRENCH FIFTEEN** 9-0.........................11
2012 **LOCH GARMAN** 9-0............................6
2013 **ECTOT** 9-0..................................4
2014 **VERT DE GRECE** 9-0..........................9
2015 **JOHANNES VERMEER** 9-0.......................8
2016 **THUNDER SNOW** 9-0...........................9
2017 ABANDONED
* 2018 **ROYAL MEETING** 9-0.........................6
** 2019 **ALSON** 9-0................................2
* Run at Chantilly
** Run at ParisLongChamp

CRITERIUM DE SAINT-CLOUD (2y)
Saint-Cloud-1m 2f
2010 **RECITAL** 9-0................................10
2011 **MANDAEAN** 9-0...............................8
2012 **MORANDI** 9-0................................8
2013 **PRINCE GIBRALTAR** 9-0......................12
2014 **EPICURIS** 9-0...............................6
2015 **ROBIN OF NAVAN** 9-0........................10
2016 **WALDGEIST** 9-0.............................13
2017 ABANDONED
2018 **WONDERMENT** 8-10............................9
2019 **MKFANCY** 9-0................................8

WINNERS OF OTHER OVERSEAS RACES

DUBAI WORLD CUP
Meydan-1m 2f Tapeta

2010	GLORIA DE CAMPEAO 7-9-0	14
2011	VICTOIRE PISA 4-9-0	14
2012	MONTEROSSO 5-9-0	13
2013	ANIMAL KINGDOM 5-9-0	13
2014	AFRICAN STORY 7-9-0	16
2015	PRINCE BISHOP 8-9-0	9
2016	CALIFORNIA CHROME 5-9-0	12
2017	ARROGATE 4-9-0	14
2018	THUNDER SNOW 4-9-0	10
2019	THUNDER SNOW 5-9-0	12

KENTUCKY DERBY
Churchill Downs-1m 2f dirt

2010	SUPER SAVER 9-0	20
2011	ANIMAL KINGDOM 9-0	19
2012	I'LL HAVE ANOTHER 9-0	20
2013	ORB 9-0	19
2014	CALIFORNIA CHROME 9-0	19
2015	AMERICAN PHAROAH 9-0	18
2016	NYQUIST 9-0	20
2017	ALWAYS DREAMING 9-0	20
2018	JUSTIFY 9-0	20
* 2019	COUNTRY HOUSE 9-0	19

* Maximum Security disqualified from first place

BREEDERS' CUP TURF
Various courses-1m 4f

2010	DANGEROUS MIDGE 4-9-0	7
2011	ST NICHOLAS ABBEY 4-9-0	9
2012	LITTLE MIKE 5-9-0	12
2013	MAGICIAN 3-8-10	12
2014	MAIN SEQUENCE 5-9-0	12
2015	FOUND 3-8-7	12
2016	HIGHLAND REEL 4-9-0	12
2017	TALISMANIC 4-9-0	13
2018	ENABLE 4-8-11	13
2019	BRICKS AND MORTAR 5-9-0	12

BREEDERS' CUP CLASSIC
Various courses-1m 2f dirt/pro-ride

2010	BLAME 4-9-0	12
2011	DROSSELMEYER 4-9-0	12
2012	FORT LARNED 4-9-0	12
2013	MUCHO MACHO MAN 5-9-0	11
2014	BAYERN 3-8-10	14
2015	AMERICAN PHAROAH 3-8-10	8
2016	ARROGATE 3-8-10	9
2017	GUN RUNNER 4-9-0	11
2018	ACCELERATE 5-9-0	14
2019	VINO ROSSO 4-9-0	11

MELBOURNE CUP
Flemington-2m

2010	AMERICAIN 5-8-8	23
2011	DUNADEN 5-8-8	23
2012	GREEN MOON 5-8-6	24
2013	FIORENTE 5-8-9	24
2014	PROTECTIONIST 4-8-13	22
2015	PRINCE OF PENZANCE 6-8-5	24
2016	ALMANDIN 6-8-3	24
2017	REKINDLING 3-8-2	23
2018	CROSS COUNTER 3-8-0	24
2019	VOW AND DECLARE 4-8-3	24

JAPAN CUP
Tokyo-1m 4f

* 2010	ROSE KINGDOM 3-8-9	18
2011	BUENA VISTA 5-8-9	16
2012	GENTILDONNA 3-8-5	17
2013	GENTILDONNA 4-8-9	17
2014	EPIPHANEIA 4-9-0	18
2015	SHONAN PANDORA 4-8-9	18
2016	KITASAN BLACK 4-9-0	17
2017	CHEVAL GRAND 5-9-0	17
2018	ALMOND EYE 3-8-5	14
2019	SUAVE RICHARD 5-9-0	15

* Buena Vista disqualified from first place

WINNERS OF PRINCIPAL NATIONAL HUNT RACES

BETVICTOR GOLD CUP (HANDICAP CHASE)
Cheltenham-2m 4f 78yds

2010	LITTLE JOSH 8-10-5	18
2011	GREAT ENDEAVOUR 7-10-3	20
2012	AL FEROF 7-11-8	18
2013	JOHNS SPIRIT 6-10-2	20
2014	CAID DU BERLAIS 5-10-13	18
2015	ANNACOTTY 7-11-0	20
2016	TAQUIN DU SEUIL 9-11-11	17
2017	SPLASH OF GINGE 9-10-6	17

2018	BARON ALCO 7-10-11	18
2019	HAPPY DIVA 8-11-0	17

BETFAIR CHASE
Haydock-3m 1f 125yds (3m 24yds before 2017)

2010	IMPERIAL COMMANDER 9-11-7	7
2011	KAUTO STAR 11-11-7	6
2012	SILVINIACO CONTI 6-11-7	5
2013	CUE CARD 7-11-7	8
2014	SILVINIACO CONTI 8-11-7	9
2015	CUE CARD 9-11-7	5

2016	**CUE CARD** 10-11-7	6
2017	**BRISTOL DE MAI** 6-11-7	6
2018	**BRISTOL DE MAI** 7-11-7	5
2019	**LOSTINTRANSLATION** 7-11-7	4

LADBROKES TROPHY HANDICAP CHASE
Newbury-3m 1f 214yds
(Run as Hennessy Gold Cup before 2017)

2010	**DIAMOND HARRY** 7-10-0	20
2011	**CARRUTHERS** 8-10-4	18
2012	**BOBS WORTH** 7-11-6	19
2013	**TRIOLO D'ALENE** 6-11-1	21
2014	**MANY CLOUDS** 7-11-6	19
2015	**SMAD PLACE** 8-11-4	15
2016	**NATIVE RIVER** 6-11-1	19
2017	**TOTAL RECALL** 8-10-8	20
2018	**SIZING TENNESSEE** 10-11-3	12
2019	**DE RASHER COUNTER** 7-10-10	24

TINGLE CREEK CHASE
Sandown-2m

* 2010	**MASTER MINDED** 7-11-7	9
2011	**SIZING EUROPE** 9-11-7	7
2012	**SPRINTER SACRE** 6-11-7	7
2013	**SIRE DE GRUGY** 7-11-7	7
2014	**DODGING BULLETS** 6-11-7	10
2015	**SIRE DE GRUGY** 9-11-7	7
2016	**UN DE SCEAUX** 8-11-7	6
2017	**POLITOLOGUE** 6-11-7	6
2018	**ALTIOR** 8-11-7	4
2019	**DEFI DU SEUIL** 6-11-7	8

* Run at Cheltenham over 2m 110yds

CHRISTMAS HURDLE
Kempton-2m

* 2010	**BINOCULAR** 7-11-7	6
2011	**BINOCULAR** 7-11-7	6
2012	**DARLAN** 5-11-7	7
2013	**MY TENT OR YOURS** 6-11-7	6
2014	**FAUGHEEN** 6-11-7	5
2015	**FAUGHEEN** 7-11-7	6
2016	**YANWORTH** 6-11-7	5
2017	**BUVEUR D'AIR** 6-11-7	4
2018	**VERDANA BLUE** 6-11-0	5
2019	**EPATANTE** 5-11-0	10

* Run in January 2011

KING GEORGE VI CHASE
Kempton-3m

* 2010	**LONG RUN** 6-11-10	9
2011	**KAUTO STAR** 11-11-10	7
2012	**LONG RUN** 7-11-10	9
2013	**SILVINIACO CONTI** 7-11-10	9
2014	**SILVINIACO CONTI** 8-11-10	10
2015	**CUE CARD** 9-11-10	9
2016	**THISTLECRACK** 8-11-10	9
2017	**MIGHT BITE** 8-11-10	8
2018	**CLAN DES OBEAUX** 6-11-10	10
2019	**CLAN DES OBEAUX** 7-11-10	5

* Run in January 2011

WELSH GRAND NATIONAL (HANDICAP CHASE)
Chepstow-3m 5f 110yds

* 2010	**SYNCHRONISED** 8-11-6	18
2011	**LE BEAU BAI** 8-10-1	20
** 2012	**MONBEG DUDE** 8-10-1	17
2013	**MOUNTAINOUS** 8-10-0	20
2014	**EMPEROR'S CHOICE** 7-10-8	19
*** 2015	**MOUNTAINOUS** 11-10-6	20
2016	**NATIVE RIVER** 6-11-12	20
**** 2017	**RAZ DE MAREE** 13-10-10	20
2018	**ELEGANT ESCAPE** 6-11-8	20
2019	**POTTERS CORNER** 9-10-4	17

* Run in January 2011
** Run in January 2013
*** Run in January 2016
**** Run in January 2018

CLARENCE HOUSE CHASE
(Victor Chandler Chase before 2014)
Ascot-2m 167yds

2011	**MASTER MINDED** 8-11-7	9
2012	**SOMERSBY** 8-11-7	8
* 2013	**SPRINTER SACRE** 7-11-7	7
2014	**SIRE DE GRUGY** 8-11-7	7
2015	**DODGING BULLETS** 7-11-7	5
2016	**UN DE SCEAUX** 8-11-7	5
* 2017	**UN DE SCEAUX** 9-11-7	7
2018	**UN DE SCEAUX** 10-11-7	5
2019	**ALTIOR** 9-11-7	3
2020	**DEFI DU SEUIL** 7-11-7	5

* Run at Cheltenham

BETFAIR HANDICAP HURDLE
Newbury-2m 69yds(Totesport Trophy before 2012)

2011	**RECESSION PROOF** 5-10-8	15
2012	**ZARKANDAR** 5-11-4	20
2013	**MY TENT OR YOURS** 6-11-2	21
2014	**SPLASH OF GINGE** 6-10-3	20
2015	**VIOLET DANCE** 5-10-9	23
2016	**AGRAPART** 5-10-5	22
2017	**BALLYANDY** 6-11-7	16
2018	**KALASHNIKOV** 5-11-5	24
* 2019	**AL DANCER** 6-11-8	14
2020	**PIC D'ORHY** 5-11-5	24

* run at Ascot over 1m 7 ½f

SUPREME NOVICES' HURDLE
Cheltenham-2m 87yds

2010	**MENORAH** 5-11-7	18
2011	**AL FEROF** 6-11-7	15
2012	**CINDERS AND ASHES** 5-11-7	19
2013	**CHAMPAGNE FEVER** 6-11-7	12
2014	**VAUTOUR** 5-11-7	18
2015	**DOUVAN** 5-11-7	12
2016	**ALTIOR** 6-11-7	14
2017	**LABAIK** 6-11-7	14
2018	**SUMMERVILLE BOY** 6-11-7	19
2019	**KLASSICAL DREAM** 5-11-7	16

ARKLE CHALLENGE TROPHY (NOVICES' CHASE)
Cheltenham-1m 7f 199yds

2010	SIZING EUROPE 8-11-7	12
2011	CAPTAIN CHRIS 7-11-7	10
2012	SPRINTER SACRE 6-11-7	6
2013	SIMONSIG 7-11-7	7
2014	WESTERN WARHORSE 6-11-4	9
2015	UN DE SCEAUX 7-11-4	11
2016	DOUVAN 6-11-4	7
2017	ALTIOR 7-11-4	9
2018	FOOTPAD 6-11-4	5
2019	DUC DES GENIEVRES 6-11-4	12

CHAMPION HURDLE
Cheltenham-2m 87yds

2010	BINOCULAR 6-11-10	12
2011	HURRICANE FLY 7-11-10	11
2012	ROCK ON RUBY 7-11-10	10
2013	HURRICANE FLY 9-11-10	9
2014	JEZKI 6-11-10	9
2015	FAUGHEEN 7-11-10	8
2016	ANNIE POWER 8-11-3	12
2017	BUVEUR D'AIR 6-11-10	11
2018	BUVEUR D'AIR 7-11-10	11
2019	ESPOIR D'ALLEN 5-11-10	10

QUEEN MOTHER CHAMPION CHASE
Cheltenham-1m 7f 199yds

2010	BIG ZEB 9-11-10	9
2011	SIZING EUROPE 9-11-10	11
2012	FINIAN'S RAINBOW 9-11-10	8
2013	SPRINTER SACRE 7-11-10	7
2014	SIRE DE GRUGY 8-11-10	11
2015	DODGING BULLETS 6-11-10	11
2016	SPRINTER SACRE 10-11-10	10
2017	SPECIAL TIARA 10-11-10	10
2018	ALTIOR 8-11-10	9
2019	ALTIOR 9-11-10	10

BALLYMORE NOVICES' HURDLE
Cheltenham-2m 5f 26yds

2010	PEDDLERS CROSS 5-11-7	17
2011	FIRST LIEUTENANT 6-11-7	12
2012	SIMONSIG 6-11-7	17
2013	THE NEW ONE 5-11-7	8
2014	FAUGHEEN 6-11-7	15
2015	WINDSOR PARK 6-11-7	10
2016	YORKHILL 6-11-7	11
2017	WILLOUGHBY COURT 6-11-7	15
2018	SAMCRO 6-11-7	14
2019	CITY ISLAND 6-11-7	16

RSA CHASE
(Royal & SunAlliance Chase before 2009)
Cheltenham-3m 80yds

2010	WEAPON'S AMNESTY 7-11-4	9
2011	BOSTONS ANGEL 7-11-4	12
2012	BOBS WORTH 7-11-4	9
2013	LORD WINDERMERE 7-11-4	11
2014	O'FAOLAINS BOY 7-11-4	15
2015	DON POLI 6-11-4	8
2016	BLAKLION 7-11-4	8
2017	MIGHT BITE 8-11-4	12
2018	PRESENTING PERCY 7-11-4	10
2019	TOPOFTHEGAME 7-11-4	12

STAYERS' HURDLE
(World Hurdle before 2017)
Cheltenham-2m 7f 213 yds

2010	BIG BUCK'S 7-11-10	14
2011	BIG BUCK'S 8-11-10	13
2012	BIG BUCK'S 9-11-10	11
2013	SOLWHIT 9-11-10	13
2014	MORE OF THAT 6-11-10	10
2015	COLE HARDEN 6-11-10	16
2016	THISTLECRACK 8-11-10	12
2017	NICHOLS CANYON 7-11-10	12
2018	PENHILL 7-11-10	15
2019	PAISLEY PARK 7-11-10	18

TRIUMPH HURDLE (4y)
Cheltenham-2m 179yds

2010	SOLDATINO 11-0	17
2011	ZARKANDAR 11-0	23
2012	COUNTRYWIDE FLAME 11-0	20
2013	OUR CONOR 11-0	17
2014	TIGER ROLL 11-0	15
2015	PEACE AND CO 11-0	16
2016	IVANOVICH GORBATOV 11-0	15
2017	DEFI DU SEUIL 11-0	15
2018	FARCLAS 11-0	9
2019	PENTLAND HILLS 11-0	14

CHELTENHAM GOLD CUP
Cheltenham-3m 2f 110yds

2010	IMPERIAL COMMANDER 9-11-10	11
2011	LONG RUN 6-11-10	13
2012	SYNCHRONISED 9-11-10	14
2013	BOBS WORTH 8-11-10	9
2014	LORD WINDERMERE 8-11-10	13
2015	CONEYGREE 8-11-10	16
2016	DON COSSACK 9-11-10	9
2017	SIZING JOHN 7-11-10	13
2018	NATIVE RIVER 8-11-10	15
2019	AL BOUM PHOTO 7-11-10	16

RYANAIR CHASE (FESTIVAL TROPHY)
Cheltenham-2m 4f 166yds

2010	ALBERTAS RUN 9-11-10	13
2011	ALBERTAS RUN 10-11-10	11
2012	RIVERSIDE THEATRE 8-11-10	12
2013	CUE CARD 7-11-10	8
2014	DYNASTE 8-11-10	11
2015	UXIZANDRE 7-11-10	14
2016	VAUTOUR 7-11-10	15
2017	UN DE SCEAUX 9-11-10	8
2018	BALKO DES FLOS 7-11-10	6
2019	FRODON 7-11-10	12

BOWL CHASE
Aintree-3m 210yds

2010	WHAT A FRIEND 7-11-7	5
2011	NACARAT 10-11-7	6
2012	FOLLOW THE PLAN 9-11-7	11
2013	FIRST LIEUTENANT 8-11-7	8
2014	SILVINIACO CONTI 8-11-7	6
2015	SILVINIACO CONTI 9-11-7	7
2016	CUE CARD 10-11-7	9
2017	TEA FOR TWO 8-11-7	7
2018	MIGHT BITE 9-11-7	6
2019	KEMBOY 7-11-7	6

MELLING CHASE
Aintree-2m 3f 200yds

2010	**ALBERTAS RUN** 9-11-10	11
2011	**MASTER MINDED** 8-11-10	10
2012	**FINIAN'S RAINBOW** 9-11-10	8
2013	**SPRINTER SACRE** 7-11-10	6
2014	**BOSTON BOB** 9-11-10	10
2015	**DON COSSACK** 8-11-10	10
2016	**GOD'S OWN** 8-11-10	6
2017	**FOX NORTON** 7-11-7	9
2018	**POLITOLOGUE** 7-11-7	6
2019	**MIN** 8-11-7	6

AINTREE HURDLE
Aintree-2m 4f

2010	**KHYBER KIM** 8-11-7	7
2011	**OSCAR WHISKY** 6-11-7	8
2012	**OSCAR WHISKY** 7-11-7	5
2013	**ZARKANDAR** 6-11-7	9
2014	**THE NEW ONE** 6-11-7	7
2015	**JEZKI** 7-11-7	6
2016	**ANNIE POWER** 8-11-0	6
2017	**BUVEUR D'AIR** 6-11-7	6
2018	**L'AMI SERGE** 8-11-7	9
2019	**SUPASUNDAE** 9-11-7	7

SCOTTISH GRANDNATIONAL (H'CAP CHASE)
Ayr-3m 7f 176 yds

2010	**MERIGO** 9-10-0	30
2011	**BESHABAR** 9-10-4	28
2012	**MERIGO** 11-10-2	24
2013	**GODSMEJUDGE** 7-11-3	24
2014	**AL CO** 9-10-0	29
2015	**WAYWARD PRINCE** 11-10-1	29
2016	**VICENTE** 7-11-3	28
2017	**VICENTE** 8-11-10	30
2018	**JOE FARRELL** 9-10-6	29
2019	**TAKINGRISKS** 10-10-1	23

BET365 GOLD CUP (H'CAP CHASE)
Sandown-3m 4f 166yds

2010	**CHURCH ISLAND** 11-10-5	19
2011	**POKER DE SIVOLA** 8-10-12	18
2012	**TIDAL BAY** 11-11-12	19
2013	**QUENTIN COLLONGES** 9-10-12	19
2014	**HADRIAN'S APPROACH** 7-11-0	19
2015	**JUST A PAR** 8-10-0	20
2016	**THE YOUNG MASTER** 7-10-12	20
2017	**HENLLAN HARRI** 9-10-0	13
2018	**STEP BACK** 8-10-0	20
2019	**TALKISCHEAP** 7-10-11	15

DISTANCE CONVERSION

5f	1,000m	10f	2,000m	15f	3,000m	20f	4,000m
6f	1,200m	11f	2,200m	16f	3,200m	21f	4,200m
7f	1,400m	12f	2,400m	17f	3,400m	22f	4,400m
8f	1,600m	13f	2,600m	18f	3,600m		
9f	1,800m	14f	2,800m	19f	3,800m		

LEADING TRAINERS ON THE FLAT: 1903-2019

1903 G Blackwell	1942 F Darling	1981 M Stoute
1904 P P Gilpin	1943 W Nightingall	1982 H Cecil
1905 W T Robinson	1944 Frank Butters	1983 W Hern
1906 Hon G Lambton	1945 W Earl	1984 H Cecil
1907 A Taylor	1946 Frank Butters	1985 H Cecil
1908 C Morton	1947 F Darling	1986 M Stoute
1909 A Taylor	1948 C F N Murless	1987 H Cecil
1910 A Taylor	1949 Frank Butters	1988 H Cecil
1911 Hon G Lambton	1950 C H Semblat	1989 M Stoute
1912 Hon G Lambton	1951 J L Jarvis	1990 H Cecil
1913 R Wootton	1952 M Marsh	1991 P Cole
1914 A Taylor	1953 J L Jarvis	1992 R Hannon Snr
1915 P P Gilpin	1954 C Boyd-Rochfort	1993 H Cecil
1916 R C Dawson	1955 C Boyd-Rochfort	1994 M Stoute
1917 A Taylor	1956 C F Elsey	1995 J Dunlop
1918 A Taylor	1957 C F N Murless	1996 Saeed bin Suroor
1919 A Taylor	1958 C Boyd-Rochfort	1997 M Stoute
1920 A Taylor	1959 C F N Murless	1998 Saeed bin Suroor
1921 A Taylor	1960 C F N Murless	1999 Saeed bin Suroor
1922 A Taylor	1961 C F N Murless	2000 Sir M Stoute
1923 A Taylor	1962 W Hern	2001 A O'Brien
1924 R C Dawson	1963 P Prendergast	2002 A O'Brien
1925 A Taylor	1964 P Prendergast	2003 Sir M Stoute
1926 F Darling	1965 P Prendergast	2004 Saeed bin Suroor
1927 Frank Butters	1966 M V O'Brien	2005 Sir M Stoute
1928 Frank Butters	1967 C F N Murless	2006 Sir M Stoute
1929 R C Dawson	1968 C F N Murless	2007 A O'Brien
1930 H S Persse	1969 A M Budgett	2008 A O'Brien
1931 J Lawson	1970 C F N Murless	2009 Sir M Stoute
1932 Frank Butters	1971 I Balding	2010 R Hannon Snr
1933 F Darling	1972 W Hern	2011 R Hannon Snr
1934 Frank Butters	1973 C F N Murless	2012 J Gosden
1935 Frank Butters	1974 P Walwyn	2013 R Hannon Snr
1936 J Lawson	1975 P Walwyn	2014 R Hannon Jnr
1937 C Boyd-Rochfort	1976 H Cecil	2015 J Gosden
1938 C Boyd-Rochfort	1977 M V O'Brien	2016 A O'Brien
1939 J L Jarvis	1978 H Cecil	2017 A O'Brien
1940 F Darling	1979 H Cecil	2018 J Gosden
1941 F Darling	1980 W Hern	2019 J Gosden

CHAMPION JOCKEYS ON THE FLAT: 1902-2019

1902 W Lane	170	1923 S Donoghue	89	1943 G Richards	65
1903 O Madden	154	1923 C Elliott	89	1944 G Richards	88
1904 O Madden	161	1924 C Elliott	106	1945 G Richards	104
1905 E Wheatley	124	1925 G Richards	118	1946 G Richards	212
1906 W Higgs	149	1926 T Weston	95	1947 G Richards	269
1907 W Higgs	146	1927 G Richards	164	1948 G Richards	224
1908 D Maher	139	1928 G Richards	148	1949 G Richards	261
1909 F Wootton	165	1929 G Richards	135	1950 G Richards	201
1910 F Wootton	137	1930 F Fox	129	1951 G Richards	227
1911 F Wootton	187	1931 G Richards	145	1952 G Richards	231
1912 F Wootton	118	1932 G Richards	190	1953 Sir G Richards	191
1913 D Maher	115	1933 G Richards	259	1954 D Smith	129
1914 S Donoghue	129	1934 G Richards	212	1955 D Smith	168
1915 S Donoghue	62	1935 G Richards	217	1956 D Smith	155
1916 S Donoghue	43	1936 G Richards	174	1957 A Breasley	173
1917 S Donoghue	42	1937 G Richards	216	1958 D Smith	165
1918 S Donoghue	66	1938 G Richards	206	1959 D Smith	157
1919 S Donoghue	129	1939 G Richards	155	1960 L Piggott	170
1920 S Donoghue	143	1940 G Richards	68	1961 A Breasley	171
1921 S Donoghue	141	1941 H Wragg	71	1962 A Breasley	179
1922 S Donoghue	102	1942 G Richards	67	1963 A Breasley	176

1964 L Piggott	140	1983 W Carson	159	2002 K Fallon	144
1965 L Piggott	160	1984 S Cauthen	130	2003 K Fallon	208
1966 L Piggott	191	1985 S Cauthen	195	2004 L Dettori	192
1967 L Piggott	117	1986 Pat Eddery	176	2005 J Spencer	163
1968 L Piggott	139	1987 S Cauthen	197	2006 R Moore	180
1969 L Piggott	163	1988 Pat Eddery	183	2007 S Sanders	190
1970 L Piggott	162	1989 Pat Eddery	171	J Spencer	190
1971 L Piggott	162	1990 Pat Eddery	209	2008 R Moore	186
1972 W Carson	132	1991 Pat Eddery	165	2009 R Moore	174
1973 W Carson	164	1992 M Roberts	206	2010 P Hanagan	191
1974 Pat Eddery	148	1993 Pat Eddery	169	2011 P Hanagan	165
1975 Pat Eddery	164	1994 L Dettori	233	2012 R Hughes	172
1976 Pat Eddery	162	1995 L Dettori	211	2013 R Hughes	203
1977 Pat Eddery	176	1996 Pat Eddery	186	2014 R Hughes	161
1978 W Carson	182	1997 K Fallon	196	2015 S De Sousa	132
1979 J Mercer	164	1998 K Fallon	185	2016 J Crowley	148
1980 W Carson	166	1999 K Fallon	200	2017 S De Sousa	155
1981 L Piggott	179	2000 K Darley	152	2018 S De Sousa	148
1982 L Piggott	188	2001 K Fallon	166	2019 O Murphy	168

CHAMPION APPRENTICES ON THE FLAT 1984-2019

1984 T Quinn	62	1996 D O'Neill	79	2008 W Buick	50
1985 G Carter	37	1997 R Ffrench	77	D Probert	50
W Ryan	37	1998 C Lowther	72	2009 F Tylicki	60
1986 G Carter	34	1999 R Winston	49	2010 M Lane	41
1987 G Bardwell	27	2000 L Newman	87	2011 M Harley	57
1988 G Bardwell	39	2001 C Catlin	71	2012 A Ryan	40
1989 L Dettori	71	2002 P Hanagan	81	2013 J Hart	51
1990 J Fortune	46	2003 R Moore	52	2014 O Murphy	74
1991 D Holland	79	2004 T Queally	59	2015 T Marquand	54
1992 D Harrison	56	2005 S Golam	44	2016 J Gordon	50
1993 J Weaver	60	H Turner	44	2017 D Egan	61
1994 S Davies	45	2006 S Donohoe	44	2018 J Watson	77
1995 S Sanders	61	2007 G Fairley	65	2019 C Fallon	50

LEADING OWNERS ON THE FLAT: 1897-2019

1897 Mr J Gubbins	1922 Ld Woolavington	1947 H.H. Aga Khan
1898 Ld de Rothschild	1923 Ld Derby	1948 H.H. Aga Khan
1899 Duke of Westminster	1924 H.H. Aga Khan	1949 H.H. Aga Khan
1900 H.R.H. The Prince of Wales	1925 Ld Astor	1950 M M Boussac
1901 Sir G Blundell Maple	1926 Ld Woolavington	1951 M M Boussac
1902 Mr R S Sievier	1927 Ld Derby	1952 H.H. Aga Khan
1903 Sir James Miller	1928 Ld Derby	1953 Sir Victor Sassoon
1904 Sir James Miller	1929 H.H. Aga Khan	1954 Her Majesty
1905 Col W Hall Walker	1930 H.H. Aga Khan	1955 Lady Zia Wernher
1906 Ld Derby (late)	1931 Mr J A Dewar	1956 Maj L B Holliday
1907 Col W Hall Walker	1932 H.H. Aga Khan	1957 Her Majesty
1908 Mr J B Joel	1933 Ld Derby	1958 Mr J McShain
1909 Mr "Fairie"	1934 H.H. Aga Khan	1959 Prince Aly Khan
1910 Mr "Fairie"	1935 H.H. Aga Khan	1960 Sir Victor Sassoon
1911 Ld Derby	1936 Ld Astor	1961 Maj L B Holliday
1912 Mr T Pilkington	1937 H.H. Aga Khan	1962 Maj L B Holliday
1913 Mr J B Joel	1938 Ld Derby	1963 Mr J R Mullion
1914 Mr J B Joel	1939 Ld Rosebery	1964 Mrs H E Jackson
1915 Mr L Neumann	1940 Lord Rothermere	1965 M J Ternynck
1916 Mr E Hulton	1941 Ld Glanely	1966 Lady Zia Wernher
1917 Mr "Fairie"	1942 His Majesty	1967 Mr H J Joel
1918 Lady James Douglas	1943 Miss D Paget	1968 Mr Raymond R Guest
1919 Ld Glanely	1944 H.H. Aga Khan	1969 Mr D Robinson
1920 Sir Robert Jardine	1945 Ld Derby	1970 Mr C Engelhard
1921 Mr S B Joel	1946 H.H. Aga Khan	1971 Mr P Mellon

1972 Mrs J Hislop
1973 Mr N B Hunt
1974 Mr N B Hunt
1975 Dr C Vittadini
1976 Mr D Wildenstein
1977 Mr R Sangster
1978 Mr R Sangster
1979 Sir M Sobell
1980 S Weinstock
1981 H.H. Aga Khan
1982 Mr R Sangster
1983 Mr R Sangster
1984 Mr R Sangster
1985 Sheikh Mohammed
1986 Sheikh Mohammed
1987 Sheikh Mohammed

1988 Sheikh Mohammed
1989 Sheikh Mohammed
1990 Mr Hamdan Al-Maktoum
1991 Sheikh Mohammed
1992 Sheikh Mohammed
1993 Sheikh Mohammed
1994 Mr Hamdan Al-Maktoum
1995 Mr Hamdan Al-Maktoum
1996 Godolphin
1997 Sheikh Mohammed
1998 Godolphin
1999 Godolphin
2000 H.H. Aga Khan
2001 Godolphin
2002 Mr Hamdan Al-Maktoum
2003 K Abdullah

2004 Godolphin
2005 Mr Hamdan Al-Maktoum
2006 Godolphin
2007 Godolphin
2008 HRH Princess Haya of Jordan
2009 Mr Hamdan Al-Maktoum
2010 K Abdullah
2011 K Abdullah
2012 Godolphin
2013 Godolphin
2014 Mr Hamdan Al-Maktoum
2015 Godolphin
2016 Godolphin
2017 Godolphin
2018 Godolphin
2019 Mr Hamdan Al-Maktoum

LEADING SIRES ON THE FLAT: 1897-2019

1897 Kendal
1898 Galopin
1899 Orme
1900 St Simon
1901 St Simon
1902 Persimmon
1903 St Frusquin
1904 Gallinule
1905 Gallinule
1906 Persimmon
1907 St Frusquin
1908 Persimmon
1909 Cyllene
1910 Cyllene
1911 Sundridge
1912 Persimmon
1913 Desmond
1914 Polymelus
1915 Polymelus
1916 Polymelus
1917 Bayardo
1918 Bayardo
1919 The Tetrarch
1920 Polymelus
1921 Polymelus
1922 Lemberg
1923 Swynford
1924 Son-in-Law
1925 Phalaris
1926 Hurry On
1927 Buchan
1928 Phalaris
1929 Tetratema
1930 Son-in-Law
1931 Pharos
1932 Gainsborough
1933 Gainsborough
1934 Blandford
1935 Blandford
1936 Fairway
1937 Solario

1938 Blandford
1939 Fairway
1940 Hyperion
1941 Hyperion
1942 Hyperion
1943 Fairway
1944 Fairway
1945 Hyperion
1946 Hyperion
1947 Nearco
1948 Big Game
1949 Nearco
1950 Fair Trial
1951 Nasrullah
1952 Tehran
1953 Chanteur II
1954 Hyperion
1955 Alycidon
1956 Court Martial
1957 Court Martial
1958 Mossborough
1959 Petition
1960 Aureole
1961 Aureole
1962 Never Say Die
1963 Ribot
1964 Chamossaire
1965 Court Harwell
1966 Charlottesville
1967 Ribot
1968 Ribot
1969 Crepello
1970 Northern Dancer
1971 Never Bend
1972 Queen's Hussar
1973 Vaguely Noble
1974 Vaguely Noble
1975 Great Nephew
1976 Wolver Hollow
1977 Northern Dancer
1978 Mill Reef (USA)

1979 Petingo
1980 Pitcairn
1981 Great Nephew
1982 Be My Guest (USA)
1983 Northern Dancer
1984 Northern Dancer
1985 Kris
1986 Nijinsky (CAN)
1987 Mill Reef (USA)
1988 Caerleon (USA)
1989 Blushing Groom (FR)
1990 Sadler's Wells (USA)
1991 Caerleon (USA)
1992 Sadler's Wells (USA)
1993 Sadler's Wells (USA)
1994 Sadler's Wells (USA)
1995 Sadler's Wells (USA)
1996 Sadler's Wells (USA)
1997 Sadler's Wells (USA)
1998 Sadler's Wells (USA)
1999 Sadler's Wells (USA)
2000 Sadler's Wells (USA)
2001 Sadler's Wells (USA)
2002 Sadler's Wells (USA)
2003 Sadler's Wells (USA)
2004 Sadler's Wells (USA)
2005 Danehill (USA)
2006 Danehill (USA)
2007 Danehill (USA)
2008 Galileo (IRE)
2009 Danehill Dancer (IRE)
2010 Galileo (IRE)
2011 Galileo (IRE)
2012 Galileo (IRE)
2013 Galileo (IRE)
2014 Galileo (IRE)
2015 Galileo (IRE)
2016 Galileo (IRE)
2017 Galileo (IRE)
2018 Galileo (IRE)
2019 Galileo (IRE)

LEADING BREEDERS ON THE FLAT: 1913-2019

1913 Mr J B Joel	1949 H.H. Aga Khan	1984 Mr E P Taylor
1914 Mr J B Joel	1950 M M Boussac	1985 Dalham Stud Farms
1915 Mr L Neumann	1951 M M Boussac	1986 H.H. Aga Khan
1916 Mr E Hulton	1952 H. H. Aga Khan	1987 Cliveden Stud
1917 Mr "Fairie"	1953 Mr F Darling	1988 H. H. Aga Khan
1918 Lady James Douglas	1954 Maj L B Holliday	1989 Mr Hamdan Al-Maktoum
1919 Ld Derby	1955 Someries Stud	1990 Capt. Macdonald- Buchanan
1920 Ld Derby	1956 Maj L B Holliday	1991 Barronstown Stud
1921 Mr S B Joel	1957 Eve Stud	1992 Swettenham Stud
1922 Ld Derby	1958 Mr R Ball	1993 Juddmonte Farms
1923 Ld Derby	1959 Prince Aly Khan and the late	1994 Shadwell Farm & Estate Ltd
1924 Lady Sykes	H.H. Aga Khan	1995 Shadwell Farm & Estate Ltd
1925 Ld Astor	1960 Eve Stud Ltd	1996 Sheikh Mohammed
1926 Ld Woolavington	1961 Eve Stud Ltd	1997 Sheikh Mohammed
1927 Ld Derby	1962 Maj L B Holliday	1998 Sheikh Mohammed
1928 Ld Derby	1963 Mr H F Guggenheim	1999 H. H. The Aga Khan's Studs
1929 Ld Derby	1964 Bull Run Stud	2000 H. H. The Aga Khan's Studs
1930 Ld Derby	1965 Mr J Ternynck	2001 Shadwell Farm & Estate Ltd
1931 Ld Dewar	1966 Someries Stud	2002 Gainsborough Stud
1932 H.H. Aga Khan	1967 Mr H J Joel	2003 Juddmonte
1933 Sir Alec Black	1968 Mill Ridge Farm	2004 Juddmonte
1934 H.H. Aga Khan	1969 Lord Rosebery	2005 Shadwell Farm & Estate Ltd
1935 H.H. Aga Khan	1970 Mr E P Taylor	2006 Darley
1936 Ld Astor	1971 Mr P Mellon	2007 Darley
1937 H.H. Aga Khan	1972 Mr J Hislop	2008 Darley
1938 Ld Derby	1973 Claiborne Farm	2009 Darley
1939 Ld Rosebery	1974 Mr N B Hunt	2010 Juddmonte
1940 Mr H E Morriss	1975 Overbury Stud	2011 Juddmonte
1941 Ld Glanely	1976 Dayton Ltd	2012 Juddmonte
1942 National Stud	1977 Mr E P Taylor	2013 Darley
1943 Miss D Paget	1978 Cragwood Estates Inc	2014 Darley
1944 Ld Rosebery	1979 Ballymacoll Stud	2015 Darley
1945 Ld Derby	1980 P Clarke	2016 Darley
1946 Lt- Col H Boyd-Rochfort	1981 H.H. Aga Khan	2017 Darley
1947 H.H. Aga Khan	1982 Someries Stud	2018 Godolphin
1948 H.H. Aga Khan	1983 White Lodge Stud	2019 Godolphin

LEADING TRAINERS OVER JUMPS: 1948-2019

1948-49 F T T Walwyn	1972-73 F T Winter	1996-97 M C Pipe
1949-50 P V F Cazalet	1973-74 F T Winter	1997-98 M C Pipe
1950-51 T F Rimell	1974-75 F T Winter	1998-99 M C Pipe
1951-52 N Crump	1975-76 T F Rimell	1999-00 M C Pipe
1952-53 M V O'Brien	1976-77 F T Winter	2000-01 M C Pipe
1953-54 M V O'Brien	1977-78 F T Winter	2001-02 M C Pipe
1954-55 H R Price	1978-79 M H Easterby	2002-03 M C Pipe
1955-56 W Hall	1979-80 M H Easterby	2003-04 M C Pipe
1956-57 N Crump	1980-81 M H Easterby	2004-05 M C Pipe
1957-58 F T T Walwyn	1981-82 M W Dickinson	2005-06 P F Nicholls
1958-59 H R Price	1982-83 M W Dickinson	2006-07 P F Nicholls
1959-60 P V F Cazalet	1983-84 M W Dickinson	2007-08 P F Nicholls
1960-61 T F Rimell	1984-85 F T Winter	2008-09 P F Nicholls
1961-62 H R Price	1985-86 N J Henderson	2009-10 P F Nicholls
1962-63 K Piggott	1986-87 N J Henderson	2010-11 P F Nicholls
1963-64 F T T Walwyn	1987-88 D R C Elsworth	2010-11 P F Nicholls
1964-65 P V F Cazalet	1988-89 M C Pipe	2011-12 P F Nicholls
1965-66 H R Price	1989-90 M C Pipe	2012-13 N J Henderson
1966-67 H R Price	1990-91 M C Pipe	2013-14 P F Nicholls
1967-68 Denys Smith	1991-92 M C Pipe	2014-15 P F Nicholls
1968-69 T F Rimell	1992-93 M C Pipe	2015-16 P F Nicholls
1969-70 T F Rimell	1993-94 D Nicholson	2016-17 N J Henderson
1970-71 F T Winter	1994-95 D Nicholson	2017-18 N J Henderson
1971-72 F T Winter	1995-96 M C Pipe	2018-19 P F Nicholls

CHAMPION JOCKEYS OVER JUMPS: 1903-2019
Prior to the 1925-26 season the figure relates to racing between January and December

1903 P Woodland 54	1942-43 No racing	1980-81 J Francome 105
1904 F Mason.........................59	1943-44 No racing	1981-82 J Francome 120
1905 F Mason.........................73	1944-45 H Nicholson 15	P Scudamore 120
1906 F Mason.........................58	T F Rimell 15	1982-83 J Francome 106
1907 F Mason.........................59	1945-46 T F Rimell 54	1983-84 J Francome 131
1908 P Cowley........................65	1946-47 J Dowdeswell...........58	1984-85 J Francome 101
1909 R Gordon 45	1947-48 B Marshall 66	1985-86 P Scudamore 91
1910 E Piggott........................67	1948-49 T Moloney 60	1986-87 P Scudamore 123
1911 W Payne 76	1949-50 T Moloney 95	1987-88 P Scudamore 132
1912 I Anthony 78	1950-51 T Moloney 83	1988-89 P Scudamore 221
1913 E Piggott........................60	1951-52 T Moloney 99	1989-90 P Scudamore 170
1914 Mr J R Anthony 60	1952-53 F Winter 121	1990-91 P Scudamore 141
1915 E Piggott........................44	1953-54 R Francis 76	1991-92 P Scudamore 175
1916 C Hawkins 17	1954-55 T Moloney 67	1992-93 R Dunwoody 173
1917 W Smith..........................15	1955-56 F Winter 74	1993-94 R Dunwoody 197
1918 G Duller 17	1956-57 F Winter 80	1994-95 R Dunwoody 160
1919 Mr H Brown 48	1957-58 F Winter 82	1995-96 A P McCoy 175
1920 F B Rees 64	1958-59 T Brookshaw 83	1996-97 A P McCoy 190
1921 F B Rees 65	1959-60 S Mellor 68	1997-98 A P McCoy 253
1922 J Anthony 78	1960-61 S Mellor 118	1998-99 A P McCoy 186
1923 F B Rees 64	1961-62 S Mellor 80	1999-00 A P McCoy 245
1924 F B Rees 108	1962-63 J Gifford 70	2000-01 A P McCoy 191
1925 E Foster 76	1963-64 J Gifford 94	2001-02 A P McCoy 289
1925-26 T Leader 61	1964-65 T Biddlecombe 114	2002-03 A P McCoy 256
1926-27 F B Rees....................59	1965-66 T Biddlecombe 102	2003-04 A P McCoy 209
1927-28 W Stott 88	1966-67 J Gifford 122	2004-05 A P McCoy 200
1928-29 W Stott 65	1967-68 J Gifford 82	2005-06 A P McCoy 178
1929-30 W Stott 77	1968-69 B R Davies 77	2006-07 A P McCoy 184
1930-31 W Stott 81	T Biddlecombe 77	2007-08 A P McCoy 140
1931-32 W Stott 77	1969-70 B R Davies 91	2008-09 A P McCoy 186
1932-33 G Wilson 61	1970-71 G Thorner 74	2009-10 A P McCoy 195
1933-34 G Wilson 56	1971-72 B R Davies 89	2010-11 A P McCoy 218
1934-35 G Wilson 73	1972-73 R Barry 125	2011-12 A P McCoy 199
1935-36 G Wilson 57	1973-74 R Barry 94	2012-13 A P McCoy 185
1936-37 G Wilson 45	1974-75 T Stack 82	2013-14 A P McCoy 218
1937-38 G Wilson 59	1975-76 J Francome 96	2014-15 A P McCoy 231
1938-39 T F Rimell 61	1976-77 T Stack 97	2015-16 R Johnson 235
1939-40 T F Rimell 24	1977-78 J J O'Neill 149	2016-17 R Johnson 189
1940-41 G Wilson 22	1978-79 J Francome 95	2017-18 R Johnson 176
1941-42 R Smyth.....................12	1979-80 J J O'Neill 117	2018-19 R Johnson 200

LEADING OWNERS OVER JUMPS: 1948-2019
(Please note that prior to the 1994-95 season the leading owner was determined by win prizemoney only)

1948-49 Mr W F Williamson	1968-69 Mr B P Jenks	1988-89 Mr R Burridge
1949-50 Mrs L Brotherton	1969-70 Mr E R Courage	1989-90 Mrs Harry J Duffey
1950-51 Mr J Royle	1970-71 Mr F Pontin	1990-91 Mr P Piller
1951-52 Miss D Paget	1971-72 Capt T A Forster	1991-92 Whitcombe Manor
1952-53 Mr J H Griffin	1972-73 Mr N H Le Mare	Racing Stables Ltd
1953-54 Mr J H Griffin	1973-74 Mr N H Le Mare	1992-93 Mrs J Mould
1954-55 Mrs W H E Welman	1974-75 Mr R Guest	1993-94 Pell-Mell Partners
1955-56 Mrs L Carver	1975-76 Mr P B Raymond	1994-95 Roach Foods Limited
1956-57 Mrs Geoffrey Kohn	1976-77 Mr N H Le Mare	1995-96 Mr A T A Wates
1957-58 Mr D J Coughlan	1977-78 Mrs O Jackson	1996-97 Mr R Ogden
1958-59 Mr J E Bigg	1978-79 Snailwell Stud Co Ltd	1997-98 Mr D A Johnson
1959-60 Miss W H Wallace	1979-80 Mr H J Joel	1998-99 Mr J P McManus
1960-61 Mr C Vaughan	1980-81 Mr R J Wilson	1999-00 Mr R Ogden
1961-62 Mr N Cohen	1981-82 Sheikh Ali Abu Khamsin	2000-01 Sir R Ogden
1962-63 Mr P B Raymond	1982-83 Sheikh Ali Abu Khamsin	2001-02 Mr D A Johnson
1963-64 Mr J K Goodman	1983-84 Sheikh Ali Abu Khamsin	2002-03 Mr D A Johnson
1964-65 Mrs M Stephenson	1984-85 T Kilroe and Son Ltd	2003-04 Mr D A Johnson
1965-66 Duchess of Westminster	1985-86 Sheikh Ali Abu Khamsin	2004-05 Mr D A Johnson
1966-67 Mr C P T Watkins	1986-87 Mr H J Joel	2005-06 Mr J P McManus
1967-68 Mr H S Alper	1987-88 Miss Juliet E Reed	2006-07 Mr J P McManus

2007-08 Mr D A Johnson	2011-12 Mr J P McManus	2015-16 Gigginstown House Stud
2008-09 Mr J P McManus	2012-13 Mr J P McManus	2016-17 Mr J P McManus
2009-10 Mr J P McManus	2013-14 Mr J P McManus	2017-18 Mr J P McManus
2010-11 Mr T Hemmings	2014-15 Mr J P McManus	2018-19 Mr J P McManus

LEADING AMATEUR RIDERS OVER JUMPS: 1952-2019

1952-53 Mr A H Moralee 22	1974-75 Mr R Lamb 22	1996-97 Mr R Thornton 30
1953-54 Mr A H Moralee 22	1975-76 Mr P Greenall 25	1997-98 Mr S Durack 41
1954-55 Mr A H Moralee 16	Mr G Jones 25	1998-99 Mr A Dempsey 47
1955-56 Mr R McCreery 13	1976-77 Mr P Greenall 27	1999-00 Mr P Flynn 41
Mr A H Moralee 13	1977-78 Mr G Sloan 23	2000-01 Mr T Scudamore 24
1956-57 Mr R McCreery 23	1978-79 Mr T G Dun.................. 26	2001-02 Mr D Crosse 19
1957-58 Mr J Lawrence 18	1979-80 Mr O Sherwood 29	2002-03 Mr C Williams 23
1958-59 Mr J Sutcliffe 18	1980-81 Mr P Webber 32	2003-04 Mr O Nelmes 14
1959-60 Mr G Kindersley............... 22	1981-82 Mr D Browne 28	2004-05 Mr T Greenall 31
1960-61 Sir W Pigott-Brown 28	1982-83 Mr D Browne 33	2005-06 Mr T O'Brien................. 32
1961-62 Mr A Biddlecombe........... 30	1983-84 Mr S Sherwood............. 28	2006-07 Mr T Greenall................ 31
1962-63 Sir W Pigott-Brown 20	1984-85 Mr S Sherwood............. 30	2007-08 Mr T Greenall................ 23
1963-64 Mr S Davenport 32	1985-86 Mr T Thomson Jones 25	2008-09 Mr O Greenall 23
1964-65 Mr M Gifford.................. 15	1986-87 Mr T Thomson Jones 19	2009-10 Mr O Greenall 41
1965-66 Mr C Collins.................. 24	1987-88 Mr T Thomson Jones 15	2010-11 Mr R Mahon 19
1966-67 Mr C Collins.................. 33	1988-89 Mr P Fenton 18	2011-12 Miss E Sayer 11
1967-68 Mr R Tate.................... 30	1989-90 Mr P McMahon............. 15	2012-13 Mr N de Boinville............ 16
1968-69 Mr R Tate.................... 17	1990-91 Mr K Johnson 24	2013-14 Mr H Bannister 11
1969-70 Mr M Dickinson 23	1991-92 Mr M P Hourigan 24	2014-15 Mr H Bannister 15
1970-71 Mr J Lawrence 17	1992-93 Mr A Thornton 26	2015-16 Mr D Noonan 19
1971-72 Mr W Foulkes 26	1993-94 Mr J Greenall................ 21	2016-17 Mr J King 15
1972-73 Mr R Smith................... 56	1994-95 Mr D Parker 16	2017-18 Miss F Fuller 16
1973-74 Mr A Webber 21	1995-96 Mr J Culloty 40	2018-19 Mr D Maxwell 18

LEADING SIRES OVER JUMPS: 1990-2019

1989-90 Deep Run	1999-00 Strong Gale	2009-10 Presenting
1990-91 Deep Run	2000-01 Be My Native (USA)	2010-11 Presenting
1991-92 Deep Run	2001-02 Be My Native (USA)	2011-12 King's Theatre
1992-93 Deep Run	2002-03 Be My Native (USA)	2012-13 Beneficial
1993-94 Strong Gale	2003-04 Be My Native (USA)	2013-14 King's Theatre
1994-95 Strong Gale	2004-05 Supreme Leader	2014-15 King's Theatre
1995-96 Strong Gale	2005-06 Supreme Leader	2015-16 King's Theatre
1996-97 Strong Gale	2006-07 Presenting	2016-17 King's Theatre
1997-98 Strong Gale	2007-08 Old Vic	2017-18 King's Theatre
1998-99 Strong Gale	2008-09 Presenting	2018-19 Flemensfirth

JOCKEYS' AGENTS

Jockeys' Agents and their Contact Details

Agent	Telephone	Mobile/Email
NICKY ADAMS	01488 72004/72964	07796 547659 nickadams2594@hotmail.com
NEIL ALLAN	01243 543870	07985 311141 email: aneilallan@aol.com
NIGEL BAXTER	01942 803247	07973 561521 email: sales@clubfactfile.com
NIKKI BLOSS	01473 741444	07881 933577 nikki@hopefarmsuffolk.co.uk
CHRIS BROAD	01452 760482/447	07836 622858 chrisd.broad@yahoo.co.uk
ADAM BROOK	01422 378597	07399 390303 atbrookgb@gmail.com
GLORIA CHARNOCK	01653 695004	07951 576912 gloriacharnock@hotmail.com
PAUL CLARKE	01638 660804	07885 914306 paul.clarke79@btinternet.com
RAY COCHRANE	01223 812008	07798 651247 ray@raysagency.co.uk
STEVEN CROFT		07809 205556 steven.croft6@googlemail.com
SIMON DODDS	01509 734496	07974 924735 simon.dodds@btinternet.com
SHELLEY DWYER	01638 493123	07949 612256 shelleydwyer4031@outlook.com
TIM ELEY		07813 546079 timeley@hotmail.co.uk

Agent	Telephone	Mobile/Email
SHIPPY ELLIS	01638 668484	07860 864864 shippysjockeys@jockeysagent.com
MARK FURNASS		07474 242332 jockeysagent@gmail.com
MICHAEL HAGGAS	01638 660811	07740 624550 mhaggas@ntlworld.com
RICHARD HALE	01768 88699	07909 520542 richardhale77@hotmail.co.uk
NIALL HANNITY	01677 423363	07710 141084 niallhannity@yahoo.co.uk
ALAN HARRISON	01969 625006	07846 187991 ahjockagent60@yahoo.co.uk
TONY HIND	01638 724997	07807 908599 tonyhind@jockeysagent.com
GAVIN HORNE	01392 433610	07914 897170 gavin.horne@hotmail.co.uk
CHRIS HUMPLEBY		07712 608969 chris.humpleby13@gmail.com
ROSS HYSLOP		07894 634067 r.hyslop91@gmail.com
RUSS JAMES	01653 699466	07947 414001 russjames2006@btconnect.com
BRUCE JEFFREY	01750 21521	07747 854684 brucejeffrey@live.co.uk
GUY JEWELL	01672 861231	07765 248859 guyjewell@btconnect.com
ANDY LEWIS	01908 386983	07838 506594 andrew.lewis11@sky.com
SARA-LOUISE METCALFE	01635 269647	07918 525354 troopersjockeys@hotmail.co.uk

Agent	Telephone	Mobile/Email
JOHN NEILSON	01388 730249	07813 874970 john@jlnjockeys.co.uk
JACK NICOL		07538 136449 racingjack@hotmail.com
GARETH OWEN	01603 569390	07958 335206 garethowenracing@gmail.com
TIMOTHY PLATT	01544 267672	07837 473852 carol@kerrylee.co.uk
IAN POPHAM	01789 488758	07791 225707 ianpophamracing@yahoo.com
SHASHI RIGHTON	01353 688594	07825 381350 srighton.sr@googlemail.com
DAVE ROBERTS	01737 221368	07860 234342 daveroberts.racing@gmail.com
PHILIP SHEA	01638 667456	07585 120297 psheajockeysagent@gmail.com
BRIAN STOREY	01228 675168	07950 925576 bstoreyracing@aol.com
ANNA WALLACE		07867 923642 awallace51@yahoo.com
IAN WARDLE	01793 688858	07831 865974 ian.wardlex@googlemail.com
LAURA WAY	01704 834488	07775 777494 laura.way@btconnect.com
IAN WOOD		07733 156380 ianwood@chase3c.com

FLAT JOCKEYS

Riding weights and contact details
An index of agents appears on page 720

Jockey	Weight	Agent
LUCY ALEXANDER	9 - 7	Mr R. A. Hale
DAVID ALLAN	8 - 10	Mrs G. S. Charnock
PADDY ASPELL	8 - 7	07841091125
ANDREA ATZENI	8 - 5	Mr Tony Hind
CONNOR BEASLEY	8-6	Mr G. R. Owen
KATHERINE BEGLEY	8 - 12	M. Furnass
CHARLIE BENNETT	8 - 6	Mr G. D. Jewell
HARRY BENTLEY	8 - 7	Mr Paul Clarke
SHELLEY BIRKETT	8 - 4	07969777694
CHARLES BISHOP	8 - 10	Mr Neil Allan
DANNY BROCK	8 - 6	07494288789
WILLIAM BUICK	8 - 6	Mr Tony Hind
WILLIAM CARSON	8 - 7	Mr Neil Allan
TIM CLARK	8 - 13	Mr L. R. James
PAT COSGRAVE	8 - 9	Mr Paul Clarke
DOUGIE COSTELLO	8 - 11	Mr A. T. Brook
HECTOR CROUCH	8 - 11	Mr G. D. Jewell
JIM CROWLEY	8 - 7	Mr Tony Hind
NICOLA CURRIE	8 - 0	P. C. Shea
BEN CURTIS	8 - 5	Mr S. T. Dodds
RAUL DA SILVA	8 - 0	M. Furnass
RAY DAWSON	8 - 4	Mr S. T. Dodds
PHIL DENNIS	8 - 4	Mr Alan Harrison
SILVESTRE DE SOUSA	8 - 0	Mrs Shelley Dwyer
FRANKIE DETTORI	8 - 9	Mr R. Cochrane
PAT DOBBS	8-9	Mr Tony Hind
STEVIE DONOHOE	8 - 8	Mr L. R. James
ROBBIE DOWNEY	8 - 4	Mrs L. H. Way
GEORGE DOWNING	8 - 9	Mr N. M. Adams
HOLLIE DOYLE	8 - 0	Mr G. D. Jewell
JAMES DOYLE	8 - 10	Mr Chris Humpleby
MARTIN DWYER	8 - 3	Mr S. T. Dodds
TOM EAVES	8 - 7	Mr R. A. Hale
LEWIS EDMUNDS	8 - 9	Mr S. T. Dodds
JOHN EGAN	8 - 3	07796929375
ANDREW ELLIOTT	8 - 4	M. Furnass
NATHAN EVANS	8 - 2	Mr R. A. Hale
JOHN FAHY	8 - 6	Mr L. R. James
JOE FANNING	8 - 2	Mr N. Hannity
DURAN FENTIMAN	8 - 2	Mr Alan Harrison
ROYSTON FFRENCH	8 - 3	Mr S. M. Righton
JONATHAN FISHER	8 - 4	Mr S. T. Dodds
ROB J. FITZPATRICK	8 - 6	07437417026
KIEREN FOX	8 - 5	M. Furnass
JACK GARRITTY	8 - 10	Mr R. A. Hale
JOSEPHINE GORDON	8 - 4	P. C. Shea
JAMIE GORMLEY	8 - 0	Mr R. A. Hale
SHANE GRAY	8 - 4	Mr N. Hannity
EDWARD GREATREX	8 - 5	Mr G. J. Horne
TONY HAMILTON	8 - 8	Mr N. Hannity
PAUL HANAGAN	8 - 3	Mr R. A. Hale
CAM HARDIE	8 - 0	Mr R. A. Hale
JASON HART	8 - 9	Mr Alan Harrison
ROBERT HAVLIN	8 - 7	Mr I. P Wardle
JOEY HAYNES	8 - 5	Mr S. T. Dodds
SAM HITCHCOTT	8 - 5	07818068508
ROB HORNBY	8 - 10	Mr N. M. Adams
SAM JAMES	8 - 6	Mrs L. H. Way
AARON JONES	8 - 0	Miss S. L. Metcalfe
JAMIE JONES	8 - 9	07596267870
LIAM JONES	8 - 4	Mr G. D. Jewell
SHANE KELLY	8 - 7	Mr N. M. Adams
LIAM KENIRY	8 - 8	Mr N. M. Adams
RICHARD KINGSCOTE	8 - 8	Mr G. D. Jewell
ADAM KIRBY	9 - 0	Mr N. M. Adams
RACHEAL KNELLER	8 - 0	07951820668
CLIFFORD LEE	8 - 10	Mr G. R. Owen
GRAHAM LEE	8 - 9	Mr R. A. Hale
SEAN LEVEY	8 - 10	Mr S. M. Righton
KEVIN LUNDIE	8 - 10	Mrs G. S. Charnock
NICKY MACKAY	8 - 2	Mr N. A. Baxter
ELLIE MACKENZIE	8 - 0	Miss A. Wallace
GINA MANGAN	8 - 0	Andy Lewis
TOM MARQUAND	8 - 7	Mr S. M. Righton
PADDY MATHERS	8 - 0	M. Furnass
ADRIAN MCCARTHY	8 - 4	M. Furnass
P. J. MCDONALD	8 - 4	Mr G. R. Owen
BARRY MCHUGH	8 - 6	Mrs L. H. Way
FAYE MCMANOMAN	7 - 13	Miss S. L. Metcalfe
ADAM MCNAMARA	8 - 10	P. C. Shea
JACK MITCHELL	8 - 9	Mr S. Croft
RYAN MOORE	8 - 9	Mr Tony Hind
LUKE MORRIS	8 - 0	Mr Neil Allan
GERALD MOSSE	8 - 8	Mrs Shelley Dwyer
ANDREW MULLEN	8 - 0	Mr R. A. Hale
PAUL MULRENNAN	8 - 10	Mr R. A. Hale
OISIN MURPHY	8 - 6	Mr G. J. Horne
DANIEL MUSCUTT	8 - 9	Mr Paul Clarke
DAVID NOLAN	9 - 1	Mr R. A. Hale
FRANNY NORTON	8 - 7	Mr I. P Wardle
DANE O'NEILL	8 - 7	Mr N. M. Adams
KIERAN O'NEILL	8 - 0	Mr N. M. Adams
BRENDAN POWELL	9 - 0	Mr Dave Roberts\
		Mr G. D. Jewell
RYAN POWELL	8 - 0	Andy Lewis
PHILIP PRINCE	8 - 5	07597836396
DAVID PROBERT	8 - 7	Mr Neil Allan
TOM QUEALLY	8 - 11	Mr L. R. James
JIMMY QUINN	8 - 0	Mr G. J. Horne\
		Mr A. T. Brook
SOPHIE RALSTON	7 - 11	Miss A. Wallace
ALISTAIR RAWLINSON	8 - 11	Mr S. Croft
RACHEL RICHARDSON	8 - 3	Mr Alan Harrison
BEN ROBINSON	8 - 0	Mr R. A. Hale
CALLUM RODRIGUEZ	8 - 10	Mr R. A. Hale
ROSSA RYAN	8 - 7	Mr S. Croft
VICTOR SANTOS	8 - 0	07096534107
KIERAN SCHOFIELD	8 - 0	Mr S. T. Dodds
CALLUM SHEPHERD	8 - 9	Mr N. M. Adams
KIERAN SHOEMARK	8 - 10	Mr Tony Hind
JAMIE SPENCER	8 - 7	Mr N. Hannity
MICHAEL STAINTON	8 - 10	M. Furnass
LOUIS STEWARD	8 - 11	Mr Tony Hind
KEVIN STOTT	8-9	Mr R. A. Hale

JAMES SULLIVAN	8 - 0	Mr R. A. Hale
RYAN TATE	8 - 6	Mr Neil Allan
DANIEL TUDHOPE	8 - 11	Mrs L. H. Way
HAYLEY TURNER	8 - 2	Mr S. Croft
GEMMA TUTTY	8 - 10	07970095355

EOIN WALSH	8 - 6	Mr N. M. Adams
ROBBIE WALSH	7 - 8	Mr A. T. Brook
JASON WATSON	8 - 4	Mr Tony Hind
TREVOR WHELAN	8 - 12	07500318885

Are your contact details missing
or incorrect?
If so please update us by
email: richard.lowther@racingpost.com

APPRENTICES

Riding weights and contact details
An index of agents appears on page 720

GAVIN ASHTON (Shaun Keightley)	8 - 2	Miss A. Wallace
LUKE BACON (Dean Ivory)	7 - 6	Miss A. Wallace
NICK BARRATT-ATKIN (Philip Kirby)	8 - 4	Mr N. Hannity
GEORGE BASS (Mick Channon)	8 - 3	Mr S. Croft
ALED BEECH (Charlie Fellowes)	7 - 13	Mr L. R. James
CHARLOTTE BENNETT (Ralph Beckett)	7 - 8	c/o 01264 772278
AIDEN BLAKEMORE (Ruth Jefferson)	9 - 0	Mr R. A. Hale
ELLA BOARDMAN (Mick Channon)	7 - 12	c/o 01635 281 166
GAIA BONI (William Jarvis)	7 - 11	c/o 01638 669873
PADDY BRADLEY (Pat Phelan)	8 - 11	Miss S. L. Metcalfe
JOE BRADNAM (Michael Bell)	8 - 3	c/o 07802264514
ANDREW BRESLIN (Mark Johnston)	7 - 9	Mr N. Hannity
POPPY BRIDGWATER (David Simcock)	8 - 6	Mr L. R. James
JOSHUA BRYAN (Andrew Balding)	8 - 7	Mr G. D. Jewell
IMOGEN CARTER (Clive Cox)	7 - 10	c/o 01488 73072
WILLIAM CARVER (Andrew Balding)	8 - 3	Mr S. T. Dodds
LUKE CATTON (Richard Hannon)	8 - 7	Mr G. D. Jewell
STEFANO CHERCHI (Marco Botti)	8 - 3	Mr Paul Clarke
JACOB CLARK (Martin Smith)	8 - 3	c/o 07712493589
IZZY CLIFTON (Nigel Tinkler)	7 - 7	Miss S. L. Metcalfe
RHYS CLUTTERBUCK (Gary Moore)	8 - 10	P. C. Shea
MORGAN COLE (Marco Botti)	7 - 11	P. C. Shea
MICHAEL COLES (K. R. Burke)	8 - 3	c/o 01969 625088
JESSICA COOLEY (Keith Dalgleish)	8 - 8	c/o 01555 773375
LAURA COUGHLAN (Tom Ward)	7 - 13	Mrs G. S. Charnock
GEORGIA COX (William Haggas)	8 - 2	Mr G. R. Owen
WILLIAM COX (Andrew Balding)	8 - 2	Mr N. M. Adams
MARK CREHAN (Richard Hannon)	8 - 3	Mr S. Croft
PAM DU CROCQ (Chris Wall)	8 - 7	c/o 01638 661 999
SEAN DAVIS (Richard Fahey)	7 - 12	Mr N. Hannity
ROSE DAWES (Archie Watson)	7 - 7	c/o 07717 133844
GEORGIA DOBIE (Eve Johnson Houghton)	8 - 3	Mr S. T. Dodds
TOBY ELEY (Steph Hollinshead)	8 - 4	Mr T. Eley
JANE ELLIOTT (Tom Dascombe)	7 - 11	Mr S. Croft
CIEREN FALLON (William Haggas)	8 - 5	P. C. Shea
POPPY FIELDING (Tom Dascombe)	8 - 9	c/o 01948 820485 Alex
ISOBEL FRANCIS (Mark Usher)	7 - 7	Mr L. R. James
HANNAH FRASER (Ed Walker)	7 - 2	c/o 01488 674148
PAGE FULLER (Jamie Snowden)	8 - 10	Mr L. R. James
LOUIS GAROGHAN (Gary Moore)	8 - 3	c/o 01403 891 912
MARCO GHIANI (Stuart Williams)	8 - 2	Mr S. M. Righton
AMELIA GLASS (Clive Cox)	8 - 2	Mr N. M. Adams
MITCH GODWIN (Harry Dunlop)	8 - 7	Miss S. L. Metcalfe
JADE GOODWIN (Richard Fahey)	7 - 5	c/o 01653 698915
SELMA GRAGE (Robert Eddery)	8 - 4	Mr A. T. Brook
THOMAS GREATREX (Roger Charlton)	8 - 6	Mr Tony Hind
THORE HAMMER HANSEN (Richard Hannon)	8 - 0	Mrs Shelley Dwyer
BRADLEY HARRIS (Andrew Balding)	8 - 5	c/o 01635 298210
RUSSELL HARRIS (Michael Bell)	8 - 5	Mrs L. H. Way
TYLER HEARD (Richard Hughes)	8 - 0	c/o 01488 71198
DYLAN HOGAN (David Simcock)	8 - 5	Mr N. Hannity
CALLUM HUTCHINSON (Andrew Balding)	8 - 0	c/o 01635 29821
CAMERON ILES (David Evans)	8 - 4	c/o 01873 890837
RHIAIN INGRAM (Paul George)	7 - 11	Mr L. R. James
PIERRE-LOUIS JAMIN (Archie Watson)	8 - 3	Mr G. D. Jewell
ALEX JARY (George Scott)	8 - 2	c/o 07833461294
ELINOR JONES (Sylvester Kirk)	6 - 10	c/o 07768855261
DARRAGH KEENAN (John Ryan)	8 - 0	Mr S. T. Dodds
THEODORE LADD (Michael Appleby)	8 - 0	Mr G. D. Jewell

KATE LEAHY (Archie Watson)	8 - 5	Mr L. R. James
HARRIETT LEES (Kevin Ryan)	8 - 4	c/o 01845 597622
OWEN LEWIS (Charles Hills)	7 - 2	P. C. Shea
COREY MADDEN (Jim Goldie)	8 - 0	c/o 077782441522
GABRIELE MALUNE (Amy Murphy)	8 - 3	Mr S. T. Dodds
FINLEY MARSH (Richard Hughes)	8 - 9	Mr G. D. Jewell
ELLA MCCAIN (Donald McCain)	8 - 5	Mr R. A. Hale
GRACE MCENTEE (Phil McEntee)	8 - 7	P. C. Shea
CONOR MCGOVERN (Seb Spencer)	8 - 5	Mr R. A. Hale
SHARIQ MOHD (Sylvester Kirk)	7 - 10	c/o 0768 855 261
RYAN M. MOORE (John Best)	8 - 5	c/o 01795842531
PAULA MUIR (Roger Fell)	7 - 13	Mr R. A. Hale
CONNOR MURTAGH (Richard Fahey)	8 - 6	Mr R. A. Hale
MEGAN NICHOLLS	8 - 2	01749 860656
ELLIE NORRIS (Richard Hannon)	8 - 3	c/o 01264 850254
GER O'NEILL (Michael Easterby)	8 - 7	c/o 01347 878 368
ERIKA PARKINSON (Michael Appleby)	8 - 0	c/o 01572 722772
OWEN PAYTON (Jedd O'Keeffe)	7 - 4	c/o 07710 476 705
APRIL PEARSON (Pam Sly)	8 - 3	c/o 01733 270 298
LAURA PEARSON (David Evans)	8 - 0	P. C. Shea
MARIE PERRAULT (Andrew Balding)	7 - 13	c/o 01635 298210
MOLLIE PHILLIPS (Mark Loughnane)	7 - 12	c/o 07806 531021
ABIGAIL PIERCE (George Margarson)	8 - 3	c/o 07860 198 303
RHONA PINDAR (K. R. Burke)	7 - 12	Mr S. T. Dodds
MATTEO PINNA (Stuart Williams)	8 - 1	c/o 01638 663984
MICHAEL PITT (Denis Coakley)	8 - 4	c/o 01635 281622
DANNY REDMOND (Tim Easterby)	8 - 10	Mr R. A. Hale
AIDAN REDPATH (Michael Dods)	7 - 7	c/o 07860 411 590
SOPHIE REED (J. S. Moore)	7 - 12	c/o 0148873887
GEORGE ROOKE (Richard Hughes)	7 - 13	Mr N. M. Adams
HARRY RUSSELL (Brian Ellison)	8 - 7	Mr R. A. Hale
BEN SANDERSON (Keith Dalgleish)	8 - 7	Mr N. Hannity
GIANLUCA SANNA (William Haggas)	8 - 4	M. Furnass
TYLER SAUNDERS (Jonathan Portman)	8 - 7	c/o 01488 73894
ROWAN SCOTT (Nigel Tinkler)	8 - 7	Mr N. Hannity
OLIVER SEARLE (Rod Millman)	7 - 12	c/o 07885 168 447
HARRISON SHAW (K. R. Burke)	8 - 5	Mr R. A. Hale
SOPHIE SMITH (Ed Dunlop)	7 - 7	c/o 01638 661998
AIDEN SMITHIES (Nigel Tinkler)	8 - 4	Miss S. L. Metcalfe
OLIVER STAMMERS (Mark Johnston)	8 - 4	Mr G. R. Owen
LEWIS STONES (Olly Murphy)	8 - 12	Mr I. P. Popham
EMMA TAFF (Henry Candy)	8 - 7	c/o 07836211264
JOSHUA THORMAN (Ian Williams)	8 - 3	c/o 01564 822 392
ANGUS VILLIERS (Richard Hughes)	7 - 12	Mr Tony Hind
ZAK WHEATLEY (Declan Carroll)	8 - 5	Mr R. A. Hale
RYAN WHILE (Bill Turner)	8 - 13	c/o 07967 242404
ELISHA WHITTINGTON (Tony Carroll)	7 - 10	Andy Lewis
LEVI WILLIAMS (Joseph Tuite)	8 - 0	c/o 01488 72630
SEBASTIAN WOODS (Hugo Palmer)	8 - 9	P. C. Shea

JUMP JOCKEYS

Riding weights and contact details

An index of agents appears on page 720

Jockey	Weight	Agent
LUCY ALEXANDER	9 - 7	Mr R. A. Hale
BRIDGET ANDREWS	9 - 5	07921 394107
LEIGHTON ASPELL	10 - 3	Mr Dave Roberts
HARRY BANNISTER	9 - 7	Mr C. D. Broad
JAMIE BARGARY	10 - 0	Mr C. D. Broad
LUCY K. BARRY	9 - 8	07889275412
DAVID BASS	10 - 5	Mr C. D. Broad
MATTIE BATCHELOR	10 - 0	07767 400753
TOM BELLAMY	10 - 7	Mr C. D. Broad
JAMES BEST	10 - 0	Mr Dave Roberts
CALLUM BEWLEY	10 - 0	Mr R. A. Hale
JONATHON BEWLEY	10 - 0	01450860651
JAMES BOWEN	10 - 0	Mr Dave Roberts
SEAN BOWEN	9 - 7	Mr Dave Roberts
PADDY BRENNAN	9 - 12	Mr Dave Roberts
HENRY BROOKE	10 - 0	Mr R. A. Hale
JONATHAN BURKE	10 - 0	Mr C. D. Broad
TOM CANNON	10 - 5	Mr Dave Roberts
GRAHAM CARSON	9 - 10	Mr L. R. James
ALAIN CAWLEY	9 - 10	Mr R. A. Hale
ROSS CHAPMAN	9 - 8	Mr R. A. Hale
TOM CHEESMAN	9 - 9	07513 109598
ALISON CLARKE	9 - 7	07549142203
HARRY COBDEN	10 - 0	Mr Dave Roberts
GRANT COCKBURN	10 - 2	Mr L. R. James
AIDAN COLEMAN	9 - 10	Mr Dave Roberts
JOE COLLIVER	10 - 0	Mr R. A. Hale
DANNY COOK	10 - 7	Mr J. B. Jeffrey
JAMES CORBETT	9 - 7	07861 726940
DOUGIE COSTELLO	10 - 0	Mr A. T. Brook
DAVE CROSSE	10 - 0	Mr C. D. Broad
JAMES DAVIES	10 - 0	Mr L. R. James
RYAN DAY	10 - 6	Mr R. A. Hale
NICO DE BOINVILLE	10 - 0	Mr Dave Roberts
CHARLIE DEUTSCH	10 - 0	Mr Dave Roberts\ Mr C. D. Broad
THOMAS DOWSON	10 - 0	Mr R. A. Hale
ROBERT DUNNE	10 - 7	Mr Dave Roberts
KIERON EDGAR	10 - 4	Mr L. R. James
LEE EDWARDS	10 - 0	Mr C. D. Broad
DAVID ENGLAND	10 - 0	Mr I. P. Popham
JONATHAN ENGLAND	9 - 10	07747 390455
DEREK FOX	10 - 0	Mr J. B. Jeffrey
BRYONY FROST	9 - 12	Mr Dave Roberts
LUCY GARDNER	10 - 0	07814 979 699
THOMAS GARNER	10 - 0	Mr L. R. James
CIARAN GETHINGS	10 - 2	Mr Dave Roberts
MARC GOLDSTEIN	10 - 0	Mr Dave Roberts
MARK GRANT	10 - 4	Mr C. D. Broad
MATT GRIFFITHS	10 - 7	Mr I. P. Popham
JAMIE HAMILTON	10 - 0	Mr R. A. Hale
JOEY HAYNES	8 - 5	Mr S. T. Dodds
LIAM HEARD	10 - 5	Mr I. P. Popham
A. P. HESKIN	10 - 0	Mr Dave Roberts
DANIEL HISKETT	9 - 10	Mr I. P. Popham
BRIAN HUGHES	9 - 7	Mr R. A. Hale
WAYNE HUTCHINSON	10 - 3	01793 815009
DARYL JACOB	10 - 3	Mr Dave Roberts
ALAN JOHNS	10 - 0	Mr I. P. Popham
RICHARD JOHNSON	10 - 0	Mr Dave Roberts
KEVIN JONES	10 - 4	Mr Dave Roberts
LIZZIE KELLY	10 - 6	07724 839047
WILLIAM KENNEDY	10 - 0	Mr Dave Roberts
JOHN KINGTON	10 - 0	Mr R. A. Hale
GRAHAM LEE	8 - 9	Mr R. A. Hale
RYAN MANIA	10 - 7	Mr J. B. Jeffrey
COLM MCCORMACK	10 - 0	01287 650456
RACHAEL MCDONALD	9 - 5	Mr Ross Hyslop
JEREMIAH MCGRATH	10 - 0	Mr Dave Roberts
RICHIE MCLERNON	9 - 10	Mr Dave Roberts
JAMIE MOORE	10 - 0	Mr Dave Roberts
JOSHUA MOORE	10 - 5	Mr Dave Roberts
KILLIAN MOORE	10 - 4	07528 234223
NATHAN MOSCROP	10 - 5	Mr R. A. Hale
STEPHEN MULQUEEN	10 - 0	Mr J. B. Jeffrey
CRAIG NICHOL	10 - 0	Mr J. L. Neilson
ADAM NICOL	9 - 11	Mr J. B. Jeffrey\ Mr T. J. Nicol
JAMES NIXON	10 - 2	Mr L. R. James
MICHEAL NOLAN	10 - 4	Mr Dave Roberts
DAVID NOONAN	10 - 0	Mr Dave Roberts
PAUL O'BRIEN	10 - 3	Mr I. P. Popham
TOM O'BRIEN	10 - 2	Mr Dave Roberts
CONOR O'FARRELL	10 - 3	Mr B. Storey
KATIE O'FARRELL	9 - 11	Mr Dave Roberts
TOMMY PHELAN	10 - 0	Mr L. R. James
BEN POSTE	9 - 10	Mr Dave Roberts
BRENDAN POWELL	9 - 11	Mr Dave Roberts\ Mr G. D. Jewell
TOM QUEALLY	9 - 0	Mr L. R. James
JACK QUINLAN	9 - 10	Mr Dave Roberts
SEAN QUINLAN	10 - 0	Mr R. A. Hale
CONOR RING	10 - 5	Mr C. D. Broad
DANIEL SANSOM	10 - 0	Mr L. R. James
NICK SCHOLFIELD	10 - 4	Mr Dave Roberts
TOM SCUDAMORE	10 - 0	Mr Dave Roberts
WILLIAM SHANAHAN	10 - 4	Mr J. L. Neilson
GAVIN SHEEHAN	10 - 0	Mr C. D. Broad
CONOR SHOEMARK	10 - 0	Mr I. P. Popham
HARRY SKELTON	10 - 0	Mr I. P. Popham
MAXIME TISSIER	9 - 9	07724 398734
LIAM TREADWELL	10 - 0	Mr I. P. Popham
SAM TWISTON-DAVIES	10 - 0	Mr C. D. Broad
EOIN WALSH	9 - 10	Mr N. M. Adams
ADAM WEDGE	9 - 11	Mr Dave Roberts
CALLUM WHILLANS	9 - 11	07894 573557
KIELAN WOODS	10 - 3	Mr C. D. Broad

CONDITIONALS

Their employer and contact details
An index of agents appears on page 720

JOE ANDERSON (Nicky Henderson)	9 - 12	Mr Dave Roberts
EDWARD AUSTIN (Jonjo O'Neill)	9 - 10	Mr I. P. Popham
MITCHELL BASTYAN (Evan Williams)	9 - 10	Mr L. R. James
CERIS BIDDLE (Robin Dickin)	9 - 4	c/o 07979 518 593
AIDEN BLAKEMORE (Ruth Jefferson)	9 - 0	Mr R. A. Hale
CONNOR BRACE (Fergal O'Brien)	9 - 3	Mr Dave Roberts
NATHAN BRENNAN (Henry Oliver)	9 - 10	c/o 07756 015836
TOM BUCKLEY (Charlie Longsdon)	9 - 1	Mr L. R. James
BLAIR CAMPBELL (Lucinda Russell)	9 - 10	Mr R. A. Hale
BRYAN CARVER (Paul Nicholls)	9 - 7	Mr Dave Roberts
SAM COLTHERD (Sue Smith)	9 - 12	Mr J. B. Jeffrey
LEE COSGROVE (Warren Greatrex)	10 - 4	Mr R. A. Hale
PATRICK COWLEY (Martin Keighley)	10 - 0	Mr I. P. Popham
NED CURTIS (Kim Bailey)	10 - 0	Mr C. D. Broad
REX DINGLE (Anthony Honeyball)	9 - 7	Mr Dave Roberts
JASON DIXON (Ben Pauling)	9 - 7	Mr I. P. Popham
PHILIP DONOVAN (Neil Mulholland)	9 - 7	Mr I. P. Popham
EDDIE EDGE (Amy Murphy)	9 - 10	c/o 01638484907
ALEXANDER FIELDING (Neil King)	9 - 11	c/o 01793 845011
PAGE FULLER (Jamie Snowden)	9 - 3	Mr L. R. James
BILLY GARRITTY (Micky Hammond)	9 - 7	Mr R. A. Hale
THEO GILLARD (Donald McCain)	10 - 7	Mr R. A. Hale
BEN GODFREY (Anthony Honeyball)	9 - 4	Mr Dave Roberts
FERGUS GREGORY (Olly Murphy)	10 - 0	Mr Dave Roberts
CHARLIE HAMMOND (Dr Richard Newland)	9 - 7	Mr Dave Roberts
BEN HICKS (Jamie Snowden)	9 - 12	Mr C. D. Broad
NIALL HOULIHAN (Gary Moore)	9 - 7	Mr Dave Roberts
SEAN HOULIHAN (Philip Hobbs)	9 - 7	Mr Dave Roberts
DILLAN HURST (Sandy Thomson)	9 - 7	Mr J. B. Jeffrey
DALE IRVING (Maurice Barnes)	10 - 0	Mr J. B. Jeffrey
BEN JONES (Philip Hobbs)	10 - 0	Mr Dave Roberts
CHARLOTTE JONES (James Moffatt)	8 - 11	Mr J. L. Neilson
ALFIE JORDAN (Nicky Henderson)	9 - 1	c/o 01488 722 59
JONJO O'NEILL JR. (Jonjo O'Neill)	10 - 0	Mr Dave Roberts
MAX KENDRICK (Graeme McPherson)	9 - 9	Mr Dave Roberts
HARRY KIMBER (Colin Tizzard)	9 - 0	Mr C. D. Broad
CILLIN LEONARD (Dr Richard Newland)	9 - 11	Mr Dave Roberts
BRUCE LYNN (Iain Jardine)	10 - 0	Mr R. A. Hale
AIDAN MACDONALD (Micky Hammond)	9 - 10	c/o 07808 572777
WILLIAM MARSHALL (Dan Skelton)	9 - 6	Mr I. P. Popham
CALLUM MCKINNES (Olly Murphy)	10 - 0	Mr I. P. Popham
DANNY MCMENAMIN (Nicky Richards)	9 - 7	Mr R. A. Hale
LUCA MORGAN (Ben Pauling)	10 - 3	Mr Dave Roberts
LORCAN MURTAGH (Donald McCain)	9 - 7	Mr R. A. Hale
JORDAN NAILOR (Nigel Twiston-Davies)	9 - 7	Mr C. D. Broad
HUGH NUGENT (Venetia Williams)	9 - 7	Mr C. D. Broad
RICHARD PATRICK (Kerry Lee)	9 - 7	Mr Dave Roberts
HENRY PLATT (Emma Lavelle)	9 - 12	c/o 01672 511544
CHARLIE PRICE (Tim Vaughan)	9 - 2	Mr I. P. Popham
SHANE QUINLAN (Dai Williams)	9 - 7	Mr L. R. James
HARRY REED (Neil Mulholland)	9 - 7	Mr Dave Roberts
CRAWFORD ROBERTSON (N. W. Alexander)	9 - 0	c/o 07831 488210
BAILEY SAGAR (Sue Smith)	9 - 10	c/o 07903 311959
STAN SHEPPARD (Tom Lacey)	10 - 0	Mr C. D. Broad
EMMA SMITH-CHASTON (Micky Hammond)	9 - 7	Mr R. A. Hale
LEWIS STONES (Olly Murphy)	9 - 7	Mr I. P. Popham
ALEXANDER THORNE (Alan King)	9 - 7	Mr Dave Roberts
CHARLIE TODD (Ian Williams)	9 - 5	Mr I. P. Popham
JACK TUDOR (Christian Williams)	9 - 7	Mr Dave Roberts

ROSS TURNER (Oliver Greenall)	9 - 7	Mr I. P Popham
CHESTER WILLIAMS (Kim Bailey)	10 - 0	Mr C. D. Broad
ISABEL WILLIAMS (Evan Williams)	9 - 7	c/o 01446 754069
LORCAN WILLIAMS (Paul Nicholls)	10 - 4	Mr Dave Roberts
ROBERT WILLIAMS (Bernard Llewellyn)	10 - 5	c/o 07971 233473
JOE WILLIAMSON (Gillian Boanas)	9 - 7	Mr R. A. Hale
THOMAS WILLMOTT (Lucinda Russell)	9 - 7	Mr J. B. Jeffrey
TABITHA WORSLEY (Laura Morgan)	9 - 9	Mr J. B. Jeffrey
KANE YEOMAN (Rebecca Menzies)	9 - 7	Mr B. Storey

Are your contact details missing
or incorrect?
If so please update us by
email: richard.lowther@racingpost.com

AMATEUR RIDERS

Riding weights and contact details
An index of agents appears on page 720

An index of agents appears on page 720

ADAMS, K. L. 8 - 6 07739414365
ALEXANDER, C. 9 - 10..........................07799191093
ALEXANDER, J. F. 11 - 7........................0131 332 8850
ALEXANDER, K. 9 - 7............................07939263113
ANDERSON, A. 9 - 7....................................Mr B. Storey
ANDREWS, D. I. J. 10 - 10....................07817322974
ANDREWS, G. 9 - 12..........................Mr C. D. Broad
ANDREWS, J. 10 - 10........................Mr I. P Popham
ANDREWS, J. M. 10 - 7........................07815543452
APRAHAMIAN, B. 11 - 3........................07739819804
ARMSON, P. M. 9 - 7............................07857714538
BAKER, Z. C. N. 10 - 10....................Mr C. D. Broad
BALL, C. 10 - 0..................................07947861711
BAMENT, J. J. 9 - 10............................07964587682
BANHAM, C. 8 - 12..............................07387169781
BANKS, A. P. 10 - 7............................07927308486
BANKS, J. 9 - 12................................01223279210
BARFOOT-SAUNT, G. C. 10 - 12..............01684 833227
BARLOW, P. C. F. 8 - 5........................07873177808
BARTLEY, C. A. 8 - 10..........................07734303862
BEAUMONT, G. 10 - 7............................07824902088
BEDI, J. I. 8 - 10..............................01642 780202
BELL, A. 9 - 4..................................Mr L. R. James
BESWICK, H. 10 - 0..........................Mr I. P Popham
BEVIN, R. 11 - 5................................07842213901
BIDDICK, W. E. T. 11 - 0........................07976556823
BINGHAM, G. F. 11 - 1..........................07766204154
BIRKETT, R. A. 9 - 10..........................07855065036
BLOSS, A. Z. 8 - 5..........................Mrs N. J. Bloss
BLUNDELL, M. R. 8 - 0..........................07736713203
BOWEN, S. L. 9 - 0..........................Mr S. M. Righton
BRACKENBURY, B. E. 10 - 11..................07921618635
BRADSTOCK, L. A. N. 9 - 6....................07972161732
BRIDGE, E. L. 10 - 0............................01980 845921
BROMLEY, B. W. 9 - 5............................07585973675
BROOKE, L. 9 - 4................................07786962911
BROOKS, K. S. 8 - 2............................07740966311
BROPHY, O. 8 - 8................................07703421038
BROTHERTON, S. 8 - 12..........................07740257110
BROUGHTON, T. P. 10 - 0........................07769311749
BROWN, L. 10 - 0................................07852830401
BROWN, M. W. 9 - 12............................07482639103
BROWNE, M. M. 9 - 4............................07873599555
BRYAN, P. J. 11 - 0............................07538655128
BRYANT, M. P. 9 - 12............................07976217542
BUCKLE, C. 11 - 0..............................07471890558
BUCKLEY, K. 10 - 12............................07484826987
BULLOCK, E. 8 - 0..............................07593951904
BURCHELL, D. G. 10 - 0........................07884263625
BURTON, S. 10 - 7..............................07786438076
CAGNEY, E. 9 - 0................................07944624286
CAREDDU, C. 8 - 3..............................07775342193
CARTER, S. 9 - 0................................07751971316
CASE, C. 10 - 10................................07807652305
CHADWICK, A. 10 - 0............................07495477109
CHATFEILD-ROBERTS, T. 10 - 7................07794743577
CHELEDA, A. 9 - 7..............................07398769954
CHENERY, M. 11 - 0............................07967911360

CHERRIMAN, D. J. 10 - 7........................07900963271
CLESHAM, W. 9 - 4..............................07802607678
CLOVER, C. 10 - 4..............................07866738717
COLEMAN, P. R. 10 - 0..........................07796123798
COLL, S. A. 10 - 0..............................07715637416
COLLIER, A. 9 - 0..............................01751430666
COLLIER, E. J. 9 - 8............................07918975329
COOPER, L. 9 - 12..............................07864537080
COX, A. 8 - 2....................................07813386642
CRANE, C. R. 9 - 8..............................07837965183
CROSS, S. P. 10 - 7............................07774876008
CROW, G. M. 10 - 12............................01928740555
CROW, H. 10 - 7................................07794379295
CUTHBERT, H. E. 9 - 0..........................01228 560700
DALY, G. 9 - 8..................................07469811361
DANDO, C. 11 - 4..............................07901522080
DAVIES, S. P. 12 - 0............................07801393851
DAVISON, S. A. 8 - 4............................07760300176
DAWSON, J. A. 10 - 7............................07525984547
DAYKIN, O. 9 - 4................................07557796895
DENIEL, A. 8 - 10..............................07786621752
DINNEEN, J. 10 - 0..............................07858435952
DISNEY, G. F. 10 - 10..........................07816847947
DIXON, J. 9 - 7................................07761998988
DOBB, L. 8 - 6..................................07960174107
DODS, C. A. 8 - 13..............................07590048619
DODS, S. E. 9 - 3..............................0790048618
DOGGRELL, T. 9 - 7............................07983249050
DOOLAN, S. M. 10 - 4............................07975736480
DUN, C. 9 - 12..................................07766592287
DUNNE, M. P. 10 - 0............................07872590083
DUNSDON, D. 10 - 7............................07885110826
DURRELL, T. 9 - 1..............................07591238094
EASTERBY, E. A. 8 - 7..........................07854733689
EASTERBY, W. H. 9 - 7........................Mr J. L. Neilson
EDDERY, G. 9 - 6................................07747535702
EDWARDS, A. W. 10 - 0..........................07590683295
EDWARDS, D. M. 11 - 4..........................07811898002
EDWARDS, H. 10 - 4............................07709506046
ELLIOT, J. A. 9 - 8............................07543740125
EMSLEY, C. J. R. 9 - 3..........................07951838378
ENGSTROM, J. 8 - 5............................07366323072
ENNIS, M. C. 9 - 11..........................Mrs L. H. Way
EYSTON, T. 9 - 10..............................07801108050
FEILDEN, S. 8 - 2..............................07384395475
FENWICK, L. 10 - 0............................07917694494
FERGUSON, A. R. D. 10 - 0......................07788876161
FIELDING, M. 9 - 10............................07592874494
FOX, M. 9 - 0....................................07769170926
FURNESS, C. J. W. 10 - 6......................07871449210
GALLIGAN, M. 9 - 7............................Mr J. B. Jeffrey
GARVEN, A. M. 8 - 12..........................Mr J. B. Jeffrey
GEORGE, N. A. C. 10 - 7......................Mr C. D. Broad
GIBBS, B. 10 - 10..............................07818407883
GILBERTSON, G. P. 10 - 5......................07729509150
GILLAM, J. E. 9 - 7............................01653668566
GILLARD, F. 9 - 7..............................07824644261
GLANVILLE, P. 10 - 0............................07949227578

GLASSONBURY, E. 10 - 12	07917167236
GOODWIN, C. L. 7 - 8	07772090280
GORMAN, G. 10 - 0	07429557863
GOSCHEN, A. B. 10 - 5	07719611301
GOWING, K. 10 - 7	07501474589
GREENWOOD, T. O. M. 10 - 0	07904889779
GREGORY, H. J. 8 - 0	07772008845
HAMBLETT, L. S. 9 - 3	07979102805
HAMPSON, B. 9 - 12	Mr S. Croft
HAMPTON, M. L. 11 - 0	07515269391
HARBISON, J. E. A. 10 - 7	01280 812057
HARDING, J. 9 - 10	Miss A. Wallace
HARDWICK, C. V. 9 - 10	07808511705
HARRIS, Z. 9 - 0	07850587881
HARRISON, W. 9 - 4	Mr I. P. Popham
HAWKER, R. 10 - 12	07891960356
HAWKINS, S. 9 - 4	07733265836
HAYNES, A. 9 - 3	07585558717
HENDERSON, F. 11 - 0	07824954461
HENRY, D. M. 7 - 9	07977794002
HICKMAN, W. H. W. 11 - 0	07841488935
HILL, R. L. 9 - 0	07714918127
HILLHOUSE, C. J. 8 - 10	07702394302
HISCOCK, G. 10 - 7	07815475518
HODGINS, L. W. 9 - 0	07585440230
HOLMES, D. 9 - 2	07487640802
HOLMES, R. J. 8 - 10	07827889627
HOOPER, M. 8 - 0	07984847633
HOPKINSON, G. J. 10 - 8	07800974583
HOPPER, P. 8 - 7	07931873497
HOWARTH, R. 9 - 6	07825708510
HUGHES, J. 9 - 7	07884432672
HUMPHREY, L. A. 10 - 2	07557772679
HUMPHREY, W. 8 - 0	07468606622
HUSKISSON, R. 9 - 0	07860346508
JACK, E. L. 9 - 3	07544538965
JAMES-THOMAS, K. 8 - 0	07376251541
JEAVONS, J. 10 - 0	07972871875
JEFFRIES, M. G. 10 - 0	07985327140
JOHNSON, B. 9 - 7	07866012885
JOHNSON, M. S. 9 - 10	07816609314
JONES, C. A. 8 - 8	07808073411
JONES, L. 8 - 6	07397384816
JORDAN, M. 9 - 0	07860661260
JUKES, S. M. 10 - 7	07860130833
KATTENHORN, B. 10 - 0	07501643988
KELLARD, W. A. 11 - 0	07779008698
KERR, D. 9 - 5	Mrs G. S. Charnock
KERSLAKE, N. 9 - 0	07944586394
KING, G. 8 - 6	07741244698
KING, J. 10 - 0	Mr I. P. Popham
KIRWAN, S. T. 9 - 6	07725434605
KNIGHT, E. 9 - 12	07465221688
LAVERGNE, A. C. 10 - 0	07542271688
LAVERY, G. 10 - 0	07585943298
LAW-EADIE, R. 9 - 2	07516722074
LEE, C. 8 - 13	07789713855
LEE, S. 9 - 7	07745327430
LEGG, M. D. 9 - 7	07590690898
LENIHAN, K. G. C. 9 - 6	07486309239
LEWIS, A. 8 - 13	07890311200
LEWIS, H. M. 9 - 7	07899649644
LLEWELLYN, J. 8 - 3	07805394892
LOVE, B. 10 - 6	07534598918
MAGER, L. R. 9 - 3	07738605077
MAINS, C. 9 - 6	07375496629
MARGARSON, R. A. 8 - 2	07595888757
MARSHALL, C. 10 - 10	07516296716
MARSHALL, I. 9 - 0	07581371480
MARTIN, J. 10 - 1	07732269216
MARTIN, J. I. 10 - 3	07815698359
MASON, J. L. 8 - 10	Mr N. Hannity
MASON, P. W. 11 - 4	07921707292
MATHIAS, J. 7 - 8	07227514423
MAXWELL, D. 11 - 0	0207 799 3429
MCBRIDE, A. 10 - 0	07465253505
MCBRIDE, C. 9 - 7	07496887118
MCCAIN, A. 9 - 7	Mr R. A. Hale
MCCAIN-MITCHELL, T. 9 - 13	07715511113
MCCANN, N. 8 - 11	07948780869
MCCANN, N. M. 7 - 10	07948780869
MCCLUNG, A. E. 9 - 4	07775740004
MCGIVERN, C. 9 - 5	07838996002
MCINTYRE, M. J. 10 - 4	07557360664
MICKLEWRIGHT, M. 8 - 4	07525466455
MILBURN, W. J. 10 - 7	07769618732
MILLMAN, P. B. 9 - 7	Mr Ian Wood
MITCHELL, G P 10 - 4	07974238776
MOORCROFT, B. 10 - 0	07971806968
MORGAN, S. A. 9 - 11	07397565965
MULLINEAUX, M. 8 - 10	01829 261440
MULRINE, F. M. 9 - 5	07946882342
MYDDELTON, H. 9 - 7	07713837857
NEWCOMBE, H. 9 - 7	07495650303
NEWMAN, J. 9 - 7	07920464705
O'BRIEN, D. J. 11 - 0	07764304906
O'BRIEN, T. M. 10 - 0	07826516 394
O'NEILL, A. J. 10 - 2	07585400544
O'SHEA, A. 9 - 7	07464819462
O'SHEA, C. 10 - 10	07779788748
OBREY, A. 9 - 4	07506007082
OLIVEIRA, H. 9 - 6	07398345994
OLIVER, N. H. 11 - 7	07791590544
ORPWOOD, N. 11 - 0	07831836 626
OSBORNE, M. 10 - 7	07398278349
PAHLMAN, J. V. 9 - 0	07712714226
PARKER, N. L. 9 - 5	07877151521
PECK, A. 8 - 7	Miss A. Wallace
PERRETT, J. E. 10 - 0	07399533551
PETERS, D. M. 11 - 3	07789 997367
PETTIS, W. 9 - 10	07908572141
PHILLIPS, T. 8 - 7	07857137135
PICKARD, E. M. G. 9 - 2	07921088893
PIKE, C. 10 - 0	07749457386
PINCHIN, L. M. 9 - 9	Mr I. P. Popham
POTTER, W. E. 10 - 7	07872933534
POWER, J. 10 - 0	07340424290
POWNALL, C. L. 9 - 1	07825064776
PRESLAND, M. 7 - 3	07885659856
PRICE, C. 10 - 4	07598925913
PRICHARD, D. G. 10 - 0	07983162251
PRINCE, G. 11 - 0	07912481157
PROCTER, F. 9 - 7	07772241195
PROVAN, L. B. 10 - 0	07703053186
QUINN, C. 9 - 7	07840312004
RAHMAN, N. 9 - 7	07772968541
RAMSAY, W. B. 11 - 12	07764960054
RAWDON-MOGG, C. J. D. 11 - 0	07759451287
RAYNER, K. P. 8 - 13	07511949914
REES, E. M. 8 - 0	07506574715
REYNOLDS, N. 10 - 0	07768630278
RIDLEY, J. M. 10 - 7	07557879646
RIPPON, S. 9 - 7	07812165566
ROBERTS, B. 9 - 8	07871504897

ROBINSON, I. P. B. 9 - 2 07581361986
ROBINSON, M. G. 10 - 10..................07715563038
ROBINSON, S. C. 12 - 0......................01424 204190
ROBOTTOM, J. P. 9 - 6.......................07455152103
SANDERS, L. 9 - 2.............................07791244494
SAVAGE, J. A. 10 - 2..........................Mr C. D. Broad
SCHILDER, N. J. 8 - 10.......................07572603297
SCOTT, D. C. 9 - 2.............................01372426200
SCOTT, J. J. 9 - 3.............................07903735554
SCOTT, L. R. B. 9 - 4..........................07399063895
SEERY, N. S. 9 - 7.............................07377842916
SENSOY, H. 9 - 8..............................07595985025
SHARP, M. 9 - 3................................07471823014
SHARPE, R. E. L. 9 - 5.......................07446907489
SHAW, B. A. S. 10 - 6.........................07502332884
SINCLAIR, K. S. 9 - 0.........................07554457681
SMITH-MAXWELL, J. 11 - 1 07535459701
SMOULT, B. G. 9 - 0...........................07917466200
SOLE, J. D. 10 - 1.............................07968947091
SOLLITT, V. A. 10 - 6.........................07540229941
SPARKES, G. 8 - 4.............................07736511591
SPENCER, L. 9 - 0.............................07393814238
SPRAKE, C. G. 9 - 3...........................07938474314
STEARN, R. R. P. 11 - 0.....................07879412 414
STEVENS, A. L. 9 - 7..........................07917602116
STEVENS, S. 9 - 2.............................07972365372
STRAWSON, T. R. F. 11 - 7..................07809444373
SUMMERS, P. F. 10 - 0.......................07552219962
SWIFT, C. 9 - 7.................................07779082171
TAILFORD, C. E. 9 - 7.........................07807650142
TAYLOR, R. M. 8 - 12.........................07973774660
TEAL, J. 10 - 9.................................07984649070
TETT, F. 9 - 0...................................07786314587
THIRLBY, W. 11 - 0............................07773885256
THOMAS, P. J. 9 - 0...........................07548790661
THORPE-CODMAN, H. 10 - 10.............07557763513
TICEHURST, L. 8 - 2..........................07825432531
TODD, E. L. 9 - 3..............................Mr J. B. Jeffrey
TRAINOR, M. 9 - 7.............................07554992851

TREGONING, G. 10 - 2.......................07818441714
TROTT, L. 10 - 5...............................07814537290
TUCKER, A. J. 8 - 8...........................07562710235
TUFNELL, A. 10 - 7............................07739748736
TURNER, D. I. 9 - 6...........................Miss A. Wallace
TURNER, J. 9 - 4..............................07955080203
TURNER, L. M. 10 - 0........................07984531836
TURNER, R. M. 9 - 6..........................07787121404
VOIKHANSKY, M. 9 - 9.......................01213772133
WADGE, C. 10 - 5.............................Mr J. B. Jeffrey
WAGGOTT, J. J. 10 - 7.......................07789465482
WALEY-COHEN, S. B. 10 - 0................07887848425
WALKER, S. A. 9 - 7...........................Mr S. T. Dodds
WALLACE, H. A. R. 11 - 0....................07974360462
WALTON, C. M. 9 - 0..........................Mr R. A. Hale
WARD, J. 11 - 0................................07969524777
WATTS, S. 8 - 3...............................07487736209
WAUGH, A. 8 - 5...............................Mr J. B. Jeffrey
WEBB, K. 9 - 3.................................07939147230
WEDMORE, O. Z. F. 9 - 10..................01424 838667
WELCH, H. J. 9 - 10...........................07501060620
WELCH, T. 10 - 5..............................07570183150
WHITAKER, J. S. 11 - 0......................01226 792143
WHITTLE, S. R. 9 - 7..........................07890510714
WILKINSON, E. J. 8 - 5.......................07964145161
WILLIAMS, C. 9 - 7............................07540858880
WILLIAMS, E. L. 10 - 0.......................07714170651
WILLIAMS, S. A. 7 - 7........................07864515150
WILLIAMS, S. R. 10 - 12.....................07590208675
WILLIAMSON, L. 9 - 7........................07428536012
WILSON, R. 10 - 7.............................07510888442
WINSTONE, M. 9 - 10........................07411290539
WONNACOTT, M. 9 - 4.......................07710461900
WOOD, C. 9 - 7.................................07446081304
WOOD, K. 10 - 6...............................07429078066
WOOD, S. 10 - 11.............................07983797331
WRIGHT, A. 10 - 10...........................07515373070
WRIGHT, J. 11 - 0.............................07787365500
YORK, P. 10 - 7.................................07774962168

Are your contact details missing
or incorrect?
If so please update us by
email: richard.lowther@racingpost.com

NOTES

NOTES

NOTES

NOTES

NOTES

NOTES

NOTES

NOTES

NOTES

NOTES

NOTES

NOTES

Want the BIGGEST offers?

Daily PROMOS?

Biggest BOOKIES?

racingpost.com/freebets

For The Must-Have Racing Offers

RACING POST

Racing Post backs responsible gambling.
18+ begambleaware.org 0808 8020 133

RACING POST
SHOP

Classic
reads

£20

HENRIETTA KNIGHT

STARTING FROM
SCRATCH
INSPIRED TO
BE A JUMP
JOCKEY

Foreword by Sir Anthony McCoy

RACING POST
LEGENDS

TIGER
ROLL
THE LITTLE LEGEND

EDITED BY ANDREW PENNINGTON

£20

Order now

 racingpost.com/shop   01933 304858

ARIONEO

THE NEW GENERATION SENSOR
EQUIMETRE

Quality control of physiological parameters:

Mesure of physical capacities and progress

Detect the early signs of pathological issues

Assist in identifing future stars

Heart rate

Speed + Split times

Distance

Stride length

Stride frequency

Automatic identification

DATA GATHERING

Our patented technology encompasses precise analysis of the heart rate, a horse's performance aligned to GPS data - speed, distance, stride frequency, stride lenght.

PLATFORM OF ANALYSIS

Due to the reliability of our data and our exacting scientific algorithms, Equimetre provides ongoing analysis of the physiological and physical capacity of each horse during training.

DATA SCIENCE

Our team of equine experts along with our veterinary partners are available to work alongside you to maximise the use of both the system and the data available to you.

For more details please visit www.arioneo.com
or contact sales@arioneo.com

WINDSOR CLIVE
INTERNATIONAL

SMALL, PURCHASES,
LETTINGS AND
VALUATIONS
OF TRAINING YARDS
AND STUD FARMS.

+44 (0)1672 521155

info@windsorclive.co.uk   windsorclive.co.uk

Unbeatable in equine supplements

Horse Victory is a well-known company specialising in High Quality nutritional supplements for sport horses. The aim of Horse Victory is to make equestrians, owners, trainers and caretakers worldwide aware of the nutritional deficiencies in horse feed, in order to optimise the athletic performance of horses. The products were developed in a top laboratory by the cooperative efforts of scientists and veterinary surgeons specialising in horses, with many years of experience in this field. In the meantime, the quality of our products has been confirmed by top international equestrians and horse owners.

Horse Victory HQ supplements are currently regarded as one of the most powerful and highest-quality products of their kind, completely safe and conforming to FEI standards.

email info@horsevictory.com | **phone** 0031 (0)653492570
www.horsevictory.com

Lacta Sport Performance

The nutritional supplement to optimise energy processing, support muscle metabolism, enhance the absorption of oxygen in the blood and reduce production of lactic acid.

P-Solution

P-Solution is frequently administered to sport horses in order to promote optimal performance by masking minor discomforts, allowing the horse's feeling of superb well-being to dominate.

Tendon Care

Very high value nutritional supplement for speedy recuperation from injured tendons, muscles and ligaments and for preventative use.

Muscle XL

Muscle XL is currently the most powerful supplement used to build and strengthen muscles in order to deliver top performance.

email info@horsevictory.com | **phone** 0031 (0)653492570
www.horsevictory.com

- pure flake® extra wood shavings
- pure flake® premium wood shavings
- pure flake® ultra wood shavings
- pure flake® excel wood shavings
- pure green® flax horse bedding
- pure green® plus, flax and wood shavings mix
- pure gold®, chopped straw bedding

bedtime®

01666 510054 | sales@equisupplies.co.uk | equisupplies.co.uk

Let equilume lighting give your horses the winning edge

Mimicking Nature, Maximising Health & Performance

"*I was amazed at the overall change in the horses after about six weeks under the Equilume lights, by the condition they were carrying and the way their coats looked. We were quietly surprised at how clean their throats were on scoping, clear of pharyngitis, all mucus and guttural pouch infections. For me, who is sceptical of most things new, I found these Stable Lights to be one of the only new technologies that worked really well.*"

Eddie Woods, Leading Consignor of 2-year-olds, Ocala, FL

www.equilume.com | **+353 45 407040**

equilume
performance lighting

NEH
NEWMARKET EQUINE HOSPITAL

Available whenever you need us

Outstanding equine
veterinary care

Committed to Service

Over 40 veterinary experts providing outstanding services to the
Thoroughbred industry

Unrivalled facilities and expertise backed by advanced technology

An array of mobile digital equipment to provide diagnostic
assessment on-site

24-hour emergency cover

www.**newmarketequinehospital**.com
Tel **01638 782000**

STABLE SHIELD
LEADERS IN EQUINE BIO SECURITY

Double Protection
Against Infectious Diseases

Prevention is Cheaper than Cure

Stable Shield Disinfectant is an advanced hard surface/multi surface cleaner and sanitiser that is manufactured to contain one of the fastest acting and most powerful germ killing products available today.

Approved product by the BHAGI for a Level One clean at racing yards.

Stable Shield is the leading anti-bacterial paint formulated specifically for stables and working yards.

Telephone: 07949 929256 or 07766 221473
www.stableshield.co.uk

BOTANICA
NATURES HEALING ENERGY

Award Winning Products

Unique blend of natural ingredients that promote effective and complete recovery - Naturally!

"Used by top trainers, studs & professionals worldwide"

Botanica Herbal Wash & Creams treat:

- OVERREACH WOUNDS
- WAR WOUNDS
- GIRT SCALDS
- MUD RASH
- RINGWORM
- RAIN SCALD
- WASHING & GROOMING
- CAPPED HOCKS
- SWEAT RASH
- CRACKED HEELS
- CUTS AND GRAZES
- SORE TENDONS
- SORE SHINS
- SUNBURN
- THRUSH
- HAIR LOSS
- FISTULOUS WITHERS

Botanica products are all Antiseptic, Anti-Fungal, Anti-Bacterial, Anti-Inflammatory, Antihistamine and Insect Repellent

www.botanica.ie E: enquiries@botanica.ie
Sales Line: +44 (0) 28 417 39151

Units 12-13 Warrenpoint Enterprise Centre, Newry Rd, Warrenpoint, Co Down BT34 3LA

FEED YOUR DESIRE TO WIN

Connolly's **RED MILLS** SINCE 1908

Jessica Harrington

"I have been using RED MILLS feed for over 25 years. Their feeds are high quality and the range caters for all our needs from yearling flat horses to our national hunt horses - I highly recommend them."

By kind permission of trainer

Connolly's **RED MILLS** SINCE 1908

Contact our specialist thoroughbred team:
Ireland: +353 599 775 800
UK: +44 1386 552066

www.redmills.com

NOPS BETA
UFAS

OUR SCIENCE, YOUR SUCCESS

FOR-RECOVERY

FOR-LIFE

Support the equine athlete with
the power of Ubiquinol CoQ10
The body's first choice of antioxidant

Utilising the natural antioxidant and energy production activity of Ubiquinol CoQ10, FOR-RECOVERY is the ideal support for the elite equine athlete during both pre-training and a busy racing or competition schedule, helping to maintain performance throughout the season.

Products from the Foran Equine FOR-LIFE range are the ONLY CoQ10 products available for horses that contain pure Ubiquinol CoQ10, formulated to ensure consistent top quality, as nature intended.

Foran Equine
A division of Foran Healthcare,
2 Cherry Orchard Ind. Est., Dublin 10, Ireland
T +353 (0)1 626 8058 E info@foranequine.com

Ireland & International – Technical
Kirsty McCann
t:+353 879161712
e: kirstymccann@forans.com

UK – Technical
Nichola Reynolds
t: +44 7739 658469
e: nichola.reynolds@foranequine.co.uk

NO MORE BUTE

Does exactly what it says on the container...

- ☑ Highly Absorbable & Bioavailable Curcumin

- ☑ Powerful Antioxidant

- ☑ Ideal during periods of Intensive Exercise & Maintenance

- ☑ No Withdrawal Period

Tel: (0191) 264 5536
Email: info@equineproducts-ukltd.com

 equineproductsukltd   EquineProductsUk   @equineprodsuk